Small Business Sourcebook

T0387291

ISSN 0883-3397

Small Business Sourcebook

The Entrepreneur's Resource

FORTY-SECOND EDITION

Volume 4

General Small Business Topics

(Entries 26479-36039)

Holly M. Selden
Project Editor

 GALE

Small Business Sourcebook, 42nd edition

Project Editor: Holly M. Selden

Editorial Support Services: Pranav Kokate

Composition and Electronic Prepress: Carolyn Roney

Manufacturing: Rita Wimberley

For product information and technology assistance, contact us at
Gale Customer Support, 1-800-877-4253.
For permission to use material from this text or product,
submit all requests online at **www.cengage.com/permissions.**
Further permissions questions can be emailed to
permissionrequest@cengage.com.

Gale, part of Cengage Group
5191 Natorp Blvd.
Mason, OH 45040

978-1-5358-7663-6 (set)
978-1-5358-7664-3 (vol. 1)
978-1-5358-7665-0 (vol. 2)
978-1-5358-7666-7 (vol. 3)
978-1-5358-7667-4 (vol. 4)
978-1-5358-7668-1 (vol. 5)
978-1-5358-7669-8 (vol. 6)

ISSN 0883-3397

This title is also available as an e-book.
978-1-5358-7670-4
Contact your Gale sales representative for ordering information.

Contents

The appeal of small business ownership remains perpetually entrenched in American culture as one of the most viable avenues for achieving the American Dream. To many entrepreneurs, going into business for themselves represents financial independence, an increased sense of identity and self-worth, and the fulfillment of personal goals. Small business owners strive to make their mark in today's competitive marketplace by establishing healthy businesses that can, over time, become legacies handed down from one generation to the next. Entrepreneurs from each generation tackle the obstacles and adversities of the current business and economic climate to test their business savvy and generate opportunities. Today's entrepreneurs face many of the problems of their predecessors, as well as some distinctly new challenges.

With the rightsizing, downsizing, and reorganization of corporate America, many individuals have decided to confront the risks of developing and operating their own businesses. Small business ownership is rapidly becoming a viable alternative to what is perceived as an equally unstable corporate environment. These entrepreneurs, many of whom have firsthand experience with the problems and inefficiencies inherent in today's large corporations, seek to improve upon an archaic business model and to capitalize on their own ingenuity and strengths. Led by their zeal, many would-be entrepreneurs let their desire, drive, and determination overshadow the need for business knowledge and skill. Ironically, aids in obtaining these components of entrepreneurial success are widely available, easily accessible, and often free of charge.

Small Business Sourcebook (SBS) is a six-volume annotated guide to nearly 17,000 listings of live and print sources of information designed to facilitate the start-up, development, and growth of specific small businesses, as well as more than 19,500 similar listings on general small business topics. An additional 12,500 state-specific listings and nearly 1,100 U.S. federal government agencies and offices specializing in small business issues, programs, and assistance are also included. *SBS* covers more than 300 specific small business profiles more than 100 general small business topics.

Features of This Edition

This edition of *Small Business Sourcebook* has been revised and updated, incorporating thousands of changes to names, addresses, contacts, and descriptions of listings from the previous edition. We have also added several hundred podcasts that will help users better understand topics on entrepreneurship and small business ownership.

Contents and Arrangement

The geographical scope of *SBS* encompasses the United States and Canada, with expanded coverage for resources pertaining to international trade and for resources that have a U.S. or Canadian distributor or contact. Internet sites that are maintained outside of the U.S. and Canada are also included if they contain relevant information for North American small businesses. Resources that do not relate specifically to small businesses are generally not included.

The information presented in *SBS* is grouped within four sections: Specific Small Business Profiles, General Small Business Topics, State Listings, and Federal Government Assistance. Detailed outlines of these sections may be found in the Users' Guide following this Introduction. Also included is a Master Index to Volumes 1 through 6.

Specific Small Business Profiles This section includes the following types of resources: start-up information, associations and other organizations, educational programs, directories of educational programs, reference works, sources of supply, statistical sources, trade periodicals, videos and podcasts, trade shows and conventions, consultants, franchises, and business opportunities, computerized databases, computer systems/software, Internet databases, libraries, and research centers. All resources are arranged by business type. Entries range from Accounting Service to Word Processing Service, and include such businesses as Cannabis Dispensaries, Computer Consulting, Food Trucks, and Web Site Design.

General Small Business Topics This section offers such resources as associations, books, periodicals, articles, pamphlets, educational programs, directories of educational programs, trade shows and conventions, consultants, computerized databases, Internet databases, software, libraries, and research centers. All resources in this section are arranged alphabetically by business topic.

State Listings Entries include government, academic, and commercial agencies and organizations, as well as select coverage of relevant state-specific publications. Listings are arranged alphabetically by state, territory, and Canadian province. Some examples include small business development consultants, SCORE offices, financing and loan programs, better business bureaus, and chambers of commerce.

Federal Government Assistance Listings Entries include federal organizations and agencies specializing in small business issues, programs, assistance, and policy. Listings are arranged alphabetically by U.S. government agency or office; regional or branch offices are listed alphabetically by state.

Master Index All entries in Volumes 1 through 6 are arranged in one alphabetic index for convenience.

Entries in *SBS* include (as appropriate and available):

- Organization, institution, or product name

- Contact information, including contact name, address and phone, toll-free, and fax numbers

- Author/editor, date(s), and frequency

- Availability, including price

- Brief description of purpose, services, or content

- Company and/or personal E-mail addresses

- Web site addresses

SBS also features the following:

Guide to Publishers—An alphabetic listing of nearly 1,000 companies, associations, institutions, and individuals that publish the periodicals, directories, guidebooks, and other publications noted in the Small Business Profiles and General Topics sections. Users are provided with full contact information, including address, phone, fax, and e-mail and URL when available. The Guide to Publishers facilitates contact with publishers and provides a one-stop resource for valuable information.

Method of Compilation

SBS was compiled by consulting small business experts and entrepreneurs, as well as a variety of resources, including direct contact with the associations, organizations, and agencies through Internet research or materials provided by those listees; government resources; and data obtained from other relevant Gale directories. *SBS* was reviewed by a team of small business advisors, all of whom have numerous years of expertise in small business counseling and identification of small business information resources. The last and perhaps most important resource we utilize is direct contact with our readers, who provide valuable comments and suggestions to improve our publication. *SBS* relies on these comprehensive market contacts to provide today's entrepreneurs with relevant, current, and accurate information on all aspects of small business.

Available in Electronic Formats

Licensing. Small Business Sourcebook is available for licensing. The complete database is provided in a fielded format and is deliverable on various forms of media. For more information, contact Gale's Business Development Group at 1-800-877-GALE, or visit our website at www.gale .com.

Comments and Suggestions Welcome

Associations, agencies, business firms, publishers, and other organizations that provide assistance and information to the small business community are encouraged to submit material about their programs, activities, services, or products. Comments and suggestions from users of this directory are also welcomed and appreciated. Please contact:

Project Editor
Small Business Sourcebook
27555 Executive Dr., Ste. 270
Farmington Hills, MI 48331
Gale, part of Cengage Group
URL: www.gale.com

Small Business Sourcebook (*SBS*) provides information in a variety of forms and presentations for comprehensive coverage and ease of use. The directory contains four parts within six volumes:

- Specific Small Business Profiles
- General Small Business Topics
- State Listings
- Federal Government Assistance

Information on specific businesses is arranged by type of business; the many general topics that are of interest to the owners, operators, or managers of all small businesses are grouped in a separate section for added convenience. Users should consult the various sections to benefit fully from the information *SBS* offers. For example, an entrepreneur with a talent or interest in the culinary arts could peruse a number of specific small business profiles, such as Restaurant, Catering Service, Cooking School, Specialty/ Gourmet Food/Wine Shop, Food Truck, Healthy Restaurant, or Candy/Chocolate Shop. Secondly, the General Small Business Topics section could be consulted for any applicable subjects, such as Service Industry, Retailing, Franchising, and other relevant topics. Then, the appropriate state within the State Listings section would offer area programs and offices providing information and support to small businesses, including venture capital firms and small business development consultants. Finally, the Federal Government Assistance section could supply relevant government offices, such as procurement contacts.

Features Included in Volumes 1 and 2

List of Small Business Profiles. This list provides an alphabetic outline of the small businesses profiled. The page number for the beginning of each profile is indicated.

Standard Industrial Classification (SIC) Codes for Profiled Small Businesses. This section lists four-digit SIC codes and corresponding classification descriptions for the small businesses profiled in this edition. The SIC system, which organizes businesses by type, is a product of the Statistical Policy Division of the U.S. Office of Management and Budget. Statistical data produced by government, public, and private organizations is usually categorized according to SIC codes, thereby facilitating the collection, comparison, and analysis of data as well as providing a uniform method for presenting statistical information. Hence, knowing the SIC code for a particular small business increases access and the use of a variety of statistical data from many sources.

Guide to Publishers. This resource lists alphabetically the companies, associations, institutions, and individuals that publish the periodicals, directories, guidebooks, and other publications noted in the "Small Business Profiles" and "General Topics" sections. Users are provided with full contact information, including address, phone, fax, and e-mail and URL when available. The "Guide" facilitates contact with publishers and provides a one-stop resource for valuable information.

Glossary of Small Business Terms. This glossary defines nearly 400 small business terms, including financial, governmental, insurance, procurement, technical, and general business definitions. Cross-references and acronyms are also provided.

Small Business Profiles A-Z. More than 300 small business profiles are represented in volumes 1 and 2. Profiles are listed alphabetically by business type. Each profile may contain up to sixteen subheadings that correlate to a resource type; entries within are listed alphabetically. These resource types are detailed below:

- *Start-up Information*—Includes periodical articles, books, manuals, book excerpts, kits, and other sources of information. Entries offer title; publisher; address; phone, fax, toll-free numbers; company e-mail and URL addresses; and a description. Bibliographic data is provided for cited periodical articles whenever possible.

- *Associations and Other Organizations*—Includes trade and professional associations whose members gather and disseminate information of interest to small business owners. Entries offer the association's name; address; phone, toll-free and fax numbers; company e-mail address; contact name; purpose and objective; a description of membership; telecommunication services; and a listing of its publications, including publishing frequency.

- **Educational Programs**—Includes university and college programs, schools, training opportunities, association seminars, correspondence courses, and other educational programs. Entries offer name of program or institution, sponsor name, address, phone, toll-free and fax numbers, e-mail and URL addresses; and description of program.

- **Directories of Educational Programs**—Includes directories and other publications that list educational programs. Entries offer name of publication; publisher name, address, and phone, toll-free and fax numbers; editor; frequency or date of publication; price; and description of contents, including directory arrangement and indexes.

- **Reference Works**—Includes handbooks, manuals, textbooks, guides, directories, dictionaries, encyclopedias, and other published reference materials. Entries offer name of publication; publisher name, address, and phone, toll-free and fax numbers; e-mail and URL addresses; and, when available, name of author or editor, publication year or frequency, and price. A brief description is often featured.

- **Sources of Supply**—Includes buyer's guides, directories, special issues of periodicals, and other publications that list sources of equipment, supplies, and services related to the operation of the profiled small business. Entries offer publication name; publisher name, address, and phone, toll-free and fax numbers; e-mail and URL addresses; and, when available, editor's name, frequency or publication year, and price. A brief description of the publication, including directory arrangement and indexes, is often provided.

- **Statistical Sources**—Includes books, reports, pamphlets, and other sources of statistical data of interest to an owner, operator or manager of the profiled small business, such as wage, salary, and compensation data; financial and operating ratios; prices and costs; demographics; and other statistical information. Entries offer publication/data source name; publisher (if applicable); address; phone, toll-free and fax numbers of data source; publication date or frequency; and price. A brief description of the publication/data source is often provided.

- **Trade Periodicals**—Includes trade journals, newsletters, magazines, and other serials that offer information about the management and operation of the profiled small business. Such periodicals often contain industry news; trends and developments; reviews; articles about new equipment and supplies;

and other information related to business operations. Entries offer publication name; publisher name, address, phone, toll-free and fax numbers, and e-mail and URL addresses; editor name; publication frequency; and price. A brief description of the publication's content is also included, when known.

- **Video/Audio Media**—Includes videos, podcasts, and other audiovisual media offering information on the profiled small business. Entries offer program title; creator or distributor name, address, phone, toll-free and fax numbers, and e-mail and URL addresses; description of program; price; and format(s).

- **Trade Shows and Conventions**—Includes tradeshows, exhibitions, expositions, conventions, and other industry meetings that provide prospective and existing business owners with the opportunity to meet and exchange information with their peers, review commercial exhibits, establish business or sales contacts, and attend educational programs. Entries offer event name; sponsor or management company name, address, phone, toll-free and fax numbers, and e-mail and URL addresses; a description of the event, including audience, frequency, principal exhibits, and dates and locations of event for as many years ahead as provided by the event's sponsor.

- **Consultants**—Includes consultants and consulting organizations that provide services specifically related to the profiled small business. Entries offer individual consultant or consulting organization name, address, and phone, toll-free and fax numbers; company and individual e-mail addresses; and a brief description of consulting services. (For e-mail and URL addresses, see the Small Business Development Consultants subheadings in the State Listings section in Volume 2.)

- **Franchises and Business Opportunities**—Includes companies granting franchise licenses for enterprises falling within the scope of the profiled small business, as well as other non-franchised business opportunities that operate within a given network or system. Entries offer franchise name, address, phone, toll-free and fax numbers, and e-mail and URL addresses, as well as a description of the franchise or business opportunity, which has been expanded whenever possible to include the number of existing franchises, the founding date of the franchise, franchise fees, equity capital requirements, royalty fees, any managerial assistance offered, and available training.

- **Computerized Databases**—Includes diskettes, magnetic tapes, CD-ROMs, online systems, and other computer-readable databases. Entries offer database name; producer name, address, phone, toll-free and fax numbers, e-mail and URL addresses; description; and available format(s), including vendor name.

(Many university and public libraries offer online information retrieval services that provide searches of databases, including those listed in this category.)

- ***Computer Systems/Software***—Includes software and computerized business systems designed to assist in the operation of the profiled small business. Entries offer name of the software or system; publisher name, address, phone, toll-free and fax numbers; price; and description.

- ***Libraries***—Includes libraries and special collections that contain material especially applicable to the profiled small business. Entries offer library or collection name; parent organization (where applicable); address; phone, toll-free and fax numbers; e-mail and URL addresses; contact name and title; scope of collection; and description of holdings, subscriptions, and services.

- ***Research Centers***—Includes university-related and independently operated research institutes and information centers that generate, through their research programs, data related to the operation of the profiled small business. Also listed are associations and other business-related organizations that conduct research programs. Entries offer name of organization; address; phone, toll-free and fax numbers; company web site address; contact name and personal e-mail; a description of principal fields of research or services; publications, including title and frequency; and related conferences.

Features Included in Volumes 3 and 4

General Small Business Topics. This section offers chapters on different topics in the operation of any small business, for example, venture capital and other funding, or compensation. Chapters are listed alphabetically by small business topic; entries within each chapter are arranged alphabetically, within up to 14 subheadings, by resource type:

- ***Associations and Other Organizations***—Includes trade and professional associations that gather and disseminate information of interest to small business owners. Entries offer the association's name; address; phone, toll-free and fax numbers; organization e-mail and URL addresses; contact name; purpose and objectives; a description of membership; telecommunication services; and a listing of its publications, including publishing frequency.

- ***Educational Programs***—Includes university and college programs, schools, training opportunities, association seminars, correspondence courses, and other educational programs. Entries offer name of program or institution, sponsor name, address, phone, toll-free and fax numbers, e-mail and URL addresses, and description of program.

- ***Directories of Educational Programs***—Includes directories and other publications that list educational programs. Entries offer name of publication; publisher name, address, phone, toll-free and fax numbers, and e-mail and URL addresses; editor; frequency or date of publication; price; and description of contents, including arrangement and indexes.

- ***Reference Works***—Includes articles, handbooks, manuals, textbooks, guides, directories, dictionaries, encyclopedias, and other published reference materials. Entries offer title of article, including bibliographic information; name of publication; publisher name, address, phone, toll-free and fax numbers, and e-mail and URL addresses; and, when available, name of author or editor, publication year or frequency, and price. A brief description is often featured.

- ***Sources of Supply***—Includes buyer's guides, directories, special issues of periodicals, and other publications that list sources of equipment, supplies, and services. Entries offer publication name; publisher name, address, phone, toll-free and fax numbers, and e-mail and URL addresses; editor's name, frequency or publication year, price, and a brief description of the publication, when available.

- ***Statistical Sources***—Includes books, reports, pamphlets, and other sources of statistical data of interest to an owner, operator, or manager of a small business, such as wage, salary, and compensation data; financial and operating ratios; prices and costs; demographics; and other statistical information. Entries offer publication/data source name; publisher (if applicable); address; phone, toll-free and fax numbers of data source; publication date or frequency; and price. A brief description is often provided.

- ***Trade Periodicals***—Includes journals, newsletters, magazines, and other serials. Entries offer name of publication; publisher name, address, phone, toll-free and fax numbers, and e-mail and URL addresses; and name of editor, frequency, and price. A brief description of the periodical's content is included when known.

- ***Video/Audio Media***—Includes videos, podcasts, and other audiovisual media. Entries offer program title; distributor name, address, phone, toll-free and fax numbers, and e-mail and URL addresses; price; description of program; and format(s).

- ***Trade Shows and Conventions***—Includes tradeshows, exhibitions, expositions, seminars, and conventions. Entries offer event name; sponsor or management company name, address, phone, toll-free and fax numbers, and e-mail and URL addresses; frequency of event; and dates and locations of the event for as many years ahead as known.

- **Consultants**—Includes consultants and consulting organizations. Entries offer individual consultant or consulting organization name, address, and phone, toll-free and fax numbers; company and individual e-mail addresses; and a brief description of consulting services. (See also Consultants in the State Listings section.)

- **Computerized Databases**—Includes diskettes, CD-ROMs, magnetic tape, online systems and other computer-readable databases. Entries offer database name; producer, address, phone, toll-free and fax numbers, and e-mail and URL addresses; description; and available format(s), including vendor name. (Many university and public libraries offer online information retrieval services that provide searches of databases, including those listed in this category.)

- **Computer Systems/Software**—Includes software and computerized business systems. Entries offer name of the software or system; publisher name, address, phone, toll-free and fax numbers, and e-mail and URL addresses; price; and description.

- **Libraries**—Includes libraries and special collections that contain material applicable to the small business topic. Entries offer library or collection name, parent organization (where applicable), address, phone and fax numbers, e-mail and URL addresses, scope of collection, and description of holdings and services.

- **Research Centers**— Includes university-related and independently operated research institutes and information centers that generate, through their research programs, data related to specific small business topics. Entries offer name of organization, address, phone, toll-free and fax numbers, e-mail and URL addresses, a description of principal fields of research or services, and related conferences.

Features Included in Volumes 5 and 6

State Listings. This section lists various sources of information and assistance available within given states, territories, and Canadian provinces; entries include governmental, academic, and commercial agencies, and are arranged alphabetically within up to 15 subheadings by resource type:

- **Small Business Development Center Lead Office**— Includes the lead small business development center (SBDC) for each state.

- **Small Business Development Centers**—Includes any additional small business development centers (SBDC) in the state, territory, or province. SBDCs provide support services to small businesses, including individual counseling, seminars, conferences, and learning center activities.

- **Small Business Assistance Programs**—Includes state small business development offices and other programs offering assistance to small businesses.

- **SCORE Offices**—Includes SCORE office(s) for each state. The Service Corps of Retired Executives Association (SCORE), a volunteer program sponsored by the Small Business Administration, offers counseling, workshops, and seminars across the U.S. for small business entrepreneurs.

- **Better Business Bureaus**—Includes various better business bureaus within each state. By becoming a member of the local Better Business Bureau, a small business owner can increase the prestige and credibility of his or her business within the community, as well as make valuable business contacts.

- **Chambers of Commerce**—Includes various chambers of commerce within each state. Chambers of Commerce are valuable sources of small business advice and information; often, local chambers sponsor SCORE counseling several times per month for a small fee, seminars, conferences, and other workshops to its members. Also, by becoming a member of the local Chamber of Commerce, a small business owner can increase the prestige and credibility of his or her business within the community, as well as make valuable business contacts.

- **Minority Business Assistance Programs**—Includes minority business development centers and other sources of assistance for minority-owned business.

- **Financing and Loan Programs**—Includes venture capital firms, small business investment companies (SBIC), minority enterprise small business investment companies (MESBIC), and other programs that provide funding to qualified small businesses.

- **Procurement Assistance Programs**—Includes state services such as counseling, set-asides, and sheltered-market bidding, which are designed to aid small businesses in bidding on government contracts.

- **Incubators/Research and Technology Parks**— Includes small business incubators, which provide newly established small business owners with work sites, business services, training, and consultation; also includes research and technology parks, which sponsor research and facilitate commercialization of new technologies.

- **Educational Programs**—Includes university and college programs, as well as those sponsored by other organizations that offer degree, nondegree, certificate, and correspondence programs in entrepreneurship and in small business development.

- **Legislative Assistance**—Includes committees, subcommittees, and joint committees of each state's senate and house of representatives that are concerned with small business issues and regulations.

- **Consultants**—Includes consultants and consulting firms offering expertise in small business development.

- **Publications**—Includes publications related to small business operations within the profiled state.

- **Publishers**—Includes publishers operating in or for the small business arena within the profiled state.

- **Early Stage Financing**—Includes organizations offering early-stage capital needed to launch and grow new businesses.

- **Venture Capital Firm**—Includes organizations offering financial support to small, early-stage and emerging firms.

Federal Government Assistance. This section lists federal government agencies and offices, many with additional listings for specific offices, as well as regional or district branches. Main agencies or offices are listed alphabetically; regional, branch, or district offices are listed after each main office or agency.

Master Index. This index provides an alphabetic listing of all entries contained in Volumes 1 through 6. Citations are referenced by their entry numbers. Publication titles are rendered in italics.

List of General Small Business Topics

This section covers sources of assistance applicable to a variety of small businesses. Resources are arranged by topic and include associations, educational programs, directories of educational programs, reference works, sources of supply, statistical sources, periodicals, videocassettes/audiocassettes, trade shows and conventions, consultants, computerized databases, computer systems/software, Internet databases, libraries, and research centers.

START-UP INFORMATION

26479 ▪ *"The Toughest Sell: Women Hate to Buy Swimsuits, So Firms Try New Tack"* in *Inc. (Vol. 36, September 2014, No. 7, pp. 69)*
Pub: Mansueto Ventures L.L.C.
Contact: Stephanie Mehta, Chief Executive Officer
Description: Finding top talent for a new startup company is challenging. It is suggested that entrepreneurs should sell the challenges faced by the new firm when hiring new workers. Startup recruiting is examined. **Availability:** Print; Online.

REFERENCE WORKS

26480 ▪ *"4 Essential Hires if You're Starting a Business in 2020"* in *Bplans*
Ed: Andrew Deen. **Description:** Discusses the importance of investing in the expertise of select professionals with specialized skills in the early stages of your company. **Availability:** Online.

26481 ▪ *"4 Great Resources to Simplify Hiring"* in *Small Business Trends(December 10, 2018)*
URL(s): smallbiztrends.com/2018/12/simplify-hiring-small-business.html
Description: Discusses new tools available to small business owners for use in hiring. **Availability:** Online.

26482 ▪ *"5 Tips to Stay Labor Law Compliant"* in *Legal Zoom (February 10, 2023)*
URL(s): www.legalzoom.com/articles/5-tips-to-stay-labor-law-compliant
Ed: Belle Wong, J.D. **Released:** February 10, 2023.
Description: Make sure your small business is following labor laws by following the checklist provided. **Availability:** Online.

26483 ▪ *"7 Steps for Small Businesses To Hire Great Employees*
URL(s): www.salesforce.com/blog/small-business-hiring/
Ed: Noah Kravitz. **Description:** Offers information on how your small business can stay competitive in a job market that has more open positions than qualified candidates to fill them. **Availability:** Online.

26484 ▪ *12-Step Checklist for Hiring Employees*
URL(s): www.xero.com/us/resources/small-business-guides/checklists/hiring-employees/
Description: Discusses the importance of hiring the right employees for your small business and provides 12 steps to ensure you follow federal and state regulations before and after hiring employees. **Availability:** Online.

26485 ▪ *"14 Best Job Apps for Listing Your Open Positions"* in *Small Business Trends (January 19, 2022)*
URL(s): smallbiztrends.com/2021/10/best-job-apps.html

Ed: Annie Pilon. **Released:** October 21, 2021.
Description: Searching for employees can be difficult but small businesses can use some particular apps to help them find the best fit for their open positions. This article describes the top apps in this category. **Availability:** Online.

26486 ▪ *"14 Employee Recruitment Strategies for Success"* in *Business News Daily (Nov. 19, 2021)*
URL(s): www.businessnewsdaily.com/15821-small-business-recruitment-strategies.html
Ed: Adam Uzialko. **Released:** November 19, 2021.
Description: Presents 14 best practices for employee recruitment. **Availability:** Online.

26487 ▪ *"50 Best Companies for Diversity"* in *Black Enterprise (Vol. 38, July 2008, No. 12, pp. 12)*
Pub: Earl G. Graves Ltd.
Contact: Earl Graves, Jr., President

Description: Maintaining excellence in a company's diversity efforts requires critical challenges such as recruiting, retaining and developing talent in the executive pipeline. Top young and diverse emerging executives in corporate America are featured. **Availability:** Online.

26488 ▪ *"77% of Companies Expect to Encounter a Talent Shortage"* in *Small Business Trends (August 10, 2021)*
URL(s): smallbiztrends.com/2021/08/small-business-talent-shortage.html
Ed: Michael Guta. **Released:** August 10, 2021.
Description: Now that the economy is opening back up after the COVID pandemic, employers are expecting a talent shortage within their respective industries and are having issues with hiring. **Availability:** Online.

26489 ▪ *"$161.9M 'Pit Stop' Fix-Up Will Create About 1,600 Jobs"* in *Orlando Business Journal (Vol. 26, January 22, 2010, No. 34, pp. 1)*
Pub: Orlando Business Journal
Contact: Julie Swyers, Director
E-mail: jswyers@bizjournals.com
Ed: Anjali Fluker. **Description:** State of Florida will be providing $161.9 million to renovate eight service plazas November 2010. The project is expected to create 1,600 jobs across the state and is expected to be completed by 2012. Details on bid advertisements and facilities slated for improvement are discussed. **Availability:** Print; Online.

26490 ▪ *"Advancing the Ball"* in *Inside Healthcare (Vol. 6, December 2010, No. 7, pp. 31)*
Description: Profile of Medicalodges an elder-care specialty company that provides both patient care and technology development. President and CEO of the firm believes that hiring good employees is key to growth for any small business. **Availability:** Online.

26491 ▪ *"After Recession, Texas Cities Lead National Recovery"* in *Dallas Business Journal (Vol. 37, June 27, 2014, No. 42, pp. 28)*
Pub: American City Business Journals, Inc.
Contact: Mike Olivieri, Executive Vice President
Released: Weekly. **Price:** $4, introductory 4-week offer(Digital only). **Description:** A study of 510 U.S. cities by NeredWallet finds that 11 Texas cities are among those showing the fastest recovery since the recession began. NerdWallet analyst Sreekar Jasthi attributes this to growing business investment, rising employment, and an increase in median home values in cities such as Richardson and Gran Prairie. **Availability:** Print; Online.

26492 ▪ *"Apprenticeship: Earn While You Learn"* in *Occupational Outlook Quarterly (Vol. 54, Fall 2010, No. 3, pp. 24)*
Description: Paid training, or apprenticeships, are examined. Registered apprenticeship programs conform to certain guidelines and industry-established training standards and may be run by businesses, trade or professional associations, or partnerships with business and unions. **Availability:** Online.

26493 ▪ *"Ask Inc.: Managing and Real Estate to Build Value"* in *Inc. (December 2007, pp. 83-84)*
Ed: Ari Weinzweig. **Price:** $8.95. **Description:** Questions regarding knowledge management in the case of a retiring CFO, issues involved in opening a satellite office for a New York realtor, and information for hiring a multicultural workforce are all discussed. **Availability:** PDF; Online.

26494 ▪ *"At the Drugstore, the Nurse Will See You Now"* in *Globe & Mail (April 13, 2007, pp. B1)*
Ed: Marina Strauss. **Description:** The appointment of several health professionals including nurse, podiatrists, etc. by Rexall Co. at its drugstores to face competition from rivals, is discussed. **Availability:** Online.

26495 ▪ *"Austin-Based Insuraprise Growing Fast"* in *Austin Business Journal (Vol. 31, April 22, 2011, No. 7, pp. 1)*
Pub: Austin Business Journal
Contact: Rachel McGrath, Director
E-mail: rmcgrath@bizjournals.com
Ed: Sandra Zaragoza. **Description:** Austin, Texas-based Insuraprise Inc. is finalizing the purchase of a 24,000-square-foot office at 12116 Jekel Circle. The firm, with 23 salespeople and sales that are growing nearly 300 percent over the past 18 months, will now have room to grow. Insuraprise plans to hire 35 new salespersons for its call center. **Availability:** Print; Online.

26496 ▪ *"Baltimore-Area Hospital Tower Projects Could Add Hundreds of New Jobs"* in *Baltimore Business Journal (Vol. 28, June 25, 2010, No. 7, pp. 1)*
Pub: Baltimore Business Journal
Contact: Rhonda Pringle, President

E-mail: rpringle@bizjournals.com
Ed: Scott Graham. **Description:** Greater Baltimore, Maryland has four hospitals that are in the middle of transforming their campuses with new facilities for treating various patients. Construction at Mercy Medical Center, Johns Hopkins Hospital, Franklin Square Hospital and Anne Rundle Hospital has helped bring the construction industry back to life. Insights into the hiring plans of these hospitals are also included.

26497 ■ "Baptist Health System Plans to Expand Stone Oak-Area Hospital: $32 Million Project Will Add Two Floors, 100 Beds" in San Antonio Business Journal (Vol. 26, May 25, 2012, No. 17, pp. 1)
Pub: Baltimore Business Journal
Contact: Rhonda Pringle, President
E-mail: rpringle@bizjournals.com
Price: $4, introductory 4-week offer(Digital & Print).
Description: Baptist Health System is planning to start the $32 million expansion of the North Central Baptist Hospital in San Antonio, Texas that will include the addition of two floors and 100 beds. An estimate of hiring 200 new health care workers will be created by the expansion. **Availability:** Print; Online.

26498 ■ "BBB Tips: 7 Tips for Hiring a Cleaning Service" in International Association of Better Business Bureaus (April 28, 2020)
Released: April 28, 2020. **Description:** Provides tips on what customers are looking for when hiring cleaning services for their homes, home offices, and businesses. **Availability:** Online.

26499 ■ "The Bell Tolls for Thee" in Canadian Business (Vol. 81, March 3, 2008, No. 3, pp. 36)
Description: Bell Canada has formed the Canadian Coalition for Tomorrow's IT Skills to solve the shortage of technology talent in the country. Canada's total workforce has only around 4%, or 600,000 people employed in information technology-related fields. The aims of the Bell-led coalition, which is supported by different industry associations and 30 corporations, are investigated. **Availability:** Print; Online.

26500 ■ "Best Layoff Practices: Can You Lay Off and Hire at the Same Time?" in Business News Daily (March 7, 2023)
URL(s): www.businessnewsdaily.com/15913-lay-off -new-hires.html
Ed: Patrick Proctor. **Released:** March 07, 2023. **Description:** This article advises on how to handle layoffs at your small business. **Availability:** Online.

26501 ■ "Best (Professional) Foot Forward: Effective Marketing Strategies for any Phase of Your Career" in Black Enterprise (Vol. 44, June 2014, No. 10, pp. 44)
Pub: Earl G. Graves Ltd.
Contact: Earl Graves, Jr., President
Description: Because hiring managers face long-term vacancies and skills gaps, the importance of creating a professional marketing strategy when applying for a professional position is stressed. Advice is given to help guide applicants through the entire application, interviewing, and hiring process.

26502 ■ "BETC Backers Plot Future" in Business Journal Portland (Vol. 27, December 10, 2010, No. 41, pp. 1)
Pub: Portland Business Journal
Contact: Andy Giegerich, Managing Editor
E-mail: agiegerich@bizjournals.com
Ed: Erik Siemers. **Description:** A coalition of clean energy groups and industrial manufacturers have spearheaded a campaign aimed at persuading Oregon legislators that the state's Business Energy Tax Credit (BETC) is vital in job creation. Oregon's BETC grants tax credits for 50 percent of an eligible renewable or clean energy project's cost. However, some legislators propose BETC's abolition. **Availability:** Print; Online.

26503 ■ "Better than Advertised: Chip Plant Beats Expectations" in Business Review Albany (Vol. 41, June 27, 2014, No. 14, pp. 4)
Pub: American City Business Journals, Inc.
Contact: Mike Olivieri, Executive Vice President
Released: Weekly. **Price:** $4, introductory 4-week offer(Digital only). **Description:** The $8.5 billion computer chip manufacturing plant and research center of GlobalFoundries in Malta, New York has strengthened the local economy in Saratoga County and helped the local manufacturing and construction industries recover from the recession. The Malta Plant construction project created more than 2,000 direct new construction jobs and over 10,000 indirect positions. **Availability:** Print; Online.

26504 ■ "BioRASI Aims to Fill Larger HQ With More Jobs" in South Florida Business Journal (Vol. 34, April 11, 2014, N. 38, pp. 4)
Pub: American City Business Journals, Inc.
Contact: Mike Olivieri, Executive Vice President
Released: Weekly. **Price:** $8, Introductory 4-week offer(Digital & Print). **Description:** BioRASI has announced plans to hire an additional 20 or 30 workers in Florida in 2014 after moving into a larger headquarters in Aventura. The contract research organization added 40 employees during 2013 and now has 80 working in Florida. Other insights on BioRASI's growing presence in Florida are given. **Availability:** Print; Online.

26505 ■ "Bioscience Hiring Flat in Florida" in South Florida Business Journal (Vol. 34, July 4, 2014, No. 50, pp. 8)
Pub: American City Business Journals, Inc.
Contact: Mike Olivieri, Executive Vice President
Released: Weekly. **Price:** $8, introductory 4-week offer(Digital only); $8, introductory 4-week offer(Digital & Print). **Description:** The bioscience industry in Florida showed little growth in job creation since 2007, despite heavy state investments. The bioscience sector lost 1 percent of its jobs from 2007 to 2010, while the following two years only recovered the losses of previous years. **Availability:** Print; Online.

26506 ■ "Birmingham Tech Firms Eye Growth in 2014" in Birmingham Business Journal (Vol. 31, January 10, 2014, No. 2, pp. 4)
Pub: American City Business Journals, Inc.
Contact: Mike Olivieri, Executive Vice President
Released: Weekly. **Price:** $4, introductory 4-week offer(Digital & Print). **Description:** Birmingham, Alabama-based high-tech firms, ProctorU and Chronicle Studio are planning to expand their work forces in 2014. ProctorU will add more than 50 employees, while Chronicle will add three more positions to their staff. **Availability:** Print; Online.

26507 ■ "Black Gold: Jobs Aplenty" in Canadian Business (Vol. 79, August 14, 2006, No. 16-17, pp. 57)
Pub: Rogers Media Inc.
Contact: Neil Spivak, Chief Executive Officer
Ed: Erin Pooley. **Description:** A list of the top ten jobs in the petroleum industry in Canada along with pay and nature of jobs, is presented. **Availability:** Print; Online.

26508 ■ "Bob's Discount Furniture Moving into Harford County, Region" in Baltimore Business Journal (Vol. 27, January 22, 2010, No. 38, pp. 1)
Pub: Baltimore Business Journal
Contact: Rhonda Pringle, President
E-mail: rpringle@bizjournals.com
Ed: Daniel J. Sernovitz. **Description:** Manchester, Connecticut-based Bob's Discount Furniture signed a lease for 672,000 square feet of space in Harford County, Maryland. The site will become the discount furniture retailer's distribution center in mid-Atlantic US. As many as 200 jobs could be generated when the center opens. **Availability:** Print; Online.

26509 ■ "Boom has Tech Grads Mulling Their Options" in Globe & Mail (March 14, 2006, pp. B1)
Ed: Grant Robertson. **Description:** Internet giant Google Inc. has stepped up its efforts to hire the talented people, in Canada, at Waterloo University in southern Ontario, to expand its operations. The details of the job market and increasing salaries are analyzed. **Availability:** Online.

26510 ■ "Building a Workforce" in Business Journal Milwaukee (Vol. 29, July 27, 2012, No. 44, pp. 1)
Ed: Rich Kirchen. **Description:** Governor Scott Walker's 'Wisconsin Working' initiative head Tim Sullivan announced that he will recommend the encouragement of immigration to meet current and future employment needs of the state. Sullivan believes immigration could help address the worker skills shortage that affected many southeaster Wisconsin businesses. **Availability:** Print; Online.

26511 ■ "Business Looks for Results in Congress" in Baltimore Business Journal (Vol. 28, November 5, 2010, No. 26, pp. 1)
Pub: Baltimore Business Journal
Contact: Rhonda Pringle, President
E-mail: rpringle@bizjournals.com
Ed: Kent Hoover. **Description:** Republican candidates in the 2010 Congressional elections were overwhelmingly supported by the business community. Republican John Boehner, who will be the next Speaker of the House, says that the party's victory would end economic uncertainty and would assist small businesses to rehire workers. **Availability:** Print; Online.

26512 ■ "Call for Superblock Jobs Tie-In Lacks Baltimore Backing" in Baltimore Business Journal (Vol. 30, June 1, 2012, No. 4, pp. 1)
Pub: American City Business Journals, Inc.
Contact: Mike Olivieri, Executive Vice President
Ed: James Briggs. **Description:** Officials of Baltimore, Maryland are seen to turn down the proposal to mandate local hiring rules for Lexington Square Partners. The plan is in line with the company's push for tax breaks on its superblock project. **Availability:** Print; Online.

26513 ■ "Campbell Clinic in Expansion Mode: Plans to Triple Size of Surgery Center, Add Employees" in Memphis Business Journal (Vol. 34, August 24, 2012, No. 19, pp. 1)
Pub: Baltimore Business Journal
Contact: Rhonda Pringle, President
E-mail: rpringle@bizjournals.com
Description: The Campbell Clinic Inc. is pushing forward with its plan to expand and hire new employees. The clinic has filed a Certificate of Need with the Tennessee Health Services Development Agency worth $13 million. Expansion projects include the enlargement of the surgery center, which handles 700 cases a month, a figure which is expected to rise to 750 in August 2012. **Availability:** Print; Online.

26514 ■ "Cancer-Fighting Entrepreneurs" in Austin Business Journal (Vol. 31, August 5, 2011, No. 22, pp. 1)
Pub: Austin Business Journal
Contact: Rachel McGrath, Director
E-mail: rmcgrath@bizjournals.com
Ed: Sandra Zaragoza. **Description:** Cancer Prevention and Research Institute of Texas has invested $10 million in recruiting known faculty to the University of Texas. The move is seen to bolster Austin's position as a major cancer research market. The institute has awarded grants to researchers Jonghwan Kim, Guangbin Dong and Kyle Miller. **Availability:** Print; Online.

26515 ■ "Capital One Expanding Campus in Plano" in Dallas Business Journal (Vol. 35, April 20, 2012, No. 2, pp. 1)
Pub: Baltimore Business Journal
Contact: Rhonda Pringle, President
E-mail: rpringle@bizjournals.com

Ed: Candace Carlisle. **Description:** The financial services division of Capital One Financial Corporation in Plano, Texas will hire an additional 300 employees and start construction of two office buildings and 2,600-space parking garage in summer 2012. Cost of the 400,000-square-foot office space is estimated at $76 million and $19.5 million for the garage. **Availability:** Print; Online.

26516 ■ *"Capital Position: M&I Acquisition Opens the Door for Rivals to Gain Market Share"* in *Business Journal-Milwaukee (Vol. 28, December 24, 2010, No. 12, pp. A1)*
Pub: The Business Journal
Contact: Heather Ladage, President
E-mail: hladage@bizjournals.com

Ed: Rich Kirchen. **Description:** Canada-based BMO Financial Group has purchased Marshall and Isley Corporation (M and I), which dominated lending among Wisconsin businesses for decades. The sale of M and I will enable other banks to recruit M and I's customers but BMO Financial remains a stronger competitor since it possesses a more potent capital position. **Availability:** Print; Online.

26517 ■ *"Capitol Ideas: Regions to Lansing: Focus on Taxes, Reform, Keeping Talent"* in *Crain's Detroit Business (Vol. 24, October 6, 2008)*
Pub: Crain Communications Inc.
Contact: Barry Asin, President

Ed: Amy Lane. **Description:** Michigan must make bold and dramatic changes in public policy regarding business legislation. The tax structure, unemployment issues and attracting and retaining talent are among the issues the state must confront, especially in this tough economic climate. **Availability:** Online.

26518 ■ *"The CEO Poll: Split on Migrant Workers"* in *Canadian Business (Vol. 83, September 14, 2010, No. 15, pp. 23)*
Pub: Rogers Media Inc.
Contact: Neil Spivak, Chief Executive Officer

Ed: Jacqueline Nelson. **Description:** A survey of Canadian CEOs shows that 49 percent of the respondents believe it was wrong to suspend the immigration programs and companies should be allowed to hire the most skilled workers regardless of citizenship. However, 42 percent believe the suspension was right because employment of Canadians must take precedence. **Availability:** Print; Online.

26519 ■ *"Charged Up for Sales"* in *Charlotte Business Journal (Vol. 25, October 15, 2010, No. 30, pp. 1)*
Description: Li-Ion Motors Corporation is set to expand its production lines of electric cars in Sacramento, California. The plan is seen to create up to 600 jobs. The company's total investment is seen to reach $500 million. **Availability:** Print; Online.

26520 ■ *"Cincinnati Consults Executives on Police Chief Hire"* in *Business Courier (Vol. 27, August 27, 2010, No. 17, pp. 1)*
Pub: Business Courier

Ed: Dan Monk, Lucy May. **Description:** The City of Cincinnati, Ohio has begun a selection process for the new police chief by consulting the city's business executives. The city charter amendment known as Issue 5 has removed civil service protection from the chief's post and enables City Manager Milton Dohoney to hire a chief from outside the department. **Availability:** Print; Online.

26521 ■ *"Citadel Hires Three Lehman Execs"* in *Chicago Tribune (October 2, 2008)*
Description: Citadel Investment Group LLC, Chicago hedge-fund operator, has hired three former senior executives of bankrupt investment banker Lehman Brothers Holding Inc. Citadel believes that the company's hiring spree will help them to further expand the firm's capabilities in the global fixed income business. **Availability:** Online.

26522 ■ *"CitiMortgage to Hire Hundreds in Dallas-Fort Worth"* in *Dallas Business Journal (Vol. 35, April 20, 2012, No. 32, pp. 1)*
Pub: Baltimore Business Journal
Contact: Rhonda Pringle, President
E-mail: rpringle@bizjournals.com

Ed: Jeff Bounds. **Description:** Citibank NA mortgage lending and servicing arm of CitMortgage is hiring at least 750 employees to work with borrowers in relation to a $2.2 billion settlement of alleged questionable foreclosure practices. Most of the staff will work in Dallas-Fort Worth, Texas in areas such as default servicing, refinancing an single points of contact as required under the settlement. **Availability:** Print; Online.

26523 ■ *"Colorado Statehouse Races Key for Business"* in *Denver Business Journal (Vol. 64, August 31, 2012, No. 15, pp. 1)*
Pub: Baltimore Business Journal
Contact: Rhonda Pringle, President
E-mail: rpringle@bizjournals.com

Description: The elections for Colorado's Senate and House of Representatives can have a great impact on the state's economy. Republicans are focusing on regulatory-reform measures, while Democrats are pushing for bidding priorities given to companies that buy and hire locally. Experts state that Republican and Democratic candidates seem to agree on job-creation proposals. **Availability:** Print; Online.

26524 ■ *"Conducting Effective Reference Checks For Your Food Truck"* in *Mobile-Cuisine.com (2020)*
Ed: Richard Myrick. **Description:** Provides steps on successfully hiring food truck staff members. **Availability:** Online.

26525 ■ *"CradlePoint Is Adding Workers, Seeking More Space"* in *Idaho Business Review (September 3, 2014)*
Pub: BridgeTower Media
Contact: Adam Reinebach, President

Price: $11.99, Print, Digital & Mobile(1 Month); 149, Print, Digital & Mobile(1 Year); 99, Digital & Mobile Only(1 Year); $99, Digital & Mobile Only(For 1 Year); $9.95, Print, Digital & Mobile (For 1 Month Intro Rate); $149, Print, Digital & Mobile(For 1 Year). **Description:** CradlePoint makes networking routers and software, focusing on security for businesses. The firm is hiring new workers at a rate higher than predicted and is seeking new office space in downtown Boise, Idaho. CradlePoint is a major player in the growing wireless service and cloud platform market and is growing faster than its competitors. **Availability:** Print; Online.

26526 ■ *"Crain's Makes Ad Sales, Custom Marketing Appointments"* in *Crain's Chicago Business (Vol. 34, October 24, 2011, No. 42, pp. 13)*
Pub: Crain Communications Inc.
Contact: Barry Asin, President

Description: Crain's Chicago Business announced key appointments in its sales department: David Denor has been named first director of custom marketing services and Kate Van Etten will succeed Denor as advertising director. **Availability:** Online.

26527 ■ *"Craning for Workers: Seattle Is Full of Cranes, but Not Enough Operators"* in *Puget Sound Business Journal (Vol. 35, August 15, 2014, No. 17, pp. 4)*
Pub: American City Business Journals, Inc.
Contact: Mike Olivieri, Executive Vice President

Released: August 15, 2014. **Description:** The U.S. Department of Labor statistics show that Washington State has 15, 510 laborers in 2013. However, construction companies are having difficulty hiring skilled workers, particularly as apprentices. The Associated General Contractors of Washington's expansion of training slots for crane and other heave equipment operators is discussed. **Availability:** Print; Online.

26528 ■ *"Crucible: Battling Back from Betrayal"* in *Harvard Business Review (Vol. 88, December 2010, No. 12, pp. 130)*
Pub: Harvard Business Publishing
Contact: Diane Belcher, Managing Director

Ed: Daniel McGinn. **Price:** $8.95, PDF. **Description:** Stephen Greer's scrap metal firm, Hartwell Pacific, lost several million dollars due to a lack of efficient and appropriate inventory audits, accounting procedures, and new-hire reference checks for his foreign operations. Greer believes that balancing growth with control is a key component of success. **Availability:** Print; PDF.

26529 ■ *"Crucible: Losing the Top Job - And Winning It Back"* in *Harvard Business Review (Vol. 88, October 2010, No. 10, pp. 136)*
Pub: Harvard Business Publishing
Contact: Diane Belcher, Managing Director

Ed: Alison Beard. **Price:** $8.95, PDF. **Description:** Michael Mack chronicles the changes in perspectives that occurred when he was fired from Garden Fresh, a restaurant firm he co-owned. Once again at the company helm, he is now more receptive to outside input and acknowledges the importance of work-life balance. **Availability:** Online; PDF.

26530 ■ *"Cultural Due Diligence"* in *Canadian Business (Vol. 80, April 23, 2007, No. 9, pp. 60)*
Description: The factors to be considered by job seekers during judging good workplace with relation to corporate culture are presented. **Availability:** Download; PDF; Online.

26531 ■ *"Custom Fit"* in *Canadian Business (Vol. 80, November 19, 2007, No. 23, pp. 42)*
Description: Proper employee selection will help ensure a company has the people with the skills it really needs. Employee development is integral in coping with changes in the company. The importance of hiring the right employee and developing his skills is examined. **Availability:** Print; Online.

26532 ■ *"Customizing a Job Application Template to Fit Your Business"* in *Legal Zoom (February 15, 2023)*
URL(s): www.legalzoom.com/articles/customizing-a-job-application-template-to-fit-your-business

Ed: Diane Faulkner. **Released:** February 15, 2023. **Description:** Follow these tips to create a job application template that will help you hire the people you need. **Availability:** Online.

26533 ■ *"Dallas Top-Performing City for Small Business Growth"* in *Dallas Business Journal (Vol. 37, July 11, 2014, No. 44, pp. 13)*
Pub: American City Business Journals, Inc.
Contact: Mike Olivieri, Executive Vice President

Released: Weekly. **Price:** $4, introductory 4-week offer(Digital only). **Description:** Dallas has been ranked as Texas' top-performing metropolitan area for small business job growth in 2014. The 1.07 percent growth rate spike placed Dallas at 104.02 on the index, and it was observed that the market conditions and economy of Dallas made it easier to start a new business. It is reported that though the index indicated a drop, small business job growth in Dallas remained at a record high. **Availability:** Print; Online.

26534 ■ *"Data Deep Dive: Supporting and Hiring Individuals with Disabilities and Neurodivergence"* in *U.S. Chamber of Commerce (Aug. 25, 2022)*
URL(s): www.uschamber.com/workforce/data-deep-dive-supporting-and-hiring-individuals-with-disabilities-and-neurodivergence

Ed: Stephanie Ferguson. **Released:** August 25, 2022. **Description:** Discusses how businesses can give themselves a competitive edge when it comes to hiring by demonstrating their commitment to diversity, equity, and inclusion (DEI). **Availability:** Online.

26535 ■ "David Maus Debuting New Dealership" in Orlando Business Journal (Vol. 26, February 5, 2010, No. 36, pp. 1)
Pub: Orlando Business Journal
Contact: Julie Swyers, Director
E-mail: jswyers@bizjournals.com

Ed: Anjali Fluker. **Description:** Automotive dealers David Maus Automotive Group and Van Tuyl Automotive Investment Group will launch David Maus Chevrolet in Sanford, Florida in fall 2010. The 12-acre site of the Chevy dealership will be located adjacent to the David Maus Toyota dealership. The new store is expected to generate nearly 125 new jobs. **Availability:** Print; Online.

26536 ■ "Dealer Gets a Lift with Acquisitions at Year's End" in Crain's Detroit Business (Vol. 26, January 11, 2010, No. 2, pp. 3)
Pub: Crain Communications Inc.
Contact: Barry Asin, President

Ed: Ryan Beene. **Description:** Alta Equipment Co., a forklift dealer, closed 2009 with a string of acquisitions expecting to double the firm's employee headcount and triple its annual revenue. Alta Lift Truck Services, Inc., as the company was known before the acquisitions, was founded in 1984 as Michigan's dealer for forklift manufacturer Yale Materials Handling Corp. **Availability:** Print; Online.

26537 ■ "Debt-Collection Agency to Lay Off 368 in Hampton Center" in Virginian-Pilot (December 4, 2010)
Pub: The Virginian-Pilot
Contact: Kevin Goyette, Director
E-mail: kgoyette@dailypress.com

Ed: Tom Shean. **Description:** NCO Financial Systems Inc., provider of debt-collection and outsourcing services, will permanently lay off 368 workers at its Hampton call center in 2011. **Availability:** Print; Online.

26538 ■ "Decorated Marine Sues Contractor" in Wall Street Journal Eastern Edition (November 29, 2011, pp. A4)
Pub: Dow Jones & Company Inc.
Contact: Almar Latour, Chief Executive Officer

Ed: Julian E. Barnes. **Description:** Marine Devon Maylie, who was awarded the Congressional Medal of Honor for bravery, has filed a lawsuit against defense contractor BAE Systems PLC claiming that the company prevented his hiring by another firm by saying he has a mental condition and a drinking problem. Maylie says that this was in retaliation for his objections to the company's plan to sell the Pakistani military high-tech sniper scopes. **Availability:** Online.

26539 ■ "Determining Your Food Truck Employee Needs" in Mobile-Cuisine.com (September 8, 2020)
Ed: Richard Myrick. **Released:** September 08, 2020. **Description:** Detailed information on determining food truck employee wants and needs. **Availability:** Online.

26540 ■ "Dexter Gauntlett Gauges the Wind" in Business Journal Portland (Vol. 30, January 31, 2014, No. 48, pp. 6)
Pub: American City Business Journals, Inc.
Contact: Mike Olivieri, Executive Vice President

Released: Weekly. **Price:** $4, Introductory 4-week offer(Digital & Print). **Description:** Navigant Research senior research analyst, Dexter Gauntlett says Vestas-American Wind Systems could boost its revenues. He added that the company has being hiring employees at its manufacturing plants. Gauntlett also said that wind energy will greatly boost state renewable portfolios. **Availability:** Print; Online.

26541 ■ "Disunion in the House: the Steep Price We Pay" in Philadelphia Business Journal (Vol. 33, March 28, 2014, No. 7, pp. 4)
Pub: American City Business Journals, Inc.
Contact: Mike Olivieri, Executive Vice President

Released: Weekly. **Price:** $4, introductory 4-week offer(Digital & Print). **Description:** Some members of the Ironworkers Local 401 Union in Philadelphia, Pennsylvania face federal indictment on charges of participating in an alleged conspiracy to commit extortion, arson, assault and destruction of property. The alleged motive of their actions was to force construction contractors to hire union ironworkers. **Availability:** Print; Online.

26542 ■ "Do You Have A Retirement Parachute?" in Barron's (Vol. 88, July 7, 2008, No. 27, pp. 32)
Pub: Dow Jones & Company Inc.
Contact: Almar Latour, Chief Executive Officer

Ed: Jane White. **Description:** The idea that American companies should emulate the Australian retirement system which implements a forced contribution rate for all employers regarding an adequate retirement plan for their employees is discussed. **Availability:** Online.

26543 ■ "Downtowns Must Court Young, CEOs for Cities President Says" in Crain's Detroit Business (Vol. 24, October 6, 2008, No. 40, pp. 18)
Description: It is important to produce more college graduates, and keep them in Michigan, according to CEOs for Cities President Carol Coletta when she spoke to a session at the West Michigan Regional Policy Conference which was held in September in Grand Rapids. Ways in which city leaders can connect students to communities, resulting in employees who have vested interest in the region, are also discussed.

26544 ■ "Duro Bag to Expand, Add 130 Jobs" in Business Courier (Vol. 27, August 6, 2010, No. 14, pp. 1)
Pub: Business Courier
Ed: Jon Newberry. **Description:** Duro Bag Manufacturing Company will expand capacity at its Florence, Kentucky plant and will add around 130 jobs over the next few years. The state of Kentucky has given preliminary approval for up to $1 million in tax incentives over 10 years, tied to the creation of new jobs. The company's investment will include new production and packaging equipment and building improvements. **Availability:** Print; Online.

26545 ■ "Electrolux Nears Product Testing" in Memphis Business Journal (Vol. 34, September 21, 2012, No. 23, pp. 1)
Pub: Baltimore Business Journal
Contact: Rhonda Pringle, President
E-mail: rpringle@bizjournals.com

Ed: Michael Sheffield. **Description:** Electrolux Home Products Inc.'s new manufacturing facility is expected to be ready for use by the end of September 2012. The company will start producing 'pilot' products once the testing of manufacturing systems is completed. Electrolux will also hire 200 employees who will assemble the first products ready for shipmenht in the first quarter of 2013. **Availability:** Print; Online.

26546 ■ "Elon Musk's Solar Firm Is Nearly Doubling Its Massachusetts Workforce" in Boston Business Journal (Vol. 34, May 30, 2014, No. 17, pp. 3)
Pub: American City Business Journals, Inc.
Contact: Mike Olivieri, Executive Vice President

Released: Weekly. **Description:** SolarCity is planning to add 100 jobs to its Massachusetts operations. The solar panel firm opened a second operations center in the state. State business incentives have enabled the company to expand presence in the area. **Availability:** Print; Online.

26547 ■ "Empathy: An Entrepreneur's Killer App" in Women Entrepreneur (February 3, 2009)
Description: It is just as important to treat employees with courtesy and respect during bad economic times as it is in a good economy. Employers sometimes take advantage of such bad economic times since they realize that employees are grateful to have a job

and cannot just quit and easily find work elsewhere. The importance of empathy in a company's leadership personnel is discussed. **Availability:** Online.

26548 ■ "Employee vs. Independent Contractor: What Employers Need to Know" in Legal Zoom (March 24, 2023)
URL(s): www.legalzoom.com/articles/employee-vs-independent-contractor-what-employers-need-to-know

Ed: Diane Faulkner. **Released:** March 24, 2023. **Description:** Discusses the differences between hiring someone as an employee versus an independent contractor. A list of things to look for from the Department of Labor is given. **Availability:** Online.

26549 ■ "Employer Guide to Tax Credits for Hiring Employees With Disabilities" in U.S. Chamber of Commerce (Aug. 25, 2022)
URL(s): www.uschamber.com/workforce/employer-guide-to-tax-credits-for-hiring-employees-with-disabilities

Ed: Jenna Shrove. **Released:** August 25, 2022. **Description:** Provides tax credit information for businesses that hire employees with disabilities. **Availability:** Online.

26550 ■ "Employment and Unemployment Among Youth - Summer 2010" in Montly Labor Review (Vol. 133, September 2010, No. 9, pp. 2)
Pub: U.S. Department of Labor Bureau of Labor Statistics
Contact: Amrit Kohli, Director
E-mail: kohli.amrit@bls.gov

Description: The number of youth 16 to 24 years old rose by 1.8 million from April to July 2010. Statistical data included. **Availability:** PDF; Online.

26551 ■ "End of an Era" in Barron's (Vol. 88, July 7, 2008, No. 27, pp. 3)
Ed: Alan Abelson. **Released:** January 01, 2016. **Description:** June 2008 was a very bad month for US stocks, with investors losing as much as 41.9 percent in the first half of 2008 signaling an end to the financial environment that prevailed around the world since the 1980's. The US job market lost 62,000 jobs in June 2008. **Availability:** Print; Online.

26552 ■ "Enriching the Ecosystem: A Four-Point Plan for Linking Innovation, Enterprises, and Jobs" in Harvard Business Review (Vol. 90, March 2012, No. 3, pp. 140)
Pub: Harvard Business Review Press
Contact: Moderna V. Pfizer, Contact

Ed: Rosabeth Moss Kanter. **Price:** $8.95, hardcopy black and white. **Description:** The four goals for enriching the ecosystem include: linking venture creation and knowledge creation to speed up the idea-to-enterprise transition; revitalizing small-, medium-, and large-sized firms via partnerships; improving matches between education and employment opportunities; and bringing together leaders across different sectors to create regional strategies. **Availability:** Print; PDF; Online.

26553 ■ "Essex Leases Space for Largest Retail Store" in Memphis Business Journal (Vol. 34, September 28, 2012, No. 24, pp. 1)
Pub: Baltimore Business Journal
Contact: Rhonda Pringle, President
E-mail: rpringle@bizjournals.com

Description: Essex Technology Group Inc. will build its third Memphis, Tennessee-area store in DeSoto County. The company signed a five-year, 69,342-square-foot lease at Stateline Square in Southaven. The new facility, which could open by January 2013, is expected to hire 30-35 employees. **Availability:** Print; Online.

26554 ■ "Evaluating the 1996-2006 Employment Projections" in Montly Labor Review (Vol. 133, September 2010, No. 9, pp. 33)
Pub: U.S. Department of Labor Bureau of Labor Statistics
Contact: Amrit Kohli, Director

E-mail: kohli.amrit@bls.gov
Description: Bureau of Labor Statistics employment projections outperformed alternative naive models, but not projecting the housing bubble or the rise in oil prices caused some inaccuracies in the projects. These projections are used by policymakers, economists, and students. **Availability:** PDF; Online.

26555 ■ *"Even Money on Recession"* in *Barron's (Vol. 88, March 10, 2008, No. 10, pp. M9)*
Pub: Dow Jones & Company Inc.
Contact: Almar Latour, Chief Executive Officer
Ed: Gene Epstein. **Description:** Discusses the US unemployment rate which was steady in February 2008 at 4.8 percent, while nonfarm payroll employment decreased by 63,000 in the same month, with the private sector losing 101,000 jobs. The economic indicators showed mixed signals on whether or not the US economy is in a recession. **Availability:** Online.

26556 ■ *"Face Time: Fastenal founder Bob Kierlin and CEO Will Oberton"* in *Business Journal (Vol. 31, January 31, 2014, No. 36, pp. 9)*
Pub: American City Business Journals, Inc.
Contact: Mike Olivieri, Executive Vice President
Released: Weekly. **Price:** $4, Introductory 4-week offer(Digital & Print). **Description:** Fastenal founder, Bob Kierline, keeps hiring standards high in order to promote his firm's growth. He also said Fastenal's School of Business employs 40 licensed teachers. Their CEO, Will Oberton, said the company has done a better job in customer relations than its competitors. **Availability:** Print; Online.

26557 ■ *"Falcons' Blank Kicking Off 'Westside Works' Job Training Program"* in *Atlanta Business Chronicle (May 30, 2014, pp. 6A)*
Pub: American City Business Journals, Inc.
Contact: Mike Olivieri, Executive Vice President
Description: Arthur Blank, owner of the Atlanta Falcons, is kicking off 'Westside Works', an initiative to build a world-class football/soccer stadium in Atlanta and transform the adjacent communities. Westside Works, a partnership between The Arthur M. Blank Family Foundation, the Construction Education Foundation of Georgia, and Integrity CDC will provide construction jobs for at least 100 men and women from the Westside neighborhoods in the next 12 months. The program will also provide job training, skills assessment, adult education programs, interview preparedness, and job placement. **Availability:** Print; Online.

26558 ■ *"Filling the Business Gap"* in *Hispanic Business (December 2010)*
Description: New York group seeks to increase state diversity supplier spending to help create jobs and boost the economy. According to a recent study, six out of 10 small business owners will increase capital spending but delay hiring in 2011. However, potential job creation is good among businesses owned by women and minorities. **Availability:** Print; Online.

26559 ■ *"FirstMerit's Top Executive Turns Around Credit Quality"* in *Crain's Cleveland Business (Vol. 28, October 15, 2007, No. 41, pp. 3)*
Pub: Crain Communications Inc.
Contact: K. C. Crain, President
Ed: Shawn A. Turner. **Description:** Discusses the ways in which chairman and CEO Paul Greig has been able to improve FirstMerit Corp.'s credit quality and profit margin. Strategies included selling more than $70 million in bad loans, hiring a new chief credit officer and redirecting its focus on cross-selling its wealth and investment services to its commercial customers. Statistical data included. **Availability:** Online.

26560 ■ *"Four Common Hiring Mistakes Small Businesses Should Avoid in This Unprecedented Labor Market"* in *The Business Journals (Sept. 29, 2021)*
URL(s): www.bizjournals.com/bizjournals/news/2021/09/23/hiring-mistakes-avoid.html

Ed: Ty West. **Released:** September 23, 2021. **Description:** Small business hiring has become extremely competitive in the Covid-19 era. This article details four common hiring mistakes small business owners should avoid in this unique labor market. **Availability:** Online.

26561 ■ *"Frontage Labs Moves, Plans to Hire 100"* in *Philadelphia Business Journal (Vol. 28, July 13, 2012, No. 22, pp. 1)*
Pub: Baltimore Business Journal
Contact: Rhonda Pringle, President
E-mail: rpringle@bizjournals.com
Ed: Natalie Kostelni, John George. **Description:** Frontage Pharmaceuticals will relocate its headquarters from the Valley Creek Corporate Center in Exton, Pennsylvania after signing a long-term lease on 80,000 square feet of space at the Eagleview Corporate Center. The relocation came as the company intended to consolidate its offices. Frontage Pharmaceuticals will also hire up to 100 new employees. **Availability:** Print; Online.

26562 ■ *"The Future Is Another Country; Higher Education"* in *The Economist (Vol. 390, January 3, 2009, No. 8612, pp. 43)*
Description: Due to the growth of the global corporation, more ambitious students are studying at universities abroad; the impact of this trend is discussed. **Availability:** Print; Online.

26563 ■ *"Gilt Groupe's CEO On Building a Team of A Players"* in *Harvard Business Review (Vol. 90, January-February 2012, No.1-2, pp. 43)*
Pub: Harvard Business Review Press
Contact: Moderna V. Pfizer, Contact
Ed: Kevin Ryan. **Description:** The author stresses the role of human capital in a firm's success, and the importance of employment references in determining a candidate's talents. Key questions include whether the reference would hire the person, whether people enjoy working with him or her, and what areas could use improvements.

26564 ■ *"The Great Fall: Here Comes The Humpty Dumpty Economy"* in *Barron's (Vol. 88, March 10, 2008, No. 10, pp. 5)*
Pub: Dow Jones & Company Inc.
Contact: Almar Latour, Chief Executive Officer
Ed: Alan Abelson. **Description:** Discusses the US economy is considered to be in a recession, with the effects of the credit crisis expected to intensify as a result. Inflation is estimated at 4.3 percent in January 2008, while 63,000 jobs were lost in February 2008. **Availability:** Online.

26565 ■ *"The Green Industry Jobs Gap"* in *Green Industry Pro (Vol. 23, October 2011)*
Ed: Gregg Wartgow. **Description:** According to the U.S. Bureau of Labor Statistics, the landscaping industry employs over 829,000 workers. According to another private study, the industry would employ more if they were able to find more people interested in performing the required work. **Availability:** Online.

26566 ■ *"Green Light"* in *The Business Journal-Portland (Vol. 25, July 11, 2008, No. 18, pp. 1)*
Description: Ecos Consulting, a sustainability consulting company based in Portland, Oregon, is seeing a boost in revenue as more businesses turn to sustainable practices. The company's revenue rose by 50 percent in 2007 and employees increased from 57 to 150. Other details about Ecos' growth are discussed. **Availability:** Print; Online.

26567 ■ *"Growing Encryptics Trades Frisco for Austin"* in *Austin Business Journal (Vol. 34, April 25, 2014, No. 10, pp. A8)*
Pub: American City Business Journals, Inc.
Contact: Mike Olivieri, Executive Vice President
Released: Weekly. **Price:** $4, Introductory 4-week offer(Digital & Print). **Description:** Frisco, Texas-based Encryptics Inc. has announced plans to relocate its headquarters with its 21 employees and negotiating for office space in West Austin's Loop

360 area. Encryptics also plans to increase the number of its employees to about 80 next year. Insights into Encryptics' email security software area also given. **Availability:** Print; Online.

26568 ■ *"Guidance On Career Guidance for Offender Reentry"* in *Occupational Outlook Quarterly (Vol. 54, Fall 2010, No. 3, pp. 24)*
Description: Stable employment is a key factor in the successful rehabilitation of law offenders. The National Institute of Corrections hopes to improve offenders' long-term employment prospects. **Availability:** Print; Online.

26569 ■ *"Hello, and Goodbye"* in *Entrepreneur (June 2014)*
Released: December 19, 2015. **Description:** Companies must implement strategies to ensure the creation of an ethical workplace. They must be able to deal with clients that experience problems and try to bully their counterparts as a result. Executive search firms must be responsible for compensating new executive hires by helping them find new jobs. Businesses must communicate to their employees about their importance as a way of making them feel appreciated and, thus, contribute to ethical behavior. **Availability:** Online.

26570 ■ *"Help Wanted: Only the Best Need Apply"* in *Pet Product News (Vol. 66, April 2012, No. 4, pp. 24)*
Description: Simi Valley, California-based pet supplies store, Theresa's Country Feed and Pet is said to have achieved success by hiring quality customer-oriented employees. In view of its receipt of the Pet Product News International's 2011-2012 Retailer of the Year Award for Outstanding General Pet Store, Theresa's approach to recruitment and customer relations are discussed. **Availability:** Print; Online.

26571 ■ *"Hickory Unemployment Stays Steady"* in *Charlotte Observer (February 2, 2007)*
Description: Unemployment rates remained unchanged in Hickory, North Carolina area; the region reported 6.1 percent unemployment.

26572 ■ *"High-Tech Job-Apalooza!"* in *Orlando Business Journal (Vol. 26, January 15, 2010, No. 33, pp. 1)*
Pub: Orlando Business Journal
Contact: Julie Swyers, Director
E-mail: jswyers@bizjournals.com
Ed: Christopher Boyd. **Description:** Science Applications International Corporation, Saab Training USA LLC, CAE USA, and Pelliconi &C.SPA attempt to obtain $939,000 in tax incentives to generate 222 technology and defense-related jobs in Orange County, Florida. Each job will provide an average salary of $67,000. Future plans of each technology and defense firm are also presented. **Availability:** Print; Online.

26573 ■ *"Highmark-Owned Glasses Chain Eyeing Phila. Expansion"* in *Philadelphia Business Journal (Vol. 28, May 18, 2012, No. 14, pp. 1)*
Pub: Baltimore Business Journal
Contact: Rhonda Pringle, President
E-mail: rpringle@bizjournals.com
Description: Pittsburgh, Pennsylvania-based Highmark's subsidiary, Visionworks, has outlined its plan to open 25 stores in the Philadelphia region. The retail eyeglasses store chain has also been trying to recruit opticians to hire in the area. **Availability:** Print; Online.

26574 ■ *"Hire Education: An Emerging Cohort"* in *Canadian Business (Vol. 79, September 11, 2006, No. 18, pp. 114)*
Pub: LNRS Data Services Limited
Contact: Mark Vickers Kelsey, Director
Ed: Erin Pooley. **Description:** Study results showing the perceptions of students while considering full-time employment and the attributes they look for in their future employers are presented. **Availability:** Online.

26575 ■ *Hire and Manage Employees*
URL(s): www.sba.gov/business-guide/manage-your
-business/hire-manage-employees
Description: Discusses how to establish a payroll structure to help you hire employees as well as how to manage employees with an understanding of state and federal labor laws. **Availability:** Online.

26576 ■ *"The Hiring Handbook: Tips & Tactics to Attract Top Tier Talent"*
Pub: CreateSpace
Released: October 22, 2014. **Price:** $7, Paperback. **Description:** All the information needed to recruit and hire the best talent for any small business is presented. While intended for hiring managers, the information is useful for any human resources executives as well as job seekers. **Availability:** Print.

26577 ■ *Hiring Mistakes Small Business Owners Make and How to Avoid Them*
URL(s): www.hg.org/legal-articles/hiring-mistakes
-small-business-owners-make-and-how-to-avoi
d-them-49879
Description: Discusses hiring mistakes small business owners make and how you can avoid them. **Availability:** Online.

26578 ■ *"Hiring Unpaid Interns: Failing To Comply With Labor Laws Can Lead to Legal Trouble" in Black Enterprise (Vol. 44, June 2014, No. 10, pp. 22)*
Pub: Earl G. Graves Ltd.
Contact: Earl Graves, Jr., President
Description: Before hiring an intern for a small business it is critical to study the Department of Labor's legal criteria, determine whether the internship should be paid or unpaid, weigh the pros and cons, focus on the training aspect, and work with local colleges.

26579 ■ *"Hold the McJobs: Canada's High-End Employment Boom" in Globe & Mail (February 17, 2006, pp. B1)*
Ed: Heather Scoffield. **Description:** A focus the increasing rate of high-end or professional jobs Canada and its negative influence on low-end and middle level jobs is presented. **Availability:** Print; Online.

26580 ■ *"How to Create a Great Employee Referral Program" in Business News Daily (March 8, 2023)*
URL(s): www.businessnewsdaily.com/8737-employee
-referral-program.html
Ed: Saige Driver. **Released:** March 08, 2023. **Description:** Networking and word-of-mouth are great ways to find employees, and sometimes a little incentive is needed. Learn how to create an employee incentive program that will bring in the results you want plus reward your staff. **Availability:** Online.

26581 ■ *"How to Heal a Broken Legg" in Barron's (Vol. 92, September 17, 2012, No. 38, pp. 18)*
Description: Legg Mason is looking for a new chief executive officer after Mark Fetting announced his resignation effective October 1, 2012. Fetting is credited with saving the company by reducing operating expenses, but had a tense relationship with the firm's affiliates. The company has limited options in finding a replacement and undertaking reorganization. **Availability:** Online.

26582 ■ *"How to Legally Hire an Intern" in Legal Zoom (March 16, 2023)*
URL(s): www.legalzoom.com/articles/how-to-legally
-hire-an-intern
Ed: Kylie Ora Lobell. **Released:** March 16, 2023. **Description:** Advice on how to start an intern program through your business. **Availability:** Online.

26583 ■ *"How Mobile Devices Can Be Used in Food Truck Hiring" in Mobile-Cuisine.com (September, 23, 2020)*
Ed: Richard Myrick. **Released:** September 23, 2020. **Description:** Details how to utilize mobile devices in your recruiting and hiring processes. **Availability:** Online.

26584 ■ *How to Start a Home-Based Senior Care Business: Develop a Winning Business Plan*
Ed: James L. Ferry. **Released:** Second edition. **Price:** paperback; softback; Electronic Book. **Description:** Everything needed to know in order to start and run a profitable, ethical, and satisfying senior care business from your home. Information covers writing a good business plan, marketing services to families, creating a fee structure, and developing a network of trusted caregivers and service providers. **Availability:** E-book; Print.

26585 ■ *"How To Reduce the Risk of Discrimination" in Idaho Business Review (September 11, 2014)*
Pub: BridgeTower Media
Contact: Adam Reinebach, President
Description: Human resource departments in small businesses in Boise are aware of the city's discrimination ordinance making it unlawful to use sexual orientation and gender identity/expression in any consideration of hiring or terminating an employee, or for any other issue. The impact of the ordinance is yet to be determined.

26586 ■ *"How to Write a Job Applicant Rejection Letter" in Legal Zoom (February 15, 2023)*
URL(s): www.legalzoom.com/articles/how-to-write-a
-job-applicant-rejection-letter
Ed: Belle Wong, J.D. **Released:** February 15, 2023. **Description:** While searching for ideal employees and going through the interview process, it is inevitable that you will need to reject some candidates. Here's how to handle the situation with class and professionalism. **Availability:** Online.

26587 ■ *"Immigration: Give Us Your Skilled" in Canadian Business (Vol. 80, October 8, 2007, No. 20, pp. 78)*
Pub: Rogers Media Inc.
Contact: Neil Spivak, Chief Executive Officer
Ed: Zena Olijnyk. **Description:** Demand for skilled workers in Canada is discussed. Despite a strong demand, as evidenced by shortages in both skilled and unskilled labor, the country's immigration policy is affecting the recruitment process. Peter Veress, founder and president of Vermax Group, believes the country is wasting opportunities to take advantage of its attractiveness as a destination for foreign workers. **Availability:** Online.

26588 ■ *"Incapital Set to Add Jobs, Expand Space" in South Florida Business Journal (Vol. 33, August 3, 2012, No. 1, pp. 1)*
Pub: Baltimore Business Journal
Contact: Rhonda Pringle, President
E-mail: rpringle@bizjournals.com
Description: Chicago, Illinois-based Incapital has announced plans to hire 25 to 30 more financial professionals over the next 12 months. Incapital is also planning to expand its Boca Raton, Florida with construction totalling 5,000 additional square feet to accommodate future growth. **Availability:** Print; Online.

26589 ■ *"Income Tax Credit for Business Pushes the Job Creation Button" in Idaho Business Review (August 27, 2014)*
Pub: BridgeTower Media
Contact: Adam Reinebach, President
Description: Idaho's new Reimbursement Incentive Act program creates a tax credit for businesses with a qualifying project that will add new jobs that are paid at or above the average wage for work performed. Legislation and technical requirements for small businesses to quality are outlined.

26590 ■ *"Indiana Collection Agency Announces Expansion Plans" in PaymentsSource (March 23, 2012)*
Description: DECA Financial Services plans to buy a vacant building in Fishers, Indiana and renovate the property. The agency specializes in collection consumer and tax debts for both companies and

government agencies. The company plans to hire 140 new employees over the next 3 years. **Availability:** Print; Mailing list.

26591 ■ *"Information Technology Changes Roles, Highlights Hiring Needs" in South Florida Business Journal (Vol. 34, February 14, 2014, No. 30, pp. 3)*
Pub: American City Business Journals, Inc.
Contact: Mike Olivieri, Executive Vice President
Released: Weekly. **Price:** $8, Introductory 4-week offer(Digital & Print). **Description:** Results of the Steven Douglas Associates survey of 218 senior and mid-level information technology executives in South Florida are presented. About 75 percent of the respondents cited cloud services, mobile technologies, big data and enterprise reporting planning as having the most profound impact on their roles. The challenges they face with the expected hiring growth are also examined. **Availability:** Print; Online.

26592 ■ *"Jobs Gain Cast Shadow On Recovery" in Providence Business News (Vol. 29, April 7, 2014, No. 1, pp. 1)*
Pub: American City Business Journals, Inc.
Contact: Mike Olivieri, Executive Vice President
URL(s): pbn.com/job-gains-cast-shadow-on-recov-
ery96249
Description: Rhode Island Department of Labor and Training data has indicated the creation of nearly 21,000 jobs in the state since summer of 2009. However, the 503,300 state's residents working in February 2014, was 45,586 fewer than pre-recession peak in December 2006, despite the job gains. The factors separating job growth from resident employment and the economic impact is discussed.

26593 ■ *"Job Seeker's Readiness Guide: Unemployment's High and Competition is Tough" in Black Enterprise (Vol. 40, July 2010, No. 12, pp. 83)*
Description: Five key areas to help someone seeking employment gain the competitive edge are listed. **Availability:** Print; Online.

26594 ■ *"A Jobs Compact for America's Future: Badly Needed Investments In Human Capital Are Not Being Made. What We Can Do - Together - To Jump-Start the Process?" in Harvard Business Review (Vol. 90, March 2012, No. 3, pp. 64)*
Pub: Harvard Business Review Press
Contact: Moderna V. Pfizer, Contact
Ed: Thomas A. Kochan. **Price:** $8.95. **Description:** Obstacles to strengthening US human capital are a lack of focus on obtaining both high wages and high productivity, and a lack of value placed on human capital as a competitive advantage. Business schools are well positioned to address these obstacles via curricula, programs, and partnerships. **Availability:** Online; PDF.

26595 ■ *"Jobs Data Show A Slow Leak" in Barron's (Vol. 88, July 7, 2008, No. 27, pp. 34)*
Pub: Dow Jones & Company Inc.
Contact: Almar Latour, Chief Executive Officer
Ed: Gene Epstein. **Description:** In June 2008, the United States manufacturing sector showed an expansion, with the purchasing managers' index rising to 50.2 from 49.6; the unemployment rate in the US, which stayed steady at 5.5 percent in June 2008 is also discussed. Statistical data included. **Availability:** Online.

26596 ■ *"Jobs Data Show Wild Card" in Barron's (Vol. 90, September 6, 2010, No. 36, pp. M12)*
Pub: Barron's Editorial & Corporate Headquarters
Ed: Gene Epstein. **Description:** August 2010 jobs report revealed a 54,000 decline in non-farm payrolls and that the unemployment rate remains unchanged at 9.6 percent. The report also shows a welcome rise of 848,999 in the household-data category. The unemployment rate shows a reversed trend where men's 10.6 percent unemployment is higher than women's 8.6 percent rate. **Availability:** Online.

26597 ■ *"Kinnser: Sales In Overdrive"* in *Austin Business Journal (Vol. 32, March 30, 2012, No. 4, pp. 1)*
Pub: American City Business Journals, Inc.
Contact: Mike Olivieri, Executive Vice President

Ed: Christopher Calnan. **Description:** Kinnser Software Inc.'s receipt of fresh capitalization is seen to enable the company to pursue its acquisition strategy. The company is planning to grow organically. It is also planning to double the number of its employees. **Availability:** Online.

26598 ■ *"Labor Pains"* in *Canadian Business (Vol. 79, August 14, 2006, No. 16-17, pp. 80)*
Description: Canada's employment insurance is analyzed in view of the growing shortage of labor. **Availability:** Print; Online.

26599 ■ *"LaSalle St. Firms Cherry-Pick Talent As Wall St. Tanks"* in *Crain's Chicago Business (Vol. 31, November 17, 2008, No. 46)*
Pub: Crain Communications Inc.
Contact: Barry Asin, President

Ed: H. Lee Murphy. **Description:** Many local businesses are taking advantage of the lay offs that many major Wall Street firms are undergoing in their workforces; these companies see the opportunity to woo talent and expand their staff with quality executives. **Availability:** Online.

26600 ■ *"Leaders: 11 Tips to Consider When a Key Employee Quits"* in *Small Business Trends (March 21, 2022)*
URL(s): smallbiztrends.com/2022/11/things-to-do
-when-a-key-employee-quits.html

Released: November 27, 2022. **Description:** A guide on how to handle the aftermath of your key employee quitting. **Availability:** Online.

26601 ■ *"Leading Ohio Internet Marketing Firm Announces Growth in September"* in *Marketing Weekly News (September 26, 2009, pp. 24)*
Pub: Investment Weekly News

Description: Despite a poor economy, Webbed Marketing, a leading social media marketing and search engine optimization firm in the Midwest, has added five additional professionals to its fast-growing team. The company continues to win new business, provide more services and hire talented employees. **Availability:** Online.

26602 ■ *"Looking To Hire Young? Be Careful"* in *Boston Business Journal (Vol. 30, November 19, 2010, No. 43, pp. 1)*
Pub: Boston Business Journal
Contact: Carolyn M. Jones, President
E-mail: cmjones@bizjournals.com

Ed: Lisa van der Pool. **Released:** Weekly. **Description:** The Massachusetts Commission Against Discrimination (MCAD) has been using undercover job applicants to expose discrimination. Cabot's Ice Cream and Restaurant has been accused of denying older workers equal employment opportunities. MCAD has discovered unfair hiring practices such as hiring high school and college students. **Availability:** Print; Online.

26603 ■ *"Looming Labor Crunch Already Pushing Up Construction Prices"* in *Business Journal (Vol. 32, August 8, 2014, No. 11, pp. 10)*
Pub: American City Business Journals, Inc.
Contact: Mike Olivieri, Executive Vice President

Released: Weekly. **Price:** $4, introductory 4-week offer(Digital & Print). **Description:** Minneapolis, Minnesota's construction sector is expected to suffer from a worker shortage. An increase in the demand for construction labor will result in higher wages. Meanwhile, higher wages are expected to drive up construction costs. **Availability:** Print; Online.

26604 ■ *"Managing the Facebookers; Business"* in *The Economist (Vol. 390, January 3, 2009, No. 8612, pp. 10)*
Pub: Economist Newspaper Ltd.
Contact: Lara Boro, Chief Executive Officer

Description: According to a report from PricewaterhouseCoopers, a business consultancy, workers from Generation Y, also known as the Net Generation, are more difficult to recruit and integrate into companies that practice traditional business acumen. 61 percent of chief executive managers say that they have trouble with younger employees who tend to be more narcissistic and more interested in personal fulfillment with a need for frequent feedback and an over-precise set of objectives on the path to promotion which can be hard for managers who are used to a different relationship with their subordinates. Older bosses should prepare to make some concessions to their younger talent since some of the issues that make them happy include cheaper online ways to communicate and additional coaching, both of which are good for business. **Availability:** Online.

26605 ■ *Managing the Older Worker: How to Prepare for the New Organizational Order*
Pub: Harvard Business Press
Contact: Gabriela Allmi, Regional Manager
E-mail: gabriela.allmi@hbsp.harvard.edu

Ed: Peter Cappelli, Bill Novelli. **Description:** Your organization needs older workers more than ever: They transfer knowledge between generations, transmit your company's values to new hires, make excellent mentors for younger employees, and provide a 'just in time' workforce for special projects. **Availability:** Print; Audio.

26606 ■ *"Managing Yourself: Job-Hopping to the Top and Other Career Fallacies"* in *Harvard Business Review (Vol. 88, July-August 2010, No. 7-8, pp. 154)*
Pub: Harvard Business Publishing
Contact: Diane Belcher, Managing Director

Ed: Monika Hamori. **Price:** $8.95, PDF. **Description:** Fallacies identified and discussed include the belief that a career move should always be a move up, that industry and career switches are penalized, and that large corporations are the only loci for reaping large rewards. **Availability:** Online; PDF.

26607 ■ *"M&A Weakness Takes Toll on Phila. Law Firms"* in *Philadelphia Business Journal (Vol. 28, August 10, 2012, No. 26, pp. 1)*
Pub: Baltimore Business Journal
Contact: Rhonda Pringle, President
E-mail: rpringle@bizjournals.com

Released: Weekly. **Price:** $4, introductory 4-week offer(Digital & Print). **Description:** Slowdown in mergers and acquisitions impact law firms in Philadelphia, Pennsylvania. Data show that M&A activity involving the US has decreased by 35 percent in the first half of 2012. With the number of deals decreasing, local firms have become cautious about hiring transactional lawyers in terms of selecting those from high revenue areas such as intellectual property. **Availability:** Print; Online.

26608 ■ *"Market Resource Set for Expansion: Supply Chain Firm to Add Up to 700 Employees"* in *Memphis Business Journal (Vol. 34, May 11, 2012, No. 4, pp. 1)*
Pub: Baltimore Business Journal
Contact: Rhonda Pringle, President
E-mail: rpringle@bizjournals.com

Description: Market Resource Packaging LLC is planning to expand its operation in Memphis, Tennessee under the new ownership of IAM Acquisition. The supply chain services company plans to increase its distribution space from 260,000 square feet to 1 million square feet in three years and to grow its employees from 300 to 1,000 in 18 months. **Availability:** Print; Online.

26609 ■ *"MBAs for Hire, By the Hour"* in *Entrepreneur (August 2014)*
Pub: Entrepreneur Media Inc.
Contact: Dan Bova, Director

E-mail: dbova@entrepreneur.com

Description: HourlyNerd started from a classroom project by Pat Petitti and Rob Biederman at Harvard Business School in Boston, Massachusetts in 2003. the temporary-staffing firm recruits business students to act as consultants to small businesses that hire them. Consultants must come from one of the top 40 Master of Business Administration Programs in the U.S. in order to bid on a project. The firm receives 15 percent of the project fee from the hiring company while the business consultants pay 5 percent to the company. **Availability:** Online.

26610 ■ *"Medical Tech Jobs Take More Than a Month To Fill"* in *Austin Business Journal (Vol. 34, July 11, 2014, No. 21, pp. 10)*
Pub: American City Business Journals, Inc.
Contact: Mike Olivieri, Executive Vice President

Released: July 11, 2014. **Price:** $4, introductory 4-week offer(Digital only). **Description:** A report by Brookings Institute has revealed that nearly half of Austin's jobs require STEM - science, technology, engineering and mathematical skills. However, these jobs generally take more than a month to fill. **Availability:** Print; Online.

26611 ■ *"Memphis Pays Healthy Price To Compete for Jobs, Investment"* in *Memphis Business Journal (Vol. 35, January 3, 2014, No. 39, pp. 4)*
Pub: American City Business Journals, Inc.
Contact: Mike Olivieri, Executive Vice President

Released: Weekly. **Price:** $4, introductory 4-week offer(Digital & Print). **Description:** Memphis, Tennessee Mayor A.C. Wharton announced that Economic Development Growth Engine (EDGE) had a solid year and he thinks 2014 will be even better. EDGE has committed $103,718 in pilot-lieu-of-tax property tax reductions for every job created in 2013. The economic development projects in Memphis and in peer cities are also presented. **Availability:** Print; Online.

26612 ■ *"Michigan Means Growth: Sustaining Growth Through Thick and Thin: Michigan Companies Sustain Growth with Well-Timed Access to Capital"* in *Inc. (Vol. 36, September 2014, No. 7, pp. 164)*
Pub: Mansueto Ventures L.L.C.
Contact: Stephanie Mehta, Chief Executive Officer

Description: Successful companies possess flexibility, foresight and resources to turn adversity into opportunity. The small businesses in Michigan who have sustained experienced sales growth despite the recession of 2007. The Michigan Economic Development Corporation has introduced three initiatives to help Michigan businesses grow, including venture capital, collateral support and loan participation through the State Small Business Credit Initiative, and cash incentives for businesses looking to invest in urban communities or grow jobs. **Availability:** Print; Online.

26613 ■ *"Microsoft's Diversity Program Clicks into High Speed"* in *Hispanic Business (Vol. 30, July-August 2008, No. 7-8, pp. 54)*
Ed: Derek Reveron. **Description:** Microsoft's diversity hiring and vendor diversity program to capture more Hispanic consumer and business-to-business market is described. One of the main goals of these programs is to hire more Hispanic executives and managers who will help the company develop and market products and services that will appeal and benefit Hispanic consumers.

26614 ■ *"Mobis to Set Up Lancaster Distribution Center"* in *Dallas Business Journal (Vol. 35, April 6, 2012, No. 30, pp. 1)*
Pub: Baltimore Business Journal
Contact: Rhonda Pringle, President
E-mail: rpringle@bizjournals.com

Description: Irvine, California-based Mobis Parts America bought a 442,000-square-foot Saint Pointe Building in Lancaster, Texas from KTR Capital Partners for an undisclosed price. Mobisplans to make the building a distribution center for regional Hyundai and Kia dealerships, creating more than 30 jobs to start. **Availability:** Print; Online.

26615 ■ "A Model Development" in Crain's Cleveland Business (Vol. 28, October 1, 2007, No. 39, pp. 12)
Pub: Crain Communications Inc.
Contact: K. C. Crain, President
Ed: Scott Suttell. **Description:** Profile a Forest City Enterprises Inc., a firm that is developing a project in New Mexico called Mesa del Sol. The Albuquerque development is being seen as the vanguard of master-planned communities with its high-tech economic development center which is expected to become the site of 60,000 jobs, 38,000 homes and a town center. **Availability:** PDF.

26616 ■ "Monogram Foods Eyes Acquisition: Midwest Manufacturer Target of Latest Expansion" in Memphis Business Journal (Vol. 34, August 10, 2012, No. 17, pp. 1)
Pub: Baltimore Business Journal
Contact: Rhonda Pringle, President
E-mail: rpringle@bizjournals.com
Description: Monogram Food Solutions, a Memphis-based food company is raising $12.5 million for the acquisition of an undisclosed company or companies. The acquistion is expected to generate $50 million revenue, add 200 new employees for Monogram, and strengthen its manufacturing arm. **Availability:** Print; Online.

26617 ■ "Morgan Keegan Feeds Wunderlich" in Memphis Business Journal (Vol. 34, May 18, 2012, No. 5, pp. 1)
Pub: Baltimore Business Journal
Contact: Rhonda Pringle, President
E-mail: rpringle@bizjournals.com
Ed: Cole Epley. **Description:** Wunderlich Securities Inc. has augmented its equity markets group with a dozen former Morgan Keegan & Company Inc. professionals. Wunderlich assigned ten of the new hires in Memphis, Tennessee while the two joined its institutional sales department in New York. **Availability:** Print; Online.

26618 ■ "Mortgage Companies are Adding Staff" in Sacramento Business Journal (Vol. 29, September 14, 2012, No. 29, pp. 1)
Pub: Baltimore Business Journal
Contact: Rhonda Pringle, President
E-mail: rpringle@bizjournals.com
Ed: Sanford Nax. **Description:** Mortgage companies have been increasing their hiring as a result of persistently low interest rates and tough new government regulations. The mortgage industry has gained 1,335 jobs in the second quarter nationally, while the number of applications to receive a mortgage loan originator license is rising in California. **Availability:** Print; Online.

26619 ■ "Mortgage Servicer Wingspan Portfolio Advisors Makes Mark in Frisco" in Dallas Business Journal (Vol. 35, September 7, 2012, No. 52, pp. 1)
Pub: Baltimore Business Journal
Contact: Rhonda Pringle, President
E-mail: rpringle@bizjournals.com
Ed: Candace Carlisle. **Description:** Carrollton, Texas-based Wingspan Portfolio Advisors LLC has seen rapid growth in its business and the company plans to hire another 500 employees. Wingspan has subleased a 125,000-square-foot building in Firsco, Texa to accommodate the expansion and making it the company's third site in North Texas.

26620 ■ "The Myth of the Overqualified Worker" in Harvard Business Review (Vol. 88, December 2010, No. 12, pp. 30)
Pub: Harvard Business Publishing
Contact: Diane Belcher, Managing Director
Ed: Andrew O'Connell. **Price:** $6, PDF. **Description:** It is recommended to seriously consider job candidates with qualifications exceeding the position being recruited because research shows these individuals

work harder, but do not quit any sooner than those whose qualifications more closely match the position. **Availability:** Online; PDF.

26621 ■ "Networking Web Sites: a Two-Edge Sword" in Contractor (Vol. 56, October 2009, No. 10, pp. 52)
Ed: H. Kent Craig. **Description:** People need to be careful about the information that they share on social networking Web sites. They should realize that future bosses, coworkers, and those that might want to hire them might read those information. Posting on these sites can cost career opportunities and respect. **Availability:** Print; Online.

26622 ■ The New Job Security: The 5 Best Strategies for Taking Control of Your Career
Released: September 07, 2010. **Price:** $14.99, paperback. **Description:** This book will help individuals to uncover interesting alternative jobs, generate multiple income streams, shape their job to reflect values and goals, move successfully through the company, and plan for career transitions to keep them in control. Online resources, real-life examples, practical exercises and a no-nonsense approach will aid in job stability. **Availability:** E-book; Print.

26623 ■ "New Jobs Coming From New Breed" in Memphis Business Journal (Vol. 34, September 21, 2012, No. 23, pp. 1)
Pub: Baltimore Business Journal
Contact: Rhonda Pringle, President
E-mail: rpringle@bizjournals.com
Ed: Andy Ashby. **Description:** New Breed Logistics has opened a new distribution center in Southeast Memphis, Tennessee. It is believed that this new service will create hundreds of new jobs over the next two years. The company may become the largest-third party logistics company operating in Memphis. **Availability:** Print; Online.

26624 ■ "No Time to Grieve" in Women In Business (Vol. 63, Fall 2011, No. 3, pp. 22)
Pub: American Business Women's Association
Contact: Rene Street, Executive Director
Ed: Diane Stafford. **Released:** September 22, 2011. **Description:** Individuals who have experienced job loss must go through the emotional stages related to this event in order to gain the best re-employment opportunities. The first step towards re-employment is to make the job search public. Tips for improving one's online footprint are also given. **Availability:** Online.

26625 ■ "NYC Tops Hub in Tech VC Dollars" in Boston Business Journal (Vol. 31, August 5, 2011, No. 28, pp. 1)
Pub: Boston Business Journal
Contact: Carolyn M. Jones, President
E-mail: cmjones@bizjournals.com
Ed: Kyle Alspach. **Description:** New York City has been outdoing Boston in terms of venture capital for technology firms since second quarter 2010. New York tech firms raised $865 million during the first two quarters of 2011 against Boston techs' $682 million. Boston has the edge, though, when it comes to hiring engineering talent as it is home to the Massachusetts Institute of Technology. **Availability:** Print; Online.

26626 ■ "Oakland County to Survey Employers on Needed Skills" in Crain's Detroit Business (Vol. 24, April 14, 2008, No. 15, pp. 30)
Pub: Crain Communications Inc.
Contact: Barry Asin, President
Ed: Chad Halcom. **Description:** In an attempt to aid educators and attract talent, Oakland County plans to collect data from 1,000 local employers on workforce skills they need now or will need soon. **Availability:** Online.

26627 ■ "Old Ford Plant to Sign New Tenants" in Business Courier (Vol. 27, August 13, 2010, No. 15, pp. 1)
Pub: Business Courier

Ed: Dan Monk. **Description:** Ohio Realty Advisors LLC, a company handling the marketing of the 1.9 million-square-foot former Ford Batavia plant is on the brink of landing one distribution and three manufacturing firms as tenants. These tenants are slated to occupy about 20 percent of the facility and generate as many as 250 jobs in Ohio. **Availability:** Print; Online.

26628 ■ "OmniSYS Plans Big Richardson Expansion" in Dallas Business Journal (Vol. 35, June 8, 2012, No. 39, pp. 1)
Pub: Baltimore Business Journal
Contact: Rhonda Pringle, President
E-mail: rpringle@bizjournals.com
Ed: Bill Hethcock. **Description:** OmniSYS LLC will hire about 250 more people in the next two years and open a 50,000-square-foot office in Richardson, Texas in October 2012. The Medicare claims processing company posted revenue growth of more than 30 percent in 2011 primarily in the Medicare audit and compliance area. **Availability:** Print; Online.

26629 ■ "Overqualified. Underemployed" in Philadelphia Business Journal (Vol. 33, August 1, 2104, No. 25, pp. 14)
Pub: American City Business Journals, Inc.
Contact: Mike Olivieri, Executive Vice President
Description: Overqualified workers often find themselves in employment situations where their education, experience and skills are beyond the requirements of the job. The implications of underemployment for the worker, the organization and the overall U.S. economy are discussed. **Availability:** Print; Online.

26630 ■ "Overseas Overtures" in Business Journal-Portland (Vol. 24, October 26, 2007, No. 35, pp. 1)
Pub: Portland Business Journal
Contact: Andy Giegerich, Managing Editor
E-mail: agiegerich@bizjournals.com
Ed: Robin J. Mood. **Description:** Oregon has a workforce shortage, specifically for the health care industry. Recruiting agencies, such as the International Recruiting Network Inc., answers the high demand for workforce by recruiting foreign employees. The difficulties recruiting companies experience with regards to foreign labor laws are investigated. **Availability:** Print; Online.

26631 ■ "Pentagon Awards $17.6B Contract for EB-Built Subs Through 2018" in Providence Business News (Vol. 29, April 28, 2014, No. 4)
Pub: American City Business Journals, Inc.
Contact: Mike Olivieri, Executive Vice President
URL(s): pbn.com/pentagon-awards-176b-contract-for-eb-built-subs-through-20189678
Description: The U.S. Navy has signed a $17.6 billion contract with Newport News Shipbuilding and General Dynamics Corporation for construction of 10 new naval submarines. The deal will help employment at General Dynamics' Quonset Business Park Electric Boat production site. The submarines are scheduled to be built between 2014-2018. Electric Boat expects to hire 650 additional workers.

26632 ■ "The People Puzzle; Re-Training America's Workers" in The Economist (Vol. 390, January 3, 2009, No. 8612, pp. 32)
Description: With thousands of workers losing their jobs, America is now facing the task of getting them back to work. With an overall unemployment rate of 6.7 percent, the federal government has three main ways for leading workers back to employment: training them for new jobs, providing unemployment insurance in order to replace lost wages during the period of job-hunting; and matching employers who desire a skill with workers who have that skill. Specialized staffing agencies provide employers and potential employees with the help necessary to find a job in some of the more niche markets. **Availability:** Online.

26633 ■ *"Philadelphia's Largest Employers Will Fill 6,000 Jobs Within 6 Months"* in *Philadelphia Business Journal (Vol. 28, February 5, 2010, No. 51, pp. 1)*
Pub: Philadelphia Business Journal
Contact: Sierra Quinn, Director
E-mail: squinn@bizjournals.com
Ed: Peter Van Allen. **Description:** Philadelphia, Pennsylvania's largest employers have openings for at least 6,000 jobs. But businesses remain cautious and are selective in hiring or waiting to see what happens to federal policy changes. **Availability:** Online.

26634 ■ *"Plan Your Future with My Next Move"* in *Occupational Outlook Quarterly (Vol. 55, Summer 2011, No. 2, pp. 22)*
Description: My Next Move, an online tool offering a variety of user-friendly ways to browse more than 900 occupations was created by the National Center for O NET Development for the US Department of Labor's Employment and Training Administration. Clicking on an occupation presents a one-page profile summarizing key information for specific careers. **Availability:** Print; Online.

26635 ■ *"Plenty of Jobs, Will Workers Follow?"* in *Providence Business News (Vol. 28, January 27, 2014, No. 43, pp. 1)*
Pub: American City Business Journals, Inc.
Contact: Mike Olivieri, Executive Vice President
URL(s): pbn.com/plenty-of-jobs-will-workers-follow9 4642
Description: Electric Boat announced a plan to hire 650 employees in 2014 for its facility at Quonset Business Park in North Kingstown, Rhode Island. However, meeting the hiring goals will be a challenge because of smaller educational pipeline for welders, electricians, shipfitters, and pipefitters. Rhode Island's internship programs to fill the skills gap are also discussed. **Availability:** Online.

26636 ■ *"Predicting Success: Evidence-Based Strategies to Hire the Right People and Build the Best Team"*
Pub: John Wiley & Sons, Inc.
Contact: Christina Van Tassell, Executive Vice President Chief Financial Officer
Released: October 2014. **Price:** $16.99, e-book; $25, hardcover. **Description:** Guide for human resource management teams choose the right employee when hiring. It teaches how to apply the principles and tools of human analytics to the work place to avoid bad culture fits, mismatched skillsets, entitled workers, and other hiring mistakes that hurt employee motivation and morale. The Predictive Index TM, behavior analytics, hiring assessments, and other resources for better outcomes are presented. **Availability:** E-book; Print.

26637 ■ *"Prichard the Third"* in *Canadian Business (Vol. 83, October 12, 2010, No. 17, pp. 34)*
Pub: Rogers Media Inc.
Contact: Neil Spivak, Chief Executive Officer
Ed: Thomas Watson. **Description:** Robert Prichard, the new chair of international business law firm Torys, talks about his current role; his job involved advising clients, representing the firm, being part of the leadership team, and recruiting talent. He considers 'Seven Days in Tibet' as the first book to have an influence on his world view. **Availability:** Online.

26638 ■ *"Private-Sector Is Back, Roadblocks Be Damned"* in *Business Review Albany (Vol. 41, July 4, 2014, No. 15, pp. 4)*
Pub: American City Business Journals, Inc.
Contact: Mike Olivieri, Executive Vice President
Released: Weekly. **Price:** $4, introductory 4-week offer(Digital only). **Description:** Private sector jobs in New York experienced significant growth, reaching an all-time high of almost 7.6 million jobs in May 2014, as government jobs suffered a decline. Large international corporations, including General Electric, are tapping into cash reserves, adding jobs and expanding operations after years of cutting staff. **Availability:** Print; Online.

26639 ■ *"Putting Vets to Work"* in *Business Week (September 22, 2008, No. 4100, pp. 18)*
Pub: Bloomberg L.P.
Contact: Michael Bloomberg, Chief Executive Officer
Ed: Deborah Stead. **Description:** Advice is provided by former Marine Sal Cepeda, a consultant who advises employers on hiring veterans, for former military personnel coming back into the workforce. **Availability:** Print; Online.

26640 ■ *"PwC to Add 400 Workers in North Texas"* in *Dallas Business Journal (Vol. 35, April 6, 2012, No. 30, pp. 1)*
Pub: Baltimore Business Journal
Contact: Rhonda Pringle, President
E-mail: rpringle@bizjournals.com
Description: London, England-headquartered PwC, formerly known as PricewaterhouseCoopers LLP, announced plans to hire 400 employees for its North Texas operations during the next 12 months. The firm provides auditing, consulting, and tax services to public, private and government clients. **Availability:** Print; Online.

26641 ■ *"Questioning Authority"* in *Entrepreneur (June 2014)*
Pub: Society for the Study of Myth and Tradition
Contact: Tracy Cochran, Director
Description: Smarterer is a platform that facilitates the evaluation of prospective hires through crowd-sourced assessment tests quantifying their professional skills and strengths. The platform has more than 900 multiple-choice tests covering a variety of professions. It uses an adaptive machine-learning algorithm that ensures the uniqueness of every test. Users can choose to make their test results public and can perform do-overs on some tests. The platform was launched in 2010 as a way of identifying potential talent and identifying skill inventories among existing employees. **Availability:** Print; Online.

26642 ■ *"Quick Earnings Revival Unlikely"* in *Barron's (Vol. 88, June 30, 2008, No. 26, pp. 31)*
Description: Analysts are pushing back their prediction of a U.S. economy turnaround to 2009. A recession in the first half of 2008 may not have happened but unemployment is rising and house prices continue to fall.

26643 ■ *"A Quick Guide to Hiring Freelancers in a Time of Crisis"* in *Legal Zoom (February 21, 2023)*
URL(s): www.legalzoom.com/articles/a-quick-guide-to -hiring-freelancers-in-a-time-of-crisis
Ed: Diane Faulkner. **Released:** February 21, 2023. **Description:** Gives advice on how to hire freelancers, including where to start looking. **Availability:** Online.

26644 ■ *"Region Wins as GE Puts Plants Close to R&D"* in *Business Review Albany (Vol. 41, July 4, 2014, No. 15, pp. 8)*
Pub: American City Business Journals, Inc.
Contact: Mike Olivieri, Executive Vice President
Description: General Electric Company (GE) invested over $400 million into the expansion of its health care, battery and renewable energy businesses in the Albany, New York region. The company's local growth secured about 7,000 private-sector jobs in the area and strengthened the relationship between GE research and manufacturing. **Availability:** Print; Online.

26645 ■ *"Reps Have Needs Too!"* in *Agency Sales Magazine (Vol. 39, December 2009, No. 11, pp. 16)*
Description: There is common information that a sales representatives needs to know prior to choosing a manufacturer to represent. Both parties must keep promises made to customers and prospects. Reps also need the support from the manufacturers and to clear matters regarding their commission. Interviewing tips for representatives to get this vital information are presented. **Availability:** Online.

26646 ■ *"Reps Vs. Factory Direct Sales Force..Which Way to Go?"* in *Agency Sales Magazine (Vol. 39, September-October 2009, No. 9, pp. 28)*
Description: Hiring independent manufacturers' sales representative is a cost-effective alternative to a direct sales force. Sales reps have predictable sales costs that go up and down with sales, stronger local relationships and better market intelligence. **Availability:** Print; Online.

26647 ■ *"'Resume Mining' Services Can Save Time, Money"* in *HR Specialist (Vol. 8, September 2010, No. 9, pp. 7)*
Pub: Capitol Information Group Inc.
Contact: Allie Ash, Chief Executive Officer
Description: Low-cost resume mining services can help human resource departments save time and money by searching online resume databases for candidates matching specific job qualifications. **Availability:** PDF; Online.

26648 ■ *"Retiring Baby Boomers and Dissatisfied Gen-Xers Cause..Brain Drain"* in *Agency Sales Magazine (Vol. 39, November 2009, No. 10)*
Description: Due to the impending retirement of the baby boomers a critical loss of knowledge and experience in businesses will result. Creating a plan to address this loss of talent centered on the development of the younger generation is discussed.

26649 ■ *"Rudy's Tortillas Wraps Up Expansion Plan in Carrollton"* in *Dallas Business Journal (Vol. 35, August 31, 2012, No. 51, pp. 1)*
Pub: Baltimore Business Journal
Contact: Rhonda Pringle, President
E-mail: rpringle@bizjournals.com
Ed: Candace Carlisle. **Released:** Weekly. **Description:** Rudy's Tortillas Corporation, a 67-year old family business based in Dallas, Texas, is moving into a new plant on Belt Line Road, Carrollton. The expansion will also involve the hiring of 150 new workers and enable the company to expand its operations. Rudy's will spend $14 million dollars on construction and equipment on the new tortilla plant. **Availability:** Print; Online.

26650 ■ *"A Safety Net In Need of Repair"* in *The Economist (Vol. 390, January 3, 2009, No. 8612, pp. 33)*
Description: America's unemployment-insurance scheme is outdated and skimpy compared to other industrialized countries despite the fact that Americans tend to work harder at returning to the job market; the benefits are lower and available for a smaller amount of time and less unemployed workers are even able to collect these benefits. Statistical data included.

26651 ■ *"Safety Products Firm Expanding"* in *Memphis Business Journal (Vol. 33, March 16, 2012, No. 49, pp. 1)*
Pub: Baltimore Business Journal
Contact: Rhonda Pringle, President
E-mail: rpringle@bizjournals.com
Description: Safety products importer and supplier International Sourcing Company Inc., the parent firm of Cordova Safety Products and Cordova Consumer Products, has purchased the 1 million-square-foot Cleo property in southeast Memphis, Tennessee. Aside from relocating its warehouse and office operations to the facility, the firm will add 20 new jobs as part of its growth initiative. **Availability:** Print; Online.

26652 ■ *"Samsung's Metamorphosis in Austin"* in *Austin Business Journal (Vol. 31, May 20, 2011, No. 11, pp. 1)*
Pub: Austin Business Journal
Contact: Rachel McGrath, Director
E-mail: rmcgrath@bizjournals.com
Ed: Christopher Calnan. **Description:** Samsung Austin Semiconductor LP, a developer of semiconductors for smartphones and tablet computers, plans to diversify its offerings to include niche products: flash

memory devices and microprocessing devices. In light of this strategy, Samsung Austin will be hiring 300 engineers as part of a $3.6 billion expansion of its plant. **Availability:** Print; Online.

26653 ■ *"Screening-Oriented Recruitment Messages: Antecedents and Relationships with Applicant Pool Quality"* in *Human Resource Management (Vol. 51,May- June 2012, No. 3, pp. 343-360)*
Pub: John Wiley & Sons, Inc.
Contact: Christina Van Tassell, Executive Vice President Chief Financial Officer

Ed: Brian R. Dineen, Ian O. Williamson. **Released:** May 25, 2012. **Description:** Factors associated with the use of screening-oriented messages for recruitment are investigated. Results indicate that labor supply perceptions, the reputation of recruiting firms and quality-based compensation incentives are associated with the use of screening-oriented messages, which are associated with the quality of the applicant pool. **Availability:** Print; PDF; Online.

26654 ■ *"Second to None"* in *Crain's Detroit Business (Vol. 26, January 18, 2010, No. 3, pp. 9)*
Pub: Crain Communications Inc.
Contact: Barry Asin, President

Ed: Nancy Kaffer. **Description:** Second-stage companies are beginning to attract more attention from government entities and the business community alike, due in part to their ability to create jobs more rapidly than their counterparts both smaller and larger. Second-stage companies have between 10-99 employees and consistently have supplied the most jobs, despite overall job declines in recent years. **Availability:** Online.

26655 ■ *"Sign of the Times: Temp-To-Perm Attorneys"* in *HRMagazine (Vol. 54, January 2009, No. 1, pp. 24)*
Description: A growing number of law firms are hiring professional staff on a temp-to-perm basis according to the president of Professional Placement Services in Florida. Firms can save money while testing potential employees on a temporary basis. **Availability:** Print; Online.

26656 ■ *"Six Things for Employers to Consider When Hiring Individuals With Disabilities"* in *U.S. Chamber of Commerce (Aug. 25, 2022)*
URL(s): www.uschamber.com/workforce/six-things -for-employers-to-consider-when-hiring-individuals -with-disabilities
Ed: Jenna Shrove. **Released:** August 25, 2022. **Availability:** Online.

26657 ■ *"Six Ways Employees on LinkedIn Benefit the Boss"* in *South Florida Business Journal (Vol. 34, April 25, 2014, No. 40)*
Pub: American City Business Journals, Inc.
Contact: Mike Olivieri, Executive Vice President

Released: Weekly. **Price:** $8, Introductory 4-week offer(Digital & Print). **Description:** LinkedIn can be a useful tool for executives. In addition to finding staff when hiring, the information service can give U.S.-based users a more global perspective. It can also be a way to share recent company accomplishment. **Availability:** Print; Online.

26658 ■ *"Skill Seekers"* in *South Florida Business Journal (Vol. 34, February 7, 2014, No. 29, pp. 15)*
Pub: American City Business Journals, Inc.
Contact: Mike Olivieri, Executive Vice President

Description: Executives talk about the need for schools to help businesses find talent to hire. Robin Sandler of Charter School USA reveals that the organization's 'Leading Edge' program allows teachers to participate in leadership opportunities, while Mason Jackson of WorkForce One Employment Solutions believes that schools need to customize the curriculum in order to support internships. **Availability:** Print; Online.

26659 ■ *"Small Bank Has Big Lending Plans, New Hire"* in *Silicon Valley/San Jose Business Journal (Vol. 30, September 21, 2012, No. 26, pp. 1)*
Pub: Baltimore Business Journal
Contact: Rhonda Pringle, President
E-mail: rpringle@bizjournals.com

Description: Santa Cruz County Bank has hired government-backed loans specialist Sat Kanwar in addition to Susan Chandler, Jorge Reguerin and Daljit Bains to boost the bank's Small Business Administration lending department. According to Chandler, the bank will take on loans ranging from $25,000 to several million dollars. **Availability:** Print; Online.

26660 ■ *"Small Business Economic Trends: Moderate Improvement but No Clear Direction"* in *Small Business Economic Trends (March 2008, pp. 3)*
Pub: National Federation of Independent Business
Contact: Brad Close, President

Ed: William C. Dunkelberg, Holly Wade. **Description:** Commentary on the economic trends for small businesses in the U.S. is presented. Analysis of the labor market and low interest rates is given. The effect of the Federal Reserve's policy announcement on small business owner optimism is also discussed. **Availability:** Print; Online.

26661 ■ *"Small Business Employment in 22 Rich Economies"* in *Small Business Economic Trends (January 2008, pp. 9)*
Pub: National Federation of Independent Business
Contact: Brad Close, President

Ed: William C. Dunkelberg, Holly Wade. **Description:** Table from a survey of small businesses in the U.S. is given, representing actual employment changes from January 2002 to December 2007. A graph comparing planned employment and current job openings from January 1986 to December 2007 is also supplied. Tables showing job opening, hiring plans, and qualified applicants for job openings are also presented. **Availability:** Online.

26662 ■ *"Small Business Employment"* in *Small Business Economic Trends (September 2010, pp. 9)*
Pub: National Federation of Independent Business
Contact: Brad Close, President

Description: A table from a survey of small businesses in the U.S. is given, representing actual employment changes from January 2005 to August 2010. A graph comparing planned employment and current job openings from January 1986 to August 2010 is also supplied. Tables showing job openings, hiring plans, and qualified applicants for job openings are also presented. **Availability:** Online.

26663 ■ *"Smart Recruiting Strategies for Hiring"* in *Business News Daily (Nov. 18, 2021)*
URL(s): www.businessnewsdaily.com/9692-recruiting -strategies.html
Ed: Bennett Conlin. **Released:** November 18, 2021. **Description:** Discusses the challenges small businesses face when it comes to recruiting talented employees and presents smart recruiting strategies to attract the best talent. **Availability:** Online.

26664 ■ *"Soft Skills, Hard Success: Employers Seek Leaders Who Offer More than Just Education and Credentials"* in *Black Enterprise (Vol. 45, July-August 2014, No. 1, pp. 44)*
Pub: Earl G. Graves Ltd.
Contact: Earl Graves, Jr., President

Description: The top ten soft skills employer look for include: strong work ethic, dependability, positive attitude, self-motivation, team oriented, organizational skills, works well under pressure, effective communication, flexibility, and confidence.

26665 ■ *"Start Filling Your Talent Gap - Now"* in *Business Strategy Review (Vol. 21, Spring 2010, No. 1, pp. 56)*
Ed: Alan Bird, Lori Flees, Paul DiPaola. **Released:** March 22, 2010. **Description:** As businesses steer their way out of turbulence, they have a unique op-

portunity to identify their leadership supply and demand and then to close the talent gap in their organization. Authors explain how to take immediate steps to build the right team now and lay the groundwork for a long-term approach for nurturing talent within the organization. **Availability:** Online; Electronic publishing.

26666 ■ *"Startup Activity Among Jobless Execs is the Highest Since 2009, Survey Says"* in *South Florida Business Journal (Vol. 34, February 21, 2014, No. 31, pp. 3)*
Pub: American City Business Journals, Inc.
Contact: Mike Olivieri, Executive Vice President

Released: Weekly. **Price:** $8, Introductory 4-week offer(Digital & Print). **Description:** The percentage of startup activity among former managers and executives in the U.S. increased 31 percent in 2013 according to consulting firm Challenger, Gray & Christmas. According to the survey, 5.5 percent of job-seeking executive launched their own business during each quarter in 2013, compared with 4.2 percent in 2012 and 3.2 percent in 2011. **Availability:** Print; Online.

26667 ■ *"Steeling Themselves: Price Hikes Testing The Mettle of Scrap Dealers"* in *Baltimore Business Journal (Vol. 30, July 6, 2012, No. 9, pp. 1)*
Ed: James Bach. **Description:** Members of Maryland's steel sector have been seeking to revive the Sparrows Point steel plant. The plan also involves saving 2,000 jobs. Comments from executives included. **Availability:** Print; Online.

26668 ■ *"The Story Of Diane Greene"* in *Barron's (Vol. 88, July 14, 2008, No. 28, pp. 31)*
Pub: Dow Jones & Company Inc.
Contact: Almar Latour, Chief Executive Officer

Ed: Mark Veverka. **Description:** Discusses the ousting of Diane Greene as a chief executive of VMWare, a developer of virtualization software, after the firm went public; in this case Greene, a brilliant engineer, should not be negatively impacted by the decision because it is common for companies to bring in new executive leadership that is more operations oriented after the company goes public. **Availability:** Online.

26669 ■ *"SunBank Plans Expansion Via Wal-Mart"* in *Business Journal-Serving Phoenix and the Valley of the Sun (Vol. 10, November 8, 2007)*
Pub: Phoenix Business Journal
Contact: Alex McAlister, Director
E-mail: amcalister@bizjournals.com

Ed: Chris Casacchia. **Description:** SunBank plans to install 12 to 14 branches in Wal-Mart stores in Arizona and hire 100 bankers by the end of 2008. Wal-Mart also offers financial products at other stores through partnerships with other banks. **Availability:** Print; Online.

26670 ■ *"A Supply-Side Solution for Health Care"* in *Barron's (Vol. 92, July 23, 2012, No. 30, pp. 30)*
Pub: Dow Jones & Company Inc.
Contact: Almar Latour, Chief Executive Officer

Ed: H. Woody Brock. **Description:** The United States should increase the supply of new doctors, nurses and other health care professionals to improve the American health care system by increasing supply. Health care reform proposals in the US Congress fail to address the supply side of the problem. **Availability:** Online.

26671 ■ *"Talent Shows"* in *Canadian Business (Vol. 81, December 24, 2007, No. 1, pp. 14)*
Description: Canadian companies are increasingly turning to marketing to promote themselves as employers, as concerns on employee recruitment increase with the nearing retirement age of the baby boomers. Details on skills shortage, the potential advantage for the immigrant workforce, and employee retention are discussed. **Availability:** Online.

26672 ■ *"Technology Companies are Increasing Their Hiring"* in Philadelphia Business Journal (Vol. 31, March 16, 2012, No. 5, pp. 1)
Pub: Baltimore Business Journal
Contact: Rhonda Pringle, President
E-mail: rpringle@bizjournals.com
Description: Technology firms in Pennsylvania have been expanding their work force. Online advertisements for computer and math science hiring have increased. **Availability:** Print; Online.

26673 ■ *"Three Steps to Follow when Job Hunting"* in Contractor (Vol. 56, September 2009, No. 9, pp. 62)
Ed: H. Kent Craig. **Description:** Advice on how project managers in the United States plumbing industry should look for jobs in view of the economic crisis. Job seekers should consider relocating to places where there are an abundance of project management jobs. Resumes should also be revised to make an applicant stand out. **Availability:** Print; Online.

26674 ■ *"Tips and Tricks for Seasonal Employment Hiring"* in Legal Zoom (February 21, 2023)
URL(s): www.legalzoom.com/articles/tips-and-tricks-for-seasonal-employment-hiring
Ed: Diane Faulkner. **Released:** February 21, 2023. **Description:** It can often be too busy and overwhelming for your regular employees during a seasonal rush. One way to alleviate the stress is by hiring seasonal employees to help take over the extra workload. **Availability:** Online.

26675 ■ *"Top 10 Hiring Platforms for Small Business"* in Entrepreneur (Oct. 19, 2021)
URL(s): www.entrepreneur.com/article/392077
Released: October 19, 2021. **Description:** Provides information on 10 hiring platforms that small business owners can utilize to recruit the best talent for your small business. **Availability:** Online.

26676 ■ *"Toyota Revs Up Plans for Ontario Plant"* in Globe & Mail (February 7, 2006, pp. B1)
Description: The production output and workforce addition proposals of Toyota Motor Corp., at Ontario plant, are presented. **Availability:** Online.

26677 ■ *"Trade Craft: Take Pride in Your Trade, Demand Excellence"* in Contractor (Vol. 56, October 2009, No. 10, pp. 24)
Ed: Al Schwartz. **Description:** There is a need for teaching, developing, and encouraging trade craft. An apprentice plumber is not only versed in the mechanical aspects of the trade but he also has a working knowledge of algebra, trigonometry, chemistry, and thermal dynamics. Contractors should be demanding on their personnel regarding their trade craft and should only keep and train the very best people they can hire. **Availability:** Print; Online.

26678 ■ *"Tri-State Lags Peer Cities in Jobs, Human Capital, Study Says"* in Business Courier (Vol. 27, September 24, 2010, No. 21, pp. 1)
Pub: Business Courier
Ed: Dan Monk, Lucy May. **Description:** Greater Cincinnati, Ohio has ranked tenth overall in the 'Agenda 360/Vision 2015 Regional Indicators Project' report. The study ranked 12-city-peer groups in categories such as job indicators standing and people indicators standing. The ranking of jobs and human capital study is topped by Minneapolis, followed by Denver, Raleigh, and Austin. **Availability:** Print; Online.

26679 ■ *"Tuesday Morning's Corporate Clearance Rack"* in Dallas Business Journal (Vol. 37, February 28, 2014, No. 25, pp. 4)
Pub: American City Business Journals, Inc.
Contact: Mike Olivieri, Executive Vice President
Released: October 30, 2015. **Description:** Tuesday Morning CEO, Michael Rouleau, has been working to help the company recover from its financial problems.

Rouleau has improved the shopping experience from garage sale to discount showroom. The company has also been hiring different executives in the past few years. **Availability:** Print; Online.

26680 ■ *"Under Pressure"* in Canadian Business (Vol. 81, July 21, 2008, No. 11, pp. 18)
Description: According to a survey conducted by COMPASS Inc., meeting revenue targets is the main cause of job stress for chief executive officers. Staffing and keeping expenditures lower also contribute to the workplace stress experienced by business executives. Other results of the survey are presented. **Availability:** Online.

26681 ■ *"Unemployment Rates"* in The Economist (Vol. 390, January 3, 2009, No. 8612, pp. 75)
Description: Countries that are being impacted the worst by rising unemployment rates are those that have also been suffering from the housing market crisis. Spain has been the hardest hit followed by Ireland. America and Britain are also seeing levels of unemployment that indicate too much slack in the economy. **Availability:** Print; Online.

26682 ■ *"Urban League Training Program Finds Jobs for Cincinnati's 'Hard to Serve'"* in Business Courier (Vol. 27, July 2, 2010, No. 9, pp. 1)
Pub: Business Courier
Ed: Lucy May. **Description:** Stephen Tucker, director of workforce development for the Urban League of Greater Cincinnati, is an example of how ex-offenders can be given chances for employment after service jail sentences. How the Urban Leagues' Solid Opportunities for Advancement job training program helped Tucker and other ex-offenders is discussed. **Availability:** Print; Online.

26683 ■ *"Use Benefits Checklist to Smooth New-Hire Onboarding"* in HR Specialist (Vol. 8, September 2010, No. 9, pp. 4)
Pub: Capitol Information Group Inc.
Contact: Allie Ash, Chief Executive Officer
Description: Checklist to help employees enroll in a company's benefit offerings is provided, courtesy of Wayne State University in Detroit, Michigan. **Availability:** Print; Online.

26684 ■ *"Veteran-Owned Business Energizes Employees To Give Back"* in Investment Weekly News (June 23, 2012, pp. 768)
Description: Service Disabled Veteran-Owned Small Business (SDVOSB) and Certified (AITC) are commited to American veterans. AITC's staff is composed of 50 percent veterans and sees this model as a means of giving back to the soldiers, a cause they proudly support. Details of programs that support wounded warriors and their families, and are supported by AITC, are described. **Availability:** Print; Online.

26685 ■ *"Veterans Train to Use Military Skills In Civilian Workforce"* in South Florida Business Journal (Vol. 34, April 18, 2014, No. 39, pp. 10)
Pub: American City Business Journals, Inc.
Contact: Mike Olivieri, Executive Vice President
Released: Weekly. **Price:** $8, Introductory 4-week offer(Digital & Print). **Description:** United Way of Broward County has launched the Mission United program that offers a one-stop shop of information and resources to meet the needs of military veterans. Mission United aims to reduce the jobless rate among veterans by creating two programs to help veterans and connect them with potential employers who are hiring. Details of the job training program is explored. **Availability:** Print; Online.

26686 ■ *"Village at Waugh Chapel $275M Expansion Begins"* in Baltimore Business Journal (Vol. 28, August 27, 2010, No. 16, pp. 1)
Pub: Baltimore Business Journal
Contact: Rhonda Pringle, President

E-mail: rpringle@bizjournals.com
Ed: Daniel J. Sernovitz. **Description:** Developer Greenberg Gibbons Corporation has broken ground on a $275 million, 1.2 million-square-foot addition to its Village at the Waugh Chapel mixed-use complex. Aside from creating 2,600 permanent jobs, the addition, named Village South, is expected to lure Target and Wegmans Food Markets to Crofton, Maryland. Funding for this project is discussed. **Availability:** Print.

26687 ■ *"Wal-Mart Sharpens Focus on Roxbury"* in Boston Business Journal (Vol. 31, July 8, 2011, No. 24, pp. 1)
Pub: Boston Business Journal
Contact: Carolyn M. Jones, President
E-mail: cmjones@bizjournals.com
Ed: Mary Moore. **Price:** $4. **Description:** Wal-Mart Stores is boosting its search for a possible location in the Roxbury section of Boston, Massachusetts. The search is focused on underserved communities in terms of jobs and access to reasonably-priced merchandise. The extent Boston's African American community has clashed with Mayor Thomas M. Menino over the accommodations of the retailer in Roxbury is discussed. **Availability:** Print; Online.

26688 ■ *"Walker Seeks More Business Participation"* in Business Journal-Milwaukee (Vol. 28, December 10, 2010, No. 10, pp. A1)
Pub: The Business Journal
Contact: Heather Ladage, President
E-mail: hladage@bizjournals.com
Ed: Rich Kirchen. **Description:** Wisconsin governor Scott Walker is seeking the aid of Milwaukee business leaders to participate in resolving the challenges posed by the economic crisis. Walker is aiming to create 250,000 jobs. He is also planning to call a special session of the legislature to enact strategies to jumpstart the economy. **Availability:** Print; Online.

26689 ■ *"Wanted: African American Professional for Hire"* in Black Enterprise (Vol. 37, November 2006, No. 4, pp. 93)
Pub: Earl G. Graves Ltd.
Contact: Earl Graves, Jr., President
Ed: Joe Watson. **Description:** Excerpt from the book, Without Excuses: Unleash the Power of Diversity to Build Your Business, speaks to the lack of diversity in the corporate arena and why executives, recruiters, and HR professionals claim they are unable to find qualified individuals of different races when hiring. **Availability:** Online.

26690 ■ *"Wayne, Oakland Counties Create Own 'Medical Corridor'"* in Crain's Detroit Business (Vol. 24, October 6, 2008, No. 40, pp. 8)
Pub: Crain Communications Inc.
Contact: Barry Asin, President
Ed: Jay Greene. **Description:** Woodward Medical Corridor that runs along Woodward Avenue and currently encompasses twelve hospitals and is rapidly growing with additional physician offices, advanced oncology centers and new hospitals. Beaumont Hospital is building a $160 million proton-beam therapy cancer center on its Royal Oak campus in a joint venture with Procure Treatment Centers of Bloomington Ind. That is expected to open in 2010 and will employ approximately 145 new workers. **Availability:** Online.

26691 ■ *"Wealth and Jobs: the Broken Link"* in Harvard Business Review (Vol. 88, November 2010, No. 11, pp. 44)
Pub: Harvard Business Publishing
Contact: Diane Belcher, Managing Director
Ed: Nitin Nohria. **Price:** $6, PDF. **Description:** Rebuilding the link between business and job creation to shore up the middle class is advocated. A blend of government policies and business strategies that foster entrepreneurship and innovation are essential. **Availability:** Online; PDF.

26692 ■ *"Web Site Focuses on Helping People Find Jobs, Internships with Area Businesses"* in *Crain's Detroit Business (Vol. 26, Jan. 4, 2010)*
Pub: Crain Communications Inc.
Contact: Barry Asin, President
Ed: Dustin Walsh. **Description:** DetroitIntern.com, LLC is helping metro Detroit college students and young professionals find career-advancing internships or jobs with local businesses. **Availability:** Print; Online.

26693 ■ *"Wegmans Adding 1,600-Plus Jobs Here Over the Next Year"* in *Boston Business Journal (Vol. 34, February 14, 2014, No. 2, pp. 3)*
Pub: American City Business Journals, Inc.
Contact: Mike Olivieri, Executive Vice President
Description: Wegmans, a family-owned grocery chain, is planning to add the most jobs of any firm in Massachusetts in 2014. The company will create more than 1,600 full- and part-time positions by opening three stores. Bill Congdon, Wegmans' New England division manager, reveals that the company is also planning to open a store in the city of Boston. **Availability:** Print; Online.

26694 ■ *"What You Need to Know about the Federal Overtime Rules"* in *Business News Daily (March 17, 2023)*
URL(s): www.businessnewsdaily.com/9110-federal -overtime-rules.html
Ed: Max Freedman. **Released:** March 17, 2023. **Description:** Every small business owner should be well acquainted with the Fair Labor Standards Act (FLSA) in order to remain compliant in federal overtime law. **Availability:** Online.

26695 ■ *"What You Need to Know about Hiring Independent Contractors"* in *Legal Zoom (March 22, 2023)*
URL(s): www.legalzoom.com/articles/what-you-nee d-to-know-about-hiring-independent-contractors
Released: March 23, 2023. **Description:** Independent contractors are an attractive choice for saving some costs, but are they the best choice for your small business? Read about the pros and cons of hiring ICs. **Availability:** Online.

26696 ■ *"What's More Important: Talent or Engagement? A Study With Retailer ANN INC. Seeks To Find the Essential Ingredients To High-Performing Managers and Employees"* in *Gallup Business Journal (April 22, 2014)*
Pub: Gallup, Inc.
Contact: Jon Clifton, Chief Executive Officer
Description: ANN INC. is a leading women's clothing retailer that is exploring the necessary steps to achieving both high-performing managers and employees. The firm found that hiring people with the right talent and engaging them will maximize performance. **Availability:** Online.

26697 ■ *"What's Working Now: In Providing Jobs for North Carolinians"* in *Business North Carolina (Vol. 28, February 2008, No. 2, pp. 16)*
Pub: Business North Carolina
Contact: Peggy Knaack, Manager
E-mail: pknaack@businessnc.com
Ed: Edward Martin, Frank Maley. **Description:** Individuals previously employed in the furniture, tobacco, or textile manufacturing sectors have gone back to school to be trained in new sectors in the area such as life sciences, finances and other emerging sectors. **Availability:** Online.

26698 ■ *"When To Make Private News Public: Should a Job Candidate Reveal That She's Pregnant?"* in *Harvard Business Review (Vol. 90, March 2012, No. 3, pp. 161)*
Pub: Harvard Business Review Press
Contact: Moderna V. Pfizer, Contact
Ed: Tiziana Casciaro, Victoria W. Winston. **Price:** $8.95, hardcopy black and white. **Description:** A fictitious hiring scenario is presented, with contributors providing advice on whether a candidate for a position involving extensive business travel should inform her manager that she is expecting. Contributors agree the employee should inform her manager, but not necessarily before she is offered the position, and that the conversation remains focused on how she will perform the job and address challenges. **Availability:** Print; PDF; Online.

26699 ■ *"When You Need Strong Millennials in Your Workplace"* in *Agency Sales Magazine (Vol. 39, November 2009, No. 10, pp. 22)*
Description: Millennials are bringing a new set of skills and a different kind of work ethics to the workplace. This generation is used to receiving a great deal of positive feedback and they expect to continue receiving this on the job. Expectations should be made clear to this generation and long-term career plans and goals should also be discussed with them. **Availability:** Online.

26700 ■ *"Why Does Firm Reputation In Human Resource Policies Influence College Students? The Mechanisms Underlying Job Pursuit Intentions"* in *Human Resource Management (Vol. 51, January-February 2012, No. 1, pp. 121-142)*
Pub: John Wiley & Sons, Inc.
Contact: Christina Van Tassell, Executive Vice President Chief Financial Officer
Ed: Julie Holliday Wayne, Wendy J. Casper. **Released:** January 26, 2012. **Description:** The effects of reputational information about human resource practices of companies on college students seeking employment are examined. The reputation of firms in compensation, work-family, and diversity efforts are found to increase intentions to pursue employment in these firms. **Availability:** Print; PDF; Online.

26701 ■ *"Why Entrepreneurs Matter More Than Innovators"* in *Gallup Management Journal (November 22, 2011)*
Ed: Jim Clifton. **Released:** November 22, 2011. **Description:** In the race to create good jobs, leaders are not paying enough attention to cultivating talented entrepreneurs, rather they invest too much attention on innovation. **Availability:** Print; Online.

26702 ■ *"Why Great Managers Are So Rare; Companies Fail To Choose the Candidate With the Right Talent For the Job 82 Percent of the Time, Gallup Finds"* in *Gallup Business Journal (March 25, 2014)*
Pub: Gallup, Inc.
Contact: Jon Clifton, Chief Executive Officer
Description: Gallup research suggests that companies hire the wrong person to manage their firm about 82 percent of the time. Many times management talent already exists within the company, but for some reason, companies look elsewhere for that talent. Bad managers cost billions of dollars to businesses annually. **Availability:** Print.

26703 ■ *"Why I Stopped Firing Everyone and Started Being a Better Boss"* in *Inc. (Vol. 34, September 2012, No. 7, pp. 86)*
Pub: Mansueto Ventures L.L.C.
Contact: Stephanie Mehta, Chief Executive Officer
Ed: April Joyner. **Released:** August 28, 2012. **Description:** Indigo Johnson, former Marine, discusses her management style when starting her business. She fired employees regularly. Johnson enrolled in a PhD program in leadership and established a better hiring program and learned to utilize her workers' strengths. **Availability:** Print; Online.

26704 ■ *"Why Is It So Hard To Find Good People? The Problem Might Be You"* in *Inc. (Vol. 33, November 2011, No. 9, pp. 100)*
Description: Entrepreneurs sometimes struggle to find good workers. A recent survey shows hiring as their top concern. Four common mistakes that can occur during the hiring process our outlined. **Availability:** Online.

26705 ■ *"Why My Company Prioritizes Hiring Employees with Disabilities"* in *U.S. Chamber of Commerce (Sept. 14, 2022)*
URL(s): www.uschamber.com/workforce/why-my -company-prioritizes-hiring-employees-with-disabili ties
Ed: Kristen Barnfield. **Released:** September 14, 2022. **Description:** Addresses outdated, ill-informed misperceptions of people with disabilities in the workplace and provides information on diversity, equity, and inclusion practices. **Availability:** Online.

26706 ■ *"Why Small Businesses Struggling to Hire New Employees Should Embrace Gig Workers"* in *Entrepreneur (Sept. 8, 2021)*
URL(s): www.entrepreneur.com/article/383109
Ed: Tim Hentschel. **Released:** September 08, 2021. **Description:** Explores the use of gig-based independent contracts for small businesses that are struggling to find and retain employees. **Availability:** Online.

26707 ■ *"Work/Life Balance"* in *Dallas Business Journal (Vol. 37, June 20, 2014, No. 41, pp. 4)*
Pub: Routledge, Taylor & Francis Group
Description: Younger generations of corporate employees are increasingly looking for a more engaged workplace community. Research firm, Quantum Workplace, identifies several trends that help to attract and retain employees, including jobs that align with the workers' own values, growth opportunities within the firm, social interactions with co-workers, and employee health benefits. **Availability:** Print; Online.

26708 ■ *"Xymogen Poised for Huge Growth, Hiring"* in *Orlando Business Journal (Vol. 29, September 14, 2012, No. 13, pp. 1)*
Pub: Baltimore Business Journal
Contact: Rhonda Pringle, President
E-mail: rpringle@bizjournals.com
Description: Xymogen has made changes to its business model. The company is planning to hire at least 50 new workers in 2013. Xymogen posted $39.3 million in profits in 2011. **Availability:** Print; Online.

26709 ■ *"Your First 100 Days on Your New Job"* in *Women In Business (Vol. 63, Spring 2011, No. 1, pp. 28)*
Pub: American Business Women's Association
Contact: Rene Street, Executive Director
Ed: Diane Stafford. **Released:** March 22, 2011. **Description:** The first 100 days on the job are crucial if the person's permanent hiring is conditional on surviving a probationary period. The new hire must do more than just master the job's technical details to maximize the chance of success. Details of some basic tips to fit into the corporate culture and get along with coworkers are also discussed. **Availability:** Print; Online.

26710 ■ *"Your Web Brand Counts"* in *Black Enterprise (Vol. 44, June 2014, No. 10, pp. 46)*
Pub: Earl G. Graves Ltd.
Contact: Earl Graves, Jr., President
Description: Forty-eight percent of employers use Google or other search engines to find information about job applicants and 25 percent of executives hired were originally identified or contacted through social media, thus the importance of a good Web presence is outlined.

TRADE PERIODICALS

26711 ■ *Insight into Diversity: The EEO Recruitment Publication*
Pub: INSIGHT Into Diversity
Contact: Lenore Pearlstein, Publisher
E-mail: lpearlstein@insightintodiversity.com
URL(s): www.insightintodiversity.com
Facebook: www.facebook.com/insightintodiversity
Linkedin: www.linkedin.com/company/insight-into -diversity
X (Twitter): x.com/INSIGHT_News

Ed: Alexandra Vollman. **Released:** Monthly **Description:** Journal for business, academia, non-profit organizations and the government to use in recruiting females, Native Americans, minorities, veterans, and persons with disabilities. **Availability:** Print; PDF; Online.

VIDEO/AUDIO MEDIA

26712 ■ *Elevated Entrepreneurship: Amber Hurdle: The Science of Recruiting Well*
URL(s): mikemichalowicz.com/podcast/amber-hurdle -the-science-of-recruting-the-right-people
Ed: Mike Michalowiicz. **Released:** July 13, 2020. **Description:** Podcast explains the science behind hiring the right people.

26713 ■ *HBR Ideacast: People with Disabilities Are an Untapped Talent Pool*
URL(s): hbr.org/podcast/2023/09/people-with-disabili ties-are-an-untapped-talent-pool
Ed: Alison Beard. **Released:** March 28, 2024. **Description:** Podcast outlines four ways that hiring employees with disabilities can be a competitive advantage.

26714 ■ *How to Build a Busines with No Employees with Ian Blair*
URL(s): podcasts.apple.com/us/podcast/how-to-buil d-a-business-with-no-employees-with-ian-blair/id7 41544976?i=1000627456319
Released: September 11, 2023. **Description:** Podcast offers strategies for leveraging hiring agencies for cost efficiency.

26715 ■ *The How of Business: Andrea Hoffer - Hire Higher*
URL(s): www.thehowofbusiness.com/437-andrea -hoffer-hire-higher
Ed: Henry Lopez. **Released:** August 29, 2022. **Description:** Podcast explains how to attract ideal candidates.

26716 ■ *The How of Business: Kurt Wilkin - Hire Better*
URL(s): www.thehowofbusiness.com/418-kurt-wilkin -hire-better
Ed: Henry Lopez. **Released:** April 18, 2022. **Description:** Podcast offer tips on recruiting and hiring, including common mistakes, interview questions, and assessment tools. .

26717 ■ *The How of Business: Thad Price - Hring Front-Line Workers*
URL(s): www.thehowofbusiness.com/517-thad-price -hiring-workers
Ed: Henry Lopez. **Released:** April 22, 2024. **Description:** Podcast discusses hiring staff who work directly with your customers.

26718 ■ *The How of Business: Travis Reiter - Employee Background Checks*
URL(s): www.thehowofbusiness.com/467-travis-reiter -employee-background-checks

Ed: Henry Lopez. **Released:** April 10, 2023. **Description:** Podcast discusses how to screen and hire the right employees.

26719 ■ *Making Key Hires*
URL(s): www.startuphustlepodcast.com/making-key -hires
Ed: Matt Watson. **Released:** April 04, 2024. **Description:** Podcast outlines hiring mistakes and identifying talented individuals with potential. .

26720 ■ *Marketplace: At This Detroit Frame Shop, It Might Be Time to Bring Another Employee into the Picture*
URL(s): www.marketplace.org/2023/06/30/at-detroi t-frame-shop-it-might-be-time-to-bring-another-em-ployee-into-the-picture
Ed: Sean McHenry. **Released:** June 30, 2023. **Description:** Podcast discusses increasing a lean crew.

26721 ■ *Marketplace: Small Businesses Are Still Struggling to Hire. But the Situation's Improving.*
URL(s): www.marketplace.org/2023/09/01/small-busi nesses-hiring-labor-shortage
Ed: Justin Ho. **Released:** September 01, 2023. **Description:** Podcast discusses staffing issues in small businesses.

26722 ■ *Nurture Small Business: Leveraging Skills-Based Hiring for a Stronger Workforce*
URL(s): nurturesmallbusiness.buzzsprout.com/900 445/episodes/15478702-leveraging-skills-base d-hiring-for-a-stronger-workforce
Ed: Denise Cagan. **Released:** July 30, 2024. **Description:** Podcast explores skills-based hiring, fostering a more inclusive workforce, overcoming hiring challenges, and finding employees who align with your company culture.

26723 ■ *Nurture Small Business: Navigating Onboarding: Discover How to Create Smooth Employee Starts*
URL(s): nurturesmallbusiness.buzzsprout.com/900 445/episodes/1574895-navigating-onboarding -discover-how-to-create-smooth-employee-starts
Ed: Denise Cagan. **Released:** May 20, 2024. **Description:** Podcast discusses the importance of effective onboarding to reduce stress for both owners and new hires and offers tips on how to optimize existing resources before introducing new tools.

26724 ■ *Profit First Nation: Fixing the Errors of Mis-Hires*
URL(s): www.profitfirstnation.com/episodes/ep -144-fixing-the-errors-of-mishires
Ed: Danielle Mulvey. **Released:** October 31, 2023. **Description:** Podcast discusses hiring mistakes that could have been avoided.

26725 ■ *Small Business, Big Mindset: Mastering the Art of the Hire*
URL(s): podcast.musclecreative.com/924061/episo des/12483157-mastering-the-art-of-the-hire

Ed: Erin Geiger. **Released:** April 04, 2023. **Description:** Podcast discusses how to hire the right person for the right role at the right time.

CONSULTANTS

26726 ■ **Barada Associates Inc.**
130 E Second St.
Rushville, IN 46173
Ph: (765)932-5917
Free: 866-400-1663
Fax: (877)576-2806
Co. E-mail: info@baradainc.com
URL: http://baradainc.com
Contact: William C. Barada, President
Facebook: www.facebook.com/BaradaAssociates
Linkedin: www.linkedin.com/company/barada -associates
X (Twitter): x.com/baradainc
Description: Firm provides professional employment screening services for client companies with dependent and objective reference reports on candidates for salaried and hourly employment. **Scope:** Firm provides professional employment screening services for client companies with dependent and objective reference reports on candidates for salaried and hourly employment. **Founded:** 1979. **Publications:** "Reference Checking for Everyone," 2004; "Reference Checking is More Than Ever," Human Resource Magazine, 1996; "The Paper Chase," Indianapolis Monthly, 1995; "Check it Out-Hiring? What You Don't Know Could Hurt You," the American School Board Journal, 1994; "Reference Checking: Increased Necessity to Exercise Reasonable Care," Kin cannon & Reed, 1994; "Reference Checking More Critical Than Ever," Association of Executive Search Consultants Inc, Dec, 1993; "Honest References," Human Resource Executive, Sep, 1993; "Check References with Care," Nation's Business, May, 1993; "Don't Overlook Reference Checks," the School Administrator, May, 1992.

26727 ■ **Business Technology Group Inc. (BTG)**
2024 Seagate Ave.
Neptune Beach, FL 32266
Description: Firm that provides IT staffing and services. **Scope:** Firm that provides IT staffing and services. **Founded:** 1995.

COMPUTERIZED DATABASES

26728 ■ *ABI/INFORM*
ProQuest LLC
789 E Eisenhower Pky.
Ann Arbor, MI 48108
Ph: (734)761-4700
Free: 800-521-0600
URL: http://www.proquest.com
Contact: Matti Shem Tov, Chief Executive Officer
URL(s): about.proquest.com/en/products-services/abi _inform_complete
Availability: Online. **Type:** Full-text; Bibliographic; Image.

Home-Based Business

START-UP INFORMATION

26729 ▪ *101 Internet Businesses You Can Start from Home: How to Choose and Build Your Own Successful E-Business*
Pub: Maximum Press

Ed: Susan Sweeney. **Released:** Third edition. **Description:** Guide for starting and growing an Internet business; information for developing a business plan, risk levels, and promotional techniques are included.

26730 ▪ *"Breakthrough: How to Build a Million Dollar Business by Helping Others Succeed"*
Pub: CreateSpace

Released: October 23, 2014. **Price:** $3.72, paperback. **Description:** Instruction for starting and growing a thriving business from home is provided. The book teaches how to listing to the small voice within, follow your instincts, deliver effective presentations, attract customers who require your products or services, host home meetings, develop leadership skills, discover purpose, and clarify your entrepreneurial visions and goals. **Availability:** Print.

26731 ▪ *"Caring Concern" in Small Business Opportunities (September 2010)*
Pub: Harris Publishing, Inc.
Contact: Janet Chase, Contact

Description: Profile of Joshua Hoffman, founder and CEO of HomeWell Senior Care, Inc., provider of non-medical live-in and hourly personal care, companionship and homemaker services for seniors so they can remain in their own homes. **Availability:** Online.

26732 ▪ *"Etsy: Etsy Business for Beginners! Master Etsy and Build a Profitable Business In No Time"*

Released: December 23, 2014. **Price:** $6.99, regular price is $13.99. **Description:** Craft artisans take note: information is offered to start an online business through Etsy. Whether handmade home accessories, clothing, or knick-knacks, Etsy is the perfect option for artists and crafters to start a home-based, online retail operation. **Availability:** Print; Download.

26733 ▪ *Going Solo: Developing a Home-Based Consulting Business from the Ground Up*

Description: Ways to turn specialized knowledge into a home-based successful consulting firm, focusing on targeting client needs, business plans, and growth.

26734 ▪ *"Green Clean Machine" in Small Business Opportunities (Winter 2010)*
Pub: Harris Publishing, Inc.
Contact: Janet Chase, Contact

Description: Eco-friendly maid franchise plans to grow its $62 million sales base. Profile of Maid Brigade, a green-cleaning franchise is planning to expand across the country. **Availability:** Print; Online.

26735 ▪ *How to Open & Operate a Financially Successful Landscaping, Nursery, or Lawn Service Business: With Companion CD-ROM*
Pub: Atlantic Publishing Co.
Contact: Dr. Heather L. Johnson, Contact

Ed: Lynn Wasnak. **Released:** 2010. **Description:** Guide provides understanding of the basic concepts of starting and running a service business, focusing on the operation of a small nursery, landscaping, or lawn service or combining the three operations. It also offers tips for running the business from the home. **Availability:** CD-ROM; Print; Online.

26736 ▪ *How to Start a Home-Based Consulting Business: Define Your Specialty Build a Client Base Make Yourself Indispensable*

Ed: Bert Holtje. **Released:** January 06, 2010. **Price:** Paperback. **Description:** Everything needed for starting and running a successful consulting business from home. **Availability:** Print.

26737 ▪ *How to Start a Home-based Craft Business*

Ed: Kenn Oberrecht, Patrice Lewis. **Released:** Sixth edition. **Price:** $18.99, e-book; Paperback. **Description:** Step-by-step guide for starting and growing a home-based craft business. **Availability:** Print.

26738 ▪ *How to Start a Home-Based Event Planning Business*

Ed: Jill Moran. **Released:** 4th edition. **Price:** $19.95, paperback; $9.99; Paperback. **Description:** Guide to starting and growing a business planning events from a home-based firm. **Availability:** E-book; Print.

26739 ▪ *How to Start a Home-Based Landscaping Business*

Ed: Owen E. Dell. **Released:** 7th edition. **Price:** $21.95, paperback(£14.95); $9.99, e-book(£6.95); $18.95; Electronic Book. **Description:** Guide to starting and running a home-based landscaping business. **Availability:** E-book; Print.

26740 ▪ *How to Start a Home-Based Mail Order Business*

Ed: Georganne Fiumara. **Released:** June 01, 2011. **Price:** Paperback. **Description:** Step-by-step guide for starting and growing a home-based mail order business. Information about equipment, pricing, online marketing, are included along with worksheets and checklists for planning. **Availability:** Print; Online.

26741 ▪ *How to Start a Home-Based Online Retail Business*

Ed: Jeremy Shepherd. **Released:** November 08, 2011. **Price:** paperback, softback. **Description:** Information for starting an online retail, home-based business is shared. **Availability:** E-book; Print.

26742 ▪ *How to Start a Home-Based Personal Chef Business*

Ed: Denise Vivaldo. **Released:** January 04, 2011. **Price:** paperback/softback. **Description:** Everything

needed to know to start a personal chef business is featured. **Availability:** E-book; Print.

26743 ▪ *How to Start a Home-Based Professional Organizing Business*

Ed: Dawn Noble. **Released:** April 01, 2011. **Price:** paperback, softback. **Description:** Tips for starting a home-based professional organizing business are presented. **Availability:** E-book; Print.

26744 ▪ *How to Start a Home-Based Senior Care Business: Develop a Winning Business Plan*

Ed: James L. Ferry. **Released:** Second edition. **Price:** paperback; softback; Electronic Book. **Description:** Everything needed to know in order to start and run a profitable, ethical, and satisfying senior care business from your home. Information covers writing a good business plan, marketing services to families, creating a fee structure, and developing a network of trusted caregivers and service providers. **Availability:** E-book; Print.

26745 ▪ *How to Start a Home-Based Web Design Business*

Ed: Jim Smith. **Released:** 4th edition. **Price:** paperback/softback. **Description:** Information for starting a home-based Web design firm is given. **Availability:** Print.

26746 ▪ *How to Start a Home-Based Web Design Business, 4th Edition*

Ed: Jim Smith. **Released:** Fourth edition. **Price:** Paperback. **Description:** Comprehensive guide contains all the necessary tools and strategies required to successfully launch and grow a Web design business. **Availability:** Print.

26747 ▪ *"Moms Mean Business: A Guide to Creating a Successful Company and Happy Life as a Mom Entrepreneur"*
Pub: Career Press Inc.

Released: October 20, 2014. **Price:** $15.99, Trade Paperback,plus S&H. **Description:** Currently, more women are starting new businesses than men and there are 9 million women-owned businesses in the United States; most of these women are also moms. A guide to help women start and run a successful home-based business is presented. **Availability:** Print.

26748 ▪ *"Road Map to Riches" in Small Business Opportunities (September 2010)*
Pub: Harris Publishing, Inc.
Contact: Janet Chase, Contact

Description: Profile of Philip Nenadov who launched The Transportation Network Group during the recession. This franchise is low cost and can earn six figures while working from home by becoming a trucking agent. **Availability:** Online.

26749 ▪ *Scrapbooking for Profit: Cashing in on Retail, Home-Based and Internet Opportunities*
Pub: Allworth Press
Contact: Tad Crawford, Founder

Ed: Rebecca Pittman. **Released:** June 01, 2005. **Price:** $16.95, paperback; $19.99, Ebook; $19.95, Paperback. **Description:** Eleven strategies for starting a scrapbooking business, including brick-and-mortar stores, home-based businesses, and online retail and wholesale outlets. **Availability:** E-book; Print.

26750 ■ Start and Run a Home-Based Food Business
Pub: Self-Counsel Press Inc.
Contact: Diana Douglas, Governor
Ed: Mimi Shortland Fix. **Price:** C$23.95; C$23.95, E pub; $12.99. **Description:** Information is shared to help start and run a home-based food business, selling your own homemade foods. **Availability:** Electronic publishing; PDF.

26751 ■ Start Your Own Fashion Accessories Business
Pub: Entrepreneur Media Inc.
Contact: Dan Bova, Director
E-mail: dbova@entrepreneur.com
Ed: Eileen Figure Sandlin. **Released:** Second edition. **Description:** Entrepreneurs wishing to start a fashion accessories business will find important information for setting up a home workshop and office, exploring the market, managing finances, publicizing and advertising the business and more.

26752 ■ "This Biz Is Booming" in Small Business Opportunities (Winter 2010)
Description: Non-medical home care is a $52 billion industry. Advice to start a non-medical home care business is provided, focusing on franchise FirstLight HomeCare, but showing that independent home care agencies are also successful.

26753 ■ "Working From Home: A Guide to Setting Up You Own Work From Home Income: On Your Own Terms with Real Companies"
Pub: CreateSpace
Released: October 19, 2014. **Price:** $19.98, $8.99 paperback. **Description:** A guide for starting and running a home business is provided. **Availability:** Print.

ASSOCIATIONS AND OTHER ORGANIZATIONS

26754 ■ American Independent Business Alliance (AMIBA)
524 Boston Post Rd.
Wayland, MA 01778
Ph: (513)202-4081
Co. E-mail: amibaoffice@gmail.com
URL: http://amiba.net
Contact: Laury Hammel, Treasurer
Facebook: www.facebook.com/theAMIBA
Linkedin: www.linkedin.com/company/amiba
-american-independent-business-alliance
X (Twitter): x.com/theAMIBA
Description: Represents small business owners. Works to fill the professional needs of small and home-based business owners. Hosts conferences. **Founded:** 2001. **Geographic Preference:** National.

26755 ■ Business Barometer
401-4141 Yonge St.
Toronto, ON, Canada M2P 2A6
Co. E-mail: cfib@cfib.ca
URL: http://www.cfib-fcei.ca/en
Contact: Dan Kelly, President
URL(s): www.cfib-fcei.ca/en/research-economic
-analysis/business-barometer
Released: Monthly **Availability:** Print; PDF.

26756 ■ Canadian Federation of Independent Business (CFIB) - Research Library
401-4141 Yonge St.
Toronto, ON, Canada M2P 2A6
Co. E-mail: cfib@cfib.ca
URL: http://www.cfib-fcei.ca/en
Contact: Dan Kelly, President
Facebook: www.facebook.com/CFIB

Linkedin: www.linkedin.com/company/canadian-fe
deration-of-independent-business
X (Twitter): x.com/CFIBNews
Instagram: www.instagram.com/cfib_fcei
YouTube: www.youtube.com/user/cfibdotca
Description: Promotes economic well-being of members and seeks to maintain a healthy domestic business climate. **Scope:** Business. **Founded:** 1971. **Holdings:** Figures not available. **Publications:** Mandate (Quarterly); Business Barometer (Monthly). **Geographic Preference:** National.

26757 ■ Home-Based Working Moms (HBWM)
4057 Riley Fuzzel Rd., Ste. 500-117
Spring, TX 77386
Co. E-mail: contact@hiremymom.com
URL: http://www.hiremymom.com
Contact: Lesley Pyle, Founder Owner
YouTube: www.youtube.com/user/hiremymom
Pinterest: www.pinterest.com/hiremymomcom
Description: Individuals who work at home or would like to. Promotes working at home as an option for people in applicable positions; seeks to enhance the careers of members currently working at home. Serves as a forum for exchange of information among members. Makes available member matching service. Advocates for creation of more work-at-home opportunities by American businesses. **Founded:** 1995. **Publications:** Our Place (10/year); Basics of Starting a Home Business; How to Promote Your Home Business; Over 200 Home Business Opportunities; Tips for Selecting a Home Business; Twenty Ways to Cut Your Living Expenses. **Geographic Preference:** National.

REFERENCE WORKS

26758 ■ "5 Straightforward Ways to Go from Employed to Self-Employed" in Forbes.com(October 26, 2022)
URL(s): www.forbes.com/sites/jodiecook/2022/10/26/
5-straightforward-ways-to-go-from-employed-to-self
-employed/?sh=9857d4b6304a
Ed: Jodie Cook. **Description:** Transition from your ourrent job working for someone else to being your own boss. Tips are discussed to help ease through this process.

26759 ■ "7 Ways to Advertise Your Home-Based Small Business for Free" in Citizens General blog (Dec. 7, 2018)
URL(s): citizensgeneral.com/business-insurance
-news/postid/130/7-ways-to-advertise-your-home
-based-small-business-for-free
Released: December 07, 2018. **Description:** Maximizing the return-on-investment for a home-based business is crucial. This article takes a look at some of the best ways to advertise your business for free. **Availability:** Online.

26760 ■ "20 Business Ideas for Stay-at-Home Parents" in Entrepreneur (May 15, 2021)
URL(s): www.entrepreneur.com/slideshow/299781
Ed: Preethi Buckholder. **Released:** May 15, 2021. **Description:** Provides twenty business ideas that stay-at-home parents can start from home with very little money. **Availability:** Online.

26761 ■ "25 Home Based Business Ideas That Let You Work From Home" in Shopify Blog (Jan. 6, 2022)
URL(s): www.shopify.com/blog/home-business
Ed: Braveen Kumar. **Released:** January 06, 2022. **Description:** Discusses the possibility of using remote work to pursue entrepreneurship. Includes information on what makes a home-based business, 25 profitable home business ideas, finding an idea that works for you, and and FAQ.

26762 ■ "25 Social Media Business Ideas" in Small Business Trends(January 26, 2023)
URL(s): smallbiztrends.com/2023/01/social-media
-business-ideas.html

Ed: Kevin Ocasio. **Released:** January 26, 2023. **Description:** Social media can provide some good opportunities to start a small business. Discussed are ideas anyone can use to build a social media based business. **Availability:** Online.

26763 ■ 30+ Small Business Ideas That Use Skills You Already Have
URL(s): articles.bplans.com/business-ideas/small
-business-ideas/thirty-small-business-ideas/
Ed: Briana Morgaine. **Description:** Includes more than 30 small business ideas that use skills you already have and provides information on how to launch your business. **Availability:** Online.

26764 ■ 42 Home-Based Businesses You Can Start Today
URL(s): www.businesstown.com/42-home-base
d-businesses-you-can-start-today/
Ed: Bob Adams. **Description:** Provides a quiz to help entrepreneurs understand what type of home-based business suits your personality. Offers 42 home-based business ideas and provides eight steps to getting started. **Availability:** Online.

26765 ■ "50 Creative Business Ideas to Start in 2023" in Small Business Trends(February 7, 2023)
URL(s): smallbiztrends.com/2023/02/creative-busi
ness-ideas.html
Ed: Annie Pilon. **Released:** February 07, 2023. **Description:** A list of 50 small business ideas that are on the creative side and how to best achieve pursuing those ideas. **Availability:** Online.

26766 ■ "50 Handmade Business Ideas to Start in 2023" in Small Business Trends(February 8, 2023)
URL(s): smallbiztrends.com/2023/02/handmade-busi
ness-ideas.html
Ed: Annie Pilon. **Released:** February 08, 2023. **Description:** A list of 50 businesses ideas focused on handmade products you can run from your home. **Availability:** Online.

26767 ■ "101 Secrets to Running a Successful Home-Based Business" in allBusiness
URL(s): www.allbusiness.com/101-secrets-running
-successful-home-based-business-15645-1.html
Ed: Sara Wilson. **Description:** Provides information for those interested in running a home-based business. Includes 101 tips, lessons, pitfalls, etc. **Availability:** Online.

26768 ■ "As Traditional Web Site Adoption Slows, Facebook and Other Social Networks Become Key Platforms for Home-Based Business Promotional and Commercial Activity Online" in Marketing Weekly News (June 16, 2012)
Description: Websites have provided an inexpensive means for businesses to market their products and services. However, home-based businesses are using social networking, email marketing, search engine optimization, search engine marketing, Website optimization for mobile devices, banner advertisements, and the use of ecommerce platforms such as eBay, Craigs list, and Amazon. **Availability:** Print; Online.

26769 ■ Business Directory
Pub: Greater Phoenix Chamber of Commerce
Contact: Todd Sanders, President
E-mail: tsanders@phoenixchamber.com
URL(s): business.phoenixchamber.com/list
Description: Covers 67 home-based businesses in the greater Phoenix, Arizona area. **Entries include:** Contact details. **Availability:** Online.

26770 ■ Business Know-How: An Operational Guide for Home-Based and Micro-Sized Businesses with Limited Budgets

26771 ■ "California vs. Freelance Writers" in National Review (October 22, 2019)
URL(s): www.nationalreview.com/corner/new-califor
nia-labor-law-hits-freelance-writers-hard/

Ed: Robert Verbruggen. **Released:** October 22, 2019. **Description:** Freelancers in California are gearing up for major changes to their work when a new law takes effect that will force all companies to treat freelancers as regular employees. **Availability:** Online.

26772 ■ *Careers for Homebodies & Other Independent Souls*

Ed: Jan Goldberg. **Released:** Second Edition. **Description:** The books offers insight into choosing the right career for individuals. Jobs range from office to outdoors, job markets, and levels of education requirements. **Availability:** Print; Online.

26773 ■ *"Check Out How a Nurse Made Millions with Her Etsy Business"* in *Small Business Trends* (February 22, 2023)

URL(s): smallbiztrends.com/2023/02/nurse-makes -millions-etsy-side-business.html

Ed: Gabrielle Pickard-Whitehead. **Released:** February 22, 2023. **Description:** Profile of Stephanee Beggs, a nurse who made millions from her side-hustle Etsy store. **Availability:** Online.

26774 ■ *"A Comprehensive Guide on How to Start a Packaging Business"* in *Home Business* (August 3, 2022)

URL(s): homebusinessmag.com/business-start-up/ how-to-guides/comprehensive-guide-how-to-star t-packaging-business/

Released: August 03, 2022. **Description:** If you are starting a packaging business, be sure to follow the steps given in this article. Tips on suppliers and marketing are included. **Availability:** Online.

26775 ■ *"Does Your Home-Based Business Need Business Insurance?"* in *Legal Zoom* (March 22, 2023)

URL(s): www.legalzoom.com/articles/does-your -home-based-business-need-business-insurance

Released: March 22, 2023. **Description:** Discusses the available business insurance small business owners should look into to have themselves covered in case of property damage, liability coverage, and even auto insurance for any company vehicles. **Availability:** Online.

26776 ■ *"Effective Organizing for the Home Business"* in *Gaebler Ventures Resources for Entrepreneurs*

URL(s): www.gaebler.com/Effective-Organizing-For -The-Home-Business.htm

Ed: Angela Ly. **Description:** Provides tips and suggestions on how to get your home start-up organization underway. **Availability:** Online.

26777 ■ *"Family Child Care Record-Keeping Guide, Ninth Edition (Redleaf Business Series)"*

Pub: Redleaf Press

Contact: Barbara Yates, President

Released: 9th edition. **Price:** $21.95, soft bound. **Description:** Writer, trainer, lawyer, and consultant provides concise information for home-based family child care (day care) providers. The book covers tracking expenses, being profitable, filing taxes, and meeting government regulations. This resources covers the process of accurate bookkeeping and record-keeping to take advantage of all allowable tax deductions. Changes in depreciation rules, adjustments to food and mileage rates, and clarifications on how to calculate the Time-Space percentage are defined. **Availability:** Print.

26778 ■ *"Floral-Design Kiosk Business Blossoming"* in *Colorado Springs Business Journal* (September 24, 2010)

Pub: Dolan Media Newswires

Ed: Monica Mendoza. **Description:** Profile of Shellie Greto and her mother Jackie Martin who started a wholesale flower business in their garage. The do-it-yourself floral arrangement firm started a kiosk business in supermarkets called Complete Design. **Availability:** Online.

26779 ■ *"The Gig's Up for Freelancers"* in *The Wall Street Journal* (October 27, 2019)

URL(s): www.wsj.com/articles/the-gigs-up-for -freelancers-11572208945

Ed: Andy Kessler. **Released:** October 27, 2019. **Description:** Assembly Bill 5 is set to take effect, meaning that most independent contractors will now be considered full-time employees in California. While it could mean that more contract workers receive sick leave and health care but more than likely, contractors will find their livelihoods taken away as employers will stop hiring freelancers from California. **Availability:** Online.

26780 ■ *"A Guide to Starting a Driveway Paving Business"* in *Home Business* (September 27, 2022)

URL(s): homebusinessmag.com/business-start-up/ how-to-guides/guide-starting-driveway-paving-busi ness/

Released: September 27, 2022. **Description:** Describes what you need to consider before starting a driveway paving business. Includes tips on marketing, registering your business, and creating a business plan. **Availability:** Online.

26781 ■ *"Guide to Starting a Flower Delivery Business"* in *Home Business* (Home Business (September 6, 2022)

URL(s): homebusinessmag.com/business-start-up/ how-to-guides/guide-starting-flower-delivery-busi ness/

Released: September 06, 2022. **Description:** Itemizes the steps needed to take before starting a flower delivery service. **Availability:** Online.

26782 ■ *"A Guide to Starting a Food Truck Business"* in *Home Business* (June 30, 2022)

URL(s): homebusinessmag.com/business-start-up/ how-to-guides/guide-starting-food-truck-business/

Released: June 30, 2022. **Description:** With the popularity of food trucks increasing, it could be the ideal time to start your own food truck business. Follow these steps to ensure you get the most out of the experience. **Availability:** Online.

26783 ■ *"Guide to Starting Your Own Roofing Business"* in *Home Business* (May 24, 2022)

URL(s): homebusinessmag.com/business-start-up/ how-to-guides/guide-starting-roofing-business/

Released: May 24, 2022. **Description:** Starting your own roofing business may be the solution you need to break away from working for someone else. Included are tips to consider while doing so. **Availability:** Online.

26784 ■ *"Home-Based Business Advantages and Disadvantages"* in *The Balance Small Business* (Apr 16, 2021)

URL(s): www.thebalancesmb.com/home-based-busi ness-2948188

Ed: Susan Ward. **Released:** April 16, 2021. **Description:** Discusses the variety of home-based business types as well as advantages and disadvantages of running a home-based business. **Availability:** Online.

26785 ■ *"Home Business Ideas: 40 Remote Jobs to Explore in 2022"* in *NerdWallet* (Jan. 7, 2021)

URL(s): www.nerdwallet.com/article/small-business/ home-business-ideas

Ed: Sally Lauckner. **Released:** January 07, 2021. **Description:** Discusses the compelling reasons a person might choose to work from home and provides a list of 40 home-based business options. Also offers tips on how to get started. **Availability:** Online.

26786 ■ *Home Business Magazine*

URL(s): homebusinessmag.com

Facebook: www.facebook.com/ homebusinessmagazineonline/

X (Twitter): twitter.com/homebusinessmag

Instagram: www.instagram.com/ homebusinessmagazine/#

YouTube: www.youtube.com/channel/UC20vTcKqfKy 3Uuqj_ehVliw

Description: Provides home-based business articles that encompass a breadth of topics covering all aspects of home-based business. **Availability:** Online. **Telecommunication Services:** editor@ homebusinessmag.com.

26787 ■ *Home Business Tax Deductions: Keep What You Earn*

Pub: Nolo

Contact: Chris Braun, President

Ed: Stephen Fishman. **Released:** November 2020. **Price:** $27.99, book and e-book; $24.99, e-book (downloadable). **Description:** Home business tax deductions are outlined. Basic information on the ways various business structures are taxed and how deductions work is included. **Availability:** E-book; Print.

26788 ■ *Housecleaning Business: Organize Your Business - Get Clients and Referrals - Set Rates and Services*

Ed: Laura Jorstad, Melinda Morse. **Price:** Paperback, softback. **Description:** This book shares insight into starting a housecleaning business. It shows how to develop a service manual, screen clients, serve customers, select cleaning products, competition, how to up a home office, using the Internet to grow the business and offering green cleaning options to clients. **Availability:** E-book; Print.

26789 ■ *"How to Create a Home-Based Business Without a Product or Service"* in *Entrepreneur* (July 31, 2021)

URL(s): www.entrepreneur.com/article/375244

Ed: Sid Peddinti. **Released:** July 31, 2021. **Description:** Provides four steps to create a home-based business that does not require the creation of a product or service. **Availability:** Online.

26790 ■ *"How to Set Up an Effective Home Office"* in *Women Entrepreneur* (August 22, 2008)

Description: Checklist provides ways in which one can arrange their home office to provide the greatest efficiency which will allow maximum productivity and as a result the greater the chance of success. **Availability:** Online.

26791 ■ *How to Start a Home-Based Senior Care Business*

Ed: James L. Ferry. **Released:** 2nd edition. **Price:** Paperback, softback; Electronic Book. **Description:** Information is provided to start a home-based senior care business. **Availability:** E-book; Print.

26792 ■ *"How to Start a Home-Based Tax Preparation Business"* in *Home Business* (June 3, 2022)

URL(s): homebusinessmag.com/business-start-up/ how-to-guides/how-to-start-home-based-tax -preparation-business/

Released: June 03, 2022. **Availability:** Online.

26793 ■ *"How to Start Your Home Business in 2023"* in *Home Business* (September 22, 2022)

URL(s): homebusinessmag.com/business-start-up/ how-to-guides/how-to-start-home-business-2023/

Released: September 22, 2023. **Description:** Itemizes steps that should be taken before embarking on creating a home-based business. **Availability:** Online.

26794 ■ *"I Quit My Day Job 4 Months Ago to Become a Freelance Writer. Here's What My Family of 4 Spends in a Typical Week"* in *Business Insider* (October 14, 2019)

URL(s): www.businessinsider.com/spending-diary -family-freelance-income-daytona-beach-florida

Ed: Clint Proctor. **Released:** October 14, 2019. **Description:** An honest look at one family's budeting with the breadwinner working a freelance writing job. **Availability:** Online.

26795 ■ *"Independent Contractor, Sole Proprietor, and LLC Taxes Explained in 100 Pages or Less"*
Description: A small business tax primer which includes information of home office deduction, estimated tax payments, self-employment tax, business retirement plans, numerous business deductions, and audit protection. **Availability:** Print; Online.

26796 ■ *"Knife Sharpening Tools – Your List for Starting a Business"* in Small Business Trends(March 2, 2023)
URL(s): smallbiztrends.com/2023/03/knife-sharpening-tools.html
Ed: Rob Starr. **Released:** March 02, 2023. **Description:** Discusses operating a knife sharpening businesses as a side-hustle or as a small business. **Availability:** Online.

26797 ■ *Make Money As a Freelance Writer: 7 Simple Steps to Start Your Freelance Writing Business and Earn Your First $1,000*
Ed: Sally Miller, Gina Horkey. **Released:** April 19, 2018. **Price:** $9.99, Paperback. **Description:** A how-to guide for turning your writing hobby into a freelance business. **Availability:** Print.

26798 ■ *"Marcia Tiago Shares How to Start and Run a Successful Business in 2023"* in Home Business (March 2, 2023)
URL(s): homebusinessmag.com/business-start-up/how-to-guides/marcia-tiago-shares-how-to-start-run-successful-business-2023/
Released: March 02, 2023. **Description:** Presents Marcia Tiago's best tips for launching a new business. **Availability:** Online.

26799 ■ *"Opportunity Knocks"* in Small Business Opportunities (September 2008)
Description: Profile of YourOffice USA, a franchise that provides home-based and small businesses cost-effective and efficient support through "virtual" offices that are available as much or as little as the client needs it; they also supply necessary tools such as a professional business address, private mailbox service, personalized telephone answering and more that supports clients who want to look, act and operate with an advanced business image. **Availability:** Online.

26800 ■ *"The Pandemic Scramble to Legalize Home-Based Businesses"* in Bloomberg CityLab (Jan. 31, 2022)
URL(s): www.bloomberg.com/news/articles/2022-01-31/zoning-rules-shouldn-t-hurt-home-based-businesses
Ed: M. Nolan Gray. **Released:** January 31, 2022. **Description:** With businesses moving to a home-based environment amidst the pandemic, many entrepreneurs have discovered that U.S. zoning codes have an impact on their home-based business. This article discusses zoning standards related to home-based businesses. **Availability:** Online.

26801 ■ *"Remote: Office Not Required"*
Released: 2018. **Description:** The growing trend in working from home, or anywhere else, and the challenges and benefits from working from home are explored. Technology has enabled one in five global workers to telecommute and about ten percent of employees work from home. Some of the advantages in remote jobs is an increase in the talent pool, reduces turnover, lessens a firm's real estate footprint, and improves the ability to conduct business across time zones.

26802 ■ *"Remote Work in Construction: 3 Tips for Success"* in Home Business Magazine (Jan. 27, 2022)
URL(s): homebusinessmag.com/businesses/success-tips/remote-work-construction-3-tips-success/
Ed: Alex Minett. **Released:** January 27, 2022. **Description:** Discusses how remote work during the pandemic has changed aspects of the construction business. Provides tips for construction business owners to set up a remote team for success. **Availability:** Online.

26803 ■ *"Right at Home China Celebrates 1 Year Anniversary as U.S. In-Home Senior Care Master Franchise"* in Professional Service Close-Up (June 24, 2012)
Description: Franchisor, Right at Home International Inc., provides in-home senior care and assistance and has experienced a one year franchise license agreement in China. Right at Home China predicts growth because China has 200 million adults over 65 years of age. **Availability:** Print; Online.

26804 ■ *Shedworking: The Alternative Workplace Revolution*
Pub: Frances Lincoln Ltd.
Contact: Philip Cooper, Publisher
E-mail: philip.cooper@quarto.com
Ed: Alex Johnson. **Description:** Shedworking is an alternative office space for those working at home. The book features shedworkers and shedbuilders from around the world who are leading this alternative workplace revolution and why this trend is working. **Availability:** Print.

26805 ■ *"Should Freelancers Establish Themselves as an LLC?"* in Small Business Trends (August 9, 2021)
URL(s): smallbiztrends.com/2020/12/should-freelancers-establish-themselves-as-llc.html
Ed: Rob Starr. **Released:** August 09, 2021. **Description:** Discusses the particulars of setting up your home-based freelance business as a LLC. **Availability:** Online.

26806 ■ *Side Hustles for Dummies*
URL(s): www.wiley.com/en-us/Side+Hustles+For+Dummies-p-9781119870159
Ed: Alan R. Simon. **Released:** April 2022. **Price:** $15, e-book; $24.99, paperback. **Description:** A side hustle gig may be the best choice for people who crave more flexibility in their lives while still earning a living. Starting a small home-based business is discussed. **Availability:** E-book; Print.

26807 ■ *Start Your Own Freelance Writing Business: The Complete Guide to Starting and Scaling from Scratch*
Ed: Laura Pennington Briggs. **Released:** July 16, 2019. **Price:** $13.49, Paperback; $9.99. E-Book. **Description:** A helpful guide for those seeking to pursue a freelance writing career. **Availability:** E-book; Print.

26808 ■ *"Starting a Business from Home - Legal, Tax, and Financial Concerns"* in CPA Journal (July 2017)
URL(c): www.opajournal.com/2017/07/05/starting-business-home/
Ed: James Grimaldi. **Released:** July 2017. **Description:** Covers legal, tax, and financial concerns related to starting a business from home. **Availability:** Online.

26809 ■ *"Starting a Home Business With a Spouse"* in Gaebler Ventures Resources for Entrepreneurs*
URL(s): www.gaebler.com/Starting-a-Home-Business-With-a-Spouse.htm
Description: Provides information and considerations related to starting a home-based business with your spouse. **Availability:** Online.

26810 ■ *"Starting a Successful Home Security Company: Step-By-Step Guide"* in Home Business (January 30, 2023)
URL(s): homebusinessmag.com/business-start-up/how-to-guides/starting-successful-home-security-company-step-by-step-guide/
Released: January 30, 2023. **Description:** Relates tips on starting a home security company, including developing a business model and deciding on inventory. **Availability:** Online.

26811 ■ *"Tax Breaks for Home-Based Businesses Go Unclaimed"* in Legal Zoom (March 29, 2023)
URL(s): www.legalzoom.com/articles/tax-breaks-for-home-based-businesses-go-unclaimed

Ed: C. Yoder. **Released:** March 29, 2023. **Description:** Discusses how home-based businesses are not claiming items on their taxes when they really should. **Availability:** Online.

26812 ■ *"Teleworkers Confess Biggest At-Home Distractions"* in Employee Benefit News (Vol. 25, November 1, 2011, No. 14, pp. 7)
Pub: SourceMedia LLC
Contact: Gemma Postlethwaite, Chief Executive Officer
Ed: Kelley M. Butler. **Description:** Telecommuting can actually make some workers more efficient and productive versus working inside the office.

26813 ■ *"Top 5 Health Insurance Tips for the Self-Employed"* in Legal Zoom (March 24, 2023)
URL(s): www.legalzoom.com/articles/top-5-health-insurance-tips-for-the-self-employed
Ed: Douglas Dalrymple. **Released:** March 24, 2023. **Description:** Self-employed people need to provide their health insurance since there is no big corporation that will give that to them as a benefit. This is often a big expense and the options can be confusing. Included are tips on what to consider. **Availability:** Online.

26814 ■ *The Travel Agent's Complete Desk Reference, 5th Edition*
Released: Fifth edition. **Description:** Reference book that provides essential information to the home-based travel agent.

26815 ■ *"Turning Uncertainty Into Opportunity: Creating A Home-Based Business"* in Forbes (Apr 27, 2020)
URL(s): www.forbes.com/sites/forbescoachescouncil/2020/04/27/turning-uncertainty-into-opportunity-creating-a-home-based-business/?sh=15635be87c28
Ed: Pasha Carter. **Released:** April 27, 2020. **Description:** Discusses opportunities in creating your own home-based business. **Availability:** Online.

26816 ■ *"TW Trade Shows to Offer Seminars On Niche Selling, Social Media"* in Travel Weekly (Vol. 69, October 4, 2010, No. 40, pp. 9)
Pub: NorthStar Travel Media
Description: Travel Weekly's Leisure World 2010 and Fall Home Based Travel Agent Show focused on niche selling, with emphasis on all-inclusives, young consumers, groups, incentives, culinary vacations, and honeymoon or romance travel. **Availability:** Print; Online.

26817 ■ *"What Not to Do When Starting a Home-Based Business"* in Home Business (March 22, 2023)
URL(s): homebusinessmag.com/business-start-up/start-up-fundamentals/what-not-do-starting-home-based-business/
Ed: Chandler Peterson. **Released:** March 22, 2023. **Description:** Reviews some helpful tips on home business culture to make your venture a success. **Availability:** Online.

26818 ■ *"What You Need to Know about Hiring Independent Contractors"* in Legal Zoom (March 22, 2023)
URL(s): www.legalzoom.com/articles/what-you-need-to-know-about-hiring-independent-contractors
Released: March 23, 2023. **Description:** Independent contractors are an attractive choice for saving some costs, but are they the best choice for your small business? Read about the pros and cons of hiring ICs. **Availability:** Online.

26819 ■ *"What You Should Know about Zoning Laws"* in Legal Zoom (March 15, 2023)
URL(s): www.legalzoom.com/articles/what-you-should-know-about-zoning-laws

Ed: Stephanie Vozza. **Released:** March 15, 2023. **Description:** Make sure your small business is not breaking the law by not being zoned properly. Discusses zoning laws and what you need to know before forming your small business. **Availability:** Online.

26820 ■ *Working for Yourself: Law & Taxes for Independent Contractors, Freelancers & Consultants*

Pub: Nolo

Contact: Chris Braun, President

Ed: Stephen Fishman. **Released:** 12th Edition. **Price:** $27.99, e-book(downloadable); $34.99, book and e-book; $27.99, E-book. **Description:** In-depth information is shared for contractors, freelancers and consultants involving business law and small business taxes. **Availability:** E-book; Print; Electronic publishing; PDF.

VIDEO/AUDIO MEDIA

26821 ■ *The How of Business: Jessica Rhodes - Home-Based Business*

URL(s): www.thehowofbusiness.com/episode-0 41-jessica-rhodes

Ed: Henry Lopez. **Released:** September 26, 2016. **Description:** Podcast offers tips on starting a home-based business.

TRADE SHOWS AND CONVENTIONS

26822 ■ National Association of Home Based Businesses Convention

Small Business Network Inc. (SBN)
  8213 Brigantine Dr.
  Colorado Springs, CO 80920
Contact: Susan Dalton, Contact
URL(s): www.usahomebusiness.com

Description: Home based business products and services, support associations, trade supplies, and related equipment. **Audience:** Industry professionals. **Principal Exhibits:** Home based business products and services, support associations, trade supplies, and related equipment.

CONSULTANTS

26823 ■ Organize Your Space

CA
Ph: (216)235-8376
URL: http://www.organizeyourspace.com

Description: Office and home organization specialists with emphasis on space planning and paper control and storage. Other areas of specialization include filing systems, accounting systems, super bills and office furniture. Also offers expertise in medical or dental, legal and color-coded filing systems. **Scope:** Office and home organization specialists with emphasis on space planning and paper control and storage. Other areas of specialization include filing systems, accounting systems, super bills and office furniture. Also offers expertise in medical or dental, legal and color-coded filing systems. **Founded:** 1982. **Publications:** "De-Clutter, De-Stress and Design Your Office Space". **Training:** Quick Start Office Systems; Quick Start Plus Office Systems; Total Office Makeover Plan.

FRANCHISES AND BUSINESS OPPORTUNITIES

26824 ■ CMIT Solutions Inc.

925 S Mo Pac Expy. St. b225
  Austin, TX 78746
Ph: (512)879-4555
Co. E-mail: cmit@cmitsolutions.com
URL: http://cmitsolutions.com

Contact: Mario Zambrano, President
Facebook: www.facebook.com/CMITdtaustin
Linkedin: www.linkedin.com/company-beta/3743915
X (Twitter): x.com/cmitatx
YouTube: www.youtube.com/user/cmitsolutions

Description: Firm provides it services and computer support to small businesses. **Founded:** 1996. **Training:** Offers 3 weeks training at headquarters, 1 week onsite with ongoing support.

26825 ■ Crock A Doodle

299 Wayne Gretzky Pky.
  Brantford, ON, Canada N3R 8A5
Ph: (519)752-8080
Co. E-mail: headoffice@crockadoo.com
URL: http://crockadoodle.com
Contact: Annette Brennan, Founder
X (Twitter): x.com/crockadoodle
Instagram: www.instagram.com/crockadoodlepyop
YouTube: www.youtube.com/user/CrockADoodlePo ttery
Pinterest: www.pinterest.ca/crockadoodle

Description: Provider of pottery painting services for kids birthday parties, ladies nights, teambuilding and corporate events. **Founded:** 2002. **Equity Capital Needed:** $75,000-$120,000. **Franchise Fee:** $20,000. **Training:** Provides 2 weeks plus ongoing support.

26826 ■ Decorating Den Interiors (DDI)

8659 Commerce Dr.
  Easton, MD 21601
Ph: (410)648-4793
Free: 800-DEC-DENS
Co. E-mail: info@decoratingden.com
URL: http://decoratingden.com
Contact: Jim Bugg, Sr., President
Facebook: www.facebook.com/DecoratingDen
X (Twitter): x.com/decoratingden
Instagram: www.instagram.com/decoratingden
YouTube: www.youtube.com/user/DecoratingDen
Pinterest: www.pinterest.com/decorating dencorporate

Description: Interiors by Decorating is one of the oldest, international, shop-at-home interior decorating franchises in the world. **Founded:** 1969. **Training:** Training combines classroom work, home study, meetings, seminars and on-the-job experience including working with an experienced interior decorator. Secondary, advanced and graduate certification training continue throughout the franchise owner's career with Interiors by Decorating Den.

26827 ■ DEI International L.L.C.

2944 Turpin Woods Ct.
  Cincinnati, OH 45244-3563
Contact: Steve Mulch, Contact

Description: Provider of business development services. **Founded:** 1979. **Training:** Offers 2 weeks home-based training and 2 weeks at headquarters with ongoing support.

26828 ■ Home Video Studio (HVS)

Apex, NC 27502
Free: 800-660-8273
Co. E-mail: info@homevideostudio.com
URL: http://apex.homevideostudio.com/169
Contact: Robert Hanley, President

Description: Firm offers video production services. **Founded:** 1991. **Financial Assistance:** Yes **Training:** Yes.

26829 ■ Liquid Capital Canada Corp.

5075 Yonge St., Ste. 700
  Toronto, ON, Canada M2N 6C6
Free: 877-228-0800
URL: http://liquidcapitalcorp.com
Contact: Robert Thompson-So, President
Facebook: www.facebook.com/liquid.capital
X (Twitter): x.com/Liquid_Capital
YouTube: www.youtube.com/channel/UCgFXxyEM 4Lk1FjBms-H8Rng

Description: Provider of short term financing services including factoring, financing receivables, purchase financing and much more. **Founded:** 1999. **Training:** Yes.

26830 ■ Padgett Business Services

1200 Speers Rd., Unit 22
  Oakville, ON, Canada L6L 2X4
Ph: (905)842-5812
Fax: (905)842-8366
URL: http://smallbizpros.ca
Contact: Alphonse Nachla, Owner
E-mail: anachla@cogeco.net

Description: Provider of business advice and consultation, tax preparation, government compliance, financial reporting, complete payroll services and other services. **No. of Franchise Units:** 120. **Founded:** 1966. **Franchised:** 1975. **Equity Capital Needed:** $42,500-$50,000. **Franchise Fee:** $25,000. **Training:** Complete program of training and support.

26831 ■ Par-T-Perfect Party Planners

Bowen Island, BC, Canada

Description: Provider of event and party planners and services for business events, birthday, schools and festivals. **Founded:** 1988. **Equity Capital Needed:** $4,995-$6,995. **Franchise Fee:** $19,000-$35,000. **Training:** 2 weeks and ongoing.

26832 ■ Suburban Cylinder Express

Blauvelt, NJ

Description: The franchise is a home-based business opportunity center. It provides propane cylinders to residential and commercial customers. **Founded:** 2001. **Franchised:** 2002. **Training:** Provides initial start-up training, ongoing business consultation, customized business software, scheduling and route optimization software, national phone customer sales center, technology help desk, a consumer website, brochures, flyers, coupons and other direct mail and mass marketing tools and materials.

26833 ■ Travel Lines Express Franchise Group

9858 Glades Rd., No. 208
  Boca Raton, FL 33434
Ph: (561)482-9557
Co. E-mail: tley2k@aol.com
URL: http://www.travellinesexpress.com
Contact: Bernard Korn, President

Description: Full service home based travel agency. **No. of Franchise Units:** 150. **Founded:** 1980. **Franchise Fee:** $500. **Royalty Fee:** $75/Month. **Financial Assistance:** No **Training:** Yes.

PUBLICATIONS

26834 ■ *"A Brave New World — Working From Home" in Innovation & Tech Today (October 8, 2021)*

URL(s): innotechtoday.com/a-brave-new-worl d-working-from-home

Ed: Pete Villari. **Released:** October 08, 2021. **Description:** Discusses the impacts a work-from-home workforce can have on a company. Gives tips on how to succeed in the post-pandemic business world while implementing new work-from-home strategies.

26835 ■ *Starting a Business from Home*

45 Gee St., 2nd Fl.
  London EC1V 3RS, United Kingdom
Ph: 44 20 7278-0433
Co. E-mail: kpinfo@koganpage.com
URL: http://www.koganpage.com
Contact: Christina Lindeholm, Manager, Sales
URL(s): www.koganpage.com/general-business-in terest/starting-a-business-from-home-9780749 480844

Price: $32.99, for paperback; $32.99, for paperback + book bundle; $32.99, for eBook. **Description:** Offers information about running a profitable and successful business from your own home with particular emphasis on opportunities provided by the internet. **Availability:** E-book; Print.

ASSOCIATIONS AND OTHER ORGANIZATIONS

26836 ■ Association for Talent Development (ATD) - Library
1640 King St.
Alexandria, VA 22313-1443
Ph: (703)683-8100
Free: 800-628-2783
Fax: (703)683-1523
Co. E-mail: customercare@td.org
URL: http://www.td.org
Contact: Tony Bingham, President
Facebook: www.facebook.com/ATD
Linkedin: www.linkedin.com/company/15989
X (Twitter): x.com/ATD
Instagram: www.instagram.com/atdnational
Pinterest: www.pinterest.com/ATDofficial

Description: Supports the talent development profession by providing trusted content in the form of research, books, webcasts, events, and education programs. **Scope:** Management; leadership. **Services:** Library open to members only. **Founded:** 1943. **Holdings:** 170 monographs; 100 books; 100 newspapers. **Publications:** *American Society Training and Development Buyer's Guide and Consultant Directory* (Annual); *Technical Training Basics*; *ASTD Buyer's Guide & Consultant Directory* (Annual); *TD at Work* (Monthly); *Learning Circuits* (Monthly); *TD Magazine* (Monthly); *Member Information Exchange (MIX)*; *TRAINET*; *ATD Buyer's Guide*; *ATD Buyer's Guide*; *American Society for Training and Development--Training Video Directory*; *Who's Who in Training and Development* (Annual). **Educational Activities:** ATD International Conference and Exposition (Annual); ATD TechKnowledge Conference (Annual); TechKnowledge Conference and Exposition (Annual). **Awards:** ATD BEST Award (Annual); Awards in the Advancing Workplace Learning and Performance; ATD Excellence in Practice Awards (Annual); Gordon M. Bliss Memorial Award (Annual); ATD Dissertation Award (Annual); ASTD Talent Development Thought Leader Award (Annual); ATD Torch Award (Annual). **Geographic Preference:** Multinational.

26837 ■ HR Policy Association (HRPA)
1001 19th St. N, Ste. 1002
Arlington, VA 22209
Ph: (202)789-8670
Fax: (202)789-0064
Co. E-mail: info@hrpolicy.org
URL: http://www.hrpolicy.org
Contact: Timothy J. Bartl, President

Description: Senior human resource executives of Fortune 500 companies. Conducts research and publishes findings on matters relating to federal human resources policy and its application and effects. Maintains task forces to study pending employment issues; conducts seminars, and offers a suite of labor relations and HR effectiveness training courses. **Founded:** 1968. **Publications:** *NLRB Watch* (Bi-monthly). **Educational Activities:** CHRO Summit (Annual); Washington Policy Conference (Annual). **Geographic Preference:** National.

26838 ■ Human Resources Research Organization (HumRRO) - Library
Human Resources Research Organization (HumRRO)
66 Canal Center Plz., Ste. 700
Alexandria, VA 22314
Ph: (703)549-3611
Fax: (703)548-2860
URL: http://www.humrro.org/corpsite
Contact: Dr. Suzanne Tsacoumis, President
Facebook: www.facebook.com/HumRRO
Linkedin: www.linkedin.com/company/humrro
X (Twitter): x.com/HumRROorg
YouTube: www.youtube.com/user/humrro

Description: Behavioral and social science researchers seeking to improve human performance, particularly in organizational settings, through behavioral and social science research, development, consultation and instruction. Promotes research and development to solve specific problems in: training and education; development, refinement, and instruction in the technology of training and education; measurement and evaluation of human performance under varying circumstances; organizational development studies, including performance counseling, group decision-making, and factors that affect organizational competence; development of manpower information systems and the application of management science on personnel systems. Encourages use of high technology for instructional purposes by means of computer assisted instruction, interactive video, and computer literacy. Offers technical publication services including data analysis and editorial, word processing, production, and printing services. **Scope:** An independent, nonprofit corporation which strives to improve human performance (primarily in organizational settings) through behavioral and social science research, product development, consultation, and instruction. Active in the fields of education and training, testing and assessment, survey research, program evaluation, and human factors engineering. **Founded:** 1951. **Holdings:** Figures not available. **Training:** An examination of the properties of local dependence measures when applied to adaptive data, Computing and communicating test accuracy for high-stakes decisions, Development of cross-cultural perspective taking skills, Developing, implementing, and scoring valid job simulations, Executive and senior leader development: A best practices review, Integrating reliability and validity based perspectives on error in performance ratings, Job incumbent perceptions of faking on noncognitive inventories, Modeling the psychometric properties of multisource ratings: CFA vs. GLMM, Performance level descriptions: Similarities and differences among select states, Reducing bias through propensity scoring: A study of SAT coaching, Retaining personality measures after failure: Changes in scores and strategies, Review of information and communication technology literacy measures, Self-presentation on personality measures: A meta-analysis, Using cases as a proxy for experience in leadership development, Using patterns to understand the dynamics of leader behavior, Verification testing in unproctored internet testing programs, A cross-cultural look at items of logic-based reasoning, An overlooked problem with standard practices for analyzing ratings data from ill-structured measurement designs, Context effects in internet testing: A literature review, Differentiating in the Upper Tail: Selecting Among High-Scoring Applicants, Gaining insight into situational judgment test functioning via spline regression, Ill-Structured measurement designs and reliability: The tale of a HumRRO IR&D project, Influence of subject matter expert (SME) personality on job analysis ratings, Modeling intraindividual change in soldiers attitudes and values during the first term of enlistment SES and admissions test validity: Within race analyses, The Feasibility of using O NET to study skill changes, Validation of a person organization personality hybrid measure, Validating psychological screening examinations and background investigations for applicant screening. **Awards:** Meredith Crawford Fellowship for Industrial and Organizational Psychology (Annual), Scholarship to graduate students in Industrial and Organizational Psychology for completing dissertations; Meredith P. Crawford Fellowship in I-O Psychology (Annual). **Geographic Preference:** National.

26839 ■ Institute for Performance and Learning (I4PL)
411 Richmond St. E, Ste. 200
Toronto, ON, Canada M5A 3S5
Ph: (416)367-5900
Free: 866-257-4275
Co. E-mail: hello@performanceandlearning.ca
URL: http://performanceandlearning.ca
Contact: Erin Spink, Executive Director
E-mail: executivedirector@performanceandlearning.ca
Facebook: www.facebook.com/institutepl
Linkedin: www.linkedin.com/company/the-institute-for-performance-and-learning
X (Twitter): x.com/InstitutePL

Description: Works for the profession of training, workplace learning and human resources development. **Founded:** 2003. **Publications:** *Performance and Learning* (Quarterly). **Awards:** Volunteer Award; Institute for Performance and Learning - President's Award; Institute for Performance and Learning - Volunteer Recognition Award. **Geographic Preference:** National.

26840 ■ Integrated Business Resources Inc.
3016 Old Mill Run
Grapevine, TX 76051-4239
Contact: Karen Houston-Johnson, President

Description: A full-service HR consulting firm offering assistance in all areas of human resources, including management and staff training. **Scope:** A full-service HR consulting firm offering assistance in all areas of human resources, including management and staff training.

26841 ■ International Personnel Management Association - Canada (IPMA) [L'Association internationale de la gestion du personnel - Canada]
PO Box 4011
  Mount Pearl, NL, Canada NL A1N 0A1
Free: 888-226-5002
Co. E-mail: national@ipmaigp.ca
URL: http://ipma-aigp.com
Contact: Cheryl Van Blaricom, President
E-mail: cherylvanblaricom@ipma-aigp.com
X (Twitter): x.com/IPMACanada
Description: Human resources professionals employed by public agencies. Seeks to advance the practice of personnel management. Facilitates ongoing professional development of members; sponsors research and educational programs. **Awards:** Gold Star Agency Award (Annual). **Geographic Preference:** National.

26842 ■ National Human Resources Association (NHRA)
1502 W Broadway St., Ste. 100
  Monona, WI 53713
Free: 866-523-4417
Co. E-mail: info@humanresources.org
URL: http://www.humanresources.org
Facebook: www.facebook.com/nationalhra
X (Twitter): x.com/nationalNHRA
Description: Represents human resource executives in business, industry, education and government. Established to expand and improve the professionalism of those in human resource management. **Founded:** 1951. **Publications:** Membership Directory (Annual); HR Yellowpages Directory. **Geographic Preference:** National.

26843 ■ Public Risk Management Association (PRIMA) - Library
700 S Washington St., Ste. 218
  Alexandria, VA 22314
Ph: (703)528-7701
Fax: (703)739-0200
Co. E-mail: info@primacentral.org
URL: http://www.primacentral.org
Contact: Melissa Steger, President
E-mail: msteger@utsystem.edu
Linkedin: www.linkedin.com/company/prima-central
X (Twitter): x.com/PRIMAcentral
Description: Public agency risk, insurance, human resources, attorneys, and/or safety managers from cities, counties, villages, towns, school boards, and other related areas. Provides an information clearinghouse and communications network for public risk managers to share resources, ideas, and experiences. Offers information on risk, insurance, and safety management. Monitors state and federal legislative actions and court decisions that deal with immunity, tort liability, and intergovernmental risk pools. **Scope:** Risk management. **Founded:** 1978. **Holdings:** Figures not available. **Publications:** Public Risk (Bimonthly); PRIMA Public Risk (Quarterly). **Educational Activities:** PRIMA's Annual Conference (Annual); Government Risk Management Seminar. **Awards:** PRIMA Outstanding Achievement Award for Enterprise Risk Management (ERM) (Annual); Public Risk Manager of the Year Award (Annual); Public Sector Risk Manager of the Year (Annual). **Geographic Preference:** National.

26844 ■ SHRM Executive Network
1800 Duke St.
  Alexandria, VA 22314
Free: 888-602-3270
Co. E-mail: executivenetwork@shrm.org
URL: http://www.shrm.org/executive
X (Twitter): x.com/TIAonline
Description: Human resource planning professionals representing 160 corporations and 3,000 individual members, including strategic human resources planning and development specialists, staffing analysts, business planners, line managers, and others who function as business partners in the application of strategic human resource management practices. Seeks to increase the impact of human resource planning and management on business and organiza-

tional performance. Sponsors program of professional development in human resource planning concepts, techniques, and practices. **Founded:** 1977. **Publications:** HR People + Strategy Membership; People and Strategy (Quarterly). **Geographic Preference:** National.

EDUCATIONAL PROGRAMS

26845 ■ Advanced Diversity Strategies (Onsite)
Seminar Information Service Inc. (SIS)
  250 El Camino Real., Ste. 112
  Tustin, CA 92780
Ph: (714)508-0340
Free: 877-736-4636
Fax: (714)734-8027
Co. E-mail: info@seminarinformation.com
URL: http://www.seminarinformation.com
Contact: Catherine Bellizzi, President
URL(s): www.seminarinformation.com/details.cfm?qc=qqbdxv
Description: Covers the fundamentals of carrying out an evaluation and the acknowledging and rewarding progress, including best practices for senior managers, line managers, and employees. **Audience:** HR and EEO/AA, diversity managers. **Principal Exhibits:** Covers the fundamentals of carrying out an evaluation and the acknowledging and rewarding progress, including best practices for senior managers, line managers, and employees.

26846 ■ Advanced Employee Complaint Handling (Onsite)
Seminar Information Service Inc. (SIS)
  250 El Camino Real., Ste. 112
  Tustin, CA 92780
Ph: (714)508-0340
Free: 877-736-4636
Fax: (714)734-8027
Co. E-mail: info@seminarinformation.com
URL: http://www.seminarinformation.com
Contact: Catherine Bellizzi, President
URL(s): www.seminarinformation.com
Description: Advanced skills needed to handle complex employee internal complaints and investigations. **Audience:** Human resource professionals. **Principal Exhibits:** Advanced skills needed to handle complex employee internal complaints and investigations.

26847 ■ Advanced Issues in EEO Law
Seminar Information Service Inc. (SIS)
  250 El Camino Real., Ste. 112
  Tustin, CA 92780
Ph: (714)508-0340
Free: 877-736-4636
Fax: (714)734-8027
Co. E-mail: info@seminarinformation.com
URL: http://www.seminarinformation.com
Contact: Catherine Bellizzi, President
URL(s): www.seminarinformation.com
Description: Interactive workshop provides advanced skills needed to identify and address more complex issues in Equal Opportunity Law and procedure. **Audience:** HR managers and professionals. **Principal Exhibits:** Interactive workshop provides advanced skills needed to identify and address more complex issues in Equal Opportunity Law and procedure.

26848 ■ Affirmative Action Plan Workshop (Onsite)
Seminar Information Service Inc. (SIS)
  250 El Camino Real., Ste. 112
  Tustin, CA 92780
Ph: (714)508-0340
Free: 877-736-4636
Fax: (714)734-8027
Co. E-mail: info@seminarinformation.com
URL: http://www.seminarinformation.com
Contact: Catherine Bellizzi, President
URL(s): www.seminarinformation.com/details.cfm?qc=qqayrr

Description: Learn how to write an affirmative action plan, including the preparation statistical analysis. **Audience:** Affirmative action professionals. **Principal Exhibits:** Learn how to write an affirmative action plan, including the preparation statistical analysis.

26849 ■ AMA Recruiting, Interviewing and Selecting Employees (Onsite)
American Management Association (AMA)
  1601 Broadway
  New York, NY 10019
Ph: (212)586-8100
Free: 800-262-9699
Fax: (212)903-8168
Co. E-mail: customerservice@amanet.org
URL: http://www.amanet.org
Contact: Manny Avramidis, President
URL(s): www.amanet.org/training/seminars/onsite/Recruiting-Interviewing-and-Selecting-Employees.aspx
Description: Covers recruitment sources, filtering applicants, interview techniques and questions, and EEO and affirmative action guidelines. **Audience:** Professionals with two years or less of experience in hiring, including newly hired HR professionals, HR practitioners who lack formal training, non-HR specialists who recruit, interview and/or hire as part of their jobs, and long-time HR practioners who want to reinforce or update their skills. **Principal Exhibits:** Covers recruitment sources, filtering applicants, interview techniques and questions, and EEO and affirmative action guidelines.

26850 ■ Applying Diversity Management to Innovation, Decision Making, Complex Problem Solving and Business Results (Onsite)
Seminar Information Service Inc. (SIS)
  250 El Camino Real., Ste. 112
  Tustin, CA 92780
Ph: (714)508-0340
Free: 877-736-4636
Fax: (714)734-8027
Co. E-mail: info@seminarinformation.com
URL: http://www.seminarinformation.com
Contact: Catherine Bellizzi, President
URL(s): www.seminarinformation.com
Description: Learn to look at diversity to create value and results versus recruiting and retention, including how to determine "true diversity" based on perspectives, interpretations, and predictive models, how to use diversity as a trigger for innovation, and examples of how diversity produces performance, productivity, creativity, quality decisions, and commercial value. **Audience:** Industry professionals. **Principal Exhibits:** Learn to look at diversity to create value and results versus recruiting and retention, including how to determine "true diversity" based on perspectives, interpretations, and predictive models, how to use diversity as a trigger for innovation, and examples of how diversity produces performance, productivity, creativity, quality decisions, and commercial value.

26851 ■ Bob Pike's Train-the-Trainer Boot Camp (Onsite)
Seminar Information Service Inc. (SIS)
  250 El Camino Real., Ste. 112
  Tustin, CA 92780
Ph: (714)508-0340
Free: 877-736-4636
Fax: (714)734-8027
Co. E-mail: info@seminarinformation.com
URL: http://www.seminarinformation.com
Contact: Catherine Bellizzi, President
URL(s): www.seminarinformation.com/qqadlf/bob-pikes-train-the-trainer-boot-camp
Description: Gives you the powerful high content, high involvement skills you'll need to add new energy and excitement to your own training sessions. **Audience:** Human resource development/organizational development personnel, private sector suppliers and presenters of seminars, conferences, and workshops. **Principal Exhibits:** Gives you the powerful high content, high involvement skills you'll need to add new energy and excitement to your own training sessions.

26852 ■ The Complete Course on Interviewing People (Onsite)

National Seminars Training L.L.C. (NST)
14502 W 105th St.
Lenexa, KS 66215
Free: 800-349-1935
Co. E-mail: info@findaseminar.com
URL: http://www.findaseminar.com/tpd/Padge
tt-Thompson-Seminars.asp
URL(s): www.findaseminar.com/event1.asp?eventID
=8234#dates-locations

Description: A one-day seminar that teaches insider techniques for going beyond the basics to master the art of interviewing people. **Audience:** Professionals. **Principal Exhibits:** A one-day seminar that teaches insider techniques for going beyond the basics to master the art of interviewing people.

26853 ■ Creative Problem Solving and Strategic Thinking (Onsite)

URL(s): www.pryor.com

Description: Learn to think beyond traditional thinking patterns and behaviors gaining a new set of skills for developing strategies that generate results. **Audience:** Professionals. **Principal Exhibits:** Learn to think beyond traditional thinking patterns and behaviors gaining a new set of skills for developing strategies that generate results.

26854 ■ The Essentials of HR Law

Fred Pryor Seminars & CareerTrack
5700 Broadmoor, Ste. 300
Mission, KS 66202
Free: 800-780-8476
Fax: (913)967-8849
Co. E-mail: customerservice@pryor.com
URL: http://www.pryor.com
Contact: Janet Turner, Contact
E-mail: dmca@pryor.com
URL(s): www.pryor.com/training-seminars/essentials
-hr-law

Frequency: Irregular. **Description:** Learn what you need to know to handle the legal issues and gray areas you face every day keeping your organization compliant. **Audience:** HR professionals. **Principal Exhibits:** Learn what you need to know to handle the legal issues and gray areas you face every day keeping your organization compliant.

26855 ■ The Essentials of Human Resources Law

Fred Pryor Seminars & CareerTrack
5700 Broadmoor, Ste. 300
Mission, KS 66202
Free: 800-780-8476
Fax: (913)967-8849
Co. E-mail: customerservice@pryor.com
URL: http://www.pryor.com
Contact: Janet Turner, Contact
E-mail: dmca@pryor.com
URL(s): www.pryor.com/training-seminars/essentials
-hr-law

Frequency: Irregular. **Description:** How to keep your organization legally sound and compliant while learning how to think like a lawyer, so you can anticipate problems before they arise. **Audience:** Industry professionals. **Principal Exhibits:** How to keep your organization legally sound and compliant while learning how to think like a lawyer, so you can anticipate problems before they arise.

26856 ■ Essentials for Personnel and HR Assistants (Onsite)

National Seminars Training L.L.C. (NST)
14502 W 105th St.
Lenexa, KS 66215
Free: 800-349-1935
Co. E-mail: info@findaseminar.com
URL: http://www.findaseminar.com/tpd/Padge
tt-Thompson-Seminars.asp
URL(s): www.findaseminar.com/event1.asp?eventID
=1750

Description: A one-day seminar that covers the important trends and changes facing HR professionals today. **Audience:** Personnel and HR assistants.

Principal Exhibits: A one-day seminar that covers the important trends and changes facing HR professionals today.

26857 ■ FMLA Compliance (Onsite)

National Seminars Training L.L.C. (NST)
14502 W 105th St.
Lenexa, KS 66215
Free: 800-349-1935
Co. E-mail: info@findaseminar.com
URL: http://www.findaseminar.com/tpd/Padge
tt-Thompson-Seminars.asp
URL(s): www.findaseminar.com/event1.asp?eventID
=7604

Description: Seminar covers the top five issues that land companies in the courtroom over FMLA disputes. **Audience:** Human resource and benefits professionals, business managers, office managers, administrators, directors, payroll professionals, attorneys, supervisors, and managers. **Principal Exhibits:** Seminar covers the top five issues that land companies in the courtroom over FMLA disputes.

26858 ■ Fundamentals of Employee Benefits (Onsite)

Seminar Information Service Inc. (SIS)
250 El Camino Real., Ste. 112
Tustin, CA 92780
Ph: (714)508-0340
Free: 877-736-4636
Fax: (714)734-8027
Co. E-mail: info@seminarinformation.com
URL: http://www.seminarinformation.com
Contact: Catherine Bellizzi, President
URL(s): www.seminarinformation.com

Description: Course will provide a comprehensive overview of the full-range of benefits responsibilities, as well as an in-depth look at the key aspects of benefits, alternatives for your organization and approaches for containing costs. **Audience:** Professionals. **Principal Exhibits:** Course will provide a comprehensive overview of the full-range of benefits responsibilities, as well as an in-depth look at the key aspects of benefits, alternatives for your organization and approaches for containing costs.

26859 ■ Fundamentals of Human Resources Management

URL(s): cmcoutperform.com/fundamentals-human
-resource-management

Price: C$2,195, Members; C$2,395, Non-members. **Description:** Covers HR planning and administration, staffing, training, technology, compensation, and legal issues. **Audience:** Non-HR professionals, managers, and HR specialists. **Principal Exhibits:** Covers HR planning and administration, staffing, training, technology, compensation, and legal issues. **Telecommunication Services:** cmcinfo@cmcout-perform.com.

26860 ■ HR Administration and the Law (Onsite)

Seminar Information Service Inc. (SIS)
250 El Camino Real., Ste. 112
Tustin, CA 92780
Ph: (714)508-0340
Free: 877-736-4636
Fax: (714)734-8027
Co. E-mail: info@seminarinformation.com
URL: http://www.seminarinformation.com
Contact: Catherine Bellizzi, President
URL(s): www.seminarinformation.com

Description: Offers practical compliance suggestions for the most common employment law-related issues faced today. **Audience:** Administrative professionals. **Principal Exhibits:** Offers practical compliance suggestions for the most common employment law-related issues faced today.

26861 ■ Human Resources for Anyone with Newly Assigned HR Responsibilities

Fred Pryor Seminars & CareerTrack
5700 Broadmoor, Ste. 300
Mission, KS 66202
Free: 800-780-8476
Fax: (913)967-8849
Co. E-mail: customerservice@pryor.com

URL: http://www.pryor.com
Contact: Janet Turner, Contact
E-mail: dmca@pryor.com
URL(s): www.pryor.com/training-seminars/human
-resources-newly-assigned-hr-responsibilities

Frequency: Irregular. **Description:** A comprehensive primer on all the issues including recordkeeping, hiring, firing, discrimination, and more. **Audience:** HR professionals. **Principal Exhibits:** A comprehensive primer on all the issues including recordkeeping, hiring, firing, discrimination, and more.

26862 ■ Human Resources and the Law (Onsite)

Seminar Information Service Inc. (SIS)
250 El Camino Real., Ste. 112
Tustin, CA 92780
Ph: (714)508-0340
Free: 877-736-4636
Fax: (714)734-8027
Co. E-mail: info@seminarinformation.com
URL: http://www.seminarinformation.com
Contact: Catherine Bellizzi, President
URL(s): www.seminarinformation.com/details.cfm?qc
=qqblnt

Description: Provides the human resources professional with an understanding of the laws that obligate employers, recent legislation and court cases defining employer/employee rights and obligations, legal and business considerations bearing on employer decisions, practical implications of the laws in day-to-day human resources operations, impact of the laws on the development of policies and procedures, and alternatives for minimizing the company's exposure to employee lawsuits and administrative charges. **Audience:** Human resources professionals. **Principal Exhibits:** Provides the human resources professional with an understanding of the laws that obligate employers, recent legislation and court cases defining employer/employee rights and obligations, legal and business considerations bearing on employer decisions, practical implications of the laws in day-to-day human resources operations, impact of the laws on the development of policies and procedures, and alternatives for minimizing the company's exposure to employee lawsuits and administrative charges.

26863 ■ Human Resources for Professionals who've Recently Assumed HR Responsibilities (Onsite)

Seminar Information Service Inc. (SIS)
250 El Camino Real., Ste. 112
Tustin, CA 92780
Ph: (714)508-0340
Free: 877-736-4636
Fax: (714)734-8027
Co. E-mail: info@seminarinformation.com
URL: http://www.seminarinformation.com
Contact: Catherine Bellizzi, President
URL(s): www.seminarinformation.com

Description: Fast-paced and information-rich, this program condenses the most important of the most important HR basics into clear, concise, easy-to-understand training. **Audience:** Professionals. **Principal Exhibits:** Fast-paced and information-rich, this program condenses the most important of the most important HR basics into clear, concise, easy-to-understand training.

26864 ■ Human Resources for Professionals Who've Recently Assumed HR Responsibilities (Onsite)

National Seminars Training L.L.C. (NST)
14502 W 105th St.
Lenexa, KS 66215
Co. E-mail: info@findaseminar.com
URL: http://www.findaseminar.com/tpd/Padge
tt-Thompson-Seminars.asp
URL(s): www.nationalseminarstraining.com

Description: Workshop provides the information and confidence needed to meet tough HR challenges. **Audience:** HR assistants, HR specialists, office managers, executive assistants, and administrative assistants. **Principal Exhibits:** Workshop provides the information and confidence needed to meet tough HR challenges.

26865 ■ Instructional Design for Participant-Centered Training (Onsite)

Seminar Information Service Inc. (SIS)
250 El Camino Real., Ste. 112
Tustin, CA 92780
Ph: (714)508-0340
Free: 877-736-4636
Fax: (714)734-8027
Co. E-mail: info@seminarinformation.com
URL: http://www.seminarinformation.com
Contact: Catherine Bellizzi, President
URL(s): www.seminarinformation.com/details.cfm?qc=qqbmbv

Description: Learn to apply the eight step design process to create a training course from nothing or enhance an existing program. **Audience:** Trainers. **Principal Exhibits:** Learn to apply the eight step design process to create a training course from nothing or enhance an existing program.

26866 ■ Instructional Design for Trainers (Onsite)

Seminar Information Service Inc. (SIS)
250 El Camino Real., Ste. 112
Tustin, CA 92780
Ph: (714)508-0340
Free: 877-736-4636
Fax: (714)734-8027
Co. E-mail: info@seminarinformation.com
URL: http://www.seminarinformation.com
Contact: Catherine Bellizzi, President
URL(s): www.seminarinformation.com/details.cfm?qc=qqargh

Price: $2,345. **Description:** Applications-based workshop where you will prepare a training plan designed to meet your company's every need. **Audience:** Trainers. **Principal Exhibits:** Applications-based workshop where you will prepare a training plan designed to meet your company's every need.

26867 ■ Succession Planning: Developing Talent from Within (Onsite)

American Management Association (AMA)
1601 Broadway
New York, NY 10019
Ph: (212)586-8100
Free: 800-262-9699
Fax: (212)903-8168
Co. E-mail: customerservice@amanet.org
URL: http://www.amanet.org
Contact: Manny Avramidis, President
URL(s): www.amanet.org/succession-planning-developing-talent-from-within

Price: $2,195, Non-members; $1,995, Members AMA; $1,889, Members GSA. **Description:** Learn to implement a succession plan to minimize gaps in leadership. **Audience:** Mid to senior level managers, business unit heads, human resources personnel and operational development professionals. **Principal Exhibits:** Learn to implement a succession plan to minimize gaps in leadership.

26868 ■ Train the Trainer: Facilitation Skills Workshop Onsite

Canadian Management Centre (CMC)
150 King St. W Ste. 271
Toronto, ON, Canada M5H 1J9
Ph: (416)214-5678
Free: 877-262-2519
Fax: (416)214-6047
Co. E-mail: cmcinfo@cmcoutperform.com
URL: http://cmcoutperform.com
Contact: Chris Peacock, Director
URL(s): cmcoutperform.com/train-the-trainer

Description: Gain practical, proven techniques and strategies for facilitating high impact learning experiences. **Audience:** Facilitators. **Principal Exhibits:** Gain practical, proven techniques and strategies for facilitating high impact learning experiences.

26869 ■ Training for Impact

Seminar Information Service Inc. (SIS)
250 El Camino Real., Ste. 112
Tustin, CA 92780
Ph: (714)508-0340
Free: 877-736-4636
Fax: (714)734-8027
Co. E-mail: info@seminarinformation.com
URL: http://www.seminarinformation.com
Contact: Catherine Bellizzi, President
URL(s): www.seminarinformation.com

Description: Designed for those accountable for delivering face-to-face training programs. **Audience:** Personnel officers, training managers and coordinators. **Principal Exhibits:** Designed for those accountable for delivering face-to-face training programs.

26870 ■ The Workshop for Personnel/HR Assistants (Onsite)

Seminar Information Service Inc. (SIS)
250 El Camino Real., Ste. 112
Tustin, CA 92780
Ph: (714)508-0340
Free: 877-736-4636
Fax: (714)734-8027
Co. E-mail: info@seminarinformation.com
URL: http://www.seminarinformation.com
Contact: Catherine Bellizzi, President
URL(s): www.seminarinformation.com/details.cfm?qc=qqbjbs

Description: Learn the essentials of accepted human resources procedures, as well as a clear understanding of current employment law, rules and regulations. **Audience:** Personnel, and Human Resource staff. **Principal Exhibits:** Learn the essentials of accepted human resources procedures, as well as a clear understanding of current employment law, rules and regulations.

REFERENCE WORKS

26871 ■ "5 Tips to Stay Labor Law Compliant" in Legal Zoom (February 10, 2023)

URL(s): www.legalzoom.com/articles/5-tips-to-stay-labor-law-compliant

Ed: Belle Wong, J.D. **Released:** February 10, 2023. **Description:** Make sure your small business is following labor laws by following the checklist provided. **Availability:** Online.

26872 ■ "6 Tips for Open-Office Etiquette" in Business News Daily (March 7, 2023)

URL(s): www.businessnewsdaily.com/10913-open-office-etiquette.html

Ed: Kiely Kuligowski. **Released:** March 07, 2023. **Description:** Open offices are becoming more prevalent, so learning some tips to function within one will be beneficial to anyone who works in this type of space. **Availability:** Online.

26873 ■ "16 Creative and Cheap Ways to Say 'Thank You'" in HR Specialist (Vol. 8, September 2010, No. 9, pp. 8)

Pub: Capitol Information Group Inc.
Contact: Allie Ash, Chief Executive Officer

Released: October 14, 2010. **Description:** Tips for starting an employee appreciation program for a small company are presented. **Availability:** Print; PDF; Online.

26874 ■ "Advancing the Ball" in Inside Healthcare (Vol. 6, December 2010, No. 7, pp. 31)

Description: Profile of Medicalodges an elder-care specialty company that provides both patient care and technology development. President and CEO of the firm believes that hiring good employees is key to growth for any small business. **Availability:** Online.

26875 ■ Aging and Working in the New Economy: Changing Career Structures in Small IT Firms

Pub: Edward Elgar Publishing Inc.
Contact: Edward Elgar, Founder Chairman

Ed: Juliie Ann McMullin, Victor W. Marshall. **Released:** 2010. **Description:** Case studies and analyses provide insight into the structural features of small- and medium-sized firms in the information technology sector, and the implications of these features for the careers of people employed by them.

26876 ■ American Bar Association Legal Guide for Small Business: Everything You Need to Know About Small Business, from Start-up to Employment to Financing and Selling

Released: Second edition. **Description:** The American Bar Association provides insight into financial, health and family issues affecting small business, including start up issues, employment laws, financing a business, and selling a business.

26877 ■ "American Chemistry Council Launches Flagship Blog" in Ecology,Environment & Conservation Business (October 29, 2011, pp. 5)

Pub: PR Newswire Association LLC.

Description: American Chemistry Council (ACC) launched its blog, American Chemistry Matters, where interactive space allows bloggers to respond to news coverage and to discuss policy issues and their impact on innovation, competitiveness, job creation and safety. **Availability:** Online.

26878 ■ "The Anatomy of a High Potential" in Business Strategy Review (Vol. 21, Autumn 2010, No. 3, pp. 52)

Ed: Doug Ready, Jay Conger, Linda Hill, Emily Stecker. **Released:** September 22, 2010. **Description:** Companies have long been interested in identifying high potential employees, but few firms know how to convert top talent into game changers, or people who can shape the future of the business. The authors have found the 'x factors' that can make a high-potential list into a strong competitive advantage. **Availability:** Print; Electronic publishing; PDF; Online.

26879 ■ "Apprenticeship: Earn While You Learn" in Occupational Outlook Quarterly (Vol. 54, Fall 2010, No. 3, pp. 24)

Description: Paid training, or apprenticeships, are examined. Registered apprenticeship programs conform to certain guidelines and industry-established training standards and may be run by businesses, trade or professional associations, or partnerships with business and unions. **Availability:** Online.

26880 ■ Atiyah's Accidents, Compensation and the Law

Pub: Cambridge University Press
Contact: Peter Phillips, Chief Executive Officer

Ed: Peter Cane. **Released:** 9th edition. **Description:** Leading authority on the law of personal injuries compensation and the social, political and economic issues surrounding it.

26881 ■ "Austin on Verge of Losing 7,500 Jobs" in Austin Business Journal (Vol. 31, May 6, 2011, No. 9, pp. 1)

Pub: Austin Business Journal
Contact: Rachel McGrath, Director
E-mail: rmcgrath@bizjournals.com

Ed: Jacob Dirr. **Description:** Proposed state budget cuts are seen to result in the loss of as many as 7,500 public and private sector jobs in Austin, Texas, with the private sector losing the majority of workers. Comments from analysts are included. **Availability:** Print; Online.

26882 ■ "Baltimore-Area Hospital Tower Projects Could Add Hundreds of New Jobs" in Baltimore Business Journal (Vol. 28, June 25, 2010, No. 7, pp. 1)

Pub: Baltimore Business Journal
Contact: Rhonda Pringle, President
E-mail: rpringle@bizjournals.com

Ed: Scott Graham. **Description:** Greater Baltimore, Maryland has four hospitals that are in the middle of transforming their campuses with new facilities for treating various patients. Construction at Mercy Medical Center, Johns Hopkins Hospital, Franklin Square Hospital and Anne Rundle Hospital has helped bring the construction industry back to life. Insights into the hiring plans of these hospitals are also included.

26883 ■ "Best Layoff Practices: Can You Lay Off and Hire at the Same Time?" in Business News Daily (March 7, 2023)
URL(s): www.businessnewsdaily.com/15913-lay-off -new-hires.html
Ed: Patrick Proctor. **Released:** March 07, 2023. **Description:** This article advises on how to handle layoffs at your small business. **Availability:** Online.

26884 ■ "Best (Professional) Foot Forward: Effective Marketing Strategies for any Phase of Your Career" in Black Enterprise (Vol. 44, June 2014, No. 10, pp. 44)
Pub: Earl G. Graves Ltd.
Contact: Earl Graves, Jr., President
Description: Because hiring managers face long-term vacancies and skills gaps, the importance of creating a professional marketing strategy when applying for a professional position is stressed. Advice is given to help guide applicants through the entire application, interviewing, and hiring process.

26885 ■ "BETC Backers Plot Future" in Business Journal Portland (Vol. 27, December 10, 2010, No. 41, pp. 1)
Pub: Portland Business Journal
Contact: Andy Giegerich, Managing Editor
E-mail: agiegerich@bizjournals.com
Ed: Erik Siemers. **Description:** A coalition of clean energy groups and industrial manufacturers have spearheaded a campaign aimed at persuading Oregon legislators that the state's Business Energy Tax Credit (BETC) is vital in job creation. Oregon's BETC grants tax credits for 50 percent of an eligible renewable or clean energy project's cost. However, some legislators propose BETC's abolition. **Availability:** Print; Online.

26886 ■ "Bracing for More Layoffs: This Week's Oil and Gas Jobs News" in Sacramento Business Journal (Vol. 28, September 30, 2011, No. 31, pp. 1)
Released: April 1, 2016. **Description:** Sacramento, California workers are preparing for a fresh wave of layoffs. The weak economy is seen to drive the development. **Availability:** Online.

26887 ■ "Breaking Bad: Rid Yourself of Negative Habits" in Black Enterprise (Vol. 40, July 2010, No. 12, pp. 104)
Pub: Earl G. Graves Ltd.
Contact: Earl Graves, Jr., President
Ed: Renita Burns. **Description:** Tardiness, procrastination, chronic complaining are among the bad habits that can make people bad employees; tips for breaking these habits are outlined. **Availability:** Online.

26888 ■ "Bridging the Worlds" in Academy of Management Journal (Vol. 50, No. 5, October 1, 2007, pp. 1043)
Pub: Academy of Management
Contact: Sharon Alvarez, President
Ed: Lise Saari. **Description:** Need to transfer human resource research information published in journals to practitioners and organizations is investigated, along with suggestions on ways of achieving this goal. **Availability:** Electronic publishing; PDF; Download; Online.

26889 ■ "Brief: Janitorial Company Must Pay Back Wages" in Buffalo News (September 24, 2011)
Description: Knights Facilities Management, located in Michigan, provides grounds maintenance and janitorial services at the Ralph Wilson Stadium in Buffalo, New York. The US Department of Labor ordered the firm to pay $22,000 in back wages and damages to 26 employees for overtime and minimum wage compensation. Details of the company's violation of the Fair Labor Standards Act are included. **Availability:** Online.

26890 ■ "Building a Workplace Harassment Policy That Keeps You and Your Employees Safe" in Legal Zoom (March 9, 2023)
URL(s): www.legalzoom.com/articles/building-a -workplace-harassment-policy-that-keeps-you-an d-your-employees-safe
Ed: Lorlei Laird. **Released:** March 09, 2023. **Description:** Keep your small business free from various forms of harassment so you can retain and attract top talent with suggestions from these professionals on how to build a policy that will protect all who enter your business. **Availability:** Online.

26891 ■ Business Black Belt: Develop the Strength, Flexibility and Agility to Run Your Company
Price: $15.99. **Description:** Manual offering insights that will enable anyone to become successful in small business. Seventy short chapters included topics such as attitude, management, marketing, selling, employees, money, MBAs, lawyers, consultants, and investors. **Availability:** Print.

26892 ■ "Business Guide and Employment Role"
Pub: AuthorHouse Inc.
Contact: William Elliott, President
Released: July 10, 2014. **Price:** $4.99, e-book; $15. 18, softcover. **Description:** Financial expert discusses the importance of economic and business and their role in employment. The business and finance manager is crucial to any small business. The guide is an essential tool for any entrepreneur, the investor in business enterprise, the individual businessman, the human resources manager, and the business and finance professional to learn the merits to do business and play a role in employment. **Availability:** E-book; Print.

26893 ■ "Business Leaders Share Their Predictions about the Lasting Impact of COVID-19" in Legal Zoom (February 21, 2023)
URL(s): www.legalzoom.com/articles/business-lea ders-share-their-predictions-about-the-lasting-impac t-of-covid-19
Ed: Katherine Gustafson. **Released:** February 21, 2023. **Description:** When the COVID-19 pandemic hit, many businesses had to do some massive adjusting really fast in order to keep employees and an income coming in. Many changes were positive for the workforce and are becoming the new normal, such as work at home options. **Availability:** Online.

26894 ■ Business Warrior: Strategy for Entrepreneurs
Price: $9.99. **Description:** Advice to help entrepreneurs understand competitive strategies in order to succeed, focusing on sales, marketing, and personnel management. **Availability:** Print; Download; PDF.

26895 ■ "But Is It Legal? Dogs in the Office" in Legal Zoom (March 21, 2023)
Ed: Chas Rampenthal. **Released:** March 21, 2023. **Description:** Discusses the legality of employees bringing their dogs into an office setting. While some companies use this as a perk to retain or attract top talent, not everyone appreciates dogs, and their fur, in the office. **Availability:** Online.

26896 ■ "Capital Position: M&I Acquisition Opens the Door for Rivals to Gain Market Share" in Business Journal-Milwaukee (Vol. 28, December 24, 2010, No. 12, pp. A1)
Pub: The Business Journal
Contact: Heather Ladage, President
E-mail: hladage@bizjournals.com
Ed: Rich Kirchen. **Description:** Canada-based BMO Financial Group has purchased Marshall and Isley Corporation (M and I), which dominated lending among Wisconsin businesses for decades. The sale of M and I will enable other banks to recruit M and I's customers but BMO Financial remains a stronger competitor since it possesses a more potent capital position. **Availability:** Print; Online.

26897 ■ "The CEO of General Electric On Sparking an American Manufacturing Renewal" in Harvard Business Review (Vol. 90, March 2012, No. 3, pp. 43)
Pub: Harvard Business Review Press
Contact: Moderna V. Pfizer, Contact
Ed: Jeffrey R. Immelt. **Price:** $8.95, hardcover. **Description:** General Electric Company utilized human innovation and lean manufactring to improve the firm's competitiveness. By engaging the firm's entire workforce, utilizing technology and improving labor-management relations, GE boosted efficiency and reduced cost and waste. **Availability:** PDF; Online.

26898 ■ "CEO Pay: Best Bang for Buck" in Philadelphia Business Journal (Vol. 30, September 30, 2011, No. 33, pp. 1)
Pub: Philadelphia Business Journal
Contact: Sierra Quinn, Director
E-mail: squinn@bizjournals.com
Ed: Jeff Blumenthal. **Description:** A study by Strategic Research Solutions on the compensation of chief executive officers in Philadelphia, Pennsylvania-based public companies reveals that only a few of them performed according to expectations. These include Brian Roberts of Comcast, John Conway of Crown Holdings, and Frank Hermance of Ametek Inc. **Availability:** Online.

26899 ■ "CEO Pay: The Details" in Crain's Detroit Business (Vol. 25, June 22, 2009, No. 25)
Pub: Crain Communications Inc.
Contact: Barry Asin, President
Description: Total compensation packages for CEOs at area companies our outlined. These packages include salary, bonuses, stock awards, and options. **Availability:** Online.

26900 ■ "The CEO Poll: Split on Migrant Workers" in Canadian Business (Vol. 83, September 14, 2010, No. 15, pp. 23)
Pub: Rogers Media Inc.
Contact: Neil Spivak, Chief Executive Officer
Ed: Jacqueline Nelson. **Description:** A survey of Canadian CEOs shows that 49 percent of the respondents believe it was wrong to suspend the immigration programs and companies should be allowed to hire the most skilled workers regardless of citizenship. However, 42 percent believe the suspension was right because employment of Canadians must take precedence. **Availability:** Print; Online.

26901 ■ "Cincinnati Consults Executives on Police Chief Hire" in Business Courier (Vol. 27, August 27, 2010, No. 17, pp. 1)
Pub: Business Courier
Ed: Dan Monk, Lucy May. **Description:** The City of Cincinnati, Ohio has begun a selection process for the new police chief by consulting the city's business executives. The city charter amendment known as Issue 5 has removed civil service protection from the chief's post and enables City Manager Milton Dohoney to hire a chief from outside the department. **Availability:** Print; Online.

26902 ■ "Cincinnati Hospitals Mandate Flu Shots" in Business Courier (Vol. 27, November 19, 2010, No. 29, pp. 1)
Pub: Business Courier
Ed: James Ritchie. **Description:** TriHealth has mandated that employees who refuse to get the vaccination shot for 2010 could be penalized with unpaid administrative leave. Other hospital employers, such as University Hospital and Cincinnati Children's Hospital and Medical Center have fired employees for forgoing flu shots. Vaccination rates among hospital employees are given. **Availability:** Print; Mailing list; Online.

26903 ■ "The Classless Workplace: The Digerati and the New Spirit of Technocapitalism" in WorkingUSA (Vol. 11, June 2008, No. 2, pp. 181)
Description: Article argues the formation of a new type of economic actor at the intersection of a new capitalism and a new technology: The Dierati. The

discourse in based on the analysis of the popular magazine Wired, which registers the culture of contemporary technocapitalism. The suggestion that the new persona of the digerati is constructed as a rejection of the ethics, which dominated the Fordist workplace and Fordist society: Hierarchy and differentiation between workers, on the one hand and capitalists and managers, on the other hand. The transformation of these two categories, workers and capitalists into the digerati worker and the digerati entrepreneur, is described. Set within the context of the structural transformations of capitalism from Fordism to post-Fordism, the article shows the ideological fit of the new ethics of the digerati to the new working arrangements of post-Fordist capitalism, characterized by more privatizes, flexible, and precarious working arrangements. **Availability:** Print; Online.

26904 ■ *"Cloud Computing for a Crowd"* in *CIO (Vol. 24, October 2, 2010, No. 1, pp. 16)*
Pub: CIO

Ed: Stephanie Overby. **Description:** Information about a project which aimed to implement a cloud-based crowdsourcing platform and innovation-management process is provided. Chubb Group of Insurance Companies wanted to mine revenue-generating ideas from its 10,400 employees and hundreds of thousands of external agents. The company hosted its first innovation event using its new system in October 2008. **Availability:** Online.

26905 ■ *"Coffee Breaks Don't Boost Productivity After All"* in *Harvard Business Review (Vol. 90, May 2012, No. 5, pp. 34)*
Pub: Harvard Business Review Press
Contact: Moderna V. Pfizer, Contact

Ed: Charlotte Fritz. **Price:** $6. **Description:** Research shows no statistical correlation between taking a short break at work and one's fatigue and vitality levels. However, a link was found between personal productivity and assisting a coworker. Employees detach from work more successfully during long breaks rather than short ones. **Availability:** Online; PDF.

26906 ■ *"Collateral Damage"* in *Business Courier (Vol. 26, October 16, 2009, No. 25, pp. 1)*
Pub: American City Business Journals, Inc.
Contact: Mike Olivieri, Executive Vice President

Ed: Jon Newberry. **Description:** Non-union construction firms representing Ohio Valley Associated Builders and Contractors Inc. have filed cases against unionized shops claiming violations of wage law in Ohio. Defendants say the violations are minor, however, they believe they are caught in the middle of the group's campaign to change the state's wage law. **Availability:** Print; Online.

26907 ■ *"Column: What 17th-Century Pirates Can Teach Us About Job Design"* in *Harvard Business Review (Vol. 88, October 2010, No. 10, pp. 44)*
Pub: Harvard Business Publishing
Contact: Diane Belcher, Managing Director

Ed: Hayagreeva Rao. **Price:** $6, PDF. **Description:** Ways in which pirates typify the importance of separating star tasks, or strategic work, from guardian tasks, or the operational work are outlined. **Availability:** Online; PDF.

26908 ■ *"A Comparison of Adverse Impact Levels Based on Top-Down, Multisource, and Assessment Center Data: Promoting Diversity and Reducing Legal Challenges"* in *Human Resource Management (Vol. 51, May-June 2012, No. 3, pp. 313-341)*
Pub: John Wiley & Sons, Inc.
Contact: Christina Van Tassell, Executive Vice President Chief Financial Officer

Ed: H. John Bernardin, Robert Konopaske, Christine M. Hagan. **Released:** May 25, 2012. **Description:** Levels of adverse impact against minorities and women were compared based on promotional deci-

sion methods. Results indicate significant effects for race and minority status in favor of white people but not for gender. **Availability:** Print; PDF; Online.

26909 ■ *"Competing on Talent Analytics"* in *Harvard Business Review (Vol. 88, October 2010, No. 10, pp. 52)*
Pub: Harvard Business Publishing
Contact: Diane Belcher, Managing Director

Ed: Thomas H. Davenport, Jeanne Harris, Jeremy Shapiro. **Price:** $8.95, PDF. **Description:** Six ways to use talent analytics to obtain the highest level of value from employees are listed. These include human-capital investment analysis, talent value models, workforce forecasts, and talent supply chains. **Availability:** Online; PDF.

26910 ■ *Complete Employee Handbook: A Step-by-Step Guide to Create a Custom Handbook That Protects Both the Employer and the Employee*
Description: Comprehensive guide for employers deal with personnel issues; CD-ROM contains sample employee handbooks, federal regulations and laws, forms for complying with government programs and worksheets for assessing personnel needs and goals. **Availability:** Online.

26911 ■ *"The Consequences of Tardiness"* in *Modern Machine Shop (Vol. 84, August 2011, No. 3, pp. 34)*
Description: Five point addressing motivating factors behind employees who are tardy and those who choose to be on time in the workplace are shared. **Availability:** Online.

26912 ■ *"A Conversation with: Renea Butler"* in *Crain's Detroit Business (Vol. 25, June 8, 2009, No. 23, pp. 12)*
Pub: Crain Communications Inc.
Contact: Barry Asin, President

Ed: Ryan Beene. **Description:** Renea Butler, vice president of administration and human resources for Real Estate One Inc. in Southfield as well as vice president for public relations for the Human Resource Association of Greater Detroit, talks about how the economy has affected human resource services. **Availability:** Print; Online.

26913 ■ *"Corporate Responsibility"* in *Professional Services Close-Up (July 2, 2010)*
Description: List of firms awarded the inaugural Best Corporate Citizens in Government Contracting by the Corporate Responsibility Magazine is presented. The list is based on the methodology of the Magazine's Best Corporate Citizen's List, with 324 data points of publicly-available information in seven categories which include: environment, climate change, human rights, philanthropy, employee relations, financial performance, and governance. **Availability:** Online.

26914 ■ *Create Your Own Employee Handbook: A Legal & Practical Guide for Employers*
Pub: Nolo
Contact: Chris Braun, President

Ed: Amy DelPo, Lisa Guerin. **Released:** 10th edition. **Price:** $39.99, book and e-book; $34.99, ebook (downloadable); $39.99, book and e-book. **Description:** Information for business owners to develop an employee handbook that covers company benefits, policies, procedures, and more. **Availability:** E-book; PDF.

26915 ■ *"Creative In-Sourcing Boosts Franchisee Performance"* in *Franchising World (Vol. 42, September 2010, No. 9, pp. 16)*
Pub: International Franchise Association
Contact: Matthew Haller, President
E-mail: mhaller@franchise.org

Ed: Daniel M. Murphy. **Released:** 2010. **Description:** Operational training and support is usually provided by franchisors. To be successful in this process it is important to balance the reality of limited financial and human resources. **Availability:** Online.

26916 ■ *"Crucible: Battling Back from Betrayal"* in *Harvard Business Review (Vol. 88, December 2010, No. 12, pp. 130)*
Pub: Harvard Business Publishing
Contact: Diane Belcher, Managing Director

Ed: Daniel McGinn. **Price:** $8.95, PDF. **Description:** Stephen Greer's scrap metal firm, Hartwell Pacific, lost several million dollars due to a lack of efficient and appropriate inventory audits, accounting procedures, and new-hire reference checks for his foreign operations. Greer believes that balancing growth with control is a key component of success. **Availability:** Print; PDF.

26917 ■ *"Crucible: Losing the Top Job - And Winning It Back"* in *Harvard Business Review (Vol. 88, October 2010, No. 10, pp. 136)*
Pub: Harvard Business Publishing
Contact: Diane Belcher, Managing Director

Ed: Alison Beard. **Price:** $8.95, PDF. **Description:** Michael Mack chronicles the changes in perspectives that occurred when he was fired from Garden Fresh, a restaurant firm he co-owned. Once again at the company helm, he is now more receptive to outside input and acknowledges the importance of work-life balance. **Availability:** Online; PDF.

26918 ■ *"Custom Fit"* in *Canadian Business (Vol. 80, November 19, 2007, No. 23, pp. 42)*
Description: Proper employee selection will help ensure a company has the people with the skills it really needs. Employee development is integral in coping with changes in the company. The importance of hiring the right employee and developing his skills is examined. **Availability:** Print; Online.

26919 ■ *"Cutting Health Care Costs: the 3-Legged Stool"* in *HR Specialist (Vol. 8, September 2010, No. 9, pp. 1)*
Pub: Capitol Information Group Inc.
Contact: Allie Ash, Chief Executive Officer

Description: Employer spending on health insurance benefits to employees is investigated. **Availability:** Print; Online; PDF.

26920 ■ *"Debt-Collection Agency to Lay Off 368 in Hampton Center"* in *Virginian-Pilot (December 4, 2010)*
Pub: The Virginian-Pilot
Contact: Kevin Goyette, Director
E-mail: kgoyette@dailypress.com

Ed: Tom Shean. **Description:** NCO Financial Systems Inc., provider of debt-collection and outsourcing services will permanently lay off 368 workers at its Hampton call center in 2011. **Availability:** Print; Online.

26921 ■ *"Developing the Next Generation of Rosies"* in *Employee Benefit News (Vol. 25, November 1, 2011, No. 14, pp. 36)*
Pub: SourceMedia LLC
Contact: Gemma Postlethwaite, Chief Executive Officer

Ed: Kathleen Koster. **Description:** According to the research group Catalyst, women made up 46.7 percent of the American workforce in 2010, however only 14.4 percent was Fortune 500 executive officers and 15.7 percent held Fortune 500 board seats. Statistical data included.

26922 ■ *"Dispelling Rocky Mountain Myths Key to Wellness"* in *Employee Benefit News (Vol. 25, November 1, 2011, No. 14, pp. 12)*
Pub: SourceMedia LLC
Contact: Gemma Postlethwaite, Chief Executive Officer

Ed: Andrea Davis. **Description:** Andrew Sykes, chairman of Health at Work Wellness Actuaries, states that it is a myth that Colorado is ranked as the healthiest state in America. Sykes helped implement a wellness programs at Brighton School District in the Denver area.

26923 ■ *The Diversity Code: Unlock the Secrets to Making Differences Work in the Real World*
Pub: HarperCollins Leadership
Contact: Donald Miller, Chief Executive Officer
Ed: Michelle T. Johnson. **Released:** January 24, 2019. **Description:** The most diligent compliance with laws and regulations can't foster true work place diversity. The best organizations have become genuine cross-cultural communities that believe equality in reconciling difference and valuing them. The book promotes understanding by answering many of the toughest questions that professionals and their employers are afraid to ask. **Availability:** Print.

26924 ■ *Diversity and Inclusion Matters: Tactics and Tools to Inspire Equity and Game-Changing Performance*
Pub: John Wiley & Sons, Inc.
Contact: Christina Van Tassell, Executive Vice President Chief Financial Officer
URL(s): www.wiley.com/en-us/Diversity+and+Inclusion+Matters%3A+Tactics+and+Tools+to+Inspire+Equity+and+Game+Changing+Performance-p-978 1119799535
Ed: Jason R. Thompson. **Released:** December 2021. **Price:** $18, e-book; $29.95, hardcover. **Description:** Discusses how to implement a diversity and inclusion program into your business. **Availability:** E-book; Print.

26925 ■ *"DOL Stiffens Child Labor Penalties" in HR Specialist (Vol. 8, September 2010, No. 9, pp. 2)*
Pub: Capitol Information Group Inc.
Contact: Allie Ash, Chief Executive Officer
Description: U.S. Department of Labor (DOL) will impose new penalties for employers that violate U.S. child labor laws. Details of the new law are included.

26926 ■ *"Downturn Tests HCL's Pledge to Employees" in Workforce Management (Vol. 88, November 16, 2009, No. 12, pp. 23)*
Pub: Crain Communications Inc.
Contact: Barry Asin, President
Ed: Ed Frauenheim. **Description:** HCL Technologies has kept its promise to keep from laying any employees off during the recession which served as a test for the tech firm's Employee First program, which seeks to give workers greater income security as well as a stronger voice in the firm. **Availability:** Online.

26927 ■ *Employee Management for Small Business*
Pub: Self-Counsel Press Inc.
Contact: Diana Douglas, Governor
Ed: Lin Grensing-Pophal. **Released:** Third edition. **Price:** C$12.99, EPUB. **Description:** Management tools to help entrepreneurs maintain an effective human resources plan for a small company. **Availability:** E-book; Print; PDF; Download.

26928 ■ *"Employees Change Clothes at Work? Heed New Pay Rules" in HR Specialist (Vol. 8, September 2010, No. 9, pp. 1)*
Pub: Capitol Information Group Inc.
Contact: Allie Ash, Chief Executive Officer
Description: U.S. Department of Labor issued a new interpretation letter that states times spent changing in and out of 'protective clothing' (e.g., helmets, smocks, aprons, gloves, etc.) is considered paid time. It also says time spent changing 'ordinary clothes' (i.e., uniform) may not be compensable itself, but could start the clock on the workday, meaning all activities after - such as walking to the workstation - would be paid time. More details and a link to the DOL are included. **Availability:** PDF; Online.

26929 ■ *Employer Legal Forms Simplified*
Released: First edition. **Description:** Business reference containing the following forms needed to handle employees in any small business environment: application, notice, confidentiality, absence, federal employer forms and notices, and many payroll forms. All forms are included on a CD that comes in both PDF and text formats. Adobe Acrobat Reader software is also included on the CD. The forms are valid in all fifty states and Washington, DC. **Availability:** Print.

26930 ■ *"Employment and Unemployment Among Youth - Summer 2010" in Montly Labor Review (Vol. 133, September 2010, No. 9, pp. 2)*
Pub: U.S. Department of Labor Bureau of Labor Statistics
Contact: Amrit Kohli, Director
E-mail: kohli.amrit@bls.gov
Description: The number of youth 16 to 24 years old rose by 1.8 million from April to July 2010. Statistical data included. **Availability:** PDF; Online.

26931 ■ *"Encouraging Study in Critical Languages" in Occupational Outlook Quarterly (Vol. 55, Summer 2011, No. 2, pp. 23)*
Description: Proficiency in particular foreign languages is vital to the defense, diplomacy, and security of the United States. Several federal programs provide scholarships and other funding to encourage high school and college students to learn languages of the Middle East, China, and Russia. **Availability:** Print; Online.

26932 ■ *Encyclopedia of Social Work*
URL(s): oxfordre.com/socialwork/page/99
Released: Continuous. **Description:** A online resource from the National Association of Social Workers and Oxford University Press that contains up-to-date articles, biographies, and links to further resources. **Availability:** Database.

26933 ■ *"The End of Clock-Punching" in Canadian Business (Vol. 83, September 14, 2010, No. 15, pp. 96)*
Pub: Rogers Media Inc.
Contact: Neil Spivak, Chief Executive Officer
Ed: Lyndsie Bourgon. **Description:** Workplace consultant Peter Hadwen is pushing for the transformation of Canada's government departments into results-only work environments (ROWE). ROWE does not require employees to show up to work at a certain time as long as they are meeting goals and achieving results in their jobs. Details of studies regarding ROWE in US companies are examined. **Availability:** Online.

26934 ■ *"Evaluating the 1996-2006 Employment Projections" in Montly Labor Review (Vol. 133, September 2010, No. 9, pp. 33)*
Pub: U.S. Department of Labor Bureau of Labor Statistics
Contact: Amrit Kohli, Director
E-mail: kohli.amrit@bls.gov
Description: Bureau of Labor Statistics employment projections outperformed alternative naive models, but not projecting the housing bubble or the rise in oil prices caused some inaccuracies in the projects. These projections are used by policymakers, economists, and students. **Availability:** PDF; Online.

26935 ■ *"Evidence-Based Management and the Marketplace For Ideas" in Academy of Management Journal (Vol. 50, No. 5, October 2007, pp. 1009)*
Pub: Academy of Management
Contact: Sharon Alvarez, President
Ed: Wayne F. Cascio. **Description:** Study examines the relevance of material to actual usage in human resource management. Results reveal that it is important to design modules with execution in mind in seeking advice from professionals in relevant organizations. **Availability:** Electronic publishing; PDF; Download; Online.

26936 ■ *"Executive Compensation: Both Eyes on the Prize" in Canadian Business (Vol. 83, September 14, 2010, No. 15, pp. 42)*
Pub: Rogers Media Inc.
Contact: Neil Spivak, Chief Executive Officer
Ed: Jacqueline Nelson. **Description:** North American executive compensation has fundamentally shifted partly due to pressure from the US government and recent adjustments in the way CEO pay packages are structured. The changes have also become common practice in Canada and helped in scrutinizing the executive pay. **Availability:** Online.

26937 ■ *"Experts Share How to Create Company Culture That Gets Results" in Small Business Trends (October 29, 2022)*
URL(s): smallbiztrends.com/2022/10/how-to-create-company-culture-that-gets-results.html
Ed: Annie Pilon. **Released:** October 29, 2022. **Description:** The culture within a company is a big deal since employees are required to spend the majority of their day there. Having a culture that is positive helps your current employees stay engaged and it can also attract top talent when you are hiring. **Availability:** Online.

26938 ■ *"Explaining Organizational Responsiveness to Work-Life Balance Issues: the Role of Business Strategy and High-Performance Work Systems" in Human Resource Management (Vol. 51, May- June 2012, No. 3, pp. 407-432)*
Pub: John Wiley & Sons, Inc.
Contact: Christina Van Tassell, Executive Vice President Chief Financial Officer
Ed: Jing Wang, Anil Verma. **Released:** May 25, 2012. **Description:** The effects of business strategies and high-performance work systems on the adoption of work-life balance programs are examined. Results indicate a mediating role of high-performance work systems in the relationship between business strategies and the adoption of work-life balance programs. **Availability:** Print; PDF; Online.

26939 ■ *"Exploring Supportive and Developmental Career Management Through Business Strategies and Coaching" in Human Resource Management (Vol. 51, January-February 2012, No. 1, pp. 99-120)*
Pub: John Wiley & Sons, Inc.
Contact: Christina Van Tassell, Executive Vice President Chief Financial Officer
Ed: Jesse Segers, Ilke Inceoglu. **Released:** January 26, 2012. **Description:** Coaching and other career practices that are part of supportive and developmental career management are examined. Such practices are found to be most present in organizations with a prospector strategy. **Availability:** Print; PDF; Online.

26940 ■ *"Falling Local Executive Pay Could Suggest a Trend" in Tampa Bay Business Journal (Vol. 30, January 15, 2010, No. 4, pp. 1)*
Pub: Tampa Bay Business Journal
Contact: Ian Anderson, President
E-mail: ianderson@bizjournals.com
Ed: Margie Manning. **Description:** Tampa Bay, Florida-based Raymond James Financial Inc. and MarineMax Inc.'s proxy statements have shown the decreasing compensation of the companies' highest paid executives. The falling trend in executive compensation was a result of intensified shareholder scrutiny and the economy. **Availability:** Print; Online.

26941 ■ *"Feds Finalize I-9 Form Rules Allowing Electronic Storage" in HR Specialist (Vol. 8, September 2010, No. 9, pp. 5)*
Pub: Capitol Information Group Inc.
Contact: Allie Ash, Chief Executive Officer
Description: U.S. Department of Homeland Security issued regulations that give employers more flexibility to electronically sing and store I-9 employee verification forms. **Availability:** Print; PDF; Online.

26942 ■ *"Filling the Business Gap" in Hispanic Business (December 2010)*
Description: New York group seeks to increase state diversity supplier spending to help create jobs and boost the economy. According to a recent study, six out of 10 small business owners will increase capital

spending but delay hiring in 2011. However, potential job creation is good among businesses owned by women and minorities. **Availability:** Print; Online.

26943 ■ *"Future Autoworkers will Need Broader Skills" in Crain's Detroit Business (Vol. 25, June 8, 2009, No. 23, pp. 13)*
Pub: Crain Communications Inc.
Contact: Barry Asin, President
Ed: Ryan Beene. **Description:** Auto industry observers report that new workers in the industry will need advanced skills and educational backgrounds in engineering and technical fields because jobs in the factories will become more technology-based and multidisciplinary. **Availability:** Online.

26944 ■ *"The Future of Work" in Black Enterprise (Vol. 41, August 2010, No. 1, pp. 65)*
Pub: Earl G. Graves Ltd.
Contact: Earl Graves, Jr., President
Ed: Annya M. Lott. **Description:** Technology, globalization, and outsourcing will continue to shape the future of work. Social media is a means for small companies to market goods and services. **Availability:** Online.

26945 ■ *"The Future of Work" in Business Strategy Review (Vol. 21, Autumn 2010, No. 3, pp. 16)*
Pub: Wiley-Blackwell
Ed: Lynda Gratton. **Released:** August 28, 2017. **Description:** Work is universal. But how, why, where and when we work has never been so open to individual interpretation. The certainties of the past have been replaced by ambiguity, questions and the steady hum of technology. Now, in a groundbreaking research project covering 21 global companies and more than 200 executives, the author is making sense of the future of work. **Availability:** Print; PDF; Online.

26946 ■ *"Generation Y: Engaging the Invincibles" in Employee Benefit News (Vol. 25, November 1, 2011, No. 14, pp. 22)*
Pub: SourceMedia LLC
Contact: Gemma Postlethwaite, Chief Executive Officer
Ed: Brenna Shebel, Dannel Dan. **Description:** Employers will need to engage younger workers about healthcare decisions and lifestyle improvement as they become the majority worker as boomers retire. **Availability:** Online.

26947 ■ *"Get Prepared for New Employee Free Choice Act" in HRMagazine (Vol. 53, December 2008, No. 12, pp. 22)*
Description: According to the director of global labor and employee relations with Ingersoll Rand Company, unions may have started having employees signing authorization cards in anticipation of the Employee Free Choice Act. Once signed, the cards are good for one year and employers would have only ten days in which to prepare for bargaining with unions over the first labor contract. The Act also requires these negotiations be subject to mandatory arbitration if a contract is not reached within 120 days of negotiations with unions, resulting in employers' wage rates, health insurance, retirement benefits and key language about flexibility would be determined by an arbitrator with no vested interest in the success of the company. **Availability:** Print; Online.

26948 ■ *"Gilt Groupe's CEO On Building a Team of A Players" in Harvard Business Review (Vol. 90, January-February 2012, No.1-2, pp. 43)*
Pub: Harvard Business Review Press
Contact: Moderna V. Pfizer, Contact
Ed: Kevin Ryan. **Description:** The author stresses the role of human capital in a firm's success, and the importance of employment references in determining a candidate's talents. Key questions include whether the reference would hire the person, whether people enjoy working with him or her, and what areas could use improvements.

26949 ■ *"The Global Talent Hunt" in Business Strategy Review (Vol. 21, Spring 2010, No. 1, pp. 78)*
Ed: Richard Emerton. **Released:** February 09, 2010. **Description:** Richard Emerton explains how the new 'triple context' of economy, environment and society will have profound implications for human resource practices. He suggests that viewing talent as abundant is the right perspective for a manager. **Availability:** Print; PDF; Online.

26950 ■ *"Glossary of Health Benefit Terms" in HRMagazine (Vol. 53, August 2008, No. 8, pp. 78)*
Pub: Society for Human Resource Management
Contact: Johnny C. Taylor, Jr., President
E-mail: shrmceo@shrm.org
Description: Glossary of health benefit terms is presented to help when choosing a health benefits package. **Availability:** Print; Online.

26951 ■ *"The Green Industry Jobs Gap" in Green Industry Pro (Vol. 23, October 2011)*
Ed: Gregg Wartgow. **Description:** According to the U.S. Bureau of Labor Statistics, the landscaping industry employs over 829,000 workers. According to another private study, the industry would employ more if they were able to find more people interested in performing the required work. **Availability:** Online.

26952 ■ *"Grooming Your Online Persona" in Women In Business (Vol. 62, June 2010, No. 2, pp. 36)*
Description: Employees' use of online social networks could become a basis on how their employers, clients, or business partners would judge them. Personal details, pictures and other online data should be filtered to avoid inappropriate or uncomfortable situations and distinguish personal from professional or work life. **Availability:** Online.

26953 ■ *"Guidance On Career Guidance for Offender Reentry" in Occupational Outlook Quarterly (Vol. 54, Fall 2010, No. 3, pp. 24)*
Description: Stable employment is a key factor in the successful rehabilitation of law offenders. The National Institute of Corrections hopes to improve offenders' long-term employment prospects. **Availability:** Print; Online.

26954 ■ *"Hickory Unemployment Stays Steady" in Charlotte Observer (February 2, 2007)*
Description: Unemployment rates remained unchanged in Hickory, North Carolina area; the region reported 6.1 percent unemployment.

26955 ■ *"High-Tech Job-Apalooza!" in Orlando Business Journal (Vol. 26, January 15, 2010, No. 33, pp. 1)*
Pub: Orlando Business Journal
Contact: Julie Swyers, Director
E-mail: jswyers@bizjournals.com
Ed: Christopher Boyd. **Description:** Science Applications International Corporation, Saab Training USA LLC, CAE USA, and Pelliconi &C.SPA attempt to obtain $939,000 in tax incentives to generate 222 technology and defense-related jobs in Orange County, Florida. Each job will provide an average salary of $67,000. Future plans of each technology and defense firm are also presented. **Availability:** Print; Online.

26956 ■ *"The Hiring Handbook: Tips & Tactics to Attract Top Tier Talent"*
Pub: CreateSpace
Released: October 22, 2014. **Price:** $7, Paperback. **Description:** All the information needed to recruit and hire the best talent for any small business is presented. While intended for hiring managers, the information is useful for any human resources executives as well as job seekers. **Availability:** Print.

26957 ■ *"Host"*
Pub: Solutions Business Publishing

Released: April 13, 2010. **Price:** $16.99, paperback; $19.98, audiobook CD; $19.98, audiobook downloadable; $7.99, e-book; $9.99, mass market; $10, mass market; $42.99, paperback large print; $25.99, hardcover. **Description:** Great engagement is the key to any successful business leadership. Host leadership involves six new roles in employee engagement: adopt the four positions for a Host Leader; understand how to step into and out of the six new roles of engagement; achieve greater agility, flexibility, and responsiveness; become a leader with a highly tuned sense of relationship building and engagement. **Availability:** CD-ROM; E-book; Print.

26958 ■ *"How to Avoid Leave-Related Lawsuits" in Employee Benefit News (Vol. 25, December 1, 2011, No. 15, pp. 12)*
Pub: SourceMedia LLC
Contact: Gemma Postlethwaite, Chief Executive Officer
Ed: John F. Galvin. **Description:** Tips for employers when adding disability and maternity leave benefits to workers are outlined, with focus on ways to avoid leave-related lawsuits.

26959 ■ *"How to Build a Great Employee Benefits Package" in Business News Daily (February 21, 2023)*
URL(s): www.businessnewsdaily.com/9494-small -business-benefits-package.html
Ed: Andreas Rivera. **Description:** Small business owners may need to start providing a benefits package to entice quality employees. Details about what to included are discussed. **Availability:** Online.

26960 ■ *"How Hard Could It Be? The Four Pillars of Organic Growth" in Inc. (January 2008, pp. 69-70)*
Ed: Joel Spolsky. **Description:** Revenue, head count, public relations, and quality are the four most important aspects of any growing business. **Availability:** Online.

26961 ■ *"How to Keep Your Top Employees" in Archery Business (December 14, 2018)*
URL(s): www.archerybusiness.com/keep-top -employees
Ed: Phillip M. Perry. **Released:** December 14, 2018. **Description:** A guide on how to retain the best employees to help run your business. Gives tips on recognizing the top performers and how to compensate them so they stay, and points out how to create a respectful and supportive work environment. **Availability:** Online.

26962 ■ *"How to Legally Hire an Intern" in Legal Zoom (March 16, 2023)*
URL(s): www.legalzoom.com/articles/how-to-legally -hire-an-intern
Ed: Kylie Ora Lobell. **Released:** March 16, 2023. **Description:** Advice on how to start an intern program through your business. **Availability:** Online.

26963 ■ *"How to Manage the New Expectations of the Younger Workforce" in Entrepreneur (March 21, 2023)*
URL(s): www.entrepreneur.com/leadership/how-to -manage-the-new-expectations-of-the-younger -workforce/447205
Ed: Cheri Beranek. **Released:** March 21, 2023. **Description:** With a smaller workforce to choose from, employers are now being confronted with a workforce that has different expectations than previous generations had. This article discusses what's changed and what procedures workplaces need to adjust. **Availability:** Online.

26964 ■ *"How to Prevent Sexual Harassment in Your Workplace" in Legal Zoom (March 15, 2023)*
URL(s): www.legalzoom.com/articles/how-to-preven t-sexual-harassment-in-your-workplace
Ed: Jane Haskins, Esq. **Released:** March 15, 2023. **Description:** Advice on how to be proactive and prevent sexual hasassment in your small business is given. **Availability:** Online.

26965 ▪ *How to Start and Run Your Own Corporation: S-Corporations For Small Business Owners*
Pub: HCM Publishing

Ed: Peter I. Hupalo. **Description:** Basics of corporate business structure are explained. Topics include discovering the best business structure for your company; how to decided between an S-Corporation and LLC; choosing the state in which to incorporate, how to form a corporation, angel investing, special issues for one-person corporations, the role of bylaws and corporate minutes, board of directors, taxes, workers' compensation issues, retirement plans, and more. **Availability:** Print.

26966 ▪ *"How To Reduce the Risk of Discrimination"* in *Idaho Business Review* (September 11, 2014)
Pub: BridgeTower Media
Contact: Adam Reinebach, President

Description: Human resource departments in small businesses in Boise are aware of the city's discrimination ordinance making it unlawful to use sexual orientation and gender identity/expression in any consideration of hiring or terminating an employee, or for any other issue. The impact of the ordinance is yet to be determined.

26967 ▪ *"How to Turn Employee Conflict Into a Positive, Productive Force"* in *HR Specialist* (Vol. 8, September 2010, No. 9, pp. 6)
Pub: Capitol Information Group Inc.
Contact: Allie Ash, Chief Executive Officer

Description: Ways to help manage a team of workers are presented, focusing on ways to avoid conflict within the group are discussed. **Availability:** Print; Online; PDF.

26968 ▪ *"Human Capital: When Change Means Terminating an Employee"* in *Black Enterprise* (Vol. 41, November 2010, No. 4, pp. 40)
Pub: Earl G. Graves Ltd.
Contact: Earl Graves, Jr., President

Ed: Tamara E. Holmes. **Description:** Covering successful business change strategies, this article focuses on how the law and nondiscrimination policies can affect this aspect of the workplace. **Availability:** Online.

26969 ▪ *"Human Resource Management: Challenges for Graduate Education"* in *Business Horizons* (Vol. 51, March-April 2008, No. 2, pp. 151)
Pub: Elsevier Advanced Technology Publications

Ed: James C. Wimbush. **Description:** Human resource management education at the master's and doctoral degree levels is discussed. There is an ever-increasing need to produce human resource managers who understand the value of human resource management as a strategic business contributor. **Availability:** PDF; Online.

26970 ▪ *Human Resource Management: Functions, Applications, and Skill Development*
Ed: John R. Hendon. **Released:** 2022. **Description:** Provides a discussion of applications and skills needed to learn about human resource management. Contains real-world cases and exercises.

26971 ▪ *Human Resources Kit for Dummies*
Pub: John Wiley & Sons, Inc.
Contact: Christina Van Tassell, Executive Vice President Chief Financial Officer
URL(s): www.wiley.com/en-us/Human+Resources+Ki t+For+Dummies%2C+4th+Edition-p-978 1119989899

Ed: Andrea Butcher. **Released:** 4th edition. **Price:** $21, e-book; $34.99, paperback. **Description:** Everything you need to know about maximizing your HR department while creating strong and talented teams for your company. **Availability:** E-book; Print.

26972 ▪ *"Immigration: Give Us Your Skilled"* in *Canadian Business* (Vol. 80, October 8, 2007, No. 20, pp. 78)
Pub: Rogers Media Inc.
Contact: Neil Spivak, Chief Executive Officer

Ed: Zena Olijnyk. **Description:** Demand for skilled workers in Canada is discussed. Despite a strong demand, as evidenced by shortages in both skilled and unskilled labor, the country's immigration policy is affecting the recruitment process. Peter Veress, founder and president of Vermax Group, believes the country is wasting opportunities to take advantage of its attractiveness as a destination for foreign workers. **Availability:** Online.

26973 ▪ *"The Incentive Bubble: Outsourcing Pay Decisions To Financial Markets Has Skewed Compensation and, With It, American Capitalism"* in *Harvard Business Review* (Vol. 90, March 2012, No. 3, pp. 124)
Pub: Harvard Business Review Press
Contact: Moderna V. Pfizer, Contact

Ed: Mihir A. Desai. **Price:** $8.95. **Description:** Basing incentive contracts and executive compensation on financial markets actually rewards luck rather than performance, and can promote dangerous risk taking. This has led to America's two main crises of capitalism: growing income inequality and governance failures. Boards of directors must focus on performance rather than stocks, and endowments and foundations must focus on incentives for long-term growth. **Availability:** Online; PDF.

26974 ▪ *"Increasing HR's Strategic Participation: the Effect of HR Service Quality and Contribution Expectations"* in *Human Resource Management* (Vol. 51, January-February 2012, No. 1, pp. 3-23)
Pub: John Wiley & Sons, Inc.
Contact: Christina Van Tassell, Executive Vice President Chief Financial Officer

Ed: Jin Feng Uen, David Ahlstrom, Shu-Yuan Chen, Pai-Wei Tseng. **Released:** January 26, 2012. **Description:** The impact of human resources service quality and human resources contribution expectations on the strategic participation of human resources in organizations is examined. Human resource professionals are found to increase the organizational value of human resources through improving quality and addressing the needs of potential internal customers. **Availability:** Print; PDF; Online.

26975 ▪ *"International Benefits Roundup"* in *Employee Benefit News* (Vol. 25, December 1, 2011, No. 15)
Pub: SourceMedia LLC
Contact: Gemma Postlethwaite, Chief Executive Officer

Description: Employee contributions to an employer-sponsored defined contribution plan in Japan are allowed on a tax-deductible basis; however, currently employee contributions are not allowed. The defined contribution plan is outlined for better understanding.

26976 ▪ *International Handbook of Entrepreneurship and HRM*
Pub: Edward Elgar Publishing Inc.
Contact: Edward Elgar, Founder Chairman

Ed: Rowena Barrett, Susan Mayson. **Released:** 2008. **Description:** Conceived on the basis that there is a growing recognition of the interplay between human resource management and entrepreneurship, this volume offers insights into the role of HRM and entrepreneurial firms.

26977 ▪ *"Interning Your Way to the Right Career"* in *Business Review Albany* (Vol. 41, June 20, 2014, No. 12, pp. 9)
Pub: American City Business Journals, Inc.
Contact: Mike Olivieri, Executive Vice President

Released: Weekly. **Price:** $4, introductory 4-week offer(Digital only). **Description:** The degree boom has made it increasingly important for students to

participate in internship programs in order to stand out. Internship programs also provide companies with several benefits. **Availability:** Print; Online.

26978 ▪ *"Is It Time to Ban Swearing in the Workplace?"* in *HR Specialist* (Vol. 8, September 2010, No. 9, pp. 2)
Pub: Capitol Information Group Inc.
Contact: Allie Ash, Chief Executive Officer

Description: Screening software has been developed to identify profanity used in business correspondence. **Availability:** PDF; Online.

26979 ▪ *"Is Your Employees' BMI Your Business?"* in *Canadian Business* (Vol. 83, September 14, 2010, No. 15, pp. 98)
Pub: Rogers Media Inc.
Contact: Neil Spivak, Chief Executive Officer

Ed: Jacqueline Nelson. **Description:** Canada's Public Health Agency's research shows that there is a solid business case for companies to promote active living to their employees. However, employers must toe the line between being helpful and being invasive. Insights into the issues faces by companies when introducing health programs are discussed. **Availability:** Online.

26980 ▪ *"Job Corps Center Remains Vacant After Operator is Booted"* in *Tampa Bay Business Journal* (Vol. 30, January 15, 2010, No. 4, pp. 1)
Pub: Tampa Bay Business Journal
Contact: Ian Anderson, President
E-mail: ianderson@bizjournals.com

Ed: Jane Meinhardt. **Description:** Pinellas County, Florida Job Corps Center has remained vacant due to a conflict over the $16 million contract awarded to Res-Care Inc. by the US Department of Labor (DOL) The DOL has ordered Res-Care to stop operation at the center and it is uncertain when it will open or what company will operate it. **Availability:** Print; Online.

26981 ▪ *"Job Reviews: Annual Assessments Still the Norm"* in *HR Specialist* (Vol. 8, September 2010, No. 9, pp. 1)
Description: An OfficeTeam survey of 500 HR professionals asked how their organizations conduct formal performance appraisals. Responses to the questions are examined.

26982 ▪ *"Job Seeker's Readiness Guide: Unemployment's High and Competition is Tough"* in *Black Enterprise* (Vol. 40, July 2010, No. 12, pp. 83)
Description: Five key areas to help someone seeking employment gain the competitive edge are listed. **Availability:** Print; Online.

26983 ▪ *"A Jobs Compact for America's Future: Badly Needed Investments In Human Capital Are Not Being Made. What We Can Do - Together - To Jump-Start the Process?"* in *Harvard Business Review* (Vol. 90, March 2012, No. 3, pp. 64)
Pub: Harvard Business Review Press
Contact: Moderna V. Pfizer, Contact

Ed: Thomas A. Kochan. **Price:** $8.95. **Description:** Obstacles to strengthening US human capital are a lack of focus on obtaining both high wages and high productivity, and a lack of value placed on human capital as a competitive advantage. Business schools are well positioned to address these obstacles via curricula, programs, and partnerships. **Availability:** Online; PDF.

26984 ▪ *"Jobs Data Show Wild Card"* in *Barron's* (Vol. 90, September 6, 2010, No. 36, pp. M12)
Pub: Barron's Editorial & Corporate Headquarters

Ed: Gene Epstein. **Description:** August 2010 jobs report revealed a 54,000 decline in non-farm payrolls and that the unemployment rate remains unchanged at 9.6 percent. The report also shows a welcome rise of 848,999 in the household-data category. The unemployment rate shows a reversed trend where men's 10.6 percent unemployment is higher than women's 8.6 percent rate. **Availability:** Online.

26985 ■ *"Layoffs Continue to Be a Drag on Region's Recovery"* in *Philadelphia Business Journal (Vol. 28, January 22, 2010, No. 49, pp. 1)*
Pub: Philadelphia Business Journal
Contact: Sierra Quinn, Director
E-mail: squinn@bizjournals.com
Ed: Athena D. Merritt. **Description:** Mass layoffs continue to hamper Pennsylvania's economic recovery. Job losses are predicted to decline in 2010. **Availability:** Online.

26986 ■ *"Leaders: 11 Tips to Consider When a Key Employee Quits"* in *Small Business Trends (March 21, 2022)*
URL(s): smallbiztrends.com/2022/11/things-to-do-when-a-key-employee-quits.html
Released: November 27, 2022. **Description:** A guide on how to handle the aftermath of your key employee quitting. **Availability:** Online.

26987 ■ *"The Leadership Equation: 10 Practices That Build Trust, Spark Innovation, and Create High-Performing Organizations"*
Pub: Greenleaf Book Group Press
Contact: Tanya Hall, Chief Executive Officer
Released: September 30, 2014. **Price:** $18.95, U.S., paperback. **Description:** Entrepreneur and business consultant draws upon his work with corporations, government agencies, and nonprofit organizations and their human resource departments to explain the workings of high-performing organizations with his equation: Trust + Spark = Leadership Culture. He describes the ten more important practices for building trust and spark that improves team performance, the business unit, and the entire organization. **Availability:** Print.

26988 ■ *"Linking HRM and Knowledge Transfer Via Individual-Level Mechanisms"* in *Human Resource Management (Vol. 51,May-June 2012, No. 3, pp. 387-405)*
Pub: John Wiley & Sons, Inc.
Contact: Christina Van Tassell, Executive Vice President Chief Financial Officer
Ed: Dana B. Minbaeva, Kristina Makela, Larissa Rabbiosi. **Released:** May 25, 2012. **Description:** The relationship between human resource management and knowledge transfer and the role of individual-level mechanisms in this relationship are examined. Results indicate that individual-level perceptions of organizational commitment to knowledge sharing and extrinsic motivation affect internal knowledge exchange among employees. **Availability:** Print; PDF; Online.

26989 ■ *"Linking Human Capital to Competitive Advantages: Flexibility in a Manufacturing Firm's Supply Chain"* in *Human Resource Management (Vol. 49, September-October 2010, No. 5)*
Pub: John Wiley & Sons, Inc.
Contact: Christina Van Tassell, Executive Vice President Chief Financial Officer
Ed: Yan Jin, Margaret M. Hopkins, Jenell L.S. Wittmer. **Released:** September 01, 2010. **Description:** A study was conducted to confirm the links among human capital, firm flexibility, and firm performance. The study also examines the emerging role of flexibility for a company's performance. A total of 201 senior supply chain management professionals from several manufacturing companies were included in the study.

26990 ■ *"Looking To Hire Young? Be Careful"* in *Boston Business Journal (Vol. 30, November 19, 2010, No. 43, pp. 1)*
Pub: Boston Business Journal
Contact: Carolyn M. Jones, President
E-mail: cmjones@bizjournals.com
Ed: Lisa van der Pool. **Released:** Weekly. **Description:** The Massachusetts Commission Against Discrimination (MCAD) has been using undercover job applicants to expose discrimination. Cabot's Ice Cream and Restaurant has been accused of denying older workers equal employment opportunities. MCAD has discovered unfair hiring practices such as hiring high school and college students. **Availability:** Print; Online.

26991 ■ *"Lowering Retirement System Barriers for Women"* in *Employee Benefit News (Vol. 25, December 1, 2011, No. 15)*
Pub: SourceMedia LLC
Contact: Gemma Postlethwaite, Chief Executive Officer
Ed: Mary Nell Billings. **Description:** Challenges faced by small business for lowering retirement benefits barriers for women and minorities, which is difficult to put into practice, is discussed.

26992 ■ *"Macroeconomic Policy and U.S. Competitiveness: A Reformed Fiscal Policy Is Vital To Renewing America's Productivity"* in *Harvard Business Review (Vol. 90, March 2012, No. 3, pp. 112)*
Pub: Harvard Business Review Press
Contact: Moderna V. Pfizer, Contact
Ed: Matthew Weinzierl, Richard H.K. Vietor. **Description:** Improving productivity requires increasing physical capital (such as equipment or technology), raising human capital, or using both of these types of capital more efficiently. The authors promote a plan that blends cuts in defense and health care spending, adjustments to Social Security, and carbon and gas taxes.

26993 ■ *Managing the Older Worker: How to Prepare for the New Organizational Order*
Pub: Harvard Business Press
Contact: Gabriela Allmi, Regional Manager
E-mail: gabriela.allmi@hbsp.harvard.edu
Ed: Peter Cappelli, Bill Novelli. **Description:** Your organization needs older workers more than ever: They transfer knowledge between generations, transmit your company's values to new hires, make excellent mentors for younger employees, and provide a 'just in time' workforce for special projects. **Availability:** Print; Audio.

26994 ■ *"Managing Risks: A New Framework: Smart Companies Match Their Approach to the Nature of the Threats They Face"* in *Harvard Business Review (Vol. 90, June 2012, No. 6, pp. 48)*
Pub: Harvard Business Review Press
Contact: Moderna V. Pfizer, Contact
Ed: Anette Mikes, Robert S. Kaplan. **Description:** The importance of strategic planning in effect risk management practices is stressed. Discussion includes preventable risks, strategy risks, and external risks and provides objectives, control models, staff functions, and the business-unit interrelationships of each.

26995 ■ *"Managing Yourself: Job-Hopping to the Top and Other Career Fallacies"* in *Harvard Business Review (Vol. 88, July-August 2010, No. 7-8, pp. 154)*
Pub: Harvard Business Publishing
Contact: Diane Belcher, Managing Director
Ed: Monika Hamori. **Price:** $8.95, PDF. **Description:** Fallacies identified and discussed include the belief that a career move should always be a move up, that industry and career switches are penalized, and that large corporations are the only loci for reaping large rewards. **Availability:** Online; PDF.

26996 ■ *"Mapping Out a Career: An Analysis of Geographic Concentration of Occupations"* in *Occupational Outlook Quarterly (Vol. 54, Fall 2010, No. 3, pp. 12)*
Pub: U.S. Department of Labor Bureau of Labor Statistics
Contact: Amrit Kohli, Director
E-mail: kohli.amrit@bls.gov
Ed: Audrey Watson. **Description:** Geographic distribution of occupations is studied, along with lifestyle considerations when choosing a career. **Availability:** PDF; Online.

26997 ■ *"Mismanaging Pay and Performance"* in *Business Strategy Review (Vol. 21, Summer 2010, No. 2, pp. 54)*
Ed: Rupert Merson. **Released:** June 24, 2010. **Description:** Understanding the relationship between performance measurement and desired behaviors is an important element of a company's talent management. **Availability:** Print; PDF; Online.

26998 ■ *"Miss Manners Minds Your Business"*
Released: October 01, 2014. **Price:** $16.95, paperback. **Description:** Office etiquette is outlined. Practical, pertinent and correct advice is given covering office manners for anyone from convening a focus group to Human Resources management. **Availability:** Print.

26999 ■ *"The Moderating Effects of Organizational Context On the Relationship Between Voluntary Turnover and Organizational Performance: Evidence from Korea"* in *Human Resource Management (Vol. 51, January-February 2012, No. 1, pp. 47-70)*
Pub: John Wiley & Sons, Inc.
Contact: Christina Van Tassell, Executive Vice President Chief Financial Officer
Ed: Kiwook Kwon, Kweontaek Chung, Hyuntak Roh, Clint Chadwick, John J. Lawler. **Released:** January 26, 2012. **Description:** The ability of organizational context to moderate the relationship between voluntary employee turnover and organizational performance is examined using data from South Korean firms. The effects of employee involvement practices, investment in employee training and development, and the availability of potential workers on this relationship are studied. **Availability:** Print; PDF; Online.

27000 ■ *"The Moment You Can't Ignore: When Big Trouble Leads to a Great Future"*
Pub: PublicAffairs
Contact: Jaime Leifer, Director
Released: October 07, 2014. **Price:** $14.99, E-book; $25.99, hardcover. **Description:** New forms of work, communication, and technology are exposing the ways in which an organization's culture conflicts with new competitive demands. Questions for small companies to ask about identity, leadership, and capacity for innovation are addressed. **Availability:** E-book; Print.

27001 ■ *"More Small Businesses in Baltimore Willing to Fund Employees' Health Benefits"* in *Baltimore Business Journal (Vol. 28, June 18, 2010, No. 6, pp. 1)*
Pub: Baltimore Business Journal
Contact: Rhonda Pringle, President
E-mail: rpringle@bizjournals.com
Ed: Scott Graham. **Description:** An increasing number of small businesses in Maryland are tapping into potentially cheaper self-funded health plans instead of providing fully insured benefits to employees through traditional health plans. Self-funded health plans charge employers for health care up to a specified level. Economic implications of self-funded plans to small businesses are discussed.

27002 ■ *"The Myth of the Overqualified Worker"* in *Harvard Business Review (Vol. 88, December 2010, No. 12, pp. 30)*
Pub: Harvard Business Publishing
Contact: Diane Belcher, Managing Director
Ed: Andrew O'Connell. **Price:** $6, PDF. **Description:** It is recommended to seriously consider job candidates with qualifications exceeding the position being recruited because research shows these individuals work harder, but do not quit any sooner than those whose qualifications more closely match the position. **Availability:** Online; PDF.

27003 ■ *The New Job Security: The 5 Best Strategies for Taking Control of Your Career*
Released: September 07, 2010. **Price:** $14.99, paperback. **Description:** This book will help individuals to uncover interesting alternative jobs, generate

multiple income streams, shape their job to reflect values and goals, move successfully through the company, and plan for career transitions to keep them in control. Online resources, real-life examples, practical exercises and a no-nonsense approach will aid in job stability. **Availability:** E-book; Print.

27004 ■ *"No Time to Grieve"* in *Women In Business (Vol. 63, Fall 2011, No. 3, pp. 22)*
Pub: American Business Women's Association
Contact: Rene Street, Executive Director

Ed: Diane Stafford. **Released:** September 22, 2011. **Description:** Individuals who have experienced job loss must go through the emotional stages related to this event in order to gain the best re-employment opportunities. The first step towards re-employment is to make the job search public. Tips for improving one's online footprint are also given. **Availability:** Online.

27005 ■ *Non-Standard Employment under Globalization: Flexible Work and Social Security in the Newly Industrializing Countries*
Pub: Palgrave Macmillan

Ed: Koichi Usami. **Released:** First edition. **Description:** Expansion of non-standard employment under globalization is being recognized in all of the newly industrialized countries. The book examines deregulation of labor markets, social protection for nonstandard workers, and social security reforms in accordance with the transformation of employment.

27006 ■ *"Notes on Current Labor Statistics"* in *Montly Labor Review (Vol. 133, September 2010, No. 9, pp. 75)*
Pub: U.S. Department of Labor Bureau of Labor Statistics
Contact: Amrit Kohli, Director
E-mail: kohli.amrit@bls.gov

Description: Principal statistics and calculated by the Bureau of Labor Statistics are presented. The series includes statistics on labor force; employment; unemployment; labor compensation; consumer, producer, and international prices; productivity; international comparisons; and injury and illness statistics. **Availability:** Online; PDF.

27007 ■ *"The Office Christmas Party and Legal Liability"* in *Legal Zoom (March 23, 2023)*
URL(s): www.legalzoom.com/articles/the-office-chris tmas-party-and-legal-liability
Ed: Ann MacDonald. **Released:** March 23, 2023. **Description:** Discusses some of the settings that could get a small business owner in legal trouble during the annual office Christmas party. Also includes alternatives and rules to have in order to avoid compromising situations. **Availability:** Online.

27008 ■ *"Olympus is Urged to Revise Board"* in *Wall Street Journal Eastern Edition (November 28, 2011, pp. B3)*
Pub: Dow Jones & Company Inc.
Contact: Almar Latour, Chief Executive Officer

Ed: Phred Dvorak. **Description:** Koji Miyata, once a director on the board of troubled Japanese photographic equipment company, is urging the company to reorganize its board, saying the present group should resign their board seats but keep their management positions. The company has come under scrutiny for its accounting practices and costly acquisitions. **Availability:** Online.

27009 ■ *"Open Enrollment: Staying Healthy During Enrollment Season"* in *Employee Benefit News (Vol. 25, November 1, 2011, No. 14, pp. 41)*
Pub: SourceMedia LLC
Contact: Gemma Postlethwaite, Chief Executive Officer

Ed: Shana Sweeney. **Description:** Tips for staying healthy during your benefit open enrollment period are outlined.

27010 ■ *"Open Enrollment: What Small Businesses Need to Know About the Affordable Care Act"* in *Business News Daily (February 21, 2023)*
URL(s): www.businessnewsdaily.com/8535-open -enrollment-tips.html
Ed: Marisa Sanfilippo. **Released:** February 21, 2023. **Description:** Get the information you need to put together a benefits package for your employees using the Affordable Care Act. **Availability:** Online.

27011 ■ *"Organization Redesign and Innovative HRM"* in *Human Resource Management (Vol. 49, July-August 2010, No. 4, pp. 809-811)*
Pub: John Wiley & Sons, Inc.
Contact: Christina Van Tassell, Executive Vice President Chief Financial Officer

Ed: Pat Lynch. **Released:** July 01, 2010. **Description:** An overview of the book, 'Organization Redesign and Innovative HRM' is presented. **Availability:** PDF; Online.

27012 ■ *Organizations Alive!: Six Things That Challenge - Seven That Bring Success*
Pub: Yuill & Associates

Ed: Jan Yuill. **Price:** C$18.95, paperback. **Description:** New insight into understanding how organizations function as individuals is presented by an international consultant. Customer service, resource management, outsourcing, and management are among the issues covered.

27013 ■ *"Overqualified. Underemployed"* in *Philadelphia Business Journal (Vol. 33, August 1, 2104, No. 25, pp. 14)*
Pub: American City Business Journals, Inc.
Contact: Mike Olivieri, Executive Vice President

Description: Overqualified workers often find themselves in employment situations where their education, experience and skills are beyond the requirements of the job. The implications of underemployment for the worker, the organization and the overall U.S. economy are discussed. **Availability:** Print; Online.

27014 ■ *"Pack Mentality: Why Black Can Be Slimming"* in *Crain's Chicago Business (Vol. 31, April 21, 2008, No. 16, pp. 31)*
Pub: Crain Communications Inc.
Contact: Barry Asin, President

Ed: Sarah A. Klein. **Description:** Jill Smart, the head of human resources for a company with 170,000 employees worldwide, frequently travels to India, London and Singapore; Ms. Smart provides advice concerning efficiency, time management and avoiding jet-lag. **Availability:** Online.

27015 ■ *"Paid to Persuade: Careers in Sales"* in *Occupational Outlook Quarterly (Vol. 55, Summer 2011, No. 2, pp. 24)*
Pub: U.S. Department of Labor Bureau of Labor Statistics
Contact: Amrit Kohli, Director
E-mail: kohli.amrit@bls.gov

Ed: Ilka Maria Torpey. **Description:** Sales workers are paid to persuade others to buy goods and services. There were over 13 million wage and salary sales workers in the US in 2010. Wages in sales careers can vary and some become lucrative, lifelong career positions. Seven sales occupations with annual wages higher than $33,000 are profiled. **Availability:** Online; PDF.

27016 ■ *"Pay Fell for Many Baltimore Execs in '09"* in *Baltimore Business Journal (Vol. 28, July 2, 2010, No. 8, pp. 1)*
Pub: Baltimore Business Journal
Contact: Rhonda Pringle, President
E-mail: rpringle@bizjournals.com

Ed: Gary Haber. **Description:** Compensation for the 100 highest-paid executives in the Baltimore, Maryland area decreased in 2009, compared with 2008. At least $1 million were received by 59 out of 100

executives in 2009, while 75 earned the said amount in 2008. Factors that contributed to the executives' decisions to take pay cuts are discussed. **Availability:** Print.

27017 ■ *"Paychecks of Some Bank CEOs Have a Pre-Recession Look"* in *Boston Business Journal (Vol. 29, May 13, 2011, No. 1, pp. 1)*
Pub: Boston Business Journal
Contact: Carolyn M. Jones, President
E-mail: cmjones@bizjournals.com

Ed: Gary Haber. **Description:** The salaries of United States-based bank chief executive officers have increased to pre-recession levels. Wells Fargo and Company's John G. Stumpf received $17.6 million in 2010. Community bank executives, on the other hand, have seen minimal increases. **Availability:** Print; Online.

27018 ■ *People Operations: Automate HR, Design a Great Employee Experience, and Unleash Your Workforce*
Pub: John Wiley & Sons, Inc.
Contact: Christina Van Tassell, Executive Vice President Chief Financial Officer
URL(s): www.wiley.com/en-us/People+Operations% 3A+Automate+HR%2C+Design+a+Great+Em ployee+Experience%2C+and+Unleash+Your +Workforce-p-9781119785231
Ed: Jay Fulcher, Tracy Cote, Kevin Marasco. **Released:** May 2021. **Price:** $18, e-book; $30, hardcover. **Description:** Gives tips to automate HR work so focus can be put on the actual people who work in the business. **Availability:** E-book; Print.

27019 ■ *"People Tools for Business: 50 Strategies for Building Success, Creating Wealth, and Finding Happiness"*
Released: September 30, 2014. **Price:** $14.91; $9.43. **Description:** Tools required to enjoy success in both career and life are given. People Tools are help to develop self-confidence, improve management skills, and find constructive ways for Human Resource managers to fire workers and ways for workers to respond. Each people tool is concise and provides a straightforward strategy to produce positive results. **Availability:** Print.

27020 ■ *"Perks Still Popular: Jets May be Out, but CEO Benefits Abound"* in *Crain's Detroit Business (Vol. 25, June 22, 2009)*
Pub: Crain Communications Inc.
Contact: Barry Asin, President

Ed: Ryan Beene. **Description:** Benefits packages of local CEOs are outlined. Statistical data included. **Availability:** Online.

27021 ■ *"Plan Your Future with My Next Move"* in *Occupational Outlook Quarterly (Vol. 55, Summer 2011, No. 2, pp. 22)*
Description: My Next Move, an online tool offering a variety of user-friendly ways to browse more than 900 occupations was created by the National Center for O NET Development for the US Department of Labor's Employment and Training Administration. Clicking on an occupation presents a one-page profile summarizing key information for specific careers. **Availability:** Print; Online.

27022 ■ *"Predicting Success: Evidence-Based Strategies to Hire the Right People and Build the Best Team"*
Pub: John Wiley & Sons, Inc.
Contact: Christina Van Tassell, Executive Vice President Chief Financial Officer

Released: October 2014. **Price:** $16.99, e-book; $25, hardcover. **Description:** Guide for human resource management teams choose the right employee when hiring. It teaches how to apply the principles and tools of human analytics to the work place to avoid bad culture fits, mismatched skillsets, entitled workers, and other hiring mistakes that hurt employee motivation and morale. The Predictive Index TM, behavior analytics, hiring assessments, and other resources for better outcomes are presented. **Availability:** E-book; Print.

27023 ■ *"Privacy Concern: Are 'Group' Time Sheets Legal?"* in *HR Specialist (Vol. 8, September 2010, No. 9, pp. 4)*
Pub: Capitol Information Group Inc.
Contact: Allie Ash, Chief Executive Officer
Description: Under the Fair Labor Standards Act (FLSA) employers are required to maintain and preserve payroll or other records, including the number of hours worked, but it does not prescribe a particular order or form in which these records must be kept. **Availability:** PDF; Online.

27024 ■ *""PTO vs. Vacation Time: Which Is Right for Your Company?"* in *Legal Zoom (February 14, 2023)*
URL(s): www.legalzoom.com/articles/pto-vs-vacation-time-which-is-right-for-your-company
Ed: Brette Sember, J.D. **Released:** February 14, 2023. **Description:** The pros and cons of offering PTO versus vacation time are discussed. **Availability:** Online.

27025 ■ *"Questioning Authority"* in *Entrepreneur (June 2014)*
Pub: Society for the Study of Myth and Tradition
Contact: Tracy Cochran, Director
Description: Smarterer is a platform that facilitates the evaluation of prospective hires through crowd-sourced assessment tests quantifying their professional skills and strengths. The platform has more than 900 multiple-choice tests covering a variety of professions. It uses an adaptive machine-learning algorithm that ensures the uniqueness of every test. Users can choose to make their test results public and can perform do-overs on some tests. The platform was launched in 2010 as a way of identifying potential talent and identifying skill inventories among existing employees. **Availability:** Print; Online.

27026 ■ *"Quitting Your Job Might Be Tougher Than You Think"* in *Canadian Business (Vol. 85, July 16, 2012, No. 11-12, pp. 71)*
Ed: Matthew McClearn. **Description:** Employees who are planning to resign should consider the notice period, the time it will take for employers to find a replacement and the reason for leaving. Departing employees can use their knowledge and skills to compete directly with their former employer, but they should be wary of unfair competition. **Availability:** Online.

27027 ■ *Race and Entrepreneurial Success: Black-, Asian-, and White-Owned Businesses in the United States*
Pub: The MIT Press
Ed: Robert W. Fairlie, Alicia M. Robb. **Released:** 2008. **Description:** Trends in minority small business ownership are explored, focusing on the importance of human capital, financial capital, and family business background in successful business ownership. **Availability:** E-book; Print; PDF.

27028 ■ *"Rawlings-Blake Unveils Business Plan for Next Four Years"* in *Baltimore Business Journal (Vol. 29, September 16, 2011, No. 19, pp. 1)*
Pub: Boston Business Journal
Contact: Carolyn M. Jones, President
E-mail: cmjones@bizjournals.com
Ed: Gary Haber. **Description:** Mayor Stephanie Rawlings-Blake of Baltimore, Maryland unveiled her plan to push the economy forward. Her key objectives include giving more support for the city's technology companies and refocusing the Baltimore Development Corporation on job creation and retention. **Availability:** Online.

27029 ■ *Reality-Based Leadership: Ditch the Drama, Restore Sanity to the Workplace, & Turn Excuses into Results*
Pub: Jossey-Bass
Ed: Cy Wakeman. **Released:** August 01, 2010. **Price:** $27.95, hardcover; $27.95, hardcover. **Description:** Recent polls show that 71 percent of workers think about quitting their jobs every day. That

number would be shocking if people actually were quitting. Worse, they go to work, punching time clocks and collecting pay checks, while checked out emotionally. Cy Wakeman reveals how to be the kind of leader who changes the way people think about and perceive their circumstances, one who deals with the facts, clarifies roles, gives clean and direct feedback, and insists that everyone do the same without drama or defensiveness. **Availability:** E-book; Print.

27030 ■ *"Recruiting Diversifies"* in *Advertising Age (Vol. 83, October 8, 2012, No. 36, pp. 25)*
Description: Heidrick & Struggles launches a data and analytics practice that filles the void as marketing becomes more data-riven. H&S specializes in recruiting and filling CEO and other senior-level positions for human resource departments of large firms. **Availability:** Print; Online.

27031 ■ *"Renren Partners With Recruit to Launch Social Wedding Services"* in *Benzinga.com (June 7, 2011)*
Pub: PR Newswire Association LLC.
Description: Renren Inc., the leading real name social networking Internet platform in China has partnered with Recruit Company Limited, Japan's largest human resource and classified media group to form a joint venture to build a wedding social media catering to the needs of engaged couples and newlyweds in China.

27032 ■ *"'Resume Mining' Services Can Save Time, Money"* in *HR Specialist (Vol. 8, September 2010, No. 9, pp. 7)*
Pub: Capitol Information Group Inc.
Contact: Allie Ash, Chief Executive Officer
Description: Low-cost resume mining services can help human resource departments save time and money by searching online resume databases for candidates matching specific job qualifications. **Availability:** PDF; Online.

27033 ■ *"Retirement Plan Disclosures: Prepare Now for Fiduciary Rules"* in *Employee Benefit News (Vol. 25, November 1, 2011, No. 14, pp. 24)*
Pub: SourceMedia LLC
Contact: Gemma Postlethwaite, Chief Executive Officer
Ed: Brian M. Pinheiro, Kurt R. Anderson. **Description:** Department of Labor has delayed the deadlines on new affirmative obligations for fiduciaries of retirement plans subject to the Employee Retirement Income Security Act. Details included. **Availability:** Online; PDF; Download.

27034 ■ *"Retirement Plans in a Quandary"* in *Employee Benefit News (Vol. 25, December 1, 2011, No. 15, pp. 18)*
Pub: SourceMedia LLC
Contact: Gemma Postlethwaite, Chief Executive Officer
Ed: Terry Dunne. **Description:** Complex issues arise when employees don't cash their 401(k) balance checks. The US Department of Labor permits plans to cash out accounts of former employees with less than $1,000 to reduce the cost and time required to manage them.

27035 ■ *"Reviving Entrepreneurship: Policy Decisions in 12 Areas Could Nurture - Or Cripple - America's Greatest Asset"* in *Harvard Business Review (Vol. 90, March 2012, No. 3, pp. 116)*
Pub: Harvard Business Review Press
Contact: Moderna V. Pfizer, Contact
Ed: Josh Lerner, William A. Sahlman. **Price:** $8.95, hardcover. **Description:** Government policies should address entrepreneurship as a process, rather than an act. Several key areas for policymaking include basic and translational science, supply and quality of human capital, information availability, tax treatment of rewards and risks, intellectual property rights, workforce healthcare, and mobility of financial and human capital. **Availability:** PDF; Online.

27036 ■ *"The Rise of the Supertemp: The Best Executive and Professional Jobs May No Longer Be Full-Time Gigs"* in *Harvard Business Review (Vol. 90, May 2012, No. 5, pp. 50)*
Pub: Harvard Business Review Press
Contact: Moderna V. Pfizer, Contact
Ed: Jody Grenstone Miller, Matt Miller. **Price:** $8.95, hardcopy and PDF. **Description:** Supertemps are independent contractors who perform mission-critical work on a project basis. Supertemps enjoy a high degree of flexibility and freedom, and offer companies new opportunities for innovation and growth. **Availability:** Print; Online; PDF.

27037 ■ *"The Role of Leadership In Successful International Mergers and Acquisitions: Why Renault-Nissan Succeeded and DaimlerChrysler-Mitsubishi Failed"* in *Human Resource Management (Vol. 51, May-June 2012, No. 3, pp. 433-456)*
Pub: John Wiley & Sons, Inc.
Contact: Christina Van Tassell, Executive Vice President Chief Financial Officer
Ed: Carol Gill. **Released:** May 25, 2012. **Description:** The effects of national and organizational culture on the performance of Nissan and Mitsubishi after their mergers with Renault and DaimlerChrysler respectively are examined. Japanese national culture was found to influence organizational culture and human resource management practices, while leadership affected the success of their turnaround efforts.

27038 ■ *"Screening-Oriented Recruitment Messages: Antecedents and Relationships with Applicant Pool Quality"* in *Human Resource Management (Vol. 51, May- June 2012, No. 3, pp. 343-360)*
Pub: John Wiley & Sons, Inc.
Contact: Christina Van Tassell, Executive Vice President Chief Financial Officer
Ed: Brian R. Dineen, Ian O. Williamson. **Released:** May 25, 2012. **Description:** Factors associated with the use of screening-oriented messages for recruitment are investigated. Results indicate that labor supply perceptions, the reputation of recruiting firms and quality-based compensation incentives are associated with the use of screening-oriented messages, which are associated with the quality of the applicant pool. **Availability:** Print; PDF; Online.

27039 ■ *"Shocks and Final Straws: Using Exit-Interview Data to Examine the Unfolding Model's Decision Paths"* in *Human Resource Management (Vol. 51, January-February 2012, No. 1, pp. 25-46)*
Pub: John Wiley & Sons, Inc.
Contact: Christina Van Tassell, Executive Vice President Chief Financial Officer
Ed: Carol T. Kulik, Gerry Treuren, Prashant Bordia. **Released:** January 26, 2012. **Description:** Employees leaving their organizations are examined according to the unfolding model using data from exit interviews. Results indicate that employees along the same exit path may experience different kinds and combinations of shocks, while some experience shock-like events. **Availability:** Print; PDF; Online.

27040 ■ *"Shorts Season: Is It Time for a Dress Code?"* in *Legal Zoom (March 21, 2023)*
URL(s): www.legalzoom.com/articles/shorts-season-is-it-time-for-a-dress-code
Ed: Chas Rampenthal. **Released:** March 21, 2023. **Description:** How to address employees and the attire they wear that may not be exactly appropriate for an office setting. **Availability:** Online.

27041 ■ *"Small Business Economic Trends: Moderate Improvement but No Clear Direction"* in *Small Business Economic Trends (March 2008, pp. 3)*
Pub: National Federation of Independent Business
Contact: Brad Close, President
Ed: William C. Dunkelberg, Holly Wade. **Description:** Commentary on the economic trends for small businesses in the U.S. is presented. Analysis of the

labor market and low interest rates is given. The effect of the Federal Reserve's policy announcement on small business owner optimism is also discussed. **Availability:** Print; Online.

27042 ■ "Small Business Employment in 22 Rich Economies" in Small Business Economic Trends (January 2008, pp. 9)
Pub: National Federation of Independent Business
Contact: Brad Close, President
Ed: William C. Dunkelberg, Holly Wade. **Description:** Table from a survey of small businesses in the U.S. is given, representing actual employment changes from January 2002 to December 2007. A graph comparing planned employment and current job openings from January 1986 to December 2007 is also supplied. Tables showing job opening, hiring plans, and qualified applicants for job openings are also presented. **Availability:** Online.

27043 ■ "Small Business Employment" in Small Business Economic Trends (September 2010, pp. 9)
Pub: National Federation of Independent Business
Contact: Brad Close, President
Description: A table from a survey of small businesses in the U.S. is given, representing actual employment changes from January 2005 to August 2010. A graph comparing planned employment and current job openings from January 1986 to August 2010 is also supplied. Tables showing job openings, hiring plans, and qualified applicants for job openings are also presented. **Availability:** Online.

27044 ■ "Sometimes You Have to Ignore the Rule Book" in Canadian Business (Vol. 83, September 14, 2010, No. 15, pp. 13)
Pub: Rogers Media Inc.
Contact: Neil Spivak, Chief Executive Officer
Ed: Richard Branson. **Released:** September 14, 2010. **Description:** The rule book has provided a clear framework for employees particularly when cash and accounting are at issue. However, sometimes rules were made to be broken and the rule book should not become an excuse for poor customer service or hinder great service. How Virgin Atlantic practices this type of corporate culture is discussed. **Availability:** Print; Online.

27045 ■ "A Stakeholder--Human Capital Perspective on the Link Between Social Performance and Executive Compensation" in Business Ethics Quarterly (Vol. 24, January 2014, No. 1, pp. 1)
Pub: Business Ethics Quarterly
Contact: Dawn Elm, Executive Director
E-mail: drelm@stthomas.edu
Description: The link between firm corporate social performance (CSP) and executive compensation could be driven by a sorting effect (a firm's CSP is related to the initial levels of compensation of newly hired executives), or by an incentive effect (incumbent executives are rewarded for past firm CSP). An exploration of the sorting effect of firm CSP on the initial compensation of newly hired executives is discussed. **Availability:** Download; PDF; Online.

27046 ■ "Stand Out Via Service: How Volunteering Can Boost Your Professional Bottom Line" in Black Enterprise (Vol. 44, June 2014, No. 10, pp. 42)
Pub: Earl G. Graves Ltd.
Contact: Earl Graves, Jr., President
Description: According to the 2013 Deloitte Volunteer IMPACT Survey, more than three of every four human resource executives volunteer. This strategy can lead to career satisfaction and help a business advance and fuel growth for individuals and the firm. Tips for finding the right volunteer opportunity are included.

27047 ■ "Start Filling Your Talent Gap - Now" in Business Strategy Review (Vol. 21, Spring 2010, No. 1, pp. 56)
Ed: Alan Bird, Lori Flees, Paul DiPaola. **Released:** March 22, 2010. **Description:** As businesses steer their way out of turbulence, they have a unique opportunity to identify their leadership supply and

demand and then to close the talent gap in their organization. Authors explain how to take immediate steps to build the right team now and lay the groundwork for a long-term approach for nurturing talent within the organization. **Availability:** Online; Electronic publishing.

27048 ■ "Stung by Recession, Hemmer Regroups with New Strategy" in Business Courier (Vol. 27, June 4, 2010, No. 5, pp. 1)
Pub: Business Courier
Ed: Lucy May. **Description:** Paul Hemmer Companies reduced its work force and outsourced operations such as marketing and architecture, in order for the commercial and construction firm to survive the recession. Hammer's total core revenue in 2009 dropped to less than $30 million forcing the closure of its Chicago office. **Availability:** PDF; Online.

27049 ■ "Surprise Package" in Business Courier (Vol. 27, June 25, 2010, No. 8, pp. 1)
Pub: Business Courier
Ed: Dan Monk, Jon Newberry, Steve Watkins. **Description:** More than 60 percent of the chief executive officers (CEOs) in Greater Cincinnati's 35 public companies took a salary cut in 2009, but stock grants resulted in large paper gains for the CEOs. The salary cuts show efforts of boards of directors to observe austerity. Statistics on increased values of stock awards for CEOs, median pay for CEOs, and median shareholder return are also presented. **Availability:** Online.

27050 ■ "Survey Profile" in Small Business Economic Trends (September 2010, pp. 19)
Pub: National Federation of Independent Business
Contact: Brad Close, President
Ed: William C. Dunkelberg, Holly Wade. **Description:** Two graphs and a table presenting the profile of small businesses that participated in the National Federation of Independent Business (NFIB) survey are provided. The actual number of firms, their industry types, and the number of full and part-time employees are presented. **Availability:** Print; PDF; Online.

27051 ■ "Swinging For the Fences: The Effects of Ceo Stock Options on Company Risk Taking and Performance" in Academy of Management Journal (Vol. 50, No. 5, October 1, 2007, pp. 1055)
Pub: Academy of Management
Contact: Sharon Alvarez, President
Ed: Gerard Sanders, Donald C. Hambrick. **Description:** Study examines managerial risk-taking vis-a-vis stock options of the company; results reveal that stock options instigate CEOs to take unwise risks that could bring huge losses to the company. **Availability:** Electronic publishing; PDF; Download; Online.

27052 ■ The Talent Masters: Why Smart Leaders Put People Before Numbers
Released: November 09, 2010. **Price:** $27.50, hardcover; $7.99, e-book; $20, audiobook download. **Description:** This book helps leaders recognize talent in their employees, and to put that talent to work to help achieve business success. **Availability:** E-book; Print.

27053 ■ "Talent Shows" in Canadian Business (Vol. 81, December 24, 2007, No. 1, pp. 14)
Description: Canadian companies are increasingly turning to marketing to promote themselves as employers, as concerns on employee recruitment increase with the nearing retirement age of the baby boomers. Details on skills shortage, the potential advantage of the immigrant workforce, and employee retention are discussed. **Availability:** Online.

27054 ■ "Teleworkers Confess Biggest At-Home Distractions" in Employee Benefit News (Vol. 25, November 1, 2011, No. 14, pp. 7)
Pub: SourceMedia LLC

Contact: Gemma Postlethwaite, Chief Executive Officer
Ed: Kelley M. Butler. **Description:** Telecommuting can actually make some workers more efficient and productive versus working inside the office.

27055 ■ "The Ten Commandments of Legal Risk Management" in Business Horizons (Vol. 51, January-February 2008, No. 1, pp. 13)
Pub: Elsevier Advanced Technology Publications
Ed: Michael B. Metzger. **Description:** Effective legal risk management is tightly linked with ethical and good management, and managers' behaviors have to be professional and based on ethically defensible principles of action. Basic human tendencies cannot be used in justifying questionable decisions in court. Guidelines for legal risk management are presented. **Availability:** Print; Online.

27056 ■ "To Win With Natural Talent, Go For Additive Effects; Four Human Capital Strategies Combine to Drive Up to 59 Percent More Growth In Revenue Per Employee" in Gallup Business Journal (June 3, 2014)
Pub: Gallup, Inc.
Contact: Jon Clifton, Chief Executive Officer
Description: Four human capital strategies, when used together, can drive growth in revenue per employee by as much as 59 percent. The strategies for selecting and implementing the right managers are explored. **Availability:** Print.

27057 ■ "'Tone-Deaf' Suitor or True Harasser: How to Tell" in HR Specialist (Vol. 8, September 2010, No. 9, pp. 1)
Pub: Capitol Information Group Inc.
Contact: Allie Ash, Chief Executive Officer
Description: Details are critical to any harassment charge in the workplace. Courts now list factors employers should consider when trying to determine whether an employee has been sexually harassed at work. **Availability:** PDF; Online.

27058 ■ "TrendHR Changes Rockwall Landscape with $25M Office Tower" in Dallas Business Journal (Vol. 35, May 25, 2012, No. 37, pp. 1)
Pub: Baltimore Business Journal
Contact: Rhonda Pringle, President
E-mail: rpringle@bizjournals.com
Ed: Candace Carlisle. **Description:** TrendHR Services is planning to build an executive tower in Rockwall, Texas. The company provides human resource outsourcing, employee benefits, and consulting services. **Availability:** Print; Online.

27059 ■ "Tri-State Lags Peer Cities in Jobs, Human Capital, Study Says" in Business Courier (Vol. 27, September 24, 2010, No. 21, pp. 1)
Pub: Business Courier
Ed: Dan Monk, Lucy May. **Description:** Greater Cincinnati, Ohio has ranked tenth overall in the 'Agenda 360/Vision 2015 Regional Indicators Project' report. The study ranked 12-city-peer groups in categories such as job indicators standing and people indicators standing. The ranking of jobs and human capital study is topped by Minneapolis, followed by Denver, Raleigh, and Austin. **Availability:** Print; Online.

27060 ■ "Unfair Distraction of Employees" in Business Owner (Vol. 35, March-April 2011, No. 2, pp. 8)
Description: Fair Credit Collection Practices Act makes it illegal for collectors to contact a debtor at his or her place of employment if the collector is made aware that it is against personnel policy of the employer for the worker to take such a call. **Availability:** Print; Online.

27061 ■ "Urban League Training Program Finds Jobs for Cincinnati's 'Hard to Serve'" in Business Courier (Vol. 27, July 2, 2010, No. 9, pp. 1)
Pub: Business Courier

Ed: Lucy May. **Description:** Stephen Tucker, director of workforce development for the Urban League of Greater Cincinnati, is an example of how ex-offenders can be given chances for employment after service jail sentences. How the Urban Leagues' Solid Opportunities for Advancement job training program helped Tucker and other ex-offenders is discussed. **Availability:** Print; Online.

27062 ■ *"URI Centre Seen as Bridge From Campus to Employment" in Providence Business News (Vol. 29, June 30, 2014, No. 13, pp. 4)*

Pub: American City Business Journals, Inc.

Contact: Mike Olivieri, Executive Vice President

URL(s): pbn.com/uri-center-seen-as-bridge-from -campus-to-employment98182

Description: Kimberly S. Washor is the first director of University of Rhode Island's (URIs) new Centre for Career and Experiential Education that combines the missions of Experiential Learning and Community Engagement along with Career Services and Employer Relations. By joining the two offices, URI is implementing a new database that will meet the needs of both career and internship advising, where adviser will be able to track industry human resource partners. **Telecommunication Services:** Daddona@ pbn.com.

27063 ■ *"Use Benefits Checklist to Smooth New-Hire Onboarding" in HR Specialist (Vol. 8, September 2010, No. 9, pp. 4)*

Pub: Capitol Information Group Inc.

Contact: Allie Ash, Chief Executive Officer

Description: Checklist to help employees enroll in a company's benefit offerings is provided, courtesy of Wayne State University in Detroit, Michigan. **Availability:** Print; Online.

27064 ■ *"Village at Waugh Chapel $275M Expansion Begins" in Baltimore Business Journal (Vol. 28, August 27, 2010, No. 16, pp. 1)*

Pub: Baltimore Business Journal

Contact: Rhonda Pringle, President

E-mail: rpringle@bizjournals.com

Ed: Daniel J. Sernovitz. **Description:** Developer Greenberg Gibbons Corporation has broken ground on a $275 million, 1.2 million-square-foot addition to its Village at the Waugh Chapel mixed-use complex. Aside from creating 2,600 permanent jobs, the addition, named Village South, is expected to lure Target and Wegmans Food Markets to Crofton, Maryland. Funding for this project is discussed. **Availability:** Print.

27065 ■ *"Voices From the Front Lines: Four Leaders on the Cross-Border Challenges They've Faced" in Harvard Business Review (Vol. 92, September 2014, No. 9, pp. 77)*

Pub: Harvard Business Publishing

Contact: Diane Belcher, Managing Director

Price: $8.95. **Description:** Points presented include building cultural sensitivity into organizations, employing varying talent to respond to market specifics, creating standard human resource practices worldwide, and emphasizing the importance of emerging markets. **Availability:** Online; PDF.

27066 ■ *"Wal-Mart China Woes Add Up" in Wall Street Journal Eastern Edition (October 17, 2011, pp. B3)*

Pub: Dow Jones & Company Inc.

Contact: Almar Latour, Chief Executive Officer

Ed: Laurie Burkitt. **Description:** Woes for Wal-Mart Inc.'s subsidiary in China are adding up as Wal-Mart China president and chief executive Ed Chan stepped down, as well as the company's senior vice president for human resources, Clara Wong. The company has been charged by regulators with mislabeling pork products, the result which has forced stores to close. Sales in China have been slow at the retail stores. **Availability:** Online.

27067 ■ *"Walker Seeks More Business Participation" in Business Journal-Milwaukee (Vol. 28, December 10, 2010, No. 10, pp. A1)*

Pub: The Business Journal

Contact: Heather Ladage, President

E-mail: hladage@bizjournals.com

Ed: Rich Kirchen. **Description:** Wisconsin governor Scott Walker is seeking the aid of Milwaukee business leaders to participate in resolving the challenges posed by the economic crisis. Walker is aiming to create 250,000 jobs. He is also planning to call a special session of the legislature to enact strategies to jumpstart the economy. **Availability:** Print; Online.

27068 ■ *"Wanted: African American Professional for Hire" in Black Enterprise (Vol. 37, November 2006, No. 4, pp. 93)*

Pub: Earl G. Graves Ltd.

Contact: Earl Graves, Jr., President

Ed: Joe Watson. **Description:** Excerpt from the book, Without Excuses: Unleash the Power of Diversity to Build Your Business, speaks to the lack of diversity in the corporate arena and why executives, recruiters, and HR professionals claim they are unable to find qualified individuals of different races when hiring. **Availability:** Online.

27069 ■ *"Ways AI is Changing HR Departments" in Business News Daily (March 21, 2023)*

URL(s): www.businessnewsdaily.com/how-ai-is -changing-hr

Ed: Gem Siocon. **Released:** March 21, 2023. **Description:** AI can improve some human resource tasks and this article discusses those options. **Availability:** Online.

27070 ■ *"Wealth and Jobs: the Broken Link" in Harvard Business Review (Vol. 88, November 2010, No. 11, pp. 44)*

Pub: Harvard Business Publishing

Contact: Diane Belcher, Managing Director

Ed: Nitin Nohria. **Price:** $6, PDF. **Description:** Rebuilding the link between business and job creation to shore up the middle class is advocated. A blend of government policies and business strategies that foster entrepreneurship and innovation are essential. **Availability:** Online; PDF.

27071 ■ *"A Well-Crafted Employee Handbook Can Make Work Run More Smoothly" in Idaho Business Review (September 17, 2014)*

Pub: BridgeTower Media

Contact: Adam Reinebach, President

Description: An employee handbook will provide a complaint process, provide company management flexibility and clarity and keep a company out of legal problems. Training, compensation, benefits, security, health, performance appraisals, and safety issues must be covered. Human resource managers and other mangers should cover basics to help communicate with workers.

27072 ■ *"What Employees Worldwide Have in Common" in Gallup Management Journal (September 22, 2011)*

Description: According to a Gallup study, workplace conditions are strongly tied to personal wellbeing, regardless of geographic region. The employee study covered 116 countries. **Availability:** Print; Online.

27073 ■ *"What Is a Business Casual Policy?" in Business News Daily (March 9, 2023)*

URL(s): www.businessnewsdaily.com/15346-busi -ness-casual-attire.html

Ed: Skye Schooley. **Released:** March 09, 2023. **Description:** Defines and gives examples of a business casual dress code policy. **Availability:** Online.

27074 ■ *"What Meal and Break Laws Does Your Business Need to Know?" in Business News Daily (March 17, 2023)*

URL(s): www.businessnewsdaily.com/15942-meal -rest-break-laws.html

Ed: Adam Uzialko. **Released:** March 17, 2023. **Description:** Avoid breaking laws and catch up on federal and state laws regarding meals and breaks for your employees. **Availability:** Online.

27075 ■ *"What Small Businesses Need to Know about Holiday Pay" in Legal Zoom (February 17, 2023)*

URL(s): www.legalzoom.com/articles/what-small -businesses-need-to-know-about-holiday-pay

Ed: Diane Faulkner. **Released:** February 17, 2023. **Description:** Advice on how to determine holiday pay for your employees, taking into consideration if they are nonexempt, salaried, etc. **Availability:** Online.

27076 ■ *"What You Need to Know about the Federal Overtime Rules" in Business News Daily (March 17, 2023)*

URL(s): www.businessnewsdaily.com/9110-federal -overtime-rules.html

Ed: Max Freedman. **Released:** March 17, 2023. **Description:** Every small business owner should be well acquainted with the Fair Labor Standards Act (FLSA) in order to remain compliant in federal overtime law. **Availability:** Online.

27077 ■ *"What You Need to Know about Hiring Independent Contractors" in Legal Zoom (March 22, 2023)*

URL(s): www.legalzoom.com/articles/what-you-nee d-to-know-about-hiring-independent-contractors

Released: March 23, 2023. **Description:** Independent contractors are an attractive choice for saving some costs, but are they the best choice for your small business? Read about the pros and cons of hiring ICs. **Availability:** Online.

27078 ■ *"What's Working Now: In Providing Jobs for North Carolinians" in Business North Carolina (Vol. 28, February 2008, No. 2, pp. 16)*

Pub: Business North Carolina

Contact: Peggy Knaack, Manager

E-mail: pknaack@businessnc.com

Ed: Edward Martin, Frank Maley. **Description:** Individuals previously employed in the furniture, tobacco, or textile manufacturing sectors have gone back to school to be trained in new sectors in the area such as life sciences, finances and other emerging sectors. **Availability:** Online.

27079 ■ *"When R&D Spending Is Not Enough: The Critical Role of Culture When You Really Want to Innovate" in Human Resource Management (Vol. 49, July-August 2010, No. 4, pp. 767-792)*

Pub: John Wiley & Sons, Inc.

Contact: Christina Van Tassell, Executive Vice President Chief Financial Officer

Ed: Sheng Wang, Rebecca M. Guidice, Judith W. Tansky, Zhong-Ming Wang. **Released:** July 19, 2010. **Description:** A study was conducted to examine the effect of contextual contingencies on innovation. Findings indicate that Chinese manufacturers with cultures emphasizing innovation and teamwork more effectively utilize financial resources in the innovation process. Results also show that a culture emphasizing outcomes and stability leads to lower levels innovation irrespective of investments. **Availability:** Print; PDF; Online.

27080 ■ *"When To Make Private News Public: Should a Job Candidate Reveal That She's Pregnant?" in Harvard Business Review (Vol. 90, March 2012, No. 3, pp. 161)*

Pub: Harvard Business Review Press

Contact: Moderna V. Pfizer, Contact

Ed: Tiziana Casciaro, Victoria W. Winston. **Price:** $8.95, hardcopy black and white. **Description:** A fictitious hiring scenario is presented, with contributors providing advice on whether a candidate for a position involving extensive business travel should inform her manager that she is expecting. Contributors agree the employee should inform her manager, but not necessarily before she is offered the position, and that the conversation remains focused on how she will perform the job and address challenges. **Availability:** Print; PDF; Online.

27081 ■ *"Who Is Eligible for Maternity and Paternity Leave?" in Legal Zoom (February 15, 2023)*
URL(s): www.legalzoom.com/articles/who-is-eligible -for-maternity-and-paternity-leave
Ed: Diane Faulkner. **Released:** February 15, 2023. **Description:** Discusses employee qualifications for maternity or paternity leave. **Availability:** Online.

27082 ■ *"Why Does Firm Reputation In Human Resource Policies Influence College Students? The Mechanisms Underlying Job Pursuit Intentions" in Human Resource Management (Vol. 51, January-February 2012, No. 1, pp. 121-142)*
Pub: John Wiley & Sons, Inc.
Contact: Christina Van Tassell, Executive Vice President Chief Financial Officer
Ed: Julie Holliday Wayne, Wendy J. Casper. **Released:** January 26, 2012. **Description:** The effects of reputational information about human resource practices of companies on college students seeking employment are examined. The reputation of firms in compensation, work-family, and diversity efforts are found to increase intentions to pursue employment in these firms. **Availability:** Print; PDF; Online.

27083 ■ *"Why His Merit Raise Is Bigger Than Hers" in Harvard Business Review (Vol. 90, April 2012, No. 4, pp. 26)*
Pub: Harvard Business Review Press
Contact: Moderna V. Pfizer, Contact
Ed: Stephen Benard. **Price:** $6, hardcover. **Description:** Research indicates that companies that utilize meritocracy as their pay-for-performance system are paradoxically more likely to award pay on biases, and specifically, to give smaller increases to women. Tranparency and accountability are therefore key in the implementation of merit pay. **Availability:** PDF; Online.

27084 ■ *"Why HR Practices Are Not Evidence-Based" in Academy of Management Journal (Vol. 50, No. 5, October 1, 2007, pp. 1033)*
Pub: Academy of Management
Contact: Sharon Alvarez, President
Ed: Edward E. Lawler. **Description:** A suggestion that an Evidence-Based Management Collaboration (EBMC) can be established to facilitate effective transfer of ideas between science and practice is presented. **Availability:** Electronic publishing; PDF; Download; Online.

27085 ■ *"Why Is It So Hard To Find Good People? The Problem Might Be You" in Inc. (Vol. 33, November 2011, No. 9, pp. 100)*
Description: Entrepreneurs sometimes struggle to find good workers. A recent survey shows hiring as their top concern. Four common mistakes that can occur during the hiring process our outlined. **Availability:** Online.

27086 ■ *"Why Make Diversity So Hard to Achieve?" in (Vol. 90, June 2012, No. 6, pp. 40)*
Pub: Harvard Business Review Press
Contact: Moderna V. Pfizer, Contact
Ed: John H. Rice. **Price:** $6, PDF and hardcover black and white. **Description:** Four obstacles to workplace diversity are identified: distributing the responsibility for improving diversity; managing activities rather than outcomes; focusing on correcting the culture rather than on promotion rates; and prioritizing minority candidates for diversity department positions without enabling them to transcend problems they themselves may be facing. **Availability:** Print; PDF; Online.

27087 ■ *"Why Men Still Get More Promotions Than Women" in Harvard Business Review (Vol. 88, September 2010, No. 9, pp. 80)*
Pub: Harvard Business Publishing
Contact: Diane Belcher, Managing Director

Ed: Herminia Ibarra, Nancy M. Carter, Christine Silva. **Price:** $8.95, PDF. **Description:** Sponsorship, rather than mentoring, is identified as the main difference in why men still receive more promotions than women. Active executive sponsorship is key to fostering career advancement. **Availability:** Online; PDF.

27088 ■ *"Why Motivating People Doesn't Work...and What Does: The New Science of Leading, Energizing, and Engaging"*
Released: September 30, 2014. **Price:** $20.95, Nonmembers, PDF e-book; $18.86, Members, electronic publishing; $20.95, Nonmembers, paperback; $18.86, Members, paperback; $24.95, Nonmembers, hardcover; $22.46, Members, hardcover; $20.95, Nonmembers, electronic publishing; $14.67, Members, electronic publishing; $18.95, PDF e-book; $14.67, Members, PDF e-book. **Description:** Leadership researcher, consultant, and business coach, Susan Fowler, shares the latest research on the nature of human motivation to present a tested model and course of action to help Human Resource leaders and managers guide workers towards motivation that will not only increase productivity and engagement but will provide employees with a sense of purpose and fulfillment. **Availability:** E-book; Print; PDF; Electronic publishing.

27089 ■ *"Why Noncompete Agreements Are Falling out of Favor" in Legal Zoom (February 13, 2023)*
URL(s): www.legalzoom.com/articles/why-noncompe te-agreements-are-falling-out-of-favor
Ed: Michelle Kaminsky, Esq. **Released:** February 13, 2023. **Description:** Many businesses, especially niche ones, would make employees sign noncompete agreements so they couldn't leave and take confidential information with them. Nowadays, courts have been in favor of employees and not enforcing these agreements. **Availability:** Online.

27090 ■ *"Why Top Young Managers Are In a Nonstop Job Hunt" in Harvard Business Review (Vol. 90, July-August 2012, No. 7-8, pp. 28)*
Pub: Harvard Business Review Press
Contact: Moderna V. Pfizer, Contact
Ed: Monika Hamori, Jie Cao, Burak Koyuncu. **Price:** $6. **Description:** Managers are moving from firm to firm in part because companies are not addressing formal training, coaching, and mentoring needs. While these are costly, companies might benefit from the investment, as managers may tend to stay longer in firms where they are provided. **Availability:** Online; PDF.

27091 ■ *"A Woman's Advantage" in Black Enterprise (Vol. 38, December 2007, No. 5, pp. 86)*
Pub: Earl G. Graves Ltd.
Contact: Earl Graves, Jr., President
Ed: Marcia A. Reed-Woodard. **Description:** Leadership development is essential for any small business. Simmons College's Strategic Leadership for Women educational course offers a five-day program for professional women teaching powerful strategies to perform, compete, and win in the workplace. **Availability:** Online.

27092 ■ *"Workplaces: The Human Element" in Canadian Business (Vol. 80, April 23, 2007, No. 9, pp. 78)*
Pub: National Association of EMS Educators
Contact: Bryan Ericson, President
Ed: Jeff Sanford. **Description:** The effects of human resource programs on stocks and investor relations are presented. **Availability:** Print; Online.

27093 ■ *"Your First 100 Days on Your New Job" in Women In Business (Vol. 63, Spring 2011, No. 1, pp. 28)*
Pub: American Business Women's Association
Contact: Rene Street, Executive Director
Ed: Diane Stafford. **Released:** March 22, 2011. **Description:** The first 100 days on the job are crucial if the person's permanent hiring is conditional on surviving a probationary period. The new hire must

do more than just master the job's technical details to maximize the chance of success. Details of some basic tips to fit into the corporate culture and get along with coworkers are also discussed. **Availability:** Print; Online.

STATISTICAL SOURCES

27094 ■ *Human Resources & Benefits Administration Industry in the US - Market Research Report*
URL(s): www.ibisworld.com/united-states/market-re search-reports/human-resources-benefits-adminis tration-industry/
Price: $925. **Description:** Downloadable report analyzing data about current and future trends in the human resources and benefits administration industries. **Availability:** Download.

TRADE PERIODICALS

27095 ■ *Employee Benefit Plan Review*
Released: Monthly **Price:** $495, Single issue. **Description:** Magazine serving decision-makers who administer, design, install, and service employee benefit plans. **Availability:** Print.

27096 ■ *Human Factors and Ergonomics in Manufacturing & Service Industries*
Pub: Wiley Periodicals Inc.
Contact: Brian Napack, Chief Executive Officer
URL(s): onlinelibrary.wiley.com/journal/15206564
Ed: Paul Salmon. **Released:** Bimonthly **Price:** $2,115, Institutions for online only Canada and US, India. **Description:** International journal focusing on the discovery, integration, application, and translation of scientific knowledge within the field of human factors and ergonomics (HFE). **Availability:** Print; Download; PDF; Online.

VIDEO/AUDIO MEDIA

27097 ■ *The Best Small Business Show: Business Fears - What If You Lose Your Best Employee?*
URL(s): richgee.libsyn.com/234-business-fears-wha t-if-you-lose-your-best-employee
Ed: Rich Gee. **Released:** March 14, 2021. **Description:** Podcast discusses how to navigate the upheaval if you lose your best employee.

27098 ■ *The Best Small Business Show: Mangers with Empathy Are the Best Leaders*
URL(s): richgee.libsyn.com/279-managers-with-empa thy-are-the-best-leaders
Released: January 23, 2023. **Description:** Podcast discusses the importance of empathy in personnel management.

27099 ■ *Better Hiring Strategies for Your Small Business with Dana Kaye*
URL(s): beingboss.club/podcast/better-hiring-stra tegies-for-your-small-business
Ed: Emily Thompson. **Released:** December 20, 2022. **Description:** Podcast discuses knowing when you need to hire, identifying roles to fill, and how to hire people that reflect your company values.

27100 ■ *Disruptors for Good: Innovative Approach to Upskilling Overlooked and Hidden Talent*
URL(s): share.transistor.fm/s/4d252599
Description: Podcast offers tips on upskilling overlooked talent.

27101 ■ *HBR Ideacast: The Real Reasons Employees Quit - and How to Retain Them*
URL(s): hbr.org/podcast/2024/10/the-real-reasons -employees-quit-and-how-to-retain-them
Ed: Alison Beard. **Released:** October 22, 2024. **Description:** Podcast explains what causes employees to leave and how to retain them.

27102 ■ *HBR Ideacast: You're Overlooking a Source of Diversity: Age*

URL(s): hbr.org/podcast/2022/03/youre-overlooking-a-source-of-diversity-age

Ed: Alison Beard. **Released:** March 08, 2022. **Description:** Podcast discusses how age diverse teams foster collaboration.

27103 ■ *The How of Business: Managing Hourly-Wage Employees*

URL(s): www.thehowofbusiness.com/393-managing-hourly-wage-employees

Ed: Henry Lopez. **Released:** October 11, 2021. **Description:** Podcast discusses challenges and tips for managing hourly-wage employees.

27104 ■ *The How of Business: Matt Tierney - Employee Retention*

URL(s): www.thehowofbusiness.com/449-matt-tenney-employee-retention

Ed: Henry Lopez. **Released:** January 02, 2023. **Description:** Podcast offers tips on retaining employees. Includes developing strong leaders, offering development opportunities, giving regular feedback and recognition, and synchronizing leadership and feedback. .

27105 ■ *The How of Business: Six Stages of Successful Employee On-Boarding*

URL(s): www.thehowofbusiness.com/episode-542-employee-on-boarding

Ed: Henry Lopez. **Released:** October 21, 2024. **Description:** Podcast outlines a successful onboarding process. .

27106 ■ *Kevin Herring - Redefining Roles in a Challenging Business Landscape*

URL(s): podcast.imanet.org/231

Ed: Adam Larson. **Released:** August 14, 2023. **Description:** Podcast discusses support functions in organizations in the current market with Kevin Herring, founder of Ascent Management Consulting. Highlights the roles of accountants, finance, IT, HR, engineering, and supply chain.

27107 ■ *Leveraging Fractional Talent*

URL(s): www.startuphustlepodcast.com/leveraging-fractional-talent

Ed: Matt Watson. **Released:** January 25, 2024. **Description:** Podcast discusses the pros and cons of hiring fractional talent.

27108 ■ *Nurture Small Business: Harnessing the Power of People*

URL(s): nurturesmallbusiness.buzzsprout.com/900445/episodes/15272669-harnessing-the-power-of-people

Ed: Denise Cagan. **Released:** July 01, 2024. **Description:** Podcast explains how to help businesses run more efficiently by understanding how people interact with systems and technology. .

27109 ■ *Nurture Small Business: How Organizational Psychology Transforms Leadership*

URL(s): nurturesmallbusiness.buzzsprout.com/900445/episodes/15470309-from-data-to-decisions-how-organizational-psychology-transforms-leadership

Ed: Denise Cagan. **Released:** September 17, 2024. **Description:** Podcast explains how organizations identify, develop, and place the right leaders for strategic objectives.

27110 ■ *The People Playbook: How to Build Your Dream Team*

URL(s): theceoschool.co/suneera-madhani-the-people-playbook-how-to-build-your-dream-team

Ed: Suneera Madhani. **Released:** January 23, 2023. **Description:** Podcast discusses analyzing your leadership, identifying key roles and responsibilities, creating your ideal organizational chart, sharpening your interviewing skills, and training/retaining A-players.

27111 ■ *Profit First Nation: How and Why to Let Employees Go*

URL(s): www.profitfirstnation.com/episodes/ep-134-how-and-why-to-let-employees-go

Ed: Danielle Mulvey. **Released:** August 22, 2023. **Description:** Podcast outlines four reasons to let employees go and offers tips for that conversation.

27112 ■ *Profit First Naton: Unlocking Employee Loyalty: The Five-Star Retention Strategy Revealed!*

URL(s): www.profitfirstnation.com/episodes/ep-119-unlocking-employee-loyalty-the-five-star-retention-strategy-revealed

Ed: Danielle Mulvey. **Released:** June 12, 2023. **Description:** Podcast offers a comprehensive breakdown of an employee-retention-strategy.

27113 ■ *The Small Business Show: Recruitment, Retention, and Labor Quality*

URL(s): richgee.libsyn.com/266-recruitment-retention-labor-quality

Ed: Rich Gee. **Released:** October 22, 2022. **Description:** Podcast discusses hiring and retaining employees.

27114 ■ *This Is Small Business: How to Hire Your First Employee*

URL(s): www.smallbusiness.amazon/podcast-episodes/ep-34-how-to-hire-your-first-employee

Ed: Andrea Marquez. **Released:** September 12, 2023. **Description:** Podcast offers tips on finding and retaining employees. Offered through Amazon Small Business Academy.

27115 ■ *Why You Can't Afford Not to Hire with Kira La Forgia*

URL(s): theceoschool.co/250-why-you-cant-afford-not-to-hire-with-kira-la-forgia

Ed: Suneera Madhani. **Released:** July 17, 2023. **Description:** Podcast discusses the importance of successful team building, the challenges of hiring international talent, the cost of traditional benefits, and strategies to compete with corporations and attract talent for small businesses. Features Kira La Forgia, CEO of Paradigm Consulting.

27116 ■ *Women Amplified: How to Navigate Age in a Multigenerational Workplace*

URL(s): www.conferencesforwomen.org/how-to-navigate-age-in-a-multigenerational-workplace

Ed: Celeste Headlee. **Released:** September 06, 2024. **Description:** Podcast discusses how to harness an age-diverse workforce in a multigenerational environment.

TRADE SHOWS AND CONVENTIONS

27117 ■ California HR Conference
Professionals in Human Resources Association (PIHRA)
18080 Crenshaw Blvd. No. 7909
Torrance, CA 90504-9998
Ph: (424)329-0200
Fax: (310)416-9055
Co. E-mail: info@pihra.org
URL: http://www.pihra.org
Contact: Tara Fournier, President
E-mail: president@pihra.org
URL(s): www.mypihra.org/events/EventDetails.aspx?id=1866593&group=
X (Twitter): twitter.com/cahrconference

Frequency: Annual. **Description:** Offer exemplary teaching and training programs. **Audience:** Human resources professionals. **Principal Exhibits:** Offer exemplary teaching and training programs. **Telecommunication Services:** programs@pihra.org.

27118 ■ Human Resource Executive Health & Benefits Leadership Conference
URL(s): www.benefitsconf.com

Frequency: Annual. **Description:** Promotes key topics sessions on best practices for Human Resource executives. Also hosts a Health and Benefits Expo.

Principal Exhibits: Promotes key topics sessions on best practices for Human Resource executives. Also hosts a Health and Benefits Expo.

27119 ■ LeadingAge Minnesota
URL(s): www.leadingagemn.org/education-events/annual-meeting-and-leadership-forum

Frequency: Annual. **Description:** Conference and expo for human resources professionals. Provides educational opportunities and networking. **Principal Exhibits:** Conference and expo for human resources professionals. Provides educational opportunities and networking.

27120 ■ SHRM Talent Management Conference and Exposition
URL(s): conferences.shrm.org/talent-conference?_ga=1.9915253.1508110229.1484164102

Frequency: Annual. **Description:** Provides key topic sessions on hiring and recruitment. **Principal Exhibits:** Provides key topic sessions on hiring and recruitment.

CONSULTANTS

27121 ■ A.E. Schwartz and Associates
Boston, MA
Ph: (781)436-3763
Co. E-mail: info@aeschwartz.com
URL: http://www.aeschwartz.com
Contact: Andrew E. Schwartz, Chief Executive Officer

Description: Firm provides management training services. **Scope:** Firm provides management training services. **Founded:** 1982. **Publications:** "Assertiveness: Responsible Communication," 2003; "Change, Challenge and Innovation," 2003; "Coaching Towards Excellence," 2003; "Delegating for Results," 2003; "Goal Setting for Results"; "Coaching Towards Excellence". **Training:** Assertiveness; Becoming a Successful Consultant; Communication Skills, Conflict Resolution; Delegation; Interns/Volunteers; Leadership; Long Range Planning; Making Effective Presentations; Motivating Staff; Office Management Effectiveness; Organizational Development; Performance Appraisals; Problem Solving/Decision Making; Stress Management; Supervising and Leading. **Special Services:** The Training Consortium™.

27122 ■ Benefit Partners Inc.
People Corporation Inc.
1-2140 Regent St.
Sudbury, ON, Canada P3E 5S8
Ph: (204)940-3900
Free: 866-940-3950
Co. E-mail: info@peoplecorporation.com
URL: http://www.peoplecorporation.com

Description: Firm provides employee benefits, pension and human resources management consulting services. **Scope:** Firm provides employee benefits, pension and human resources management consulting services.

27123 ■ Bijan International Inc.
15008 Natural Springs
Austin, TX 78728
Contact: Bijan Afkhami, President

Description: Outsourced consulting and training firm offers leadership and corporate training, executive coaching workshops, seminars and programs for individuals, teams, and organizations. **Publications:** "Coaching firm Rallies Businesses," Jan, 2003; "A Journey of 1000 Miles". **Training:** Emotional Intelligence; Discovering Diversity; Empowered Women; High-Velocity Change; The Positive Power of Feedback; Team work; Customer Service; Sexual Harassment; Leaders In Sales; Body Therapy; Personal Effectiveness; Teamwork Skills; Leadership Abilities.

27124 ■ Blankinship & Associates Inc.
1615 5th St., Ste. A
Davis, CA 95616
Ph: (530)757-0941
URL: http://www.h2osci.com
Contact: Michael Blankinship, President

Description: Provider of consulting services to support water resources, agriculture and risk evaluation and communication, water resources management and regulatory. **Scope:** Provider of consulting services to support water resources, agriculture and risk evaluation and communication, water resources management and regulatory. **Founded:** 2000. **Publications:** "Air Blast Sprayer Calibration and Chlorpyrifos Irrigation Study," Oct, 2007; "How Green is your golf course," Prosper Magazine, 2007. **Training:** CDFG Wildlands IPM Seminar, Oct, 2009.

27125 ■ The Business Center (TBC)
120 Westview Ln.
 Oak Ridge, TN 37830
Ph: (865)483-5850
Co. E-mail: tbc@bizcenter.com
URL: http://www.bizcenter.com
Contact: Don Barkman, President

Description: Provider of practical consulting assistance dealing with organizational change and creation of high-performance work systems. **Scope:** Provider of practical consulting assistance dealing with organizational change and creation of high-performance work systems. **Founded:** 1988. **Publications:** "Skill-Based Pay: Design and Implementation," 2002; "Open Book Management, Your EZ Intro to OBM," 1997; "BIZ WIZ® Universal"; "Business Basics"; "START-UP!, A Guide to Getting Off On the Right Foot"; "Money: Make Manage, & Multiply It!". **Training:** DiSC Management Strategies; Adventures in Attitudes; BIZ WIZ - Basic Business Education; Journey to Excellence; Building Better Meetings; Training Others; Team Leadership; Effective Teams, Skill-Based Pay Design; New Plant Start-Ups; Disc Sales Strategies; Professional Service Works.

27126 ■ The Business Research Lab
397 River St.
 Chester, VT 05143
Ph: (802)875-1788
Free: 844-288-2349
Co. E-mail: info@employeesurveys.com
URL: http://www.employeesurveys.com
Contact: Gregg Campa, Director
Facebook: www.facebook.com/EmployeeEngagementSurveys

Description: Firm provides a range of employee survey analysis and consulting services. **Scope:** Firm provides a range of employee survey analysis and consulting services. **Founded:** 1995. **Publications:** "Bloomberg Online"; "Kiplinger Magazine".

27127 ■ Business Resource Consulting L.L.C. (BRC)
9742 Pleasant Gate Ln.
 Potomac, MD 20854

Description: The firm develops innovative human resource solutions. Assists small and large organizations in compensation design, employee relations, training and communication design, technical and non-technical recruiting. **Scope:** The firm develops innovative human resource solutions. Assists small and large organizations in compensation design, employee relations, training and communication design, technical and non-technical recruiting. **Training:** Supervisory and Management Skills; Performance Management; Team Building; Recruitment and Interviewing Skills; Human Resource Basics; Introduction to Policy Statements; Performance Management Training.

27128 ■ Business Staffing Inc.
27350 Blueberry Hill Dr., Ste. 11
 Conroe, TX 77385-8965
Contact: Harry E. Sewill, President

Description: Human resource firm offers staffing, management consulting, and financial management expertise.

27129 ■ The Center for Organizational Excellence, Inc. (COE)
15204 Omega Dr., Ste. 300
 Rockville, MD 20850
Contact: Stephen P. Goodrich, Contact
E-mail: sgoodrich@center4oe.com

Description: Firm provides consulting services such as designing and delivering consulting solutions in the areas of organizational effectiveness, human capital, information technology, and data management. **Scope:** Firm provides consulting services such as designing and delivering consulting solutions in the areas of organizational effectiveness, human capital, information technology, and data management. **Founded:** 1984.

27130 ■ CFI Group USA L.L.C.
3916 Ranchero Dr.
 Ann Arbor, MI 48108
Ph: (734)930-9090
Fax: (734)930-0911
Co. E-mail: info@cfigroup.se
URL: http://cfigroup.com
Contact: Sheri Petras, Chief Executive Officer
Facebook: www.facebook.com/CFIGroup
Linkedin: www.linkedin.com/company/cfi-group
X (Twitter): x.com/cfigroup

Description: Management consulting firm helps its clients worldwide to maximize shareholder value by optimizing customer and employee satisfaction, their clients span from a variety of industries including manufacturing, telecommunication, retail and government. **Scope:** Management consulting firm helps its clients worldwide to maximize shareholder value by optimizing customer and employee satisfaction, their clients span from a variety of industries including manufacturing, telecommunication, retail and government. **Founded:** 1988. **Publications:** "Customer Satisfaction and Stock Prices: High Returns, Low Risk," American Marketing Association, Jan, 2006; "Customer Satisfaction Index Climbs," The Wall Street Journal, Feb, 2004; "What's Next? Customer Service is Key to Post-Boom Success," The Bottom Line, Mar, 2003; "Boost Stock Performance, Nation's Economy," Quality Progress, Feb, 2003.

27131 ■ Choice Coaching and Consulting
9 Pk., Place Cir. W
 Hartford, CT 06110
Ph: (860)461-0105
URL: http://www.choicecoaching.net
Contact: Jackie Johnson, Contact

Description: Certified professional coach specializes in organizational coaching and personal coaching, the firm works with business leaders, groups, and teams to improve organizational effectiveness, with individuals to make positive, lasting lifestyle change. **Scope:** Certified professional coach specializes in organizational coaching and personal coaching, the firm works with business leaders, groups, and teams to improve organizational effectiveness, with individuals to make positive, lasting lifestyle change. **Founded:** 2003.

27132 ■ Cole Financial Service Inc.
1321 Joliet Pl.
 Detroit, MI 48207

Description: Services: Office management and computer consultant. **Scope:** A full service human capital development firm providing services in recruiting, coaching, retaining, developing and retiring. Works with front line staff, managers and executive level decision makers that set strategy. Industries served: Engineering, construction, government and other business entities. **Founded:** 1983. **Training:** How to Run Your Own Business; 25Ways to stay in Business 25Years; How to Tap Your Potential and Discover Your GENIUS; The Job Ladder Steps to SUCCESS; Making and Keeping a Budget; Records Retention and Disposal; Take Control of Your Life; Time and Priority Management; TQM - Total Quality Management; Leadership 101; Leadership 201; Diversity Agent or Opponent A Personal Development Workshop; Coaching in a Diverse Workplace.

27133 ■ Consulting & Conciliation Service (CCS)
Sacramento, CA
Ph: (916)396-0480
URL: http://conciliation.org
Contact: Jane McCluskey, Contact
E-mail: jane@conciliation.org

Description: Firm offers consulting and conciliation services, they provide pre-mediation counseling, training and research on preparing for a peaceful society, mediation and facilitation, preparation for shifts in structure, policy, and personnel, it offers sliding scale business rates and free individual consultation. **Scope:** Firm offers consulting and conciliation services, they provide pre-mediation counseling, training and research on preparing for a peaceful society, mediation and facilitation, preparation for shifts in structure, policy, and personnel, it offers sliding scale business rates and free individual consultation. **Publications:** "Native America and Tracking Shifts in US Policy"; "Biogenesis: A Discussion of Basic Social Needs and the Significance of Hope". **Training:** Positive Approaches to Violence Prevention: Peace building in Schools and Communities.

27134 ■ CoStaff Services L.L.C.
26555 Evergreen Rd., Ste. 1070
 Southfield, MI 48076
Ph: (248)671-1400
Free: 866-426-7823
Fax: (248)692-0816
URL: http://www.costaffservices.com
Contact: Michael Bulgarelli, Contact
E-mail: michael@costaffservices.com
Facebook: www.facebook.com/CoStaff-Services
-114953525265441

Description: Provider of human resource outsourcing services. **Scope:** Provider of human resource outsourcing services. **Founded:** 2000.

27135 ■ DJT Consulting Group L.L.C.
3154 Granada Dr.
 Cameron Park, CA 95682
Ph: (530)387-7089
Co. E-mail: sherry@djtconsulting.com
URL: http://www.djtconsulting.com
Contact: Dan Armenta, Principal
E-mail: dan@djtconsulting.com

Description: Provider of consulting services such as grant writing and fund development, grant monitoring and reporting, project management, program development, implementation, evaluation, and much more. **Founded:** 2000. **Training:** Finding and Winning Government Grants.

27136 ■ Eastern Point Consulting Group Inc.
75 Oak St.
 Newton, MA 02465
Ph: (617)965-4141
URL: http://www.eastpt.com
Contact: Katherine Herzog, President

Description: Firm specializes in bringing practical solutions to complex challenges and provides consulting and training in managing diversity, comprehensive sexual-harassment policies and programs, organizational development, benchmarks 360-degree skills assessment, executive coaching, strategic human resource planning, team building, leadership development for women, mentoring programs, and gender issues in the workplace. **Scope:** Firm specializes in bringing practical solutions to complex challenges and provides consulting and training in managing diversity, comprehensive sexual-harassment policies and programs, organizational development, benchmarks 360-degree skills assessment, executive coaching, strategic human resource planning, team building, leadership development for women, mentoring programs, and gender issues in the workplace. **Training:** Leadership Development for Women.

27137 ■ Effective Compensation Inc. (ECI)
5856 S Lowell Blvd., Ste. 32 No 322
 Littleton, CO 80123
Ph: (303)854-1000
Co. E-mail: eci@effectivecompensation.com
URL: http://www.effectivecompensation.com
Contact: Terry Isselhardt, President

Description: Independent compensation consulting firm specializing in working with clients on a collaborative basis to improve their organization's efficiency through competitive, focused total compensation processes. Helps organizations determine how to competitively pay their employees. Provides quality, culture sensitive, compensation consulting assistance to all types of employers. **Scope:** Independent compensation consulting firm specializing in working with clients on a collaborative basis to improve their organization's efficiency through competitive, focused total compensation processes. Helps organizations determine how to competitively pay their employees. Provides quality, culture sensitive, compensation consulting assistance to all types of employers. **Founded:** 1991. **Publications:** "Alternative Job Evaluation Approaches"; "Broad Banding: A Management Overview"; "Job Evaluation: Understanding the Issues"; "Industry Compensation Surveys"; "Skill Based Pay"; "Four Levels of Team Membership"; "Factors in Designing an Incentive Plan"; "Key Stock Allocation Issues"; "Stock Plans Primer". **Training:** Alternative Job Evaluation Approaches; Broad Banding: A Management Overview; Skill Based Pay; Job Evaluation: Understanding the Issues; Designing Compensation Programs that Motivate Employees; Master the Compensation Maze; Base Salary Administration Manual.

27138 ■ The Executive Group

1645 Parkhill Dr., Ste. 4
Billings, MT 59102
Free: 800-755-5161
URL: http://www.executivegroup.biz
Contact: Chris Adam, Contact
Facebook: www.facebook.com/The-Executive-Group
-1390936761161135
Linkedin: www.linkedin.com/company/the-executive
-group

Description: Firm provides recruitment and executive placement services for banking and financial, oil and gas, civil engineering, construction, and various other sectors. **Scope:** Firm provides recruitment and executive placement services for banking and financial, oil and gas, civil engineering, construction, and various other sectors. **Founded:** 1985.

27139 ■ Goren & Associates Inc.

32000 NW Hwy., Ste. 128
Farmington Hills, MI 48334
Ph: (248)851-0824
Co. E-mail: info@gorentrain.com
URL: http://www.gorentrain.com
Contact: Dr. Keith Levick, Chief Executive Officer
Linkedin: www.linkedin.com/company/gorentrain

Description: Firm provides organizational and workforce education and training related services such as simple, flexible and durable solutions, and much more. **Scope:** Firm provides organizational and workforce education and training related services such as simple, flexible and durable solutions, and much more. **Founded:** 1981. **Publications:** "The healthy child cookbook: 146 healthy snacks, meals, and desserts," The wellness institute; "Why is my child so overweight". **Training:** Instituting Change; Adjusting to Stress and Change; Initiating and Managing Change For Leaders; Deterring Sexual Harassment; Deterring Workplace Violence; Diversity in the Workplace; Collaborative Negotiation; Customizing our Service, Servicing our Customers; Dealing with Difficult Customers; Stress Management; Conducting Successful Meetings; How to Deliver a Dynamic Presentation; Creating a Motivating Team; Coaching Skills for Leaders.

27140 ■ Harvey A. Meier Co. (HAM)

410 W Nevada St.
Ashland, OR 97520-1043
Ph: (509)458-3210
Fax: (541)488-7905
Co. E-mail: harvey@harveymeier.com
URL: http://www.harveymeier.com
Contact: Dr. Harvey A. Meier, President
E-mail: harvey@harveymeier.com

Description: Services: Management consulting. **Scope:** Services: Management consulting. **Publications:** "The D'Artagnan Way".

27141 ■ HR Advice.com

PO Box 313
Mountain Lakes, NJ 07046
URL: http://hradvice.com

Description: Firm provides human resources solutions and specializing in employee relations, business planning and strategy, recruiting, human resources policy, compensation and benefits, training, development and performance systems.

27142 ■ HR Answers Inc. (HRA)

7650 SW Beveland St., Ste. 130
Tigard, OR 97223
Ph: (503)885-9815
Co. E-mail: info@hranswers.com
URL: http://hranswers.com
Contact: Laurie Grenya, President
E-mail: lgrenya@hranswers.com
Facebook: www.facebook.com/HRAnswersPortland
Linkedin: www.linkedin.com/company/hranswersinc
YouTube: www.youtube.com/channel/UC08puI0e
tWsbQKDrU2BkfIA

Description: Provider of human resource management consulting services. Offers expertise in: compensation program design and support, benefit plan assessment, policy and procedure development, AAP and EEO/OFCCP compliance, human resource function audits, supervisory, managerial and employee training, employee relation issues, employment law compliance, employee handbooks, risk management, performance management design, and information and organizational development and transition strategies. **Founded:** 1985. **Training:** Creating Your Safety Committee, Oct, 2006; Top Ten Best Practicesforl-9's, Oct, 2006; Sailing the Rough C's - Communication, Counseling & Conflict Resolution; Breaking the Secret Codes of Communication; Can We Talk; Coach or Discipline - What Action is Appropriate; Catch Your Employees Doing Something Right; The Future of Human Resources.

27143 ■ HR Business Solutions

7107 Riverside Dr.
Richmond, VA 23225
Ph: (804)740-7952
Fax: (866)889-7954
Co. E-mail: info@hrbsolutions.com
URL: http://hrbsolutions.com
Contact: Colleen Baybutt, President
E-mail: colleen@hrbsolutions.com

Description: Provider of management consulting services. **Scope:** Provider of management consulting services. **Founded:** 1999. **Training:** ServSafe Serving Safe Food Manager; Gualala, May, 2004. **Special Services:** ServeSafe®.

27144 ■ The HR Dept.

22 W Pennsylvania Ave.
Bel Air, MD 21014
Ph: (410)893-0901
Fax: (410)893-0901
Co. E-mail: info@hrdept.com
URL: http://www.hrdept.com

Description: Provider of human resources management support to small business employers on a part-time basis. Standard support services include the review of the human resources functions, compliance issues, performance appraisal programs, handbooks and policy manuals, annual human resources calendar, quarterly human resources reports, formal compensation structure, benefit plans analysis and more. **Scope:** Provider of human resources management support to small business employers on a part-time basis. Standard support services include the review of the human resources functions, compliance issues, performance appraisal programs, handbooks and policy manuals, annual human resources calendar, quarterly human resources reports, formal compensation structure, benefit plans analysis and more. **Founded:** 1998.

27145 ■ Human Resource Specialties, Inc. (HRS)

DCI Consulting Group Inc.
PO Box 1995
Missoula, MT 59806
Ph: (202)828-6900
URL: http://www.dciconsult.com
Contact: Sandy L. Henderson, President

Description: Provider of human resources assistance to organizations. Offers preparation of affirmative action plans, support documents, and adverse impact studies of personnel activities. Also offers customized consultations in small business services, diversity and discrimination, and investigations, complaints and grievances. Provides investigations, including allegations of unfair treatment, equal employment opportunity (EEO) and racial or sexual harassment. Offers customized web-based training (webinars) on a variety of HR, EEO and AAP-related topics. **Scope:** Provider of human resources assistance to organizations. Offers preparation of affirmative action plans, support documents, and adverse impact studies of personnel activities. Also offers customized consultations in small business services, diversity and discrimination, and investigations, complaints and grievances. Provides investigations, including allegations of unfair treatment, equal employment opportunity (EEO) and racial or sexual harassment. Offers customized web-based training (webinars) on a variety of HR, EEO and AAP-related topics. **Founded:** 1984.

27146 ■ In Plain English

14501 Antigone Dr.
Gaithersburg, MD 20878-2484
Ph: (301)340-2821
Free: 800-274-9645
Fax: (301)279-0115
URL: http://www.inplainenglish.com

Description: Management consultants helping government and businesses research, design, write and produce user oriented management information for human resources, employee benefits, business process, corporate and marketing needs. Services include: GSA mob is schedule for consulting to the government; employee benefit communications, plain English business writing workshops for print and electronic media; communicating strategy and tactics; marketing research, business planning and communications; readability testing; usability testing and monitoring strategy. **Scope:** Management consultants helping government and businesses research, design, write and produce user oriented management information for human resources, employee benefits, business process, corporate and marketing needs. Services include: GSA mob is schedule for consulting to the government; employee benefit communications, plain English business writing workshops for print and electronic media; communicating strategy and tactics; marketing research, business planning and communications; readability testing; usability testing and monitoring strategy. **Founded:** 1977. **Publications:** "The Benefits Communication"; "The Employee Benefits Communication ToolKit," Commerce Clearinghouse; "Benefits Communication," Business and Legal Reports. **Training:** Plain English Writing Training; Summary Plan Description Compliance workshops; Re-Humanizing the Corporation, Human Resources and Employee Benefits Communication Workshop; 21 Writing Tips for the 21st Century; Make the Write Impression; Writing to Inform and Instruct; The Dreaded Nuts and Bolts; Writing to Persuade; Writing Policy and Procedure Manuals In Plain English; Writing for Accountants and Auditors In Plain English. **Special Services:** In Plain English®.

27147 ■ Incentive Solutions Inc. (ISI)

2299 Perimeter Pk. Dr., Ste. 150
Atlanta, GA 30341
Ph: (678)514-0200
Free: 866-567-7432
URL: http://www.incentivesolutions.com
Contact: Mark Herbert, President
Facebook: www.facebook.com/IncentiveSolutionsInc
Linkedin: www.linkedin.com/company/incentive-solu
tions
X (Twitter): x.com/Incentive_Sols
Instagram: www.instagram.com/incentive_sols
YouTube: www.youtube.com/user/IncentiveSolu
tionsIn

Description: Firm provides corporate incentive and motivation programs from group travel to incentive debit cards and merchandise gift certificates and specializing in business meeting and planning, audio and visual services, and internet development to support business communications. **Scope:** Firm provides corporate incentive and motivation programs from group travel to incentive debit cards and merchandise gift certificates and specializing in business meeting and planning, audio and visual services, and internet development to support business communications. **Founded:** 1994. **Special Services:** RewardTrax®.

27148 ■ KEYGroup
1121 Boyce Rd., Ste. 1800
    Pittsburgh, PA 15241
Ph: (724)942-7900
Co. E-mail: info@keygroupconsulting.com
URL: http://www.keygroupconsulting.com
Contact: Dr. Jan Ferri-Reed, President
Description: Firm provides consulting and training services. **Scope:** Firm provides consulting and training services. **Founded:** 1980. **Publications:** "Keeping the Millennials"; "Leading a Multi-Generational Workforce"; "Keys That Open Doors to Success - Key Words for Leaders"; "The Power of Partnering"; "The Keys to Conquering Change: 100 Tales of Success"; "The Keys to Putting Change in Your Pocket"; "The Keys to Mastering Leadership"; "Training Games for Managing Change"; "Private Sector: We Get You! Make Work Cultures Fit the Needs and Aspirations of Young Adults, and They Will Stay Here," Sep, 2005. **Training:** Performance Management, Enhancing Creativity Leading Others; Coaching for Improved Performance; Team-Building; Supervisory Development; Train-the-Trainer; Stress Management; Presentation Skills; Think-on-Your-Feet; Communicating Your BEST; leadership training team building. **Special Services:** KEYGroup®.

27149 ■ LRP Media Group - Library
360 Hiatt Dr.
    Palm Beach Gardens, FL 33418
Ph: (561)622-6520
Free: 800-341-7874
Fax: (561)622-2423
Co. E-mail: custserve@lrp.com
URL: http://www.lrp.com
Contact: Julie J. Kline, Director, Editorial
Facebook: www.facebook.com/LRPMediaGroup1
Linkedin: www.linkedin.com/company/lrp-publications
Instagram: www.instagram.com/lrpmediagroup
Description: Publishes legal loose-leaf and information in the areas of workers 'compensation, federal government employee relations, labor arbitration, bankruptcy and education law and state and local employment law. Offers online employment litigation tracking service and arbitration searches. Accepts unsolicited manuscripts. Reaches market through direct mail and telephone sales. **Scope:** Publisher of books, pamphlets, videos, newsletter and online content for businesses and educational institutions. **Founded:** 1977. **Holdings:** Figures not available. **Publications:** *Workers' Compensation Monitor*; *California Special Education Alert*; *Risk & Insurance Magazine*; *The AIDS Directory*; *Hospitality Law*; *Missouri Workers' Compensation Law Reporter* (Monthly); *Current Award Trends in Personal Injury* (Annual); *Early Childhood Law and Policy Reporter (ECLPR)* (Monthly); *Today's School Psychologist* (11/year); *Risk & Insurance*; *Federal Human Resources Week: News, Strategies and Best Practices for the HR Professional*; *AIDS Policy and Law: The Biweekly Newsletter on Legislation, Regulation, and Litigation Concerning AIDS* (11/year); *Special Education Law on CD-ROM*; *cyberFEDS® eLearning*; *Arbsearch.com*; *Human Resource Executive's Market Resource* (Annual); *Instant Computer Arbitration Search*; *Human Resource Executive* (6/year; Monthly); *EducationDaily.com®*; *Special Ed Connection®*; *CTD News* (Monthly); *Counterpoint* (Quarterly); *Disability Law on CD-ROM*.

27150 ■ Michigan CFO Associates Inc.
43230 Garfield Rd., Ste. 130
    Clinton Township, MI 48038
Ph: (586)580-3285
Free: 844-739-0116
Co. E-mail: info@michigancfo.com
URL: http://www.michigancfo.com
Contact: Todd Rammler, President

E-mail: trammler@michigancfo.com
Facebook: www.facebook.com/MichiganCFO
X (Twitter): x.com/michigancfo

Description: Firm offers CFO services, accounting and financial management advising for small businesses. **Founded:** 2006. **Publications:** "Is the Flight Attendant Flying the Plane? Mismatching Skills Causes Many Businesses to Crash"; "Are You Worth $15/per hour? Getting Maximum Value Out of YOUR Time"; "CFO Insider Tools: Flexible Budgets". **Training:** 10 Keys to a Healthy Business.

27151 ■ Nightingale Associates
7445 Setting Sun Way
    Columbia, MD 21046
Ph: (410)381-4280
URL: http://www.nightingaleassociates.net
Contact: Frederick C. Nightingale, Managing Director
E-mail: fredericknightingale@nightingaleassociates
    .net
X (Twitter): x.com/FCNightingale

Description: Management training and consulting firm offering the following skills productivity and accomplishment, leadership skills for the experienced manager, management skills for the new manager, leadership and teambuilding, supervisory development, creative problem solving, real strategic planning. **Scope:** Management training and consulting firm offering the following skills productivity and accomplishment, leadership skills for the experienced manager, management skills for the new manager, leadership and teambuilding, supervisory development, creative problem solving, real strategic planning. **Founded:** 1984. **Training:** Productivity and Accomplishment Management Skills for the New Manager; Leadership and Team building; Advanced Management; Business Process Re engineering; Strategic Thinking; Creative Problem Solving; Customer Service; International Purchasing and Materials Management; Fundamentals of Purchasing; Negotiation Skills Development; Providing superior customer service; Leadership skills for the experienced manager.

27152 ■ Norman Peterson and Associates (NPA)
526 Washington St., Ste. 1
    Ashland, OR 97520
Free: 800-497-1368
Fax: (541)488-5408
Co. E-mail: info@returntowork.com
URL: http://www.returntowork.com
Contact: Erik Peterson, President
E-mail: epeterson@returntowork.com
Facebook: www.facebook.com/return
    toworkspecialists
Linkedin: www.linkedin.com/company/norman-pe
    terson-and-associates

Description: Firm provides return to work service for employers and employees. **Scope:** Firm provides return to work service for employers and employees. **Founded:** 1985. **Publications:** "Planning Pays Off in Back to Work Programs," Ohio Association of School Business Officials Chronicle; "Diving into a pool Return-to-Work program," Public Risk Magazine. **Special Services:** OUR®; BridgIt.

27153 ■ Pamela K. Henry & Associates
13329 Kingman Dr., Ste. B
    Austin, TX 78729
Ph: (512)335-1237
Co. E-mail: info@pamelakhenry.com
URL: http://www.pamelakhenry.com
Contact: Pamela K. Henry, Contact

Description: Provider of career management, marketing strategies, life cycle employment strategies, coaching and human resource consulting services. **Publications:** "Diversity and the Bottom Line: Prospering in the Global Economy". **Training:** Competency-based Interviewing; Executive Interviewing; Selection Best Practices; Career Transitioning; Effectively Recruiting a Diverse Workforce; Creating Cultural Competence & Inclusion on Teams; Preventing Sexual Harassment.

27154 ■ Pitts - Aldrich Associates (PAA)
1501 Oxford Rd.
    Grosse Pointe Woods, MI 48236
Ph: (313)881-3433
URL: http://www.pittsaldrichassociates.com
Contact: Christina Pitts, President
E-mail: christina@pittsaldrichassociates.com
Description: Provides coaching, consulting, and facilitation services through publications and specifically tailored workshops for individuals, private industry, and not-for-profit organizations across market sectors. **Founded:** 1990. **Publications:** "At the Podium/In the Press: Optimize 5"; "Leadership Basics"; "Managing Change"; "A Gift of the Four-Legs: Presence, Trust, Vulnerability and..."; "Leadership Has Gone to the Horses'; "Brown Paper Bag"; "The Phoenix Challenge: Rising to Fulfillment"; "Navigating the Badlands- Leadership in the New Century," 2009; "Color Me Purple- Embracing Differences to Optimize Performance"; "The End of Work & Rise of the Nonprofit Sector"; "Building Mentoring Inside Your Organization". **Training:** Journey to Authencity; Optimize5-From the World of Horses- Practical Wisdom for Success; The Phoenix Challenge: Rising to Fulfillment; Optimizing Relationship, Partnership & Teamwork; Change: Your Ally For Success.

27155 ■ The Plotkin Group
5650 El Camino Real, Ste. 223
    Carlsbad, CA 92008
Ph: (760)603-8791
Free: 800-877-5685
URL: http://www.plotkingroup.com
Contact: Hank Plotkin, Founder

Description: Provider of employee assessment solutions and services. **Scope:** Provider of employee assessment solutions and services. **Founded:** 1968. **Publications:** "Building a Winning Team"; "Achieving Above and Beyond Service"; "American Businesses Face Mountain of Problomo". **Training:** Building a Winning Team; Above and Beyond Customer Service Training; Taking the Guess Work Out of Hiring and Promoting.

27156 ■ PSP Metrics - Library
The Frick Bldg., 437 Grant St., Ste. 1333
    Pittsburgh, PA 15219
Ph: (412)261-1333
Fax: (412)261-5014
Co. E-mail: info@pspmetrics.com
URL: http://www.pspmetrics.com
Instagram: www.instagram.com/pspmetrics

Description: Human resource consulting firm providing organizational consulting services in new plant start-up, employee selection, management development and succession planning, employee opinion surveys, outplacement and organizational change. **Scope:** Human resource consulting firm providing organizational consulting services in new plant start-up, employee selection, management development and succession planning, employee opinion surveys, outplacement and organizational change. **Founded:** 1946. **Holdings:** Figures not available. **Publications:** "Hiring Star Performers in Sales"; "Selecting Supervisors and Managers"; "Improving Selection Decisions Around the World"; "Management Competencies for the Global Marketplace"; "Leadership Development is Key for Middle Managers"; "Executive Development - Why Successful Executives Continue to Change"; "Gain Competitive Advantage Through Employment Testing," American Management Association, 1993. **Training:** Effectively Managing Organizational Change; The Use of Employee Section Systems; Corporate Succession Planning; How to Use Employee Surveys for Organizational Development; Handling Confrontation and Conflict; Executive Development: Why Successful Executives Continue to Change; Hire Right-The First Time; Strategic Innovation for Breakthrough Performance. **Special Services:** Quick Response Testing System (QRTS).

27157 ■ Shannon Staffing Inc.
1590-B Coshocton Ave.
    Mount Vernon, OH 43050
Ph: (740)397-2040

Co. E-mail: mountvernon@shannonstaffing.com
URL: http://www.shannonstaffing.com
Facebook: www.facebook.com/shannonstaffing
Linkedin: www.linkedin.com/company/shannon-s
taffing-inc.
X (Twitter): x.com/shannonstaffing

Description: Provides human resources recruiting and outplacement counseling services to industries and public sector organizations. **Founded:** 1985. **Publications:** "Powells Rules for Picking People". **Training:** Time Management workshop.

27158 ■ Siebrand-Wilton Associates Inc. (S-WA)

PO Box 193
Rocky Hill, NJ 08553-0193
URL: http://www.s-wa.com
Contact: John S. Sturges, Principal

Description: Firm provides nationwide human resources consulting support and also offers executive coaching and counseling, benefit plan design, and other related services. **Founded:** 1986. **Publications:** "Should Government or Business Try to Save Medicare," HR News; "Executive Temping," HR Horizons; "When is an Employee Truly an Employee," HR Magazine; "Examining Your Insurance Carrier," HR Magazine.

27159 ■ Speech Coach for Executives

Burlington, ON, Canada
Ph: (905)335-1997
Co. E-mail: coach@torok.com
URL: http://www.speechcoachforexecutives.com
Contact: George Torok, Contact

Description: Firm provides speaking and presentation skills training for executives, professional speakers and sales teams. **Scope:** Firm provides speaking and presentation skills training for executives, professional speakers and sales teams. **Publications:** "Too much information: not enough time"; "Establish Your Believability"; "Smile: say cheese"; "Master the pause: it will make you a master"; "Presentation Power does not come from PowerPoint"; "Boardroom Presentations: Sweat Like a Horse"; "Presentation Skills Success"; "How to write your speech in five minutes"; "10 Power Tips for Presentations with Computer Projection". **Training:** Superior presentations, strengthened my ability to speak and many more. **Special Services:** Power Presentations™.

27160 ■ Verbit & Co.

152 Union Ave.
Bala Cynwyd, PA 19004
Contact: Alan C. Verbit, Owner

Description: Management consulting firm to assist executives and managers fulfill their mission and to assure that adequate planning of day-to-day operations occurs, that controls sufficient to safeguard valuable resources and that results of decisions reviewed in sufficient time to effect continuing action. **Scope:** Management consulting firm to assist executives and managers fulfill their mission and to assure that adequate planning of day-to-day operations occurs, that controls sufficient to safeguard valuable resources and that results of decisions reviewed in sufficient time to effect continuing action. **Training:** Integrating Manufacturing Management Systems with Business Systems; Negotiating Information Systems Agreements with Suppliers.

27161 ■ Vital Business Solutions (VBS)

1325 G St. NW, Ste. 500
Washington, DC 20005
Ph: (202)832-1388
Co. E-mail: info@vbs-hr.com
URL: http://www.vbs-hr.com
Contact: Hennrietta Smith, Owner
Facebook: www.facebook.com/VBShr
Linkedin: www.linkedin.com/company/vi
talbusinesssolutionshr
X (Twitter): x.com/HrVBS

Description: Firm provides human resource management services to non-profit organizations, they offer employee training, personnel policies and procedures manuals, employment advice, employee manuals, needs assessments, program specific measurement systems, human resource audits, employee and compensation surveys, career pathing, benefits assessments, job descriptions and other human resource services as needed. **Scope:** Firm provides human resource management services to non-profit organizations, they offer employee training, personnel policies and procedures manuals, employment advice, employee manuals, needs assessments, program specific measurement systems, human resource audits, employee and compensation surveys, career pathing, benefits assessments, job descriptions and other human resource services as needed. **Publications:** "No Better Time Than the Present". **Training:** Basics of Human Resource Management; Management Development; Custom Client Specific Sessions.

27162 ■ Wheeler & Associates Inc.

6935 Barney Rd., Ste. 110
Houston, TX 77092
Ph: (713)462-8906
Fax: (713)690-7203
Co. E-mail: contact.us@wheelerassoc.com
URL: http://www.wheelerassoc.com
Contact: Catherine Wheeler, Chief Executive Officer

Description: Provider of services in career and vocational counseling, human resources development and training, managerial development assistance for all levels of management and offers organizational effectiveness studies and organizational design assistance for private and public enterprises and serves educational institutions, training schools, small businesses, and engineering companies. **Scope:** Provider of services in career and vocational counseling, human resources development and training, managerial development assistance for all levels of management and offers organizational effectiveness studies and organizational design assistance for private and public enterprises and serves educational institutions, training schools, small businesses, and engineering companies.

27163 ■ Workplace Dimensions Inc.

7004 Lakewood Dr.
Richmond, VA 23229
Contact: Carol R. Losee, President

Description: Offers human resources services including designing salary programs and performance management systems, customizing employee handbooks and personnel policy manuals, conducting employee and management training on harassment prevention and other relevant topics and reviewing business practices for compliance. **Scope:** Offers

human resources services including designing salary programs and performance management systems, customizing employee handbooks and personnel policy manuals, conducting employee and management training on harassment prevention and other relevant topics and reviewing business practices for compliance. **Founded:** 1995. **Special Services:** Interviewer's Toolkit; Employer's Toolkit.

LIBRARIES

27164 ■ Association for Talent Development (ATD) - Library

1640 King St.
Alexandria, VA 22313-1443
Ph: (703)683-8100
Free: 800-628-2783
Fax: (703)683-1523
Co. E-mail: customercare@td.org
URL: http://www.td.org
Contact: Tony Bingham, President
Facebook: www.facebook.com/ATD
Linkedin: www.linkedin.com/company/15989
X (Twitter): x.com/ATD
Instagram: www.instagram.com/atdnational
Pinterest: www.pinterest.com/ATDofficial

Description: Supports the talent development profession by providing trusted content in the form of research, books, webcasts, events, and education programs. **Scope:** Management; leadership. **Services:** Library open to members only. **Founded:** 1943. **Holdings:** 170 monographs; 100 books; 100 newspapers. **Publications:** American Society Training and Development Buyer's Guide and Consultant Directory (Annual); Technical Training Basics; ASTD Buyer's Guide & Consultant Directory (Annual); TD at Work (Monthly); Learning Circuits (Monthly); TD Magazine (Monthly); Member Information Exchange (MIX); TRAINET; ATD Buyer's Guide; ATD Buyer's Guide; American Society for Training and Development--Training Video Directory; Who's Who in Training and Development (Annual). **Educational Activities:** ATD International Conference and Exposition (Annual); ATD TechKnowledge Conference (Annual); TechKnowledge Conference and Exposition (Annual). **Awards:** ATD BEST Award (Annual); Awards in the Advancing Workplace Learning and Performance; ATD Excellence in Practice Awards (Annual); Gordon M. Bliss Memorial Award (Annual); ATD Dissertation Award (Annual); ASTD Talent Development Thought Leader Award (Annual); ATD Torch Award (Annual). **Geographic Preference:** Multinational.

27165 ■ Walt Disney World Global Business Technology Strategy Library

PO Box 10000
Lake Buena Vista, FL 32830
URL: http://disneyworld.disney.go.com

Scope: Computer science, human resources, general business. **Services:** Center not open to the public. **Founded:** 1986. **Holdings:** 4,000 books, videos, DVDs, and CD-ROMs; 100 AV equipment. **Subscriptions:** 200 journals and other serials; 3 newspapers.

REFERENCE WORKS

27166 ■ *"5 Business Structures: Find the Right One for Your Small Business"* in *Business News Daily (April 12, 2022)*
URL(s): smallbiztrends.com/2014/01/5-common-business-structures.html

Released: April 12, 2022. **Description:** Five common business structures are discussed with the purpose of providing information to help you choose which structure would benefit your small business the most. **Availability:** Online.

27167 ■ *"5 Mistakes to Avoid When Choosing Your Business Entity"* in *Legal Zoom (March 14, 2023)*
URL(s): www.legalzoom.com/articles/5-mistakes-to-avoid-when-choosing-your-business-entity

Ed: Marcia Layton Turner. **Released:** March 14, 2023. **Description:** Be sure to research corporate structures and choose one that will work for your business. This article discusses the options you have when choosing a business entity. **Availability:** Online.

27168 ■ *"7 Places to Incorporate Your Small Business Online"* in *Small Business Trends (March 18, 2022)*
URL(s): smallbiztrends.com/2018/06/incorporate-on-line.html

Ed: Gabrielle Pickard-Whitehead. **Released:** March 18, 2022. **Description:** Discusses the advantages of forming a LLC for your small businesses and how to do it online. **Availability:** Online.

27169 ■ *"Adding Partners to an LLC"* in *Legal Zoom (March 16, 2023)*
URL(s): www.legalzoom.com/articles/adding-partners-to-an-llc

Ed: Belle Wong, J.D. **Released:** March 16, 2023. **Description:** Follow this guide for adding new members to your LLC, so that your business remains compliant. **Availability:** Online.

27170 ■ *"Articles of Incorporation: What New Business Owners Should Know"* in *Business News Daily (February 28, 2023)*
URL(s): www.businessnewsdaily.com/4038-articles-of-incorporation.html

Ed: Max Freedman. **Released:** February 28, 2023. **Description:** Provides details about the requirements for submitting articles of incorporation for your small business. **Availability:** Online.

27171 ■ *"Can I Have More Than One LLC?"* in *Legal Zoom (February 17, 2023)*
URL(s): www.legalzoom.com/articles/can-i-have-more-than-one-llc

Ed: Jane Haskins, Esq. **Released:** February 17, 2023. **Description:** Discusses filing for multiple LLCs and the pros and cons of doing so. **Availability:** Online.

27172 ■ *"A Checklist for Maintaining Your Corporate Veil"* in *Legal Zoom (March 13, 2023)*
URL(s): www.legalzoom.com/articles/a-checklist-for-maintaining-your-corporate-veil

Ed: Matthew A. Griffith. **Released:** March 13, 2023. **Description:** Many people set up a corporate veil, usually in the form of a LLC, LP, or LLP, in order to separate their personal assets from the business in case they get sued. This checklist will help you maintain that corporate veil to protect your personal property. **Availability:** Online.

27173 ■ *Choosing the Right Legal Form of Business: The Complete Guide to Becoming a Sole Proprietor, Partnership, LLC, or Corporation*
Pub: Atlantic Publishing Co.
Contact: Dr. Heather L. Johnson, Contact

Ed: Pat Mitchell. **Released:** 2010. **Description:** According to the U.S. Small Business Administration, nearly 250,000 new businesses start up annually; currently there are over nine million small companies in the nation. The importance of choosing the proper legal form of business is stressed. **Availability:** Print; Online.

27174 ■ *"The Complete Guide to Starting a Business"* in *Legal Zoom (March 15, 2023)*
URL(s): www.legalzoom.com/articles/the-complete-guide-to-starting-a-business

Released: March 15, 2023. **Description:** A comprehensive guide on the steps needed to start your own business. **Availability:** Online.

27175 ■ *"The Difference Between a DBA, Sole Proprietor, Corporation and LLC"* in *Small Business Trends (June 9, 2022)*
URL(s): smallbiztrends.com/2013/09/business-structures-difference.html

Ed: Nellie Akalp. **Released:** June 09, 2022. **Description:** Discusses the various structures small businesses can legally take. **Availability:** Online.

27176 ■ *"'Doing Business As': How to Register a DBA Name"* in *Business News Daily (February 21, 2023)*
URL(s): www.businessnewsdaily.com/48-doing-business-as-how-to-register-a-dba-name.html

Ed: Simone Johnson. **Released:** February 21, 2023. **Description:** Gives details on how to file your small business as a Doing Business As (DBA). **Availability:** Online.

27177 ■ *"Federal Employer Identification Number (FEIN): How to Get One"* in *Business News Daily (February 28, 2023)*
URL(s): www.businessnewsdaily.com/17-federal-employer-identification-number-criteria.html

Ed: Sean Peek. **Released:** February 28, 2023. **Description:** If your small business plans on hiring employees, it will need a federal employer identifica-

tion number. This article discusses the steps needed to take to obtain that number so your business is compliant. **Availability:** Online.

27178 ■ *"How to Avoid Double Taxation with an S Corporation"* in *Small Business Trends (May 22, 2017)*
URL(s): smallbiztrends.com/2017/02/double-taxation-s-corporation.html

Ed: Nellie Akalp. **Released:** May 22, 2018. **Description:** Describes how S corporations are taxed and gives tips on how to avoid double taxation. **Availability:** Online.

27179 ■ *"How to Change a Corporation to an LLC without Dissolving the Corporation"* in *Legal Zoom (March 16, 2023)*
URL(s): www.legalzoom.com/articles/how-to-change-a-corporation-to-an-llc-without-dissolving-the-corporation

Ed: Belle Wong, J.D. **Released:** March 16, 2023. **Description:** Discusses the reasons why shareholders in a business may want to restructure from a corporation to an LLC. **Availability:** Online.

27180 ■ *"How to Create an LLC"* in *Small Business Trends (June 29, 2021)*
URL(s): smallbiztrends.com/2021/06/how-to-create-an-llc.html

Ed: Lisa Price. **Released:** September 29, 2021. **Description:** Discusses the steps small business owners need to take to set up their new company as a LLC. **Availability:** Online.

27181 ■ *"How to get an LLC"* in *Legal Zoom (October 27, 2022)*
URL(s): www.legalzoom.com/articles/how-to-apply-for-an-llc

Ed: Belle Wong. **Released:** October 27, 2022. **Description:** Gives advice on how to set up an LLC for your small business. **Availability:** Online.

27182 ■ *"How Much Does it Cost to Incorporate in Each State?"* in *Business News Daily (June 7, 2016)*
URL(s): smallbiztrends.com/2015/04/much-cost-incorporate-state.html

Released: June 07, 2016. **Description:** Provides details on each state and their filing fees for incorporating your business there. **Availability:** Online.

27183 ■ *"How to Place Property in an LLC"* in *Legal Zoom (February 17, 2023)*

Ed: Jane Haskins, Esq. **Released:** February 17, 2023. **Description:** Details what is involved with placing property into a LLC to protect it. **Availability:** Online.

27184 ■ *"How to Remove a Member from an LLC"* in *Legal Zoom (March 16, 2023)*
URL(s): www.legalzoom.com/articles/how-to-remove-a-member-from-an-llc

Ed: Jane Haskins, Esq. **Released:** March 16, 2023. **Description:** A guide on what to do if you need to remove a LLC member, even if the member leaves voluntarily. **Availability:** Online.

27185 ■ *"How to Start a Business with a Partner"* in *Legal Zoom (March 14, 2023)*

URL(s): www.legalzoom.com/articles/how-to-start-a-business-with-a-partner

Ed: Michelle Kaminsky. **Released:** March 14, 2023. **Description:** Business partnerships can be fragile, so be sure you are doing it right by following the steps listed in this article so you, and your partner, are treated fairly. **Availability:** Online.

27186 ■ *"How To Set Up and Structure Multiple Businesses"* in *Small Business Trends (May 21, 2013)*

Released: May 21, 2013. **Description:** Often, small business owners are able to expand and start new ventures. This article explains how to do that and set up multiple companies. **Availability:** Online.

27187 ■ *"If My Business Name Is Registered with the State, Do I Still Need a Trademark?"* in *Legal Zoom (March 21, 2023)*

URL(s): www.legalzoom.com/articles/if-my-business-name-is-registered-with-the-state-do-i-still-need-a-trademark

Ed: Jane Haskins, Esq. **Released:** March 21, 2023. **Description:** Be aware of the limitations your state business entity registration entails. You may need to trademark your company name if it's important to you that another business doesn't use a similar name. **Availability:** Online.

27188 ■ *"Incorporated Versus Unincorporated Self Employment"* in *Small Business Trends (January 14, 2014)*

URL(s): smallbiztrends.com/2013/11/incorporated-versus-unincorporated-self-employment.html

Ed: Scott Shane. **Released:** January 17, 2014. **Description:** Discusses the two types of self employment. **Availability:** Online.

27189 ■ *"Legal Structure: The Difference Between LLCs And LLPs"* in *Small Business Trends (May 21, 2013)*

URL(s): smallbiztrends.com/2012/04/legal-structure-difference-llc-llp.html

Ed: Nellie Akalp. **Released:** May 21, 2013. **Description:** Explains the differences between setting your small business up as an LLP or as an LLC. **Availability:** Online.

27190 ■ *"Piercing the Corporate Veil: Understanding the Limits of LLC Protection"* in *Legal Zoom (February 15, 2023)*

URL(s): www.legalzoom.com/articles/piercing-the-corporate-veil-understanding-the-limits-of-llc-protection

Ed: Brette Sember, J.D. **Released:** February 15, 2023. **Description:** A discussion on what a LLC can and cannot do for your small business. **Availability:** Online.

27191 ■ *"The Right and Wrong Reasons to Incorporate or Form an LLC"* in *Small Business Trends (February 8, 2016)*

URL(s): smallbiztrends.com/2016/02/reasons-to-incorporate-form-llc.html

Ed: Nellie Akalp. **Released:** February 08, 2016. **Description:** Not every business needs to be structured as a LLC. This article guides you the reasoning behind incorporation. **Availability:** Online.

27192 ■ *"Should Freelancers Establish Themselves as an LLC?"* in *Small Business Trends (August 9, 2021)*

URL(s): smallbiztrends.com/2020/12/should-freelancers-establish-themselves-as-llc.html

Ed: Rob Starr. **Released:** August 09, 2021. **Description:** Discusses the particulars of setting up your home-based freelance business as a LLC. **Availability:** Online.

27193 ■ *"Tax and Business Forms You'll Need to Start a Small Business"* in *Business News Daily (February 21, 2023)*

URL(s): www.businessnewsdaily.com/9-tax-and-business-forms-needed-to-start-a-small-business.html

Ed: Andrew Martins. **Released:** February 21, 2023. **Description:** Properly filing the right forms is a crucial step in starting a business. This article explains which forms you need based on your company's structure. **Availability:** Online.

27194 ■ *"Thinking about Names for Your New Business? These 20 Startup Name Generators Could Help"* in *Small Business Trends (January 27, 2023)*

URL(s): smallbiztrends.com/2018/06/startup-name-generator.html

Ed: Annie Pilon. **Released:** January 27, 2023. **Description:** Get help with naming your new business with these listed name generators. **Availability:** Online.

27195 ■ *"Top 6 Ways Your Company Could Lose Its Corporate Veil: Is Your Business at Risk?"* in *Small Business Trends(June 1, 2017)*

URL(s): smallbiztrends.com/2017/06/small-business-compliance-checklist.html

Ed: Nellie Akalp. **Released:** June 01, 2017. **Description:** Discusses the obligations small business owners must face in order to keep their LLC in good order and in good legal standing. **Availability:** Online.

27196 ■ *"Top Reasons to Incorporate Your Business"* in *Small Business Trends (August 5, 2014)*

Ed: Nellie Akalp. **Released:** August 05, 2014. **Description:** Provides the reasons why you should incorporate your small business so both you and your business are protected. **Availability:** Online.

27197 ■ *"What is a DBA (Doing Business As) and How to Register One"* in *Business News Daily (February 8, 2023)*

URL(s): smallbiztrends.com/2023/02/dba.html

Ed: Joshua Sophy. **Released:** February 08, 2023. **Description:** Discusses the definition of DBA (Doing Business As) and the pros and cons of setting that up for your small business. **Availability:** Online.

27198 ■ *"What Is an Annual Report?"* in *Legal Zoom (March 15, 2023)*

URL(s): www.legalzoom.com/articles/what-is-an-annual-report

Ed: Jonathan Layton, J.D. **Released:** March 15, 2023. **Description:** Explains everything you need to know about annual reports for your business. **Availability:** Online.

27199 ■ *"What Is a C Corporation?"* in *Business News Daily (February 21, 2023)*

URL(s): www.businessnewsdaily.com/3771-c-corporation.html

Ed: Sean Peek. **Released:** February 21, 2023. **Description:** Discusses the C corporation business structure so you can make in informed decision about setting up your small business. **Availability:** Online.

27200 ■ *"What Is the Difference between S Corp and C Corp?"* in *Legal Zoom (February 15, 2023)*

URL(s): www.legalzoom.com/articles/what-is-the-difference-between-s-corp-and-c-corp

Released: February 15, 2023. **Description:** Discusses the differences between S and C corporations. **Availability:** Online.

27201 ■ *"What Is an LLC?"* in *Business News Daily (February 21, 2022)*

URL(s): www.businessnewsdaily.com/3747-limited-liability-company.html

Ed: Simone Johnson. **Released:** February 21, 2023. **Description:** Defines and discusses the limited liability company (LLC) structure. **Availability:** Online.

27202 ■ *"What Noncitizens Need to Know about Filing an LLC"* in *Legal Zoom (March 15, 2023)*

URL(s): www.legalzoom.com/articles/what-noncitizens-need-to-know-about-filing-an-llc

Ed: Ronna L. DeLoe. **Released:** March 15, 2023. **Description:** Explains what non-U.S. citizens need to know before filing for an LLC for their small business. **Availability:** Online.

27203 ■ *"What Solo Owners of Corporations Need to Know about Annual Meetings"* in *Small Business Trends (November 12, 2019)*

URL(s): smallbiztrends.com/2019/11/single-owner-corporation.html

Ed: Nellie Akalp. **Released:** November 12, 2019. **Description:** Explains annual shareholder meetings for small business owners who incorporate. **Availability:** Online.

27204 ■ *"What's the Difference Between a Tax ID Number and a Corporate Number?"* in *Business News Daily (February 21, 2023)*

URL(s): www.businessnewsdaily.com/15094-tax-id-corporate-numbers-explained.html

Ed: Simone Johnson. **Released:** February 21, 2023. **Description:** Discusses the differences between a tax ID number and a corporate number so small business can remain compliant with tax laws. **Availability:** Online.

27205 ■ *"Which LLC Taxes Must Your Business File?"* in *Business News Daily (February 28, 2023)*

URL(s): www.businessnewsdaily.com/15744-llc-tax-guide.html

Ed: Andrew Martins. **Released:** February 28, 2023. **Description:** Small businesses structured as an LLC file differently during tax time than other businesses. This article guides business owners on what to expect during tax time. **Availability:** Online.

27206 ■ *"Writing Annual Reports for Your Business"* in *Legal Zoom (March 15, 2023)*

URL(s): www.legalzoom.com/articles/writing-annual-reports-for-your-business

Ed: Ronna L. DeLoe, Esq. **Released:** March 15, 2023. **Description:** Explains the purpose of annual reports and how to prepare them to file with your state. **Availability:** Online.

START-UP INFORMATION

27207 ■ *"Alpharetta Seeding Startups To Encourage Job Growth" in Atlanta Business Chronicle(June 20, 2014, pp. 3A)*
Pub: American City Business Journals, Inc.
Contact: Mike Olivieri, Executive Vice President
Description: The City of Alpharetta is witnessing several incubators and accelerators that will create the physical and educational infrastructure to convert ideas into sustainable businesses. This will help startups develop a go-to-market strategy, prepare for FDA certification and insurance reimbursement as well as see that the company reaches a point where it can attract private equity or venture capital. **Availability:** Print; Online.

27208 ■ *"Consumer Startup Hub Set for Downtown" in Atlanta Business Chronicle (June 13, 2014, pp. 3A)*
Pub: American City Business Journals, Inc.
Contact: Mike Olivieri, Executive Vice President
Description: Michael Tavani, co-founder of Scoutmob, believes that Atlanta is fast becoming the hub for consumer- and design-focused startups. He is planning to locate his consumer-focused startup, Switchyards, in a 1920s building downtown, which will become a hive for mobile app, media, and ecommerce startups. **Availability:** Print; Online.

27209 ■ *"A Messy Job" in Washington Business Journal (Vol. 33, May 30, 2014, No. 6, pp. 6)*
Pub: American City Business Journals, Inc.
Contact: Mike Olivieri, Executive Vice President

Description: Mess Hall founder, Al Goldberg, shares his views on business incubators for culinary entrepreneurs in District of Columbia. Goldberg says he expects to accommodate up to 100 members in the space of the former warehouse turned culinary center for entrepreneurs wishing to start restaurants, bakeries or bars. **Availability:** Print; Online.

REFERENCE WORKS

27210 ■ *"How a Business Incubator Is Different from an Accelerator Program" in Denton Record-Chronicle (Aug. 16, 2022)*
URL(s): dentonrc.com/business/how-a-business
-incubator-is-different-from-an-accelerator-program/
article_7e3486e9-a5b4-5743-b739-d2e5973aa5b
2.html
Ed: Tracy Irby. **Released:** August 16, 2022. **Description:** Startup education is one of the most important things an early-stage entrepreneur can do for his or her business. Incubator and accelerator programs help businesses in ideation or the startup phase grow and scale. This article provides information about how incubators are different from accelerators. **Availability:** Online.

27211 ■ *"Incubators Experiencing a Baby Boom" in Philadelphia Business Journal (Vol. 31, March 23, 2012, No. 6, pp. 1)*
Pub: Baltimore Business Journal
Contact: Rhonda Pringle, President
E-mail: rpringle@bizjournals.com

Description: At least seven business incubators have opened in Philadelphia, Pennsylvania since November 2011. Five of the seven incubators are nonprofit organizations. **Availability:** Print; Online.

27212 ■ *"Life Science Companies in I-35 Corridor Get New Booster" in Dallas Business Journal (Vol. 35, March 16, 2012, No. 2, pp. 1)*
Pub: Baltimore Business Journal
Contact: Rhonda Pringle, President
E-mail: rpringle@bizjournals.com

Description: The Texas Bio Corridor Alliance intends to promote the development of life science firms along the Interstate 35 corridor. It comprises business incubators, cities, economic development organizations and companies in Texas. **Availability:** Print; Online.

27213 ■ *"Spreading Your Wings" in Canadian Business (Vol. 81, March 17, 2008, No. 4, pp. 31)*
Ed: Megan Harman. **Released:** February 09, 2017.
Description: Financing from angel Investors is one avenue that should be explored by startups. Angel investors are typically affluent individuals who invest their own money. Angel investors usually want at least 10 times their initial investment within eight years but they benefit the businesses through their help in decision-making and the industry expertise they provide. **Availability:** Download; Online.

Insurance

START-UP INFORMATION

27214 ■ *"An Insurer Stretches Out" in Business Journal Portland (Vol. 30, February 21, 2014, No. 51, pp. 4)*
Pub: American City Business Journals, Inc.
Contact: Mike Olivieri, Executive Vice President
Released: Weekly. **Price:** $4, Introductory 4-week offer(Digital & Print). **Description:** The diversification strategy of Cambia Health Solutions has led to investments in several health care startups. The company earned $5.8 billion in revenue from insurance premiums in 2012 and posted a profit margin of about 2 percent for its net income of $173 million. **Availability:** Print; Online.

27215 ■ *"One of the Best Ways to Build Wealth...Is to Take Equity In a Company" in Business Journal (Vol. 31, May 2, 2014, No. 49, pp. 9)*
Pub: American City Business Journals, Inc.
Contact: Mike Olivieri, Executive Vice President
Released: Weekly. **Price:** $4, introductory 4-week offer(Digital only). **Description:** Entrepreneur Abir Sen reveals that he was not planning to start a business after selling Bloom Health, but he soon discovered that he wanted to do something productive. He believes that the traditional model of employer-paid health care insurance is dying. His opinion on health care entrepreneurial activity in Minnesota is also examined. **Availability:** Print; Online.

ASSOCIATIONS AND OTHER ORGANIZATIONS

27216 ■ America's Health Insurance Plans (AHIP)
601 Pennsylvania Ave. NW, S Bldg., Ste. 500
  Washington, DC 20004
Ph: (207)778-3200
Fax: (202)331-7487
Co. E-mail: info@ahip.org
URL: http://www.ahip.org
Contact: Matt Eyles, President
Facebook: www.facebook.com/AHIP
Linkedin: www.linkedin.com/company/america%27s
  -health-insurance-plans-ahip-
X (Twitter): x.com/ahipcoverage
Instagram: www.instagram.com/ahipcoverage
YouTube: www.youtube.com/channel/UCj4Yn_50zPln
  6eq2AV-1kog
Description: Publishes materials for health insurance plans. **Founded:** 1948. **Publications:** *National Directory of Health Plans and Utilization Review Organizations* (Annual); *AAHP/Dorland 2001 National Directory of Health Plans* (Annual); *AHIP Coverage* (Bimonthly); *The Employers' Guide to Medicare Managed Care in 1998 and Beyond*; *HIAA Research Bulletins* (Periodic); *Sourcebook of Health Insurance Data* (Biennial); *Healthplan: The Magazine of Trends, Insights, and Best Practices* (Quarterly). **Educational**

Activities: American Association of Health Plans/ Institute and Display Forum (Annual). **Geographic Preference:** National.

27217 ■ Association of Average Adjusters of the United States and Canada (AAAUS) - Library
c/o Ms. Eileen Fellin
  126 Midwood Ave.
  Farmingdale, NY 11735
URL: http://averageadjustersusca.org
Contact: Eileen M. Fellin, Contact
Description: Marine insurance adjusters, marine insurers, admiralty lawyers and appraisers of ships and cargoes. Promotes correct principles in the Adjustment of Marine Hull Claims and uniformity of practice among Average Adjusters. **Scope:** Insurance; risk management and actuarial science. **Founded:** 2011. **Holdings:** Books. **Geographic Preference:** National.

27218 ■ Association of Finance and Insurance Professionals (AFIP)
4104 Felps Dr., Ste. H
  Colleyville, TX 76034
Ph: (817)428-2434
Fax: (817)428-2534
Co. E-mail: info@afip.com
URL: http://afip.com
Contact: Linda Robertson, President
Facebook: www.facebook.com/LikeAFIP
Linkedin: www.linkedin.com/company/association-of
  -finance-&-insurance-professionals
X (Twitter): x.com/AFIP
Instagram: www.instagram.com/afip
Description: Provides state and federal regulatory information and ethical-practice standards to franchised automobile, RV, motorcycle, and watercraft dealers. **Founded:** 1989. **Publications:** *Management & Technology* (Monthly). **Geographic Preference:** National.

27219 ■ Association of Professional Insurance Women (APIW)
990 Cedar Bridge Ave., Ste. B7
  PMB210
  Brick, NJ 08723
Ph: (973)941-6024
Co. E-mail: scb@thebeaumontgroup.com
URL: http://www.apiw.org/cpages/home
Contact: Liz Kramer, President
E-mail: elizabeth.kramer@zurichna.com
X (Twitter): x.com/apiw_1
Description: Professional women from the insurance/reinsurance industry. Promotes cooperation and understanding among members; maintains high professional standards in the insurance industry; provides a strong network of professional contacts and educational aid; recognizes the contributions of women to insurance; encourages women to seek employment in the insurance community. **Founded:** 1976. **Publications:** *APIW News* (Irregular). **Awards:**

Lana James Memorial Scholarship (Annual); APIW Insurance Woman of the Year (Annual). **Geographic Preference:** National.

27220 ■ Big I Michigan
1141 Centennial Way
  Lansing, MI 48917
Ph: (517)323-9473
Co. E-mail: jburnett@michagent.org
URL: http://www.michagent.org
Contact: Bev Barney, Chief Executive Officer
E-mail: bbarney@michagent.org
Facebook: www.facebook.com/BigIMichigan
Description: Trade organization representing independent insurance agencies across Michigan. **Founded:** 1992. **Publications:** *Michigan Agent* (6/ year). **Geographic Preference:** State.

27221 ■ International Association of Insurance Receivers (IAIR)
c/o Lori D. Kirch, Account Manager
  230 Washington Ave., Extension, Ste. 101
  Albany, NY 12203
Ph: (518)417-2882
Fax: (518)463-8656
Co. E-mail: office@iair.org
URL: http://www.iair.org
Contact: Lori D. Kirch, Account Manager
Description: Professional insurance receivers. Promotes adherence to high standards of ethics and professional practice in the administration of insurance receiverships. Seeks to raise public awareness of insurance receivership services. **Founded:** 1991. **Geographic Preference:** Multinational.

27222 ■ National Association of Insurance and Financial Advisors - Wisconsin
600 State St., Ste. A
  Cedar Falls, IA 50613
Ph: (608)455-6674
Fax: (703)770-8224
Co. E-mail: info@naifawisconsin.org
URL: http://wi.naifa.org
Contact: Brendon DeRouin, President
Facebook: www.facebook.com/NAIFAWI
Linkedin: www.linkedin.com/in/naifa-wisconsin-3705b
  1143
X (Twitter): x.com/naifawisconsin
Instagram: www.instagram.com/naifawisconsin
Description: Advocates for a positive legislative and regulatory environment, enhances business and professional skills, and promote the ethical conduct of their members. **Founded:** 1890. **Geographic Preference:** State.

27223 ■ National Association of Mutual Insurance Cos (NAMIC)
3601 Vincennes Rd.
  Indianapolis, IN 46268
Ph: (317)875-5250
URL: http://www.namic.org
Contact: Neil Alldredge, President
E-mail: nalldredge@namic.org
Facebook: www.facebook.com/NAMICorg
Linkedin: www.linkedin.com/company/namicorg

X (Twitter): x.com/namic
YouTube: www.youtube.com/user/NAMICorg
Description: Strengthens and supports its members and the property/casualty insurance industry by providing effective and high value advocacy, member services and public policy development. **Founded:** 1895. **Publications:** *NAMIC Magazine* (Quarterly); *IN Magazine* (Quarterly); *NAMIC National Affairs Insider* (Semimonthly); *NAMIC State Government Observer* (Monthly). **Educational Activities:** National Association of Mutual Insurance Companies Annual Convention (Annual). **Geographic Preference:** National.

27224 ■ National Association of Public Insurance Adjusters (NAPIA)
1400 Village Sq., Blvd., Ste. 3, No. 187
Tallahassee, FL 32312-1231
Ph: (703)433-9217
Co. E-mail: info@napia.com
URL: http://www.napia.com
Contact: Gjergj Ndoja, Executive Director
Linkedin: www.linkedin.com/company/national -association-of-public-insurance-adjusters
X (Twitter): x.com/NAPIAforPAs
Instagram: www.instagram.com/napiaadjuster
Description: Professional society of public insurance adjusters. Sponsors certification and professional education programs. **Founded:** 1951. **Publications:** *The Professional Public Insurance Adjuster-Working For You...On Your Side!*. **Educational Activities:** National Association of Public Insurance Adjusters Annual Meeting (Annual). **Geographic Preference:** National.

27225 ■ National Council of Self-Insurers (NCSI)
Contact UsNational Council of Self-Insurersc/o Loyd Hudson, President
8545 Libra Rd.
Dublin, OH 43016
Ph: (513)850-1941
Co. E-mail: natcouncilsi@gmail.com
URL: http://www.natcouncil.com
Contact: Loyd Hudson, President
Facebook: www.facebook.com/ncsiforyou
Linkedin: www.linkedin.com/company/national -council-of-self-insurers
X (Twitter): x.com/natcouncilofsi
YouTube: www.youtube.com/channel/UCM 6tt1HCEcVWMvvyPl2rCag
Description: Promotes and protects, at all governmental levels, the interests of self-insurers or legally non-insured employers and their employees in matters of legislative and administrative activity affecting workmen's compensation; assists, advises, and uses its resources in developing and implementing common objectives among self-insurers. **Founded:** 1946. **Publications:** *Self-Insurance Requirements of the States* (Periodic). **Educational Activities:** NCSI Annual Meeting (Annual). **Geographic Preference:** National.

27226 ■ Ohio Insurance Agents Association Inc. (OIA)
175 S 3RD St., Ste. 940
Columbus, OH 43215
Ph: (614)552-8000
Free: 800-555-1742
Fax: (614)552-0115
Co. E-mail: oia@ohioinsuranceagents.com
URL: http://ohioinsuranceagents.com
Contact: Jeff Smith, Chief Executive Officer
E-mail: jeff@ohioinsuranceagents.com
Facebook: www.facebook.com/OhioInsuranceAgents
Linkedin: www.linkedin.com/company/ohio-insurance -agents
X (Twitter): x.com/ohioinsagents
Instagram: www.instagram.com/ohioinsuranceagents
YouTube: www.youtube.com/channel/UCM58HKibT tgzZzVwj-1loog
Description: Independent insurance agents. Provides legislative representation. Offers educational programs and insurance benefits. **Founded:** 1933.

Publications: *Inside Insurance; ProAction, PIAA of Ohio* (Monthly); *Professional Insurance Agents (PIA)*. **Geographic Preference:** State.

INCUBATORS/RESEARCH AND TECHNOLOGY PARKS

27227 ■ Plug and Play - Insurtech
440 N Wolfe Rd.
Sunnyvale, CA 94085
Ph: (408)524-1400
URL: http://www.plugandplaytechcenter.com/indus tries/insurtech
Linkedin: www.linkedin.com/showcase/plugan dplayinsurtech
Description: An accelerator for startups in the insurtech industry. Provides support with venture and angel partners, mentorship, a data center, office space, and networking opportunities. Has a focus on general insurance, property and casual insurance, and life and health. **Founded:** 2015.

EDUCATIONAL PROGRAMS

27228 ■ AMA's Insurance and Risk Management Workshop (Onsite)
URL(s): www.amanet.org
Description: Covers everything from coverage and cost to liability limits, retention and broker services. **Audience:** Insurance and risk management professionals . **Principal Exhibits:** Covers everything from coverage and cost to liability limits, retention and broker services.

REFERENCE WORKS

27229 ■ "6 Biggest Business Insurance Risks (and How to Mitigate Them)" in Business News Daily (February 21, 2023)
URL(s): www.businessnewsdaily.com/9024-bigges t-business-insurance-risks.html
Ed: Nicole Fallon. **Released:** February 21, 2023. **Description:** Having proper insurance coverage for your small business is necessary, since there is a lot of risk out in the world. This article discusses what you need to know about what could happen and how to cover your losses with insurance. **Availability:** Online.

27230 ■ "26 Types of Insurance Your Small Business Should Consider" in Business News Daily (February 21, 2023)
URL(s): www.businessnewsdaily.com/15781-types-of -business-insurance.html
Ed: Skye Schooley. **Released:** February 21, 2023. **Description:** There are many options for business insurance and this list goes through 26 of them so you can choose which coverage you need. **Availability:** Online.

27231 ■ "7.7% Workers' Comp Decrease Recommended in Missouri" in Insurance Journal (November 16, 2021)
Released: November 16, 2021. **Description:** The largest decrease in workers' compensation insurance loss costs sine 2009 is being recommended in Missouri. This is due to a decline in loss-time claim frequency since workplaces have increased safety standards. **Availability:** Online.

27232 ■ "2010 Book of Lists" in Business Courier (Vol. 26, December 26, 2009, No. 36, pp. 1)
Price: $49.95. **Description:** Rankings of companies and organizations within the business services, education, finance, health care, hospitality and tourism, real estate, and technology industries in the Cincinnati, Ohio-Northern Kentucky area are presented. Rankings are based on sales, business size, or other statistics. **Availability:** PDF; Online.

27233 ■ "ACE Expands M&A Practice" in Economics & Business Week (March 22, 2014, pp. 2)
Pub: NewsRX LLC.
Contact: Kalani Rosell, Contact
Description: ACE Group announced an expansion of its mergers and acquisitions practice focusing on insurance solutions for private equity firms, their portfolio companies as well as their M&A transactions. **Availability:** Online.

27234 ■ "All-Star Advice 2010" in Black Enterprise (Vol. 41, October 2010, No. 3, pp. 97)
Pub: Earl G. Graves Ltd.
Contact: Earl Graves, Jr., President
Ed: Renita Burns, Sheiresa Ngo, Marcia Wade Talbert. **Description:** Financial experts share tips on real estate, investing, taxes, insurance and debt management. **Availability:** Online.

27235 ■ "Alpharetta Seeding Startups To Encourage Job Growth" in Atlanta Business Chronicle(June 20, 2014, pp. 3A)
Pub: American City Business Journals, Inc.
Contact: Mike Olivieri, Executive Vice President
Description: The City of Alpharetta is witnessing several incubators and accelerators that will create the physical and educational infrastructure to convert ideas into sustainable businesses. This will help startups develop a go-to-market strategy, prepare for FDA certification and insurance reimbursement as well as see that the company reaches a point where it can attract private equity or venture capital. **Availability:** Print; Online.

27236 ■ "The Annual Entitlement Lecture Medicare Elephantiasis" in Barron's (March 31, 2008)
Pub: Dow Jones & Company Inc.
Contact: Almar Latour, Chief Executive Officer
Ed: Thomas G. Donlan. **Description:** Expenditures on Medicare hospital insurance and the revenues available to pay for it have led to a gap of capital valued at $38.6 trillion. Slashing the benefits or raising taxes will not solve the gap which exists unless the government saves the money and invests it in private markets. **Availability:** Online.

27237 ■ "Anthem Becomes First to Penalize Small-Business Employees for Smoking" in Denver Business Journal (Vol. 64, August 17, 2012, No. 13, pp. 1)
Pub: Baltimore Business Journal
Contact: Rhonda Pringle, President
E-mail: rpringle@bizjournals.com
Description: Health insurance companies Anthem Blue Cross and Blue Shield of Colorado are first to impose higher premiums on employee smokers who are under their small-group policies. The premiums may increase up to 15 percent starting September, to be paid by the smoking employees or the company. The law aims to help reduce tobacco-related health problems, as well as health care costs.

27238 ■ "Are Prepaid Legal Services Worthwhile?" in Contractor (Vol. 56, December 2009, No. 12, pp. 31)
Ed: Susan Linden McGreevy. **Description:** Companies' provision of legal insurance as an employee benefit in the United States is discussed. Stoppage of premium payment halts employee coverage. It also does not cover all kinds of personal issues. **Availability:** Print; Online.

27239 ■ "Are You Overinsured? Some Policies May Not Offer Much Additional Benefit" in Black Enterprise (Vol. 38, March 1, 2008, No. 8, pp. 126)
Pub: Earl G. Graves Ltd.
Contact: Earl Graves, Jr., President
Ed: Tamara E. Holmes. **Description:** Travel insurance, identity-theft insurance, specific disease or health condition insurance policies are described. Advice is given to help determine if you are overinsured. **Availability:** Online.

27240 ■ "Austin-Based Insuraprise Growing Fast" in Austin Business Journal (Vol. 31, April 22, 2011, No. 7, pp. 1)
Pub: Austin Business Journal
Contact: Rachel McGrath, Director
E-mail: rmcgrath@bizjournals.com
Ed: Sandra Zaragoza. Description: Austin, Texas-based Insuraprise Inc. is finalizing the purchase of a 24,000-square-foot office at 12116 Jekel Circle. The firm, with 23 salespeople and sales that are growing nearly 300 percent over the past 18 months, will now have room to grow. Insuraprise plans to hire 35 new salespersons for its call center. Availability: Print; Online.

27241 ■ "Baldwin Connelly Partnership Splits" in Business Journal Serving Greater Tampa Bay (Vol. 30, November 19, 2010, No. 48, pp. 1)
Pub: Tampa Bay Business Journal
Contact: Ian Anderson, President
E-mail: ianderson@bizjournals.com
Description: The fast-growing insurance brokerage Baldwin Connelly is now breaking up after five years. Two different entrepreneurial visions have developed within the organization and founders Lowry Baldwin and John Connell will not take separate tracks. Staffing levels in the firm are expected to remain the same. Availability: Print; Online.

27242 ■ "Bills Raise Blues Debate: An Unfair Edge or Level Playing Field?" in Crain's Detroit Business (Vol. 24, January 21, 2008, No. 3)
Pub: Crain Communications Inc.
Contact: Barry Asin, President
Ed: Sherri Begin. Description: Changes in Michigan state law would change the way health insurance can be sold to individuals. Michigan Blue Cross Blue Shield is working to keep its tax-exempt status while staying competitive against for-profit insurers and nonprofit HMOs. Availability: Print; Online.

27243 ■ "Blue Cross to Put Kiosk in Mall" in News & Observer (November 9, 2010)
Pub: News and Observer
Contact: Bill Church, Editor
Ed: Alan M. Wolf. Description: Blue Cross and Blue Shield of North Carolina has placed a kiosk in Durham's Streets of Southpoint in order to market its health insurance. Availability: Online.

27244 ■ "Business Insurance: When You Need It and When You Don't" in Legal Zoom (March 23, 2023)
URL(s): www.legalzoom.com/articles/business-insurance-when-you-need-it-and-when-you-dont
Ed: Jane Haskins, Esq. Released: March 23, 2023. Description: Talks about business insurance, how much to purchase, and what kind is needed for your small business. Availability: Online.

27245 ■ "Changes Sought to Health Law" in Baltimore Business Journal (Vol. 28, July 30, 2010, No. 12, pp. 1)
Pub: Baltimore Business Journal
Contact: Rhonda Pringle, President
E-mail: rpringle@bizjournals.com
Ed: Kent Hoover. Description: Business groups that opposed health care reform are working to undo parts of the new laws even before they go into effect. Business groups are gaining support for one legislative fix, which is repealing the law's provision that requires all businesses to file 1099 forms with the IRS any time they pay more than $600 a year to another business. Availability: Print; Online.

27246 ■ "Cincinnati Hospitals Wage War on 'Bounce-Backs" in Business Courier (Vol. 27, July 30, 2010, No. 13, pp. 1)
Pub: Business Courier
Ed: James Ritchie. Description: Health care organizations in Greater Cincinnati area have tried a number of care and follow up programs, primarily focused on congestive heart failure to prevent readmissions to hospitals. Hospital administrators

have made the averting of bounce-backs a priority due to new federal government plans on reimbursement. Availability: Print; Online.

27247 ■ "Collision Centers See Business Boom" in Atlanta Business Chronicle (February 7, 2014, pp. 3A)
Pub: American City Business Journals, Inc.
Contact: Mike Olivieri, Executive Vice President
Released: February 07, 2014. Price: $4, Introductory 4-Week Offer(Digital & Print). Description: Collision repair shops in Atlanta, Georgia are benefitting from the recent snow storm. The storm resulted in $10 million insured losses to homes and automobiles. Meanwhile, collision centers have also extended business hours to accommodate more customers. Availability: Print; Online.

27248 ■ "Commissioner Wants to Expand Private Market for Insurance" in South Florida Business Journal (Vol. 32, June 8, 2012, No. 46, pp. 1)
Pub: Baltimore Business Journal
Contact: Rhonda Pringle, President
E-mail: rpringle@bizjournals.com
Description: Florida insurance commissioner Keven McCarty shares his views about the major risks to the state's property insurance system. McCarty believes the bigger issue is what might happen to the market in the aftermath of a catastrophe. He also shared their activities in bringing more private property insurers into Florida. Availability: Print; Online.

27249 ■ "Consulting Firm Goes Shopping" in Crain's Chicago Business (Vol. 31, April 28, 2008, No. 17, pp. 45)
Pub: Crain Communications Inc.
Contact: Barry Asin, President
Ed: Phuong Ly. Description: Clark & Wamberg LLC was created last year after the merger of Clark Inc. to a Dutch insurance conglomerate. Clark Inc. was a life insurance and benefits consultancy which had been on a downslide, returning just 5.6 percent a year to shareholders. In contrast Clark & Wamberg posted first-year revenue of $106.8 million, fueled by business from its executive compensation and health care clients. Availability: Online.

27250 ■ "Continuously Monitoring Workers' Comp Can Limit Costs" in Crain's Cleveland Business (Vol. 28, October 8, 2007, No. 40, pp. 21)
Pub: Crain Communications Inc.
Contact: K. C. Crain, President
Ed: Michael Agnoni. Description: When operating without a plan for managing its workers' compensation program, a company risks losing money. For most companies workers' compensation insurance premiums are often reduced to an annual budget entry but employers who are actively involved in the management of their programs are more likely to experience reductions in premiums and limit indirect costs associated with claims. Availability: Online.

27251 ■ "Controversial Bill Could Raise Rates for Homeowners" in Orlando Business Journal (Vol. 26, January 22, 2010, No. 34, pp. 1)
Pub: Orlando Business Journal
Contact: Julie Swyers, Director
E-mail: jswyers@bizjournals.com
Ed: Oscar Pedro Musibay, Christopher Boyd. Description: Florida Senate Bill 876 and its companion House Bill 447 are pushing for the deregulation of rates in the state's home insurance market. The bill is being opposed by consumer advocates as it could mean higher rates for homeowner insurance policies. Availability: Print; Online.

27252 ■ "Cost of Creating Health Insurance Exchange in Md. 'Largely Unknown'" in Baltimore Business Journal (Vol. 28, September 3, 2010, No. 17, pp. 1)
Pub: Baltimore Business Journal
Contact: Rhonda Pringle, President
E-mail: rpringle@bizjournals.com

Ed: Emily Mullin. Description: United States health reform is seen to result in increased health insurance prices in Maryland. However, health care reform advocates claim a new marketplace and increased competition will help keep costs down. Availability: Print.

27253 ■ "Cover Your Assets: An Insurance Primer for Small Businesses" in Business News Daily (March 15, 2023)
URL(s): www.businessnewsdaily.com/335-small-business-insuranc-policy-primer.html
Ed: Leslie Pankowski. Released: March 15, 2023. Description: If you never purchased insurance for your small business, this article will explain what it is you need to do to make sure your business is fully covered in case there is an emergency. Multiple types of coverage are discussed. Availability: Online.

27254 ■ "Covered California Adds Dental Benefits" in Sacramento Business Journal (Vol. 31, August 29, 2014, No. 27, pp. 8)
Pub: American City Business Journals, Inc.
Contact: Mike Olivieri, Executive Vice President
Released: Weekly. Price: $4, introductory 4-week offer(Digital only). Description: Health benefit exchange, Covered California, is introducing stand-alone family dental benefits for consumers who enroll in health insurance coverage for 2015. The Governor has yet to sign a bill that would establish a separate vision care marketplace linked to Covered California's Website. Availability: Print; Online.

27255 ■ "Crop Insurance Harvest Prices in 2011" in Farm Industry News (November 9, 2011)
Pub: Informa Business Media, Inc.
Contact: Charlie McCurdy, President
Ed: Gary Schnitkey. Description: Risk Management Agency (RMA) reported harvest prices for corn and soybean grown in the Midwest with corn at $6.32 per bushel, 31 cents higher than the project $6.01; soybeans were at $12.14 per bushel, down $1.35 from the projected price of $13.49. Availability: Print; Online.

27256 ■ "Cutting Health Care Costs: the 3-Legged Stool" in HR Specialist (Vol. 8, September 2010, No. 9, pp. 1)
Pub: Capitol Information Group Inc.
Contact: Allie Ash, Chief Executive Officer
Description: Employer spending on health insurance benefits to employees is investigated. Availability: Print; Online; PDF.

27257 ■ Dictionary of Real Estate Terms
Pub: Barron's Educational Series Inc.
Contact: Manuel H. Barron, Contact
Ed: Jack P. Friedman, Jack C. Harris, J. Bruce Lindeman. Released: 9th edition. Price: $16.99, paperback, plus shipping charges $5.99. Description: More than 2,500 real estate terms relating to mortgages and financing, brokerage law, architecture, rentals and leases, property insurance, and more. Availability: E-book; Print.

27258 ■ "Discovery Communications: Don't Sell, But Don't Buy" in Workforce Management (Vol. 88, December 14, 2009, No. 13, pp. 17)
Pub: Crain Communications Inc.
Contact: Barry Asin, President
Ed: Jeremy Smerd. Description: Discovery Communications provides its employees a wealth of free health services via a comprehensive work-site medical clinic that is available to its employees and their dependents. Overview of the company's innovative approach to healthcare is presented. Availability: Online.

27259 ■ "Distribution Dilemma: Standard Process of Tariff Revisions Across States Can Make Discoms Viable" in Best's Review (Vol. 113, September 2012, No. 5, pp. 15)
Description: Life insurance companies are addressing the obstacles prohibiting them from increasing sales. Availability: Print; Online.

27260 ∎ *"Doctor Shortage Continues to Plague Region"* in *Business First of Buffalo (Vol. 30, April 11, 2014, No. 30, pp. 6)*
Pub: American City Business Journals, Inc.
Contact: Mike Olivieri, Executive Vice President
Released: April 11, 2014. **Price:** $140, Digital & Print; $115, Digital only. **Description:** New York hospitals need at least 1,000 additional physicians, particularly primary care doctors, as they try to meet the criteria set by Federal health reform's Affordable Care Act. The Western New York region gained only 421 new physicians, while losing 544 in 2013. **Availability:** Print; Online.

27261 ∎ *"Does Your Home-Based Business Need Business Insurance?"* in *Legal Zoom (March 22, 2023)*
URL(s): www.legalzoom.com/articles/does-your -home-based-business-need-business-insurance
Released: March 22, 2023. **Description:** Discusses the available business insurance small business owners should look into to have themselves covered in case of property damage, liability coverage, and even auto insurance for any company vehicles. **Availability:** Online.

27262 ∎ *"Ducking the New Health-Care Taxes"* in *Barron's (Vol. 92, September 15, 2012, No. 38, pp. 34)*
Pub: Dow Jones & Company Inc.
Contact: Almar Latour, Chief Executive Officer
Ed: Elizabeth Ody. **Description:** Strategies that investors can use to avoid paying higher taxes starting January 2013 are discussed. These include selling assets by December 2012, distributing dividends, purchasing private-placement life insurance and converting individual retirement accounts. **Availability:** Online.

27263 ∎ *"E-Medical Records Save Money, Time in Ann Arbor"* in *Crain's Detroit Business (Vol. 24, January 21, 2008, No. 3, pp. 6)*
Pub: Crain Communications Inc.
Contact: Barry Asin, President
Ed: Jay Greene. **Description:** Ann Arbor Area Health Information Exchange is improving patient outcomes by sharing clinical and administrative data in electronic medical record systems. **Availability:** Online.

27264 ∎ *"Elder Care Costs Surge"* in *National Underwriter Life & Health (Vol. 114, November 8, 2020, No. 21, pp. 25)*
Ed: Trevor Thomas. **Description:** Nursing home and assisted living rates rose from 2009 to 2010, according to MetLife Mature Market Institute. Statistical data included. **Availability:** Online.

27265 ∎ *"Employer Jobless Tax Could Rise"* in *Sacramento Business Journal (Vol. 28, May 27, 2011, No. 13, pp. 1)*
Pub: Sacramento Business Journal
Contact: Stephanie Fretwell, Director
E-mail: sfretwell@bizjournals.com
Ed: Kathy Robertson. **Description:** The government of California is facing an estimated $16 billion deficit in its unemployment insurance fund. Unemployment insurance spending has exceeded employer contributions to the fund. Statistics on unemployment insurance is included. **Availability:** Online.

27266 ∎ *"FEMA Postpones Switch to New Risk-Based Flood Insurance Rating Until 2021"* in *Insurance Journal (November 8, 2019)*
URL(s): www.insurancejournal.com/news/national/20 19/11/08/548044.htm
Ed: Andrew G. Simpson. **Released:** November 08, 2019. **Description:** Risk Rating 2.0, FEMA's new methodology for calculating its pricing for federal flood insurance is being delayed. More time is needed to complete a comprehensive analysis of the rating structure and will let NFIP policies switch to the new rating system instead of using a phased approach. **Availability:** Online.

27267 ∎ *"Firms Sue Doracon to Recoup More Than $1M in Unpaid Bills"* in *Baltimore Business Journal (Vol. 28, July 9, 2010, No. 9, pp. 1)*
Pub: Baltimore Business Journal
Contact: Rhonda Pringle, President
E-mail: rpringle@bizjournals.com
Ed: Scott Dance. **Description:** Concrete supplier Paul J. Rach Inc., Selective Insurance Company, and equipment leasing firm Colonial Pacific Leasing Corporation intend to sue Baltimore, Maryland-based Doracon Contracting Inc. for $1 million in unpaid bills. Doracon owed Colonial Pacific $794,000 and the equipment is still in Doracon's possession. Selective Insurance and Paul J. Rach respectively seek $132,000 and $88,000. **Availability:** Print.

27268 ∎ *"For 2020, Expect Biggest Commercial Insurance Hikes in Years: Willis Towers Watson"* in *Insurance Journal (November 15, 2019)*
URL(s): www.insurancejournal.com/news/national/20 19/11/15/548582.htm
Released: November 15, 2019. **Description:** According to insurance broker Willis Towers Watson, North American commercial insurance buyers will face sizable price increases starting in 2020. Property, umbrella, and public company directors and officers are expected to to experience the most widespread hikes. **Availability:** Online.

27269 ∎ *"Ground Forces: Insurance Companies Should Help Agents to Build the Skills and Relationships that Translate Into More Business"* in *Best's Review (Vol. 113, September 2012, No. 5, pp. 25)*
Description: The economic challenges of the past few years required insurance agents and financial professionals to better trained. Insurance companies should help their agents build skills and relationships in order to grow. **Availability:** Print; Online.

27270 ∎ *"Harleysville Eyes Growth After Nationwide Deal"* in *Philadelphia Business Journal (Vol. 30, October 7, 2011, No. 34, pp. 1)*
Pub: Philadelphia Business Journal
Contact: Sierra Quinn, Director
E-mail: squinn@bizjournals.com
Ed: Jeff Blumenthal. **Price:** $4, introductory 4-week offer(Digital & Print). **Description:** Harleysville Group announced growth plans after the company was sold to Columbus, Ohio-based Nationwide Mutual Insurance Company for about $1.63 billion. Nationwide gained an independent agency platform in 32 states with the Harleysville deal. **Availability:** Print; Online.

27271 ∎ *"Health Care of the Future"* in *Business Journal Serving Greater Tampa Bay (Vol. 30, November 19, 2010, No. 48, pp. 1)*
Pub: Tampa Bay Business Journal
Contact: Ian Anderson, President
E-mail: ianderson@bizjournals.com
Description: Information about accountable care organizations (ACO), which are integrated care systems with doctors and hospitals working closely together to handle patient care, is provided. The Patient Protection and Affordable Care Act paved the way for ACOs as Medicare demonstration projects. **Availability:** Online.

27272 ∎ *"Health Centers Plan Expansion: $3M from D.C. Expected; Uninsured a Target"* in *Crain's Detroit Business (Vol. 25, June 15, 2009, No. 24, pp. 3)*
Pub: Crain Communications Inc.
Contact: Barry Asin, President
Ed: Jay Greene. **Description:** Detroit has five federally qualified health centers that plan to receive over $3 million in federal stimulus money that will be used to expand projects that will care for uninsured patients. **Availability:** Print; Online.

27273 ∎ *"Health IT Regulations Generate Static Among Providers"* in *Philadelphia Business Journal (Vol. 28, January 29, 2010, No. 50, pp. 1)*
Pub: Philadelphia Business Journal
Contact: Sierra Quinn, Director
E-mail: squinn@bizjournals.com
Ed: John George. **Description:** US Centers for Medicaid and Medicare Services and the Office of the National Coordinator for Health Information Technology have proposed rules regarding the meaningful use of electronic health records. The rules must be complied with by hospitals and physicians to qualify for federal stimulus funds. **Availability:** Online.

27274 ∎ *"Health Reform Could Expand HSA-Based Plans"* in *Workforce Management (Vol. 88, December 14, 2009, No. 13, pp. 6)*
Description: HSA-qualified plans are the cheapest insurance plans on the market as they have a higher deductible but cost less upfront. If health care reform passes, HSA-qualified plans should benefit greatly. **Availability:** Print; Online.

27275 ∎ *"Health Reform: How to Make it Cheaper"* in *Business Courier (Vol. 26, December 11, 2009, No. 33, pp. 1)*
Description: Greater Cincinnati health care leaders shared views about the health care reform bill. Respondents included the Cincinnati Visiting Nurse's Wallen Falberg, healthcare consultant Hirsch Cohen, Greater Cincinnati Health Council's Coleen O'Toole, Employer Health Care Alliance's Sharron DiMario, Legal Aid Society of Greater Cincinnati's Col Owens, Christ Hospital's Susan Croushore, and Humana of Ohio's Tim Cappel. **Availability:** Online.

27276 ∎ *"Hospitals Say Medicaid Expansion is Critical"* in *Dallas Business Journal (Vol. 35, August 3, 2012, No. 47, pp. 1)*
Pub: Baltimore Business Journal
Contact: Rhonda Pringle, President
E-mail: rpringle@bizjournals.com
Ed: Bill Hethcock, Matt Joyce. **Description:** Governor Rick Perry's rejection of the Texas expansion of Medicaid is met with disapproval by health organizations such as the Methodist Health System. The federal government has extended $70 billion in financing to help more Texans become eligible for primary health care. Expansion supporters argue that Medicaid is critical in lowering insurance osts for those who need it. **Availability:** Print; Online.

27277 ∎ *"Hospitals Vying to Buy Physician Associates LLC"* in *Orlando Business Journal (Vol. 29, August 31, 2012, No. 11, pp. 1)*
Pub: Baltimore Business Journal
Contact: Rhonda Pringle, President
E-mail: rpringle@bizjournals.com
Description: Hospitals are battling it out on who gets to buy Physician Associates LLC, the largest multispecialty practice in Central Florida. The most likely candidates to purchase the practice are Orlando Health and Florida Hospital. The deal could be worth $20 million to $60 million and it could also hike health care costs since Physician Associates serves 19 percent of Central Florida's uninsured population. **Availability:** Print; Online.

27278 ∎ *"How to Avoid Leave-Related Lawsuits"* in *Employee Benefit News (Vol. 25, December 1, 2011, No. 15, pp. 12)*
Pub: SourceMedia LLC
Contact: Gemma Postlethwaite, Chief Executive Officer
Ed: John F. Galvin. **Description:** Tips for employers when adding disability and maternity leave benefits to workers are outlined, with focus on ways to avoid leave-related lawsuits.

27279 ∎ *"How to Build a Great Employee Benefits Package"* in *Business News Daily (February 21, 2023)*
URL(s): www.businessnewsdaily.com/9494-small -business-benefits-package.html

Ed: Andreas Rivera. **Description:** Small business owners may need to start providing a benefits package to entice quality employees. Details about what to included are discussed. **Availability:** Online.

27280 ■ "How to Buy Small Business Insurance" in Business News Daily (February 21, 2023)
URL(s): www.businessnewsdaily.com/138-de terminating-small-business-insurance-needs.html
Ed: Mona Bushnell. **Released:** February 21, 2023. **Description:** Small business owners should investigate the various business insurance they need to cover their business in emergencies. Insurance provides are listed. **Availability:** Online.

27281 ■ "How to Choose the Best Driving School for Your Teen" in Drivingguide.com (September 24, 2018)
URL(s): www.drivingguide.com/articles/choose-bes t-teen-driving-school/
Ed: Jim Thompson. **Released:** September 24, 2018. **Description:** A guide to finding the best driving school that will meet your child's needs. With teen crashes in the forefront of parents' minds, it's important to find a place that will train your teen to drive safely and responsibly. This guide also discusses car insurance and the state graduated driving license programs. **Availability:** Online.

27282 ■ "How to Get a Workplace Wellness Program for Your Office" in Entrepreneurs (June 2014)
Pub: Entrepreneur Media Inc.
Contact: Dan Bova, Director
E-mail: dbova@entrepreneur.com
Description: Workplace wellness programs can be started by checking with insurers who may provide program and activity suggestions promotional materials or other resources. Teaming up with others is encouraged. For instance, employees from various departments or nearby companies can get flu shots or blood pressure screening. Management should also get involved in these programs, because it will then be known among employees that wellness is taken seriously. It is also important that workplace wellness programs are kept safe and legally sound. **Availability:** Online.

27283 ■ "How to Maximize Your Investment Income" in Contractor (Vol. 56, December 2009, No. 12, pp. 33)
Ed: Irving L. Blackman. **Description:** Private placement life insurance (PPLI) can minimize taxes and protect assets. PPLI is a form of variable universal insurance that is offered privately. Risk of insurance company illiquidity is avoided as investments are placed in separate accounts. **Availability:** Online.

27284 ■ "Handling New Health Insurance Regulations" in Baltimore Business Journal (Vol. 31, April 25, 2014, No. 52, pp. 25)
Pub: American City Business Journals, Inc.
Contact: Mike Olivieri, Executive Vice President
Released: March 13, 2014. **Description:** Research and consulting firm, Mercer, surveyed businesses in January 2014 to examine their employer-sponsored health plans following enrollment in the Affordable Care Act-created exchanges. The survey found employers were taking advantage of a delay to a key regulation in the Act on offering insurance to employees who work at least 30 hours a week. **Availability:** Print; Online.

27285 ■ How to Start a Home-Based Senior Care Business
Ed: James L. Ferry. **Released:** 2nd edition. **Price:** Paperback,softback; Electronic Book. **Description:** Information is provided to start a home-based senior care business. **Availability:** E-book; Print.

27286 ■ "Humana Planning Pa. HMO" in Philadelphia Business Journal (Vol. 28, August 10, 2012, No. 26, pp. 1)
Pub: Baltimore Business Journal
Contact: Rhonda Pringle, President
E-mail: rpringle@bizjournals.com

Description: Humana plans to establish an HMO in Philadelphia and other areas of Pennsylvania. Along with this plan is an insurance offering in the Medicare Advantage market focused on senior citizens. The new offering would complement the company's existing preferred provider organization product. **Availability:** Print; Online.

27287 ■ "Humana Seeks Higher Stake in Memphis Market" in Memphis Business Journal (Vol. 33, February 17, 2012, No. 45, pp. 1)
Pub: Baltimore Business Journal
Contact: Rhonda Pringle, President
E-mail: rpringle@bizjournals.com
Ed: Christopher Sheffield. **Description:** Humana of Tennessee has been hoping to get a bigger share of the West Tennessee insurance market through its new three-year contract with Baptist Memorial Health Care Corporation. Louisville, Kentucky-based Humana Inc. has a business relationship with Baptist that stretches back more than two decades. **Availability:** Print; Online.

27288 ■ "Independence Blue Cross Reverses Membership Slide" in Philadelphia Business Journal (Vol. 30, September 23, 2011, No. 32, pp. 1)
Pub: Philadelphia Business Journal
Contact: Sierra Quinn, Director
E-mail: squinn@bizjournals.com
Ed: John George. **Description:** Health insurer Independence Blue Cross (IBC) added more than 40,000 members across all product lines since the start of 2011. It has 2.2 million members in Pennsylvania's Philadelphia region and 3.1 million members across the U.S. Services and other growth-related plans of IBC are covered. **Availability:** Online.

27289 ■ "Insurance Firm Consolidates Offices: Integro Finds the Right Price Downtown" in Crain's New York Business (January 13, 2008)
Pub: Crain Communications, Inc.
Contact: Jessica Botos, Manager, Marketing
E-mail: jessica.botos@crainsnewyork.com
Description: Integro insurance brokers is relocating its headquarters to 1 State Street Plaza, where it will consolidate its operations in March. The firm feels that the upscale design will provide an appropriate setting for entertaining clients and an engaging work environment for employees. **Availability:** Online.

27290 ■ "Insurers Enter Ridesharing Dispute" in Sacramento Business Journal (Vol. 31, June 6, 2014, No. 15, pp. 8)
Pub: American City Business Journals, Inc.
Contact: Mike Olivieri, Executive Vice President
Released: Weekly. **Price:** $4, Introductory 4-week offer(Digital & Print). **Description:** Insurance companies have been lobbying the California Assembly to pass legislation requiring ridesharing drivers to carry commercial liability insurance. Ridesharing companies provide drivers with liability coverage as a backup when an accident is not covered by personal insurance. The passage of such a bill would boost ridesharing companies' revenues. **Availability:** Print; Online.

27291 ■ "Insurers No Longer Paying Premium for Advertising" in Brandweek (Vol. 49, April 21, 2008, No. 16, pp. SR3)
Description: Insurance companies are cutting their advertising budgets after years of accelerated double-digit growth in spending due to the economic downturn, five years of record-breaking ad spend and a need to cut expenditures as claims costs rise and a competitive market keeps premiums in place. Statistical data included. **Availability:** Print; Online.

27292 ■ "Internet Marketing 2.0: Closing the Online Chat Gap" in Agent's Sales Journal (November 2009, pp. 14)
Ed: Jeff Denenholz. **Description:** Advice regarding the implementation of an Internet marketing strategy for insurance agencies includes how and why to incorporate a chat feature in which a sales agent can

communicate in real-time with potential or existing customers. It is important to understand if appropriate response mechanisms are in place to convert leads into actual sales. **Availability:** Print; Online.

27293 ■ "Is Peer-to-Peer Insurance Right for Your Business?" in Business News Daily (February 21, 2023)
URL(s): www.businessnewsdaily.com/10362-peer-to -peer-insurance.html
Ed: Adam Uzialko. **Released:** February 21, 2023. **Description:** Discusses the role peer-to-peer insurance programs play within the small business industry. **Availability:** Online.

27294 ■ "Is There a Doctor In the House?" in Black Enterprise (Vol. 41, December 2010, No. 5, pp. 42)
Pub: Earl G. Graves Ltd.
Contact: Earl Graves, Jr., President
Ed: Renita Burns. **Description:** Health insurance premiums have increased between 15 percent and 20 percent for small business owners, making it one of the most expensive costs. Ways to evaluate a health plan's costs and effectiveness are examined. **Availability:** Online.

27295 ■ "Is Your Business Disaster Proof? How To Keep Your Company Up and Running Even After an Emergency" in Black Enterprise (Vol. 44, March 2014, No. 7, pp. 15)
Pub: Earl G. Graves Ltd.
Contact: Earl Graves, Jr., President
Description: Nearly 40 percent of all small businesses never reopen following a disaster. Floods are the most common event causing thousands of dollars in damages and shutting down companies. Commercial property insurance rarely covers flood damage. It usually covers physical assets such as buildings, equipment, inventory, computers, and records damaged by the event. Flood insurance must be purchased separately.

27296 ■ "It's Time for Insurance Carriers To Win More Customers; About One-Third of Insurance Customers are Engaged. This Means the Industry Has a Massive Opportunity to Gain More Business" in Gallup Business Journal (May 28, 2014)
Pub: Gallup, Inc.
Contact: Jon Clifton, Chief Executive Officer
Description: The insurance industry has the opportunity to engage and increase business and profits. Only one-third of insurance customers are engaged. Tips to help engage customers are offered. **Availability:** Print; Online.

27297 ■ "JK Lasser's New Rules for Estate, Retirement, and Tax Planning"
Pub: John Wiley & Sons, Inc.
Contact: Christina Van Tassell, Executive Vice President Chief Financial Officer
Released: 6th Edition. **Price:** $24.95, paperback; $16.99, E-book. **Description:** The authoritative guide to estate, retirement and tax planning is fully updated and reflects the new changes and legal updates. Estate planning section covers: planning, taxation, investing, wills, executors, trusts, life insurance, retirement planning, Social Security, business planning, succession, asset protection and family limited partnerships. **Availability:** E-book; Print.

27298 ■ "The Keeper of Records" in Black Enterprise (Vol. 41, December 2010, No. 5, pp. 54)
Pub: Earl G. Graves Ltd.
Contact: Earl Graves, Jr., President
Ed: Denise A. Campbell. **Description:** Medical billing and coding, submission of claims to health insurance companies and Medicare or Medicaid for payment is one of the fastest growing disciplines in healthcare. **Availability:** Online.

27299 ■ *"Labor Pains"* in Canadian Business (Vol. 79, August 14, 2006, No. 16-17, pp. 80) **Description:** Canada's employment insurance is analyzed in view of the growing shortage of labor. **Availability:** Print; Online.

27300 ■ *"The List: Top Insurance Agencies"* in South Florida Business Journal (Vol. 34, May 2, 2014, No. 41, pp. 10) Pub: American City Business Journals, Inc. Contact: Mike Olivieri, Executive Vice President **Released:** Weekly. **Price:** $8, Introductory 4-week offer(Digital & Print). **Description:** Rankings of insurance agencies in the South Florida area are presented. Rankings were based on the 2013 premium volume. **Availability:** Print; Online.

27301 ■ *"Markel American Insurance Company Announces Wedding and Special Event Insurance for Consumers"* in Benzinga.com (February 16, 2011) Pub: Benzinga.com Contact: Jason Raznick, Founder **Description:** Markel American Insurance Company, headquartered in Waukesha, Wisconsin has launched its new special event insurance and wedding insurance to protect both liabilities and cancellations associated with these events. **Availability:** Print; Online.

27302 ■ *"Maryland Hospitals Cope with Rare Drop in Patient Admissions"* in Baltimore Business Journal (Vol. 29, September 23, 2011, No. 20, pp. 1) Pub: Boston Business Journal Contact: Carolyn M. Jones, President E-mail: cmjones@bizjournals.com **Ed:** Scott Dance. **Description:** Admissions to Maryland hospitals have dropped to less than 700,000 in fiscal year 2010 and initial figures for fiscal 2011 show in-patient admissions are now nearing 660,000. The decline can be partly attributed to new ways health insurers are paying hospitals for care and to the financial reward hospitals get for cutting back on admissions. **Availability:** Online.

27303 ■ *"The Massachusetts Mess"* in Barron's (Vol. 89, July 27, 2009, No. 30, pp. 39) Pub: Dow Jones & Company Inc. Contact: Almar Latour, Chief Executive Officer **Ed:** Thomas G. Donlan. **Description:** Massachusetts' mandatory health insurance has produced the highest rate of insurance coverage among the states but the state is now unable to afford its dream of universal coverage just three years after they enacted it. This supposed model for federal health-care reform is turning out to be a joke. **Availability:** Online.

27304 ■ *"MCM Bulks Up by Merging With Maritime Insurer"* in Puget Sound Business Journal (Vol. 33, June 1, 2012, No. 6, pp. 1) Pub: Baltimore Business Journal Contact: Rhonda Pringle, President E-mail: rpringle@bizjournals.com **Ed:** Peter Neurath. **Description:** Seattle, Washington-based brokerage and benefits company MCM has formed a merger with Global Insurance Specialists that would strengthen its property-casualty insurance brokerage division. MCM has 2012 premium volume of $794.7 million, a total of 75 employees and provides service in areas such as employee benefits, executive benefits, and retirement plans. **Availability:** Print; Online.

27305 ■ *"Md. Faces Daunting Task of Educating Masses About Health Reform Law"* in Baltimore Business Journal (Vol. 28, October 15, 2010, No. 23, pp. 1) Pub: Baltimore Business Journal Contact: Rhonda Pringle, President E-mail: rpringle@bizjournals.com **Ed:** Emily Mullin. **Description:** The Henry J. Kaiser Family Foundation's survey shows nearly 53 percent of Americans remain confused about health care reform and it was up to the states to educate the people. However, Maryland is still trying to figure out how to conduct the campaign without guidance or funding from the Federal government. **Availability:** Print.

27306 ■ *"Meadowbrook To Acquire ProCentury in $272.6 Million Deal"* in Crain's Detroit Business (Vol. 24, February 21, 2008, No. 8, pp. 4) Pub: Crain Communications Inc. Contact: Barry Asin, President **Ed:** Jay Greene. **Description:** Meadowbrook Insurance Group, based in Southfield, Michigan reports its proposed acquisition of ProCentury Corporation based in Columbus, Ohio. Meadowbrook provides risk-management to agencies, professional and trade associations and small-to-midsize businesses. **Availability:** Print; Online.

27307 ■ *"Medicaid Insurers See Growth in Small Biz Market"* in Boston Business Journal (Vol. 31, July 15, 2011, No. 25, pp. 1) Pub: Boston Business Journal Contact: Carolyn M. Jones, President E-mail: cmjones@bizjournals.com **Ed:** Julie M. Donnelly. **Description:** BMC HealthNet Plan announced plans to launch small business products to serve small businesses that are priced out of rising premium rates at large Massachusetts insurers. BMC joined competitors CeltiCare Health Plan and Neighborhood Health Plan in augmenting its core business. **Availability:** Print; Online.

27308 ■ *"Medicare Plans Step Up Battle for Subscribers"* in Sacramento Business Journal (Vol. 28, October 21, 2011, No. 34, pp. 1) Pub: Sacramento Business Journal Contact: Stephanie Fretwell, Director E-mail: sfretwell@bizjournals.com **Ed:** Kathy Robertson. **Description:** California's market for health plans have become increasingly competitive as more than 313,000 seniors try to figure out the best plans to meet their needs for 2012. Health plans are rated on Medicare materials to help consumers distinguish among the Medicare health maintenance organizations (HMOs). **Availability:** Online.

27309 ■ *"Michigan Governor: Drivers to See More Savings Under Auto Insurance Reform Law"* in Insurance Journal (November 16, 2021) **Released:** November 16, 2021. **Description:** Michigan's new auto insurance law went into effect in 2019, which reduced rates for drivers. Now, Michigan drivers will see more savings through another piece of legislation that will allow them to choose their level of medical coverage. **Availability:** Online.

27310 ■ *"More Small Businesses in Baltimore Willing to Fund Employees' Health Benefits"* in Baltimore Business Journal (Vol. 28, June 18, 2010, No. 6, pp. 1) Pub: Baltimore Business Journal Contact: Rhonda Pringle, President E-mail: rpringle@bizjournals.com **Ed:** Scott Graham. **Description:** An increasing number of small businesses in Maryland are tapping into potentially cheaper self-funded health plans instead of providing fully insured benefits to employees through traditional health plans. Self-funded health plans charge employers for health care up to a specified level. Economic implications of self-funded plans to small businesses are discussed.

27311 ■ *"The New Janus CEO of Battle-Hardened Money Manager Plots Comeback"* in Denver Business Journal (Vol. 64, August 31, 2012, No. 15, pp. 1) Pub: Baltimore Business Journal Contact: Rhonda Pringle, President E-mail: rpringle@bizjournals.com **Description:** Richard Well, chief executive officer of Janus Capital Group Inc., discusses the strategic plans of the mutual fund company. He touches on the firm's alliance with Dai-chi Life Insurance Company Ltd., the future of equity markets, and the company's intelligent diversification strategy. **Availability:** Print; Online.

27312 ■ *"Nixon Assails Insurance Rules"* in Globe & Mail (March 4, 2006, pp. B5) **Ed:** Sinclair Stewart. **Description:** The opinions of chief executive officer Gordon Nixon of Royal Bank of Canada on the need to amend banking regulations, in order to provide insurance services, are presented. **Availability:** Print; Online.

27313 ■ *"North American Pet Health Insurance Market Poised for Growth"* in Pet Product News (Vol. 64, December 2010, No. 12, pp. 4) **Ed:** David Lummis. **Description:** The pet health insurance market is expected to further grow after posting about $350 million in sales in 2009, a gain of more than $40 million. Pet insurance firms have offered strategies such as product humanization in response to this growth forecast. Meanwhile, pet insurance shoppers have been provided more by insurance firms with wider choices. **Availability:** Online.

27314 ■ *"Northwestern Mutual Promotes Exec to Chief Insurance Officer"* in Bizwomen (March 24, 2023) URL(s): www.bizjournals.com/bizwomen/news/lates t-news/2023/03/northwestern-mutual-promotes -exec-to-chief.html **Ed:** Anne Stych. **Released:** March 24, 2023. **Description:** Kamilah Williams-Kemp has been promoted from VP of Risk Products to Executive VP and Chief Insurance Officer. **Availability:** Online.

27315 ■ *"Norvax University Health Insurance Sales Training and Online Marketing Conference"* in Marketwired (January 27, 2010) Pub: Comtex News Network Inc. Contact: Kan Devnani, President **Description:** Overview of the Norvax University Marketing and Sales Success Conference Tour which includes insurance sales training seminars, proven and innovative online marketing techniques and a host of additional information and networking opportunities. **Availability:** Print; Online.

27316 ■ *"Number-Cruncher Gets 'Pushback"* in Philadelphia Business Journal (Vol. 33, August 22, 2014, No. 28, pp. 10) Pub: American City Business Journals, Inc. Contact: Mike Olivieri, Executive Vice President **Released:** Weekly. **Price:** $4, introductory 4-week offer(Digital only). **Description:** Bryan Wellen, senior director of clinical informatics for Continuum Health Alliance (CHA), asserts that while some physicians are receptive to patient information, others respond with an element of 'pushback' and criticism of the data. CHA and Horizon Blue Cross Blue Shield of New Jersey are using data analysis to create strategies that improve health care and reduce costs. **Availability:** Print; Online.

27317 ■ *"Of Paper Towels and Health Insurance"* in Philadelphia Business Journal (Vol. 28, May 11, 2012, No. 13, pp. 1) Pub: Baltimore Business Journal Contact: Rhonda Pringle, President E-mail: rpringle@bizjournals.com **Description:** Health insurance companies are using different strategies to take advantage of the demand growth in health coverage in markets such as Philadelphia. Horizon Blue Cross Iue Shield of New Jersey, for example, is creating a retail center where customers can get information from specially trained staff about insurance, health and wellness. IBC, on the other hand, has partnered with AAA Mid-Atlantic to market its plan option to AAA members. **Availability:** Print; Online.

27318 ■ *"Open Enrollment: Staying Healthy During Enrollment Season"* in Employee Benefit News (Vol. 25, November 1, 2011, No. 14, pp. 41) Pub: SourceMedia LLC

Contact: Gemma Postlethwaite, Chief Executive Officer

Ed: Shana Sweeney. **Description:** Tips for staying healthy during your benefit open enrollment period are outlined.

27319 ■ "Open Enrollment: What Small Businesses Need to Know About the Affordable Care Act" in Business News Daily (February 21, 2023)
URL(s): www.businessnewsdaily.com/8535-open -enrollment-tips.html
Ed: Marisa Sanfilippo. **Released:** February 21, 2023. **Description:** Get the information you need to put together a benefits package for your employees using the Affordable Care Act. **Availability:** Online.

27320 ■ "Patients to Elect to Cut Care" in The Business Journal-Serving Metropolitan Kansas City (Vol. 27, November 21, 2008, No. 11, pp. 1)
Pub: American City Business Journals, Inc.
Contact: Mike Olivieri, Executive Vice President
Ed: Rob Roberts. **Description:** Patients in Kansas City, Missouri are cutting down on health care services due to the economic crisis. A decline in diagnostic procedures has been observed at Northland Cardiology. Elective reconstructive procedures have also been reduced by 25 percent. Additional information and statistics regarding the healthcare sector is included. **Availability:** Online.

27321 ■ "The People Puzzle; Re-Training America's Workers" in The Economist (Vol. 390, January 3, 2009, No. 8612, pp. 32)
Description: With thousands of workers losing their jobs, America is now facing the task of getting them back to work. With an overall unemployment rate of 6.7 percent, the federal government has three main ways for leading workers back to employment: training them for new jobs, providing unemployment insurance in order to replace lost wages during the period of job-hunting; and matching employers who desire a skill with workers who have that skill. Specialized staffing agencies provide employers and potential employees with the help necessary to find a job in some of the more niche markets. **Availability:** Online.

27322 ■ "Planning a Wedding Fit for a Royal? Read This First, Urge Legal & General" in Marketwired (April 21, 2011)
Released: April 21, 2011. **Description:** When planning a wedding, the author suggests checking life insurance to be sure you are covered for any situations that may arise. **Availability:** Print; Online.

27323 ■ "The Price of Citizenship" in Canadian Business (Vol. 79, August 14, 2006, No. 16-17, pp. 13)
Description: Safety and insurance benefits provided by the Canadian government to Canadian passport holders returning from Lebanon, is discussed. **Availability:** Print; Online.

27324 ■ "Private Health-Care Services Growing in Canada" in Canadian Business (Vol. 85, June 11, 2012, No. 10, pp. 10)
Ed: Laura Cameron. **Description:** Some public-private partnerships in Canada include the acquisition of clinics by Centric Health Corporation and the partnership between Westbank First National and Johns Hopkins Hospital. Private healthcare providers have operated by dividing their funding among government contracts, clients not covered by Medicare and patients paying out of pocket and noninsured services. **Availability:** Print; Online.

27325 ■ "Public Health Care Funding and the Montana Economy" in Montana Business Quarterly (Vol. 49, Spring 2011, No. 1, pp. 23)
Pub: University of Montana Bureau of Business and Economic Research
Contact: Patrick Barkey, Director
E-mail: patrick.barkey@business.umt.edu

Ed: Gregg Davis. **Released:** Quarterly. **Description:** Montana has more baby boomers and veterans per capita than any other state in the nation. The role of public health in the state is a crucial part of the state's economy. **Availability:** Online.

27326 ■ "Questions Abound in Voluminous Health Care Reform Law" in Memphis Business Journal (Vol. 34, July 6, 2012, No. 12, pp. 1)
Pub: Baltimore Business Journal
Contact: Rhonda Pringle, President
E-mail: rpringle@bizjournals.com
Ed: Cole Epley. **Description:** US Supreme Court has upheld the health care reform legislation, also known as Obamacare, as the law of the land. However, key questions remain and conjecture surrounding which direction states and insurance providers will pursue abounds. Insights on possible impact of health care providers of TennCare are also given. **Availability:** Print; Online.

27327 ■ Quitting Your Day Job? The Basics on Benefits Coverage for Entrepreneurs
URL(s): www.businessnewsdaily.com/8927-self-em-ployed-benefits-coverage.html
Released: February 21, 2023. **Description:** If you are quitting your corporate job to launch a small business, be prepared to leave behind your benefits. This article discusses the various benefits and insurance along with what you need to do to gain coverage in your new venture. **Availability:** Online.

27328 ■ "Reaching Out: the LIFE Foundation Provides Free Tools and Resources to Help Agents Boost Their Life Insurance Sales" in Best's Review (Vol. 113, September 2012, No. 5, pp. 26)
Description: The LIFE Foundation's LIFE program is profiled. The program offers free tools and resources for life insurance agents. **Availability:** Print; Online.

27329 ■ "Recovery on Tap for 2010?" in Orlando Business Journal (Vol. 26, January 1, 2010, No. 31, pp. 1)
Pub: Orlando Business Journal
Contact: Julie Swyers, Director
E-mail: jswyers@bizjournals.com
Ed: Melanie Stawicki Azam, Richard Bilbao, Christopher Boyd, Anjali Fluker. **Description:** Economic forecasts for Central Florida's leading business sectors in 2010 are presented. These sectors include housing, film and TV, sports business, law, restaurants, aviation, tourism and hospitality, banking and finance, commercial real estate, retail, health care, insurance, higher education, and manufacturing. According to some local executives, Central Florida's economy will slowly recover in 2010. **Availability:** Online.

27330 ■ "Reimbursement Limitations on Home Healthcare Are Being Loosened" in Modern Healthcare (October 27, 2018)
URL(s): www.modernhealthcare.com/article/201810 27/NEWS/181029949/reimbursement-limitations-on -home-healthcare-are-being-loosened
Ed: Shelby Livingston. **Released:** October 27, 2018. **Description:** Insurers are now focused on keeping patients out of the hospital and letting them be cared for at home, which actually saves money in the long-term. More and more care is being done at home, leading to better patient response and preventing them from returning to the hospital for more care. **Availability:** Online.

27331 ■ "Rich or Poor, Hospitals Must Work Together" in Crain's Chicago Business (Vol. 31, April 28, 2008, No. 17, pp. 22)
Pub: Crain Communications Inc.
Contact: Barry Asin, President
Description: Chicago-area safety-net hospitals that serve the poor, uninsured and underinsured are struggling to stay open while wealthier areas compete to build advanced facilities for the expensive surgical procedures their privately insured patients can afford. If these safety-net hospitals close, their patients, many of them in ambulances, will show up at the

remaining hospitals resulting in a strain that will test the ability of hospitals across the region to care for all of their patients. Hospitals need to address the threats to the local health care system before it slips into crisis since the current every-hospital-for-itself approach that pays off big for some will eventually will make losers of everyone. **Availability:** Online.

27332 ■ "Ride Apps Uber, Lyft, Sidecar Hit Speed Bumps" in San Francisco Business Times (Vol. 28, January 24, 2014, No. 27, pp. 4)
Pub: American City Business Journals, Inc.
Contact: Mike Olivieri, Executive Vice President
Released: Weekly. **Price:** $4, Introductory 4-week offer(Digital & Print). **Description:** California's Public Utilities Commission (PUC) has reversed its earlier prohibition and allowed mobile app ride services, while imposing insurance and safety regulations on these alternatives to taxicabs and limousine services. However, the PUC did not take action when the issue of liability and insurance were raised due to the death of Sofia Liu, who was hit by an Uber driver. The lawsuits against Uber are discussed. **Availability:** Print; Online.

27333 ■ "Riding Herd on Health Care" in Business Journal Portland (Vol. 30, February 7, 2014, No. 49, pp. 8)
Pub: American City Business Journals, Inc.
Contact: Mike Olivieri, Executive Vice President
Released: February 07, 2014. **Description:** Singing rancher and aspiring gubernatorial candidate, Jon Justesen, explains his views on universal healthcare. He expresses support for health care reform and Cover Oregon and he is looking at his options after dropping his Republican primary bid. **Availability:** Print; Online.

27334 ■ "Rising Above Flood-Insurance Costs" in Providence Business News (Vol. 28, February 3, 2014, No. 44, pp. 1)
Pub: American City Business Journals, Inc.
Contact: Mike Olivieri, Executive Vice President
Released: February 01, 2014. **Description:** Businesses are advised to examine flood insurance costs when rebuilding or expanding their facilities. Some firms choose to elevate their buildings in response to the redrawing of Federal Emergency Management Agency flood maps and regulations. The process for getting a flood-elevation survey is also explored. **Availability:** Print; Online.

27335 ■ "RPA Preps for Building Radiant Conference, Show" in Contractor (Vol. 57, January 2010, No. 1, pp. 5)
Description: Radiant Panel Association is accepting registrations for its Building Radiant 2010 Conference and Trade Show. The conference will discuss radiant heating as well as insurance and other legal matters for mechanical contractors. **Availability:** Print; Online.

27336 ■ "A Safety Net in Need of Repair" in The Economist (Vol. 390, January 3, 2009, No. 8612, pp. 33)
Description: America's unemployment-insurance scheme is outdated and skimpy compared to other industrialized countries despite the fact that Americans tend to work harder at returning to the job market; the benefits are lower and available for a smaller amount of time and less unemployed workers are even able to collect these benefits. Statistical data included.

27337 ■ "Small Biz Owners Are Tapping Into Health Savings Plans" in Small Business Opportunities (Fall 2007)
Description: Health savings accounts were developed by Golden Rule, a United Healthcare company. Today, more than 40 percent of the company's customers are covered by health savings account plans.

27338 ■ *Small Businesses Without Insurance Take Dangerous Risks*
URL(s): www.businessnewsdaily.com/5896-small
-business-insurance-tips.html
Released: February 21, 2023. **Description:** Business insurance is there to protect your business from certain types of risk, and some are required by law. However, that could end up costing you if something happens and the business isn't covered. Included are details about various types of insurance and what they cover. **Availability:** Online.

27339 ■ *"Small, But Mighty" in Employee Benefit News (Vol. 25, November 1, 2011, No. 14, pp. 32)*
Pub: SourceMedia LLC
Contact: Gemma Postlethwaite, Chief Executive Officer
Ed: Andrea Davis. **Description:** Three consulting firms are facing the challenge of helping clients understand the new health care reform in a tight economy. **Availability:** Print; PDF; Online.

27340 ■ *"The Smell of Fear: Is a Bottom Near?" in Barron's (Vol. 88, March 17, 2008, No. 11, pp. M3)*
Pub: Dow Jones & Company Inc.
Contact: Almar Latour, Chief Executive Officer
Ed: Kopin Tan. **Description:** Liquidity problems at Bear Stearns frightened investors in markets around the world due to the fear of the prospects of a big bank's failure. Shares of health maintenance organizations got battered led by WellPoint, and Humana but longer-term investors who could weather short-term volatility may find value here. The value of J. Crew shares is also discussed. **Availability:** Online.

27341 ■ *"Spouses, Health Coaching Added to Mix" in Pittsburgh Business Times (Vol. 33, June 6, 2014, No. 47, pp. 5)*
Pub: American City Business Journals, Inc.
Contact: Mike Olivieri, Executive Vice President
Released: Weekly. **Price:** $4, introductory 4-week offer (Digital & Print). **Description:** Hospital giant, UPMC, was the Category Winner in the 5,000+ employees group of Healthiest Employers in Western Pennsylvania, for its initiative in expanding its health assessment and wellness programs to the spouses and partners of all its employees, regardless of their health insurance carrier. In addition, UPMC Health Plan expanded its individual health coaching option for members as well as corporate clients. **Availability:** Print; Online.

27342 ■ *Starting & Running Your Own Horse Business*
Pub: Storey Publishing L.L.C.
Contact: Maribeth Casey, Director
E-mail: maribeth.casey@storey.com
Ed: Mary Ashby McDonald. **Released:** Second edition. **Price:** $19.95, trade paper. **Description:** Insight into starting and running a successful equestrian business is given. The book covers safety, tips for operating a riding school or horse camp, strategies for launching a carriage business, along with tax and insurance advice. **Availability:** E-book; Print.

27343 ■ *"State Pressure Keeps Rates Low" in Sacramento Business Journal (Vol. 31, August 8, 2014, No. 24, pp. 4)*
Pub: American City Business Journals, Inc.
Contact: Mike Olivieri, Executive Vice President
Description: The proposed California Covered rate increases are likely to hit an average 4.2 percent in 2015, with the average increase in Sacramento expected at 3.7 percent. The health insurance exchange was set up to be an active purchaser so that it differs with the proposed exchange in other states, which range from 8 percent to 20 percent. Insights on the advantages of Covered California are presented. **Availability:** Print; Online.

27344 ■ *"Steeling for Battle" in Crain's Chicago Business (Vol. 31, April 21, 2008, No. 16, pp. 3)*
Pub: Crain Communications Inc.
Contact: Barry Asin, President

Ed: Bob Tita. **Description:** Discusses contract negotiations between the United Steelworkers union and ArcelorMittal USA Inc., the nation's largest steelmaker, and U.S. Steel Corp., the third-largest; the union sees these negotiations as the best chance in two decades to regain lost ground but industry experts predict the companies will try to reduce benefits, demand a separate, lower wage scale for new hires and look for relief from the rising costs for retirees' health insurance coverage. **Availability:** Online.

27345 ■ *"Symbility Solutions Joins Motion Computing Partner Program" in Marketwired (May 14, 2007)*
Pub: Comtex News Network Inc.
Contact: Kan Devnani, President
Description: Symbility Solutions Inc., a wholly owned subsidiary of Automated Benefits Corp., announced an agreement with Alliance Partner of Motion Computing, a leader in wireless communications and mobile computing, in which both companies will invest in a sales and marketing strategy that focuses specifically on the insurance market. **Availability:** Print; Online.

27346 ■ *"Taking Full Advantage: What You Need To Know During Open-Enrollment Season" in Black Enterprise (Vol. 38, November 2007, No. 4)*
Pub: Earl G. Graves Ltd.
Contact: Earl Graves, Jr., President
Ed: Donald Jay Korn. **Description:** Employees can change or enroll in new insurance benefits during the fall season. It is important to assess each plan offered and to determine your deductible. Statistical data included. **Availability:** Online.

27347 ■ *"Top 5 Health Insurance Tips for the Self-Employed" in Legal Zoom (March 24, 2023)*
URL(s): www.legalzoom.com/articles/top-5-health
-insurance-tips-for-the-self-employed
Ed: Douglas Dalrymple. **Released:** March 24, 2023. **Description:** Self-employed people need to provide their health insurance since there is no big corporation that will give that to them as a benefit. This is often a big expense and the options can be confusing. Included are tips on what to consider. **Availability:** Online.

27348 ■ *"Top 50 In Total Revenue" in Canadian Business (Vol. 81, Summer 2008, No. 9, pp. 119)*
Description: Table showing the top 50 Canadian companies in terms of total revenue is presented. Manulife Financial Corp. topped the list with revenue of 34.5 billion. The financial services firm is the 6th largest provider of life insurance in the world and the second largest in North America. **Availability:** Print; Online.

27349 ■ *"Tropeano Takes Charge" in Philadelphia Business Journal (Vol. 33, August 22, 2014, No. 28, pp. 11)*
Pub: American City Business Journals, Inc.
Contact: Mike Olivieri, Executive Vice President
Released: Weekly. **Price:** $4, introductory 4-week offer(Digital only). **Description:** Dan Tropeano will serve as the new head of United Healthcare of Pennsylvania, while continuing in his position as executive director of United Healthcare's Pennsylvania and Delaware health plans. Tropeano discusses his new role and notes that the medical insurance market has become increasingly competitive as consumers seek cheaper and more flexible products. **Availability:** Print; Online.

27350 ■ *"Trusted Choice: Mobile App" in Best's Review (Vol. 113, September 2012, No. 5, pp. 14)*
Description: Profile of Trusted Choice, the new mobile app launched in March 2012 for use on smartphones and tablet computers. The app helps clients contact their independent insurance agent. Consumers can keep an inventory of insured personal possessions, document a car accident with photos,

read insurance tips, communicate with Trusted Choice agent and ask insurance-related questions. **Availability:** Online.

27351 ■ *"U.S. Combined Life and Health Writers--Industry's Reported Admitted Assets of $5.7 Trillion" in Best's Review (Vol. 113, September 2012, No. 5, pp. 33)*
Description: U.S. Combined Life and Health Writers--Industry's Reported Admitted Assets of $5.7 Trillion report is presented. Companies/Groups are ranked in 2011 by admitted assets. **Availability:** Print; Online.

27352 ■ *"Virtually Secure" in Rough Notes (Vol. 155, February 2012, No. 2, pp. 46)*
Pub: The Rough Notes Company Inc.
Contact: Walter J. Gdowski, President
E-mail: waltg@roughnotes.com
Ed: Nabeel Sayegh. **Availability:** PDF; Online.

27353 ■ *"VPA to Pay $9.5 Million to Settle Whistle-Blower Lawsuits" in Crain's Detroit Business (Vol. 26, January 11, 2010, No. 2, pp. 13)*
Pub: Crain Communications Inc.
Contact: Barry Asin, President
Ed: Jay Greene. **Description:** According to Terrence Berg, first assistant with the U.S. Attorney's Office in Detroit, Voluntary Physicians Association, a local home health care company, has agreed to pay $9.5 million to settle four whistle-blower lawsuits; the agreement settles allegations that VPA submitted claims to TriCare, the Michigan Medicaid program and Medicare for unnecessary home visits, tests and procedures. **Availability:** Online.

27354 ■ *"Week on the Web" in Crain's Detroit Business (Vol. 25, June 22, 2009, No. 25, pp. 19)*
Pub: Crain Communications Inc.
Contact: Barry Asin, President
Description: Blue Cross Blue Shield of Michigan, in a class-action lawsuit, will pay about 100 families whose children were either denied coverage for autism treatment or paid for treatment out of pocket. The settlement is worth about $ million. **Availability:** Print; Online.

27355 ■ *"Western & Southern to Trim Rich Retirement Plan" in Business Courier (Vol. 27, October 15, 2010, No. 24, pp. 1)*
Pub: Business Courier
Ed: Dan Monk. **Description:** Insurance firm Western & Southern Financial Group announced that it will reduce the pension benefits of its 4,000 associates by more than 30 percent starting January 1, 2011. The move is expected to reduce annual retirement payments by several thousand dollars per associate. Western is a Fortune 500 company and has $34 billion in total assets. **Availability:** Print; Online.

27356 ■ *"What Choice Did I Have?" in Entrepreneur (Vol. 37, October 2009, No. 10, pp. 88)*
Pub: Entrepreneur Media Inc.
Contact: Dan Bova, Director
E-mail: dbova@entrepreneur.com
Ed: Craig Matsuda. **Description:** Profile of a worker at a financial services company who acquired firsthand knowledge concerning the relationship between health insurance costs and coverage. The worker's son got severely ill, forcing the worker to spend above what is covered by health insurance. **Availability:** Print; Online.

27357 ■ *"What Should Your Insurance Agent Do for You?" in U.S. News & World Report (May 24, 2018)*
URL(s): money.usnews.com/money/personal-finance/
saving-and-budgeting/articles/2018-05-24/wha
t-should-your-insurance-agent-do-for-you
Ed: Maryalene LaPonsie. **Released:** May 24, 2018. **Description:** Discusses traits that good insurance agents possess, since not all agents and agencies operate the same way. Ones that offer personalized attention and make an effort to check in well after the

papers are signed, are two of the most important things an agent to do to go above and beyond. **Availability:** Online.

27358 ■ "Why Seattle Children's Appealed" in Puget Sound Business Journal (Vol. 35, May 30, 2014, No. 6, pp. 6)
Pub: American City Business Journals, Inc.
Contact: Mike Olivieri, Executive Vice President
Description: Seattle Children's Hospital filed an appeal against the Washing State Office of the Insurance Commissioner for approving several health exchange plans that excluded the hospital. Children's argues that it offers unique services and treatments only available through their medical facility and health insurance plans excluding them is putting children at risk. **Availability:** Online.

27359 ■ "Work/Life Balance" in Dallas Business Journal (Vol. 37, June 20, 2014, No. 41, pp. 4)
Pub: Routledge, Taylor & Francis Group
Description: Younger generations of corporate employees are increasingly looking for a more engaged workplace community. Research firm, Quantum Workplace, identifies several trends that help to attract and retain employees, including jobs that align with the workers' own values, growth opportunities within the firm, social interactions with co-workers, and employee health benefits. **Availability:** Print; Online.

STATISTICAL SOURCES

27360 ■ *Online Insurance Brokers Industry in the US - Market Research Report*
URL(s): www.ibisworld.com/united-states/market-research-reports/online-insurance-brokers-industry/
Price: $925. **Description:** Downloadable report analyzing the current and future trends in the online insurance broker industry. **Availability:** Download.

TRADE PERIODICALS

27361 ■ *The John Liner Letter*
Pub: Standard Publishing Corp.
Contact: John C. Cross, President
E-mail: j.cross@spcpub.com
URL(s): www.spcpub.com/page.cfm?name=John _Liner_letter&teaser=72
Released: Monthly **Price:** $427.50, for per year for combination print edition and single-user online access; $339, for online edition 12 monthly issue; $339, for print edition 12 monthly issue. **Description:** Provides risk management and technical insurance advice for business firms, such as broadening coverage, cutting costs, and anticipating special insurance problems. **Availability:** Print; Online.

VIDEO/AUDIO MEDIA

27362 ■ *The Best Small Business Show: Securing Success - Why Insurance Matters for Your Small Business*
URL(s): richgee.libsyn.com/298-securing-success -why-insurance-matters-for-your-small-business
Ed: Rich Gee. **Released:** June 05, 2023. **Description:** Podcast discusses the importance of insurance for small businesses.

27363 ■ *The How of Business: Kevin Ring - Workers' Compensation Insurance*
URL(s): www.thehowofbusiness.com/497-kevin-ring -workers-compensation-insurance
Ed: Henry Lopez. **Released:** November 04, 2023. **Description:** Podcast discusses the importance of understanding and managing workers' compensation insurance to balance both employee safety/benefits and the financial impact.

27364 ■ *The How of Business: LeRoy Wilkerson - Health Insurance Business*
URL(s): www.thehowofbusiness.com/epidose-047 -leroy-wilkerson

Ed: Henry Lopez. **Released:** October 17, 2016. **Description:** Podcast discusses both staring an insurance agency and offering insurance benefits as a small business,.

TRADE SHOWS AND CONVENTIONS

27365 ■ Capitol Conference
National Association of Health Underwriters (NAHU)
    999 E St. NW, Ste. 400
    Washington, DC 20004
Ph: (202)552-5060
Fax: (202)747-6820
Co. E-mail: info@nahu.org
URL: http://nahu.org
Contact: Janet Trautwein, Chief Executive Officer
E-mail: jtrautwein@nahu.org
URL(s): nabip.org/capitol-conference
Frequency: Annual. **Description:** Insurance agents and brokers engaged in the promotion, sale, and administration of disability income and health insurance. **Audience:** Licensed health insurance agents, brokers, general agents, consultants, and benefit professionals. **Principal Exhibits:** Insurance agents and brokers engaged in the promotion, sale, and administration of disability income and health insurance. Dates and Locations: Hyatt Regency Capitol Hill, Washington, DC; 2025 Feb 23-26; 2026 Feb 22-25; 2027 Feb 21-24; 2028 Feb 27-Mar 01. **Telecommunication Services:** meetings@nahu.org.

27366 ■ Houston Insurance Day
URL(s): www.iiah.org/events/EventDetails.aspx?i d=1425390&group=
Frequency: Annual. **Description:** Tradeshow and networking for insurance professionals. **Audience:** Insurance professionals. **Principal Exhibits:** Tradeshow and networking for insurance professionals.

27367 ■ ICMG Annual Meeting
URL(s): www.icmg.org//conference
Frequency: Annual. **Description:** Conference to network and develop business partnerships in the insurance and financial product industries. **Principal Exhibits:** Conference to network and develop business partnerships in the insurance and financial product industries.

27368 ■ IFCA Life Communicators Association Convention
URL(s): www.ifcaonline.com
Frequency: Annual. **Description:** Presentations on the latest trends and to participate in skill enhancing workshops. **Audience:** Communicators from insurance and financial services. **Principal Exhibits:** Presentations on the latest trends and to participate in skill enhancing workshops.

27369 ■ International Claim Association Annual Education Conference
International Claim Association (ICA)
    1800 M St., NW 400 S
    Washington, DC 20036
Ph: (202)452-0143
Fax: (202)530-0659
Co. E-mail: memberservices@claim.org
URL: http://www.claim.org
Contact: Kimberly Tomaselli, President
URL(s): www.claim.org/events/ica-2024-annual-e ducation-conference-2
Frequency: Annual; every September to October. **Description:** Insurance claims industry research, training, and communications. **Audience:** Industry professionals. **Principal Exhibits:** Insurance claims industry research, training, and communications. Dates and Locations: 2025 Sep 27-30 New Orleans Marriott, New Orleans, LA; 2026 Sep 13-16 Gaylord Texan, Grapevine, TX. **Telecommunication Services:** memberservices@claim.org.

27370 ■ National Association of Catastrophe Adjusters Annual Convention
URL(s): www.nacatadj.org/convention

Price: $799, Members On-site.; $979, Non-members On-site. **Description:** Offers education, networking, and access to new products and companies within the adjustor industry. **Audience:** Independent adjusters. **Principal Exhibits:** Offers education, networking, and access to new products and companies within the adjustor industry.

27371 ■ National Education Association Annual Meeting
National Education Association (NEA)
    1201 16th St. NW
    Washington, DC 20036-3290
Ph: (202)833-4000
Free: 800-637-4636
Fax: (202)822-7974
Co. E-mail: neamobilealerts@nea.org
URL: http://www.nea.org
Contact: Becky Pringle, President
URL(s): www.nea.org/professional-excellence/ conferences-events/annual-meeting-and-representa tive-assembly
Frequency: Annual. **Description:** Insurance providers, educational programs and services. **Audience:** Education professionals and students. **Principal Exhibits:** Insurance providers, educational programs and services. Dates and Locations: 2025 Jul 02-06 Portland, OR; 2026 Jul 03-07 Denver, CO; 2027 Jul 01-05 Indianapolis, IN; 2028 Jul 01-05 Washington, DC; 2029 Jul 01-05 Kansas City, MO.

CONSULTANTS

27372 ■ Business Insurance Consultants Inc. (BIC)
30 Freneau Ave., Ste. 2A
    Matawan, NJ 07747
Ph: (732)946-9300
Fax: (732)946-7505
Co. E-mail: bicinc@businessinsure.com
URL: http://businessinsure.com
Description: Firm provides personal and business insurance, payroll processing, request, human resources, IT security and related services. **Scope:** Firm provides personal and business insurance, payroll processing, request, human resources, IT security and related services. **Founded:** 1990. **Special Services:** Trusted Choice.

27373 ■ Health Insurance Specialists Inc. (HISI)
PO Box 5743
    Derwood, MD 20855
Ph: (301)590-0006
Fax: (301)590-0661
Co. E-mail: info@his-inc.com
URL: http://his-inc.com
Facebook: www.facebook.com/Heal thInsuranceSpecialistsInc
Description: Firm provides insurance and business financial planning solutions. **Scope:** Firm provides insurance and business financial planning solutions. **Founded:** 1982.

27374 ■ Leonard R. Friedman Risk Management Inc.
1979 Marcus Ave., Ste. E100
    Lake Success, NY 11042
Contact: Alice B. Weiss, Chief Executive Officer
Description: Provider of independent insurance and risk management and also provides related services. **Scope:** Provider of independent insurance and risk management and also provides related services.

27375 ■ Siver Insurance Consultants
13575 58th St. N ste. 238
    Clearwater, FL 33760
Ph: (727)577-2780
Fax: (727)579-8692
URL: http://www.siver.com
Contact: James Marshall, Jr., President
E-mail: jmarshall@siver.com
Description: Firm provides insurance advice and consultancy. **Scope:** Firm provides insurance advice and consultancy. **Founded:** 1970. **Training:** Third

Party Administrators Performance Audit: Self Funded Group Medical Programs; Self Funded Workers Compensation Programs.

27376 ■ United Insurance Consultants Inc. (UIC)

500 N Franklin Turnpike Ste. 220
  Ramsey, NJ 07446
Ph: (201)661-5010
Co. E-mail: riskadvisory@uici.com
URL: http://uici.com
Facebook: www.facebook.com/UICInc
Linkedin: www.linkedin.com/company/uic-inc----risk
  -management-consultants

Description: Firm provides program audits, enterprise risk management and much more. **Founded:** 1978.

FRANCHISES AND BUSINESS OPPORTUNITIES

27377 ■ A.D. Banker & Co.

7311 W 130th St., Ste. 160
  Overland Park, KS 66213
Free: 800-866-2468
Co. E-mail: help@adbanker.com
Facebook: www.facebook.com/adbanker

Description: Provides prelicensing candidates with the information needed to pass insurance and securities licensing exams.

27378 ■ Paul Davis Restoration Inc. (PDR)

FirstService Brands
  7251 Salisbury Rd.
  Jacksonville, FL 32256
Free: 866-366-0420
Fax: (601)549-7973
URL: http://www.fsvbrands.com
Contact: Rich Wilson, President
URL(s): www.fsvbrands.com/our_companies/paul
  _davis.html
Facebook: www.facebook.com/PaulDavisRestora
  tionInc
Linkedin: www.linkedin.com/company/paul-davis-res
  toration
X (Twitter): x.com/PDRestoration
YouTube: www.youtube.com/user/PDRestorationInc

Description: Computerized contracting and cleaning services to the insurance industry. **No. of Operating Units:** 300. **Founded:** 1966. **Financial Assistance:** Yes **Training:** 4 week training at corporate headquarters, followed by 1 week of onsite training at new franchise location.

27379 ■ Puroclean-The Paramedics of Property Damage

4360 Oakes Rd., Unit 526
  Davie, FL 33314
Ph: (954)233-1100
Free: 800-775-7876
Co. E-mail: info.davie@puroclean.com
URL: http://www.puroclean.com
Contact: Steve White, President
X (Twitter): twitter.com/puroclean
YouTube: www.youtube.com/purosystems
Pinterest: www.pinterest.com/puroclean

Description: Firm provides property damage restoration, mold and mildew removal and biohazard cleanup solutions. **Founded:** 1989. **Financial Assistance:** Yes **Training:** Provides 3 weeks at corporate training center & 1 week field training covering customer service, marketing/advertising, computer software, product knowledge, management, & hands-on application with ongoing 24 hour support. **Educational Activities:** PLRB Claims Conference & Insurance Services Expo (Annual).

COMPUTERIZED DATABASES

27380 ■ *Business Insurance*

Crain Communications Inc.
  1155 Gratiot Ave.
  Detroit, MI 48207-2732
Ph: (313)446-6000
Co. E-mail: info@crain.com
URL: http://www.crain.com
Contact: Barry Asin, President
URL(s): www.businessinsurance.com
Facebook: www.facebook.com/BusInsMagazine
Linkedin: www.linkedin.com/company/business
  -insurance
X (Twitter): x.com/BusInsMagazine

Released: Biweekly **Description:** International newsweekly reporting on corporate risk and employee benefit management news. **Availability:** Print; Online. **Type:** Full-text.

LIBRARIES

27381 ■ Anderson Kill P.C. - Library

1717 Pennsylvania Ave. NW, Ste. 200
  Washington, DC 20006
Ph: (202)416-6500
Co. E-mail: information@andersonkill.com
URL: http://www.andersonkill.com
Contact: Rhonda D. Orin, Managing Partner
E-mail: rorin@andersonkill.com
Facebook: www.facebook.com/AndersonKillLaw
Linkedin: www.linkedin.com/company/andersonkilllaw
X (Twitter): x.com/andersonkilllaw

Description: A law firm in United States. **Scope:** Insurance - property, fire, medical disability, casualty; law - civil, insurance. **Services:** Interlibrary loan; library not open to the public. **Holdings:** Books and periodicals.

27382 ■ Buffalo & Erie County Public Library-Business, Science & Technology

1 Lafayette Sq.
  Buffalo, NY 14203
URL: http://www.buffalolib.org

Scope: Investments, real estate, economics, marketing, engineering, computer science, technology, medical information for laymen, consumer information, automotive repair. **Services:** Interlibrary loan; copying; library open to the public. **Founded:** 1952. **Holdings:** 312,916 books; 60,516 bound periodical volumes; 600 periodical.

27383 ■ Long & Levit Library

465 California St., Fifth Fl.
  San Francisco, CA 94104
Ph: (415)397-2222
URL: http://www.longlevit.com
Contact: Jennifer W. Suzuki, Partner
E-mail: jsuzuki@longlevit.com

Scope: Insurance; environment; professional liability; construction. **Services:** Interlibrary loan; copying; library open to the public at librarian's discretion. **Founded:** 1927. **Holdings:** 10,000 books.

27384 ■ National Association of Professional Insurance Agents (PIA) - Library

419 North Lee St.
  Alexandria, VA 22314
Ph: (703)836-9340
Fax: (703)836-1279
URL: http://www.pianational.org
Contact: Lauren Pachman, Director
E-mail: lpachman@pianational.org
Facebook: www.facebook.com/PIANational
Linkedin: www.linkedin.com/company/pianational
X (Twitter): x.com/PIANational
Instagram: www.instagram.com/pia_national

Description: Represents independent agents in all fifty states, Puerto Rico and the District of Columbia. Represents members' interests in government and industry; provides educational programs; compiles statistics; conducts research programs; develops products/services unique to independent agencies; provides information and networking opportunities. **Scope:** Advocacy; insurance. **Founded:** 1931. **Holdings:** Figures not available. **Publications:** *Consumer Brochures for Your Clients*; *PIA Connection* (10/year); *Professional Agent* (Monthly). **Awards:** PIA National Company Award of Excellence (Annual); PIA National Company Representative of the Year Award (Annual); PIA National Professional Agent of the Year (Annual); The PIA National Customer Service Representative (CSR) of the Year Award (Annual); Agent of the Year (Annual); Company Representative of the Year (Annual). **Geographic Preference:** National; Regional.

FARM CREDIT ADMINISTRATION

27385 ■ *"Transforming the Business Portfolio: How Multinationals Reinvent Themselves" in Journal of Business Strategy (Vol. 35, May-June 2014, No. 3, pp. 4-17)*
Emerald Group Publishing Limited
120 Beacon St., Ste. 202
Somerville, MA 02143
Contact: Erika Valenti, President
Description: Study on the process of business portfolio transformations to investigate its precursors, practices, and outcomes, including repositioning, refocusing, and diversifying of portfolio restructurings is presented. It is observed that poor performance and over-diversification induce portfolio restructuring. The results also revealed that diversifying or repositioning transformations feature a low success rate, whereas refocusing transformations generally happen to be more successful. **Availability:** Download; Online.

TENNESSEE VALLEY AUTHORITY

27386 ■ *"Six Ways Employees on LinkedIn Benefit the Boss" in South Florida Business Journal (Vol. 34, April 25, 2014, No. 40)*
American City Business Journals, Inc. (ACBJ)
120 W Morehead St.
Charlotte, NC 28202
Co. E-mail: circhelp@bizjournals.com
URL: http://www.acbj.com
Contact: Mike Olivieri, Executive Vice President
Released: Weekly. **Price:** $8, Introductory 4-week offer(Digital & Print). **Description:** LinkedIn can be a useful tool for executives. In addition to finding staff when hiring, the information service can give U.S.-based users a more global perspective. It can also be a way to share recent company accomplishment. **Availability:** Print; Online.

START-UP INFORMATION

27387 ■ *Canadian Small Business Kit for Dummies*
Ed: Margaret Kerr, JoAnn Kurtz, Andrew Dagys. **Released:** 4th edition. **Price:** $26.60, paperback; $39.99, paperback. **Description:** Resources include information on changes to laws and taxes for small businesses in Canada. **Availability:** Print; Online.

27388 ■ *"CrowdFunding Platform, START.ac, Announces It Is Expanding Its International Scope From the US, Canada and the UK to 36 Countries Including Australia, India, Israel, Italy and Africa" in Benzinga.com (July 11, 2012)*
Pub: Benzinga.com
Contact: Jason Raznick, Founder

Ed: Aaron Wise. **Description:** START.ac is expanding its CrowdFunding site to include 36 countries and increasing its scope to include business startups, teen projects, as well as medical products. START.ac projects are in the fundraising stage at this point, with 23 percent located outside the United States. **Availability:** Online.

27389 ■ *International Entrepreneurship: Starting, Developing, and Managing a Global Venture*
Pub: SAGE Publications
Contact: Tracey Ozmina, President
Ed: Robert D. Hisrich. **Released:** Third edition. **Price:** $95, paperback. **Description:** International entrepreneurship combines the aspects of domestic entrepreneurship along with other disciplines, including anthropology, economics, geography, history, jurisprudence, and language. **Availability:** Print; Online.

27390 ■ *"Savvy Solutions" in Black Enterprise (Vol. 41, December 2010, No. 5, pp. 42)*
Pub: Earl G. Graves Ltd.
Contact: Earl Graves, Jr., President
Ed: Tennille M. Robinson. **Description:** Individual asks for advice in launching a graphic design business, particularly grants available in a slow economy.

ASSOCIATIONS AND OTHER ORGANIZATIONS

27391 ■ **American Association of Exporters and Importers (AAEI) - Essential Library**
1717 K St. NW, Ste. 1120
Washington, DC 20006
Ph: (202)857-8009
Fax: (202)857-7843
Co. E-mail: hq@aaei.org
URL: http://aaei.org
Contact: Eugene Laney, Jr., President
Facebook: www.facebook.com/AAEITrade
Linkedin: www.linkedin.com/company/american
-association-of-exporters-and-importers
X (Twitter): x.com/aaeitrade
Description: Exporters and importers of goods, products, and raw materials; wholesalers and retailers; customs brokers and forwarders; banks; insurance underwriters; steamship companies; customs attorneys and others engaged directly or indirectly in dealing with exports and imports. **Scope:** Harmonized tariff schedule; international trade references; food & drug industry CFR set; international trade CFR set. **Founded:** 1921. **Holdings:** Figures not available. **Publications:** *International Trade Alert* (Weekly); *American Association of Exporters and Importers--Membership Directory* (Irregular). **Geographic Preference:** National.

27392 ■ **American Hellenic Institute (AHI)**
1220 16th St. NW
Washington, DC 20036

Ph: (202)785-8430
Co. E-mail: info@ahiworld.org
URL: http://www.ahiworld.org
Contact: Nick Larigakis, President
E-mail: nlarigakis@ahiworld.org
Facebook: www.facebook.com/AmericanHellenicInsti
tute
X (Twitter): x.com/theahiindc
Instagram: www.instagram.com/american.hellenic.ins
titute
YouTube: www.youtube.com/channel/UCIFH0HVPj
te7lk_-dnSAszQ
Description: Seeks to strengthen political, cultural, trade, commerce, and related matters between the US. and Greece, Cyprus, and the American Hellenic community. Conducts research on issues such as Turkish threats to the Aegean, Cyprus, the rule of law, and human rights. Sponsors internship program and seminars. **Founded:** 1974. **Publications:** *AHI Report* (Irregular); *American Hellenic Who's Who*; *General News*; *Handbook on United States Relations with Greece and Cyprus*; *Rule of Law and Conditions on Foreign Aid to Turkey*. **Geographic Preference:** National.

27393 ■ **American Indonesian Chamber of Commerce (AICC)**
521 5th Ave., Ste. 1700
New York, NY 10175
Ph: (212)687-4505
Fax: (212)687-5844
Co. E-mail: director@aiccusa.org
URL: http://www.aiccusa.org
Contact: Wayne Forrest, President
Description: Holds briefings on new trade policies in Indonesia and offers orientation workshops for American company personnel traveling to Indonesia. **Founded:** 1949. **Publications:** *American Business Directory for Indonesia* (Periodic); *Executive Diary*; *Members Bulletin* (Periodic); *Outlook Indonesia* (Monthly); *Sourcing Products in Indonesia: A Guide for Importers*. **Geographic Preference:** National.

27394 ■ **American-Uzbekistan Chamber of Commerce (AUCC)**
2020 Pennsylvania Ave., NW No. 274
Washington, DC 20006
Ph: (202)509-3744
Co. E-mail: info@aucconline.com
URL: http://aucconline.com
Contact: Steven Nadherny, President
Description: Brings together companies and individual professionals interested in promoting trade and investment between Uzbekistan and the United States. Represents business and industry to promote growth in interest of the U.S. business community in Uzbekistan. **Founded:** 1993. **Geographic Preference:** National.

27395 ■ **Australian Trade and Investment Commission (AUSTRADE)**
150 E 42nd St., 34th Fl.
New York, NY 10017
Ph: (646)344-8111

Fax: (212)867-7710
URL: http://www.austrade.gov.au
Contact: Xavier Simonet, Chief Executive Officer
Linkedin: www.linkedin.com/company/australian-tra
 de-commission
X (Twitter): x.com/Austrade
YouTube: www.youtube.com/user/austrade

Description: Works in the promotion of Australian products and investments in the U.S. **Publications:** *Export Update.* **Geographic Preference:** National.

27396 ■ Austrian Trade Commissions in the United States (ATCUSC)
11601 Wilshire Blvd., Ste. 2420
 Los Angeles, CA 90025
Ph: (310)477-9988
Fax: (310)477-1643
Co. E-mail: losangeles@advantageaustria.org
URL: http://www.advantageaustria.org/us/servicecen
 ter/Buero-Los-Angeles.en.html
Contact: Laura Miller, Manager, Business Development

Description: Corporations in Austria, Canada and the United States. Promotes increased trade between the U.S., Canada, and Austria. Works to remove legislative barriers to international trade; represents members before international trade organizations and agencies; facilitates establishment of joint ventures and other international business connections involving members. **Geographic Preference:** National.

27397 ■ Brazilian-American Chamber of Commerce (BACC)
485 Madison Ave., Ste. 401
 New York, NY 10022
Ph: (212)751-4691
Co. E-mail: info@brazilcham.com
URL: http://www.brazilcham.com
Contact: Simoni Morato, President
Facebook: www.facebook.com/BrazilUSCham
Linkedin: www.linkedin.com/in/brazilian-american
 -chamber-of-commerce
X (Twitter): x.com/brazilcham
Instagram: www.instagram.com/braziluscham
YouTube: www.youtube.com/user/brazilcham

Description: Corporations. partnerships, financial institutions, and individuals either in the U.S. or Brazil interested in fostering two-way trade and investment between the countries. **Founded:** 1969. **Publications:** *Brazilian-American Who's Who* (Irregular); *Brazilian-American Business Review/Directory* (Annual). **Awards:** Brazilian-American Chamber of Commerce Person of the Year (Annual). **Geographic Preterence:** National.

27398 ■ Brazilian Government Trade Bureau of the Consulate General of Brazil in New York
225 E 41st St. between 2nd & 3rd Ave.
 New York, NY 10017
Ph: (917)777-7777
Fax: (212)827-0225
Co. E-mail: cg.novayork@itamaraty.gov.br
URL: http://www.gov.br/mre/pt-br/consulado-nova
 -york

Description: Commercial Office of the Brazil Consulate in New York. Offers online match between Brazilian exporters of goods and services and U.S. importers. **Geographic Preference:** National.

27399 ■ British Trade Office at Consulate-General
1 Dag Hammarskjold Plz.
 885 Second Ave.
 New York, NY 10017-6927
Ph: (212)745-0200
Fax: (212)745-0463
Co. E-mail: public.affairsny@fcdo.gov.uk
URL: http://www.gov.uk/world/organisations/british
 -consulate-general-new-york
Contact: Hannah Young, Contact
X (Twitter): x.com/ukinnewyork
Instagram: www.instagram.com/ukinnewyork

Description: British government office that promotes trade with the U.S.; assists British companies selling in the U.S.; aids American companies that wish to import goods from or invest in Britain. **Geographic Preference:** National.

27400 ■ BritishAmerican Business Inc. of New York and London (BAB)
52 Vanderbilt Ave., 20th Fl.
 New York, NY 10017
Ph: (212)661-4060
Fax: (212)661-4074
Co. E-mail: nyinfo@babinc.org
URL: http://www.babinc.org
X (Twitter): x.com/BritAmBusiness
Instagram: www.instagram.com/BritAmBusiness
YouTube: www.youtube.com/channel/UCDDgj-0KfS
 3Ny6Rwlrc6v6A

Description: Works to increase the trade and investment between the U.S. and the U.K. by offering member companies a full range of transatlantic business services, information, and contacts. **Publications:** *UK and USA Directory of Investment* (Semi-monthly); *American British Business Handbook* (Annual); *British American Business Handbook* (Annual); *BritishAmerican Business Inc. - Membership Directory*; *Investment News* (Monthly); *Issue Insight* (Quarterly); *Network London / New York* (Quarterly); *Network New York* (Quarterly); *British American Business Inc.--Membership Directory*; *British-American Chamber of Commerce--UK and US Investment Directory* (Biennial); *The UK/USA Investment Directory & Business Resource* (Biennial); *UK & USA* (Quarterly). **Geographic Preference:** Multinational.

27401 ■ Business and Industry Advisory Committee to the OECD (BIAC) [Comite Consultatif Economique et Industriel aupres de l'O.C.D.E.]
13/15, Chaussee de la Muette
 75016 Paris, France
URL: http://www.businessatoecd.org
Contact: Hanni Rosenbaum, Executive Director
X (Twitter): x.com/businessatoecd

Description: Sponsored by United States Council for International Business. Represents the United States on the Business and Industry Advisory Committee to the Organization for Economic Co-Operation and Development. **Founded:** 1962. **Geographic Preference:** Multinational; National.

27402 ■ Business Sweden
150 N Michigan Ave., Ste. 1950
 Chicago, IL 60601-7550
Ph: (321)781-6222
Fax: (321)276-8606
Co. E-mail: info@business-sweden.se
URL: http://www.business-sweden.com
Contact: Anna Stellinger, President
Facebook: www.facebook.com/BusinessSweden
X (Twitter): x.com/BusinessSweden
Instagram: www.instagram.com/businesssweden

Description: Promotes Swedish exports and assists American companies in contacting Swedish suppliers. Performs market developments studies and research, partner searches, and project management. **Founded:** 2013. **Publications:** *Swedish Export Directory.* **Geographic Preference:** National.

27403 ■ Canada-United States Business Association (CUSBA)
c/o Clayton & McKervey, P. C.
 2000 Town Ctr., Ste. 1800
 Southfield, MI 48075
Co. E-mail: info@cusbaonline.com
URL: http://www.cusbaonline.com
Contact: Laurie Tannous, President

Description: Consists of supporters of business such as labor, banking, consulting, government, and academia. Promotes stronger business and trading lineages between the U.S. and Canada by providing a forum to exchange information and ideas and to build relationships. Conducts educational programs; maintains speakers' bureau, panels, and special events. **Founded:** 1992. **Geographic Preference:** National.

27404 ■ Canadian American Business Council (CABC) [Conseil Des Affaires Canado-Americanes]
1725 1st NW, Ste. 300
 Washington, DC 20006
Co. E-mail: info@cabc.co
URL: http://cabc.co
Contact: Nancy Ziuzin Schlegel, Chairman
Facebook: www.facebook.com/cabc.co
Linkedin: www.linkedin.com/company/canadian
 -american-business-council
X (Twitter): x.com/cabc_co
YouTube: www.youtube.com/channel/UCyNK
 2bhIHDF4oq8d0neYuHw

Description: Individuals, corporations, institutions and organizations with an interest in trade between the United States and Canada. Promotes free trade. Gathers and disseminates information; maintains speakers' bureau. **Founded:** 1987. **Awards:** Canadian-American Business Achievement Award (Annual). **Geographic Preference:** Multinational.

27405 ■ Colombian American Association (CAA)
135 E 57th St., Ste. 18-117
 New York, NY 10022
Ph: (212)233-7776
Co. E-mail: programs@andean-us.com
URL: http://www.colombianamerican.org
Contact: Stephanie Junger-Moat, President
Facebook: www.facebook.com/
 ColombianAmericanNY
X (Twitter): x.com/caa_ny
Instagram: www.instagram.com/
 colombianamerican_ny
YouTube: www.youtube.com/channel/UCtNP0D
 dq0nmCeU3o4CyxMEw

Description: Facilitates commerce and trade between the Republic of Colombia and the U.S. Fosters and advances cultural relations and goodwill between the two nations. Encourages sound investments in Colombia by Americans and in the U.S. by Colombians. Disseminates information in the U.S. concerning Colombia. **Founded:** 1927. **Geographic Preference:** National.

27406 ■ Conexx: America Israel Business Connector
5805 State Bridge Rd.
 Marietta, GA 30068
Ph: (404)843-9426
Co. E-mail: info@conexx.org
URL: http://conexx.org
Contact: Randall Foster, Chairman of the Board
E-mail: randallmarkfoster@gmail.com
Facebook: www.facebook.com/conexx.AIBC
Linkedin: www.linkedin.com/company/american-israel
 -chamber-of-commerce-se
X (Twitter): x.com/conexx_AIBC

Description: Promotes increased trade between Israel and the United States, with emphasis on increasing Israeli-American trade involving companies in the southeastern US. Facilitates networking and contact development involving Israeli and US corporations; makes available trade mentoring and matchmaking services; sponsors educational programs. **Founded:** 1992. **Publications:** *Latest Southeast-Israel Business News* (Monthly). **Geographic Preference:** National.

27407 ■ Council of the Americas (CoA)
680 Pk. Ave.
 New York, NY 10065
Ph: (212)249-8950
Co. E-mail: ascoa.online@as-coa.org
URL: http://www.as-coa.org
Contact: Susan L. Segal, President
Facebook: www.facebook.com/ASCOA
Linkedin: www.linkedin.com/company/ascoaonline
X (Twitter): x.com/ascoa
Instagram: www.instagram.com/ascoa
YouTube: www.youtube.com/ascoaonline

Description: Promotes on behalf of its members, policies and practices favoring free trade and investment, market economies and the rule of law in the Western Hemisphere. Provides a forum for its members to discuss economic, political and social issues relevant to the Hemisphere with public and private sector leaders. Represents the membership in public policy discussions. Assists members in the achievement of their business objectives in the region. **Founded:** 1965. **Geographic Preference:** National.

27408 ■ Danish American Chamber of Commerce (DACC)
253 W 73rd St.
New York, NY 10023
Ph: (212)933-1800
Co. E-mail: daccny@daccny.com
URL: http://www.daccny.com
Contact: Laust Hemig, President
X (Twitter): x.com/daccny

Description: Danish and American business leaders; firms and institutions. Functions as an advisory board to support and promote commercial relations between the United States and Denmark, in both directions; makes itself available for consultation with the Danish diplomatic representatives in the U.S. and to the U.S. Department of Commerce, as well as to trade groups and members in Denmark and the U.S. Attempts to avoid duplication of governmental activities. **Founded:** 1931. **Geographic Preference:** National.

27409 ■ Federation of International Trade Associations (FITA)
172 5th Ave., No. 118
Brooklyn, NY 11217
Free: 888-491-8833
Co. E-mail: info@fita.org
URL: http://www.fita.org
Contact: Kimberly Park, President
E-mail: kim@fita.org

Description: Fosters international trade by strengthening the role of local, regional, and national associations throughout the United States, Mexico, and Canada that have an international mission; affiliates are 450 independent international associations. **Founded:** 1984. **Publications:** *Directory of North American Trade Association* (Annual); *FITA's Really Useful Sites* (Biweekly). **Geographic Preference:** Multinational.

27410 ■ Finnish American Chamber of Commerce (FACC)
2 Pk. Ave.
New York, NY 10016
Ph: (917)622-7076
Co. E-mail: info@facc-ny.com
URL: http://facc-ny.com
Contact: Kati Kaivonen, President
Facebook: www.facebook.com/FaccNY
X (Twitter): x.com/FACCNY

Description: Promotes trade and professional interests between the U.S. and Finland. Maintains liaison with similar groups abroad; conducts seminars; arranges meetings with speakers. **Founded:** 1948. **Geographic Preference:** National.

27411 ■ French-American Chamber of Commerce (FACC)
33 W 46th St., Ste. 800
New York, NY 10036
Ph: (212)867-0123
Fax: (212)867-9050
Co. E-mail: info@faccnyc.org
URL: http://www.faccnyc.org
Contact: Marc Somnolet, President
Facebook: www.facebook.com/faccnyc
Linkedin: www.linkedin.com/company/french
-american-chamber-of-commerce
X (Twitter): x.com/faccnyc

Description: Promotes trade between the U.S. and France and fosters economic, commercial and financial relations between the two countries. Functions in an advisory and informative capacity and assists in organizing business contacts for its members. Holds round table discussions. **Founded:** 1896. **Publications:** *French-American Chamber of Commerce--Membership Directory*; *National Membership Directory of the French-American Chamber of Commerce*. **Geographic Preference:** National.

27412 ■ Global Industrial Cooperation Association (GICA)
3855 SW 153rd Dr.
Beaverton, OR 97003
Ph: (503)619-2694
Co. E-mail: info@gica.org
URL: http://gica.org
Contact: Stephanie Schultz, Executive Director
X (Twitter): x.com/gica_global

Description: Promotes trade and commerce between companies and their foreign customers who engage in reciprocal trade, including offset and countertrade, as a form of doing business. **Founded:** 1986. **Geographic Preference:** Multinational.

27413 ■ Guam Chamber of Commerce (GCC)
372 W Soledad Ave.
Hagatna, GU 96910
Ph: (671)472-6311
Co. E-mail: info@guamchamber.com.gu
URL: http://www.guamchamber.com.gu
Contact: Catherine S. Castro, President
Facebook: www.facebook.com/Guamchamber
Linkedin: www.linkedin.com/company/guam-chamber
-of-commerce
X (Twitter): x.com/GUChamber

Description: Promotes increased international trade and tourism. Gathers and disseminates information; conducts promotional activities; represents members' interests. **Founded:** 1924. **Publications:** *Guam Chamber of Commerce--Member Directory*; *The President's Report* (Monthly); *Small Business Focus* (Quarterly). **Educational Activities:** Guam Chamber of Commerce Meeting (Monthly). **Awards:** Dave J. Santos Scholarships (Annual). **Geographic Preference:** National; Local.

27414 ■ Hellenic-American Chamber of Commerce (HACC)
140 E 156th St., Ste. 1D
New York, NY 10022
Ph: (212)629-6380
Co. E-mail: info@hellenicamerican.cc
URL: http://www.hellenicamerican.cc
Contact: Clay Maitland, President
Facebook: www.facebook.com/HACCNY
Instagram: www.instagram.com/haccny

Description: Promotes commerce and trade between Greece and the United States; represents members' interests. **Founded:** 1947. **Geographic Preference:** National.

27415 ■ Hong Kong Trade Development Council (HKTDC)
38/F, Office Tower, Convention Plz., 1 Harbour Rd.
Wan chai 10017, Hong Kong, China
Ph: 86 852 1830-668
Fax: 86 852 2824 0249
URL: http://www.hktdc.com
Contact: Margaret Fong, Executive Director
Facebook: www.facebook.com/hktdc.hk
Linkedin: www.linkedin.com/company/hong-kong-tra
de-development-council
X (Twitter): x.com/hktdc
YouTube: www.youtube.com/user/HKTDC

Description: Quasi-governmental body responsible for promoting Hong Kong trade with the rest of the world and creating a favorable image for Hong Kong as a trading partner and international trade center. Sponsors trade missions and participates in major trade shows around the world. Maintains library of trade publications in both Hong Kong and its North American offices. Compiles statistics. **Founded:** 1966. **Publications:** *Hong Kong Apparel* (Semiannual; Quarterly); *HKTDC Electronics* (Quarterly); *HKTDC Enterprise*; *Hong Kong for the Business Visitor* (Annual); *Hong Kong Gifts and Premiums* (Annual). **Educational Activities:** HIMSS Annual Conference & Exhibition (HIMSS) (Annual); Hong Kong Electronics Fair (Annual); Hong Kong Fashion Week for Fall/Winter (Annual); Hong Kong Toys and Games Fair (Annual); Hong Kong Watch and Clock Fair (Annual). **Geographic Preference:** National.

27416 ■ Innovation Norway - United States
54 W 40th St.
New York, NY 10018

Co. E-mail: newyork@innovationnorway.no
URL: http://www.innovasjonnorge.no/en/start-page/
about/our-offices/offices-abroad/usa---new-york
Contact: David DiGrigorio, Specialist Consultant
E-mail: david.digregorio@innovationnorway.no

Description: Assists Norwegian companies in marketing their goods and services in the US. Provides information to Norwegian exporters on US. markets, tariffs and statistics, trade constraints, and distribution channels. Establishes contacts with US. authorities, marketing and manufacturing firms, local lawyers, accountants, banks, patent offices, advertising and public relations agencies, consultants, and credit and debt collection agencies. **Founded:** 1945. **Geographic Preference:** National.

27417 ■ Italian-American Chamber of Commerce (IACC)
728 Anthony Trl.
Northbrook, IL 60062
Ph: (312)553-9137
Fax: (312)553-9142
Co. E-mail: info@iacc-chicago.com
URL: http://www.iacc-chicago.com
Contact: Fulvio Calcinardi, Executive Director
Facebook: www.facebook.com/IACCMidwest
Linkedin: www.linkedin.com/in/iaccmidwest
X (Twitter): x.com/IACCMidwest
Instagram: www.instagram.com/iaccchicago
YouTube: www.youtube.com/channel/UCHy7U3FwD
_74pZbH9jqN3GA

Description: Promotes trade between Italy and the U.S. and helps Italian organizations and companies promote their products and services in the U.S. **Founded:** 1907. **Publications:** *Italian American Chamber of Commerce of Chicago Bulletin* (Bimonthly). **Geographic Preference:** National.

27418 ■ Italy-America Chamber of Commerce (IACC)
11 E 44th St., Ste. 1400
New York, NY 10017
Ph: (212)459-0044
Fax: (212)459-0090
Co. E-mail: info@italchamber.org
URL: http://italchamber.org
Contact: Alberto Milani, President
Facebook: www.facebook.com/iaccnewyork
Linkedin: www.linkedin.com/company/italy-america
-chamber-of-commerce-new-york
Instagram: www.instagram.com/iaccnewyork

Description: Represents companies that have business relationships in Italy and the U.S. Advances the interests of its members through contacts and interaction with government agencies, trade associations and leading international organizations. **Founded:** 1887. **Publications:** *IACC Newsletter* (Monthly); *Trade with Italy* (Biennial; Annual; Bimonthly). **Educational Activities:** Mifur: International Fur and Leather Exhibition (Annual). **Geographic Preference:** National.

27419 ■ Japanese Chamber of Commerce and Industry of New York, Inc. (JCCINY)
145 W 57th St. No. 6
New York, NY 10019
Ph: (212)246-8001
Co. E-mail: info@jcciny.org
URL: http://www.jcciny.org
Contact: Kosuke Takechi, Chief Executive Officer
Facebook: www.facebook.com/jcciny

Description: Japanese and non-Japanese corporations. Fosters improved trade relations between the U.S. and Japan. Conducts seminars and surveys. **Founded:** 1932. **Publications:** *Japan's Industries and Trade: Profiles and Interrelationships with the United States*; *Joining In! A Handbook for Better Corporate Citizenship in the U.S.*. **Geographic Preference:** National.

27420 ■ JETRO New York (JETRO)
565 5th Ave., 4th Fl.
New York, NY 10017
Ph: (212)997-0400
Fax: (212)997-0464
URL: http://www.jetro.go.jp/usa
Contact: Ryota Hiramoto, Director

E-mail: ryota_hiramoto@jetro.go.jp
Linkedin: www.linkedin.com/company/jetro
X (Twitter): x.com/JETROUSA

Description: Supports foreign companies in export and/or investment to Japan-related business ventures. Disseminates comprehensive information on the Japanese economy and market through surveys, reports, publications, and newsletters. Conducts trade and investment promotion seminars and symposia. Sponsors trade shows and exhibitions. Provides professional business consultation services and handles trade-related inquiries and provides opportunities for international exchange. **Founded:** 1958. **Geographic Preference:** National.

27421 ■ The Latin Chamber of Commerce of the United States [Camara de Comercio Latina de los EEUU (CAMACOL)]
1401 W Flagler St.
  Miami, FL 33135
Ph: (305)642-3870
Fax: (305)642-3961
Co. E-mail: info@camacol.org
URL: http://www.camacol.org
Contact: Joe Chi, President
Facebook: www.facebook.com/camacol.org
Linkedin: www.linkedin.com/company/camacol-latin
  -chamber-of-commerce-of-u-s-a
X (Twitter): x.com/camacolusa

Description: Represents Latino business owners in Florida. Provides placement services; compiles statistics. Maintains information and referral service. **Founded:** 1965. **Educational Activities:** CAMACOL Hemispheric Congress (Annual). **Geographic Preference:** National.

27422 ■ Moroccan American Business Council, Ltd. (AMBC)
10375 Richmond Ave., No. 190
  Houston, TX 77042
Co. E-mail: media@ambchouston.com
Facebook: www.facebook.com/ambchouston

Description: Promotes commerce and business between Morocco and the United States. **Geographic Preference:** National.

27423 ■ National Association of Export Companies (NEXCO)
396 Broadway, Ste. 603
  New York, NY 10013

Description: Established independent international trade firms, bilateral chambers of commerce, banks, law firms, accounting firms, trade associations, insurance companies, and product/service providers; export trading companies; export management companies. Promotes expansion of U.S. trade. Promotes the participation of members in international trade. Conducts educational programs. **Founded:** 1963. **Geographic Preference:** National.

27424 ■ National Association of Foreign-Trade Zones (NAFTZ)
National Press Bldg.
  529 14th St. NW, Ste. 1071
  Washington, DC 20045
Ph: (202)331-1950
Fax: (202)331-1994
URL: http://www.naftz.org
Contact: Erik Autor, President
E-mail: eautor@naftz.org
Facebook: www.facebook.com/naftzdc
Linkedin: www.linkedin.com/company/the-national
  -association-of-foreign-trade-zones
X (Twitter): x.com/NAFTZ
Instagram: www.instagram.com/_naftz
YouTube: www.youtube.com/user/NAFTZUS

Description: Aims to promote, stimulate, and improve foreign-trade zones and their utilization as integral and valuable tools in the international commerce of the U.S.; to encourage the establishment of foreign-trade zones to foster investment and the creation of jobs in the US. Sponsors seminars. **Founded:** 1973. **Publications:** *The Impact of Foreign Trade Zones on the 50 States and Puerto Rico*; *U.S. Foreign Trade Zones*; *Zones Report* (Monthly). **Geographic Preference:** National.

27425 ■ Netherlands Chamber of Commerce in the United States (NLCOC)
535 5th Ave.
  New York, NY 10017
Ph: (212)265-6460
Co. E-mail: info@netherlands.org
URL: http://netherlands.org
Contact: Andre Grift, President
E-mail: agrift@netherlands.org
Facebook: www.facebook.com/Netherlands.org

Description: Aims to maintain and expand business relations between The Netherlands and the United States. **Founded:** 1903. **Geographic Preference:** National.

27426 ■ Norwegian American Chamber of Commerce, Inc. (NACC)
450 Lexington Ave., 4th Fl.
  New York, NY 10017
Ph: (646)883-1760
Co. E-mail: info@naccusa.org
URL: http://www.naccusa.org
Contact: Clay Maitland, President
Facebook: www.facebook.com/naccusa
X (Twitter): x.com/naccusa

Description: Promotes business and trade among members and between Norway and the United States. Provides networking opportunities and source information. **Founded:** 1915. **Publications:** *Norwegian American Chamber of Commerce--Business Directory*; *Norwegian American Commerce* (Quarterly). **Awards:** NACC Achievement Award (Annual); NACC Trade Award (Annual). **Geographic Preference:** National.

27427 ■ Organization of Women in International Trade (OWIT)
1776 K St., N W, Ste., 200
  Washington, DC 20006
Co. E-mail: admin@owit.org
URL: http://owit.org
Contact: Frida Owinga, President
E-mail: president@owit.org
Facebook: www.facebook.com/OWITIntl
Linkedin: www.linkedin.com/company/organization-of
  -women-in-international-trade-owit
X (Twitter): x.com/owitintl
Instagram: www.instagram.com/owit_intl

Description: Fosters international trade and the advancement of women in business. Offers educational programs, conventions and other activities to promote the employment of women in international trade. Facilitates networking and exchange of information and ideas among members. **Founded:** 1989. **Geographic Preference:** Local.

27428 ■ Romanian-U.S. Business Council (AMRO)
c/o Henry Homans, Vice President
  1201 Pennsylvania Ave., Ste. 800
  Washington, DC 20004
Ph: (202)973-5979
Co. E-mail: info@amrobiz.org
URL: http://www.amrobc.org
Contact: Eric Stewart, President

Description: Advocates American business interests with respect to U.S. Romanian trade and investments. Provides the American and Romanian business communities with a means of discussing bilateral trade and investment issues and the formulation of policy positions that will promote and expand economic relations between the two countries. Facilitates appropriate legislation and policies regarding trade between the U.S. and Romania. Has sponsored seminars on topics such as possibilities for cooperative commercial efforts in other countries and cooperation in energy development. **Founded:** 1974. **Geographic Preference:** National.

27429 ■ Society of International Business Fellows (SIBF)
715 Peachtree St. NE, Ste. 200
  Atlanta, GA 30308
Ph: (470)378-1156
Co. E-mail: contactus@sibf.org
URL: http://sibf.org/#home-ask

Contact: Nancy Haselden, Executive Director
E-mail: nancy.haselden@sibf.org
X (Twitter): x.com/TheSIBF

Description: Businesspeople active or with an interest in international trade. Promotes "enhancement of the international competitiveness and prosperity of its members and the growth of the South as a vital region for global business." Works to strengthen personal and professional relations among members; conducts educational programs in international business and trade. **Founded:** 1981. **Geographic Preference:** Multinational.

27430 ■ Spain-United States Chamber of Commerce - Library [Camara de Comercio Espana - Estados Unidos]
80 Broad St., Ste. 2103
  New York, NY 10004
Ph: (212)967-2170
Co. E-mail: info@spainuscc.org
URL: http://spainuscc.org
Contact: Gemma Cortijo, Executive Director

Description: Promotes business investment and trade between the U.S. and Spain. **Scope:** Business; marketing. **Founded:** 1959. **Holdings:** Figures not available. **Publications:** *Business Directories*; *Visa and Work Permits for the USA*; *Spain-United States Chamber of Commerce--Membership Directory*. **Awards:** Business Leader of the Year Award (Annual). **Geographic Preference:** Multinational.

27431 ■ Trans-Atlantic Business Council (TABC)
Washington, DC 20006
Ph: (202)778-9073
Co. E-mail: admin@transatlanticbusiness.org
URL: http://transatlanticbusiness.org
Contact: Bart Gordon, Director
Linkedin: www.linkedin.com/company/transatlantic
  -business-council
X (Twitter): x.com/TABC_Council

Description: Represents over 50 major European and North American companies with a focus on promoting trans-Atlantic growth, bilateral trade, and investment in order to foster prosperity and stability between the U.S. and Europe. Committed to fortifying EU-US economic integration, growth and competitiveness. **Founded:** 1989. **Geographic Preference:** National.

27432 ■ U.S. Austrian Chamber of Commerce
c/o AT Consult
  405 Lexington Ave., 37th Fl.
  New York, NY 10174
Ph: (212)819-0117
Co. E-mail: office@usaustrianchamber.org
URL: http://usaustrianchamber.org
Contact: Chris Hoedl, President

Description: Promotes the development of business and education between the U.S. and Austria. Hosts receptions and luncheons. Sponsors Viennese Opera Ball, panel discussions, and business assistance. **Founded:** 1946. **Educational Activities:** Viennese Opera Ball (VOB) (Annual). **Geographic Preference:** National.

27433 ■ United States Council for International Business (USCIB)
1212 Avenue of the Americas
  New York, NY 10036
Ph: (212)354-4480
Fax: (212)575-0327
Co. E-mail: info@uscib.org
URL: http://uscib.org
Contact: Whitney Y. Baird, President
E-mail: wbaird@uscib.org
Linkedin: www.linkedin.com/company/uscib-united-s
  tates-council-for-international-business
X (Twitter): x.com/USCIB

Description: Serves as the US. National Committee of the International Chamber of Commerce. Enables multinational enterprises to operate effectively by representing their interests to intergovernmental and governmental bodies and by keeping enterprises advised of international developments having a major impact on their operations. **Founded:** 1945. **Publica-**

tions: *USCF Occasional Paper.* **Awards:** USCIB International Leadership Award (Annual). **Geographic Preference:** National.

27434 ■ United States-Mexico Chamber of Commerce (USMCOC)
207 Mandalay Canal
Irving, TX 75039
Ph: (469)567-0923
Co. E-mail: info@usmcoc.org
URL: http://usmcoc.org
Contact: Al Zapanta, President
Facebook: www.facebook.com/usmcoc
Linkedin: www.linkedin.com/company/united-states
-mexico-chamber-of-commerce
X (Twitter): x.com/USMCOC
Description: Works to promote private sector trade and investment between the United States and Mexico. **Founded:** 1973. **Publications:** *United States-Mexico Chamber of Commerce--Membership Directory and Resource Guide; Chamber News* (Monthly); *United States-Mexico Chamber of Commerce--Regional Newsletters* (Periodic). **Awards:** USMCOC Good Neighbor Award (Annual). **Geographic Preference:** National.

27435 ■ U.S. Pan Asian American Chamber of Commerce (USPAACC)
1329 18th St. NW
Washington, DC 20036
Ph: (202)296-5221
Free: 800-696-7818
Co. E-mail: info@uspaacc.com
URL: http://uspaacc.com
Contact: Susan Au Allen, President
Facebook: www.facebook.com/
UsPanAsianAmericanChamberOfCommerce
Linkedin: www.linkedin.com/company/uspaacc-ef
X (Twitter): x.com/uspaacc
Instagram: www.instagram.com/uspaacc_official
YouTube: www.youtube.com/channel/UCU
51aqkGkEfxn1pCEF-a7Rw
Description: Promotes contact, education, and business opportunities for Asian American businesses and their partners in corporate and government settings. **Founded:** 1984. **Publications:** *East West Report* (Semiannual). **Educational Activities:** CelebrAsian Procurement Conference (Annual). **Awards:** USPAACC Government Agency of the Year (Annual); USPAACC College Hallmark Scholarships (Annual); USPAACC/Wells Fargo Asian Business Leadership Award (Annual); USPAACC College Scholarships (Annual); USPAACC Denny's Hungry for Education Scholarship (Annual); USPAACC Microgrants (Annual). **Geographic Preference:** National.

27436 ■ U.S.-Russia Business Council (USRBC) - Library
1101 17th St. NW
Washington, DC 20036
Ph: (202)739-9180
Co. E-mail: info@usrbc.org
URL: http://www.usrbc.org
Contact: Daniel A. Russell, President
E-mail: dan.russell@usrbc.org
Linkedin: www.linkedin.com/company/u-s--russia
-business-council
Description: Conducts lobbying activities; facilitates establishment of joint ventures involving US. and Russian companies; maintains bank of job listings; compiles trade statistics. Gathers and disseminates information on political, economic, and social issues affecting trade with Russia. **Scope:** Trade. **Founded:** 1993. **Holdings:** Figures not available. **Publications:** *Russia Business Watch* (Quarterly). **Geographic Preference:** Multinational.

27437 ■ Venezuelan American Association of the United States (VAAUS)
641 Lexington Ave.
New York, NY 10022
Ph: (212)233-7776
Co. E-mail: info@andean-us.com
URL: http://www.venezuelanamerican.org
Contact: Herman G. Brock, President
Facebook: www.facebook.com/An
deanAmericanAssociations

X (Twitter): x.com/Andean_US
Description: Financial institutions, businesses, organizations, and individuals interested in the expansion and improvement of trade relations between Venezuela and the US. Fosters cultural and commercial relations, facilitates investment between the US. and Venezuela, and promotes improved understanding between businesspersons of the two nations. **Founded:** 1936. **Publications:** *Venezuela News Bulletin* (Monthly). **Geographic Preference:** National.

EDUCATIONAL PROGRAMS

27438 ■ Creating a Positive, High-Energy Workplace (Onsite)
National Seminars Training L.L.C. (NST)
14502 W 105th St.
Lenexa, KS 66215
Free: 800-349-1935
Co. E-mail: info@findaseminar.com
URL: http://www.findaseminar.com/tpd/Padge
tt-Thompson-Seminars.asp
URL(s): www.findaseminar.com/event1.asp?eventID
=6680
Description: A seminar for those who want to gain crucial insights into increasing their bottom line by fostering an energized climate where anything is possible. **Audience:** Managers, supervisors, and team leaders . **Principal Exhibits:** A seminar for those who want to gain crucial insights into increasing their bottom line by fostering an energized climate where anything is possible.

27439 ■ Foreign Military Sales (Onsite)
Seminar Information Service Inc. (SIS)
250 El Camino Real., Ste. 112
Tustin, CA 92780
Ph: (714)508-0340
Free: 877-736-4636
Fax: (714)734-8027
Co. E-mail: info@seminarinformation.com
URL: http://www.seminarinformation.com
Contact: Catherine Bellizzi, President
URL(s): www.seminarinformation.com/qqbkmv/
foreign-military-sales
Description: Contractors who want to engage in international contracting successfully and profitably must be able to navigate a complex web of statutes, regulations and policies governing FRMS, FMF and U.S. export controls. **Audience:** Manufacturers, exporters and advisors . **Principal Exhibits:** Contractors who want to engage in international contracting successfully and profitably must be able to navigate a complex web of statutes, regulations and policies governing FRMS, FMF and U.S. export controls.

REFERENCE WORKS

27440 ■ "2015 Corporate Counsel Legal Pricing Guide - Mergers & Acquisitions" in Economics & Business Week (August 16, 2014, pp. 3)
Pub: NewsRX LLC.
Contact: Kalani Rosell, Contact
Description: Research and Markets has added the 2015 Corporate Counsel Legal Pricing Guide - Mergers & Acquisitions to its report. The guide details how the mergers and acquisitions market for law firms has increased since the downturn in 2008-2009 due mostly to an improved economy, increased corporate liquidity and sometimes corporate tax policies of certain countries. **Availability:** Print; Online.

27441 ■ "Acquisition to Give Mylan Tax Benefits, Boost Sales" in Pittsburgh Business Times (Vol. 33, July 18, 2014, No. 53, pp. 3)
Pub: American City Business Journals, Inc.
Contact: Mike Olivieri, Executive Vice President
Released: Weekly. **Price:** $4, introductory 4-week offer(Digital & Print). **Description:** Mylan Inc.'s acquisition of Abbot's foreign specialty and branded generic drug business is a win situation for the company. The acquisition will help Mylan expand and diversify in the largest markets outside the U.S. as

well as prove beneficial in growth through enhanced financial flexibility and a more competitive global tax structure. **Availability:** Print; Online.

27442 ■ "Actian, Data Transformed and Yellowfin BI Mashup Helps Kollaras Group Reap Big Data Rewards" in Computer Business Week (August 28, 2014, pp. 22)
Pub: NewsRX LLC.
Contact: Kalani Rosell, Contact
Description: Actian announced that Australian liquor, hospitality and property investment company, Kollaras Group can now access real-time analytics; fast, simple and accurate data warehousing; and Yellowfin's Business Intelligence (BI) platform is examined. The BI provides better insights and decision-making across diverse business units. **Availability:** Online.

27443 ■ "Addition by Subtraction in Tokyo" in Barron's (Vol. 92, August 25, 2012, No. 38, pp. 20)
Pub: Dow Jones & Company Inc.
Contact: Almar Latour, Chief Executive Officer
Ed: Kopin Tan. **Description:** Investors in Japan could benefit from the increase in management buyouts, particularly of small capitalization stocks. This increase would shrink the number of Japanese stocks, many of which are trading below book value. **Availability:** Online.

27444 ■ "Adidas' Brand Ambitions" in Business Journal Portland (Vol. 27, December 10, 2010, No. 41, pp. 1)
Pub: Portland Business Journal
Contact: Andy Giegerich, Managing Editor
E-mail: agiegerich@bizjournals.com
Ed: Erik Siemers. **Description:** Adidas AG, the second-largest sporting goods brand in the world, hopes to increase global revenue by 50 percent by 2015. The German company, which reported $14.5 billion sales, plans to improve its U.S. market. The U.S. is Adidas' largest, but also the most underperforming market for the firm. **Availability:** Print; Online.

27445 ■ "Africa Rising" in Harvard Business Review (Vol. 86, September 2008, No. 9, pp. 36)
Pub: Harvard Business Review Press
Contact: Moderna V. Pfizer, Contact
Ed: Vijay Mahajan. **Description:** Review of the book entitled, "Africa Rising: How 900 Million African Consumers Offer More Than You Think" provides advice for marketing to those on the African continent. **Availability:** Print; Online.

27446 ■ "All About The Benjamins" in Canadian Business (Vol. 81, September 29, 2008, No. 16, pp. 92)
Description: Discusses real estate developer Royal Indian Raj International Corp., a company that planned to build a $3 billion "smart city" near the Bangalore airport; to this day nothing has ever been built. The company was incorporated in 1999 by Manoj C. Benjamin one investor, Bill Zack, has been sued by the developer for libel due to his website that calls the company a scam. Benjamin has had a previous case of fraud issued against him as well as a string of liabilities and lawsuits. **Availability:** Online.

27447 ■ "All-Star Execs: Top CEO: Gordon Nixon" in Canadian Business (Vol. 80, November 24, 2008, No. 22, pp. 9)
Pub: Rogers Media Inc.
Contact: Neil Spivak, Chief Executive Officer
Ed: Jeff Sanford. **Description:** Royal Bank of Canada (RBC) CEO, Gordon Nixon, believes the Canadian financial services segment is heavily regulated. Nixon also feels that it has become difficult for local banks to enter the market since foreign banks can easily come in and compete with them. His views on RBC's success are provided. **Availability:** Print; Online.

27448 ■ *"Alliance Offers to Help Italian Workers Settle In"* in *Crain's Detroit Business* (Vol. 25, June 15, 2009, No. 24, pp. 21)
Pub: Crain Communications Inc.
Contact: Barry Asin, President
Ed: Nancy Kaffer. **Description:** Italian American Alliance for Business and Technology will help workers arriving from Italy to transition to their new homes in the Detroit area. **Availability:** Online.

27449 ■ *"Allied Brands Loses Baskin-Robbins Franchise Down Under"* in *Ice Cream Reporter* (Vol. 23, November 20, 2010, No. 12, pp. 2)
Description: Dunkin Brands, worldwide franchisor of Baskin-Robbins, terminated the master franchise agreement for Australia held by the food marketer Allied Brands Services. **Availability:** Print; Online.

27450 ■ *"American Airlines Works to Keep Its Brand Aloft"* in *Dallas Business Journal* (Vol. 35, May 18, 2012, No. 36, pp. 1)
Pub: Baltimore Business Journal
Contact: Rhonda Pringle, President
E-mail: rpringle@bizjournals.com
Ed: Matt Joyce. **Description:** As American Airlines is undergoing restructuring, the company is planning to redesign its international aircraft as part of its marketing strategy. But the airline's efforts to improve its brand image present a challenge made difficult by labor relations. Labor unions representing American Airlines employees are fighting the company over their collective bargaining agreements. **Availability:** Print; Online.

27451 ■ *"The Americans Are Coming"* in *The Economist* (Vol. 390, January 3, 2009, No. 8612, pp. 44)
Description: Student recruitment consultancies, which help place international students at universities in other countries and offer services such as interpreting or translating guidelines, are discussed; American universities who have shunned these agencies in the past; the result has been that America underperforms in relation to its size with a mere 3.5 percent of students on its campuses that are from abroad. **Availability:** Print; Online.

27452 ■ *"Ampm Focus Has BP Working Overtime"* in *Crain's Chicago Business* (April 28, 2008)
Pub: Crain Communications Inc.
Contact: Barry Asin, President
Ed: John T. Slania. **Description:** Britian's oil giant BP PLC is opening its ampm convenience stores in the Chicago market and has already begun converting most of its 78 Chicago-area gas stations to ampms. The company has also started to franchise the stores to independent operators. BP is promoting the brand with both traditional and unconventional marketing techniques such s real or simulated 3D snacks embedded in bus shelter ads and an in-store Guitar Hero contest featuring finalists from a recent contest at the House of Blues. **Availability:** Online.

27453 ■ *"Another Determinant of Entrepreneurship: The Belief In Witchcraft and Entrepreneurship"* in *International Journal of Entrepreneurship and Small Business* (Vol. 10, July 6, 2010)
Ed: Felix Pauligard Ntep, Wilton Wilton. **Description:** Interviews were carried out with entrepreneurs of Douala, Cameroon. These entrepreneurs believe that witchcraft existed and could bring harm to them or their enterprises. **Availability:** Download; PDF; Online.

27454 ■ *"Areva Diversifies Further Into Wind"* in *Wall Street Journal Eastern Edition* (November 29, 2011, pp. B7)
Pub: Dow Jones & Company Inc.
Contact: Almar Latour, Chief Executive Officer
Ed: Max Colchester, Noemie Bisserbe. **Description:** French engineering company Areva SA is diversifying and moving away from nuclear energy projects. One sign of that is its recent discussion to construct 120

wind turbines to be located at two German wind farms. Such a deal, if signed, would be worth about US$1.59 billion. **Availability:** Online.

27455 ■ *"Asia Breathes a Sigh of Relief"* in *Business Week* (September 22, 2008, No. 4100, pp. 32)
Description: Foreign bankers, such as those in Asia, that had been investing heavily in the United States began to worry as the housing crisis deepened and the impact on Freddie Mac and Fannie Mae became increasingly clear. Due to the government bailout, however, central banks will most likely continue to buy American debt. **Availability:** Print; Online.

27456 ■ *"Au Revoir Or Goodbye?"* in *Barron's* (Vol. 88, July 14, 2008, No. 28, pp. 5)
Pub: Dow Jones & Company Inc.
Contact: Almar Latour, Chief Executive Officer
Ed: Alan Abelson. **Description:** Former Senator Phil Gramm's opinion that the U.S. is a "nation of whiners" as they moan about recession is another example of the disconnection between Washington and Wall Street on one hand and the real world on the other. It would be a catastrophe for most of the world if Fannie Mae and Freddie Mac were to go under and take their trillions of mortgage debt with them. **Availability:** Online.

27457 ■ *"AV Concept Expands Into Green Energy Storage"* in *Wireless News* (January 25, 2010)
Description: Electronics distributor and manufacturer AV Concept Holdings Limited announced a marketing partnership with Boston-Power, a provider of lithium-ion batteries, with a focus in the Chinese and Korean markets. **Availability:** Online.

27458 ■ *"Back in the Race. New Fund Manager Has Whipped Sentinel International Equity Back into Shape"* in *Barron's* (Vol. 88, March 17, 2008, No. 11, pp. 43)
Pub: Dow Jones & Company Inc.
Contact: Almar Latour, Chief Executive Officer
Ed: Leslie P. Norton. **Description:** Katherine Schapiro was able to get Sentinel International Equity's Morningstar classification to blended fund from a value fund rating after joining Sentinel from her former jobs at Strong Overseas Fund. Schapiro aims to benefit from the global rebalancing as the U.S.'s share of the world economy shrinks. **Availability:** Online.

27459 ■ *"Bargain Hunting In Vietnam"* in *Barron's* (Vol. 88, July 14, 2008, No. 28, pp. M6)
Pub: Dow Jones & Company Inc.
Contact: Almar Latour, Chief Executive Officer
Ed: Elliot Wilson. **Description:** Vietnam's economy grew by just 6.5 percent for the first half of 2008 and its balance of payments ballooned to $14.4 billion. The falling stock prices in the country is a boon for bargain hunters and investing in the numerous domestic funds is one way of investing in the country. Some shares that investors are taking an interest in are also discussed. **Availability:** Online.

27460 ■ *"Baskin-Robbins Expanding in China and U.S."* in *Ice Cream Reporter* (Vol. 21, August 20, 2008, No. 9, pp. 1)
Description: Baskin-Robbins will open its first store in Shanghai, China along with plans for 100 more shops in that country. They will also be expanding their market in the Dallas/Fort Worth, Texas area as well as Greater Cincinnati/Northern Kentucky regions. **Availability:** Print; Online.

27461 ■ *"Baskin-Robbins: New in U.S., Old in Japan"* in *Ice Cream Reporter* (Vol. 23, August 20, 2010, No. 9, pp. 2)
Description: Baskin-Robbins is celebrating its first franchise in Japan. **Availability:** Print; Online.

27462 ■ *"BayTSP, NTT Data Corp. Enter Into Reseller Pact to Market Online IP Monitoring"* in *Professional Services Close-Up* (Sept. 11, 2009)
Description: Due to incredible interest from distributors and content owners across Asia, NTT Data Corp.

will resell BayTSP's online intellectual property monitoring, enforcement, business intelligence and monetization services in Japan.

27463 ■ *"Be a Better Manager: Live Abroad"* in *Harvard Business Review* (Vol. 88, September 2010, No. 9, pp. 24)
Pub: Harvard Business Publishing
Contact: Diane Belcher, Managing Director
Ed: William W. Maddux, Adam D. Galinsky, Carmit T. Tadmor. **Price:** $6, PDF. **Description:** Interrelationship between international experience and entrepreneurship is discussed. Individuals with international experience are likelier to be promoted and to develop new products and businesses. **Availability:** Online; PDF.

27464 ■ *"Bedandbreakfast.eu: Bed & Breakfast Emerging in Europe"* in *Travel & Leisure Close-Up* (January 11, 2012)
Pub: Close-Up Media Inc.
Contact: Caroline S. Moore, President
E-mail: cms@closeupmedia.com
Description: According to experts, only 15 percent of all bed and breakfast operations in Europe were launched before the year 2000, with the majority opening after 2005. Reports show approximately 2,400 new operations opening on a monthly basis. Bedandbreakfast.eu offer current offerings for vacationers interested in staying at a bed and breakfast while visiting Europe. **Availability:** Online.

27465 ■ *"A Better Way to Tax U.S. Businesses"* in *(Vol. 90, July-August 2012, No. 7-8, pp. 134)*
Pub: Harvard Business Review Press
Contact: Moderna V. Pfizer, Contact
Ed: Mihir A. Desai. **Price:** $8.95, PDF and hardcover black and white. **Description:** Correcting the US corporate tax code will require ending the disconnect botwoon oarningo otatod to invootoro and taxable income, implementing rate reductions, eliminating the taxing of overseas income, and securing an agreement by business leaders to acknowledge taxes as a responsibility. **Availability:** Print; PDF; Online.

27466 ■ *"Betting On Volatile Materials"* in *Barron's* (Vol. 88, July 14, 2008, No. 28, pp. M11)
Pub: Dow Jones & Company Inc.
Contact: Almar Latour, Chief Executive Officer
Ed: John Marshall. **Description:** Economic slowdowns in the U.S., Europe and China could cause sharp short-term declines in the materials sector. The S&P Materials sector is vulnerable to shifts in the flow of funds. Statistical data included. **Availability:** Online.

27467 ■ *"Beware this Chinese Export"* in *Barron's* (Vol. 90, August 30, 2010, No. 35, pp. 21)
Pub: Barron's Editorial & Corporate Headquarters
Ed: Bill Alpert, Leslie P. Norton. **Description:** A look at 158 China reverse-merger stocks in the U.S. reveal that the median underperformed the index of U.S. listed Chinese companies by 75 percent in their first three years. These reverse merger stocks also lagged the Russell 2000 index of small cap stocks by 66 percent. **Availability:** Online.

27468 ■ *"Blood Diamonds are Forever"* in *Canadian Business* (Vol. 83, August 17, 2010, No. 13-14, pp. 59)
Description: The failed case against Donald McKay who was found in possession of rough diamonds in a raid by Royal Canadian Mounted Police has raised doubts about Kimberley Process (KP) attempts to stop the illicit global trade in diamonds. KP has managed to reduce total global trade of blood diamonds by 1 percent in mid-2000. **Availability:** Print; Online.

27469 ■ *"Bodovino Is a World Leader in Self-Service Wine Tasting"* in *Idaho Business Review* (September 8, 2014)
Pub: BridgeTower Media
Contact: Adam Reinebach, President

Description: Bodovino's wine bar and retail shop offers self-service wine tasting for its customers. It is the largest outlet globally for the Italian wine dispenser manufacturer WineEmotion. Visitors to the shop can choose from 144 wines set up in the dispensing machines.

27470 ■ *"Bombardier Deja Vu" in Canadian Business (Vol. 83, August 17, 2010, No. 13-14, pp. 28)*
Pub: Rogers Media Inc.
Contact: Neil Spivak, Chief Executive Officer
Ed: Laura Cameron. **Description:** Foreign competitors have accused the Quebec government and the Societe de transport de Montreal of giving Bombardier preferential treatment when it bids for contract to replace Montreal metro's rail cars. Bombardier was in a similar situation in 1974 when it won the contract to build the metro's second generation rail cars. **Availability:** Online.

27471 ■ *"Border Boletin: UA to Take Lie-Detector Kiosk to Poland" in Arizona Daily Star (September 14, 2010)*
Pub: Arizona Daily Star
Contact: John D'Orlando, President
E-mail: jdorlando@tucson.com
Ed: Brady McCombs. **Description:** University of Arizona's National Center for Border Security and Immigration Research will send a team to Warsaw, Poland to show border guards from 27 European Union countries the center's Avatar Kiosk. The Avatar technology is designed for use at border ports and airports to assist Customs officers detect individuals who are lying. **Availability:** Print; Online.

27472 ■ *"Bottom-Fishing and Speed-Dating in India-How Investors Feel About the Indian Market" in Barron's (Vol. 88, March 24, 2008, No. 12, pp. M12)*
Pub: Dow Jones & Company Inc.
Contact: Almar Latour, Chief Executive Officer
Ed: Elliot Wilson. **Description:** Indian stocks have fallen hard in 2008, with Mumbai's Sensex 30 down 30 percent from its January 2008 peak of 21,000 to 14,995 in March. The India Private Equity Fair 2008 attracted 140 of the world's largest private equity firms and about 24 of India's fastest-growing corporations. Statistical data included. **Availability:** Online.

27473 ■ *"Bountiful Barrels: Where to Find $140 Trillion" in Barron's (Vol. 88, July 14, 2008, No. 28, pp. 40)*
Pub: Dow Jones & Company Inc.
Contact: Almar Latour, Chief Executive Officer
Ed: Andrew Bary. **Description:** Surge in oil prices has caused a large transfer of wealth to oil-producing countries thereby reshaping the global economy. Oil reserves of oil exporting countries are now valued at $140 trillion. Economist Stephen Jen believes that this wealth will be transformed into paper assets as these countries invest in global stocks and bonds. **Availability:** Online.

27474 ■ *"Brazil's New King of Food" in Barron's (Vol. 89, July 13, 2009, No. 28, pp. 28)*
Pub: Dow Jones & Company Inc.
Contact: Almar Latour, Chief Executive Officer
Ed: Kenneth Rapoza. **Description:** Perdigao and Sadia's merger has resulted in the creation of Brasil Foods and the shares of Brasil Foods provides a play on both Brazil's newly energized consumer economy and its role as a major commodities exporter. Brasil Foods shares could climb as much as 36 percent. **Availability:** Online.

27475 ■ *"Bubble Trouble? Many Experts Say Seattle Housing Market Is Headed for a Fall" in Puget Sound Business Journal (Vol. 34, April 18, 2014, No. 53, pp. 4)*
Pub: American City Business Journals, Inc.
Contact: Mike Olivieri, Executive Vice President
Description: Redfin disclosed that nearly one third of homes listed in the real estate market in King County, Washington were sold above the listing price in February 2014 and it is forecast that the housing

market is headed into a new bubble. Statistics indicate that the trend in rising prices is slowing even in the face of a declining supply of available homes. The impact of international buyers is also discussed.

27476 ■ *"Buhler Versatile Launches Next Generation of Equipment" in Farm Industry News (November 23, 2011)*
Pub: Informa Business Media, Inc.
Contact: Charlie McCurdy, President
Ed: Jodie Wehrspann. **Description:** Canadian owned Versatile is expanding its four-wheel drive tractor division with sprayers, tillage, and seeding equipment. **Availability:** Online.

27477 ■ *"Building Inclusive Markets in Rural Bangladesh: How Intermediaries Work Institutional Voids" in Academy of Management Journal (Vol. 55, August 1, 2012, No. 4, pp. 819)*
Pub: Academy of Management
Contact: Sharon Alvarez, President
Ed: Johanna Mair, Ignasi Marti, Marc J. Ventresca. **Description:** The process of building inclusive markets in rural Bangladesh through Building Resources Across Communities program is analyzed. Results identifying institutional voids as the source of market exclusion and that redefining market architecture and the effort to legitimate new market actors are critical to building inclusive markets. **Availability:** Download; Electronic publishing; PDF; Online.

27478 ■ *"Building a Portfolio, BRIC by BRIC" in Barron's (Vol. 92, August 25, 2012, No. 38, pp. M8)*
Pub: Dow Jones & Company Inc.
Contact: Almar Latour, Chief Executive Officer
Ed: Reshma Kapadia. **Availability:** Online.

27479 ■ *"Building Wealth in China: 36 True Stories of Chinese Millionaires and How They Made Their Fortunes*
Released: April 27, 2010. **Price:** $7.99, e-book.
Description: Thirty-six of China's most successful and innovative entrepreneurs discuss valuable lessons for growing a business in China. **Availability:** E-book.

27480 ■ *"Business Without Borders: All For One, None for All?" in Canadian Business (Vol. 83, October 12, 2010, No. 17, pp. 60)*
Pub: Rogers Media Inc.
Contact: Neil Spivak, Chief Executive Officer
Ed: Michael McCullogh. **Description:** The effect of the growth of Canada's overseas provincial trade offices on Canadian trade is discussed. Economic development commissions in the country have devised a single 'Consider Canada' campaign to pitch foreign investors. It is hoped that large cities will gain from banding together rather than competing against one another. **Availability:** Print; Online.

27481 ■ *"Cabi to Develop Major Retail Project" in South Florida Business Journal (Vol. 32, July 6, 2012, No. 50, pp. 1)*
Pub: Baltimore Business Journal
Contact: Rhonda Pringle, President
E-mail: rpringle@bizjournals.com
Description: Aventura, Florida-based Cabi Developers has received a bankruptcy court approval to begin construction of a major retail project called Capital Brickell Place in the Brickell neighborhood. Mexican real estate developer GICSA will finance the project and Cabi has been talking with retailers like Costco, Targt and Trader Joe's as potential tenants. **Availability:** Print; Online.

27482 ■ *"Calendar" in Crain's Detroit Business (Vol. 24, March 10, 2008, No. 10, pp. 21)*
Pub: Crain Communications Inc.
Contact: Barry Asin, President
Description: Listing of events in the Detroit area include conferences addressing entrepreneurialism, economic development, and women business ownership. **Availability:** Print; Online.

27483 ■ *"Cameco to Supply Reactors With Recycled Nukem Warheads" in Canadian Business (Vol. 85, August 13, 2012, No. 13, pp. 10)*
Ed: Richard Warnica. **Description:** Cameco Corporation has acquired Nukem Energy gmbH from private equity firm Advent International for $136 million as part of the Canadian mining company's plan to double annual uranium production to 40 million pounds by 2018. Such agreement gives Cameco access to some of the last of the uranium supply in the Megatons to Megawatt deal between Russia and the U.S. which expires in 2013. **Availability:** Print; Online.

27484 ■ *"Canada Joins TPP Free Trade Talks" in Canadian Business (Vol. 85, August 13, 2012, No. 13, pp. 7)*
Ed: Tim Shufelt. **Description:** The decision of the Canadian government to join the Trans-Pacific Partnership (TPP) has potential economic benefits in terms of trading with China and the U.S.Failure of the World Trade Ogranization's Doha Round and the admission of the U.S. to the TPP prompted Canada to join the trade agreement. **Availability:** Print; Online.

27485 ■ *"Canada Nears European Trade Treaty" in Globe & Mail (February 5, 2007, pp. B1)*
Ed: Steven Chase. **Description:** The probable establishment of a treaty by Canada with Norway, Switzerland and Iceland for free-trade is discussed. The treaty will allow an annual business of $11 billion to take place in Canada. **Availability:** Print; Online.

27486 ■ *"Canada, Not China, Is Partner In Our Economic Prosperity" in Crain's Chicago Business (Vol. 31, April 14, 2008, No. 15, pp. 14)*
Pub: Crain Communications Inc.
Contact: Barry Asin, President
Ed: Paul O'Connor. **Description:** In 2005 more than $500 billion in two-way trade crossed the friendly border between the Great Lakes states and Canadian provinces and for decades Canada is every Great Lakes State's number one and growing export market. **Availability:** Online.

27487 ■ *"Canadian Hydronics Businesses Promote 'Beautiful Heat" in Indoor Comfort Marketing (Vol. 70, September 2011, No. 9, pp. 20)*
Pub: Spray Technology & Marketing
Contact: Ava Caridad, Director, Editorial
E-mail: acaridad@spraytm.com
Released: September 01, 2011. **Description:** Canadian hydronics companies are promoting their systems as beautiful heat. Hydronics is the use of water as the heat-transfer medium in heating and cooling system. **Availability:** Print; Online.

27488 ■ *"Canadian Patients Give Detroit Hospitals a Boost" in Crain's Detroit Business (Vol. 24, April 14, 2008, No. 15, pp. 10)*
Pub: Crain Communications Inc.
Contact: Barry Asin, President
Ed: Jay Greene. **Description:** Each year thousands of Canadians travel to Detroit area hospitals seeking quicker solutions to medical problems or access to services that are limited or unavailable in Canada. **Availability:** Online.

27489 ■ *"Canadian Solar Expands Into Puerto Rico With Planned 26MW Solar Power Plant Installation" in Benzinga.com (October 2, 2012)*
Pub: Benzinga.com
Contact: Jason Raznick, Founder
Description: Canadian Solar Inc. is expanding into Puerto Rico with the delivery of 26mg of CS6P-P solar power modules for the San Fermin solar power plant. Canadian Solar is one of the world's largest

solar firms. The solar power system is expected to be completed and connected to the national grid by December 2012.

27490 ■ "The Canadians Are Coming!" in Canadian Business (Vol. 80, October 22, 2007, No. 21, pp. 15)
Description: Toronto-Dominion Bank declared its acquisition of the New Jersey-based Commerce Bancorp for C$8.5 billion. Royal Bank of Canada has scooped up Trinidad-based Financial Group for C$2.2 billion. Details of the foreign acquisitions, as well as the impact of high Canadian dollars on the mergers are discussed. **Availability:** Online.

27491 ■ "Capitalizing On Our Intellectual Capital" in Harvard Business Review (Vol. 90, May 2012, No. 5, pp. 42)
Pub: Harvard Business Review Press
Contact: Moderna V. Pfizer, Contact
Ed: Iqbal Quadir. **Price:** $6, hardcopy and PDF. **Description:** By managing education as an export, the US can benefit not only from revenue received from tuition, but also from the relationships forged with foreign students. The students will import the networks and technologies they used while in the US and their education levels will help create global growth. **Availability:** Print; Online; PDF.

27492 ■ "Caterpillar to Expand Research, Production in China" in Chicago Tribune (August 27, 2008)
Description: Caterpillar Inc., the Peoria-based heavy-equipment manufacturer, plans to establish a new research-and-development center at the site of its rapidly growing campus in Wuxi. **Availability:** Print; Online.

27493 ■ "Cemex Paves a Global Road to Solid Growth" in Barron's (Vol. 88, March 10, 2008, No. 10, pp. 24)
Pub: Dow Jones & Company Inc.
Contact: Almar Latour, Chief Executive Officer
Ed: Sandra Ward. **Description:** Shares of Cemex are expected to perform well with the company's expected strong performance despite fears of a US recession. The company has a diverse geographical reach and benefits from a strong worldwide demand for cement. **Availability:** Online.

27494 ■ "Central Valley Local Fund II Has $110M to Invest" in Sacramento Business Journal (Vol. 29, May 25, 2012, No. 13, pp. 1)
Pub: Baltimore Business Journal
Contact: Rhonda Pringle, President
E-mail: rpringle@bizjournals.com
Description: CVF Capital Partners has raised $110 million to fund investments in mature companies. CVF's Central Valley Fund II is twice the size of the fund launched by the company in December 2005. The second hand, which was established by a total of 10 banks and a Mexican equity fund, is considered a vote of confidence in Central Valley industries. **Availability:** Print; Online.

27495 ■ "The CEO Poll: Potash Sale Must Be Blocked" in Canadian Business (Vol. 83, October 12, 2010, No. 17, pp. 24)
Pub: Rogers Media Inc.
Contact: Neil Spivak, Chief Executive Officer
Ed: Kasey Coholan. **Description:** Chief executive officers (CEOs) and corporate leaders in Canada are concerned about the possible sale of Potash Corporation to foreign buyers. A Compas Inc. poll recently asked CEOs whether the Canadian Government should step in to block the sale of the country's largest fertilizer firm. **Availability:** Print; Online.

27496 ■ "CEO Putting Rubber to Road at Lanxess Corporation" in Pittsburgh Business Times (Vol. 33, May 2, 2014, No. 42, pp. 4)
Pub: American City Business Journals, Inc.
Contact: Mike Olivieri, Executive Vice President
Released: May 02, 2014. **Price:** $4, introductory 4-week offer(Digital only). **Description:** Flemming Bjoernslev, CEO for the North American operations of Germany-based Lanxess Corporation, discusses

their recovery efforts following their first financial loss in 2013. He is confident that the U.S. tire manufacturing industry will help their business further in North America. **Availability:** Print; Online.

27497 ■ "CEOs Decry Budget Taxation Change" in Globe & Mail (April 2, 2007, pp. B1)
Ed: Steven Chase. **Description:** The views of the chief executive officers of Canadian firms, on the changes in the country's policy governing the taxation of foreign deals, are presented. **Availability:** Print; Online.

27498 ■ "A Change Would Do You Good" in Canadian Business (Vol. 80, November 19, 2007, No. 23, pp. 15)
Description: Western Glove Works will be manufacturing clothing offshore, including Sheryl Crow's jeans collection, in countries such as China and the Philippines. The company decided to operate offshore after 86 years of existence due to the high price of manufacturing jeans in Canada. Western Glove's focus on producing celebrity-endorsed goods is discussed. **Availability:** Print; Online.

27499 ■ "Changing the Rules of the Accounting Game" in Canadian Business (Vol. 81, December 8, 2008, No. 21, pp. 19)
Description: Interference from world politicians in developing accounting standards is believed to have resulted in untested rules that are inferior to current standards. European lawmakers have recently asked to change International Financial Reporting Standards. **Availability:** Online.

27500 ■ "Charlotte Pipe Launches Satirical Campaign" in Contractor (Vol. 57, January 2010, No. 1, pp. 6)
Description: Charlotte Pipe and Foundry Co. launched an advertising campaign that uses social media and humor to make a point about how it can be nearly impossible to determine if imported cast iron pipes and fittings meet the same quality standards as what is made in the U.S. The campaign features 'pipe whisperers' and also spoofs pipe sniffing dogs. **Availability:** Print; Online.

27501 ■ "Cheap Tubing Risk to Local Jobs, Execs Caution" in Pittsburgh Business Times (Vol. 33, May 23, 2014, No. 45, pp. 4)
Pub: American City Business Journals, Inc.
Contact: Mike Olivieri, Executive Vice President
Released: Weekly. **Price:** $4, introductory 4-week offer(Digital only). **Description:** U.S. Steel Corporation requests the U.S. Department of Commerce to take action against unfairly traded steel imports in the market because thousands of jobs are at risk. At least 26,400 jobs in Pennsylvania may be affected by the unfair trading practices of foreign exporters according to the office of Governor Tom Corbett. **Availability:** Print; Online.

27502 ■ "The China Connection" in Crain's Chicago Business (Vol. 31, March 24, 2008, No. 12, pp. 26)
Ed: Samantha Stainburn. **Description:** Interview with Ben Munoz who studied abroad in Beijing, China for three months to study international economics, e-commerce and global leadership. **Availability:** Print; Online.

27503 ■ "China Vs the World: Whose Technology Is It?" in Harvard Business Review (Vol. 88, December 2010, No. 12, pp. 94)
Pub: Harvard Business Publishing
Contact: Diane Belcher, Managing Director
Ed: Thomas M. Hout, Pankaj Ghemawat. **Price:** $8.95, PDF. **Description:** Examination of the regulation the Chinese government is implementing that require foreign corporations wishing to do business in the country to give up their new technologies. These regulations avoid World Trade Organization technology transfer provisions and complicate the convergence of socialism and capitalism. **Availability:** Online; PDF.

27504 ■ China's Rational Entrepreneurs: The Development of the New Private Business Sector
Pub: Routledge, Taylor & Francis Group
Ed: Barbara Krug. **Released:** First edition. **Description:** Difficulties faced by entrepreneurs in China are discussed, including analysis for understanding their behavior and relations with local governments in order to secure long-term business success.

27505 ■ "China's Slowing Growth Could Benefit the Global Economy; An Expert On China's Economy Says the Country Is Seeing an Upside to Slowing Down" in Gallup Business Journal (April 8, 2014)
Pub: Gallup, Inc.
Contact: Jon Clifton, Chief Executive Officer
Description: An expert on China's economy reports that the country is acknowledging an upside to slowing down, and is creating opportunities for a market economy never seen before. Ways that China is looking to expand its economy, thus expand the global economy, is investigated. **Availability:** Online.

27506 ■ "China's Super Consumers: What 1 Billion Customers Want and How to Sell It to Them"
Pub: John Wiley & Sons, Inc.
Contact: Christina Van Tassell, Executive Vice President Chief Financial Officer
Released: September 22, 2014. **Price:** $25, hardcover; $16.99, e-book. **Description:** China has become the largest consumer market in the world. An exploration into the birth of consumerism in China and what the Chinese consumer buys, how they buy, and why they buy is presented. Advice for successfully entering this international market include a hands-on resource, real stories of companies making an impact in China, what the Chinese consumer wants and how to deliver the goods. **Availability:** E-book; Print.

27507 ■ "China's Transition to Green Energy Systems: The Economics of Home Solar Water Heaters and Their Popularization in Dezhou City" in Energy Policy (Vol. 39, October 2011, No. 10, pp. 5909-5919)
Ed: Wei Li, Guojun Song, Melanie Beresford, Den Ma. **Released:** 2011. **Description:** The economics of home solar water heaters and their growing popularity in Dezhous City, China is discussed. **Availability:** PDF; Online.

27508 ■ "Chinese Coal Giant Shifts Focus with ECA Pact" in Pittsburgh Business Times (Vol. 33, January 10, 2014, No. 26, pp. 3)
Pub: American City Business Journals, Inc.
Contact: Mike Olivieri, Executive Vice President
Description: China Shenhua Energy Company has signed a deal with Energy Corporation of America (ECA) for a joint venture with its U.S. subsidiary, Shenhua America Holdings Corporation, to drill 25 wells in Greene County, Pennsylvania. Shenhua will initially provide $90 million to cover the costs of drilling and production for the wells in ECA-owned land. **Availability:** Online.

27509 ■ Cities from the Arabian Desert: The Building of Jubail and Yambu in Saudi Arabia
Ed: Andrea H. Pampanini. **Description:** An overview of Saudi Arabia's government to take control of the nation's natural resources and change the government, educational system, and its culture by evolving into a modern industrial society. **Availability:** Print.

27510 ■ "Closed Minds and Open Skies" in Barron's (Vol. 88, March 10, 2008, No. 10, pp. 50)
Pub: Dow Jones & Company Inc.
Contact: Almar Latour, Chief Executive Officer
Ed: Thomas G. Donlan. **Description:** American politicians have closed minds when it comes to fair trade. The American government must not interfere with the country's manufacturing industries or worry about outsourcing defense contracts to European aerospace company Airbus. **Availability:** Online.

27511 ■ "Column: Want People to Save? Force Them" in Harvard Business Review (Vol. 88, September 2010, No. 9, pp. 36)

Pub: Harvard Business Publishing

Contact: Diane Belcher, Managing Director

Ed: Dan Ariely. Price: $6, PDF. Description: Contrasts in U.S. attitudes towards savings and government regulation with those of Chile, where all employees are required to save 11 percent of their salary in a retirement account, are highlighted. Availability: Online; PDF.

27512 ■ "Coming: Cheaper Oil and a Stronger Buck" in Barron's (Vol. 88, March 24, 2008, No. 12, pp. 53)

Pub: Dow Jones & Company Inc.

Contact: Almar Latour, Chief Executive Officer

Ed: Lawrence C. Strauss. Description: Carl C. Weinberg, the chief economist of High Frequency Economics, forecasts that Chinese economic growth will slow down and that oil prices will drop to $80 a barrel in 2008. He also believes that the US dollar will start rising the moment the Federal Reserve stops cutting interest rates. Availability: Online.

27513 ■ "Coming: The End of Fiat Money" in Barron's (Vol. 92, July 23, 2012, No. 30, pp. 32)

Pub: Dow Jones & Company Inc.

Contact: Almar Latour, Chief Executive Officer

Ed: Leslie P. Norton. Description: Stephanie Pomboy, founder of MicroMavens, discusses her views on the global financial system. She believes that the global fiat currency system may collapse within five years and be replaced by a gold-backed currency system. Availability: Online.

27514 ■ Connect with SmartBook: Online Access for Canadian Entrepreneurship and Small Business Management

Ed: D. Wesley Balderson. Released: 10th Edition. Price: C$89, connect with smartbook; C$143.95, print text plus connect with smartbook; C$133.95, print text; C$89, Digital(Connect with SmartBook); C$143.95, Print (Print text + Connect with Smart-Book); C$133.95, Print text. Description: Successful entrepreneurship and small business management is shown through the use of individual Canadian small business experiences. Availability: Print; Online.

27515 ■ "Coping With a Shrinking Planet" in Agency Sales Magazine (Vol. 39, December 2009, No. 11, pp. 46)

Description: China and India are forcing big changes in the world and are posing a huge threat to U.S. manufacturers and their sales representatives. Reps may want to consider expanding into these territories. Helping sell American products out of the country presents an opportunity for economic expansion. Availability: Online.

27516 ■ "Copy Karachi?" in Barron's (Vol. 88, June 30, 2008, No. 26, pp. 5)

Pub: Dow Jones & Company Inc.

Contact: Almar Latour, Chief Executive Officer

Ed: Randall W. Forsyth. Description: Karachi bourse had a historic 8.6 percent one-day gain because the bourse banned short-selling for a month and announced a 30 billion rupee fund to stabilize the market. The shares of General Motors are trading within the same values that it had in 1974. The reasons for this decline are discussed. Availability: Online.

27517 ■ "Corporate Governance Reforms in China and India: Challenges and Opportunities" in Business Horizons (January-February 2008)

Pub: Elsevier Advanced Technology Publications

Ed: Nandini Rajagopalan, Yan Zhang. Description: The evolution of corporate governance reforms and the role of privatization and globalization in India and China are studied. Shortage of qualified independent directors and lack of incentives were found to be two

of the major challenges in governance. The implications of and solutions to these challenges are highlighted. Availability: Download; PDF; Online.

27518 ■ "Corporate Social Responsibility and Trade Unions: Perspectives Across Europe"

Pub: Routledge, Taylor & Francis Group

Released: First edition. Description: Although interest in corporate social responsibility (CSR) is focused on the relationship between business and key stakeholders such as NGOs and local communities, the role of trade unions is rarely connected to CSR. Experts discuss the gap in the literature on both CSR and employment relations, namely trade union policies toward CSR as well as union engagement with particular CSR initiatives. The research covers eleven European countries which represent a sample of industrial relations structures across the continent.

27519 ■ "Cost Remains Top Factor In Considering Green Technology" in Canadian Sailings (June 30, 2008)

Description: Improving its environmental performance remains a priority in the shipping industry; however, testing new technologies can prove difficult due to the harsh conditions that ships endure as well as installation which usually requires a dry dock. Availability: Online.

27520 ■ "Counterfeits Plague Many Collectibles" in Coin World (September 16, 2019)

URL(s): www.coinworld.com/news/us-coins/monday-morning-brief-for-sept-16-2019-counterfeits-plague-many-collectibles

Ed: William T. Gibbs. Released: September 16, 2019. Description: Counterfeit stamps are sold on eBay and other internet sites, in order to get quick cash. Most of the time the postal service will kick out these stamps if they are placed on envelopes and return to sender. Others make it through. Coins and other collectibles are also taking a hit, as counterfeits are manufactured overseas in China. Availability: Online.

27521 ■ "CPR-CN Deal to Ease Vancouver Logjam" in Globe & Mail (January 27, 2006, pp. B4)

Description: In a bid to lessen West coast port grid lock Canadian Pacific Railway Ltd and Canadian National Railway Co. has agreed to share tracks in the Vancouver region. This will allow the trains to operate more efficiently from the Vancouver Port. Availability: Print; Online.

27522 ■ "A Crash Course in Global Relations" in Canadian Business (Vol. 87, July 2014, No. 7, pp. 77)

Description: Teach Away Inc. is a global education firm based in Toronto, Ontario that recruits English-speaking teachers to work abroad. The firm's revenues have grown by 1,621 percent from 2008 to 2013, placing it in the 37th spot on the 2014 Profit ranking of fastest growing companies in Canada. Availability: Online.

27523 ■ "Critics Target Bribery Law" in Wall Street Journal Eastern Edition (November 28, 2011, pp. B1)

Pub: Dow Jones & Company Inc.

Contact: Almar Latour, Chief Executive Officer

Ed: Joe Palazzolo. Description: Concern about how the Foreign Corrupt Practices Act, the United States' anti-bribery law, is enforced has drawn the focus of corporate lobbyists. Corporations have paid some $4 billion in penalties in cases involving the law, which prohibits companies from paying foreign officials bribes. The US Chamber of Commerce believes amending the act should be a priority. Availability: Online.

27524 ■ "Crucible: Battling Back from Betrayal" in Harvard Business Review (Vol. 88, December 2010, No. 12, pp. 130)

Pub: Harvard Business Publishing

Contact: Diane Belcher, Managing Director

Ed: Daniel McGinn. Price: $8.95, PDF. Description: Stephen Greer's scrap metal firm, Hartwell Pacific, lost several million dollars due to a lack of efficient and appropriate inventory audits, accounting procedures, and new-hire reference checks for his foreign operations. Greer believes that balancing growth with control is a key component of success. Availability: Print; PDF.

27525 ■ Currency Internationalization: Global Experiences and Implications for the Renminbi

Pub: Palgrave Macmillan

Released: First edition. Description: A collection of academic studies relating to the potential internationalization of China's remninbi. It also discusses the increasing use of China's remninbi currency in international trade and finance.

27526 ■ "Deere to Open Technology Center in Germany" in Chicago Tribune (September 3, 2008)

Description: Deere & Co. plans to open a technology and innovation center in Germany; details of the company's expansion plans are discussed. Availability: Print; Online.

27527 ■ "Delivering the Milk" in Barron's (Vol. 92, July 23, 2012, No. 30, pp. M7)

Pub: Dow Jones & Company Inc.

Contact: Almar Latour, Chief Executive Officer

Ed: Kopin Tan. Description: The stocks of China Mengniu Dairy could continue losing value in the short term but could gain value in the long term. The company's revenue growth and profit margins face downward pressure due to aggressive pricing after food safety scandals. Availability: Online.

27528 ■ "Direct Recovery Associates Debt Collection Agency Beats Industry Record" in Internet Wire (June 24, 2010)

Description: Direct Recovery Associates Inc. was named as one of the highest collection records in the industry, which has consistently improved over 18 years. The firm is an international attorney-based debt collection agency. Availability: Print; Online.

27529 ■ "Disney's High Hopes for Duffy" in Canadian Business (Vol. 83, October 12, 2010, No. 17, pp. 14)

Pub: Rogers Media Inc.

Contact: Neil Spivak, Chief Executive Officer

Ed: James Cowan. Description: The reintroduction of Duffy is expected to create a new, exclusive product line that distinguishes Disney's parks and stores from competitors. Duffy, a teddy bear, was first introduced at a Disney World store in Florida in 2002. The character was incorporated into the Disney mythology when its popularity grew in Japan. Availability: Online.

27530 ■ "Diversity Knocks" in Canadian Business (Vol. 83, October 12, 2010, No. 17, pp. 62)

Ed: Angelina Chapin. Released: October 12, 2010. Description: Canadian companies have a global edge because of their multicultural workforce. However, most of these organizations do not take advantage and avoid doing business abroad. Canadian firms could leverage their multicultural staff with language skills and knowledge of local customs. Availability: Print; Online.

27531 ■ "DocuSign Raises $85 Million for Electronic Signatures" in San Francisco Business Times (Vol. 28, March 7, 2014, No. 33, pp. 6)

Pub: American City Business Journals, Inc.

Contact: Mike Olivieri, Executive Vice President

Released: Weekly. Description: DocuSign, the market leader in electronic signatures, reported that it was able to raise another $85 million in capital. The company is expected to file an initial public offering in 2014 or 2015. CFO, Mike Dinsdale, shares that the firm also wants to expand internationally. Availability: Print; Online.

27532 ■ "Don't Bet Against The House" in Barron's (Vol. 88, July 14, 2008, No. 28, pp. 20)
Pub: Dow Jones & Company Inc.
Contact: Almar Latour, Chief Executive Officer

Ed: Sandra Ward. Description: Shares of Nasdaq OMX have lost more than 50 percent of their value from November 2007 to July 2008 but the value of these shares could climb 50 percent on the strength of world security exchanges. Only 15 percent of the company's revenues come from the U.S. and the shares are trading at 12.5 times the amount expected for 2008. Availability: Online.

27533 ■ "Don't Tweak Your Supply Chain - Rethink It End to End" in Harvard Business Review (Vol. 88, October 2010, No. 10, pp. 62)
Pub: Harvard Business Publishing
Contact: Diane Belcher, Managing Director

Ed: Hau L. Lee. Price: $8.95, PDF. Description: Hong Kong apparel firm Esquel Apparel Ltd. is used to illustrate supply chain reorganization to improve a firm's sustainability. Discussion focuses on taking a broad approach rather than addressing individual steps or processes. Availability: Online; PDF.

27534 ■ "Dow Champions Innovative Energy Solutions for Auto Industry at NAIAS" in Business of Global Warming (January 25, 2010, pp. 7)
Description: This year's North American International Auto Show in Detroit will host the "Electric Avenue" exhibit sponsored by the Dow Chemical Company. The display will showcase the latest in innovative energy solutions from Dow as well as electric vehicles and the technology supporting them. This marks the first time a non-automotive manufacturer is part of the main floor of the show. Availability: Print; PDF; Online.

27535 ■ "Drilling Deep and Flying High" in Barron's (Vol. 88, June 30, 2008, No. 26, pp. 34)
Pub: Dow Jones & Company Inc.
Contact: Almar Latour, Chief Executive Officer

Ed: Kenneth Rapoza. Description: Shares of Petrobras could rise another 25 percent if the three deepwater wells that the company has found proves as lucrative as some expect. Petrobras will become an oil giant if the reserves are proven. Availability: Online.

27536 ■ EBay Income: How ANYONE of Any Age, Location, and/or Background Can Build a Highly Profitable Online Business with eBay
Pub: Atlantic Publishing Co.
Contact: Dr. Heather L. Johnson, Contact

Description: A complete overview of eBay is given and guides any small company through the entire process of creating the auction and auction strategies, photography, writing copy, text and formatting, multiple sales, programming tricks, PayPal, accounting, creating marketing, merchandising, managing email lists, advertising plans, taxes and sales tax, best time to list items and for how long, sniping programs, international customers, opening a storefront, electronic commerce, buy-it now pricing, keywords, Google marketing and eBay secrets.

27537 ■ "Economic Distance and the Survival of Foreign Direct Investments" in Academy of Management Journal (Vol. 50, No. 5, October 1, 2007, pp. 1156)
Pub: Academy of Management
Contact: Sharon Alvarez, President

Ed: Eric W.K. Tsang, Paul S.L. Yip. Description: Study was undertaken to assess the relationship between economic disparities of various countries and foreign direct investments, focusing on Singapore. Results revealed that economic distance has a definite impact on foreign direct investment hazard rates. Availability: Electronic publishing; Download; PDF; Online.

27538 ■ "Economics: The User's Guide"
Released: 1st edition. Price: $27, hardback ; $18, paperback ; $16, ebook. Description: Cambridge economist explains how the global economy is working. He provides a concise knowledge of history with a disregard for conventional economic traditions and offers insights into economic behavior. Availability: E-book.

27539 ■ "An Educated Play on China" in Barron's (Vol. 88, June 30, 2008, No. 26, pp. M6)
Pub: Dow Jones & Company Inc.
Contact: Almar Latour, Chief Executive Officer

Ed: Mohammed Hadi. Description: New Oriental Education & Technology Group sells English-language courses to an increasingly competitive Chinese workforce that values education. The shares in this company have been weighed down by worries on the impact of the Beijing Olympics on enrollment and the Sichuan earthquake. These shares could be a great way to get exposure to the long-term growth in China. Availability: Online.

27540 ■ "Elastic Path Software Joins Canada in G20 Young Entrepreneur Summit" in Marketwire (June 14, 2010)
Pub: Comtex News Network Inc.
Contact: Kan Devnani, President

Description: The Canadian Youth Business Foundation hosted the G20 Young Entrepreneur Summit and announced that Harry Chemko of British Columbia's Elastic Path Software will be a member of the Canadian delegation at the G20 Young Entrepreneur Summit. Details are included. Availability: Print; Online.

27541 ■ Electronic Commerce
Ed: Gary P. Schneider, Bryant Chrzan, Charles Mc-Cormick. Released: 12th edition. Price: $29.49, e-book. Description: E-commerce can open the door to more opportunities than ever before for small business. Packed with real-world examples and cases, the book delivers comprehensive coverage of emerging online technologies and trends and their influence on the electronic marketplace. It details how the landscape of online commerce is evolving, reflecting changes in the economy and how business and society are responding to those changes. Balancing technological issues with the strategic business aspects of successful e-commerce, the new edition includes expanded coverage of international issues, social networking, mobile commerce, Web 2.0 technologies, and updates on spam, phishing, and identity theft. Availability: Print.

27542 ■ Emerging Business Online: Global Markets and the Power of B2B Internet Marketing
Pub: FT Press

Ed: Lara Fawzy, Lucas Dworski. Released: First edition. Price: $39.99, Members, watermarked. Description: An introduction into ebocube (emerging business online), a comprehensive proven business model for Internet B2B marketing in emerging markets. Availability: E-book; Print; Online; PDF; Electronic publishing.

27543 ■ "End of the Beginning" in Canadian Business (Vol. 81, November 10, 2008, No. 19, pp. 17)
Ed: David Wolf. Released: September 30, 2016. Description: The freeze in the money markets and historic decline in equity markets around the world finally forced governments into aggressive coordinated action. The asset price inflation brought on by cheap credit will now work in reverse and the tightening of credit will be difficult economically. Canada is exposed to the fallout everywhere, given that the U.S, the U.K. and Japan buy 30 percent of Canada's output. Availability: Print; Online.

27544 ■ "The End of RIM" in Canadian Business (Vol. 85, August 13, 2012, No. 13, pp. 22)
Ed: Joe Castaldo. Description: The potential implications of the collapse of Research in Motion (RIM) on the Canadian technology sector are examined. The

country is expected to lose its biggest training ground for technology talent without RIM, but the company's decline will not stop Canadians from trying to build and sustain multinational technology companies. Availability: Print; Online.

27545 ■ Entrepreneurship and Small Business Development in the Former Soviet Bloc
Description: Examination of entrepreneurship and small business in Russia and other key countries of Eastern Europe, showing how far small businesses have developed in the region. Availability: Online; PDF.

27546 ■ "ESolar Partners With Penglai on Landmark Solar Thermal Agreement for China" in Business of Global Warming (January 25, 2010, pp. 8)
Description: Penglai Electric, a privately-owned Chinese electrical power equipment manufacturer, and eSolar, a global provider of cost-effective and reliable solar power plants, announced a master licensing agreement in which eSolar will build at least 2 gigawatts of solar thermal power plants in China over the next 10 years. Availability: Print; Online.

27547 ■ "Europe's Meltdown" in Canadian Business (Vol. 83, June 15, 2010, No. 10, pp. 76)
Description: As European countries such as Greece, Spain, and Portugal struggle with debt problems, it is worth noting that its equities trade at a 30 percent discount to the U.S. and that a 10 percent drop in the Euro translates to a 10 percent rise in profitability for exporters. Investors may also want to focus on business-to-business operations rather than consumer-focused ones. Availability: Online.

27548 ■ "Everybody Wants To Save the World: But When You Start a Charity Overseas, Good Intentions Often Go Awry" in Inc. (December 2007)
Ed: Dalia Fahmy. Description: Unique set of challenges faced by small businesses wanting to create a charity overseas. Five key issues to explore before starting a charity overseas are examined. Availability: Online.

27549 ■ "Ex-Im Bank Accepts $105 Million in Financing for Aquarium in Brazil" in Travel & Leisure Close-Up (October 8, 2012)
Description: Export-Import Bank of the United States authorized a $105 million direct loan to the Brazilian state of Ceara to finance the export of American goods and services for the construction of an aquarium in Fortaleza, Brazil. This transaction will support 700 American jobs and at least 90 percent of the export contract value will be provided by U.S. small businesses. Availability: Print; Online.

27550 ■ "Export Opportunity" in Business Journal-Portland (Vol. 24, October 12, 2007, No. 33, pp. 1)
Description: U.S. dollar is weak, hitting an all-time low against the Euro, while the Canadian dollar is also performing well it hit parity for the first time after more than thirty years. The weak U.S. dollar is making companies that sell overseas benefit as it makes their goods cheaper to buy.

27551 ■ Facilitating Sustainable Innovation through Collaboration: A Multi-Stakeholder Perspective
Ed: Joseph Sarkis, James J. Cordeiro, Diego Vazquez Brust. Description: An international perspective of sustainable innovation with contributions from Australia, Europe, and North America, by prominent policy makers, scientific researchers and others. Availability: E-book; Print; Electronic publishing.

27552 ■ "Fast 50: HNM Global Logistics" in Orlando Business Journal (Vol. 30, June 27, 2014, No. 53, pp. 8)
Pub: American City Business Journals, Inc.
Contact: Mike Olivieri, Executive Vice President

Released: Weekly. **Description:** Tony L. McGee is the CEO of HNM Global Logistics, a full service freight forwarder that reduced its logistic spending by 22 percent in 2013. He believes that America will see a revival in manufacturing coupled with more free trade agreements. **Availability:** Print; Online.

27553 ■ Faster Cheaper Better
Released: December 28, 2010. **Price:** $27.50, hardcover. **Description:** Nine levels for transforming work in order to achieve business growth are outlined. The book helps small business compete against the low-wage countries. **Availability:** E-book; Print.

27554 ■ Female Entrepreneurship in East and South-East Asia: Opportunities and Challenges
Ed: Philippe Debroux. **Released:** 2010. **Description:** A detailed study of female entrepreneurship in Asia, where public authorities are slowly realizing the importance of women as workers and entrepreneurs. **Availability:** E-book; Print.

27555 ■ "Finally! Windsor Gets a New Bridge" in Canadian Business (Vol. 85, August 21, 2012, No. 14, pp. 20)
Ed: Tim Shufelt. **Description:** Canadian Prime Minister Stephen Harper agreed to loan Michigan $550 million to build its new highway interchange and customs plaza linking Windsor, Ontario and Detroit, Michigan. Billionaire Manuel Maroun, owner of the Ambassador Bridge, has initiated a signature campaign for a referendum on any new border crossings. **Availability:** Print; Online.

27556 ■ "Finding Life Behind the Numbers" in Crain's Chicago Business (Vol. 31, March 24, 2008, No. 12, pp. 25)
Pub: Crain Communications Inc.
Contact: Barry Asin, President
Ed: Samantha Stainburn. **Description:** Interview with Phillip Capodice who is a graduate student at DePaul University's Kellstadt Graduate School of Business and studied abroad in Lima, Peru where he visited a number of companies including some who are trade partners with the United States. **Availability:** Online.

27557 ■ "Finding the Right Resources to Get Started Overseas" in Pittsburgh Business Times (Vol. 33, January 3, 2014, No. 25, pp. 4)
Pub: American City Business Journals, Inc.
Contact: Mike Olivieri, Executive Vice President
Description: Pittsburgh, Pennsylvania-based companies can develop relationships abroad and take advantage of the market opportunity to expand. Companies are unaware of the many helpful agencies, organizations and Websites that help them become international. Tips for developing relationships overseas are presented. **Availability:** Online.

27558 ■ "Finding Your Place in the World: Global Diversity Has Become a Corporate Catchphrase" in Black Enterprise (November 2007)
Pub: Earl G. Graves Ltd.
Contact: Earl Graves, Jr., President
Ed: Wendy Harris. **Description:** Does the inclusion of workers from other countries mean exclusion of African American workers in the U.S.?. **Availability:** Online.

27559 ■ "Flying the Unfriendly Skies" in Crain's Chicago Business (Vol. 31, April 21, 2008, No. 16, pp. 26)
Pub: Crain Communications Inc.
Contact: Barry Asin, President
Ed: Sarah A. Klein. **Description:** Due to the number of Chicago companies and entrepreneurs who are traveling overseas more frequently in order to strengthen ties with customers, companies and oftentimes even business partners, the number of flights leaving O'Hare International Airport for destinations abroad has surged; In 2007, international passengers departing O'Hare totaled 5.7 million, up from 2.4 million in 1990. **Availability:** Online.

27560 ■ "ForeSee Finds Satisfaction On Web Sites, Bottom Line" in Crain's Detroit Business (Vol. 24, February 25, 2008, No. 8, pp. 3)
Pub: Crain Communications Inc.
Contact: Barry Asin, President
Ed: Tom Henderson. **Description:** Ann Arbor-based ForeSee Results Inc. evaluates user satisfaction on Web sites. The company expects to see an increase of 40 percent in revenue for 2008 with plans to expand to London, Germany, Italy and France by the end of 2009.

27561 ■ "The Foundations of Supplier Engagement; Companies' Relationships With Their Suppliers Are Vital To Their Success. Here Are the Fundamental Ways Businesses Can Measure and Manage Those Relationships" in Gallup Business Journal (June 26, 2014)
Pub: Gallup, Inc.
Contact: Jon Clifton, Chief Executive Officer
Description: The global economy has changed the nature of supplier-customer relationships. A company's relationship with their suppliers is critical to success. Fundamental ways any business can measure and manage their relationships with suppliers and become a customer of choice are examined. **Availability:** Print.

27562 ■ "The Four Cheapest Plays in Emerging Markets" in Barron's (Vol. 89, July 27, 2009, No. 30, pp. 34)
Pub: Dow Jones & Company Inc.
Contact: Almar Latour, Chief Executive Officer
Ed: Lawrence C. Strauss. **Description:** Portfolio manager Arjun Divecha of the GMO Emerging Markets III Fund says that the main thing in investing in emerging markets is getting the country right since getting it wrong makes it harder to add value. Divecha says that the four countries that they are positive on are Turkey, Russia, South Korea, and Thailand. **Availability:** Online.

27563 ■ "From American Icon to Global Juggernaut" in Automotive News (Vol. 86, October 31, 2011, No. 6488, pp. S003)
Pub: Crain Communications Inc.
Contact: Barry Asin, President
Ed: Peter Brown. **Description:** Chevrolet celebrates its 100th Anniversary. The brand revolutionized its market with affordable cars that bring technology to the masses. Chevys have been sold in 140 countries and the company is responding to a broader market. **Availability:** Print; Online.

27564 ■ "From Malls to Steel Plants" in Crain's Chicago Business (Vol. 31, April 28, 2008, No. 17, pp. 30)
Pub: Crain Communications Inc.
Contact: Barry Asin, President
Ed: Samantha Stainburn. **Description:** Profile of the company Graycor Inc. which started out as a sand-blasting and concrete-breaking firm but has grown into four businesses due to innovation and acquisitions. Graycor's businesses include: Graycor Industrial Constructors Inc., which builds and renovates power plants and steel mills; Graycor Construction Co., which erects stores, medical centers and office buildings; Graycor Blasting Co., which uses explosives and blasts tunnels for industrial cleaning, and Graycor International Inc., which provides construction services in Mexico. **Availability:** Online.

27565 ■ "Furniture Making May Come Back--Literally" in Business North Carolina (Vol. 28, March 2008, No. 3, pp. 32)
Pub: Business North Carolina
Contact: Peggy Knaack, Manager
E-mail: pknaack@businessnc.com
Description: Due to the weak U.S. dollar and the fact that lumber processors never left the country, foreign furniture manufacturers are becoming interested in moving manufacturing plants to the U.S. **Availability:** Online.

27566 ■ "Future of Diversity: Cultural Inclusion Is a Business Imperative" in Black Enterprise (Vol. 41, August 2010, No. 1, pp. 75)
Pub: Earl G. Graves Ltd.
Contact: Earl Graves, Jr., President
Ed: Annya M. Lott. **Description:** As globalization continues to make the world a smaller place, workforce diversity will be imperative to any small company in order to be sustainable.

27567 ■ "The Future Is Another Country; Higher Education" in The Economist (Vol. 390, January 3, 2009, No. 8612, pp. 43)
Description: Due to the growth of the global corporation, more ambitious students are studying at universities abroad; the impact of this trend is discussed. **Availability:** Print; Online.

27568 ■ "The Future of Work" in Black Enterprise (Vol. 41, August 2010, No. 1, pp. 65)
Pub: Earl G. Graves Ltd.
Contact: Earl Graves, Jr., President
Ed: Annya M. Lott. **Description:** Technology, globalization, and outsourcing will continue to shape the future of work. Social media is a means for small companies to market goods and services. **Availability:** Online.

27569 ■ "The Future of Work" in Business Strategy Review (Vol. 21, Autumn 2010, No. 3, pp. 16)
Pub: Wiley-Blackwell
Ed: Lynda Gratton. **Released:** August 28, 2017. **Description:** Work is universal. But how, why, where and when we work has never been so open to individual interpretation. The certainties of the past have been replaced by ambiguity, questions and the steady hum of technology. Now, in a groundbreaking research project covering 21 global companies and more than 200 executives, the author is making sense of the future of work. **Availability:** Print; PDF; Online.

27570 ■ "G20 Young Entrepreneur Alliance Signs Charter Outlining Commitment to Entrepreneurship" in Marketwire (November 10, 2010)
Pub: Comtex News Network Inc.
Contact: Kan Devnani, President
Description: G20 Young Entrepreneur Summit members created a charter document that outlines their support for the G20 process to include entrepreneurship on its agenda. Details of the Summit are included. **Availability:** Online.

27571 ■ "Gamesa Office Closing Part of Political Reality" in Pittsburgh Business Times (Vol. 33, February 7, 2014, No. 30, pp. 6)
Pub: American City Business Journals, Inc.
Contact: Mike Olivieri, Executive Vice President
Description: Due to political uncertainty surrounding the production tax credit for wind energy and changes in the supply chain needs in the North America wind market, a Spanish wind blade maker Gamesa will be shutting down its manufacturing unit in Ebensburg March 31, 2014. The general counsel for Gamesa, Frank Fuselier, stated that optimizing the company's supply chain will help them survive in a market devoid of a production tax credit. **Availability:** Online.

27572 ■ "Gaming Infrastructure Paves Ready Path for Manufacturing" in Memphis Business Journal (No. 35, February 14, 2014, No. 45, pp. 4)
Pub: American City Business Journals, Inc.
Contact: Mike Olivieri, Executive Vice President
Description: The city of Tunica, Mississippi is trying to expand its reputation as a gaming destination into manufacturing in an effort seek new opportunities for economic development and revenue. German crankshaft manufacturer, Feurer Powertrain, is building a $140 million manufacturing facility that will open in late 2014. **Availability:** Online.

27573 ■ *"German Win Through Sharing"* in *Canadian Business (Vol. 83, September 14, 2010, No. 15, pp. 16)*
Pub: Rogers Media Inc.
Contact: Neil Spivak, Chief Executive Officer
Ed: Jordan Timm. **Released:** September 14, 2010. **Description:** German economic historian Eckhard Hoffner has a two-volume work showing how German's relaxed attitude toward copyright and intellectual property helped it catch up to industrialized United Kingdom. Hoffner's research was in response to his interest in the usefulness of software patents. Information on the debate regarding Canada's copyright laws is given. **Availability:** Print; Online.

27574 ■ *"Getting Rid of Global Glitches: Choosing Software For Trade Compliance"* in *Black Enterprise (Vol. 41, September 2010, No. 2, pp. 48)*
Pub: Earl G. Graves Ltd.
Contact: Earl Graves, Jr., President
Ed: Marcia Wade Talbert. **Description:** Compliance software for trading with foreign companies must be compatible with the U.S. Census Bureau's Automated Export System (www.aesdirect.gov). It has to be current with regulatory requirements for any country in the world. Whether owners handle their own compliance or hire a logistics company, they need to be familiar with this software in order to access reports and improve transparency and efficiency of theft supply chain. **Availability:** Online.

27575 ■ *"Global Business Speaks English: Why You Need a Language Strategy Now"* in *Harvard Business Review (Vol. 90, May 2012, No. 5, pp. 116)*
Pub: Harvard Business Review Press
Contact: Moderna V. Pfizer, Contact
Ed: Tsedal Neeley. **Price:** $8.95. **Description:** English is rapidly becoming the language of businesses regardless of where they are located. To improve efficiency, the author advocates implementing an English-only policy. However, this must be conducted with sufficient training and support, and appropriate cultural sensitivity. **Availability:** PDF; Online.

27576 ■ *Global E-Commerce: Impacts of National Environment and Policy*
Pub: Cambridge University Press
Contact: Peter Phillips, Chief Executive Officer
Released: September 01, 2011. **Description:** Global assessment of the impact of e-business on companies as well as countries.

27577 ■ *"Global Economy: The World Tomorrow"* in *Canadian Business (Vol. 81, December 19, 2007, No. 1, pp. 35)*
Pub: Rogers Media Inc.
Contact: Neil Spivak, Chief Executive Officer
Ed: Zena Olijnyk. **Description:** Global economy is predicted to be in a difficult period as analysts expect a slowdown in economic growth. Germany's Deutsche Bank wrote in a report about 'growth recession' that the chances of the world growth falling below two percent being one in three. Forecasts on other global economic aspects are explored. **Availability:** Online.

27578 ■ *"The Global Environment Movement is Bjorn Again"* in *Canadian Business (Vol. 83, September 14, 2010, No. 15, pp. 11)*
Pub: Rogers Media Inc.
Contact: Neil Spivak, Chief Executive Officer
Ed: Steve Maich. **Description:** Danish academic Bjorn Lomborg is in favor of decisive action to combat climate change in his new book and was given front page treatment by a London newspaper. Environmentalist groups see this as a victory since Lomborg had not previously considered climate change an immediate issue. **Availability:** Online.

27579 ■ *"The Global Talent Hunt"* in *Business Strategy Review (Vol. 21, Spring 2010, No. 1, pp. 78)*
Ed: Richard Emerton. **Released:** February 09, 2010. **Description:** Richard Emerton explains how the new 'triple context' of economy, environment and society

will have profound implications for human resource practices. He suggests that viewing talent as abundant is the right perspective for a manager. **Availability:** Print; PDF; Online.

27580 ■ *"The Globe: A Cautionary Tale for Emerging Market Giants"* in *Harvard Business Review (Vol. 88, September 2010, No. 9, pp. 99)*
Pub: Harvard Business Publishing
Contact: Diane Belcher, Managing Director
Ed: J. Stewart Black, Allen J. Morrison. **Price:** $8.95. **Description:** Key factors that negatively affected Japan corporate growth and organizational effectiveness include: devotion to established path, isolated domestic markets, homogenous executive teams, and a non-contentious labor force. Solutions include leadership development programs, multicultural input, and cross-cultural training. **Availability:** Online; PDF.

27581 ■ *"The Globe: How to Conquer New Markets With Old Skills"* in *Harvard Business Review (Vol. 88, November 2010, No. 11, pp. 118)*
Pub: Harvard Business Publishing
Contact: Diane Belcher, Managing Director
Ed: Mauro F. Guillen, Esteban Garcia-Canal. **Price:** $8.95, PDF. **Description:** Exploration of business-networking factors that have helped lead to the success of Spain's multinational companies is provided. These include development of political skills, access to capabilities and resources, globalization partnerships, and speed of implementation. **Availability:** Online; PDF.

27582 ■ *"The Globe: Let Emerging Market Customers Be Your Teachers"* in *Harvard Business Review (Vol. 88, December 2010, No. 12, pp. 115)*
Pub: Harvard Business Publishing
Contact: Diane Belcher, Managing Director
Ed: Guillermo D'Andrea, David Marcotte, Gwon Dixon Morrison. **Price:** $8.95, PDF. **Description:** Examination of effective strategies for emerging markets is presented. These include helping educate customers as well as selling to them, adapting to customers' habits, and focusing brands appropriately. Magazine Luiza, a chain store in Brazil, is used to illustrate these points. **Availability:** Online; PDF.

27583 ■ *"Golden Spoon Accelerates Expansion Here and Abroad"* in *Ice Cream Reporter (Vol. 22, December 20, 2008, No. 1, pp. 2)*
Description: Golden Spoon frozen yogurt franchise chain is developing 35 more locations in the Phoenix, Arizona area along with plans to open a store in Japan. **Availability:** Print; Online.

27584 ■ *"The Great Fall of China"* in *Canadian Business (Vol. 85, June 11, 2012, No. 10, pp. 26)*
Ed: Michael McCullough. **Description:** China has a growing influence over the future of Canada's economy as emerging economies and commodity prices recover from the recession. Among the problems unique to China which could impact the Canadian economy are the housing market, its demographic risk and the lack of transparency in the corporate and financial sector. **Availability:** Online.

27585 ■ *"The Growth Opportunity That Lies Next Door: How Will the Logic of Globalization Change for Corporations from Countries such as India, China, Indonesia, Brazil, and Turkey if the Growth Opportunities..."* in *(Vol. 90, July-August 2012, No. 7-8, pp. 141)*
Pub: Harvard Business Review Press
Contact: Moderna V. Pfizer, Contact
Ed: Geoffrey G. Jones. **Description:** Brazilian company Natura Cosmeticos found that focusing on expanding into the emerging markets represented by neighboring countries, rather than on well-established markets in developed nations, offered more opportunities and greater rewards.

27586 ■ *"Half a World Away"* in *Tampa Bay Business Journal (Vol. 30, December 4, 2009, No. 50, pp. 1)*
Description: Enterprise Florida has offered four trade grants for Florida's marine industry businesses to give them a chance to tap into the Middle East market at the Dubai International Boat Show on March 9 to 13, 2010. The grants pay for 50 percent of the exhibition costs for the qualifying business. **Availability:** Online.

27587 ■ *"H&M Offers a Dress for Less"* in *Canadian Business (Vol. 83, September 14, 2010, No. 15, pp. 20)*
Pub: Rogers Media Inc.
Contact: Neil Spivak, Chief Executive Officer
Ed: Laura Cameron. **Description:** Swedish clothing company H&M has implemented loss leader strategy by pricing some dresses at extremely low prices. The economy has forced retailers to keep prices down despite the increasing cost of manufacturing, partly due to Chinese labor becoming more expensive. How the trend will affect apparel companies is discussed. **Availability:** Print; Online.

27588 ■ *"HBR Case Study: Setting Up Shop in a Political Hot Spot"* in *Harvard Business Review (Vol. 88, October 2010, No. 10, pp. 141)*
Pub: Harvard Business Publishing
Contact: Diane Belcher, Managing Director
Ed: Patrick Chun, John Coleman, Nabil El-Hage. **Price:** $8.95, PDF. **Description:** A fictitious foreign operations scenario is presented, with contributors providing comments and advice. The scenario involves a politically charged North Korean-South Korean business venture; suggestions range from ensuring financial flexibility in case of adverse events to avoiding any business venture until political stability is achieved. **Availability:** Online; PDF.

27589 ■ *"The HBR Interview: "We Had to Own the Mistakes""* in *Harvard Business Review (Vol. 88, July-August 2010, No. 7-8, pp. 108)*
Pub: Harvard Business Publishing
Contact: Diane Belcher, Managing Director
Ed: Adi Ignatius. **Description:** Interview with Howard Schultz, CEO of Starbucks, covers topics that include investment in retraining, the impact of competition, premium quality, authenticity, customer services, strategy development, work-and-life issues, and international presence. **Availability:** Online.

27590 ■ *"Headwinds From the New Sod Slow Aer Lingus"* in *Barron's (Vol. 88, March 10, 2008, No. 10, pp. M6)*
Pub: Dow Jones & Company Inc.
Contact: Almar Latour, Chief Executive Officer
Ed: Sean Walters, Arindam Nag. **Description:** Aer Lingus faces a drop in its share prices with a falling US market, higher jet fuel prices, and lower long-haul passenger load factors. British media companies Johnston Press and Yell Group are suffering from weaker ad revenue and heavier debt payments due to the credit crunch. **Availability:** Online.

27591 ■ *"Heavy Duty: The Case Against Packing Lightly"* in *Crain's Chicago Business (Vol. 31, April 21, 2008, No. 16, pp. 29)*
Pub: Crain Communications Inc.
Contact: Barry Asin, President
Ed: Sarah A. Klein. **Description:** Penelope Biggs, a Northern Trust executive who manages sales teams in North America, Europe and Asia gives advice on traveling abroad for business including time management skills, handling time-zone hops and avoiding jet-lag. **Availability:** Online.

27592 ■ *"Helping Apple Go Wearable"* in *Austin Business Journal (Vol. 34, July 4, 2014, No. 20, pp. 13)*
Pub: American City Business Journals, Inc.
Contact: Mike Olivieri, Executive Vice President
Released: July 04, 2014. **Price:** $4, introductory 4-week offer(Digital only). **Description:** Andrew Hamra, CEO and designer at Red Street Ventures

will launch the Runnur Hands Free iPad Clip and Carry Case across the U.S. in July 2014 following the success of his flagship product the Hands Free Carry-All. Hamra builds and designs the products and controls startup costs by outsourcing most of the production to China's Xiamen Uptex Industrial Company Ltd. **Availability:** Print; Online.

27593 ■ *"The High-Intensity Entrepreneur" in Harvard Business Review (Vol. 88, September 2010, No. 9, pp. 74)*
Pub: Harvard Business Publishing
Contact: Diane Belcher, Managing Director
Ed: Anne S. Habiby, Deirdre M. Coyle, Jr. **Price:** $8. 95, PDF. **Description:** Examination of the role of small companies in promoting global economic growth is presented. Discussion includes identifying entrepreneurial capability. **Availability:** Online; PDF.

27594 ■ *"Hong Kong's Boom in IPOs" in Barron's (Vol. 89, July 13, 2009, No. 28, pp. M7)*
Pub: Dow Jones & Company Inc.
Contact: Almar Latour, Chief Executive Officer
Ed: Nick Lord. **Description:** Hong Kong's IPO (initial public offering) market is booming with 13 Chinese IPOs already on the market for the year as July 2009. One of them is Bawang International which raised $214 million after generating $9 billion in order which makes it 42 times oversubscribed. **Availability:** Online.

27595 ■ *"Hoop Culture Opens Showroom, Expands Reach Globally" in Orlando Business Journal (Vol. 30, February 28, 2014, No. 36, pp. 3)*
Pub: American City Business Journals, Inc.
Contact: Mike Olivieri, Executive Vice President
Released: Weekly. **Description:** Hoop Culture Inc. president, Mike Brown, shares how the online basketball apparel retailer/wholesaler online store has expanded globally. He mentions that Orlando, Florida is one of their biggest markets. **Availability:** Print; Online.

27596 ■ *"How Bad Is It?" in Hawaii Business (Vol. 54, July 2008, No. 1, pp. 35)*
Pub: PacificBasin Communications
Contact: Chuck Tindle, Director
E-mail: chuckt@pacificbasin.net
Ed: Jolyn Okimoto Rosa. **Description:** Donald G. Horner, chief executive officer of First Hawaiian Bank, says that the current Hawaiian economic situation is a cyclical slowdown. Maurice Kaya, an energy consultant, says the slowdown is due to overdependence on imported fuels. Other local leaders, such as Constance H. Lau, also discuss their view on the current economic situation in Hawaii.

27597 ■ *"How Baltimore's Largest Private Companies Weathered the Recession's Punch; Top Private Companies" in Baltimore Business Journal (Vol. 28, August 27, 2010, No. 16, pp. 1)*
Pub: Baltimore Business Journal
Contact: Rhonda Pringle, President
E-mail: rpringle@bizjournals.com
Ed: Gary Haber. **Description:** The combined revenue of the 100 largest private firms in Maryland's Baltimore region dropped from about $22.7 billion in 2008 to $21 billion in 2009, an annual decrease of more than 7 percent. To survive the recession's impact, these firms resorted to strategies such as government contracting and overseas expansion. How these strategies affected the revenue of some firms is described. **Availability:** Print; Online.

27598 ■ *"How Exports Could Save America" in Barron's (Vol. 89, July 20, 2009, No. 29, pp. 15)*
Pub: Dow Jones & Company Inc.
Contact: Almar Latour, Chief Executive Officer
Ed: Jonathan R. Laing. **Description:** Increase in US exports should help drive up the nation's economic growth, according to Wells Capital Management strategist Jim Paulsen. He believes US gross domes-

tic product could grow by 3-3.5 percent annually starting in 2010 due to a more favorable trade balance. **Availability:** Online.

27599 ■ *"How Foreigners Could Disrupt U.S. Markets" in Barron's (Vol. 90, September 13, 2010, No. 37, pp. 30)*
Pub: Barron's Editorial & Corporate Headquarters
Ed: Jim McTague. **Description:** An informal meeting by the House Homeland Security Panel concluded that U.S. stock exchanges and related trading routes can be the subject of attacks from rogue overseas traders. A drop in funding for the U.S. Department of Defense is discussed. **Availability:** Online.

27600 ■ *"How High Can Soybeans Fly?" in Barron's (Vol. 88, March 10, 2008, No. 10, pp. M14)*
Pub: Dow Jones & Company Inc.
Contact: Almar Latour, Chief Executive Officer
Ed: Kenneth Rapoza. **Description:** Prices of soybeans have risen to $14.0875 a bushel, up 8.3 percent for the week. Increased demand, such as in China and in other developing economies, and the investment-driven commodities boom are boosting prices. **Availability:** Online.

27601 ■ *"How Not to Raise Bank Capital" in Barron's (Vol. 88, June 30, 2008, No. 26, pp. M6)*
Pub: Dow Jones & Company Inc.
Contact: Almar Latour, Chief Executive Officer
Ed: Sean Walters. **Description:** French bank Natixis wants to raise 1 billion euros from cash provided by their two major owners. Natixis will reimburse Banque Populaire and Caisses d'Epargne with hybrid securities so this move will not benefit Natixis' core Tier 1 ratio. This has also given the impression that the company is afraid of a full rights issue which could shake investors' faith in the bank. **Availability:** Online.

27602 ■ *"How To Win In Emerging Markets: Lessons From Japan" in Harvard Business Review (Vol. 90, May 2012, No. 5, pp. 126)*
Pub: Harvard Business Review Press
Contact: Moderna V. Pfizer, Contact
Ed: Shigeki Ichii, Susumu Hattori, David Michael. **Price:** $8.95. **Description:** Corporate Japan's four challenges in engaging emerging markets are an aversion to mergers and acquisitions, an aversion to low- and middle-end segments, lack of organizational or financial commitments to emerging markets, and a shortage of executive talent placed in emerging markets. By addressing these weaknesses, Japan can succeed in global expansion. **Availability:** Online; PDF.

27603 ■ *"How Young Professionals Can Position Themselves for Board Membership: 4 Quick Tips to Get You Started" in Black Enterprise (Vol. 45, July-August 2014, No. 1, pp. 46)*
Pub: Earl G. Graves Ltd.
Contact: Earl Graves, Jr., President
Description: Four tips to help young professionals secure a position on a company's board focus on: starting with nonprofits, focus on key areas of interest, continue to growth through networking and training programs, and to gain global experience.

27604 ■ *"Husband-Wife Team Opens Somali Interpreting Business in Willmar, Minn." in West Central Tribune (May 22, 2012)*
Ed: Linda Vanderwerf. **Description:** Profile of husband and wife team who launched an interpreting service in Somali. Details of the business are included. **Availability:** Online.

27605 ■ *"IBR Breakfast Series: Idaho's Dairy Industry Quietly Grows" in Idaho Business Review (August 15, 2014)*
Pub: BridgeTower Media
Contact: Adam Reinebach, President
Description: Several dairy industry members were called to a breakfast to discuss the past, present and future of the Idaho dairy farms and products. The

impact of technology changes and rising foreign market demands as well as creating more and different products was addressed.

27606 ■ *"Ideas at Work: Sparkling Innovation" in Business Strategy Review (Vol. 21, Summer 2010, No. 2, pp. 07)*
Ed: Julian Birkinshaw, Peter Robbins. **Released:** June 24, 2010. **Description:** GlaxoSmithKline faced a situation common to large global organizations: how to allocate marketing resources to smaller, regional brands. The company's approach to worldwide marketing that led to the development of a unique and productive network is outlined. **Availability:** Print; PDF; Online.

27607 ■ *"Ill Winds; Cuba's Economy" in The Economist (Vol. 390, January 3, 2009, No. 8612, pp. 20)*
Description: Cuba's long-term economic prospects remain poor with the economy forecasted to grow only 4.3 percent for the year, about half of the original forecast, due in part to Hurricane Gustav which caused $10 billion in damage and disrupted the food-supply network and devastated farms across the region; President Raul Castro made raising agricultural production a national priority and the rise in global commodity prices hit the country hard. The only bright spot has been the rise in tourism which is up 9.3 percent over 2007. **Availability:** Online.

27608 ■ *Import/Export Kit For Dummies*
Pub: John Wiley & Sons, Inc.
Contact: Christina Van Tassell, Executive Vice President Chief Financial Officer
Ed: John J. Capela. **Released:** 3rd Edition. **Price:** $26.99, paperback; $17.99, E-book. **Description:** Provides entrepreneurs and small- to medium-size businesses with information required to start exporting products globally and importing goods to the U.S. Topics covered include the ins and outs of developing or expanding operations to gain market share, with details on the top ten countries in which America trades, from Canada to Germany to China. **Availability:** E-book; Print.

27609 ■ *"In China, Railways to Riches" in Barron's (Vol. 88, July 7, 2008, No. 27, pp. M9)*
Pub: Dow Jones & Company Inc.
Contact: Almar Latour, Chief Executive Officer
Ed: Assif Shameen. **Description:** Shares of Chinese railway companies look to benefit from multimillion-dollar investments aimed at upgrading the Chinese railway network. Investment in the sector is expected to reach $210 billion for the 2006-2010 period. **Availability:** Online.

27610 ■ *"In India, A Gold-Price Threat?" in Barron's (Vol. 88, June 30, 2008, No. 26, pp. M12)*
Pub: Dow Jones & Company Inc.
Contact: Almar Latour, Chief Executive Officer
Ed: Melanie Burton. **Description:** Gold purchases in India are falling as record prices take its toll on demand. Gold imports to India fell by 52 percent in May 2008 from the previous year and local prices are higher by one-third from the previous year to 12,540 rupees for 10 grams. **Availability:** Online.

27611 ■ *"In the Wake of Pet-Food Crisis, Iams Sales Plummet Nearly 17 Percent" in Advertising Age (Vol. 78, May 14, 2007, No. 18, pp. 3)*
Pub: Crain Communications, Inc.
Contact: Jessica Botos, Manager, Marketing
E-mail: jessica.botos@crainsnewyork.com
Ed: Jack Neff. **Description:** Although the massive U.S. pet-food recall impacted more than 100 brands, Procter & Gamble Co.'s Iams lost more sales and market share than any other industry player. According to Information Resources Inc. data, the brand's sales dropped 16.5 percent in the eight-week period ended April 22. Many analysts feel that the company could have handled the crisis in a better manner. **Availability:** Online.

27612 ■ *"Indigenous Tourism Operators: The Vanguard of Economic Recovery in the Chatham Islands"* in *International Journal of Entrepreneurship and Small Business (Vol. 10, July 6, 2010, No. 4)*

Ed: Andrew Cardow, Peter Wiltshier. **Description:** Emergent enthusiasm for tourism as a savior for economic development in the Chatham Islands of New Zealand is highlighted. **Availability:** Online.

27613 ■ *Innovate to Great: Re-Igniting Sustainable Innovation to Win in the Global Economy*

Description: The author explores innovation and creativity as a means for small companies to survive and expand in the global economy. **Availability:** Print; PDF.

27614 ■ *"Innovating Globally"* in *Business Strategy Review (Vol. 21, Spring 2010, No. 1, pp. 24)*

Ed: Costas Markides, Stuart Crainer. **Description:** Costas Markides has spent over two decades studying business strategy and innovation. Recently, he has been focusing on the bigger picture of how people can address major social problems. Can the techniques used by managers to create innovation inside organizations work with global change?. **Availability:** Download; PDF; Online.

27615 ■ *"Innovating Low-Cost Business Models"* in *Strategy and Leadership (Vol. 39, March-April 2011, No. 2, pp. 43)*

Pub: Emerald Group Publishing Limited
Contact: Erika Valenti, President

Ed: Nicolas Kachaner, Zhenya Lindgardt, David Michael. **Description:** A process that can be used to implement low-cost innovation is presented. The process can be used to address the competitive challenges presented by multinationals' practice of presenting applications and price points that are intended for developing markets into developed markets. The process involves targeting large, and low-income segments of the market.

27616 ■ *"Innovators Critical in Technical Economy"* in *Crain's Cleveland Business (Vol. 28, November 5, 2007, No. 44, pp. 10)*

Pub: Crain Communications Inc.
Contact: K. C. Crain, President

Ed: Peter Rea. **Description:** Discusses the importance to attract, develop and retain talented innovators on Ohio's economy. Also breaks down the four fronts on which the international battle for talent is being waged. **Availability:** Online.

27617 ■ *"International Benefits Roundup"* in *Employee Benefit News (Vol. 25, December 1, 2011, No. 15)*

Pub: SourceMedia LLC
Contact: Gemma Postlethwaite, Chief Executive Officer

Description: Employee contributions to an employer-sponsored defined contribution plan in Japan are allowed on a tax-deductible basis; however, currently employee contributions are not allowed. The defined contribution plan is outlined for better understanding.

27618 ■ *International Business*

Pub: John Wiley & Sons, Inc.
Contact: Christina Van Tassell, Executive Vice President Chief Financial Officer
URL(s): www.wiley.com/en-us/International+Business%2C+2nd+Edition-p-9781119679745

Ed: Shad Morris, James Oldroyd. **Released:** 2nd edition. **Price:** $119.50, e-book. **Description:** Discusses the global marketplace with updates regarding the COVID pandemic, Brexit, and the US-China trade war. **Availability:** E-book.

27619 ■ *"International Business Law: Interpreting the Term 'Like Products"* in *Business Recorder (June 7, 2012)*

Ed: Zafar Azeem. **Description:** The term 'like products' needs to be defined for international trade. The battle between the United States and Indonesia

regarding this issue is discussed. A technical barrier clause being used by foreign countries is prohibiting imports and hurting competitiveness. **Availability:** Online.

27620 ■ *"International ETFs: Your Passport to the World"* in *Barron's (Vol. 89, July 13, 2009, No. 28, pp. L10)*

Pub: Dow Jones & Company Inc.
Contact: Almar Latour, Chief Executive Officer

Ed: John Hintze. **Description:** International exchange traded funds give investors more choices in terms of investment plays and there are 174 U.S. ETF listings worth $141 billion as of July 2009. Suggestions on how to invest in these funds based on one's conviction on how the global economy will unfold are presented. **Availability:** Online.

27621 ■ *International Growth of Small and Medium Enterprises*

Pub: Routledge, Taylor & Francis Group

Released: First edition. **Description:** This volume focuses on how companies expand their operations across borders through opportunity exploration and exploitation, and identification and development of innovations.

27622 ■ *International Journal of Entrepreneurship and Small Business (IJESB)*

Pub: Inderscience Publishers
URL(s): www.inderscience.com/jhome.php?jcode=ijesb

Released: Monthly **Price:** $99, for airmail hardcopy; $11,073.20, for online only per year 20+ users; $698, for print and multi-user; $2,484, for hardcopy and online; $1,786, for hardcopy annual; $8,215.60, for 10 to 14 users; $9,376.50, for 15 to 19 users; $3,036.20, for 2 to 3 users; $4,465, for 4 to 5 users; $5,804.50, for 6 to 7 users; $7,054.70, for 8 to 9 users; $1,700, for 1 user only. **Description:** Journal publishing and fostering discussion on international, cross cultural, and comparative academic research about entrepreneurs, including corporate intrapreneurs and founders of domestic new ventures. **Availability:** Print; PDF; Online.

27623 ■ *"Investment In Israel Is Investment in the Future of Georgia"* in *Atlanta Business Chronicle (May 30, 2014, pp. 22A)*

Pub: American City Business Journals, Inc.
Contact: Mike Olivieri, Executive Vice President

Description: Georgia Governor Nathan Deal will travel to Israel to lead an economic and trade mission and consolidate Georgia's trade ties with Israel. Israel and the State of Georgia are already collaborating in the fields of health information technology, agrotechnology, homeland security, defense, aerospace and cybersecurity, and microelectronics and nanotechnology. The proposed visit by the Governor will build on this particular partnership from which both parties will benefit. **Availability:** Print; Online.

27624 ■ *"Is the Sun Setting on Oil Sector's Heydey?"* in *Globe & Mail (January 25, 2007, pp. B3)*

Description: The effects of fuel efficiency management policies of the United States on Canadian petroleum industry are discussed. Canada is the largest exporter of crude oil to America after the Middle East. **Availability:** Online.

27625 ■ *"It May Be Cheaper to Manufacture At Home"* in *Harvard Business Review (Vol. 88, October 2010, No. 10, pp. 84)*

Pub: Harvard Business Publishing
Contact: Diane Belcher, Managing Director

Ed: Suzanne de Treville, Lenos Trigeorgis. **Price:** $8.95, PDF. **Description:** Using a real options framework rather than a discounted cash flow model to assess and value supply chain processes is examined. This enables companies to assess costs for a variety of situations, not just ideal or normal circumstances, which can make the difference between domestic and foreign manufacturing decisions. **Availability:** Online; PDF.

27626 ■ *"It's Good To Be King"* in *South Florida Business Journal (Vol. 35, August 29, 2014, No. 5, pp. 12)*

Released: December 01, 2013. **Description:** The $11.4 billion deal that will create a new holding company for Burger King Worldwide and Tim Hortons will be based in Oakville, Ontario, Canada and was met with public outrage. Burger King declares that the merger with the Canadian coffee and doughnut franchise chain was about global growth, not a strategy to avoid millions of dollars in corporate income tax payments to the U.S. government. **Availability:** Print; Online.

27627 ■ *"It's Time To Swim"* in *Canadian Business (Vol. 81, March 3, 2008, No. 3, pp. 37)*

Description: Canadian manufacturers should consider Asian markets such as India and the United Arab Emirates as the U.S. economic downturn continues. Canada's shortage in skilled labor is also expected to negatively affect manufacturing industries. Ontario's plans to assist manufacturers are also presented. **Availability:** Print; PDF; Download; Online.

27628 ■ *"It's What You Know. It's Who You Know. It's China"* in *Inc. (Vol. 33, October 2011, No. 8, pp. 80)*

Description: Michael Lee will be the first American entrepreneur to build big in China. The company is piloting two large commercial real estate developments, one in New York City the other in Nanjing, China. **Availability:** Print; Online.

27629 ■ *"Keeping Railcars 'Busy At All Times' At TTX"* in *Crain's Chicago Business (Vol. 31, April 28, 2008, No. 17, pp. 6)*

Pub: Crain Communications Inc.
Contact: Barry Asin, President

Ed: Bob Tita. **Description:** Profile of the president of Chicago railcar pool operator TTX Co. and his business plan for the company which includes improving fleet management and car purchasing through better use of data on railroad demand. **Availability:** Online.

27630 ■ *"Ketchup King Heinz Seeks to Boost Soy-Sauce Empire in China"* in *Advertising Age (Vol. 83, October 8, 2012, No. 36, pp. 3)*

Description: Heinz is buying up local soy sauce firms in China with a buy-and-build strategy to expand into other markets in the country. Soy sauce total sales are about $4 billion annually in China, while ketchup sales amount to $100 million to $200 million there. **Availability:** Print; Online.

27631 ■ *"Kinetico Exec Going Global to Increase Growth Flow"* in *Crain's Cleveland Business (Vol. 28, October 1, 2007, No. 39, pp. 5)*

Pub: Crain Communications Inc.
Contact: K. C. Crain, President

Ed: David Bennett. **Description:** Shamus Hurley, the new CEO and president of Kinetico Inc., a manufacturer of water filtering and softening equipment for residential, commercial and municipal use, plans to expand the company to target markets overseas. **Availability:** Online.

27632 ■ *"The Latin Beat Goes On"* in *Barron's (Vol. 88, July 7, 2008, No. 27, pp. L5)*

Pub: Dow Jones & Company Inc.
Contact: Almar Latour, Chief Executive Officer

Ed: Tom Sullivan. **Description:** Latin American stocks have outperformed other regional markets due to rising commodities prices and favorable economic climate. Countries such as Brazil, Mexico, Chile, and Peru provide investment opportunities, while Argentina and Venezuela are tougher places to invest. **Availability:** Online.

27633 ■ *"Lobster Mania Hits China: They Just Had to Get Used to the Claws"* in *Canadian Business (Vol. 85, July 16, 2012, No. 11-12, pp. 10)*

Ed: Joe Castaldo. **Description:** Canadian lobster exports to China have tripled to almost $30 million annually since 2010 as a result of marketing efforts by Maritimes governments including pitching lobster to cooking shows and organizing training sessions for Chinese chefs. Canadian exporters must decide whether their lobster is a premium product or a commodity product to solidify its image in China. **Availability:** Print; Online.

27634 ■ "Loonie Tunes: When Will the Dollar Rise Again?" in Canadian Business (Vol. 81, November 10, 2008, No. 19, pp. 62)
Pub: Rogers Media Inc.
Contact: Neil Spivak, Chief Executive Officer

Ed: Joe Castaldo. **Description:** The Canadian dollar has weakened against the U.S. Dollar as the U.S. financial crisis rocked global markets. A currency strategist says that the strength of the U.S. dollar is not based on people's optimism on the U.S. economy but on a structural demand where U.S. non-financial corporations have been repatriating greenbacks from foreign subsidiaries. **Availability:** Print; Online.

27635 ■ "Loonies Buy U.S. Cable" in Canadian Business (Vol. 85, September 17, 2012, No. 14, pp. 8)
Ed: Jeff Beer. **Description:** The move by two Canadian companies to invest in the U.S. cable industry get mixed reactions from analyst and observers. Cogeco Cable purchased Atlantic Broadband for $1.36 billion while the Canada Pension Plan Investment Board announced its partnership with European private equity firm BC Partners to acquire Suddenlink Communications for $6.6 billion. **Availability:** Online.

27636 ■ Macrowikinomics: Rebooting Business and the World
Pub: Portfolio Hardcover
Contact: Adrian Zackheim, President

Ed: Don Tapscott, Anthony D. Williams. **Released:** May 29, 2012. **Price:** $18, paperback; $6.99, e-book. **Description:** Wikinomics Don Tapscott and Anthony Williams showed how mass collaboration was changing the way businesses communicate, create value, and compete in the new global marketplace in 2007. Now, in the wake of the global financial crisis, the principles of wikinomics have become more powerful than ever. **Availability:** E-book; Print.

27637 ■ "Magpower May Build Solar Panels in Pflugerville" in Austin Business Journal (Vol. 31, May 13, 2011, No. 10, pp. A1)
Pub: Austin Business Journal
Contact: Rachel McGrath, Director
E-mail: rmcgrath@bizjournals.com

Ed: Christopher Calnan. **Description:** RRE Austin Solar LLC CEO Doven Mehta has revealed plans to partner with Portugal-based Magpower SA, only if Austin energy buys electricity from planned solar energy farm in Pflugerville. Austin Energy has received 100 bids from 35 companies to supply 200 megawatts of solar- and wind-generated electricity. **Availability:** Print; Online.

27638 ■ "Major Advances in Heat Pump Technology - Part Two" in Contractor (Vol. 57, February 2010, No. 2, pp. 22)
Ed: Mark Eatherton. **Description:** Chinese and Japanese companies have come up with refrigerant based heat pump products that are air based which will significantly lower the installed cost of heat pump based systems. Some of these newer models have variable speed, soft start compressors and have the ability to perform high-efficiency heat pump operation on a modulating basis. **Availability:** Print; Online.

27639 ■ Make It in America: How International Companies and Entrepreneurs Can Successfully Enter and Scale in U.S. Markets
Pub: John Wiley & Sons, Inc.
Contact: Christina Van Tassell, Executive Vice President Chief Financial Officer
URL(s): www.wiley.com/en-us/Make+It+in+America%3A+How+International+Companies+and+En trepreneurs+Can+Successfully+Enter+and+Scale+in+U+S+Markets-p-9781119885146

Ed: Matthew Lee Sawyer. **Released:** November 2022. **Price:** $18, e-book; $30, hardcover. **Description:** Includes case studies of international companies who successfully launched inside the U.S. **Availability:** E-book; Print.

27640 ■ "Managerial Ties with Local Firms and Governments: an Analysis of Japanese Firms In China" in International Journal of Business and Emerging Markets (Vol. 4, July 11, 2012, No. 3, pp. 181)
Pub: Inderscience Publishers

Ed: Naoki Ando, Daniel Z. Ding. **Description:** This study explores how managerial ties between foreign firms and local firms and those between foreign firms and local government officials affect the performance of firms operating in transition economies. Using survey data collected from Japanese firms operating in China, this study finds that managerial ties between foreign firms and local firms and local government officials are positively associated with the performance of Japanese firms in China. **Availability:** Print; PDF; Online.

27641 ■ Managing Economies, Trade and International Business
Pub: Palgrave Macmillan

Released: 1st edition. **Price:** $89, e-book; $115, Hardcover; $110, softcover. **Description:** An in-depth look at the areas that affect and influence international business, exploring specific issues businesses face in terms of economic development, trade law, and international marketing and management. **Availability:** E-book; Print.

27642 ■ "Manufacturing Behind the Great Wall: What Works, What Doesn't" in Canadian Electronics (Vol. 23, February 2008, No. 1, pp. 6)
Description: Electronic component producers are increasingly transitioning their manufacturing operations to China in order to take advantage of the growing Chinese manufacturing industry. It is believed that manufacturers have to carefully consider whether their run sizes are appropriate for Chinese manufacturing before moving their operations. **Availability:** PDF.

27643 ■ "Market Watch" in Barron's (Vol. 88, March 24, 2008, No. 12, pp. M18)
Ed: Ashraf Laidi, Marc Pado, David Kotok. **Released:** 2018. **Description:** Latest measures implemented by the Federal Reserve to address the credit crisis did not benefit the US dollar, with the Japanese yen and the euro recouping earlier losses against the dollar. Goldman Sachs reported earnings of $3.23 per share, claiming a stronger liquidity position. The US markets bottomed early on 22 January 2007, according to evidence. **Availability:** Print; Online.

27644 ■ "Market Watch: A Sampling of Advisory Opinion" in Barron's (Vol. 88, March 17, 2008, No. 11, pp. M10)
Pub: Dow Jones & Company Inc.
Contact: Almar Latour, Chief Executive Officer

Ed: Paul Schatz, William Gibson, Michael Darda, Peter Greene, Ian Wyatt, Stephanie Pomboy. **Released:** January 25, 2014. **Description:** S&P 500 bank stocks were down 46 percent from their 2007 peak while the peak to through fall in 1989-1990 was just over 50 percent. This suggests that the bottom on the bank stocks could be near. The Federal Reserve Board announced they will lend up to $200 billion to primary lenders in exchange other securities. **Availability:** Print; Online.

27645 ■ "Market Watch: A Sampling of Advisory Opinion US Stock Price Trends, Economic Effects of Global Trade, Chinese Economic Trends" in Barron's (Vol. 92, July 23, 2012, No. 30, pp. M14)
Ed: Richard M. Salsman, Jack Ablin, Francois Sicart. **Description:** US stocks are considered inexpensive due to their low price-earnings ratios compared to levels before the global financial crisis. The US economy is becoming more dependent on the rest of the world as a result of global trade. The Chinese economy continues to have strong economic growth despite a slowdown. **Availability:** Online.

27646 ■ "Massage Heights Chasing Big Expansion Opportunities" in San Antonio Business Journal (Vol. 28, April 25, 2014, No. 11, pp. 6)
Pub: American City Business Journals, Inc.
Contact: Mike Olivieri, Executive Vice President

Released: Weekly. **Price:** $4, Introductory 4-week offer(Digital only). **Description:** Massage Heights, offering deep tissue massage, hot stone massage and facials, has opened a second corporate-owned facility in Stone Oak, Texas. The company, founded in April 2004, is focusing on expansion plans due to investor interest in the firm's growth. Massage Heights currently has five facilities in Canada. **Availability:** Print; Online.

27647 ■ "Maybe We're Exploiting China" in Canadian Business (Vol. 85, September 17, 2012, No. 14, pp. 4)
Ed: Duncan Hood. **Description:** The proposed deal by China National Offshore Oil Corp. (CNOOC) to acquire Canada's Nexen for $27.50 a share is met with uncertainty by the public. The U.S. is believed to be opposing the deal because it would no longer have quite as much power to set oil prices in Canada. **Availability:** Online.

27648 ■ "Medtronic Heading to Foreign Markets" in Memphis Business Journal (Vol. 34, September 28, 2012, No. 24, pp. 1)
Pub: Baltimore Business Journal
Contact: Rhonda Pringle, President
E-mail: rpringle@bizjournals.com

Description: Medtronics Inc.'s Spinal and Biologics Division will launch a new spinal surgery system in 2012. The spinal fusion procedure has not yet been approved by international surgical governing bodies, but the company is already rolling it out in different countries. The new service uses the company's various surgical systems and implants. **Availability:** Print; Online.

27649 ■ "Melamine Analytical Methods Released" in Feedstuffs (Vol. 80, October 6, 2008, No. 41, pp. 2)
Pub: Miller Publishing Company

Description: Romer Labs has released new validations for its AgraQuant Melamine enzyme-linked immunosorbent assay. The test kit screens for melamine in feed and diary products, including pet foods, milk and milk powder. Melamine by itself is nontoxic in low doses, but when combined with cyanuric acid it can cause fatal kidney stones. The Chinese dairy industry is in the midst of a huge melamine crisis; melamine-contaminated dairy and food products from China have been found in more than 20 countries. **Availability:** Print; Online.

27650 ■ "Micro-Finance Agencies and SMEs: Model of Explication of Tacit Knowledge" in International Journal of Entrepreneurship and Small Business (Vol. 11, August 3, 2010)
Ed: Patricia A. Rowe, Michael J. Christie, Frank Hoy. **Description:** Institutional preparedness of economic development agencies for developing small and medium-sized enterprises (SMEs) is discussed. The cases presented illustrate variations in the micro-finance lender agency-enterprise development of processes for sharing vision and interdependence. **Availability:** Online.

27651 ■ "Mine Woes Could Rouse Zinc" in Barron's (Vol. 88, July 7, 2008, No. 27, pp. M12)
Pub: Dow Jones & Company Inc.
Contact: Almar Latour, Chief Executive Officer

Ed: Andrea Hotter. **Description:** Prices of zinc could increase due to supply problems in producing countries such as Australia and China. London Metal Exchange prices for the metal have dropped about 36 percent in 2008. **Availability:** Online.

27652 ■ *"Mission to China"* in *Canadian Business (Vol. 81, December 8, 2008, No. 21, pp. 28)*
Ed: Andrew Wahl. **Released:** October 26, 2016. **Description:** Canada China Business Council and the Council of the Federation visited China for a three-city trade mission. The trade mission aims to re-establish the strong relationship between China and Canada. **Availability:** Online.

27653 ■ *"The Moderating Effects of Organizational Context On the Relationship Between Voluntary Turnover and Organizational Performance: Evidence from Korea"* in *Human Resource Management (Vol. 51, January-February 2012, No. 1, pp. 47-70)*
Pub: John Wiley & Sons, Inc.
Contact: Christina Van Tassell, Executive Vice President Chief Financial Officer
Ed: Kiwook Kwon, Kweontaek Chung, Hyuntak Roh, Clint Chadwick, John J. Lawler. **Released:** January 26, 2012. **Description:** The ability of organizational context to moderate the relationship between voluntary employee turnover and organizational performance is examined using data from South Korean firms. The effects of employee involvement practices, investment in employee training and development, and the availability of potential workers on this relationship are studied. **Availability:** Print; PDF; Online.

27654 ■ *"Mover and Sheika"* in *Conde Nast Portfolio (Vol. 2, June 2008, No. 6, pp. 104)*
Ed: John Arlidge. **Description:** Profile of Princess Sheika Lubna who is the first female foreign trade minister in the Middle East, the United Arab Emirates biggest business envoy, paving the way for billions in new investment, and also a manufacturer of her own perfume line. **Availability:** Online.

27655 ■ *"A Muddle at Marks & Spencer"* in *Barron's (Vol. 88, July 7, 2008, No. 27, pp. M7)*
Pub: Dow Jones & Company Inc.
Contact: Almar Latour, Chief Executive Officer
Ed: Molly Neal. **Description:** British retail outfit Marks & Spencer is encountering turbulent financial conditions but remains confident in spending 900 million pounds sterling. The company has not made a profit forecast for the first half of 2008 and is suffering from a shrinking cash flow. **Availability:** Online.

27656 ■ *The Multinational Enterprise Revisited: The Essential Buckley and Casson*
Pub: Palgrave Macmillan
Ed: Peter J. Buckley, Mark Casson. **Released:** 2010. **Price:** $89, e-book; $120, hardcover; $120, hardcover. **Description:** A compilation of essays gathered from over thirty years discussing the future of the multinational enterprise, and includes a new introduction and conclusion to bond the pieces together in a comprehensive overview of the theory of the multinational enterprise. **Availability:** E-book; Print.

27657 ■ *"MyReviewsNow.net Announces New Affiliate Partner Gift Baskets Overseas"* in *M2 EquityBites (EQB) (June 22, 2012)*
Description: MyReviewsNow.net has partnered with Gift Baskets Overseas in order to offer gift baskets to be shipped overseas. Gift Baskets Overseas works with local florists and shippers worldwide. No financial details were disclosed. **Availability:** Online.

27658 ■ *"Needed: A Strategy; Banking In China"* in *The Economist (Vol. 390, January 3, 2009, No. 8612, pp. 54)*
Description: International banks are competing for a role in China but are finding obstacles in their paths such as a reduction in the credit their operations may receive from Chinese banks and the role they can play in the public capital markets which remain limited. **Availability:** Print; Online.

27659 ■ *"Nestle Acquires Waggin' Train Dog Treat Company"* in *Pet Product News (Vol. 64, November 2010, No. 11, pp. 7)*
Description: Vevey, Switzerland-based Nestle has acquired South Carolina-based dog treat firm Waggin' Train LLC from private equity firm VMG Partners in

September 2010. Waggin' Train LLC, which will be operated as a wholly owned subsidiary, is expected to fill a gap in Nestle's dog treat product portfolio. **Availability:** Online.

27660 ■ *"A New Alliance For Global Change"* in *Harvard Business Review (Vol. 88, September 2010, No. 9, pp. 56)*
Pub: Harvard Business Publishing
Contact: Diane Belcher, Managing Director
Ed: Bill Drayton, Valeria Budinich. **Price:** $8.95, PDF. **Description:** Collaboration between social organizations and for-profit firms through the development of hybrid value chains to target complex global issues is promoted. While social organizations offer links to communities and consumers, firms provide financing and scale expertise. **Availability:** Online; PDF.

27661 ■ *"New Argentine Investment Taps Real Estate"* in *South Florida Business Journal (Vol. 32, June 22, 2012, No. 48, pp. 1)*
Pub: Baltimore Business Journal
Contact: Rhonda Pringle, President
E-mail: rpringle@bizjournals.com
Description: Industry experts believe that Miami, Florida is becoming the go-to-investment destination of Argentines looking for real estate development opportunities. For example, Consultatio paid $220 million for 5.5 acres in Bal Harbour where it plans to construct condominiums. It appears Argentines are selecting sites in Miami as investments. **Availability:** Print; Online.

27662 ■ *"New Game Plan to Grow Trade?"* in *Providence Business News (Vol. 29, May 19, 2014, No. 7, pp. 1)*
Pub: American City Business Journals, Inc.
Contact: Mike Olivieri, Executive Vice President
Released: May 17, 2014. **Description:** The state of Rhode Island is trying a new approach for expanding its foreign trade connections by offering its location to foreign businesses instead of taking local companies abroad. The four-member Rhode Island delegation visited companies and their leadership teams in Ireland and Italy. **Availability:** Online.

27663 ■ *"New Generation Deans Lead Atlanta Area Business Schools Into the Future"* in *Atlanta Business Chronicle (July 25, 2014, pp. 3A)*
Pub: American City Business Journals, Inc.
Contact: Mike Olivieri, Executive Vice President
Released: Weekly. **Price:** $4, introductory 4-week offer(Digital only). **Description:** An interview with five business school deans from Georgia share their views on the future of business education, changing business education needs, and other issues affecting the Atlanta area business schools. The growing demands for greater global competences, good communication skills across various cultures, and other challenges faced by the students and employers are discussed. Other topics include the role of women in the corporate world. **Availability:** Print; Online.

27664 ■ *"New Institutional Accounting and IFRS"* in *Accounting and Business Research (Vol. 41, Summer 2011, No. 3, pp. 309)*
Pub: Routledge, Taylor & Francis Group
Ed: Peter Wysocki. **Description:** A new framework for institutional accounting research is presented. It has five fundamental components: efficient versus inefficient results, interdependencies, causation, level of analysis, and institutional structure. The use of the framework for evaluation accounting institutions such as the international financial reports standards (IFRS) is discussed. **Availability:** PDF; Online; Download.

27665 ■ *The New Role of Regional Management*
Pub: Palgrave Macmillan
Ed: Bjorn Ambos, Bodo B. Schlegelmilch. **Released:** 2010. **Description:** Regional management is becoming more important to companies as they expand globally. This book explores the challenges of European, United States and Asian companies and

outlines how regional headquarters can develop into Dynamic Competence Relay centers to master these issues. **Availability:** E-book; Print.

27666 ■ *"New Texas South-International Alliance Seeking to Net Foreign Firms for South Texas"* in *San Antonio Business Journal (Vol. 26, June 22, 2012, No. 21, pp. 1)*
Pub: Baltimore Business Journal
Contact: Rhonda Pringle, President
E-mail: rpringle@bizjournals.com
Description: The city of San Antonio, Texas is partnering with Brownsville, Corpus Christi, Edinburg, Laredo, and San Marcos, to form the Texas South-International Alliance. The alliance is aimed at attracting more international economic development opportunities and investment to South Texas. **Availability:** Print; Online.

27667 ■ *"New Zealand Natural Co-Branding with Mrs. Fields"* in *Ice Cream Reporter (Vol. 23, November 20, 2010, No. 12, pp. 2)*
Description: Mrs. Fields has partnered with a New Zealand firm to co-brand ice cream and cookies in Australian markets. **Availability:** Print; Online.

27668 ■ *"The Next Wave"* in *Hawaii Business (Vol. 53, January 2008, No. 7, pp. 27)*
Pub: PacificBasin Communications
Contact: Chuck Tindle, Director
E-mail: chuckt@pacificbasin.net
Ed: Cathy S. Cruz-George. **Description:** Only 40,000 Koreans took a visit to Hawaii in 2007, a decline from the pre-September averages of 123,000 visits. The number of Korean visitors in Hawaii could increase if the visa waiver proposal is passed. Efforts to improve Hawaiian tourism are presented. **Availability:** Print; Online.

27669 ■ *"No Shortage of Challenges for Cross-Border Trade"* in *Canadian Sailings (June 30, 2008)*
Description: Pros and cons of the North American Free Trade Agreement are examined. The agreement between the U.S. and Canada concerning trade was an essential step toward securing economic growth for Canadian citizens. Two-way trade between the counties has tripled since the agreement and accounts for 7.1 million American and 3 million Canadian jobs. **Availability:** Print; Online; PDF.

27670 ■ *Non-Standard Employment under Globalization: Flexible Work and Social Security in the Newly Industrializing Countries*
Pub: Palgrave Macmillan
Ed: Koichi Usami. **Released:** First edition. **Description:** Expansion of non-standard employment under globalization is being recognized in all of the newly industrialized countries. The book examines deregulation of labor markets, social protection for nonstandard workers, and social security reforms in accordance with the transformation of employment.

27671 ■ *"No. 381: Metallica and Other Forms of Hardware"* in *Inc. (Vol. 36, September 2014, No. 7, pp. 107)*
Pub: Mansueto Ventures L.L.C.
Contact: Stephanie Mehta, Chief Executive Officer
Released: August 20, 2014. **Description:** Profile of Mikhail Orlov, who stayed in American instead of fighting a war he did not believe in while living in Chechnya, Russia. Orlov discovered his entrepreneurial spirit when he began importing Russian army surplus gear. He operates his startup online store selling guns, ammo, and hunting accessories. **Availability:** Print; Online.

27672 ■ *"Olympus is Urged to Revise Board"* in *Wall Street Journal Eastern Edition (November 28, 2011, pp. B3)*
Pub: Dow Jones & Company Inc.
Contact: Almar Latour, Chief Executive Officer
Ed: Phred Dvorak. **Description:** Koji Miyata, once a director on the board of troubled Japanese photographic equipment company, is urging the company to reorganize its board, saying the present group

should resign their board seats but keep their management positions. The company has come under scrutiny for its accounting practices and costly acquisitions. **Availability:** Online.

27673 ■ *"OMERS Joins Bid for U.K. Port Giant" in Globe & Mail (March 28, 2006, pp. B1)*

Ed: Paul Waldie. **Description:** The plans of Ontario Municipal Employees Retirement Board to partner with Goldman Sachs Group Inc., in order to acquire Associated British Ports PLC, are presented. **Availability:** Online.

27674 ■ *"On the U.S. Election: Shaky on Free Trade" in Canadian Business (Vol. 81, December 19, 2007, No. 1, pp. 29)*

Pub: Rogers Media Inc.

Contact: Neil Spivak, Chief Executive Officer

Ed: Rachel Pulfer. **Description:** Rhetoric at the U.S. presidential elections seems to be pointing toward a weaker free trade consensus, with Democratic candidates being against the renewal of free trade deals, while Republican candidates seem to be for free trade. **Availability:** Online.

27675 ■ *"Oracle: No Profit of Doom" in Barron's (Vol. 88, March 31, 2008, No. 13, pp. 40)*

Pub: Dow Jones & Company Inc.

Contact: Almar Latour, Chief Executive Officer

Ed: Mark Veverka. **Description:** Oracle's revenues grew by 21 percent but fell short of expectation and their profits came in at the low-end of expectations. The company's shares dropped 8 percent but investors are advised to pay more attention to the company's earnings expansion rather than revenue growth in a slow economy. Nokia's Rick Simonson points out that their markets in Asia and particularly India is growing so they are not as affected by the U.S. economic conditions. **Availability:** Online.

27676 ■ *"Ottawa to Push for Gas Deal Between Petrocan, Gazprom" in Globe & Mail (February 13, 2006, pp. B1)*

Ed: Greame Smith. **Description:** Jim Flaherty, finance minister of Canada is negotiating a 1.3 billion dollar deal between state owned Petro-Canada and Russia's OAO Gazprom. This once again highlighted the country's increasing dependence on Russia for its energy requirements. **Availability:** Online.

27677 ■ *"Overseas Marketing Key to Success of Chicago Spire" in Commercial Property News (March 17, 2008)*

Description: New construction of the Chicago Spire, a condominium project located on Lake Michigan's shore, is being marketed to would-be clients in Asia where Chicago is viewed as an emerging world city. **Availability:** Online.

27678 ■ *"Overseas Overtures" in Business Journal-Portland (Vol. 24, October 26, 2007, No. 35, pp. 1)*

Pub: Portland Business Journal

Contact: Andy Giegerich, Managing Editor

E-mail: agiegerich@bizjournals.com

Ed: Robin J. Mood. **Description:** Oregon has a workforce shortage, specifically for the health care industry. Recruiting agencies, such as the International Recruiting Network Inc., answers the high demand for workforce by recruiting foreign employees. The difficulties recruiting companies experience with regards to foreign labor laws are investigated. **Availability:** Print; Online.

27679 ■ *"An Overview of Energy Consumption of the Globalized World Economy" in Energy Policy (Vol. 39, October 2011, No. 10, pp. 5920-2928)*

Ed: Z. M. Chen, G. Q. Chen. **Released:** October 01, 2011. **Description:** Energy consumption and its impact on the global world economy is examined. **Availability:** Print; Online.

27680 ■ *"Pack Mentality: Why Black Can Be Slimming" in Crain's Chicago Business (Vol. 31, April 21, 2008, No. 16, pp. 31)*

Pub: Crain Communications Inc.

Contact: Barry Asin, President

Ed: Sarah A. Klein. **Description:** Jill Smart, the head of human resources for a company with 170,000 employees worldwide, frequently travels to India, London and Singapore; Ms. Smart provides advice concerning efficiency, time management and avoiding jet-lag. **Availability:** Online.

27681 ■ *"Parent Firm's Global Reach, Stricter Air Quality Rules Have Stock Smiling" in Crain's Cleveland Business (October 15, 2007)*

Pub: Crain Communications Inc.

Contact: K. C. Crain, President

Ed: David Bennett. **Description:** Since Stock Equipment Co., a firm that makes industrial pollution control equipment, was acquired by Schenck Process Group, a diversified global manufacturer based in Germany, the company's orders from abroad have been on the rise. The purchase has opened the doors to regions such as Eastern and Central Europe, Latin America and Australia. **Availability:** Online.

27682 ■ *"Patience Will Pay Off in Africa" in Barron's (Vol. 92, September 17, 2012, No. 38, pp. M8)*

Description: The stocks of African companies present long-term capital appreciation opportunities for investors. This is due to a commodities boom, economic reform and relative political stability in many African countries. **Availability:** Online.

27683 ■ *"Paying for the Recession: Rebalancing Economic Growth" in Montana Business Quarterly (Vol. 49, Spring 2011, No. 1, pp. 2)*

Pub: University of Montana Bureau of Business and Economic Research

Contact: Patrick Barkey, Director

E-mail: patrick.barkey@business.umt.edu

Ed: Patrick M. Barkey. **Released:** Quarterly. **Description:** Four key issues required to address in order to rebalance economic growth in America are examined. They include: savings rates, global trade imbalances, government budgets and most importantly, housing price correction. **Availability:** Online.

27684 ■ *"PBSJ Launches Internal Probe" in Tampa Bay Business Journal (Vol. 30, January 8, 2010, No. 3, pp. 1)*

Pub: Tampa Bay Business Journal

Contact: Ian Anderson, President

E-mail: ianderson@bizjournals.com

Ed: Margie Manning. **Description:** Florida-based engineering firm PBSJ Corporation has started an internal investigation into possible violations of any laws, including the Foreign Corrupt Practices Act. Projects handled by subsidiary PBS&J International in foreign countries are the focus of the investigation. **Availability:** Print; Online.

27685 ■ *"The Perils of Partnering in Developing Markets: How a Health Care Provider Addresses the Risks That Come With Globalization" in Harvard Business Review (Vol. 90, June 2012, No. 6, pp23)*

Pub: Harvard Business Review Press

Contact: Moderna V. Pfizer, Contact

Ed: Steven J. Thompson. **Price:** $6. **Description:** Effective evaluation of international risk includes assessing the opportunity; ramping up processes, operations, and metrics; and establishing long-term functionality. Warning signs for each stage are also presented. **Availability:** Online; PDF.

27686 ■ *"Play It Safe At Home, Or Take a Risk Abroad? A US Lease-To-Own Chain Considers Whether To Test Its Business In Mexico" in Harvard Business Review (Vol. 90, January-February 2012, No.1-2, pp. 145)*

Pub: Harvard Business Review Press

Contact: Moderna V. Pfizer, Contact

Ed: Michael Chu. **Price:** $8.95, hardcopy black and white. **Description:** A fictitious foreign-market entry scenario is presented, with contributors providing advice. Recommendations include ensuring that expansion will not compromise the firm's core business, and that expansion, while necessary to growth, must be done carefully. **Availability:** Print; Online; PDF.

27687 ■ *"Political Environments and Business Strategy: Implications for Managers" in Business Horizons (Vol. 51, January-February 2008)*

Pub: Elsevier Advanced Technology Publications

Ed: Gerald D. Keim, Amy J. Hillman. **Description:** Various government bodies and business organizations work together in shaping new business opportunities and policies that arise from globalization. Presented is framework of public policy considerations for business managers. The framework is based on Nobel laureate Douglas North's work. **Availability:** PDF; Online.

27688 ■ *"Port in the Storm" in Canadian Business (Vol. 81, October 13, 2008, No. 17, pp. 101)*

Description: Interport Inc.'s state-of-the-art studio complex in Toronto is discussed. The strong Canadian dollar, along with disputes within the movie industry, are creating challenges for the studio to secure Hollywood projects. Interport plans to compete for Hollywood projects based on quality. **Availability:** Print; Online.

27689 ■ *"Putting the World at Your Fingertips" in Barron's (Vol. 88, July 7, 2008, No. 27, pp. L13)*

Pub: Dow Jones & Company Inc.

Contact: Almar Latour, Chief Executive Officer

Ed: Neil A. Martin. **Description:** Currency-traded exchange funds allow investors to diversify their assets and take advantage of investment opportunities such as speculation and hedging. Investors can use these funds to build positions in favor of or against the US dollar. **Availability:** Online.

27690 ■ *"Q&A: RBC's Gordon Nixon" in Canadian Business (Vol. 80, May 31, 2011, No. 22, pp. 9)*

Pub: Rogers Media Inc.

Contact: Neil Spivak, Chief Executive Officer

Ed: Rachel Pulfer. **Description:** Royal Bank of Canada (RBC) chief executive officer Gordon Nixon believes that the Canadian financial services segment is heavily regulated. Nixon also feels that it has become difficult for local banks to enter the market since foreign banks can easily come in and compete with Canadian banks. His views on RBC's success are provided. **Availability:** Online.

27691 ■ *"Qorvis Communications Gets Sabre Award for Search Engine Optimization" in Entertainment Close-Up (May 29, 2012)*

Description: Qorvis Communications received the Gold Sabre Award by the Holmes Report for Search Engine Optimization for its work on the Marca Paid Imagen de Mexico on the MexicoToday campaign. MexicoToday.org is a next-generation Website and external branding initiative which focuses on digital and social media. The site hopes to change the world's perception of Mexico, particularly Europeans and Americans. **Availability:** Print; Online.

27692 ■ *"Quality Performance of SMEs in a Developing Economy: Direct and Indirect Effects of Service Innovation and Entrepreneurial Orientation" in Journal of Business & Industrial Marketing (Vol. 29, July 2014, No. 6)*

Pub: Emerald Group Publishing Limited

Contact: Erika Valenti, President

Description: A study was conducted to investigate the effects of innovation and EO (entrepreneurial orientation) on organizational performance in Asian small enterprise context. Strategic management literature and the relationship between EO, innovation, and quality performance was tested. The results indicated that a noteworthy direct and indirect positive relationship exists between EO dimensions, innovation, and quality performance. **Availability:** Download; Online.

27693 ■ "Raising the Game" in Birmingham Business Journal (Vol. 31, May 2, 2014, No. 18, pp. 4)
Pub: American City Business Journals, Inc.
Contact: Mike Olivieri, Executive Vice President

Description: Birmingham, Alabama has grown its reputation in the sports world in recent years by hosting global events that draw tourists and overage from around the world. However, the Metro needs a facilities upgrade to further elevate its game. The long-debated project to replace the Birmingham-Jefferson Convention Complex and Legion Field is also examined. **Availability:** Online.

27694 ■ "R&R Launches Upscale Spoony's and Low Fat Dragon's Den" in Ice Cream Reporter (Vol. 23, August 20, 2010, No. 9, pp. 3)
Description: European ice cream manufacturer R&R has acquired French ice cream maker Rolland and will position itself as an upscale challenger to brands like Ben & Jerry's. **Availability:** Print; Online.

27695 ■ Reading Financial Reports for Dummies
Pub: John Wiley & Sons, Inc.
Contact: Christina Van Tassell, Executive Vice President Chief Financial Officer
URL(s): www.amazon.com/gp/product/1119871360/ref=as_li_tl?ie=UTF8&tag=wiley01-20
Ed: Lita Epstein. **Released:** 4th Edition. **Price:** $27.18, paperback; $18, e-book. **Description:** The fourth edition contains more new and updated information. This book is meant as a guide to help the reader interpret and understand financial reports, annual reports, balance sheets, income statements, statements of cash flow and consolidated statements. Real-world examples are given. . **Availability:** E-book; Print.

27696 ■ "Religious Revival" in Canadian Business (Vol. 81, December 8, 2008, No. 21, pp. 57)
Pub: Rogers Media Inc.
Contact: Neil Spivak, Chief Executive Officer
Ed: Paul Webster. **Description:** Canada-based lawyer Cyndee Todgham Cherniak believes that Canadians wishing to do business in China should have professional competence, as well as cultural and spiritual sensitivity. Chinese government officials also acknowledge the role of religion in China's economy. **Availability:** Online.

27697 ■ "Renren Partners With Recruit to Launch Social Wedding Services" in Benzinga.com (June 7, 2011)
Pub: PR Newswire Association LLC.
Description: Renren Inc., the leading real name social networking Internet platform in China has partnered with Recruit Company Limited, Japan's largest human resource and classified media group to form a joint venture to build a wedding social media catering to the needs of engaged couples and newlyweds in China.

27698 ■ "RES Stakes Its Claim in Area" in Philadelphia Business Journal (Vol. 28, January 29, 2010, No. 50, pp. 1)
Pub: Philadelphia Business Journal
Contact: Sierra Quinn, Director
E-mail: squinn@bizjournals.com
Ed: Peter Key. **Description:** RES Software Company Inc. of Amsterdam, Netherlands appointed Jim Kirby as president for the Americas and Klaus Besier as chairman in an effort to boost the firm's presence in the US. Brief career profiles of Kirby and Besier are included. RES develops software that allows management of information flow between an organization and its employees regardless of location. **Availability:** Online.

27699 ■ "Research and Markets Adds Report: Cyprus: Convergence, Broadband and Internet Market" in Wireless News (September 4, 2009)
Description: Overview of a new report by Research and Markets entitled, "Cyprus Convergence, Broadband and Internet Market - Overview, Statistics and Forecasts." Highlights include information regarding broadband accounts which now account for the majority of household Internet connections. **Availability:** Print; Online.

27700 ■ "Retail Doesn't Cross Borders: Here's Why and What To Do About It" in Harvard Business Review (Vol. 90, April 2012, No. 4, pp. 104)
Pub: Harvard Business Review Press
Contact: Moderna V. Pfizer, Contact
Ed: Marcel Corstjens, Rajiv Lal. **Description:** Globalization poses challenges for retailers, such as competing directly with well established local businesses. To succeed, retailers should enter markets at the right time, focus not on synergies but on differentiation, and introduce new and innovative products and services.

27701 ■ "Reversal of Fortune" in Canadian Business (Vol. 85, June 11, 2012, No. 10, pp. 32)
Ed: Matthew McClearn. **Description:** First Quantum Minerals of Vancouver, British Columbia contested the decisio of the Democratic Republic of Congo to revoke their mining license in the Kolwezi Tailings by means of political pressure and international law. Eurasian National Resources Corporation agreed to pay First Quantum $1.25 billion in return for uncontested title to Congo mines and a ceasefire in January 2012. **Availability:** Print; Online.

27702 ■ "A Reverse-Innovation Playbook. Insights From a Company That Developed Products For Emerging Markets and Then Brought Them Back Home" in Harvard Business Review (Vol. 90, April 2012, No. 4, pp. 120)
Pub: Harvard Business Review Press
Contact: Moderna V. Pfizer, Contact
Ed: Vijay Govindarajan. **Price:** $8.95, hardcover. **Description:** An overview is presented on the organizational change implemented by Harman International Industries Inc. to create products for emerging markets and ensure that they would be accepted in already established middle markets. Components include setting radical goals, selecting team leaders with no competing interests, and leveraging global resources. **Availability:** PDF; Online.

27703 ■ "RIAC: Green Air Link to Ireland No Flight of Fancy" in Providence Business News (Vol. 29, May 26, 2014, No. 8, pp. 1)
Pub: American City Business Journals, Inc.
Contact: Mike Olivieri, Executive Vice President
URL(s): pbn.com/riac-green-air-link-to-ireland-no-flight-of-fancy97335
Ed: Kelly Anderson. **Description:** Rhode Island Airport Corporation president and CEO, Kelly Fredericks, joined the European trade mission led by the state government to pitch nonstop flights from T.F. Green Airport in Warwick, RI to Ireland. Fredericks is in discussions with Shannon Airport and Ireland West Airport Knock about cargo/freight forwarding and passenger services.

27704 ■ "Rice & Roll Onigiri Food Truck to Tour Los Angeles Area" in Entertainment Close-Up (July 30, 2012)
Description: Rice & Roll Onigiri food truck service is entering the US market, offering Japanese stuffed rice balls in a variety of flavors and fillings. Asian cuisine is popular in restaurants and markets. The ten locations to visit Rice & Roll in California are listed.

27705 ■ "Riding the Export Wave: How To Find a Good Distributor Overseas" in Inc. (January 2008, pp. 49)
Ed: Sarah Goldstein. **Description:** Small companies should contact the U.S. embassy in foreign companies in order to connect with the U.S. Commercial Service's Gold Key program that is designed to work with small and midsize exporters. **Availability:** Online.

27706 ■ "Right at Home China Celebrates 1 Year Anniversary as U.S. In-Home Senior Care Master Franchise" in Professional Service Close-Up (June 24, 2012)
Description: Franchisor, Right at Home International Inc., provides in-home senior care and assistance and has experienced a one year franchise license agreement in China. Right at Home China predicts growth because China has 200 million adults over 65 years of age. **Availability:** Print; Online.

27707 ■ "Rising in the East; Research and Development" in The Economist (Vol. 390, January 3, 2009, No. 8612, pp. 47)
Description: Impressive growth of the technological research and development in Asian countries is discussed. Statistical data included. **Availability:** Online.

27708 ■ "Risk and Reward" in Canadian Business (Vol. 81, October 13, 2008, No. 17, pp. 21)
Description: Macro-economist and currency analyst Mark Venezia believes that stable financial institutions, free-market reforms, and the role of central banks in keeping inflation and exchange rates stable could make emerging-market bonds strong performers for better future returns. Venezia's other views on emerging-market bonds are discussed. **Availability:** Print; Online.

27709 ■ "Rough Trade: the Canada-Chile Free Trade Agreement" in Canadian Business (Vol. 79, September 11, 2006, No. 18, pp. 31)
Pub: Rogers Media Inc.
Contact: Neil Spivak, Chief Executive Officer
Ed: Christina Campbell. **Description:** The divergence between trade policy agreements entered into by Chile and the Canadian government are highlighted. Canada-Chile Free Trade Agreement and the myth around the big benefits to be reaped by bilateral trade policy agreements are discussed. **Availability:** Print; Mailing list; Online.

27710 ■ "Russia: Uncle Volodya's Flagging Christmas Spirit" in The Economist (Vol. 390, January 3, 2009, No. 8612, pp. 22)
Description: Overview of Russia's struggling economy as well as unpopular government decisions such as raising import duties on used foreign vehicles so as to protect Russian carmakers. **Availability:** Print; Online.

27711 ■ "Russian Renaissance" in Chicago Tribune (September 22, 2008)
Pub: Tribune News Service
Contact: Jack Barry, Vice President, Operations
E-mail: jbarry@tribpub.com
Ed: Alex Rodriguez. **Description:** Winemakers from Russia are returning to the craft and quality of wine-making now that they are free from Soviet restraints. **Availability:** Print; Online.

27712 ■ "Sedo Keeps Trucking in Good Times and Bad" in Crain's Chicago Business (Vol. 31, April 28, 2008, No. 17, pp. 35)
Description: Discusses Seko Worldwide Inc., an Itasca-based freight forwarder, and its complicated road to growth and expansion on a global scale. **Availability:** Print; Online.

27713 ■ "Selling Michigan; R&D Pushed as Reason For Chinese To Locate In State" in Crain's Detroit Business (Vol. 24, January 14, 2008)
Pub: Crain Communications Inc.
Contact: Barry Asin, President

Ed: Marti Benedetti. **Description:** Southeast Michigan Economic Development organizations are working to develop relationships with Chinese manufacturers so they will locate their automotive research and development operations in the state.

27714 ■ "The Service Imperative" in Business Horizons (Vol. 51, January-February 2008, No. 1, pp. 39)
Pub: Elsevier Advanced Technology Publications
Ed: Mary Jo Bitner, Stephen W. Brown. **Description:** The importance of services is growing in developing countries like India and China, but little attention is given to service research, education and innovation. The 'service imperative' seeks to promote the advancement of services. The scope, objectives and philosophy of the service imperative platform are outlined. **Availability:** Online.

27715 ■ "Shattering the Myths About U.S. Trade Policy: Stop Blaming China and India. A More Active Trade Policy Can Lead to a Stronger U.S. Economy" in Harvard Business Review (Vol. 90, March 2012, No. 3, pp. 149)
Pub: Harvard Business Review Press
Contact: Moderna V. Pfizer, Contact
Ed: Robert Z. Lawrence, Lawrence Edwards. **Price:** $8.95, hardcopy black and white. **Description:** Myths debunked include the belief that the US open trade policy has caused job losses, and that living standards are falling due to export market competition. American must leverage China's need for global economic engagement and secure an open domestic market in China. It must also persuade the World Trade Organization to improve market access. **Availability:** Print; PDF; Online.

27716 ■ "Shire Seeking New Digs for Headquarters" in Philadelphia Business Journal (Vol. 30, September 2, 2011, No. 29, pp. 1)
Pub: Philadelphia Business Journal
Contact: Sierra Quinn, Director
E-mail: squinn@bizjournals.com
Ed: Natalie Kostelni. **Description:** Dublin, Ireland-based Shire PLC announced plans to relocate its North American headquarters from Chesterbrook Corporate Center in Wayne, Pennsylvania and currently evaluating their options. The specialty biopharmaceutical firm is also considering a move to New Jersey or Delaware. **Availability:** Online.

27717 ■ "Size Does Matter" in International Journal of Globalisation and Small Business (Vol. 4, September 21, 2010, No. 1, pp. 61)
Ed: Julia Connell, Ranjit Voola. **Description:** Examination of how members of an Australian-based manufacturing and engineering cluster share knowledge through networking as a means to improve competitive advantage. **Availability:** Online.

27718 ■ "Sky Harvest Windpower Corp. - Operational Update" in Investment Weekly News (March 10, 2012, pp. 744)
Pub: PR Newswire Association LLC.
Description: Sky Harvest Windpower Corporation is rebranding its focus on gas and power activities both nationally and internationally. The firm's Canadian projects are outlined as well as its commitment to purse the Green Options Partners Program in 2012. **Availability:** Online.

27719 ■ "A Slice of Danish; Fixing Finance" in The Economist (Vol. 390, January 3, 2009, No. 8612, pp. 55)
Description: Denmark's mortgage-holders and the county's lending system is presented. **Availability:** Print; Online.

27720 ■ "Slimmed-Down Supplier TI Automotive Relaunches" in Crain's Detroit Business (Vol. 26, January 11, 2010, No. 2, pp. 14)
Pub: Crain Communications Inc.
Contact: Barry Asin, President

Ed: Robert Sherefkin. **Description:** TI Automotive Ltd., one of the world's largest suppliers of fuel storage and delivery systems, has reorganized the company by splitting it into five global divisions and is relaunching its brand which is now more focused on new technology. **Availability:** Print; Online.

27721 ■ "Small Firms Punch Ticket for Growth" in Houston Business Journal (Vol. 40, January 29, 2010, No. 38, pp. 1)
Pub: Houston Business Journal
Contact: Bob Charlet, President
E-mail: bcharlet@bizjournals.com
Ed: Allison Wollam. **Description:** Independent ticket agencies anticipate growth as American and Canadian authorities approved a merger between Ticketmaster and concert promoter Live Nation. Expansion of service offerings and acquisition of venues have also been done by independent ticket agencies in light of the merger. Details of the merger are included. **Availability:** Print; Online.

27722 ■ "Some Relief Possible Following Painful Week" in Barron's (Vol. 88, July 14, 2008, No. 28, pp. M3)
Pub: Dow Jones & Company Inc.
Contact: Almar Latour, Chief Executive Officer
Ed: Kopin Tan. **Description:** Dow Chemical is offering a 74 percent premium to acquire Rohm & Haas' coatings and electronics materials operations. Frontline amassed a 5.6 percent stake in rival Overseas Shipholding Group and a merger between the two would create a giant global fleet with pricing power. Highlights of the U.S. stock market during the week that ended in July 11, 2008 are discussed. Statistical data included. **Availability:** Online.

27723 ■ "Speaking In Tongues: Rosetta Stone's TOTALE Adds 'Social' To Language Learning" in Black Enterprise (Vol. 41, September 2010, No. 2)
Pub: Earl G. Graves Ltd.
Contact: Earl Graves, Jr., President
Ed: Sonya A. Donaldson. **Description:** As small businesses become more globalized, it is necessary to learn new languages in order to compete. Rosetta Stone's TOTALe is profiled. **Availability:** Online.

27724 ■ Start-Up Nation
Released: September 07, 2011. **Price:** Paperback. **Description:** Amid the turmoil in the Middle East, Israel's economy continues to thrive. **Availability:** Print; Download.

27725 ■ "StubHub Launches in the UK" in Entertainment Close-Up (March 25, 2012)
Description: StubHub, an eBay company, is expanding to the United Kingdom. The firm sells tickets, third party, to music, sport, and entertainment events by connecting buyers and sellers. Details of the service and expansion are explored. **Availability:** Online.

27726 ■ "Suit: Bank Bypassing Minorities" in Providence Business News (Vol. 29, June 9, 2014, No. 10, pp. 1)
Pub: American City Business Journals, Inc.
Contact: Mike Olivieri, Executive Vice President
URL(s): pbn.com/suit-bank-bypassing-minori ties97644
Description: The City of Providence, Rhode Island filed a lawsuit against the U.S. operations of Santander Bank for purposely bypassing minority neighborhoods in prime mortgage lending. The lawsuit alleges the Madrid, Spain-based bank of violating the Fair Housing Act by not lending into the minority communities of the city.

27727 ■ "The Superpower Dilemma" in Canadian Business (Vol. 83, August 17, 2010, No. 13-14, pp. 42)
Description: Canada has been an energy superpower partly because it controls the energy source and the production means, particularly of fossil fuels. However, Canada's status as superpower could diminish if it replaces petroleum exports with renewable technology for using sources of energy available globally. **Availability:** Online.

27728 ■ "Suppliers May Follow Fiat: Local Group Says Italian Firms are Inquiring" in Crain's Detroit Business (Vol. 25, June 15, 2009, No. 24, pp. 1)
Pub: Crain Communications Inc.
Contact: Barry Asin, President
Ed: Ryan Beene. **Description:** Italian suppliers to Fiat SpA are looking toward Detroit after the formation of Chrysler Group LLC, the Chrysler-Fiat partnership created from Chrysler's bankruptcy. The Italian American Alliance for Business and Technology is aware of two Italy-based powertrain component suppliers that are considering a move to Detroit. **Availability:** Online.

27729 ■ "Surge in the South" in Canadian Business (Vol. 85, June 11, 2012, No. 10, pp. 48)
Ed: Jeff Beer. **Description:** Canada should get involved as a trading partner in the emerging markets as South-South trade, which is between these markets, is projected to grow between 2012 and 2030 from 13 percent of global trade to 26 percent. Canadian firms can join the South-South trade by setting up operations in an emeging market and use it as a base for trade or by acting as facilitator between trade partners. **Availability:** Online.

27730 ■ The Swedish-American Chamber of Commerce, Inc.--Membership Directory
Pub: Swedish-American Chamber of Commerce Inc.
Contact: Anna Throne-Holst, President
URL(s): www.saccny.org/memberships
Description: Covers over 300 company members and professional individuals, spanning across more than 30 industries and sectors. **Entries include:** Company name, address, phone, fax. **Arrangement:** Alphabetical. **Availability:** Print.

27731 ■ "Taking the Over-the-Counter Route to U.S." in Barron's (Vol. 88, July 7, 2008, No. 27, pp. 24)
Pub: Dow Jones & Company Inc.
Contact: Almar Latour, Chief Executive Officer
Ed: Eric Uhlfelder. **Description:** Many multinational companies have left the New York Stock Exchange and allowed their shares to trade over-the-counter. The companies have taken advantage of a 2007 SEC rule allowing publicly listed foreign companies to change trading venues if less than 5 percent of global trading volume in the past 12 months occurred in the US. **Availability:** Online.

27732 ■ "Talent Shows" in Canadian Business (Vol. 81, December 24, 2007, No. 1, pp. 14)
Description: Canadian companies are increasingly turning to marketing to promote themselves as employers, as concerns on employee recruitment increase with the nearing retirement age of the baby boomers. Details on skills shortage, the potential advantage from the immigrant workforce, and employee retention are discussed. **Availability:** Online.

27733 ■ "Tales of the City" in Canadian Business (Vol. 81, December 8, 2008, No. 21, pp. 37)
Description: Key information on doing business in Hong Kong are shared by an entrepreneur, a consultant, an exporter, and a financier who were from Canada. Hong Kong hosts about 3,900 regional headquarters or offices of international companies. **Availability:** Online.

27734 ■ "Tao of Downfall: the Failures of High-profile Entrepreneurs in the Chinese Economic Reform" in International Journal of Entrepreneurship and Small Business (Vol. 11, August 31, 2010, No. 2, pp. 121)
Ed: Wenxian Zhang, Ilan Alon. **Description:** Through historical reviews and case studies, this research seeks to understand why some initially successful entrepreneurs failed in the economic boom of past decades. Among various factors contributing to their

downfall are a unique political and business environment, fragile financial systems, traditional cultural influences and personal characteristics. **Availability:** Online.

27735 ■ *"Tasti D-Lite Has Franchise Agreement for Australia"* in Ice Cream Reporter (Vol. 23, November 20, 2010, No. 12, pp. 3)

Description: Tasti D-Lite signed an international master franchise agreement with Friezer Australia Pty. Ltd. and will open 30 units throughout Australia over the next five years. **Availability:** Print; Online.

27736 ■ *"Tax Services Firm Ryan Prepares for Growth"* in Dallas Business Journal (Vol. 35, June 29, 2012, No. 42, pp. 1)

Pub: Baltimore Business Journal

Contact: Rhonda Pringle, President

E-mail: rpringle@bizjournals.com

Ed: Candace Carlisle. **Description:** Ryan LLC is seen to grow with three pending acquisitions. The tax services firm has opened offices in Australia and Singapore. **Availability:** Print; Online.

27737 ■ *"Thai Ice Cream Cremo Expanding to Middle East"* in Ice Cream Reporter (Vol. 23, September 20, 2010, No. 10, pp. 3)

Description: Thai-based frozen dessert manufacturer Chomthana, maker of Cremo brand ice cream, is expanding into the Middle East. **Availability:** Print; Online.

27738 ■ *"The Three Amigos"* in Canadian Business (Vol. 81, March 17, 2008, No. 4, pp. 19)

Description: Mexican president Felipe Calderon said that Mexico exported 30 percent more to Europe and 25 percent more to other countries in Latin America in 2000 in light of the downturn in the U.S. economy. Calderon made this announcement in a speech at Harvard University while protestors marched outside protesting against NAFTA. **Availability:** Online.

27739 ■ *"Three Ways Columbia's Stock Can Keep Rising"* in Business Journal Portland (Vol. 30, February 21, 2014, No. 51, pp. 8)

Pub: American City Business Journals, Inc.

Contact: Mike Olivieri, Executive Vice President

Released: Weekly. **Price:** $4, Introductory 4-week offer(Digital & Print). **Description:** The shares of Columbia Sportswear Company reached a record high of $88.25 in February 2014. The company's cold-weather gear, its TurboDown technology and its new joint venture with China are expected to contribute significantly in keeping stock prices high. **Availability:** Print; Online.

27740 ■ *"Time For a Change at Canon?"* in Barron's (Vol. 92, July 23, 2012, No. 30, pp. 17)

Pub: Dow Jones & Company Inc.

Contact: Almar Latour, Chief Executive Officer

Ed: Neil A. Martin. **Description:** Stocks of Japanese imaging equipment maker Canon could lose value unless the company undergoes changes in operations and governance. Prices of the company's American Depositary Receipts could fall 20 percent from $37.22 per share within 12 months. **Availability:** Online.

27741 ■ *"Timken's Bearings Rolling in China, India"* in Crain's Cleveland Business (Vol. 28, October 29, 2007, No. 43, pp. 14)

Pub: Crain Communications Inc.

Contact: K. C. Crain, President

Ed: David Bennett. **Description:** Canton-based Timken Co., a manufacturer of bearings and specialty metals, is seeing growing demand for its line of tapered roller bearings, which allow rail users to carry heavy car loads. The company is finding significant growth in China and India due to their rapidly growing rail markets. **Availability:** PDF; Online.

27742 ■ *"To Keep Freight Rolling, Ill. Has to Grease the Hub"* in Crain's Chicago Business (Vol. 31, April 21, 2008, No. 16, pp. 22)

Pub: Crain Communications Inc.

Contact: Barry Asin, President

Ed: Paul O'Connor. **Description:** Discusses the importance of upgrading Chicago's continental-hub freight rail system which is integral to moving international products as well as domestic ones. Global tonnage is expected to double by 2020 and unless more money is designated to upgrade the infrastructure the local and national economy will suffer. **Availability:** Online.

27743 ■ *"Too Much Precaution About Biotech Corn"* in Barron's (Vol. 88, March 17, 2008, No. 11, pp. 54)

Pub: Dow Jones & Company Inc.

Contact: Almar Latour, Chief Executive Officer

Ed: Mark I. Schwartz. **Description:** In the U.S., 90 percent of cultivated soybeans are biotech varietals as well as 60 percent of the corn. Farmers have significantly reduced their reliance on pesticides in the growing of biotech corn. Biotech cotton cultivation has brought hundreds of millions of dollars in net financial gains to farmers. The European Union has precluded the cultivation or sale of biotech crops within its border. **Availability:** Online.

27744 ■ *"Trade Mission Provides Global Entry Point"* in Pittsburgh Business Times (Vol. 33, January 3, 2014, No. 25, pp. 4)

Pub: American City Business Journals, Inc.

Contact: Mike Olivieri, Executive Vice President

Description: Carnegie, Pennsylvania-based Neural Ware CEO, Jack Cooper, claims trade missions can give companies a focal point when they trade overseas. Neural Ware uses the high respect for mayors in China and builds trust with potential customers. Insights into Cooper's advice for visiting target countries are discussed. **Availability:** Online.

27745 ■ *"Trade Winds"* in Canadian Sailings (June 30, 2008)

Description: Trade between Canada and the United States is discussed as well as legislation concerning foreign trade and the future of this trade relationship. **Availability:** Online.

27746 ■ *"The Transparent Supply Chain"* in Harvard Business Review (Vol. 88, October 2010, No. 10, pp. 76)

Pub: Harvard Business Publishing

Contact: Diane Belcher, Managing Director

Ed: Steve New. **Price:** $8.95, PDF. **Description:** Examination of the use of new technologies to create a transparent supply chain, such as next-generation 2D bar codes in clothing labels that can provide data on a garment's provenance. **Availability:** Online; PDF.

27747 ■ *"Tri-State to Get New Headquarters"* in Business Courier (Vol. 27, October 22, 2010, No. 25, pp. 1)

Description: Hong Kong-based corn processing firm Global Bio-Chem Technology is set to choose Greater Cincinnati, Ohio as a location of its North American headquarters. The interstate access, central location, and low labor and property costs might have enticed Global Bio-Chem to invest in the region. Statistics on Chinese direct investment in U.S. are also presented. **Availability:** Online; PDF.

27748 ■ *"Twitter Hack: Made in Japan? User Says Attack Showed Security Flaw"* in Houston Chronicle (September 24, 2010, pp. 3)

Description: Details of the attack on Twitter caused by a Japanese computer hacker are revealed. **Availability:** Print; Mailing list; Online.

27749 ■ *"Unemployment Rates"* in The Economist (Vol. 390, January 3, 2009, No. 8612, pp. 75)

Description: Countries that are being impacted the worst by rising unemployment rates are those that have also been suffering from the housing market crisis. Spain has been the hardest hit followed by Ireland. America and Britain are also seeing levels of unemployment that indicate too much slack in the economy. **Availability:** Print; Online.

27750 ■ *"Unilever Acquiring EVGA's Ice Cream Brands in Greece"* in Ice Cream Reporter (Vol. 23, October 20, 2010, No. 11, pp. 1)

Description: Unilever will acquire the ice cream brands and distribution network of the Greek frozen dessert manufacturer EVGA. **Availability:** Print; Online.

27751 ■ *"U.S. Competitiveness and the Chinese Challenge"* in Harvard Business Review (Vol. 90, March 2012, No. 3, pp. 40)

Pub: Harvard Business Review Press

Contact: Moderna V. Pfizer, Contact

Ed: Xu Xiaonian. **Price:** $6, hardcover. **Description:** Although China's shift from cntral planningto market-oriented policies has boosted innovation, intellectual property rights and original research are still insufficiently valued. The U.S. has the edge on China in this respect; it remains for the U.S. to restore confidence in its innovation and creativity. **Availability:** PDF; Online.

27752 ■ *"U.S. Primaries: An Amazing Race"* in Canadian Business (Vol. 81, February 12, 2008, No. 3, pp. 25)

Pub: Rogers Media Inc.

Contact: Neil Spivak, Chief Executive Officer

Ed: Rachel Pulfer. **Description:** U.S. presidential candidates Barack Obama and Hilary Clinton lead the Democratic Part primaries while John McCain is a frontrunner at the Republican Party. These leading candidates have different plans for the U.S. economy which will affect Canada's own economy particularly concerning trade policies. The presidential candidates' proposals and the impacts of U.S. economic downturn on Canada are examined. **Availability:** Print; Online.

27753 ■ *"Up On The Farm"* in Canadian Business (Vol. 81, March 31, 2008, No. 5, pp. 23)

Description: Agricultural products have outperformed both energy and metal and even the prospect of a global economic slowdown does not seem to hinder its prospects. The Organization for Economic Cooperation and Development sees prices above historic equilibrium levels during the next ten years given that fuel and fertilizers remain high and greater demand from India and China remain steady. **Availability:** Print; Online.

27754 ■ *"Upsurge"* in Puget Sound Business Journal (Vol. 33, July 13, 2012, No. 12, pp. 1)

Description: Kent, Washington-based Flow International Corporation posted a record of $254 million in annual sales for fiscal 2012 and it is expected to reach about $300 million by 2014. Flow is being lifted by a global manufacturing revival and by its machines' ability to handle the carbon-fiber composites used in aerospace. Insights on Flow's water jet cutting tools are also given.

27755 ■ *"VASCO DIGIPASS GO3 in Combination With IDENTIKEY Enhances the Security of Business Intelligence Solution Developed by CDS for General Motors Brazil"* in News Bites US (March 29, 2012)

Description: VASCO Data Security International Inc. will provide Condominio de Corporativas, a vendor and business solutions integrator, its DIGIPASS GO 3 authentication solution along with IDENTIKEY Authentacation Server to provide security to the BI Retail Program developed for General Motors Brazil. VASCO is a leading software security firm specializing in authentication products. **Availability:** Print; Online.

27756 ■ *"Vision Statement: Mapping the Social Internet"* in Harvard Business Review (Vol. 88, July-August 2010, No. 7-8, pp. 32)

Pub: Harvard Business Publishing

Contact: Diane Belcher, Managing Director

Ed: Mikolaj Jan Piskorski, Tommy McCall. **Price:** $6, PDF. **Description:** Chart compares and contrasts online social networks in selected countries. **Availability:** Online; PDF.

27757 ■ *"Vision Statement: Why Mumbai at 1 PM is the Center of the Business World"* in *Harvard Business Review (Vol. 88, October 2010, No. 10, pp. 38)*
Pub: Harvard Business Publishing
Contact: Diane Belcher, Managing Director
Ed: Michael Segalla. **Price:** $6, PDF. **Description:** A time zone chart is presented for assisting in the planning of international conference calls. **Availability:** Online; PDF.

27758 ■ *"Viva Brazil"* in *Business Strategy Review (Vol. 21, Autumn 2010, No. 3, pp. 24)*
Ed: Georgina Peters. **Released:** September 29, 2010. **Description:** Brazil's current status as a major emerging market with a boundless economic horizon is a radical shift from its place in the world in the late 1960s to the mid 1990s. Lessons Brazil can teach other countries are outlined. **Availability:** Print; PDF; Online.

27759 ■ *"Voices From the Front Lines: Four Leaders on the Cross-Border Challenges They've Faced"* in *Harvard Business Review (Vol. 92, September 2014, No. 9, pp. 77)*
Pub: Harvard Business Publishing
Contact: Diane Belcher, Managing Director
Price: $8.95. **Description:** Points presented include building cultural sensitivity into organizations, employing varying talent to respond to market specifics, creating standard human resource practices worldwide, and emphasizing the importance of emerging markets. **Availability:** Online; PDF.

27760 ■ *"Wabtec Delivering Strategic Plan for Long-term Growth"* in *Pittsburgh Business Times (Vol. 33, July 11, 2014, No. 52, pp. 10)*
Pub: American City Business Journals, Inc.
Contact: Mike Olivieri, Executive Vice President
Released: July 2014. **Description:** Raymond Betler, new CEO of Wabtec Corporation, the only company with a 13-year streak of annual stock price increase on US exchanges is profiled. Betler attributes the company's growth to four corporate strategies, including to grow internationally, focus on new product development, expand after-market opportunities, and pursue acquisitions. **Availability:** Print; Online.

27761 ■ *"Wal-Mart China Woes Add Up"* in *Wall Street Journal Eastern Edition (October 17, 2011, pp. B3)*
Pub: Dow Jones & Company Inc.
Contact: Almar Latour, Chief Executive Officer
Ed: Laurie Burkitt. **Description:** Woes for Wal-Mart Inc.'s subsidiary in China are adding up as Wal-Mart China president and chief executive Ed Chan stepped down, as well as the company's senior vice president for human resources, Clara Wong. The company has been charged by regulators with mislabeling pork products, the result which has forced stores to close. Sales in China have been slow at the retail stores. **Availability:** Online.

27762 ■ *"A Warning Sign From Global Companies"* in *Harvard Business Review (Vol. 90, March 2012, No. 3, pp. 74)*
Pub: Harvard Business Review Press
Contact: Moderna V. Pfizer, Contact
Ed: Laura D'Andrea Tyson, Matthew J. Slaughter. **Price:** $8.95, hardcover. **Description:** Multiple charts demonstrate the importance of the multinational corporation to the American economy, and that the US needs to become more attractive to these types of firms. **Availability:** PDF; Online.

27763 ■ *"Wegmans Uses Database for Recall"* in *Supermarket News (Vol. 56, September 22, 2008, No. 38)*
Pub: Informa USA, Inc.
Contact: Stephen A. Carter, Chief Executive Officer

Ed: Carol Angrisani. **Description:** Wegmans used data obtained through its loyalty card that, in turn, sent automated telephone calls to every customer who had purchased tainted pet food when Mars Petcare had recalled dog food products.

27764 ■ *"What Keeps Global Leaders Up at Night"* in *Harvard Business Review (Vol. 90, April 2012, No. 4, pp. 32)*
Pub: Harvard Business Review Press
Contact: Moderna V. Pfizer, Contact
Price: $6. **Description:** A chart uses colored squares to portray economic, environmental, geopolitical, societal, and technological concerns of industry leaders, and ranks them according to likelihood and impact. **Availability:** PDF; Online.

27765 ■ *What Works: Success in Stressful Times*
Ed: Hamish McRae. **Released:** August 04, 2011. **Price:** $14.95, paperback; $5.99, e-book. **Description:** Exploration of success stories from across the glove, and what Michelle Obama referred to as 'the flimsy difference between success and failure.' Why do some initiatives take off while others flounder? How have communities managed to achieve so much while others struggle? What distinguishes the good companies from the bad? What lessons can be learned from the well-ordered Mumbai community made famous by 'Slumdog Millionaire'? Why have Canadian manners helped Whistler become the most popular ski resort in North America?. **Availability:** E-book; Print.

27766 ■ *"Why Change?"* in *Canadian Business (Vol. 80, October 8, 2007, No. 20, pp. 9)*
Description: The need for economic change in Canada is discussed. Despite the country's economic growth and low unemployment rate, economic reform is needed in order to maximize its economic potential in the future. Other reasons for the need to further develop its economy, such as the rise of manufacturing and service industries in Asia and the emergence of regional trade pacts in South America are also tackled.

27767 ■ *"Why 'I'm Sorry' Doesn't Always Translate"* in *(Vol. 90, June 2012, No. 6, pp. 26)*
Pub: Harvard Business Review Press
Contact: Moderna V. Pfizer, Contact
Ed: Jeanne Brett, Peter H. Kim, Tetsushi Okumura, William W. Maddux. **Description:** Studies indicate that Americans associate an apology with culpability and personal responsibility, while Japan and other countries with group-oriented cultures view an apology as an acknowledgement that a transgression has occurred and that it is unfortunate. Implications for the role of the apology in negotiations and establishing trust are presented.

27768 ■ *"Why Japan Is So Interested In Alabama"* in *Birmingham Business Journal (Vol. 31, August 1, 2014, No. 31, pp. 11)*
Pub: American City Business Journals, Inc.
Contact: Mike Olivieri, Executive Vice President
Description: Kazuo Sunaga, Consul General of Japan in Atlanta, Georgia lists several reasons why Alabama presents several opportunities for Japanese companies, including fewer labor laws, low tax rates and the availability of trained workers. The state's relationship with Japan will be further enhanced when Birmingham hosts the Southeast U.S./Japan Association meeting in 2015, which will be attended by leaders from the business, political, and nonprofit sectors. **Availability:** Print; Online.

27769 ■ *"Why Optimism Over Europe Won't Last"* in *Barron's (Vol. 92, August 25, 2012, No. 38, pp. M6)*
Pub: Dow Jones & Company Inc.
Contact: Almar Latour, Chief Executive Officer
Ed: Jonathan Buck. **Description:** European markets could experience losses in the second half of 2012 as uncertainty over political events could wipe out market gains. Greece has to abide by the terms of ts

agreements with creditors to receive bailout funds. The stock prices of BG Group could gain as much as 20 percent in 2013 due to its strong lifquified natural gas business. **Availability:** Online.

27770 ■ *"Why U.S. Competitiveness Matters to All of Us: The World Wants America to Regain Its Vibrancy. Let's Stop Assigning Blame and Instead Focus on Solutions"* in *Harvard Business Review (Vol. 90, March 2012, No. 3, pp. 49)*
Pub: Harvard Business Review Press
Contact: Moderna V. Pfizer, Contact
Ed: Nitin Nohria. **Description:** The introduction to this special issue presents perspectives on the US economy from citizens of other nations. While they realize globalization means countries are interdependent and that a strong America provides an international boost, they feel US leaders are concerned more with politics than economic growth. Action is needed instead.

27771 ■ *"Why You Aren't Buying Venezuelan Chocolate "* in *Harvard Business Review (Vol. 88, December 2010, No. 12, pp. 25)*
Pub: Harvard Business Publishing
Contact: Diane Belcher, Managing Director
Ed: Rohit Deshpande. **Price:** $6, PDF. **Description:** The concept of provenance paradox is defined as the preconceived notions consumers have about the country of origin of a given product, which can pose significant difficulties for emerging markets. Five strategies are presented for combating this problem, including building on historic events that have informed cultural perspectives. **Availability:** Online; PDF.

27772 ■ *"With Whom Do You Trade? Defensive Innovation and the Skill-Bias"* in *Canadian Journal of Electronics (Vol. 43, November 2010)*
Pub: Journal of the Canadian Economics Association
Ed: Pushan Dutt, Daniel Traca. **Released:** Vol. 43, No. 4. **Price:** $5. **Description:** Examination into whether increased trade with ineffective protection of intellectual property has contributed to the skill-deepening of the 1980s. An index of effective protection of intellectual property at the country level, combining data on protection of patents and rule of law are presented. An industry-specific version of this index is given using as weights each country's trade share in the total trade of the industry. A decline is seen in this trade-weighted index, owing to a rise in trade with countries with low effective protection of intellectual property, which explains 29 percent of the rise within-industry skill-intensity. **Availability:** Print; Online; Download.

27773 ■ *"The World Is Your Oyster"* in *Canadian Business (Vol. 80, October 22, 2007, No. 21, pp. 140)*
Description: Business graduates are not that keen on working abroad. Fortune 500 companies are requiring executives to have a multi-country focus. The skill required for jobs abroad, as well as employment opportunities are discussed.

27774 ■ *"A World of Opportunity: Foreign Markets Offer Diversity to Keen Investors"* in *Canadian Business (Vol. 81, Summer 2008, No. 9)*
Description: International Monetary Fund projected in its 'World Economy Outlook' that there is a 25 percent chance that a global recession will occur in 2008 and 2009. Global growth rate is forecasted at 3.7 percent in 2008. Inflation in Asia emerging markets and forecasts on stock price indexes are presented. **Availability:** Online.

27775 ■ *"The World is Their Classroom"* in *Crain's Chicago Business (Vol. 31, March 24, 2008, No. 12, pp. 24)*
Ed: Samantha Stainburn. **Released:** January 17, 2017. **Description:** Due to globalization more business students are studying abroad; 89 percent of

eligible students in its executive MBA program went overseas in 2007 compared to 15 percent ten years ago. **Availability:** Print; Online.

27776 ■ *"World Watch: Where Michigan Does Business" in Crain's Detroit Business (Vol. 30, October 13, 2014, No. 41, pp. 22)*
Pub: Crain Communications Inc.
Contact: Barry Asin, President
Description: Canada is Michigan's closest trading partner. Canada's most significant industries include chemicals, minerals, wood/paper products, food products, transportation equipment, petroleum and natural gas. Canada is also the largest energy supplier to the United States, thus helping Canada's petroleum sector grow. Major export partners of Canada include: U.S. (74.5 percent), China (4.3 percent) and the United Kingdom (4.1 percent). Major exports include motor vehicles and parts, aircraft, telecommunication equipment, chemicals, crude petroleum and natural gas. **Availability:** Online.

27777 ■ *"Wrigley's Newest Taste: Wolfberry" in Crain's Chicago Business (Vol. 31, March 31, 2008, No. 13, pp. 1)*
Pub: Crain Communications Inc.
Contact: Barry Asin, President
Ed: David Sterrett. **Description:** Wm. Wrigley Jr. Co. has introduced a gum line in China that touts the medicinal advantages of aloe vera to improve skin and wolfberry to boost energy in an attempt to keep the company positioned as the top candy firm in China. **Availability:** Online.

27778 ■ *"Yao Ming Courts China's Wine Boom" in Wall Street Journal Eastern Edition (November 28, 2011, pp. B4)*
Pub: Dow Jones & Company Inc.
Contact: Almar Latour, Chief Executive Officer
Ed: Jason Chow. **Description:** Yao Ming, the former NBA 7-foot 6-inch Chinese basketball star, is set to cash in on the market potential for wine in China. He has created his own winery in California, Yao Family Wines, which will produce wines solely for the Chinese market. **Availability:** Online.

27779 ■ *"You Won't Go Broke Filling Up On The Stock" In Barron's (Vol. 88, July 14, 2008, No. 28, pp. 38)*
Pub: Dow Jones & Company Inc.
Contact: Almar Latour, Chief Executive Officer
Ed: Assif Shameen. **Description:** Due to high economic growth, pro-business policies and a consumption boom, the Middle East is a good place to look for equities. The best ways in which to gain exposure to this market include investing in the real estate industry and telecommunications markets as well as large banks that serve corporations and consumers. **Availability:** Online.

TRADE PERIODICALS

27780 ■ *The International Trade Journal: Western Hemispheric Studies*
Pub: Taylor And Francis Group
Contact: Annie Callanan, Chief Executive Officer
URL(s): www.tandfonline.com/journals/uitj20freetrade .tamiu.edu/itj.shtml
Ed: George R. G. Clarke, George R.G. Clarke. **Released:** 6/year; volume 38, issue 4. **Price:** $1,354, Institutions for print and online; $720, Individuals for print and online; $1,110, Institutions for online only; $720, Individuals for print only. **Description:** Professional journal dealing with theoretical and practical aspects of business and economic issues in the Western Hemisphere. **Availability:** Print; Download; PDF; Online.

27781 ■ *Journal of East-West Business*
Pub: Taylor And Francis Group
Contact: Annie Callanan, Chief Executive Officer
URL(s): www.tandfonline.com/journals/wjeb20
Released: Quarterly; volume 30, issue 2. **Price:** $295, Individuals for print and online; $257, Individuals for online only; $895, Institutions for online only; $1,091, Institutions for print and online. **Description:**

Journal dealing with contemporary and emerging topics of business studies, strategies, development, and practice relating to Eastern Europe and Asia. **Availability:** Print; Download; PDF; Online.

27782 ■ *Political Risk Letter (PRL)*
Pub: The PRS Group Inc.
Contact: Dr. Christopher McKee, Chief Executive Officer
E-mail: cmckee@prsgroup.com
URL(s): epub.prsgroup.com/products/political-risk-le tter
Released: Monthly **Price:** $93, Individuals for current issue pdf; $595, Individuals for 12-month pdf. **Description:** Offers concise political and economic forecasts for both 18 month and 5 year time spans. Provides country risk forecasts and analysis on 100 countries around the world and provides indepth coverage on 20 countries. **Availability:** Download; PDF. **Type:** Full-text.

27783 ■ *Washington Tariff & Trade Letter*
Contact: Samuel M. Gilston, Editor
URL(s): www.wttlonline.com
Ed: Samuel M. Gilston. **Released:** Weekly **Price:** $597, Individuals online. **Description:** Reports on U.S. trade policies, negotiations, regulations, and legislation. **Availability:** Print; PDF; Online.

CONSULTANTS

27784 ■ **International Business Resource Center**
50 Frida Kahlo Way
Cloud Hall 119, 1st Fl.
San Francisco, CA 94112
Ph: (415)239-3200
Fax: (415)239-3065
Co. E-mail: helpdesk@ccsf.edu
URL: http://www.ccsf.edu/academics/ccsf-catalog/ courses-by-department/courses-by-subject/52111
Contact: Brigitte Davila, President
Description: International business and educational resources for San Francisco are offered through forums and private appointments with consultants who assist in international trade transactions, dialog groups with international experts, workshops, seminars and conferences on international business issues and topics. **Scope:** International business and educational resources for San Francisco are offered through forums and private appointments with consultants who assist in international trade transactions, dialog groups with international experts, workshops, seminars and conferences on international business issues and topics.

27785 ■ **Nightingale Associates**
7445 Setting Sun Way
Columbia, MD 21046
Ph: (410)381-4280
URL: http://www.nightingaleassociates.net
Contact: Frederick C. Nightingale, Managing Director
E-mail: fredericknightingale@nightingaleassociates .net
X (Twitter): x.com/FCNightingale
Description: Management training and consulting firm offering the following skills productivity and accomplishment, leadership skills for the experienced manager, management skills for the new manager, leadership and teambuilding, supervisory development, creative problem solving, real strategic planning. **Scope:** Management training and consulting firm offering the following skills productivity and accomplishment, leadership skills for the experienced manager, management skills for the new manager, leadership and teambuilding, supervisory development, creative problem solving, real strategic planning. **Founded:** 1984. **Training:** Productivity and Accomplishment Management Skills for the New Manager; Leadership and Team building; Advanced Management; Business Process Re engineering; Strategic Thinking; Creative Problem Solving; Customer Service; International Purchasing and Materials Management; Fundamentals of Purchasing;

Negotiation Skills Development; Providing superior customer service; Leadership skills for the experienced manager.

PUBLICATIONS

27786 ■ *CaseBase: Case Studies in Global Business*
200 Pier 4 Blvd.
Boston, MA 02210
URL: http://www.cengage.co.in
Contact: Michael E. Hansen, Chief Executive Officer
URL(s): www.gale.com/ebooks/9781414486932/ casebase-case-studies-in-global-business
Released: Latest Volume 001. **Description:** Details business case studies; focused on worldwide emerging markets and industries. **Availability:** E-book.

27787 ■ *ie: The Business of International Events*
10400 Overland Rd No.356
Boise, ID 83709
Ph: (208)433-0950
Co. E-mail: ifea@ifea.com
URL: http://www.ifea.com
Contact: Steven Wood Schmader, President
E-mail: schmader@ifea.com
URL(s): www.ifea.com/p/resources/iemagazine
Released: Quarterly; Spring, Summer, Fall and Winter. **Description:** Includes industry updates, trends and issues. **Availability:** Online.

27788 ■ *Journal of International Business and Cultural Studies (JIBCS)*
PO Box 350997
Jacksonville, FL 32099-0997
URL: http://www.aabri.com
Contact: Russell Baker, Executive Director
URL(s): www.aabri.com/jibcs.html
Ed: Dr. Frank LaPira, Dr. Frank LaPira, Dr. George Gresham. **Released:** Latest Volume 13-June 2023. **Description:** Journal containing manuscripts related to international business and cultural relations issues. **Availability:** Print; PDF; Online.

27789 ■ *Journal of International Business Studies (JIBS)*
4 Crinan St.
London N1 9XW, United Kingdom
Ph: 44 20 78334000
Co. E-mail: palgrave@macmillan.com.au
URL: http://www.palgrave.com
Contact: Beth Farrow, Editor
E-mail: beth.farrow@palgrave.com
URL(s): www.aib.world/publications/journal-of-interna tional-business-studieswww.palgrave.com/gp/jour- nal/41267
Facebook: www.facebook.com/JIBSupdates
Released: 9/year **Description:** Scholarly business journal, covering topics from e-commerce to foreign markets. **Availability:** Print; Download; PDF; Online.

27790 ■ *Knowledge Ecology in Global Business: Managing Intellectual Capital*
701 E Chocolate Ave.
Hershey, PA 17033
Ph: (717)533-8845
Free: 866-342-6657
Fax: (717)533-8661
Co. E-mail: cust@igi-global.com
URL: http://www.igi-global.com
Contact: Jan Travers, Director
URL(s): www.igi-global.com/book/knowledge-ecology -global-business/673
Price: $195, for hardcover; $195, for e-book; $235, for hardcover + eBook; $37.50, for on demand. **Description:** Provides ideas on how intellectual capital through emerging technologies can support business performance. Covers topics such as competitive strategy, human resource management, and organizational learning. **Availability:** E-book; Print; PDF.

27791 ■ *Nations of the World: A Political, Economic and Business Handbook*
4919 Rte. 22
  Amenia, NY 12501-0056
Ph: (518)789-8700
Free: 800-562-2139
Fax: (518)789-0556
URL: http://www.greyhouse.com
Contact: Richard Gottlieb, President
URL(s): www.greyhouse.com/nations_of_the_world
Released: Latest Edition February 2018,17th edition.
Price: $180, Individuals for softcover. **Description:** Covers political, economic and business information for 231 nations and self-governing territories around the world. Includes five regional chapters. **Entries include:** Key facts, political and economic issues, country profile, business information, maps, demographics, GDP figures, climate, chambers of commerce, media, travel information, and contact information for government offices. **Availability:** Print; Online; PDF.

27792 ■ *Thunderbird International Business Review (TIBR)*
111 River St.
  Hoboken, NJ 07030-5774
Ph: (201)748-6000
Fax: (201)748-6088
Co. E-mail: creditriskdept@wiley.com
URL: http://www.wiley.com/en-in
Contact: Brian Napack, Chief Executive Officer
URL(s): onlinelibrary.wiley.com/journal/15206874
Ed: Mary B. Teagarden. **Released:** 6/year **Price:** $1,284, Institutions for online US, Canada, India, Japan; $1,442, Institutions for print + online US, Canada, India, Japan; $1,340, Institutions for print US, Canada, India, Japan; $337, Individuals for online US, Canada, India, Japan. **Description:** Refereed journal covering innovative ideas and current research on understanding the challenges confronting global business. Published in association between Wiley and the Thunderbird School of Global Management. **Availability:** Print; PDF; Online. **Type:** Full-text.

COMPUTERIZED DATABASES

27793 ■ *International Trade Reporter*
Bloomberg Industry Group
  1801 S Bell St.
  Arlington, VA 22202
Ph: (703)341-1818
URL: http://www.bloombergindustry.com
Contact: Josh Eastright, Chief Executive Officer
URL(s): lawcat.berkeley.edu/record/1281051
Released: Daily; Daily. **Availability:** Print; Online. **Type:** Full-text.

27794 ■ *OneSource Business Browser North America*
URL(s): custom.onesource.com/businessbrowserus
  .aspx
Type: Directory; Numeric; Statistical; Full-text.

27795 ■ *Ward's Business Directory of U.S. Private and Public Companies*
Gale, part of Cengage Group
  27555 Executive Dr., Ste. 270
  Farmington Hills, MI 48331
Free: 800-877-4253

Co. E-mail: gale.customerservice@cengage.com
URL: http://www.gale.com
Contact: Paul Gazzolo, General Manager Senior Vice President
URL(s): www.gale.com/ebooks/9781414453064/war
  ds-business-directory-of-u.s.-private-and-public
  -companies
Description: Covers approximately 112,000 companies, 90% of which are privately owned, representing all industries. **Entries include:** Company name, address, phone, fax, toll-free, e-mail, URL, names and titles of up to five officers, up to four Standard Industrial Classification (SIC) codes, NAICS code, revenue figure, number of employees, year founded, ticker symbol, stock exchange, immediate parent, fiscal year end, import/export, type of company (public, private, subsidiary, etc.). In Vol. 4, lists of top 1,000 privately held companies ranked by sales vol., top 1,000 publicly held companies ranked by sales volume, and top 1,000 employers ranked by number of employees; analyses of public and private companies by state, revenue per employee for top 1,000 companies, public and private companies by SIC code and NAICS code. In volume 5, national Standard Industrial Classification (SIC) code rankings are listed, while volumes 6 and 7 lists Standard Industrial Classification (SIC) code rankings by state. In all volumes, guide to abbreviations, codes, and symbols; explanation of classification system; numerical and alphabetical listings of SIC and NAICS codes. In volume 8, NAICS rankings. In the supplement, 10,000 new listings not contained in the main edition are included. **Arrangement:** Volumes 1, 2, and 3, alphabetical; volume 4 is geographical by state, then ascending zip; volume 5 is classified by 4-digit SIC code, then ranked by sales; volumes 6 and 7 are classified by Standard Industrial Classification (SIC) code within state; volume 8 classified by NAICS, then ranked; supplement arranged alphabetical and Standard Industrial Classification (SIC) code. **Indexes:** Company name index in volumes 5, 7, and 8. **Availability:** E-book; Print; Download. **Type:** Directory; Numeric.

LIBRARIES

27796 ■ Canadian International Trade Tribunal Library [Tribunal Canadien du Commerce Exterieur]
333 Laurier Ave. W, 17th Fl.
  Ottawa, ON, Canada K1A 0G7
URL: http://www.citt-tcce.gc.ca/en/publications/cana
  dian-international-trade-tribunal-25-years
  -excellence
Contact: Frederic Seppey, Chairperson
Scope: Trade; tariffs; customs and excise; Canadian law; commerce; economics. **Services:** Interlibrary loan; copying; library open to the public by appointment. **Founded:** 1989. **Holdings:** 6,000 books; 1,000 bound periodical volumes. **Subscriptions:** 300 journals and other serials; 12 newspapers.

27797 ■ Woodbury University Library
7500 N Glenoaks Blvd.
  Burbank, CA 91510
Ph: (818)252-5200
Co. E-mail: reference@woodbury.edu
URL: http://library.woodbury.edu
Contact: Eric Garcia, Librarian, Reference
E-mail: eric.garcia@woodbury.edu

Facebook: www.facebook.com/wulibrary
X (Twitter): x.com/woodburylib
Instagram: www.instagram.com/woodburyuniversi
  tylibrary
Scope: Education. **Services:** Interlibrary loan (limited). **Founded:** 1884. **Holdings:** Books; journals.

RESEARCH CENTERS

27798 ■ Georgia Tech Enterprise Innovation Institute (EI2) [Georgia Institute of Technology Enterprise Innovation Institute]
75 5th St. NW., Centergy One Bldg
  Atlanta, GA 30308
Ph: (404)894-2000
URL: http://innovate.gatech.edu
Contact: John Avery, Director
E-mail: john.avery@atdc.org
Facebook: www.facebook.com/ei2gt
X (Twitter): x.com/gtei2
Description: Integral unit of Georgia Institute of Technology. Offers market and product analysis, quality assessments, re-engineering and design services, standards interpretation, and standards updating service. **Scope:** Provides university-based program of business and industry assistance, technology commercialization and economic development. Helps companies, entrepreneurs, economic developers, and communities improve competitiveness through the application of science, technology and innovation. **Publications:** *European Market Bulletin*; *European Standards Directory* (Annual); *Standards Newsletter* (Monthly).

27799 ■ University of Maryland at College Park - Center for Global Business Education (CGBE)
2308 Van Munching Hall
  College Park, MD 20742-1815
Co. E-mail: helpme@rhsmith.umd.edu
URL: http://www.rhsmith.umd.edu/centers
  -excellence/global-business
Contact: Rebecca L. Bellinger, Executive Director
E-mail: rbellinger@rhsmith.umd.edu
Description: Integral unit of Smith School of Business, University of Maryland at College Park. **Scope:** Global business and management. **Educational Activities:** CGBE Conferences and workshops.

27800 ■ University of Maryland at College Park - International Communications and Negotiations Simulations (ICONS)
5245 Greenbelt Rd.
  College Park, MD 20740
Ph: (301)405-4172
Co. E-mail: icons@umd.edu
URL: http://www.icons.umd.edu
Contact: Devin H. Ellis, Director
E-mail: ellisd@umd.edu
Facebook: www.facebook.com/iconsproject
Linkedin: www.linkedin.com/company/icons-project-a
  t-the-university-of-maryland
X (Twitter): x.com/iconsproject
Description: Integral unit of Department of Government and Politics, University of Maryland at College Park. **Scope:** Focuses on the critical connections between international issues and the perspectives that different cultures bring to negotiations. Also teaches cross cultural negotiation and develops international economic, environmental, and political scenarios/curriculum materials for university and high school students. **Founded:** 1982.

ASSOCIATIONS AND OTHER ORGANIZATIONS

27801 ■ American Marketing Association (AMA)

American Marketing Association (AMA)
130 E Randolph St., 22nd Fl.
Chicago, IL 60601
Ph: (312)542-9000
Free: 800-262-1150
Co. E-mail: customersupport@ama.org
URL: http://www.ama.org
Contact: Bennie F. Johnson, Chief Executive Officer
Facebook: www.facebook.com/AmericanMarketing
Linkedin: www.linkedin.com/company/american
-marketing-association
X (Twitter): x.com/ama_marketing
Description: Serves as a professional society of marketing and market research executives, sales and promotion managers, advertising specialists, academics, and others interested in marketing. Fosters research; sponsors seminars, conferences, and student marketing clubs; provides educational placement service and doctoral consortium. **Founded:** 1937. **Publications:** *Journal of International Marketing (JIM)* (Quarterly); *Journal of Public Policy & Marketing (JPP&M)* (Quarterly); *Marketing Health Services* (Quarterly); *Journal of Marketing Research (JMR)* (Bimonthly); *Marketing News: Reporting on the Marketing Profession* (Monthly); *AMA Conference Proceedings*; *Marketing Academics at AMA* (Bimonthly); *Marketing Matters* (Biweekly); *Journal of Marketing* (Bimonthly); *Marketing Management* (Bimonthly); *Marketing Executive Report* (Monthly); *Services Marketing Today* (Bimonthly); *Marketing News--Directory of Professional Courses for Marketing Issue*; *American Marketing Association--The M Guide Services Directory* (Annual); *International Membership Directory and Marketing Services Guide* (Annual); *Marketing News--Software Directory* (Annual); *Marketing Insights* (Quarterly). **Educational Activities:** AMA International Collegiate Conference (Annual); AMA Research and Strategy Summit; AMA Summer Academic Conference (Annual); Winter Academic Conference (Annual). **Awards:** AMA Explor Award (Annual); AMA/Irwin/McGraw-Hill Distinguished Marketing Educator Award (Annual); Shelby D. Hunt/Harold H. Maynard Award (Annual); Weitz-Winer-O'Dell Award (Annual); Charles Coolidge Parlin Marketing Research Award (Annual); AMA/Marketing Science Institute/H. Paul Root Award (Annual). **Geographic Preference:** National; Local.

27802 ■ Internet Marketing Association (IMA)

638 Camino De Los Mares, Ste. H130-612
San Clemente, CA 92673
Ph: (949)443-9300

Fax: (949)443-2215
Co. E-mail: info@imanetwork.org
URL: http://imanetwork.org
Contact: Sinan Kanatsiz, Founder Chairman
Facebook: www.facebook.com/IMAnetwork
Linkedin: www.linkedin.com/company/internetmarke
tingassociation
X (Twitter): x.com/IMA_Network
YouTube: www.youtube.com/user/IMAnetworking
Description: Promotes the internet marketing industry; offers training and networking opportunities for members. **Founded:** 2001.

REFERENCE WORKS

27803 ■ "10 Reasons You Need a Digital Marketing Strategy in 2020" in Smart Insights (October 12, 2020)

Ed: Dave Chaffey. **Released:** October 12, 2020. **Description:** Discusses the importance of creating and using a digital marketing plan to support digital transformation and company growth. Details challenges, recommends a marketing approach, and provides ten reasons why you may need a digital strategy. **Availability:** Online.

27804 ■ 10 Small Business Internet Marketing Tips

Description: Acknowledges that there are hundreds of suggestions to make about internet marketing tips, this article details ten tips that 90 percent of small business owners will find useful. **Availability:** Online.

27805 ■ "21 Ways to Market Your Business Online" in Entrepreneur (October, 26, 2016)

Ed: R.L. Adams. **Released:** October 26, 2016. **Description:** Discusses the importance of online marketing and how to get your business to rise to the top of a Google search. Also discusses the use of tools like blogs, social media, email marketing, and optimizing your website for SEO. **Availability:** Online.

27806 ■ "Best Internet Marketing Services for Small Businesses--2020" in Inc.

Ed: Constance Brinkley-Badgett. **Description:** Shares some of the best email platforms, free internet marketing services, sales automation, and overall platforms that small businesses can utilize to enhance marketing. **Availability:** Online.

27807 ■ "Cash Flow Analysis for Small Business Owners" in The Balance Small Business (April 13, 2020)

Ed: Susan Ward. **Released:** April 13, 2020. **Description:** Cash flow analysis is the study of the cycle of your business's cash inflows and outflows. This article discusses how to achieve the goal of maintain-

ing adequate cash flow for your business and provides the basis for cash flow management. **Availability:** Online.

27808 ■ "How to Choose the Best Digital Marketing Agency for Your Business in 2020" in Single Grain

Ed: Eric Siu. **Description:** With tens of thousands of digital agencies, how does a small business owner decide who to work with? This article deals with why to work with an agency, what marketing agencies do, questions to ask, and whether to stay in-house or to hire an agency for your digital marketing needs. **Availability:** Online.

27809 ■ "Internet Marketing 101 for Small Businesses" in The Balance Small Business (June 25, 2019)

Ed: Randy Duermyer. **Released:** June 25, 2019. **Description:** Discusses internet marketing types and tactics, costs, and how to track results. **Availability:** Online.

27810 ■ "Online Marketing for Small Businesses in 2020: The Essentials" in International Business Times (June 16, 2020)

Released: June 16, 2020. **Description:** A detailed guide on digital marketing including information on metrics, online traffic, and conversion (which refers to how a website visitor takes any desired action intended by the marketing funnel). **Availability:** Online.

27811 ■ "A Quick Guide to Digital Marketing for Newbies" in Forbes (June 14, 2020)

Ed: Mike Wood. **Released:** June 14, 2020. **Description:** Discusses the state of digital marketing as well as the basics of digital marketing to provide a solid framework. **Availability:** Online.

27812 ■ Small Business Internet Marketing - How Do I Know My Target Audience?

Ed: Jessie Carballo. **Released:** July 28, 2017. **Description:** Discusses the importance of focusing marketing energy that is focused on a small group rather than a general audience. This direct approach will reach people who are interested in your product or service and will help your business get new leads, conversions, and results. **Availability:** Online.

27813 ■ "The Ultimate Digital Marketing Guide for Small Business" in Just Creative Blog (March 3, 2020)

Ed: Steven Novak. **Released:** March 03, 2020. **Description:** Discusses the importance of creating a digital marketing strategy as a perfect way to advertise your services, get a loyal following, and grow your business' brand beyond the borders of your location. **Availability:** Online.

REFERENCE WORKS

27814 ■ *"Black Gold: Jobs Aplenty" in Canadian Business (Vol. 79, August 14, 2006, No. 16-17, pp. 57)*
Pub: Rogers Media Inc.
Contact: Neil Spivak, Chief Executive Officer
Ed: Erin Pooley. **Description:** A list of the top ten jobs in the petroleum industry in Canada along with pay and nature of jobs, is presented. **Availability:** Print; Online.

VIDEO/AUDIO MEDIA

27815 ■ *BS-Free Service Business Show: Consumer Caution: Understanding the Risks of Payment Plans in Online Business*
URL(s): duped.online/2024/05/06/risks-of-paymen t-plans

Ed: Maggie Patterson. **Released:** May 06, 2024. **Description:** Podcast discusses the pros and cons of payment plans, how they can be weaponized, possible pitfalls, the problems of paying in full, and issues with third-party services. .

27816 ■ *The End of the Golden Age of Online Business with Erica Courdae & Tasha L. Harrison*
URL(s): beingboss.club/podcast/the-end-of-the-gol den-age-of-online-business
Ed: Emily Thompson. **Released:** June 06, 2023. **Description:** Podcast discusses the shift in the online business realm and offers two things to help grow and sustain your business.

27817 ■ *How I Built This: Casper: Philip Krim*
URL(s): www.npr.org/2021/06/23/1009551702/casper -philip-krim

Ed: Guy Raz. **Released:** June 28, 2021.

27818 ■ *Staying Inspired as a Content Creator with Tieghan Gerard of Half-Baked Harvest*
URL(s): beingboss.club/podcast/staying-inspired-as-a -content-creator-with-tieghan-gerard-of-half-bake d-harvest
Ed: Emily Thompson. **Released:** October 04, 2022. **Description:** Podcast discusses the power of work that feels aligned, how to stay inspired, and content creation.

START-UP INFORMATION

27819 ■ *"Brand Storytelling Becomes a Booming Business"* in Entrepreneur (April 2012)
Pub: Entrepreneur Media Inc.
Contact: Dan Bova, Director
E-mail: dbova@entrepreneur.com
Ed: Paula Andruss. **Description:** San Francisco-based Story House Creative engages in helping small businesses connect with their audience in communicating their brand identity. Web content, bios and tag lines are some of the marketing materials Story House Creative creates for its clients. The company also does search engine optimization, video, design, and copywriting. The Brandery, another brand-building company, helps startups promote their business. Eight to ten Brandery mentors are assigned to assist each startup client. Meanwhile, Brand Journalists is a Tennessee based company focusing on corporate storytelling. It offers Web and blog content, human stories reporting and ghostwriting services. **Availability:** Print; Online.

27820 ■ *"Do Cool Sh*t: Quit Your Day Job, Start Your Own Business, and Live Happily Ever After"*
Pub: Harper Business
Contact: Hollis Heimbouch, Senior Vice President Publisher
Released: January 20, 2015. **Price:** $16.61, hardcover; $11.97, paperback; $11.49, e-book; $3.13, kindle; $0.05, hardcover(99 used from $0.05); $8, hardcover(44 new from $8.00); $2, paperback(76 used from $2.00); $5.47, paperback(64 new from $5.47). **Description:** Serial social entrepreneur, angel investor, and woman business leader, Miki Agrawal, teaches how to start and run a successful new business. She covers all issues from brainstorming, to raising money to getting press without any connections, and still have time to enjoy life. She created WILD, a farm-to-table pizzeria in New York City and Las Vegas. She also partnered in a children's multimedia company called Super Sprowtz--a story-driven nutrition program for children, and she launched a patented high-tech underware business called THINX. Agrawal also discusses the growth in her businesses. **Availability:** E-book; Print.

27821 ■ *"The Innovator's Method: Bringing the Lean Start-up into Your Organization"*
Pub: Harvard Business Review Press
Contact: Moderna V. Pfizer, Contact
Released: September 09, 2014. **Price:** $35, Hardcover/Hardcopy. **Description:** The innovator's method was developed using research inside corporations and successful startups to create, refine, and bring ideas and inventions to the marketplace. Advice is provided to test, validate and commercialize ideas with the lean, design, and agile techniques used by successful startups. **Availability:** E-book; Print.

27822 ■ *"Made@Mayo: Mayo Professor Doubles As Founder of Text Tech Company"* in Business Journal (Vol. 32, June 6, 2014, No. 2, pp. 10)
Pub: American City Business Journals, Inc.
Contact: Mike Olivieri, Executive Vice President

Description: Rochester, Minnesota-based Mayo Clinic Ventures has managed the licensing of Mayo Clinic technologies and invests in startups. Mayo Clinic Ventures has a $100 million growth fund for investing in startups and two smaller funds worth about $500,000 combined. Insights on the stories of Mayo researchers leading startups are also provided. **Availability:** Online.

27823 ■ *"Making 'Freemium' Work: Many Start-Ups Fail to Recgonize the Challenges of This Popular Business Model"* in Harvard Business Review (Vol. 92, May 2014, No. 5, pp. 27)
Pub: Harvard Business Publishing
Contact: Diane Belcher, Managing Director
Price: $6. **Description:** The key to successful 'freemium' business model is identifying which features to offer free of charge, and how to price the remaining features. Target conversion rates conversion life cycle preparation, and commitment to innovation are also discussed. **Availability:** Online, PDF.

27824 ■ *"The Self Starting Entrepreneurs Handbook"*
Pub: CreateSpace
Released: September 24, 2014. **Price:** $17.99; $11.03, paperback. **Description:** Information for starting a business is provided. Advice is given for writing a business plan, naming your new business, obtaining a business license if required, and building a marketing strategy for entrepreneurs. **Availability:** Print.

27825 ■ *"So You Want To Be a Food Truck Vendor?"* in Philadelphia Business Journal (Vol. 33, August 15, 2014, No. 27, pp. 7)
Pub: American City Business Journals, Inc.
Contact: Mike Olivieri, Executive Vice President
Released: Weekly. **Price:** $4, introductory 4-week offer(Digital only). **Description:** Food truck vendors assert that the most challenging part of starting a food truck business is acquiring a license as well as the price and number of licenses and permits required. Other costs include additional fees to vend in prime locations, maintenance, and inventory. **Availability:** Print; Online.

27826 ■ *"Troy Patent Law Firm Launches Rent-Free Tech Incubator"* in Crain's Detroit Business (Vol. 25, June 8, 2009, No. 23, pp. 4)
Pub: Crain Communications Inc.
Contact: Barry Asin, President
Ed: Tom Henderson. **Description:** Young Basile Hanlon MacFarlane & Helmholdt PC, a patent law firm located in Troy, Michigan has created a small, rent-free technology incubator on site. The incubator will be called North Woodward Tech Incubator and has room for four or five startups. The incubator is for the earliest or pre-seed stage for entrepreneurs who have not yet gotten significant investment capital. **Availability:** Online.

ASSOCIATIONS AND OTHER ORGANIZATIONS

27827 ■ **American Society of Inventors (ASI)**
600 W Germantown Pke.
Plymouth Meeting, PA 19462

Ph: (215)546-6601
Co. E-mail: ask@asoi.org
URL: http://asoi.org
Contact: Marie Kraft, President
Facebook: www.facebook.com/AmericanSocie tyofInventors
X (Twitter): x.com/AsoiTweetus
Description: Aims to encourage invention and innovation, helps the independent inventor become self-sufficient, and promotes a networking system for inventors and business people to solve problems. Sponsors educational programs. **Founded:** 1953. **Publications:** Inventors Digest (Annual). **Geographic Preference:** National.

27828 ■ **International Licensing Industry Merchandisers' Association (LIMA)**
350 5th Ave., Ste. 6410
New York, NY 10118
Ph: (212)244-1944
Fax: (212)563-6552
Co. E-mail: info@licensing.org
URL: http://licensinginternational.org
Contact: Maura Regan, President
E-mail: mregan@licensing.org
Facebook: www.facebook.com/limalicensingintl
Linkedin: www.linkedin.com/company/2677729/a dmin
X (Twitter): x.com/Licensing_Intl
Instagram: www.instagram.com/licensing_intl
YouTube: www.youtube.com/channel/UCjGhK dDSELFbUQje3EQc8Yg
Description: Companies and individuals engaged in the marketing and servicing of licensed properties, both as agents and as property owners; manufacturers and retailers in the licensing business; supporters of the licensing industry. Professional association for the licensing industry worldwide. Objectives are to establish a standard reflecting a professional and ethical management approach to the marketing of licensed properties; to become the leading source of information in the industry; to communicate this information to members and others in the industry through publishing, public speaking, seminars, and an open line; to represent the industry in trade and consumer media and in relationships with the government, retailers, manufacturers, other trade associations, and the public. **Founded:** 1985. **Publications:** LIMA BottomLine (Monthly); LIMA Worldwide Licensing Resource Directory (Annual). **Educational Activities:** Licensing University. **Awards:** LIMA Licensing Excellence Awards for sports (Annual). **Geographic Preference:** Multinational.

27829 ■ **International Trademark Association (INTA) - Library**
675 3rd Ave., 3rd Fl.
New York, NY 10017
Ph: (212)642-1700
Fax: (212)768-7796
URL: http://www.inta.org
Contact: Zeeger Vink, President
Facebook: www.facebook.com/GoINTA
Linkedin: www.linkedin.com/company/gointa

X (Twitter): x.com/INTA
Instagram: www.instagram.com/intaglobal
YouTube: www.youtube.com/channel/UCfoSgeal
dEpL1f32YWS5nPw
Description: Trademark owners; associate members are lawyers, law firms, advertising agencies, designers, market researchers, and others in the trademark industries. Seeks to: protect the interests of the public in the use of trademarks and trade names; promote the interests of members and of trademark owners generally in the use of their trademarks and trade names; disseminate information concerning the use, registration, and protection of trademarks in the United States, its territories, and in foreign countries. Maintains job bank and speakers' bureau. **Scope:** Branding; practitioners. **Founded:** 1878. **Holdings:** Figures not available. **Publications:** *International Trademark Association--Membership Directory*; *INTA Bulletin* (Weekly (Wed.)); *The Trademark Report (TMR)* (6/year); *The Trademarker Reporter* (Bimonthly). **Educational Activities:** INTA Annual Meeting (Annual). **Awards:** The Ladas Memorial Award - Student Category (Annual). **Geographic Preference:** National.

27830 ■ Juneau County Inventors & Entrepreneurs Club
PO Box 322
Camp Douglas, WI 54618
URL: http://www.juneaucounty.com/inventors--en
trepreneurs-club.html
Contact: Bonnie Peterson, President
Description: Represents inventors' organizations and providers of services to inventors. Seeks to facilitate the development of innovation conceived by independent inventors. Provides leadership and support services to inventors and inventors' organizations. **Founded:** 2003. **Geographic Preference:** Local.

27831 ■ United Inventors Association of the United States of America (UIA)
1025 Connecticut Ave., Ste. 1000
Washington, DC 20036
Co. E-mail: admin@uiausa.org
URL: http://uiausa.org
Contact: Carmine Denisco, Author
Facebook: www.facebook.com/uiausa
X (Twitter): x.com/uiausa
YouTube: www.youtube.com/c/UIATV
Description: Inventors' organizations and providers of services to inventors.Facilitates the development of innovation conceived by independent inventors. Provides leadership and support services to inventors and inventors' organizations. **Founded:** 1990. **Publications:** *Inventors' Resource Guide* (Periodic). **Geographic Preference:** National.

REFERENCE WORKS

27832 ■ *"26 Things Holding Canadians Back"* in Canadian Business (Vol. 85, August 13, 2012, No. 13, pp. 27)
Description: A list of the problems that Canada needs to address in order to succeed as an economic superpower is presented. Some of these barriers include declining fertility rate, rising percentage of overweight and obese, and obsolete copyright laws. **Availability:** Print; Online.

27833 ■ *"100 Brilliant Companies"* in Entrepreneur (May 2014)
Pub: Entrepreneur Media Inc.
Contact: Dan Bova, Director
E-mail: dbova@entrepreneur.com
Description: Entrepreneur magazine annually selects 100 companies, ideas, innovations and applications which the editors feel offer unique, simple and high-tech solutions to various everyday problems. These may include design developments, innovations in wearable gadgets, travel applications and other new ideas which represent 21st Century breakthroughs and thinking outside the box. The list is divided into ten categories, including Fashion, The Human Factor, and Travel and Transportation. **Availability:** Online.

27834 ■ *"American Chemistry Council Launches Flagship Blog"* in Ecology,Environment & Conservation Business (October 29, 2011, pp. 5)
Pub: PR Newswire Association LLC.
Description: American Chemistry Council (ACC) launched its blog, American Chemistry Matters, where interactive space allows bloggers to respond to news coverage and to discuss policy issues and their impact on innovation, competitiveness, job creation and safety. **Availability:** Online.

27835 ■ *"Are You a Young Canadian Entrepreneur Looking for Recognition?"* in CNW Group (November 10, 2010)
Pub: Comtex News Network Inc.
Contact: Kan Devnani, President
Description: Business Development Bank of Canada is looking for young Canadian entrepreneurs ages 19 to 35 for its 2011 Young Entrepreneur Awards. The awards pay tribute to remarkable young Canadian entrepreneurs for their creativity, innovative spirit and community development, as well as business success. **Availability:** Online.

27836 ■ *"The Art of Rapid, Hands-On Execution Innovation"* in Strategy and Leadership (Vol. 39, March-April 2011, No. 2, pp. 28)
Pub: Emerald Group Publishing Limited
Contact: Erika Valenti, President
Ed: Anssi Tuulenmaki, Liisa Valikangas. **Description:** A model of 'rapid execution innovation' that can be used to increase the chances of achieving innovations that develop into successful new business models is introduced. The model involves company experiments that inspire the radical rethinking business opportunities, and by continuing these experiments until the idea evolves into a product. **Availability:** Download; Online.

27837 ■ *"Top 25 Engineering Firms"* in South Florida Business Journal (Vol. 34, February 14, 2014, No. 30, pp. 12)
Pub: American City Business Journals, Inc.
Contact: Mike Olivieri, Executive Vice President
Released: Weekly. **Price:** $25, Print. **Description:** Rankings of the companies within the engineering services in South Florida are presented. Rankings are based on the number of licensed engineers in the region. **Availability:** Print; Online.

27838 ■ *"Attention Songwriters: Protect Your Valuable Assets with a Copyright"* in Legal Zoom (March 24, 2023)
URL(s): www.legalzoom.com/articles/attention
-songwriters-protect-your-valuable-assets-with-a
-copyright
Ed: Peter Smith. **Released:** March 24, 2023. **Description:** A discussion of copyrighting songs and why it's important to do so. **Availability:** Online.

27839 ■ *"Auto Show Aims to Electrify"* in Crain's Detroit Business (Vol. 26, January 11, 2010, No. 2, pp. 1)
Pub: Crain Communications Inc.
Contact: Barry Asin, President
Ed: Ryan Beene. **Description:** Overview of the North American International Auto show include sixteen production and concept vehicles including eight from the Detroit 3. High-tech battery suppliers as well as hybrid and electric vehicles will highlight the show. **Availability:** Print; Online.

27840 ■ *"Auxilium Drug's New Use: Putting the Squeeze On Cellulite"* in Philadelphia Business Journal (Vol. 30, September 16, 2011, No. 31, pp. 1)
Pub: Philadelphia Business Journal
Contact: Sierra Quinn, Director
E-mail: squinn@bizjournals.com
Ed: John George. **Description:** Auxilium Pharmaceuticals and BioSpecifics Technologies are getting on with their plans of finding new uses for their drug Xiaflex, a possible treatment for cellulite. The two firms have dismissed their pending litigations and

mapped out an amended licensing agreement for their search for the potential uses of the drug. **Availability:** Online.

27841 ■ *"Baltimore Vendors Brave Heat, Red Tape to Eke Out a Living: Working the Streets"* in Baltimore Business Journal (Vol. 28, July 30, 2010, No. 12, pp. 1)
Pub: Baltimore Business Journal
Contact: Rhonda Pringle, President
E-mail: rpringle@bizjournals.com
Ed: Amanda Pino. **Description:** Reports show that street vendors are popping up on new corners in Baltimore, Maryland, with city-inspected stainless steel food carts in tow. Applications for street vending licenses shot up at the end of 2009 and into this summer. It is believed that pinning down the exact number of vendors operating at any one point is difficult. **Availability:** Print.

27842 ■ *"Bitumen Oilsands: Slick Science"* in Canadian Business (Vol. 81, September 15, 2008, No. 14-15, pp. 55)
Pub: Rogers Media Inc.
Contact: Neil Spivak, Chief Executive Officer
Ed: Andrew Nikiforuk. **Description:** N-Solv Corp's John Nenniger has discovered a better alternative to steam-assisted gravity drainage methods for extracting bitumen. Nenniger's technique also relies on gravity but replaces steam with propane, which leaves behind impurities like asphaltenes and heavy metals that are too dirty to burn. **Availability:** Print; Mailing list; Online.

27843 ■ *Borrowing Brilliance: The Six Steps to Business Innovation by Building on the Ideas of Others*
Released: October 05, 2010. **Price:** $16, paperback; $9.99, e-book. **Description:** The author builds the case that cherry-picking the ideas of others is a vital part of the research and development process for any small firm. **Availability:** E-book; Print.

27844 ■ *"Bridging the Talent Gap Through Partnership and Innovation"* in Canadian Business (Vol. 81, October 27, 2008, No. 18, pp. 88)
Description: Research revealed that North America is short by more than 60,000 qualified networking professionals. Businesses, educators and communities are collaborating in order to address the shortfall. **Availability:** Print; Online.

27845 ■ *"A Burning Issue: Lives Are at Stake Every Day"* in Contractor (Vol. 56, October 2009, No. 10, pp. 29)
Description: American Society of Plumbing Engineers has been accused of being biased for supporting rules that require residential fire sprinklers although the society's members will not receive any benefit from their installation. The organization trains and certifies plumbing engineers who design life-saving fire protection systems. **Availability:** Online.

27846 ■ *"The Call of the City"* in Puget Sound Business Journal (Vol. 35, September 5, 2014, No. 20, pp. 16)
Pub: American City Business Journals, Inc.
Contact: Mike Olivieri, Executive Vice President
Description: A number of large companies have moved their headquarters to Seattle, Washington. The area is known to be transit-accessible with mixed-use offices and retail space, making it a great site selection. Seattle also embraces innovations and inventions in area districts that bring a diverse workforce. **Availability:** Print; Online.

27847 ■ *"Calling All Creatives, Innovators, 'Expats': Detroit Is Hopping In September"* in Crain's Detroit Business (Vol. 30, September 1, 2014, No. 35, pp. 6)
Pub: Crain Communications Inc.
Contact: Barry Asin, President

Description: Wayne State University is hosting a seminar September 16, 2014 which will focus on Detroit, Michigan as a center for innovation. Six other such seminars seeking investment in the city will be held in September. **Availability:** Online.

27848 ■ "Can Fashion Designs Be Copyrighted?" in Legal Zoom (March 27, 2023)
URL(s): www.legalzoom.com/articles/can-fashion-designs-be-copyrighted
Ed: Michelle Kaminsky, Esq. **Released:** March 27, 2023. **Description:** Discusses if fashion designs can be copyrighted and discusses the case of Gwen Stefani filing suit against Forever 21 for using her trademarked patterns. **Availability:** Online.

27849 ■ "Can He Win the Patent Game?" in Globe & Mail (February 20, 2006, pp. B1)
Ed: Simon Avery, Paul Waldie. **Description:** A profile on managerial abilities of chief executive officer Jim Balsillie of Research In Motion Ltd., who will face the patent case with NTP Inc., is presented. **Availability:** Online.

27850 ■ "A Chinese Approach to Management: A Generation of Entrepreneurs Is Writing Its Own Rules" in Harvard Business Review (Vol. 92, September 2014, No. 9, pp. 103)
Pub: Harvard Business Publishing
Contact: Diane Belcher, Managing Director
Price: $8.95. **Description:** The Chinese approach to management include simple structures for organizations, quick development of products, responsiveness to local values and needs, and investment in source firms and vendors. Manufacturing and engineering operations are typically co-located. **Availability:** Online; PDF.

27851 ■ "Clash of the Titans" in Canadian Business (Vol. 80, March 12, 2007, No. 6, pp. 27)
Description: The frequent allegations of Google Inc. and Microsoft Corp. against each other over copyright and other legal issues, with a view to taking away other's market share, is discussed. **Availability:** Print; Online.

27852 ■ Clicking Through: A Survival Guide for Bringing Your Company Online
Released: First edition. **Description:** Summary of legal compliance issues faced by small companies doing business on the Internet, including copyright and patent laws.

27853 ■ "Clusters Last Stand?" in Canadian Electronics (Vol. 23, February 2008, No. 1, pp. 6)
Description: Survival of technology clusters was the focus of Strategic Microelectronics Council's conference entitled, "The Power of Community: Building Technology Clusters in Canada". Clusters can help foster growth in the microelectronics sector, and it was recognized that government intervention is needed to maintain these clusters. **Availability:** Download; PDF; Online.

27854 ■ "Code Name: Inventors: Go from Golden Idea to Agent of Invention" in Black Enterprise (Vol. 41, November 2010, No. 4, pp. 78)
Pub: Earl G. Graves Ltd.
Contact: Earl Graves, Jr., President
Ed: Renita Burns. **Description:** Profile of Andre Woolery, inventor of a magnetic wristband that holds small nails, screws, drill bits, and small tools, allowing handymen to keep essential tools at hand while working. **Availability:** Online.

27855 ■ "Companies Must Innovate, Regardless of Economy" in Crain's Detroit Business (Vol. 25, June 1, 2009, No. 22, pp. M007)
Pub: Crain Communications Inc.
Contact: Barry Asin, President

Ed: Sherri Begin Welch. **Description:** Despite the economy, leaders of Michigan's successful companies stress that small businesses must innovate in order to grow. **Availability:** Print; PDF; Online.

27856 ■ Content Rich: Writing Your Way to Wealth on the Web
Released: 1st Edition. **Description:** A definitive search engine optimization (SEO) copywriting guide for search engine rankings and sales conversion. It includes topics not covered in other books on the subject and targets the small to medium sized business looking for ways to maximize online marketing activities as well as designers and Web developers seeking to incorporate more SEO techniques into design and content.

27857 ■ "Copyright Clearance Center (CCC) Partnered with cSubs" in Information Today (Vol. 28, November 2011, No. 10, pp. 14)
Description: Copyright Clearance Center (CCC) partnered with cSubs to integrate CCC's point-of-content licensing solution RightsLink Basic directly into cSubs workflow. The partnership will allow cSubs' customers a user-friendly process for obtaining permissions. Csubs is a corporate subscription management service for books, newspapers, and econtent. **Availability:** Online.

27858 ■ "The Copyright Evolution" in Information Today (Vol. 28, November 2011, No. 10, pp. 1)
Pub: Information Today Inc.
Contact: Thomas H. Hogan, President
Ed: Nancy Davis Kho. **Description:** For information professionals, issues surrounding copyright compliance have traditionally been on the consumption side. However, today, content consumption is only half the program because blogging, tweeting, and commenting is a vital part of more standard duties for workers as corporations aim to create authentic communications with customers.

27859 ■ "DFW Inventors Psyched for New, Local Patent Office" in Dallas Business Journal (Vol. 35, August 3, 2012, No. 47, pp. 1)
Pub: Baltimore Business Journal
Contact: Rhonda Pringle, President
E-mail: rpringle@bizjournals.com
Ed: Jeff Bounds. **Description:** The United States Patent & Trademark Office is planning to expand by adding three satellite offices, including one in Dallas-Fort Worth, Texas. Inventors look forward to the planned expansion as it is expected to make the process of patent licensing more effective. **Availability:** Print; Online.

27860 ■ "Disabled Inventors: Necessity Is the Mother of Invention" in Legal Zoom (March 27, 2023)
URL(s): www.legalzoom.com/articles/disabled-inventors-necessity-is-the-mother-of-invention
Ed: Katherine Butler. **Released:** March 27, 2023. **Description:** Disabled inventors and their inventions that solved problems and made lives easier are recounted. **Availability:** Online.

27861 ■ "Does Your Website Violate Copyright Law? in Legal Zoom (March 27, 2023)
URL(s): www.legalzoom.com/articles/does-your-website-violate-copyright-law
Ed: Heleigh Bostwick. **Released:** March 27, 2023. **Description:** Make sure your business website is compliant and not violating anyone's hard-earned copyright with these suggestions. **Availability:** Online.

27862 ■ "Economy: The Case for a Bright Future" in Canadian Business (Vol. 83, July 20, 2010, No. 11-12, pp. 58)
Pub: Rogers Media Inc.
Contact: Neil Spivak, Chief Executive Officer
Ed: Andrew Potter. **Description:** Writer Matt Ridley argues that trade is the determinant of development and that it is the reason why humans got rich. Ridley

believes that the important innovations are often low-tech and is often processes rather than products. **Availability:** Print; Online.

27863 ■ "Entrepreneurial Orientation and Firm Performance: The Unique Impact of Innovativeness, Proactiveness, and Risk-taking" in Journal of Small Business and Entrepreneurship (Vol. 23, Winter 2010, No. 1)
Pub: Canadian Council for Small Business and Entrepreneurship
Contact: John MacRitchie, President
Ed: Patrick M. Kreisera, Justin Davis. **Description:** The article develops a theoretical model of the relationship between firm-level entrepreneurship and firm performance. This model is intended to further clarify the consequences of an 'entrepreneurial orientation', paying particular attention to the differential relationship that exists between the three sub-dimensions of entrepreneurial orientation and firm performance. Included in the theoretical model are other important variables (such as organizational structure and environmental characteristics) that may impact the EO-performance relationship. Propositions are developed regarding the various configurations of the sub-dimensions of EO and organizational structure that would be most appropriate in a given environmental context. Future research may also benefit from considering the important role that organizational strategy and life cycle stage play in this model. The implications of this model for both researchers and managers are discussed.

27864 ■ "Entrepreneurship and Service Innovation" in Journal of Business & Industrial Marketing (Vol. 29, July 2014, No. 6)
Pub: Emerald Group Publishing Limited
Contact: Erika Valenti, President
Description: An overview of entrepreneurship and service innovation and the association between entrepreneurial orientation, innovation, and entrepreneurship or new entry. Analysis of secondary data was performed and observed that EO (entrepreneurial orientation), innovation, and entrepreneurship feature a triadic connect. EO supports innovation, innovation endorses new venture creation, and it in turn commercializes innovations. **Availability:** Download; Online.

27865 ■ "Evolutionary Psychology in the Business Sciences"
Pub: Springer Publishing Co.
Contact: Bernhard Springer, Founder
Released: First edition. **Description:** All individuals operating in the business sphere share a common biological heritage, including consumers, employers, employees, entrepreneurs, or financial traders, to name a few. The evolutionary behavioral sciences and specific business contexts including marketing, consumer behavior, advertising, innovation and creativity and invention, intertemporal choice, negotiations, competition and cooperation in organizational settings, sex differences in workplace patterns, executive leadership, business ethics, store and office design, behavioral decision making, and electronic communications and commerce are all addressed. **Availability:** E-book; Print.

27866 ■ "Facebook, Google, LinkedIn Line Up In Patent Case Before Supreme Court" in San Francisco Business Times (Vol. 28, March 28, 2014, No. 36)
Pub: American City Business Journals, Inc.
Contact: Mike Olivieri, Executive Vice President
Released: Weekly. **Description:** The U.S. Supreme Court is set to hear a case involving Alice Corporation Pty. Ltd. and CLS Bank International in a dispute over a patented computer-implemented escrow service. The case has larger implications to tech companies concerning whether a business method can be patented if it is made electronic. **Availability:** Print; Online.

27867 ■ "Facilitating and Rewarding Creativity During New Product Development" in Journal of Marketing (Vol. 75, July 2011, No. 4, pp. 53)
Pub: American Marketing Association
Contact: Bennie F. Johnson, Chief Executive Officer

Ed: James E. Burroughs, Darren W. Dahl, C. Page Moreau, Amitava Chattopadhay, Gerald J. Gorn. **Description:** A study to determine the effects of rewards to creativity in the process of new product development is presented. The findings show that the effect of rewards can be made positive if combined with appropriate creativity training. **Availability:** PDF.

27868 ■ *Facilitating Sustainable Innovation through Collaboration: A Multi-Stakeholder Perspective*

Ed: Joseph Sarkis, James J. Cordeiro, Diego Vazquez Brust. **Description:** An international perspective of sustainable innovation with contributions from Australia, Europe, and North America, by prominent policy makers, scientific researchers and others. **Availability:** E-book; Print; Electronic publishing.

27869 ■ *"Feeding the Elephants While Searching for Greener Pastures"* in Inc. (Volume 32, December 2010, No. 10, pp. 34)

Pub: Mansueto Ventures L.L.C.

Contact: Stephanie Mehta, Chief Executive Officer

Ed: April Joyner. **Released:** December 2010. **Description:** Innovation is the future for small business. A new book, Inside Real Innovation: How the Right Approach Can Move Ideas from R&D to Market - And Get the Economy Moving helps to break down the process by which innovation occurs. **Availability:** Print.

27870 ■ *"FinOvation 2009"* in Farm Industry News (Vol. 42, January 1, 2009, No. 1)

Ed: Karen McMahon, Mark Moore, David Hest. **Description:** New and innovative products and technologies are presented.

27871 ■ *"Fledgling Brands May Take the Fall With Steve & Barry's"* in Advertising Age (Vol. 79, July 7, 2008, No. 26, pp. 6)

Pub: Crain Communications, Inc.

Contact: Jessica Botos, Manager, Marketing

E-mail: jessica.botos@crainsnewyork.com

Ed: Natalie Zmuda. **Description:** Steve & Barry's, a retailer that holds licensing deals with a number of designers and celebrities, may have to declare bankruptcy; this leaves the fate of the retailer's hundreds of licensing deals and exclusive celebrity lines in question. **Availability:** Online.

27872 ■ *"For Tech Companies, Holding Onto Prized Patents Can Be Expensive"* in Puget Sound Business Journal (Vol. 33, May 18, 2012, No. 4, pp. 1)

Pub: Baltimore Business Journal

Contact: Rhonda Pringle, President

E-mail: rpringle@bizjournals.com

Description: Patent lawsuits have been rising steadily over the past 20 years and the damage rewards are also growing. Microsoft is currently engaged in more than 60 patent infringement lawsuits worldwide and the largest is a 2 year fight over a series of patents that Motorola holds and Microsoft uses. **Availability:** Print; Online.

27873 ■ *"Foreign Flavor of U.S. Innovation: Report Makes New Case for Immigration Reform"* in Silicon Valley/San Jose Business Journal (Vol. 30, July 20, 2012, No. 17, pp. 1)

Pub: Baltimore Business Journal

Contact: Rhonda Pringle, President

E-mail: rpringle@bizjournals.com

Released: Weekly. **Description:** The results of a recent study show that 76 percent of the patents created at the top 10 patent-producing universities include at least one foreign-born inventor. Findings also indicate that immigrants are three times more likely and US-born individuals to file a patent. Information about H1-B Visas is also provided. **Availability:** Print; Online.

27874 ■ *From Concept To Consumer: How to Turn Ideas Into Money*

Ed: Phil Baker. **Released:** 1st edition. **Price:** $27.99, paperback. **Description:** Renowned product developer Phil Baker explains how a great idea accounts

for only 5 percent of all the factors of success and why the majority of success is dependent upon a myriad of other factors, including the time it takes to get to market, price, marketing and distribution. By being their own best competition, a small company can stay one step ahead of competitors. **Availability:** Print.

27875 ■ *"Full-Court Press for Apple"* in Barron's (Vol. 88, March 24, 2008, No. 12, pp. 47)

Pub: Dow Jones & Company Inc.

Contact: Mark Veverka, Chief Executive Officer

Ed: Mark Veverka. **Description:** Apple Inc. is facing more intellectual property lawsuits in 2008, with 30 patent lawsuits filed compared to 15 in 2007 and nine in 2006. The lawsuits, which involve products such as the iPod and the iPhone, present some concern for Apple's shareholders. **Availability:** Online.

27876 ■ *"German Win Through Sharing"* in Canadian Business (Vol. 83, September 14, 2010, No. 15, pp. 16)

Pub: Rogers Media Inc.

Contact: Neil Spivak, Chief Executive Officer

Ed: Jordan Timm. **Released:** September 14, 2010. **Description:** German economic historian Eckhard Hoffner has a two-volume work showing how German's relaxed attitude toward copyright and intellectual property helped it catch up to industrialized United Kingdom. Hoffner's research was in response to his interest in the usefulness of software patents. Information on the debate regarding Canada's copyright laws is given. **Availability:** Print; Online.

27877 ■ *"Getting Inventive With..Ed Spellman"* in Crain's Cleveland Business (Vol. 28, October 22, 2007, No. 42, pp. 18)

Pub: Crain Communications Inc.

Contact: K. C. Crain, President

Ed: Kimberly Bonvissuto. **Description:** Profile featuring Ed Spellman, a mechanical engineer who decided to quit his job at Invacare Corp., a medical equipment manufacturer and distributor, in order to devote his full attention to promoting his numerous inventions, including the DV-Grip, a vehicle mount for portable DVD players. **Availability:** Online.

27878 ■ *"Getting the Word Out"* in Modern Machine Shop (Vol. 84, September 2011, No. 4, pp. 16)

Pub: Gardner Business Media Inc.

Contact: Rick Kline, Jr., President

E-mail: rkline2@gardnerweb.com

Ed: Derek Korn. **Description:** Many times machine shops create devices to streamline their own machining processes and find these devices can be used by other shops, thus developing a marketable product. Tips for this process are outlined. **Availability:** Print; Online.

27879 ■ *"The Globe: Singapore Airlines' Balancing Act"* in Harvard Business Review (Vol. 88, July-August 2010, No. 7-8, pp. 145)

Pub: Harvard Business Publishing

Contact: Diane Belcher, Managing Director

Ed: Loizos Heracleous, Jochen Wirtz. **Price:** $8.95. **Description:** Singapore Airlines is used as an illustration of organizational effectiveness. The article includes the firm's 4-3-3 rule of spending, its promotion of centralized as well as decentralized innovation, use of technology, and strategic planning. **Availability:** Online; PDF.

27880 ■ *The Gridlock Economy: How Too Much Ownership Wrecks Markets, Stops Innovation, and Costs Lives*

Ed: Michael Heller. **Released:** February 23, 2010. **Price:** $11.99, paperback; C$14.99. **Description:** While private ownership generally creates wealth, the author believes that economic gridlock results when too many people own pieces of one thing, which results in too many people being able to block each other from creating or using a scarce source. **Availability:** E-book; Print.

27881 ■ *"GTI Licenses TMC to Cannon Boiler Works"* in Contractor (Vol. 56, December 2009, No. 12, pp. 6)

Description: Gas Technology Institute has licensed Cannon Boiler Works Inc. to use its transport membrane condenser technology. The technology can be applied to elevated-temperature industrial processes such as boilers. It allows the capture and beneficial use of latent waste heat and water vapor from exhaust/flue gas. **Availability:** Online.

27882 ■ *"Health and the City: How Close Is Too Close in Trademarks?"* in Legal Zoom (March 27, 2023)

URL(s): www.legalzoom.com/articles/health-and-the-city-how-close-is-too-close-in-trademarks

Ed: Michelle Kaminsky, Esq. **Released:** March 27, 2023. **Description:** Discusses what happens when the business name you try to trademark is too similar to another established business or concept. **Availability:** Online.

27883 ■ *"How Innovative Is Michigan? Index Aims To Keep Track"* in Crain's Detroit Business (Vol. 24, February 4, 2008, No. 5, pp. 1)

Pub: Crain Communications Inc.

Contact: Barry Asin, President

Ed: Chad Halcom. **Description:** Profile of the newly created "Innovation Index", released by the University of Michigan-Dearborn. The report showed a combination of indicators that gauged innovation activity in the state slightly lower for second quarter 2007, but ahead of most levels for most of 2006. Statistical data included. **Availability:** Print; Online.

27884 ■ *"How to Register and Trademark a Brand Name"* in Business News Daily (February 21, 2023)

URL(s): businessnewsdaily.com/15762-how-to-register-trademark-brand-name.html

Ed: Marisa Sanfilippo. **Released:** February 21, 2023. **Description:** Tips on how to register any brands associated with your business. Your intellectual property should be protected and the process is outlined in the article. **Availability:** Online.

27885 ■ *"How Sharing Sent Record Sales Soaring"* in Business Strategy Review (Vol. 25, Summer 2014, No. 2, pp. 7)

Released: June 02, 2014. **Description:** Removing copy protection from songs actually increased music sales. **Availability:** Print; PDF; Online.

27886 ■ *How to Start an Internet Sales Business Without Making the Government Mad*

Pub: Lulu Press Inc.

Ed: Dan Davis. **Released:** October 01, 2011. **Price:** $19.95, paperback; $14.38, PDF; $14.38, e-book. **Description:** Small business guide for launching an Internet sales company. Topics include business structure, licenses, and taxes. **Availability:** E-book; Print; PDF.

27887 ■ *"How to Turn Your Idea Into a Product (and Launch It!)"* in Business News Daily (February 21, 2023)

URL(s): businessnewsdaily.com/8773-turn-your-idea-into-a-product.html

Ed: Kiely Kuligowski. **Released:** February 21, 2023. **Description:** Goes into detail about taking your idea and what to do to make it into a business. **Availability:** Online.

27888 ■ *"Hunhu Healthcare Gets Some Mayo Help"* in Business Journal (Vol. 32, August 29, 2014, No. 14, pp. 4)

Pub: American City Business Journals, Inc.

Contact: Mike Olivieri, Executive Vice President

Description: Hunhu Healthcare Inc. has signed a licensing agreement with Mayo Clinic to develop mobile and Web applications that will enable patients to communicate with the company's network using social networking tools. The firm is expected to charge a monthly fee for the service. **Availability:** Print; Online.

27889 ■ *"Ideas at Work: Sparkling Innovation"* in *Business Strategy Review (Vol. 21, Summer 2010, No. 2, pp. 07)*

Ed: Julian Birkinshaw, Peter Robbins. **Released:** June 24, 2010. **Description:** GlaxoSmithKline faced a situation common to large global organizations: how to allocate marketing resources to smaller, regional brands. The company's approach to worldwide marketing that led to the development of a unique and productive network is outlined. **Availability:** Print; PDF; Online.

27890 ■ *"If My Business Name Is Registered with the State, Do I Still Need a Trademark?"* in *Legal Zoom (March 21, 2023)*

URL(s): www.legalzoom.com/articles/if-my-business-name-is-registered-with-the-state-do-i-still-need-a-trademark

Ed: Jane Haskins, Esq. **Released:** March 21, 2023. **Description:** Be aware of the limitations your state business entity registration entails. You may need to trademark your company name if it's important to you that another business doesn't use a similar name. **Availability:** Online.

27891 ■ *"Illinois Regulators Revoke Collection Agency's License"* in *Collections & Credit Risk (Vol. 15, August 1, 2010, No. 7, pp. 13)*

Pub: SourceMedia LLC

Contact: Gemma Postlethwaite, Chief Executive Officer

Description: Creditors Service Bureau of Springfield, Illinois had its license revoked by a state regulatory agency and was fined $55,000 because the owner and president, Craig W. Lewis, did not turn over portions of collected funds to clients. **Availability:** Print; Online.

27892 ■ *"The Impact of Acquisitions On the Productivity of Inventors at Semiconductor Firms: A Synthesis of Knowledge-Based and Incentive-Based Perspective"* in *Academy of Management Journal (Vol. 50, No. 5, October 1, 2007, pp. 1133)*

Pub: Academy of Management

Contact: Sharon Alvarez, President

Ed: Rahul Kapoor, Kwanghui Lim. **Description:** Study examined the relation between knowledge-based and incentive-based outlook in explaining the impact of acquisitions on the productivity of inventors at acquired semiconductor firms. Results showed a definite relation between the two perspectives. **Availability:** Electronic publishing; Download; PDF; Online.

27893 ■ *"In Chesterfield: Paletta's Operations Raise Competitors' Blood Pressure"* in *St. Louis Business Journal (Vol. 33, August 17, 2012, No. 52, pp. 1)*

Pub: Baltimore Business Journal

Contact: Rhonda Pringle, President

E-mail: rpringle@bizjournals.com

Description: The proposed relocation of Doctor George Paletta Jr.'s Orthopedic Center of Saint Louis to a new 62,000-square-foot facility was met with opposition by local hospital officials and the Missouri Hospital Association. Officials state the facility must be licensed as a hospital in order to provide overnight post-operative care as planned by Paletta.

27894 ■ *Innovate to Great: Re-Igniting Sustainable Innovation to Win in the Global Economy*

Description: The author explores innovation and creativity as a means for small companies to survive and expand in the global economy. **Availability:** Print; PDF.

27895 ■ *"Innovate or Stagnate: How Doing Things Differently Helps Business"* in *South Florida Business Journal (Vol. 34, January 10, 2014, No. 25, pp. 10)*

Pub: American City Business Journals, Inc.

Contact: Mike Olivieri, Executive Vice President

Released: Weekly. **Price:** $8, Introductory 4-week offer(Digital & Print). **Description:** Business enterprises can drive growth by focusing on innovations. Companies are advised to consider radical ideas, invent different ways of working and avoid bureaucracy. Peter Drucker, a management consultant, believes that business has two functions: marketing and innovation. **Availability:** Print; Online.

27896 ■ *"Innovating Globally"* in *Business Strategy Review (Vol. 21, Spring 2010, No. 1, pp. 24)*

Ed: Costas Markides, Stuart Crainer. **Description:** Costas Markides has spent over two decades studying business strategy and innovation. Recently, he has been focusing on the bigger picture of how people can address major social problems. Can the techniques used by managers to create innovation inside organizations work with global change?. **Availability:** Download; PDF; Online.

27897 ■ *"Innovating Low-Cost Business Models"* in *Strategy and Leadership (Vol. 39, March-April 2011, No. 2, pp. 43)*

Pub: Emerald Group Publishing Limited

Contact: Erika Valenti, President

Ed: Nicolas Kachaner, Zhenya Lindgardt, David Michael. **Description:** A process that can be used to implement low-cost innovation is presented. The process can be used to address the competitive challenges presented by multinationals' practice of presenting applications and price points that are intended for developing markets into developed markets. The process involves targeting large, and low-income segments of the market.

27898 ■ *"Innovation Central: Tech, Tweets, and Trolls"* in *Inc. (Vol. 36, September 2014, No. 7, pp. 102)*

Pub: Mansueto Ventures L.L.C.

Contact: Stephanie Mehta, Chief Executive Officer

Description: Results of a survey regarding the ways small business is using technology to grow their businesses is presented. Information covers social media applications, government software patents, trends impacting small business, and the most innovative technology companies. **Availability:** Print; Online.

27899 ■ *"Innovation Station"* in *Canadian Business (Vol. 80, October 8, 2007, No. 20, pp. 42)*

Description: Study and teaching of entrepreneurship at the University of Waterloo is discussed. Research projects in the university are expected to be influential in Canada's economic development. In spite of the success of these studies, financing is still a problem for the university, especially in technological innovations. **Availability:** Online.

27900 ■ *"Innovation's Holy Grail"* in *Harvard Business Review (Vol. 88, July-August 2010, No. 7-8, pp. 132)*

Pub: Harvard Business Publishing

Contact: Diane Belcher, Managing Director

Ed: C.K. Prahalad, R.A. Mashelkar. **Price:** $8.95. **Description:** Three forms of business innovation are presented, inspired by the tenets of Mahatma Gandhi. They are: changing organizational capabilities, sourcing or creating new capabilities, and disrupting conventional business models. Illustrations for these methods are also included. **Availability:** Online; PDF.

27901 ■ *"Innovative Ability and Entrepreneurial Activity: Two Factors to Enhance 'Quality of Life"'* in *Journal of Business & Industrial Marketing (Vol. 29, July 2014, No. 6)*

Pub: Emerald Group Publishing Limited

Contact: Erika Valenti, President

Description: Examination of how aspects of knowledge economy covered by the KEI (Knowledge Economy Index) and those of entrepreneurial activity covered by the GEI (Global Entrepreneurship Index) affect QOL (quality of Life) in a country. KEI, GEI, and QOL data gathered from different countries was analyzed using correlation and regression analyses. It was observed that KEI and GEI feature a momen-

tous effect on QOL, while innovation index and total early stage entrepreneurship improve it. **Availability:** Download; Online.

27902 ■ *The Innovators: How a Group of Hackers, Geniuses, and Geeks Created the Digital Revolution*

Pub: Simon & Schuster, Inc.

Contact: Jonathan Karp, President

Released: October 2014. **Price:** $17.99, paperback; $29.99, abridged compact disk; $13.99, e-book; $29.99, unabridged audio download; $49.99, abridged audio download; $29.99, unabridged compact disk, plus shipping charges; 13.99, trade paperback. **Description:** Profiles of the individuals who created the computer and the Internet are provided describing the talents of certain inventors and entrepreneurs who are able to turn their business visions and goals into realities, while others have failed. The author begins with Ada Lovelace, Lord Byron's daughter, who pioneered computer programming back in the 1840s and continues by exploring the minds of Vannevar Bush, Alan Turing, John von Neumann, J.C.R. Licklider, Doug Englebart, Robert Noyce, Bill Gates, Steve Wozniak, Steve Jobs, Tim Berners-Lee and Larry Page. **Availability:** CD-ROM; E-book; Print; Audio.

27903 ■ *"The Innovator's Solution: Creating and Sustaining Successful Growth"*

Pub: Harvard Business Review Press

Contact: Moderna V. Pfizer, Contact

Released: November 19, 2013. **Price:** $35, Hardcover/Hardcopy. **Description:** Even in today's hyper-accelerated business environment any small company can transform their business. Advice on business decisions crucial to achieving truly disruptive growth and purpose guidelines for developing their own disruptive growth engine is given. The forces that cause managers to make bad decisions as they plan new ideas for their company are identified and new frameworks to help develop the right conditions, at the right time, for a disruption to succeed. Managers and business leaders responsible for innovation and growth will benefit their business and their teams with this information. **Availability:** E-book; Print.

27904 ■ *"Inside Out"* in *Playthings (Vol. 107, January 1, 2009, No. 1, pp. 3)*

Description: Mattel signed on as the global master toy licensee for Cartoon Network's The Secret Saturdays while Toy Island signed a deal for wooden toys based on several leading Nick Jr. properties. **Availability:** Print; Online.

27905 ■ *"The Intel Trinity: How Robert Noyce, Gordon Moore, and Andy Grove Built the World's Most Important Company"*

Pub: Harper Business

Contact: Hollis Heimbouch, Senior Vice President Publisher

Released: July 15, 2014. **Price:** $34.99, hardcover; $11.74, e-book; $4.34, kindle; $19.42, hardcover; $4.30, hardcover(69 used from $4.30); $15.17, hardcover(56 new from $15.17); $19.99, hardcover(1 collectible from $19.99); $31.74, paperback; $22.95, paperback(10 used from $22.95); $19.13, paperback(4 new from $19.13). **Description:** A complete history of Intel Corporation, the essential company of the digital age, is presented. After over four decades Intel remains the most important company in the world, a defining company of the global digital economy. The inventors of the microprocessor that powers nearly every intelligent electronic device worldwide are profiled. These entrepreneurs made the personal computer, Internet, telecommunications, and personal electronics all possible. The challenges and successes of the company and its ability to maintain its dominance, its culture and its legacy are examined. **Availability:** E-book; Print; Online.

27906 ■ *International Growth of Small and Medium Enterprises*

Pub: Routledge, Taylor & Francis Group

Released: First edition. **Description:** This volume focuses on how companies expand their operations across borders through opportunity exploration and exploitation, and identification and development of innovations.

27907 ■ *"Invention Submission Companies: Scams or Valuable Services?"* in *Legal Zoom (March 27, 2023)*

URL(s): www.legalzoom.com/articles/invention -submission-companies-scams-or-valuable-services

Ed: Stephanie Morrow. **Released:** March 27, 2023. **Description:** Outsourcing the legwork to patent or trademark your invention or idea may seem like a great idea, until you find out the company you used is a scam. Included are profiles on inventors who fell for scams. **Availability:** Online.

27908 ■ *"Inventive Doctor New Venture Partner"* in *Houston Business Journal (Vol. 40, January 29, 2010, No. 38, pp. A2)*

Pub: Houston Business Journal

Contact: Bob Charlet, President

E-mail: bcharlet@bizjournals.com

Ed: Ford Gunter. **Description:** Dr. Billy Cohn, a surgeon from Houston, Texas has been named as venture partner for venture firm Sante Ventures LLC of Austin, Texas. Cohn will be responsible for seeing marketable developing technologies in the medical industry. The motivation for Cohn's naming as venture partner is his development of a minimally invasive therapy for end-stage renal disease. **Availability:** Print; Online.

27909 ■ *"Judge Gives RIM One Last Chance"* in *Globe & Mail (February 24, 2006, pp. B5)*

Ed: Barrie McKenna, Paul Waldie. **Description:** United States District Court Judge James Spencer offers more time for Research In Motion Ltd. (RIM) to settle the patent infringement dispute with NTP Inc. RIM's shares increase by 6.2 percent following the decision. **Availability:** Online.

27910 ■ *"Kaiser Permanente's Innovation on the Front Lines"* in *Harvard Business Review (Vol. 88, September 2010, No. 9, pp. 92)*

Pub: Harvard Business Publishing

Contact: Diane Belcher, Managing Director

Ed: Lew McCreary. **Price:** $8.95. **Description:** Kaiser Permanente's human-centered model for organizational effectiveness emphasizes the roles of patients and providers as collaborators driving quality improvement and innovation. **Availability:** Online; PDF.

27911 ■ *"Lawyers Sued Over Lapsed Lacrosse Patent"* in *Crain's Detroit Business (Vol. 25, June 8, 2009, No. 23, pp. 5)*

Pub: Crain Communications Inc.

Contact: Barry Asin, President

Ed: Chad Halcom. **Description:** Warrior Sports Inc., a manufacturer of lacrosse equipment located in Warren, Michigan is suing the law firm Dickinson Wright PLLC and two of its intellectual property lawyers over patent rights to lacrosse equipment. **Availability:** Print; Online.

27912 ■ *"Life's Work: James Dyson"* in *Harvard Business Review (Vol. 88, July-August 2010, No. 7-8, pp. 172)*

Pub: Harvard Business Publishing

Contact: Diane Belcher, Managing Director

Ed: Alison Beard. **Price:** $8.95. **Description:** The founder of appliance company Dyson Ltd. discusses the role of making mistakes in learning and innovation, and emphasizes the importance of hands-on involvement to make a company successful. **Availability:** Online; PDF.

27913 ■ *"Local Company Seeks Patent For Armored Trucks"* in *Crain's Detroit Business (Vol. 24, February 4, 2008, No. 5, pp. 10)*

Pub: Crain Communications Inc.

Contact: Barry Asin, President

Description: Profile of James LeBlanc Sr., mechanical engineer and defense contractor, discusses his eleven utility patents pending for a set of vehicles and subsystems that would work as countermeasures to explosively formed projectiles. **Availability:** Print; Online.

27914 ■ *"Look Out, Barbie, Bratz are Back"* in *Canadian Business (Vol. 83, August 17, 2010, No. 13-14, pp. 18)*

Pub: Rogers Media Inc.

Contact: Neil Spivak, Chief Executive Officer

Ed: Joe Castaldo. **Description:** California-based MGA Entertainment has wrestled back control over Bratz from Mattel after a six-year legal battle. However, MGA owner Isaac Larian could still face legal hurdles if Mattel pursues a retrial. He now has to revive the brand which virtually disappeared from stores when Mattel won the rights for Bratz. **Availability:** Online.

27915 ■ *"Managing Yourself: How to Save Good Ideas"* in *Harvard Business Review (Vol. 88, October 2010, No. 10, pp. 129)*

Pub: Harvard Business Publishing

Contact: Diane Belcher, Managing Director

Ed: Jeff Kehoe. **Price:** $8.95, PDF. **Description:** Harvard Business School Professor John P. Kotter identifies situations that may hinder the development and implementation of ideas, and discusses effective ways to counter them. **Availability:** Online; PDF.

27916 ■ *"Market and Technology Orientations for Service Delivery Innovation: the Link of Innovative Competence"* in *Journal of Business & Industrial Marketing (Vol. 29, July 2014, No. 6)*

Pub: Emerald Group Publishing Limited

Contact: Erika Valenti

Description: A study to formulate an alternative method of predicting service delivery innovation based on market and technology orientations and innovative competence is examined. Five hypotheses were proposed and tested using the Partial Least Square (PLS) analysis. It was observed that proactive market orientation and technology orientation regulate exploratory and exploitative innovative competences, while exploitative competence influences service delivery innovation. **Availability:** Download; Online.

27917 ■ *"Maximizing Your Patent Application"* in *Legal Zoom (March 22, 2023)*

URL(s): www.legalzoom.com/articles/maximizing -your-patent-application

Ed: Stephanie Morrow. **Released:** March 22, 2023. **Description:** Describes the process of applying for a patent for your invention with an emphasis for making sure it gets approved. **Availability:** Online.

27918 ■ *"Monsanto Wins Patent Case Against DuPont"* in *Farm Journal (Vol. 136, September 2012, No. 8, pp. 8)*

Pub: Farm Journal Media Inc.

Description: Monsanto Company was awarded a $1 billion settlement by a federal jury for a patent infringement lawsuit the company filed againt DuPont regarding Roundup Ready seed technolgy. Details of the lawsuit are included. **Availability:** Online.

27919 ■ *"Mortgage Companies are Adding Staff"* in *Sacramento Business Journal (Vol. 29, September 14, 2012, No. 29, pp. 1)*

Pub: Baltimore Business Journal

Contact: Rhonda Pringle, President

E-mail: rpringle@bizjournals.com

Ed: Sanford Nax. **Description:** Mortgage companies have been increasing their hiring as a result of persistently low interest rates and tough new government regulations. The mortgage industry has gained 1,335 jobs in the second quarter nationally, while the number of applications to receive a mortgage loan originator license is rising in California. **Availability:** Print; Online.

27920 ■ *"Mosaid Grants First Wireless Patent License To Matsushita"* in *Canadian Electronics (Vol. 23, June-July 2008, No. 5, pp. 1)*

Pub: Annex Buisness Media

Contact: Mike Fredericks, President

Description: Matsushita Electric Industrial Co. Ltd. has been granted a six-and-a-half-year license by Mosaid Technologies Inc. to manufacture the latter's products. The patent portfolio license agreement covers Mosaid's Wi-Fi, Wi-Max, CDMA-enabled notebook computers and other products.

27921 ■ *"Much Work Still To Be Done on Meadows Deal"* in *Pittsburgh Business Times (Vol. 33, May 16, 2014, No. 44, pp. 3)*

Pub: American City Business Journals, Inc.

Contact: Mike Olivieri, Executive Vice President

Released: Weekly. **Price:** $4, introductory 4-week offer(Digital only). **Description:** Real estate investment trust, Gaming and Leisure Properties Inc., is acquiring the Meadows Racetrack & Casino in Washington, Pennsylvania from Cannery Casino & Resorts LLC in a $465 million deal. The process of finding an operator and getting the license transfers approved will be the next critical step following the deal. **Availability:** Print; Online.

27922 ■ *"Necessity Mother of This Startup"* in *Providence Business News (Vol. 28, January 6, 2014, No. 40, pp. 1)*

Pub: American City Business Journals, Inc.

Contact: Mike Olivieri, Executive Vice President

URL(s): pbn.com/necessity-mother-of-this-startup9 4159

Description: Kailas Narendran, founder of kiinde LLC, invented a device that can quickly thaw breast milk to precisely the right temperature for feeding a baby without losing nutrients. Innovative products for mothers and babies are now being sold by kiine throughout the U.S., Canada and South Korea. New product development is discussed by Narendran. **Availability:** Online.

27923 ■ *"The Next Great Canadian Idea: Peripiteia Generator"* in *Canadian Business (Vol. 81, July 21, 2008, No. 11, pp. 45)*

Pub: Rogers Media Inc.

Contact: Neil Spivak, Chief Executive Officer

Ed: Sharda Prashad. **Description:** Thane Heins has invented a generator that produces energy in an isolated system which contradicts the law of conservation of energy. Perepiteia generator is referred to as a 'perpetual motion machine.' Other inventions slated for the Canadian invention competition include Rob Matthies' batteries and Frank Naumann's Smart Trap. **Availability:** Online.

27924 ■ *"The Next Step in Patent Reform"* in *Information Today (Vol. 28, November 2011, No. 10, pp. 1)*

Pub: Information Today Inc.

Contact: Thomas H. Hogan, President

Ed: George H. Pike. **Description:** The Leahy-Smith America Invents Act was signed into law in September 2011. The new act reformed the previous US patent system. Information involving the new patent law process is discussed.

27925 ■ *"Of Marks and Men"* in *Canadian Business (Vol. 80, March 12, 2007, No. 6, pp. 59)*

Description: The importance on the part of business enterprises to register for trademarks to avoid any threat of litigation in future is discussed. **Availability:** Print; Online.

27926 ■ *"Organization Redesign and Innovative HRM"* in *Human Resource Management (Vol. 49, July-August 2010, No. 4, pp. 809-811)*

Pub: John Wiley & Sons, Inc.

Contact: Christina Van Tassell, Executive Vice President Chief Financial Officer

Ed: Pat Lynch. **Released:** July 01, 2010. **Description:** An overview of the book, 'Organization Redesign and Innovative HRM' is presented. **Availability:** PDF; Online.

27927 ■ *"Orlando Patents Forecast Biz Diversity and Growth" in Orlando Business Journal (Vol. 30, April 18, 2014, No. 43, pp. 4)*
Pub: American City Business Journals, Inc.
Contact: Mike Olivieri, Executive Vice President
Released: Weekly. **Price:** $8, introductory 4-week offer(Digital & Print). **Description:** Orlando, Florida ranked among cities in the state in terms of number of patents filed. Around 275 patents were issued to Orlando-based inventors and businesses in 2013. The increase in the number of high technology companies entering the city has contributed to this trend. **Availability:** Print; Online.

27928 ■ *"The Overlicensed Society" in Harvard Business Review (Vol. 90, April 2012, No. 4, pp. 38)*
Pub: Harvard Business Review Press
Contact: Moderna V. Pfizer, Contact
Ed: Robert E. Litan. **Price:** $6, hardcover. **Description:** The author argues that certification and licensing requirements are hindering professionals who might otherwise be able to find positions and provide services inexpensively. To key areas are healthcare and law. Federal mutual recognition agreements may be one method of addressing both practice and consumer protection issues. **Availability:** PDF; Online.

27929 ■ *"Patent Squatters: Is It Possible to Patent an Invention That Everyone's Been Using for Years?" in Legal Zoom (March 27, 2023)*
URL(s): www.legalzoom.com/articles/patent-squatters-is-it-possible-to-patent-an-invention-that-everyones-been-using-for-years
Ed: Stephanie Morrow. **Released:** March 27, 2023. **Description:** Discussion about patents and If It's possible to patent something that has been around for a long time. Examples are given. **Availability:** Online.

27930 ■ *"Patently Absurd" in Globe & Mail (January 28, 2006, pp. B4)*
Description: An overview of facts about patent dispute between Research In Motion Ltd. and NTP Inc. is presented. **Availability:** Online.

27931 ■ *"Patently (Un)Clear" in Business Strategy Review (Vol. 21, Spring 2010, No. 1, pp. 28)*
Ed: Markus Reitzig, Stefan Wagner. **Released:** 2010. **Description:** After developing a great product or process, it's important to protect it. The benefits of using internal patent lawyers versus outsourcing the task are examined. **Availability:** Print; PDF; Online.

27932 ■ *Patent's Handbook: A Guide for Inventors and Researchers to Searching Patent Documents and Preparing and Making an Application*
Pub: McFarland & CPI, Publishers
Contact: Shelia Baldwin, Contact
E-mail: sbaldwin@mcfarlandpub.com
URL(s): mcfarlandbooks.com/product/patents-handbook
Price: $39.95, Individuals for stock. **Description:** Publication includes list of information sources for researching patents and inventorship. Principal content of publication is an overview of the patent system in the United States. Includes diagrams, facsimiles, appendix. **Indexes:** Master. **Availability:** E-book; Print; Online.

27933 ■ *"Phillip Frost: 'Technology Is the Future'" in South Florida Business Journal (Vol. 34, June 20, 2014, No. 48, pp. 16)*
Pub: American City Business Journals, Inc.
Contact: Mike Olivieri, Executive Vice President
Released: Weekly. **Price:** $8, introductory 4-week offer(Digital only). **Description:** Entrepreneur, Phillip Frost, shares his strategies and perspectives on the business climate of Miami, Florida. He describes

investment strategy for the diverse holdings of Opko Health and his criteria for buying companies and licensing technologies. **Availability:** Print; Online.

27934 ■ *"Pioneering Strategies for Entrepreneurial Success" in Business Horizons (Vol. 51, January-February 2008, No. 1, pp. 21)*
Pub: Elsevier Advanced Technology Publications
Ed: Candida G. Brush. **Price:** $8.95, hardcopy black and white. **Description:** Entrepreneurs are known for new products, services, processes, markets and industries. In order to achieve success, they have to develop a clear vision, creatively manage finances, and use social skills to persuade others to commit to the venture. Pioneering strategies and their implementation are examined. **Availability:** Print; PDF; Online.

27935 ■ *"Plagiarism: What Is It, Exactly?" in Legal Zoom (March 27, 2023)*
URL(s): www.legalzoom.com/articles/plagiarism-what-is-it-exactly
Ed: Stephanie Morrow. **Released:** March 27, 2023. **Description:** Defines plagiarism and discusses ways people plagiarize, often without knowing they are doing it. Gives an example of popstar Madonna being sued for plagiarism. **Availability:** Online.

27936 ■ *"Presidential Address: Innovation in Retrospect and Prospect" in Canadian Journal of Electronics (Vol. 43, November 2010, No. 4)*
Pub: Journal of the Canadian Economics Association
Ed: James A. Brander. **Description:** Has innovation slowed in recent decades? While there has been progress in information and communications technology, the recent record of innovation in agriculture, energy, transportation and healthcare sectors is cause for concern. **Availability:** PDF; Online.

27937 ■ *"Probability Processing Chip: Lyric Semiconductor" in Inc. (Volume 32, December 2010, No. 10, pp. 52)*
Pub: Inc. Magazine
Ed: Christine Lagorio. **Description:** Lyric Semiconductor, a start up located in Cambridge, Massachusetts, has developed a computer chip that also uses values that fall between zero and one, resulting in a chip that can process information using probabilities, considering many possible answers that find the best fit. **Availability:** Online.

27938 ■ *"Protect Your Domain Name From Cybersquatters" in Idaho Business Review (September 1, 2014)*
Pub: BridgeTower Media
Contact: Adam Reinebach, President
Description: Cybersquatting is the practice of registering, trafficking in or using domain names with the intent to profit from the goodwill of recognizable trade names or trademarks of other companies. Companies can protect their Website domain by following these steps: register domain names, promptly renew registrations, maintain proper records, obtain additional top-level domains, and monitor your site for cybersquatters.

27939 ■ *"Quality Performance of SMEs in a Developing Economy: Direct and Indirect Effects of Service Innovation and Entrepreneurial Orientation" in Journal of Business & Industrial Marketing (Vol. 29, July 2014, No. 6)*
Pub: Emerald Group Publishing Limited
Contact: Erika Valenti, President
Description: A study was conducted to investigate the effects of innovation and EO (entrepreneurial orientation) on organizational performance in Asian small enterprise context. Strategic management literature and the relationship between EO, innovation, and quality performance was tested. The results indicated that a noteworthy direct and indirect positive relationship exists between EO dimensions, innovation, and quality performance. **Availability:** Download; Online.

27940 ■ *"The Quest for a Smart Prosthetic" in Canadian Business (Vol. 83, October 12, 2010, No. 17, pp. 26)*
Pub: Rogers Media Inc.
Contact: Neil Spivak, Chief Executive Officer
Ed: Jacqueline Nelson. **Description:** Information about a two-year research project led by Southern Methodist University (SMU) and funded by the Defense Advance Research Projects Agency (DARPA) is provided. The agency aims to create a 'smart prosthetic' which will improve the lives of military amputees. The planned prosthetic will use a sensor that can carry nerve signals through synthetic channels. **Availability:** Print; Online.

27941 ■ *"Racing to Beam Electricity to Devices Wirelessly" in San Francisco Business Times (Vol. 28, April 11, 2014, No. 38, pp. 6)*
Pub: American City Business Journals, Inc.
Contact: Mike Olivieri, Executive Vice President
Description: Pleasanton, California-based Energous Corporation has developed a technology that safely converts radio waves into electrical current. The innovation makes it possible to charge multiple/cellular mobile phones or other electrical devices from a distance of 15 feet. The prototype of Energous founder, Michael Leabman's invention is also outlined. **Availability:** Print; Online.

27942 ■ *"Region to Be Named Innovation Hub" in Business Courier (Vol. 27, July 2, 2010, No. 9, pp. 1)*
Pub: Business Courier
Ed: Dan Monk. **Description:** The selection of Cincinnati's consumer-marketing cluster as a 'Hub of Innovation' by the Ohio Department of Development could boost Cincinnati's chances of receiving $100 million in grants from Ohio's Third Frontier program and other funding sources. Implications of the University of Cincinnati's designation as a Center of Excellence in Advanced Transportation and Aerospace are also discussed. **Availability:** Print; Online.

27943 ■ *"Rethinking the Organization" in Strategy & Leadership (Vol. 38, September-October 2010, No. 5, pp. 13-19)*
Pub: Emerald Inc.
Ed: Stephen Denning. **Description:** A study identifies the changes needed to be adopted by top managers to achieve game-changing innovation at an organization-wide level. Findings indicate that CEOs should practice pull management in order to nurture fruitful communication between employees and customers and achieve organizational involvement of customers. **Availability:** Print; PDF.

27944 ■ *"Reversal of Fortune" in Canadian Business (Vol. 85, June 11, 2012, No. 10, pp. 32)*
Ed: Matthew McClearn. **Description:** First Quantum Minerals of Vancouver, British Columbia contested the decisio of the Democratic Republic of Congo to revoke their mining license in the Kolwezi Tailings by means of political pressure and international law. Eurasian National Resources Corporation agreed to pay First Quantum $1.25 billion in return for uncontested title to Congo mines and a ceasefire in January 2012. **Availability:** Print; Online.

27945 ■ *"Reviving Entrepreneurship: Policy Decisions in 12 Areas Could Nurture - Or Cripple - America's Greatest Asset" in Harvard Business Review (Vol. 90, March 2012, No. 3, pp. 116)*
Pub: Harvard Business Review Press
Contact: Moderna V. Pfizer, Contact
Ed: Josh Lerner, William A. Sahlman. **Price:** $8.95, hardcover. **Description:** Government policies should address entrepreneurship as a process, rather than an act. Several key areas for policymaking include basic and translational science, supply and quality of human capital, information availability, tax treatment of rewards and risks, intellectual property rights, workforce healthcare, and mobility of financial and human capital. **Availability:** PDF; Online.

27946 ■ "The Service Imperative" in Business Horizons (Vol. 51, January-February 2008, No. 1, pp. 39)
Pub: Elsevier Advanced Technology Publications
Ed: Mary Jo Bitner, Stephen W. Brown. Description: The importance of services is growing in developing countries like India and China, but little attention is given to service research, education and innovation. The 'service imperative' seeks to promote the advancement of services. The scope, objectives and philosophy of the service imperative platform are outlined. Availability: Online.

27947 ■ "Shedding Light on Innovation" in Rental Product News (Vol. 33, June 2011)
Description: Light tower manufacturers have introduced numerous new products that feature alternative power sources, LED lighting and a second generation of performance and value. Availability: Online.

27948 ■ "Sinai Doctor's Research May Lead to Rival Plavix Drug" in Baltimore Business Journal (Vol. 28, July 16, 2010, No. 10, pp. 1)
Pub: Baltimore Business Journal
Contact: Rhonda Pringle, President
E-mail: rpringle@bizjournals.com
Ed: Emily Mullin. Description: Paul Gurbel, Sinai Hospital Center for Thrombosis Research director, is seeking an FDA approval of Brilinta, a drug which he helped create and test. Gurbel says that the approval could bring the drug to market as early as December 2010. The drug is expected to rival Bristol-Myers' Plavix, which generated almost $6.2 billion in 2009. Availability: Print; Online.

27949 ■ "The Sky's the Limit" in Retail Merchandiser (Vol. 51, July-August 2011, No. 4, pp. 64)
Description: Mars Retail Group (MRG) is the licensing division handling M&M's Brand Candies. Since taking over the brand they have expanded from 12 licensees to 50 licensees with new offerings. Availability: Online.

27950 ■ "Stop the Innovation Wars" in Harvard Business Review (Vol. 88, July-August 2010, No. 7-8, pp. 76)
Pub: Harvard Business Publishing
Contact: Diane Belcher, Managing Director
Ed: Vijay Govindarajan, Chris Trimble. Price: $8.95, PDF. Description: Methods for managing conflicts between partners during the innovation initiative process are highlighted. These include dividing the labor, assembling a dedicated team, and mitigating likelihood for any potential conflict. Availability: Online; PDF.

27951 ■ "The 'Supply Side' of the Auto Industry" in Montly Labor Review (Vol. 133, September 2010, No. 9, pp. 72)
Pub: U.S. Department of Labor Bureau of Labor Statistics
Contact: Amrit Kohli, Director
E-mail: kohli.amrit@bls.gov
Description: Restructuring and geographic change in the automobile industry is discussed. Availability: PDF; Online.

27952 ■ "Tastee-Freez Celebrates 60th Anniversary" in Ice Cream Reporter (Vol. 23, July 20, 2010, No. 8, pp. 2)
Description: Tastee-Freez founders, Leo Moranz (inventor) and Harry Axene, an inventor partnered to market the soft-serve pump and freezer for serving frozen treats back in 1950. Availability: Print; Online.

27953 ■ "Think Disruptive! How to Manage In a New Era of Innovation" in Strategy & Leadership (Vol. 38, July-August 2010, No. 4, pp. 5-10)
Pub: Emerald Inc.
Ed: Brian Leavy, John Sterling. Price: $32, online only 30 days. Description: The views expressed by Scott Anthony, president of an innovation consultancy Innosight, on the need for corporate leaders to apply disruptive innovation in a recessionary environment

are presented. His suggestion that disruptive innovation is the only way to survive during the economic crisis is discussed. Availability: Online; PDF.

27954 ■ Trade-Off: The Ever-Present Tension Between Quality and Conscience
Released: August 17, 2010. Price: $15. Description: The tension between fidelity (the quality of a consumer's experience) and convenience (the ease of getting and paying for a product) are shown to be the forces that determine the success or failure of new products and services in the marketplace.

27955 ■ "Trademark and Patent Scams: What to Watch out For" in Legal Zoom (February 17, 2023)
URL(s): www.legalzoom.com/articles/trademark-an
d-patent-scams-what-to-watch-out-for
Ed: Stephanie Morrow. Released: February 17, 2023. Description: Read thought this article to learn about how scammers could take advantage of your trademarks and patents. Availability: Online.

27956 ■ "Under Armour Wants to Equip Athletes, Too" in Boston Business Journal (Vol. 29, July 8, 2011, No. 9, pp. 1)
Pub: Boston Business Journal
Contact: Carolyn M. Jones, President
E-mail: cmjones@bizjournals.com
Ed: Ryan Sharrow. Description: Baltimore sportswear maker Under Armour advances plans to enter into the equipment field, aiming to strengthen its hold on football, basketball and lacrosse markets where it already has a strong market share. The company is now cooking up licensing deals to bolster the firm's presence among athletes. Availability: Print; Online.

27957 ■ "Unlicensed Utah Collection Agency Settles with State Finance Department" in Idaho Business Review, Boise (July 15, 2010)
Pub: Idaho Business Review
Contact: Autumn Kersey, Sales Executive
E-mail: akersey@idahobusinessreview.com
Description: Federal Recovery Acceptance Inc., doing business as Paramount Acceptance in Utah, agreed to pay penalties and expenses after the firm was investigated by the state for improprieties. The firm was charged with conducting unlicensed collection activity. Availability: Print; Online.

27958 ■ "Voices: The Strategic Innovation Cube" in Business Strategy Review (Vol. 23, Spring 2012, No. 1, pp. 84)
Description: Companies that innovate tend to prosper. Yet the process used by most innovative firms remains a mystery. Is there a way that any company can discern whether to commit resources to an innovation idea? Kiriti Rambhatla has blended the fields of science and management and offers a new way of thinking about innovation inside any company. Availability: Online.

27959 ■ "Wall Street Is No Friend to Radical Innovation" in Harvard Business Review (Vol. 88, July-August 2010, No. 7-8, pp. 28)
Pub: Harvard Business Publishing
Contact: Diane Belcher, Managing Director
Ed: Julia Kirby. Price: $6, PDF. Description: Research indicates that investors are skittish about backing a business that proposes significant changes to its product or service status quo. Availability: Online; PDF.

27960 ■ "What Is Creative Commons? 5 Frequently Asked Questions" in Legal Zoom (March 27, 2023)
URL(s): www.legalzoom.com/articles/what-is-creative
-commons-5-frequently-asked-questions
Ed: Michelle Kaminsky, Esq. Released: March 27, 2023. Description: A summary of the nonprofit Creative Commons, which distributes creative licenses so it is easier for permission to be granted to use the work that is being protected. Availability: Online.

27961 ■ "What Kind of Business Methods Can You Patent?" in Legal Zoom (March 13, 2023)
URL(s): www.legalzoom.com/articles/what-kind-of
-business-methods-can-you-patent
Ed: Heleigh Bostwick. Released: March 13, 2023. Description: E-commerce has given entrepreneurs an opportunity to do business in a new way and in doing so, new methods and business procedures have emerged. But, can these processes be patented by those who develop them?. Availability: Online.

27962 ■ "When and How to Innovate Your Business Model" in Strategy & Leadership (Vol. 38, July-August 2010, No. 4, pp. 17-26)
Pub: Emerald Inc.
Ed: Edward Giesen, Eric Riddleberger, Richrd Christner, Ragna Bell. Description: A study uses survey data to identify factors that are considered by corporate leaders regarding when and how they should innovate their business model. Findings identify a set of characteristics called the 'Three A's, Namely, Aligned, Analytical and Adaptable, which corporate leaders use consistently to successfully design and execute business-model innovation. Availability: PDF; Online.

27963 ■ "When R&D Spending Is Not Enough: The Critical Role of Culture When You Really Want to Innovate" in Human Resource Management (Vol. 49, July-August 2010, No. 4, pp. 767-792)
Pub: John Wiley & Sons, Inc.
Contact: Christina Van Tassell, Executive Vice President Chief Financial Officer
Ed: Sheng Wang, Rebecca M. Guidice, Judith W. Tansky, Zhong-Ming Wang. Released: July 19, 2010. Description: A study was conducted to examine the effect of contextual contingencies on innovation. Findings indicate that Chinese manufacturers with cultures emphasizing innovation and teamwork more effectively utilize financial resources in the innovation process. Results also show that a culture emphasizing outcomes and stability leads to lower levels innovation irrespective of investments. Availability: Print; PDF; Online.

27964 ■ "Where Good Ideas Come From: The Natural History of Innovation" in Business Owner (Vol. 35, July-August 2011, No. 4, pp. 6)
Description: A history of ideas, concepts, innovations and technologies that have created a successful small business environment are explored. Availability: Print; Online.

27965 ■ "Where New Economy Initiative Grants Have Gone" in Crain's Detroit Business (Vol. 25, June 1, 2009, No. 22, pp. M014)
Pub: Crain Communications Inc.
Contact: Barry Asin, President
Ed: Sherri Begin Welch. Description: Listing of grants totaling $20.5 million focusing on talent development, attraction and retention; innovation and entrepreneurship; and shifting to a culture that values learning, work and innovation, is presented. Availability: Online; PDF.

27966 ■ "A Whiteboard that Peels and Sticks" in Inc. (Volume 32, December 2010, No. 10, pp. 58)
Pub: Inc. Magazine
Ed: Issie Lapwosky. Description: Profile of an affordable adhesive whiteboard that can be restuck multiple times; the whiteboard was created by three college friends. The students share insight in the contacts they used in order to promote the sale of their invention. Availability: Online.

27967 ■ "Why Entrepreneurs Matter More Than Innovators" in Gallup Management Journal (November 22, 2011)
Ed: Jim Clifton. Released: November 22, 2011. Description: In the race to create good jobs, leaders are not paying enough attention to cultivating talented entrepreneurs, rather they invest too much attention on innovation. Availability: Print; Online.

27968 ■ *"Why Life Science Needs Its Own Silicon Valley: Human Genomics Won't Reach Its Full Potential Until It Has a Sizable Industry Cluster" in Harvard Business Review (Vol. 90, July-August 2012, No. 7-8, pp. 25)*
Pub: Harvard Business Review Press
Contact: Moderna V. Pfizer, Contact

Ed: Fariborz Ghadar, John Sviokla, Dietrich A. Stephan. **Price:** $6, PDF and hardcover black and white. **Description:** The creation of an industry cluster will be key to advancing human genomics research. High degrees of specialization via multiple contributors will be needed to generate significant innovations; an accessible, coherent data source will also be necessary. **Availability:** Print; PDF; Online.

27969 ■ *"With Whom Do You Trade? Defensive Innovation and the Skill-Bias" in Canadian Journal of Electronics (Vol. 43, November 2010)*
Pub: Journal of the Canadian Economics Association

Ed: Pushan Dutt, Daniel Traca. **Released:** Vol. 43, No. 4. **Price:** $5. **Description:** Examination into whether increased trade with ineffective protection of intellectual property has contributed to the skill-deepening of the 1980s. An index of effective protection of intellectual property at the country level, combining data on protection of patents and rule of law are presented. An industry-specific version of this index is given using as weights each country's trade share in the total trade of the industry. A decline is seen in this trade-weighted index, owing to a rise in trade with countries with low effective protection of intellectual property, which explains 29 percent of the rise within-industry skill-intensity. **Availability:** Print; Online; Download.

27970 ■ *"Your Guide to Getting a Business License" in Business News Daily (February 21, 2023)*
URL(s): www.businessnewsdaily.com/15764-how-to-get-a-business-license.html
Ed: Skye Schooley. **Released:** February 21, 2023. **Description:** This article discusses business licenses, including how to go about obtaining one. **Availability:** Online.

VIDEO/AUDIO MEDIA

27971 ■ *Create a Successful Product with Your Invention Idea with Kevin Mako*
URL(s): www.eofire.com/podcast/kevinmako
Ed: Jon Lee Dumas. **Released:** April 06, 2024. **Description:** Podcast discusses hardware startups: new inventions, gadgets, gizmos, or other physical objects in day-to-day life.

27972 ■ *The How of Business: Trademarks and Copyrights with Andrea Sager*
URL(s): www.thehowofbusiness.com/episode-312-andrea-sager
Ed: Henry Lopez. **Released:** May 25, 2020. **Description:** Podcast explains when you need a trademark and whether you have to register a copyright.

27973 ■ *This Is Small Business: How a Patent Can Protect Your Idea*
URL(s): www.smallbusiness.amazon/podcast-episodes/ep-51-how-a-patent-can-protect-your-idea
Ed: Andrea Marquez. **Released:** April 02, 2024. **Description:** Podcast explains the patent process for someone new to entrepreneurship.

27974 ■ *This Is Small Business: Why You Should Protect Your Intellectual Property*
URL(s): www.smallbusiness.amazon/podcast-episodes/ep-33-why-you-should-protect-your-intellectual-property
Ed: Andrea Marquez. **Released:** September 05, 2023. **Description:** Podcast discusses the IP process, rebranding, trademark disputes, logo registration, and legal support for small businesses. Offered as part of Amazon Small Business Academy.

COMPUTERIZED DATABASES

27975 ■ *Canadian Patent Reporter Plus (CPR)*
Carswell
2075 Kennedy Rd.
Toronto, ON, Canada M1T 3V4
URL: http://store.thomsonreuters.ca/en-ca/products/carswells-pension-manual-formerly-mercer-pension-manual-30843906
Contact: Steve Hasker, President
URL(s): store.thomsonreuters.ca/en-ca/products/canadian-patent-reporter-index--inet-svc-42699501
Ed: Marcus Gallie. **Released:** Annual **Price:** C$684, for 1 quantity. **Availability:** Print; Online. **Type:** Full-text.

27976 ■ *CLAIMS® Direct Database*
IFI CLAIMS Patent Services
195 Church St., 11th Fl.
New Haven, CT 06510
Ph: (203)779-5301
Co. E-mail: info@ificlaims.com
URL: http://www.ificlaims.com
Contact: Mike Baycroft, Chief Executive Officer
URL(s): www.ificlaims.com/product/product-data-collection.htm
Availability: Online. **Type:** Bibliographic.

27977 ■ *Health & Wellness InSite*
Type: Full-text.

27978 ■ *Industrial Patent Activity in the United States Parts 1 and 2, 1974-1998*
U.S. Department of Commerce United States Patent and Trademark Office
Ph: (571)272-1000
Free: 800-786-9199
URL: http://www.uspto.gov
Contact: Joseph Matal, Director
URL(s): www.ntis.govwww.uspto.gov
Type: Full-text.

INTERNET DATABASES

27979 ■ *African Americans in Business and Entrepreneurship: A Resource Guide*
URL(s): guides.loc.gov/african-americans-in-business
Description: A guide providing key topics on the history of African Americans in various business industries. **Availability:** Online.

LIBRARIES

27980 ■ **Chicago Public Library Central Library - Business/Science/Technology Division**
400 S State St.
Chicago, IL 60605
URL: http://www.chipublib.org/resources/science-technology
Scope: Small business; marketing; technology; sciences; computer science; careers and environmental information. **Services:** Interlibrary loan; library open to the public. **Founded:** 1977. **Holdings:** Figures not available.

27981 ■ **Finnegan, Henderson, Farabow, Garrett & Dunner, LLP - Library**
Finnegan, Henderson, Farabow, Garrett & Dunner, LLP
901 New York Ave. NW
Washington, DC 20001-4413
Ph: (202)408-4000
Co. E-mail: info@finnegan.com
URL: http://www.finnegan.com
Contact: Aaron L. Parker, Partner
E-mail: aaron.parker@finnegan.com
Facebook: www.facebook.com/finnegan
Linkedin: www.linkedin.com/company/finnegan-henderson-farabow-garrett-&-dunner-llp
X (Twitter): x.com/FinneganIPLaw
Description: Services: Law firm specializing in intellectual property. **Scope:** Law. **Founded:** 1965. **Holdings:** Figures not available. **Awards:** Finnegan Diversity Scholarship (Annual).

27982 ■ **O'Melveny & Myers LLP - Library**
Two Embarcadero Ctr.
28th Fl.
San Francisco, CA 94111
Ph: (415)984-8700
URL: http://www.omm.com/locations/san-francisco
Contact: Caitlin M. Bair, Partner
E-mail: cbair@omm.com
Facebook: www.facebook.com/OMelvenyandMyersLLP
X (Twitter): x.com/omelvenymyers
Instagram: www.instagram.com/omelvenymyers
Scope: Law. **Services:** Library not open to the public. **Founded:** 1989. **Holdings:** 8,000 books. **Subscriptions:** 75 journals and other serials; 10 newspapers.

27983 ■ **Public Library of Cincinnati and Hamilton County - Government Resources**
800 Vine St.
Cincinnati, OH 45202
URL: http://chpl.org/services/small-business/government-resources
Scope: Organization behaviors. **Services:** Library open to the public. **Founded:** 2005. **Holdings:** Figures not available.

RESEARCH CENTERS

27984 ■ **Indiana State University - Office of Sponsored Programs (OSP)**
200 North Seventh St.
Terre Haute, IN 47809-1902
Ph: (812)237-3088
Free: 800-468-6478
Fax: (812)237-3092
Co. E-mail: research@indstate.edu
URL: http://www.indstate.edu/research
Description: Integral unit of Indiana State University. Offers individual assistance in the preparation and submission of proposals. **Scope:** Coordinates pre-award activities associated with external funding and supports research and proposal development. Assists with patents, licensing, and technology transfer. Also facilitates the administrative review and approval of proposals. **Publications:** *Creating a Grant Proposal Budget* (Annual); *Finding Money for Your Project*; *Preparing a Winning Grant Proposal*.

27985 ■ **University of Wisconsin - Whitewater - Wisconsin Innovation Service Center (WISC)**
800 W Main St.
Whitewater, WI 53190
Ph: (262)472-1703
URL: http://www.uww.edu/wisc
Description: Integral unit of University of Wisconsin—Whitewater, University of Wisconsin—Extension Small Business Development Center, and the Small Business Administration. Offers market information to clients; technical reviews. **Scope:** Performs early-stage market research for independent inventors and manufacturers. **Founded:** 1980.

EARLY STAGE FINANCING

27986 ■ *"Acacia Subsidiary Acquires Patents Related to Shared Memory for Multimedia Processing from a Major Corporation" in Economics & Business Week (April 26, 2014, pp. 5)*
NewsRX LLC.
PO Box 724823
Atlanta, GA 31139
Ph: (770)507-7777
Co. E-mail: info@newsrx.com
URL: http://www.newsrx.com/NewsRxWebsite
Contact: Kalani Rosell, Contact
Description: Acacia Research Corporation that a subsidiary has acquired U.S. patents and foreign counterparts related to the use of shared memory in multimedia processing systems such as mobile phones, tablets and other consumer electronic devices. **Availability:** Online.

Inventory

START-UP INFORMATION

27987 ■ *"So You Want To Be a Food Truck Vendor?"* in Philadelphia Business Journal (Vol. 33, August 15, 2014, No. 27, pp. 7)
Pub: American City Business Journals, Inc.
Contact: Mike Olivieri, Executive Vice President
Released: Weekly. **Price:** $4, introductory 4-week offer(Digital only). **Description:** Food truck vendors assert that the most challenging part of starting a food truck business is acquiring a license as well as the price and number of licenses and permits required. Other costs include additional fees to vend in prime locations, maintenance, and inventory. **Availability:** Print; Online.

EDUCATIONAL PROGRAMS

27988 ■ **Best Practices for Managing Inventories and Cycle Counts (Onsite)**
Seminar Information Service Inc. (SIS)
250 El Camino Real., Ste. 112
Tustin, CA 92780
Ph: (714)508-0340
Free: 877-736-4636
Fax: (714)734-8027
Co. E-mail: info@seminarinformation.com
URL: http://www.seminarinformation.com
Contact: Catherine Bellizzi, President
URL(s): www.seminarinformation.com/details.cfm?qc =qqbqhk
Description: Learn how to use specific techniques that will actually improve speed and accuracy when counting inventory. **Audience:** Industry professionals. **Principal Exhibits:** Learn how to use specific techniques that will actually improve speed and accuracy when counting inventory.

27989 ■ **Fred Pryor Seminars & CareerTrack How to Manage Inventories and Cycle Counts**
Fred Pryor Seminars & CareerTrack
5700 Broadmoor, Ste. 300
Mission, KS 66202
Free: 800-780-8476
Fax: (913)967-8849
Co. E-mail: customerservice@pryor.com
URL: http://www.pryor.com
Contact: Janet Turner, Contact
E-mail: dmca@pryor.com
URL(s): www.pryor.com/mkt_info/seminars/desc/IV .asp
Description: Cost saving methods and time saving techniques to ensure accurate counts and inventories. **Audience:** Administrative professionals. **Principal Exhibits:** Cost saving methods and time saving techniques to ensure accurate counts and inventories.

27990 ■ **Inventory Management Techniques (Onsite)**
Seminar Information Service Inc. (SIS)
250 El Camino Real., Ste. 112
Tustin, CA 92780
Ph: (714)508-0340

Free: 877-736-4636
Fax: (714)734-8027
Co. E-mail: info@seminarinformation.com
URL: http://www.seminarinformation.com
Contact: Catherine Bellizzi, President
URL(s): www.seminarinformation.com/details.cfm?qc =qqajau
Description: Learn how to assure less inventory where the product pipeline begins and greater customer satisfaction where it ends. **Audience:** Material inventory, control purchasing, logistics, and distribution professionals. **Principal Exhibits:** Learn how to assure less inventory where the product pipeline begins and greater customer satisfaction where it ends.

27991 ■ **Managing Inventories and Cycle Counts (Onsite)**
National Seminars Training L.L.C. (NST)
14502 W 105th St.
Lenexa, KS 66215
Free: 800-349-1935
Co. E-mail: info@findaseminar.com
URL: http://www.findaseminar.com/tpd/Padge tt-Thompson-Seminars.asp
URL(s): www.findaseminar.com/event1.asp?eventID =893
Description: One-day workshop focusing on methods to streamline processes and keep a warehouse running smoothly. **Audience:** Inventory, quality control or warehouse management professionals. **Principal Exhibits:** One-day workshop focusing on methods to streamline processes and keep a warehouse running smoothly.

27992 ■ **Successful Inventory Management (Onsite)**
URL(s): www.pryor.com
Description: Learn proven cost saving methods that improve inventory and cycle count accuracy. **Audience:** Professionals. **Principal Exhibits:** Learn proven cost saving methods that improve inventory and cycle count accuracy.

REFERENCE WORKS

27993 ■ *"Beyond Zipcar: Collaborative Consumption"* in Harvard Business Review (Vol. 88, October 2010, No. 10, pp. 30)
Pub: Harvard Business Publishing
Contact: Diane Belcher, Managing Director
Ed: Rachel Botsman, Roo Rogers. **Price:** $6, PDF. **Description:** Description of the rise of collaborative consumption, the sharing or redistributing of products, rather than the purchasing thereof is discussed. **Availability:** Online; PDF.

27994 ■ *"The CEO of TJX On How To Train First-Class Buyers"* in Harvard Business Review (Vol. 92, May 2014, No. 5, pp. 45)
Pub: Harvard Business Press
Contact: Gabriela Allmi, Regional Manager
E-mail: gabriela.allmi@hbsp.harvard.edu

Released: 2014. **Price:** $8.95. **Description:** The CEO of clothing retailer TJX Companies Inc. emphasizes the importance of buyer training to ensure that store merchandise inventory optimizes consumer response. Buyers must be curious, knowledgeable about customers, and willing to take risks. **Availability:** Print; Online; PDF.

27995 ■ *"Commercial Real Estate May Be Cooling, While Residential Clamors to Meet Demand"* in Houston Business Journal (Vol. 44, January 3, 2014, No. 35, pp. 6)
Pub: American City Business Journals, Inc.
Contact: Mike Olivieri, Executive Vice President
Released: January 03, 2014. **Description:** Greater Houston Partnership has predicted that the real estate industry will remain active for the years ahead in Houston, Texas. However, commercial real estate might cool down while residential sales are expected to remain hot with demand outpacing supply. Houston's construction boom in each sector is also discussed. **Availability:** Print; Online.

27996 ■ *"Crucible: Battling Back from Betrayal"* in Harvard Business Review (Vol. 88, December 2010, No. 12, pp. 130)
Pub: Harvard Business Publishing
Contact: Diane Belcher, Managing Director
Ed: Daniel McGinn. **Price:** $8.95, PDF. **Description:** Stephen Greer's scrap metal firm, Hartwell Pacific, lost several million dollars due to a lack of efficient and appropriate inventory audits, accounting procedures, and new-hire reference checks for his foreign operations. Greer believes that balancing growth with control is a key component of success. **Availability:** Print; PDF.

27997 ■ *"Dean Foods: Uh Oh. Here Comes Wal-Mart"* in Ice Cream Reporter (Vol. 23, September 20, 2010, No. 10, pp. 8)
Description: Dean Foods promoted Joseph Scalzo to President and Chief Operating Officer to oversee the firm's operational turnaround and near-term strategic initiatives as well as business units. Key functions will include worldwide supply chain and research and development. **Availability:** Online.

27998 ■ *"Don't Tweak Your Supply Chain - Rethink It End to End"* in Harvard Business Review (Vol. 88, October 2010, No. 10, pp. 62)
Pub: Harvard Business Publishing
Contact: Diane Belcher, Managing Director
Ed: Hau L. Lee. **Price:** $8.95, PDF. **Description:** Hong Kong apparel firm Esquel Apparel Ltd. is used to illustrate supply chain reorganization to improve a firm's sustainability. Discussion focuses on taking a broad approach rather than addressing individual steps or processes. **Availability:** Online; PDF.

27999 ■ *eBay Business the Smart Way*
Released: 3rd edition. **Description:** eBay commands ninety percent of all online auction business. Computer and software expert and online entrepreneur shares information to help online sellers get started

and move merchandise on eBay. Tips include the best ways to build credibility, find products to sell, manage inventory, create a storefront Website, and more. **Availability:** Print; PDF.

28000 ■ *"Economic Trends for Small Business" in Small Business Economic Trends (April 2008, pp. 1)*

Description: Summary of economic trends for small businesses in the U.S. is presented. Economic indicators such as capital spending, inventories and sales, inflation, and profits are given. Analysis of credit markets is also provided. **Availability:** Online.

28001 ■ *Housecleaning Business: Organize Your Business - Get Clients and Referrals - Set Rates and Services*

Ed: Laura Jorstad, Melinda Morse. **Price:** Paperback,softback. **Description:** This book shares insight into starting a housecleaning business. It shows how to develop a service manual, screen clients, serve customers, select cleaning products, competition, how to up a home office, using the Internet to grow the business and offering green cleaning options to clients. **Availability:** E-book; Print.

28002 ■ *"Iconic Boise Skateboard Shop to Close" in Idaho Business Review (August 19, 2014)*

Pub: BridgeTower Media

Contact: Adam Reinebach, President

Description: Lori Wright and Lori Ambur have owned Newt & Harold's for over 30 years. The partners are closing the firm that sold skateboards and snowboards. Wright focused on the marketing and inventory aspects of the retail shop, while Ambur ran the organizational and financial end. Wright and Ambur say they are leaving retail because the industry has faced so many changes since they first opened, particularly competing with online stores.

28003 ■ *"Is Your Supply Chain Sustainable?" in Harvard Business Review (Vol. 88, October 2010, No. 10, pp. 74)*

Pub: Harvard Business Publishing

Contact: Diane Belcher, Managing Director

Price: $8.95, PDF. **Description:** Charts and models are presented to help a firm assess its sustainability. **Availability:** Online; PDF.

28004 ■ *"It May Be Cheaper to Manufacture At Home" in Harvard Business Review (Vol. 88, October 2010, No. 10, pp. 84)*

Pub: Harvard Business Publishing

Contact: Diane Belcher, Managing Director

Ed: Suzanne de Treville, Lenos Trigeorgis. **Price:** $8.95, PDF. **Description:** Using a real options framework rather than a discounted cash flow model to assess and value supply chain processes is examined. This enables companies to assess costs for a variety of situations, not just ideal or normal circumstances, which can make the difference between domestic and foreign manufacturing decisions. **Availability:** Online; PDF.

28005 ■ *"Miller's Crossroad" in Canadian Business (Vol. 83, September 14, 2010, No. 15, pp. 58)*

Ed: Joe Castaldo. **Released:** September 14, 2010. **Description:** Future Electronics founder and billionaire Robert Miller shares the secret of Future's unique operating model, which is based on inventory and market research. Miller attributes much of the company's success to its privately held status that enables quick movement against competitors. **Availability:** Print; Online.

28006 ■ *"No. 252: H. Bloom: Floral Subscriptions" in Inc. (Vol. 36, September 2014, No. 7, pp. 132)*

Pub: Mansueto Ventures L.L.C.

Contact: Stephanie Mehta, Chief Executive Officer

Released: September 2014. **Description:** Spoilage is the largest problem facing flower shops. H. Bloom provides custom floral designs to high-end hotels, spas, restaurants, retailers, and apartment and office buildings through their subscription service. The firm found that regular orders provides better inventory control and less waste. Weekly, biweekly, or monthly deliveries are available. **Availability:** Print; Online.

28007 ■ *"Oreos, Mercedes Join Super Bowl Ad Lineup; 90 Percent of Inventory Sold" in Advertising Age (Vol. 83, October 8, 2012, No. 36, pp. 3)*

Description: Mercedes-Benz and Oreo cookes, along with Coca-Cola and Best Buy, announced marketing plans to advertise during Super Bowl XLVII. **Availability:** Print; Online.

28008 ■ *"Perfecting Customer Services" in Pet Product News (Vol. 64, November 2010, No. 11, pp. 18)*

Ed: Alison Bour. **Description:** Pet supply retailers are encouraged to emphasize customer experience and sales representatives' knowledge of the store's product offerings to foster repeat business. Employee protocols could be implemented to improve customer interaction. Other guidelines on developing a pet supply retail environment that advances repeat business are presented. **Availability:** Online.

28009 ■ *"Small Business Economic Trends: Moderate Improvement but No Clear Direction" in Small Business Economic Trends (March 2008, pp. 3)*

Pub: National Federation of Independent Business

Contact: Brad Close, President

Ed: William C. Dunkelberg, Holly Wade. **Description:** Commentary on the economic trends for small businesses in the U.S. is presented. Analysis of the labor market and low interest rates is given. The effect of the Federal Reserve's policy announcement on small business owner optimism is also discussed. **Availability:** Print; Online.

28010 ■ *"Small Business Inventories" in Small Business Economic Trends (February 2008, pp. 14)*

Pub: National Federation of Independent Business

Contact: Brad Close, President

Ed: William C. Dunkelberg, Holly Wade. **Description:** Three tables and a graph presenting the inventories of small businesses in the U.S. are given. The tables include figures on actual inventory changes, inventory satisfaction, and inventory plans. **Availability:** Print; Online.

28011 ■ *"Summary. Economic Trends for Small Business" in Small Business Economic Trends (February 2008, pp. 1)*

Pub: National Federation of Independent Business

Contact: Brad Close, President

Ed: William C. Dunkelberg, Holly Wade. **Description:** Summary of economic trends for small businesses in the U.S. is provided. Economic indicators such as capital spending, inventories and sales, inflation, and profits are given. Analysis of credit markets is also provided.

28012 ■ *"A Supply-Side Solution for Health Care" in Barron's (Vol. 92, July 23, 2012, No. 30, pp. 30)*

Pub: Dow Jones & Company Inc.

Contact: Almar Latour, Chief Executive Officer

Ed: H. Woody Brock. **Description:** The United States should increase the supply of new doctors, nurses and other health care professionals to improve the American health care system by increasing supply. Health care reform proposals in the US Congress fail to address the supply side of the problem. **Availability:** Online.

28013 ■ *"The Sustainable Supply Chain" in Harvard Business Review (Vol. 88, October 2010, No. 10, pp. 70)*

Pub: Harvard Business Publishing

Contact: Diane Belcher, Managing Director

Ed: Steven Prokesch. **Price:** $8.95, PDF. **Description:** Peter Senge, founder of the Society for Organizational Learning, emphasizes the importance of assessing the system as a whole under which one is operating, and learning how to work with individuals with which one has not worked previously. He also points to nongovernmental organizations to provide assistance and legitimacy. **Availability:** Online; PDF.

28014 ■ *"The Transparent Supply Chain" in Harvard Business Review (Vol. 88, October 2010, No. 10, pp. 76)*

Pub: Harvard Business Publishing

Contact: Diane Belcher, Managing Director

Ed: Steve New. **Price:** $8.95, PDF. **Description:** Examination of the use of new technologies to create a transparent supply chain, such as next-generation 2D bar codes in clothing labels that can provide data on a garment's provenance. **Availability:** Online; PDF.

28015 ■ *"An Unfair Knock on Nokia" in Barron's (Vol. 88, March 10, 2008, No. 10, pp. 36)*

Pub: Dow Jones & Company Inc.

Contact: Almar Latour, Chief Executive Officer

Ed: Mark Veverka. **Description:** Discusses the decision by the brokerage house Exane to recommend a Sell on Nokia shares, presumably due to higher inventories, which is unfounded. The news that the company's inventories are rising is not an indicator of falling demand for its products. The company is also benefiting from solid management and rising market share. **Availability:** Online.

28016 ■ *"Waterloo Gardens Files for Bankruptcy" in Philadelphia Business Journal (Vol. 28, July 20, 2012, No. 23, pp. 1)*

Pub: Baltimore Business Journal

Contact: Rhonda Pringle, President

E-mail: rpringle@bizjournals.com

Description: Nursery and garden center Waterloo Gardens Inc. has voluntarily filed Chapter 11 bankruptcy protection in the Eastern District of Pennsylvania as it attempts to reorganize. Watrloos' Devon location will be closing, while its inventory will be relocated to its Exton location. Factors that might have contributed to the bankruptcy filing are also discussed. **Availability:** Print; Online.

28017 ■ *"Weathering the Economic Storm" in Playthings (Vol. 107, January 1, 2009, No. 1, pp. 10)*

Ed: J. Tol Broome, Jr. **Description:** Six steps for toy companies to survive the economic turndown are outlined: Outline your business model; seek professional input; meet with your banker; cut your costs; manage your inventory; and use your trade credit. **Availability:** Print; Online.

28018 ■ *"Zacks Industry Outlook Highlights: Target, Cabela's and Family Dollar Stores" in Marketing Weekly News (April 28, 2012, pp. 351)*

Description: Zacks Industry Outlook focuses on retailers such as Target, Cabela's and Family Dollar Stores. An examination of ways retailers are working to improve sales and profits and productivity is given, including supply-chain management, cost containment, inventory management, and merchandise initiatives. **Availability:** Print; Online.

FRANCHISES AND BUSINESS OPPORTUNITIES

28019 ■ **AccuTrak Inventory Specialists**

PO Box 14782

Surfside Beach, SC 29587

Ph: (843)536-8701
URL: http://www.accutrakinventory.com
Contact: Vince Perrin, Co-Founder
Description: Provider of inventory auditing and loss prevention consulting services. **Training:** Provides 4 days at headquarters, 4 days at approved franchisee training site with ongoing support.

28020 ■ Sculpture Hospitality
601-505 Consumers Rd.
 Toronto, ON, Canada M2J 4V8

Ph: (512)572-6123
Free: 888-238-4626
Co. E-mail: info@sculpturehospitality.com
URL: http://www.sculpturehospitality.com
Contact: Vanessa De Caria, President
Facebook: www.facebook.com/sculpturehospitality
Linkedin: www.linkedin.com/company/sculpturehospi
 tality
X (Twitter): x.com/sculptureHQ
Instagram: www.instagram.com/sculpture.hospitality

YouTube: www.youtube.com/channel/UCMzz
 -FD7WmK2W4FGI41O-BQ
Description: Firm provides technology solutions and services to bar and restaurant operators. **Founded:** 1987. **Financial Assistance:** Yes **Training:** 7 days corporate training in Toronto, 5-10 days regional training with state master franchise.

ASSOCIATIONS AND OTHER ORGANIZATIONS

28021 ■ **Strategic and Competitive Intelligence Professionals (SCIP)**
7550 IH 10 W, Ste. 400
  San Antonio, TX 78229
Co. E-mail: memberservices@scip.org
URL: http://www.scip.org
Contact: Cam Mackey, Executive Director
Linkedin: www.linkedin.com/company/scip
X (Twitter): x.com/SCIP

Description: Acts as a forum for the exchange of news and ideas among professionals involved in competitive intelligence and analysis. Addresses legal and ethical concerns; provides opportunities for improving professional expertise. Conducts programs of interest to members. **Founded:** 1986. **Publications:** *Competitive Intelligence*; *Journal of Competitive Intelligence and Management* (Quarterly); *Strategic and Competitive Intelligence Professionals-Membership Directory*; *SCIP.ORG In-box* (Weekly). **Awards:** SCIP Catalyst Award (Annual); Faye Brill Award (Biennial); SCIP Meritorious Award (Annual). **Geographic Preference:** Multinational.

REFERENCE WORKS

28022 ■ *"Ask Inc.: Managing and Real Estate to Build Value"* in *Inc.* (December 2007, pp. 83-84)
Ed: Ari Weinzweig. **Price:** $8.95. **Description:** Questions regarding knowledge management in the case of a retiring CFO, issues involved in opening a satellite office for a New York realtor, and information for hiring a multicultural workforce are all discussed. **Availability:** PDF; Online.

28023 ■ *"Bridging the Worlds"* in *Academy of Management Journal (Vol. 50, No. 5, October 1, 2007, pp. 1043)*
Pub: Academy of Management
Contact: Sharon Alvarez, President

Ed: Lise Saari. **Description:** Need to transfer human resource research information published in journals to practitioners and organizations is investigated, along with suggestions on ways of achieving this goal. **Availability:** Electronic publishing; PDF; Download; Online.

28024 ■ *"Bring Out the Best in Your Team"* in *Harvard Business Review Vol. 92, September 2014, No. 9, pp. 26)*
Pub: Harvard Business Publishing
Contact: Diane Belcher, Managing Director

Price: $6. **Description:** Social influence often impacts team decision making, as more outgoing members tend to dominate discussion. To replace social influence with informational influence, have team members state at the beginning what knowledge they have regarding the task at hand. **Availability:** Online; PDF.

28025 ■ *"Capitalizing On Our Intellectual Capital"* in *Harvard Business Review (Vol. 90, May 2012, No. 5, pp. 42)*
Pub: Harvard Business Review Press
Contact: Moderna V. Pfizer, Contact

Ed: Iqbal Quadir. **Price:** $6, hardcopy and PDF. **Description:** By managing education as an export, the US can benefit not only from revenue received from tuition, but also from the relationships forged with foreign students. The students will import the networks and technologies they used while in the US and their education levels will help create global growth. **Availability:** Print; Online; PDF.

28026 ■ *"Contextual Intelligence: Despite 30 Years of Experimentation and Study, We are Only Starting to Understand that Some Managerial Knowledge is Universal and Some is Specific to a Market or a Culture"* in *Harvard Business Review (Vol. 92, September 2014, No. 9, pp. 58)*
Pub: Harvard Business Publishing
Contact: Diane Belcher, Managing Director

Price: $8.95. **Description:** Contextual intelligence is defined as the ability to adapt knowledge to circumstances different from those under which the knowledge was initially developed. Firms should observe both employees and customers to understand local variations. **Availability:** Online; PDF.

28027 ■ *"Dynamically Integrating Knowledge in Teams: Transforming Resources Into Performance"* in *Academy of Management Journal (Vol. 55, August 1, 2012, No. 4, pp. 998)*
Pub: Academy of Management
Contact: Sharon Alvarez, President

Ed: Heidi K. Gardner, Francesca Gino, Bradley R. Staats. **Description:** A method for developing a knowledge-integration capability to dynamically integrate the resources of team members into higher performance is proposed. Results suggest that the development of this capability is aided by the use of relational, structural, and experiential resources while uncertainty plays a moderating role in these relationships. **Availability:** Electronic publishing; Download; PDF; Online.

28028 ■ *"Enriching the Ecosystem: A Four-Point Plan for Linking Innovation, Enterprises, and Jobs"* in *Harvard Business Review (Vol. 90, March 2012, No. 3, pp. 140)*
Pub: Harvard Business Review Press
Contact: Moderna V. Pfizer, Contact

Ed: Rosabeth Moss Kanter. **Price:** $8.95, hardcopy black and white. **Description:** The four goals for enriching the ecosystem include: linking venture creation and knowledge creation to speed up the idea-to-enterprise transition; revitalizing small-, medium-, and large-sized firms via partnerships; improving matches between education and employment opportunities; and bringing together leaders across different sectors to create regional strategies. **Availability:** Print; PDF; Online.

28029 ■ *"Expatriate Knowledge Transfer, Subsidiary Absorptive Capacity, and Subsidiary Performance"* in *Academy of Management Journal (Vol. 55, August 1, 2012, No. 4, pp. 927)*
Pub: Academy of Management
Contact: Sharon Alvarez, President

Ed: Yi-Ying Chang, Yaping Gong, Mike W. Peng. **Description:** The influence of expatriate competencies in knowledge transfer on the performance of subsidiary companies is examined. Results suggest that the success of knowledge transfer and subsidiary performance rely on the expatriates' ability and motivation to transfer knowledge as well as on the action taken by multinational corporations to develop subsidiary absorptive capacity. **Availability:** Electronic publishing; Download; PDF; Online.

28030 ■ *"From the Battlefield to the Boardroom"* in *Business Horizons (Vol. 51, March-April 2008, No. 2, pp. 79)*
Pub: Elsevier Advanced Technology Publications

Ed: Catherine M. Dalton. **Description:** Effective intelligence gathering, a thorough understanding of the mission, efficient use of resources, and strategic leadership are vital to achieving success in business as well as in the battlefield. Examples of effective leadership in the battle of Gettysburg are cited. **Availability:** Online.

28031 ■ *"From Common To Uncommon Knowledge: Foundations of Firm-Specific Use of Knowledge as a Resource"* in *Academy of Management Journal (Vol. 55, April 1, 2012, No. 2, pp. 421)*
Pub: Academy of Management
Contact: Sharon Alvarez, President

Ed: Rajiv Nag. **Description:** A model of how top managers seek, use, and transform common knowledge into distinctive, uncommon knowledge as an approach to competitive advantage is developed. In this context, knowledge is not just regarded as a basis for strategy but also a strategic resource. Characteristics of knowledge adaptation and augmentation are also described as distinct forms of knowledge-use-in-practice. **Availability:** Electronic publishing; Download; PDF; Online.

28032 ■ *"German Win Through Sharing"* in *Canadian Business (Vol. 83, September 14, 2010, No. 15, pp. 16)*
Pub: Rogers Media Inc.
Contact: Neil Spivak, Chief Executive Officer

Ed: Jordan Timm. **Released:** September 14, 2010. **Description:** German economic historian Eckhard Hoffner has a two-volume work showing how German's relaxed attitude toward copyright and intellectual property helped it catch up to industrialized United Kingdom. Hoffner's research is in response to his interest in the usefulness of software patents. Information on the debate regarding Canada's copyright laws is given. **Availability:** Print; Online.

28033 ■ *"How Business Intelligence Can Affect Bottomline"* in *Canadian Electronics* (Vol. 23, February 2008, No. 1, pp. 6)

Description: Business intelligence has an important role in delivering the right information in a secured manner. However, coping with data volume, cost, workload, time, availability and compliance have been a problem for business intelligence projects. Ways to avoid problems in business intelligence projects and examples of business intelligence applications are provided. **Availability:** Online.

28034 ■ *"The Impact of Acquisitions On the Productivity of Inventors at Semiconductor Firms: A Synthesis of Knowledge-Based and Incentive-Based Perspective"* in *Academy of Management Journal* (Vol. 50, No. 5, October 1, 2007, pp. 1133)

Pub: Academy of Management

Contact: Sharon Alvarez, President

Ed: Rahul Kapoor, Kwanghui Lim. **Description:** Study examined the relation between knowledge-based and incentive-based outlook in explaining the impact of acquisitions on the productivity of inventors at acquired semiconductor firms. Results showed a definite relation between the two perspectives. **Availability:** Electronic publishing; Download; PDF; Online.

28035 ■ *"Innovative Ability and Entrepreneurial Activity: Two Factors to Enhance 'Quality of Life"* in *Journal of Business & Industrial Marketing* (Vol. 29, July 2014, No. 6)

Pub: Emerald Group Publishing Limited

Contact: Erika Valenti, President

Description: Examination of how aspects of knowledge economy covered by the KEI (Knowledge Economy Index) and those of entrepreneurial activity covered by the GEI (Global Entrepreneurship Index) affect QOL (quality of Life) in a country. KEI, GEI, and QOL data gathered from different countries was analyzed using correlation and regression analyses. It was observed that KEI and GEI feature a momentous effect on QOL, while innovation index and total early stage entrepreneurship improve it. **Availability:** Download; Online.

28036 ■ *"Lawyers Sued Over Lapsed Lacrosse Patent"* in *Crain's Detroit Business* (Vol. 25, June 8, 2009, No. 23, pp. 5)

Pub: Crain Communications Inc.

Contact: Barry Asin, President

Ed: Chad Halcom. **Description:** Warrior Sports Inc., a manufacturer of lacrosse equipment located in Warren, Michigan is suing the law firm Dickinson Wright PLLC and two of its intellectual property lawyers over patent rights to lacrosse equipment. **Availability:** Print; Online.

28037 ■ *"Legislating the Cloud"* in *Information Today* (Vol. 28, October 2011, No. 9, pp. 1)

Pub: Information Today Inc.

Contact: Thomas H. Hogan, President

Ed: Kurt Schiller. **Description:** Internet and telecommunications industry leaders are asking for legislation to address the emerging market in cloud computing. Existing communications laws do not adequately govern the modern Internet.

28038 ■ *"LIBOR's Hidden Lesson: Instant Messages Are Deadly"* in *Canadian Business* (Vol. 85, August 12, 2012, No. 14, pp. 75)

Ed: Vanessa Farquharson. **Description:** The appropriate use of instant messaging in the workplace is discussed. Employees involved in a business that deals with other people's finances or intellectual property are advised to keep all of their work and private email accounts separate. **Availability:** Print; Online.

28039 ■ *"Linking HRM and Knowledge Transfer Via Individual-Level Mechanisms"* in *Human Resource Management* (Vol. 51,May-June 2012, No. 3, pp. 387-405)

Pub: John Wiley & Sons, Inc.

Contact: Christina Van Tassell, Executive Vice President Chief Financial Officer

Ed: Dana B. Minbaeva, Kristina Makela, Larissa Rabbiosi. **Released:** May 25, 2012. **Description:** The relationship between human resource management and knowledge transfer and the role of individual-level mechanisms in this relationship are examined. Results indicate that individual-level perceptions of organizational commitment to knowledge sharing and extrinsic motivation affect internal knowledge exchange among employees. **Availability:** Print; PDF; Online.

28040 ■ *Managing the Older Worker: How to Prepare for the New Organizational Order*

Pub: Harvard Business Press

Contact: Gabriela Allmi, Regional Manager

E-mail: gabriela.allmi@hbsp.harvard.edu

Ed: Peter Cappelli, Bill Novelli. **Description:** Your organization needs older workers more than ever: They transfer knowledge between generations, transmit your company's values to new hires, make excellent mentors for younger employees, and provide a 'just in time' workforce for special projects. **Availability:** Print; Audio.

28041 ■ *"Managing Your Innovation Portfolio: People Throughout Your Organization Are Energetically Pursuing the New. But Does All That Add Up To a Strategy?"* in *Harvard Business Review* (Vol. 90, May 2012, No. 5, pp. 66)

Pub: Harvard Business Review Press

Contact: Moderna V. Pfizer, Contact

Ed: Bansi Nagji, Geoff Tuff. **Price:** $8.95. **Description:** Returns on innovation are higher with transformational initiatives than with core or adjacent pursuits, but require unique management methods. These include establishing a diverse talent set, separating teams from daily operations, and obtaining funding from outside the regular budget cycle. **Availability:** Online; PDF.

28042 ■ *Organizations Alive!: Six Things That Challenge - Seven That Bring Success*

Pub: Yuill & Associates

Ed: Jan Yuill. **Price:** C$18.95, paperback. **Description:** New insight into understanding how organizations function as individuals is presented by an international consultant. Customer service, resource management, outsourcing, and management are among the issues covered.

28043 ■ *"Perfecting Customer Services"* in *Pet Product News* (Vol. 64, November 2010, No. 11, pp. 18)

Ed: Alison Bour. **Description:** Pet supply retailers are encouraged to emphasize customer experience and sales representatives' knowledge of the store's product offerings to foster repeat business. Employee protocols could be implemented to improve customer interaction. Other guidelines on developing a pet supply retail environment that advances repeat business are presented. **Availability:** Online.

28044 ■ *"Quitting Your Job Might Be Tougher Than You Think"* in *Canadian Business* (Vol. 85, July 16, 2012, No. 11-12, pp. 71)

Ed: Matthew McClearn. **Description:** Employees who are planning to resign should consider the notice period, the time it will take for employers to find a replacement and the reason for leaving. Departing employees can use their knowledge and skills to compete directly with their former employer, but they should be wary of unfair competition. **Availability:** Online.

28045 ■ *"Reviving Entrepreneurship: Policy Decisions in 12 Areas Could Nurture - Or Cripple - America's Greatest Asset"* in *Harvard Business Review* (Vol. 90, March 2012, No. 3, pp. 116)

Pub: Harvard Business Review Press

Contact: Moderna V. Pfizer, Contact

Ed: Josh Lerner, William A. Sahlman. **Price:** $8.95, hardcover. **Description:** Government policies should address entrepreneurship as a process, rather than an act. Several key areas for policymaking include basic and translational science, supply and quality of human capital, information availability, tax treatment of rewards and risks, intellectual property rights, workforce healthcare, and mobility of financial and human capital. **Availability:** PDF; Online.

28046 ■ *"Size Does Matter"* in *International Journal of Globalisation and Small Business* (Vol. 4, September 21, 2010, No. 1, pp. 61)

Ed: Julia Connell, Ranjit Voola. **Description:** Examination of how members of an Australian-based manufacturing and engineering cluster share knowledge through networking as a means to improve competitive advantage. **Availability:** Online.

28047 ■ *Successful Proposal Strategies for Small Businesses: Using Knowledge Management to Win Government, Private-Sector, and International Contracts*

Pub: Artech House Inc.

Contact: Ed Waltz, Editor

Ed: Robert S. Frey. **Released:** Sixth edition. **Price:** $153, print; $153, e-book, CD-ROM included; $39, hardback; $76.50, digital download and online; $80. **Description:** Front-end proposal planning and storyboarding, focusing on the customer mission in proposals, along with the development of grant proposals. **Availability:** E-book; Print; Online; Download.

28048 ■ *"U.S. Competitiveness and the Chinese Challenge"* in *Harvard Business Review* (Vol. 90, March 2012, No. 3, pp. 40)

Pub: Harvard Business Review Press

Contact: Moderna V. Pfizer, Contact

Ed: Xu Xiaonian. **Price:** $6, hardcover. **Description:** Although China's shift from cntral planningto market-oriented policies has boosted innovation, intellectual property rights and original research are still insufficiently valued. The U.S. has the edge on China in this respect; it remains for the U.S. to restore confidence in its innovation and creativity. **Availability:** PDF; Online.

28049 ■ *"Valuation of Intangible Assets in Franchise Companies and Multinational Groups: A Current Issue"* in *Franchise Law Journal* (Vol. 27, No. 3, Winter 2008)

Ed: Bruce D. Schaeffer, Susan J. Robins. **Released:** Volume 27. **Description:** Intangible assets, also known as intellectual properties are the most valuable assets for companies today. Legal intellectual property issues faced by franchises firms are discussed.

28050 ■ *"Why HR Practices Are Not Evidence-Based"* in *Academy of Management Journal* (Vol. 50, No. 5, October 1, 2007, pp. 1033)

Pub: Academy of Management

Contact: Sharon Alvarez, President

Ed: Edward E. Lawler. **Description:** A suggestion that an Evidence-Based Management Collaboration (EBMC) can be established to facilitate effective transfer of ideas between science and practice is presented. **Availability:** Electronic publishing; PDF; Download; Online.

28051 ■ *"With Whom Do You Trade? Defensive Innovation and the Skill-Bias" in Canadian Journal of Electronics (Vol. 43, November 2010)*

Pub: Journal of the Canadian Economics Association

Ed: Pushan Dutt, Daniel Traca. **Released:** Vol. 43, No. 4. **Price:** $5. **Description:** Examination into whether increased trade with ineffective protection of intellectual property has contributed to the skill-deepening of the 1980s. An index of effective protection of intellectual property at the country level, combining data on protection of patents and rule of law are presented. An industry-specific version of this index is given using as weights each country's trade share in the total trade of the industry. A decline is seen in this trade-weighted index, owing to a rise in trade with countries with low effective protection of intellectual property, which explains 29 percent of the rise within-industry skill-intensity. **Availability:** Print; Online; Download.

VIDEO/AUDIO MEDIA

28052 ■ *The Power of Knowledge & Bootstrapping for 20 Years*

URL(s): www.startuphustlepodcast.com/the-power-of-knowledge-bootstrapping-for-20-years

Ed: Matt Watson. **Released:** May 14, 2024. **Description:** Podcast discusses knowledge management, training materials, and onboarding.

START-UP INFORMATION

28053 ■ *"3rd Annual 'OneMedForum NY 2012', July 11th-12th, to Spotlight JOBS Act, Crowdfunding, and Promising Areas for Healthcare Investment" in Investment Weekly (June 23, 2012)*
Description: Third annual forum presented by OneMed provided sessions for understanding the changes in regulation due to the new JOBS Act, which will create opportunities for investors and entrepreneurs. Experts in healthcare and life science investments will be featured. Details of the event are covered. **Availability:** Online.

28054 ■ *"Allied Brokers of Texas Looking to Fill Private Lending Gap" in San Antonio Business Journal (Vol. 26, March 23, 2012, No. 8, pp. 1)*
Pub: Baltimore Business Journal
Contact: Rhonda Pringle, President
E-mail: rpringle@bizjournals.com
Description: San Antonio, Texas-based Allied Brokers of Texas has announced the expansion of its services to offer private lending. The move would provide direct private financing of $250,000 to $5 million to entrepreneurs looking to buy or sell a small business. Insights into the firm's new subsidiary, Allied Lending Services, are also offered. **Availability:** Print; Online.

28055 ■ *"Alpharetta Seeding Startups To Encourage Job Growth" in Atlanta Business Chronicle(June 20, 2014, pp. 3A)*
Pub: American City Business Journals, Inc.
Contact: Mike Olivieri, Executive Vice President
Description: The City of Alpharetta is witnessing several incubators and accelerators that will create the physical and educational infrastructure to convert ideas into sustainable businesses. This will help startups develop a go-to-market strategy, prepare for FDA certification and insurance reimbursement as well as see that the company reaches a point where it can attract private equity or venture capital. **Availability:** Print; Online.

28056 ■ *"Begslist.org Launches Crowdfunding On Its Website" in Computer Business Week (August 2, 2012)*
Description: Donation Website called Begslist has added crowdfunding to its site. Crowdfunding and begging are popular among small startups wishing to procure funding for their new companies. **Availability:** Online.

28057 ■ *"Beyond Bootstrapping" in Inc. (Vol. 36, September 2014, No. 7, pp. 64)*
Pub: Mansueto Ventures L.L.C.
Contact: Stephanie Mehta, Chief Executive Officer
Price: $15, Nonmembers. **Description:** Dave Lerner, serial entrepreneur, angel investor, B-school professor, and author, explains the challenges entrepreneurs face when self-funding their startup business. **Availability:** PDF; Online.

28058 ■ *"Crowdfunding Becomes Relevant for Medical Start-Ups as TCB Medical Launches Campaign On Idiegogo to Bring Life-Saving Epinephrine Key to Market" in PR Newswire (July 31, 2012)*
Pub: PR Newswire Association LLC.
Ed: Hilton Head. **Description:** Startup company, TCB Medical Devices, is hoping to raise money through crowdfunding to launch its life-saving Epinephrine Key to the marketplace. According to allergist, Thomas C. Beller, MD, epinephrine provides safe and effective relief to allergy sufferers. **Availability:** Online.

28059 ■ *"CrowdFunding Platform, START.ac, Announces It Is Expanding Its International Scope From the US, Canada and the UK to 36 Countries Including Australia, India, Israel, Italy and Africa" in Benzinga.com (July 11, 2012)*
Pub: Benzinga.com
Contact: Jason Raznick, Founder
Ed: Aaron Wise. **Description:** START.ac is expanding its CrowdFunding site to include 36 countries and increasing its scope to include business startups, teen projects, as well as medical products. START.ac projects are in the fundraising stage at this point, with 23 percent located outside the United States. **Availability:** Online.

28060 ■ *"Entrepreneurs: Search Party" in Business Strategy Review (Vol. 21, Autumn 2010, No. 3, pp. 30)*
Ed: Georgina Peters. **Released:** September 22, 2010. **Description:** Entrepreneurs tend to be fixated on coming up with a foolproof idea for a new business and then raising money to start it. Raising startup funds is difficult, but it doesn't have to be that way. Search funds offer an innovative alternative, and the results are often impressive. **Availability:** Electronic publishing; Online.

28061 ■ *Entrepreneurship*
Pub: John Wiley & Sons, Inc.
Contact: Christina Van Tassell, Executive Vice President Chief Financial Officer
Ed: William D. Bygrave, Andrew Zacharakis. **Released:** Fourth edition. **Price:** $75.95, paperback. **Description:** Information for starting a new business is shared, focusing on marketing and financing a product or service. **Availability:** Print.

28062 ■ *"Equity 'Crowdfunding' Platform, RelayFund, Launched by Michigan Investor Group" in Economics Week (July 20, 2012)*
Description: RelayFund was launched by a group of Michigan venture capitalists, entrepreneurs, and investment bankers to link small investors with startup firms under the new JOBS (Jumpstart Our Business Startups) Act. Crowdfunding is money raised for charities, projects or pre-selling products or services and allows online micro investments for startup companies.

28063 ■ *"ETF Process May be Tweaked" in Austin Business JournalInc. (Vol. 28, December 26, 2008, No. 41, pp. 3)*
Description: Some government officials are proposing for an adjustment of the Texas Emerging Technology Fund's (ETF) policies. The ETF was created to get startup companies capital to get off the ground. Reports show that the global recession had made it more difficult for startup companies to garner investment. **Availability:** Online.

28064 ■ *"iAM Scientist Launches To Provide a Crowdfunding Platform for Science, Technology, and Medicine" in Benzinga.com (July 31, 2012)*
Pub: Benzinga.com
Contact: Jason Raznick, Founder
Ed: Aaron Wise. **Description:** Medical, technology, and science researchers will be able to seach for funding through the newly launched iAMscientist platform. The sitewill provide a site with funding and shared research opportunities. The new tools, better models, and quicker data collection processes will help make research interdisciplinary, collaborative, data driven, and less predictable. Open Access Funding Platform (OAFP) can be used to solicit funding required to carry out research projects. **Availability:** Print; Online.

28065 ■ *"Kickstarter Funds the Future; Crowdfunding Services Such as Kickstarter Have Been Hailed as a New Way To Get Started In Business and Cut Out the Traditional Money Men" in Telegraph Online (August 24, 2012)*
Pub: Telegraph Media Group Limited
Contact: Nick Hugh, Chief Executive Officer
Ed: Monty Munford. **Description:** More than 530 crowdfunding services are expected to hit the net by the end of the year. Crowdfunding helps companies raise money from investors for specific projects. A musician was able to raise over $1 million to fund a new record. **Availability:** Online.

28066 ■ *"Legal Matters: 'Crowdfunding' a Boon for Entrepreneurs, If They Clear Regulatory Hurdles" in Finance and Commerce (July 17, 2012)*
Pub: BridgeTower Media
Contact: Adam Reinebach, President
Ed: Dan Heilman. **Description:** Part of the Jumpstart Our Business Startups Act (JOBS) is crowdfunding, which allows the funding of a company by selling small parts of equity to a group of investors. Kickstarter, a Website for raising funds for business entities, is primarily used for film and book projects. Most businesses cannot adopt Kickstarter's model because of the legality of receiving investor funds without offering security.

28067 ■ *"MicroVentures: New Crowdfunding Game Makes Startups the Stars, Prepares Players for a New Kind of Investing" in Health & Beauty Close-Up (July 31, 2012)*
Description: MicroVentures created the MicroVentures Investor Challenge as a game on Facebook.

The game features real startups such as AirBnB, Etsy, and Pinterest and players invest in these firms. The game has real startups face off in six weekly rounds and the players act as venture capitalists. One startup and one investor will win the game. **Availability:** Print; Online.

28068 ■ *"Military Vet Uses SBA Program to Help Fund His Business"* in *Philadelphia Business Journal (Vol. 33, May 9, 2014, No. 13, pp. 6)*

Pub: American City Business Journals, Inc.

Contact: Mike Olivieri, Executive Vice President

Released: Weekly. **Description:** Colonel Richard Elam and his wife Kimberly, both with the Florida Army National Guard, secured funding through the Small Business Administration's (SBA's) Veterans Advantage program to launch iPlay, which rents mobile entertainment equipment such as rock walls and laser-tag setups for group events. The capital access initiative, launched in January 2014, waives the origination fee for SBA Express loans to qualified veteran entrepreneurs. **Availability:** Print; Online.

28069 ■ *"No. 64: Scaling the Business Meant Rebuilding a Bridge"* in *Inc. (Vol. 36, September 2014, No. 7, pp. 48)*

Pub: Mansueto Ventures L.L.C.

Contact: Stephanie Mehta, Chief Executive Officer

Released: September 2014. **Description:** Profile of Susan Meitner, mortgage industry veteran who founded Centennial Lending Group, a mortgage lending institution. Meitner and her family helped raise the needed $2.5 million to launch the firm in order to provide loans to new customers. **Availability:** Print; Online.

28070 ■ *Raising Capital*

Released: Third edition. **Price:** $34.95, Paperback/E-book. **Description:** Corporate attorney provides a comprehensive guide using in-depth, practical advice on raising money to start and grow a business. A 115-page appendix contains samples of financing agreements, forms and questionnaires. **Availability:** E-book; Print.

28071 ■ *"SBA Program Helped New Company Survive As It Built Company Base"* in *Philadelphia Business Journal (Vol. 33, May 9, 2014, No. 13, pp. 4)*

Pub: American City Business Journals, Inc.

Contact: Mike Olivieri, Executive Vice President

Released: Weekly. **Description:** The Small Business Administration (SBA) Indiana District Business Office helped Netwise Resources set up its information technology (IT) consulting business with a six-month SBA-backed loan and the 8(a) Business Development Program for small disadvantaged businesses. Owner, Mark Gibson, attributes Netwise Resources' success to its focus on branding, recruiting skilled staff, and establishing relationships with clients within the target market. **Availability:** Print; Online.

28072 ■ *"SEC, NASAA Tell Small Businesses: Wait To Join the 'Crowd': Crowdfunding Is 'Not Yet Legal Until the Commission Appoints Rules', Says SEC's Kim"* in *Investment Advisor (Vol. 3, August 2012, No. 8, pp. 13)*

Ed: Melanie Waddell. **Description:** Securities and Exchange Commission along with state regulators have advised small businesses and entrepreneurs to wait until the SEC has produced rules governing crowdfunding practices. Until that happens, federal and state securities laws prohibit publicly accessible Internet securities offerings. An overview of crowdfunding and the JOBS Act is included. **Availability:** Online.

28073 ■ *"So What Is Crowdfunding Anyway? New Legislation by Obama and Congress Relaxes Solicitation by Startups"* in *Accounting Today (August 6, 2012)*

Ed: Jim Brendel. **Description:** An introduction to crowdfunding provides a concise description to the process in which a group of investors partner to fund

small business and startups. Rules from the SEC regarding crowdfunding are expected to be in place by the end of the year. **Availability:** Print; Online.

28074 ■ *"State Fund That Aids New Companies Likely To Wither"* in *Crain's Detroit Business (Vol. 24, February 25, 2008, No. 8, pp. 16)*

Pub: Crain Communications Inc.

Contact: Barry Asin, President

Ed: Tom Henderson. **Description:** Officials are committed to fighting to save funding for the statewide Strategic Economic Investment and Commercialization Board which provides pre-seed money to start-up firms. **Availability:** Print; PDF; Online.

28075 ■ *"Three Common Computer Repair Franchise Funding Sources Revealed by SP Home Run Inc."* in *Investment Weekly News (May 12, 2012)*

Description: SP Home Run discusses three popular sources for initial funding capital when starting a computer repair franchise: family, friends, and fools. It is advised that if money could become a problem within any relationship it is best to avoid that type of funding source. **Availability:** Online.

28076 ■ *The Toilet Paper Entrepreneur: The Tell-It-Like-It-Is Guide to Cleaning Up In Business, Even If You Are At the End of Your Roll*

Pub: Obsidian Launch L.L.C.

Contact: Kelsey Ayres, President

Ed: Mike Michalowicz. **Description:** The founder of three multimillion-dollar companies, including Obsidian Launch, a company that partners with first-time entrepreneurs to grow their concepts into industry leaders. **Availability:** Print; Online.

ASSOCIATIONS AND OTHER ORGANIZATIONS

28077 ■ **Greater Midwest Lenders Association (GMLA)**
PO Box 70
Elwood, IL 60421
Ph: (630)916-7720
Fax: (630)396-3501
URL: http://www.gmlaonline.org
Contact: Robert C. Perry, Executive Director
E-mail: bperry@gmlaonline.org

Description: Trade organization representing mortgage brokers, mortgage bankers, and affiliates throughout the midwestern United States. **Founded:** 1987. **Geographic Preference:** State.

28078 ■ **National Association of Development Companies (NADCO)**
10319 Westlake Dr., Unit 197
Bethesda, MD 20817
Ph: (202)349-0070
Co. E-mail: news@nadco.org
URL: http://www.nadco.org
Contact: Rhonda Pointon, President
E-mail: rpointon@nadco.org
Facebook: www.facebook.com/NADCO504
Linkedin: www.linkedin.com/company/nadco-national
  -association-of-development-companies
X (Twitter): x.com/NADCO504

Description: Provides long-term financing to small and medium-sized businesses. **Founded:** 1981. **Publications:** *NADCO News* (Monthly). **Educational Activities:** Winter Board Meeting (Annual). **Geographic Preference:** National.

28079 ■ **Risk Management Association (RMA)**
1801 Market St., Ste. 300
Philadelphia, PA 19103-1613
Free: 800-677-7621
Fax: (215)446-4100
Co. E-mail: rmaar@rmahq.org
URL: http://www.rmahq.org/Default.aspx
Contact: Nancy Foster, President
Linkedin: www.linkedin.com/company/the-risk
  -management-association
X (Twitter): x.com/RMAHQ

Description: A non-profit professional organization consisting of banks, trust companies, economic development corporations, finance companies, and governmental agencies that conduct research and professional development activities in areas of loan administration, asset management, and commercial lending and credit to increase professionalism. **Founded:** 1914. **Publications:** *Annual Statement Studies: Industry Default Probabilities and Cash Flow Measures* (Annual); *Directory of Credit Information Personnel*; *The RMA Journal*; *Member Roster* (Annual); *RMA Annual Statement Studies* (Annual). **Educational Activities:** Loan Management Seminar; PASLA/RMA Conference on Asian Securities Lending (Annual); RMA's Annual Annual Risk Management Conference (Annual); RMA's Conferences (Annual). **Awards:** RMA Award for Journalistic Excellence (Annual); RMA National Paper Writing Competition Award (Annual). **Geographic Preference:** National.

28080 ■ **Secured Finance Network (SFNet)**
370 7th Ave., Ste. 1801
New York, NY 10001
Ph: (212)792-9390
Fax: (212)564-6053
URL: http://community.cfa.com/home
Contact: Michele Ocejo, Director, Communications
E-mail: mocejo@sfnet.com
URL(s): www.sfnet.comc
X (Twitter): x.com/SFNet_National
Instagram: www.instagram.com/secured_finance_ne
  twork

Description: Organizations engaged in asset-based financial services including commercial financing and factoring and lending money on a secured basis to small- and medium-sized business firms. Acts as a forum for information and consideration about ideas, opportunities and legislation concerning asset-based financial services. Seeks to improve the industry's legal and operational procedures. Offers job placement and reference services for members. Sponsors School for Field Examiners and other educational programs. Compiles statistics; conducts seminars and surveys; maintains speaker's bureau and 21 committees. **Founded:** 1944. **Publications:** *The Secured Lender* (6/year). **Educational Activities:** Annual SFNet Convention (Annual). **Geographic Preference:** Multinational.

SMALL BUSINESS ASSISTANCE PROGRAMS

28081 ■ **LiftFund**
2014 S Hackberry St.
San Antonio, TX 78210
Free: 888-215-2373
Co. E-mail: communications@liftfund.com
URL: http://www.liftfund.com
Contact: Janie Barrera, Founder
E-mail: jbarrera@liftfund.com
Facebook: www.facebook.com/LiftFundUS
Linkedin: www.linkedin.com/company/liftfund
X (Twitter): x.com/LiftFundUS
Instagram: www.instagram.com/liftfundus
YouTube: www.youtube.com/c/liftfundus

Description: Offers small business loans and minority business loans to startups and entrepreneurs. Partners with SBA lenders and other institutions in Texas and throughout the Southeast.

FINANCING AND LOAN PROGRAMS

28082 ■ **California Business Bank (CBB)**
3200 El Camino Real, Ste. 220
Irvine, CA 92602
Ph: (714)389-9964
Free: 866-495-4042
Co. E-mail: aalvarez@californiabusinessbank.com
URL: http://www.californiabusinessbank.com
Contact: Richard Tan, Chairman of the Board

Linkedin: www.linkedin.com/company/california -business-bank

Description: A state-chartered community oriented commercial bank that offers a wide range of business and loan products and services to individuals, professionals, and small to medium-sized businesses. **Founded:** 2005.

28083 ■ Community LendingWorks (CLW)
212 Main St.
 Springfield, OR 97477
Ph: (541)345-0446
Fax: (541)345-9584
Co. E-mail: info@communitylendingworks.org
URL: http://communitylendingworks.org
Contact: Emily Reiman, Executive Director
E-mail: emily@nedcocdc.org
Facebook: www.facebook.com/communitylen dingworks
Linkedin: www.linkedin.com/company/community-len dingworks
X (Twitter): x.com/clendingworks

Description: CDFI (Community Development Financial Institution) offers loans to small businesses. **Founded:** 2011.

28084 ■ Evergreen Business Capital (EBC)
13925 Interurban Ave. S, Ste. 100
 Seattle, WA 98168
Ph: (206)622-3731
Free: 800-878-6613
Fax: (206)623-6613
URL: http://www.evergreen504.com
Contact: Patti Kibbe, President
E-mail: patti.kibbe@evergreen504.com
Facebook: www.facebook.com/ EvergreenBusinessCapital
X (Twitter): x.com/evergreen504
YouTube: www.youtube.com/channel/UCnMv_u-Lggb 2Y_pVs2mWSHA

Description: Provides economic development solutions that support small business stability, growth, and job creation. Partners with lenders in Washington, Oregon, Alaska, and Northern Idaho to provide loans for small businesses in the Northwest. **Founded:** 1980.

EDUCATIONAL PROGRAMS

28085 ■ SBA Loan Options and Best Borrowing Practices for Women
URL(s): wewbc.ecenterdirect.com/events/977255

Description: An online class offered by the Center for Women and Enterprise that discusses the different types of SBA loans, their criteria, and how to apply. **Principal Exhibits:** An online class offered by the Center for Women and Enterprise that discusses the different types of SBA loans, their criteria, and how to apply.

REFERENCE WORKS

28086 ■ "5 Things You Should Know About Getting a Small Business Loan: Insights From a Banking Executive to Improve Your Odds" in Black Enterprise (Vol. 44, June 2014, No. 10, pp. 20)
Pub: Earl G. Graves Ltd.
Contact: Earl Graves, Jr., President

Description: Five important tips for small businesses seeking a loan, include a credit profile, positive feedback from vendors and customers, presence on social media, bringing banker to business on a regular basis, and every six months to three times a year talk to banker about your industry.

28087 ■ "$353 Million in SSBCI Funds Going to Small Businesses in 4 States" in Small Business Trends(March 1, 2023)
URL(s): smallbiztrends.com/2023/03/ssbci-funds-for -small-businesses-in-4-states.html

Ed: Gabrielle Pickard-Whitehead. **Released:** March 01, 2023. **Description:** The State Small Business Credit Initiative is releasing four additional state plans, totaling up to $353.4 million. **Availability:** Online.

28088 ■ American Bar Association Legal Guide for Small Business: Everything You Need to Know About Small Business, from Start-up to Employment to Financing and Selling
Released: Second edition. **Description:** The American Bar Association provides insight into financial, health and family issues affecting small business, including start up issues, employment laws, financing a business, and selling a business.

28089 ■ "Angel Investors Across Texas Collaborate" in Austin Business Journal (Vol. 31, May 20, 2011, No. 11, pp. 1)
Pub: Austin Business Journal
Contact: Rachel McGrath, Director
E-mail: rmcgrath@bizjournals.com

Ed: Christopher Calnan. **Description:** Texas' twelve angel investing groups are going to launch the umbrella organization Alliance of Texas Angel Networks (ATAN) to support more syndicated deals and boost investments in Texas. In 2010, these investing groups infused more than $24 million to startups in 61 deals. **Availability:** Print; Online.

28090 ■ "Asia Breathes a Sigh of Relief" in Business Week (September 22, 2008, No. 4100, pp. 32)
Description: Foreign bankers, such as those in Asia, that had been investing heavily in the United States began to worry as the housing crisis deepened and the impact on Freddie Mac and Fannie Mae became increasingly clear. Due to the government bailout, however, central banks will most likely continue to buy American debt. **Availability:** Print; Online.

28091 ■ "Au Revoir Or Goodbye?" in Barron's (Vol. 88, July 14, 2008, No. 28, pp. 5)
Pub: Dow Jones & Company Inc.
Contact: Almar Latour, Chief Executive Officer

Ed: Alan Abelson. **Description:** Former Senator Phil Gramm's opinion that the U.S. is a "nation of whiners" as they moan about recession is another example of the disconnection between Washington and Wall Street on one hand and the real world on the other. It would be a catastrophe for most of the world if Fannie Mae and Freddie Mac were to go under and take their trillions of mortgage debt with them. **Availability:** Online.

28092 ■ "Auto Loan Demand On the Upswing" in Memphis Business Journal (Vol. 34, May 25, 2012, No. 6, pp. 1)
Pub: Baltimore Business Journal
Contact: Rhonda Pringle, President
E-mail: rpringle@bizjournals.com

Ed: Cole Epley. **Description:** Demand for auto loans in the US has increased in April 2012. Auto loans have surpassed consumerm loans during the first quarter of the year. **Availability:** Print; Online.

28093 ■ "Bad Loans Start Piling Up" in Crain's New York Business (Vol. 24, January 6, 2008, No. 1, pp. 2)
Pub: Crain Communications, Inc.
Contact: Jessica Botos, Manager, Marketing
E-mail: jessica.botos@crainsnewyork.com

Ed: Tom Fredrickson. **Description:** Problems in the subprime mortgage industry have extended to other lending activities as evidenced by bank charge-offs on bad commercial and industrial loans which have more than doubled in the third quarter.

28094 ■ "Baltimore Commercial Real Estate Foreclosures Continue to Rise" in Baltimore Business Journal (Vol. 28, October 1, 2010, No. 21, pp. 1)
Pub: Baltimore Business Journal
Contact: Rhonda Pringle, President
E-mail: rpringle@bizjournals.com

Ed: Daniel J. Sernovitz. **Description:** Foreclosures of commercial real estate across the Greater Baltimore area have continued to rise. The region is now host to about $2 billion worth of commercial properties that carry a maturing debt or have been foreclosed. Commercial real estate owners are unable to finance their debts because banks have become stricter in passing out loans. **Availability:** Print; Online.

28095 ■ "Baltimore Eyeing Tax Breaks for New Arena" in Boston Business Journal (Vol. 29, June 3, 2011, No. 4, pp. 1)
Pub: Boston Business Journal
Contact: Carolyn M. Jones, President
E-mail: cmjones@bizjournals.com

Ed: Daniel J. Sernovitz. **Description:** Baltimore City is opting to give millions of dollars in tax breaks and construction loans to a group of private investors led by William Hackerman who is proposing to build a new arena and hotel at the Baltimore Convention Center. The project will cost $500 million with the state putting up another $400 million for the center's expansion.

28096 ■ "Banks Continue March Out of Bad-Loan Numbers: Total Loans Up, Non-Performing Loans Decline" in Memphis Business Journal (Vol. 34, August 24, 2012, No. 19, pp. 1)
Pub: Baltimore Business Journal
Contact: Rhonda Pringle, President
E-mail: rpringle@bizjournals.com

Description: Banks in Memphis, Tennessee continue to improve their capital status throughout the second quarter of 2012. The twenty-five banks observed showed improvements in total loan volume, as well as in non-performing loans and real estate. Total loans grew $723.26 million, while non-performing loans and real-estate-owned assets fell $322.4 million. **Availability:** Print; Online.

28097 ■ "Banks Looking to Lend, Compete to Make Small-Business Loans" in Puget Sound Business Journal (Vol. 33, August 17, 2012, No. 17, pp. 1)
Pub: Baltimore Business Journal
Contact: Rhonda Pringle, President
E-mail: rpringle@bizjournals.com

Ed: Greg Lamm. **Description:** Mobile Tool Management has grown from four employees to 30 during the past five years, and its expansion was completed after owner Mike woogerd applied for a loan from Chase. Figures show that Chase lent $132 million in the second quarter of 2012 to businesses. A report by the Federal Reserve shows that large banks are owering their standatrds for lending to large and medium-sized companies. **Availability:** Print; Online.

28098 ■ "BankUnited, Banco do Brasil Lead Local Lenders" in South Florida Business Journal (Vol. 35, September 12, 2014, No. 7, pp. 5)
Pub: American City Business Journals, Inc.
Contact: Mike Olivieri, Executive Vice President

Description: South Florida banks have reported a $7.54 billion increase in loans in 2014. BankUnited registered the highest growth with a total of $3.75 billion in loans. National Bank of Florida came in second with $585 million.

28099 ■ "The Bear Stearns-JPMorgan Deal - Rhymes with Steal - Of A Lifetime" in Barron's (Vol. 88, March 24, 2008, No. 12, pp. 24)
Pub: Dow Jones & Company Inc.
Contact: Almar Latour, Chief Executive Officer

Ed: Andrew Bary. **Description:** JPMorgan Chase's impending acquisition of Bear Stearns for $2.50 a share is a huge steal for the former. JPMorgan is set to acquire a company with a potential annual earnings of $1 billion while the Federal Reserve funds Bear's illiquid assets by providing $30 billion in non-recourse loans. **Availability:** Online.

28100 ■ *"The Beauty of Banking's Big Ugly"* in Barron's (Vol. 89, July 27, 2009, No. 30, pp. 31)
Pub: Dow Jones & Company Inc.
Contact: Almar Latour, Chief Executive Officer
Ed: Andrew Bary. **Description:** Appeal of the shares of Citigroup comes from its sharp discount to its tangible book value and the company's positive attributes include a strong capital position, high loan-loss reserves, and their appealing global-consumer. The shares have the potential to generate nice profits and decent stock gains as the economy turns. **Availability:** Online.

28101 ■ *"Best Turnaround Stocks"* in Canadian Business (Vol. 81, Summer 2008, No. 9, pp. 65)
Description: Share prices of Sierra Wireless Inc. and EXFO Electro Optical Engineering Inc. have fallen over the past year but have good chance at a rebound considering that the companies have free cash flow and no long-term debt. One-year stock performance analysis of the two companies is presented. **Availability:** Print; Online.

28102 ■ *"Big Deals With More To Come"* in Business Journal Portland (Vol. 30, January 24, 2014, No. 47, pp. 14)
Pub: American City Business Journals, Inc.
Contact: Mike Olivieri, Executive Vice President
Released: January 24, 2014. **Price:** $4, Introductory 4-Week Offer(Digital & Print). **Description:** D.A. Davidson & Company investment banking head, Brad Gevurtz, describes the local mergers and acquisitions (M&A) market in Portland, Oregon in 2013. Gevurtz says 2014 will be a good year for M&A because corporations have a lot of cash and lenders are lending. **Availability:** Print; Online.

28103 ■ *"BofA Goes for Small Business"* in Austin Business Journal (Vol. 31, July 22, 2011, No. 20, pp. A1)
Pub: Austin Business Journal
Contact: Rachel McGrath, Director
E-mail: rmcgrath@bizjournals.com
Ed: Christopher Calnan. **Description:** Bank of America is planning to target small businesses as new customers. The bank lost its number one market share in Austin, Texas in 2010. **Availability:** Print; Online.

28104 ■ *"Bouncing Back"* in Orlando Business Journal (Vol. 29, September 7, 2012, No. 12, pp. 1)
Description: The Federal Financial Institutions Examination Council's data has shown the total value of small business loans originated in Central Florida by regional and national banks increased by 21.4 percent in 2011 after three years of decline. The total value reached $911 million compared to $750.7 million in 2010. **Availability:** Print; Online.

28105 ■ *"Bracing for a Bear of a Week"* in Barron's (Vol. 88, March 17, 2008, No. 11, pp. 24)
Pub: Dow Jones & Company Inc.
Contact: Almar Latour, Chief Executive Officer
Ed: Jacqueline Doherty. **Description:** JPMorgan Chase and the Federal Reserve Bank of New York's opening of a line of credit to Bear Stearns cut the stock price of Bear Stearns by 47 percent to 30 followed by speculation of an imminent sale. JP Morgan may be the only potential buyer for the firm and some investors say Bears could be sold at $20 to $30. Bears prime assets include its enormous asset base worth $395 billion. **Availability:** Online.

28106 ■ *"Builders: Land Prices Up, Bank Lending Down"* in Orlando Business Journal (Vol. 30, January 31, 2014, No. 32, pp. 5)
Pub: American City Business Journals, Inc.
Contact: Mike Olivieri, Executive Vice President
Released: Weekly. **Price:** $8, introductory 4-week offer(Digital & Print). **Description:** A look at the views of residential real estate executives on the rising land prices and financing of construction is presented.

The limited supply of lots in great locations has resulted in landowners raising asking prices. The real estate downturn has also resulted in the reluctance of many banks to lend money to home builders to finance construction in Central Florida. **Availability:** Print; Online.

28107 ■ *"Can You Say $1 Million? A Language-Learning Start-Up Is Hoping That Investors Can"* in Inc. (Vol. 33, November 2011, No. 9, pp. 116)
Pub: Inc. Magazine
Ed: April Joyner. **Description:** Startup, Verbling is a video platform that links language learners and native speakers around the world. The firm is working to raise money to hire engineers in order to build the product and redesign their Website. **Availability:** Online.

28108 ■ *"Capital Position: M&I Acquisition Opens the Door for Rivals to Gain Market Share"* in Business Journal-Milwaukee (Vol. 28, December 24, 2010, No. 12, pp. A1)
Pub: The Business Journal
Contact: Heather Ladage, President
E-mail: hladage@bizjournals.com
Ed: Rich Kirchen. **Description:** Canada-based BMO Financial Group has purchased Marshall and Isley Corporation (M and I), which dominated lending among Wisconsin businesses for decades. The sale of M and I will enable other banks to recruit M and I's customers but BMO Financial remains a stronger competitor since it possesses a more potent capital position. **Availability:** Print; Online.

28109 ■ *"Cautions on Loans with Your Business"* in Business Owner (Vol. 35, July-August 2011, No. 4, pp. 5)
Description: Caution must be used when borrowing from or lending to any small business. Tax guidelines for the borrowing and lending practice are also included. **Availability:** Print; Online.

28110 ■ *"Chasing Credit"* in Canadian Business (Vol. 81, November 10, 2008, No. 19, pp. 59)
Pub: Rogers Media Inc.
Contact: Neil Spivak, Chief Executive Officer
Ed: Joe Castaldo. **Description:** Small and medium sized companies are dealing with tightening credit because they appear riskier than usual. Some of these businesses are turning to private investors, but this is not easy since many have invested everything in the stock market. The sector is expected to weaken with the broader Canadian market in the next six months from October 2008. **Availability:** Online.

28111 ■ *"Cincinnati Hospitals Feel Pain from Slow Economy"* in Business Courier (Vol. 27, September 3, 2010, No. 18, pp. 1)
Pub: Business Courier
Ed: James Ritchie. **Description:** Hospitals in Cincinnati, Ohio have suffered from decreased revenues owing to the economic crises. Declining patient volumes and bad debt have also adversely impacted hospitals. **Availability:** Print; Online.

28112 ■ *"Cleanup to Polish Plating Company's Bottom Line"* in Crain's Cleveland Business (Vol. 28, October 29, 2007, No. 43, pp. 4)
Pub: Crain Communications Inc.
Contact: K. C. Crain, President
Ed: Jay Miller. **Description:** Barker Products Co, a manufacturer of nuts and bolts, is upgrading its aging facility which will allow them to operate at capacity and will save the company several hundred thousand dollars a year in operating costs. The new owners secured a construction loan from the county's new Commercial Redevelopment Fund which will allow them to upgrade the building which was hampered by years of neglect. **Availability:** Online.

28113 ■ *"Clock Ticks On Columbia Sussex Debt"* in Business Courier (Vol. 27, July 30, 2010, No. 13, pp. 1)
Pub: Business Courier

Ed: Dan Monk. **Description:** Cincinnati, Ohio-based Columbia Sussex Corporation has made plans to restructure a $1 billion loan bundle that was scheduled to mature in October 2010. The privately held hotel has strived in a weak hotel market to keep pace with its $3 billion debt load. **Availability:** Print; Online.

28114 ■ *"Co-Op Launches Revolving Loan Program for Farmers"* in Bellingham Business Journal (Vol. February 2010, pp. 3)
Pub: Sound Publishing Inc.
Contact: Josh O'Connor, President
Ed: Lance Henderson. **Description:** Community Food Co-op's Farm Fund received a $12,000 matching grant from the Sustainable Whatcom Fund of the Whatcom Community Foundation. The Farm Fund will create a new revolving loan program for local farmers committed to using sustainable practices.

28115 ■ *"Coming Soon: Bailouts of Fannie and Freddie"* in Barron's (Vol. 88, July 14, 2008, No. 28, pp. 14)
Pub: Dow Jones & Company Inc.
Contact: Almar Latour, Chief Executive Officer
Ed: Jonathan R. Laing. **Description:** Assurances from the government that Fannie Mae and Freddie Mac are adequately capitalized and able to carry on their duties as guarantors or owners of over $5 trillion of U.S. home mortgages are designed to keep both entities afloat until they attempt to raise $10 billion in new equity. The government would assume any losses in a bailout and owners of the banks' papers would profit as yields drop. **Availability:** Online.

28116 ■ *"Commercial Loans Ready for Refinance: High Number of Mortgages Creates Buying Opportunities"* in Memphis Business Journal (Vol. 34, June 22, 2012, No. 10, pp. 1)
Pub: Baltimore Business Journal
Contact: Rhonda Pringle, President
E-mail: rpringle@bizjournals.com
Ed: Cole Epley. **Description:** Commercial mortgage lending in Memphis, Tennessee improves as area volume loan increased from 2010 to 2011. The industry is projecting $600 billion in commercial mortgages held by banks coming to term over the next four to eight quarters.

28117 ■ *The Complete Guide to Buying a Business*
Pub: Nolo
Contact: Chris Braun, President
Ed: Fred S. Steingold. **Released:** 2015. **Description:** Key steps in buying a business are highlighted, focusing on legal issues, tax considerations, approaches for valuing a business, financing, structuring the deal, along with forms and documents for taking ownership are included. **Availability:** Print.

28118 ■ *"Condos Becoming FHA No-Lending Zones"* in Providence Business News (Vol. 29, June 2, 2014, No. 9, pp. 7)
Pub: American City Business Journals, Inc.
Contact: Mike Olivieri, Executive Vice President
Description: Federal policy changes and decisions by condominium boards of directors have made the condominium development ineligible for Federal Housing Administration (FHA) loans, making several communities prohibited lending zones. As a result, the number of condo developments approved for FHA funding has fallen by more than half, presenting a growing problem for first-time buyers, those with modest down payment cash, and senior citizens using a reverse mortgage. **Availability:** Online.

28119 ■ *"A Conversation With: Ron Gantner, Jones Lang LaSalle"* in Crain's Detroit Business (Vol. 24, October 6, 2008, No. 40, pp. 9)
Pub: Crain Communications Inc.
Contact: Barry Asin, President
Description: Interview with Ron Gantner who is a corporate real estate adviser with the real estate company Jones Lang LaSalle as well as the company's executive vice president and part of the tenant

advisory team; Gantner speaks about the impact that the Wall Street crisis is having on the commercial real estate market in Detroit. **Availability:** Print; Online.

28120 ■ "Corus Eases Off Ailing Condo Market" in Crain's Chicago Business (April 28, 2008)
Pub: Crain Communications Inc.
Contact: Barry Asin, President

Ed: H. Lee Murphy. **Description:** Corus Bankshares Inc., a specialist in lending for the condominium high-rise construction market, is diversifying its portfolio by making loans to office developers and expects to be investing in hotels through the rest of the year. Corus' $7.57 billion loan portfolio is also discussed in detail as well as the company's earnings and share price. Statistical data included. **Availability:** Online.

28121 ■ "Credit Conditions Improve for Small Businesses" in Small Business Economic Trends (February 2008, pp. 12)
Pub: National Federation of Independent Business
Contact: Brad Close, President

Ed: William C. Dunkelberg, Holly Wade. **Description:** Graphs and tables that present the credit conditions of small businesses in the U.S. are provided. The tables include figures on availability of loans, interest rates, and expected credit conditions. **Availability:** Print; PDF; Online.

28122 ■ "The Credit Crisis Continues to Take Victims" in Barron's (Vol. 88, March 10, 2008, No. 10, pp. M12)
Pub: Dow Jones & Company Inc.
Contact: Almar Latour, Chief Executive Officer

Ed: Randall W. Forsyth. **Description:** Short-term Treasury yields dropped to new cyclical lows in early March 2008, with the yield for the two-year Treasury note falling to 1.532 percent. Spreads of the mortgage-backed securities of Fannie Mae and Freddie Mac rose on suspicion of collapses in financing. **Availability:** Online.

28123 ■ "Credit Unions Buck Trend, Lend Millions More" in Saint Louis Business Journal (Vol. 32, September 9, 2011, No. 2, pp. 1)
Pub: Saint Louis Business Journal
Contact: Robert Bobroff, President
E-mail: rbobroff@bizjournals.com

Ed: Greg Edwards. **Description:** St. Louis, Missouri-based credit unions have been making more loans despite the weak economy. Credit unions have made a total of $3.46 billion in outstanding loans as of June 30, 2011. **Availability:** Print; Online.

28124 ■ "Credit Unions Seek to Raise Lending for Small Business" in Denver Business Journal (Vol. 64, September 28, 2012, No. 64, pp. 1)
Pub: Baltimore Business Journal
Contact: Rhonda Pringle, President
E-mail: rpringle@bizjournals.com

Description: United States Senator Mark Udall has introduced the Small Business Lending Enhancement Act, which aims to increase the commercial lending authority of credit unions. The bill's supporters claim that small business owners are still experiencing problems getting credit, and that the legislation will increase small business lending by $13 milliion within its first year of enactment. **Availability:** Print; Online.

28125 ■ "Crowdfunding Author Thinks Google Will Beat Facebook to the Punch on InvestP2P Acquisition" in GlobeNewswire (July 17, 2012)
Pub: Comtex News Network Inc.
Contact: Kan Devnani, President

Description: Author, Mark Kanter, explores the potentials of crowdfunding Websites, especially InvestP2P (aka: peer to peer lending) in his new book, "Street Smart CEO". Invest P2P has social networking tools built into its system. Kanter predicts Google to acquire InvestP2P.

28126 ■ "CrowdFunding Made Simple Conference at University of Utah Ignites Ecosystem of Entrepreneurs and Investors" in Economics Week (June 29, 2012)
Description: The first national conference on crowdfunding was held at the University of Utah Guest House and Conference Center May 31 through June 1, 2012. The event, CrowdFunding Made Simple, gathered entrepreneurs, business owners, professional service providers, investors, government officials and students to provide understanding and potential of crowdfunding, including information on the Jumpstart Our Business Startups (JOBS) Act. **Availability:** Print; Online.

28127 ■ "Data: Nearly 80% of Black Entrepreneurs Believe They Run Thriving Businesses, Yet Gaining Access to Capital Still a Hurdle" in Black Enterprise(February 24, 2023)
URL(s): www.blackenterprise.com/data-nearly-80-of -black-entrepreneurs-believe-they-run-thriving-busi -nesses-yet-gaining-access-to-capital-still-a-hurdle/
Ed: Jeffrey McKinney. **Released:** February 24, 2023. **Description:** After navigating a world-wide pandemic, many Black entrepreneurs are focused on building up their businesses and creating generational wealth while also supporting other Black-owned businesses. Even with these commitments, issues obtaining financing have been encountered. Tips for circumventing these hurdles are discussed. **Availability:** Online.

28128 ■ "Death Spiral" in Business Journal Serving Greater Tampa Bay (Vol. 30, October 29, 2010, No. 45, pp. 1)
Pub: Tampa Bay Business Journal
Contact: Ian Anderson, President
E-mail: ianderson@bizjournals.com

Description: Bay Cities Bank has started working on the loan portfolio of its acquisition, Progress Bank of Florida. Regulators closed Progress Bank in October 2010 after capital collapsed due to charge-offs and increases in the provision for future loan losses. **Availability:** Print; Online.

28129 ■ "EDF Ventures Dissolves Fund, Begins Anew On Investment" in Crain's Detroit Business (Vol. 24, February 25, 2008, No. 8, pp. 14)
Pub: Crain Communications Inc.
Contact: Barry Asin, President

Ed: Tom Henderson. **Description:** EDF Ventures is Michigan's oldest venture capital firm and was part of the second round of investments by the state's 21st Century Investment Fund and the Venture Michigan Fund. **Availability:** Print; Online.

28130 ■ "Editorial: Find Private Money for FutureGen Plant" in Crain's Chicago Business (Vol. 34, September 12, 2011, No. 37, pp. 18)
Pub: Crain Communications Inc.
Contact: Barry Asin, President

Description: FutureGen is a clean-coal power plant being developed in Southern Illinois. The need for further funding is discussed. **Availability:** Print.

28131 ■ "Evolve Bank Ramps Up Staff for SBA Lending" in Memphis Business Journal (Vol. 33, February 24, 2012, No. 46, pp. 1)
Pub: Baltimore Business Journal
Contact: Rhonda Pringle, President
E-mail: rpringle@bizjournals.com

Ed: Christopher Sheffield. **Description:** Memphis, Tennessee-based Evolve Bank has hired Marty Ferguson and Tre Luckett to handle its national and local Small Business Administration (SBA) lending operations. The two are long-time leaders in SBA lending. **Availability:** Print; Online.

28132 ■ "Ex-Im Bank Accepts $105 Million in Financing for Aquarium in Brazil" in Travel & Leisure Close-Up (October 8, 2012)
Description: Export-Import Bank of the United States authorized a $105 million direct loan to the Brazilian state of Ceara to finance the export of American goods and services for the construction of an aquarium in Fortaleza, Brazil. This transaction will support 700 American jobs and at least 90 percent of the export contract value will be provided by U.S. small businesses. **Availability:** Print; Online.

28133 ■ "Extortion: How Politicians Extract Your Money, Buy Votes, and Line Their Own Pockets"
Pub: Mariner Books

Released: October 22, 2013. **Price:** $12.79, Paperback. **Description:** Politicians and lawmakers have developed a new set of legislative tactics designed to extort wealthy industries and donors into huge contributions. This money is then funneled into the pockets of their friends and family members. Schweizer reveals the secret 'fees' each political party charges politicians for top committee assignments; how fourteen members of Congress received hundreds of thousands of dollars using a self-loan loophole; how PAC money is used to bankroll their lavish lifestyles; and more. The first time these unethical issues have been reported to the public. **Availability:** E-book; Print.

28134 ■ "Fight Ensues Over Irreplaceable Princess Diana Gowns" in Tampa Bay Business Journal (Vol. 30, January 15, 2010, No. 4, pp. 1)
Pub: Tampa Bay Business Journal
Contact: Ian Anderson, President
E-mail: ianderson@bizjournals.com

Ed: Janet Leiser. **Description:** People's Princess Charitable Foundation Inc. founder Maureen Rorech Dunkel has sought Chapter 11 bankruptcy protection before a state court decides on the fate of the five of 13 Princess Diana Gowns. Dunkel and the nonprofit were sued by Patricia Sullivan of HRH Venture LLC who claimed they defaulted on $1.5 million in loans. **Availability:** Print; Online.

28135 ■ Financing Your Small Business
Released: First edition. **Description:** Tips for raising venture capital, dealing with bank officials, and initiating public offerings of stock shares for small business.

28136 ■ "A Good Step, But There's a Long Way to Go" in Business Week (September 22, 2008, No. 4100, pp. 10)
Ed: James C. Cooper. **Description:** Despite the historic action by the U.S. government to nationalize the mortgage giants Freddie Mac and Fannie Mae, rising unemployment rates may prove to be an even bigger roadblock to bringing back the economy from its downward spiral. The takeover is meant to restore confidence in the credit markets and help with the mortgage crisis but the rising rate in unemployment may make many households unable to take advantage of any benefits which arise from the bailout. Statistical data included. **Availability:** Online.

28137 ■ "Goodwill Haunts Local Companies" in Crain's Chicago Business (Apr. 28, 2008)
Pub: Crain Communications Inc.
Contact: Barry Asin, President

Ed: Ann Saphir. **Description:** Many companies are having to face the reality that they overpaid for acquisitions made in better economic times; investors often dismiss such one-time charges as mere accounting adjustments but writeoffs related to past acquisitions can signal future problems because they mean the expected profits that justified the purchase have not materialized. Writeoffs are particularly worrisome for firms with a lot of debt and whose banks require them to have enough assets to back up their borrowings. **Availability:** Online.

28138 ■ "Grounded Condo Development Poised for Construction Takeoff" in Memphis Business Journal (Vol. 35, February 7, 2014, No. 44, pp. 4)
Pub: American City Business Journals, Inc.
Contact: Mike Olivieri, Executive Vice President

Released: Weekly. **Price:** $4, introductory 4-week offer(Digital only). **Description:** Developers in Memphis, Tennessee are hoping that the economic recovery will help revive the condominium market. However, industry experts believe that inventory will have to all and prices will have to rise before the market recovers. The impact of loose lending practices on condominium developers is also discussed. **Availability:** Print; Online.

28139 ▪ *"Growing Field"* in *Crain's Detroit Business (Vol. 26, January 11, 2010, No. 2, pp. 3)*
Pub: Crain Communications Inc.
Contact: Barry Asin, President
Description: Detroit's TechTown was awarded a combination loan and grant of $4.1 million from the U.S. Department of Housing and Urban Development to build a 15,000-square-foot stem cell center, a collection of laboratories that will be available to both for-profit companies and university researchers. **Availability:** Online.

28140 ▪ *"Hayes Lemmerz Reports Some Good News Despite Losses"* in *Crain's Detroit Business (Vol. 24, April 14, 2008, No. 15, pp. 4)*
Pub: Crain Communications Inc.
Contact: Barry Asin, President
Ed: Nancy Kaffer. **Description:** Hayes Lemmerz International Inc., a wheel manufacturer from Northville that has reported a positive free cash flow for the first time in years, a narrowed net loss in the fourth quarter and significant restructuring of the company's debt. **Availability:** Print; Online.

28141 ▪ *How to Start and Run Your Own Corporation: S-Corporations For Small Business Owners*
Pub: HCM Publishing
Ed: Peter I. Hupalo. **Description:** Basics of corporate business structure are explained. Topics include discovering the best business structure for your company; how to decided between an S-Corporation and LLC; choosing the state in which to incorporate, how to form a corporation, angel investing, special issues for one-person corporations, the role of bylaws and corporate minutes, board of directors, taxes, workers' compensation issues, retirement plans, and more. **Availability:** Print.

28142 ▪ *"How To Get a Loan the Web 2.0 Way"* in *Black Enterprise (Vol. 41, December 2010, No. 5, pp. 23)*
Pub: Earl G. Graves Ltd.
Contact: Earl Graves, Jr., President
Ed: John Simons. **Description:** People are turning to online peer-to-peer network for personal loans as banks are lending less money. **Availability:** Online.

28143 ▪ *"Identity Theft Can Have Long-Lasting Impact"* in *Providence Business News (Vol. 28, February 10, 2014, No. 45, pp. 7)*
Pub: American City Business Journals, Inc.
Contact: Mike Olivieri, Executive Vice President
URL(s): pbn.com/identity-theft-can-have-long-lasting-impact94959
Description: According to mortgage credit experts, recently reported massive data breaches at Nieman Marcus, Target, and other merchants could have negative impacts on several real estate deals scheduled for the upcoming months. Although victims are not liable for the unlawful debts, their credit reports and scores can be damaged for months, thus endangering loan applications for mortgages on home sale transactions. **Availability:** Online.

28144 ▪ *"In 2011, Wichita-Area Banks Cleaned Up Books, Grew Earnings"* in *Wichita Business Journal (Vol. 27, February 17, 2012, No. 7, pp. 1)*
Pub: Baltimore Business Journal
Contact: Rhonda Pringle, President
E-mail: rpringle@bizjournals.com
Description: Wichita, Kansas-based banks have reported smaller loan portfolios and higher loan-loss allowances at the end of 2011 compared to the previous year. The earnings of the 35 banks in the metro area also grew strongly both for the quarter and for

the year, while their assets increased. How the banks managed to generate positive earnings results is also discussed. **Availability:** Print; Online.

28145 ▪ *"In the News: Hundreds of Millions of Dollars Available to Small Businesses from SSBCI"* in *Small Business Trends(March 3, 2023)*
URL(s): smallbiztrends.com/2023/03/weeklsmall-business-news-roundup-march-3-2023.html
Released: March 03, 2023. **Description:** Small businesses can apply for funding through the State Small Business Credit Initiative in order to provide help for their long-term survival. **Availability:** Online.

28146 ▪ *"In the SBA's Face"* in *American Small Business League (December 2010)*
Ed: Richard Larsen. **Description:** Lloyd Chapman uses the American Small Business League to champion small business. Statistical data included.

28147 ▪ *"Industry Escalates Lobbying Efforts For Loan Program"* in *Crain's Detroit Business (Vol. 24, September 22, 2008, No. 38, pp. 22)*
Pub: Crain Communications Inc.
Contact: Barry Asin, President
Ed: Jay Greene, Ryan Beene, Harry Stoffer. **Description:** Auto suppliers such as Lear Corp., which is best known for vehicle seating, also supplies high-voltage wiring for Ford hybrids and is developing other hybrid components. These suppliers are joining automakers in lobbying for the loan program which would promote the accelerated development of fuel-efficient vehicles. **Availability:** Print; PDF; Online.

28148 ▪ *"Inside the Mind of an Investor: Lessons from Bill Draper"* in *Inc. (Volume 32, December 2010, No. 10, pp. 140)*
Pub: Mansueto Ventures L.L.C.
Contact: Stephanie Mehta, Chief Executive Officer
Released: December 01, 2010. **Description:** Profile of the three-generation Draper family, the first venture capital firm west of the Mississippi. **Availability:** Online.

28149 ▪ *"Investment Bank Predicts Shakeup in Farm Equipment Industry"* in *Farm Industry News (November 16, 2011)*
Pub: Informa Business Media, Inc.
Contact: Charlie McCurdy, President
Ed: Jodie Wehrspann. **Description:** Farming can expect to see more mergers and acquisitions in the agricultural equipment industry, as it appears to be in the early stages of growth over the next few years. **Availability:** Online.

28150 ▪ *"Is Fannie Mae the Next Government Bailout?"* in *Barron's (Vol. 88, March 10, 2008, No. 10, pp. 21)*
Pub: Dow Jones & Company Inc.
Contact: Almar Latour, Chief Executive Officer
Ed: Jonathan R. Laing. **Description:** Fannie Mae may need a government bailout as it faces huge hits brought about by the effects of the housing crisis. The shares of the government-sponsored enterprise have dropped 65 percent since the housing crisis began. **Availability:** Online.

28151 ▪ *"Is Fierce Competition Loosening Standards?"* in *Birmingham Business Journal (Vol. 31, February 14, 2014, No. 7, pp. 6)*
Pub: American City Business Journals, Inc.
Contact: Mike Olivieri, Executive Vice President
Released: Weekly. **Price:** $4, introductory 4-week offer(Digital only). **Description:** Bankers have been seeing an intense competition for business loans in the Birmingham, Alabama market because of the limited number of qualified borrowers. However, some bankers expressed concerns that the trend signals a return to pre-recession habits for lenders. **Availability:** Print; Online.

28152 ▪ *"Law Firms See Improvement in Financing Climate"* in *Sacramento Business Journal (Vol. 28, October 14, 2011, No. 33, pp. 1)*
Pub: Sacramento Business Journal
Contact: Stephanie Fretwell, Director
E-mail: sfretwell@bizjournals.com
Ed: Kathy Robertson. **Description:** Sacramento, California-based Weintraub Genshlea Chediak Law Corporation has helped close 26 financing deals worth more than $1.6 billion in 2010, providing indication of improvement in Sacramento's economy. Lawyers have taken advantage of low interest rates to make refinancing agreements and help clients get new funds. **Availability:** Online.

28153 ▪ *"Leaning Tower"* in *Business Courier (Vol. 27, June 4, 2010, No. 5, pp. 1)*
Pub: Business Courier
Ed: Jon Newberry. **Description:** New York-based developer Armand Lasky, owner of Tower Place Mall in downtown Cincinnati, Ohio has sued Birmingham, Alabama-based Regions Bank to prevent the bank's foreclosure on the property. Regions Bank claims Lasky was in default on an $18 million loan agreement. Details on the mall's leasing plan are also discussed. **Availability:** Online.

28154 ▪ *"Legal Barriers Keep 16-Story Horizon at Ground Level"* in *Memphis Business Journal (Vol. 34, August 24, 2012, No. 19, pp. 1)*
Pub: Baltimore Business Journal
Contact: Rhonda Pringle, President
E-mail: rpringle@bizjournals.com
Description: Construction on the Horizon building at 717 Riverside Drive remains unfinished as legal battles ensue among banks and construction firms involved in the project. The root of the legal proceedings is the Bryan Company's defaulting from a $58.6 million loan from four banks and the foreclosureof the property. **Availability:** Print; Online.

28155 ▪ *"Lenders Get Boost from Low Rates"* in *Saint Louis Business Journal (Vol. 32, September 9, 2011, No. 2, pp. 1)*
Pub: Saint Louis Business Journal
Contact: Robert Bobroff, President
E-mail: rbobroff@bizjournals.com
Ed: Greg Edwards. **Description:** St. Louis, Missouri-based lenders have benefitted from record low mortgage interest rates. Housing loan applications have increased in view of the development. **Availability:** Print; Online.

28156 ▪ *"Lending Door Slams"* in *Puget Sound Business Journal (Vol. 29, October 24, 2008, No. 27, pp. 1)*
Description: KeyBank's closure of its Puget Sound unit that services single-family homebuilders is part of a nationwide shutdown that includes similar closures in other cities. Bank of America is adopting more conservative terms for homebuilding loans while Union Bank of California is still offering credit for market rate housing. **Availability:** Print; Online.

28157 ▪ *"Lending Grows as Banks Make Moves"* in *Pittsburgh Business Times (Vol. 33, May 9, 2014, No. 43, pp. 4)*
Pub: American City Business Journals, Inc.
Contact: Mike Olivieri, Executive Vice President
Released: May 2014. **Price:** $4, introductory 4-week offer(Digital only). **Description:** Pittsburgh, Pennsylvania-based biggest retail banks have bigger loan portfolios at the end of 2014s first quarter compared with the same period in 2013. Business lending has been driving activity and the surge also includes the impact of merger and acquisition strategies to capture customers in Ohio. The rising loan portfolio of the banks are examined. **Availability:** Print; Online.

28158 ▪ *"The Loan Arranger"* in *Canadian Business (Vol. 80, October 22, 2007, No. 21, pp. 15)*
Description: Muhammad Yunus received the Nobel Prize in 2006 for the organization that he founded, the Grameen Bank. The bank has helped women in

developing countries and has also begun helping millions of individuals to make loans in the U.S. through the Grameen Bank. An evaluation of the Grameen model is provided. **Availability:** Online.

28159 ■ *"Loans Aplenty From Local Banks in Q4" in South Florida Business Journal (Vol. 34, February 7, 2014, No. 29, pp. 4)*
Pub: American City Business Journals, Inc.
Contact: Mike Olivieri, Executive Vice President

Released: Weekly. **Price:** $8, Introductory 4-week offer(Digital & Print). **Description:** Figures show that eight of the 25 largest banks in South Florida increased loans by more than $50 million in the fourth quarter of 2013. Ocean Bank, Legacy Bank of Florida, Intercredit Bank and Anchor Commercial Bank regained well capitalized status. The decrease in Regent Bank's capital ratios is also discussed. **Availability:** Print; Online.

28160 ■ *"Loans Are Plentiful for Small Businesses" in South Florida Business Journal (Vol. 35, September 12, 2014, No. 7, pp. 16)*
Pub: American City Business Journals, Inc.
Contact: Mike Olivieri, Executive Vice President

Description: Banks have relaxed requirements for small business loans in South Florida. Total bank loans increased by 11.4 percent in 2014. It has also become easier for small businesses to secure credit for acquisitions and mergers and growth. **Availability:** Online.

28161 ■ *"Lotus Starts Slowly, Dodges Subprime Woes" in Crain's Detroit Business (Vol. 24, April 14, 2008, No. 15, pp. 3)*
Pub: Crain Communications Inc.
Contact: Barry Asin, President

Ed: Tom Henderson. **Description:** Discusses Lotus Bancorp Inc. and their business plan, which although is not right on target due to the subprime mortgage meltdown, is in a much better position than its competitors due to the quality of their loans. **Availability:** Online.

28162 ■ *"Market Watch: A Sampling of Advisory Opinion" in Barron's (Vol. 88, March 17, 2008, No. 11, pp. M10)*
Pub: Dow Jones & Company Inc.
Contact: Almar Latour, Chief Executive Officer

Ed: Paul Schatz, William Gibson, Michael Darda, Peter Greene, Ian Wyatt, Stephanie Pomboy. **Released:** January 25, 2014. **Description:** S&P 500 bank stocks were down 46 percent from their 2007 peak while the peak to through fall in 1989-1990 was just over 50 percent. This suggests that the bottom on the bank stocks could be near. The Federal Reserve Board announced they will lend up to $200 billion to primary lenders in exchange other securities. **Availability:** Print; Online.

28163 ■ *"Marketing is Everything, But Timing Helps" in Idaho Business Review (September 9, 2014)*
Pub: BridgeTower Media
Contact: Adam Reinebach, President

Description: Profile of Ladd Family Pharmacy, founded by husband and wife Kip and Elaine, who borrowed money from Idaho Banking Company to start their pharmacy. The firm has expanded from three workers in 2008 to 22 to date and reported $6.2 million in revenue for 2013.

28164 ■ *"A Matter of Interest: Payday Loans" in Canadian Business (Vol. 79, July 17, 2006, No. 14-15, pp. 21)*
Pub: Rogers Media Inc.
Contact: Neil Spivak, Chief Executive Officer

Ed: Jeff Sanford. **Description:** With the steady decrease in savings, the need for growth in Canada's payloan industry is discussed. Also emphasized are the challenges faced by payloan operators. **Availability:** Online.

28165 ■ *"Md. Bankers Say 'Devil Is In the Details' of New $30B Loan Fund" in Baltimore Business Journal (Vol. 28, October 8, 2010, No. 22)*
Pub: Baltimore Business Journal
Contact: Rhonda Pringle, President
E-mail: rpringle@bizjournals.com

Ed: Gary Haber. **Description:** Maryland community bankers have expressed doubts over a new federal loan program for small business. The new law will also earmark $80 billion for community banks. Comments from executives also given. **Availability:** Print.

28166 ■ *"Md. Banks Beef Up Deposits, But Lending Lags" in Baltimore Business Journal (Vol. 28, October 29, 2010, No. 25, pp. 1)*
Pub: Baltimore Business Journal
Contact: Rhonda Pringle, President
E-mail: rpringle@bizjournals.com

Ed: Gary Haber. **Description:** Bank deposits in the Greater Baltimore area have increased but commercial loans have not. Small business owners complain that banks do not help them expand their businesses, but banks argue that they want to lend but the borrowers have to meet standard qualifications. **Availability:** Print; Online.

28167 ■ *"Md. Housing Leaders Race to Stem Rising Tide of Foreclosures: Neighborhood Watch" in Baltimore Business Journal (Vol. 28, July 23, 2010, No. 11, pp. 1)*
Pub: Baltimore Business Journal
Contact: Rhonda Pringle, President
E-mail: rpringle@bizjournals.com

Ed: Daniel J. Sernovitz. **Description:** Maryland government and housing leaders are set to spend $100 million in federal funding to stem the increase in foreclosures in the area. The federal funding is seen as inadequate to resolve the problem of foreclosures. **Availability:** Print.

28168 ■ *"Michigan Means Growth: Sustaining Growth Through Thick and Thin: Michigan Companies Sustain Growth with Well-Timed Access to Capital" in Inc. (Vol. 36, September 2014, No. 7, pp. 164)*
Pub: Mansueto Ventures L.L.C.
Contact: Stephanie Mehta, Chief Executive Officer

Description: Successful companies possess flexibility, foresight and resources to turn adversity into opportunity. The small businesses in Michigan who have sustained experienced sales growth despite the recession of 2007. The Michigan Economic Development Corporation has introduced three initiatives to help Michigan businesses grow, including venture capital, collateral support and loan participation through the State Small Business Credit Initiative, and cash incentives for businesses looking to invest in urban communities or grow jobs. **Availability:** Print; Online.

28169 ■ *"Micro-Finance Agencies and SMEs: Model of Explication of Tacit Knowledge" in International Journal of Entrepreneurship and Small Business (Vol. 11, August 3, 2010)*
Ed: Patricia A. Rowe, Michael J. Christie, Frank Hoy. **Description:** Institutional preparedness of economic development agencies for developing small and medium-sized enterprises (SMEs) is discussed. The cases presented illustrate variations in the microfinance lender agency-enterprise development of processes for sharing vision and interdependence. **Availability:** Online.

28170 ■ *"Microlending Seen as Having a Major Impact" in Business Journal Serving Greater Tampa Bay (Vol. 30, November 26, 2010, No. 49, pp. 1)*
Pub: Tampa Bay Business Journal
Contact: Ian Anderson, President
E-mail: ianderson@bizjournals.com

Ed: Margie Manning. **Description:** There are several organizations that are planning to offer microlending services in Tampa Bay, Florida. These include the Children's Board of Hillsborough County, and OUR Microlending Florida LLC. Organizations that are

already offering these services in the area include the Small Business Administration and the Tampa Bay Black Business Investment Corp. **Availability:** Print; Online.

28171 ■ *"Morgan Hill Attracts Manufacturing to South County" in Silicon Valley/San Jose Business Journal (Vol. 30, September 21, 2012, No. 26, pp. 1)*
Pub: Baltimore Business Journal
Contact: Rhonda Pringle, President
E-mail: rpringle@bizjournals.com

Description: The Grow Morgan Hill Fund offers $2 million in loans to qualifying businesses off of an initial $500,000 city investment. The fund is a way for the city of Morgan Hill, California to help local businesses expand int he absence of redevelopment agencies. **Availability:** Print; Online.

28172 ■ *"Multifamily Banks on Fannie, Freddie" in Memphis Business Journal (Vol. 33, February 24, 2012, No. 46, pp. 1)*
Pub: Baltimore Business Journal
Contact: Rhonda Pringle, President
E-mail: rpringle@bizjournals.com

Ed: Andy Ashby. **Description:** The possible demise of Fannie Mae and Freddie Mac is seen to adversely impact the multifamily apartment market of Memphis, Tennessee. The apartment market relies on federal loans for funding. **Availability:** Print; Online.

28173 ■ *"A New Kid on the Block" in Barron's (Vol. 88, March 17, 2008, No. 11, pp. 58)*
Pub: Dow Jones & Company Inc.
Contact: Almar Latour, Chief Executive Officer

Ed: Thomas G. Donlan. **Description:** Discusses the Federal Reserve which has offered to lend $100 billion in cash to banks and $200 billion in Treasuries to Wall Street investment banks that have problems with liquidity. The reluctance of the banks to lend money to meet a margin call on securities that could still depreciate is the reason why the agency is going into the direct loan business. **Availability:** Online.

28174 ■ *"No End to the Nightmare; America's Car Industry" in The Economist (Vol. 390, January 3, 2009, No. 8612, pp. 46)*
Description: Detroit's struggling auto industry and the government loan package is discussed as well as the United Auto Worker union, which is loathed by Senate Republicans. **Availability:** Print; Online.

28175 ■ *"Ohio Commerce Draws Closer to Profitability" in Crain's Cleveland Business (Vol. 28, October 29, 2007, No. 43, pp. 14)*
Pub: Crain Communications Inc.
Contact: K. C. Crain, President

Ed: Shawn A. Turner. **Description:** Overview of the business plan of Ohio Commerce Bank, a de novo, or startup bank that is close to turning the corner to profitability. The bank opened in November 2006 and focuses on dealing with small businesses totaling $5 million or less in annual revenues. **Availability:** Online.

28176 ■ *"OK, Bring in the Lawyers" in Crain's Chicago Business (Vol. 31, November 17, 2008, No. 46, pp. 26)*
Pub: Crain Communications Inc.
Contact: Barry Asin, President

Ed: Daniel Rome Levine. **Description:** Bankruptcy attorneys are finding the economic and credit crisis a benefit for their businesses due to the high number of business owners and mortgage holders that are need of their services. One Chicago firm is handling ten times the number of cases they did the previous year and of that about 80 percent of their new clients are related to the real estate sector. **Availability:** Online.

28177 ■ *"Past Due: $289 Million in Loans - University Club Tower, Sheraton St. Louis City Center in Default" in Saint Louis Business Journal (Vol. 32, September 23, 2011, No. 4, pp. 1)*
Pub: Saint Louis Business Journal
Contact: Robert Bobroff, President

E-mail: rbobroff@bizjournals.com

Ed: Evan Binns. **Description:** New York-based Trepp LLC research found about $289 million in local commercial mortgage-backed securities loans on 20 properties delinquent in payments by 30 days or more as of August 31, 2011. The report also placed the delinquency rate for St. Louis at that time at 9.64 percent. **Availability:** Online.

28178 ■ *"Proposed Accounting Changes Could Complicate Tenants' Leases" in Baltimore Business Journal (Vol. 28, July 2, 2010, No. 8, pp. 1)*
Pub: Baltimore Business Journal
Contact: Rhonda Pringle, President
E-mail: rpringle@bizjournals.com

Ed: Daniel J. Sernovitz. **Description:** The Financial Accounting Standards Board has proposed that companies must indicate the value of real estate leases as assets and liabilities on balance sheets instead of expenses. The proposals could cause some companies to document millions of dollars in charges on their books or find difficulty in getting loans. **Availability:** Print.

28179 ■ *Race and Entrepreneurial Success: Black-, Asian-, and White-Owned Businesses in the United States*
Pub: The MIT Press

Ed: Robert W. Fairlie, Alicia M. Robb. **Released:** 2008. **Description:** Trends in minority small business ownership are explored, focusing on the importance of human capital, financial capital, and family business background in successful business ownership. **Availability:** E-book; Print; PDF.

28180 ■ *"Race, Not Income, Played Role in Subprime Loans" in Black Enterprise (Vol. 40, July 2010, No. 12, pp. 26)*
Pub: Earl G. Graves Ltd.
Contact: Earl Graves, Jr., President

Ed: Deborah Creighton Skinner. **Description:** African Americans were 80 percent more likely than whites to receive a subprime loan and were almost 20 percent more likely to go into foreclosure, according to a study done by the National Community Reinvestment Coalition. Statistical data included.

28181 ■ *"Radisson Hotel San Jose Airport Headed Into Foreclosure" in Silicon Valley/San Jose Business Journal (Vol. 29, February 3, 2012, No. 45, pp. 1)*
Pub: Baltimore Business Journal
Contact: Rhonda Pringle, President
E-mail: rpringle@bizjournals.com

Description: The Radisson Hotel San Jose Airport is set to be foreclosed. Hotel owner, Silicon Valley Hwang LLC has yet to pay a $15.9 million loan. **Availability:** Print; Online.

28182 ■ *Raising Capital*
Pub: HarperCollins Leadership
Contact: Donald Miller, Chief Executive Officer

Ed: Andrew J. Sherman. **Released:** 2nd edition. **Availability:** Print.

28183 ■ *"Ready for a Rally?" in The Economist (Vol. 390, January 3, 2009, No. 8612, pp. 54)*
Description: Analysts predict that the recession could end by 2010. The current economic crisis is presented in detail. **Availability:** Print; Online.

28184 ■ *"Refinance: To Do Or Not To Do?" in Real Estate Review (Vol. 41, Spring 2012, No. 1, pp. 91)*
Description: An author's experiences in home mortgage refinancing are presented. The author's encounter with home appraisers is mentioned. Special or streamlined loans can be secured by parties with existing conforming loans. **Availability:** Print; Online.

28185 ■ *"Region's Small Business Lending Rises by $440M" in South Florida Business Journal (Vol. 33, September 7, 2012, No. 6, pp. 1)*
Pub: Baltimore Business Journal
Contact: Rhonda Pringle, President
E-mail: rpringle@bizjournals.com

Description: Reports show that small business lending in South Florida increased by $440 million in 2011. Figures also indicate that banks originated $3.24 billion in small business loans during the same period, up from $2.8 billion in the previous year. It is believed that the region's economy is slowly improving. **Availability:** Print; Online.

28186 ■ *"Research Reports" in Barron's (Vol. 88, March 24, 2008, No. 12, pp. M10)*
Pub: Dow Jones & Company Inc.
Contact: Almar Latour, Chief Executive Officer

Ed: Anita Peltonen. **Description:** Investors are recommending purchasing shares of Ampco Pittsburgh due to an expected surge in earnings. Deteriorating credit quality presents problems for the shares of BankAtlantic Bancorp, whose price targets have been lowered from $7 to $5 each. Shares of Helicos Biosciences are expected to move sideways from their $6 level. Statistical data included.

28187 ■ *"Return to Wealth; Bank Strategy" in The Economist (Vol. 390, January 3, 2009, No. 8612, pp. 56)*
Description: UBS' strategy to survive these trying economic times is presented. Statistical data included. UBS has a stronger balance-sheet than most of its investment-banking peers and has reduced its portfolio. **Availability:** Print; Online.

28188 ■ *"Ryan Gilbert Wants SBA To Mean Speedy Business Administration" in Philadelphia Business Journal (Vol. 33, May 9, 2014, No. 13, pp. 8)*
Pub: American City Business Journals, Inc.
Contact: Mike Olivieri, Executive Vice President

Released: May 23, 2014. **Description:** Ryan Gilbert, CEO of San Francisco, California-based Better Finance explains that his company uses its financial technology, SmartBiz, to help banks expedite Small Business Administration (SBA) loans. Better Finance, formerly known as BillFloat, helps small business owners receive SBA 7(a) loans between $5,000 and $150,000 within five business days instead of several week, offering easy online access to SBA loans at low interest rates. **Availability:** Print; Online.

28189 ■ *"St. Louis Lending Tumbles $10 Billion Since '08" in Saint Louis Business Journal (Vol. 31, August 26, 2011, No. 53, pp. 1)*
Pub: Saint Louis Business Journal
Contact: Robert Bobroff, President
E-mail: rbobroff@bizjournals.com

Ed: Greg Edwards. **Description:** St. Louis, Missouri-based banks lending fell by more than 30 percent in less than three years, from about $30 billion in third and fourth quarters 2008 to about $20 billion in the most recent quarter. However, community banks revealed that they want to lend but there is no loan demand. **Availability:** Print; Online.

28190 ■ *"St. Louis Restaurants Rewrite Menu to Get Financing" in Saint Louis Business Journal (Vol. 31, August 19, 2011, No. 52, pp. 1)*
Pub: Saint Louis Business Journal
Contact: Robert Bobroff, President
E-mail: rbobroff@bizjournals.com

Ed: E.B. Solomont. **Description:** St. Louis, Missouri-based restaurants are finding new ways to secure financing. The weak economy has made it difficult for restaurants to secure bank financing. **Availability:** Print; Online.

28191 ■ *"Savvy Solutions" in Black Enterprise (Vol. 41, December 2010, No. 5, pp. 42)*
Pub: Earl G. Graves Ltd.
Contact: Earl Graves, Jr., President

Ed: Tennille M. Robinson. **Description:** Individual asks for advice in launching a graphic design business, particularly grants available in a slow economy.

28192 ■ *"Savvy Solutions" in Black Enterprise (Vol. 41, November 2010, No. 4, pp. 42)*

Description: Society of Children's Book Writers and Illustrators offers members many benefits, including directories of agencies looking for new writers of books. **Availability:** Online.

28193 ■ *"SBA Can Improve Your Cash Flow" in Business Owner (Vol. 35, September-October 2011, No. 5, pp. 3)*

Description: Federal assistance available to small business is examined. The Small Business Administration loan guarantee program is designed to improve availability and attractiveness of small business loans. **Availability:** Print; Online.

28194 ■ *"SBA Lending Hits Record" in Saint Louis Business Journal (Vol. 32, September 30, 2011, No. 5, pp. 1)*
Pub: Saint Louis Business Journal
Contact: Robert Bobroff, President
E-mail: rbobroff@bizjournals.com

Ed: Rick Desloge. **Description:** US Small Business Administration loans have reached a record high of $200 million in 2011. The agency decreased the usual loan fees. **Availability:** Print; Online.

28195 ■ *"Science Museum, Theater Seeking State Loans" in Sacramento Business Journal (Vol. 31, May 30, 2014, No. 14, pp. 4)*
Pub: American City Business Journals, Inc.
Contact: Mike Olivieri, Executive Vice President

Released: Weekly. **Price:** $4, Introductory 4-week offer(Digital & Print). **Description:** The Powerhouse Science Center and B Street Theatre in Sacramento, California are hoping to secure loans from the California Infrastructure and Economic Development Bank. Both nonprofit organizations are planning to start their own construction projects as soon as loans are received. **Availability:** Print; Online.

28196 ■ *"Seminar on Crowdfunding Set for Aug. 1" in Gazette (July 25, 2012)*
URL(s): gazette.com/seminar-on-crowdfunding-set-for-aug.-1/article/142192#!

Description: Senator Michael Bennet is co-hosting a seminar with Epicentral Coworking on crowdfunding featuring two panels with local entrepreneurs and business owners, legal experts, and representatives from investment firms. The seminar will be held August 1, 2012. **Availability:** Print; Online.

28197 ■ *"Sense of Discovery" in Business Journal Portland (Vol. 27, November 19, 2010, No. 38, pp. 1)*
Pub: Portland Business Journal
Contact: Andy Giegerich, Managing Editor
E-mail: agiegerich@bizjournals.com

Description: Tigard, Oregon-based Exterro Inc. CEO Bobby Balachandran announced plans to go public without the help of an institutional investor. Balachandran believes Exterro could grow to a $100 million legal compliance software company in the span of three years. Insights on Exterro's growth as market leader in the $1 billion legal governance software market are also given. **Availability:** Print; Online.

28198 ■ *"Sentiment Split on Financials: Is the Worse Over or Still to Come?" in Barron's (Vol. 88, March 24, 2008, No. 12, pp. M14)*
Pub: Dow Jones & Company Inc.
Contact: Almar Latour, Chief Executive Officer

Ed: Steven M. Sears. **Description:** Experts in the financial sector are split as to whether or not the worst of the financial crisis brought on by the credit crunch is over. Some options traders are trading on are defensive puts, expecting the worst, while investors buying calls are considered as bullish. **Availability:** Online.

28199 ■ "Shining a Light on Entrepreneurial Opportunities" in San Antonio Business Journal (Vol. 28, July 11, 2014, No. 22, pp. 4)
Pub: American City Business Journals, Inc.
Contact: Mike Olivieri, Executive Vice President
Released: Weekly. **Price:** $4, Introductory 4-week offer(Digital & Print). **Description:** Café Commerce is a small business and entrepreneurship development program launched by the City of San Antonio in partnership with microlender Accion Texas. The goal of the new resource center is to make entrepreneurship easier by complementing existing programs and serving as a platform to introduce new ones to the business community. **Availability:** Print; Online.

28200 ■ "A Slice of Danish; Fixing Finance" in The Economist (Vol. 390, January 3, 2009, No. 8612, pp. 55)
Description: Denmark's mortgage-holders and the county's lending system is presented. **Availability:** Print; Online.

28201 ■ "Small Bank Has Big Lending Plans, New Hire" in Silicon Valley/San Jose Business Journal (Vol. 30, September 21, 2012, No. 26, pp. 1)
Pub: Baltimore Business Journal
Contact: Rhonda Pringle, President
E-mail: rpringle@bizjournals.com
Description: Santa Cruz County Bank has hired government-backed loans specialist Sat Kanwar in addition to Susan Chandler, Jorge Reguerin and Daljit Bains to boost the bank's Small Business Administration lending department. According to Chandler, the bank will take on loans ranging from $25,000 to several million dollars. **Availability:** Print; Online.

28202 ■ "Small Business Lending Rebounds to 3-Year High" in Washington Business Journal (Vol. 31, August 31, 2012, No. 19, pp. 1)
Pub: Baltimore Business Journal
Contact: Rhonda Pringle, President
E-mail: rpringle@bizjournals.com
Description: Loans made to small companies in the Washington DC area rose to 83,522 in 2011, up 14 percent from 2010 levels. The amount lent in 2011 reached $3.3 billion, up 9 percent from 2010, but down 44 percent from 2007 levels. **Availability:** Print; Online.

28203 ■ "Small Business Loan Approval Rates Up with Some Lenders" in Small Business Trends (September 15, 2022)
URL(s): smallbiztrends.com/2022/09/biz2credit-small-lending-index-september-2022.html
Ed: Lisa Price. **Released:** September 15, 2022. **Description:** Small banks and non-bank lenders are slowly approving more loans, as opposed to the larger banks who have been approving less loans. **Availability:** Online.

28204 ■ "Small Businesses Finding It Easier To Get Capital" in Birmingham Business Journal (Vol. 31, July 11, 2014, No. 28, pp. 10)
Pub: American City Business Journals, Inc.
Contact: Mike Olivieri, Executive Vice President
Description: According to the Federal Reserve Bank of Atlanta, small businesses that applied for credit received the financing requested, showing increased confidence among Birmingham businesses. With a robust lending environment, Birmingham is expecting the trend to continue in 2014 with more business plans for expansion and new capital spends. **Availability:** Print; Online.

28205 ■ "Soldiers as Consumers: Predatory and Unfair Business Practices Harming the Military Community"
Pub: CreateSpace
Released: October 05, 2014. **Price:** $9.81, paperback. **Description:** Soldiers, airmen, sailors, and marines are young consumers and are appealing targets for unscrupulous businesses. There are lending organizations that prey upon our military offering products to help them bridge financial problems.

Unethical elements of these loans includes higher interest rates and/or high fees or waivers of certain rights in fine print of contracts. A Federal Law called the Military Lending Act is supposed to protect service members from this kind of abuse, but the law only covers loans with terms of six months or less. **Availability:** Print.

28206 ■ "Some Credit Unions Are Big on Business Loans" in South Florida Business Journal (Vol. 35, September 5, 2014, No. 6, pp. 4)
Pub: American City Business Journals, Inc.
Contact: Mike Olivieri, Executive Vice President
Description: Business loans provided by credit unions in Florida have increased in 2014. Business loans in the state have risen to $1.36 billion. Jetstream Federal Credit Union increased its business loans by 456 percent. **Availability:** Online.

28207 ■ "South Jersey Office Space in Doldrums" in Philadelphia Business Journal (Vol. 31, March 16, 2012, No. 5, pp. 1)
Pub: Baltimore Business Journal
Contact: Rhonda Pringle, President
E-mail: rpringle@bizjournals.com
Description: Morgage lenders have been trying to boost office building occupancies in preparation of eventual sales. They are also selling loans at discounted prices. **Availability:** Print; Online.

28208 ■ "State Investment Goes Sour" in Business Journal Portland (Vol. 26, December 4, 2009, No. 39, pp. 1)
Pub: Portland Business Journal
Contact: Andy Giegerich, Managing Editor
E-mail: agiegerich@bizjournals.com
Ed: Erik Siemers. **Description:** Oregon might recoup only $500,000 of a $20 million loan to Vancouver-based Cascade Grain Products LLC. Cascade Grain's ethanol plant in Clatskanie, OR will be put into auction under the supervision of a bankruptcy court. **Availability:** Print; Online.

28209 ■ "State VC Fund To Get At Least $7.5 Million" in Crain's Detroit Business (Vol. 24, February 25, 2008, No. 8, pp. 14)
Pub: Crain Communications Inc.
Contact: Barry Asin, President
Ed: Tom Henderson. **Description:** Michigan's 21st Century Investment Fund is expected to receive $7.5 million, financed by tobacco-settlement money. The Michigan Strategic Fund Board will determine which firms will receive venture capital, which is mandated by legislation to invest the fund within three years. **Availability:** Online.

28210 ■ "State Wants to Add Escape Clause to Leases" in Sacramento Business Journal (Vol. 28, October 14, 2011, No. 33, pp. 1)
Pub: Sacramento Business Journal
Contact: Stephanie Fretwell, Director
E-mail: sfretwell@bizjournals.com
Ed: Michael Shaw. **Description:** California Governor Jerry Brown's administration has decided to add escape clauses to new lease agreements, which created new worry for building owners and brokers in Sacramento, California. Real estate brokers believe the appropriation of funds clauses have been making the lenders nervous and would result in less competition. **Availability:** Online.

28211 ■ "Sterotaxis Needs $10 Million in 60 Days" in Saint Louis Business Journal (Vol. 32, October 7, 2011, No. 6, pp. 1)
Pub: Saint Louis Business Journal
Contact: Robert Bobroff, President
E-mail: rbobroff@bizjournals.com
Ed: E.B. Solomont. **Description:** Medical device firm Stereotaxis signed a loan modification deal with Silicon Valley Bank. The company suffered massive losses during second quarter 2011. Under the deal, the company waived the minimum tangible net work covenant of the original loan in exchange for reduction in its credit line. **Availability:** Print; Online.

28212 ■ "Still No Arena Financing Plan" in Sacramento Business Journal (Vol. 28, May 27, 2011, No. 13, pp. 1)
Pub: Sacramento Business Journal
Contact: Stephanie Fretwell, Director
E-mail: sfretwell@bizjournals.com
Ed: Kelly Johnson. **Description:** The government of Sacramento, California has yet to devise a plan to finance the construction of a proposed stadium. The arena is estimated to cost $387 million. A brief description of the facility is also included. **Availability:** Online.

28213 ■ "Stuck With Two Mortgages" in Crain's Chicago Business (Vol. 31, April 21, 2008, No. 16)
Pub: Crain Communications Inc.
Contact: Barry Asin, President
Ed: Darci Smith. **Description:** Discusses the problem a number of people are facing due to the slump in the housing market: being stuck with two mortgages when they move because their former homes have not sold. Many thought they could afford to move to a larger home, anticipating significant equity appreciation that did not occur; now they are left with lowering their price and competing with the host of new developments. **Availability:** Online.

28214 ■ "Survey: Ag Lenders Less Optimistic" in Idaho Business Review (June 27, 2014)
Pub: BridgeTower Media
Contact: Adam Reinebach, President
Price: $11.99, Print, Digital & Mobile (For 1 Month Intro Rate); $149, Print, Digital & Mobile (For 1 Year); $99, Digital & Mobile Only(For 1 Year). **Description:** According to a survey conducted by Kansas State University, agricultural lenders are showing less optimism than previously felt last fall. Lenders are expecting interest rates to rise, while the spread over cost of funds is expected to increase in the long term. Statistical data included. **Availability:** Print; Online.

28215 ■ "This Just In: TechTown, Partners Get $1M to Start Tech Exchange" in Crain's Detroit Business (Vol. 25, June 1, 2009, No. 22, pp. 1)
Pub: Crain Communications Inc.
Contact: Barry Asin, President
Ed: Daniel Duggan. **Description:** Three veterans of the auto industry have partnered to create, Revitalizing Michigan, a nonprofit dedicated to help manufacturers improve their processes. The firm is seeking federal, state and private grants to fund the mission. **Availability:** Print; Online.

28216 ■ "TMC Development Closes $1.1 Million Real Estate Purchase for Mansa, LLC Using SBA 504 Real Estate Financing" in Marketwired (September 17, 2009)
Pub: Comtex News Network Inc.
Contact: Kan Devnani, President
Description: TMC Development announced the closing of a $1.1 million real estate purchase for Mansa, LLC dba Kwikee Mart, a Napa-based convenience store; TMC helped the company secure a Small Business Administration 504 loan in order to purchase the acquisition of a 3,464 square foot building. SBA created the 504 loan program to provide financing for growing small and medium-sized businesses. **Availability:** Online.

28217 ■ "Today's Business Sale Climate" in Business Owner (Vol. 35, September-October 2011, No. 5, pp. 10)
Description: Despite the weak economy, there is a surplus of individuals wanting to purchase a small business. The Small Business Administration loan guarantees program helps with its loans for purchase/sale of business assistance. **Availability:** Print; Online.

28218 ■ "Too Much Information?" in Black Enterprise (Vol. 37, December 2006, No. 5, pp. 59)
Pub: Earl G. Graves Ltd.
Contact: Earl Graves, Jr., President

Ed: James C. Johnson. **Description:** African American business owners often face the dilemma of whether or not to divulge their minority status when soliciting new customers and financial institutions. The quality of the products or services is always the key factor and race should never define one's business; however, it is appropriate to market oneself as a minority- or women-owned business, especially if the company is in an industry where those clients are offered top-tier contracts. **Availability:** Online.

28219 ■ *"Triad, Fortune Dump TARP Cut Costs, Boost Lending" in Saint Louis Business Journal (Vol. 32, October 7, 2011, No. 6, pp. 1)*
Pub: Saint Louis Business Journal
Contact: Robert Bobroff, President
E-mail: rbobroff@bizjournals.com
Ed: Greg Edwards. **Description:** St. Louis, Missouri-based Triad Bank and Fortune Bank have been using an alternative federal loan program to pay back financing from the Troubled Asset Relief Program. Triad got a $5 million loan at one percent interest rate from the US Small Business Lending Fund. **Availability:** Print; Online.

28220 ■ *"U-Swirl Added to SBA's Franchise Registry" in Ice Cream Reporter (Vol. 23, September 20, 2010, No. 10, pp. 1)*
Description: Healthy Fast Food Inc., parent to the U-SWIRL Frozen Yogurt cafe chain announced that the U.S. Small Business Administration listed U-SWIRL Frozen Yogurt on its official franchise registry. This move will allow U-SWIRL the benefits of a streamlined review process for SBA financing. **Availability:** Print; Online.

28221 ■ *"VA Exceeds Government-Wide Goal for Veteran-Owned Business Procurement" in Benzinga.com (July 3, 2012)*
Pub: Benzinga.com
Contact: Jason Raznick, Founder
Ed: Aaron Wise. **Description:** Department of Veterans Affairs has surpassed its goal of government procurements of the Small Business Adminstration by more than six times. The VA's committment to the success of veteran-owned small businesses is covered.

28222 ■ *"Valenti: Roots of Financial Crisis Go Back to 1998" in Crain's Detroit Business (Vol. 24, October 6, 2008, No. 40, pp. 25)*
Pub: Crain Communications Inc.
Contact: Barry Asin, President
Ed: Tom Henderson, Nathan Skid. **Description:** Interview with Sam Valenti III who is the chairman and CEO of Valenti Capital L.L.C., a wealth-management firm; Valenti discusses in detail the history that led up to the current economic crisis as well as his prediction for the future of the country. **Availability:** Print; Online.

28223 ■ *"VC Money Down In State, Number of Deals Up" in Crain's Detroit Business (Vol. 24, January 28, 2008, No. 4, pp. 18)*
Pub: Crain Communications Inc.
Contact: Barry Asin, President
Ed: Tom Henderson. **Description:** Despite the amount of money invested by venture capitalists in Michigan is down, the number of deals rose according to the annual Money Tree report. Venture capital firms invested a combined $105.4 million in 22 deals that involved 19 companies in the state. **Availability:** Online.

28224 ■ *"What's In a Relationship? The Case of Commercial Lending" in Business Horizons (Vol. 51, March-April 2008, No. 2, pp. 93)*
Pub: Elsevier Advanced Technology Publications
Ed: Gregory F. Udell. **Description:** Academic literature on relationship lending and banking to small and medium enterprises is analyzed. This practice is best suited to some SME types but creates special challenges for bank managers. Relationship lending may also be better delivered by community banks. **Availability:** PDF; Online.

28225 ■ *"Where Small Biz Gets a 'Yes' More Often" in Denver Business Journal (Vol. 65, February 28, 2014, No. 42, pp. A10)*
Pub: American City Business Journals, Inc.
Contact: Mike Olivieri, Executive Vice President
Released: Weekly. **Price:** $4, Introductory 4-week offer(Digital & Print). **Description:** The Biz2Credit Small Business Lending Index has found that alternative lenders granted 66.9 percent of funding requests in Colorado compared to the 15.1 percent approval of loans requests by big banks. The big banks' low approval rates were attributed to their less aggressive lending efforts and the state's fewer restrictions on alternative lending. Other findings from the study are discussed. **Availability:** Print; Online.

28226 ■ *"Where to Stash Your Cash" in Barron's (Vol. 88, March 17, 2008, No. 11, pp. 41)*
Pub: Dow Jones & Company Inc.
Contact: Almar Latour, Chief Executive Officer
Ed: Mike Hogan. **Description:** Investors are putting their money in money-market mutual funds seeking fractionally better yields and a safe haven from the uncertainties that was brought about by subprime lending. These funds, however, are hovering near 3.20 percent which is less than the 4 percent inflation rate. **Availability:** Online.

28227 ■ *Women Entrepreneurs in The Global Marketplace*
Pub: Edward Elgar Publishing Inc.
Contact: Edward Elgar, Founder Chairman
Ed: Andrea E. Smith-Hunter. **Released:** 2013. **Description:** Focus is on women entrepreneurs; information includes human capital, network structures and financial capital, with comparative analysis across racial lines.

28228 ■ *"The Worst Lies Ahead for Wall Street: More Losses Certain; More Expensive Capital to Be Needed" in Crain's New York Business (Vol. 24, January 20, 2008, No. 3, pp. 1)*
Pub: Crain Communications, Inc.
Contact: Jessica Botos, Manager, Marketing
E-mail: jessica.botos@crainsnewyork.com
Ed: Aaron Elstein. **Description:** Due to the weakening economy, many financial institutions will face further massive losses forcing them to borrow more at higher interest rates and dragging down their earnings for years to come. The effects on commercial real estate and credit card loans are also discussed as well as the trend to investing in Asia and the Middle East. **Availability:** Online.

28229 ■ *"You Better Shop Around: Four Steps to Getting the Best Deal on a Home Loan" in Black Enterprise (Vol. 40, July 2010, No. 12, pp. 78)*
Pub: Earl G. Graves Ltd.
Contact: Earl Graves, Jr., President
Ed: Tara-Nicholle Nelson. **Description:** Four steps to help anyone seeking a mortgage for a home purchase are listed. **Availability:** Online.

28230 ■ *"Your Exposure to Bear Stearns" in Barron's (Vol. 88, March 17, 2008, No. 11, pp. 45)*
Pub: Dow Jones & Company Inc.
Contact: Almar Latour, Chief Executive Officer
Ed: Tom Sullivan, Jack Willoughby. **Description:** Bear Stearns makes up 5.5 percent of Pioneer Independence's portfolio, 1.4 percent of Vanguard Windsor II's portfolio, 1.2 percent of Legg Mason Value Trust, about 1 percent of Van Kampen Equity & Income, and 0.79 percent of Putnam Fund for Growth & Income. Ginnie Mae securities are now trading at 1.78 percentage points over treasuries due to the mortgage crises. **Availability:** Online.

28231 ■ *Your Guide to Arranging Bank & Debt Financing for Your Own Business in Canada*
Pub: Productive Publications
Contact: Iain Williamson, Author Publisher

Ed: Iain Williamson. **Released:** 2022-2023 Edition. **Price:** C$99.95, softcover, Postage/handling $19.95 on first title, Add postage/handling of $3.50 per title thereafter. **Description:** Bank financing for small businesses in Canada is discussed. **Availability:** Print.

28232 ■ *Your Guide to Canadian Export Financing: Successful Techniques for Financing Your Exports from Canada*
Pub: Productive Publications
Contact: Iain Williamson, Author Publisher
Ed: Iain Williamson. **Released:** 2022-2023 Edition. **Price:** C$74.95, softcover, Postage/handling $19.95 on first title, Add postage/handling of $3.50 per title thereafter. **Description:** Canadian export financing is covered. **Availability:** Print.

28233 ■ *Your Guide to Preparing a Plan to Raise Money for Your Own Business*
Pub: Productive Publications
Contact: Iain Williamson, Author Publisher
Ed: Iain Williamson. **Released:** Revised edition. **Price:** C$68.95, softcover, Postage/handling $19.95 on first title, Add postage/handling of $3.50 per title thereafter. **Description:** A good business plan is essential for raising money for any small business. **Availability:** Print.

28234 ■ *"Zions Offers Step-by-Step Small Business Guidance" in Idaho Business Review (September 1, 2014)*
Pub: BridgeTower Media
Contact: Adam Reinebach, President
Description: Zions bank provides small business guidance to clients through its Zions Bank Idaho Business Resource Center. The program helps entrepreneurs learn the basic rules of running a small business. Free courses teach the essentials of finance, marketing and selling, .

TRADE PERIODICALS

28235 ■ *National Mortgage News*
Pub: SourceMedia LLC
Contact: Gemma Postlethwaite, Chief Executive Officer
URL(s): www.nationalmortgagenews.com
Facebook: www.facebook.com/NationalMortgageNews
Linkedin: www.linkedin.com/company/nationalmortgagenews
X (Twitter): x.com/NatMortgageNews
Released: 8/year **Description:** Magazine covering technological trends and developments within the mortgage industry. **Availability:** Print; Online.

VIDEO/AUDIO MEDIA

28236 ■ *The How of Business: Ray Drew - SBA Loans*
URL(s): www.thehowofbusiness.com/456-ray-drew-sba-loans
Ed: Henry Lopez. **Released:** January 23, 2023. **Description:** Podcast discusses SBA lending, specifically the SBA 7a loan program, for entrepreneurs.

28237 ■ *How to Launch Your Venture with 0% Funding and Profit by Helping Others with Leo Kanell*
URL(s): www.eofire.com/podcast/leokanell
Ed: Jon Lee Dumas. **Released:** April 27, 2024. **Description:** Podcast shares the formula to make a business fundable.

28238 ■ *Marketplace: With Higher Interest Rates, Small Businesses and Lenders Proceed with Caution*
URL(s): www.marketplace.org/2023/10/10/higher-interest-rates-cautions-small-businesses-their-lenders
Ed: Sean McHenry. **Released:** October 10, 2023. **Description:** Podcast discusses cautious approaches to lending.

28239 ■ *Think Business: Learn Loan Essentials for Entrepreneurs from Mark Ritter*
URL(s): thinktyler.com/podcast_episode/loan-for-entrepreneurs-mark-ritter
Ed: Tyler Martin. **Released:** March 18, 2024. **Description:** Podcast explores the lending climate, the impact of personal situations on loan approvals, working with credit unions for small business owners, and the advantages of SBA loans for growing businesses.

28240 ■ *This Is Small Business: Business Loans Dos and Don'ts*
URL(s): www.smallbusiness.amazon/podcast-episodes/ep-48-business-loans-dos-and-donts
Ed: Andrea Marquez. **Released:** March 12, 2024. **Description:** Podcast explains how to start when looking for a business loan.

28241 ■ *What Is an SBA Loan?*
URL(s): podcasts.apple.com/us/podcast/what-is-an-sba-loan/id1377376636?i=1000590146681
Ed: Mike Jesowshek. **Released:** December 14, 2022. **Description:** Podcast discusses SBA loans and who is eligible for them.

RESEARCH CENTERS

28242 ■ University of Nebraska at Kearney - Nebraska Business Development Center (NBDC)
1917 West 24th St.
  Kearney, NE 68849-4440
Ph: (308)865-8344
Fax: (308)865-8153
Co. E-mail: nbdcunk@unk.edu
URL: http://www.unk.edu/academics/nbdc/index.php
Contact: Odee Ingersoll, Director
E-mail: ingersollo@unk.edu

Description: A cooperative program of the U.S. Small Business Administration and University of Nebraska at Kearney. Offers consulting services. **Scope:** Management education, market research, business and marketing plans, strategic planning, financial planning, cash flow budgeting, capital budgeting and loan packaging. **Founded:** 1977. **Publications:** *NBDC Business Calendar* (Quarterly). **Educational Activities:** NBDC Continuing education programs.

TENNESSEE VALLEY AUTHORITY

28243 ■ *"What Direction Is Your Company Moving In?"* in South Florida Business Journal (Vol. 35, August 29, 2014, No. 5, pp. 8)
American City Business Journals, Inc. (ACBJ)
120 W Morehead St.
Charlotte, NC 28202
Co. E-mail: circhelp@bizjournals.com
URL: http://www.acbj.com
Contact: Mike Olivieri, Executive Vice President
Released: Weekly. **Price:** $8, introductory 4-week offer(Digital only). **Description:** Senior management should have a clear perspective about the direction of a company and work hard to effectively communicate such perspective to all stakeholders. Some ways on how corporate leaders can clarify the strategic plan of a company to its key stakeholders are suggested. **Availability:** Print; Online.

U.S. POSTAL SERVICE

28244 ■ *Business As a Force for Good and Impact Leadership with Catherine Bell*
URL(s): www.awarepreneurs.com/podcast/335-impact-leadership
Ed: Paul Zelizer. **Released:** May 21, 2024. **Description:** Podcast offers an overview on impactful leadership.

START-UP INFORMATION

28245 ■ *"'Entrepreneurial Spirit' Leads Executives to Form New Tower Company"* in South Florida Business Journal (Vol. 34, February 21, 2014, No. 31, pp. 6)
Pub: American City Business Journals, Inc.
Contact: Mike Olivieri, Executive Vice President
Released: Weekly. **Price:** $8, Introductory 4-week offer(Digital & Print). **Description:** Phoenix Tower International is a new company in Boca Raton, Florida formed by the former executives of Global Tower Partners, a multibillion-dollar company that was sold in October 2013. Phoenix is self-funded and will focused on owning, leasing, and managing cellular phone service towers. **Availability:** Print; Online.

28246 ■ *"The Hard Thing About Hard Things: Building a Business When There Are No Easy Answers"*
Pub: HarperCollins Publishers L.L.C.
Contact: Brian Murray, President
Released: 2014. **Price:** $29.99, Hardcover; $14.99, E-book; $23.99, Digital Audiobook Unabridged. **Description:** Cofounder of Andreessen Horowitz and well-respected Silicon Valley entrepreneur, offers advice for building and running a startup small business. Horowitz analyzes issues confronting leaders

daily and shares insights he gained from managing, selling, buying investing in, and supervising technology firms. **Availability:** E-book; Print; Download.

28247 ■ *"The Introvert's Guide to Entrepreneurship: How to Become a Successful Entrepreneur as an Introvert"*
Pub: CreateSpace
Released: October 17, 2014. **Price:** $4.27, kindle; $12.99, paperback . **Description:** The five main strengths and the five harmful weaknesses for an introvert wishing to become an entrepreneur are listed. Three key strategies to help an introvert run his new company are examined. Five key attributes of a good business partner are considered. Management tips are also shared for introverted leaders. **Availability:** Print.

28248 ■ *"The Responsible Entrepreneur: Four Game-Changing Archetypes for Founders, Leaders, and Impact Investors"*
Pub: Jossey-Bass
Released: July 14, 2014. **Description:** Responsible entrepreneurs are special people who are able to transform industries as well as society. They challenge and refine cultural assumptions, laws, regulations, along with the processes of governance. They think beyond the status quo of entrepreneurship. Sanford provides the makings for this new type of business leadership, describing the ways in which any entrepreneur can achieve a higher level of work. Four archetypes are cover to help managers and entrepreneurs start and scale any business venture.

28249 ■ *Small Business Management: Launching and Growing New Ventures*
Pub: Nelson Education Ltd.
Contact: Steve Brown, President
Ed: Justin G. Longenecker. **Released:** 6th edition. **Price:** $133.95, paperback. **Description:** Tips for starting and running a successful new company are provided. **Availability:** E-book; Print.

28250 ■ *"Startup Activity Among Jobless Execs is the Highest Since 2009, Survey Says"* in South Florida Business Journal (Vol. 34, February 21, 2014, No. 31, pp. 3)
Pub: American City Business Journals, Inc.
Contact: Mike Olivieri, Executive Vice President
Released: Weekly. **Price:** $8, Introductory 4-week offer(Digital & Print). **Description:** The percentage of startup activity among former managers and executives in the U.S. increased 31 percent in 2013 according to consulting firm Challenger, Gray & Christmas. According to the survey, 5.5 percent of job-seeking executive launched their own business during each quarter in 2013, compared with 4.2 percent in 2012 and 3.2 percent in 2011. **Availability:** Print; Online.

ASSOCIATIONS AND OTHER ORGANIZATIONS

28251 ■ **American Management Association (AMA)**
American Management Association (AMA)
1601 Broadway
New York, NY 10019

Ph: (212)586-8100
Free: 800-262-9699
Fax: (212)903-8168
Co. E-mail: customerservice@amanet.org
URL: http://www.amanet.org
Contact: Manny Avramidis, President
Facebook: www.facebook.com/AmericanManagementAssn
Linkedin: www.linkedin.com/company/american-management-association
X (Twitter): x.com/amanet
Instagram: www.instagram.com/americanmanagementassociation
YouTube: www.youtube.com/user/AmericanManagement
Description: Provides educational forums worldwide where members and their colleagues learn superior, practical business skills and explore best practices of world-class organizations through interaction with each other and expert faculty practitioners. Maintains a publishing program providing tools individuals use to extend learning beyond the classroom in a process of lifelong professional growth and development through education. **Holdings:** 15,000 multilingual learning objects. **Publications:** *Small Business Reports: For Decision Makers in America's Small and Mid-Size Companies* (Monthly); *AMA's Directory of Human Resource Products and Services*; *Management Review* (Monthly); *The Take-Charge Assistant* (Monthly); *Organizational Dynamics: A Quarterly Review of Organizational Behavior for Management Executives*; *HR Focus* (Monthly). **Educational Activities:** Negotiating to Win (Continuous); Writing for the Web; AMA Management Skills for Administrative Professionals (Continuous); AMA Project Management for Administrative Professionals (Onsite); AMA Managing Chaos: Dynamic Time Management, Recall, Reading, and Stress Management Skills for Administrative Professionals (Onsite); AMA The Voice of Leadership: How Leaders Inspire, Influence, and Achieve Results (Onsite); AMA Making the Transition to Management (Onsite); AMA Making the Transition from Staff Member to Supervisor (Onsite); AMA Principles of Professional Selling (Continuous); AMA Technical Project Management (Onsite); AMA Leading Virtual Teams (Continuous); AMA Successful Product Management (Onsite); AMA's Course on Mergers and Acquisitions (Onsite); AMA Improving Your Project Management Skills: The Basics for Success (Continuous); AMA Partnering with Your Boss: Strategic Skills for Administrative Professionals (Continuous); AMA Effective Technical Writing (Onsite); AMA Strategies for Developing Effective Presentation Skills (Onsite); AMA Developing Your Personal Brand and Professional Image (Continuous); AMA Customer Service Excellence: How to Win and Keep Customers (Continuous); AMA Fundamentals of Cost Accounting (Onsite); AMA Recruiting, Interviewing and Selecting Employees (Onsite); AMA Managing Emotions in the Workplace: Strategies for Success (Onsite); AMA Responding to Conflict: Strategies for Improved Communication (Continuous); Assertiveness Training for Women in Business (Continuous); Leadership and Team Development for Managerial

Success (Onsite); AMA's Leading with Emotional Intelligence (Onsite); AMA's 5-Day MBA Workshop (Continuous); Taking on Greater Responsibility: Step-up Skills for Nonmanagers (Onsite) (Irregular); Successfully Managing People (Continuous); Managing Chaos: How to set Priorities and Make Decisions Under Pressure (Continuous); Moving Ahead: Breaking Behavior Patterns That Hold You Back (Onsite); The Effective Facilitator: Maximizing Involvement and Results (Continuous); Conquering Your Management Challenges: Advanced Management Skills for Supervisors (Onsite); Coaching and Counseling for Outstanding Job Performance (Continuous); Advanced Critical Thinking Applications Workshop (Onsite); AMA's Advanced Course in Strategic Marketing (Onsite); AMA's Advanced Executive Leadership Program (Onsite); AMA's Comprehensive Budgeting Workshop (Continuous); AMA's Comprehensive Project Management Workshop (Onsite) (Continuous); AMA's Advanced Financial Forecasting and Modeling Workshop (Onsite) (Continuous); AMA's PMP Exam Prep Express (Onsite); Building Better Work Relationships: New Techniques for Results-oriented Communication (Continuous); Assertiveness Training for Managers (Onsite); Managing Chaos: Tools to Set Priorities and Make Decisions Under Pressure (Onsite) (Continuous); Developing Your Analytical Skills: How to Research and Present Information (Onsite); AMA's 2-Day Business Writing Workshop (Live Online) (Continuous); Business Writing for the Multilingual Professional; Effective Executive Speaking (Onsite) (Continuous); Communication and Interpersonal Skills: A Seminar for IT and Technical Professionals (Onsite) (Continuous); Communicating with Confidence (Onsite) (Continuous); Developing Effective Business Conversation Skills (Onsite); Interpersonal Skills for Managers (Onsite); How to Present Online: A Skills-Based Workshop; Succession Planning: Developing Talent from Within (Onsite); Collaborative Leadership Skills (Onsite) (Continuous); Fundamentals of Marketing: Your Action Plan for Success (Continuous); Information Technology Project Management (Continuous); Best Practices for the Multi-project Manager (Continuous); Fundamentals of Purchasing for the New Buyer (Onsite); Selling to Major Accounts: A Strategic Approach (Onsite); Strategic Sales Negotiations (Onsite) (Continuous); Advanced Sales Management (Onsite); Effective Technical Writing (Onsite) (Continuous); Essentials of Project Management for the Nonproject Manager (Continuous). **Geographic Preference:** Multinational; National.

28252 ■ Association of Change Management Professionals (ACMP)

1032 15th St., NW, Ste. 261
  Washington, DC 20005
Ph: (202)991-8790
Co. E-mail: info@acmpglobal.org
URL: http://www.acmpglobal.org
Contact: Rich Batchelor, President
Facebook: www.facebook.com/ACMPGlobal
Linkedin: www.linkedin.com/company/acmpglobal
X (Twitter): x.com/acmpglobal
Instagram: www.instagram.com/acmpglobal

Description: Provides networking and collaboration for change management professionals who lead the people-side of change, ensuring that the needs of infrastructure, systems, culture and personnel are addressed. Focuses on developing industry standards and a professional certification program to ensure globally recognized standards for the discipline. **Founded:** 2011. **Geographic Preference:** National.

28253 ■ Association for Corporate Growth - Toronto Chapter (ACG) [Canadian Angus Association]

411 Richmond St. E, Ste. 200
  Toronto, ON, Canada M5A 3S5
Ph: (416)868-1881
Fax: (416)929-5256
Co. E-mail: toronto@acg.org
URL: http://www.acg.org/toronto
Contact: Mike Fenton, President

Linkedin: www.linkedin.com/company/association-for
  -corporate-growth-toronto-chapter
X (Twitter): x.com/ACGGlobal

Description: Professionals with a leadership role in strategic corporate growth. Seeks to facilitate the professional advancement of members, and the practice of corporate growth management. Fosters communication and cooperation among members; conducts continuing professional education programs. **Founded:** 1954. **Educational Activities:** Annual Capital Connection Conference (Annual). **Geographic Preference:** National.

28254 ■ Association of Strategic Alliance Professionals (ASAP)

935 Great Plain Ave., No. 127
  Needham, MA 02492
Ph: (781)562-1630
URL: http://www.strategic-alliances.org
Contact: Mike Leonetti, President
E-mail: mleonetti@strategic-alliances.org
Facebook: www.facebook.com/ASAPGlobal
Linkedin: www.linkedin.com/company/association-of
  -strategic-alliance-professionals
X (Twitter): x.com/ASAP_Global
YouTube: www.youtube.com/channel/UCGbGvB
  duVByljHeq_hWkkkA

Description: Seeks to create a distinct professional identity for executives and managers of strategic alliances. Sets standards of professional performance in the formation and management of strategic alliances. Creates awareness of the contributions of strategic alliances and strategic alliance professionals among corporate managers and executives and among the general public. **Founded:** 1998. **Publications:** *Best Practices* (Monthly). **Awards:** ASAP Alliance Program Excellence Award (Annual); ASAP Individual Alliance Excellence Award (Annual). **Geographic Preference:** Multinational.

28255 ■ Business Modeling and Integration Domain Task Force (BMIDTF)

9C Medway Rd., PMB 274
  Milford, MA 01757
URL: http://www.omg.org/bmi
Contact: Claude Baudoin, Chairman
E-mail: bmi-chair@omg.org

Description: Aims to empower all companies, across all industries, to develop and operate business processes that span multiple applications and business partners, behind the firewall and over the Internet. **Founded:** 2000. **Geographic Preference:** National.

28256 ■ Canadian Institute of Management (CIM) [Institut Canadien de Gestion]

311 - 80 Bradford St.
  Barrie, ON, Canada L4N 6S7
Ph: (705)725-8926
Fax: (705)725-8196
Co. E-mail: office@cim.ca
URL: http://www.cim.ca
Contact: Bob Fisher, President
E-mail: bob.fisher@cim.ca
Facebook: www.facebook.com/CanadianInstitu
  teofManagement
Linkedin: www.linkedin.com/company/canadian-insti
  tute-of-management
X (Twitter): x.com/CIM_National
Instagram: www.instagram.com/cim_charteredman
  ager
YouTube: www.youtube.com/channel/UC4K-tWjVD
  4cD1UnHye8xU-A

Description: Seeks to advance the practice of business management; promotes continuing professional development of members. **Founded:** 1942. **Publications:** *Canadian Manager: The Magazine for Managers* (Quarterly); *The Canadian Manager* (Quarterly). **Geographic Preference:** National.

28257 ■ Canadian Management Centre (CMC)

150 King St. W Ste. 271
  Toronto, ON, Canada M5H 1J9
Ph: (416)214-5678
Free: 877-262-2519
Fax: (416)214-6047
Co. E-mail: cmcinfo@cmcoutperform.com

URL: http://cmcoutperform.com
Contact: Chris Peacock, Director
Facebook: www.facebook.com/CanadianMgmt
Linkedin: www.linkedin.com/company/cana
  dianmanagementcentre
X (Twitter): x.com/canadianmgmt
YouTube: www.youtube.com/user/CdnMgmtCtr

Description: Managers of corporations and organizations. Promotes excellence in management. Conducts educational and training programs for management personnel. **Scope:** Provides courses in areas such as general management, communications, marketing, sales, project management and finance. Specialized services include customized on-site training and programs tailored for the government sector. **Founded:** 1963. **Publications:** "The Seven-Second Advantage"; "Stress and Coaching"; "Great Managers Attract and Keep) Great Talent"; "Why Aren't There More Good Managers?"; "Don't Delegate More - Delegate More Effectively"; "Managing in Uncertain Times: Transforming Employees from "Comfeartable" to Courageous"; "Ten Obstacles to Successful Decision Making"; "How to Be a Super Supervisor"; "The Evolution of Diversity: From 'The Right Thing' to Business Strategy"; "Okay, Okay, We Get It About Talent Management, But Do We Really"; "What High-Performing Companies Are Doing Now to Retain Talent Later"; "How Do You Want To Be Treated"; "The Ethics Dilemma"; "Understanding and Coping With Difficult Managers"; "Great Managers Lead Differently"; "Time Management for the Hurried and the Harried Professional"; "Well-Trained People Are Priceless"; "What Should We Be Measuring-Satisfaction or Engagement". **Training:** Skills Plus: Selling Different Clients Differently, Toronto, May, 2007; Management Skills for New Managers, Calgary, May, 2007; Time and Territory Management for Salespeople, Toronto, May, 2007; Developing Executive Leadership, Toronto, Apr, 2007; Building Business Acumen for Learning Professionals, Toronto, Apr, 2007; Communicating Up, Down and Across the Organization, Toronto, Mar, 2007; Managing Customer Conflict, Toronto, Feb, 2007; Negotiating to Win, Toronto, Jan, 2007. **Educational Activities:** Fundamentals of Marketing: Your Action Plan for Success; Assertiveness Training for Managers; Negotiating to Win; Preparing for Leadership: What It Takes to Take the Lead; Train the Trainer: Facilitation Skills Workshop Onsite; Maximum Performance Leadership Canada; Improving Your Project Management Skills: The Basics for Success; CMC Communicating Up, Down and Across the Organization; Advanced Financial Forecasting and Modeling Workshop; Management Skills for New Supervisors and Managers; The Comprehensive Project Management Workshop (Onsite).

28258 ■ *The Canadian Manager*

311 - 80 Bradford St.
  Barrie, ON, Canada L4N 6S7
Ph: (705)725-8926
Fax: (705)725-8196
Co. E-mail: office@cim.ca
URL: http://www.cim.ca
Contact: Bob Fisher, President
E-mail: bob.fisher@cim.ca
URL(s): cim.ca/resources/cim-publications/canadian
  -manager-magazine

Released: Quarterly; Winter, Spring, Summer, Fall. **Availability:** Print; Online.

28259 ■ International Council for Small Business (ICSB)

2201 G St. NW Funger Hall, Ste. 315
  Washington, DC 20052
Ph: (202)994-0704
Fax: (202)994-4930
Co. E-mail: info@icsb.org
URL: http://icsb.org
Contact: Dr. Ayman El Tarabishy, President
E-mail: ayman@gwu.edu
Facebook: www.facebook.com/icsb.org
Linkedin: www.linkedin.com/company/international
  -council-for-small-business-icsb-
X (Twitter): x.com/icsb
Instagram: www.instagram.com/icsbglobal

YouTube: www.youtube.com/channel/UCvWy8wfz
5nMk9a6yr5ZS0hQ

Description: Promotes and supports the interests and advancement of small businesses globally. **Founded:** 1955. **Publications:** *Journal of Small Business Management (JSBM)* (6/year). **Geographic Preference:** Multinational.

28260 ■ Machinery Information Management Open Systems Alliance (MIMOSA)
2200 Jack Warner Pky., Ste. 300
Tuscaloosa, AL 35401
Ph: (949)625-8616
Fax: (949)625-8616
URL: http://www.mimosa.org
Contact: Alan T. Johnston, President

Description: Encourages the adoption of open information standards for Operations and Maintenance and Collaborative Asset Lifecycle Management in commercial and military applications. Provides a forum for the members, bringing together subject matter experts in cross disciplinary technologies, to enable complex solutions for Equipment Operators, Maintainers, and Fleet Managers. **Geographic Preference:** National.

28261 ■ National Emergency Management Association (NEMA)
1776 Avenue of the States
Lexington, KY 40511
Ph: (859)244-8162
Co. E-mail: nemaadmin@csg.org
URL: http://www.nemaweb.org
Contact: Erica Bornemann, President
X (Twitter): x.com/NEMA_web
YouTube: www.youtube.com/user/NEMAforyou

Description: A U.S.-based resource for the emergency management community, providing information, support, and expertise. Promotes state emergency management programs, represents the state emergency management community before the federal government, and facilitates coordination of efforts between government and the private sector. **Founded:** 1974. **Awards:** Lacy E. Suiter Distinguished Service in Emergency Management Award (Annual). **Geographic Preference:** National.

28262 ■ NMA - The Leadership Development Organization (NMA)
3055 Kettering Blvd., Ste. 210
Dayton, OH 45439
Ph: (937)294-0421
Co. E-mail: nma@nma1.org
URL: http://nma1.org
Contact: Brian Berg, Executive Director
E-mail: brian@nma1.org
Facebook: www.facebook.com/NMAtheLeader
Linkedin: www.linkedin.com/company/nma-the-lea
dership-organization
X (Twitter): x.com/nmaleaders
Instagram: www.instagram.com/nmaleaders
YouTube: www.youtube.com/channel/UCcqiLHrxWe
_J4HpUp5buueA

Description: Business and industrial management personnel; membership comes from supervisory level, with the remainder from middle management and above. Seeks to develop and recognize management as a profession and to promote the free enterprise system. Prepares chapter programs on basic management, management policy and practice, communications, human behavior, industrial relations, economics, political education, and liberal education. Maintains speaker's bureau and hall of fame. Maintains educational, charitable, and research programs. Sponsors charitable programs. **Founded:** 1925. **Publications:** *National Speakers' Directory* (Periodic); *Manage* (Quarterly; Bimonthly). **Awards:** NMA Executive of the Year Award (Annual); NMA Leadership Speech Contest (Annual). **Geographic Preference:** National.

28263 ■ Organization Design Forum (ODF)
Phoenix, AZ
Ph: (602)510-9105
Co. E-mail: info@organizationdesignforum.org
URL: http://organizationdesignforum.org
Contact: Stacy Conti, Treasurer

E-mail: sconti@brighthealthinc.com
Facebook: www.facebook.com/organization
designforum
X (Twitter): x.com/orgdesignforum

Description: Works to promote the knowledge and practice of organizational design. Focuses on the effect organization structure and processes have on the performance of individuals, groups, and the organization itself. Offers basic and advanced training in organization design techniques. **Founded:** 1989. **Publications:** *Organization Design.* **Geographic Preference:** Multinational.

28264 ■ Professional Association of Health Care Office Management (PAHCOM)
1497 Main St., Ste. 136
Dunedin, FL 34698
Co. E-mail: info@pahcom.com
URL: http://my.pahcom.com
Contact: Karen Blanchette, Executive Director
Facebook: www.facebook.com/PAHCOM
Linkedin: www.linkedin.com/company/pahcom---pro
fessional-association-of-health-care-office
-management
X (Twitter): x.com/PAHCOM
Instagram: www.instagram.com/pahc0m

Description: Office managers of small group and solo medical practices. Conducts certification program for health care office managers. **Founded:** 1988. **Educational Activities:** Annual PAHCOM Conference (Annual). **Awards:** PAHCOM Medical Manager of the Year (Annual). **Geographic Preference:** National.

28265 ■ Professional Managers Association (PMA)
700 12th St., NW, Ste. 700, No 95968
Washington, DC 20005
Ph: (202)793-6262
URL: http://www.promanager.org
Contact: James Collins, President
Facebook: www.facebook.com/VoiceOfPMA
Linkedin: www.linkedin.com/company/voiceotpma
X (Twitter): x.com/voiceofpma
Instagram: www.instagram.com/voiceofpma

Description: Seeks to: improve the management, compensation, and public image of the federal workforce; provide a vehicle for the advancement of interests and views of professional managers. Concentrates on issues affecting the interests of professional managers and their ability to efficiently conduct their duties. **Founded:** 1981. **Geographic Preference:** National.

28266 ■ Project Management Institute - Dallas Chapter - Library
PO Box 251231
Plano, TX 75025-1231
Co. E-mail: education@pmidallas.org
URL: http://pmidallas.org
Contact: Jerry Glasscock, President
Facebook: www.facebook.com/pmidallaschapter
Linkedin: www.linkedin.com/company/pmidallas
X (Twitter): x.com/pmidallas
Instagram: www.instagram.com/pmidallas

Description: Corporations and individuals engaged in the practice of project management; project management students and educators. Seeks to advance the study, teaching, and practice of project management. **Scope:** Professional and educational materials. **Services:** Library open to public with restrictions; interlibrary loan. **Founded:** 1984. **Holdings:** Books. **Geographic Preference:** Local.

28267 ■ SCORE [Score Association]
712 H St. NE
Washington, DC 20002
Free: 800-634-0245
Co. E-mail: help@score.org
URL: http://www.score.org
Contact: Bridget Weston, Chief Executive Officer
Facebook: www.facebook.com/SCOREMentors
Linkedin: www.linkedin.com/company/score-mentors
X (Twitter): x.com/SCOREMentors
YouTube: www.youtube.com/user/
SCORESmallBusiness
Pinterest: www.pinterest.com/scorementors

Description: Provides free business counseling to regarding the start-up of a small business, problems with their business, or expanding their business. Offers free one-on-one and online counseling as well as low cost workshops on a variety of business topics. **Founded:** 1964. **Publications:** *SCORE eNews*; *SCORE Today.* **Awards:** SCORE Chapter of the Year Award (Annual); SCORE Outstanding Woman-Owned Small Business Award (Annual). **Geographic Preference:** National.

28268 ■ Society for Advancement of Management (SAM)
Marshall University - Provost Office 1 John Marshall Dr.
Huntington, WV 25755
Ph: (407)279-0890
Co. E-mail: sam@samnational.org
URL: http://samnational.org
Contact: Reza Kheirandish, President
Facebook: www.facebook.com/SAMnational
Linkedin: www.linkedin.com/company/samnational
X (Twitter): x.com/SAM_samnational
Instagram: www.instagram.com/samnational_news

Description: Represents management executives in industry commerce, government, and education. Fields of interest include management education, policy and strategy, MIS, international management, administration, budgeting, collective bargaining, distribution, incentives, materials handling, quality control, and training. **Founded:** 1912. **Publications:** *SAM Advanced Management Journal* (Quarterly); *SAM Management In Practice* (Quarterly); *The SAM News International* (Quarterly); *Society for Advancement of Management--International Business Conference Proceedings* (Annual); *Advanced Management Journal* (Quarterly). **Educational Activities:** Society for Advancement of Management Meeting (Annual); Society for Advancement of Management International Business Conference (Annual). **Geographic Preference:** National.

28269 ■ Strategic Management Society (SMS)
134 N LaSalle St., Ste. 1005
Chicago, IL 60602
Ph: (312)492-6224
Fax: (312)492-6223
Co. E-mail: sms@strategicmanagement.net
URL: http://www.strategicmanagement.net
Contact: Africa Ariño, President
X (Twitter): x.com/Strategic_Mgmt
YouTube: www.youtube.com/user/StrategicMgm
tSociety

Description: Aims to promote and encourage superior research and practice in the field of strategic management. **Scope:** Serves the Chicago business community in the areas of strategic planning and its application to the management of organizations. **Founded:** 1981. **Publications:** *Global Strategy Journal (GSJ)* (Quarterly). **Training:** Rolling Out The ($75) Barrel Forecasting Volatile Energy Prices, Chicago, Oct, 2006; Bricks and Clicks Transformation, Chicago, May, 2005; Branding Strategy for a Category Leader: How I Love My Dremel Found Its Target, Chicago, Apr, 2005; Successful Strategy: Recognizing Who You're Up Against, Chicago, Mar, 2005; Discover What the Best New Product Companies Do, Chicago, Feb, 2005. **Geographic Preference:** Multinational.

28270 ■ WIM Fox Valley (WIM)
PO Box 6690
Elgin, IL 60121-6690
Co. E-mail: wimfoxvalley@gmail.com
URL: http://www.wimfoxvalley.org
Contact: Joy Symonds, President

Description: Supports network of women in professional and management positions that facilitate the exchange of experience and ideas. Promotes self-growth in management; provides speakers who are successful in management; sponsors workshops and special interest groups to discuss problems and share job experiences. **Founded:** 1976. **Publications:** *Women in Management--National Directory* (Annual). **Geographic Preference:** Local; National.

28271 ■ World Confederation of Productivity Science (WCPS)

c/o Linda Carbone, Executive Secretary
500 Sherbrooke St. W, Ste. 900
Montreal, QC, Canada H3A 3C6
Co. E-mail: secretariat@wcps.info
URL: http://wcps.info
Contact: Linda Carbone, Executive Secretary
E-mail: secretariat@wcps.info
Description: Brings together a set of independent organizations and individuals who share common aims. **Founded:** 1969. **Educational Activities:** World Productivity Congress (Quadrennial). **Geographic Preference:** Multinational.

EDUCATIONAL PROGRAMS

28272 ■ The 8th Habit: From Effectiveness to Greatness

URL(s): www.amanet.org
Price: $2,195, Non-members; $1,995, Members AMA; $1,708, Members GSA. **Description:** Learn to reach your full potential and inspire others through the teachings of Dr. Stephen R. Covey of Franklin-Covey. **Audience:** Directors, VPs, team leaders, executives, department heads and experienced managers. **Principal Exhibits:** Learn to reach your full potential and inspire others through the teachings of Dr. Stephen R. Covey of FranklinCovey.

28273 ■ Achieving Leadership Success Through People (Onsite)

URL(s): www.amanet.org/training/seminars/onsite/
achieving-leadership-success-through-people.aspx
Description: Learn to lead more effectively by creating rapport, synergy, and two-way trust in this two-day course. **Audience:** Senior managers, directors, vice presidents and other executives, as well as midlevel managers. **Principal Exhibits:** Learn to lead more effectively by creating rapport, synergy, and two-way trust in this two-day course.

28274 ■ Advanced Issues in Employee Relations

Seminar Information Service Inc. (SIS)
250 El Camino Real., Ste. 112
Tustin, CA 92780
Ph: (714)508-0340
Free: 877-736-4636
Fax: (714)734-8027
Co. E-mail: info@seminarinformation.com
URL: http://www.seminarinformation.com
Contact: Catherine Bellizzi, President
URL(s): www.seminarinformation.com
Description: Key topics include coaching managers to more effectively manage high performing employees who consistently demonstrate one serious performance failing, collaborating with managers to assist them in focusing on performance issues without being influenced by employees' personal circumstances, working with managers on dealing more effectively with strong negative employee reactions to direction or feedback, and addressing managers' behavior that is inappropriate and potentially high risk. **Audience:** Industry professionals. **Principal Exhibits:** Key topics include coaching managers to more effectively manage high performing employees who consistently demonstrate one serious performance failing, collaborating with managers to assist them in focusing on performance issues without being influenced by employees' personal circumstances, working with managers on dealing more effectively with strong negative employee reactions to direction or feedback, and addressing managers' behavior that is inappropriate and potentially high risk.

28275 ■ Advanced IT Audit School (Onsite)

Seminar Information Service Inc. (SIS)
250 El Camino Real., Ste. 112
Tustin, CA 92780
Ph: (714)508-0340
Free: 877-736-4636
Fax: (714)734-8027
Co. E-mail: info@seminarinformation.com
URL: http://www.seminarinformation.com
Contact: Catherine Bellizzi, President

URL(s): www.seminarinformation.com
Description: This advanced hands-on workshop will show you how to use software tools to identify and test key control points in your organization's network infrastructure. **Audience:** IT auditors managers, and supervisors. **Principal Exhibits:** This advanced hands-on workshop will show you how to use software tools to identify and test key control points in your organization's network infrastructure.

28276 ■ AMA Improving Your Project Management Skills: The Basics for Success

American Management Association (AMA)
1601 Broadway
New York, NY 10019
Ph: (212)586-8100
Free: 800-262-9699
Fax: (212)903-8168
Co. E-mail: customerservice@amanet.org
URL: http://www.amanet.org
Contact: Manny Avramidis, President
URL(s): www.amanet.org/training/seminars/Improving
-Your-Project-Management-Skills-The-Basics-for
-Success.aspx
Frequency: Continuous. **Description:** Covers the basic principles of project management, including setting goals and schedules, managing a project plan, estimating, and budgeting. **Audience:** Project managers, business analysts and industry professionals. **Principal Exhibits:** Covers the basic principles of project management, including setting goals and schedules, managing a project plan, estimating, and budgeting. **Telecommunication Services:** customerservice@amanet.org.

28277 ■ AMA Leading Virtual Teams

American Management Association (AMA)
1601 Broadway
New York, NY 10019
Ph: (212)586-8100
Free: 800-262-9699
Fax: (212)903-8168
Co. E-mail: customerservice@amanet.org
URL: http://www.amanet.org
Contact: Manny Avramidis, President
URL(s): www.amanet.org/training/seminars/Leading
-Virtual-and-Remote-Teams.aspx
Frequency: Continuous. **Description:** Covers leadership models, communication between teams, virtual team development, measuring performance, and utilizing technology effectively. **Audience:** Experienced managers, leaders and project managers who are currently leading virtual teams and are seeking to enhance their overall performance as virtual leaders, as well as those who will be moving into a virtual leadership role in the future. **Principal Exhibits:** Covers leadership models, communication between teams, virtual team development, measuring performance, and utilizing technology effectively. **Telecommunication Services:** customerservice@amanet.org.

28278 ■ AMA Making the Transition to Management (Onsite)

American Management Association (AMA)
1601 Broadway
New York, NY 10019
Ph: (212)586-8100
Free: 800-262-9699
Fax: (212)903-8168
Co. E-mail: customerservice@amanet.org
URL: http://www.amanet.org
Contact: Manny Avramidis, President
URL(s): www.amanet.org/training/seminars/onsite/
Making-the-Transition-to-Management.aspx
Description: Covers various aspects of the transition to manager, understanding what managers do, effective communication and coaching skills, setting attainable goals, and creating a positive atmosphere. **Audience:** Newly appointed or prospective managers with less than one year of management experience who are interested in mastering basic management skills. **Principal Exhibits:** Covers various aspects of the

transition to manager, understanding what managers do, effective communication and coaching skills, setting attainable goals, and creating a positive atmosphere.

28279 ■ AMA Making the Transition from Staff Member to Supervisor (Onsite)

American Management Association (AMA)
1601 Broadway
New York, NY 10019
Ph: (212)586-8100
Free: 800-262-9699
Fax: (212)903-8168
Co. E-mail: customerservice@amanet.org
URL: http://www.amanet.org
Contact: Manny Avramidis, President
URL(s): www.amanet.org/training/seminars/onsite/
Making-the-Transition-from-Staff-Member-to-Super-
visor.aspx
Description: Covers various aspects of taking on a management position, setting goals, motivation, behavior styles, and time management. **Audience:** Newly promoted supervisors with less than one year of experience in this position. **Principal Exhibits:** Covers various aspects of taking on a management position, setting goals, motivation, behavior styles, and time management.

28280 ■ AMA Management Skills for Administrative Professionals

American Management Association (AMA)
1601 Broadway
New York, NY 10019
Ph: (212)586-8100
Free: 800-262-9699
Fax: (212)903-8168
Co. E-mail: customerservice@amanet.org
URL: http://www.amanet.org
Contact: Manny Avramidis, President
URL(s): www.amaseminars.org/training/seminars/
Management-Skills-for-Administrative-Professionals
.aspx
Frequency: Continuous. **Description:** Covers effective communication skills, conflict resolution, organizational skills, partnering with your boss, and setting attainable goals. **Audience:** Experienced administrative professionals, including executive secretaries, administrative assistants, secretaries or other members of the administrative support staff who need to expand their management skills so they can better support their organization and enhance their careers. **Principal Exhibits:** Covers effective communication skills, conflict resolution, organizational skills, partnering with your boss, and setting attainable goals. **Telecommunication Services:** customerservice@amanet.org.

28281 ■ AMA Managing Chaos: Dynamic Time Management, Recall, Reading, and Stress Management Skills for Administrative Professionals (Onsite)

American Management Association (AMA)
1601 Broadway
New York, NY 10019
Ph: (212)586-8100
Free: 800-262-9699
Fax: (212)903-8168
Co. E-mail: customerservice@amanet.org
URL: http://www.amanet.org
Contact: Manny Avramidis, President
URL(s): www.amaseminars.org/training/seminars/
onsite/managing-chaos-dynamic-time-managemen
t.aspx
Description: Covers learning techniques, productive planning, setting goals, and methods of controlling stress. **Audience:** Executive secretaries, secretaries and administrative/executive/sales assistants. **Principal Exhibits:** Covers learning techniques, productive planning, setting goals, and methods of controlling stress.

28282 ■ AMA Managing a World-Class IT Department (Onsite)

URL(s): www.amanet.org

Description: Covers leadership techniques, common challenges, budgeting, planning, testing, and decision making. **Audience:** New or prospective IT managers. **Principal Exhibits:** Covers leadership techniques, common challenges, budgeting, planning, testing, and decision making. **Telecommunication Services:** customerservice@amanet.org.

28283 ■ AMA Master Organizational Politics, Influence and Alliances (Onsite)

URL(s): www.amanet.org

Description: Covers driving high performance, relationship management, coaching, delegating, and your political image. **Audience:** Industry professionals. **Principal Exhibits:** Covers driving high performance, relationship management, coaching, delegating, and your political image. **Telecommunication Services:** customerservice@amanet.org.

28284 ■ AMA Project Management for Administrative Professionals (Onsite)

American Management Association (AMA)
  1601 Broadway
  New York, NY 10019
Ph: (212)586-8100
Free: 800-262-9699
Fax: (212)903-8168
Co. E-mail: customerservice@amanet.org
URL: http://www.amanet.org
Contact: Manny Avramidis, President
URL(s): www.amanet.org/training/seminars/onsite/
  Project-Management-for-Administrative-Profession-
  als.aspx

Description: Covers methods for planning, controlling, organizing, and tracking projects; problem solving techniques; and time management. **Audience:** Executive secretaries and assistants, administrative assistants and administrative support personnel, office managers, sales assistants and any administrative professional who is responsible for projects. **Principal Exhibits:** Covers methods for planning, controlling, organizing, and tracking projects; problem solving techniques; and time management.

28285 ■ AMA Technical Project Management (Onsite)

American Management Association (AMA)
  1601 Broadway
  New York, NY 10019
Ph: (212)586-8100
Free: 800-262-9699
Fax: (212)903-8168
Co. E-mail: customerservice@amanet.org
URL: http://www.amanet.org
Contact: Manny Avramidis, President
URL(s): www.amanet.org/training/seminars/onsite/
  Technical-Project-Management.aspx

Description: Covers defining cost, time, and scope; project leadership; utilizing status reports; and scheduling with milestones. **Audience:** R&D professionals, IT, engineers, scientists, principal investigators, plant managers and anyone else who administers IT and technical projects. **Principal Exhibits:** Covers defining cost, time, and scope; project leadership; utilizing status reports; and scheduling with milestones.

28286 ■ AMA The Voice of Leadership: How Leaders Inspire, Influence, and Achieve Results (Onsite)

American Management Association (AMA)
  1601 Broadway
  New York, NY 10019
Ph: (212)586-8100
Free: 800-262-9699
Fax: (212)903-8168
Co. E-mail: customerservice@amanet.org
URL: http://www.amanet.org
Contact: Manny Avramidis, President
URL(s): www.amanet.org/training/seminars/onsite/
  The-Voice-of-Leadership-How-Leaders-Inspire-In-
  fluence-and-Achieve-Results.aspx

Description: Covers managing change, how to inspire and influence, effective communication skills, coaching, and addressing conflict. **Audience:** Experienced managers and executives. **Principal Exhibits:** Covers managing change, how to inspire and influence, effective communication skills, coaching, and addressing conflict.

28287 ■ AMA's 5-Day MBA Workshop

American Management Association (AMA)
  1601 Broadway
  New York, NY 10019
Ph: (212)586-8100
Free: 800-262-9699
Fax: (212)903-8168
Co. E-mail: customerservice@amanet.org
URL: http://www.amanet.org
Contact: Manny Avramidis, President
URL(s): www.amanet.org/training/seminars/5-Day
  -MBA-Workshop.aspx
Price: $3,995, Non-members; $3,595, Members; $3,026, General Services Administration (GSA). **Frequency:** Continuous. **Description:** Provides information on recognize how effective risk management maximizes returns while mitigating, minimizing, and eliminating risks. **Audience:** All business professionals. **Principal Exhibits:** Provides information on recognize how effective risk management maximizes returns while mitigating, minimizing, and eliminating risks. **Telecommunication Services:** customerservice@amanet.org.

28288 ■ AMA's Advanced Executive Leadership Program (Onsite)

American Management Association (AMA)
  1601 Broadway
  New York, NY 10019
Ph: (212)586-8100
Free: 800-262-9699
Fax: (212)903-8168
Co. E-mail: customerservice@amanet.org
URL: http://www.amanet.org
Contact: Manny Avramidis, President
URL(s): www.amanet.org/training/seminars/onsite/a
  dvanced-executive-leadership-program.aspx
Price: $2,745, Non-members; $2,495, Members AMA; $2,268, Members GSA. **Description:** An intensive three day seminar focusing on executive leadership. **Audience:** Executives, directors and managers. **Principal Exhibits:** An intensive three day seminar focusing on executive leadership.

28289 ■ AMA's Comprehensive Project Management Workshop (Onsite)

American Management Association (AMA)
  1601 Broadway
  New York, NY 10019
Ph: (212)586-8100
Free: 800-262-9699
Fax: (212)903-8168
Co. E-mail: customerservice@amanet.org
URL: http://www.amanet.org
Contact: Manny Avramidis, President
URL(s): www.amanet.org/top-courses
Price: $3,095, Non-members; $2,795, Members AMA; $2,647, Members GSA. **Frequency:** Continuous. **Description:** Five-day seminar examining the framework, reviewing project management body of knowledge, initiating the project, planning the project, executing project plan, monitoring and controlling project and closing the project. **Audience:** Project managers, program managers and project team leaders who have several years of experience initiating, planning and managing projects, and project team members who are interested in enhancing their career by preparing to become a certified PMP. **Principal Exhibits:** Five-day seminar examining the framework, reviewing project management body of knowledge, initiating the project, planning the project, executing project plan, monitoring and controlling project and closing the project.

28290 ■ AMA's Leading with Emotional Intelligence (Onsite)

American Management Association (AMA)
  1601 Broadway
  New York, NY 10019
Ph: (212)586-8100
Free: 800-262-9699
Fax: (212)903-8168
Co. E-mail: customerservice@amanet.org

URL: http://www.amanet.org
Contact: Manny Avramidis, President
URL(s): www.amanet.org/training/seminars/onsite/lea
  ding-with-emotional-intelligence.aspx
Description: Covers the importance of emotional intelligence in the workplace, and developing a style to effectively communicate and use emotions positively. **Audience:** Senior managers and leaders who need to create a healthy, productive workplace and organizational culture by enhancing their overall effectiveness through EI. **Principal Exhibits:** Covers the importance of emotional intelligence in the workplace, and developing a style to effectively communicate and use emotions positively.

28291 ■ The Art of Coaching Employees to Excel (Onsite)

National Seminars Training L.L.C. (NST)
  14502 W 105th St.
  Lenexa, KS 66215
Free: 800-349-1935
Co. E-mail: info@findaseminar.com
URL: http://www.findaseminar.com/tpd/Padge
  tt-Thompson-Seminars.asp
URL(s): www.findaseminar.com/event1.asp?eventID
  =10000
Description: Teaches managers how to approach performance issues, set morale, and create self-esteem in the workplace. **Audience:** Professionals. **Principal Exhibits:** Teaches managers how to approach performance issues, set morale, and create self-esteem in the workplace.

28292 ■ Assertive Management (Onsite)

Seminar Information Service Inc. (SIS)
  250 El Camino Real., Ste. 112
  Tustin, CA 92780
Ph: (714)508-0340
Free: 877-736-4636
Fax: (714)734-8027
Co. E-mail: info@seminarinformation.com
URL: http://www.seminarinformation.com
Contact: Catherine Bellizzi, President
URL(s): www.seminarinformation.com
Description: Develop the qualities necessary for successful, assertive management. Participants gain confidence and skill in being 'pro-active' in communicating with others, including how to use positive, win-win approaches and to defuse emotionally charged situations in order to work more effectively with their fellow workers, supervisors and subordinates. **Audience:** Supervisors and managers. **Principal Exhibits:** Develop the qualities necessary for successful, assertive management. Participants gain confidence and skill in being 'pro-active' in communicating with others, including how to use positive, win-win approaches and to defuse emotionally charged situations in order to work more effectively with their fellow workers, supervisors and subordinates. **Telecommunication Services:** info@seminarinformation.com.

28293 ■ Assertiveness Skills for Managers and Supervisors (Onsite)

National Seminars Training L.L.C. (NST)
  14502 W 105th St.
  Lenexa, KS 66215
Free: 800-349-1935
Co. E-mail: info@findaseminar.com
URL: http://www.findaseminar.com/tpd/Padge
  tt-Thompson-Seminars.asp
URL(s): www.findaseminar.com/event1.asp?eventID
  =859
Description: Attendees will gain assertiveness skills they need to achieve the recognition they deserve. **Audience:** Professionals, managers and supervisors. **Principal Exhibits:** Attendees will gain assertiveness skills they need to achieve the recognition they deserve.

28294 ■ Assertiveness Training for Managers (Onsite)

American Management Association (AMA)
  1601 Broadway
  New York, NY 10019
Ph: (212)586-8100
Free: 800-262-9699

Fax: (212)903-8168
Co. E-mail: customerservice@amanet.org
URL: http://www.amanet.org
Contact: Manny Avramidis, President
URL(s): www.amanet.org/training/seminars/onsite/
assertiveness-training-for-managers.aspx

Price: $2,495, Non-members; $2,245, Members AMA; $1,984, Members GSA. **Description:** Learn how your behavior impacts your performance and how to take control without isolating others. **Audience:** Managers, and professionals. **Principal Exhibits:** Learn how your behavior impacts your performance and how to take control without isolating others.

28295 ■ Become a World Class Assistant (Onsite)

Seminar Information Service Inc. (SIS)
    250 El Camino Real., Ste. 112
    Tustin, CA 92780
Ph: (714)508-0340
Free: 877-736-4636
Fax: (714)734-8027
Co. E-mail: info@seminarinformation.com
URL: http://www.seminarinformation.com
Contact: Catherine Bellizzi, President
URL(s): www.seminarinformation.com/qqbqyw/be-
come-a-world-class-assistant

Description: Offer exemplary teaching and training programs. **Audience:** Seasoned executive assistants and other high-caliber assistants. **Principal Exhibits:** Offer exemplary teaching and training programs.

28296 ■ Best Practices for the Multi-project Manager

American Management Association (AMA)
    1601 Broadway
    New York, NY 10019
Ph: (212)586-8100
Free: 800-262-9699
Fax: (212)903-8168
Co. E-mail: customerservice@amanet.org
URL: http://www.amanet.org
Contact: Manny Avramidis, President
URL(s): www.amanet.org/best-practices-for-the-multi
-project-manager

Price: $2,195, Non-members; $1,995, Members; $1,795, General Services Administration (GSA). **Frequency:** Continuous. **Description:** Covers balancing work load, reducing risk and conflict, time management, prioritizing, and monitoring and reporting on multiple projects. **Audience:** Project managers who are working on multiple projects simultaneously and would like to learn tips and techniques to improve their effectiveness and efficiency. **Principal Exhibits:** Covers balancing work load, reducing risk and conflict, time management, prioritizing, and monitoring and reporting on multiple projects. **Telecommunication Services:** customerservice@amanet.org.

28297 ■ Building a Positive, Motivated and Cooperative Team (Onsite)

Seminar Information Service Inc. (SIS)
    250 El Camino Real., Ste. 112
    Tustin, CA 92780
Ph: (714)508-0340
Free: 877-736-4636
Fax: (714)734-8027
Co. E-mail: info@seminarinformation.com
URL: http://www.seminarinformation.com
Contact: Catherine Bellizzi, President
URL(s): www.seminarinformation.com

Price: $199. **Description:** Learn to create positive and productive results within the workplace utilizing real world examples. **Audience:** Professionals. **Principal Exhibits:** Learn to create positive and productive results within the workplace utilizing real world examples.

28298 ■ Building a Successful Business Analysis Work Plan

URL(s): www.learningtree.com/investor/releases/
pr090507.htm

Description: Learn to develop and execute a work plan using practical project management tools, methods, and techniques. **Audience:** Business industry professionals. **Principal Exhibits:** Learn to develop and execute a work plan using practical project management tools, methods, and techniques.

28299 ■ Business Analysis Essentials (Onsite)

Seminar Information Service Inc. (SIS)
    250 El Camino Real., Ste. 112
    Tustin, CA 92780
Ph: (714)508-0340
Free: 877-736-4636
Fax: (714)734-8027
Co. E-mail: info@seminarinformation.com
URL: http://www.seminarinformation.com
Contact: Catherine Bellizzi, President
URL(s): www.seminarinformation.com/qqbuxn/busi-
ness-analysis-essentials

Description: Learn to define the scope of work and master requirements-gathering techniques that will work for a variety of projects and audiences. **Audience:** Systems analysts, business analysts, requirements analysts, developers, software engineers, IT project managers, project managers, project analysts, project leaders, senior project managers, team leaders, program managers. **Principal Exhibits:** Learn to define the scope of work and master requirements-gathering techniques that will work for a variety of projects and audiences.

28300 ■ Business Process Analysis

Seminar Information Service Inc. (SIS)
    250 El Camino Real., Ste. 112
    Tustin, CA 92780
Ph: (714)508-0340
Free: 877-736-4636
Fax: (714)734-8027
Co. E-mail: info@seminarinformation.com
URL: http://www.seminarinformation.com
Contact: Catherine Bellizzi, President
URL(s): www.seminarinformation.com/qqbuxp/
business-process-analysis

Description: Learn to model business processes as they are currently enacted, assess the quality of those business processes, and collaborate with the stakeholders to identify improvements. **Audience:** Systems analysts, business analysts, IT project managers, associate project managers, project managers, project coordinators, project analysts, project leaders, senior project managers, team leaders, product managers, and program managers. **Principal Exhibits:** Learn to model business processes as they are currently enacted, assess the quality of those business processes, and collaborate with the stakeholders to identify improvements.

28301 ■ CMC Confronting the Tough Stuff: Turning Managerial Challenges into Positive Results

URL(s): cmcoutperform.com

Description: Seminar that covers the challenges and the problem-solving skills in the workplace, including coaching uncooperative employees, constructive and destructive conflict, techniques for using conflict to increase cohesion, four stages of mediation and techniques to mediate disputes between employees, and avoid potentially litigious situations. Held in Mississauga, ON and Toronto, ON. **Audience:** Supervisors and managers. **Principal Exhibits:** Seminar that covers the challenges and the problem-solving skills in the workplace, including coaching uncooperative employees, constructive and destructive conflict, techniques for using conflict to increase cohesion, four stages of mediation and techniques to mediate disputes between employees, and avoid potentially litigious situations. Held in Mississauga, ON and Toronto, ON.

28302 ■ CMC Developing Executive Leadership

URL(s): cmcoutperform.com/developing-executive
-leadership-online

Description: Seminar that covers leadership in today's business environment, including techniques to improve effectiveness, leading individuals and

groups, keys to developing influence, and how to create your own leadership development plan. **Audience:** Midlevel managers and executives. **Principal Exhibits:** Seminar that covers leadership in today's business environment, including techniques to improve effectiveness, leading individuals and groups, keys to developing influence, and how to create your own leadership development plan. **Telecommunication Services:** cmcinfo@cmctraining.org.

28303 ■ CMC Process Management: Applying Process Mapping to Analyze and Improve Your Operation

URL(s): www.cmctraining.org

Description: Seminar that covers process mapping techniques, and application and documentation of standard operation procedures, including work simplification analysis and value added versus non-value added activity analysis. **Audience:** Project and program directors and managers. **Principal Exhibits:** Seminar that covers process mapping techniques, and application and documentation of standard operation procedures, including work simplification analysis and value added versus non-value added activity analysis. **Telecommunication Services:** cmcinfo@cmctraining.org.

28304 ■ CMC Stepping Up to Leadership

URL(s): cmcoutperform.com

Description: Seminar that covers the role of leadership, including attitudes and barriers that prevent you from taking a leadership role, create partnerships that get you the information you need, team leading without the authority, Emotional Intelligence (EI), and career development strategies. **Audience:** Industry professionals. **Principal Exhibits:** Seminar that covers the role of leadership, including attitudes and barriers that prevent you from taking a leadership role, create partnerships that get you the information you need, team leading without the authority, Emotional Intelligence (EI), and career development strategies.

28305 ■ Coaching: A Strategic Tool for Effective Leadership

URL(s): cmcoutperform.com/coaching-effective-lea
dership

Price: C$2,195, Members; C$2,395, Non-members. **Description:** Covers creating a successful environment, problem resolution, teamwork, soliciting valuable feedback, and models for successful coaching. **Audience:** Individuals who are responsible for the performance and development of other employees. **Principal Exhibits:** Covers creating a successful environment, problem resolution, teamwork, soliciting valuable feedback, and models for successful coaching. **Telecommunication Services:** cmcinfo@cmcoutperform.com.

28306 ■ Coaching and Counseling for Outstanding Job Performance

American Management Association (AMA)
    1601 Broadway
    New York, NY 10019
Ph: (212)586-8100
Free: 800-262-9699
Fax: (212)903-8168
Co. E-mail: customerservice@amanet.org
URL: http://www.amanet.org
Contact: Manny Avramidis, President
URL(s): www.amanet.org/training/seminars/Coaching
-and-Counseling-for-Outstanding-Job-Performance
.aspx

Price: $2,345, Non-members; $2,095, Members; $1,889, General Services Administration (GSA). **Frequency:** Continuous. **Description:** Covers creating a successful environment, problem resolution, teamwork, soliciting valuable feedback, and models for successful coaching. Held in Arlington, VA; San Francisco, CA; and Washington, DC. Also available live online. **Audience:** Managers who want to improve results and get higher performance from their team. **Principal Exhibits:** Covers creating a successful environment, problem resolution, teamwork, soliciting valuable feedback, and models for successful coaching. Held in Arlington, VA; San Francisco, CA; and Washington, DC. Also available live online. **Telecommunication Services:** customerservice@ amanet.org.

28307 ■ Coaching, Mentoring & Team-Building Skills (Onsite)

Seminar Information Service Inc. (SIS)
250 El Camino Real., Ste. 112
Tustin, CA 92780
Ph: (714)508-0340
Free: 877-736-4636
Fax: (714)734-8027
Co. E-mail: info@seminarinformation.com
URL: http://www.seminarinformation.com
Contact: Catherine Bellizzi, President
URL(s): www.seminarinformation.com/details.cfm?qc
=qqdqvk

Description: Learn how to motivate, inspire and guide people to success, including tools for improving cooperation, communication, and a high-energy environment that fosters teamwork. **Audience:** Managers, supervisors, team leaders and business owners. **Principal Exhibits:** Learn how to motivate, inspire and guide people to success, including tools for improving cooperation, communication, and a high-energy environment that fosters teamwork.

28308 ■ Collaborative Leadership Skills (Onsite)

American Management Association (AMA)
1601 Broadway
New York, NY 10019
Ph: (212)586-8100
Free: 800-262-9699
Fax: (212)903-8168
Co. E-mail: customerservice@amanet.org
URL: http://www.amanet.org
Contact: Manny Avramidis, President
URL(s): www.amanet.org/collaborative-leadership
-skills

Price: $2,195, Non-members; $1,995, Members AMA, $1,889, Members GSA. **Frequency:** Continuous. **Description:** Learn to develop a collaborative style to build a mutual trust with your team and other departments. **Audience:** Midlevel managers who want to inspire greater involvement, creativity and knowledge sharing in their employees. **Principal Exhibits:** Learn to develop a collaborative style to build a mutual trust with your team and other departments.

28309 ■ The Comprehensive Project Management Workshop (Onsite)

Canadian Management Centre (CMC)
150 King St. W Ste. 271
Toronto, ON, Canada M5H 1J9
Ph: (416)214-5678
Free: 877-262-2519
Fax: (416)214-6047
Co. E-mail: cmcinfo@cmcoutperform.com
URL: http://cmcoutperform.com
Contact: Chris Peacock, Director
URL(s): cmcoutperform.com/courses-on-request

Description: Promotes project management expertise and prepares participants for PMP certification in this five-day seminar. **Audience:** Project managers. **Principal Exhibits:** Promotes project management expertise and prepares participants for PMP certification in this five-day seminar.

28310 ■ Conducting Employee Performance Evaluations (Onsite)

National Seminars Training L.L.C. (NST)
14502 W 105th St.
Lenexa, KS 66215
Free: 800-349-1935
Co. E-mail: info@findaseminar.com
URL: http://www.findaseminar.com/tpd/Padge
tt-Thompson-Seminars.asp
URL(s): www.findaseminar.com/event1.asp?eventID
=921

Description: Learn more about conducting fair, legal evaluations and make the review process an integral part of improving employee performance. **Audience:** Human resource professionals, managers, and

supervisors. **Principal Exhibits:** Learn more about conducting fair, legal evaluations and make the review process an integral part of improving employee performance.

28311 ■ Conquering Your Management Challenges: Advanced Management Skills for Supervisors (Onsite)

American Management Association (AMA)
1601 Broadway
New York, NY 10019
Ph: (212)586-8100
Free: 800-262-9699
Fax: (212)903-8168
Co. E-mail: customerservice@amanet.org
URL: http://www.amanet.org
Contact: Manny Avramidis, President
URL(s): www.amanet.org/training/seminars/onsite/
confronting-the-tough-stuff-management-skills-for
-supervisors.aspx

Price: $2,095, Non-members; $1,895, Members; $1,700, General Services Administration (GSA). **Description:** Covers diffusing potential legal situations, dealing with challenges, writing performance evaluations, enhancing productivity, and managing diversity. **Audience:** Managers and supervisors. **Principal Exhibits:** Covers diffusing potential legal situations, dealing with challenges, writing performance evaluations, enhancing productivity, and managing diversity.

28312 ■ Creative Leadership Workshop for Managers, Supervisors, and Team Leaders

Seminar Information Service Inc. (SIS)
250 El Camino Real., Ste. 112
Tustin, CA 92780
Ph: (714)508-0340
Free: 877-736-4636
Fax: (714)734-8027
Co. E-mail: info@seminarinformation.com
URL: http://www.seminarinformation.com
Contact: Catherine Bellizzi, President
URL(s): www.seminarinformation.com/details.cfm?qc
=qqbsje

Price: $348. **Description:** Learn a bold new approach to motivate employees for greater productivity, stronger teamwork and improved morale in today's complex workforce. **Audience:** Managers, supervisors and team leaders. **Principal Exhibits:** Learn a bold new approach to motivate employees for greater productivity, stronger teamwork and improved morale in today's complex workforce.

28313 ■ Critical Thinking: A New Paradigm for Peak Performance (Onsite)

Seminar Information Service Inc. (SIS)
250 El Camino Real., Ste. 112
Tustin, CA 92780
Ph: (714)508-0340
Free: 877-736-4636
Fax: (714)734-8027
Co. E-mail: info@seminarinformation.com
URL: http://www.seminarinformation.com
Contact: Catherine Bellizzi, President
URL(s): www.seminarinformation.com/details.cfm?qc
=qqaxga

Description: Learn different styles of thinking and identify your personal preferences, including how to challenge assumptions and expand perceptions about situations. **Audience:** Executives, directors, managers, team leaders and business professionals. **Principal Exhibits:** Learn different styles of thinking and identify your personal preferences, including how to challenge assumptions and expand perceptions about situations.

28314 ■ Criticism & Discipline Skills for Managers and Supervisors (Onsite)

URL(s): www.pryor.com/training-seminars/criticism
-discipline-skills-managers-supervisors

Description: Learn proven techniques for managing difficult employees without incurring resentment, making enemies, or destroying relationships, including how to discipline employees who have a bad attitude, are chronically tardy, miss work often, refuse to take responsibility and challenge your authority. **Audience:** Industry professionals. **Principal Exhibits:**

Learn proven techniques for managing difficult employees without incurring resentment, making enemies, or destroying relationships, including how to discipline employees who have a bad attitude, are chronically tardy, miss work often, refuse to take responsibility and challenge your authority.

28315 ■ Developing Into a Powerful Leader (Onsite)

Seminar Information Service Inc. (SIS)
250 El Camino Real., Ste. 112
Tustin, CA 92780
Ph: (714)508-0340
Free: 877-736-4636
Fax: (714)734-8027
Co. E-mail: info@seminarinformation.com
URL: http://www.seminarinformation.com
Contact: Catherine Bellizzi, President
URL(s): www.seminarinformation.com/details.cfm?qc
=qqbeak

Description: Enhance your ability to lead others and have them feel good about the process. **Audience:** Managers. **Principal Exhibits:** Enhance your ability to lead others and have them feel good about the process.

28316 ■ Developing Your Emotional Intelligence (Onsite)

National Seminars Training L.L.C. (NST)
14502 W 105th St.
Lenexa, KS 66215
Free: 800-349-1935
Co. E-mail: info@findaseminar.com
URL: http://www.findaseminar.com/tpd/Padge
tt-Thompson-Seminars.asp
URL(s): www.findaseminar.com/PERSONAL-DEVEL-
OPMENT-Training/Developing-Your-Emotional-In
telligence-Seminar-by-American-Managemen
t-Association-Seminars/8018.html?filter=ON&city
=ARLINGTON&state=VA

Description: Seminar provides skills to the eliminate stress and frustration brought on by others in the workplace. **Audience:** Business professionals, admin professionals. **Principal Exhibits:** Seminar provides skills to the eliminate stress and frustration brought on by others in the workplace.

28317 ■ The Difference Between Good and Great Supervisors

National Seminars Training L.L.C. (NST)
14502 W 105th St.
Lenexa, KS 66215
Free: 800-349-1935
Co. E-mail: info@findaseminar.com
URL: http://www.findaseminar.com/tpd/Padge
tt-Thompson-Seminars.asp
URL(s): www.findaseminar.com/event1.asp?eventID
=9782

Description: Workshop presents positive solutions, real-world tips, and strategies for managers and supervisors. **Audience:** Supervisors and professionals. **Principal Exhibits:** Workshop presents positive solutions, real-world tips, and strategies for managers and supervisors.

28318 ■ Driving Innovation: Proven Processes, Tools and Strategies for Growth (Onsite)

Seminar Information Service Inc. (SIS)
250 El Camino Real., Ste. 112
Tustin, CA 92780
Ph: (714)508-0340
Free: 877-736-4636
Fax: (714)734-8027
Co. E-mail: info@seminarinformation.com
URL: http://www.seminarinformation.com
Contact: Catherine Bellizzi, President
URL(s): www.seminarinformation.com

Description: Learn to use proven processes and tools to imagine and execute new innovation opportunities, regardless of your creative disposition or your role in the organization. **Audience:** Internal trainers and leadership development professionals interested in becoming certified to deliver Linkage's 2-day Driving Innovation workshop to their leaders, managers and staff. **Principal Exhibits:** Learn to use proven processes and tools to imagine and execute new innovation opportunities, regardless of your creative disposition or your role in the organization.

28319 ■ EEI Communications Earned Value Management Systems (EVMS) for Project Managers
URL(s): www.eeicom.com

Description: Seminar based on ANSI/EIA-748-A, Earned Value Management Systems, and the Project Management Institute's (PMI) Project Management Body of Knowledge (PMBOK) that covers resource planning and estimating, project budgeting, EVM (Earned Value Management) performance metrics, variance analyses, and EVMS reports. **Audience:** Newly assigned program managers, project managers and project administrators . **Principal Exhibits:** Seminar based on ANSI/EIA-748-A, Earned Value Management Systems, and the Project Management Institute's (PMI) Project Management Body of Knowledge (PMBOK) that covers resource planning and estimating, project budgeting, EVM (Earned Value Management) performance metrics, variance analyses, and EVMS reports. **Telecommunication Services:** info@eeicom.com.

28320 ■ EEI Communications Introduction to Project Management (Onsite)
URL(s): www.eeicom.com

Description: Topics include understanding project management, characteristics of an effective manager, documentation, and quality control. **Audience:** Project managers. **Principal Exhibits:** Topics include understanding project management, characteristics of an effective manager, documentation, and quality control. **Telecommunication Services:** train@eeicom.com.

28321 ■ EEI Communications Project Management for Streaming DVD, and Multimedia
URL(s): www.eeicom.com

Description: Covers an overview of the steps involved in bringing a multimedia or CD-ROM project to completion, including audience and purpose analysis, information and graphic design, planning and resources, managing the creative process, scheduling and budgeting, quality control, and video and sound options. **Audience:** Project managers and professionals. **Principal Exhibits:** Covers an overview of the steps involved in bringing a multimedia or CD-ROM project to completion, including audience and purpose analysis, information and graphic design, planning and resources, managing the creative process, scheduling and budgeting, quality control, and video and sound options. **Telecommunication Services:** info@eeicom.com.

28322 ■ Effective Meeting Management (Onsite)
Seminar Information Service Inc. (SIS)
  250 El Camino Real., Ste. 112
  Tustin, CA 92780
Ph: (714)508-0340
Free: 877-736-4636
Fax: (714)734-8027
Co. E-mail: info@seminarinformation.com
URL: http://www.seminarinformation.com
Contact: Catherine Bellizzi, President
URL(s): www.seminarinformation.com

Description: Learn how to keep control throughout the meeting, while creating a receptive, engaging, and energetic atmosphere. **Audience:** Individuals in lead worker or group leader positions who are not officially management employees. **Principal Exhibits:** Learn how to keep control throughout the meeting, while creating a receptive, engaging, and energetic atmosphere.

28323 ■ Effective Negotiating
Karrass USA Ltd.
  1625 Stanford St.
  Santa Monica, CA 90404
Ph: (323)866-3800
Co. E-mail: info@karrass.com
URL: http://www.karrass.com

Contact: Gary Karrass, Co-Founder Chairman
URL(s): www.karrass.com/seminars/effective-negotiating-two-day-seminar
Frequency: Irregular; Two days. **Description:** Seminar topics include, sticking to your own game plan, what people forget to do, you have more power than you think, and using hidden leverage. **Audience:** Business professionals. **Principal Exhibits:** Seminar topics include, sticking to your own game plan, what people forget to do, you have more power than you think, and using hidden leverage.

28324 ■ Effective Project Communications, Negotiations and Conflict (Onsite)
URL(s): www.eeicom.com

Description: Learn what you need to know to lead projects through their initiation, planning, execution, and control phases, including the skills needed to find common ground, overcome resistance, resolve disputes, and gain commitment to project management efforts. **Audience:** Industry professionals, administrative. **Principal Exhibits:** Learn what you need to know to lead projects through their initiation, planning, execution, and control phases, including the skills needed to find common ground, overcome resistance, resolve disputes, and gain commitment to project management efforts.

28325 ■ Effective Training Techniques for Group Leaders (Onsite)
Seminar Information Service Inc. (SIS)
  250 El Camino Real., Ste. 112
  Tustin, CA 92780
Ph: (714)508-0340
Free: 877-736-4636
Fax: (714)734-8027
Co. E-mail: info@seminarinformation.com
URL: http://www.seminarinformation.com
Contact: Catherine Bellizzi, President
URL(s): www.seminarinformation.com/details.cfm?qc=qqadnm

Description: Provides group leaders precise and practical methods to train their employees. Leaders also learn to spot worker training needs and provide effective on-the-job training. **Audience:** Group leaders. **Principal Exhibits:** Provides group leaders precise and practical methods to train their employees. Leaders also learn to spot worker training needs and provide effective on-the-job training.

28326 ■ Enhancing Your Management Skills (Onsite)
Seminar Information Service Inc. (SIS)
  250 El Camino Real., Ste. 112
  Tustin, CA 92780
Ph: (714)508-0340
Free: 877-736-4636
Fax: (714)734-8027
Co. E-mail: info@seminarinformation.com
URL: http://www.seminarinformation.com
Contact: Catherine Bellizzi, President
URL(s): www.seminarinformation.com/qqbsee/enhancing-your-management-skills

Description: Learn the critical success factors for driving results through goal alignment, coaching for performance, building trust, and driving committed action through stronger leadership. Receive practical, state-of-the-art tools and techniques for holding conversations that set clear expectations, provide focused feedback, create a motivational environment, and build commitment for needed change. **Audience:** Industry professionals. **Principal Exhibits:** Learn the critical success factors for driving results through goal alignment, coaching for performance, building trust, and driving committed action through stronger leadership. Receive practical, state-of-the-art tools and techniques for holding conversations that set clear expectations, provide focused feedback, create a motivational environment, and build commitment for needed change.

28327 ■ Essential Facilitation Workshop
Interaction Associates
  50 Milk St.
  Boston, MA 02110
Ph: (617)535-7000
Co. E-mail: success@interactionassociates.com

URL: http://interactionassociates.com
Contact: Kim Doyle, Director
E-mail: kdoyle@interactionassociates.com
URL(s): www.tickettailor.com/events/interactionassociates1/1058347
Frequency: Irregular. **Audience:** General public.

28328 ■ Essentials of Project Management for the Nonproject Manager
American Management Association (AMA)
  1601 Broadway
  New York, NY 10019
Ph: (212)586-8100
Free: 800-262-9699
Fax: (212)903-8168
Co. E-mail: customerservice@amanet.org
URL: http://www.amanet.org
Contact: Manny Avramidis, President
URL(s): www.amanet.org/essentials-of-project-management-for-the-non-project-manager
Frequency: Continuous. **Description:** Learn and apply basic elements of project management to your job. Also available live online. **Audience:** Subject matter experts, team members, project sponsors, contributors, facilitators and coordinators. **Principal Exhibits:** Learn and apply basic elements of project management to your job. Also available live online.

28329 ■ Excelling as A Manager or Supervisor (Onsite)
Seminar Information Service Inc. (SIS)
  250 El Camino Real., Ste. 112
  Tustin, CA 92780
Ph: (714)508-0340
Free: 877-736-4636
Fax: (714)734-8027
Co. E-mail: info@seminarinformation.com
URL: http://www.seminarinformation.com
Contact: Catherine Bellizzi, President
URL(s): www.seminarinformation.com/details.cfm?qc=qqbfmk

Description: Offers solutions to help you fully achieve your potential as a true leader. **Audience:** Newly appointed managers and supervisors. **Principal Exhibits:** Offers solutions to help you fully achieve your potential as a true leader.

28330 ■ Excelling as a Highly Effective Team Leader (Onsite)
Seminar Information Service Inc. (SIS)
  250 El Camino Real., Ste. 112
  Tustin, CA 92780
Ph: (714)508-0340
Free: 877-736-4636
Fax: (714)734-8027
Co. E-mail: info@seminarinformation.com
URL: http://www.seminarinformation.com
Contact: Catherine Bellizzi, President
URL(s): www.seminarinformation.com/details.cfm?qc=qqbjfh

Description: Learn the personal leadership characteristics and skills that create energy and enthusiasm increasing productivity and performance. **Audience:** Leaders of teams and potential leaders. **Principal Exhibits:** Learn the personal leadership characteristics and skills that create energy and enthusiasm increasing productivity and performance.

28331 ■ Exceptional Management Skills
URL(s): www.bakercommunications.com/Exceptional-Management-Skills.htm

Description: This two-day interactive workshop will provide the tools to make the most of interactions with subordinates. Cloud-based training also available. **Audience:** Managers, industry professionals. **Principal Exhibits:** This two-day interactive workshop will provide the tools to make the most of interactions with subordinates. Cloud-based training also available.

28332 ■ Facilitation Skills (Onsite)
Seminar Information Service Inc. (SIS)
  250 El Camino Real., Ste. 112
  Tustin, CA 92780
Ph: (714)508-0340
Free: 877-736-4636
Fax: (714)734-8027

Co. E-mail: info@seminarinformation.com
URL: http://www.seminarinformation.com
Contact: Catherine Bellizzi, President
URL(s): www.seminarinformation.com/details.cfm?qc
=qqbnuu
Description: Learn how to facilitate goal-oriented results through planning, collaboration and consensus; Maintain facilitative focus by adopting the right frame of mind; Create a targeted agenda to make meetings productive; Start-up, manage and close effective meetings; Resolve disagreement using a range of consensus-building techniques; Develop and implement a facilitative action plan. **Audience:** Team leaders, team members, human resource specialists, and internal organization development consultants. **Principal Exhibits:** Learn how to facilitate goal-oriented results through planning, collaboration and consensus; Maintain facilitative focus by adopting the right frame of mind; Create a targeted agenda to make meetings productive; Start-up, manage and close effective meetings; Resolve disagreement using a range of consensus-building techniques; Develop and implement a facilitative action plan.

28333 ■ Facilitative Leadership® Workshop
Interaction Associates
  50 Milk St.
  Boston, MA 02110
Ph: (617)535-7000
Co. E-mail: success@interactionassociates.com
URL: http://interactionassociates.com
Contact: Kim Doyle, Director
E-mail: kdoyle@interactionassociates.com
URL(s): www.tickettailor.com/events/interac
  tionassociates1/1074986
Description: Two-day seminar that offers seven principles to form a strategic framework for leadership. **Audience:** Project managers, department heads, team leaders and supervisors. **Principal Exhibits:** Two-day seminar that offers seven principles to form a strategic framework for leadership.

28334 ■ Facilities Management (Onsite)
URL(s): www.pryor.com
Description: Covers techniques used by leading facilities managers to run a safe, cost-effective, and employee friendly environment. **Audience:** Industry professionals. **Principal Exhibits:** Covers techniques used by leading facilities managers to run a safe, cost-effective, and employee friendly environment.

28335 ■ Foundation for Leading Teams (Onsite)
Seminar Information Service Inc. (SIS)
  250 El Camino Real., Ste. 112
  Tustin, CA 92780
Ph: (714)508-0340
Free: 877-736-4636
Fax: (714)734-8027
Co. E-mail: info@seminarinformation.com
URL: http://www.seminarinformation.com
Contact: Catherine Bellizzi, President
URL(s): www.seminarinformation.com/details.cfm?qc
=qqazet
Description: Learn to develop a clear understanding of effective team behaviors. **Audience:** Team leaders. **Principal Exhibits:** Learn to develop a clear understanding of effective team behaviors.

28336 ■ Fred Pryor Seminars & CareerTrack Creative Leadership for Managers, Supervisors, and Team Leaders
Fred Pryor Seminars & CareerTrack
  5700 Broadmoor, Ste. 300
  Mission, KS 66202
Free: 800-780-8476
Fax: (913)967-8849
Co. E-mail: customerservice@pryor.com
URL: http://www.pryor.com
Contact: Janet Turner, Contact
E-mail: dmca@pryor.com
URL(s): www.pryor.com/mkt_info/seminars/desc/KL
  .asp?zip=12140
Description: Learn techniques that increase your leadership skills and get employees on track in performance and productivity including, why tradi-

tional management models just don't measure up in today's workplace and what to use instead. **Audience:** Managers, supervisors, and team leaders. **Principal Exhibits:** Learn techniques that increase your leadership skills and get employees on track in performance and productivity including, why traditional management models just don't measure up in today's workplace and what to use instead.

28337 ■ Fundamentals of Project Management
Fred Pryor Seminars & CareerTrack
  5700 Broadmoor, Ste. 300
  Mission, KS 66202
Free: 800-780-8476
Fax: (913)967-8849
Co. E-mail: customerservice@pryor.com
URL: http://www.pryor.com
Contact: Janet Turner, Contact
E-mail: dmca@pryor.com
URL(s): www.pryor.com/training-seminars/fundamen
  tals-project-management
Frequency: Irregular. **Description:** Learn to plan, budget and schedule project in on time and within a budget. **Audience:** Project managers. **Principal Exhibits:** Learn to plan, budget and schedule project in on time and within a budget.

28338 ■ Fundamentals of Successful Project Management (Onsite)
Seminar Information Service Inc. (SIS)
  250 El Camino Real., Ste. 112
  Tustin, CA 92780
Ph: (714)508-0340
Free: 877-736-4636
Fax: (714)734-8027
Co. E-mail: info@seminarinformation.com
URL: http://www.seminarinformation.com
Contact: Catherine Bellizzi, President
URL(s): www.seminarinformation.com/details.cfm?qc
=qqbdrn
Description: How to create a plan, implement it, monitor progress, correct as necessary and deliver as promised. **Audience:** Managers. **Principal Exhibits:** How to create a plan, implement it, monitor progress, correct as necessary and deliver as promised.

28339 ■ Getting Results Without Authority
URL(s): cmcoutperform.com/results-without-authority
Price: C$2,195, Members; C$2,395, Non-members. **Description:** Covers how to achieve results via other employees despite not having direct authority over them. Held in Vancouver, BC; Toronto, ON; Edmonton, AB; Calgary, AB; and Mississauga, ON. **Audience:** Professionals who need to improve their influencing skills to achieve results through others. **Principal Exhibits:** Covers how to achieve results via other employees despite not having direct authority over them. Held in Vancouver, BC; Toronto, ON; Edmonton, AB; Calgary, AB; and Mississauga, ON.

28340 ■ Global Competencies for Diversity Leaders (Onsite)
Seminar Information Service Inc. (SIS)
  250 El Camino Real., Ste. 112
  Tustin, CA 92780
Ph: (714)508-0340
Free: 877-736-4636
Fax: (714)734-8027
Co. E-mail: info@seminarinformation.com
URL: http://www.seminarinformation.com
Contact: Catherine Bellizzi, President
URL(s): www.seminarinformation.com
Description: Through the use of case studies, exercises, discussion with peers, and guidance from experts in the field, participants will develop a toolkit of competencies to achieve success, including why a global diversity strategy is essential, differences between U.S. and multinational diversity implementation, and key steps in creating a global diversity strategy. **Audience:** Diversity leaders. **Principal Exhibits:** Through the use of case studies, exercises, discussion with peers, and guidance from experts in the field, participants will develop a toolkit of competencies to achieve success, including why a global

diversity strategy is essential, differences between U.S. and multinational diversity implementation, and key steps in creating a global diversity strategy.

28341 ■ High-Impact Decision Making (Onsite)
URL(s): cmcoutperform.com
Description: Learn to make the best decision every time by reducing risks and maximizing results. **Audience:** Managers, and professionals. **Principal Exhibits:** Learn to make the best decision every time by reducing risks and maximizing results.

28342 ■ How to Be a Highly Successful Team Leader (Onsite)
Seminar Information Service Inc. (SIS)
  250 El Camino Real., Ste. 112
  Tustin, CA 92780
Ph: (714)508-0340
Free: 877-736-4636
Fax: (714)734-8027
Co. E-mail: info@seminarinformation.com
URL: http://www.seminarinformation.com
Contact: Catherine Bellizzi, President
URL(s): www.seminarinformation.com
Description: Intensive two-day workshop that teaches the many dimensions of effective leadership and develop the skills needed to lead your team to maximum performance. **Audience:** New team leaders. **Principal Exhibits:** Intensive two-day workshop that teaches the many dimensions of effective leadership and develop the skills needed to lead your team to maximum performance.

28343 ■ How to Be a Highly Successful Team Leader (Onsite)
National Seminars Training L.L.C. (NST)
  14502 W 105th St.
  Lenexa, KS 66215
Free: 800-349-1935
Co. E-mail: info@findaseminar.com
URL: http://www.findaseminar.com/tpd/Padge
  tt-Thompson-Seminars.asp
URL(s): www.findaseminar.com/event1.asp?eventID
  =965
Description: Two-day workshop to help explore the many dimensions of effective leadership and develop the skills needed to lead a team to peak performance. **Audience:** Team leaders and industry professionals. **Principal Exhibits:** Two-day workshop to help explore the many dimensions of effective leadership and develop the skills needed to lead a team to peak performance.

28344 ■ How to Deal with Unacceptable Employee Behavior
Fred Pryor Seminars & CareerTrack
  5700 Broadmoor, Ste. 300
  Mission, KS 66202
Free: 800-780-8476
Fax: (913)967-8849
Co. E-mail: customerservice@pryor.com
URL: http://www.pryor.com
Contact: Janet Turner, Contact
E-mail: dmca@pryor.com
URL(s): www.pryor.com/training-seminars/how-to
  -deal-unacceptable-employee-behavior
Description: Learn effective management techniques for dealing with problem employees, and how to tailor an individual approach for each employee's situation. **Audience:** Industry professionals. **Principal Exhibits:** Learn effective management techniques for dealing with problem employees, and how to tailor an individual approach for each employee's situation.

28345 ■ How to Effectively Manage Multiple Locations (Onsite)
Seminar Information Service Inc. (SIS)
  250 El Camino Real., Ste. 112
  Tustin, CA 92780
Ph: (714)508-0340
Free: 877-736-4636
Fax: (714)734-8027
Co. E-mail: info@seminarinformation.com
URL: http://www.seminarinformation.com
Contact: Catherine Bellizzi, President

URL(s): www.seminarinformation.com/details.cfm?qc =qqbsuu

Description: Gain critical know-how for realizing full potential as a manager and a leader in one of the most challenging situations any manager could find themselves in. **Audience:** Those who manage multiple locations. **Principal Exhibits:** Gain critical know-how for realizing full potential as a manager and a leader in one of the most challenging situations any manager could find themselves in.

28346 ■ How to Effectively Supervise People: Fundamentals of Leading With Success! (Onsite)

Seminar Information Service Inc. (SIS)
    250 El Camino Real., Ste. 112
    Tustin, CA 92780
Ph: (714)508-0340
Free: 877-736-4636
Fax: (714)734-8027
Co. E-mail: info@seminarinformation.com
URL: http://www.seminarinformation.com
Contact: Catherine Bellizzi, President
URL(s): www.seminarinformation.com

Description: This seminar teaches the fundamentals of leading with success, including what's expected of you and how to deal with various personalities and problem employees. **Audience:** Supervisors. **Principal Exhibits:** This seminar teaches the fundamentals of leading with success, including what's expected of you and how to deal with various personalities and problem employees.

28347 ■ How to Excel at Managing and Supervising People (Onsite)

Seminar Information Service Inc. (SIS)
    250 El Camino Real., Ste. 112
    Tustin, CA 92780
Ph: (714)508-0340
Free: 877-736-4636
Fax: (714)734-8027
Co. E-mail: info@seminarinformation.com
URL: http://www.seminarinformation.com
Contact: Catherine Bellizzi, President
URL(s): www.seminarinformation.com/details.cfm?qc =qqbpmt

Description: Learn skills to manage change, motivate, discipline, delegate, including problem solving for success. **Audience:** Managers and supervisors. **Principal Exhibits:** Learn skills to manage change, motivate, discipline, delegate, including problem solving for success.

28348 ■ How to Gather and Document User Requirements (Onsite)

Seminar Information Service Inc. (SIS)
    250 El Camino Real., Ste. 112
    Tustin, CA 92780
Ph: (714)508-0340
Free: 877-736-4636
Fax: (714)734-8027
Co. E-mail: info@seminarinformation.com
URL: http://www.seminarinformation.com
Contact: Catherine Bellizzi, President
URL(s): www.seminarinformation.com/qqbqak/how-to -gather-and-document-user-requirements

Price: $2,295. **Description:** Introduces the roles of the business analyst as they relate to the analysis and documentation requirements. **Audience:** Business analysts. **Principal Exhibits:** Introduces the roles of the business analyst as they relate to the analysis and documentation requirements.

28349 ■ How to Get More Organized (Onsite)

National Seminars Training L.L.C. (NST)
    14502 W 105th St.
    Lenexa, KS 66215
Free: 800-349-1935
Co. E-mail: info@findaseminar.com
URL: http://www.findaseminar.com/tpd/Padge tt-Thompson-Seminars.asp
URL(s): www.findaseminar.com/event1.asp?eventID =923

Description: Seminar will teach how to meet deadlines by getting more done in less time. **Audience:** Business industry professionals. **Principal Exhibits:** Seminar will teach how to meet deadlines by getting more done in less time.

28350 ■ How to Handle Conflict and Confrontation (Onsite)

National Seminars Training L.L.C. (NST)
    14502 W 105th St.
    Lenexa, KS 66215
Free: 800-349-1935
Co. E-mail: info@findaseminar.com
URL: http://www.findaseminar.com/tpd/Padge tt-Thompson-Seminars.asp
URL(s): www.findaseminar.com/event1.asp?eventID =7032

Description: A change management seminar that shows participants how to find positive solutions to negative situations. **Audience:** People having to deal with conflict and confrontation . **Principal Exhibits:** A change management seminar that shows participants how to find positive solutions to negative situations.

28351 ■ How to Manage Emotions and Excel Under Pressure (Onsite)

National Seminars Training L.L.C. (NST)
    14502 W 105th St.
    Lenexa, KS 66215
Free: 800-349-1935
Co. E-mail: info@findaseminar.com
URL: http://www.findaseminar.com/tpd/Padge tt-Thompson-Seminars.asp
URL(s): www.findaseminar.com/event1.asp?eventID =7345

Description: Workshop teaches the skills required to maintain emotional control in the workplace. **Audience:** People having deal with conflict, anger, confrontation and stress. **Principal Exhibits:** Workshop teaches the skills required to maintain emotional control in the workplace.

28352 ■ How to Supervise People (Onsite)

Seminar Information Service Inc. (SIS)
    250 El Camino Real., Ste. 112
    Tustin, CA 92780
Ph: (714)508-0340
Free: 877-736-4636
Fax: (714)734-8027
Co. E-mail: info@seminarinformation.com
URL: http://www.seminarinformation.com
Contact: Catherine Bellizzi, President
URL(s): www.seminarinformation.com/details.cfm?qc =qqbwjn

Description: Participants learn how to rate performance, relate to former peers, maintain a positive motivational climate, and handle conflicts. **Audience:** Supervisors. **Principal Exhibits:** Participants learn how to rate performance, relate to former peers, maintain a positive motivational climate, and handle conflicts.

28353 ■ Improving Your Managerial Effectiveness

URL(s): cmcoutperform.com/improving-managerial -effectiveness

Price: C$2,195, Members; C$2,395, Non-members. **Description:** Addresses issues faced by most management professionals, including personal, operational, organizational, and interpersonal effectiveness in today's workplace. Course on request. **Audience:** Managers with a few years of experience who are interested in enhancing their managerial effectiveness. **Principal Exhibits:** Addresses issues faced by most management professionals, including personal, operational, organizational, and interpersonal effectiveness in today's workplace. Course on request. **Telecommunication Services:** cmcinfo@ cmcoutperform.com.

28354 ■ Improving Your Project Management Skills: The Basics for Success

Canadian Management Centre (CMC)
    150 King St. W Ste. 271
    Toronto, ON, Canada M5H 1J9
Ph: (416)214-5678
Free: 877-262-2519

Fax: (416)214-6047
Co. E-mail: cmcinfo@cmcoutperform.com
URL: http://cmcoutperform.com
Contact: Chris Peacock, Director
URL(s): cmcoutperform.com/ottawa

Price: C$2,195, Members; C$2,395, Non-members. **Description:** Topics include understanding project management, project planning and scheduling, documentation and reporting, and quality control. Held in Edmonton, AB; Calgary, AB; Vaughan, ON; Ottawa, ON; Mississauga, ON; Vancouver, BC; and Toronto, ON. **Audience:** Industry professionals. **Principal Exhibits:** Topics include understanding project management, project planning and scheduling, documentation and reporting, and quality control. Held in Edmonton, AB; Calgary, AB; Vaughan, ON; Ottawa, ON; Mississauga, ON; Vancouver, BC; and Toronto, ON.

28355 ■ Information Technology Project Management

American Management Association (AMA)
    1601 Broadway
    New York, NY 10019
Ph: (212)586-8100
Free: 800-262-9699
Fax: (212)903-8168
Co. E-mail: customerservice@amanet.org
URL: http://www.amanet.org
Contact: Manny Avramidis, President
URL(s): www.amanet.org/technical-projec t-management

Price: $2,345, Non-members; $2,095, Members; $1,889, General Services Administration (GSA). **Frequency:** Continuous. **Description:** Covers the entire information systems process from start to finish, including budgeting, software tools, and scheduling. **Audience:** Directors and managers of IT, project managers and team leaders, programmers/analysts, systems analysts, and project office staff members. **Principal Exhibits:** Covers the entire information systems process from start to finish, including budgeting, software tools, and scheduling. **Telecommunication Services:** customerservice@amanet.org.

28356 ■ Interpersonal Skills for Managers (Onsite)

American Management Association (AMA)
    1601 Broadway
    New York, NY 10019
Ph: (212)586-8100
Free: 800-262-9699
Fax: (212)903-8168
Co. E-mail: customerservice@amanet.org
URL: http://www.amanet.org
Contact: Manny Avramidis, President
URL(s): www.amanet.org/training/seminars/onsite/In terpersonal-Skills-for-Managers.aspx

Price: $2,445, Non-members; $2,195, Members AMA; $1,984, Members GSA. **Description:** Covers organizational change, diversity and electronic communication channels in the workplace. **Audience:** Managers, team leaders and supervisors who want to maximize their positive impact on others through effective interpersonal skills. **Principal Exhibits:** Covers organizational change, diversity and electronic communication channels in the workplace.

28357 ■ IT Relationship Management: Aligning IT with the Business (Onsite)

Seminar Information Service Inc. (SIS)
    250 El Camino Real., Ste. 112
    Tustin, CA 92780
Ph: (714)508-0340
Free: 877-736-4636
Fax: (714)734-8027
Co. E-mail: info@seminarinformation.com
URL: http://www.seminarinformation.com
Contact: Catherine Bellizzi, President
URL(s): www.seminarinformation.com/qqbuuk/it-rela tionship-management-aligning-it-with-the

Description: Learn the best practices of an IT Relationship Manager (ITRM) for facilitating IT solutions that provide value to the business and satisfy the needs of business stakeholders. **Audience:** Business analysts, project managers, IT department managers, and IT executives. **Principal Exhibits:** Learn the best practices of an IT Relationship Manager (ITRM) for facilitating IT solutions that provide value to the business and satisfy the needs of business stakeholders.

28358 ■ Keys to Effectively Supervising People (Onsite)

National Seminars Training L.L.C. (NST)
  14502 W 105th St.
  Lenexa, KS 66215
Free: 800-349-1935
Co. E-mail: info@findaseminar.com
URL: http://www.findaseminar.com/tpd/Padge tt-Thompson-Seminars.asp
URL(s): www.findaseminar.com/event1.asp?eventID =6692

Description: One-day seminar that immerses participants in the supervisory techniques, tools, and solutions needed to be more effective. **Audience:** Managers, supervisors, and team leaders. **Principal Exhibits:** One-day seminar that immerses participants in the supervisory techniques, tools, and solutions needed to be more effective.

28359 ■ Leadership Development for Women

Seminar Information Service Inc. (SIS)
  250 El Camino Real., Ste. 112
  Tustin, CA 92780
Ph: (714)508-0340
Free: 877-736-4636
Fax: (714)734-8027
Co. E-mail: info@seminarinformation.com
URL: http://www.seminarinformation.com
Contact: Catherine Bellizzi, President
URL(s): www.seminarinformation.com/qqbwgh/lea dership-development-for-women

Description: Provides the knowledge, network, and impetus necessary to thrive at work, at home, and within your community. **Audience:** Women business professionals. **Principal Exhibits:** Provides the knowledge, network, and impetus necessary to thrive at work, at home, and within your community.

28360 ■ Leadership Skills: Building Success Through Teamwork (Onsite)

Seminar Information Service Inc. (SIS)
  250 El Camino Real., Ste. 112
  Tustin, CA 92780
Ph: (714)508-0340
Free: 877-736-4636
Fax: (714)734-8027
Co. E-mail: info@seminarinformation.com
URL: http://www.seminarinformation.com
Contact: Catherine Bellizzi, President
URL(s): www.seminarinformation.com/qqbtjm/lea dership-skills-building-success-through-teamwork

Description: Learn how to: Develop your teams to maximize their strengths and enhance productivity; Optimize organization and work design for success in service delivery teams; Motivate your team with effective performance measurement; Integrate your role as a leader into your management style; Leverage the complementary skills and styles of your team; Eliminate barriers and chokepoints that block teamwork; Apply a diverse and multilevel approach to minimize communication breakdowns. **Audience:** Industry professionals. **Principal Exhibits:** Learn how to: Develop your teams to maximize their strengths and enhance productivity; Optimize organization and work design for success in service delivery teams; Motivate your team with effective performance measurement; Integrate your role as a leader into your management style; Leverage the complementary skills and styles of your team; Eliminate barriers and chokepoints that block teamwork; Apply a diverse and multilevel approach to minimize communication breakdowns.

28361 ■ Leadership Skills: Building Success Through Teamwork (Onsite)

Learning Tree International Inc.
  13650 Dulles Technology Dr., Ste. 400
  Herndon, VA 20171-6156
Free: 888-843-8733
Co. E-mail: info@learningtree.com
URL: http://www.learningtree.com

URL(s): www.learningtree.com/info/pdfs/gsa-pricing 1.pdf

Description: Learn to develop teams to maximize their strengths and enhance productivity. **Audience:** Industry professionals. **Principal Exhibits:** Learn to develop teams to maximize their strengths and enhance productivity.

28362 ■ Leadership Skills for Supervisors

URL(s): cmcoutperform.com

Description: Covers empowering supervisors and staff; using flow chart techniques as a means of assessing work flow and streamlining processes; coaching, mentoring, and providing feedback; organizing and leading productive meetings; and using brainstorming to cultivate ideas. **Audience:** Supervisors. **Principal Exhibits:** Covers empowering supervisors and staff; using flow chart techniques as a means of assessing work flow and streamlining processes; coaching, mentoring, and providing feedback; organizing and leading productive meetings; and using brainstorming to cultivate ideas. **Telecommunication Services:** cmcinfo@cmcoutperform.com.

28363 ■ Leadership Skills and Team Development for IT and Technical Professionals (Onsite)

Seminar Information Service Inc. (SIS)
  250 El Camino Real., Ste. 112
  Tustin, CA 92780
Ph: (714)508-0340
Free: 877-736-4636
Fax: (714)734-8027
Co. E-mail: info@seminarinformation.com
URL: http://www.seminarinformation.com
Contact: Catherine Bellizzi, President
URL(s): www.seminarinformation.com/details.cfm?qc =qqatpm

Description: Interactive seminar provides hands-on exercises designed to help technical professionals build and lead a team, evaluate the team's performance, and develop an action plan for leadership success. **Audience:** IT and Technical team leaders, technical managers and technical professionals. **Principal Exhibits:** Interactive seminar provides hands-on exercises designed to help technical professionals build and lead a team, evaluate the team's performance, and develop an action plan for leadership success.

28364 ■ Leadership and Supervisory Skills for Women (Onsite)

National Seminars Training L.L.C. (NST)
  14502 W 105th St.
  Lenexa, KS 66215
Free: 800-349-1935
Co. E-mail: info@findaseminar.com
URL: http://www.findaseminar.com/tpd/Padge tt-Thompson-Seminars.asp
URL(s): www.findaseminar.com/event1.asp?eventID =891

Description: A one-day workshop to learn strategies for effective leadership at all levels. **Audience:** Women leaders, and supervisors . **Principal Exhibits:** A one-day workshop to learn strategies for effective leadership at all levels.

28365 ■ Leadership and Team Development for Managerial Success (Onsite)

American Management Association (AMA)
  1601 Broadway
  New York, NY 10019
Ph: (212)586-8100
Free: 800-262-9699
Fax: (212)903-8168
Co. E-mail: customerservice@amanet.org
URL: http://www.amanet.org
Contact: Manny Avramidis, President
URL(s): www.amanet.org/training/seminars/onsite/lea dership-and-team-development-for-managerial-suc cess.aspx

Description: Covers the difference between managing and leading, developing and communicating goals, motivating a team, and various team concepts. **Audience:** New managers, team leaders and business professionals interested in acquiring effective

leadership skills for managers. **Principal Exhibits:** Covers the difference between managing and leading, developing and communicating goals, motivating a team, and various team concepts.

28366 ■ Leading Effective Teams II - Communicating with Your Teammates (Onsite)

Seminar Information Service Inc. (SIS)
  250 El Camino Real., Ste. 112
  Tustin, CA 92780
Ph: (714)508-0340
Free: 877-736-4636
Fax: (714)734-8027
Co. E-mail: info@seminarinformation.com
URL: http://www.seminarinformation.com
Contact: Catherine Bellizzi, President
URL(s): www.seminarinformation.com

Description: Leaders learn their communication style and how it relates to their team members, as well as how to motivate through communication. **Audience:** Members, industry professionals. **Principal Exhibits:** Leaders learn their communication style and how it relates to their team members, as well as how to motivate through communication.

28367 ■ Leading High-Performance Project Teams

Seminar Information Service Inc. (SIS)
  250 El Camino Real., Ste. 112
  Tustin, CA 92780
Ph: (714)508-0340
Free: 877-736-4636
Fax: (714)734-8027
Co. E-mail: info@seminarinformation.com
URL: http://www.seminarinformation.com
Contact: Catherine Bellizzi, President
URL(s): www.seminarinformation.com/qqbmxs/lea ding-high-performing-project-teams

Description: Fast-paced, highly engaging workplace simulation enables you to integrate and apply five practices of exemplary leaders, and eight dimensions of high-performing teams, becoming a confident and competent leader. **Audience:** Managers with a thorough understanding of basic project management including knowledge of Gantt charts, resource leveling and general leadership principles. **Principal Exhibits:** Fast-paced, highly engaging workplace simulation enables you to integrate and apply five practices of exemplary leaders, and eight dimensions of high-performing teams, becoming a confident and competent leader.

28368 ■ Leading High Performance Teams

Seminar Information Service Inc. (SIS)
  250 El Camino Real., Ste. 112
  Tustin, CA 92780
Ph: (714)508-0340
Free: 877-736-4636
Fax: (714)734-8027
Co. E-mail: info@seminarinformation.com
URL: http://www.seminarinformation.com
Contact: Catherine Bellizzi, President
URL(s): www.seminarinformation.com/qqbmxs/lea ding-high-performing-project-teams

Description: Builds awareness and skill in the areas of team dynamics, group problem solving, and group decision making. You will develop leadership skills applicable to many areas, but especially suited to self-directed work teams, employee participation teams, interdepartmental task groups, and other group situations where combined efforts are needed to reach optimal performance levels. **Audience:** Team leaders and project managers. **Principal Exhibits:** Builds awareness and skill in the areas of team dynamics, group problem solving, and group decision making. You will develop leadership skills applicable to many areas, but especially suited to self-directed work teams, employee participation teams, interdepartmental task groups, and other group situations where combined efforts are needed to reach optimal performance levels. **Telecommunication Services:** info@seminarinformation. com.

28369 ■ Leading Project Managers: A Guide to Success (Onsite)

Seminar Information Service Inc. (SIS)
250 El Camino Real., Ste. 112
Tustin, CA 92780
Ph: (714)508-0340
Free: 877-736-4636
Fax: (714)734-8027
Co. E-mail: info@seminarinformation.com
URL: http://www.seminarinformation.com
Contact: Catherine Bellizzi, President
URL(s): www.seminarinformation.com/details.cfm?qc=qqbmxr

Description: Gain perspectives and review best practices on issues critical to those who manage project managers. **Audience:** Managers of project managers with a basic understanding of project management. **Principal Exhibits:** Gain perspectives and review best practices on issues critical to those who manage project managers.

28370 ■ Legal Issues for Managers (Onsite)

Seminar Information Service Inc. (SIS)
250 El Camino Real., Ste. 112
Tustin, CA 92780
Ph: (714)508-0340
Free: 877-736-4636
Fax: (714)734-8027
Co. E-mail: info@seminarinformation.com
URL: http://www.seminarinformation.com
Contact: Catherine Bellizzi, President
URL(s): www.seminarinformation.com

Description: Using a case study, practical examples, and discussions participants will explore the law as it relates to making nondiscriminatory employment decisions, compliance with wage and hour laws, safety and health rights and responsibilities, required versus discretionary leaves of absence, managing employees covered by labor agreements, and individual rights and wrongful discharge. **Audience:** Managers. **Principal Exhibits:** Using a case study, practical examples, and discussions participants will explore the law as it relates to making nondiscriminatory employment decisions, compliance with wage and hour laws, safety and health rights and responsibilities, required versus discretionary leaves of absence, managing employees covered by labor agreements, and individual rights and wrongful discharge.

28371 ■ Making Successful Business Decisions: Getting it Right the First Time (Onsite)

Seminar Information Service Inc. (SIS)
250 El Camino Real., Ste. 112
Tustin, CA 92780
Ph: (714)508-0340
Free: 877-736-4636
Fax: (714)734-8027
Co. E-mail: info@seminarinformation.com
URL: http://www.seminarinformation.com
Contact: Catherine Bellizzi, President
URL(s): www.seminarinformation.com

Description: Learn how to make intelligent decisions with limited time and information, how to convert conflicting opinions into useful insights, foster efficient and effective group decision making, and ensure decisions are implemented by the organization. **Audience:** Managers, professionals. **Principal Exhibits:** Learn how to make intelligent decisions with limited time and information, how to convert conflicting opinions into useful insights, foster efficient and effective group decision making, and ensure decisions are implemented by the organization.

28372 ■ Making the Transition to Supervising and Managing Others

URL(s): cmcoutperform.com/supervising-managing-others

Description: This seminar prepares you for a complete change of responsibilities and helps eliminate the anxiety that can accompany it. Held in Montreal, PQ; Ottawa, ON; Regina, SK; Toronto, ON; Calgary, AB; Edmonton, AB; Vaughan, ON; Mississauga, ON; and Vancouver, BC. **Audience:** Newly appointed supervisors and managers, professionals.

Principal Exhibits: This seminar prepares you for a complete change of responsibilities and helps eliminate the anxiety that can accompany it. Held in Montreal, PQ; Ottawa, ON; Regina, SK; Toronto, ON; Calgary, AB; Edmonton, AB; Vaughan, ON; Mississauga, ON; and Vancouver, BC.

28373 ■ Management and Leadership Skills for First-Time Supervisors and Managers (Onsite)

National Seminars Training L.L.C. (NST)
14502 W 105th St.
Lenexa, KS 66215
Free: 800-349-1935
Co. E-mail: info@findaseminar.com
URL: http://www.findaseminar.com/tpd/Padgett-Thompson-Seminars.asp
URL(s): www.findaseminar.com/event1.asp?eventID=895&venueID=1173363

Description: An intensive two-day workshop for new supervisors who want to develop their management skills quickly. **Audience:** Supervisors, managers, team leaders, and professionals. **Principal Exhibits:** An intensive two-day workshop for new supervisors who want to develop their management skills quickly.

28374 ■ Management Skills: Building Performance and Productivity

Seminar Information Service Inc. (SIS)
250 El Camino Real., Ste. 112
Tustin, CA 92780
Ph: (714)508-0340
Free: 877-736-4636
Fax: (714)734-8027
Co. E-mail: info@seminarinformation.com
URL: http://www.seminarinformation.com
Contact: Catherine Bellizzi, President
URL(s): www.seminarinformation.com/qqbdnc/management-skills-building-performance-and-productivity

Description: Learn how to: Develop the vision and skills that result in real team commitment; Build and lead empowered and motivated teams; Delegate tasks and authority while maintaining control; Communicate effectively at all levels; Create world-class team performance; Become a skilled and effective leader. **Audience:** New and experienced managers. **Principal Exhibits:** Learn how to: Develop the vision and skills that result in real team commitment; Build and lead empowered and motivated teams; Delegate tasks and authority while maintaining control; Communicate effectively at all levels; Create world-class team performance; Become a skilled and effective leader.

28375 ■ Management Skills: Building Performance and Productivity (Onsite)

Learning Tree International Inc.
13650 Dulles Technology Dr., Ste. 400
Herndon, VA 20171-6156
Free: 888-843-8733
Co. E-mail: info@learningtree.com
URL: http://www.learningtree.com
URL(s): www.learningtree.com

Description: Provides information on how to become a skilled and effective leader. **Audience:** Managers and professionals. **Principal Exhibits:** Provides information on how to become a skilled and effective leader.

28376 ■ Management Skills for First-Time Supervisors (Onsite)

National Seminars Training L.L.C. (NST)
14502 W 105th St.
Lenexa, KS 66215
Free: 800-349-1935
Co. E-mail: info@findaseminar.com
URL: http://www.findaseminar.com/tpd/Padgett-Thompson-Seminars.asp
URL(s): www.findaseminar.com/event1.asp?eventID=13084

Description: Through accelerated learning techniques, teaches skills and supervisory how-to's. **Audience:** Supervisors, and managers. **Principal Exhibits:** Through accelerated learning techniques, teaches skills and supervisory how-to's.

28377 ■ Management Skills for an IT Environment (Onsite)

Seminar Information Service Inc. (SIS)
250 El Camino Real., Ste. 112
Tustin, CA 92780
Ph: (714)508-0340
Free: 877-736-4636
Fax: (714)734-8027
Co. E-mail: info@seminarinformation.com
URL: http://www.seminarinformation.com
Contact: Catherine Bellizzi, President
URL(s): www.seminarinformation.com/qqbuun/management-skills-for-an-it-environment

Description: Learn how to apply a proven management model for leading technical staff to excellence; identify key success criteria for leadership in an IT environment; leverage emotion to optimize communication and performance; motivate and empower technical professionals to achieve results; delegate proactively to focus on strengths of IT teams and build accountability. **Audience:** IT managers. **Principal Exhibits:** Learn how to apply a proven management model for leading technical staff to excellence; identify key success criteria for leadership in an IT environment; leverage emotion to optimize communication and performance; motivate and empower technical professionals to achieve results; delegate proactively to focus on strengths of IT teams and build accountability.

28378 ■ Management Skills for New Supervisors and Managers

Canadian Management Centre (CMC)
150 King St. W Ste. 271
Toronto, ON, Canada M5H 1J9
Ph: (416)214-5678
Free: 877-262-2519
Fax: (416)214-6047
Co. E-mail: cmcinfo@cmcoutperform.com
URL: http://cmcoutperform.com
Contact: Chris Peacock, Director
URL(s): cmcoutperform.com/management-skills-supervisors-managers

Description: Learn the tools to plan, organize, communicate, and monitor every situation effectively. Held in Calgary, AB; Montreal, QC; Vancouver, BC; Halifax, NS; Regina, SK; Ottawa, ON; and Toronto, ON. Also offers course on request. **Audience:** Supervisors and managers. **Principal Exhibits:** Learn the tools to plan, organize, communicate, and monitor every situation effectively. Held in Calgary, AB; Montreal, QC; Vancouver, BC; Halifax, NS; Regina, SK; Ottawa, ON; and Toronto, ON. Also offers course on request.

28379 ■ Management Skills for Secretaries, Administrative Assistants, and Support Staff

Fred Pryor Seminars & CareerTrack
5700 Broadmoor, Ste. 300
Mission, KS 66202
Free: 800-780-8476
Fax: (913)967-8849
Co. E-mail: customerservice@pryor.com
URL: http://www.pryor.com
Contact: Janet Turner, Contact
E-mail: dmca@pryor.com
URL(s): www.pryor.com/training-seminars/management-skills-secretaries-administrative-assistants

Description: Learn how to make decisions, manage change, solve problems, and negotiate what you need. **Audience:** Secretaries, administrative assistants and support staff. **Principal Exhibits:** Learn how to make decisions, manage change, solve problems, and negotiate what you need.

28380 ■ Managerial Skills of the New Supervisors

1601 Broadway
New York, NY 10019
URL: http://www.amanet.org/management-skills-for-new-supervisors

Description: Program topics include handling managerial responsibilities; utilizing leadership style; facilitating communication; motivating staff; coaching staff; delegating responsibilities; doing performance appraisals; and time management.

28381 ■ Managerial and Team-building Skills for Project Managers

URL(s): www.amanet.org

Description: Covers improving people skills in order to create a powerful, cooperative project team. **Audience:** Business professionals. **Principal Exhibits:** Covers improving people skills in order to create a powerful, cooperative project team.

28382 ■ Managing Change: People and Process (Onsite)

Seminar Information Service Inc. (SIS)
250 El Camino Real., Ste. 112
Tustin, CA 92780
Ph: (714)508-0340
Free: 877-736-4636
Fax: (714)734-8027
Co. E-mail: info@seminarinformation.com
URL: http://www.seminarinformation.com
Contact: Catherine Bellizzi, President
URL(s): www.seminarinformation.com

Description: Learn how to manage change through the total integration of people and process, design and implement a framework for managing change, evaluate best practice approaches to people and process for delivering successful change, reduce the impact of risk while maximizing the benefit of change, overcome resistance to change, and assemble a practical toolkit tailored to the needs of your organization. **Audience:** Industry professionals. **Principal Exhibits:** Learn how to manage change through the total integration of people and process, design and implement a framework for managing change, evaluate best practice approaches to people and process for delivering successful change, reduce the impact of risk while maximizing the benefit of change, overcome resistance to change, and assemble a practical toolkit tailored to the needs of your organization.

28383 ■ Managing Chaos: How to set Priorities and Make Decisions Under Pressure

American Management Association (AMA)
1601 Broadway
New York, NY 10019
Ph: (212)586-8100
Free: 800-262-9699
Fax: (212)903-8168
Co. E-mail: customerservice@amanet.org
URL: http://www.amanet.org
Contact: Manny Avramidis, President
URL(s): amanet.org/managing-chaos-tools-to-set-priorities-and-make-decisions-under-pressure

Price: $1,995, Non-members; $1,795, Members; $1,700, General Services Administration (GSA). **Frequency:** Continuous. **Description:** Covers practical tools to prepare for unpredictable demands and balance changing priorities. Also available live online. **Audience:** Anyone facing expanding workloads, shifting priorities, complex organizational dynamics, organizational restructuring and increased uncertainty. **Principal Exhibits:** Covers practical tools to prepare for unpredictable demands and balance changing priorities. Also available live online. **Telecommunication Services:** customerservice@amanet.org.

28384 ■ Managing Chaos: Tools to Set Priorities and Make Decisions Under Pressure (Onsite)

American Management Association (AMA)
1601 Broadway
New York, NY 10019
Ph: (212)586-8100
Free: 800-262-9699
Fax: (212)903-8168
Co. E-mail: customerservice@amanet.org
URL: http://www.amanet.org
Contact: Manny Avramidis, President
URL(s): www.amanet.org/managing-chaos-tools-to-set-priorities-and-make-decisions-under-pressure

Price: $1,995, Non-members; $1,795, Members AMA; $1,700, Members GSA. **Frequency:** Continuous. **Description:** Two-day seminar where you will learn techniques to adjust to the shifting challenges

and demands. **Audience:** Anyone working with multiple projects and/or faces expanding workloads, tight deadlines and increased uncertainty. **Principal Exhibits:** Two-day seminar where you will learn techniques to adjust to the shifting challenges and demands.

28385 ■ Managing Information Overload: Techniques for Working Smarter (Onsite)

Seminar Information Service Inc. (SIS)
250 El Camino Real., Ste. 112
Tustin, CA 92780
Ph: (714)508-0340
Free: 877-736-4636
Fax: (714)734-8027
Co. E-mail: info@seminarinformation.com
URL: http://www.seminarinformation.com
Contact: Catherine Bellizzi, President
URL(s): www.seminarinformation.com

Description: Learn how to increase your productivity with effective information management skills, apply creative strategies, including mind maps, for processing information, adopt speed-reading techniques to quickly digest reports, and develop advanced memory skills to retain important information. **Audience:** Business industry professionals. **Principal Exhibits:** Learn how to increase your productivity with effective information management skills, apply creative strategies, including mind maps, for processing information, adopt speed-reading techniques to quickly digest reports, and develop advanced memory skills to retain important information.

28386 ■ Managing Multiple Project, Competing Priorites and Tight Deadlines (Onsite)

National Seminars Training L.L.C. (NST)
14502 W 105th St.
Lenexa, KS 66215
Free: 800-349-1935
Co. E-mail: info@findaseminar.com
URL: http://www.findaseminar.com/tpd/Padge
tt-Thompson-Seminars.asp
URL(s): findaseminar.com/event1.asp?eventID
=13079&Category=PROJECT+MANAGEMENT
&venueID=993335&x=44&y=11

Description: Seminar provides the skills needed to immediately and effectively deal with multiple projects. **Audience:** Project managers, administrators, administrative assistants, receptionists, secretaries and professionals. **Principal Exhibits:** Seminar provides the skills needed to immediately and effectively deal with multiple projects.

28387 ■ Managing Multiple Projects and Priorities (Onsite)

Seminar Information Service Inc. (SIS)
250 El Camino Real., Ste. 112
Tustin, CA 92780
Ph: (714)508-0340
Free: 877-736-4636
Fax: (714)734-8027
Co. E-mail: info@seminarinformation.com
URL: http://www.seminarinformation.com
Contact: Catherine Bellizzi, President
URL(s): www.seminarinformation.com/details.cfm?qc
=qqbpaj

Description: Learn to gain control of your time, your projects and your priorities. **Audience:** Professionals. **Principal Exhibits:** Learn to gain control of your time, your projects and your priorities.

28388 ■ Managing Organizational Transition (Onsite)

Seminar Information Service Inc. (SIS)
250 El Camino Real., Ste. 112
Tustin, CA 92780
Ph: (714)508-0340
Free: 877-736-4636
Fax: (714)734-8027
Co. E-mail: info@seminarinformation.com
URL: http://www.seminarinformation.com
Contact: Catherine Bellizzi, President
URL(s): www.seminarinformation.com/qqbqfl/manag-ing-organizational-transition

Description: Learn the critical elements for driving successful change and develop coaching skills to create a change-ready culture. **Audience:** Managers. **Principal Exhibits:** Learn the critical elements for driving successful change and develop coaching skills to create a change-ready culture.

28389 ■ Managing People in Projects (Onsite)

Seminar Information Service Inc. (SIS)
250 El Camino Real., Ste. 112
Tustin, CA 92780
Ph: (714)508-0340
Free: 877-736-4636
Fax: (714)734-8027
Co. E-mail: info@seminarinformation.com
URL: http://www.seminarinformation.com
Contact: Catherine Bellizzi, President
URL(s): www.seminarinformation.com

Description: Learn how to have people want to work on your projects and how to improve your project results by applying a powerful approach to managing the people who work on them. **Audience:** Project managers and leaders . **Principal Exhibits:** Learn how to have people want to work on your projects and how to improve your project results by applying a powerful approach to managing the people who work on them.

28390 ■ Managing Subcontracts (Onsite)

Seminar Information Service Inc. (SIS)
250 El Camino Real., Ste. 112
Tustin, CA 92780
Ph: (714)508-0340
Free: 877-736-4636
Fax: (714)734-8027
Co. E-mail: info@seminarinformation.com
URL: http://www.seminarinformation.com
Contact: Catherine Bellizzi, President
URL(s): www.seminarinformation.com/qqbqmz/man-aging-subcontracts

Description: Examines effective management and administration of subcontracts and complex purchase orders, including tailoring of the terms and conditions. **Audience:** Sellers, buyers, industry representatives, government officials, contract administrators, lawyers. **Principal Exhibits:** Examines effective management and administration of subcontracts and complex purchase orders, including tailoring of the terms and conditions.

28391 ■ Managing in Tough Times (Onsite)

Seminar Information Service Inc. (SIS)
250 El Camino Real., Ste. 112
Tustin, CA 92780
Ph: (714)508-0340
Free: 877-736-4636
Fax: (714)734-8027
Co. E-mail: info@seminarinformation.com
URL: http://www.seminarinformation.com
Contact: Catherine Bellizzi, President
URL(s): www.seminarinformation.com

Description: Learn how to demonstrate authentic and strong leadership to create an atmosphere of confidence and trust in tough times, share your vision and display confidence that the problems your team currently faces will be solved, and minimize stress and maximize productivity and performance during difficult times. **Audience:** Industry professionals, managers. **Principal Exhibits:** Learn how to demonstrate authentic and strong leadership to create an atmosphere of confidence and trust in tough times, share your vision and display confidence that the problems your team currently faces will be solved, and minimize stress and maximize productivity and performance during difficult times.

28392 ■ Maximum Performance Leadership Canada

Canadian Management Centre (CMC)
150 King St. W Ste. 271
Toronto, ON, Canada M5H 1J9
Ph: (416)214-5678
Free: 877-262-2519
Fax: (416)214-6047
Co. E-mail: cmcinfo@cmcoutperform.com
URL: http://cmcoutperform.com

Contact: Chris Peacock, Director
URL(s): cmcoutperform.com/files/CMC_Spring%2020
11_FINAL.pdf
Description: Covers advanced leadership skills for managers with several years of experience. **Audience:** Experienced managers who are ready to re-assess, re-focus and recharge to gain the effective edge that makes them an authentic leader. **Principal Exhibits:** Covers advanced leadership skills for managers with several years of experience.

28393 ■ Motivation and Trust Building for Group Leaders (Onsite)

Seminar Information Service Inc. (SIS)
    250 El Camino Real., Ste. 112
    Tustin, CA 92780
Ph: (714)508-0340
Free: 877-736-4636
Fax: (714)734-8027
Co. E-mail: info@seminarinformation.com
URL: http://www.seminarinformation.com
Contact: Catherine Bellizzi, President
URL(s): www.seminarinformation.com/details.cfm?qc
    =qqaakg
Description: A practical understanding of basic leadership skills, work values, and organizational responsibility. **Audience:** Group leaders. **Principal Exhibits:** A practical understanding of basic leadership skills, work values, and organizational responsibility.

28394 ■ Moving Ahead: Breaking Behaviour Patterns That Hold You Back

URL(s): cmcoutperform.com/moving-ahead-info
    -request
Description: Change your professional image by overcoming destructive workplace behavior. **Audience:** Managers, supervisors and team leaders . **Principal Exhibits:** Change your professional image by overcoming destructive workplace behavior.

28395 ■ Performance Management, Leading Change, and Putting It All Together (Onsite)

Seminar Information Service Inc. (SIS)
    250 El Camino Real., Ste. 112
    Tustin, CA 92780
Ph: (714)508-0340
Free: 877-736-4636
Fax: (714)734-8027
Co. E-mail: info@seminarinformation.com
URL: http://www.seminarinformation.com
Contact: Catherine Bellizzi, President
URL(s): www.seminarinformation.com
Description: Participants will learn a performance management system including how to prepare for and conduct performance reviews, how to manage individual and group change and the manager's role in the organizational change process. **Audience:** General public. **Principal Exhibits:** Participants will learn a performance management system including how to prepare for and conduct performance reviews, how to manage individual and group change and the manager's role in the organizational change process.

28396 ■ Personal Skills for Professional Excellence (Onsite)

Seminar Information Service Inc. (SIS)
    250 El Camino Real., Ste. 112
    Tustin, CA 92780
Ph: (714)508-0340
Free: 877-736-4636
Fax: (714)734-8027
Co. E-mail: info@seminarinformation.com
URL: http://www.seminarinformation.com
Contact: Catherine Bellizzi, President
URL(s): www.seminarinformation.com/qqbtkd/
    personal-skills-for-professional-excellence
Description: Learn how to: Achieve maximum productivity and effectiveness in your organization; Build and leverage your professional reputation; Get results working with different and difficult personality types; Maintain focus in pressure situations; Work productively within the political environment of your organization; Build and present persuasive proposals; Make a balanced choice between professional and personal commitments. **Audience:** Industry

professionals. **Principal Exhibits:** Learn how to: Achieve maximum productivity and effectiveness in your organization; Build and leverage your professional reputation; Get results working with different and difficult personality types; Maintain focus in pressure situations; Work productively within the political environment of your organization; Build and present persuasive proposals; Make a balanced choice between professional and personal commitments.

28397 ■ Persuasive Communications

URL(s): www.eeicom.com
Description: Course designed for department heads and project managers, as well as mid-level communications professionals who want to expand their public relations and marketing skills. **Audience:** Industry professionals, students. **Principal Exhibits:** Course designed for department heads and project managers, as well as mid-level communications professionals who want to expand their public relations and marketing skills.

28398 ■ Persuasive Leadership: Storytelling that Inspires (Onsite)

Seminar Information Service Inc. (SIS)
    250 El Camino Real., Ste. 112
    Tustin, CA 92780
Ph: (714)508-0340
Free: 877-736-4636
Fax: (714)734-8027
Co. E-mail: info@seminarinformation.com
URL: http://www.seminarinformation.com
Contact: Catherine Bellizzi, President
URL(s): www.seminarinformation.com/details.cfm?qc
    =qqbfng
Description: Participants develop their storytelling abilities and learn how to use humor to persuade and motivate others, as well as polish their existing speaking skills and develop powerful new ones. **Audience:** Executives, managers, others in positions of influence and experienced speakers. **Principal Exhibits:** Participants develop their storytelling abilities and learn how to use humor to persuade and motivate others, as well as polish their existing speaking skills and develop powerful new ones.

28399 ■ PMP Exam Prep Workshop (Onsite)

URL(s): cmcoutperform.com/pmp-exam-prep
Description: This three-day, PMP certification exam prep seminar covers the Guide to the Project Management Body of Knowledge on which the exam is based. **Audience:** Project management professionals. **Principal Exhibits:** This three-day, PMP certification exam prep seminar covers the Guide to the Project Management Body of Knowledge on which the exam is based.

28400 ■ Positive Assertive Management (Onsite)

Seminar Information Service Inc. (SIS)
    250 El Camino Real., Ste. 112
    Tustin, CA 92780
Ph: (714)508-0340
Free: 877-736-4636
Fax: (714)734-8027
Co. E-mail: info@seminarinformation.com
URL: http://www.seminarinformation.com
Contact: Catherine Bellizzi, President
URL(s): www.seminarinformation.com/qqbeah/posi
    tive-assertive-management
Description: Covers the meaning of assertiveness, how assertiveness can benefit you, using assertive behavior, constructive confrontation and assertive listening. **Audience:** Supervisors and managers . **Principal Exhibits:** Covers the meaning of assertiveness, how assertiveness can benefit you, using assertive behavior, constructive confrontation and assertive listening.

28401 ■ A Practical Guide to Controls for IT Professionals (Onsite)

Seminar Information Service Inc. (SIS)
    250 El Camino Real., Ste. 112
    Tustin, CA 92780
Ph: (714)508-0340
Free: 877-736-4636
Fax: (714)734-8027

Co. E-mail: info@seminarinformation.com
URL: http://www.seminarinformation.com
Contact: Catherine Bellizzi, President
URL(s): www.seminarinformation.com
Description: Designed to provide all levels of IT personnel with an understanding of what controls are and why they are critical to safeguarding information assets. Discover why it is important to have a business-process view of IT controls and review the critical role they play in providing for a smooth running, efficiently manager IT environment. **Audience:** IT management and staff, other IT personnel and IT auditors. **Principal Exhibits:** Designed to provide all levels of IT personnel with an understanding of what controls are and why they are critical to safeguarding information assets. Discover why it is important to have a business-process view of IT controls and review the critical role they play in providing for a smooth running, efficiently manager IT environment.

28402 ■ Preparing for Leadership: What It Takes to Take the Lead

Canadian Management Centre (CMC)
    150 King St. W Ste. 271
    Toronto, ON, Canada M5H 1J9
Ph: (416)214-5678
Free: 877-262-2519
Fax: (416)214-6047
Co. E-mail: cmcinfo@cmcoutperform.com
URL: http://cmcoutperform.com
Contact: Chris Peacock, Director
URL(s): cmcoutperform.com/preparing-leadership
    -take-lead-live-online
Price: C$1,845, Members; C$1,995, Non-members.
Description: Covers leadership roles, the characteristics of leaders, dealing with organizational politics, and creating an action plan. Held in Ottawa, ON; Calgary, AB; Vancouver, BC; Regina, SK; and Toronto, ON. **Audience:** High potential individuals and managers who are candidates for a leadership role or those who are about to take on a new leadership responsibility. **Principal Exhibits:** Covers leadership roles, the characteristics of leaders, dealing with organizational politics, and creating an action plan. Held in Ottawa, ON; Calgary, AB; Vancouver, BC; Regina, SK; and Toronto, ON.

28403 ■ The Proactive Leader I: Develop an Effective Agenda, Build Support, and Gain Traction

Seminar Information Service Inc. (SIS)
    250 El Camino Real., Ste. 112
    Tustin, CA 92780
Ph: (714)508-0340
Free: 877-736-4636
Fax: (714)734-8027
Co. E-mail: info@seminarinformation.com
URL: http://www.seminarinformation.com
Contact: Catherine Bellizzi, President
URL(s): www.seminarinformation.com
Description: Learn to identify and prioritize arenas where you can effect change in your organization, including the skills of political competence to take the next steps toward building support and gaining traction for your idea. **Audience:** Industry professionals. **Principal Exhibits:** Learn to identify and prioritize arenas where you can effect change in your organization, including the skills of political competence to take the next steps toward building support and gaining traction for your idea.

28404 ■ Problem Solving and Decision Making (Onsite)

Seminar Information Service Inc. (SIS)
    250 El Camino Real., Ste. 112
    Tustin, CA 92780
Ph: (714)508-0340
Free: 877-736-4636
Fax: (714)734-8027
Co. E-mail: info@seminarinformation.com
URL: http://www.seminarinformation.com
Contact: Catherine Bellizzi, President
URL(s): www.seminarinformation.com/details.cfm?qc
    =qqabgu

Description: Based on the principles of rational process and a systematic approach to problem solving and decision making pioneered by Drs. Benjamin Tregoe and Charles Kepner. Participants develop an in-depth understanding of systematic process through case study practice, and apply these principles to urgent job-related concerns. Focus is on immediate, practical results. **Audience:** Managers and professionals. **Principal Exhibits:** Based on the principles of rational process and a systematic approach to problem solving and decision making pioneered by Drs. Benjamin Tregoe and Charles Kepner. Participants develop an in-depth understanding of systematic process through case study practice, and apply these principles to urgent job-related concerns. Focus is on immediate, practical results.

28405 ■ Project Change Management (Onsite)

URL(s): www.eeicom.com

Description: Seminar based on the Project Management Institute's (PMI) Project Management Body of Knowledge (PMBOK) that covers the principles of change management as applied to project management and products, including change control system, configuration management, coordinating changes throughout the project, and change management and project closure. **Audience:** Negotiators, manager, supervisors and team leaders. **Principal Exhibits:** Seminar based on the Project Management Institute's (PMI) Project Management Body of Knowledge (PM-BOK) that covers the principles of change management as applied to project management and products, including change control system, configuration management, coordinating changes throughout the project, and change management and project closure.

28406 ■ Project Leadership: Building High-Performance Teams (Onsite)

Seminar Information Service Inc. (SIS)
  250 El Camino Real., Ste. 112
  Tustin, CA 92780
Ph: (714)508-0340
Free: 877-736-4636
Fax: (714)734-8027
Co. E-mail: info@seminarinformation.com
URL: http://www.seminarinformation.com
Contact: Catherine Bellizzi, President
URL(s): www.seminarinformation.com/qqbtkk/projec t-leadership-building-high-performance-teams

Description: Learn how to: Develop the leadership skills to build and sustain high-performing project teams; Develop effective team performance through the Leadership Services Model; Build a strong team identity through vision, purpose and commitment; Foster positive and productive team communication and define ground rules; Protect the team and convert conflicts into advantages that promote high performance; Maximize your leadership abilities when you return to your organization. **Audience:** Team leaders and project managers. **Principal Exhibits:** Learn how to: Develop the leadership skills to build and sustain high-performing project teams; Develop effective team performance through the Leadership Services Model; Build a strong team identity through vision, purpose and commitment; Foster positive and productive team communication and define ground rules; Protect the team and convert conflicts into advantages that promote high performance; Maximize your leadership abilities when you return to your organization.

28407 ■ Project Management for Auditors (Onsite)

Seminar Information Service Inc. (SIS)
  250 El Camino Real., Ste. 112
  Tustin, CA 92780
Ph: (714)508-0340
Free: 877-736-4636
Fax: (714)734-8027
Co. E-mail: info@seminarinformation.com
URL: http://www.seminarinformation.com
Contact: Catherine Bellizzi, President
URL(s): www.seminarinformation.com

Description: Learn improved cost control, resource utilization, and more timely conclusions with project management techniques that are applicable to internal audit. **Audience:** Financial, operational, information technology, and external auditors with two more years of audit experience . **Principal Exhibits:** Learn improved cost control, resource utilization, and more timely conclusions with project management techniques that are applicable to internal audit.

28408 ■ Project Management: Skills for Success (Onsite)

Seminar Information Service Inc. (SIS)
  250 El Camino Real., Ste. 112
  Tustin, CA 92780
Ph: (714)508-0340
Free: 877-736-4636
Fax: (714)734-8027
Co. E-mail: info@seminarinformation.com
URL: http://www.seminarinformation.com
Contact: Catherine Bellizzi, President
URL(s): www.seminarinformation.com/qqaanv/projec t-management-skills-for-success

Description: Learn how to: Produce a project plan for successful delivery; Plan and run projects using best practices in a 6-step project management process; Implement risk management techniques and mitigation strategies; Estimate and schedule task work and duration with confidence; Implement monitoring tools and controls to keep you fully in command of the project; Recognize and practice the leadership skills needed to run a motivated team. **Audience:** Project managers. **Principal Exhibits:** Learn how to: Produce a project plan for successful delivery; Plan and run projects using best practices in a 6-step project management process; Implement risk management techniques and mitigation strategies; Estimate and schedule task work and duration with confidence; Implement monitoring tools and controls to keep you fully in command of the project; Recognize and practice the leadership skills needed to run a motivated team.

28409 ■ Project Management for Software Development - Planning and Managing Successful Projects (Onsite)

Seminar Information Service Inc. (SIS)
  250 El Camino Real., Ste. 112
  Tustin, CA 92780
Ph: (714)508-0340
Free: 877-736-4636
Fax: (714)734-8027
Co. E-mail: info@seminarinformation.com
URL: http://www.seminarinformation.com
Contact: Catherine Bellizzi, President
URL(s): www.seminarinformation.com/qqafqg/projec t-management-for-software-development-planning -and

Description: Learn how to: Deliver successful software projects that support your organization's strategic goals; Match organizational needs to the most effective software development model; Plan and manage projects at each stage of the software development life cycle (SDLC); Create project plans that address real-world management challenges; Develop the skills for tracking and controlling the project deliverables; Focus on key tasks for the everyday management of software projects; Build an effective and committed team and keep them motivated day to day. **Audience:** Industry professionals. **Principal Exhibits:** Learn how to: Deliver successful software projects that support your organization's strategic goals; Match organizational needs to the most effective software development model; Plan and manage projects at each stage of the software development life cycle (SDLC); Create project plans that address real-world management challenges; Develop the skills for tracking and controlling the project deliverables; Focus on key tasks for the everyday management of software projects; Build an effective and committed team and keep them motivated day to day.

28410 ■ Project Management: The Human and Technical View (Onsite)

Seminar Information Service Inc. (SIS)
  250 El Camino Real., Ste. 112
  Tustin, CA 92780

Ph: (714)508-0340
Free: 877-736-4636
Fax: (714)734-8027
Co. E-mail: info@seminarinformation.com
URL: http://www.seminarinformation.com
Contact: Catherine Bellizzi, President
URL(s): www.seminarinformation.com/details.cfm?qc =qqaucg

Description: A systematic, practical approach to successful project management, including skills to handle problems with members who won't commit, who resist change, or who won't cooperate. **Audience:** Functional managers and supervisors, and project leaders. **Principal Exhibits:** A systematic, practical approach to successful project management, including skills to handle problems with members who won't commit, who resist change, or who won't cooperate.

28411 ■ Project Management for Web Development (Onsite)

URL(s): www.eeicom.com

Description: Covers the basics of managing and maintaining the development of a website. **Audience:** Project management methodology and highly trained professionals. **Principal Exhibits:** Covers the basics of managing and maintaining the development of a website.

28412 ■ Project Management Workshop

Fred Pryor Seminars & CareerTrack
  5700 Broadmoor, Ste. 300
  Mission, KS 66202
Free: 800-780-8476
Fax: (913)967-8849
Co. E-mail: customerservice@pryor.com
URL: http://www.pryor.com
Contact: Janet Turner, Contact
E-mail: dmca@pryor.com
URL(s): www.pryor.com/training-seminars/projec t-management-workshop

Frequency: Irregular. **Description:** One-day seminar guaranteed to help you complete projects in a timely manner within a budget. **Audience:** Project management professionals. **Principal Exhibits:** One-day seminar guaranteed to help you complete projects in a timely manner within a budget.

28413 ■ Project Scope and Requirements Management (Onsite)

Seminar Information Service Inc. (SIS)
  250 El Camino Real., Ste. 112
  Tustin, CA 92780
Ph: (714)508-0340
Free: 877-736-4636
Fax: (714)734-8027
Co. E-mail: info@seminarinformation.com
URL: http://www.seminarinformation.com
Contact: Catherine Bellizzi, President
URL(s): www.seminarinformation.com

Description: Learn how to achieve project success by mastering scope control. **Audience:** Project and program managers, directors, PMO managers, team leaders and business analysts. **Principal Exhibits:** Learn how to achieve project success by mastering scope control.

28414 ■ Risk Management (Onsite)

Seminar Information Service Inc. (SIS)
  250 El Camino Real., Ste. 112
  Tustin, CA 92780
Ph: (714)508-0340
Free: 877-736-4636
Fax: (714)734-8027
Co. E-mail: info@seminarinformation.com
URL: http://www.seminarinformation.com
Contact: Catherine Bellizzi, President
URL(s): www.seminarinformation.com/qqbebx/projec t-risk-management

Description: Learn how to evaluate and respond to risk at the project and task levels. **Audience:** Project managers and team members. **Principal Exhibits:** Learn how to evaluate and respond to risk at the project and task levels.

28415 ■ Sales and Use Tax Workshop (Onsite)

Seminar Information Service Inc. (SIS)
  250 El Camino Real., Ste. 112
  Tustin, CA 92780
Ph: (714)508-0340
Free: 877-736-4636
Fax: (714)734-8027
Co. E-mail: info@seminarinformation.com
URL: http://www.seminarinformation.com
Contact: Catherine Bellizzi, President
URL(s): www.seminarinformation.com/details.cfm?qc
  =qqbsjk

Description: Gain a better understanding of sales and use tax and how to apply it to keep your bottom line in check. **Audience:** Sales and tax professionals. **Principal Exhibits:** Gain a better understanding of sales and use tax and how to apply it to keep your bottom line in check.

28416 ■ Senior Project Management

URL(s): cmcoutperform.com

Description: Covers project management basics, measuring project accomplishments, trends, human factors, and automated and administrative project support. **Audience:** Industry professionals. **Principal Exhibits:** Covers project management basics, measuring project accomplishments, trends, human factors, and automated and administrative project support. **Telecommunication Services:** cmcinfo@cmcoutperform.com.

28417 ■ Situational Leadership II Workshop (Onsite)

Seminar Information Service Inc. (SIS)
  250 El Camino Real., Ste. 112
  Tustin, CA 92780
Ph: (714)508-0340
Free: 877-736-4636
Fax: (714)734-8027
Co. E-mail: info@seminarinformation.com
URL: http://www.seminarinformation.com
Contact: Catherine Bellizzi, President
URL(s): www.seminarinformation.com/details.cfm?qc
  =qqbqnh

Description: Diagnose the needs of an individual at any particular point in time, then be able to apply the leadership style that is most responsive an productive for the situation at hand. **Audience:** Executives, managers at all levels, project managers, team leaders and supervisors. **Principal Exhibits:** Diagnose the needs of an individual at any particular point in time, then be able to apply the leadership style that is most responsive an productive for the situation at hand.

28418 ■ Strategic Agility and Resilience: Embracing Change to Drive Growth

URL(s): cmcoutperform.com

Description: Master the competencies of agile leadership. **Audience:** Executives, and managers. **Principal Exhibits:** Master the competencies of agile leadership.

28419 ■ Strategic Diversity Retention (Onsite)

Seminar Information Service Inc. (SIS)
  250 El Camino Real., Ste. 112
  Tustin, CA 92780
Ph: (714)508-0340
Free: 877-736-4636
Fax: (714)734-8027
Co. E-mail: info@seminarinformation.com
URL: http://www.seminarinformation.com
Contact: Catherine Bellizzi, President
URL(s): www.seminarinformation.com/details.cfm?qc
  =qqbppw

Description: Offer exemplary teaching programs. **Audience:** Managers, recruiters, diversity councils, EEO, AA, diversity, and other HR generalists and specialists. **Principal Exhibits:** Offer exemplary teaching programs.

28420 ■ Successfully Managing People

American Management Association (AMA)
  1601 Broadway
  New York, NY 10019

Ph: (212)586-8100
Free: 800-262-9699
Fax: (212)903-8168
Co. E-mail: customerservice@amanet.org
URL: http://www.amanet.org
Contact: Manny Avramidis, President
URL(s): www.amanet.org/successfully-managing
  -people

Price: $2,445, Non-members; $2,195, Members; $1,984, General Services Administration (GSA). **Frequency:** Continuous. **Description:** Three-day seminar covering negotiation, motivation, confidence, leadership skills, and dealing with various types of employees. **Audience:** Managers and individuals with management responsibilities. **Principal Exhibits:** Three-day seminar covering negotiation, motivation, confidence, leadership skills, and dealing with various types of employees.

28421 ■ Successfully Managing People

URL(s): cmcoutperform.com/successfully-managing
  -people

Price: C$2,195, Members; C$2,395, Non-members. **Description:** Covers negotiation, motivation, confidence, leadership skills, and dealing with various types of employees. Held in Toronto, ON; Calgary, AB; and Mississauga, ON. **Audience:** Supervisors, managers and others with management responsibilities looking to step-up their people management skills. **Principal Exhibits:** Covers negotiation, motivation, confidence, leadership skills, and dealing with various types of employees. Held in Toronto, ON; Calgary, AB; and Mississauga, ON. **Telecommunication Services:** cmcinfo@cmcoutperform.com.

28422 ■ Supporting Multiple Bosses (Onsite)

Seminar Information Service Inc. (SIS)
  250 El Camino Real., Ste. 112
  Tustin, CA 92780
Ph: (714)508-0340
Free: 877-736-4636
Fax: (714)734-8027
Co. E-mail: info@seminarinformation.com
URL: http://www.seminarinformation.com
Contact: Catherine Bellizzi, President
URL(s): www.seminarinformation.com

Description: Learn to deal with multiple bosses with different agendas, priorities, styles, and expectations. **Audience:** Executive secretaries and assistants, administrative support staff, office managers, coordinators, team members and associates and office coordinators/supervisors/managers. **Principal Exhibits:** Learn to deal with multiple bosses with different agendas, priorities, styles, and expectations.

28423 ■ Systems Thinking (Onsite)

Seminar Information Service Inc. (SIS)
  250 El Camino Real., Ste. 112
  Tustin, CA 92780
Ph: (714)508-0340
Free: 877-736-4636
Fax: (714)734-8027
Co. E-mail: info@seminarinformation.com
URL: http://www.seminarinformation.com
Contact: Catherine Bellizzi, President
URL(s): www.seminarinformation.com/qqbftp/sys
  tems-thinking

Description: Learn how to become a systems thinker so you can resolve complex, systematic business dilemmas in a practical manner. **Audience:** Industry professionals. **Principal Exhibits:** Learn how to become a systems thinker so you can resolve complex, systematic business dilemmas in a practical manner.

28424 ■ Taking on Greater Responsibility: Step-up Skills for Nonmanagers (Onsite)

American Management Association (AMA)
  1601 Broadway
  New York, NY 10019
Ph: (212)586-8100
Free: 800-262-9699
Fax: (212)903-8168
Co. E-mail: customerservice@amanet.org
URL: http://www.amanet.org
Contact: Manny Avramidis, President

URL(s): www.amanet.org/taking-on-greater
  -responsibility-step-up-skills-for-non-managers

Price: $1,995, Non-members; $1,795, Members; $1,511, General Services Administration (GSA). **Frequency:** Irregular. **Description:** Two-day seminar for new or prospective managers; covers management responsibilities, aligning with other managers, building respect with your team, coaching, motivating, and delegating. **Audience:** Career development professionals. **Principal Exhibits:** Two-day seminar for new or prospective managers; covers management responsibilities, aligning with other managers, building respect with your team, coaching, motivating, and delegating.

28425 ■ Team Leadership Effectiveness Program 'Team Top Gun' (Onsite)

Seminar Information Service Inc. (SIS)
  250 El Camino Real., Ste. 112
  Tustin, CA 92780
Ph: (714)508-0340
Free: 877-736-4636
Fax: (714)734-8027
Co. E-mail: info@seminarinformation.com
URL: http://www.seminarinformation.com
Contact: Catherine Bellizzi, President
URL(s): www.seminarinformation.com

Description: Three-day seminar using psychological profiles, 360 degree feedback, extensive experiential simulations, and state of the art content relating to success in team based organizations. **Audience:** Industry professionals. **Principal Exhibits:** Three-day seminar using psychological profiles, 360 degree feedback, extensive experiential simulations, and state of the art content relating to success in team based organizations.

28426 ■ Technical Project Management

URL(s): cmcoutperform.com/courses/pdu?t=technical

Description: Covers defining cost, time, and scope; project leadership; utilizing status reports; and technical project control systems. **Audience:** Organizations and project managers. **Principal Exhibits:** Covers defining cost, time, and scope; project leadership; utilizing status reports; and technical project control systems. **Telecommunication Services:** cmcinfo@cmcoutperform.com.

28427 ■ Thinking Outside the Lines for Managers and Supervisors (Onsite)

Seminar Information Service Inc. (SIS)
  250 El Camino Real., Ste. 112
  Tustin, CA 92780
Ph: (714)508-0340
Free: 877-736-4636
Fax: (714)734-8027
Co. E-mail: info@seminarinformation.com
URL: http://www.seminarinformation.com
Contact: Catherine Bellizzi, President
URL(s): www.seminarinformation.com

Description: Techniques and solutions for daily real world problems, including speedy decision making and motivating for results. **Audience:** Managers, supervisors, and team leaders. **Principal Exhibits:** Techniques and solutions for daily real world problems, including speedy decision making and motivating for results.

28428 ■ Thinking Outside the Lines (Onsite)

National Seminars Training L.L.C. (NST)
  14502 W 105th St.
  Lenexa, KS 66215
Free: 800-349-1935
Co. E-mail: info@findaseminar.com
URL: http://www.findaseminar.com/tpd/Padge
  tt-Thompson-Seminars.asp
URL(s): www.findaseminar.com/event1.asp?eventID
  =1747

Description: Teach yourself and others to find innovative answers and make better decisions. **Audience:** Business leaders and managers. **Principal Exhibits:** Teach yourself and others to find innovative answers and make better decisions.

28429 ■ **The Ultimate Supervisor's Workshop (Onsite)**
National Seminars Training L.L.C. (NST)
   14502 W 105th St.
   Lenexa, KS 66215
Free: 800-349-1935
Co. E-mail: info@findaseminar.com
URL: http://www.findaseminar.com/tpd/Padge
   tt-Thompson-Seminars.asp
URL(s): www.nationalseminarstraining.com/
   SeminarSearchResults/The_Ultimate_Supervi-
   sor%92s_Workshop/YSUP2/index.html
Description: A two-day workshop where leaders come for fresh ideas and proven strategies. **Audience:** Supervisors. **Principal Exhibits:** A two-day workshop where leaders come for fresh ideas and proven strategies.

28430 ■ **Uncovering Fraud in Core Business Functions (Onsite)**
Seminar Information Service Inc. (SIS)
   250 El Camino Real., Ste. 112
   Tustin, CA 92780
Ph: (714)508-0340
Free: 877-736-4636
Fax: (714)734-8027
Co. E-mail: info@seminarinformation.com
URL: http://www.seminarinformation.com
Contact: Catherine Bellizzi, President
URL(s): www.seminarinformation.com
Description: Pinpoint the areas most prone to internal fraud and identify key indicators of potential crime. **Audience:** Audit managers, corporate attorneys and information security professionals . **Principal Exhibits:** Pinpoint the areas most prone to internal fraud and identify key indicators of potential crime.

28431 ■ **Win-Win Negotiations Training**
URL(s): www.bakercommunications.com/win_negotia
   tions.htm
Description: In this hands-on workshop, participants learn through practice exercises how to strengthen their negotiation skills. Cloud-based training also available. **Audience:** Industry professionals. **Principal Exhibits:** In this hands-on workshop, participants learn through practice exercises how to strengthen their negotiation skills. Cloud-based training also available.

REFERENCE WORKS

28432 ■ **"5 Simple Project Management Organization Tips" in Small Business Trends (August 31, 2022)**
Ed: Larry Alton. **Released:** August 31, 2022 . **Description:** Project managers are vital team members and learning to take on that role can be daunting. Staying organized is key to this role and tips are given to help you stay on track. **Availability:** Online.

28433 ■ **"7 Tips for Managing Your Business While on Vacation" in Legal Zoom (March 17, 2023)**
URL(s): www.legalzoom.com/articles/7-tips-for-man-
   aging-your-business-while-on-vacation
Ed: Jane Haskins, Esq. **Released:** March 17, 2023. **Description:** Small business owners have a lot to take care of on a day-to-day basis, and that doesn't end even for a vacation! However, there are steps you can take to get away for some much needed rest while keeping your business running. **Availability:** Online.

28434 ■ **"10 Tips for Effectively Communicating with Clients, Prospects, Employees, and Other Business Stakeholders" in Small Business Trends (January 29, 2022)**
URL(s): smallbiztrends.com/2022/01/communicating
   -with-clients.html
Ed: Annie Pilon. **Released:** January 29, 2022. **Description:** Communicating clearly is a required skill when dealing with clients and stakeholders. Sharpen up those skills with the tips given in this article. **Availability:** Online.

28435 ■ **"113D Filings: Investors Report to the SEC" in Barron's (Vol. 88, March 24, 2008, No. 12, pp. M13)**
Pub: Dow Jones & Company Inc.
Contact: Almar Latour, Chief Executive Officer
Released: April 02, 2016. **Description:** HealthCor Management called as problematic the plan of Magellan Health Services to use its high cash balances for acquisitions. Carlson Capital discussed with Energy Partners possible changes in the latter's board. Investor Carl Icahn suggested that Enzon Pharmaceuticals consider selling itself or divest some of its assets. **Availability:** Print; Online.

28436 ■ **"50 Best Companies for Diversity" in Black Enterprise (Vol. 38, July 2008, No. 12, pp. 12)**
Pub: Earl G. Graves Ltd.
Contact: Earl Graves, Jr., President
Description: Maintaining excellence in a company's diversity efforts requires critical challenges such as recruiting, retaining and developing talent in the executive pipeline. Top young and diverse emerging executives in corporate America are featured. **Availability:** Online.

28437 ■ **"The 2007 Black Book" in Hawaii Business (Vol. 53, December 2007, No. 6, pp. 43)**
Description: Brief biographies of 364 top executives in Hawaii are presented. Information on their educational achievement, membership in associations, hobbies, family, present position and the company they work for are supplied. **Availability:** Print; Online.

28438 ■ **"Actions to Implement Three Potent Post-Crisis Strategies" in Strategy & Leadership (Vol. 38, September-October 2010, No. 5)**
Pub: Emerald Inc.
Ed: Saul J. Berman, Richard Christner, Ragna Bell. **Description:** The need for organizations to design and implement strategies to cope with the possible situations in the post-economic crisis environment is emphasized. The plans that organizations should implement to successfully manage uncertainty and complexity and to foster their eventual growth are discussed. **Availability:** PDF.

28439 ■ **"Addition by Subtraction in Tokyo" in Barron's (Vol. 92, August 25, 2012, No. 38, pp. 20)**
Pub: Dow Jones & Company Inc.
Contact: Almar Latour, Chief Executive Officer
Ed: Kopin Tan. **Description:** Investors in Japan could benefit from the increase in management buyouts, particularly of small capitalization stocks. This increase would shrink the number of Japanese stocks, many of which are trading below book value. **Availability:** Online.

28440 ■ **"Air Canada to Slash 600 Non-Union Jobs" in Globe & Mail (February 11, 2006, pp. B3)**
Ed: Brent Jang. **Description:** The reasons behind workforce reduction by ACE Aviation Holdings Inc. at Air Canada are presented. **Availability:** Online.

28441 ■ **Airline Without a Pilot: Lessons in Leadership**
Released: 2005. **Description:** The events that destroyed Delta Air Lines are used to define the failures when solid leadership is not at the helm of a company.

28442 ■ **"The Alliance: Managing Talent in the Networked Age"**
Pub: Harvard Business Review Press
Contact: Moderna V. Pfizer, Contact
Released: July 08, 2014. **Price:** $30, Hardcover/ Hardcopy. **Description:** It is suggested that management see their workers as allies instead of family or free agents in order to create a realistic loyalty pact between employer and employee. Both sides need to trust each other for the company to succeed and the employee to further their career with the firm. **Availability:** E-book; Print.

28443 ■ **The AMA Handbook of Project Management**
Pub: HarperCollins Leadership
Contact: Donald Miller, Chief Executive Officer
Ed: Paul C. Dinsmore, Jeannette Cabanis-Brewin. **Released:** Fifth edition. **Price:** $22.99, E-book. **Description:** A comprehensive reference presenting the critical concepts and theories all project managers must master using essays and advice from the field's top professionals. **Availability:** E-book; Print.

28444 ■ **"Amazing Apple Does It Again" in Barron's (Vol. 92, September 15, 2012, No. 38, pp. 26)**
Pub: Dow Jones & Company Inc.
Contact: Almar Latour, Chief Executive Officer
Ed: Tiernan Ray. **Description:** The introduction of the Apple iPhone 5 lacked the flair of previous product introductions by the company. New chief executive officer Tim Cook has been criticized for this lack of flair for marketing, although pre-orders for the iPhone 5 remain high. **Availability:** Online.

28445 ■ **"American Water's Ed Vallejo Chosen for 2012 Minority Business Leader Awards" in Manufacturing Close-Up (July 30, 2012)**
Description: Ed Vallejo, vice president of investor relations at American Water, has been awarded the 2012 Minority Business Leader Award from the Philadelphia Business Journal. Vallejo is responsible for developing investor relations strategies for the publicly traded water and wastewater utility firm. He also serves as the company's liaison with financial analyst and investor communities. **Availability:** Online.

28446 ■ **"The Anatomy of a High Potential" in Business Strategy Review (Vol. 21, Autumn 2010, No. 3, pp. 52)**
Ed: Doug Ready, Jay Conger, Linda Hill, Emily Stecker. **Released:** September 22, 2010. **Description:** Companies have long been interested in identifying high potential employees, but few firms know how to convert top talent into game changers, or people who can shape the future of the business. The authors have found the 'x factors' that can make a high-potential list into a strong competitive advantage. **Availability:** Print; Electronic publishing; PDF; Online.

28447 ■ **"The Art of Appreciation" in Business Horizons (November-December 2007, pp. 441)**
Ed: Catherine M. Dalton. **Released:** November 01, 2011. **Description:** The art of appreciation is an art less and less practices by employees. Employers should lead by example and practice this art to inspire employees to do the same. **Availability:** Print; Online.

28448 ■ **"The Art of War for Women" in Hawaii Business (Vol. 54, July 2008, No. 1, pp. 23)**
Pub: PacificBasin Communications
Contact: Chuck Tindle, Director
E-mail: chuckt@pacificbasin.net
Ed: Chin-Ning Chu. **Description:** Business consultant Chi-Ning Chu talks about her new book 'The Art of War for Women: Sun Tzu's Ancient Strategies and Wisdom for Winning at Work', which discusses how women can more effectively win in business. She also shares her thoughts about the advantages that women have, which they can use in businesses decisions.

28449 ■ **"avVaa World Health Care Products Rolls Out Internet Marketing Program" in Health and Beauty Close-Up (September 18, 2009)**
Description: avVaa World Health Care Products, Inc., a biotechnology company, manufacturer and distributor of nationally branded therapeutic, natural health care and skin products, has signed an agreement with Online Performance Marketing to launch of an Internet marketing campaign in order to broaden

its presence online. The impact of advertising on the Internet to generate an increase in sales is explored. **Availability:** Online.

28450 ■ *"Back in the Race. New Fund Manager Has Whipped Sentinel International Equity Back into Shape"* in Barron's (Vol. 88, March 17, 2008, No. 11, pp. 43)

Pub: Dow Jones & Company Inc.

Contact: Almar Latour, Chief Executive Officer

Ed: Leslie P. Norton. **Description:** Katherine Schapiro was able to get Sentinel International Equity's Morningstar classification to blended fund from a value fund rating after joining Sentinel from her former jobs at Strong Overseas Fund. Schapiro aims to benefit from the global rebalancing as the U.S.'s share of the world economy shrinks. **Availability:** Online.

28451 ■ *"B&B Hopes to Appeal to Fiat Execs"* in Crain's Detroit Business (Vol. 25, June 15, 2009, No. 24, pp. 21)

Pub: Crain Communications Inc.

Contact: Barry Asin, President

Ed: Daniel Duggan. **Description:** Cobblestone Manor, a ten-room bed and breakfast in Auburn Hills, Michigan is hoping to provide rooms for Fiat executives. The owners have been working with travel organizations to promote the castle-like bed and breakfast which appeals to European visitors. **Availability:** Online.

28452 ■ *"Barnes Shakes Up Sara Lee Exec Suite"* in Crain's Chicago Business (Vol. 31, April 21, 2008, No. 16, pp. 1)

Pub: Crain Communications Inc.

Contact: Barry Asin, President

Ed: David Sterrett. **Description:** In an attempt to cut costs and boost profits, Sara Lee Corp.'s CEO Brenda Barnes is restructuring the company's management team. **Availability:** Online.

28453 ■ *"Be a Better Manager: Live Abroad"* in Harvard Business Review (Vol. 88, September 2010, No. 9, pp. 24)

Pub: Harvard Business Publishing

Contact: Diane Belcher, Managing Director

Ed: William W. Maddux, Adam D. Galinsky, Carmit T. Tadmor. **Price:** $6, PDF. **Description:** Interrelationship between international experience and entrepreneurship is discussed. Individuals with international experience are likelier to be promoted and to develop new products and businesses. **Availability:** Online; PDF.

28454 ■ *"Before Happiness: The 5 Hidden Keys to Achieving Success, Spreading Happiness, and Sustaining Positive Change"*

Released: 2013. **Price:** $26, hardcover; $6.99, e-book. **Description:** Harvard trained researcher explains proven strategies for changing attitudes to positive include, the most valuable reality to see a broader range of ideas and solutions; success mapping, setting goals around things that matter to you most; the x-spot, using success accelerants to propel you more quickly towards goals; noise-canceling, boost the signal pointing to opportunities and possibilities others miss; and positive inception, transferring your skills to your team, employees and everyone around you. **Availability:** CD-ROM; E-book; Print.

28455 ■ *"Best (Professional) Foot Forward: Effective Marketing Strategies for any Phase of Your Career"* in Black Enterprise (Vol. 44, June 2014, No. 10, pp. 44)

Pub: Earl G. Graves Ltd.

Contact: Earl Graves, Jr., President

Description: Because hiring managers face long-term vacancies and skills gaps, the importance of creating a professional marketing strategy when applying for a professional position is stressed. Advice is given to help guide applicants through the entire application, interviewing, and hiring process.

28456 ■ *"The Big Idea: No, Management Is Not a Profession"* in Harvard Business Review (Vol. 88, July-August 2010, No. 7-8, pp. 52)

Pub: Harvard Business Publishing

Contact: Diane Belcher, Managing Director

Ed: Richard Barker. **Price:** $8.95, PDF. **Description:** An argument is presented that management is not a profession, as it is less focused on mastering a given body of knowledge than it is on obtaining integration and collaboration skills. Implications for teaching this new approach are also examined. **Availability:** Online; PDF.

28457 ■ *"The Big Idea: The Case for Professional Boards"* in Harvard Business Review (Vol. 88, December 2010, No. 12, pp. 50)

Pub: Harvard Business Publishing

Contact: Diane Belcher, Managing Director

Ed: Robert C. Pozen. **Price:** $8.95, PDF. **Description:** A professional directorship model can be applied to corporate governance. Suggestions for this include the reduction of board size to seven members in order to improve the effectiveness of decision making, along with the requirement that directors have industry expertise. **Availability:** Online; PDF.

28458 ■ *"BIM: What to Watch Out For"* in Contractor (Vol. 57, February 2010, No. 2, pp. 28)

Ed: Susan Linden McGreevy. **Description:** Legal and risk management issues surrounding Building Information Modeling (BIM) can be divided into three categories namely; intellectual property, liability for content, and the responsibility for the inputs into the model. The agreement should be done in a way that protects the intellectual rights of the authors when using BIM. **Availability:** Print; Online.

28459 ■ *"Black Gold: Jobs Aplenty"* in Canadian Business (Vol. 79, August 14, 2006, No. 16-17, pp. 57)

Pub: Rogers Media Inc.

Contact: Neil Spivak, Chief Executive Officer

Ed: Erin Pooley. **Description:** A list of the top ten jobs in the petroleum industry in Canada along with pay and nature of jobs, is presented. **Availability:** Print; Online.

28460 ■ *"The Blazers' Money Maker"* in Business Journal Portland (Vol. 31, April 18, 2014, No. 7, pp. 4)

Pub: American City Business Journals, Inc.

Contact: Mike Olivieri, Executive Vice President

Released: April 18, 2014. **Price:** $4, Introductory 4-Week Offer(Digital & Print). **Description:** The turnaround strategy used by CEO, Chris McGowan, to make the Portland Trail Blazers basketball team profitable by July 2016 is discussed. His personal restructuring effort was aimed at combining the Blazers' operations with day-to-day management of the Moda Center. The team also returned to selling tickets and sponsorship deals. **Availability:** Print; Online.

28461 ■ *"Blindspot: Hidden Biases of Good People"*

Pub: Ballantine/ Del Rey/Fawcett/Ivy Books

Contact: Matt Shatz, Contact

E-mail: mshatz@randomhouse.com

Released: February 12, 2013. **Price:** $14, paperback; $14.50, Hardcover. **Description:** Perceptions of social groups that shape our likes and dislikes and our judgments about people's character, abilities and potential include exposure to and attitudes about age, gender, race, ethnicity, religion, social class, sexuality, disability status, and nationality are examined. Hidden biases impact everyone, including business leaders, entrepreneurs and managers in decision making. **Availability:** E-book; Print.

28462 ■ *The Board Book: An Insider's Guide for Directors and Trustees*

Pub: W.W. Norton & Company Ltd.

Contact: Stanley Kubrick, Director

Ed: William G. Bowen. **Released:** May 06, 2008. **Price:** $16.95, paperback; $26.95, hardcover. **Description:** A primer for all directors and trustees that provides suggestions for getting back to good-governance basics in business. **Availability:** Print.

28463 ■ *"Boards That Lead: When to Take Charge, When to Partner, and When to Stay Out of the Way"*

Pub: Harvard Business Review Press

Contact: Moderna V. Pfizer, Contact

Released: December 10, 2013. **Price:** $35, Hardcover/Hardcopy. **Description:** As boards take a more active role in decision making at companies, leadership at the top is being redefined. Boardroom veterans describe the successes and pitfalls of this new leadership style and explain how to define the central idea of the company, ensure that the right CEO is in place and potential successors are identified, recruit directors who add value, root out board dysfunction, select a board leader who bridges the divide between management and the board, and to set a high bar on ethics and risk. **Availability:** E-book; Print.

28464 ■ *Bottom-Line Training: Performance-Based Results*

Pub: Training Education Management

Contact: Dr. Donald J. Ford, President

Ed: Donald J. Ford. **Released:** Second edition. **Price:** $29. **Description:** Training is critical to any successful enterprise. The key to any successful training program involves defining and constantly focusing on the desired results of the program. The author provides a training model based on five phases, known as ADDIE: analysis, design, development, implementation and evaluation. **Availability:** Print.

28465 ■ *"Boundaries for Leaders (Enhanced Edition): Results, Relationships, and Being Ridiculously In Charge"*

Pub: Harper Business

Contact: Hollis Heimbouch, Senior Vice President Publisher

Released: April 16, 2013. **Price:** $15.97, Default Title; $16.99. **Description:** Clinical psychologist and author explains how the best business leaders set boundaries within their organizations, with their teams and themselves, to improve performance and increase customer and employee satisfaction. Practical advice is given to manage teams, coach direct reports, and create an organization with strong ethics and culture. **Availability:** E-book; Print.

28466 ■ *Bradford's International Directory of Marketing Research Agencies*

Pub: Business Research Services, Inc.

URL(s): www.sba8a.com/brs.htm

Description: Covers over 2,300 marketing research agencies worldwide. Includes domestic and international demographic data and professional association contacts. **Entries include:** Company name, address, phone, name and title of contact, date founded, number of employees, description of products or services, e-mail, URL. **Arrangement:** Geographical. **Indexes:** Alphabetical by company. **Availability:** Print. **Type:** Directory.

28467 ■ *"Brief: Make a Bigger Impact by Saying Less"*

Pub: John Wiley & Sons, Inc.

Contact: Christina Van Tassell, Executive Vice President Chief Financial Officer

Released: February 23, 2014. **Price:** $24, hardcover; $15.99, e-book. **Description:** Communication is key to any business success. Today, busy executives demand respect and manage their time more efficiently than ever. The author addresses the challenges of inattention, interruptions, and impatience faced by professionals and to help leaders gain the strength required to eliminate wasteful words and stand out from others when communicating. **Availability:** E-book; Print.

28468 ■ *"Bringing Manufacturing Concerns to Springfield" in Crain's Chicago Business (Vol. 31, March 31, 2008, No. 13, pp. 6)*
Pub: Crain Communications Inc.
Contact: Barry Asin, President
Ed: Paul Merrion. **Description:** Profile of the new executive vice-president of Tooling & Manufacturing Assn., Paul Merrion, a man who plans to grow TMA's membership with an aggressive legislative agenda in Springfield. **Availability:** Online.

28469 ■ *"The Buck Stops Here" in Canadian Business (Vol. 81, November 10, 2008, No. 19, pp. 25)*
Ed: Sarka Halas. **Description:** Reputation strategist Leslie Gaines-Ross says that minimizing the damage followed by the identification of what went wrong are the first steps that companies need to take when trying to salvage their reputation. Gaines-Ross states that it is up to the CEO to ensure the company's speedy recovery and they need to be at the forefront of the process. **Availability:** Online.

28470 ■ *Business Black Belt: Develop the Strength, Flexibility and Agility to Run Your Company*
Price: $15.99. **Description:** Manual offering insights that will enable anyone to become successful in small business. Seventy short chapters included topics such as attitude, management, marketing, selling, employees, money, MBAs, lawyers, consultants, and investors. **Availability:** Print.

28471 ■ *"Business Guide and Employment Role"*
Pub: AuthorHouse Inc.
Contact: William Elliott, President
Released: July 10, 2014. **Price:** $4.99, e-book; $15.18, softcover. **Description:** Financial expert discusses the importance of economic and business and their role in employment. The business and finance manager is crucial to any small business. The guide is an essential tool for any entrepreneur, the investor in business enterprise, the individual businessman, the human resources manager, and the business and finance professional to learn the merits to do business and play a role in employment. **Availability:** E-book; Print.

28472 ■ *Business Management for Entrepreneurs*
Released: Third Edition. **Description:** Lack of good management skills are usually the reason for any small company to fail. This book introduces entrepreneurs and managers of small to medium-sized firms to all functions required to manage successfully. **Availability:** Print; Download; PDF.

28473 ■ *Business Management for Tropical Dairy Farmers*
Pub: CSIRO Publishing
Contact: Dr. Stefan Doerr, Editor-in-Chief
E-mail: s.doerr@swansea.ac.uk
Ed: John Moran. **Description:** Business management skills required for dairy farmers are addressed, focusing on financial management and ways to improve cattle housing and feeding systems. **Availability:** Print; PDF; Download.

28474 ■ *Business Warrior: Strategy for Entrepreneurs*
Price: $9.99. **Description:** Advice to help entrepreneurs understand competitive strategies in order to succeed, focusing on sales, marketing, and personnel management. **Availability:** Print; Download; PDF.

28475 ■ *"Business Wisdom from the Mountaintops" in Canadian Business (Vol. 83, October 12, 2010, No. 17, pp. 91)*
Ed: Matthew McClearn. **Released:** October 12, 2010. **Description:** Techniques used to save lives on the world's highest mountains could make companies more creative. Mountaineers have time to talk to one another, and the resulting flow of ideas help climbers reach the summit. Organizations are expected to foster communication both internally and externally. **Availability:** Print; Online.

28476 ■ *"Can He Win the Patent Game?" in Globe & Mail (February 20, 2006, pp. B1)*
Ed: Simon Avery, Paul Waldie. **Description:** A profile on managerial abilities of chief executive officer Jim Balsillie of Research In Motion Ltd., who will face the patent case with NTP Inc., is presented. **Availability:** Online.

28477 ■ *"Can You Really Manage Engagement Without Managers? Zappos May Soon Find Out, as the Online Retailer is Eliminating the Traditional Manager Role" in Gallup Business Journal (April 24, 2014)*
Pub: Gallup, Inc.
Contact: Jon Clifton, Chief Executive Officer
Description: Online retailer, Zappos, will do away with the traditional manager role to lessen the chain of control within the organization. The concept of self-managed teams is explored. **Availability:** Online.

28478 ■ *"Captain Planet" in (Vol. 90, June 2012, No. 6, pp. 112)*
Pub: Harvard Business Review Press
Contact: Moderna V. Pfizer, Contact
Ed: Paul Polman, Adi Ignatius. **Price:** $8.95, hardcopy black and white. **Description:** Paul Polman, chief executive officer of Unilever N.V., discusses his company's sustainable living plan, which integrates social responsibility with corporate objectives. Topics include sustainable sourcing, abolishing quarterly reporting in favor of long-term perspectives, the impact of the 2008 global economic crisis, and turning a company into a learning organization. **Availability:** Print; Online; PDF.

28479 ■ *"The Carpenter: A Story About the Greatest Success Strategies of All"*
Pub: John Wiley & Sons, Inc.
Contact: Christina Van Tassell, Executive Vice President Chief Financial Officer
Released: May 23, 2014. **Price:** $23, hardcover; $14.99, e-book. **Description:** John Gordon draws upon his with work with business leaders, sales people, professional and college sports teams, nonprofit organizations and schools to share a story that will inspire people to build a better life, career and team with successful business strategies. **Availability:** E-book; Print.

28480 ■ *"The Center of Success: Author Explores How Confidence Can Take You Further" in Black Enterprise (Vol. 38, March 1, 2008, No. 8)*
Pub: Earl G. Graves Ltd.
Contact: Earl Graves, Jr., President
Ed: Ayana Dixon. **Description:** Motivational speaker and author, Valorie Burton, provides a 50-question confidence quotient assessment to help business owners and managers develop confidence in order to obtain goals. **Availability:** Online.

28481 ■ *"The CEO of Anglo American On Getting Serious About Safety" in (Vol. 90, June 2012, No. 6, pp. 43)*
Pub: Harvard Business Review Press
Contact: Moderna V. Pfizer, Contact
Ed: Cynthia Carroll. **Price:** $8.95, PDF and hardcover black and white. **Description:** The author discusses her decision to shut down Anglo American PLC's platinum mine, the world's largest, for a complete overhaul of the firm's safety procedures. This involved a thorough retraining of the mine's workforce, replacing nearly all of the managers, and promoting the changes throughout the rest of the industry. **Availability:** Print; PDF; Online.

28482 ■ *"CEO Forecast: With Cloudy Economy, Executives Turn to Government Contracting" in Hispanic Business (January-February 2009, pp. 34, 36)*
Ed: Jessica Haro, Richard Kaplan. **Description:** As economic uncertainty fogs the future, executives turn to government contracts in order to boost business.

Revenue sources, health care challenges, environmental consulting and remediation services, as well as technological strides are discussed. **Availability:** Print; Online.

28483 ■ *"CEO Pay: Best Bang for Buck" in Philadelphia Business Journal (Vol. 30, September 30, 2011, No. 33, pp. 1)*
Pub: Philadelphia Business Journal
Contact: Sierra Quinn, Director
E-mail: squinn@bizjournals.com
Ed: Jeff Blumenthal. **Description:** A study by Strategic Research Solutions on the compensation of chief executive officers in Philadelphia, Pennsylvania-based public companies reveals that only a few of them performed according to expectations. These include Brian Roberts of Comcast, John Conway of Crown Holdings, and Frank Hermance of Ametek Inc. **Availability:** Online.

28484 ■ *"CEO Pay: The Details" in Crain's Detroit Business (Vol. 25, June 22, 2009, No. 25)*
Pub: Crain Communications Inc.
Contact: Barry Asin, President
Description: Total compensation packages for CEOs at area companies our outlined. These packages include salary, bonuses, stock awards, and options. **Availability:** Online.

28485 ■ *"The CEO Poll: Potash Sale Must Be Blocked" in Canadian Business (Vol. 83, October 12, 2010, No. 17, pp. 24)*
Pub: Rogers Media Inc.
Contact: Neil Spivak, Chief Executive Officer
Ed: Kasey Coholan. **Description:** Chief executive officers (CEOs) and corporate leaders in Canada are concerned about the possible sale of Potash Corporation to foreign buyers. A Compas Inc. poll recently asked CEOs whether the Canadian Government should step in to block the sale of the country's largest fertilizer firm. **Availability:** Print; Online.

28486 ■ *"The CEO Poll: Split on Migrant Workers" in Canadian Business (Vol. 83, September 14, 2010, No. 15, pp. 23)*
Pub: Rogers Media Inc.
Contact: Neil Spivak, Chief Executive Officer
Ed: Jacqueline Nelson. **Description:** A survey of Canadian CEOs shows that 49 percent of the respondents believe it was wrong to suspend the immigration programs and companies should be allowed to hire the most skilled workers regardless of citizenship. However, 42 percent believe the suspension was right because employment of Canadians must take precedence. **Availability:** Print; Online.

28487 ■ *"CEOs Decry Budget Taxation Change" in Globe & Mail (April 2, 2007, pp. B1)*
Ed: Steven Chase. **Description:** The views of the chief executive officers of Canadian firms, on the changes in the country's policy governing the taxation of foreign deals, are presented. **Availability:** Print; Online.

28488 ■ *"CEOs Gone Wild" in Canadian Business (Vol. 79, August 14, 2006, No. 16-17, pp. 15)*
Description: Stock investment decisions of chief executive officers of metal companies in Canada, are discussed. **Availability:** Print; Online.

28489 ■ *"CEOs Keep Bringing Home the Perks" in Baltimore Business Journal (Vol. 30, May 18, 2012, No. 2, pp. 1)*
Pub: American City Business Journals, Inc.
Contact: Mike Olivieri, Executive Vice President
Ed: Gary Haber. **Description:** According to the annual proxy statement of Baltimore-based Stanley Black & Decker, executive chairman Nolan D. Archibald received a $12.3 million compensation package in 2011. According to the company, Archibald's perks are part of his employment agreement which was duly approved by the shareholders during the merger of Stanley Works and Black & Decker. **Availability:** Print; Online.

28490 ■ "CEOs With Headsets" in Harvard Business Review (Vol. 88, September 2010, No. 9, pp. 21)
Pub: Harvard Business Publishing
Contact: Diane Belcher, Managing Director
Ed: Andrew Zimbalist. Price: $6, PDF. Description: Placing a salary cap on college coaches' compensation would not significantly affect coaching quality or an institution's ability to obtain talent. A salary growth rate comparison between coaches, university presidents, and full professors for the period 1986 to 2007 is also presented. Availability: Online; PDF.

28491 ■ "Certification Experts Germanischer Lloyd Wind Energy Assist NaiKun's Offshore Wind Project" in Marketwired (May 14, 2007)
Pub: Comtex News Network Inc.
Contact: Kan Devnani, President
Description: Germanischer Lloyd Wind Energy (GL Wind) will examine, inspect, and provide quality management services for the engineering, design, and construction of the offshore wind project planned by NaiKun Wind Development Inc. in northwest British Columbia. Availability: Online.

28492 ■ "CFOs Walk a Tightrope When Picking Consultants" in The Wall Street Journal (July 26, 2016)
URL(s): blogs.wsj.com/cfo/2016/07/26/cfos-walk-a-tightrope-when-picking-consultants/
Ed: Tatyana Shumsky. Released: July 26, 2016. Description: Choosing a business consultant is often tricky and picking someone who isn't a good fit for the company can waste funds and time. CFOs often bring in outside help and they need to do their due diligence to make sure this person will get the job done. That includes contacting references and making sure the consultant has actually done this type of work in the past. Giving them a small project to start is often advised, and then moving them onto bigger projects once the scope of their knowledge and skill set are known. Availability: Online.

28493 ■ "Challenges Await Quad in Going Public" in Milwaukee Business Journal (Vol. 27, January 29, 2010, No. 18, pp. A1)
Pub: The Business Journal
Contact: Heather Ladage, President
E-mail: hladage@bizjournals.com
Ed: Rich Rovito. Description: Sussex, Wisconsin-based Quad/Graphics Inc.'s impending acquisition of rival Canadian World Color Press Inc. will transform it into a publicly held entity for the first time. Quad has operated as a private company for nearly 40 years and will need to adjust to changes, such as the way management shares information with Quad/Graphics' employees. Details of the merger are included. Availability: Print; Online.

28494 ■ "Challenges, Responses and Available Resources: Success in Rural Small Businesses" in Journal of Small Business and Entrepreneurship (Vol. 23, Winter 2010, No. 1)
Pub: Canadian Council for Small Business and Entrepreneurship
Contact: John MacRitchie, President
Ed: Lynne Siemens. Description: Rural communities and their residents are exploring the potential of small business and entrepreneurship to address the economic changes they are facing. While these rural areas present many opportunities, business people in these areas face challenges which they must navigate to operate successfully. Availability: Download; PDF; Online.

28495 ■ "Chameleonic or Consistent? A Multilevel Investigation of Emotional Labor Variability and Self-Monitoring" in Academy of Management Journal (Vol. 55, August 1, 2012, No. 4, pp. 905)
Pub: Academy of Management
Contact: Sharon Alvarez, President
Ed: Brent A. Scott, Christopher M. Barnes, David T. Wagner. Description: The importance of emotional labor variability in association with job satisfaction and work withdrawal is examined. Results indicate that surface acting variability is linked to lower levels of job satisfaction and higher levels of work withdrawal and that self-monitoring influences the impact of surface acting variability on job satisfaction and work withdrawal. Availability: Electronic publishing; Download; PDF; Online.

28496 ■ "Chameleonic or Consistent? A Multilevel Investigation of Emotional Labor Variability and Self-Monitoring" in Academy of Management Journal (Vol. 55, August 2012, No. 4, pp. 905)
Released: Volume 55. No 4. Price: $30, PDF and download. Description: The importance of emotional labor variability in association with job satisfaction and work withdrawal is examined. Results indicate that surface acting variability is linked to lowe levels of job satisfaction and higher levels of work withdrawal and that self-monitoring influences the impact of surface acting variability on job satisfactionand work withdrawal. Availability: Print; Download; PDF; Online.

28497 ■ "Characteristics of Great Salespeople" in Agency Sales Magazine (Vol. 39, November 2009, No. 10, pp. 40)
Description: Tips for managers in order to maximize the performance of their sales personnel are presented through several vignettes. Using performance based commission that rewards success, having business systems that support sales activity, and having an organizational culture that embraces sales as a competitive edge are some suggestions. Availability: Online.

28498 ■ The Checklist Manifesto: How to Get Things Right
Ed: Atul Gawande. Released: January 4, 2011. Price: $32, hardcover; $16, paperback; $9.99, e-book; $34.99, CD-ROM; $9.99, hardcover(4 Collectible from $9.99); $2.87, hardcover(180 Used from $2.87); $7.76, hardcover(84 New from $7.76); $13.60, Paperback; $3.61, Paperback(191 Used from $3.61); $9.64, Paperback(90 New from $9.64); $8.99, Paperback(3 Collectible from $8.99); $25.09, Audio CD; $15.94, Audio CD; $19.29, Audio CD. Description: How tragic errors can be sharply reduced with a piece of paper, hand-drawn boxes, and a pencil. Availability: CD-ROM; E-book; Print; Audio.

28499 ■ "Chip Heath: Get Over Your Fear of Change" in Canadian Business (Vol. 83, June 15, 2010, No. 10, pp. 38)
Pub: Rogers Media Inc.
Contact: Neil Spivak, Chief Executive Officer
Ed: Michelle Magnan. Description: Organizational behavior professor Chip Heath says that resistance to change is based on the conflict between our analytical, rational side and our emotional side that is in love with comfort. Heath states that businesses tend to focus on the negatives during an economic crisis while they should be focusing on what is working and ways to do more of that. Availability: Print; Online.

28500 ■ "Chuck E. Cheese's CEO to Retire" in Dallas Business Journal (Vol. 37, March 28, 2014, No. 29, pp. 6)
Pub: American City Business Journals, Inc.
Contact: Mike Olivieri, Executive Vice President
Released: Weekly. Price: $4, introductory 4-week offer(Digital only). Description: CEC Entertainment Inc. president and CEO, Michael Magusiak, is retiring after spending almost 27 years with the parent company Chuck E. Cheese. Magusiak is confident that the future of Chuck E. Cheese's brand will continue to grow in the U.S. and globally. Availability: Print; Online.

28501 ■ "Cincinnati Consults Executives on Police Chief Hire" in Business Courier (Vol. 27, August 27, 2010, No. 17, pp. 1)
Pub: Business Courier
Ed: Dan Monk, Lucy May. Description: The City of Cincinnati, Ohio has begun a selection process for the new police chief by consulting the city's business executives. The city charter amendment known as Issue 5 has removed civil service protection from the chief's post and enables City Manager Milton Dohoney to hire a chief from outside the department. Availability: Print; Online.

28502 ■ "Citadel Hires Three Lehman Execs" in Chicago Tribune (October 2, 2008)
Description: Citadel Investment Group LLC, Chicago hedge-fund operator, has hired three former senior executives of bankrupt investment banker Lehman Brothers Holding Inc. Citadel believes that the company's hiring spree will help them to further expand the firm's capabilities in the global fixed income business. Availability: Online.

28503 ■ "Clearwire Struggling, Banks on Deals with Competitors" in Puget Sound Business Journal (Vol. 33, August 24, 2012, No. 18, pp. 1)
Pub: Baltimore Business Journal
Contact: Rhonda Pringle, President
E-mail: rpringle@bizjournals.com
Ed: Emily Parkhurst, Alyson Raletz. Description: Clearwire Corporation's chief executive, Erik Prusch, is planning to lease the wireless spectrum of the company to major mobile providers that run out of their own supply. At issue is whether the Bellevue, Washington-based telecommunication company can manage its $4 billion debt and maximize the value of its technology while managing its partners all at the same time. Availability: Print; Online.

28504 ■ "The CMO of Consequence" in Business Strategy Review (Vol. 21, Autumn 2010, No. 3, pp. 42)
Ed: D. Eric Boyd, Rajesh K. Chandy, Marcus Cunha, Jr. Released: September 29, 2010. Description: Do chief marketing officers matter? Some say that CMOs have limited effect on corporate performance and don't add significant value to the firm. The authors agree that the job in many firms is in great peril, but their research has uncovered why the contributions of some CMOs are invaluable. Availability: Print; PDF; Online.

28505 ■ "CMO Nicholson Exits Pepsi as Share Declines" in Advertising Age (Vol. 79, July 7, 2008, No. 26, pp. 4)
Pub: Crain Communications, Inc.
Contact: Jessica Botos, Manager, Marketing
E-mail: jessica.botos@crainsnewyork.com
Ed: Natalie Zmuda. Description: Cie Nicholson, the chief marketing officer at Pepsi-Cola UK, is leaving the company at a time when its market share is down; the brand, which was known for its dynamic marketing, has diverted much of its attention from its core brands and shifted attention to the ailing Gatorade brand as well as Sobe Life Water and Amp. Availability: Online.

28506 ■ Coaching & Mentoring for Dummies
Pub: John Wiley & Sons, Inc.
Contact: Christina Van Tassell, Executive Vice President Chief Financial Officer
URL(s): www.wiley.com/en-us/Coaching+%26+Mentoring+For+Dummies%2C+2nd+Edition-p-9781394181179
Ed: Leo MacLeod. Released: 2nd edition. Price: $24.99, paperback. Description: A guide for helping people transition into the role of a coach or mentor in a workplace setting. Availability: Online.

28507 ■ "Coffee Breaks Don't Boost Productivity After All" in Harvard Business Review (Vol. 90, May 2012, No. 5, pp. 34)
Pub: Harvard Business Review Press
Contact: Moderna V. Pfizer, Contact
Ed: Charlotte Fritz. Price: $6. Description: Research shows no statistical correlation between taking a short break at work and one's fatigue and vitality levels. However, a link was found between personal productivity and assisting a coworker. Employees detach from work more successfully during long breaks rather than short ones. Availability: Online; PDF.

28508 ■ *"The Color of Success: ELC Focuses On Making Diversity Work" In Black Enterprise (Vol. 41, December 2010, No. 5, pp. 59)*
Pub: Earl G. Graves Ltd.
Contact: Earl Graves, Jr., President
Ed: Sonia Alleyne. **Description:** CEOs and top ELC members at the annual recognition conference held in New York in October 2010 shared their perspective on corporate inclusion and advice for C-suite aspirants. **Availability:** Online.

28509 ■ *"Column: Good Decisions. Bad Outcomes" in Harvard Business Review (Vol. 88, December 2010, No. 12, pp. 40)*
Pub: Harvard Business Publishing
Contact: Diane Belcher, Managing Director
Ed: Dan Ariely. **Price:** $6, PDF. **Description:** Suggestions are provided for developing and implementing improved reward systems that in turn produce better decision-making processes. These include documenting critical assumptions and changing mind sets. **Availability:** Online; PDF.

28510 ■ *"Column: It's Time to Take Full Responsibility" in Harvard Business Review (Vol. 88, October 2010, No. 10, pp. 42)*
Pub: Harvard Business Publishing
Contact: Diane Belcher, Managing Director
Ed: Rosabeth Moss Kanter. **Price:** $6, PDF. **Description:** A case for corporate responsibility is cited, focusing on long-term impact and the effects of public accountability. **Availability:** Online; PDF.

28511 ■ *"Column: Redefining Failure" in Harvard Business Review (Vol. 88, September 2010, No. 9, pp. 34)*
Pub: Harvard Business Publishing
Contact: Diane Belcher, Managing Director
Ed: Seth Godin. **Price:** $6, PDF. **Description:** Specific forms of failure, including design failure, failure of priorities, failure of opportunity, and failure to quit are examined. The negative implications of maintaining the status quo are discussed. **Availability:** Online; PDF.

28512 ■ *"Column: What 17th-Century Pirates Can Teach Us About Job Design" in Harvard Business Review (Vol. 88, October 2010, No. 10, pp. 44)*
Pub: Harvard Business Publishing
Contact: Diane Belcher, Managing Director
Ed: Hayagreeva Rao. **Price:** $6, PDF. **Description:** Ways in which pirates typify the importance of separating star tasks, or strategic work, from guardian tasks, or the operational work are outlined. **Availability:** Online; PDF.

28513 ■ *"Column: Work Pray Love" in Harvard Business Review (Vol. 88, December 2010, No. 12, pp. 38)*
Pub: Harvard Business Publishing
Contact: Diane Belcher, Managing Director
Ed: Rosabeth Moss Kanter. **Price:** $6, PDF. **Description:** It is recommended to reinvest in values in order to promote better employee-company engagement and performance. **Availability:** Online; PDF.

28514 ■ *"Competing on Talent Analytics" in Harvard Business Review (Vol. 88, October 2010, No. 10, pp. 52)*
Pub: Harvard Business Publishing
Contact: Diane Belcher, Managing Director
Ed: Thomas H. Davenport, Jeanne Harris, Jeremy Shapiro. **Price:** $8.95, PDF. **Description:** Six ways to use talent analytics to obtain the highest level of value from employees are listed. These include human-capital investment analysis, talent value models, workforce forecasts, and talent supply chains. **Availability:** Online; PDF.

28515 ■ *"Conference Calendar" in Marketing to Women (Vol. 21, April 2008, No. 4, pp. 7)*
Description: Listing of current conferences and events concerning women, marketing and business. **Availability:** Print; PDF; Download; Online.

28516 ■ *Connect with SmartBook: Online Access for Canadian Entrepreneurship and Small Business Management*
Ed: D. Wesley Balderson. **Released:** 10th Edition. **Price:** C$89, connect with smartbook; C$143.95, print text plus connect with smartbook; C$133.95, print text; C$89, Digital(Connect with SmartBook); C$143.95, Print (Print text + Connect with Smart-Book); C$133.95, Print text. **Description:** Successful entrepreneurship and small business management is shown through the use of individual Canadian small business experiences. **Availability:** Print; Online.

28517 ■ *"The Consequences of Tardiness" in Modern Machine Shop (Vol. 84, August 2011, No. 3, pp. 34)*
Description: Five point addressing motivating factors behind employees who are tardy and those who choose to be on time in the workplace are shared. **Availability:** Online.

28518 ■ *"Consulting Firm Goes Shopping" in Crain's Chicago Business (Vol. 31, April 28, 2008, No. 17, pp. 45)*
Pub: Crain Communications Inc.
Contact: Barry Asin, President
Ed: Phuong Ly. **Description:** Clark & Wamberg LLC was created last year after the merger of Clark Inc. to a Dutch insurance conglomerate. Clark Inc. was a life insurance and benefits consultancy which had been on a downslide, returning just 5.6 percent a year to shareholders. In contrast Clark & Wamberg posted first-year revenue of $106.8 million, fueled by business from its executive compensation and health care clients. **Availability:** Online.

28519 ■ *"Contextual Intelligence: Despite 30 Years of Experimentation and Study, We are Only Starting to Understand that Some Managerial Knowledge is Universal and Some is Specific to a Market or a Culture" in Harvard Business Review (Vol. 92, September 2014, No. 9, pp. 58)*
Pub: Harvard Business Publishing
Contact: Diane Belcher, Managing Director
Price: $8.95. **Description:** Contextual intelligence is defined as the ability to adapt knowledge to circumstances different from those under which the knowledge was initially developed. Firms should observe both employees and customers to understand local variations. **Availability:** Online; PDF.

28520 ■ *"Corporate Governance Reforms in China and India: Challenges and Opportunities" in Business Horizons (January-February 2008)*
Pub: Elsevier Advanced Technology Publications
Ed: Nandini Rajagopalan, Yan Zhang. **Description:** The evolution of corporate governance reforms and the role of privatization and globalization in India and China are studied. Shortage of qualified independent directors and lack of incentives were found to be two of the major challenges in governance. The implications of and solutions to these challenges are highlighted. **Availability:** Download; PDF; Online.

28521 ■ *"Corporate Responsibility" in Professional Services Close-Up (July 2, 2010)*
Description: List of firms awarded the inaugural Best Corporate Citizens in Government Contracting by the Corporate Responsibility Magazine is presented. The list is based on the methodology of the Magazine's Best Corporate Citizen's List, with 324 data points of publicly-available information in seven categories which include: environment, climate change, human rights, philanthropy, employee relations, financial performance, and governance. **Availability:** Online.

28522 ■ *"The Couch in the Corner Office: Surveying the Landscape of the CEO Psyche" in Inc. (January 2008, pp. 33-34)*
Description: Profile of Leslie G. Mayer, founder of the Leadership Group, a firm that provides assistance to CEOs of firms by offering a deep understanding of the relationships, insecurities, and blind spots that can weaken strong leadership. **Availability:** Online.

28523 ■ *"The Coup Is Over, the Execution Begins" in Canadian Business (Vol. 85, June 11, 2012, No. 10, pp. 9)*
Ed: Matthew McClearn. **Description:** U.S. activist investor Bill Ackman of Pershing Square Capital Management faces the challenge of satisfying the high expectations he set when he acquired Canadian Pacific (CP) Railway and all of Pershing's nominees were elected to the CP board. Ackman promises that CP would reach an operating ratio of 65 percent by 2015. **Availability:** Online.

28524 ■ *"Creativity, Inc.: Overcoming the Unseen Forces That Stand in the Way of True Inspiration"*
Pub: Penguin Random House
Contact: Nihar Malaviya, Chief Executive Officer
Released: April 08, 2014. **Price:** $28, hardcover, plus shipping charges; $2.99, e-book; $35, CD, plus shipping charges; $17.50, audiobook download; $16.89, Hardcover; $15.79, Paperback; $28.33, Audible Audiobook. **Description:** Ed Catmull, co-founder of Pixar Animation Studios, reaches out to managers who want to lead their employees to greater heights. Pixar has dominated the world of animated films for twenty years. Catmull addresses philosophies that protect the creative process and defy convention to inspire employees and create a successful small business. **Availability:** CD-ROM; E-book; Print; Audio.

28525 ■ *"The Critical Need to Reinvent Management" in Business Strategy Review (Vol. 21, Spring 2010, No. 1, pp. 4)*
Ed: Julian Birkinshaw. **Released:** February 09, 2010. **Description:** The author believes that management is undervalued today - and for good reasons. Management, he says, has failed at the big-picture level and thinks it is time to reinvent the profession. **Availability:** Print; PDF; Online.

28526 ■ *"Cross Atlantic Commodities Launches National Internet Marketing Programs" in Manufacturing Close-Up (September 8, 2009)*
Description: Profile of the Internet campaign recently launched by Cross Atlantic Commodities, Inc., a manufacturer of specialty beauty and health products. **Availability:** Print; Online.

28527 ■ *"Crucible: A New Will to Win" in Harvard Business Review (Vol. 88, September 2010, No. 9, pp. 110)*
Pub: Harvard Business Publishing
Contact: Diane Belcher, Managing Director
Ed: Daniel McGinn. **Price:** $8.95, PDF. **Description:** Importance of succession and contingency planning are emphasized in this account of Rick Hendrick's response to business loss coupled with personal tragedy. Focus and determination in leadership are also discussed. **Availability:** Online; PDF.

28528 ■ *"Crucible: Battling Back from Betrayal" in Harvard Business Review (Vol. 88, December 2010, No. 12, pp. 130)*
Pub: Harvard Business Publishing
Contact: Diane Belcher, Managing Director
Ed: Daniel McGinn. **Price:** $8.95, PDF. **Description:** Stephen Greer's scrap metal firm, Hartwell Pacific, lost several million dollars due to a lack of efficient and appropriate inventory audits, accounting procedures, and new-hire reference checks for his foreign operations. Greer believes that balancing growth with control is a key component of success. **Availability:** Print; PDF.

28529 ■ *"Crucible: Losing the Top Job - And Winning It Back" in Harvard Business Review (Vol. 88, October 2010, No. 10, pp. 136)*
Pub: Harvard Business Publishing
Contact: Diane Belcher, Managing Director
Ed: Alison Beard. **Price:** $8.95, PDF. **Description:** Michael Mack chronicles the changes in perspectives that occurred when he was fired from Garden Fresh, a restaurant firm he co-owned. Once again at the

company helm, he is now more receptive to outside input and acknowledges the importance of work-life balance. **Availability:** Online; PDF.

28530 ■ *"The Cult of Ralph: Chrysler's Ralph Gilles" in Canadian Business (Vol. 79, September 22, 2006, No. 19, pp. 90)*

Pub: Rogers Media Inc.

Contact: Neil Spivak, Chief Executive Officer

Ed: Thomas Watson. **Description:** The contributions of Ralph Gilles to automobile manufacturing giant Daimler Chrysler AG are discussed. **Availability:** Print; Online.

28531 ■ *"Culture Club: Effective Corporate Cultures" in Canadian Business (Vol. 79, October 9, 2006, No. 20, pp. 115)*

Pub: Rogers Media Inc.

Contact: Neil Spivak, Chief Executive Officer

Ed: Calvin Leung. **Description:** Positive impacts of an effective corporate culture on the employees' productivity and the performance of the business are discussed. **Availability:** Online.

28532 ■ *"Custom Fit" in Canadian Business (Vol. 80, November 19, 2007, No. 23, pp. 42)*

Description: Proper employee selection will help ensure a company has the people with the skills it really needs. Employee development is integral in coping with changes in the company. The importance of hiring the right employee and developing his skills is examined. **Availability:** Print; Online.

28533 ■ *"Customer Retention is Proportionate to Employee Retention" in Green Industry Pro (Vol. 23, September 2011)*

Description: Presented in a question-answer format, information is provided to help retain customers as well as keeping workers happy. **Availability:** Online.

28534 ■ *"The Danger from Within: The Biggest Threat to Your Cybersecurity May Be an Employee or a Vendor" in Harvard Business Review (Vol. 92, September 2014, No. 9, pp. 94)*

Pub: Harvard Business Publishing

Contact: Diane Belcher, Managing Director

Price: $8.95. **Description:** Corporate computer crimes involving insiders are on the rise. To reduce vulnerability, firms should incorporate employees into the watchdog process, perform regular audits of distributors and suppliers, and implement security procedures involving both management and information technology personnel. **Availability:** Online; PDF.

28535 ■ *"The Darwinian Workplace: New Technology Is Helping Employers Systematically Shift More Work To Their Best Employees" in Harvard Business Review (Vol. 90, May 2012, No. 5, pp. 25)*

Pub: Harvard Business Review Press

Contact: Moderna V. Pfizer, Contact

Ed: Serguei Netessine, Valery Yakubovich. **Price:** $6. **Description:** The winners-take-all model is a productivity-based system that shifts work and incentives to a firm's most productive employees. Challenges such as unpredictable pay swings, excessive competition, and unfair comparisons are addressed. **Availability:** Online; PDF.

28536 ■ *"Davis Family Expands Cable Empire" in St. Louis Business Journal (Vol. 32, June 15, 2012, No. 43, pp. 1)*

Pub: Baltimore Business Journal

Contact: Rhonda Pringle, President

E-mail: rpringle@bizjournals.com

Description: Missouri-based Fidelity Communications has become a standout in the $98 billion cable industry through low-profile management of the Davis family, with the help of John Colbert. Fidelity has made five acquisitions since 1992 and has grown its subscriber base to more than 115,000 customers or revenue generating units. **Availability:** Print; Online.

28537 ■ *"Dean Foods: Uh Oh. Here Comes Wal-Mart" in Ice Cream Reporter (Vol. 23, September 20, 2010, No. 10, pp. 8)*

Description: Dean Foods promoted Joseph Scalzo to President and Chief Operating Officer to oversee the firm's operational turnaround and near-term strategic initiatives as well as business units. Key functions will include worldwide supply chain and research and development. **Availability:** Online.

28538 ■ *"Defend Your Research: It's Not "Unprofessional" to Gossip at Work" in Harvard Business Review (Vol. 88, September 2010, No. 9, pp. 28)*

Pub: Harvard Business Publishing

Contact: Diane Belcher, Managing Director

Ed: Giuseppe Labianca. **Price:** $6, PDF. **Description:** Gossip can be of value to a company as an exchange of information and its use as a diagnostic tool can enable managers to address problems promptly and even head them off. **Availability:** Online; PDF.

28539 ■ *"Defend Your Research: The Early Bird Really Does Get the Worm" in Harvard Business Review (Vol. 88, July-August 2010, No. 7-8, pp. 30)*

Pub: Harvard Business Publishing

Contact: Diane Belcher, Managing Director

Ed: Christoph Randler. **Price:** $6, PDF. **Description:** Research indicates that those who identify themselves as 'morning people' tend to be more proactive, and thus have a career-development advantage over those who identify themselves as 'night people'. Implications of the research are also discussed. **Availability:** Online; PDF.

28540 ■ *Delegation: The Most Rewarding, Frustrating . . . Awesome Part of Running Your Business*

URL(s): www.barnesandnoble.com/w/delegation -dave-ramsey/1142776000?ean=2940185689257

Ed: Dave Ramsey. **Released:** January 03, 2023. **Price:** $9.99, e-book. **Description:** Small business owners often feel overwhelmed because they feel like must be doing everything, even the smallest of jobs, out of fear that it won't be done correctly. Releasing that fear and learning to delegate will help your business and your own life. **Availability:** E-book; Print.

28541 ■ *"Developing the Next Generation of Rosies" in Employee Benefit News (Vol. 25, November 1, 2011, No. 14, pp. 36)*

Pub: SourceMedia LLC

Contact: Gemma Postlethwaite, Chief Executive Officer

Ed: Kathleen Koster. **Description:** According to the research group Catalyst, women made up 46.7 percent of the American workforce in 2010, however only 14.4 percent was Fortune 500 executive officers and 15.7 percent held Fortune 500 board seats. Statistical data included.

28542 ■ *"DHR Hires Carr for Sports Group" in Crain's Detroit Business (Vol. 25, June 8, 2009, No. 23, pp. 5)*

Pub: Crain Communications Inc.

Contact: Barry Asin, President

Ed: Sherri Begin Welch. **Description:** Lloyd Carr, former head football coach for University of Michigan, has taken a position with DHR International in order to expand its searches for collegiate and professional sports organizations, recruit athletic directors, head coaches and other executives. **Availability:** Print; Online.

28543 ■ *"The Difference Between Management and Project Management" in Contractor (Vol. 57, February 2010, No. 2, pp. 30)*

Ed: H. Kent Craig. **Description:** There are differences when managing a two-man crew as a foreman and a 2,000 employee company as a corporate president. A project manager should have good skills in human psychology, accounting, and the knowledge

of a mechanical engineer, architect, civil engineer, and also the meditative skills of a Zen master. **Availability:** Print; Online.

28544 ■ *"Digital Marketing: Integrating Strategy and Tactics with Values, A Guidebook for Executives, Managers, and Students"*

Pub: Routledge, Taylor & Francis Group

Released: First edition. **Price:** $59.95, Paperback-$47.96; $190, Hardback - $152; $29.98, e-book. **Description:** Guidebook filled with information on the latest digital marketing tactics and strategic insights to help small businesses generate sustainable growth and achieve competitive advantage through digital integration. A five-step program: mindset, model, strategy, implementation, and sustainability is explained. **Availability:** E-book; Print.

28545 ■ *"Digital-Physical Mashups: To Consumers, the Real and Virtual Worlds Are One. The Same Should Go For Your Company" in Harvard Business Review (Vol. 92, September 2014, No. 9, pp. 84)*

Pub: Harvard Business Publishing

Contact: Diane Belcher, Managing Director

Price: $8.95. **Description:** By merging their physical and virtual operations, companies can provide a seamless experience for customers, boosting competitive advantage. These include strengthening customer/engagement links, approaching innovation through complementary expertise, and ensure that chief executive officers possess adequate technological knowledge. **Availability:** Online; PDF.

28546 ■ *"Disagree With Your Client? 11 Ways to Find a Positive and Effective Solution" in Small Business Trends (August 21, 2022)*

URL(s): smallbiztrends.com/2022/08/effective-solu tion-to-disagreement-with-a-client.html

Released: August 21, 2022. **Description:** Not everyone is going to see eye-to-eye all the time, and that is certainly true with client relationships. Tips are given to help defuse any situation where you find yourself in disagreement with a client. **Availability:** Online.

28547 ■ *"Discovery Networks" in Brandweek (Vol. 49, April 21, 2008, No. 16, pp. SR9)*

Description: Provides contact information for sales and marketing personnel for the Discovery networks as well as a listing of the station's top programming and an analysis of the current season and the target audience for those programs running in the current season. The networks flagship station returned to the top 10 in 2007, averaging 1.28 million viewers.

28548 ■ *"Disrupt Yourself: Four Principles for Finding the Career Path You Really Want" in Harvard Business Review (Vol. 90, July-August 2012, No. 7-8, pp. 147).*

Pub: Harvard Business Review Press

Contact: Moderna V. Pfizer, Contact

Ed: Whitney Johnson. **Description:** The four principles are: target needs that need to be met more effectively; identify one's own disruptive strengths; step down or step aside to aside to achieve growth; and allow one's strategy to emerge.

28549 ■ *The Diversity Code: Unlock the Secrets to Making Differences Work in the Real World*

Pub: HarperCollins Leadership

Contact: Donald Miller, Chief Executive Officer

Ed: Michelle T. Johnson. **Released:** January 24, 2019. **Description:** The most diligent compliance with laws and regulations can't foster true work place diversity. The best organizations have become genuine cross-cultural communities that believe equality in reconciling difference and valuing them. The book promotes understanding by answering many of the toughest questions that professionals and their employers are afraid to ask. **Availability:** Print.

28550 ■ *"Do You Need to Reinvent Your Managers?" in Rental Product News (Vol. 33, June 2011)*

Description: Rental business owners need to assess their management and be sure they perform as true leaders of the organization. **Availability:** Online.

28551 ■ *"Does Rudeness Really Matter? The Effects of Rudeness on Task Performance and Helpfulness" in Academy of Management Journal (Vol. 50, No. 5, October 1, 2007, pp. 1181)*

Pub: Academy of Management

Contact: Sharon Alvarez, President

Ed: Christine L. Porath, Amir Erez. **Description:** Study assessing the effect of impoliteness on performance and helpfulness showed rude behavior lowered performance levels and also decreased attitude of helpfulness. **Availability:** Electronic publishing; Download; PDF; Online.

28552 ■ *"Don't' Hate the Cable Guy" in Saint Louis Business Journal (Vol. 31, August 5, 2011, No. 50, pp. 1)*

Pub: Saint Louis Business Journal

Contact: Robert Bobroff, President

E-mail: rbobroff@bizjournals.com

Ed: Angela Mueller. **Description:** Charter Communications named John Birrer as senior vice president of customer experience. The company experienced problems with its customer services. **Availability:** Print; Online.

28553 ■ *"Don't Leave Employees on the Outside Looking In" in Canadian Business (Vol. 83, July 20, 2010, No. 11-12, pp. 13)*

Description: Managers should be careful with employee's tendencies to use the word 'they' when problems occur since this shows that employees are not associating themselves with their company. Employees should be involved in the development of the company and improving the flow of information is important in overcoming this communication challenge. **Availability:** Print; Online.

28554 ■ *"Don't Shoot the Messenger: A Wake-Up Call For Academics" in Academy of Management Journal (Vol. 50, No. 5, October 1, 2007, pp. 1020)*

Pub: Academy of Management

Contact: Sharon Alvarez, President

Ed: David E. Guest. **Description:** Author evaluates two well-known publications: HR Magazine and People Management, to emphasize the role of U.S. academics in communicating management practice. **Availability:** Electronic publishing; PDF; Download; Online.

28555 ■ *"The Doodle Revolution: Unlock the Power to Think Differently"*

Pub: Portfolio Hardcover

Contact: Adrian Zackheim, President

Released: January 09, 2014. **Price:** $21, hardcover; $15.99, e-book. **Description:** Powerhouse minds like Albert Einstein, John F. Kennedy, Marie Curie, Thomas Edison, and Henry Ford were all doodlers. Doodling has led to countless discoveries in science, technology, medicine, architecture, literature, and art. Brown guides us through basic doodling to the info-doodle, in other words, a higher level of thinking and empowerment for anyone, especially entrepreneurs and managers. **Availability:** E-book; Print.

28556 ■ *"Doria Camaraza on the Best Advice She's Ever Received 'Leave Your Ego at the Door'" in South Florida Business Journal (Vol. 34, June 20, 2014, No. 43, pp. 13)*

Pub: American City Business Journals, Inc.

Contact: Mike Olivieri, Executive Vice President

Description: Doria Camaraza, senior vice president and general manager of American Express Service Centers in Fort Lauderdale, Mexico and Argentina, share advice for successfully running service centers for the credit card company. She describes ways in

which she inspires creativity and drive, while promoting employee team building with her workers. **Availability:** Print; Online.

28557 ■ *"Downtowns Must Court Young, CEOs for Cities President Says" in Crain's Detroit Business (Vol. 24, October 6, 2008, No. 40, pp. 18)*

Description: It is important to produce more college graduates, and keep them in Michigan, according to CEOs for Cities President Carol Coletta when she spoke to a session at the West Michigan Regional Policy Conference which was held in September in Grand Rapids. Ways in which city leaders can connect students to communities, resulting in employees who have vested interest in the region, are also discussed.

28558 ■ *"Downturn Tests HCL's Pledge to Employees" in Workforce Management (Vol. 88, November 16, 2009, No. 12, pp. 23)*

Pub: Crain Communications Inc.

Contact: Barry Asin, President

Ed: Ed Frauenheim. **Description:** HCL Technologies has kept its promise to keep from laying any employees off during the recession which served as a test for the tech firm's Employee First program, which seeks to give workers greater income security as well as a stronger voice in the firm. **Availability:** Online.

28559 ■ *"Driving With No Brakes: How a Bunch of Hooligans Built the Best Travel Company in the World"*

Pub: Grand Circle Corp.

Ed: Alan Lewis, Harriet Lewis. **Released:** 2010. **Description:** Inspirational book about how two courageous leaders built a remarkable company that can thrive in change and succeed in an unpredictable world. Important lessons for any business leader trying to create value in the 21st Century are included. **Availability:** Print.

28560 ■ *"The Dynamic Small Business Manager"*

Ed: Frank Vickers. **Released:** February 11, 2011. **Price:** $19.95, e-book, plus shipping charges; $39.91, paperback, plus shipping charges. **Description:** Practical advice is given to help small business owners successfully manage their company. **Availability:** E-book; Print.

28561 ■ *"Dynamically Integrating Knowledge in Teams: Transforming Resources Into Performance" in Academy of Management Journal (Vol. 55, August 1, 2012, No. 4, pp. 998)*

Pub: Academy of Management

Contact: Sharon Alvarez, President

Ed: Heidi K. Gardner, Francesca Gino, Bradley R. Staats. **Description:** A method for developing a knowledge-integration capability to dynamically integrate the resources of team members into higher performance is proposed. Results suggest that the development of this capability is aided by the use of relational, structural, and experiential resources while uncertainty plays a moderating role in these relationships. **Availability:** Electronic publishing; Download; PDF; Online.

28562 ■ *"Economic Development: 105 CEOs Depart in July" in South Florida Business Journal (Vol. 35, August 15, 2014, No. 3, pp. 5)*

Pub: American City Business Journals, Inc.

Contact: Mike Olivieri, Executive Vice President

Released: August 15, 2014. **Price:** $4, Introductory 4-Week Offer(Digital & Print). **Description:** Challenger, Gray & Christmas has reported 105 CEO departures in July 2014 and these include seven in Florida. US-based companies announced 766 CEO changes in management during the first seven months of 2014. CEO departure trend by industry are given. **Availability:** Print; Online.

28563 ■ *Economic Freedom and the American Dream*

Pub: Palgrave Macmillan

Ed: Joseph Shaanan. **Released:** 2010. **Price:** $80, Hardcover; $75, softcover; $59.99, e-book. **Description:** An exploration into the effects of economic freedom on American in several areas such as markets, politics, and opportunities for would-be entrepreneurs. **Availability:** E-book; Print.

28564 ■ *"The Effect of Corporate Governance on Firm's Credit Ratings: Further Evidence Using Governance Score in the United States" in Accounting and Finance (Vol. 52, June 2012, No. 2, pp. 291)*

Ed: Fatima Alali, Asokan Anandarajan, Wei Jiang. **Released:** January 06, 2012. **Description:** An investigation into whether corporate governance affects a firm's credit ratings and whether improvement in corporate governance standards is associated with improvement in investing grade rating is presented. **Availability:** Print; PDF; Online.

28565 ■ *"Eight Tips For Leaders On Protecting the Team" in Puget Sound Business Journal (Vol. 35, August 22, 2014, No. 18, pp. 13)*

Pub: American City Business Journals, Inc.

Contact: Mike Olivieri, Executive Vice President

Description: Advice on ways to protect corporate teams is given. Unnecessary information and processes should be filtered to avoid distraction of the team. Team action plans must be prioritized. **Availability:** Print; Online.

28566 ■ *"The Emergence of Governance In an Open Source Community" in Academy of Management Journal (Vol. 50, No. 5, October 1, 2007, pp. 1079)*

Pub: Academy of Management

Contact: Sharon Alvarez, President

Ed: Siobhan O'Mahony, Fabrizio Ferraro. **Description:** Study examined the method of self-governance among small communities producing collective goods, focusing on an open source software community. Results revealed that a combination of bureaucratic and democratic practices helped its governance system. **Availability:** Electronic publishing; PDF; Download; Online.

28567 ■ *"Empathy: An Entrepreneur's Killer App" in Women Entrepreneur (February 3, 2009)*

Description: It is just as important to treat employees with courtesy and respect during bad economic times as it is in a good economy. Employers sometimes take advantage of such bad economic times since they realize that employees are grateful to have a job and cannot just quit and easily find work elsewhere. The importance of empathy in a company's leadership personnel is discussed. **Availability:** Online.

28568 ■ *"Empathy, Engagement the 'Secret Sauce' for Post-Pandemic Leadership Success" in Minority Business Entrepreneur (October 11, 2022)*

URL(s): mbemag.com/articles/empathy-engagement-the-secret-sauce-for-post-pandemic-leadership-success/

Ed: Merilee Kern. **Price:** $7.95. **Description:** Discusses how businesses need to change tactics in their leadership culture in this post-pandemic world. **Availability:** Online.

28569 ■ *Employee Management for Small Business*

Pub: Self-Counsel Press Inc.

Contact: Diana Douglas, Governor

Ed: Lin Grensing-Pophal. **Released:** Third edition. **Price:** C$12.99, EPUB. **Description:** Management tools to help entrepreneurs maintain an effective human resources plan for a small company. **Availability:** E-book; Print; PDF; Download.

28570 ■ *"Empowered" in Harvard Business Review (Vol. 88, July-August 2010, No. 7-8, pp. 94)*
Pub: Harvard Business Publishing
Contact: Diane Belcher, Managing Director
Ed: Josh Bernoff, Ted Schadler. **Price:** $8.95, PDF.
Description: HERO concept (highly empowered and resourceful operative) which builds a connection between employees, managers, and IT is outlined. The resultant additional experience and knowledge gained by employees improves customer relationship management. **Availability:** Online; PDF.

28571 ■ *"Entrepreneurial Orientation and Firm Performance: The Unique Impact of Innovativeness, Proactiveness, and Risk-taking" in Journal of Small Business and Entrepreneurship (Vol. 23, Winter 2010, No. 1)*
Pub: Canadian Council for Small Business and Entrepreneurship
Contact: John MacRitchie, President
Ed: Patrick M. Kreisera, Justin Davis. **Description:** The article develops a theoretical model of the relationship between firm-level entrepreneurship and firm performance. This model is intended to further clarify the consequences of an 'entrepreneurial orientation', paying particular attention to the differential relationship that exists between the three sub-dimensions of entrepreneurial orientation and firm performance. Included in the theoretical model are other important variables (such as organizational structure and environmental characteristics) that may impact the EO-performance relationship. Propositions are developed regarding the various configurations of the sub-dimensions of EO and organizational structure that would be most appropriate in a given environmental context. Future research may also benefit from considering the important role that organizational strategy and life cycle stage play in this model. The implications of this model for both researchers and managers are discussed.

28572 ■ *Everyday Leadership: You Will Make A Difference*
URL(s): www.barnesandnoble.com/w/everyday-lea
dership-brian-unell/1141224502?ean=294018
6613671
Ed: Brian Unell. **Released:** September 25, 2022. **Price:** $9.99, e-book; $36, hardcover; $18, paperback. **Description:** Understand the concepts of leadership with this guide and use those skills not only in a work-setting, but in your home-life as well. **Availability:** E-book; Print.

28573 ■ *"Evidence-Based Management and the Marketplace For Ideas" in Academy of Management Journal (Vol. 50, No. 5, October 2007, pp. 1009)*
Pub: Academy of Management
Contact: Sharon Alvarez, President
Ed: Wayne F. Cascio. **Description:** Study examines the relevance of material to actual usage in human resource management. Results reveal that it is important to design modules with execution in mind in seeking advice from professionals in relevant organizations. **Availability:** Electronic publishing; PDF; Download; Online.

28574 ■ *"The Evolution of Carolyn Elman" in Women In Business (Vol. 62, September 2010, No. 3, pp. 11)*
Pub: American Business Women's Association
Contact: Rene Street, Executive Director
Ed: Leigh Elmore. **Description:** Carolyn Elman, former executive director of the American Business Women's Association (ABWA), provides an overview of her career. Elman grew up with the Association, and it was part of her family's existence. She believes that the ABWA provides women the opportunity to learn and improve their skills in business.

28575 ■ *"Executive Compensation: Both Eyes on the Prize" in Canadian Business (Vol. 83, September 14, 2010, No. 15, pp. 42)*
Pub: Rogers Media Inc.
Contact: Neil Spivak, Chief Executive Officer

Ed: Jacqueline Nelson. **Description:** North American executive compensation has fundamentally shifted partly due to pressure from the US government and recent adjustments in the way CEO pay packages are structured. The changes have also become common practice in Canada and helped in scrutinizing the executive pay. **Availability:** Online.

28576 ■ *"Executive Presence: The Missing Link Between Merit and Success"*
Pub: Harper Business
Contact: Hollis Heimbouch, Senior Vice President Publisher
Released: June 03, 2014. **Price:** $23.99, hardcover. **Description:** Ways to find out if you possess executive presence are discussed. Executive presence is a conglomeration of qualities exuded by true leaders, a presence that shows you are in charge. Executive presences is a dynamic, collective mix of appearance, communication and gravitas and leaders must know how to use them all to their advantage. **Availability:** E-book; Print; Audio.

28577 ■ *"Experts Share How to Create Company Culture That Gets Results" in Small Business Trends (October 29, 2022)*
URL(s): smallbiztrends.com/2022/10/how-to-create
-company-culture-that-gets-results.html
Ed: Annie Pilon. **Released:** October 29, 2022. **Description:** The culture within a company is a big deal since employees are required to spend the majority of their day there. Having a culture that is positive helps your current employees stay engaged and it can also attract top talent when you are hiring. **Availability:** Online.

28578 ■ *"Exploring Supportive and Developmental Career Management Through Business Strategies and Coaching" in Human Resource Management (Vol. 51, January-February 2012, No. 1, pp. 99-120)*
Pub: John Wiley & Sons, Inc.
Contact: Christina Van Tassell, Executive Vice President Chief Financial Officer
Ed: Jesse Segers, Ilke Inceoglu. **Released:** January 26, 2012. **Description:** Coaching and other career practices that are part of supportive and developmental career management are examined. Such practices are found to be most present in organizations with a prospector strategy. **Availability:** Print; PDF; Online.

28579 ■ *"Extreme Negotiations" in Harvard Business Review (Vol. 88, November 2010, No. 11, pp. 66)*
Pub: Harvard Business Publishing
Contact: Diane Belcher, Managing Director
Ed: Jeff Weiss, Aram Donigian, Jonathan Hughes. **Price:** $8.95, PDF. **Description:** Examination of military negotiation skills that are applicable in business situations. Skills include soliciting others' perspectives, developing and proposing multiple solutions, and inviting others to assess them. **Availability:** Online; PDF.

28580 ■ *"Falling Local Executive Pay Could Suggest a Trend" in Tampa Bay Business Journal (Vol. 30, January 15, 2010, No. 4, pp. 1)*
Pub: Tampa Bay Business Journal
Contact: Ian Anderson, President
E-mail: ianderson@bizjournals.com
Ed: Margie Manning. **Description:** Tampa Bay, Florida-based Raymond James Financial Inc. and MarineMax Inc.'s proxy statements have shown the decreasing compensation of the companies' highest paid executives. The falling trend in executive compensation was a result of intensified shareholder scrutiny and the economy. **Availability:** Print; Online.

28581 ■ *Family Business*
Pub: Cengage Learning, Inc.
Contact: Michael E. Hansen, Chief Executive Officer
Ed: Ernesto J. Poza. **Released:** 2014. **Price:** $69.99, ETextbook. **Description:** Family-owned businesses face unique challenges in today's economy. This book

provides the next generation of knowledge and skills required for profitable management and leadership in a family enterprise. **Availability:** E-book; Print.

28582 ■ *Family Business Models: Practical Solutions for the Family Business*
Pub: Palgrave Macmillan
Ed: Alberto Gimeno, Gemma Baulenas, Joan Coma-Cros. **Released:** First edition. **Description:** A unique new model for understanding family businesses gives readers the potential to build better managed and more stable family firms and to plan for a success future.

28583 ■ *"The Fatal Bias" in Business Strategy Review (Vol. 25, Summer 2014, No. 2, pp. 34)*
Description: The prevailing managerial bias towards cost efficiency is harmful to corporate performance. Management's fatal bias is discussed. **Availability:** Online; PDF.

28584 ■ *"Fearless Leaders: Sharpen Your Focus: How the New Science of Mindfulness Can Help You Reclaim Your Confidence"*
Pub: Waterfront Digital Press
Released: First edition. **Description:** Executive coaches explain the principles that make managers and entrepreneurs and business leaders fearless. **Availability:** Print.

28585 ■ *Fierce Leadership*
Price: Paperback. **Description:** A bold alternative to the worst 'best' practices of business in the 21st Century. **Availability:** Print.

28586 ■ *"Fighting The Good Fight - Against Hate" in Inc. (Vol. 33, October 2011, No. 8, pp. 8)*
Description: Rob Roy, former Navy SEAL, runs SOT-G a firm that offers an 80-hour leadership training course inspired by military combat preparations. Details of the program are outlined. **Availability:** Online.

28587 ■ *"Flurry of Activity from Restaurant Groups as Industry Strengthens" in Wichita Business Journal (Vol. 27, February 17, 2012, No. 7, pp. 1)*
Pub: Baltimore Business Journal
Contact: Rhonda Pringle, President
E-mail: rpringle@bizjournals.com
Description: Atlanta, Georgia-based Chick-fil-A chain is set to open two restaurants in Wichita, Kansas and those additions were highly anticipated. However, there were other local management groups and franchisees that are investing on new buildings and refurbishing stores. Insights on the increasing restaurant constructions are also given. **Availability:** Print; Online.

28588 ■ *"Following the Signs" in Minority Business Entrepreneur (Vol. 39, Fall, 2022, No. 4, pp. 22-26)*
URL(s): digital.mbemag.com/?m=53732&i=769780
&p=22&ver=html5
Ed: Kelly L. Anderson. **Price:** $7.95. **Description:** Profile of Kevin Cooper, CEO of Infrastructure Professional Services and Equipment LLC. **Availability:** Print; Online.

28589 ■ *"The Formula for Growth: Through a Mixture of Vision and Partnerships, Leon Richardson has ChemicoMays in Expansion Mode" in Black Enterprise (Vol. 44, June 2014, No. 10, pp. 66)*
Pub: Earl G. Graves Ltd.
Contact: Earl Graves, Jr., President
Description: Profile of Leon Richardson, who has his family-owned business poised for growth. At the age of 13, Leon helped his family in their convenience store located in West Haven, Connecticut. He has gone from managing storefronts to overseeing a chemical management business during his entrepreneurial career.

28590 ■ *"Formulating Policy With a Parallel Organization"* in *Strategy & Leadership (Vol. 38, September-October 2010, No. 5, pp. 33-38)*
Pub: Emerald Inc.

Ed: Dale E. Zand, Thomas F. Hawk. **Description:** A study analyzes a case to examine the parallel organization concept and its successful implementation by a CEO to integrate independent divisions of a firm. Findings reveal that the implementation of the parallel organization improved the policy formulation, strategic planning profitability of the firm while also better integrating its independent divisions.

28591 ■ *"Four Lessons in Adaptive Leadership"* in *Harvard Business Review (Vol. 88, November 2010, No. 11, pp. 86)*
Pub: Harvard Business Publishing
Contact: Diane Belcher, Managing Director

Ed: Michael Useem. **Price:** $8.95, PDF. **Description:** Four key factors to effective leadership are presented. These are establishing a personal link, making sound and timely decisions, developing a common purpose while avoiding personal gain, and ensuring that objectives are clear without micromanaging those implementing them. **Availability:** Online; PDF.

28592 ■ *"Four Ways to Fix Banks: A Wall Street Veteran Suggests How To Cut Through the Industry's Complexity"* in *(Vol. 90, June 2012, No. 6, pp. 106)*
Pub: Harvard Business Review Press
Contact: Moderna V. Pfizer, Contact

Ed: Sallie Krawcheck. **Description:** Despite new regulations in the post-global economic crisis of 2008, banks are sill too complex for effective management of their boards. Recommendations for improving governance include incorporating bank debt in executive compensation to increase their sensitivity to risk, and paying dividends as a percentage of company earnings to maintain capital.

28593 ■ *"Friendly Ice Cream Corporation"* in *Ice Cream Reporter (Vol. 23, August 20, 2010, No. 9, pp. 8)*
Description: Friendly Ice Cream Corporation appointed Andrea M. McKenna as vice president of marketing and chief marketing officer. **Availability:** Print; Online.

28594 ■ *"From the Battlefield to the Boardroom"* in *Business Horizons (Vol. 51, March-April 2008, No. 2, pp. 79)*
Pub: Elsevier Advanced Technology Publications

Ed: Catherine M. Dalton. **Description:** Effective intelligence gathering, a thorough understanding of the mission, efficient use of resources, and strategic leadership are vital to achieving success in business as well as in the battlefield. Examples of effective leadership in the battle of Gettysburg are cited. **Availability:** Online.

28595 ■ *"From the Editors: Plagiarism Policies and Screening at AMJ"* in *Academy of Management Journal (Vol. 55, August 2012, No. 4, pp. 749)*
Pub: Academy of Management
Contact: Sharon Alvarez, President

Description: The plagiarism policies and practices of the Academy of Management Journal (AMJ) based on the Committee on Publications Ethics and AOM guidelines are described. The function of the Cross-Check software tool for screening manuscripts for plagiarism is explained. **Availability:** Download; Electronic publishing; PDF; Online.

28596 ■ *"The Fundamentals of Contract Management"* in *Business News Daily (February 21, 2023)*
URL(s): www.businessnewsdaily.com/4813-contract-management.html

Ed: Bennett Conlin. **Released:** February 21, 2023. **Description:** Discusses how managing contracts and hiring a contract manager can help your business. This is especially beneficial to companies who take part in government contract projects. **Availability:** Online.

28597 ■ *"The Future of Work"* in *Business Strategy Review (Vol. 21, Autumn 2010, No. 3, pp. 16)*
Pub: Wiley-Blackwell

Ed: Lynda Gratton. **Released:** August 28, 2017. **Description:** Work is universal. But how, why, where and when we work has never been so open to individual interpretation. The certainties of the past have been replaced by ambiguity, questions and the steady hum of technology. Now, in a groundbreaking research project covering 21 global companies and more than 200 executives, the author is making sense of the future of work. **Availability:** Print; PDF; Online.

28598 ■ *"Game Changing"* in *Business Strategy Review (Vol. 23, Spring 2012, No. 1, pp. 26)*
Released: Spring 2012. **Description:** Barney Francis is Managing Director of Sky Sports. In a television career spanning 18 years, he has worked in the multichannel terrestrial and independent sectors. At Sky, he was executive producer for cricket, leading his team through two ICC World Cups, two Ashes Tours, England tours to nine nations, and the first Twenty20 Cup. In 2007, he became executive producer for Sky's Premier league football and in 2008 executive producer for the UEFA Champions League.

28599 ■ *"Generalizing Newcomers' Relational and Organizational Identifications: Processes and Prototypicality"* in *Academy of Management Journal (Vol. 55, August 1, 2012, No. 4, pp. 949)*
Pub: Academy of Management
Contact: Sharon Alvarez, President

Ed: David M. Sluss, Robert E. Ployhart, M. Glenn Cobb, Blake E. Ashforth. **Description:** The process in which newcomers identify themselves with a supervisor and with the employing organization is examined. Results suggest that relational identification with a supervisor converges with organizational identification through effective, cognitive and behavioral mechanisms yet only when the relational other is perceived to be prototypical. **Availability:** Electronic publishing; Download; PDF; Online.

28600 ■ *"Get Online Quick in the Office Or in the Field"* in *Contractor (Vol. 56, October 2009, No. 10, pp. 47)*

Ed: William Feldman, Patti Feldman. **Description:** Contractors can set up a web site in minutes using the www.1and1.com website. Verizon's Novatel MIFI 2372 HSPA personal hotspot device lets contractors go online in the field. The StarTech scalable business management system helps contractors manage daily operations. **Availability:** Print; Online.

28601 ■ *"Getting Drowned Out by the Brainstorm"* in *Canadian Business (Vol. 83, June 15, 2010, No. 10, pp. 91)*
Pub: Rogers Media Inc.
Contact: Neil Spivak, Chief Executive Officer

Ed: Joe Castaldo. **Description:** A study reveals that people generate more ideas when they do it alone rather than as part of a brainstorming group. The limited range of ideas is due to the fixation of group members on the first idea that gets offered. **Availability:** Online.

28602 ■ *"Getting to 'Us'"* in *Harvard Business Review (Vol. 92, September 2014, No. 9, pp. 38)*
Pub: Harvard Business Publishing
Contact: Diane Belcher, Managing Director

Price: $6. **Description:** Employee motivation and satisfaction can be enhanced through leadership that presents a shared goal that emphasizes kinship and relationship to others, rather than citing a common enemy. **Availability:** Online; PDF.

28603 ■ *"Getting to Yes: Negotiating Agreement Without Giving In"*
Pub: Penguin Publishing Group

Ed: Roger Fisher, William L. Ury, Bruce Patton. **Released:** May 03, 2011. **Price:** $17, paperback; $14.99, e-book; $11.55, paperback; $5.38, hardcover. **Description:** Strategies for negotiating mutually acceptable agreements in all types of conflict. **Availability:** E-book; Print.

28604 ■ *"The Global Talent Hunt"* in *Business Strategy Review (Vol. 21, Spring 2010, No. 1, pp. 78)*

Ed: Richard Emerton. **Released:** February 09, 2010. **Description:** Richard Emerton explains how the new 'triple context' of economy, environment and society will have profound implications for human resource practices. He suggests that viewing talent as abundant is the right perspective for a manager. **Availability:** Print; PDF; Online.

28605 ■ *"The Globe: A Cautionary Tale for Emerging Market Giants"* in *Harvard Business Review (Vol. 88, September 2010, No. 9, pp. 99)*
Pub: Harvard Business Publishing
Contact: Diane Belcher, Managing Director

Ed: J. Stewart Black, Allen J. Morrison. **Price:** $8.95. **Description:** Key factors that negatively affected Japan corporate growth and organizational effectiveness include: devotion to established path, isolated domestic markets, homogenous executive teams, and a non-contentious labor force. Solutions include leadership development programs, multicultural input, and cross-cultural training. **Availability:** Online; PDF.

28606 ■ *Go Put Your Strengths to Work*
Pub: Free Press/Simon and Schuster Inc.
Contact: Jonathan Karp, President

Ed: Marcus Buckingham. **Description:** A guide to being more productive, focused and creative at work. **Availability:** Video; Online.

28607 ■ *"Go Team! Why Building a Cohesive Organization Is a Necessary Exercise"* in *Black Enterprise (Vol. 38, February 2008, No. 7, pp. 66)*
Pub: Earl G. Graves Ltd.
Contact: Earl Graves, Jr., President

Ed: Angeli R. Rasbury. **Description:** Tips to help manage successful as well as productive teams are outlined for small business managers. **Availability:** Online.

28608 ■ *"Goodwill Haunts Local Companies"* in *Crain's Chicago Business (Apr. 28, 2008)*
Pub: Crain Communications Inc.
Contact: Barry Asin, President

Ed: Ann Saphir. **Description:** Many companies are having to face the reality that they overpaid for acquisitions made in better economic times; investors often dismiss such one-time charges as mere accounting adjustments but writeoffs related to past acquisitions can signal future problems because they mean the expected profits that justified the purchase have not materialized. Writeoffs are particularly worrisome for firms with a lot of debt and whose banks require them to have enough assets to back up their borrowings. **Availability:** Online.

28609 ■ *"Great Canadian's President Folds His Cards"* in *Globe & Mail (February 21, 2006, pp. B4)*

Ed: Peter Kennedy. **Description:** The reasons behind the resignation of Anthony Martin as president of Great Canadian Gaming Corp. are presented. **Availability:** Print; Online.

28610 ■ *"Gregory Cunningham on Taking on Farm Credit of Florida"* in *South Florida Business Journal (Vol. 34, July 18, 2014, No. 52, pp. 11)*
Pub: American City Business Journals, Inc.
Contact: Mike Olivieri, Executive Vice President

Released: Weekly. **Price:** $8, introductory 4-week offer(Digital only). **Description:** Gregory Cunningham, president and CEO of Farm Credit of Florida, shares the lessons he learned from his military background that he applies to managing a company.

He explains why he decided to take on the challenge of helping the agricultural credit group deal with its regulatory order. **Availability:** Print; Online.

28611 ■ *"Grooming Your Online Persona" in Women In Business (Vol. 62, June 2010, No. 2, pp. 36)*

Description: Employees' use of online social networks could become a basis on how their employers, clients, or business partners would judge them. Personal details, pictures and other online data should be filtered to avoid inappropriate or uncomfortable situations and distinguish personal from professional or work life. **Availability:** Online.

28612 ■ *Groundswell: Winning in a World Transformed by Social Technologies*

Pub: Harvard Business Review Press
Contact: Moderna V. Pfizer, Contact

Ed: Charlene Li, Josh Bernoff. **Released:** June 09, 2011. **Price:** $22, paperback/softbound. **Description:** Individuals are using online social technologies such as blogs, social networking sites, YouTube, and podcasts to discuss products and companies, write their own news, and find their own deals. When consumers you've never met are rating your company's products in public forums with which you have no experience or influence, your company is vulnerable. This book teaches the tools and data necessary to turn this treat into an opportunity. **Availability:** E-book; Print.

28613 ■ *"Group Thinking" in Business Strategy Review (Vol. 23, Spring 2012, No. 1, pp. 48)*

Description: Conflicts and decision making in groups has long been a subject of fascination for Randall Peterson, Professor of Organizational Behavior at London Business School. He talks to Business Strategy Review about what ignited his interest and his latest research and thinking. **Availability:** Print; Online.

28614 ■ *The Growing Business Handbook: Inspiration and Advice from Successful Entrepreneurs and Fast Growing UK Companies*

Pub: Kogan Page Ltd.
Contact: Christina Lindeholm, Manager, Sales

Ed: Adam Jolly. **Released:** 17th edition. **Price:** $90, hardback; $90, e-book. **Description:** Tips for growing and running a successful business are covered, focusing on senior managers in middle market and SME companies. **Availability:** E-book; Print.

28615 ■ *A Guide to the Project Management Body of Knowledge*

Pub: Project Management Institute
Contact: Pierre Le Manh, President

Released: Seventh edition. **Description:** A guide for project management using standard language, with new data flow diagrams; the Identify Stakeholders and Collect Requirements processes defined; and with greater attention placed on how knowledge areas integrate in the context of initiating, planning, executing, monitoring and controlling, and closing process groups. **Availability:** Print; Download.

28616 ■ *"Halls Give Hospital Drive $11 Million Infusion" in The Business Journal-Serving Metropolitan Kansas City (Vol. 26, July 18, 2008)*

Description: Don Hall, chairman of Hallmark Cards Inc., and eight family members have announced that they will give $11 million to Children's Mercy Hospitals and Clinics for its $800 million expansion plan. Hall Family Foundation president Bill Hall that contributions such as that for Children's Mercy reflect the charitable interests of the foundation's board and founders. The possible impacts of the Hall's donation are analyzed.

28617 ■ *The Halo Effect: And the Eight Other Business Delusions That Deceive Managers*

Pub: Free Press/Simon and Schuster Inc.
Contact: Jonathan Karp, President

Ed: Phil Rosenzweig. **Released:** June 17, 2014. **Description:** Nine common business delusions, including the halo effect (which the author describes as the need to attribute positive qualities to successful individuals and companies), are illustrated using case studies of Lego, Cisco, and Nokia to show how adhering to myths can be bad for any business.

28618 ■ *"HBC Enlists IBM to Help Dress Up Its On-Line Shopping" in Globe & Mail (February 7, 2006, pp. B3)*

Description: The details of management contract between Hudson's Bay Co. and International Business Machines Corp. are presented. **Availability:** Print; Online.

28619 ■ *"HBR Case Study: Play It Safe or Take a Stand?" in Harvard Business Review (Vol. 88, November 2010, No. 11, pp. 139)*

Pub: Harvard Business Publishing
Contact: Diane Belcher, Managing Director

Ed: Trish Gorman Clifford, Jay Barney. **Price:** $8.95, PDF. **Description:** A fictitious leadership scenario is presented, with contributors providing comments and recommendations. A female executive ponders whether to assert a point of view on a new venture. Both experts agree that after providing careful analysis of pros and cons, the executive should come to a well-informed conclusion. **Availability:** Online; PDF.

28620 ■ *"HBR Case Study: When the Longtime Star Fades" in Harvard Business Review (Vol. 88, September 2010, No. 9, pp. 117)*

Pub: Harvard Business Publishing
Contact: Diane Belcher, Managing Director

Ed: Jimmy Guterman. **Price:** $8.95, PDF. **Description:** A fictitious aging employee scenario is presented, with contributors offering advice. The scenario focuses on an older employee's match with a rapidly changing industry; suggestions include consolidating a niche business around the employee, and also engaging the older employee in solving the productivity issue. **Availability:** Online; PDF.

28621 ■ *"A Heart for Software; Led by Its Upbeat CEO, Menlo Spreads Joy of Technology" in Crain's Detroit Business (Vol. 30, October 13, 2014, No. 41, pp. 1)*

Pub: Crain Communications Inc.
Contact: Barry Asin, President

Description: Profile of Rich Sheridan, one of the most prominent names in IT in Ann Arbor, Michigan. Sheridan believes in common-sense solutions and manages his workers to be empowered employees to come up with their own solutions to software coding issues, and he is a consummate salesman and marketer. He runs his company so it goes beyond understanding what the user needs, and managing a great team, to being the front man selling his goods and services. **Availability:** Print; Online.

28622 ■ *"Heavy Duty: The Case Against Packing Lightly" in Crain's Chicago Business (Vol. 31, April 21, 2008, No. 16, pp. 29)*

Pub: Crain Communications Inc.
Contact: Barry Asin, President

Ed: Sarah A. Klein. **Description:** Penelope Biggs, a Northern Trust executive who manages sales teams in North America, Europe and Asia gives advice on traveling abroad for business including time management skills, handling time-zone hops and avoiding jet-lag. **Availability:** Online.

28623 ■ *"Hennelly Aims to Increase Building Work in Great Lakes Region for Ryan Cos." in Crain's Chicago Business (Vol. 34, May 23, 2011, No. 21, pp. 6)*

Pub: Crain Communications Inc.
Contact: Barry Asin, President

Ed: Eddie Baeb. **Description:** Profile of Tim Hennelly, who is working to make Ryan Company known as a pure builder rather than a developer-builder. **Availability:** Print; Online.

28624 ■ *"Henry Mintzberg: Still the Zealous Skeptic and Scold" in Strategy and Leadership (Vol. 39, March-April 2011, No. 2, pp. 4)*

Pub: Emerald Group Publishing Limited
Contact: Erika Valenti, President

Ed: Robert J. Allio. **Description:** Henry Mintzberg, professor at the McGill University in Montreal, Canada, shares his thoughts on issues such as inappropriate methods in management education and on trends in leadership and management. Mintzberg believes that US businesses are facing serious management and leadership challenges. **Availability:** Download; Online.

28625 ■ *"The Hidden Advantages of Quiet Bosses" in Harvard Business Review (Vol. 88, December 2010, No. 12, pp. 28)*

Pub: Harvard Business Publishing
Contact: Diane Belcher, Managing Director

Ed: Adam M. Grant, Francesca Gino, David A. Hofmann. **Price:** $6, PDF. **Description:** Research on organizations behavior indicates that, while extroverts most often become managers, introvert managers paired with proactive employees make a highly efficient and effective combination. **Availability:** Online; PDF.

28626 ■ *"High Energy: Gaurdie Banister Joins Aera As President and CEO" in Black Enterprise (Vol. 38, July 2008, No. 12, pp. 30)*

Pub: Earl G. Graves Ltd.
Contact: Earl Graves, Jr., President

Ed: Brenda Porter. **Description:** Gaurdie Banister Jr. has been appointed president and CEO of Aera Energy L.L.C., becoming one of the first African Americans in the nation to run a major energy corporation. His plans for the firm include utilizing new, sophisticated technologies in order to unlock the 3-1/2 billion barrels of resources the company has on their books in a safe and environmentally friendly way. He also hopes to increase production and maintain cost leadership.

28627 ■ *Hiring & Retaining Great Security Officers*

Ed: David Mathena. **Released:** December 25, 2022. **Price:** $14.95, e-book. **Description:** This guide from a former security management professional will help you not only hire the best people for security, but give you tips on retaining their services. **Availability:** E-book.

28628 ■ *"His Brother's Keeper: A Mentor Learns the True Meaning of Leadership" in Black Enterprise (Vol. 37, December 2006, No. 5, pp. 69)*

Pub: Earl G. Graves Ltd.
Contact: Earl Graves, Jr., President

Ed: Laura Egodigwe. **Description:** Interview with Keith R. Wyche of Pitney Bowes Management Services, which discusses the relationship between a mentor and mentee as well as sponsorship. **Availability:** Online.

28629 ■ *"Host"*

Pub: Solutions Business Publishing

Released: April 13, 2010. **Price:** $16.99, paperback; $19.98, audiobook CD; $19.98, audiobook downloadable; $7.99, e-book; $9.99, mass market; $10, mass market; $42.99, paperback large print; $25.99, hardcover. **Description:** Great engagement is the key to any successful business leadership. Host leadership involves six new roles in employee engagement: adopt the four positions for a Host Leader; understand how to step into and out of the six new roles of engagement; achieve greater agility, flexibility, and responsiveness; become a leader with a highly tuned sense of relationship building and engagement. **Availability:** CD-ROM; E-book; Print.

28630 ■ *"How Anger Poisons Decision Making" in Harvard Business Review (Vol. 88, September 2010, No. 9, pp. 26)*

Pub: Harvard Business Publishing
Contact: Diane Belcher, Managing Director

Ed: Jennifer S. Lerner, Katherine Shonk. **Price:** $6, PDF. **Description:** Importance of accountability in mitigating the negative effects of anger on the decision making process is stressed. **Availability:** Online; PDF.

28631 ■ *"How Employees' Strengths Make Your Company Stronger; Employees Who Use Their Strengths Are More Engaged, Perform Better, Are Less Likely To Leave -- and Boost Your Bottom Line" in Gallup Business Journal (February 20, 2014)*
Pub: Gallup, Inc.
Contact: Jon Clifton, Chief Executive Officer

Description: The best way for organizations to maximize their workers' strengths is through their managers. When staff members know and use their strongest skills, they are more engaged and will perform better, have a higher sense of well being, are less likely to seek employment elsewhere, while increasing the firm's bottom line. **Availability:** Online.

28632 ■ *"How to Get a Workplace Wellness Program for Your Office" in Entrepreneurs (June 2014)*
Pub: Entrepreneur Media Inc.
Contact: Dan Bova, Director
E-mail: dbova@entrepreneur.com

Description: Workplace wellness programs can be started by checking with insurers who may provide program and activity suggestions promotional materials or other resources. Teaming up with others is encouraged. For instance, employees from various departments or nearby companies can get flu shots or blood pressure screening. Management should also get involved in these programs, because it will then be known among employees that wellness is taken seriously. It is also important that workplace wellness programs are kept safe and legally sound. **Availability:** Online.

28633 ■ *"How Great Leaders Think: The Art of Reframing"*
Pub: Jossey-Bass

Released: July 01, 2014. **Price:** $30, hardcover. **Description:** More complex thinking is the key to better leadership. A guide to help leaders understand four major aspects of organizational life: structure, people, politics, and culture is given. The book's lessons include: how to use structural tools to organize teams and organizations for better results, how to build motivation and morale by aligning organizations and people, how to map the terrain and build a power base to navigate the political dynamics of organizations, and how to develop a leadership story that shapes culture, provides direction, and inspires commitment to excellence. **Availability:** E-book; Print.

28634 ■ *"How Has Cincinnati's City Golf Privatization Played?" in Business Courier (Vol. 27, September 10, 2010, No. 19, pp. 1)*
Pub: Business Courier

Ed: Dan Monk. **Description:** It was reported that private contractors are getting more revenue from fewer golfers on city-owned courses in Cincinnati, Ohio. In 1998, the city handed over seven municipal courses to private management. However, some believe that the city has escalated a price war among the region's golf courses. **Availability:** Print; Online.

28635 ■ *"How to Heal a Broken Legg" in Barron's (Vol. 92, September 17, 2012, No. 38, pp. 18)*
Description: Legg Mason is looking for a new chief executive officer after Mark Fetting announced his resignation effective October 1, 2012. Fetting is credited with saving the company by reducing operating expenses, but had a tense relationship with the firm's affiliates. The company has limited options in finding a replacement and undertaking reorganization. **Availability:** Online.

28636 ■ *"How Healthcare Managers Can Improve Outcomes and Patient Care; They Can Start With These Five Steps for Turning their Organization's Employee Engagement Results Into Clinical Improvements" in Gallup Business Journal (August 7, 2014)*
Pub: Gallup, Inc.
Contact: Jon Clifton, Chief Executive Officer

Description: Health care managers can improve outcomes and patient care by following the five steps outlined in this article. **Availability:** Print; Online.

28637 ■ *"How Hierarchy Can Hurt Strategy Execution" in Harvard Business Review (Vol. 88, July-August 2010, No. 7-8, pp. 74)*
Pub: Harvard Business Publishing
Contact: Diane Belcher, Managing Director

Price: $8.95, PDF. **Description:** A series of charts illustrate Harvard Business Review's Advisory Council survey results regarding perceptions of strategy development and execution identifying obstacles and key factors affecting implementation. **Availability:** Online; PDF.

28638 ■ *"How I Did It: Xerox's Former CEO On Why Succession Shouldn't Be a Horse Race" in Harvard Business Review (Vol. 88, October 2010, No. 10, pp. 47)*
Pub: Harvard Business Publishing
Contact: Diane Belcher, Managing Director

Ed: Anne Mulcahy. **Price:** $8.95, PDF. **Description:** The importance of beginning talks between chief executive officers and boards of directors as early as possible to ensure a smooth transition is stressed. This can also prevent turning successions into competitions, with the resultant loss of talent when other candidates 'lose'. **Availability:** Online; PDF.

28639 ■ *"How Investors React When Women Join Boards" in Harvard Business Review (Vol. 88, July-August 2010, No. 7-8, pp. 24)*
Pub: Harvard Business Publishing
Contact: Diane Belcher, Managing Director

Ed: Andrew O'Connell. **Price:** $6, PDF. **Description:** Research reveals a cognitive bias in blockholders regarding the presence of women on boards of directors despite evidence showing that diversity improves results. **Availability:** Online; PDF.

28640 ■ *How to Make Money with Social Media: An Insider's Guide to Using New and Emerging Media to Grow Your Business*

Ed: Jamie Turner, Reshma Shah, PhD. **Released:** 2nd edition. **Description:** Marketers, executives, entrepreneurs are shown more effective ways to utilize Internet social media to make money. This guide brings together both practical strategies and proven execution techniques for driving maximum value from social media marketing. **Availability:** E-book; Print.

28641 ■ *"How Managers Become Leaders: The Seven Seismic Shifts of Perspective and Responsibility" in Harvard Business Review (Vol. 90, June 2012, No. 6, pp. 64)*
Pub: Harvard Business Review Press
Contact: Moderna V. Pfizer, Contact

Ed: Michael D. Watkins. **Description:** The seven shifts are: from specialist to generalist, from analyst to integrator, from tactician to strategist, from bricklayer to architect, from problem solver to agenda setter, from warrior to diplomat, and from supporting cast to lead role. The specific characteristics of each transition are described.

28642 ■ *"How Many Direct Reports? Senior Leaders, Always Pressed For Time, Are Nonetheless Broadening Their Span of Control" in Harvard Business Review (Vol. 90, April 2012, No. 4, pp. 112)*
Pub: Harvard Business Review Press
Contact: Moderna V. Pfizer, Contact

Ed: Gary L. Neilson, Julie M. Wulf. **Price:** $8.95, hardcover. **Description:** A rise in market and geographical complexities has driven an expansion of chief executive officer control during the past 20 years. New executive development options enable CEOs to cross-collaborate, and functional leaders make up 80 percent of new positions reporting to the CEO. **Availability:** PDF; Online.

28643 ■ *"How To Earn Loyalty From Millenials" in Birmingham Business Journal (Vol. 31, February 28, 2014, No. 9, pp. 16)*
Pub: American City Business Journals, Inc.
Contact: Mike Olivieri, Executive Vice President

Released: Weekly. **Price:** $4, Introductory 4-week offer(Digital only). **Description:** Advice for earning loyalty from millennial employees is offered. Management need to create an environment where mistakes are openly admitted and employees should be encouraged to give back to causes that matter most to them. **Availability:** Print; Online.

28644 ■ *"How To Help New Leaders Succeed" in Birmingham Business Journal (Vol. 31, January 31, 2014, No. 5, pp. 9)*
Pub: American City Business Journals, Inc.
Contact: Mike Olivieri, Executive Vice President

Description: Advice on how new managers could attain successful careers is presented. Managers should know how their department's function fits into the organization. Reading about managerial leadership is also encouraged. **Availability:** Print; Online.

28645 ■ *"How To Identify Leadership Potential: Development and Testing of a Consensus Model" in Human Resource Management (Vol. 51,May- June 2012, No. 3, pp. 361-385)*
Pub: John Wiley & Sons, Inc.
Contact: Christina Van Tassell, Executive Vice President Chief Financial Officer

Ed: Nicky Dries, Roland Pepermans. **Released:** May 25, 2012. **Description:** A consensus model for the identification of leadership potential is proposed. This model is made up of four quadrants: analytical skills, learning agility, drive and emergent leadership.

28646 ■ *"How To Manage Your Chain of Command" in Birmingham Business Journal (Vol. 31, June 27, 2014, No. 26, pp. 12)*
Pub: American City Business Journals, Inc.
Contact: Mike Olivieri, Executive Vice President

Description: Chain of command in a small business functions through junior leaders who pass information and instructions from the CEO to subordinates. The chain of command is used more effectively when CEOs work through those leaders and not around them. **Availability:** Print; Online.

28647 ■ *"How To Win In Emerging Markets: Lessons From Japan" in Harvard Business Review (Vol. 90, May 2012, No. 5, pp. 126)*
Pub: Harvard Business Review Press
Contact: Moderna V. Pfizer, Contact

Ed: Shigeki Ichii, Susumu Hattori, David Michael. **Price:** $8.95. **Description:** Corporate Japan's four challenges in engaging emerging markets are an aversion to mergers and acquisitions, an aversion to low- and middle-end segments, lack of organizational or financial commitments to emerging markets, and a shortage of executive talent placed in emerging markets. By addressing these weaknesses, Japan can succeed in global expansion. **Availability:** Online; PDF.

28648 ■ *"How to Turn Employee Conflict Into a Positive, Productive Force" in HR Specialist (Vol. 8, September 2010, No. 9, pp. 6)*
Pub: Capitol Information Group Inc.
Contact: Allie Ash, Chief Executive Officer

Description: Ways to help manage a team of workers are presented, focusing on ways to avoid conflict within the group are discussed. **Availability:** Print; Online; PDF.

28649 ■ *How to Write a Great Business Plan for Your Small Business in 60 Minutes or Less*
Pub: Atlantic Publishing Co.
Contact: Dr. Heather L. Johnson, Contact

Ed: Sharon L. Fullen. **Released:** 2013. **Description:** A good business plan outlines goals and works as a company's resume to obtain funding, credit from suppliers, management of the operations and finances, promotion and marketing, and more. **Availability:** CD-ROM; E-book; Print; Online.

28650 ■ "How Yamana CEO First Struck Gold With Desert Sun" in Globe & Mail (February 27, 2006, pp. B3)

Ed: Andrew Willis. **Description:** The role of chief executive officer Peter Marronne of Yamana Gold Inc. in the acquisition of Desert Sun Mining Corp. is discussed. **Availability:** Online.

28651 ■ "How Young Professionals Can Position Themselves for Board Membership: 4 Quick Tips to Get You Started" in Black Enterprise (Vol. 45, July-August 2014, No. 1, pp. 46)

Pub: Earl G. Graves Ltd.

Contact: Earl Graves, Jr., President

Description: Four tips to help young professionals secure a position on a company's board focus on: starting with nonprofits, focus on key areas of interest, continue to growth through networking and training programs, and to gain global experience.

28652 ■ "How Your Team Can Work Four Days a Week and Get More Done" in Small Business Trends (November 8, 2021)

URL(s): smallbiztrends.com/2021/11/joe-sanok-four -day-work-week.html

Released: November 08, 2021. **Description:** There has been a shift in the way people want to work and who they will work for. One of the big ideas to emerge is the four-day workweek, but how will that impact your business workflow? An interview with Joe Sanok, author and podcaster, discusses this new concept. **Availability:** Online.

28653 ■ "Huberman Failing to Keep CTA on Track" in Crain's Chicago Business (Vol. 31, April 21, 2008, No. 16, pp. 22)

Pub: Crain Communications Inc.

Contact: Barry Asin, President

Description: Discusses the deplorable service of CTA, the Chicago Transit Authority, as well as CTA President Ron Huberman who, up until last week had riders hoping he had the management skills necessary to fix the system's problems; Tuesday's event left hundreds of riders trapped for hours and thousands standing on train platforms along the Blue Line waiting for trains that never came. **Availability:** Online.

28654 ■ "Human Resource Management: Challenges for Graduate Education" in Business Horizons (Vol. 51, March-April 2008, No. 2, pp. 151)

Pub: Elsevier Advanced Technology Publications

Ed: James C. Wimbush. **Description:** Human resource management education at the master's and doctoral degree levels is discussed. There is an ever-increasing need to produce human resource managers who understand the value of human resource management as a strategic business contributor. **Availability:** PDF; Online.

28655 ■ I Can't Believe I Get Paid to Do This

Ed: Stacey Mayo. **Description:** This book is targeted to anyone unhappy in their current position. It is designed to help everyone feel good about their job.

28656 ■ "IBM's Best-Kept Secret: It's Huge in Software Too" in Canadian Business (Vol. 79, September 25, 2006, No. 19, pp. 19)

Description: The contribution of IBM vice-president Steve Mills in company's development is discussed. **Availability:** Print; Online.

28657 ■ "In the Hot Finance Jobs, Women Are Still Shut Out" in Harvard Business Review (Vol. 90, July-August 2012, No. 7-8, pp. 30)

Pub: Harvard Business Review Press

Contact: Moderna V. Pfizer, Contact

Ed: Nori Gerardo Lietz. **Price:** $6, PDF and hardcover black and white. **Description:** Although women constitute a significant proportion of business school

graduates, the percentage of senior investment professionals who are female remain in a single-digit figure. Active effort will be needed to change corporate culture and industry awareness to raise this figure. **Availability:** Print; PDF; Online.

28658 ■ "The Incentive Bubble: Outsourcing Pay Decisions To Financial Markets Has Skewed Compensation and, With It, American Capitalism" in Harvard Business Review (Vol. 90, March 2012, No. 3, pp. 124)

Pub: Harvard Business Review Press

Contact: Moderna V. Pfizer, Contact

Ed: Mihir A. Desai. **Price:** $8.95. **Description:** Basing incentive contracts and executive compensation on financial markets actually rewards luck rather than performance, and can promote dangerous risk taking. This has led to America's two main crises of capitalism: growing income inequality and governance failures. Boards of directors must focus on performance rather than stocks, and endowments and foundations must focus on incentives for long-term growth. **Availability:** Online; PDF.

28659 ■ "Information Technology Changes Roles, Highlights Hiring Needs" in South Florida Business Journal (Vol. 34, February 14, 2014, No. 30, pp. 3)

Pub: American City Business Journals, Inc.

Contact: Mike Olivieri, Executive Vice President

Released: Weekly. **Price:** $8, Introductory 4-week offer(Digital & Print). **Description:** Results of the Steven Douglas Associates survey of 218 senior and mid-level information technology executives in South Florida are presented. About 75 percent of the respondents cited cloud services, mobile technologies, big data and enterprise reporting planning as having the most profound impact on their roles. The challenges they face with the expected hiring growth are also examined. **Availability:** Print; Online.

28660 ■ "The Innovator's Solution: Creating and Sustaining Successful Growth"

Pub: Harvard Business Review Press

Contact: Moderna V. Pfizer, Contact

Released: November 19, 2013. **Price:** $35, Hardcover/Hardcopy. **Description:** Even in today's hyper-accelerated business environment any small company can transform their business. Advice on business decisions crucial to achieving truly disruptive growth and purpose guidelines for developing their own disruptive growth engine is given. The forces that cause managers to make bad decisions as they plan new ideas for their company are identified and new frameworks to help develop the right conditions, at the right time, for a disruption to succeed. Managers and business leaders responsible for innovation and growth will benefit their business and their teams with this information. **Availability:** E-book; Print.

28661 ■ "Investment Funds: Friends with Money" in Canadian Business (Vol. 81, May 22, 2008, No. 9, pp. 22)

Pub: Rogers Media Inc.

Contact: Neil Spivak, Chief Executive Officer

Ed: Jeff Stanford. **Description:** Two of the most well connected managers in Canadian capital markets Rob Farquharson and Brian Gibson will launch Panoply Capital Asset Management in June. The investment management company aims to raise a billion dollars from institutions and high-net worth individuals. **Availability:** Print; Online.

28662 ■ "iRobot Appoints Former BAE Systems Vice President, Frank Wilson to Lead Defense & Security Business Unit" in News Bites US (August 9, 2012)

Description: Frank Wilson will serve as senior vice president and general manager of iRobot's Defense & Security business unit. He will focus on strategic business development and product development in order for the firm to meet military, civil defense, and security needs. Tim Trainer, previous acting interim general manager, will remain vice president of programs. **Availability:** Print; Online.

28663 ■ "Is Business Ethics Getting Better? A Historical Perspective" in Business Ethics Quarterly (Vol. 21, April 2011, No. 2, pp. 335)

Ed: Joanne B. Ciulla. **Released:** Volume 21, Issue 2. **Description:** The question 'Is Business Ethics Getting Better?' as a heuristic for discussing the importance of history in understanding business and ethics is answered. The article uses a number of examples to illustrate how the same ethical problems in business have been around for a long time. It describes early attempts at the Harvard School of Business to use business history as a means of teaching students about moral and social values. In the end, the author suggests that history may be another way to teach ethics, enrich business ethics courses, and develop the perspective and vision in future business leaders. **Availability:** Online.

28664 ■ "Is Your Anxiety Affecting Your Leadership?" in Small Business Trends (December 8, 2022)

URL(s): smallbiztrends.com/2022/12/managing-your -anxiety.html

Ed: Larry Alton. **Released:** December 08, 2022. **Description:** Discusses anxiety management options for you to take if you notice your anxiety is getting in the way of running your small business or managing your team. **Availability:** Online.

28665 ■ "It's Good To Be a CEO: Top Execs Pull Millions In Raises for 2013" in Atlanta Business Chronicle (June 20, 2014, pp. 22A)

Pub: American City Business Journals, Inc.

Contact: Mike Olivieri, Executive Vice President

Description: Discussion regarding the highest paid CEOs in Georgia in 2013, with an average of 8.8 percent increase from 2012. The largest increase went to Jeffrey C. Sprecher, chairman and CEO of Intercontinental Exchange Inc., followed by John F. Brock, chairman and CEO of Coca-Cola Enterprises Inc. **Availability:** Print; Online.

28666 ■ "It's Not the How or the What but the Who: Succeed by Surrounding Yourself with the Best"

Pub: Harvard Business Review Press

Contact: Moderna V. Pfizer, Contact

Released: June 03, 2014. **Price:** $32, Hardcover/Hardcopy. **Description:** Surrounding yourself with the best matters in every aspect of life and can mean the difference between success and failure. The author draws upon years of experience in global executive search and talent development, as well as the latest management and psychology research, to help improve the choices management makes about employees and mentors, business partners and friends, top corporate leaders and elected officials. **Availability:** E-book; Print.

28667 ■ It's Not Just Who You Know: Transform Your Life (and Your Organization) by Turning Colleagues and Contacts into Lasting Relationships

Released: August 10, 2010. **Price:** $11.99, hardcover; $29.57, paperback. **Description:** Tommy Spaulding teaches the reader how to reach out to others in order to create lasting relationships that go beyond superficial contacts. **Availability:** audiobook; E-book; Print.

28668 ■ "Jab, Jab, Jab, Right Hook: How to Tell Your Story in a Noisy Social World"

Pub: Harper Business

Contact: Hollis Heimbouch, Senior Vice President Publisher

Released: November 26, 2013. **Price:** $23.99, hardcover. **Description:** Author and social media expert shares advice on ways to connect with customers and beat the competition. Social media strategies for marketers and managers need to convert Internet traffic to sales. Communication is the key to online sales that are adapted to high quality social media platforms and mobile devices. **Availability:** E-book; Print.

28669 ■ *"J.C. Penney Head Shops for Shares"* in *Barron's* (Vol. 88, July 7, 2008, No. 27, pp. 29)

Pub: Dow Jones & Company Inc.

Contact: Almar Latour, Chief Executive Officer

Ed: Teresa Rivas. **Description:** Myron Ullman III, chairman and chief executive officer of J.C. Penney, purchased $1 million worth of shares of the company. He now owns 393,140 shares of the company and an additional 1,282 on his 401(k) plan. **Availability:** Online.

28670 ■ *"Joanna Crangle Named MBJ Publisher"* in *Sacramento Business Journal* (Vol. 31, March 28, 2014, No. 5)

Pub: American City Business Journals, Inc.

Contact: Mike Olivieri, Executive Vice President

Released: Weekly. **Description:** Joanna Crangle has been appointed the new publisher of the 'Memphis Business Journal'. She will succeed Stuart Chamblin, who is retiring as of March 31, 2014. Crangle has previously served as the newspaper's circulation director and advertising director. **Availability:** Print; Online.

28671 ■ *"Job Reviews: Annual Assessments Still the Norm"* in *HR Specialist* (Vol. 8, September 2010, No. 9, pp. 1)

Description: An OfficeTeam survey of 500 HR professionals asked how their organizations conduct formal performance appraisals. Responses to the questions are examined.

28672 ■ *"Jobs Data Show A Slow Leak"* in *Barron's* (Vol. 88, July 7, 2008, No. 27, pp. 34)

Pub: Dow Jones & Company Inc.

Contact: Almar Latour, Chief Executive Officer

Ed: Gene Epstein. **Description:** In June 2008, the United States manufacturing sector showed an expansion, with the purchasing managers' index rising to 50.2 from 49.6; the unemployment rate in the US, which stayed steady at 5.5 percent in June 2008 is also discussed. Statistical data included. **Availability:** Online.

28673 ■ *"Joe Wikert, General Manager, O'Reilly Technology Exchange"* in *Information Today* (Vol. 26, February 2009, No. 2, pp. 21)

Description: Joe Wikert, general manager of O'Reilly Technology Exchange discusses his plans to develop a free content model that will evolve with future needs. O'Reilly's major competitor is Google. Wikert plans to expand the firm's publishing program to include print, online, and in-person products and services. **Availability:** Online.

28674 ■ *"Just Be Nice: Providing Good Customer Service"* in *Canadian Business* (Vol. 79, October 9, 2006, No. 20, pp. 141)

Pub: Rogers Media Inc.

Contact: Neil Spivak, Chief Executive Officer

Ed: Joe Castaldo. **Description:** The customer relationship management strategies on customer retention and satisfaction adopted by WestJet are discussed. **Availability:** Print; Online.

28675 ■ *"Justice In Self-Managing Teams: the Role of Social Networks In the Emergence of Procedural Justice Climates"* in *Academy of Management Journal* (Vol. 55, June 1, 2012, No. 3, pp. 685)

Pub: Academy of Management

Contact: Sharon Alvarez, President

Ed: Quinetta M. Roberson, Ian O. Williamson. **Description:** The effect of social network content and structure on organizational justice in self-managing teams is studied using data from 79 project teams. Findings show that team instrumental network density has positive impact on procedural justice climate strength. Low team functional background diversity was also found to strengthen this relationship. **Availability:** Electronic publishing; Download; PDF; Online.

28676 ■ *"Keeping Railcars 'Busy At All Times' At TTX"* in *Crain's Chicago Business* (Vol. 31, April 28, 2008, No. 17, pp. 6)

Pub: Crain Communications Inc.

Contact: Barry Asin, President

Ed: Bob Tita. **Description:** Profile of the president of Chicago railcar pool operator TTX Co. and his business plan for the company which includes improving fleet management and car purchasing through better use of data on railroad demand. **Availability:** Online.

28677 ■ *"Keith Crain: Business Must Stand Up And Be Counted"* in *Crain's Detroit Business* (Vol. 24, October 6, 2008, No. 40, pp. 6)

Pub: Crain Communications Inc.

Contact: Barry Asin, President

Description: Discusses the challenges that the new mayor of Detroit faces concerning business, the state of the economy and the exceptionally tight budget the city is running on, which includes a lot of red ink. It is very likely that the city is going to see tax revenues fall substantially in the next few months and business leaders may find it in their favor to lend their support to the new mayor as well as provide him with the executive talent necessary to overcome some of these crucial issues. **Availability:** Online.

28678 ■ *"Kinetico Exec Going Global to Increase Growth Flow"* in *Crain's Cleveland Business* (Vol. 28, October 1, 2007, No. 39, pp. 5)

Pub: Crain Communications Inc.

Contact: K. C. Crain, President

Ed: David Bennett. **Description:** Shamus Hurley, the new CEO and president of Kinetico Inc., a manufacturer of water filtering and softening equipment for residential, commercial and municipal use, plans to expand the company to target markets overseas. **Availability:** Online.

28679 ■ *"Kraft Taps Cheese Head; Jordan Charged With Fixing Foodmaker's Signature Product"* in *Crain's Chicago Business* (April 14, 2008)

Pub: Crain Communications Inc.

Contact: Barry Asin, President

Ed: David Sterrett. **Description:** Kraft Foods Inc. has assigned Rhonda Jordan, a company veteran, to take charge of the cheese and dairy division which has been losing market shares to cheaper store-brand cheese among cost-sensitive shoppers as Kraft and its competitors raise prices to offset soaring dairy costs. **Availability:** Online.

28680 ■ *"Labor and Management: Working Together for a Stable Future"* in *Alaska Business Monthly* (Vol. 27, October 2011, No. 10, pp. 130)

Pub: Alaska Business Publishing Company Inc.

Contact: Charles Bell, Vice President, Sales and Marketing

E-mail: cbell@akbizmag.com

Ed: Nicole A. Bonham Colby. **Description:** Alaska unions and employers are working to ensure a consistent flow of skilled Alaska workers as current the current workforce reaches retirement age. **Availability:** Print; Online.

28681 ■ *"Laced Up and Ready to Run"* in *Barron's* (Vol. 89, July 6, 2009, No. 27, pp. 12)

Pub: Dow Jones & Company Inc.

Contact: Almar Latour, Chief Executive Officer

Ed: Christopher C. Williams. **Description:** Shares of Foot Locker could raise from $10 to about $15 a share with the improvement of the economy. The company has benefited from prudent management and merchandising as well as better cost cutting, allowing it to better survive in a recession. **Availability:** Online.

28682 ■ *"LaSalle St. Firms Cherry-Pick Talent As Wall St. Tanks"* in *Crain's Chicago Business* (Vol. 31, November 17, 2008, No. 46)

Pub: Crain Communications Inc.

Contact: Barry Asin, President

Ed: H. Lee Murphy. **Description:** Many local businesses are taking advantage of the lay offs that many major Wall Street firms are undergoing in their workforces; these companies see the opportunity to woo talent and expand their staff with quality executives. **Availability:** Online.

28683 ■ *"The Last Word Dirty Work Required"* in *Workforce Management* (Vol. 88, November 16, 2009, No. 12, pp. 34)

Pub: Crain Communications Inc.

Contact: Barry Asin, President

Ed: John Hollon. **Description:** Due to salary freezes, pay cuts, layoffs, buyouts and a number of other stress factors brought about by the recession, employee engagement has been difficult to maintain by managers. **Availability:** Online.

28684 ■ *"Laurent Beaudoin Interview: Deja Vu"* in *Canadian Business* (Vol. 81, July 22, 2008, No. 12-13, pp. 38)

Pub: Rogers Media Inc.

Contact: Neil Spivak, Chief Executive Officer

Ed: Joe Castaldo. **Description:** Laurent Beaudoin has retired as chief executive officer for Bombardier Inc.'s, a manufacturer of regional and business aircraft, but kept a role in the firm as a non-executive chairman. Beaudoin first resigned from the company in 1999, but had to return in 2004 to address challenging situations faced by the company. Beaudoin's views on management and the company are presented. **Availability:** Online.

28685 ■ *"Lead Like It Matters...Because It Does: Practical Leadership Tools to Inspire and Engage Your People and Create Great Results"*

Released: First Edition. **Price:** $33; $33. **Description:** The Ripple Effect method for increasing employee engagement, reducing turnover, and driving overall business success will help any manager or entreprenour to load hio company. Important practices like eliminating wasted meetings, addressing conflict, and aligning decisions with business needs are addressed. **Availability:** E-book; Print; Online.

28686 ■ *"Leaders: 11 Tips to Consider When a Key Employee Quits"* in *Small Business Trends* (March 21, 2022)

URL(s): smallbiztrends.com/2022/11/things-to-do-when-a-key-employee-quits.html

Released: November 27, 2022. **Description:** A guide on how to handle the aftermath of your key employee quitting. **Availability:** Online.

28687 ■ *"The Leaders Who Make M&A Work"* in *Harvard Business Review* (Vol. 92, September 2014, No. 9, pp. 28)

Pub: Harvard Business Publishing

Contact: Diane Belcher, Managing Director

Price: $6. **Description:** Leadership capabilities for both acquiring and targeting firms are predictors of merger and acquisition success. Capabilities for acquirers include motivation, influence, adaptability, and integrity; those for targets include providing direction. **Availability:** Online; PDF.

28688 ■ *The Leadership Challenge: How to Make Extraordinary Things Happen in Organizations*

Pub: Jossey-Bass

Ed: James M. Kouzes, Barry Z. Posner. **Released:** 7th edition. **Price:** $34.95, hardcover; $34.95, hardcover. **Description:** According to research by the authors, people can make extraordinary things happen by liberating the leader within everyone around them. This handbook gives practical tips to aspire leaders in retail, manufacturing, government, community, church and school settings. **Availability:** E-book; Print.

28689 ■ *"Leadership Development In the Age of the Algorithm"* in (Vol. 90, June 2012, No. 6, pp. 86)

Pub: Harvard Business Review Press

Contact: Moderna V. Pfizer, Contact

Ed: Marcus Buckingham. **Price:** $8.95. **Description:** Guidelines to tailor leadership training to specific individuals include assessing the leadership type for each person, identifying the top leaders for each type, creating practices that are effective for each type, delivering those practices to others, and integrate user feedback to fine-tune the process. **Availability:** Online; PDF.

28690 ■ *"The Leadership Equation: 10 Practices That Build Trust, Spark Innovation, and Create High-Performing Organizations"*
Pub: Greenleaf Book Group Press
Contact: Tanya Hall, Chief Executive Officer

Released: September 30, 2014. **Price:** $18.95, U.S., paperback. **Description:** Entrepreneur and business consultant draws upon his work with corporations, government agencies, and nonprofit organizations and their human resource departments to explain the workings of high-performing organizations with his equation: Trust + Spark = Leadership Culture. He describes the ten more important practices for building trust and spark that improves team performance, the business unit, and the entire organization. **Availability:** Print.

28691 ■ *"Leadership: Growing Pains"* in *Canadian Business (Vol. 80, November 19, 2007, No. 23, pp. 41)*
Pub: Rogers Media Inc.
Contact: Neil Spivak, Chief Executive Officer

Ed: Lauren McKeon. **Description:** Employee promotions must be done with consideration to the effects of ill-prepared leadership, which include high worker turnover, low morale, and ineffective management. Organizations must handle the transition period involved in promotion by setting clear expectations, providing guidelines on approaching different situations, and by welcoming the promoted employees; impacts are further analyzed. **Availability:** Online.

28692 ■ *"Leadership Is a Conversation: How To Improve Employee Engagement and Alignment In Today's Flatter, More Networked Organizations"* in *Harvard Business Review (Vol. 90, June 2012, No. 6, pp. 76)*
Pub: Harvard Business Review Press
Contact: Moderna V. Pfizer, Contact

Ed: Boris Groysberg, Michael Slind. **Description:** A two-way flow of communication is essential in promoting and maintaining employee motivation. Key points are establishing intimacy through gaining trust, interactivity via dialogue, inclusion by expanding employee roles, and intentionality through establishing an agenda.

28693 ■ *"Leading the Way"* in *Business Strategy Review (Vol. 23, Spring 2012, No. 1, pp. 10)*
Description: The ability to persevere in the face of what may seem impossible odds is the story of Ursula Burns, who began her career as an engineering intern at Xerox and rose to become CEO of the company in 2009. Burns talked with Pearl Doherty about her career at Xerox. **Availability:** Online.

28694 ■ *"Leading With Meaning: Beneficiary Contact, Prosocial Impact, and the Performance Effects of Transformational Leadership"* in *Academy of Management Journal (Vol. 55, April 1, 2012, No. 2, pp. 458)*
Pub: Academy of Management
Contact: Sharon Alvarez, President

Ed: Adam M. Grant. **Description:** Transformational leadership is shown to effectively motivate followers when they interact with the beneficiaries of their work. For instance, beneficiary contact boosted the effects on call center employees' sales and revenue with these findings being extended by a survey study with government employees. How perceived prosocial impact supports a moderated mediation model is discussed. **Availability:** Electronic publishing; Download; PDF; Online.

28695 ■ *"Legg Mason Compensation Committee Chair Defends CEO Fetting's Pay"* in *Baltimore Business Journal (Vol. 29, July 22, 2011, No. 11, pp. 1)*
Pub: Boston Business Journal
Contact: Carolyn M. Jones, President
E-mail: cmjones@bizjournals.com

Ed: Gary Haber. **Description:** Legg Mason Inc. CEO Mark R. Fetting has been awarded $5.9 million pay package and he expects to receive questions regarding it in the coming shareholders meeting. However, Baltimore, Maryland-based RKTL Associates chairman emeritus Harold R. Adams believes Fetting has done a tremendous job in bringing Legg's through a tough market. **Availability:** Print; Online.

28696 ■ *"Lessons from Turnaround Leaders"* in *Strategy and Leadership (Vol. 39, May-June 2011, No. 3, pp. 36-43)*
Pub: Emerald Group Publishing Limited
Contact: Erika Valenti, President

Ed: David P. Boyd. **Description:** A study analyzes the cases of some successful turnaround leaders to present a strategic model to help firms tackle challenges such as employee inertia, competition and slow organizational renewal. It describes a change model consisting of five major steps to be followed by firms with environmental uncertainty for the purpose. **Availability:** Download; Online.

28697 ■ *"Liespotting: Proven Techniques to Detect Deception"*
Pub: St. Martins Press/Macmillan

Ed: Pamela Meyer. **Released:** September 13, 2011. **Price:** $15.99, paperback; $25.99, hardcover. **Description:** Liespotting links three disciplines: facial recognition training, interrogation training, and a comprehensive survey of research in the field - into a specialized body of information developed specifically to help business leaders detect deception and get the information they need to successfully conduct their most important interactions and transactions. **Availability:** Paperback; E-book; Print.

28698 ■ *"Life's Work: Ben Bradlee"* in *Harvard Business Review (Vol. 88, September 2010, No. 9, pp. 128)*
Pub: Harvard Business Publishing
Contact: Diane Belcher, Managing Director

Ed: Alison Beard. **Price:** $8.95, PDF. **Description:** Newspaper publisher Ben Bradlee discusses factors that lead to success, including visible supervisors, enthusiasm, appropriate expansion, and the importance in truth in reporting. **Availability:** Online; PDF.

28699 ■ *"Life's Work: Oliver Sacks"* in *Harvard Business Review (Vol. 88, November 2010, No. 11, pp. 152)*
Pub: Harvard Business Publishing
Contact: Diane Belcher, Managing Director

Ed: Lisa Burrell. **Price:** $8.95, PDF. **Description:** Neurologist and author Oliver Sacks discusses whether different types of minds tend toward certain skills, physician-patient communication, and his own perspectives from being a patient himself. **Availability:** Online; PDF.

28700 ■ *"Linchpin: Are You Indispensable?"*
Pub: Portfolio
Contact: Adrian Zackheim, President

Ed: Seth Godin. **Released:** January 26, 2010. **Price:** $18, paperback; $26.95, hardcover; $9.99, e-book. **Description:** The best way to get what you're worth, according to the author, is to exert emotional labor, to be seen as indispensable, and to produce interactions that organizations and people care about. **Availability:** E-book; Print.

28701 ■ *"Live & Learn: Ian Delaney"* in *Canadian Business (Vol. 81, Summer 2008, No. 9, pp. 168)*
Pub: Rogers Media Inc.
Contact: Neil Spivak, Chief Executive Officer

Ed: Joe Castaldo. **Description:** Interview with Ian Delaney who is the executive chairman of chemical company Sherritt International Corp.; Delaney previ-

ously worked as chief executive for a holding company owned by Peter Munk. Details of his beliefs, profession and family life are discussed. **Availability:** Online.

28702 ■ *"Live and Learn: Penny Chapman"* in *Canadian Business (Vol. 79, July 17, 2006, No. 14-15, pp. 75)*
Pub: Rogers Media Inc.
Contact: Neil Spivak, Chief Executive Officer

Ed: Erin Pooley. **Description:** Interview with Penny Chapman, president of Chapman's Ice Cream, who speaks about her journey from rags to riches. **Availability:** Online.

28703 ■ *"Live & Learn: Thomas D'Aquino"* in *Canadian Business (Vol. 80, November 19, 2007, No. 23, pp. 92)*
Pub: Rogers Media Inc.
Contact: Neil Spivak, Chief Executive Officer

Ed: Calvin Leung. **Description:** Thomas D'Aquino is the CEO and president of the Canadian Council of Chief Executives since 1981. D'Aquino thinks he has the best job in Canada because he can change the way policies are made and the way people think. Details of his career as a lawyer and CEO and his views on Canada's economy are provided. **Availability:** Print; Online.

28704 ■ *"The Lords of Ideas"* in *Business Strategy Review (Vol. 21, Autumn 2010, No. 3, pp. 57)*
Ed: Stuart Crainer. **Released:** September 22, 2010. **Description:** True originators of modern strategy are profiled. **Availability:** Print; Electronic publishing; PDF; Online.

28705 ■ *"Lots More Mr. Nice Guy"* in *Canadian Business (Vol. 80, October 22, 2007, No. 21, pp. 58)*
Description: Galen Weston Jr., executive chairman of Loblaw and heir to the Weston family business, has his hands full running the company. Details of his turnaround strategies and ambitious plans to increase profitability of the business are discussed.

28706 ■ *"Macho Men"* in *Canadian Business (Vol. 81, November 10, 2008, No. 19, pp. 23)*
Description: Professors Robin Ely and Debra Meyerson found that oil rigs decreased accidents and increased productivity when they focused on improving safety and admitting errors rather than on a worker's individual strength. Professor Jennifer Berdahl shows there is pressure for men to be seen as masculine at work, which makes them avoid doing 'feminine' things such as parental leaves. **Availability:** Print; Online.

28707 ■ *"The Main Ingredient of Change"* in *Harvard Business Review (Vol. 92, September 2014, No. 9, pp. 36)*
Pub: Harvard Business Publishing
Contact: Diane Belcher, Managing Director

Price: $6. **Description:** Courage and leadership were key factors in driving organizational change at Campbell Soup Company. Leadership improved decision making processes, while courage gave the 145-year-old firm the impetus to expand the business and enter new markets. **Availability:** Online; PDF.

28708 ■ *Making Difficult Decisions: How to Be Decisive and Get the Business Done*
Pub: John Wiley & Sons, Inc.
Contact: Christina Van Tassell, Executive Vice President Chief Financial Officer

Ed: Peter Shaw. **Released:** February 28, 2010. **Price:** $29.95, paperback; $19.99, e-book. **Description:** Experience of others can help entrepreneurs and managers make difficult business decisions. The strategies set forth in this book have been used successfully in public, private and voluntary sectors. **Availability:** E-book; Print.

28709 ■ *"Management Matters with Mike Myatt: Are You Creating Growth in a Down Economy?"* in *Commercial Property News (March 17, 2008)*
Description: Senior executives are expected to create growth for their company regardless of recession,

economic slowdown, inflation, or tight credit and capital markets. **Availability:** PDF; Online.

28710 ■ *The Management of Small and Medium Enterprises*
Pub: Routledge, Taylor & Francis Group
Released: First edition. **Description:** Investigation into the underlying mechanisms and practices of management within small and medium enterprises is provided.

28711 ■ *"Managerial Rudeness: Bad Attitudes Can Demoralize Your Staff" in Black Enterprise (Vol. 37, January 2007, No. 6, pp. 58)*
Pub: Earl G. Graves Ltd.
Contact: Earl Graves, Jr., President
Ed: Chauntelle Folds. **Description:** Positive leadership in the managerial realm leads to a more productive workplace. Managers who are negative, hostile, arrogant, rude or fail to accept any responsibility for their own mistakes find that employees will not give their all on the job. **Availability:** Online.

28712 ■ *"Managerial Ties with Local Firms and Governments: an Analysis of Japanese Firms In China" in International Journal of Business and Emerging Markets (Vol. 4, July 11, 2012, No. 3, pp. 181)*
Pub: Inderscience Publishers
Ed: Naoki Ando, Daniel Z. Ding. **Description:** This study explores how managerial ties between foreign firms and local firms and those between foreign firms and local government officials affect the performance of firms operating in transition economies. Using survey data collected from Japanese firms operating in China, this study finds that managerial ties between foreign firms and local firms and local government officials are positively associated with the performance of Japanese firms in China. **Availability:** Print; PDF; Online.

28713 ■ *The Manager's Guide to Rewards: What You Need to Know to Get the Best of-and-from-Your Employees*
Availability: E-book.

28714 ■ *"Managers as Visionaries: a Skill That Can Be Learned" in Strategy and Leadership (Vol. 39, September-October 2011, No. 5, pp. 56-58)*
Pub: Emerald Group Publishing Limited
Contact: Erika Valenti, President
Ed: Stephen M. Millett. **Description:** A study uses research findings to examine whether visionary management can be learned. Results conclude that managers can learn visionary management through intuitive pattern recognition of trends and by using scenarios for anticipating and planning for likely future occurrences.

28715 ■ *Managing Economies, Trade and International Business*
Pub: Palgrave Macmillan
Released: 1st edition. **Price:** $89, e-book; $115, Hardcover; $110, softcover. **Description:** An in-depth look at the areas that affect and influence international business, exploring specific issues businesses face in terms of economic development, trade law, and international marketing and management. **Availability:** E-book; Print.

28716 ■ *"Managing the Facebookers; Business" in The Economist (Vol. 390, January 3, 2009, No. 8612, pp. 10)*
Pub: Economist Newspaper Ltd.
Contact: Lara Boro, Chief Executive Officer
Description: According to a report from PricewaterhouseCoopers, a business consultancy, workers from Generation Y, also known as the Net Generation, are more difficult to recruit and integrate into companies that practice traditional business acumen. 61 percent of chief executive managers say that they have trouble with younger employees who tend to be more narcissistic and more interested in personal fulfillment with a need for frequent feedback and an overprecise set of objectives on the path to promotion

which can be hard for managers who are used to a different relationship with their subordinates. Older bosses should prepare to make some concessions to their younger talent since some of the issues that make them happy include cheaper online ways to communicate and additional coaching, both of which are good for business. **Availability:** Online.

28717 ■ *Managing the Older Worker: How to Prepare for the New Organizational Order*
Pub: Harvard Business Press
Contact: Gabriela Allmi, Regional Manager
E-mail: gabriela.allmi@hbsp.harvard.edu
Ed: Peter Cappelli, Bill Novelli. **Description:** Your organization needs older workers more than ever: They transfer knowledge between generations, transmit your company's values to new hires, make excellent mentors for younger employees, and provide a 'just in time' workforce for special projects. **Availability:** Print; Audio.

28718 ■ *"Managing Risks: A New Framework: Smart Companies Match Their Approach to the Nature of the Threats They Face" in Harvard Business Review (Vol. 90, June 2012, No. 6, pp. 48)*
Pub: Harvard Business Review Press
Contact: Moderna V. Pfizer, Contact
Ed: Anette Mikes, Robert S. Kaplan. **Description:** The importance of strategic planning in effect risk management practices is stressed. Discussion includes preventable risks, strategy risks, and external risks and provides objectives, control models, staff functions, and the business-unit interrelationships of each.

28719 ■ *"Managing Your Innovation Portfolio: People Throughout Your Organization Are Energetically Pursuing the New. But Does All That Add Up To a Strategy?" in Harvard Business Review (Vol. 00, May 2012, No. 5, pp. 66)*
Pub: Harvard Business Review Press
Contact: Moderna V. Pfizer, Contact
Ed: Bansi Nagji, Geoff Tuff. **Price:** $8.95. **Description:** Returns on innovation are higher with transformational initiatives than with core or adjacent pursuits, but require unique management methods. These include establishing a diverse talent set, separating teams from daily operations, and obtaining funding from outside the regular budget cycle. **Availability:** Online; PDF.

28720 ■ *"Managing Yourself: What Brain Science Tells Us About How to Excel" in Harvard Business Review (Vol. 88, December 2010, No. 12, pp. 123)*
Pub: Harvard Business Publishing
Contact: Diane Belcher, Managing Director
Ed: Edward M. Hallowell. **Price:** $8.95, PDF. **Description:** Relevant discoveries in brain research as they apply to boosting employee motivation and organizational effectiveness are explained. Included is a checklist of 15 items for use in assessing the fitness of a person for a particular job, focusing on the intersection of what one likes to do, what one does best, and what increases organizational value. **Availability:** Print; PDF.

28721 ■ *Mastering Business Negotiation: A Working Guide to Making Deals and Resolving Conflict*
Pub: Jossey-Bass
Ed: Roy J. Lewicki, Alexander Hiam. **Released:** 2011. **Description:** Provides extensive insight into practical strategies and ideas for conducting business negotiations. **Availability:** Print; Electronic publishing; Online.

28722 ■ *"Messing with Corporate Heads? Psychological Contracts and Leadership Integrity" in Journal of Business Strategy (Vol. 35, May-June 2014, No. 3, pp. 38-46)*
Pub: Emerald Group Publishing Limited
Contact: Erika Valenti, President

Description: A model of leadership, i.e. the leadership psychological contract (LPC) and investigation of the contribution of psychological contract (PC) to the leadership domain is investigated. Contemporary literature on leadership and PC is reviewed and it was observed that the LPC is a predictive model consisting of three dependent variables namely trust, fairness, and fulfillment of expectations. The LPC model seeks to augment the value of ethical and effective leadership approaches.

28723 ■ *"Microsoft's Diversity Program Clicks into High Speed" in Hispanic Business (Vol. 30, July-August 2008, No. 7-8, pp. 54)*
Ed: Derek Reveron. **Description:** Microsoft's diversity hiring and vendor diversity program to capture more Hispanic consumer and business-to-business market is described. One of the main goals of these programs is to hire more Hispanic executives and managers who will help the company develop and market products and services that will appeal and benefit Hispanic consumers.

28724 ■ *"Miller's Crossroad" in Canadian Business (Vol. 83, September 14, 2010, No. 15, pp. 58)*
Ed: Joe Castaldo. **Released:** September 14, 2010. **Description:** Future Electronics founder and billionaire Robert Miller shares the secret of Future's unique operating model, which is based on inventory and market research. Miller attributes much of the company's success to its privately held status that enables quick movement against competitors. **Availability:** Print; Online.

28725 ■ *The Mirror Test: Is Your Business Really Breathing?*
Pub: Grand Central Publishing
Contact: Michael Pietsch, Chairman
Ed: Jeffrey W. Hayzlett. **Released:** May 05, 2010. **Price:** $0.00, e-book. **Description:** Consultant and author, Jeffrey Hayzlett, explains why a business is not doing well and asks the questions that most business managers are afraid to ask. **Availability:** E-book; Print.

28726 ■ *"Mismanaging Pay and Performance" in Business Strategy Review (Vol. 21, Summer 2010, No. 2, pp. 54)*
Ed: Rupert Merson. **Released:** June 24, 2010. **Description:** Understanding the relationship between performance measurement and desired behaviors is an important element of a company's talent management. **Availability:** Print; PDF; Online.

28727 ■ *"Miss Manners Minds Your Business"*
Released: October 01, 2014. **Price:** $16.95, paperback. **Description:** Office etiquette is outlined. Practical, pertinent and correct advice is given covering office manners for anyone from convening a focus group to Human Resources management. **Availability:** Print.

28728 ■ *"Modeling How to Grow: an Inductive Examination of Humble Leader Behaviors, Contingencies, and Outcomes" in Academy of Management Journal (Vol. 55, August 1, 2012, No. 4, pp. 787)*
Pub: Academy of Management
Contact: Sharon Alvarez, President
Ed: Bradley P. Owens, David R. Hekman. **Description:** An inductive analysis of the behaviors, outcome and contingencies of humble leadership in relation to organizational effectiveness is presented. Results suggest that effective leadership amid market complexity and diversity requires leaders to humbly show their followers how to grow by admitting their limitations and acknowledging the contributions of the people around them. **Availability:** Download; Electronic publishing; PDF; Online.

28729 ■ *"The Moment You Can't Ignore: When Big Trouble Leads to a Great Future"*
Pub: PublicAffairs
Contact: Jaime Leifer, Director

Released: October 07, 2014. **Price:** $14.99, E-book; $25.99, hardcover. **Description:** New forms of work, communication, and technology are exposing the ways in which an organization's culture conflicts with new competitive demands. Questions for small companies to ask about identity, leadership, and capacity for innovation are addressed. **Availability:** E-book; Print.

28730 ▪ "My Inglorious Road to Success" in Harvard Business Review (Vol. 88, July-August 2010, No. 7-8, pp. 38)
Pub: Harvard Business Publishing
Contact: Diane Belcher, Managing Director
Ed: Warren Bennis. **Price:** $6, PDF. **Description:** The author discusses the intersection of fortune and opportunity in his career success, and emphasizes the important role of awareness when taking advantage of both. **Availability:** Online; PDF.

28731 ▪ "The Myth of the Overqualified Worker" in Harvard Business Review (Vol. 88, December 2010, No. 12, pp. 30)
Pub: Harvard Business Publishing
Contact: Diane Belcher, Managing Director
Ed: Andrew O'Connell. **Price:** $6, PDF. **Description:** It is recommended to seriously consider job candidates with qualifications exceeding the position being recruited because research shows these individuals work harder, but do not quit any sooner than those whose qualifications more closely match the position. **Availability:** Online; PDF.

28732 ▪ "Negotiating Tips" in Black Enterprise (Vol. 37, December 2006, No. 5, pp. 70)
Pub: Earl G. Graves Ltd.
Contact: Earl Graves, Jr., President
Ed: Marcia A. Reed-Woodard. **Description:** Sekou Kaalund, head of strategy, mergers & acquisitions at Citigroup Securities & Fund Services, states that "Negotiation skills are paramount to success in a business environment because of client, employee, and shareholder relationships". He discusses how the book by George Kohlrieser, Hostage at the Table: How Leaders Can Overcome Conflict, Influence Others, and Raise Performance, has helped him negotiate more powerfully and enhance his skills at conflict-resolution. **Availability:** Online.

28733 ▪ Never Eat Alone: And Other Secrets to Success, One Relationship at a Time
Released: June 03, 2014. **Price:** $28; $13.99. **Description:** Business networking strategies are offered. **Availability:** E-book; Print.

28734 ▪ "Never Eat Alone, Expanded and Updated: And Other Secrets to Success, One Relationship at a Time"
Released: June 03, 2014. **Description:** The power of their relationships is what makes successful business leaders stand out from the rest. He lists specific steps to reach out and connect with colleagues, friends, and associates, along with successful ways to use social media to advance in business. **Availability:** Print.

28735 ▪ The New Role of Regional Management
Pub: Palgrave Macmillan
Ed: Bjorn Ambos, Bodo B. Schlegelmilch. **Released:** 2010. **Description:** Regional management is becoming more important to companies as they expand globally. This book explores the challenges of European, United States and Asian companies and outlines how regional headquarters can develop into Dynamic Competence Relay centers to master these issues. **Availability:** E-book; Print.

28736 ▪ "Nexstar Super Meeting Breaks Business Barriers" in Contractor (Vol. 56, November 2009, No. 11, pp. 3)
Ed: Candace Roulo. **Description:** Around 400 Nexstar members met to discuss the trends in the HVAC industry and the economic outlook for 2010. Former lead solo pilot John Foley for the Blue Angels made a presentation on how a business can increase

overall productivity based on the culture of the Blue Angels. Some breakout sessions tackled how to optimize workflow and marketing. **Availability:** Print; Online.

28737 ▪ "Nine Paradoxes of Problem Solving" in Strategy and Leadership (Vol. 39, May-June 2011, No. 3, pp. 25-31)
Pub: Emerald Group Publishing Limited
Contact: Erika Valenti, President
Ed: Alex Lowy. **Description:** Nine frequently-occurring inherent paradoxes in corporate decision making for solving complex problems are identified. The methods with which these paradoxes and their influence can be recognized and dealt with for firm leaders and management team members to better understand and solve the problems are discussed. **Availability:** Download; Online.

28738 ▪ "Nobel Prize Winners Provide Insight on Outsourcing, Contract Work" in Workforce Management (Vol. 88, November 16, 2009, No. 12, pp. 11)
Pub: Crain Communications Inc.
Contact: Barry Asin, President
Ed: Jeremy Smerd. **Description:** Insights into such workforce management issues as bonuses, employee contracts and outsourcing has been recognized by the Nobel Prize winners in economics whose research sheds a light on the way economic decisions are made outside markets. **Availability:** Online.

28739 ▪ "'Nobody Knows What To Do' To Make Money on the Web" in Barron's (Vol. 88, March 17, 2008, No. 11, pp. 40)
Pub: Dow Jones & Company Inc.
Contact: Almar Latour, Chief Executive Officer
Ed: Mark Veverka. **Description:** Attendees of the South by Southwest Interactive conference failed to get an insight on how to make money on the Web from former Walt Disney CEO Michael Eisner when Eisner said there's no proven business model for financing projects. Eisner said he finances his projects with the help of his connections to get product-placement deals. **Availability:** Online.

28740 ▪ Non-Standard Employment under Globalization: Flexible Work and Social Security in the Newly Industrializing Countries
Pub: Palgrave Macmillan
Ed: Koichi Usami. **Released:** First edition. **Description:** Expansion of non-standard employment under globalization is being recognized in all of the newly industrialized countries. The book examines deregulation of labor markets, social protection for nonstandard workers, and social security reforms in accordance with the transformation of employment.

28741 ▪ "Nortel Makes Customers Stars in New Campaign" in Brandweek (Vol. 49, April 21, 2008, No. 16, pp. 8)
Description: Nortel has launched a new television advertising campaign in which the business-to-business communications technology provider cast senior executives in 30-second TV case studies that show how Nortel's technology helped their businesses innovate. **Availability:** Online.

28742 ▪ "The Obstacle Is the Way: The Timeless Art of Turning Trials into Triumph"
Pub: Portfolio Hardcover
Contact: Adrian Zackheim, President
Released: May 01, 2014. **Price:** $9.99, e-book; $25, hardcover; $16.96, hardcover; $9.38, hardcover(73 used from $9.38); $12.14, hardcover(66 new from $12.14); $89.99, hardcover(2 collectible from $89.99). **Description:** The formula for success is taking any obstacle and turning it into a business opportunity. Successful leaders throughout history are profiled to show how any entrepreneur can succeed. **Availability:** E-book; Print.

28743 ▪ "The Ode: CoolBrands (1986 - 2010)" in Canadian Business (Vol. 83, September 14, 2010, No. 15, pp. 25)
Pub: Rogers Media Inc.
Contact: Neil Spivak, Chief Executive Officer

Ed: Joe Castaldo. **Description:** CoolBrands International Inc.'s merger with Swisher International Inc., a US hygiene products and services company, has formally erased the last traces of the former ice cream company. CoolBrands began as a frozen yogurt stand in 1986 and flourished across the world. How the string of acquisitions and poor corporate governance led to its demise are cited. **Availability:** Online.

28744 ▪ "The Office: Do Not Disturb" in Inc. (November 2007, pp. 144)
Ed: Leigh Buchanan. **Description:** The importance for any CEO to be accessible to his employees is stressed. **Availability:** Online.

28745 ▪ "The Office: The Bad and the Ugly" in Inc. (January 2008, pp. 120)
Description: Seven signs that you are a bad boss are outlined to help managers improve their skills. **Availability:** Online.

28746 ▪ Old Dogs New Tricks Version 2.0 - Awakening and Cultivating Leadership at Any Age
URL(s): www.barnesandnoble.com/w/old-dogs-new-tricks-version-20-awakening-and-cultivating-leadership-at-any-age-david-specht/1143035023?ean=2940185756850
Ed: David Specht. **Released:** February 14, 2023. **Price:** $9.99, e-book; $14.99, paperback. **Description:** Learning new leadership skills is something everyone can learn, not matter the age. From people just starting in the field to seasoned pros, leaders can learn new techniques based on the challenges they face. **Availability:** E-book; Print.

28747 ▪ "Olympus is Urged to Revise Board" in Wall Street Journal Eastern Edition (November 28, 2011, pp. B3)
Pub: Dow Jones & Company Inc.
Contact: Almar Latour, Chief Executive Officer
Ed: Phred Dvorak. **Description:** Koji Miyata, once a director on the board of troubled Japanese photographic equipment company, is urging the company to reorganize its board, saying the present group should resign their board seats but keep their management positions. The company has come under scrutiny for its accounting practices and costly acquisitions. **Availability:** Online.

28748 ▪ "On the Edge: The Art of High-Impact Leadership"
Released: January 07, 2014. **Price:** $30, audiobook CD; $13.99, e-book; $24.98, audiobook downloadable; $27, hardcover. **Description:** Alison Levine provides insights into leadership garnered from her various expeditions from Mount Everest to the South Pole. Levine believes that leadership principles that apply in extreme adventure sport also apply in today's extreme business environment. She discusses your survival as well as the survival of the team. **Availability:** CD-ROM; E-book; Print.

28749 ▪ On the Make: Clerks and the Quest for Capital in Nineteenth-Century America
Pub: New York University Press
Contact: Ellen Chodosh, Director
E-mail: ellen.chodosh@nyu.edu
Ed: Brian P. Luskey. **Released:** January 01, 2010. **Price:** $27, paperback; $89, cloth. **Description:** Through exploration into the diaries, newspapers, credit reports, census data, advice literature and fiction, the book presents the origins of the white collar culture, the antebellum clerk. **Availability:** E-book; Print.

28750 ▪ "On Managerial Relevance" in Journal of Marketing (Vol. 75, July 2011, No. 4, pp. 211)
Pub: American Marketing Association
Contact: Bennie F. Johnson, Chief Executive Officer
Ed: Bernard J. Jaworski. **Description:** A study to define and clarify managerial relevance, in order to act as a catalyst for debate, disagreement and future scholarship, is presented. The role of chief marketing officer (CMO) is examined to identify areas of inquiry

that are both novel and high managerially relevant. The analysis reveals the seven core tasks necessary to perform the CMO role. **Availability:** PDF.

28751 ■ *"On the Money" in San Antonio Business Journal (Vol. 28, June 27, 2014, No. 20, pp. 4)*

Description: The total compensation for the top 18 highest paid public company CEOs in San Antonio, Texas has increased 11 percent in the 2013 fiscal year to $74.8 million compared to 2012 fiscal year. The average total CEO compensation in the city was $4.15 million, an 11 percent increase from the 2013 list. The trend in the 2014 highest paid CEOs list is discussed. **Availability:** Print; Online.

28752 ■ *"One Hundred Years of Excellence in Business Education: What Have We Learned?" in Business Horizons (January-February 2008)*

Pub: Elsevier Advanced Technology Publications

Ed: Frank Acito, Patricia M. McDougall, Daniel C. Smith. **Description:** Business schools have to be more innovative, efficient and nimble, so that the quality of the next generation of business leaders is improved. The Kelley School of Business, Indiana University has long been a leader in business education. The trends that influence the future of business education and useful success principles are discussed. **Availability:** PDF; Online.

28753 ■ *"One-Time Area Trust Executive Finds Trouble in N.H." in The Business Journal-Serving Metropolitan Kansas City (September 12, 2008)*

Description: About 200 investors, some from Missouri's Kansas City area, claim that they had conducted business with Noble Trust Co. The trust company was placed under New Hampshire Banking Department's conservatorship after $15 million was discovered to be missing from its account. It is alleged that the money was lost in a Colorado Ponzi scheme. **Availability:** Print; Online.

28754 ■ *The Orange Revolution: How One Great Team Can Transform an Entire Organization*

Pub: Simon & Schuster, Inc.

Contact: Jonathan Karp, President

Ed: Adrian Gostick, Chester Elton. **Released:** September 2010. **Price:** $25, hardcover; $16.99. **Description:** Based on a 350,000-person study by the Best Companies Group, as well as research into exceptional teams at leading companies, including Zappos.com, Pepsi Beverages Company, and Madison Square Garden, the authors have determined a key set of characteristics displayed by members of breakthrough teams, and have identified a set of rules great teams live by, which generate a culture of positive teamwork and led to extraordinary results. Using specific stories from the teams they studied, they reveal in detail how these teams operate and how managers can transform their own teams into such high performers by fostering: stronger clarity of goals, greater trust among team members, more open and honest dialogue, stronger accountability for all team members, and purpose-based recognition of team member contributions. **Availability:** E-book; Print.

28755 ■ *"The Organized Mind: Thinking Straight in the Age of Information Overload"*

Pub: Penguin Publishing Group

Released: August 19, 2014. **Price:** $17, paperback; $9.99, e-book; $25, audiobook download; $6.99. **Description:** Leaders are expected to make more decisions faster than ever, despite the amount of information faced daily. Levitin uses the latest brain science to show how leaders are able to excel by successfully handling information flow. He shows how research into the cognitive neuroscience of attention and memory can be applied to everyday challenges, not only in managing a small business, but also in our personal lives. **Availability:** audiobook; E-book; Print.

28756 ■ *"The Outcome of an Organization Overhaul" in Black Enterprise (Vol. 41, December 2010, No. 5)*

Pub: Earl G. Graves Ltd.

Contact: Earl Graves, Jr., President

Ed: Tamara E. Holmes. **Description:** Savvy business owners understand the need for change in order to stay competitive and be successful. This article examines how to manage change as well as what strategies can help employees to get with the program faster. **Availability:** Online.

28757 ■ *"Pack Mentality: Why Black Can Be Slimming" in Crain's Chicago Business (Vol. 31, April 21, 2008, No. 16, pp. 31)*

Pub: Crain Communications Inc.

Contact: Barry Asin, President

Ed: Sarah A. Klein. **Description:** Jill Smart, the head of human resources for a company with 170,000 employees worldwide, frequently travels to India, London and Singapore; Ms. Smart provides advice concerning efficiency, time management and avoiding jet-lag. **Availability:** Online.

28758 ■ *A Passion for Planning: Financials, Operations, Marketing, Management, and Ethics*

Pub: University Press of America Inc.

Contact: Henry O. Dormann, Editor-in-Chief Founder Chairman

URL(s): rowman.com/ISBN/9780761818540/A-Passion-for-Planning-Financials-Operations-Marketing -Management-and-Ethics

Released: Latest Edition February 2001. **Price:** $82. 99, Individuals for paperback. **Description:** Covers small business topics, including growth, manufacturing, technology, sales, distribution, services, resources, networking, and business ethics. **Entries include:** Contact details, Web sites. **Availability:** Print; Online.

28759 ■ *"Passionate About Empowering Women" in Women in Business (Vol. 63, Spring 2011, No. 1, pp. 24)*

Pub: American Business Women's Association

Contact: Rene Street, Executive Director

Ed: Leigh Elmore. **Released:** March 22, 2011. **Description:** Krazy Coupon Ladies cofounder Joanie Demer shares her views about her book, 'Pick Another Checkout Lane, Honey', which she coauthored with Heather Wheeler. Demer believes using coupons is for everyone who wants to save money. She also believes that extreme couponing is not an exercise for those who lack organizational ability since it requires planning and discipline. **Availability:** Online.

28760 ■ *"Patience May Pay Off" in Barron's (Vol. 89, July 13, 2009, No. 28, pp. 30)*

Description: New CEO Craig Herkert can turn around Supervalu and their shares could double to $30 in three years from June 2009 according to one investment officer. Herkert knows how to run a lean and tight operation since he has worked for Albertsons and Wal-Mart in the past. **Availability:** Online.

28761 ■ *"Pay Fell for Many Baltimore Execs in '09" in Baltimore Business Journal (Vol. 28, July 2, 2010, No. 8, pp. 1)*

Pub: Baltimore Business Journal

Contact: Rhonda Pringle, President

E-mail: rpringle@bizjournals.com

Ed: Gary Haber. **Description:** Compensation for the 100 highest-paid executives in the Baltimore, Maryland area decreased in 2009, compared with 2008. At least $1 million were received by 59 out of 100 executives in 2009, while 75 earned the said amount in 2008. Factors that contributed to the executives' decisions to take pay cuts are discussed. **Availability:** Print.

28762 ■ *"Paychecks of Some Bank CEOs Have a Pre-Recession Look" in Boston Business Journal (Vol. 29, May 13, 2011, No. 1, pp. 1)*

Pub: Boston Business Journal

Contact: Carolyn M. Jones, President

E-mail: cmjones@bizjournals.com

Ed: Gary Haber. **Description:** The salaries of United States-based bank chief executive officers have increased to pre-recession levels. Wells Fargo and Company's John G. Stumpf received $17.6 million in 2010. Community bank executives, on the other hand, have seen minimal increases. **Availability:** Print; Online.

28763 ■ *"People Tools for Business: 50 Strategies for Building Success, Creating Wealth, and Finding Happiness"*

Released: September 30, 2014. **Price:** $14.91; $9. 43. **Description:** Tools required to enjoy success in both career and life are given. People Tools are help to develop self-confidence, improve management skills, and find constructive ways for Human Resource managers to fire workers and ways for workers to respond. Each people tool is concise and provides a straightforward strategy to produce positive results. **Availability:** Print.

28764 ■ *"Pep Talk: Marketing An Independent Film" in Black Enterprise (Vol. 40, July 2010, No. 12, pp. 104)*

Pub: Earl G. Graves Ltd.

Contact: Earl Graves, Jr., President

Ed: Tennille M. Robinson. **Description:** Advice for maintaining motivation in any small business is given. **Availability:** Online.

28765 ■ *"Perfecting the Process: Creating a More Efficient Organization on Your Terms" in Black Enterprise (Vol. 41, October 2010, No. 3)*

Pub: Earl G. Graves Ltd.

Contact: Earl Graves, Jr., President

Ed: Tamara E. Holmes. **Description:** More than ever, entrepreneurs need to identify new ways of doing business in a cost-effective manner in order to expand their companies, while remaining true to their customer demands. **Availability:** Online.

28766 ■ *"The Performer: Soulpepper Theatre Company's Albert Shultz" in Canadian Business (Vol. 83, August 17, 2010, No. 13-14, pp. 71)*

Pub: Rogers Media Inc.

Contact: Neil Spivak, Chief Executive Officer

Ed: Steve Maich. **Description:** Soulpepper Theater Company founder and actor/director Albert Schultz shares the key ingredient to his success both artistically and commercially. Schultz believes his success was a combination of passion and persistence, as well as team building. He believes his entrepreneurial impulse came when he began thinking of making opportunities instead of taking them.

28767 ■ *"Performing Leadership" in Business Strategy Review (Vol. 23, Spring 2012, No. 1, pp. 56)*

Description: Can you create a great performance in three days? Orchestra conductors do so time and again. Bernhard Kerres investigates how they do it and what we can learn from them. Profile of Kerres in included. **Availability:** PDF; Online.

28768 ■ *"Perks Still Popular: Jets May be Out, but CEO Benefits Abound" in Crain's Detroit Business (Vol. 25, June 22, 2009)*

Pub: Crain Communications Inc.

Contact: Barry Asin, President

Ed: Ryan Beene. **Description:** Benefits packages of local CEOs are outlined. Statistical data included. **Availability:** Online.

28769 ■ *"Pet Store Pro Adds New Curriculum" in Pet Product News (Vol. 66, February 2012, No. 2, pp. 2012)*

Description: Pet Store Pro, the Pet Industry Distributors Association's free online training program, is going to launch chapters of a curriculum intended to assist pet store managers learn effective approaches to motivate employees and boost profitability. Other management-level chapters are to be added by Pet Store Pro throughout 2012 are listed. **Availability:** Print; Online.

28770 ■ *"Pete Carroll's Winning Rule: Protect Your Team"* in Puget Sound Business Journal (Vol. 35, July 25, 2014, No. 14, pp. 12)
Pub: American City Business Journals, Inc.
Contact: Mike Olivieri, Executive Vice President
Released: Weekly. **Price:** $4, Introductory 4-week offer(Digital & Print). **Description:** Seattle Seahawks coach, Pete Carroll, has three simple rules for team success and the first rule is to always protect the team. The rule is also important in every workplace because it will help align the workers attention to their behavior. Seven ways to protect the team are outlined. **Availability:** Print; Online.

28771 ■ *"Peter Bynoe Trades Up"* in Black Enterprise (Vol. 38, July 2008, No. 12, pp. 30)
Pub: Earl G. Graves Ltd.
Contact: Earl Graves, Jr., President
Description: Chicago-based Loop Capital Markets L.L.C. has named Peter Bynoe managing director of corporate finance. Bynoe was previously a senior partner at the law firm DLA Piper U.S. L.L.P., where he worked on stadium deals.

28772 ■ *"PhotoMedex Bouncing Back from Brink of Bankruptcy"* in Philadelphia Business Journal (Vol. 30, January 6, 2012, No. 47, pp. 1)
Pub: Baltimore Business Journal
Contact: Rhonda Pringle, President
E-mail: rpringle@bizjournals.com
Description: PhotoMedex Inc. has managed to avoid bankruptcy through reorganization. The company appointed Dennis McGrath as president and chief executive. Details of the business reorganization plans are covered. **Availability:** Print; Online.

28773 ■ *"Political Environments and Business Strategy: Implications for Managers"* in Business Horizons (Vol. 51, January-February 2008)
Pub: Elsevier Advanced Technology Publications
Ed: Gerald D. Keim, Amy J. Hillman. **Description:** Various government bodies and business organizations work together in shaping new business opportunities and policies that arise from globalization. Presented is framework of public policy considerations for business managers. The framework is based on Nobel laureate Douglas North's work. **Availability:** PDF; Online.

28774 ■ *Power Ambition Glory: The Stunning Parallels between Great Leaders of the Ancient World and Today... and the Lessons You Can Learn*
Ed: Steve Forbes, John Prevas. **Released:** 2010.
Price: $4.99, e-book. **Description:** An examination into the lives of the ancient world's greatest leaders and the lessons they have for today's business leaders. **Availability:** E-book; Print.

28775 ■ *"Power Cues: The Subtle Science of Leading Groups, Persuading Others, and Maximizing Your Personal Impact"*
Pub: Harvard Business Review Press
Contact: Moderna V. Pfizer, Contact
Released: May 13, 2014. **Price:** $30, hardcover. **Description:** Renowned speaking coach and communication expert, Nick Morgan, shows how humans are programmed to respond to the nonverbal cues of others. He teaches business leaders and entrepreneurs how to take control of their communications in order to communicate more effectively while commanding influence. **Availability:** E-book; Print.

28776 ■ *"The Power of Noticing: What the Best Leaders See"*
Pub: Simon & Schuster Adult Publishing Group
Contact: Jonathan Karp, President
Released: August 05, 2014. **Price:** $17.99, paperback, plus $1.55 shipping charges. **Description:** A guide to help entrepreneurs and managers gain the advantage in negotiations, decision making, and leadership skills. Instruction is given to see and evaluate information that others overlook. **Availability:** E-book; Print; Download; Audio.

28777 ■ *"Power Play"* in Harvard Business Review (Vol. 88, July-August 2010, No. 7-8, pp. 84)
Pub: Harvard Business Publishing
Contact: Diane Belcher, Managing Director
Ed: Jeffrey Pfeffer. **Price:** $8.95, PDF. **Description:** Guidelines include in-depth understanding of resources at one's disposal, relentlessness that still provides opponents with opportunities to save face, and a determination not to be put off by the processes of politics. **Availability:** Online; PDF.

28778 ■ *The Power of Pull: How Small Moves, Smartly Made, Can Set Big Things in Motion*
Ed: John Hagel, III, John Seely Brown, Lang Davison. **Released:** April 13, 2010. **Price:** $11.99; C$14.99. **Description:** Examination of how we can effectively address the most pressing challenges in a rapidly changing and increasingly interdependent world is addressed. New ways in which passionate thinking, creative solutions, and committed action can and will make it possible for small businesses owners to seize opportunities and remain in step with change. **Availability:** E-book; Print.

28779 ■ *"Powerlessness Corrupts"* in Harvard Business Review (Vol. 88, July-August 2010, No. 7-8, pp. 36)
Pub: Harvard Business Publishing
Contact: Diane Belcher, Managing Director
Ed: Rosabeth Moss Kanter. **Price:** $6, PDF. **Description:** Studies show that individuals who perceive that they are being treated poorly and denied sufficient freedom for a certain level of autonomy are more likely to act negatively. **Availability:** Online; PDF.

28780 ■ *"Practices, Governance, and Politics: Applying MacIntyre's Ethics to Business"* in Business Ethics Quarterly (Vol. 24, April 2014, No. 2, pp. 229)
Pub: Business Ethics Quarterly
Contact: Dawn Elm, Executive Director
E-mail: drelm@stthomas.edu
Description: An argument to apply MacIntyre's positive moral theory to business ethics is problematic due to the cognitive closure of MacIntyre's concept of practice. The paper begins by outlining the notion of a practice, before turning Moore's attempt to provide a MacIntyrean account of corporate governance. It argues that Moore's attempt is mismatched with MacIntyre's account of moral education. Because the notion of practices resists general application it is argued that a negative application, which focuses on regulation, is more plausible. Large-scale regulation, usually thought anti-ethical to MacIntyre's advocacy of small-scale politics, has the potential to facilitate practice-based work and reveals that MacIntyre's own work can be used against his pessimism about the modern order. Furthermore, the conception of regulation can show how management is more amenable to ethical understanding than MacIntyre's work is often taken to imply.

28781 ■ *"Prichard the Third"* in Canadian Business (Vol. 83, October 12, 2010, No. 17, pp. 34)
Pub: Rogers Media Inc.
Contact: Neil Spivak, Chief Executive Officer
Ed: Thomas Watson. **Description:** Robert Prichard, the new chair of international business law firm Torys, talks about his current role; his job involved advising clients, representing the firm, being part of the leadership team, and recruiting talent. He considers 'Seven Days in Tibet' as the first book to have an influence on his world view. **Availability:** Online.

28782 ■ *"Problem Solving Requires Total Team Approach"* in Green Industry Pro (Vol. 23, September 2011)
Ed: Bob Coulter. **Description:** Working Smarter Training Challenge teaches that leaders are able to carry out solutions directly into their organization, develop skills and drive business results in key areas by creating a culture of energized workers who are able to take ownership of their performance as well as the performance of the company as a whole. **Availability:** Online.

28783 ■ *"Profile: Charles Handy"* in Business Strategy Review (Vol. 21, Summer 2010, No. 2, pp. 86)
Ed: Stuart Crainer. **Description:** In a new series, profiles of a major thinker who has made a significant difference in how organizations are managed and how business careers are shaped are presented. **Availability:** PDF; Online.

28784 ■ *"Project Management Courses for You"* in Small Business Trends (July 25, 2022)
URL(s): smallbiztrends.com/2022/07/best-project-management-courses.html
Ed: Yednekachew Samson. **Released:** July 25, 2022. **Description:** Listed are online project management courses to help guide you develop these skills. **Availability:** Online.

28785 ■ *"Project Managers' Creed: Learn It, Live It"* in Contractor (Vol. 56, November 2009, No. 11, pp. 46)
Ed: H. Kent Craig. **Description:** Project managers should take the health and safety of their subordinates above all else. A manager should deal with the things that distract him from his job before starting a day on the site. The manager should maintain a comfortable and relaxed attitude with his employees. **Availability:** Print; Online.

28786 ■ *"Q&A with Google's Patrick Pichette"* in Canadian Business (Vol. 81, October 13, 2008, No. 17, pp. 6)
Description: Patrick Pichette finds challenge in taking over the finances of an Internet company that has a market cap of about $140 billion. He feels, however, that serving as Google's chief financial officer is nothing compared to running Bell Canada Enterprises (BCE). Pichette's other views on Google and BCE are presented. **Availability:** Print; Online.

28787 ■ *"Quality Performance of SMEs in a Developing Economy: Direct and Indirect Effects of Service Innovation and Entrepreneurial Orientation"* in Journal of Business & Industrial Marketing (Vol. 29, July 2014, No. 6)
Pub: Emerald Group Publishing Limited
Contact: Erika Valenti, President
Description: A study was conducted to investigate the effects of innovation and EO (entrepreneurial orientation) on organizational performance in Asian small enterprise context. Strategic management literature and the relationship between EO, innovation, and quality performance was tested. The results indicated that a noteworthy direct and indirect positive relationship exists between EO dimensions, innovation, and quality performance. **Availability:** Download; Online.

28788 ■ *"The RBC Dynasty Continues"* in Globe & Mail (January 30, 2006, pp. B1)
Description: The details on business growth of Royal Bank of Canada, under chief executive officer Gordon Nixon, are presented. **Availability:** Print; Online.

28789 ■ *"The Real Job of Boards"* in Business Strategy Review (Vol. 21, Autumn 2010, No. 3, pp. 36)
Ed: Harry Korine, Marcus Alexander, Pierre-Yves Gomez. **Released:** September 29, 2010. **Description:** Widely seen as the key for ensuring quality in corporate governance, the board of directors has been a particular focal point for reform. The authors believe that more leadership at board level could avert many corporate crises in the future. **Availability:** Print; PDF; Online.

28790 ■ *The Real Leadership Lessons of Steve Jobs*
Pub: Harvard Business Review Press
Contact: Moderna V. Pfizer, Contact

Ed: Walter Isaacson. **Price:** $8.95, hardcover. **Description:** Fourteen separate leadership practices of Steve Jobs are listed. These include focus, simplify, assume end-to-end responsibility, leapfrog when behind, place products ahead of profits, engage in face-to-face, understood both the details and the big picture, blend the sciences with the humanities, push for perfection, and stay hungry. **Availability:** PDF; Online.

28791 ■ *"Real-Life Coursework for Real-Life Business People"* in *Women In Business (Vol. 63, Summer 2011, No. 2, pp. 22)*
Pub: American Business Women's Association
Contact: Rene Street, Executive Director

Ed: Leigh Elmore. **Released:** June 22, 2011. **Description:** American Business Women's Association National Women's Leadership Conference provides members with academic business training courses. Members can take a variety of MBA-level courses that are taught by University of Kansas School of Business professors. Courses include marketing, management, leadership and communication and decision making. **Availability:** Print; Online.

28792 ■ *Reality-Based Leadership: Ditch the Drama, Restore Sanity to the Workplace, & Turn Excuses into Results*
Pub: Jossey-Bass

Ed: Cy Wakeman. **Released:** August 01, 2010. **Price:** $27.95, hardcover; $27.95, hardcover. **Description:** Recent polls show that 71 percent of workers think about quitting their jobs every day. That number would be shocking if people actually were quitting. Worse, they go to work, punching time clocks and collecting pay checks, while checked out emotionally. Cy Wakeman reveals how to be the kind of leader who changes the way people think about and perceive their circumstances, one who deals with the facts, clarifies roles, gives clean and direct feedback, and insists that everyone do the same without drama or defensiveness. **Availability:** E-book; Print.

28793 ■ *Reality Check: The Irreverent Guide to Outsmarting, Outmanaging, and Outmarketing Your Competition*
Pub: Penguin Publishing Group

Ed: Guy Kawasaki. **Released:** February 22, 2011. **Price:** $13.34, paperback; $4.99, e-book; $19.89, hardcover; $20.43, audio. **Description:** Marketing guru and entrepreneur, Guy Kawasaki, provides a compilation of his blog posts on all aspects of starting and operating a business. **Availability:** E-book; Print.

28794 ■ *"Reinventing Management"* in *Harvard Business Review (Vol. 88, July-August 2010, No. 7-8, pp. 167)*
Description: Review of the book, 'Reinventing Management' is presented. **Availability:** Online.

28795 ■ *"The Reinvention of Management"* in *Strategy and Leadership (Vol. 39, March-April 2011, No. 2, pp. 9)*
Pub: Emerald Group Publishing Limited
Contact: Erika Valenti, President

Ed: Stephen Denning. **Description:** An examination found that critical changes in management practice involves five shifts. These shifts involve the firm's goals, model of coordination, the role of managers and values practiced. Other findings of the study are discussed. **Availability:** Download; Online.

28796 ■ *"Relocation, Relocation, Relocation"* in *Conde Nast Portfolio (Vol. 2, June 2008, No. 6, pp. 36)*
Pub: American City Business Journals, Inc.
Contact: Mike Olivieri, Executive Vice President

Ed: Michelle Leder. **Description:** Perks regarding executive relocation are discussed. **Availability:** Print; Online.

28797 ■ *Remarkable Leadership: Unleashing Your Leadership Potential One Skill at a Time*
Released: 2011. **Description:** Handbook for anyone wishing to be an outstanding business leader; the framework and a mechanism for learning new things

and applying current knowledge in a practical to any business situation is outlined. **Availability:** Print; Online; Electronic publishing.

28798 ■ *"A Renewed Sisterhood"* in *Women in Business (Vol. 64, Summer 2012, No. 2, pp. 6)*

Ed: Rene Street. **Description:** The American Business Women's Association (ABWA) regional conference highlighted a new sense of enthusiasm and sisterhood as well as effective visioning exercise and breakout sessions. The ABWA National Women's Leadership Conference in October 2012 will feature the graduates of the Kansas University MBA Essentials Program and keynote speakers Bob Eubanks and Francine Ward. **Availability:** Online.

28799 ■ *"Research Highlights Disengaged Workforce"* in *Workforce Management (Vol. 88, November 16, 2009, No. 12, pp. 22)*
Pub: Crain Communications Inc.
Contact: Barry Asin, President

Ed: Ed Frauenheim. **Description:** Most researchers have documented a drop in employee engagement during the recession due to such factors as layoffs, restructuring and less job security. **Availability:** Online.

28800 ■ *"Rethinking the Organization"* in *Strategy & Leadership (Vol. 38, September-October 2010, No. 5, pp. 13-19)*
Pub: Emerald Inc.

Ed: Stephen Denning. **Description:** A study identifies the changes needed to be adopted by top managers to achieve game-changing innovation at an organization-wide level. Findings indicate that CEOs should practice pull management in order to nurture fruitful communication between employees and customers and achieve organizational involvement of customers. **Availability:** Print; PDF.

28801 ■ *"Retiring Baby Boomers and Dissatisfied Gen-Xers Cause..Brain Drain"* in *Agency Sales Magazine (Vol. 39, November 2009, No. 10)*
Description: Due to the impending retirement of the baby boomers a critical loss of knowledge and experience in businesses will result. Creating a plan to address this loss of talent centered on the development of the younger generation is discussed.

28802 ■ *"RIM's Demise Stems from Arrogance: It Didn't Have To Come To This"* in *Canadian Business (Vol. 85, August 13, 2012, No. 13, pp. 4)*

Ed: James Cowan. **Description:** The business collapse of Research in Motion (RIM) was blamed on the management's arrogance in terms of recognizing that Apple's iPhone is dominating the consumer market and that corporate customers would remain loyal despite the emergence of better smartphones. It is speculated that the failure of RIM could lead to at least 5,000 job losses. **Availability:** Online.

28803 ■ *"The Risks and Rewards of Speaking Up: Managerial Responses to Employee Voice"* in *Academy of Management Journal (Vol. 55, August 1, 2012, No. 4, pp. 851)*
Pub: Academy of Management
Contact: Sharon Alvarez, President

Ed: Ethan R. Burris. **Description:** The ways in which managers respond to suggestions made by employees is examined. Positive and negative managerial reactions to employees speaking up depend on whether the type of voice exhibited is challenging or supportive as well as on the psychological mechanisms of loyalty and threat. **Availability:** Download; Electronic publishing; PDF; Online.

28804 ■ *"Robert S. McNamara and the Evolution of Modern Management"* in *Harvard Business Review (Vol. 88, December 2010, No. 12, pp. 86)*
Pub: Harvard Business Publishing
Contact: Diane Belcher, Managing Director

Ed: Phil Rosenzweig. **Price:** $8.95, PDF. **Description:** A chronicle of the emergence and development of Robert S. McNamara's management skills and perspectives, focusing on the role of his idealism. Lessons learned during the course of the Vietnam Ware are also delineated. **Availability:** Online; PDF.

28805 ■ *"The Role of Leadership In Successful International Mergers and Acquisitions: Why Renault-Nissan Succeeded and DaimlerChrysler-Mitsubishi Failed"* in *Human Resource Management (Vol. 51,May-June 2012, No. 3, pp. 433-456)*
Pub: John Wiley & Sons, Inc.
Contact: Christina Van Tassell, Executive Vice President Chief Financial Officer

Ed: Carol Gill. **Released:** May 25, 2012. **Description:** The effects of national and organizational culture on the performance of Nissan and Mitsubishi after their mergers with Renault and DaimlerChrysler respectively are examined. Japanese national culture was found to influence organizational culture and human resource management practices, while leadership affected the success of their turnaround efforts.

28806 ■ *"Run Your Business Like Clockwork"* in *Small Business Trends(October 24, 2022)*
URL(s): smallbiztrends.com/2022/10/running-your -business-like-clockwork.html

Released: October 24, 2022. **Description:** A discussion on how entrepreneurs can run successful businesses without having to do everything and micromanage everything and everyone. **Availability:** Online.

28807 ■ *"Scrum: The Art of Doing Twice the Work in Half the Time"*
Pub: Penguin Random House
Contact: Nihar Malaviya, Chief Executive Officer

Released: 2014. **Price:** $27, hardcover, plus shipping charges; $16.99, e-book; $35, CD, plus shipping charges; $17.50, audiobook download. **Description:** Scrum is a more efficient way for getting things done, particularly when managing a company. Scrum has recorded productivity gains as high as 1200 percent and is an excellent time management tool. **Availability:** CD-ROM; E-book; Print; Audio.

28808 ■ *"Secrets to Improve Your Small Business Leadership Skills"* in *Small Business Trends(January 17, 2023)*
URL(s): smallbiztrends.com/2023/01/leadership-skills .html

Ed: Michael Guta. **Released:** January 17, 2023. **Description:** Good traits for company leadership are discussed. **Availability:** Online.

28809 ■ *"Segmenting When It Matters"* in *Business Strategy Review (Vol. 21, Spring 2010, No. 1, pp. 46)*
Ed: Andreas Birnik, Richard Moat. **Released:** February 09, 2010. **Description:** Authors argue that business complexity is directly linked to the degree of segmentation implemented by a company. They propose an approach to map business activities at the segment level to make sure that complexity is only introduced when it really matters. **Availability:** Print; PDF; Online.

28810 ■ *"Selling a Job When There's Buyer's Remorse"* in *Contractor (Vol. 56, December 2009, No. 12, pp. 37)*
Ed: H. Kent Craig. **Description:** Advice on how contractors should manage low-profit jobs in the United States is presented. Efforts should be made to try and find at least one quality field foreman or superintendent. Contractors should also try to respectfully renegotiate the terms of the job. **Availability:** Online.

28811 ■ *"Seven Things Great Employers Do (That Others Don't); Unusual, Innovative, and Proven Tactics To Create Productive and Profitable Working Environments"* in *Gallup Business Journal (April 15, 2014)*
Pub: Gallup, Inc.
Contact: Jon Clifton, Chief Executive Officer

Price: $8.95. Description: Seven unusual, innovative, and proven tactics that create productive and profitable working environments are examined through researching 32 companies. These firms represented many industries, including healthcare, financial services, hospitality, manufacturing, and retail throughout the world. Availability: Print; PDF; Online.

28812 ■ *"Shared Leadership In Teams: An Investigation of Antecedent Conditions and Performance"* in *Academy of Management Journal (Vol. 50, No. 5, October 1, 2007, pp. 1217)*
Pub: Academy of Management
Contact: Sharon Alvarez, President
Ed: Jay B. Carson, Paul E. Tesluk, Jennifer A. Marrone. Description: Study assessed the advantages of distribution of leadership among team members rather than on a single person revealed advantages that ranged from support and shared functions along with higher ratings from clients on their performance. Availability: Electronic publishing; Download; PDF; Online.

28813 ■ *"Should Managers Focus on Performance or Engagement? Gallup Examined this Question and Found That the Answer Isn't as 'Either/Or' as Many Companies Might Think"* in *Gallup Business Journal (August 5, 2014)*
Pub: Gallup, Inc.
Contact: Jon Clifton, Chief Executive Officer
Description: A Gallup survey of over 8,000 employees were asked whether managers should focus on performance or engagement. High performance managers create an engaging work environment promoting peak performance in three ways. Availability: Print; Online.

28814 ■ *"Six Sears Board Members to Resign in April"* in *Globe & Mail (March 1, 2006, pp. B1)*
Ed: Marina Strauss. Description: The reasons behind the departure of six board members of Sears Canada Inc. are presented. Availability: Online.

28815 ■ *"Six Ways Employees on LinkedIn Benefit the Boss"* in *South Florida Business Journal (Vol. 34, April 25, 2014, No. 40)*
Pub: American City Business Journals, Inc.
Contact: Mike Olivieri, Executive Vice President
Released: Weekly. Price: $8, Introductory 4-week offer(Digital & Print). Description: LinkedIn can be a useful tool for executives. In addition to finding staff when hiring, the information service can give U.S.-based users a more global perspective. It can also be a way to share recent company accomplishment. Availability: Print; Online.

28816 ■ *Small Business for Dummies*
Pub: John Wiley & Sons, Inc.
Contact: Christina Van Tassell, Executive Vice President Chief Financial Officer
Ed: Eric Tyson, Jim Schell. Released: 5th Edition. Price: $24.99, paperback; $16.99, E-book. Description: Guidebook for anyone wanting to start or grow a small business; topics include information financing, budgeting, marketing, management and more. Availability: E-book; Print.

28817 ■ *Small Business Management in Canada*
Released: 8th edition. Price: $243.27. Description: Small business management in Canada. Availability: E-book; Print.

28818 ■ *"Social Media, E-Mail Remain Challenging for Employers"* in *Workforce Management (Vol. 88, December 14, 2009, No. 13, pp. 4)*
Pub: Crain Communications Inc.
Contact: Barry Asin, President
Ed: Ed Frauenheim. Description: Examining the impact of Internet social networking and the workplace; due to the power of these new technologies, it is important that companies begin to set clear policies regarding Internet use and employee privacy. Availability: Online.

28819 ■ *"Social Networks in the Workplace: The Risk and Opportunity of Business 2.0"* in *Strategy & Leadership (Vol. 38, July-August 2010, No. 4, pp. 50-53)*
Pub: Emerald Inc.
Ed: Daniel Burrus. Description: The opinions of futurist Daniel Burrus on a novel trend called 'Business 2.0', which involves the use of social networking applications as business tools, are presented. His suggestion that personal social networking technology can be used by businesses to improve collaboration, problem solving, and leadership communications to achieve continuous value innovation is discussed. Availability: Online.

28820 ■ *"Soft Skills, Hard Success: Employers Seek Leaders Who Offer More than Just Education and Credentials"* in *Black Enterprise (Vol. 45, July-August 2014, No. 1, pp. 44)*
Pub: Earl G. Graves Ltd.
Contact: Earl Graves, Jr., President
Description: The top ten soft skills employer look for include: strong work ethic, dependability, positive attitude, self-motivation, team oriented, organizational skills, works well under pressure, effective communication, flexibility, and confidence.

28821 ■ *"Sources"* in *Canadian Electronics (Vol. 23, August 2008, No. 5, pp. 12)*
Description: Directory of electronic manufacturers, distributors and representatives in Canada is provided. The list presents distributors and representatives under each manufacturer.

28822 ■ *"Spam's Biggest Fan"* in *Barron's (Vol. 92, August 25, 2012, No. 35, pp. 42)*
Pub: Dow Jones & Company Inc.
Contact: Almar Latour, Chief Executive Officer
Ed: Lawrence C. Strauss. Description: Jeffrey Ettinger, chief executive officer of meat packing and packaged food firm Hormel Foods, is credited with expanding the company's product offerings. Ettinger, who took over in 2006, involves himself in almost every aspect of the company's business. Availability: Online.

28823 ■ *"A Stakeholder--Human Capital Perspective on the Link Between Social Performance and Executive Compensation"* in *Business Ethics Quarterly (Vol. 24, January 2014, No. 1, pp. 1)*
Pub: Business Ethics Quarterly
Contact: Dawn Elm, Executive Director
E-mail: drelm@stthomas.edu
Description: The link between firm corporate social performance (CSP) and executive compensation could be driven by a sorting effect (a firm's CSP is related to the initial levels of compensation of newly hired executives), or by an incentive effect (incumbent executives are rewarded for past firm CSP). An exploration of the sorting effect of firm CSP on the initial compensation of newly hired executives is discussed. Availability: Download; PDF; Online.

28824 ■ *"Stand Out Via Service: How Volunteering Can Boost Your Professional Bottom Line"* in *Black Enterprise (Vol. 44, June 2014, No. 10, pp. 42)*
Pub: Earl G. Graves Ltd.
Contact: Earl Graves, Jr., President
Description: According to the 2013 Deloitte Volunteer IMPACT Survey, more than three of every four human resource executives volunteer. This strategy can lead to career satisfaction and help a business advance and fuel growth for individuals and the firm. Tips for finding the right volunteer opportunity are included.

28825 ■ *"Start Filling Your Talent Gap - Now"* in *Business Strategy Review (Vol. 21, Spring 2010, No. 1, pp. 56)*
Ed: Alan Bird, Lori Flees, Paul DiPaola. Released: March 22, 2010. Description: As businesses steer their way out of turbulence, they have a unique opportunity to identify their leadership supply and demand and then to close the talent gap in their organization. Authors explain how to take immediate steps to build the right team now and lay the groundwork for a long-term approach for nurturing talent within the organization. Availability: Online; Electronic publishing.

28826 ■ *"Staying Engaged: Location, Location"* in *Black Enterprise (Vol. 38, February 2008, No. 7, pp. 64)*
Pub: Earl G. Graves Ltd.
Contact: Earl Graves, Jr., President
Ed: Marcia A. Reed-Woodard. Description: Rules to help business leaders construct networking contacts in order to maximize professional success are outlined. Availability: Online.

28827 ■ *"A Step Up"* in *Black Enterprise (Vol. 38, January 2008, No. 6, pp. 53)*
Pub: Earl G. Graves Ltd.
Contact: Earl Graves, Jr., President
Ed: Aisha Sylvester. Description: Professional black women can get advice from a nonprofit program called ASCENT: Leading Multicultural Women to the Top. ASCENT's sessions last six months and are held at both Tuck School of Business at Dartmouth and UCLA Anderson School of Management.

28828 ■ *"Stop the Innovation Wars"* in *Harvard Business Review (Vol. 88, July-August 2010, No. 7-8, pp. 76)*
Pub: Harvard Business Publishing
Contact: Diane Belcher, Managing Director
Ed: Vijay Govindarajan, Chris Trimble. Price: $8.95, PDF. Description: Methods for managing conflicts between partners during the innovation initiative process are highlighted. These include dividing the labor, assembling a dedicated team, and mitigating likelihood for any potential conflict. Availability: Online; PDF.

28829 ■ *"The Story Of Diane Greene"* in *Barron's (Vol. 88, July 14, 2008, No. 28, pp. 31)*
Pub: Dow Jones & Company Inc.
Contact: Almar Latour, Chief Executive Officer
Ed: Mark Veverka. Description: Discusses the ousting of Diane Greene as a chief executive of VMWare, a developer of virtualization software, after the firm went public; in this case Greene, a brilliant engineer, should not be negatively impacted by the decision because it is common for companies to bring in new executive leadership that is more operations oriented after the company goes public. Availability: Online.

28830 ■ *"Strategic Issue Management as Change Catalyst"* in *Strategy and Leadership (Vol. 39, September-October 2011, No. 5, pp. 20-29)*
Pub: Emerald Group Publishing Limited
Contact: Erika Valenti, President
Ed: Bruce E. Perrott. Description: A study analyzes the case of a well-known Australian healthcare organization to examine how a company's periodic planning cycle is supplemented with a dynamic, real-time, strategic-issue-management system under high turbulence conditions. Findings highlight the eight steps that a company's management can use in its strategic issue management (SIM) process to track, monitor and manage strategic issues so as to ensure that the corporate, strategy, and capability are aligned with one another in turbulent times. Availability: Download; PDF; Online.

28831 ■ *Strengths Based Leadership*
Pub: Gallup, Inc.
Contact: Jon Clifton, Chief Executive Officer
Ed: Tom Rath, Barry Conchie. Price: $19.99. Description: Three keys to being a more effective leader. Availability: Print; Online.

28832 ■ *"Stress-Test Your Strategy: the 7 Questions to Ask"* in *Harvard Business Review (Vol. 88, November 2010, No. 11, pp. 92)*
Pub: Harvard Business Publishing
Contact: Diane Belcher, Managing Director

Ed: Robert Simons. **Price:** $8.95, PDF. **Description:** Seven questions organizations should use to assess crisis management capabilities are: who is the primary customer, how do core values prioritize all parties, what performance variables are being tracked, what strategic boundaries have been set, how is creative tension being produced, how committed are workers to assisting each other, and what uncertainties are causing worry?. **Availability:** Online; PDF.

28833 ■ *"Striving for Self-Verification During Organizational Entry"* in *Academy of Management Journal (Vol. 55, June 2012, No. 2, pp. 360)*
Pub: Academy of Management
Contact: Sharon Alvarez, President

Ed: Daniel M. Cable, Virginia S. Kay. **Description:** How striving for self-verification relates with self-disclosure, self-monitoring, and core self-evaluations is explored. Striving refers to bringing others to know who a person is during the organizational entry process. Relations to the validity of interviewers' evaluations, job seekers' ability to find satisfying work, and supervisors' evaluations of newcomers' performance are given. **Availability:** Electronic publishing; Download; PDF; Online.

28834 ■ *"Stuff that Works for You: In the Mobikey of Life"* in *Canadian Business (Vol. 81, June 11, 2008, No. 11, pp. 42)*
Pub: Rogers Media Inc.
Contact: Neil Spivak, Chief Executive Officer

Ed: John Gray. **Description:** Toronto-based Route1 has created a data security software system that allows employees to access files and programs stored in the head office without permanently transferring data to the actual computer being used. Mobikey technology is useful in protecting laptops of chief executive officers, which contain confidential financial and customer data. **Availability:** Online.

20035 ■ *"Stymiest's RBC Compensation Triggers Shareholder Outrage"* in *Globe & Mail (January 28, 2006, pp. B3)*
Description: The concerns of shareholders over the issue of Royal Bank of Canada's $6.6 million pay package for chief executive officer Barbara Stymiest, in 2004, are presented. **Availability:** Print; Online.

28836 ■ *"Succeeding at Succession"* in *Harvard Business Review (Vol. 88, November 2010, No. 11, pp. 29)*
Pub: Harvard Business Publishing
Contact: Diane Belcher, Managing Director

Ed: James M. Citrin, Dayton Ogden. **Price:** $6, PDF. **Description:** Analysis of various executive succession scenarios is given. The article compares insider vs. outsider performance and the effectiveness of board members assuming the CEO position. **Availability:** Online; PDF.

28837 ■ *"Surprise Package"* in *Business Courier (Vol. 27, June 25, 2010, No. 8, pp. 1)*
Pub: Business Courier

Ed: Dan Monk, Jon Newberry, Steve Watkins. **Description:** More than 60 percent of the chief executive officers (CEOs) in Greater Cincinnati's 35 public companies took a salary cut in 2009, but stock grants resulted in large paper gains for the CEOs. The salary cuts show efforts of boards of directors to observe austerity. Statistics on increased values of stock awards for CEOs, median pay for CEOs, and median shareholder return are also presented. **Availability:** Online.

28838 ■ *"Swinging For the Fences: The Effects of Ceo Stock Options on Company Risk Taking and Performance"* in *Academy of Management Journal (Vol. 50, No. 5, October 1, 2007, pp. 1055)*
Pub: Academy of Management
Contact: Sharon Alvarez, President

Ed: Gerard Sanders, Donald C. Hambrick. **Description:** Study examines managerial risk-taking vis-a-vis stock options of the company; results reveal that stock options instigate CEOs to take unwise risks that could bring huge losses to the company. **Availability:** Electronic publishing; PDF; Download; Online.

28839 ■ *"Switch: How to Change Things When Change Is Hard"*
Pub: Broadway Business

Ed: Chip Heath, Dan Heath. **Released:** February 16, 2010. **Price:** $29, U.S., hardcover; $17.50, U.S., e-book. **Description:** Change is difficult for everyone. This book helps business leaders to motivate employees as well as to help everybody motive themselves and others. **Availability:** E-book; Print; Download; Audio.

28840 ■ *"A System for Continuous Organization Renewal"* in *Strategy & Leadership (Vol. 38, July-August 2010, No. 4, pp. 34-41)*
Pub: Emerald Inc.

Ed: Oliver Sparrow, Gill Ringland. **Description:** A study presents a unique system to facilitate continuous organizational renewal. An analysis indicates that the system is effective when organizations implement all its parts to achieve organizational renewal. **Availability:** Print.

28841 ■ *"Take Command: Lessons in Leadership: How to Be a First Responder in Business"*
Released: 2018. **Price:** $25. **Description:** What do elite members of the military, first responders in a disaster zone, and successful business leaders have in common? Clarity of mind and purpose in the midst of chaos. Cofounder and CEO of Team Rubicon and former Marine Sniper Jake Wood, teaches the lessons in leadership and teamwork to help managers and entrepreneurs succeed in this hyper-competitive business environment today.

28842 ■ *"The Talent Masters: Why Smart Leaders Put People Before Numbers"*
Released: November 09, 2010. **Price:** $27.50, hardcover; $7.99, e-book; $20, audiobook download. **Description:** This book helps leaders recognize talent in their employees, and to put that talent to work to help achieve business success. **Availability:** E-book; Print.

28843 ■ *"Talk, Inc.: How Trusted Leaders Use Conversation to Power Their Organizations"* in *Canadian Business (Vol. 85, August 13, 2012, No. 13, pp. 59)*
Ed: Boris Groysberg, Michael Slind. **Price:** $32. **Description:** Review of the book entitled, "Talk, Inc.: How Trusted Leaders Use Conversation to Power Their Organizations". As the title states, this book will help business leaders deliver their messages concisely and effectively. **Availability:** E-book; Print; Online.

28844 ■ *"Tax Tip: Streamlining Sales Tax Collections"* in *Pet Product News (Vol. 66, September 2012, No. 9, pp. 38)*
Ed: Mark E. Battersby. **Description:** Pointers on how pet supplies retailers and managers can streamline sales taxes are presented. Businesses are being challenge by the pressure to collect taxes on goods sold to local customers and competititon from Internet merchants that are not required to collect sales taxes. **Availability:** Online.

28845 ■ *"Teamwork On the Fly: How To Master the New Art of Teaming"* in *Harvard Business Review (Vol. 90, April 2012, No. 4, pp. 72)*
Pub: Harvard Business Review Press
Contact: Moderna V. Pfizer, Contact

Ed: Amy C. Edmondson. **Price:** $8.95. **Description:** Description of the concept of 'teaming' or flexible teamwork is given. Teaming brings together expertise from disparate fields and forms temporary groups to identify innovations and address unanticipate problems. Project management and team leadership are important components of success. **Availability:** Online; PDF.

28846 ■ *"Temp Job, Permanent Fulfillment: How the Desire To Earn a Bit of Extra Cash Opened the Door to a Long-Term Career"* in *Black Enterprise (Vol. 44, June 2014, No. 10, pp. 41)*
Pub: Earl G. Graves Ltd.
Contact: Earl Graves, Jr., President

Description: Profile of Kay Francis who started a temporary job with Darden Restaurants to earn money during her final year of college. After graduation, Francis took a permanent position with the firm and today is the Director, Concept Support and Purchasing for the company.

28847 ■ *"Tempering Urgency Within Your Shop"* in *Modern Machine Shop (Vol. 84, October 2011, No. 5, pp. 16)*
Pub: Gardner Business Media Inc.
Contact: Rick Kline, Jr., President
E-mail: rkline2@gardnerweb.com

Ed: Derek Korn. **Released:** September 20, 2011. **Description:** Because machine shops operate under an environment of urgency, patience can commingle with the pressure to produce products efficiently and timely. **Availability:** Print; Online.

28848 ■ *"The Ten Commandments of Legal Risk Management"* in *Business Horizons (Vol. 51, January-February 2008, No. 1, pp. 13)*
Pub: Elsevier Advanced Technology Publications

Ed: Michael B. Metzger. **Description:** Effective legal risk management is tightly linked with ethical and good management, and managers' behaviors have to be professional and based on ethically defensible principles of action. Basic human tendencies cannot be used in justifying questionable decisions in court. Guidelines for legal risk management are presented. **Availability:** Print; Online.

28849 ■ *"There's Always Something Unexpected"* in *South Florida Business Journal (Vol. 34, June 6, 2014, No. 46, pp. 13)*
Pub: American City Business Journals, Inc.
Contact: Mike Olivieri, Executive Vice President

Released: Weekly. **Price:** $8, introductory 4-week offer(Digital only). **Description:** Hannah Granade, CEO of Advantix Systems, likes how her job allows her to build the business and bring people together. The company, that provides cooling and dehumidification systems for industrial and commercial applications, encourages creative thinking by building an open culture. **Availability:** Print; Online.

28850 ■ *"Think Again: What Makes a Leader?"* in *Business Strategy Review (Vol. 21, Autumn 2010, No. 3, pp. 64)*
Ed: Rob Goffee, Gareth Jones. **Released:** September 29, 2010. **Description:** Leadership cannot be faked and all the self-help books in the world won't make you a leader - but there are four characteristics any leader must possess and they are outlined. **Availability:** Print; PDF; Online.

28851 ■ *"Think Disruptive! How to Manage In a New Era of Innovation"* in *Strategy & Leadership (Vol. 38, July-August 2010, No. 4, pp. 5-10)*
Pub: Emerald Inc.

Ed: Brian Leavy, John Sterling. **Price:** $32, online only 30 days. **Description:** The views expressed by Scott Anthony, president of an innovation consultancy Innosight, on the need for corporate leaders to apply disruptive innovation in a recessionary environment are presented. His suggestion that disruptive innovation is the only way to survive during the economic crisis is discussed. **Availability:** Online; PDF.

28852 ■ *"Thinking Aloud"* in *Business Strategy Review (Vol. 21, Summer 2010, No. 2, pp. 47)*
Description: In each issue we ask an academic to explain the big question on which their research hopes to shed light. Yiorgos Mylonadis looks at how people define and solve problems. **Availability:** Print; Online.

28853 ■ *"Three Signs Your Biz Needs a COO"*
in *Birmingham Business Journal (Vol. 31,*
April 18, 2014, No. 16, pp. 10)
Pub: American City Business Journals, Inc.
Contact: Mike Olivieri, Executive Vice President
Description: Business conditions that warrant the
recruitment of a chief operations officer are discussed.
The halting of growth results in the shifting of focus
from operations to sales. Dependence on one or two
employees can result in resignations. **Availability:**
Print; Online.

28854 ■ *"Three Skills Every 21st Century*
Manager Needs" in *Harvard Business Review*
(Vol. 90, January-February 2012, No.1-2, pp.
139)
Pub: Harvard Business Review Press
Contact: Moderna V. Pfizer, Contact
Ed: Andy L. Molinsky, Bala Iyer, Cathy N. Davidson,
Thomas H. Davenport. **Description:** The first skill is
cultural code-switching, or the ability to adapt to one's
behavior to accommodate variations in cultural norms
for modern managers. The second is effective utilization of online networks. The third is maximizing the
brain's natural tendency to focus on multiple items
simultaneously.

28855 ■ *"To Win With Natural Talent, Go For*
Additive Effects; Four Human Capital
Strategies Combine to Drive Up to 59 Percent
More Growth In Revenue Per Employee" in
Gallup Business Journal (June 3, 2014)
Pub: Gallup, Inc.
Contact: Jon Clifton, Chief Executive Officer
Description: Four human capital strategies, when
used together, can drive growth in revenue per
employee by as much as 59 percent. The strategies
for selecting and implementing the right managers
are explored. **Availability:** Print.

28856 ■ *"Tough Times for the Irving Clan"* in
Canadian Business (Vol. 83, August 17, 2010,
No. 13-14, pp. 14)
Pub: Rogers Media Inc.
Contact: Neil Spivak, Chief Executive Officer
Ed: Dean Jobb. **Description:** The death of John E.
Irving and reported health problems of his nephew
Kenneth Irving was a double blow to the billionaire
Irving clan. Kenneth suddenly left his job as CEO of
Fort Reliance, holding company for Irving Oil and
new energy ventures, wherein the explanation was
for personal reasons. **Availability:** Online.

28857 ■ *"Tracking Your Fleet Can Increase*
Bottom Line" in *Contractor (Vol. 56,*
November 2009, No. 11, pp. 26)
Ed: Candace Roulo. **Description:** GPS fleet management system can help boost a contractor's profits,
employee productivity, and efficiency. These are
available as a handheld device or a cell phone that
employees carry around or as a piece of hardware
installed in a vehicle. These lets managers track assets and communicate with employees about jobs.
Availability: Online.

28858 ■ *"Trial of Enron Ex-Bosses to Begin*
Today" in *Globe & Mail (January 30, 2006, pp.*
B1)
Description: The details of the case against former
executives Kenneth L. Lay and Jeffrey Skilling of En-
ron Corp. are presented. **Availability:** Online.

28859 ■ *"The Trust Edge: How Top Leaders*
Gain Faster Results, Deeper Relationships"
Pub: Free Press Inc.
Contact: Craig Aaron, President
Released: October 09, 2012. **Price:** $28, hardcover;
$14.99, ebook; $17, unabridged audio download;
$29.99, unabridged compact disk. **Description:**
David Horsager provides the eight Pillars of Trust to
business leaders, including managers and entrepreneurs. Those eight trusts are based on research and
are practical for today's leaders. They include: clarity,
compassion, character, competency, commitment,
connection, contribution, and consistency. **Availability:** CD-ROM; E-book; Print; Audio.

28860 ■ *"Tuesday Morning's Corporate*
Clearance Rack" in *Dallas Business Journal*
(Vol. 37, February 28, 2014, No. 25, pp. 4)
Pub: American City Business Journals, Inc.
Contact: Mike Olivieri, Executive Vice President
Released: October 30, 2015. **Description:** Tuesday
Morning CEO, Michael Rouleau, has been working to
help the company recover from its financial problems.
Rouleau has improved the shopping experience from
garage sale to discount showroom. The company
has also been hiring different executives in the past
few years. **Availability:** Print; Online.

28861 ■ *"TWU Offers Course in Project*
Management" in *Bellingham Business*
Journal (Vol. February 2010, pp. 4)
Pub: Sound Publishing Inc.
Contact: Josh O'Connor, President
Ed: Lance Henderson. **Description:** Trinity Western
University in Bellinham, Washington is offering a new
certification program in project management. Stu-
dents who take and pass the certification examina-
tion of the International Project Management Institutes
will lead to positions in many industries. Details of
the program are provided.

28862 ■ *Ubuntu!: An Aspiring Story About an*
African Tradition of Teamwork and
Collaboration
Pub: Broadway Business
Ed: Bob Nelson, Stephen Lundin. **Released:** March
30, 2010. **Price:** $23, paperback; $9. **Description:**
The African tradition of teamwork and collaboration is
used to demonstrate these skills to small business
leaders. **Availability:** E-book; Print; Download; Audio.

28863 ■ *"Under Pressure"* in *Canadian*
Business (Vol. 81, July 21, 2008, No. 11, pp.
18)
Description: According to a survey conducted by
COMPASS Inc., meeting revenue targets is the main
cause of job stress for chief executive officers. Staffing and keeping expenditures lower also contribute to
the workplace stress experienced by business executives. Other results of the survey are presented.
Availability: Online.

28864 ■ *"An Unfair Knock on Nokia"* in
Barron's (Vol. 88, March 10, 2008, No. 10, pp.
36)
Pub: Dow Jones & Company Inc.
Contact: Almar Latour, Chief Executive Officer
Ed: Mark Veverka. **Description:** Discusses the decision by the brokerage house Exane to recommend a
Sell on Nokia shares, presumably due to higher
inventories, which is unfounded. The news that the
company's inventories are rising is not an indicator of
falling demand for its products. The company is also
benefiting from solid management and rising market
share. **Availability:** Online.

28865 ■ *"Unilever's CMO Finally Gets Down*
To Business" in *Advertising Age (Vol. 79, July*
7, 2008, No. 26, pp. 11)
Description: Overview of Unilever's chief marketing
officer Simon Clift's strategy for promoting its products; now that the company has restructured, Clift is
able to focus all of his energy on the challenges of
the new-media climate that marketers are having to
face. **Availability:** Print; Online.

28866 ■ *"Unveiling the Secrets Behind*
Hispanic Business' 100 Fastest-Growing
Companies" in *Hispanic Business (Vol. 30,*
July-August 2008, No. 7-8, pp. 22)
Ed: Michael Bowker. **Description:** CEO's of the five
fastest growing Hispanic-owned companies discuss
the success of their companies; most of them attribute their success to proper investment and
diversification, effective innovations and seeing
growth opportunities where others see roadblocks.
Availability: Online.

28867 ■ *"Valuable Lessons"* in *Minority*
Business Entrepreneur (Vol. 39, Fall, 2022,
No. 4, pp. 28-31)
URL(s): digital.mbemag.com/?m=53732&i=769780
   &p=28&ver=html5

Ed: Tanya Isley. **Price:** $7.95. **Description:** Profile of
William Randall, CEO of Boateng Logistics. **Availability:** Print; Online.

28868 ■ *"The Value of Conversations With*
Employees; Talk Isn't Cheap" in *Gallup*
Management Journal (June 30, 2011)
Ed: Jessica Tyler. **Released:** June 30, 2011. **Description:** When managers have meaningful exchanges
with their employees, they don't only show they care,
they also add value to their organization's bottom
line. **Availability:** Print; Online.

28869 ■ *"Voices: More Important than*
Results" in *Business Strategy Review (Vol.*
21, Summer 2010, No. 2, pp. 81)
Ed: Bert De Reyck, Zeger Degraeve. **Released:** June
24, 2010. **Description:** Managing only for results
leads to crises. It is important to reward people for
the decisions they make, not just for the results they
create. **Availability:** Print; Online.

28870 ■ *"Voices: The Strategic Innovation*
Cube" in *Business Strategy Review (Vol. 23,*
Spring 2012, No. 1, pp. 84)
Description: Companies that innovate tend to
prosper. Yet the process used by most innovative
firms remains a mystery. Is there a way that any
company can discern whether to commit resources
to an innovation idea? Kiriti Rambhatla has blended
the fields of science and management and offers a
new way of thinking about innovation inside any
company. **Availability:** Online.

28871 ■ *"Wal-Mart China Woes Add Up"* in
Wall Street Journal Eastern Edition (October
17, 2011, pp. B3)
Pub: Dow Jones & Company Inc.
Contact: Almar Latour, Chief Executive Officer
Ed: Laurie Burkitt. **Description:** Woes for Wal-Mart
Inc.'s subsidiary in China are adding up as Wal-Mart
China president and chief executive Ed Chan stepped
down, as well as the company's senior vice president
for human resources, Clara Wong. The company has
been charged by regulators with mislabeling pork
products, the result which has forced stores to close.
Sales in China have been slow at the retail stores.
Availability: Online.

28872 ■ *"Wanted: African American*
Professional for Hire" in *Black Enterprise*
(Vol. 37, November 2006, No. 4, pp. 93)
Pub: Earl G. Graves Ltd.
Contact: Earl Graves, Jr., President
Ed: Joe Watson. **Description:** Excerpt from the book,
Without Excuses: Unleash the Power of Diversity to
Build Your Business, speaks to the lack of diversity in
the corporate arena and why executives, recruiters,
and HR professionals claim they are unable to find
qualified individuals of different races when hiring.
Availability: Online.

28873 ■ *"Web-Based Solutions Streamline*
Operations" in *Contractor (Vol. 56, December*
2009, No. 12, pp. 28)
Ed: William Feldman, Patti Feldman. **Description:**
Sage Project Lifecycle Management is a Web-based
service platform for plumbing and HVAC contractors.
It enables effective workflow and document management. Projectmates, on the other hand, is a Web-
based enterprise-wide solution for managing both
commercial plumbing and HVAC projects. **Availability:** Print; Online.

28874 ■ *"Web Site Focuses on Helping*
People Find Jobs, Internships with Area
Businesses" in *Crain's Detroit Business (Vol.*
26, Jan. 4, 2010)
Pub: Crain Communications Inc.
Contact: Barry Asin, President
Ed: Dustin Walsh. **Description:** DetroitIntern.com,
LLC is helping metro Detroit college students and
young professionals find career-advancing intern-
ships or jobs with local businesses. **Availability:**
Print; Online.

28875 ■ "A Well-Crafted Employee Handbook Can Make Work Run More Smoothly" in Idaho Business Review (September 17, 2014)
Pub: BridgeTower Media
Contact: Adam Reinebach, President
Description: An employee handbook will provide a complaint process, provide company management flexibility and clarity and keep a company out of legal problems. Training, compensation, benefits, security, health, performance appraisals, and safety issues must be covered. Human resource managers and other mangers should cover basics to help communicate with workers.

28876 ■ "Weyerhaeuser's REIT Decision Shouldn't Scare Investors Away" in Barron's (Vol. 88, June 30, 2008, No. 26, pp. 18)
Pub: Dow Jones & Company Inc.
Contact: Almar Latour, Chief Executive Officer
Ed: Christopher Williams. **Description:** Weyerhaeuser Co.'s management said that a conversion to a real estate investment trust was not likely in 2009 since the move is not tax-efficient as of the moment and would overload its non-timber assets with debt. The company's shares have fallen by 19.5 percent. However, the company remains an asset-rich outfit and its activist shareholder is pushing for change. **Availability:** Online.

28877 ■ A Whack on the Side of the Head: How You Can Be More Creative
Ed: Roger von Oech. **Released:** 25th anniversary edition. **Price:** $17, paperback. **Description:** The author, a consultant, shares insight into increasing entrepreneurial creativity. **Availability:** Print.

28878 ■ "What Comes After That Job Is Cut?" in Business Review Albany (Vol. 41, August 15, 2014, No. 21, pp. 4)
Released: Weekly. **Price:** $4, Print. **Description:** Former KeyBank regional president, Jeff Stone, has joined the list of well-known banking executives who have reinvented themselves as the financial industry transforms around the Albany, NY area. Stone, as well as other leading bank leaders, have transitioned to smaller banks or other industries. Insights into the Banking Industry's Act II are provided. **Availability:** Print; Online.

28879 ■ "What It Takes to Be an Effective Leader" in Black Enterprise (Vol. 41, December 2010, No. 5, pp. 62)
Pub: Earl G. Graves Ltd.
Contact: Earl Graves, Jr., President
Ed: Sonia Alleyne. **Description:** Redia Anderson and Lenora Billings-Harris have partnered to write the book, 'Trailblazers: How Top Business Leaders Are Accelerating Results Through Inclusion and Diversity'. The book offers insight into best practices demonstrated by some of the most influential chief diversity officers in business. **Availability:** Online.

28880 ■ "What Kind of Golfer Are You?" in Baltimore Business Journal (Vol. 29, May 4, 2012, No. 53, pp. 1)
Ed: Gary Haber. **Description:** Businesspeople playing golf are classified into different profiles according to style. These profiles also describe the behavior of businessmen during and after playing golf. **Availability:** Print; Online.

28881 ■ "What Kind of Leader Are You?" in Inc. (Vol. 36, September 2014, No. 7, pp. 76)
Pub: Mansueto Ventures L.L.C.
Contact: Stephanie Mehta, Chief Executive Officer
Description: Ranking of leadership skills for entrepreneurs and managers is presented, with being a visionary leading each category. **Availability:** Print; Online.

28882 ■ What Makes People Tick: How to Understand Yourself and Others
Pub: AWC Business Solutions
Released: February 10, 2015. **Price:** $20.99, large print 16pt edition; $20.99, large print 16pt bold edition; $20.99, super large 18pt bold edition; $20.99, super large 20pt bold edition; $19.99, super large

24pt bold edition. **Description:** Management and Human Resources Development and Psychology expert offers a guide to self-discovery and personal growth. Job Compatibility Indicator is used to pinpoint the most suitable personality for each occupation. **Availability:** Large print.

28883 ■ "What Your Employees Need to Know; They Probably Don't Know How They're Performing" in Gallup Management Journal (April 13, 2011)
Ed: Steve Crabtree. **Released:** April 13, 2011. **Description:** Personalized feedback and recognition aren't just extras that make workers feel good about themselves they are critical predictors of positive performance. **Availability:** Print; Online.

28884 ■ "What's More Important: Talent or Engagement? A Study With Retailer ANN INC. Seeks To Find the Essential Ingredients To High-Performing Managers and Employees" in Gallup Business Journal (April 22, 2014)
Pub: Gallup, Inc.
Contact: Jon Clifton, Chief Executive Officer
Description: ANN INC. is a leading women's clothing retailer that is exploring the necessary steps to achieving both high-performing managers and employees. The firm found that hiring people with the right talent and engaging them will maximize performance. **Availability:** Online.

28885 ■ "What's the Ticket to a Higher-Paying Corporate Position?" in Orlando Business Journal (Vol. 29, September 14, 2012, No. 13, pp. 1)
Pub: Baltimore Business Journal
Contact: Rhonda Pringle, President
E-mail: rpringle@bizjournals.com
Description: Advice on how to land higher-paying executive jobs in the US is presented. Understanding organization politics as well as compensation is encouraged. Employment alternatives for executives are also given. **Availability:** Print; Online.

28886 ■ "When Emotional Reasoning Trumps IQ" in Harvard Business Review (Vol. 88, September 2010, No. 9, pp. 27)
Pub: Harvard Business Publishing
Contact: Diane Belcher, Managing Director
Ed: Roderick Gilkey, Ricardo Caceda, Clinton Kilts. **Price:** $6, PDF. **Description:** Strategic reasoning was found to be linked more closely to areas of the brain associated with intuition and emotion, rather than the prefrontal cortex, which is typically thought to be the center of such activity. Implications for management skills are discussed. **Availability:** Online; PDF.

28887 ■ "When and How to Innovate Your Business Model" in Strategy & Leadership (Vol. 38, July-August 2010, No. 4, pp. 17-26)
Pub: Emerald Inc.
Ed: Edward Giesen, Eric Riddleberger, Richrd Christner, Ragna Bell. **Description:** A study uses survey data to identify factors that are considered by corporate leaders regarding when and how they should innovate their business model. Findings identify a set of characteristics called the 'Three A's, Namely, Aligned, Analytical and Adaptable, which corporate leaders use consistently to successfully design and execute business-model innovation. **Availability:** PDF; Online.

28888 ■ "When Key Employees Clash: How Should a Business Owner Handle a Conflict Between Two Senior Managers?" in Harvard Business Review (Vol. 90, June 2012, No. 6, pp. 135)
Pub: Harvard Business Review Press
Contact: Moderna V. Pfizer, Contact
Ed: H. Irving Grousbeck. **Price:** $8.95. **Description:** A fictitious employee conflict scenario is presented, with contributors providing suggestions for an effective management plan. The key component is ensur-

ing that both employees receive the coaching and support necessary to enable them to perceive their roles more clearly and to build trust. **Availability:** Online; PDF.

28889 ■ "When You Need Strong Millennials in Your Workplace" in Agency Sales Magazine (Vol. 39, November 2009, No. 10, pp. 22)
Description: Millennials are bringing a new set of skills and a different kind of work ethics to the workplace. This generation is used to receiving a great deal of positive feedback and they expect to continue receiving this on the job. Expectations should be made clear to this generation and long-term career plans and goals should also be discussed with them. **Availability:** Online.

28890 ■ "Where Are They Now?" in Canadian Business (Vol. 79, October 9, 2006, No. 20, pp. 71)
Ed: Jeff Sanford, Zena Olijnyk, Andrew Wahl, Andy Holloway, John Gray. **Description:** The profile of the top chief executive officers of Canada for the year 2005 is discussed. **Availability:** Online.

28891 ■ "Where Do Women Stand? Leaders Don't Skirt the Issue" in Birmingham Business Journal (Vol. 31, April 4, 2014, No. 14, pp. 4)
Pub: American City Business Journals, Inc.
Contact: Mike Olivieri, Executive Vice President
Description: Women business executives discuss ways women are faring in the workplace. City Paper Company's Cathy Friedman says equality remains the biggest challenge for women in the workplace. Mayer Electric Supply's Nancy Goedecke, believes company's should encourage women to try new things. **Availability:** Print; Online.

28892 ■ "Why Bossy Is Better for Rookie Managers" in Harvard Business Review (Vol. 90, May 2012, No. 5, pp. 30)
Pub: Harvard Business Review Press
Contact: Moderna V. Pfizer, Contact
Ed: Stephen J. Sauer. **Price:** $6. **Description:** New managers can enhance their standing by taking control and appearing decisive and confident, especially if they may be perceived as having low status due to education, age, or experience. However, those who are already perceived as high status can be most effective by soliciting input. **Availability:** Online; PDF.

28893 ■ "Why Creating Organizational Change Is So Hard; Resistance To Change Is Entrenched In Most Companies. Here's How To Overcome Obstacles and Create Change That Lasts" in Gallup Business Journal (May 22, 2014)
Pub: Gallup, Inc.
Contact: Jon Clifton, Chief Executive Officer
Description: Poorly defined objectives, politics, and unclear metrics are come of the obstacles to implementing meaningful change in any organization. Employees are motivated to change if leaders provide hope and inspiration. Ways that companies can overcome barriers to change are examined. **Availability:** Print; Online.

28894 ■ "Why Great Managers Are So Rare; Companies Fail To Choose the Candidate With the Right Talent For the Job 82 Percent of the Time, Gallup Finds" in Gallup Business Journal (March 25, 2014)
Pub: Gallup, Inc.
Contact: Jon Clifton, Chief Executive Officer
Description: Gallup research suggests that companies hire the wrong person to manage their firm about 82 percent of the time. Many times management talent already exists within the company, but for some reason, companies look elsewhere for that talent. Bad managers cost billions of dollars to businesses annually. **Availability:** Print.

28895 ■ "Why HR Practices Are Not Evidence-Based" in Academy of Management Journal (Vol. 50, No. 5, October 1, 2007, pp. 1033)
Pub: Academy of Management
Contact: Sharon Alvarez, President
Ed: Edward E. Lawler. **Description:** A suggestion that an Evidence-Based Management Collaboration (EBMC) can be established to facilitate effective transfer of ideas between science and practice is presented. **Availability:** Electronic publishing; PDF; Download; Online.

28896 ■ "Why I Stopped Firing Everyone and Started Being a Better Boss" in Inc. (Vol. 34, September 2012, No. 7, pp. 86)
Pub: Mansueto Ventures L.L.C.
Contact: Stephanie Mehta, Chief Executive Officer
Ed: April Joyner. **Released:** August 28, 2012. **Description:** Indigo Johnson, former Marine, discusses her management style when starting her business. She fired employees regularly. Johnson enrolled in a PhD program in leadership and established a better hiring program and learned to utilize her workers' strengths. **Availability:** Print; Online.

28897 ■ "Why Men Still Get More Promotions Than Women" in Harvard Business Review (Vol. 88, September 2010, No. 9, pp. 80)
Pub: Harvard Business Publishing
Contact: Diane Belcher, Managing Director
Ed: Herminia Ibarra, Nancy M. Carter, Christine Silva. **Price:** $8.95, PDF. **Description:** Sponsorship, rather than mentoring, is identified as the main difference in why men still receive more promotions than women. Active executive sponsorship is key to fostering career advancement. **Availability:** Online; PDF.

28898 ■ "Why Motivating People Doesn't Work...and What Does: The New Science of Leading, Energizing, and Engaging"
Released: September 30, 2014. **Price:** $20.95, Nonmembers, PDF e-book; $18.86, Members, electronic publishing; $20.95, Nonmembers, paperback; $18.86, Members, paperback; $24.95, Nonmembers, hardcover; $22.46, Members, hardcover; $20.95, Nonmembers, electronic publishing; $14.67, Members, electronic publishing; $18.95, PDF e-book; $14.67, Members, PDF e-book. **Description:** Leadership researcher, consultant, and business coach, Susan Fowler, shares the latest research on the nature of human motivation to present a tested model and course of action to help Human Resource leaders and managers guide workers towards motivation that will not only increase productivity and engagement but will provide employees with a sense of purpose and fulfillment. **Availability:** E-book; Print; PDF; Electronic publishing.

28899 ■ "Why People Believe Things That Aren't True inside Your Company" in Small Business Trends (October 3, 2022)
URL(s): smallbiztrends.com/2022/10/illusionary-truth-effect.html
Released: October 03, 2022. **Description:** A discussion of how workplace leaders can use four strategies to prevent workplace misinformation from spreading. **Availability:** Online.

28900 ■ "Why Slacking Off Is Great For Business" in Canadian Business (Vol. 85, August 13, 2012, No. 13, pp. 60)
Ed: Sarah Barmak. **Description:** Procrastination can be good for busy managers to develop creative thinking which may be good for business. Ways to enhance the brain's creative engine including taking a different route to the office, reading a best seller, or playing golf. **Availability:** Print; Online.

28901 ■ "Why Successful Entrepreneurs Are Effective Delegators; Shifting from a Do-It-Yourself Executive Style to a More Hands-Off Approach Is Essential When They're Growing a Business" in Gallup Business Journal (August 26, 2014)
Pub: Gallup, Inc.
Contact: Jon Clifton, Chief Executive Officer

Description: It is critical for entrepreneurs to step away from a do-it-yourself executive style to a more hands-off approach when a company begins to grow. **Availability:** Print; Online.

28902 ■ "Why To Embrace Positive Leadership" in Birmingham Business Journal (Vol. 31, February 7, 2014, No. 6, pp. 14)
Pub: American City Business Journals, Inc.
Contact: Mike Olivieri, Executive Vice President
Released: Weekly. **Price:** $4, introductory 4-week offer(Digital only). **Description:** The benefits achieved from managers' adoption of positive leadership are discussed. Positive leadership motivates employees to achieve higher performance levels. Tips to achieve positive leadership are listed. **Availability:** Print; Online.

28903 ■ "Why Top Young Managers Are In a Nonstop Job Hunt" in Harvard Business Review (Vol. 90, July-August 2012, No. 7-8, pp. 28)
Pub: Harvard Business Review Press
Contact: Moderna V. Pfizer, Contact
Ed: Monika Hamori, Jie Cao, Burak Koyuncu. **Price:** $6. **Description:** Managers are moving from firm to firm in part because companies are not addressing formal training, coaching, and mentoring needs. While these are costly, companies might benefit from the investment, as managers may tend to stay longer in firms where they are provided. **Availability:** Online; PDF.

28904 ■ "Why Your Company Must Be Mission-Driven; A Clear Mission Inspires Employee Engagement, Fosters Customer Engagement, and Helps Boost Company Performance -- Among Other Benefits" in Gallup Business Journal (March 6, 2014)
Pub: Gallup, Inc.
Contact: Jon Clifton, Chief Executive Officer
Description: It is stressed that executives need a clear mission in order to engage their workers, foster customer engagement, and to help boost their firm's performance. **Availability:** Print; Online.

28905 ■ "Wilderness Leadership - On the Job: Five Principles From Outdoor Exploration That Will Make You a Better Manager" in Harvard Business Review (Vol. 90, April 2012, No. 4, pp. 127)
Pub: Harvard Business Review Press
Contact: Moderna V. Pfizer, Contact
Ed: John Kanengieter, Aparna Rajagopal-Durbin. **Description:** Five principles of wilderness leadership are: practicing leadership, leading from everywhere, behaving well, remaining calm, and disconnecting to connect. Key points include knowing when to offer leadership to another member, and taking a break from technological devices that can distract from critical thinking.

28906 ■ "Winners and Losers" in Crain's Detroit Business (Vol. 25, June 22, 2009, No. 25, pp. 18)
Pub: Crain Communications Inc.
Contact: Barry Asin, President
Description: Rankings for Detroit's 50 top-compensated CEOs has changed due to the economic recession. The biggest changes are discussed. **Availability:** Online.

28907 ■ "A Woman's Advantage" in Black Enterprise (Vol. 38, December 2007, No. 5, pp. 86)
Pub: Earl G. Graves Ltd.
Contact: Earl Graves, Jr., President
Ed: Marcia A. Reed-Woodard. **Description:** Leadership development is essential for any small business. Simmons College's Strategic Leadership for Women educational course offers a five-day program for professional women teaching powerful strategies to perform, compete, and win in the workplace. **Availability:** Online.

28908 ■ "Women as 21st Century Leaders" in Women In Business (Vol. 63, Summer 2011, No. 2, pp. 26)
Pub: American Business Women's Association
Contact: Rene Street, Executive Director
Ed: Leigh Elmore. **Description:** American Business Women's Association and Park University have partnered to provide a leadership training program to attendees of the 2011 National Women's Leadership Conference. The courses will incorporate introduction to concepts, development of critical thinking skills and direct application through exercises. Comments from executives are also included. **Availability:** Online.

28909 ■ "The World Is Your Oyster" in Canadian Business (Vol. 80, October 22, 2007, No. 21, pp. 140)
Description: Business graduates are not that keen on working abroad. Fortune 500 companies are requiring executives to have a multi-country focus. The skill required for jobs abroad, as well as employment opportunities are discussed.

28910 ■ "World's Best CEOs" in Barron's (Vol. 88, March 24, 2008, No. 12, pp. 33)
Pub: Dow Jones & Company Inc.
Contact: Almar Latour, Chief Executive Officer
Ed: Andrew Bary. **Description:** Listing of the 30 best chief executive officers worldwide which was compiled through interviews with investors and analysts, analysis of financial and stock market performance, and leadership and industry stature.

28911 ■ "Worth His Salt" in Hawaii Business (Vol. 53, January 2008, No. 7, pp. 45)
Pub: PacificBasin Communications
Contact: Chuck Tindle, Director
E-mail: chuckt@pacificbasin.net
Ed: Jolyn Okimoto Rosa. **Description:** Bryan Zada owns three PretzelMaker franchises, whose total loss amounted to $40,000 in 2003. Zada believes that listening to employees was one of the key steps in turning the business around. The efforts made to improve the franchises' products are also given. **Availability:** Online.

28912 ■ "You Have to Lead From Everywhere" in Harvard Business Review (Vol. 88, November 2010, No. 11, pp. 76)
Pub: Harvard Business Publishing
Contact: Diane Belcher, Managing Director
Ed: Scott Berinato. **Price:** $8.95, PDF. **Description:** U.S. Coast Guard Admiral Thad W. Allen discusses effective leadership in successful crises management. Topics include influence of media and public perspective, the applicability of military training to the business arena, and the responsibility of a leader to set morale. **Availability:** Online; PDF.

28913 ■ "Young Executives Share Leadership Lessons" in Pittsburgh Business Times (Vol. 33, April 25, 2014, No. 41, pp. 4)
Pub: American City Business Journals, Inc.
Contact: Mike Olivieri, Executive Vice President
Released: Weekly. **Price:** $4, introductory 4-week offer(Digital only). **Description:** Some members of the Pittsburgh chapter of the Young Presidents' Organization in Pennsylvania participated in a roundtable discussion exploring the different aspects of leadership. They discuss the importance of leadership, the challenges they faced and the defining moments of their careers. **Availability:** Print; Online.

28914 ■ "Your First 100 Days on Your New Job" in Women In Business (Vol. 63, Spring 2011, No. 1, pp. 28)
Pub: American Business Women's Association
Contact: Rene Street, Executive Director
Ed: Diane Stafford. **Released:** March 22, 2011. **Description:** The first 100 days on the job are crucial if the person's permanent hiring is conditional on surviving a probationary period. The new hire must do more than just master the job's technical details to maximize the chance of success. Details of some

basic tips to fit into the corporate culture and get along with coworkers are also discussed. **Availability:** Print; Online.

28915 ■ *"Your Web Brand Counts" in Black Enterprise (Vol. 44, June 2014, No. 10, pp. 46)*
Pub: Earl G. Graves Ltd.
Contact: Earl Graves, Jr., President
Description: Forty-eight percent of employers use Google or other search engines to find information about job applicants and 25 percent of executives hired were originally identified or contacted through social media, thus the importance of a good Web presence is outlined.

TRADE PERIODICALS

28916 ■ *Human Factors and Ergonomics in Manufacturing & Service Industries*
Pub: Wiley Periodicals Inc.
Contact: Brian Napack, Chief Executive Officer
URL(s): onlinelibrary.wiley.com/journal/15206564

Ed: Paul Salmon. **Released:** Bimonthly **Price:** $2,115, Institutions for online only Canada and US, India. **Description:** International journal focusing on the discovery, integration, application, and translation of scientific knowledge within the field of human factors and ergonomics (HFE). **Availability:** Print; Download; PDF; Online.

28917 ■ *Journal of Economics and Management Strategy (JEMS)*
Pub: Wiley Periodicals Inc.
Contact: Brian Napack, Chief Executive Officer
URL(s): onlinelibrary.wiley.com/journal/15309134
Facebook: www.facebook.com/jemsjournal

Ed: Daniel F. Spulber, Ramon Casadesus-Masanell. **Released:** Quarterly **Price:** $756, Institutions for print and online US, Canada; $86, Individuals for online UC, Canada, India; $1,101, Institutions for print and online India; $672, Institutions for online US, Canada; $701, Institutions for print US, Canada; $1,033, Institutions for online India; $1,078, Institutions for print India. **Description:** Journal covering theoretical and empirical industrial organization, applied game theory, and management strategy. **Availability:** Print; PDF; Download; Online.

28918 ■ *Quality Management Journal (QMJ)*
Pub: Taylor & Francis Group (Journals)
Contact: Annie Callanan, Chief Executive Officer
URL(s): www.tandfonline.com/journals/uqmj20
Released: Quarterly **Price:** $153, Individuals for print and online; $2,323, Institutions for print and online; $1,905, Institutions for online only. **Description:** Peer-reviewed journal covering research relevant to quality management practice and providing a forum for discussion of such research by academics and practitioners. An official journal of the American Society for Quality. **Availability:** Print; Download; PDF; Online.

28919 ■ *Small Business Taxes and Management*
Pub: A/N Group Inc.
Contact: Steven A. Hopfenmuller, Chief Executive Officer
URL(s): www.smbiz.com
Released: Daily; Monday thru Friday. **Description:** Offers current tax news, reviews of recent cases, tax saving tips, and personal financial planning for small business owners. Includes articles on issues such as finance and management. Remarks: Available online only. **Availability:** Print.

28920 ■ *Supervisors Legal Update*
Pub: American Future Systems Inc.
Contact: Edward G. Rendell, Governor
URL(s): www.pbp.com/divisions/publishing/newsletters/human-resources/supervisors-legal-update
Released: Semimonthly **Description:** Supplies brief updates on employment law for supervisors. Review a column titled Sharpen Your Judgment. **Availability:** Print; Online.

VIDEO/AUDIO MEDIA

28921 ■ *BS-Free Service Business Show: Antidote to Overwhelm and Overwork When You Work with Clients*
URL(s): bsfreebusiness.com/overwhelm-with-clients
Ed: Maggie Patterson. **Released:** May 27, 2024.
Description: Podcast discussed capacity planning.

28922 ■ *HBR Ideacast: An Astronaut's Advice on High-Stakes Collaboration*
URL(s): hbr.org/podcast/2024/07/an-astronauts-advice-on-high-stakes-collaboration
Ed: Alison Beard. **Released:** July 30, 2024. **Description:** Podcast discusses how to collaboratively manage team stress, assess risk, and navigate bias.

28923 ■ *HBR Ideacast: Here's How Managers Can Rediscover Their Joy at Work*
URL(s): hbr.org/podcast/2024/10/heres-how-managers-can-rediscover-their-joy-at-work
Ed: Alison Beard. **Released:** October 15, 2024.
Description: Podcast offer tips and techniques for leaders who are feeling burnt out.

28924 ■ *HBR Ideacast: Lessons from a Turnaround Expert*
URL(s): hbr.org/podcast/2024/08/lessons-from-a-turnaround-expert
Ed: Alison Beard. **Released:** August 27, 2024.
Description: Podcast explains that turnarounds are possible if you have a hard-working team, can be creative, and will embrace change.

28925 ■ *HBR Ideacast: Why You Need to Stress Test Your Strategies (and Tactics)*
URL(s): hbr.org/podcast/2024/06/why-you-need-to-stress-test-your-strategies-and-tactics
Ed: Alison Beard. **Released:** June 04, 2024. **Description:** Podcast explains the importance of testing strategies, operations, and tactics to see how they hold up against competitors, market dynamics, and unexpected events.

28926 ■ *How To Balance Empathy and Accountability with Maria Ross*
URL(s): www.eofire.com/podcast/mariaross2
Ed: Jon Dumas. **Released:** November 05, 2024.
Description: Podcast discusses the role of empathy in business and leadership.

28927 ■ *The Knowledge Project: Jim Collins: Relationships vs. Transactions*
URL(s): fs.blog/knowldege-project-podcast/jim-collins-2
Ed: Shane Parrish. **Released:** May 04, 2021. **Description:** Podcast offers a practical guide for leadership, discusses trusting by default, and explains the difference between "risk afraid" and "ambiguity afraid."

28928 ■ *The Knowledge Project: Ravi Gupta: The Realities of Success*
URL(s): fs.blog/knowldege-project-podcast/ravi-gupta
Ed: Shane Parrish. **Released:** April 18, 2023.
Description: Podcast discusses the realities of success and decision-making.

28929 ■ *The Knowledge Project: Reid Hoffman: Better Decision, Fewer Mistakes*
URL(s): fs.blog/knowldege-project-podcast/reid-hoffman
Ed: Shane Parrish. **Released:** September 19, 2022.
Description: Podcast discusses scaling, making decision, evolving your learning pattern, and adapting to the crisis at hand.

28930 ■ *The Knowledge Project: Roger Martin: Forward Thinking*
URL(s): fs.blog/knowldege-project-podcast/roger-martin
Ed: Shane Parrish. **Released:** November 24, 2020.
Description: Podcast discusses leadership, decision making, and self-sabotage.

28931 ■ *Legal Protection for Entrepreneurs and How to Leverage It for Business Growth with Attorney Nuzayra Haque*
URL(s): theceoschool.co/?s=247
Ed: Suneera Madhani. **Released:** June 26, 2023.
Description: Podcast discusses how legal can be used as an asset to protect and grow businesses, the do's and don'ts of legal contracts, and the support of professional networks to benefit entrepreneurs.

28932 ■ *Shifting Your Company's Culture*
URL(s): www.startuphustlepodcast.com/shifting-your-companys-culture
Ed: Matthews DeCoursey. **Released:** October 12, 2023. **Description:** Podcast discusses company culture, the impact of leaders who shape it, and the components of its cultivation.

28933 ■ *Side Hustle to Small Business: How Ryan Klee Leads with Purpose through Thought Leadership*
URL(s): sidehustletosmallbusiness.podbean.com/e/how-ryan-klee-leads-with-purpose-through-thought-leadership
Ed: Sanjay Parekh. **Released:** October 16, 2024.
Description: Podcast discusses venturing into entrepreneurship, strategic planning, and refining narratives.

28934 ■ *Think Business with Tyler: Leadership and Vision in Business with Bryce Henson*
URL(s): thinktyler.com/podcast_episode/leadership-and-vision-bryce-henson
Ed: Tyler Martin. **Released:** April 29, 2024. **Description:** Podcast discusses the role of leadership in scaling a business. Also covers the importance of maintaining consistency, managing cash flow, and finding strong sales and marketing strategies in franchising.

28935 ■ *This Is Small Business: How to Future-Proof Your Business*
URL(s): www.smallbusiness.amazon/podcast-episodes/eo-42-how-to-future-proof-your-business
Ed: Andrea Marquez. **Released:** December 05, 2023.
Description: Podcast explains how to use AI or technology to ease your workload.

28936 ■ *You Need THIS Mindset (Attention Small Biz Owners!) with Julie Sellers*
URL(s): www.makinggoodpodcast.com/episodes/233-1
Ed: Lauren Tilden. **Released:** April 23, 2024. **Description:** Podcast explains how "CEO" is a mindset to help you reach your goals.

TRADE SHOWS AND CONVENTIONS

28937 ■ *ARMA InfoCon*
ARMA International
312 SW Greenwich Dr., Ste. 515
Lees Summit, MO 64082
Free: 844-565-2120
Fax: (913)257-3855
Co. E-mail: education@armaintl.org
URL: http://www.arma.org
Contact: Margaret Hermesmeyer, Chairman
E-mail: margaret.hermesmeyer@armaintl.org
URL(s): s6.goeshow.com/arma/infocon/2024
Frequency: Annual. **Audience:** Governance professionals and management professionals. **Telecommunication Services:** conference@armaintl.org.

28938 ■ *Club Managers Association of America Conference and Expo*
URL(s): www.cmaa.org/conference
Frequency: Annual. **Description:** Expo for the hospitality industry showcasing products and services geared towards club management personnel. **Principal Exhibits:** Expo for the hospitality industry showcasing products and services geared towards club management personnel.

CONSULTANTS

28939 ■ 108 Ideaspace Inc.
2 Bloor St. W, 700
  Toronto, ON, Canada M4W 3E2
Ph: (416)256-7773
Free: 888-802-1147
Fax: (416)256-7763
Co. E-mail: hello@108ideaspace.com
URL: http://108ideaspace.com
Contact: Ashish Malik, Chief Executive Officer
Facebook: www.facebook.com/108ideaspace
Linkedin: www.linkedin.com/company/108ideaspace
X (Twitter): x.com/108Ideaspace
Description: Marketing consultant who teaches strategy, technology and design techniques to organizations. **Scope:** Marketing consultant who teaches strategy, technology and design techniques to organizations. **Founded:** 1994. **Publications:** "Leaving the Mother Ship"; "The Working Resume". **Training:** No Job, Now What; Social Media Executive Briefing; Career Networking for Success; Development; Work-Life Balance; Integrated marketing planning workshop.

28940 ■ ABONAR Business Consultants Ltd.
240-222 Baseline Rd., Ste. 212
  Sherwood Park, AB, Canada T8H 1S8
Ph: (780)862-0282
Fax: (866)405-4510
Co. E-mail: info@abonarconsultants.com
URL: http://www.abonarconsultants.com
Contact: Nav Khinda, Contact
E-mail: nav.khinda@abonarconsultants.com
Facebook: www.facebook.com/Abonar-Business
  -Consultants-Ltd-198161584454
X (Twitter): x.com/abonarbusiness
Description: Provider of business plans, financial, operation and strategic management business consulting services. **Scope:** Provider of business plans, financial, operation and strategic management business consulting services.

28941 ■ Advisory Management Services Inc.
9600 E 129th St.
  Kansas City, MO 64149
Contact: William H. Wood, President
Description: A management consulting and training firm specializing in employee relations, management and staff training, organizational development, strategic planning and continuous quality improvement. **Scope:** A management consulting and training firm specializing in employee relations, management and staff training, organizational development, strategic planning and continuous quality improvement. **Founded:** 1979.

28942 ■ The Alliance Management Group Inc.
38 Old Chester Rd., Ste. 300
  Gladstone, NJ 07934
Ph: (908)234-2344
Fax: (908)234-0638
URL: http://www.strategicalliance.com
Contact: Dr. Gene Slowinski, Director
Description: Firm is engaged in business management consultant such as integration, technology management and related services. **Scope:** Firm is engaged in business management consultant such as integration, technology management and related services. **Publications:** "Effective Practices For Sourcing Innovation," Jan-Feb, 2009; "Intellectual Property Issues in Collaborative Research Agreements," Nov-Dec, 2008; "Building University Relationships in China," Sep-Oct, 2008; "Reinventing Corporate Growth: Implementing the Transformational Growth Model"; "The Strongest Link"; "Allocating Patent Rights in Collaborative Research Agreements"; "Protecting Know-how and Trade Secrets in Collaborative Research Agreements," Aug, 2006; "Sourcing External Technology for Innovation," Jun, 2006. **Special Services:** "Want, Find, Get, Manage" Model®; "Want, Find, Get, Manage" Framework®; WFGM Framework®; The Alliance Implementation Program®; WFGM Paradigm®; WFGM Model®; "Want, Find, Get, Manage" Paradigm®, Transformational Growth®; T-growth®.

28943 ■ Alliance Management International Ltd.
6200 Rockside Rd.
  Cleveland, OH 44131
Contact: Carolyn K. Matheson, Contact
Description: A consulting company that helps to form national and international strategic alliances. Handles alliances between companies forming joint ventures. Staff specialized in small company-large company alliance, alliance assessment and analysis and alliance strategic planning. **Scope:** A consulting company that helps to form national and international strategic alliances. Handles alliances between companies forming joint ventures. Staff specialized in small company-large company alliance, alliance assessment and analysis and alliance strategic planning. **Training:** Joint Business Planning; Developing a Shared Vision; Current and New/Prospective Partner Assessment; Customer Service; Sales Training; Leader and Management Skills.

28944 ■ Allsup, L.L.C.
300 Allsup Pl.
  Belleville, IL 62223
Free: 800-279-4357
Fax: (866)316-3899
URL: http://www.allsup.com
Contact: Jim Allsup, Chief Executive Officer
Facebook: www.facebook.com/allsupinc
Linkedin: www.linkedin.com/company/allsup-llc
X (Twitter): x.com/allsup
YouTube: www.youtube.com/user/wecareaboutu
Description: Social Security disability claims services company understanding the specialized needs of those with disabilities. **Scope:** Social Security disability claims services company understanding the specialized needs of those with disabilities. **Founded:** 1984. **Publications:** "The Alls up Alternative".

28945 ■ Alvana Business Consulting Inc.
2108-1009 Expo Blvd.
  Vancouver, BC, Canada V6Z 2V9
Ph: (778)968-6084
URL: http://www.alvanabusinessconsulting.com
Contact: Dr. Michele Vincenti, President
X (Twitter): x.com/alvana1
Description: Firm provides management consulting services for management consulting courses, business management and strategy, change management, communication improvement, and much more. **Scope:** Firm provides management consulting services for management consulting courses, business management and strategy, change management, communication improvement, and much more. **Training:** E-Learning Facilitator; Instructional Skills Workshop Plus.

28946 ■ American Business Dynamics Corp.
4501 Silhavy Rd.
  Valparaiso, IN 46383
Contact: Yvonne Schwedland, President
Description: Small business consulting firm specializing in helping businesses prepare and execute high impact growth strategies. **Scope:** Small business consulting firm specializing in helping businesses prepare and execute high impact growth strategies. **Publications:** "Small businesses don't work," "The entrepreneurial myth," "The balanced business owner," "How to find fulfillment from your business," "Strategic objectives - more than a financial plan Management," "Make business work - by system and staff," "How to manage with success," "How to make your business truly work," "A systematic approach to business," "Base your strategy on functions," "Build success by design," "Reliable employees are essential," "Create a system that works for you," "Save time with simple reminders," "Developing a systems strategy," "Marketing," "A new way to draw customers," "Attention to quality will pay rewards," "Choose a core market, then serve it well," "Build better customers with words," "Turn business into a game," "Image is everything, Finance," "Money, money, money".

28947 ■ Apex Innovations Inc.
19951 W 162nd St.
  Olathe, KS 66062

Ph: (913)254-0250
Fax: (913)254-0320
URL: http://www.apex-innovations.com
Description: Developer of software for dynamically sharing information and processes between organizations. **Scope:** Developer of software for dynamically sharing information and processes between organizations. **Founded:** 2002. **Special Services:** i-INFO. EPR™; i-INFO.WORKS™; i-INFO Classes™.

28948 ■ Arnold S. Goldin & Associates Inc.
PO Box 276158
  Boca Raton, FL 33427
Ph: (561)994-5810
Fax: (561)431-3102
URL: http://www.arnoldgoldin.com
Description: An accounting and management consulting firm. Serves clients worldwide. Provides management services. Handles monthly write-ups and tax returns. **Scope:** An accounting and management consulting firm. Serves clients worldwide. Provides management services. Handles monthly write-ups and tax returns.

28949 ■ Aspire Business Development Inc.
10955 Lowell Ave., Ste. 400
  Overland Park, KS 66210
Ph: (913)660-9400
Co. E-mail: info@aspirekc.com
URL: http://aspirekc.com
Contact: Shawn Kinkade, President
E-mail: skinkade@aspirekc.com
Description: Firm provides business management consulting services, business aspirations models, business effectiveness analysis, and much more services. **Scope:** Firm provides business management consulting services, business aspirations models, business effectiveness analysis, and much more services.

28950 ■ Aurora Management Partners Inc.
1201 Peachtree St., Ste. 1570
  Atlanta, GA 30361
Ph: (704)377-6010
Co. E-mail: info@auroramp.com
URL: http://www.auroramp.com
Contact: David Baker, CTP, Managing Partner
Linkedin: www.linkedin.com/company/aurora
  -management-partners/about
Description: Specializes in turnaround management and reorganization consulting, the company develops strategic initiatives, organize and analyze solutions, deal with creditor issues, review organizational structures and develop time frames for decision making. **Founded:** 2000. **Publications:** "TMA Turnaround of the Year Award, Small Company, Honorable Mention," Nov, 2005; "Back From The Brink - Bland Farms," Progressive Farmer, Oct, 2004; "New Breed of Turnaround Managers," Catalyst Magazine, Aug, 2004; "Key Performance Drivers - Bland Farms," The Produce News, Apr, 2004; "Corporate Governance: Averting Crisis's Before They Happen," ABJ journal, Feb, 2004.

28951 ■ Avery, Cooper & Co.
4918-50th St.
  Yellowknife, NT, Canada X1A 2P2
Ph: (867)873-3441
Free: 800-661-0787
Fax: (867)873-2353
URL: http://averycooper.com
Contact: William Senfuma, Manager
E-mail: william.senfuma@averycooper.com
Facebook: www.facebook.com/averycooperandco
Description: Provider of public accounting and auditing services. **Scope:** Provider of public accounting and auditing services. **Founded:** 1969. **Training:** Sage Software Training. **Special Services:** ACCPAC Plus; Sage Accpac ERP.

28952 ■ Bahr International Inc.
12221 Merit Dr., Ste. 1305
  Dallas, TX 75251
Contact: C. Charles Bahr, III, President

Description: Firm provides full-service turnaround management services and its operating solutions. **Scope:** Firm provides full-service turnaround management services and its operating solutions.

28953 ■ Bayer Center for Nonprofit Management (BCNM)
6001 University Blvd.
　Moon Township, PA 15108
Ph: (412)397-3000
Free: 800-762-0097
Co. E-mail: bcnm@rmu.edu
URL: http://www.rmu.edu/about/bcnm
Contact: Welling W. Fruehauf, President
Facebook: www.facebook.com/RMUpgh
Linkedin: www.linkedin.com/school/robert-morris
　-university
X (Twitter): x.com/bayercenter
Instagram: www.instagram.com/rober
tmorrisuniversity
YouTube: www.youtube.com/user/RMUNewsTube

Description: Center offers consulting services in: Board development, business planning, collaboration and alliances, financial management, fund development, organizational effectiveness and technology planning. Also provides information and referral services, conducts applied research and serves to convene in depth discussions on the problems of society addressed by nonprofit organizations. **Scope:** Center offers consulting services in: Board development, business planning, collaboration and alliances, financial management, fund development, organizational effectiveness and technology planning. Also provides information and referral services, conducts applied research and serves to convene in depth discussions on the problems of society addressed by nonprofit organizations. **Founded:** 1999. **Training:** A Starfish Can Grow a New Arm, Why Cant I?; Carnegie Science Centers SuperFun Science Fest; Disc Driving the Electronic Mall; Steady Hand Game; Planning an Accessible World.

28954 ■ Be Cause Business Resources Inc.
Canterbury Park
　1335 3rd Ave.
　Longview, WA 98632
Ph: (360)200-5840
URL: http://becausebusiness.com
Contact: John E. Anderson, President
X (Twitter): x.com/becausebusiness

Description: Firm provides business valuation, executive coaching, facilitation, finance, growth management, marketing, organizational design and project management services. **Scope:** Firm provides business valuation, executive coaching, facilitation, finance, growth management, marketing, organizational design and project management services. **Founded:** 2003.

28955 ■ Beacon Management-Management Consultants
Pompano Beach, FL 33069
Co. E-mail: md@beaconmgmt.com
URL: http://www.beaconmgmt.com
Contact: Michael J. Donnelly, Consultant Managing
　Director Principal

Description: Provider of management consulting services such as strategic and business planning, market intelligence, decision support services, corporate finance, and much more. **Scope:** Provider of management consulting services such as strategic and business planning, market intelligence, decision support services, corporate finance, and much more. **Founded:** 1985. **Publications:** "Sun-Sentinel Article," Oct, 2012.

28956 ■ Big 2Go (B2G)
Bloomfield, NJ 07003
URL: http://big2go.com
Linkedin: www.linkedin.com/company/big-inspirations
　-2go-llc-big2go
Instagram: www.instagram.com/biginspirations2go

Description: Helps leaders, teams, and organizations foster well-being at work. Specializes in managing stress and burnout, leader development, team retreats, and diversity, equity and inclusion.

28957 ■ Biomedical Management Resources (BMR)
4131 Fortuna Way
　Salt Lake City, UT 84124
Contact: Ping Fong, Jr., Contact
E-mail: pfongbmr@gmail.com

Description: Provides business development, interim management and executive search services. Assists companies in strategic alliances, corporate partnering, business acquisition. Demonstrated success in identifying recruiting and placing key managers in difficult to hire positions. **Scope:** Provides business development, interim management and executive search services. Assists companies in strategic alliances, corporate partnering, business acquisition. Demonstrated success in identifying recruiting and placing key managers in difficult to hire positions.

28958 ■ Blankinship & Associates Inc.
1615 5th St., Ste. A
　Davis, CA 95616
Ph: (530)757-0941
URL: http://www.h2osci.com
Contact: Michael Blankinship, President

Description: Provider of consulting services to support water resources, agriculture and risk evaluation and communication, water resources management and regulatory. **Scope:** Provider of consulting services to support water resources, agriculture and risk evaluation and communication, water resources management and regulatory. **Founded:** 2000. **Publications:** "Air Blast Sprayer Calibration and Chlorpyrifos Irrigation Study," Oct, 2007; "How Green is your golf course," Prosper Magazine, 2007. **Training:** CDFG Wildlands IPM Seminar, Oct, 2009.

28959 ■ Blue Garnet Associates L.L.C.
8405 Pershing Dr., Ste. 205
　Playa del Rey, CA 90293
Ph: (310)439-1930
Co. E-mail: hello@bluegarnet.net
UHL: http://bluegarnet.net
Contact: Jen Oki, Business Manager
E-mail: jen.oki@bluegarnet.net
Linkedin: www.linkedin.com/company/blue-garne
　t-associates
X (Twitter): x.com/hellobluegarnet

Description: Provider of management consulting services including employee benefits, managed care and intranet applications. **Founded:** 2002.

28960 ■ BroadVision, Inc.
460 Seaport Ct., Ste. 102
　Redwood City, CA 94063
Ph: (650)331-1000
URL: http://broadvision.com/broadvision
Contact: Dr. Pehong Chen, President

Description: Provides application solutions for large scale, personalized business on the internet, intranets, and extranets. Serves the retail and distribution, financial services, high-tech, travel, and telecom industries. Offer expertise in areas such as task management, content sharing, email consolidation, instant messaging and chat, workflow consolidation, process improvement, social networking, internal and external communication, templates and blogs, reports and analytics, e-commerce and transactional portals. **Founded:** 1993.

28961 ■ Bruce D. Wyman Co.
6147 Poburn Landing Ct.
　Burke, VA 22015-2535
Ph: (703)503-9753
Fax: (703)503-2091
Co. E-mail: bdwyman@bdwyman.com
URL: http://www.bdwyman.com
Contact: Bruce D. Wyman, President
E-mail: bdwyman@bdwyman.com

Description: Firm provides strategic business planning and support services for-profit and not-for-profit small businesses and associations, the company aides in developing management processes as well as providing employee training, and tailored consultation services that help leverage scarce time and monetary resources. **Founded:** 1988. **Publications:** "A New Acquisition Reform Culture for the Air Force,"

Program Manager, Feb, 1999. **Training:** The Best of Both Worlds: Combining Equity 3 and Integer Programming to Allocate Resources, Oct, 2004; Implementing Massive Change: Coordination, Communication, and Campaign Management, May, 2000; Strategic Business Planning for Small and Micro Businesses and Associations; quality management and processes consulting and training (CQMgr. and CQIA).

28962 ■ Business Answers International Inc. (BAI)
1920 Palm Beach Lakes Blvd.,Ste. 216
　West Palm Beach, FL 33409
Ph: (561)775-6110
Free: 800-583-4726
Fax: (561)775-0520
Co. E-mail: info@baintl.com
URL: http://www.baintl.com
Linkedin: www.linkedin.com/company/business-an-
swers-international

Description: Firm provides solutions to enhance growth and profitability of the plastics industry and performs executive recruitment for high authority positions such as presidents, vice presidents, directors, branch and product managers, and much more. **Scope:** Firm provides solutions to enhance growth and profitability of the plastics industry and performs executive recruitment for high authority positions such as presidents, vice presidents, directors, branch and product managers, and much more. **Founded:** 1933.

28963 ■ Business Coach L.L.C.
738 Main St., Ste. No. 216
　Waltham, MA 02451
Ph: (781)647-1238
Co. E-mail: info@thebusinesscoach.com
URL: http://thebusinesscoach.com/home
Contact: Michael Kaye, President
E-mail: michael@thebuinesscoach.com
Facebook: www.facebook.com/TheBusinessCoach
Linkedin: www.linkedin.com/in/michaelkaye
thobucinocccoach
X (Twitter): x.com/thbusinesscoach

Description: Provider of management consulting and executive coaching services for assisting businesses and individuals. **Scope:** Provider of management consulting and executive coaching services for assisting businesses and individuals. **Founded:** 1997.

28964 ■ The Business Group
369-B 3rd St., Ste. 387
　San Rafael, CA 94901
Ph: (415)491-1896
Fax: (415)459-6472
URL: http://www.businessownerstoolbox.com
Contact: Mike van Horn, President
E-mail: mvh@businessgroup.biz

Description: Our company provides small business owners a resource often reserved for execs of large organizations - problem solving and accountability from savvy independent peers. Management consulting firm providing problem solving and accountability to small business owners. Services include executive coaching, growth management, human resources, and organizational design and development. **Scope:** Our company provides small business owners a resource often reserved for execs of large organizations - problem solving and accountability from savvy independent peers. Management consulting firm providing problem solving and accountability to small business owners. Services include executive coaching, growth management, human resources, and organizational design and development. **Founded:** 1984. **Publications:** "How to Grow Your Business Without Driving Yourself Crazy".

28965 ■ Business Improvement Architects (BIA)
633 Lakelands Ave.
　Innisfil, ON, Canada L9S 4E5
Co. E-mail: info@bia.ca
URL: http://bia.ca
Contact: Rowena Lamy, Consultant
E-mail: rlamy@bia.ca
Facebook: www.facebook.com/BusinessImprovemen
tArchitects

Linkedin: www.linkedin.com/company/business
-improvement-architects
Description: Provider of the following services, strategic planning, leadership development, innovation and project and quality management. Specialize in strategic planning, change management, leadership assessment and development of skills. **Scope:** Provider of the following services, strategic planning, leadership development, innovation and project and quality management. Specialize in strategic planning, change management, leadership assessment and development of skills. **Founded:** 1989. **Publications:** "Avoiding Pit falls to Innovation"; "Create a New Dimension of Performance with Innovation"; "The Power of Appreciation in Leadership"; "Why It Makes Sense To Have a Strategic Enterprise Office"; "Burning Rubber at the Start of Your Project"; "Accounting for Quality"; "How Pareto Charts Can Help You Improve the Quality of Business Processes"; "Managing Resistance to Change". **Training:** The Innovation Process From Vision to Reality, San Diego, Oct, 2007; Critical Thinking, Kuala Lump or, Sep, 2007; Critical Thinking, Brunei, Sep, 2007; Delivering Project Assurance, Auckland, Jun, 2007; From Crisis to Control: A New Era in Strategic Project Management, Prague, May, 2007; What Project Leaders Need to Know to Help Them Sleep Better At Night, London, May, 2007; Innovation Process. From Vision To Reality, Orlando, Apr, 2007. **Special Services:** Project Planning Tool™.

28966 ■ Business Management Consultants
1502 Augusta Dr., Ste. 315, Ste. D
 Houston, TX 77057
Co. E-mail: info@bmc-global.com
URL: http://www.bmc-global.com
Linkedin: www.linkedin.com/company/business
-management-consultants
X (Twitter): x.com/Merguerian
YouTube: www.youtube.com/user/GlobalBMCVideo
Description: International management consulting firm specializes in global project management training and consulting, their consultants conduct organizational development, management training, and consulting in project management. **Scope:** International management consulting firm specializes in global project management training and consulting, their consultants conduct organizational development, management training, and consulting in project management. **Founded:** 1985. **Publications:** "How The Art of Project Management improved the performance of pharmaceutical clinical trials in a Major Global Pharmaceutical Company," May, 2007. **Training:** Senior Project Management, Singapore, Oct, 2007; Fundamentals of Project Management I: Tools and Techniques, Houston, Jun, 2007; Fundamentals of Project Management II: Project Leadership and Communication, Houston, Jun, 2007; Project Management for Administrators, Singapore, Jun, 2007; Project Management for IT/IS I - Tools and Techniques, Singapore, Jun, 2007.

28967 ■ Business Performance Improvement Consorium L.L.C. (BPI)
225 S 6th St., Ste. 3900
 Minneapolis, MN 55402
Co. E-mail: consultants@bpi-consortium.com
URL: http://www.bpi-consortium.com
Contact: Rod Hagedorn, Senior Partner General Manager
E-mail: rod.hagedorn@bpi-consortium.com
Description: Firm provides management consulting services including organizational research and business performance improvement consulting. **Scope:** Firm provides management consulting services including organizational research and business performance improvement consulting. **Founded:** 1993.

28968 ■ Business Resource Group Inc.
10819 101St Ave. NE
 Kirkland, WA 98034
Contact: Janis Martinka, Governor
Description: Services: Management consulting. **Scope:** Services: Management consulting. **Training:** Dynamic and superior techniques to improve business immediately.

28969 ■ Business Ventures Corp.
3883 Rogers Bridge Rd., Ste. 205-B
 Duluth, GA 30097
Contact: King Ruth Anne, Chief Executive Officer
Description: Private equity firm provides investment services. **Scope:** Private equity firm provides investment services. **Publications:** "The Ugly Truth about Managing People," 2007; "The Ugly Truth about Small Business," 2006; "How to Write a Business Plan," Atlanta Business Chronicle; "Ask 10 Questions Before You Begin Your Business," Income Opportunities "HVAC Bookkeeping and Financial Statements"; "Service Manager's Guide to Running a Profitable Service Department"; "HVAC Career Training Manual"; "Technician's Procedures Manual"; "HVAC Residential Pricing Manual"; "21 Ways to Keep the Honest People Honest Manual"; "Keeping Score: Financial Management for Entrepreneurs"; "Keeping Score: Improving Contractor Productivity and Profitability"; "Keeping Score: Financial Management for Contractors". **Training:** The Seven Rules for Business Success; The Seven Greatest Lies of Small Business; Understanding the Financial Side of Business; Small Business Marketing; Strategic Business Planning.

28970 ■ ByrneMRG Corp.
5459 Rinker Cir.
 Doylestown, PA 18902
Ph: (215)630-7411
Co. E-mail: info@byrnemrg.com
URL: http://www.byrnemrg.com
Contact: Patrick Boyle, Founder Consultant
E-mail: pjboyle@byrnemrg.com
Description: Services: Management consulting. **Scope:** Services: Management consulting. **Founded:** 1972. **Publications:** "Implementing Solutions to Everyday Issues".

28971 ■ Cartesian, Inc.
6405 Metcalf Ave., Ste. 417
 Overland Park, KS 66202
Fax: (913)273-1395
URL: http://www.cartesian.com
Contact: Dale Reynolds, Vice President
Facebook: www.facebook.com/cartesian
Linkedin: www.linkedin.com/company/cartesian
X (Twitter): x.com/cartesiantweets
Description: Firm provides strategy, management consulting and managed solutions for the communication, media and entertainment sectors. **Founded:** 1990. **Special Services:** Lexicon™; QBC™; QSA™.

28972 ■ CBIZ, Inc.
CBIZ, Inc.
 5959 Rockside Woods Blvd. N, Ste. 600
 Independence, OH 44131
Ph: (216)447-9000
Fax: (216)447-9007
Co. E-mail: cbizwomensadvantage@cbiz.com
URL: http://www.cbiz.com
Contact: Jerome P. Grisko, Jr., President
Facebook: facebook.com/cbizmhmcareers
Linkedin: www.linkedin.com/company/cbiz
X (Twitter): twitter.com/cbz
YouTube: www.youtube.com/user/CBIZSolutions
Description: Diversified services company is engaged in providing an array of professional business services which include accounting and tax, healthcare and health benefits consulting, financial advisory, valuation, risk and advisory services, payroll, property and casualty insurance, retirement planning, managed networking and hardware services primarily to small and medium-sized businesses, as well as individuals, government agencies, and not-for-profit enterprises. **Founded:** 1996. **Training:** Health Care - What the Future Holds; Consumer Driven Health Plans; Executive Plans; Health Savings Accounts; Healthy Wealthy and Wise; Legislative Update; Medicare Part D; Retirement Plans.

28973 ■ The Center for Organizational Excellence, Inc. (COE)
15204 Omega Dr., Ste. 300
 Rockville, MD 20850
Contact: Stephen P. Goodrich, Contact

E-mail: sgoodrich@center4oe.com
Description: Firm provides consulting services such as designing and delivering consulting solutions in the areas of organizational effectiveness, human capital, information technology, and data management. **Scope:** Firm provides consulting services such as designing and delivering consulting solutions in the areas of organizational effectiveness, human capital, information technology, and data management. **Founded:** 1984.

28974 ■ CFI Group USA L.L.C.
3916 Ranchero Dr.
 Ann Arbor, MI 48108
Ph: (734)930-9090
Fax: (734)930-0911
Co. E-mail: info@cfigroup.se
URL: http://cfigroup.com
Contact: Sheri Petras, Chief Executive Officer
Facebook: www.facebook.com/CFIGroup
Linkedin: www.linkedin.com/company/cfi-group
X (Twitter): x.com/cfigroup
Description: Management consulting firm helps its clients worldwide to maximize shareholder value by optimizing customer and employee satisfaction, their clients span from a variety of industries including manufacturing, telecommunication, retail and government. **Scope:** Management consulting firm helps its clients worldwide to maximize shareholder value by optimizing customer and employee satisfaction, their clients span from a variety of industries including manufacturing, telecommunication, retail and government. **Founded:** 1988. **Publications:** "Customer Satisfaction and Stock Prices: High Returns, Low Risk," American Marketing Association, Jan, 2006; "Customer Satisfaction Index Climbs," The Wall Street Journal, Feb, 2004; "What's Next? Customer Service is Key to Post-Boom Success," The Bottom Line, Mar, 2003; "Boost Stock Performance, Nation's Economy," Quality Progress, Feb, 2003.

28975 ■ Chartered Management Co.
100 Saunders Rd., Ste. 150
 Lake Forest, IL 60045
Contact: William B. Avellone, President
Description: Operations improvement consultants. Specializes in strategic planning, feasibility studies, management audits and reports, profit enhancement, start-up businesses, mergers and acquisitions, joint ventures, divestitures, interim management, crisis management, turnarounds, business process re-engineering, venture capital and due diligence. **Scope:** Operations improvement consultants. Specializes in strategic planning, feasibility studies, management audits and reports, profit enhancement, start-up businesses, mergers and acquisitions, joint ventures, divestitures, interim management, crisis management, turnarounds, business process re-engineering, venture capital and due diligence. **Founded:** 1985.

28976 ■ Comer & Associates L.L.C. (CA)
5255 Holmes Pl.
 Boulder, CO 80303
Ph: (303)786-7986
URL: http://www.comerassociates.com
Contact: Gerald Comer, Contact
Description: Specialize in developing markets and businesses. Marketing support includes developing and writing strategic and tactical business plans, developing and writing focused, effective market plans, researching market potential and competition, implementing targeted marketing tactics to achieve company objectives, conducting customer surveys to determine satisfaction and attitudes toward client. **Scope:** Specialize in developing markets and businesses. Marketing support includes developing and writing strategic and tactical business plans, developing and writing focused, effective market plans, researching market potential and competition, implementing targeted marketing tactics to achieve company objectives, conducting customer surveys to determine satisfaction and attitudes toward client. **Training:** Developing a Strategic Market Plan; Market Research: Defining Your Opportunity; Management and Leadership Effectiveness; Team Building; Devel-

oping a Business Plan; How to Close; Using Questions to Sell; Sales System Elements and Checklist; Working With Independent Reps; Features vs. Benefits; Overcoming Objections; Sales Force Automation.

28977 ■ Consulting & Conciliation Service (CCS)

Sacramento, CA
Ph: (916)396-0480
URL: http://conciliation.org
Contact: Jane McCluskey, Contact
E-mail: jane@conciliation.org
Description: Firm offers consulting and conciliation services, they provide pre-mediation counseling, training and research on preparing for a peaceful society, mediation and facilitation, preparation for shifts in structure, policy, and personnel, it offers sliding scale business rates and free individual consultation. **Scope:** Firm offers consulting and conciliation services, they provide pre-mediation counseling, training and research on preparing for a peaceful society, mediation and facilitation, preparation for shifts in structure, policy, and personnel, it offers sliding scale business rates and free individual consultation. **Publications:** "Native America and Tracking Shifts in US Policy"; "Biogenesis: A Discussion of Basic Social Needs and the Significance of Hope". **Training:** Positive Approaches to Violence Prevention: Peace building in Schools and Communities.

28978 ■ Corporate Consulting, Inc.

100 Fillmore St.
Denver, CO 80206
Contact: Devereux C. Josephs, Contact
Description: Engaged in feasibility studies, organizational development, small business management, mergers and acquisitions, joint ventures, divestitures, interim management, crisis management, turnarounds, financing, appraisals valuations and due diligence studies. **Scope:** Engaged in feasibility studies, organizational development, small business management, mergers and acquisitions, joint ventures, divestitures, interim management, crisis management, turnarounds, financing, appraisals valuations and due diligence studies.

28979 ■ Corporate Impact

33326 Bonnieview Dr., Ste. 200
Avon Lake, OH 44012
Description: Provider of coaching, consultation, facilitation, and training services. **Scope:** Provider of coaching, consultation, facilitation, and training services. **Publications:** "8 Lies of Teamwork". **Training:** Personal Productivity Management; The Challenge of Leadership; Collaborative Problem Solving; The Creative Side of Enterprise; Teamwork and Peak Performance; Winning Customers; Conflict Resolution.

28980 ■ Crouser & Associates Inc.

235 Dutch Rd.
Charleston, WV 25302
Contact: Thomas P. Crouser, President
E-mail: tom@crouser.com
Description: Provider of management, accounting, pricing, personnel, and marketing for smaller organizations and market research for companies selling to small press printers. **Scope:** Provider of management, accounting, pricing, personnel, and marketing for smaller organizations and market research for companies selling to small press printers. **Publications:** "Dead Printer Working: A Printer's Financial Survival Guide"; "Prospering: Putting Your Business to Work for You and Your Family". **Training:** Power Pricing - Pricing Small Press Printing; Family Business Families in Small Press Printing Businesses; Getting Jobs Out - Production Management in the Small Press Shop. **Special Services:** CPrint®.

28981 ■ Daedalus Ventures Ltd.

717 Crossan Rd.
Newark, DE 19711
Contact: J. Gregory Vermeychuk, Contact
Description: Analyzes and evaluates business and investment opportunities, then develops specific plans and programs to derive value from them.

Industries served advanced materials, specialty chemicals and information systems. **Scope:** Analyzes and evaluates business and investment opportunities, then develops specific plans and programs to derive value from them. Industries served advanced materials, specialty chemicals and information systems. **Founded:** 1993.

28982 ■ David G. Schantz

29 Wood Run Cir.
Rochester, NY 14612-2271
Ph: (716)723-0760
Fax: (716)723-8724
Co. E-mail: daveschantz@yahoo.com
URL: http://www.daveschantz.freeservers.com
Description: Provider of industrial engineering services for photo finishing labs, including amateur-wholesale, professional, commercial, school and package. **Scope:** Provider of industrial engineering services for photo finishing labs, including amateur-wholesale, professional, commercial, school and package.

28983 ■ Denison Consulting

555 Briarwood Cir., Ste. 115
Ann Arbor, MI 48105
Ph: (734)302-4002
URL: http://www.denisonconsulting.com
Contact: Dave Kirchoff, President
E-mail: dkirchoff@denisonculture.com
Facebook: www.facebook.com/DenisonConsulting
Linkedin: www.linkedin.com/company/denison-consulting
X (Twitter): x.com/denisonculture
YouTube: www.youtube.com/user/denisonculture
Description: Firm provides consulting services and solutions such as leadership development, culture surveys, analytics, and more services. **Founded:** 1998. **Publications:** "Executive Coaching: Does leader behavior change with feedback and coaching," 2009; "Engagement Surveys: Gallup and Best Companies Face Criticism," 2009; "Managing Expectations-of You," 2006; "Out of the Blue," 2006; "Organizational Culture: Measuring and Developing It in Your Organization," 2005; "Riding the Tiger of Culture Change," 2004; "Like it or not, Culture Matters," 2000; "Why Mission Matters," 2000; "Ready Or Not, Here I Learn," 2000. **Training:** Building High Performance Organizations; Organizational Culture & Diagnosis; Managing Thought.

28984 ■ DevelopWell

3301 Richmond Hwy., No. 1090
Alexandria, VA 22305-3044
Co. E-mail: info@developwell.org
URL: http://www.developwell.org
Contact: Holly Witherington, Chief Executive Officer
Facebook: www.facebook.com/developwell
Linkedin: www.linkedin.com/company/developwell
Instagram: www.instagram.com/thedevelopwell
Description: A women-owned and operated coaching and consulting practice that develops leaders and teams in values-driven organizations with a holistic and innovative approach. **Founded:** 2017.

28985 ■ Don Phin, Esq.

114 C. Ave., No. 200
Coronado, CA 92118
Ph: (619)852-4580
URL: http://www.donphin.com
Contact: Don Phin, Contact
E-mail: don@donphin.com
Linkedin: www.linkedin.com/in/donphin
X (Twitter): x.com/donphin12
YouTube: www.youtube.com/donphin
Description: Firm is engaged in consulting services on training, coaching and mentoring for the individuals and small businesses. **Scope:** Firm is engaged in consulting services on training, coaching and mentoring for the individuals and small businesses. **Founded:** 1983. **Publications:** "Doing Business Right!"; "HR That Works!"; "Lawsuit Free! How to Prevent Employee Lawsuits"; "Building Powerful Employment Relationships!"; "Victims, Villains and

Heroes: Managing Emotions in The Workplace". **Training:** Doing Business Right!; HR That Works!; Building Powerful Employment Relationships; Lawsuit Free!.

28986 ■ DRI Consulting Inc. (DRIC)

Two Otter Ln.
Saint Paul, MN 55127
Ph: (651)415-1400
Co. E-mail: dric@dric.com
URL: http://www.dric.com
Contact: Dr. John Fennig, Director
Description: Provides high-quality, research-based services and training in leadership, team processes, supervision, and management, and organizational development, clients with direct and substantial impact on individual and team performance and on organizational success through proven processes for selecting, developing and deploying leaders. **Scope:** Provides high-quality, research-based services and training in leadership, team processes, supervision, and management, and organizational development, clients with direct and substantial impact on individual and team performance and on organizational success through proven processes for selecting, developing and deploying leaders. **Founded:** 1991.

28987 ■ Environmental Business Consultants (EBC)

94 Riverwood Pwy.
Toronto, ON, Canada M8Y 4E9
Co. E-mail: info@ebccanada.com
URL: http://www.ebccanada.com/index.shtml
Contact: John Nicholson, President
E-mail: john.nicholson@ebccanada.com
Description: Provider of environmental and business management consulting services. **Scope:** Provider of environmental and business management consulting services. **Publications:** "Ontario Electronic Stewardship: A Program Evaluation and Comparison of Similar Organizations".

28988 ■ Espionage Research Institute International (ERII)

4445 Corporation Ln.
Virginia Beach, VA 23462
Ph: (757)716-7353
Fax: (757)716-7353
Co. E-mail: lml@erii.org
URL: http://www.erii.org
Contact: J. D. LeaSure, Director
Facebook: www.facebook.com/EspionageResearchInstitute
Linkedin: www.linkedin.com/company/espionage-research-institute-international
X (Twitter): x.com/eriintl
Description: Dedicated to collect and promulgate information on hostile espionage activity. It attempts to keep all informed on hostile espionage activity that is directed against business and industry. **Scope:** Dedicated to collect and promulgate information on hostile espionage activity. It attempts to keep all informed on hostile espionage activity that is directed against business and industry. **Founded:** 2011. **Publications:** "A Guidebook For Beginning Sweepers"; "The Ear Volume"; "The Attack on Axnan Headquarters"; "The TSCM Threat Book"; "The Russian Eavesdropping Threat As Of 1993".

28989 ■ Family Business Institute Inc. (FBI)

3520 Ridge View Ct.
Marietta, GA 30068
Ph: (770)952-4085
URL: http://www.family-business-experts.com
Contact: Don A. Schwerzler, Founder
Description: Firm engages in business consulting and professional services. **Scope:** Assists families in business to achieve personal, family and organizational goals. **Founded:** 1995. **Publications:** "Professional Intervention in the Family Owned Business"; "Building Consensus in a Family Business"; "Professionalizing Family Business Management".

28990 ■ Family Veterinary Care of Oakdale

389 W F St.
Oakdale, CA 95361
Ph: (209)847-9077

URL: http://www.oakdalevet.com
Contact: Dr. Mel Tanner, Contact
Facebook: www.facebook.com/family-veterinary-care
  -of-oakdale-1755775344446878
Description: Provider of diagnostic and therapeutic services including surgical services, anesthesia, radiology services, ultrasound services, electrocardiography services, dental services, dietary and behavioral counselling. **Scope:** Provider of diagnostic and therapeutic services including surgical services, anesthesia, radiology services, ultrasound services, electrocardiography services, dental services, dietary and behavioral counselling. **Founded:** 1948.

28991 ■ First Strike Management Consulting Inc. (FSMC)
PO Box 1188
  Little River, SC 29566-1188
Ph: (843)385-6338
Co. E-mail: info@fsmc.com
URL: http://www.fsmc.com
Description: Offers proposal management and program management services. Specializes in enterprise systems, management systems, and staff augmentation. Serves the following industries: Nuclear/Fossil Power, Petro-Chemical, Aerospace and Defense, Telecommunications, Engineering and Construction, Information Technology, Golf Course Construction/Management, Utility Engineering/Construction, Civil Works, and Housing Development. **Scope:** Offers proposal management and program management services. Specializes in enterprise systems, management systems, and staff augmentation. Serves the following industries: Nuclear/Fossil Power, Petro-Chemical, Aerospace and Defense, Telecommunications, Engineering and Construction, Information Technology, Golf Course Construction/Management, Utility Engineering/Construction, Civil Works, and Housing Development. **Founded:** 1991. **Publications:** "Project Management for Executives"; "Project Risk Management"; "Project Communications Management"; "Winning Proposals, Four Computer Based Training (CBT) courses"; "Principles of Program Management". **Training:** Preparing Winning Proposals in Response to Government RFPs.

28992 ■ Freese & Associates Inc. (F&A)
16105 Lucky Bell Ln.
  Newbury, OH 44065
Ph: (440)487-4509
URL: http://www.freeseinc.com
Contact: Thomas L. Freese, Principal
E-mail: tfreese@freeseinc.com
Description: Provider of supply chain management and logistics consulting services such as customer service, material management, transportation, and much more. **Scope:** Provider of supply chain management and logistics consulting services such as customer service, material management, transportation, and much more. **Founded:** 1987. **Publications:** "Building Relationships is Key to Motivation," Distribution Center Management, Apr, 2006; "Getting Maximum Results from Performance Reviews," WERC Sheet, Oct, 2003; "SCM: Making the Vision a Reality," Supply Chain Management Review, Oct, 2003; "Contents Under Pressure," DC Velocity, Aug, 2003; "When Considering Outsourcing, It's Really a Financial Decision," Inventory Management Report, Mar, 2003. **Training:** WERC/CAWS Warehousing in China Conference, Sep, 2008; CSCMP Annual Conference, Denver, Oct, 2008; Keys to Retaining and Motivating Your Associates, Dallas, Mar, 2006; The Value and Challenges of Supply Chain Management, Dubai, Feb, 2006; Best Practices in Logistics in China, Jun, 2005; Keys to Motivating Associates, Dallas, May, 2005; The Goal and the Way of International Cooperation in Logistics, Jenobuk, Apr, 2005.

28993 ■ Global Technology Transfer L.L.C.
1500 Dixie Hwy.
  Park Hills, KY 41011
Contact: Anthony R. Zembrodt, Sr., Member
Description: Firm specializes in product development, quality assurance, new product development, and total quality management focusing on household chemical specialties, especially air fresheners. Utilizes latest technology from global resources. Specializes in enhancement products for home and automobile. **Scope:** Firm specializes in product development, quality assurance, new product development, and total quality management focusing on household chemical specialties, especially air fresheners. Utilizes latest technology from global resources. Specializes in enhancement products for home and automobile.

28994 ■ Glynn Law Offices
49 Locust St.
  Falmouth, MA 02540
Ph: (508)548-8282
Fax: (508)548-0020
Co. E-mail: office@glynnlawoffices.com
URL: http://www.glynnlawoffices.com
Contact: Dawn Rigby Walsh, Contact
Description: Law firm specializing in commercial and residential real estate law, estate planning, trust administration, business formation and law, zoning, and other areas. **Scope:** Law firm specializing in commercial and residential real estate law, estate planning, trust administration, business formation and law, zoning, and other areas.

28995 ■ Health Fitness Corp. (HF)
400 Field Dr.
  Lake Forest, IL 60045
Free: 800-639-7913
URL: http://www.healthfitness.com
Contact: Sean McManamy, President
Facebook: www.facebook.com/HealthFitnessCareers
Linkedin: www.linkedin.com/company/12931
X (Twitter): x.com/hfit
Description: Provider of health management, corporate fitness programs and condition management solutions. **Founded:** 1975. **Training:** How to Determine the Feasibility of Developing a Corporate Fitness Center in Your Company; Fulfilling a Dream: The Entrepreneur; How Healthy Is Your Business?; Recruiting, Retaining and Servicing Members: Delivering What They Want.

28996 ■ Hewitt Development Enterprises (HDE)
1717 N Bayshore Dr., Ste. 2154
  Miami, FL 33132
Ph: (305)372-0941
Fax: (305)372-0941
Co. E-mail: info@hewittdevelopment.com
URL: http://www.hewittdevelopment.com
Contact: Robert G. Hewitt, Contact
E-mail: bob@hewittdevelopment.com
Description: Firm specializes in strategic planning, profit enhancement, startup businesses, interim and crisis management, turnarounds, production planning, just-in-time inventory and project management, serves senior management and acquirers of distressed businesses. **Scope:** Firm specializes in strategic planning, profit enhancement, startup businesses, interim and crisis management, turnarounds, production planning, just-in-time inventory and project management, serves senior management and acquirers of distressed businesses. **Founded:** 1985.

28997 ■ Human Resource Specialties, Inc. (HRS)
DCI Consulting Group Inc.
  PO Box 1995
  Missoula, MT 59806
Ph: (202)828-6900
URL: http://www.dciconsult.com
Contact: Sandy L. Henderson, President
Description: Provider of human resources assistance to organizations. Offers preparation of affirmative action plans, support documents, and adverse impact studies of personnel activities. Also offers customized consultations in small business services, diversity and discrimination, and investigations, complaints and grievances. Provides investigations, including allegations of unfair treatment, equal employment opportunity (EEO) and racial or sexual harassment. Offers customized web-based training (webinars) on a variety of HR, EEO and AAP-related topics. **Scope:** Provider of human resources assistance to organizations. Offers preparation of affirmative action plans, support documents, and adverse impact studies of personnel activities. Also offers customized consultations in small business services, diversity and discrimination, and investigations, complaints and grievances. Provides investigations, including allegations of unfair treatment, equal employment opportunity (EEO) and racial or sexual harassment. Offers customized web-based training (webinars) on a variety of HR, EEO and AAP-related topics. **Founded:** 1984.

28998 ■ Hutar Growth Management Institute (HGMI)
912 Huber Ln.
  Glenview, IL 60025
Contact: Laddie F. Hutar, President
E-mail: laddie@hutar.com
Description: Publishes material on management and business practices. Offers audio cassettes and printed reports. It does not accept unsolicited manuscripts. Reaches the market through direct mail, telephone sales, and trade sales. **Scope:** Offers general growth management services, including research, participative process consulting, development of professional practices, publication, training and coaching for organizations. **Publications:** "What Every Business Needs to Know," L.F. Hutar, 1993; "Convention Attendance Report Kit," 1992; "Finance Operations Package," 1992; "Self-administered Management Audit Questionnaire," 1992; "Successful Techniques for Improving Sales," 1992; "DHP Report - Decorative High Profit Millwork," 1995; "Communications Improvement Manual," 1995. **Training:** Millwork/Showcase Selling/DHP Niche Workshop; Upscale Selling Techniques; Hidden Waste Reduction; Sales Personnel Performance Improvement; Positive Work Attitude Workshop; Retailers Better Management Workshop; Better Middle Management Personnel Workshop; Communications Improvement Workshop; Professionals Practice Development.

28999 ■ Impact Business Network Ltd.
3098 Midland Rd.
  Victoria, BC, Canada V8R 6P2
Ph: (250)812-6771
Co. E-mail: victoria@impact-ltd.ca
URL: http://www.impact-ltd.ca
Contact: Sandra Birrell, President
E-mail: sandra@impact-ltd.ca
Description: Provider of project management and business consulting services including training development, communications assessment and development for government and corporate organizations. **Scope:** Provider of project management and business consulting services including training development, communications assessment and development for government and corporate organizations.

29000 ■ IMPAQ Accountability Business & Human Resources Development Inc.
3221 S Hill St., Ste. 124
  Los Angeles, CA 90007
Ph: (213)536-5685
Co. E-mail: contactus@impaqcorp.com
URL: http://impaqcorp.com
Contact: Mark Samuel, Chief Executive Officer
Facebook: www.facebook.com/BStateBreakthrough
Description: Services: Management and leadership. **Scope:** Services: Management and leadership. **Founded:** 1985. **Publications:** "Making Yourself Indispensable"; "Creating the Accountable Organization"; "Success Through Accountability for Managers and Their Teams"; "The Power of Personal Accountability: Achieve What Matters to You"; "Team Interaction Questionnaire"; "Success Through Accountability"; "Situation Action Inventory"; "The Personal Accountability Card"; "The Personal Accountability Model Poster". **Training:** Designing Accountability; Transformation; Accountability Based Safety: A New Solution to an Old Problem; Sep, 2006; Making Yourself & Your Organization Indispensable; The Accountability Revolution; Breaking the Rules of Change; Driving Organizational Change; Facilitation Mastership.

29001 ■ In Plain English

14501 Antigone Dr.
  Gaithersburg, MD 20878-2484
Ph: (301)340-2821
Free: 800-274-9645
Fax: (301)279-0115
URL: http://www.inplainenglish.com

Description: Management consultants helping government and businesses research, design, write and produce user oriented management information for human resources, employee benefits, business process, corporate and marketing needs. Services include: GSA mob is schedule for consulting to the government; employee benefit communications, plain English business writing workshops for print and electronic media; communicating strategy and tactics; marketing research, business planning and communications; readability testing; usability testing and monitoring strategy. **Scope:** Management consultants helping government and businesses research, design, write and produce user oriented management information for human resources, employee benefits, business process, corporate and marketing needs. Services include: GSA mob is schedule for consulting to the government; employee benefit communications, plain English business writing workshops for print and electronic media; communicating strategy and tactics; marketing research, business planning and communications; readability testing; usability testing and monitoring strategy. **Founded:** 1977. **Publications:** "The Benefits Communication"; "The Employee Benefits Communication ToolKit," Commerce Clearinghouse; "Benefits Communication," Business and Legal Reports. **Training:** Plain English Writing Training; Summary Plan Description Compliance workshops; Re-Humanizing the Corporation, Human Resources and Employee Benefits Communication Workshop; 21 Writing Tips for the 21st Century; Make the Write Impression; Writing to Inform and Instruct; The Dreaded Nuts and Bolts; Writing to Persuade; Writing Policy and Procedure Manuals In Plain English; Writing for Accountants and Auditors In Plain English. **Special Services:** In Plain English®.

29002 ■ Institute for Business Technology (IBT) [IBT International]

2400 Walsh Ave.
  Santa Clara, CA 95051
Ph: (408)669-3289
Free: 800-915-3562
Co. E-mail: inquiries@ibttech.com
URL: http://www.ibt.edu
Facebook: www.facebook.com/santaclaraIBT

Description: The firm offers consulting and conducts training in the areas of self management, work flow management, time management, information management and project management for all levels of management, professional and administrative staff. Helps companies address a range of strategic and operational issues such as white collar productivity, optimal utilization of productivity tools, alternative officing, corporate relocations, paper reduction and files management and E-mail overload. Company has nationwide expertise in alternative design and implementation - all phases thereof. Industries served: Fortune1000 companies, government agencies and financial institutions. **Scope:** The firm offers consulting and conducts training in the areas of self management, work flow management, time management, information management and project management for all levels of management, professional and administrative staff. Helps companies address a range of strategic and operational issues such as white collar productivity, optimal utilization of productivity tools, alternative officing, corporate relocations, paper reduction and files management and E-mail overload. Company has nationwide expertise in alternative design and implementation - all phases thereof. Industries served: Fortune1000 companies, government agencies and financial institutions. **Founded:** 1945. **Publications:** "The Personal Efficiency Program - How To Get Organized To Do More Work In Less Time," John Wiley and Sons, 2004; "The Next Generation Workplace What, Why, When, Where, & How"; "Your Filing Systems Can Work!"; "The High-Tech Personal Efficiency Program," John

Wiley Sons, 1997; "Your Filing Systems Can Work!"; "Alternative Officing Day - Saluting the New Ways of Work"; "Top Five Management Mistakes"; "The Company Move: Calm or Chaos?". **Training:** Stress Management and Life Balance; Work place Strategies: Alternative Workplaces; Work Effectiveness; Making the Most of Technology; Getting Things Done; Overcoming Procrastination; TRAIN-THE-TRAINER PROGRAM.

29003 ■ Institute for Management Excellence

Trabuco Canyon, CA 92679
Ph: (949)667-1012
URL: http://www.itstime.com
Contact: Barbara Taylor, Executive Director

Description: Consulting firm and training focuses on improving productivity, using practices and creative techniques. **Scope:** Consulting firm and training focuses on improving productivity, using practices and creative techniques. **Founded:** 1995. **Publications:** "Income Without a Job," 2008; "The Other Side of Midnight, 2000: An Executive Guide to the Year 2000 Problem"; "Concordance to the Michael Teachings"; "Handbook of Small Business Advertising"; "The Personality Game"; "How to Market Yourself for Success". **Training:** The Personality Game; Power Path Seminars; Productivity Plus; Sexual Harassment and Discrimination Prevention; Worker's Comp Cost Reduction; Americans with Disabilities Act; In Search of Identify: Clarifying Corporate Culture.

29004 ■ Interminds & Federer Resources Inc.

PO Box 438
  Pasadena, CA 91102
Ph: (512)261-0761
Co. E-mail: yesyoucan@interminds.com
URL: http://www.interminds.com

Description: Firm specializes in feasibility studies, startup businesses, small business management, mergers and acquisitions, joint ventures, divestitures, interim and crisis management, turnarounds, production planning, team building, appraisals, and valuations. **Scope:** Firm specializes in feasibility studies, startup businesses, small business management, mergers and acquisitions, joint ventures, divestitures, interim and crisis management, turnarounds, production planning, team building, appraisals, and valuations. **Founded:** 1985. **Publications:** "Yes You Can: How To Be A Success No Matter Who You Are Or Where You're From".

29005 ■ International Money Management Group Inc.

110 Channel Marker Way Ste. 101
  Grasonville, MD 21638
Contact: Ernest O. Brittingham, Jr., Contact

Description: Multiservice firm created with the express purpose of guiding and assisting individuals, professionals, small businesses and corporations ineffective management of their business and personal financial planning. **Scope:** Multiservice firm created with the express purpose of guiding and assisting individuals, professionals, small businesses and corporations ineffective management of their business and personal financial planning.

29006 ■ Jewish Lights Publishing

Sunset Farms Offices, Rte. 4
  Woodstock, VT 05091
Ph: (802)457-4000
Fax: (802)457-4004
Co. E-mail: marketing@turnerpublishing.com
URL: http://www.jewishlights.com

Description: Publishes adult and children's books on Jewish spirituality, religion, philosophy, theology and culture for people of all faiths and backgrounds. Reaches market through commission representatives, direct mail, telephone sales, trade sales, advertising, wholesalers and distributors. Accepts unsolicited manuscripts. **Founded:** 1974.

29007 ■ Johnston Co.

78 Bedford St.
  Lexington, MA 02420
Ph: (781)862-7595
Fax: (781)862-9066
Co. E-mail: info@johnstoncompany.com

URL: http://johnstoncompany.com
Contact: Jim Johnston, Chief Executive Officer
E-mail: jimj@johnstoncompany.com

Description: Firm provides consulting on environmental and workplace services such as LSRP service, property acquisition and redevelopment, engineering and site remediation. **Scope:** Firm provides consulting on environmental and workplace services such as LSRP service, property acquisition and redevelopment, engineering and site remediation. **Publications:** "Why are board meetings such a waste of time," Boston Business Journal, Apr, 2004.

29008 ■ Liberty Business Strategies Ltd.

329 S 16th
  Philadelphia, PA 19102
Ph: (267)858-4021
Co. E-mail: info@libertystrategies.com
URL: http://libertystrategies.com
Contact: Emmy Miller, President
Linkedin: www.linkedin.com/company/525207
X (Twitter): x.com/LibertyBusiness

Description: Management consulting firm provides executive coaching, strategic alignment, succession planning such as healthcare, consumer products, technology, and much more. **Scope:** Management consulting firm provides executive coaching, strategic alignment, succession planning such as healthcare, consumer products, technology, and much more. **Founded:** 1980. **Training:** Winning with Talent, Morison Annual Conference, Jul, 2009.

29009 ■ Management Growth Institute (MGI)

27 Chelmsford Rd.
  Rochester, NY 14618-1727
Contact: Kathleen Barry Albertini, Contact

Description: Firm offers assistance in the specification, design, and implementation of management development programs, their clients include individuals, small businesses, national trade associations and government agencies. **Scope:** Firm offers assistance in the specification, design, and implementation of management development programs, their clients include individuals, small businesses, national trade associations and government agencies. **Publications:** "Cost Reduction Is Your Company the Target," InFocus Magazine, Apr, 2010; "Fall-I hired this great person," The Canadian Mover, Dec, 2009; "Profit Strategies," Direction Magazine, Jul, 2009; "Customer Loyalty," InFocus Magazine, Jul, 2009; "Cash Management," The Portal Magazine, Jul, 2009; "What is Customer Loyalty," In FOCUS Magazine, Dec, 2008; "Strategies to Improve Profits," Aug, 2008; "A Question of Management," Moving World. **Training:** Profit Enhancement; Family-Owned Businesses; Strategic Planning; Survival and Growth in a Down Economy.

29010 ■ Management House L.L.C.

PO Box 2708
  Carefree, AZ 85377
Contact: V. Clayton Sherman, Manager

Description: Firm offers management consulting that emphasizes management education and human resources programming for health service, business, military, and academic organizations, this programming is based on needs analysis and can be presented as keynote addresses, half-day else full-day programs, multiple-day seminars and executive retreats. **Scope:** Firm offers management consulting that emphasizes management education and human resources programming for health service, business, military, and academic organizations, this programming is based on needs analysis and can be presented as keynote addresses, half-day else full-day programs, multiple-day seminars and executive retreats. **Founded:** 2008. **Publications:** "Raising Standards in American Healthcare"; "Creating the New American Hospital"; "Total Customer Satisfaction"; "From Losers to Winners"; "Managerial Performance & Promotability"; "Make Yourself Memorable Winning Strategies to Influence Others". **Training:** Offers the following in-house programs: The Uncommon Leader; The New American Organization; The New American Hospital; Productivity & Performance Improvement; Keys to Managerial Effectiveness;

Creating Organizational Excellence; Managing Change & Conflict; Handling the Problem Employee; Gaining Power & Persuasion; Building a Winning Team; and Managing Stress, Strain, and Dis-Ease; Creating the New American Hospital: A Time For Greatness; Total Customer Satisfaction; Leading With Certainty in Uncertain Times; Raising Standards in American Health Care.

29011 ■ Management Methods Inc.
PO Box 1484
Decatur, AL 35602
Ph: (256)355-3896
URL: http://www.managementmethods.com
Contact: Davis M. Woodruff, Founder Consultant
E-mail: davisw@managementmethods.com

Description: Firm provides consulting, customized training and speaking services. **Scope:** Firm provides consulting, customized training and speaking services. **Founded:** 1984. **Publications:** "A Manager's Guide to the 10 Essentials"; "A Manager's Guide to Tqm Success"; "Leading People and Managing Processes"; "Taking Care of the Basics, 101 Success Factors for Managers," 2005. **Training:** Statistical Process Control (SPC): Concepts and Applications; Advanced Statistical Methods; Team Problem Solving; Effective Management Methods; Measurement Systems SPC and ISO 9000; What To Do When Total Quality Management Isn't Working; Seven Golden Rules for the Best Customer service; How To Make Quality Management a Success; Managing Without Unions; Five Techniques for Keeping Technical People From Failing as Managers; How To Stop the War Between Sales, Engineering and Manufacturing; Reengineer Your Company with Common Sense and Compassion; Having High Values in a Low Cost, High Quality Business.

29012 ■ Market Focus, Inc.
2307 Fenton Pkwy. No. 134
San Diego, CA 92108
Free: 800-708-9715
Co. E-mail: sales@emarketfocus.com
URL: http://www.emarketfocus.com
Contact: Chris Carter, Contact
Facebook: www.facebook.com/marketfocusinc

Description: Provider of custom qualitative and quantitative market research designed to answer key questions and then offers ideas that generate results. Provides counsel in marketing research and planning and marketing programs, particularly for financial service organizations, banking, insurance, electronics, publishing and industrial organizations. **Founded:** 1992. **Publications:** "Surviving in Hard Times," NJ Contractor. **Training:** Charting a Course for Future Company Growth; Marketing Planning; Construction Marketing in the 90's; Marketing and The CFO.

29013 ■ Max Freund
363 Omaha Ct.
Claremont, CA 91711
Ph: (909)632-1624
Co. E-mail: max@lfleadership.com
URL: http://praxsysleadership.com
Contact: Max Freund, Partner

Description: Consultant and coach provide training on leadership and success for individuals and organizations and consults with organizations, teams and communities on leadership, economic development, strategy, organizational learning and team effectiveness and other core practice areas are coaching groups and individuals, facilitating groups, training leaders and teams in skills to communicate effectively. **Scope:** Consultant and coach provide training on leadership and success for individuals and organizations and consults with organizations, teams and communities on leadership, economic development, strategy, organizational learning and team effectiveness and other core practice areas are coaching groups and individuals, facilitating groups, training leaders and teams in skills to communicate effectively. **Training:** High Desert Resource Network Fundraising Academy for Grassroots Nonprofits, Aug, 2009; Developing the Next Generation of Leaders, Sep, 2008; Coaching Skills for Staff Development and Retention, Sep, 2008; Developing Funds, Trans-

forming Leadership, San Bernardino County Grants Office, Jun, 2008; Developing Funds, Developing Leadership, High Desert Resource Network, Apr, 2008; Executive Coaching Skills; Fundraising Fundamentals for Non-profits.

29014 ■ MCR Capital Advisors Corp.
3626 N Hall St., Ste. 520
Dallas, TX 75219
Ph: (214)575-9985
Fax: (888)502-6983
Co. E-mail: colvint@mcrcapitaladvisors.com
URL: http://www.mcrcapital.com
Contact: Tom A. Colvin, Office Manager
E-mail: colvint@mcrcapitaladvisors.com

Description: Services: Strategic planning, business consulting and wealth creation. **Scope:** Services: Strategic planning, business consulting and wealth creation. **Training:** R&D Limited Partnership Organization; Tax Sheltered Investments; Mid-Management Development Seminar.

29015 ■ McShane Group L.L.C.
2119 E Franklin St.
Richmond, VA 23223
URL: http://www.mcshanegroup.com
Contact: Jim L. Huitt, Jr., Principal
E-mail: jhuitt@mcshanegroup.com

Description: Firm provides diligence services, interim management, strategic business realignments, marketing, and much more. **Scope:** Firm provides diligence services, interim management, strategic business realignments, marketing, and much more. **Founded:** 1987.

29016 ■ Medema Consulting Associates L.L.C.
3355 Eagle Park Dr. NE, Ste. 107
Grand Rapids, MI 49525
Ph: (616)581-3230
URL: http://www.medemaconsulting.com
Contact: Dave Medema, Consultant

Description: Firm creates and delivers customized training and consulting services in board governance and leadership development, diversity assessment and training, fundraising, human resources, meeting facilitation, performance improvement, strategic thinking, planning, evaluation, team building, and workshops. **Scope:** Firm creates and delivers customized training and consulting services in board governance and leadership development, diversity assessment and training, fundraising, human resources, meeting facilitation, performance improvement, strategic thinking, planning, evaluation, team building, and workshops. **Founded:** 1993.

29017 ■ Medical Imaging Consultants Inc. (MIC)
1037 US Hwy. 46, Ste. G-2
Clifton, NJ 07013-2445
Ph: (973)574-8000
Free: 800-589-5685
Fax: (973)574-8001
Co. E-mail: info@micinfo.com
URL: http://www.micinfo.com
Contact: Philip A. Femano, President

Description: Provider of professional support services in radiology management and comprehensive continuing education programs for radiologic technologists such as professional educators, life scientists, biomedical engineers, and much more. **Scope:** Provider of professional support services in radiology management and comprehensive continuing education programs for radiologic technologists such as professional educators, life scientists, biomedical engineers, and much more. **Founded:** 1991. **Training:** Sectional Anatomy and Imaging Strategies; CT Cross-Trainer; CT Registry Review Program; MR Cross Trainer; MRI Registry Review Program; Digital Mammography Essentials for Technologists; Radiology Trends for Technologists.

29018 ■ Medical Outcomes Management Inc. (MOM)
15 S Main St., Ste. 208
Sharon, MA 02067
Ph: (781)806-0275

URL: http://www.mom-inc.us
Contact: Dr. Alan Kaul, Chief Executive Officer
E-mail: alan@mom-inc.us
Facebook: www.facebook.com/akaul2019
Linkedin: www.linkedin.com/company/medical-outcomes-management

Description: Management and technology consulting firm providing a specially focused group of services such as disease management programs and pharmacoeconomic studies. Services include clinical and educational projects, medical writing and editing, marketing and sales projects, disease registries, educational seminars, strategic planning projects, managed care organizations and pharmaceutical and biotechnology companies. **Scope:** Management and technology consulting firm providing a specially focused group of services such as disease management programs and pharmacoeconomic studies. Services include clinical and educational projects, medical writing and editing, marketing and sales projects, disease registries, educational seminars, strategic planning projects, managed care organizations and pharmaceutical and biotechnology companies. **Founded:** 1991. **Publications:** "Treatment of acute exacerbation's of chronic bronchitis in patients with chronic obstructive pulmonary disease: A retrospective cohort analysis logarithmically extended release vs. Azithromycin," 2003; "A retrospective analysis of cyclooxygenase-II inhibitor response patterns," 2002; "DUE criteria for use of regional urokinase infusion for deep vein thrombosis,"2002; "The formulary management system and decision-making process at Horizon Blue Cross Blue Shield of New Jersey," Pharmaco therapy, 2001. **Training:** Economic Modeling as a Disease Management Tool, Academy of Managed Care Pharmacy, Apr, 2005; Integrating Disease State Management and Economics, Academy of Managed Care Pharmacy, Oct, 2004; Clinical and economic outcomes in the treatment of peripheral occlusive diseases, Mar, 2003.

29019 ■ Metric Business Associates Inc.
190 S Benjamin Dr.
West Chester, PA 19382
Contact: Michael E. Moore, President

Description: Company engaged in providing business services such as strategic planning and execution, leadership management, change management and tracking and management of business performances. **Scope:** Company engaged in providing business services such as strategic planning and execution, leadership management, change management and tracking and management of business performances.

29020 ■ Miller/Cook & Associates Inc.
Marco Island, FL 34145
Ph: (239)266-2761
URL: http://www.millercook.com
Contact: William B. Miller, President
E-mail: bill@millercook.com

Description: Firm is engaged in consulting services such as enrollment integration and operation, re-recruitment and retention, tuition discount and net revenue reviews, integrated communication training to colleges and universities. **Scope:** Firm is engaged in consulting services such as enrollment integration and operation, re-recruitment and retention, tuition discount and net revenue reviews, integrated communication training to colleges and universities. **Founded:** 1988. **Publications:** "Capital gains: Surviving in an increasingly for profit world"; "Making steps to a brighter future". **Training:** Admissions: An overview of a changing profession; Admission practices: Managing the admissions office; Admission practices: Internal operations often make the difference; Effective communication and the enrollment process; Telemarketing or Tele counseling: How to use the telephone to effectively enroll and re-enroll students; Graduate and professional program recruitment: An overview Re-Recruitment: What is it? Is it necessary?; The effective use of electronic mediums in the recruitment process; The use of alumni to support and sustain your recruiting efforts.

29021 ■ Miller, Leiby & Associates P.C.

32 Broadway, 13th Fl.
 New York, NY 10004
Ph: (212)227-4200
Fax: (212)504-8369
URL: http://www.millerleiby.com
Contact: Doron Leiby, Partner
Facebook: www.facebook.com/MillerLeibyAssocia
 tesPc
Linkedin: www.linkedin.com/company/1269719
Instagram: www.instagram.com/millerleiby
Description: Firm is engaged in legal counsel for individuals and businesses. **Scope:** Firm is engaged in legal counsel for individuals and businesses. **Training:** Objectives and standards/recruiting for boards of directors.

29022 ■ Murray Dropkin & Associates

390 George St.
 New Brunswick, NJ 08901
URL: http://dropkin.com
Contact: Murray Dropkin, Contact
Description: Firm specializes in feasibility studies, business management, business process reengineering, team building, healthcare, and housing. **Scope:** Firm specializes in feasibility studies, business management, business process reengineering, team building, healthcare, and housing. **Publications:** "Bookkeeping for Nonprofits," Jossey Bass, 2005; "Guide to Audits of Nonprofit Organizations," PPC; "The Nonprofit Report," Warren, Gorham & Lamont; "The Budget Building Book for Nonprofits," Jossey-Bass; "The Cash Flow Management Book for Nonprofits," Jossey-Bass.

29023 ■ Nightingale Associates

7445 Setting Sun Way
 Columbia, MD 21046
Ph: (410)381-4280
URL: http://www.nightingaleassociates.net
Contact: Frederick C. Nightingale, Managing Director
E-mail: fredericknightingale@nightingaleassociates
 .net
X (Twitter): x.com/FCNightingale
Description: Management training and consulting firm offering the following skills productivity and accomplishment, leadership skills for the experienced manager, management skills for the new manager, leadership and teambuilding, supervisory development, creative problem solving, real strategic planning. **Scope:** Management training and consulting firm offering the following skills productivity and accomplishment, leadership skills for the experienced manager, management skills for the new manager, leadership and teambuilding, supervisory development, creative problem solving, real strategic planning. **Founded:** 1984. **Training:** Productivity and Accomplishment Management Skills for the New Manager; Leadership and Team building; Advanced Management; Business Process Re engineering; Strategic Thinking; Creative Problem Solving; Customer Service; International Purchasing and Materials Management; Fundamentals of Purchasing; Negotiation Skills Development; Providing superior customer service; Leadership skills for the experienced manager.

29024 ■ Performance Consultants Group, Inc. (PCG)

1 Innovation Way., Ste. 400
 Newark, DE 19711
Ph: (302)738-7532
Free: 888-724-3578
URL: http://www.pcgius.com
Description: Firm provides consulting services in the areas of strategic planning, profit enhancement, product development, and production planning. **Scope:** Firm provides consulting services in the areas of strategic planning, profit enhancement, product development, and production planning. **Founded:** 1988.

29025 ■ Performance Consulting Associates, Inc. (PCA)

3700 Crestwood Pky., Ste. 100
 Duluth, GA 30096
Ph: (770)717-2737

Co. E-mail: info@pcaconsulting.com
URL: http://pcaconsulting.com
Contact: Richard deFazio, President
Linkedin: www.linkedin.com/company/pcaconsulting
Description: Firm provides asset management solutions, business process optimization, and much more. **Scope:** Firm provides asset management solutions, business process optimization, and much more. **Founded:** 1976. **Publications:** "Does Planning Pay," Plant Services, Nov, 2000; "Asset Reliability Coordinator," Maintenance Technology, Oct, 2000; "Know What it is You Have to Maintain," Maintenance Technology, May, 2000; "Does Maintenance Planning Pay," Maintenance Technology, Nov, 2000.; "What is Asset Management?"; "Implementing Best Business Practices".

29026 ■ Pinpoint Tactics Business Consulting

5525 West Blvd.
 Vancouver, BC, Canada V6M 3W6
Ph: (604)263-4698
Co. E-mail: info@pinpointtactics.com
URL: http://www.pinpointtactics.com
Contact: Sandy Huang, President
Facebook: www.facebook.com/PinpointTactics
X (Twitter): x.com/pinpointtactics
Description: Firm provides business consulting services such as marketing programs, small business launch program, strategic business program, market research, and much more. **Scope:** Firm provides business consulting services such as marketing programs, small business launch program, strategic business program, market research, and much more.

29027 ■ PYA GatesMoore

Resurgens Plz., Ste. 2100, 945 E Paces Ferry Rd. NE
 Atlanta, GA 30326
Ph: (404)266-9876
Free: 800-270-9629
Co. E-mail: info@pyapc.com
URL: http://www.pyapc.com
Contact: Marty Brown, President
E-mail: mbrown@pyapc.com
Facebook: www.facebook.com/pyapc
Linkedin: www.linkedin.com/company/pyapc
Description: Firm provides healthcare consulting, audit and accounting and valuation services. **Scope:** Firm provides healthcare consulting, audit and accounting and valuation services. **Founded:** 1982. **Publications:** "Practicing Medicine in the 21st Century"; "Physicians, Dentists and Veterinarians"; "Insurance Portability and Accountability Act Privacy Manual"; "How To Guide for your Medical Practice and Health Insurance Portability and Accountability Act Security Manual"; "A How To Guide for your Medical Practice"; "Cost Analysis Made Simple: A Step by Step Guide to Using Cost Accounting to Ensure Practice Profitability"; "Cost Cutting Strategies for Medical Practices"; "Cost Cutting Strategies for Medical Practices"; "Getting the Jump on Year-End Tax Planning"; "New 401(k) Safe Harbor Option: Increased Opportunities for the Physician and Practice"; "Not All Tax News is Bad News"; "Shareholder Agreements: Identifying and Addressing Five Risk Areas"; "Surprise - Your Practice has a Deferred Income Tax Liability". **Training:** Documenting and Billing High Risk Codes, 2010; Current Challenges in Ob/Gyn Recruiting, 2010; Planning for Physician Wind-down & Retirement, 2010; HITECH "How To" - Opportunities & Risks, 2010; Pediatric Coding and Audits; Recruiting and Retaining Physicians; How to Prepare for the Recovery Audit Contractors - RAC, 2010; Meaningful Use Rule, 2010; The Revenue Stream in Practice, Apr, 2008; Improving Efficiencies in a Small Family Medicine Practice, Oct, 2007; Using Compensation Models to Improve Performance, Sep, 2007; The Financial Side of Personnel Management, Sep, 2007; Pay for Performance-Is it Really Contracting for Quality?, New York State Ophthalmological Society, Sep, 2007; Beyond the Class Action Settlement Payments-Looking Prospectively at Managed Care Companies Behavior, New York State Ophthalmological Society, Sep, 2007; Protecting your clients

from Embezzlement, Jun, 2007; What P4P Means to Your Medical Practice, May, 2007; Finance for the Practicing Physician, May, 2007; Trashing, Dipping and Ghosts in Medical Practices: Protecting your clients from Embezzlement, Apr, 2006.

29028 ■ Quality Business Consulting Inc. (QBCI)

8405 Pershing Dr., Ste. 404
 Playa del Rey, CA 90293
Ph: (310)822-9008
Free: 866-636-5666
Fax: (310)822-9009
Co. E-mail: info@qbconsulting.com
URL: http://www.qbconsulting.com
Contact: Jean-Paul Issock, Contact
Description: Technology consulting firm specializing in the implementation, support and engineering of construction management and accounting systems. Offers services to heavy construction, marine salvage, property development/management, law firms and general and specialty contractors. **Scope:** Technology consulting firm specializing in the implementation, support and engineering of construction management and accounting systems. Offers services to heavy construction, marine salvage, property development/management, law firms and general and specialty contractors. **Founded:** 1987. **Special Services:** LIBRA Signature; StarBid; StarViewer; StarProject; ToolBox; ProEst.

29029 ■ Rose & Crangle Ltd.

102 E Lincoln Ave.
 Lincoln, KS 67455
Contact: S. Jeanne Crangle, Contact
Description: Provider of evaluation, planning and policy analyzes for universities, associations, foundations, governmental agencies and private companies engaged in scientific, technological or educational activities. Special expertise in the development of new institutions. Special skills in providing planning and related group facilitation workshops. **Scope:** Provider of evaluation, planning and policy analyzes for universities, associations, foundations, governmental agencies and private companies engaged in scientific, technological or educational activities. Special expertise in the development of new institutions. Special skills in providing planning and related group facilitation workshops. **Publications:** "Preface to Bulgarian Integration Into Europe and NATO: Issues of Science Policy And research Evaluation Practice," Ios Press, 2006; "Allocating Limited National Resources for Fundamental Research," 2005.

29030 ■ Sandler Travis and Rosenberg P.A. (ST&R)

5835 Blue Lagoon Dr., Ste. 200
 Miami, FL 33126
Ph: (305)267-9200
URL: http://www.strtrade.com
Contact: Gilbert Lee Sandler, President
E-mail: lsandler@strtrade.com
Facebook: www.facebook.com/STRTRADE
Linkedin: www.linkedin.com/company/sandler-travis
 -&-rosenberg-p-a
X (Twitter): x.com/STRTRADE
Description: Law firm provides legal advisory services. **Founded:** 1977.

29031 ■ Schneider Consulting Group Inc.

2801 E 4th Ave.
 Denver, CO 80206
Contact: Frank S. Schneider, Contact
Description: Firm assists family-owned and privately-held business transition to the next generation and or to a more professionally managed company, turn around consulting for small and medium-sized companies. **Scope:** Firm assists family-owned and privately-held business transition to the next generation and or to a more professionally managed company, turn around consulting for small and medium-sized companies. **Founded:** 1987. **Training:** Family Business Council; Impact of the Energy Renaissance.

29032 ■ Smart Ways to Work

300 Frank H. Ogawa Plz., Ste. 215
 Oakland, CA 94612
Free: 800-599-8463
Co. E-mail: odette@smartwaystowork.com
URL: http://www.smartwaystowork.com
Contact: Odette Pollar, Consultant
E-mail: odette@smartwaystowork.com

Description: Provider of consulting, training, and other related services and also analyze performance, speeches, and much more. **Scope:** Provider of consulting, training, and other related services and also analyze performance, speeches, and much more. **Publications:** "Surviving Information Overload driving Information Overload: How to Find, Filter, and Focus on What's Important," Crisp Publications, Sep, 2003; "Take Back Your Life: Smart Ways to Simplify Daily Living," Conari Press, Apr, 1999; "365 Ways to Simplify Your Work Life," Kaplan Business, Aug, 1996; "Dynamics of Diversity: Strategic Programs for Your Organization," Crisp Publications, 1994; "Organizing Your Workspace: A Guide to Personal Productivity," Crisp Publications, May, 1992. **Training:** Managing Multiple Demands: Surviving Ground Zero; Defending Your Life: Balancing Work And Home; Desktop Sprawl: Conquer Your Paper Pile-Up; Getting It All Done: Breaking The Time Bind; To Give or Not To Give: The Delegation Dilemma; Information Happens: Don't Let It Happen On You; Take The Terror Out Of Talk: Secrets To Successful Speaking; To Give or Not To Give: The Delegation Dilemma; Managing Meetings.

29033 ■ SPC Business Consulting Ltd.

1629 K. St. NW
 Washington, DC 20006
Free: 866-577-6749
Co. E-mail: info@spcconsulting.org
URL: http://www.spcconsulting.org
Contact: Leona Charles, Contact
Facebook: www.facebook.com/spcbusinessconsulting
Instagram: www.instagram.com/adventuresincontracting

Description: Firm specializes in management and business consulting. **Scope:** Firm specializes in management and business consulting.

29034 ■ Tamayo Consulting Inc.

662 Encinitas Blvd., Ste. 236
 Encinitas, CA 92024
Ph: (760)479-1352
URL: http://www.tamayoconsulting.com
Contact: Jennifer Dreyer, President

Description: It Provides training and consulting services. And also it specializes in leadership and team development. Industries served: private, nonprofit, government, educational. **Scope:** It Provides training and consulting services. And also it specializes in leadership and team development. Industries served: private, non-profit, government, educational. **Training:** Presentation AdvantEdge Program; Lead point Development Program; Supervisor Development Programs.Identify Presentation Objectives; Implement 360-degree presentation assessment; conduct baseline-coaching session; Develop coaching plan; Staying connected.

29035 ■ Trendzitions Inc.

25691 Atlantic Ocean, Dr. No. B13
 Lake Forest, CA 92630
Ph: (949)727-9100
URL: http://www.trendzitions.com
Contact: Chris Tooker, President
E-mail: ctooker@trendzitions.com
X (Twitter): x.com/trendzitions
Instagram: www.instagram.com/trendzitions

Description: Provider of services in the areas of communications consulting, project management, construction management, and furniture procurement. Offers information on spatial uses, building codes, ADA compliance and city ordinances. Also offers budget projections. **Scope:** Provider of services in the areas of communications consulting, project management, construction management, and furni-

ture procurement. Offers information on spatial uses, building codes, ADA compliance and city ordinances. Also offers budget projections. **Founded:** 1986.

29036 ■ Tweed-Weber Inc. (TWD)

PO Box 112
 Reading, PA 19603
Free: 800-999-6615
Co. E-mail: mail@tweedweber.com
URL: http://www.tweedweber.com
Contact: Gretchen Henion, Manager, Operations
E-mail: gkoch@tweedweber.com
Linkedin: www.linkedin.com/company/tweed-weber-inc.

Description: Firm provides marketing and sales consulting, management assistance, and advertising agency services, they assist in strategic, marketing, advertising, internet, import and export, sales, distribution, and trade shows. **Founded:** 1991.

29037 ■ Verbit & Co.

152 Union Ave.
 Bala Cynwyd, PA 19004
Contact: Alan C. Verbit, Owner

Description: Management consulting firm to assist executives and managers fulfill their mission and to assure that adequate planning of day-to-day operations occurs, that controls sufficient to safeguard valuable resources and that results of decisions reviewed in sufficient time to effect continuing action. **Scope:** Management consulting firm to assist executives and managers fulfill their mission and to assure that adequate planning of day-to-day operations occurs, that controls sufficient to safeguard valuable resources and that results of decisions reviewed in sufficient time to effect continuing action. **Training:** Integrating Manufacturing Management Systems with Business Systems; Negotiating Information Systems Agreements with Suppliers.

29038 ■ Weber Business Services L.L.C.

2909 Conococheague Ln.
 Greencastle, PA 17225
Ph: (717)597-8890
Co. E-mail: info@wbsllc.com
URL: http://www.wbsllc.com
Contact: Liz Weber, Chief Executive Officer

Description: Services include strategic planning, systems development, succession and workforce planning, performance management, and leadership training. **Scope:** Services include strategic planning, systems development, succession and workforce planning, performance management, and leadership training.

29039 ■ Western Business Services Ltd. (WBS)

1269 Lindsay St.
 Regina, SK, Canada S4N 3B4
Ph: (306)522-1493
Fax: (306)522-9076
Co. E-mail: wbs@myaccess.ca
URL: http://business.accesscomm.ca/wbs
Contact: O'Neil A. Zuck, President

Description: Provides advice and assistance to organizations on administrative management issues. **Scope:** Provides advice and assistance to organizations on administrative management issues. **Founded:** 1992.

29040 ■ Westlife Consultants and Advisors

4 Robert Speck Pkwy.
 Mississauga, ON, Canada L4Z, CA
URL: http://www.westlifeconsultants.com
Contact: Syed N. Hussain, President
E-mail: shussain@westlifeconsultants.com
Linkedin: www.linkedin.com/company/westlife-consultants-&-advisors

Description: Provider of entrepreneurs and businesses with a highly commercial and global perspectives on the international business development ideas under consideration. **Scope:** Provider of entrepreneurs and businesses with a highly commercial and global perspectives on the international business development ideas under consideration. **Founded:** 1992. **Publications:** "Innovative Management"; "Team Building and Leadership"; "Financial Planning";

"Estate Planning"; "Risk Management"; "Export/Import Trade Finance Mechanics"; "Marketing and Sales Management"; "What Your Banker Needs to Know"; "Building A Successful Financial Plan".

29041 ■ Zbikowski Business Initiatives L.L.C. (ZBI)

7319 Woodsman Cir.
 Holland, OH 43528-9561
Contact: James Zbikowski, Contact

Description: Firm provides consulting and training related to quality and environmental management systems. Takes a process approach to development and implementation activities. Assists clients in achieving certification and process improvements initially conducts on site assessment of quality or environmental management systems, and includes an action plan for development and implementation. **Scope:** Firm provides consulting and training related to quality and environmental management systems. Takes a process approach to development and implementation activities. Assists clients in achieving certification and process improvements initially conducts on site assessment of quality or environmental management systems, and includes an action plan for development and implementation.

FRANCHISES AND BUSINESS OPPORTUNITIES

29042 ■ LMI Canada Inc. (LMI)

205 Matheson Blvd. E, Unit 15
 Mississauga, ON, Canada L4Z 3E3
Free: 877-857-4083
Co. E-mail: info@lmicanada.ca
URL: http://www.lmicanada.ca
Contact: Frank Kreze, President
E-mail: fkreze@lmicanada.ca
Facebook: www.facebook.com/LMICanada
Linkedin: www.linkedin.com/company/lmi-canada-inc-
X (Twitter): x.com/lmicanada
YouTube: www.youtube.com/user/LMICanada

Description: Firm provides human development, leadership development and programs, professional training and coaching services for education, corporate and individuals. **Founded:** 1980. **Franchise Fee:** $38,000. **Training:** Initial and ongoing support provided.

PUBLICATIONS

29043 ■ *Advanced Research Journal of Business Management (ARJBM)*

2238 Pacific St., Ste. 1F
 Brooklyn, NY 11233
Co. E-mail: helpdesk@advancedscholarsjournals.org
URL: http://advancedscholarsjournals.org
Contact: Omer Abdel Aziz Mohammed Ahmed El Tigani, Manager
URL(s): advancedscholarsjournals.org/journal/arjbm

Released: Monthly; one volume per year. **Description:** Open access journal containing articles in all areas of business management and related disciplines. **Availability:** Print; PDF; Download; Online.

29044 ■ *Global Business Review*

2455 Teller Rd.
 Thousand Oaks, CA 91320
Contact: Tracey Ozmina, President
URL(s): journals.sagepub.com/home/gbr
Facebook: www.facebook.com/GBRGlobalBusinessReview

Ed: Arindam Banik. **Released:** Bimonthly **Price:** $143, Institutions for single print issue; us.sagepub.com/en-us/nam/journal/global-business-review; $33, Individuals for single print issue; $798, Institutions for print and online; $678, Institutions for online only; $150, Individuals for print only; $782, Institutions for print only. **Description:** International, multidisciplinary, peer-reviewed journal covering research and scholarship on management-related themes and topics, with an emphasis on Asian and Indian perspectives. Published in association between SAGE and the International Management Institute, New Delhi. **Availability:** Print; PDF; Download; Online.

29045 ■ *Smart Business Dealmakers*
835 Sharon Dr., Ste. 200
 Cleveland, OH 44145
Ph: (440)250-7000
Free: 800-988-4726
URL: http://sbnonline.com
Contact: Fred Koury, President
E-mail: fkoury@sbnonline.com
URL(s): www.smartbusinessdealmakers.com/about
Released: Weekly **Description:** Covers CEOs and
investors. **Availability:** Print.

29046 ■ *Who's Who in Finance and Business*
350 RXR Plz.
 Uniondale, NY 11556
Ph: (908)673-0100
Free: 844-394-6946
Fax: (908)356-0184
Co. E-mail: customerservice@marquiswhoswho.com
URL: http://marquiswhoswho.com
Contact: Kristine McCarthy, Contact
E-mail: kristine@marquiswww.com
URL(s): store.marquiswhoswho.com/collections/whos
-who-publications/products/whos-who-finance-busi-
ness?variant=23731670147
Released: Latest edition 2009. **Price:** $295, for listee
price; $349, for retail price. **Description:** Covers over
24,000 individuals. **Entries include:** Name, home
and office addresses, personal, career, and family
data; civic and political activities; memberships,
publications, awards. **Arrangement:** Alphabetical.
Availability: Print.

LIBRARIES

**29047 ■ Boston University - Frederick S.
Pardee Management Library**
Rafik B. Hariri Bldg.
 595 Commonwealth Ave.
 Boston, MA 02215
Ph: (617)353-4301
Fax: (617)353-4307
Co. E-mail: pardstf@bu.edu
URL: http://www.bu.edu/library/management
Contact: Brock Edmunds, Assistant Head
E-mail: edmundsb@bu.edu
Facebook: www.facebook.com/BUpardeelibrary
X (Twitter): x.com/bupardeelibrary
Instagram: www.instagram.com/bulibraries
Description: Provides resources and services sup-
porting the faculty and students in BU's Questrom
School of Business. **Scope:** Business management.
Services: Interlibrary loan; library open to the public;
printing, scanning & copying; reference services;
library classes; individual consultation. **Founded:**
1997. **Holdings:** 60,000 volumes.; . **Subscriptions:**
; 45,000 journals eBooks; monographs; microforms;
periodicals; ejournals.

**29048 ■ Canada School of Public Service
Library**
Asticou Ctr.
 241 de la Cite-des-Jeunes Blvd., Rm. 1323
 Gatineau, QC, Canada K1N 6Z2
Ph: (819)953-5613
Co. E-mail: librarybibliotheque@csps-efpc.gc.ca
URL: http://www.csps-efpc.gc.ca/Contact_Us/
libraryandpublications-eng.aspx
Scope: Educational materials. **Services:** Interlibrary
loan; copying; library open to public. **Holdings:**
Books. **Subscriptions:** 65 journals and other serials.

**29049 ■ Carnegie Library of Pittsburgh
Downtown & Business**
612 Smithfield St.
 Pittsburgh, PA 15222
Ph: (412)281-7141
URL: http://www.carnegielibrary.org/clp_location/
downtown-business
Contact: Andrew Medlar, President
Scope: Local history. **Services:** Library open to the
public. **Founded:** 1924. **Holdings:** Books; maga-
zines; CD-ROMs; videos.

**29050 ■ Chicago Public Library Central
Library - Business/Science/Technology
Division**
400 S State St.
 Chicago, IL 60605
URL: http://www.chipublib.org/resources/science
-technology
Scope: Small business; marketing; technology; sciences; computer science; careers and environmental
information. **Services:** Interlibrary loan; library open
to the public. **Founded:** 1977. **Holdings:** Figures not
available.

**29051 ■ Comenius University - Faculty of
Management Library**
Odbojarov 10
 820 05 Bratislava, Slovakia
URL: http://www.fm.uniba.sk/en/offices
Contact: Ján Badura, Department Head
Description: Comenius University's faculty of Man-
agement Library. **Scope:** Management. **Services:**
Library open to the public. **Founded:** 1919. **Hold-
ings:** Figures not available.

**29052 ■ Lappeenranta University of
Technology (LUT) - LUT Academic Library**
Yliopistonkatu 34
 53850 Lappeenranta, Finland
Ph: 358 294 462 111
URL: http://www.lut.fi
Contact: Juha-Matti Saksa, President
E-mail: juha-matti.saksa@lut.fi
X (Twitter): x.com/UniLUT
Instagram: www.instagram.com/unilut
YouTube: www.youtube.com/lutvideo
Description: An academic institute that provides
educational services. **Scope:** Educational material.
Services: Interlibrary loan (members only); open to
the researchers and general public. **Founded:** 1969.
Holdings: Books; journals. **Publications:** WILMA.

29053 ■ Nichols College - Conant Library
121 Center Rd.
 Dudley, MA 01571
Ph: (508)213-2334
Co. E-mail: circulation@nichols.edu
URL: http://www.nichols.edu/offices/conant-library
Contact: Carrie Grimshaw, Director
E-mail: carrie.grimshaw@nichols.edu
Scope: Sports management and education. **Ser-
vices:** Interlibrary loan; copying; information service
to groups; document delivery; library open to Dudley
and Webster residents. **Founded:** 1962. **Holdings:**
Figures not available.

29054 ■ Strategic Decisions Group (SDG)
Strategic Decisions Group (SDG)
 101 Jefferson Dr.
 Menlo Park, CA 94025
Ph: (650)475-4400
Fax: (650)475-4401
Co. E-mail: info@sdg.com
URL: http://sdg.com
Contact: Dr. Mark Seidler, Chief Executive Officer
Facebook: www.facebook.com/Stra
tegicDecisionsGroup
Linkedin: www.linkedin.com/company/strategic
-decisions-group-sdg
X (Twitter): x.com/SDGconsulting
Description: Provider of management consulting
services including employee benefits, managed care
and intranet applications. **Founded:** 1981.

**29055 ■ Touro College Lander College for
Men Library**
75-31 150th St.
 Kew Gardens Hills, NY 11367
Ph: (718)820-4894
URL: http://www.tourolib.org/about/libraries/kew-gar
dens-hills
Contact: Yeshaya Metal, Librarian
E-mail: yeshaya.metal@touro.edu
Scope: Biology; business; computer science; man-
agement information science; political science;
psychology; social sciences; Judaic. **Services:**

Interlibrary loan; copying; library open to college staff
and students. **Holdings:** Books; audio and video
tapes; CD-ROMs; DVDs; microfiche.

**29056 ■ University of Massachusetts at
Lowell - Lydon Library**
84 University Ave.
 Lowell, MA 01854
Ph: (978)934-3213
Co. E-mail: ask@uml.libanswers.com
URL: http://www.uml.edu/library
Contact: Mary Kay Martynuk, Librarian
E-mail: mary_martynuk@uml.edu
Scope: Philosophy; Psychology; Religion; American
History; Law; Education; Archeology; Biography and
much more. **Services:** Interlibrary loan; library open
to the public. **Founded:** 1984. **Holdings:** Book;
Articles.

**29057 ■ University of Southern Maine (USM)
- Lewiston-Auburn College Library (LAC)**
51 Westminster St.
 Lewiston, ME 04240
Ph: (207)753-6540
URL: http://usm.maine.edu/library
Contact: Libby Bischof, Executive Director
Description: University of Maine campus library.
Scope: Educational material. **Services:** Interlibrary
loan; library open to the public. **Subscriptions:** 200
journals 16,000 volumes; paper; microfiche; 450
videocassettes.

29058 ■ Woodbury University Library
7500 N Glenoaks Blvd.
 Burbank, CA 91510
Ph: (818)252-5200
Co. E-mail: reference@woodbury.edu
URL: http://library.woodbury.edu
Contact: Eric Garcia, Librarian, Reference
E-mail: eric.garcia@woodbury.edu
Facebook: www.facebook.com/wulibrary
X (Twitter): x.com/woodburylib
Instagram: www.instagram.com/woodburyuniversi
tylibrary
Scope: Education. **Services:** Interlibrary loan (lim-
ited). **Founded:** 1884. **Holdings:** Books; journals.

RESEARCH CENTERS

**29059 ■ The Conference Board (TCB) -
Library**
845 Third Ave.
 New York, NY 10022-6600
Ph: (212)759-0900
Co. E-mail: membership@conferenceboard.org
URL: http://www.conference-board.org/us
Contact: Steve Odland, President
Facebook: www.facebook.com/conference-board
Linkedin: www.linkedin.com/company/the-conference
-board
X (Twitter): x.com/Conferenceboard
YouTube: www.youtube.com/user/
theconferenceboard
Description: Fact-finding institution that conducts
research and publishes studies on business econom-
ics and management experience. **Scope:** Dedicated
to equipping the world's leading corporations with the
practical knowledge they need to improve their
performance and better serve society. **Founded:**
1916. **Holdings:** Figures not available. **Publications:**
StraightTalk (Quarterly); Conference Board Briefing
Charts (Quarterly); Multinational Register & Global
Business Briefing; The Conference Board Review
(Quarterly); Consumer Confidence Survey, The
Conference Board (Monthly); International Economic
Scoreboard; Across the Board (10/year); Business
Cycle Indicators (Monthly); Consumer Confidence
Survey (Monthly); E-mail Express (Monthly); Execu-
tive Action Series; The Conference Board, Inc.
Research reports; Top Executive Compensation; HR
Executive Review (Quarterly). **Educational Activi-
ties:** Executive Compensation Conference (Annual).
Geographic Preference: Multinational.

29060 ■ Organization Development Institute - Library

11234 Walnut Ridge Rd.
 Chesterland, OH 44026
Ph: (440)729-7419
Fax: (440)729-9319
Co. E-mail: don@odinstitute.org
URL: http://www.theodinstitute.org/od-library/the_o
 d_institute.htm
Contact: Donald W. Cole, President
E-mail: donwcole@aol.com

Description: Professionals, students, and individuals interested in organization development. Disseminates information on and promotes a better understanding of organization development worldwide. **Scope:** Conducts specialized education programs. Develops the International O.D. Code of Ethics and a competency test for individuals wishing to qualify as a Registered Organization Development Consultant and a statement on the knowledge and skill necessary to be competent in organization development and criteria for the accreditation of OD/OB academic programs. **Founded:** 1968. **Holdings:** Figures not available. **Publications:** "The International Registry of O.D. Professionals and O.D. Handbook," 2003; "Conflict Resolution Technology"; "Professional Suicide or Organizational Murder"; "Improving Profits Through Organization Development"; "Organization Development: A Straight forward Reference Guide for Executives Seeking to Improve Their Organizations"; "What Is New In Organization Development; Organizations and Change"; "Organization Development Journal". **Training:** What Is New in Organization Development and Human Resources Development. **Educational Activities:** Organization Development Institute Annual International Congress; International, interorganizational, interdisciplinary Research/Study Team on Nonviolent Large Systems Change Meetings, Exhibit relating to interdisciplinary peace research. **Geographic Preference:** Multinational.

29061 ■ University of British Columbia (UBC) - Sauder School of Business - Centre for Operations Excellence (COE)

2053 Main Mall
 Vancouver, BC, Canada V6T 1Z2
Co. E-mail: info@coe.ubc.ca
URL: http://www.sauder.ubc.ca/thought-leadership/
 research-outreach-centres/centre-operations
 -excellence

Description: Integral unit of Sauder School of Business, University of British Columbia. Industry Partners Program: partnership with leading companies to formulate and solve operations research problems using advanced management science methods (10/ year). **Scope:** Issues facing operations managers, and the development of methods, tools, and techniques to shape the business environment of the future. **Founded:** 1998.

29062 ■ Workplace Bullying Institute (WBI) - Library

PO Box 578
 Clarkston, WA 99403-0578
Ph: (360)656-6630
Co. E-mail: wbi@workplacebullying.org
URL: http://workplacebullying.org
Contact: Dr. Ruth Namie, Contact
Facebook: www.facebook.com/workplacebullyinginsti
 tute
YouTube: www.youtube.com/user/BullyingInstitute

Description: Aims to eradicate workplace bullying through books, websites, professional coaching/counseling, research, public education and speeches, training for professionals, legislative advocacy and solutions for bold employers. Conducts scientific national prevalence study of workplace bullying. **Scope:** Education materials. **Founded:** 1997. **Subscriptions:** 200 journals Books. **Publications:** *2003 Comprehensive Research Report on Abusive Workplaces.* **Educational Activities:** Freedom from workplace Bullies Week (Annual). **Geographic Preference:** National.

TENNESSEE VALLEY AUTHORITY

29063 ■ *"CEO Putting Rubber to Road at Lanxess Corporation"* in *Pittsburgh Business Times (Vol. 33, May 2, 2014, No. 42, pp. 4)*
American City Business Journals, Inc. (ACBJ)
120 W Morehead St.
Charlotte, NC 28202
Co. E-mail: circhelp@bizjournals.com
URL: http://www.acbj.com
Contact: Mike Olivieri, Executive Vice President
Released: May 02, 2014. **Price:** $4, introductory 4-week offer(Digital only). **Description:** Flemming Bjoernslev, CEO for the North American operations of Germany-based Lanxess Corporation, discusses their recovery efforts following their first financial loss in 2013. He is confident that the U.S. tire manufacturing industry will help their business further in North America. **Availability:** Print; Online.

START-UP INFORMATION

29064 ■ *"Red McCombs, Partner Rolling Out New Venture Capital Fund"* in *San Antonio Business Journal (Vol. 26, April 20, 2012, No. 12, pp. 1)*
Pub: Baltimore Business Journal
Contact: Rhonda Pringle, President
E-mail: rpringle@bizjournals.com
Description: Entrepreneur Red McCombs has partnered with businessman Chase Fraser to create a new venture capital fund. This new fund will focus on technology startups in the automotive sector. **Availability:** Print; Online.

29065 ■ *"Well-Heeled Startup Plots Course for a Run at Garmin"* in *Business Journal Portland (Vol. 27, November 12, 2010, No. 37, pp. 1)*
Pub: Portland Business Journal
Contact: Andy Giegerich, Managing Editor
E-mail: agiegerich@bizjournals.com
Description: Oh! Shoes LLC expects to receive about $1.5 million in funding from angel investors, while marketing a new line of high heel shoes that are comfortable, healthy, and attractive. The new line of shoes will use the technology of athletic footwear while having the look of an Italian designer. Oh! Shoes hopes to generate $35 million in sales by 2014. **Availability:** Print; Online.

29066 ■ *"Wheel Genius"* in *Entrepreneur (June 2014)*
Pub: Entrepreneur Media Inc.
Contact: Dan Bova, Director
E-mail: dbova@entrepreneur.com
Description: Electric car startup, Kenguru, has developed a hatchback that aims to improve mobility for wheelchair users, who enter the vehicle using a rear-opening tailgate and automatic ramp. The Kenguru, which is Hungarian for kangaroo, uses motorcycle-style handlebars instead of steering wheels. The 1,000-pound car has an estimated range of 60 miles and can travel up to 35 miles per hour. The Kenguru could sell for about $25,000. Founder Stacy Zoern partnered with Budapest, Hungary-based Istvan Kissaroslaki in developing the new car. **Availability:** Print; Online.

ASSOCIATIONS AND OTHER ORGANIZATIONS

29067 ■ **Alliance for American Manufacturing (AAM)**
711 D St. NW, Ste. 3
Washington, DC 20004
Ph: (202)393-3430
Co. E-mail: info@aamfg.org
URL: http://www.americanmanufacturing.org
Contact: Scott N. Paul, President
Facebook: www.facebook.com/AmericanManufacturing
X (Twitter): x.com/KeepitMadeinUSA
Instagram: www.instagram.com/americanmanufacturing
YouTube: www.youtube.com/user/AmericanMfg
Description: Seeks to strengthen manufacturing in the U.S. Provides research, public education, advocacy, strategic communications and coalition building around the issues that matter to America's manufacturing sector. Promotes policy solutions on priorities such as international trade, energy security, health care, retirement security, currency manipulation and other issues of mutual concern. **Founded:** 2007. **Geographic Preference:** National.

29068 ■ **American Composites Manufacturers Association (ACMA)**
2000 N 15th St., Ste. 250
Arlington, VA 22201
Ph: (703)525-0511
Fax: (703)525-0743
Co. E-mail: info@acmanet.org
URL: http://acmanet.org
Contact: Cindy L. Squires, President
Facebook: www.facebook.com/AmericanComposites
Linkedin: www.linkedin.com/company/american-composites-manufacturers-association
X (Twitter): x.com/ACMAcomposites
YouTube: www.youtube.com/channel/UCiEiNIz0n26UmmUZiDbmg2g
Description: Companies engaged in the hand lay up or spray up of fiberglass in open molds or engaged in filament winding or resin transfer molding. Products requiring this process include boats, swimming pools, and bathroom fixtures. Conducts educational and research programs; compiles statistics. Sponsors product specialty seminars. **Founded:** 1979. **Publications:** *Materials Interface* (Bimonthly); *SACMA Recommended Practice*; *SACMA Recommended Test Methods*; *Working Safely: A Guide for Using Advanced Composite Materials*; *Composites Manufacturing* (Bimonthly); *Government Matters* (Monthly); *Membership Directory*. **Educational Activities:** Composites Convention (Annual); Corrosion, Mining, Infrastructure and Architecture Conference. **Geographic Preference:** National.

29069 ■ **American Small Manufacturers Coalition (ASMC)**
PO Box 8
Mount Airy, MD 21771
Ph: (202)341-7066
Fax: (202)315-3906
Co. E-mail: carrie.hines@smallmanufacturers.org
URL: http://smallmanufacturers.org
Contact: Carrie Hines, President
E-mail: carrie.hines@smallmanufacturers.org
Description: Strives to help small manufacturers to succeed. Improves the innovativeness and productivity of America's manufacturing community. Advocates for legislative and programmatic resources to allow small manufacturers to compete in the global marketplace. **Founded:** 1988. **Geographic Preference:** National.

29070 ■ **Association of Equipment Manufacturers (AEM)**
6737 W Washington St., Ste. 2400
Milwaukee, WI 53214-5650
Ph: (414)272-0943
Co. E-mail: careers@aem.org
URL: http://www.aem.org
Contact: Robert B. Crain, Chairman
Facebook: www.facebook.com/AssociationofEquipmentManufacturers
X (Twitter): x.com/aemadvisor
YouTube: www.youtube.com/channel/UC5n8rzDvlEupfGz5UviK5tg
Description: Unite the Agriculture equipment and technology industry under the AEM brand to achieve a leadership position. **Founded:** 1894. **Publications:** *Pictorial Database*; *Construction Industry Manufacturers Association--Membership and Activities Directory* (Annual). **Educational Activities:** Conexpo-Con/Agg Show (Triennial); CONEXPO-CON/AGG (Triennial); AEM Board & Sector Board Meeting (Annual); CONEXPO-CON/AGG (Triennial); The Utility Expo (ICUEE) (Biennial); World of Asphalt Show and Conference (Annual). **Geographic Preference:** Multinational; National.

29071 ■ **Association for Manufacturing Excellence (AME)**
2118 Plum Grove Rd., Ste. 360
Rolling Meadows, IL 60008
Ph: (224)232-5980
Co. E-mail: info@ame.org
URL: http://www.ame.org
Facebook: www.facebook.com/ameconnect
X (Twitter): x.com/ameconnect
YouTube: www.youtube.com/user/TheAMEConnect
Description: Professional manufacturing executives united in the pursuit of excellence in manufacturing. Works to foster the understanding, analysis, and exchange of world-class productivity methods in an effort to achieve manufacturing excellence. **Founded:** 1985. **Geographic Preference:** Multinational.

29072 ■ Association for Manufacturing Technology (AMT)
7901 Jones Branch Dr., Ste. 900
 McLean, VA 22102-4206
Ph: (703)893-2900
Free: 800-524-0475
Fax: (703)893-1151
Co. E-mail: amt@amtonline.org
URL: http://www.amtonline.org/home
Contact: Douglas K. Woods, President
Facebook: www.facebook.com/amtnews
Linkedin: www.linkedin.com/company/amtonline
X (Twitter): x.com/amtonline
YouTube: www.youtube.com/user/amtinsight
Description: Supports and enhances the activities of American manufacturers. Strives to be an effective spokesman for the industry; provides members with the latest information on technical developments, training methods, economic issues, and trade and marketing opportunities; encourages higher safety and technical standards; and gathers and disseminates information about world markets. **Founded:** 1902. **Publications:** *AMT--Member Product Directory*; *Foreign Machine Tool Distributors Directory*; *Domestic Machine Tool Distributors Directory*; *Directory of Machine Tools and Manufacturing Equipment* (Annual); *AMT News*. **Educational Activities:** International Manufacturing Technology Show (IMTS) (Biennial); Westec (Biennial). **Geographic Preference:** Multinational.

29073 ■ Association des Produits Forestiers du Canada (APFC) [Forest Products Association of Canada (FPAC)]
99 Bank St., Ste. 410
 Ottawa, ON, Canada K1P 6B9
Ph: (613)563-1441
Co. E-mail: ottawa@fpac.ca
URL: http://www.fpac.ca
Contact: Derek Nighbor, President
Facebook: www.facebook.com/FPAC.APFC
Linkedin: www.linkedin.com/company/forest-products -association-of-canada
X (Twitter): x.com/fpac_apfc
YouTube: www.youtube.com/user/ForestPro dsAssocCan
Description: Represents forest product manufacturers. Lobbies government on legislation, taxation, and other policy matters. **Publications:** *Forest Products Association of Canada--Membership Directory*. **Educational Activities:** Paperweek (Annual). **Geographic Preference:** National.

29074 ■ Association of Women in the Metal Industries (AWMI)
19 Mantua Rd.
 Mount Royal, NJ 08061
Ph: (856)423-3201
Fax: (856)423-3420
Co. E-mail: awmi@talley.com
URL: http://www.awmi.org
Contact: Mary Wardle, President
Facebook: www.facebook.com/awmi.headquarters
Linkedin: www.linkedin.com/company/association-of -women-in-the-metal-industries
X (Twitter): x.com/AWMIHQ
Description: Promotes professionalism and the advancement of women in the metal industries. Advocates on behalf of women in metal-related industries; conducts educational programs and activities; provides a forum for exchanging information and networking. **Founded:** 1981. **Publications:** *Coast to Coast* (Quarterly). **Educational Activities:** National Board Conference. **Awards:** AWMI Member of the Year (Annual); AWMI Service Awards (Annual). **Geographic Preference:** National.

29075 ■ CAMUS International
Hampton, VA
URL: http://camus.org
Contact: Terry Simpkins, Treasurer
E-mail: simpkinsterry@cox.net
Description: Provides forum for manufacturing application users to interact with and learn from each other. **Founded:** 1985. **Geographic Preference:** Multinational.

29076 ■ Canadian Plastics Industry Association (CPIA) [Association Canadienne de l'industrie des Plastiques]
45 O'Connor St., Ste. 1240
 Ottawa, ON, Canada K1P 1A4
URL: http://canadianchemistry.ca
Contact: Carol Hochu, President
Facebook: www.facebook.com/CanadianPlasticsIn dustryAssociation
Linkedin: www.linkedin.com/company/canadian-plas tics-industry-association
X (Twitter): x.com/CPIA_ACIP
YouTube: www.youtube.com/user/Canadianchemistry
Description: Plastics manufacturers, distributors, importers, and exporters in Canada. Encourages research and development programs. Represents and defends members' interests. **Founded:** 1943. **Geographic Preference:** National.

29077 ■ *CTMA View*
140 McGovern Dr., Unit 3
 Cambridge, ON, Canada N3H 4R7
Ph: (519)653-7265
Fax: (519)653-6764
Co. E-mail: info@ctma.com
URL: http://ctma.com
Contact: Steve Watson, President
URL(s): ctma.com/publications/ctma-view-magazine
Released: 3/year; three times per year. **Description:** Contains information on the association and its members. **Availability:** Print; Online.

29078 ■ Manufacturing Jewelers and Suppliers of America (MJSA)
8 Hayward St.
 Attleboro, MA 02703
Ph: (508)316-2132
Free: 800-444-MJSA
Fax: (508)316-1429
Co. E-mail: info@mjsa.org
URL: http://www.mjsa.org
Contact: David W. Cochran, President
E-mail: david.cochran@mjsa.org
Facebook: www.facebook.com/theMJSA
X (Twitter): x.com/MJSAtweets
YouTube: www.youtube.com/mjsavideos
Description: Represents American manufacturers and suppliers within the jewelry industry. Seeks to foster long-term stability and prosperity of the jewelry industry. Provides leadership in government affairs and industry education. **Founded:** 1903. **Publications:** *Buyer's Guide*; *MJSA Journal* (Monthly); *Manufacturing Jewelers Buyers' Guide*; *MJSA Benchmark* (Monthly). **Educational Activities:** MJSA Expo (Annual); MJSA Expo Providence (Annual); Jeweler's Bench Conference and Trade Fair (Annual). **Awards:** MJSA Vision Awards (Annual); MJSA Education Foundation Scholarship Award (Annual); MJSA Education Foundation Scholarship (Annual). **Geographic Preference:** National.

29079 ■ National Association of Manufacturers (NAM)
733 10th St. NW, Ste. 700
 Washington, DC 20001
Ph: (202)637-3000
Free: 800-814-8468
Fax: (202)637-3182
Co. E-mail: manufacturing@nam.org
URL: http://www.nam.org
Contact: Jay Timmons, President
Facebook: www.facebook.com/NAMpage
Linkedin: www.linkedin.com/company/national -association-of-manufacturers---nam
X (Twitter): x.com/shopfloornam
YouTube: www.youtube.com/namvideo
Description: Manufacturers and cooperating non-manufacturers having a direct interest in or relationship to manufacturing. Represents industry's views on national and international problems to government. Maintains public affairs and public relations programs. Reviews current and proposed legislation, administrative rulings and interpretations, judicial decisions and legal matters affecting industry. Maintains numerous policy groups: Human Resources Policy; Small and Medium Manufacturers;

Tax Policy; Resources & Environmental Policy; Regulation and Legal Reform Policy; International Economic Affairs. Affiliated with 150 local and state trade associations of manufacturers through National Industrial Council and 250 manufacturing trade associations through the Associations Council. **Founded:** 1895. **Publications:** *NAM/NIC Speakers Directory*; *NAMonline*; *National Association of Manufacturers--Congress Directory: 109th NAM Congress Directory: Second Session* (Biennial); *National Association of Manufacturers--Associations Council Membership Directory* (Annual); *Member Focus Digital Magazine* (Monthly). **Geographic Preference:** National.

29080 ■ National Council for Advanced Manufacturing (NACFAM)
2025 M St. NW, Ste. 800
 Washington, DC 20036
Ph: (202)367-1247
URL: http://www.nacfam.org
Contact: Rusty Patterson, Chief Executive Officer
Description: Seeks to "enhance the productivity, quality and competitiveness of all tiers of the U.S. domestic industrial base." Organizes public and private technology research and development projects; serves as a network linking members; conducts workforce skills standards development programs. **Founded:** 1989. **Publications:** *Manufacturing Trends* (Weekly). **Geographic Preference:** National.

29081 ■ National Tooling and Machining Association (NTMA)
1357 Rockside Rd.
 Cleveland, OH 44134
Free: 800-248-6862
Fax: (216)264-2840
Co. E-mail: info@ntma.org
URL: http://ntma.org
Contact: Roger Atkins, President
E-mail: ratkins@ntma.org
Facebook: www.facebook.com/NTMAnow
Linkedin: www.linkedin.com/company/ntma
X (Twitter): x.com/NTMATalk
Instagram: www.instagram.com/ntmanow
YouTube: www.youtube.com/channel/ UCWz78MHNBXqkxAHKqbUArzg
Description: U.S. machinery manufacturing companies, particularly small and medium-sized businesses. Seeks to further the interests of the precision custom manufacturing industry in the United States. **Founded:** 1943. **Publications:** *National Tooling and Machining Association--Buyers Guide* (Irregular).

29082 ■ Valve Manufacturers Association of America (VMA)
1625 K St. NW, Ste. 325
 Washington, DC 20006
Ph: (202)331-8105
Fax: (202)296-0378
Co. E-mail: info@vma.org
URL: http://www.vma.org
Contact: Eric McClafferty, Legal Counsel
Facebook: www.facebook.com/ValveMfgAssn
Linkedin: www.linkedin.com/company/valve-manufac turers-association
X (Twitter): x.com/ValveMfgAssn
Description: Manufacturers of industrial valves and actuators including gate valves, globe valves, check valves, water works, IBBM gate valves, tapping sleeves and crosses, fire hydrants, ball valves, butterfly valves, nonmetal valves, corrosion resistant valves, through-conduit valves, plug valves, automatic control and regulating valves, solenoid valves, and safety and relief valves; as well as suppliers to the valve and actuator industry. Compiles statistical and biographical archives. Conducts research. **Founded:** 1938. **Holdings:** 300 volumes of technical and industrial data. **Publications:** *Catalog of U.S. and Canadian Valves & Actuators*; *Quick Read* (Weekly); *Sourcebook of U.S. and Canadian Valves* (Biennial); *VMA Directory* (Annual). **Educational Activities:** VMA Market Outlook Workshop (Annual). **Geographic Preference:** National.

EDUCATIONAL PROGRAMS

29083 ■ **Advanced Electric Motor/Generator/ Actuator Design and Analysis for Automotive Applications (Onsite)**
Seminar Information Service Inc. (SIS)
   250 El Camino Real., Ste. 112
   Tustin, CA 92780
Ph: (714)508-0340
Free: 877-736-4636
Fax: (714)734-8027
Co. E-mail: info@seminarinformation.com
URL: http://www.seminarinformation.com
Contact: Catherine Bellizzi, President
URL(s): www.seminarinformation.com

Description: Provide extensive details on design and analysis of electric motors/generators, actuators using state-of-the-art techniques, including the fundamentals of electromagnetism and basic electric machine equations will be presented along with examples. **Audience:** Industry professionals. **Principal Exhibits:** Provide extensive details on design and analysis of electric motors/generators, actuators using state-of-the-art techniques, including the fundamentals of electromagnetism and basic electric machine equations will be presented along with examples. **Telecommunication Services:** info@seminarinformation.com.

29084 ■ **Automotive Glazing Materials (Onsite)**
Seminar Information Service Inc. (SIS)
   250 El Camino Real., Ste. 112
   Tustin, CA 92780
Ph: (714)508-0340
Free: 877-736-4636
Fax: (714)734-8027
Co. E-mail: info@seminarinformation.com
URL: http://www.oominarinformation.com
Contact: Catherine Bollizzi, President
URL(s): www.seminarinformation.com

Description: An overview of the different automotive glazing materials, past, present and future, including the laws that govern their use, and manufacture, installation, usage, testing, safety aspects and how they affect automotive performance. Topics include the chemical, physical and design issues of annealed, laminated, tempered, glass-plastic and plastic glazing materials. **Audience:** Industry professionals. **Principal Exhibits:** An overview of the different automotive glazing materials, past, present and future, including the laws that govern their use, and manufacture, installation, usage, testing, safety aspects and how they affect automotive performance. Topics include the chemical, physical and design issues of annealed, laminated, tempered, glass-plastic and plastic glazing materials.

29085 ■ **Automotive Lighting (Onsite)**
Seminar Information Service Inc. (SIS)
   250 El Camino Real., Ste. 112
   Tustin, CA 92780
Ph: (714)508-0340
Free: 877-736-4636
Fax: (714)734-8027
Co. E-mail: info@seminarinformation.com
URL: http://www.seminarinformation.com
Contact: Catherine Bellizzi, President
URL(s): www.seminarinformation.com

Description: Provides broad information about automotive lighting systems with emphasis on lighting functions, effectiveness, and technologies, including the legal aspects and implications related to automotive lighting and examine safety measurements used with lighting functions and human factors costs. **Audience:** Industry professionals. **Principal Exhibits:** Provides broad information about automotive lighting systems with emphasis on lighting functions, effectiveness, and technologies, including the legal aspects and implications related to automotive lighting and examine safety measurements used with lighting functions and human factors costs.

29086 ■ **A Familiarization of Drivetrain Components (Onsite)**
Seminar Information Service Inc. (SIS)
   250 El Camino Real., Ste. 112
   Tustin, CA 92780
Ph: (714)508-0340
Free: 877-736-4636
Fax: (714)734-8027
Co. E-mail: info@seminarinformation.com
URL: http://www.seminarinformation.com
Contact: Catherine Bellizzi, President
URL(s): www.seminarinformation.com

Description: Learn to visualize both individual components and the entire drivetrain system without reference to complicated equations, with focus on the terms, functions, nomenclature, operating characteristics and effect on vehicle performance for each of the drivetrain components. **Audience:** Engineers. **Principal Exhibits:** Learn to visualize both individual components and the entire drivetrain system without reference to complicated equations, with focus on the terms, functions, nomenclature, operating characteristics and effect on vehicle performance for each of the drivetrain components. **Telecommunication Services:** info@seminarinformation.com.

29087 ■ **OSHA Compliance and Workplace Safety**
National Seminars Training L.L.C. (NST)
   14502 W 105th St.
   Lenexa, KS 66215
Free: 800-349-1935
Co. E-mail: info@findaseminar.com
URL: http://www.findaseminar.com/tpd/Padge tt-Thompson-Seminars.asp
URL(s): www.findaseminar.com/event1.asp?eventID =905
Description: This workshop offers the cost-effective solutions to keep the workplace safe and the OSHA inspectors away. **Audience:** Professionals. **Principal Exhibits:** This workshop offers the cost-effective solutions to keep the workplace safe and the OSHA inspectors away.

29088 ■ **WBENC Industry Spotlight**
URL(s): www.wbenc.org/programs/industry-spotligh t-series
Frequency: Irregular. **Description:** A series of webinars and resources for women business owners in order to learn about new trends, innovations, and sources of support in the automotive, food & beverage, utilities, healthcare, energy, financial services, and manufacturing sectors. **Principal Exhibits:** A series of webinars and resources for women business owners in order to learn about new trends, innovations, and sources of support in the automotive, food & beverage, utilities, healthcare, energy, financial services, and manufacturing sectors.

DIRECTORIES OF EDUCATIONAL PROGRAMS

29089 ■ *Scott's Directories: National Manufacturers*
Pub: Scott's Directories
URL(s): www.scottsdirectories.com/canadian-busi ness-database/national-manufacturers-all-employ ees-directory
Ed: Barbara Peard. **Released:** Annual **Description:** Covers 58,000 manufacturers throughout Canada. **Entries include:** Company name, address, phone, fax, telex, names and titles of key personnel, number of employees, parent or subsidiary companies, North American Standard Industrial (NAICS) code, product, export interest, and year established. **Availability:** Online.

REFERENCE WORKS

29090 ■ *"$3 Million in Repairs Prep Cobo for Auto Show"* in *Crain's Detroit Business (Vol. 26, January 4, 2010, No. 1, pp. 1)*
Pub: Crain Communications Inc.
Contact: Barry Asin, President

Ed: Nancy Kaffer. **Description:** Overview of the six projects priced roughly at $3 million which were needed in order to host the North American International Auto Show; show organizers stated that the work was absolutely necessary to keep the show in the city of Detroit. **Availability:** Print; Online.

29091 ■ *"The 490 Made Chevy a Bargain Player"* in *Automotive News (Vol. 86, October 31, 2011, No. 6488, pp. S22)*
Pub: Crain Communications Inc.
Contact: Barry Asin, President

Ed: David Phillips. **Description:** The first Chevrolet with the 490 engine was sold in 1913, but it was too expensive for masses. In 1914 the carmaker launched a lower-priced H-series of cars competitively priced. Nameplates such as Corvette, Bel Air, Camaro and Silverado have defined Chevrolet through the years. **Availability:** Online.

29092 ■ *"1914 Proved to Be Key Year for Chevy"* in *Automotive News (Vol. 86, October 31, 2011, No. 6488, pp. S18)*
Pub: Crain Communications Inc.
Contact: Barry Asin, President

Ed: Jamie LaReau. **Description:** Chevy Bow Tie emblem was born in 1914, creating the brand's image that has carried through to current days. **Availability:** Print; Online.

29093 ■ *"ACON Investments Acquires Igloo Products Corporation"* in *Economics & Business Week (April 19, 2014, pp. 6)*
Pub: NewsRX LLC.
Contact: Kalani Rosell, Contact

Description: ACON Investments LLC has acquired Igloo Products Corporation, the top cooler manufacturer in the world. Details of the acquisition are included. **Availability:** Online.

29094 ■ *"Aeronautics Seeking New HQ Site"* in *The Business Journal-Milwaukee (Vol. 25, September 5, 2008, No. 50, pp. 1)*
Description: Milwaukee, Wisconsin-based Aeronautics Corp. of America is planning to move its headquarters to a new site. The company has started to search for a new site. It also plans to consolidate its operations under one roof.

29095 ■ *"AgraQuest Deal Signals Growth for Biopesticide Makers"* in *Sacramento Business Journal (Vol. 29, July 13, 2012, No. 20, pp. 1)*
Pub: Baltimore Business Journal
Contact: Rhonda Pringle, President
E-mail: rpringle@bizjournals.com
Description: Industry observes claim that biotechnology irm Bayer CropScience's upcoming acquisition of AgraQuest Inc. could signal the growth of biopesticide manufacturing chemical methods for agricultural crop protection could then be complemented with environmentally friendly approaches allowed by biopesticides. **Availability:** Print; Online.

29096 ■ *"Aircraft Maker May Land in Austin"* in *Austin Business Journal (Vol. 31, April 15, 2011, No. 6, pp. 1)*
Pub: Austin Business Journal
Contact: Rachel McGrath, Director
E-mail: rmcgrath@bizjournals.com
Ed: Jacob Dirr. **Description:** Icon Aircraft Inc. is planning to build a manufacturing facility in Austin, Texas. The company needs 100,000 square feet of space in a new or renovated plant. Executive comments are included. **Availability:** Print; Online.

29097 ■ *"Albemarle to Invest $1.3B, Create 300-Plus Jobs with New Chester County Facility"* in *The Business Journals (March 22, 2023)*
URL(s): www.bizjournals.com/charlotte/news/2023/0 3/22/albemarle-chester-county-13b-investment-300 -jobs.html
Ed: Collin Huguley. **Released:** March 22, 2023. **Description:** A new lithium hydroxide processing facility is being built near Richburg. **Availability:** Online.

29098 ■ *"Alcoa: 'Going Where No Materials Scientist Has Gone Before'" in Pittsburgh Business Times (Vol. 33, July 18, 2014, No. 53, pp. 5)*

Pub: American City Business Journals, Inc.

Contact: Mike Olivieri, Executive Vice President

Released: Weekly. **Price:** $4, introductory 4-week offer(Digital & Print). **Description:** Alcoa Inc. has signed a $1.1 billion supply agreement with Pratt & Whitney to build the forging for aluminum jet-engine fan blades as well as other parts made with aluminum lithium. This partnership brings together Alcoa's proprietary alloys and unique manufacturing processes with Pratt & Whitney's design, thus forging an aluminum fan blade that is lighter and enables better fuel efficiency. **Availability:** Print; Online.

29099 ■ *"Alcoa's Quebec Deal Keeps Smelters Running" in Pittsburgh Business Times (Vol. 33, February 28, 2014, No. 33, pp. 3)*

Pub: American City Business Journals, Inc.

Contact: Mike Olivieri, Executive Vice President

Released: Weekly. **Price:** $4, Introductory 4-week offer(Digital & Print). **Description:** Alcoa Inc. has renewed its power supply contract with the Quebec provincial government for three of its smelters in 2014. The aluminum company is investing $250 million in the smelters over the next five years to support growth in the automotive manufacturing industry. **Availability:** Print; Online.

29100 ■ *"Alstom Launches the ECO 122 - 2.7MW Wind Turbine for Low Wind Sites" in CNW Group (September 28, 2011)*

Pub: CNW Group Ltd.

Description: Alstom is launching its new ECO 122, a 2.7MW onshore wind turbine that combines high power and high capacity factor (1) to boost energy yield in low wind regions around the world. The ECO 122 will produce about 25 percent increased wind farm yield that current turbines and fewer turbines would be installed in areas. **Availability:** Print; Online.

29101 ■ *"Alternative Fuels Take Center Stage at Houston Auto Show" in Houston Business Journal (Vol. 44, January 31, 2014, No. 39, pp. 8)*

Pub: American City Business Journals, Inc.

Contact: Mike Olivieri, Executive Vice President

Released: January 31, 2014. **Price:** $4, Introductory 4-Week Offer(Digital & Print). **Description:** An energy summit was held at the Houston Auto Show in Texas on January 22, 2014, where energy executives discussed new technology and initiatives. They considered the market for electric and natural gas-fueled vehicles as well as other options including hydrogen, fuel cells, and biofuels. **Availability:** Print; Online.

29102 ■ *"Analysts: Intel Site May Be Last Major U.S.-Built Fab" in Business Journal-Serving Phoenix and the Valley of the Sun (October 18, 2007)*

Pub: Phoenix Business Journal

Contact: Alex McAlister, Director

E-mail: amcalister@bizjournals.com

Ed: Ty Young. **Description:** Intel's million-square-foot manufacturing facility, called Fab 32, is expected to open in 2007. The plant will mass-produce the 45-nanometer microchip. Industry analysts believe Fab 32 may be the last of its kind to be built in the U.S., as construction costs are higher in America than in other countries. Intel's future in Chandler is examined. **Availability:** Print; Online.

29103 ■ *"Aquatic Medications Engender Good Health" in Pet Product News (Vol. 64, November 2010, No. 11, pp. 47)*

Ed: Madelaine Heleine. **Description:** Pet supply manufacturers and retailers have been exerting consumer education and preparedness efforts to help aquarium hobbyists in tackling ornamental fish disease problems. Aquarium hobbyists have been

also assisted in choosing products that facilitate aquarium maintenance before disease attacks their pet fish. **Availability:** Online.

29104 ■ *"Attorney Panel Tackles Contract Questions" in Agency Sales Magazine (Vol. 39, September-October 2009, No. 9, pp. 8)*

Description: MANAfest conference tackled issues regarding a sales representative's contract. One attorney from the panel advised reps to go through proposed agreements with attorneys who are knowledgeable concerning rep laws. Another attorney advised reps to communicate with a company to ask about their responsibilities if that company is facing financial difficulty. **Availability:** Online.

29105 ■ *"Auto Asphyxiation" in Canadian Business (Vol. 85, August 13, 2012, No. 13, pp. 38)*

Ed: Michael McCullough. **Description:** The declining car ownership and utlization has profound business implications for oil companies and automakers and may bring substantial benefit to other sectors and the economy as a whole. The transition to the post-automotive age may happen in places where there is the will to change transportation practices but not in others. **Availability:** Print; Online.

29106 ■ *"Auto Bankruptcies Could Weaken Defense" in Crain's Detroit Business (Vol. 25, June 8, 2009, No. 23, pp. 1)*

Pub: Crain Communications Inc.

Contact: Barry Asin, President

Ed: Chad Halcom. **Description:** Bankruptcy and supplier consolidation of General Motors Corporation and Chrysler LLC could interfere with the supply chains of some defense contractors, particularly makers of trucks and smaller vehicles. **Availability:** Print; Online.

29107 ■ *"Auto Show Aims to Electrify" in Crain's Detroit Business (Vol. 26, January 11, 2010, No. 2, pp. 1)*

Pub: Crain Communications Inc.

Contact: Barry Asin, President

Ed: Ryan Beene. **Description:** Overview of the North American International Auto show include sixteen production and concept vehicles including eight from the Detroit 3. High-tech battery suppliers as well as hybrid and electric vehicles will highlight the show. **Availability:** Print; Online.

29108 ■ *"Automaker Foundations Run Leaner" in Crain's Detroit Business (Vol. 26, January 11, 2010, No. 2, pp. 1)*

Pub: Crain Communications Inc.

Contact: Barry Asin, President

Ed: Sherri Welch. **Description:** Overview of the Detroit automobile industry includes restoring profitability, smarter marketing strategies and philanthropy. Each company comprising the Big 3 is examined, as is their vision for the future. **Availability:** Print; Online.

29109 ■ *"AV Concept Expands Into Green Energy Storage" in Wireless News (January 25, 2010)*

Description: Electronics distributor and manufacturer AV Concept Holdings Limited announced a marketing partnership with Boston-Power, a provider of lithium-ion batteries, with a focus in the Chinese and Korean markets. **Availability:** Online.

29110 ■ *"Backer Christmas Trade Show Preview" in Pet Product News (Vol. 66, September 2012, No. 9, pp. 12)*

Description: The 46th Annual H.H. Backer Pet Industry Christmas Trade Showand Educational Conference will beheld at the Donald E. Stephens Convention Center in Rosemont, Illinois from October 12-14, 2012. More than 600 pet supply manufacturers and about 9,000 industry professionals will attend. **Availability:** Print; Online.

29111 ■ *"Baking Up a Bigger Lance" in Charlotte Business Journal (Vol. 25, December 3, 2010, No. 37, pp. 1)*

Pub: Charlotte Business Journal

Contact: Robert Morris, Editor

E-mail: rmorris@bizjournals.com

Ed: Ken Elkins. **Description:** Events that led to the merger between Charlotte, North Carolina-based snack food manufacturer Lance Inc. and Pennsylvania-based pretzel maker Snyder's of Hanover Inc. are discussed. The merger is expected to help Lance in posting a 70 percent increase in revenue, which reached $900 million in 2009. How the merger would affect Snyder's of Hanover is also described. **Availability:** Print; Online.

29112 ■ *"Baltimore GM Plant Moves Forward" in Baltimore Business Journal (Vol. 32, July 4, 2014, No. 9, pp. 18)*

Pub: American City Business Journals, Inc.

Contact: Mike Olivieri, Executive Vice President

Released: Weekly. **Price:** $4, introductory 4-week offer(Digital only). **Description:** General Motors (GM) plant at White Marsh represents traditional and modern manufacturing, attracting young employees with the use of advanced technology, but still retaining its loyal, veteran workforce. Most workers at the plant's Allison Transmission facility have been with GM for 25 years or more, while the adjacent facility making electric motors for the Chevy Spark EV is primarily made up of workers in their late 20s. **Availability:** Print; Online.

29113 ■ *"Baltimore's Businesses: Equipment Tax Breaks Help, But Money Still Tight: Weighing the Write-Off" in Baltimore Business Journal (Vol. 28, September 10, 2010, No. 18, pp. 1)*

Pub: Baltimore Business Journal

Contact: Rhonda Pringle, President

E-mail: rpringle@bizjournals.com

Ed: Daniel J. Sernovitz. **Description:** President Barrack Obama has proposed to let business write off their investments in plant and equipment upgrades under a plan aimed at getting the economy going. The plan would allow a company to write off 100 percent of the depreciation for their new investments at one time instead of over several years. **Availability:** Print.

29114 ■ *"Bankruptcies" in Crain's Detroit Business (Vol. 24, March 24, 2008, No. 12, pp. 6)*

Pub: Crain Communications Inc.

Contact: Barry Asin, President

Description: Current list of business that filed for Chapter 7 or 11 protection in U.S. Bankruptcy Court in Detroit include a construction company, a medical care company, a physical therapy firm and a communications firm. **Availability:** Online.

29115 ■ *"Barnes Shakes Up Sara Lee Exec Suite" in Crain's Chicago Business (Vol. 31, April 21, 2008, No. 16, pp. 1)*

Pub: Crain Communications Inc.

Contact: Barry Asin, President

Ed: David Sterrett. **Description:** In an attempt to cut costs and boost profits, Sara Lee Corp.'s CEO Brenda Barnes is restructuring the company's management team. **Availability:** Online.

29116 ■ *"Battered U.S. Auto Makers in Grip of Deeper Sales Slump" in Globe & Mail (April 4, 2007, pp. B1)*

Ed: Greg Keenan. **Description:** The fall in Canadian sales and market share of Ford Motor Co., General Motors Corp. and Chrysler Group is discussed. **Availability:** Print; Online.

29117 ■ *"Bellingham Boatbuilder Norstar Yachts Maintains Family Tradition" in Bellingham Business Journal (Vol. February 2010, pp. 12)*

Description: Profile of Norstar Yachts and brothers Gary and Steve Nordtvedt who started the company in 1994. The company recently moved its operations to a 12,000 square foot space in the Fairhaven Marine Industrial Park. **Availability:** Print; Online.

29118 ■ *"Best Turnaround Stocks"* in *Canadian Business (Vol. 81, Summer 2008, No. 9, pp. 65)*

Description: Share prices of Sierra Wireless Inc. and EXFO Electro Optical Engineering Inc. have fallen over the past year but have good chance at a rebound considering that the companies have free cash flow and no long-term debt. One-year stock performance analysis of the two companies is presented. **Availability:** Print; Online.

29119 ■ *"BETC Backers Plot Future"* in *Business Journal Portland (Vol. 27, December 10, 2010, No. 41, pp. 1)*

Pub: Portland Business Journal

Contact: Andy Giegerich, Managing Editor

E-mail: agiegerich@bizjournals.com

Ed: Erik Siemers. **Description:** A coalition of clean energy groups and industrial manufacturers have spearheaded a campaign aimed at persuading Oregon legislators that the state's Business Energy Tax Credit (BETC) is vital in job creation. Oregon's BETC grants tax credits for 50 percent of an eligible renewable or clean energy project's cost. However, some legislators propose BETC's abolition. **Availability:** Print; Online.

29120 ■ *"Better than Advertised: Chip Plant Beats Expectations"* in *Business Review Albany (Vol. 41, June 27, 2014, No. 14, pp. 4)*

Pub: American City Business Journals, Inc.

Contact: Mike Olivieri, Executive Vice President

Released: Weekly. **Price:** $4, introductory 4-week offer(Digital only). **Description:** The $8.5 billion computer chip manufacturing plant and research center of GlobalFoundries in Malta, New York has strengthened the local economy in Saratoga County and helped the local manufacturing and construction industries recover from the recession. The Malta Plant construction project created more than 2,000 direct new construction jobs and over 10,000 indirect positions. **Availability:** Print; Online.

29121 ■ *"Better Made's Better Idea: Diversify Despite Rising Costs"* in *Crain's Detroit Business (Vol. 24, September 22, 2008, No. 38, pp. 18)*

Pub: Crain Communications Inc.

Contact: Barry Asin, President

Ed: Nathan Skid. **Description:** Better Made Snack Foods Inc. is planning to expand its product lines and market reach as well as boost manufacturing capability during a time in which the company is being buffeted by rising commodity and fuel costs. The company feels that diversification is the key to maintain sales and growth. **Availability:** Online.

29122 ■ *"Betting On Volatile Materials"* in *Barron's (Vol. 88, July 14, 2008, No. 28, pp. M11)*

Pub: Dow Jones & Company Inc.

Contact: Almar Latour, Chief Executive Officer

Ed: John Marshall. **Description:** Economic slowdowns in the U.S., Europe and China could cause sharp short-term declines in the materials sector. The S&P Materials sector is vulnerable to shifts in the flow of funds. Statistical data included. **Availability:** Online.

29123 ■ *"Beyond Meat (R) Completes Largest Financing Round to Date"* in *Ecology, Environment & Conservation Business (August 16, 2014, pp. 4)*

Pub: NewsRX LLC.

Contact: Kalani Rosell, Contact

Description: Beyond Meat (R) is the first company to recreate meat from plants and is dedicated to improving human health, positively impacting climate change, conserving natural resources and respecting animal welfare. The firm has completed its Series D financing round, which will also help the company promote consumer awareness and increase capacity at its manufacturing facility to meet demand. **Availability:** Online.

29124 ■ *"Birdcage Optimization"* in *Pet Product News (Vol. 64, November 2010, No. 11, pp. 54)*

Ed: Cheryl Reeves. **Description:** Manufacturers have been emphasizing size, security, quality construction, stylish design, and quick cleaning when guiding consumers on making birdcage options. Selecting a birdcage is gaining importance considering that cage purchases have become the highest expense associated with owning a bird. Other avian habitat trends are also examined. **Availability:** Online.

29125 ■ *"Black Gold: Jobs Aplenty"* in *Canadian Business (Vol. 79, August 14, 2006, No. 16-17, pp. 57)*

Pub: Rogers Media Inc.

Contact: Neil Spivak, Chief Executive Officer

Ed: Erin Pooley. **Description:** A list of the top ten jobs in the petroleum industry in Canada along with pay and nature of jobs, is presented. **Availability:** Print; Online.

29126 ■ *"BMW Revs Up for a Rebound"* in *Barron's (Vol. 89, July 13, 2009, No. 28, pp. M7)*

Pub: Dow Jones & Company Inc.

Contact: Almar Latour, Chief Executive Officer

Ed: Jonathan Buck. **Description:** Investors may like BMW's stocks because the company has maintained its balance sheet strength and has an impressive production line of new models that should boost sales in the next few years. The company's sales are also gaining traction, although their vehicle delivery was down 1.7 percent year on year on June 2009, this was still the best monthly sales figure for 2009. **Availability:** Online.

29127 ■ *"Boeing Moving 1,000 Washington Engineering Jobs to California"* in *Business Journal Portland (Vol. 31, April 11, 2014, No. 6)*

Pub: American City Business Journals, Inc.

Contact: Mike Olivieri, Executive Vice President

Released: Weekly. **Description:** Boeing plans to move 1,000 engineering jobs from Portland, Oregon to Southern California. The company says the move helps support planes in service at the company's Commercial Airplanes Engineering Center in Southern California and position the aerospace manufacturer for further growth. **Availability:** Print; Online.

29128 ■ *"The Book of Battery Manufacturing"*

Pub: CreateSpace

Released: October 06, 2014. **Price:** $7.86. **Description:** A comprehensive guide to every aspect of manufacturing batteries.

29129 ■ *"Bose Seeking Expansion Options in Framingham"* in *Boston Business Journal (Vol. 34, June 13, 2014, No. 19, pp. 15)*

Pub: American City Business Journals, Inc.

Contact: Mike Olivieri, Executive Vice President

Released: Weekly. **Description:** Bose Corporation, the Framingham-based high-end audio products manufacturer, is in talks to buy a 10-acre property near its headquarters. Bose is negotiating with the owner of three buildings on Pennsylvania Avenue near the Bose headquarters. Bose already owns five buildings in Framingham, but is looking at real estate for growth and expansion. **Availability:** Print; Online.

29130 ■ *"Branding Spree"* in *Pet Product News (Vol. 66, September 2012, No. 9, pp. 40)*

Ed: Michael Ventre. **Description:** The extent to which pet security firm PetSafe has continued to diversify into new product categories to realize growth opportunities is explored. An arm of Radio Systems Corporation, PetSafe has been known for manufacturing products such as wireless fences and electronic pet collars. **Availability:** Print; Online.

29131 ■ *"Breaking Down Walls - 2 Kinds"* in *Puget Sound Business Journal (Vol. 35, August 22, 2014, No. 18, pp. 9)*

Pub: American City Business Journals, Inc.

Contact: Mike Olivieri, Executive Vice President

Released: Weekly. **Price:** $4, Introductory 4-week offer(Digital & Print). **Description:** Boeing Company's demolition of its office building in Everett, Washington along with its plan to build a new production facility may reduce jobs. Many workers at the manufacturing facility have been replaced by robots. The plant will be used to build the company's new version of the 777 twin engine. **Availability:** Print; Online.

29132 ■ *"A Bright Spot: Industrial Space in Demand Again"* in *Sacramento Business Journal (Vol. 28, October 21, 2011, No. 34, pp. 1)*

Description: Sacramento, California's industrial sites have been eyed by potential tenants who are actively seeking space larger than 50,000 square feet. **Availability:** Print; Online.

29133 ■ *"Bringing Charities More Bang for Their Buck"* in *Crain's Chicago Business (Vol. 34, May 23, 2011, No. 21, pp. 31)*

Pub: Crain Communications Inc.

Contact: Barry Asin, President

Ed: Lisa Bertagnoli. **Description:** Marcy-Newberry Association connects charities with manufacturers in order to use excess items such as clothing, janitorial and office supplies. **Availability:** Online.

29134 ■ *"Bringing Manufacturing Concerns to Springfield"* in *Crain's Chicago Business (Vol. 31, March 31, 2008, No. 13, pp. 6)*

Pub: Crain Communications Inc.

Contact: Barry Asin, President

Ed: Paul Merrion. **Description:** Profile of the new executive vice-president of Tooling & Manufacturing Assn., Paul Merrion, a man who plans to grow TMA's membership with an aggressive legislative agenda in Springfield. **Availability:** Online.

29135 ■ *"Buhler Versatile Launches Next Generation of Equipment"* in *Farm Industry News (November 23, 2011)*

Pub: Informa Business Media, Inc.

Contact: Charlie McCurdy, President

Ed: Jodie Wehrspann. **Description:** Canadian owned Versatile is expanding its four-wheel drive tractor division with sprayers, tillage, and seeding equipment. **Availability:** Online.

29136 ■ *"Buick Prices Verano Below Rival Luxury Compacts"* in *Automotive News (Vol. 86, October 31, 2011, No. 6488, pp. 10)*

Pub: Crain Communications Inc.

Contact: Barry Asin, President

Ed: Mike Colias. **Description:** General Motors's Verano will compete with other luxury compacts such as the Lexus IS 250 and the Acura TSX, but will be prices significantly lower coming in with a starting price of $23,470, about $6,000 to $10,000 less than those competitors. **Availability:** Online.

29137 ■ *"Business Briefs: Alcoholic Beverage Manufacturing Is Big Business In Idaho"* in *Idaho Business Review (August 19, 2014)*

Pub: BridgeTower Media

Contact: Adam Reinebach, President

Description: Idaho's alcoholic beverage manufacturing industry is growing at a steady pace, reporting an $8.7 million payroll in 2013. Breweries, as well as wineries and distilleries are also strong. Statistical data included.

29138 ■ *"Buyology: Truth and Lies About Why We Buy"*

Pub: Doubleday

Ed: Martin Lindstrom. **Released:** February 02, 2010. **Price:** $15, paperback. **Description:** Marketers study brain scans to determine how consumers rate Nokia, Coke, and Ford products. **Availability:** Print.

29139 ■ *"C-Class Could Boost Auto Suppliers"* in *Birmingham Business Journal (Vol. 31, June 27, 2014, No. 26, pp. 10)*

Pub: American City Business Journals, Inc.

Contact: Mike Olivieri, Executive Vice President

Released: June 27, 2014. **Description:** The 2014 model of the Mercedes-Benz C-Class will be the first to be built at the Vance, Alabama manufacturing plant, increasing business opportunities for auto suppliers in the region. Jason Hoff, president and CEO of Mercedes-Benz US International Inc. notes that the move will impact the local economy as several companies in the area expand their operations to meet the growing demand from Mercedes.

29140 ■ *"California Water Treatment Facility Turns to Solar Power" in Chemical Business Newsbase (September 11, 2012)*
Description: Ramona, California municipal water district providing water, sewer, recycled water, fire protection, emergency medical services, and park services to the community has commissioned a 530KWp solar energy installation. Enfinity America Corporation developed and financed the solar panels and EPC services were provided by manufacturer Siliken. **Availability:** Print; Online.

29141 ■ *"Canadian Pet Charities Won't Go Hungry" in Pet Product News (Vol. 66, September 2012, No. 9, pp. 15)*
Description: Premium dog and cat food manufacturer Petcurean will donate more than 42,000 pounds of Go! and Now Fresh dry foods to 25 animal rescue organizations across Canada. The donation is deemed invaluable to Petcurean's network of dog and cat foster activities. **Availability:** Online.

29142 ■ *"Car Dealer Closings: Immoral, Slow-Death" in Crain's Detroit Business (Vol. 25, June 8, 2009, No. 23)*
Pub: Crain Communications Inc.
Contact: Barry Asin, President
Ed: Daniel Duggan. **Description:** Colleen McDonald discusses the closing of her two Chrysler dealerships located in Taylor and Livonia, Michigan, along with her Farmington Hills store, Holiday Chevrolet. **Availability:** Print; Online.

29143 ■ *"Catch the Wind to Hold Investor Update Conference Call on October 18, 2011" in CNW Group (October 4, 2011)*
Pub: CNW Group Ltd.
Description: Catch the Wind Ltd., providers of laser-based wind sensor products and technology, held a conference call for analysts and institutional investors. The high-growth technology firm is headquartered in Manassas, Virginia. **Availability:** Print; Online.

29144 ■ *"Caterpillar to Expand Research, Production in China" in Chicago Tribune (August 27, 2008)*
Description: Caterpillar Inc., the Peoria-based heavy-equipment manufacturer, plans to establish a new research-and-development center at the site of its rapidly growing campus in Wuxi. **Availability:** Print; Online.

29145 ■ *"CAW Hopes to Beat Xstrata Deadline" in Globe & Mail (January 30, 2007, pp. B3)*
Description: The decision of Canadian Auto Workers to strike work at Xstrata PLC over wage increase is discussed. **Availability:** Online.

29146 ■ *"Cemex Paves a Global Road to Solid Growth" in Barron's (Vol. 88, March 10, 2008, No. 10, pp. 24)*
Pub: Dow Jones & Company Inc.
Contact: Almar Latour, Chief Executive Officer
Ed: Sandra Ward. **Description:** Shares of Cemex are expected to perform well with the company's expected strong performance despite fears of a US recession. The company has a diverse geographical reach and benefits from a strong worldwide demand for cement. **Availability:** Online.

29147 ■ *"Centurion Signs Egypt Deal With Shell" in Globe & Mail (March 21, 2006, pp. B5)*
Ed: Dave Ebner. **Description:** Centurion Energy International Inc., a Calgary-based natural gas producer in Egypt, has signed contract with Royal

Dutch Shell PLC to explore about 320,000 hectares of land in Egypt. Details of the agreement are presented. **Availability:** Online.

29148 ■ *"The CEO of General Electric On Sparking an American Manufacturing Renewal" in Harvard Business Review (Vol. 90, March 2012, No. 3, pp. 43)*
Pub: Harvard Business Review Press
Contact: Moderna V. Pfizer, Contact
Ed: Jeffrey R. Immelt. **Price:** $8.95, hardcover.
Description: General Electric Company utilized human innovation and lean manufactring to improve the firm's competitiveness. By engaging the firm's entire workforce, utilizing technology and improving labor-management relations, GE boosted efficiency and reduced cost and waste. **Availability:** PDF; Online.

29149 ■ *"The CEO Poll: Fuel for Thought II Canadian Business Leaders on Energy Policy" in Canadian Business (Vol. 81, September 15, 2008, No. 14-15, pp. 12)*
Pub: Rogers Media Inc.
Contact: Neil Spivak, Chief Executive Officer
Ed: Joe Castaldo. **Description:** Most Canadian business leaders worry about the unreliability of the oil supply but feel that Canada is in a better position to benefit from the energy supply crisis than other countries. Many respondents also highlighted the need to invest in renewable energy sources. **Availability:** Online.

29150 ■ *"CEOs Gone Wild" in Canadian Business (Vol. 79, August 14, 2006, No. 16-17, pp. 15)*
Description: Stock investment decisions of chief executive officers of metal companies in Canada, are discussed. **Availability:** Print; Online.

29151 ■ *"Change Is in the Air" in Agency Sales Magazine (Vol. 39, August 2009, No. 8, pp. 30)*
Description: Highlights of the Power-Motion Technology Representatives Association (PTRA) 37th Annual Conference, which projected an economic upturn, are presented. Allan Bealulieu of the Institute for Trend Research gave the positive news while Manufacturer's Agents National Association (MANA) president Brain Shirley emphasized the need to take advantage of a turnaround. **Availability:** Print; Online.

29152 ■ *"A Change Would Do You Good" in Canadian Business (Vol. 80, November 19, 2007, No. 23, pp. 15)*
Description: Western Glove Works will be manufacturing clothing offshore, including Sheryl Crow's jeans collection, in countries such as China and the Philippines. The company decided to operate offshore after 86 years of existence due to the high price of manufacturing jeans in Canada. Western Glove's focus on producing celebrity-endorsed goods is discussed. **Availability:** Print; Online.

29153 ■ *"Charged Up for Sales" in Charlotte Business Journal (Vol. 25, October 15, 2010, No. 30, pp. 1)*
Description: Li-Ion Motors Corporation is set to expand its production lines of electric cars in Sacramento, California. The plan is seen to create up to 600 jobs. The company's total investment is seen to reach $500 million. **Availability:** Print; Online.

29154 ■ *"A Chinese Approach to Management: A Generation of Entrepreneurs Is Writing Its Own Rules" in Harvard Business Review (Vol. 92, September 2014, No. 9, pp. 103)*
Pub: Harvard Business Publishing
Contact: Diane Belcher, Managing Director
Price: $8.95. **Description:** The Chinese approach to management include simple structures for organizations, quick development of products, responsiveness to local values and needs, and investment in source firms and vendors. Manufacturing and engineering operations are typically co-located. **Availability:** Online; PDF.

29155 ■ *"Chrysler Unions Set Up Roadblocks to Private Equity" in Globe & Mail (March 20, 2007, pp. B3)*
Ed: Greg Keenan. **Description:** The opposition of the Canadian Auto Workers union and the United Auto Workers to any proposal to sell Chrysler Group is discussed. **Availability:** Online.

29156 ■ *"Cleanup to Polish Plating Company's Bottom Line" in Crain's Cleveland Business (Vol. 28, October 29, 2007, No. 43, pp. 4)*
Pub: Crain Communications Inc.
Contact: K. C. Crain, President
Ed: Jay Miller. **Description:** Barker Products Co, a manufacturer of nuts and bolts, is upgrading its aging facility which will allow them to operate at capacity and will save the company several hundred thousand dollars a year in operating costs. The new owners secured a construction loan from the county's new Commercial Redevelopment Fund which will allow them to upgrade the building which was hampered by years of neglect. **Availability:** Online.

29157 ■ *"Closed Minds and Open Skies" in Barron's (Vol. 88, March 10, 2008, No. 10, pp. 50)*
Pub: Dow Jones & Company Inc.
Contact: Almar Latour, Chief Executive Officer
Ed: Thomas G. Donlan. **Description:** American politicians have closed minds when it comes to fair trade. The American government must not interfere with the country's manufacturing industries or worry about outsourcing defense contracts to European aerospace company Airbus. **Availability:** Online.

29158 ■ *"CMO Nicholson Exits Pepsi as Share Declines" in Advertising Age (Vol. 79, July 7, 2008, No. 26, pp. 4)*
Pub: Crain Communications, Inc.
Contact: Jessica Botos, Manager, Marketing
E-mail: jessica.botos@crainsnewyork.com
Ed: Natalie Zmuda. **Description:** Cie Nicholson, the chief marketing officer at Pepsi-Cola UK, is leaving the company at a time when its market share is down; the brand, which was known for its dynamic marketing, has diverted much of its attention from its core brands and shifted attention to the ailing Gatorade brand as well as Sobe Life Water and Amp. **Availability:** Online.

29159 ■ *"Coca-Cola FEMSA, Family Dollar, Other Dividend Payers On a Roll" in Benzinga.com (June 21, 2012)*
Pub: Benzinga.com
Contact: Jason Raznick, Founder
Ed: Nelson Hem. **Description:** Dividend paying companies showing upward price trends are outlined. The firms highlighted include: Agnico-Eagle Mines, Coca-Cola FEMSA, Dean Foods, Expedia, Family Dollar Stores, Ferrellgas Partners, and InterContinental Hotels. **Availability:** Print; Online.

29160 ■ *"The Code-Cracker: Prominent Researcher at Miami Part of Federal Effort to Solve Protein Structures" in Business Courier (Vol. 24, January 10, 2008, No. 40, pp. 1)*
Pub: American City Business Journals, Inc.
Contact: Mike Olivieri, Executive Vice President
Ed: James Ritchie. **Description:** Michael Kennedy, a professor in the chemistry and biochemistry department at the Miami University, is a part of the Protein Structure Initiative, a project that is aimed at forming a catalog of three-dimensional protein structures. The initiative is a project of the Northeast Structural Genomics consortium, of which the Miami University is a member. The impacts of the research on drug development are discussed. **Availability:** Print; Online.

29161 ■ *"Cogs in R.I. Manufacturing Machine" in Providence Business News (Vol. 28, January 27, 2014, No. 43, pp. 1)*
Pub: American City Business Journals, Inc.
Contact: Mike Olivieri, Executive Vice President
URL(s): pbn.com/cogs-in-ri-manufacturing-machine9 4640

Description: Machine shops are capable of fixing or designing unique parts for manufacturing equipment and serve as a critical link in a company's production and distribution. Rhode Island has at least 50 machine shops capable of fabricating parts for companies. The Rhode Island Manufacturers Association's efforts to close the skills gap in machining are examined. **Availability:** Online.

29162 ■ *"Coming Soon: Electric Tractors"* in *Farm Industry News (November 21, 2011)*
Pub: Informa Business Media, Inc.
Contact: Charlie McCurdy, President

Ed: Jodie Wehrspann. **Description:** The agricultural industry is taking another look at electric farm vehicles. John Deere Product Engineering Center said that farmers can expect to see more diesel-electric systems in farm tractors, sprayers, and implements. **Availability:** Online.

29163 ■ *"Communications and Power Industries Awarded $6 Million to Support Apache Helicopter"* in *Defense & Aerospace Business (August 13, 2014, pp. 11)*
Pub: NewsRX LLC.
Contact: Kalani Rosell, Contact

Description: Communications and Power Industries LLC procured an order totaling $6 million from Lockheed Martin Missiles and Fire Control for manufacturing tactical common data links. These links will be installed on the AH-64E Guardian variant of the Apache helicopter used to support U.S. warfighters. **Availability:** Online.

29164 ■ *"Compelling Opportunities for Investors in Emerging Markets"* in *Barron's (Vol. 88, March 10, 2008, No. 10, pp. 39)*
Pub: Dow Jones & Company Inc.
Contact: Almar Latour, Chief Executive Officer

Ed: Neil A. Martin. **Description:** Michael L. Reynal, portfolio manager of Principal International Emerging Markets Fund, is bullish on the growth prospects of stocks in emerging markets. He is investing big on energy, steel, and transportation companies. **Availability:** Online.

29165 ■ *"Continuant's Big Win: A Lawsuit That Seemed Like a Lifetime"* in *Puget Sound Business Journal (Vol. 34, April 11, 2014, No. 52, pp. 4)*
Pub: American City Business Journals, Inc.
Contact: Mike Olivieri, Executive Vice President

Description: Fife, Washington-based Continuant has won a court ruling along with a $20 million verdict against Santa Clara, California-based Avaya Inc. after eight years in court. Avaya sued Continuant claiming the company did not have the right to service Avaya manufactured products. Insights into the lawsuit are given. **Availability:** Online.

29166 ■ *"ContiTech Celebrates 100 Years"* in *American Printer (Vol. 128, July 1, 2011, No. 7)*
Description: ContiTech celebrated 100 years in business. The firm started in 1911 after developing the first elastic printing blanket. Other milestones for the firm include its manufacturing process for compressible printing blankets, the Conti-Air brand and climate-neutral printing blankets. **Availability:** Print; Online.

29167 ■ *"Coping With a Shrinking Planet"* in *Agency Sales Magazine (Vol. 39, December 2009, No. 11, pp. 46)*
Description: China and India are forcing big changes in the world and are posing a huge threat to U.S. manufacturers and their sales representatives. Reps may want to consider expanding into these territories. Helping sell American products out of the country presents an opportunity for economic expansion. **Availability:** Online.

29168 ■ *"Copy Karachi?"* in *Barron's (Vol. 88, June 30, 2008, No. 26, pp. 5)*
Pub: Dow Jones & Company Inc.
Contact: Almar Latour, Chief Executive Officer

Ed: Randall W. Forsyth. **Description:** Karachi bourse had a historic 8.6 percent one-day gain because the bourse banned short-selling for a month and announced a 30 billion rupee fund to stabilize the market. The shares of General Motors are trading within the same values that it had in 1974. The reasons for this decline are discussed. **Availability:** Online.

29169 ■ *"The Cult of Ralph: Chrysler's Ralph Gilles"* in *Canadian Business (Vol. 79, September 22, 2006, No. 19, pp. 90)*
Pub: Rogers Media Inc.
Contact: Neil Spivak, Chief Executive Officer

Ed: Thomas Watson. **Description:** The contributions of Ralph Gilles to automobile manufacturing giant Daimler Chrysler AG are discussed. **Availability:** Print; Online.

29170 ■ *"DaimlerChrysler Bears Down on Smart"* in *Globe & Mail (March 27, 2006, pp. B11)*
Ed: Oliver Suess. **Description:** DaimlerChrysler AG, German automobile industry giant, is planning to cut down its workforce at its Smart division. The Chrysler is also planning to stop the production of its four-seater models, to end losses at Smart division. **Availability:** Print; Online.

29171 ■ *"Danaher to Acquire Tectronix for $2.8 Billion"* in *Canadian Electronics (Vol. 22, November-December 2007, No. 7, pp. 1)*
Description: Leading supplier of measurement, test and monitoring equipment Tektronix will be acquired by Danaher Corporation for $2.8 billion. Tektronix products are expected to complement Danaher's test equipment sector. The impacts of the deal on Tektronix shareholders and Danaher's operations are discussed. **Availability:** Print; Online.

29172 ■ *"Dealer Gets a Lift with Acquisitions at Year's End"* in *Crain's Detroit Business (Vol. 26, January 11, 2010, No. 2, pp. 3)*
Pub: Crain Communications Inc.
Contact: Barry Asin, President

Ed: Ryan Beene. **Description:** Alta Equipment Co., a forklift dealer, closed 2009 with a string of acquisitions expecting to double the firm's employee headcount and triple its annual revenue. Alta Lift Truck Services, Inc., as the company was known before the acquisitions, was founded in 1984 as Michigan's dealer for forklift manufacturer Yale Materials Handling Corp. **Availability:** Print; Online.

29173 ■ *"A Decent Proposal"* in *Hawaii Business (Vol. 53, March 2008, No. 9, pp. 52)*
Pub: PacificBasin Communications
Contact: Chuck Tindle, Director
E-mail: chuckt@pacificbasin.net

Ed: Jacy L. Youn. **Description:** Bonnie Cooper and Brian Joy own Big Rock Manufacturing Inc., a stone manufacturing company, which sells carved rocks and bowls, lava benches, waterfalls, and Buddhas. Details about the company's growth are discussed. **Availability:** Print; Online.

29174 ■ *"Deere to Open Technology Center in Germany"* in *Chicago Tribune (September 3, 2008)*
Description: Deere & Co. plans to open a technology and innovation center in Germany; details of the company's expansion plans are discussed. **Availability:** Print; Online.

29175 ■ *"Delphi Latest In Fight Over Offshore Tax Shelters"* in *Crain's Detroit Business (Vol. 30, July 7, 2014, No. 27, pp. 1)*
Pub: Crain Communications Inc.
Contact: Barry Asin, President

Description: Internal Revenue Service is investigating Delphi Automotive and other American companies over the use of offshore tax shelters. The latest in Delphi's dispute with the federal government over tax practices is expected to cost the supplier millions. Delphi manufactures electronics and technologies for vehicles. Apple Inc. and Google Inc. have also been targeted by the IRS for incorporating portions of the businesses offshore allowing them to avoid U.S. taxes as well as other foreign taxes. **Availability:** Online.

29176 ■ *"Despite FDA Approval, Heart Test No Boom for BG Medical"* in *Boston Business Journal (Vol. 31, June 17, 2011, No. 21, pp. 1)*
Pub: Boston Business Journal
Contact: Carolyn M. Jones, President
E-mail: cmjones@bizjournals.com

Ed: Julie M. Donnelly. **Description:** The Galectin-3 test failed to boost stock prices of its manufacturer, BG Medicine, which has fallen to $6.06/share. The company hopes that its revenue will be boosted by widespread adoption of an automated and faster version of the test, which diagnoses for heart failure. **Availability:** Online.

29177 ■ *"DeWind Delivering Turbines to Texas Wind Farm"* in *Professional Services Close-Up (September 25, 2011)*
Description: DeWind Company has begun shipment of turbines to the 20 MW Frisco Wind Farm located in Hansford County, Texas. DeWind is a subsidiary of Daewoo Shipbuilding and Marine Engineering Company. Details of the project are discussed. **Availability:** Online.

29178 ■ *"Dexter Gauntlett Gauges the Wind"* in *Business Journal Portland (Vol. 30, January 31, 2014, No. 48, pp. 6)*
Pub: American City Business Journals, Inc.
Contact: Mike Olivieri, Executive Vice President

Released: Weekly. **Price:** $4, Introductory 4-week offer(Digital & Print). **Description:** Navigant Research senior research analyst, Dexter Gauntlett says Vestas-American Wind Systems could boost its revenues. He added that the company has being hiring employees at its manufacturing plants. Gauntlett also said that wind energy will greatly boost state renewable portfolios. **Availability:** Print; Online.

29179 ■ *"Digital Power Management and the PMBus"* in *Canadian Electronics (Vol. 23, June-July 2008, No. 4, pp. 8)*
Pub: Annex Buisness Media
Contact: Mike Fredericks, President

Ed: Torbjorn Holmberg. **Description:** PMBus is an interface that can be applied to a variety of devices including power management devices. Information on digital power management products using this interface are also provided. **Availability:** Print; Online.

29180 ■ *"Digital Printing Walks the Plank"* in *American Printer (Vol. 128, August 1, 2011, No. 8)*
Description: Digital print manufacturing is discussed. **Availability:** Online.

29181 ■ *"Discount Beers Take Fizz Out Of Molson"* in *Globe & Mail (February 10, 2006, pp. B3)*
Description: The reasons behind the decline in profits by 60 percent for Molson Coors Brewing Co., during fourth quarter 2005, are presented. **Availability:** Online.

29182 ■ *"Does America Really Need Manufacturing? Yes, When Production Is Closely Tied to Innovation"* in *Harvard Business Review (Vol. 90, March 2012, No. 3, pp. 94)*
Pub: Harvard Business Review Press
Contact: Moderna V. Pfizer, Contact

Ed: Gary P. Pisano, Willy C. Shih. **Price:** $8.95. **Description:** A framework is presented for assessing when manufacturing and research and development are crucial to innovation and therefore should be kept in close proximity to each other. The framework denotes the degree to which product design data can be separated from manufacturing, and the opportunities to improve manufacturing. **Availability:** Online; PDF.

29183 ■ *"Dog Marketplace: Pet Waste Products Pick Up Sales" in Pet Product News (Vol. 66, September 2012, No. 9, pp. 58)*
Ed: Sandi Cain. **Description:** Pet supplies manufacturers are developing dog waste pickup bags and other convenient cleanup tools characterized by environment-friendliness and fashion. The demand for these cleanup tools has been motivated by dog owners' desire to minimize their and their dogs' environmental footprints. **Availability:** Online.

29184 ■ *"The Doomsday Scenario" in Conde Nast Portfolio (Vol. 2, June 2008, No. 6, pp. 91)*
Ed: Jeffrey Rothfeder. **Description:** Detroit and the U.S. auto industry are discussed as well as the ramifications of the demise of this manufacturing base. Similarities and differences between the downfall of the U.S. steel business and the impact it had on Pittsburg, Pennsylvania is also discussed.

29185 ■ *"Dow Champions Innovative Energy Solutions for Auto Industry at NAIAS" in Business of Global Warming (January 25, 2010, pp. 7)*
Description: This year's North American International Auto Show in Detroit will host the "Electric Avenue" exhibit sponsored by the Dow Chemical Company. The display will showcase the latest in innovative energy solutions from Dow as well as electric vehicles and the technology supporting them. This marks the first time a non-automotive manufacturer is part of the main floor of the show. **Availability:** Print; PDF; Online.

29186 ■ *"Drilling Deep and Flying High" in Barron's (Vol. 88, June 30, 2008, No. 26, pp. 34)*
Pub: Dow Jones & Company Inc.
Contact: Almar Latour, Chief Executive Officer
Ed: Kenneth Rapoza. **Description:** Shares of Petrobras could rise another 25 percent if the three deepwater wells that the company has found proves as lucrative as some expect. Petrobras will become an oil giant if the reserves are proven. **Availability:** Online.

29187 ■ *"Drop in the Bucket Makes a lot of Waves" in Globe & Mail (March 22, 2007, pp. B1)*
Ed: Greg Keenan. **Description:** The concern of several auto makers in Canada over the impact of providing heavy rebates to customers buying energy-efficient cars is discussed. **Availability:** Online.

29188 ■ *"Duro Bag to Expand, Add 130 Jobs" in Business Courier (Vol. 27, August 6, 2010, No. 14, pp. 1)*
Pub: Business Courier
Ed: Jon Newberry. **Description:** Duro Bag Manufacturing Company will expand capacity at its Florence, Kentucky plant and will add around 130 jobs over the next few years. The state of Kentucky has given preliminary approval for up to $1 million in tax incentives over 10 years, tied to the creation of new jobs. The company's investment will include new production and packaging equipment and building improvements. **Availability:** Print; Online.

29189 ■ *"The Dynamic DUO" in Canadian Electronics (Vol. 23, February 2008, No. 1, pp. 24)*
Description: Citronics Corporation not only aims to proved a good working environment for its employees, it also values the opinions of its personnel. Citronics had its employees test different workbenches before finally purchasing thirty-five of Lista's Align adjustable height workstation, which combines flexibility with aesthetics. The design of the Alin workbench is described. **Availability:** Print; Online.

29190 ■ *"Dynamic Duo: Payouts Rise at General Dynamics, Steel Dynamics" in Barron's (Vol. 88, March 10, 2008, No. 10, pp. 45)*
Pub: Dow Jones & Company Inc.
Contact: Almar Latour, Chief Executive Officer

Ed: Shirley A. Lazo. **Description:** General Dynamics, the world's sixth-largest military contractor, raised its dividend payout by 20.7 percent from 29 cents to 35 cents a share. Steel Dynamics, producer of structural steel and steel bar products, declared a 2-for-1 stock split and raised its quarterly dividend by 33 percent to a split-adjusted 10 cents a share. **Availability:** Online.

29191 ■ *"Early Spring Halts Drilling Season" in Globe & Mail (March 14, 2007, pp. B14)*
Ed: Norval Scott. **Description:** Decreased petroleum productivity in Canadian oil drilling rigs due to early spring season in western regions is discussed. **Availability:** Online.

29192 ■ *"Effective Use of Field Time" in Agency Sales Magazine (Vol. 39, July 2009, No. 7, pp. 40)*
Description: Sales representatives need to consider the value of field visits to themselves and their customers ahead of time. Several anecdotes about field visits from the perspective of manufacturers and sale representatives are presented.

29193 ■ *"Electrolux Feeding Economy: Contracts for Local Firms at $64 Million; Supplier Bids Up Next" in Memphis Business Journal (Vol. 34, June 22, 2012, No. 10, pp. 1)*
Pub: Baltimore Business Journal
Contact: Rhonda Pringle, President
E-mail: rpringle@bizjournals.com
Ed: Michael Sheffield. **Description:** Electrolux Home Products Inc. has awarded almost $64 million of its construction contracts to local companies in Memphis, Tennessee while planning the search for suppliers for its 700,000 square foot manufacturing facility. The company aims to complete the facility by the end of 2012. **Availability:** Print; Online.

29194 ■ *"Electrolux Nears Product Testing" in Memphis Business Journal (Vol. 34, September 21, 2012, No. 23, pp. 1)*
Pub: Baltimore Business Journal
Contact: Rhonda Pringle, President
E-mail: rpringle@bizjournals.com
Ed: Michael Sheffield. **Description:** Electrolux Home Products Inc.'s new manufacturing facility is expected to be ready for use by the end of September 2012. The company will start producing 'pilot' products once the testing of manufacturing systems is completed. Electrolux will also hire 200 employees who will assemble the first products ready for shipmenht in the first quarter of 2013. **Availability:** Print; Online.

29195 ■ *"Electronics Assembly" in Canadian Electronics (Vol. 23, February 2008, No. 1, pp. 12)*
Description: I&J Fisnar Inc. has launched a new system of bench top dispensing robots while Vitronics Soltec and KIC have introduced a new reflow soldering machine. Teknek, on the other hand, has announced a new product, called the CM10, which an be used in cleaning large format substrates. Other new products and their description are presented. **Availability:** Print; Online.

29196 ■ *"EnCana Axes Spending on Gas Wells" in Globe & Mail (February 16, 2006, pp. B1)*
Ed: Dave Ebner. **Description:** The reasons behind EnCana Corp.'s cost spending measures by $300 million on natural gas wells are presented. The company projects 2 percent cut in gas and oil sales for 2006. **Availability:** Print; Online.

29197 ■ *"Encore Container, Manufacturer of Plastic Drums and IBC Totes, Leads the Way in Environmental Sustainability" in Ecology, Environment & Conservation Business (January 25, 2014, pp. 33)*
Pub: NewsRX LLC.
Contact: Kalani Rosell, Contact
Description: Encore Container, a leading reconditioner of IBC totes and manufacturer and reconditioner of plastic drums describes its efforts to promote environmental sustainability within the company:

container reconditioning, plastic and steel recycling, water conservation and waste minimization. **Availability:** Online.

29198 ■ *"Energy Boom Spurring Manufacturing Growth" in Pittsburgh Business Times (Vol. 33, May 2, 2014, No. 42, pp. 7)*
Pub: American City Business Journals, Inc.
Contact: Mike Olivieri, Executive Vice President
Released: May 02, 2014. **Price:** $4, introductory 4-week offer(Digital only). **Description:** The manufacturing and energy technology sectors both showed strong growth, according to the Pittsburgh Technology Council in Pennsylvania. Data shows that the sectors added about 7,000 jobs as a result of the growth in the Marcellus Shale from 2010 to 2012. **Availability:** Print; Online.

29199 ■ *"Energy Firms Face Stricter Definitions" in Globe & Mail (March 26, 2007, pp. B3)*
Ed: David Ebner. **Description:** The Alberta Securities Commission has imposed strict securities regulations on oil and gas industries. Energy industries will have to submit revenue details to stake holders. **Availability:** Online.

29200 ■ *"Energy Slide Slows 4th-Quarter Profits" in Globe & Mail (April 13, 2007, pp. B9)*
Ed: Angela Barnes. **Description:** The decrease in the fourth quarter profits of several companies across various industries in Canada, including mining and manufacturing, due to global decrease in oil prices, is discussed.

29201 ■ *"Evaluate Your Process and Do It Better" in Modern Machine Shop (Vol. 84, October 2011, No. 5, pp. 34)*
Pub: Gardner Business Media Inc.
Contact: Rick Kline, Jr., President
E-mail: rkline2@gardnerweb.com
Ed: Wayne Chaneski. **Released:** September 15, 2011. **Description:** In order to be more competitive, many machine shops owners are continually looking at their processes and procedures in order to be more competitive. **Availability:** Print; Online.

29202 ■ *"Everyone Has a Story Inspired by Chevrolet" in Automotive News (Vol. 86, October 31, 2011, No. 6488, pp. S003)*
Pub: Crain Communications Inc.
Contact: Barry Asin, President
Description: Besides being a great ad slogan, 'Baseball, Hot Dogs, Apple Pie and Chevrolet', the brand conjures up memories for most everyone in our society. Louis Chevrolet had a reputation as a race car driver and lent his name to the car that has endured for 100 years. **Availability:** Online.

29203 ■ *"Executive Decision: Damn the Profit Margins, Sleeman Declares War on Buck-a-Beer Foes" in Globe & Mail (January 28, 2006, pp. B3)*
Description: The cost savings plans of chief executive officer John Sleeman of Sleeman Breweries Ltd. are presented. **Availability:** Online.

29204 ■ *"Expanding Middleby's Food Processing Biz" in Crain's Chicago Business (Vol. 31, April 21, 2008, No. 16, pp. 6)*
Pub: Crain Communications Inc.
Contact: Barry Asin, President
Ed: David Sterrett. **Description:** Profile of the executive vice-president of the food processing company, Middleby Corp, whose business plan is to develop new products, begin looking for acquisitions and simplify operations in order to expand the firm. **Availability:** Online.

29205 ■ *"Experts Strive to Educate on Proper Pet Diets" in Pet Product News (Vol. 64, November 2010, No. 11, pp. 40)*
Ed: Joan Hustace Walker. **Description:** Pet supply manufacturers have been bundling small mammal food and treats with educational sources to help

retailers avoid customer misinformation. This action has been motivated by the customer's quest to seek proper nutritional advice for their small mammal pets. **Availability:** Online.

29206 ■ *"Extra Rehab Time Boosts M-B's Off-Lease Profits"* in Automotive News (Vol. 86, October 31, 2011, No. 6488, pp. 22)
Pub: Crain Communications Inc.
Contact: Barry Asin, President
Ed: Arlena Sawyers. **Description:** Mercedes-Benz Financial Services USA is holding on to off-lease vehicles in order to recondition them and the move is boosting profits for the company. **Availability:** Print; Online.

29207 ■ *"Feet on the Street: Reps Are Ready to Hit the Ground Running"* in Agency Sales Magazine (Vol. 39, July 2009, No. 7, pp. 12)
Description: One of the major benefits to manufacturers in working with sales representatives is the concept of synergistic selling where the rep shows his mettle. The rep of today is a solution provider that anticipates and meets the customer's needs.

29208 ■ *"First Impressions of Robotic Farming Systems"* in Farm Industry News (September 30, 2011)
Pub: Informa Business Media, Inc.
Contact: Charlie McCurdy, President
Ed: Jodie Wehrspann. **Description:** Farm Science Review featured tillage tools and land rollers, including John Deere's GPS system where a cart tractor is automatically controlled as well as a new line of Kinze's carts and a video of their robotic system for a driver-less cart tractor. **Availability:** Print; Online.

29209 ■ *"First Sustainability Standard for Household Portable and Floor Care Appliances Developed to Identify Environmentally Responsible Products"* in Ecology, Environment & Conservation Business (September 13, 2014, pp. 39)
Pub: NewsRX LLC.
Contact: Kalani Rosell, Contact
Description: the Association of Home Appliance Manufacturers (AHAM), CSA Group, and the UL Environment released the AHAM 7002-2014/CSA SPE-7002-14/UL 7002, Sustainability Standard for Household Portable and Floor Care Appliances. This is the first voluntary sustainability standards for these appliances and is the third in a unit of product sustainability standards under development by the group. These standards are intended for use by manufacturers, governments, retailers, and others to identify products conforming to these standards in six key areas: materials, manufacturing and operations, energy consumption during use, end-of-life, consumables, and innovation. **Availability:** Online.

29210 ■ *"First Suzlon S97 Turbines Arrive in North America for Installation"* in PR Newswire (September 28, 2011)
Pub: PR Newswire Association LLC.
Description: Suzlon Energy Ltd., the world's fifth largest manufacturer of wind turbines, will install its first S97 turbine at the Amherst Wind Farm Project. These turbines will be installed on 90-meter hub height towers and at full capacity, will generate enough electricity to power over 10,000 Canadian homes. **Availability:** Online.

29211 ■ *"Five Reasons Why the Gap Fell Out of Fashion"* in Globe & Mail (January 27, 2007, pp. B4)
Description: The five major market trends that have caused the decline of fashion clothing retailer Gap Inc.'s sales are discussed. The shift in brand, workplace fashion culture, competition, demographics, and consumer preferences have lead to the Gap's brand identity. **Availability:** Online.

29212 ■ *"Foods for Thought"* in Pet Product News (Vol. 64, December 2010, No. 12, pp. 16)
Ed: Maddy Heleine. **Description:** Manufacturers have been focused at developing species-specific fish foods due to consumer tendency to assess the

benefits of the food they feed their fish. As retailers stock species-specific fish foods, manufacturers have provided in-store items and strategies to assist in efficiently selling these food products. Trends in fish food packaging and ingredients are also discussed. **Availability:** Online.

29213 ■ *"Ford Canada's Edsel of a Year: Revenue Plummets 24 Percent in '05"* in Globe & Mail (February 2, 2006, pp. B1)
Description: Ford Motor Company of Canada Ltd. posted 24% decline in revenues for 2005. The drop in earnings is attributed to plant shutdown in Oaksville, Canada. **Availability:** Online.

29214 ■ *"Ford: Down, Not Out, and Still a Buy"* in Barron's (Vol. 92, July 23, 2012, No. 30, pp. 14)
Pub: Dow Jones & Company Inc.
Contact: Almar Latour, Chief Executive Officer
Ed: Vito J. Racanelli. **Description:** Stocks of Ford Motor Company could gain value as the company continues to improve its finances despite fears of slower global economic growth. The company's stock prices could double from $9.35 per share within three years. **Availability:** Online.

29215 ■ *"Fraser and Neave Acquires King's Creameries"* in Ice Cream Reporter (Vol. 23, November 20, 2010, No. 12, pp. 1)
Description: Fraser and Neave Ltd., a Singapore-based consumer products marketer, has entered a conditional agreement to acquire all outstanding shares of King's Creameries, the leading manufacturer and distributor of frozen desserts. **Availability:** Print; Online.

29216 ■ *"From American Icon to Global Juggernaut"* in Automotive News (Vol. 86, October 31, 2011, No. 6188, pp. S003)
Pub: Crain Communications Inc.
Contact: Barry Asin, President
Ed: Peter Brown. **Description:** Chevrolet celebrates its 100th Anniversary. The brand revolutionized its market with affordable cars that bring technology to the masses. Chevys have been sold in 140 countries and the company is responding to a broader market. **Availability:** Print; Online.

29217 ■ *"Fuel King: The Most Fuel-Efficient Tractor of the Decade is the John Deere 8295R"* in Farm Industry News (November 10, 2011)
Pub: Informa Business Media, Inc.
Contact: Charlie McCurdy, President
Description: Farm Industry News compiled a list of the most fuel-efficient tractors with help from the Nebraska Tractor Test Lab, with the John Deere 8295R PTO winner of the most fuel-efficient tractor of the decade. **Availability:** Print; Online.

29218 ■ *"Full-Court Press for Apple"* in Barron's (Vol. 88, March 24, 2008, No. 12, pp. 47)
Pub: Dow Jones & Company Inc.
Contact: Almar Latour, Chief Executive Officer
Ed: Mark Veverka. **Description:** Apple Inc. is facing more intellectual property lawsuits in 2008, with 30 patent lawsuits filed compared to 15 in 2007 and nine in 2006. The lawsuits, which involve products such as the iPod and the iPhone, present some concern for Apple's shareholders. **Availability:** Online.

29219 ■ *"Funky Footwear: Walk This Way"* in Barron's (Vol. 90, August 23, 2010, No. 34, pp. 13)
Pub: Barron's Editorial & Corporate Headquarters
Ed: Christopher C. Williams. **Description:** Crocs and Skechers are selling very popular shoes and sales show no signs of winding down. The shares of both companies are attractively prices. **Availability:** Online.

29220 ■ *"Furniture Making May Come Back--Literally"* in Business North Carolina (Vol. 28, March 2008, No. 3, pp. 32)
Pub: Business North Carolina
Contact: Peggy Knaack, Manager
E-mail: pknaack@businessnc.com
Description: Due to the weak U.S. dollar and the fact that lumber processors never left the country, foreign furniture manufacturers are becoming interested in moving manufacturing plants to the U.S. **Availability:** Online.

29221 ■ *"Future Autoworkers will Need Broader Skills"* in Crain's Detroit Business (Vol. 25, June 8, 2009, No. 23, pp. 13)
Pub: Crain Communications Inc.
Contact: Barry Asin, President
Ed: Ryan Beene. **Description:** Auto industry observers report that new workers in the industry will need advanced skills and educational backgrounds in engineering and technical fields because jobs in the factories will become more technology-based and multidisciplinary. **Availability:** Online.

29222 ■ *"The Game of Operation"* in Crain's Chicago Business (Vol. 31, April 28, 2008, No. 17, pp. 26)
Pub: Crain Communications Inc.
Contact: Barry Asin, President
Ed: Samantha Stainburn. **Description:** Revenue at Medline Industries Inc., a manufacturer of medical products, has risen 12 percent a year since 1976, reaching $2.81 billion last year. Growth at the company is due to new and increasingly sophisticated operations by surgeons which brings about the need for more specialized tools. **Availability:** Online.

29223 ■ *"Gamesa Office Closing Part of Political Reality"* in Pittsburgh Business Times (Vol. 33, February 7, 2014, No. 30, pp. 6)
Pub: American City Business Journals, Inc.
Contact: Mike Olivieri, Executive Vice President
Description: Due to political uncertainty surrounding the production tax credit for wind energy and changes in the supply chain needs in the North America wind market, a Spanish wind blade maker Gamesa will be shutting down its manufacturing unit in Ebensburg March 31, 2014. The general counsel for Gamesa, Frank Fuselier, stated that optimizing the company's supply chain will help them survive in a market devoid of a production tax credit. **Availability:** Online.

29224 ■ *"Gaming Infrastructure Paves Ready Path for Manufacturing"* in Memphis Business Journal (No. 35, February 14, 2014, No. 45, pp. 4)
Pub: American City Business Journals, Inc.
Contact: Mike Olivieri, Executive Vice President
Description: The city of Tunica, Mississippi is trying to expand its reputation as a gaming destination into manufacturing in an effort seek new opportunities for economic development and revenue. German crankshaft manufacturer, Feurer Powertrain, is building a $140 million manufacturing facility that will open in late 2014. **Availability:** Online.

29225 ■ *"Gas Supplies Low Heading Into Summer Season"* in Globe & Mail (April 13, 2007, pp. B6)
Ed: Shawn McCarthy. **Description:** The decrease in the supply of gas due to maintenance problems at refineries in the United States and Canada is discussed. **Availability:** Online.

29226 ■ *"GE Milestone: 1,000th Wind Turbine Installed in Canada"* in CNW Group (October 4, 2011)
Pub: CNW Group Ltd.
Description: GE installed its 1,000th wind turbine in Canada at Cartier Wind Energy's Gros Morne project in the Gaspesie Region of Quebec, Canada. As Canada continues to expand its use of wind energy, GE plans to have over 1,100 wind turbines installed in the nation by the end of 2011. **Availability:** Online.

29227 ■ *"General Electric Touts Going Green for Business Fleet Services"* **in America's Intelligence Wire (June 1, 2012)**

Description: General Capital Fleet Services if featuring alternative-fuel vehicles in Eden Prairie for its corporate customers. GE Capital is the world's largest fleet management service and is offering its customers the first of its kind service that allows corporate lease customers to test drive alternative fuel cars from 20 different manufacturers. **Availability:** Print; Online.

29228 ■ *"German Firm Ifm Electronic to Open Second Local Unit"* **in Philadelphia Business Journal (Vol. 28, July 20, 2012, No. 23, pp. 1)**

Pub: Baltimore Business Journal

Contact: Rhonda Pringle, President

E-mail: rpringle@bizjournals.com

Description: German electronic control and sensor manufacturer, ifm electronic gmbh, has established ifm prover USA in January 2012, its second subsidiary in Exton, Pennsylvania after ifm efector Inc. Ifm prover will relocate in July 2012 to a new 36,000 square foot building that features a product development area and multiple laboraties for testing and quality control. **Availability:** Print; Online.

29229 ■ *"Getting Inventive With..Ed Spellman"* **in Crain's Cleveland Business (Vol. 28, October 22, 2007, No. 42, pp. 18)**

Pub: Crain Communications Inc.

Contact: K. C. Crain, President

Ed: Kimberly Bonvissuto. **Description:** Profile featuring Ed Spellman, a mechanical engineer who decided to quit his job at Invacare Corp., a medical equipment manufacturer and distributor, in order to devote his full attention to promoting his numerous inventions, including the DV-Grip, a vehicle mount for portable DVD players. **Availability:** Online.

29230 ■ *"Getting the Word Out"* **in Modern Machine Shop (Vol. 84, September 2011, No. 4, pp. 16)**

Pub: Gardner Business Media Inc.

Contact: Rick Kline, Jr., President

E-mail: rkline2@gardnerweb.com

Ed: Derek Korn. **Description:** Many times machine shops create devices to streamline their own machining processes and find these devices can be used by other shops, thus developing a marketable product. Tips for this process are outlined. **Availability:** Print; Online.

29231 ■ *"Global Steel Makers Circle Stelco"* **in Globe & Mail (April 19, 2007, pp. B3)**

Ed: Greg Keenan. **Description:** The details of the take over bids offered to Stelco Inc. are presented. Due to these bids the shares of Stelco Inc rose up to 70 percent. **Availability:** Online.

29232 ■ *"GM Canada Revved Up Over Camaro"* **in Globe & Mail (February 17, 2006, pp. B4)**

Ed: Greg Keenan. **Description:** General Manager of General Motors Canada is planning to start the production of company's muscle car Camaro in Canadian facility. The car was exhibited at Canadian International Auto Show held in Toronto. **Availability:** Online.

29233 ■ *"GM Scores High Marks For Its Use of Solar Power"* **in Blade (September 13, 2012)**

Pub: McClatchy Tribune Information Services

Contact: Patrick J. Talamantes, President

Ed: Tyrel Linkhorn. **Description:** General Motors scores high among top corporate generators of solar power in the United States. The Solar Energy Industries Assocation ranked GM's on-site solar power generation capacity at number 13, making GM the first in the automotive sector. Details of GM's solar projects are outlined. **Availability:** Online.

29234 ■ *"GM's Decision to Boot Dealer Prompts Sale"* **in Baltimore Business Journal (Vol. 27, November 6, 2009, No. 26, pp. 1)**

Pub: Baltimore Business Journal

Contact: Rhonda Pringle, President

E-mail: rpringle@bizjournals.com

Ed: Daniel J. Sernovitz. **Description:** General Motors Corporation's (GM) decision to strip Baltimore's Anderson Automotive Group Inc. of its GM franchise has prompted the owner, Bruce Mortimer, to close the automotive dealership and sell the land to a developer. The new project could make way for new homes, a shopping center and supermarket. **Availability:** Print; Online.

29235 ■ *"GM's Volt Woes Cast Shadow on E-Cars"* **in Wall Street Journal Eastern Edition (November 28, 2011, pp. B1)**

Pub: Dow Jones & Company Inc.

Contact: Almar Latour, Chief Executive Officer

Ed: Sharon Terlep. **Description:** The future of electric cars is darkened with the government investigation by the National Highway Traffic Safety Administration into General Motor Company's Chevy Volt after two instances of the car's battery packs catching fire during crash tests conducted by the Agency. **Availability:** Online.

29236 ■ *"Got Skills? Think Manufacturing"* **in Occupational Outlook Quarterly (Vol. 58, Summer 2014, No. 2, pp. 28)**

Pub: Government Publishing Office

Contact: Hugh Nathanial Halpern, Director

Released: June 22, 2014. **Description:** According to the U.S. Bureau of Labor Statistics, 264,000 job openings in manufacturing were reported in March 2014. Employers are finding it difficult to fill jobs for machinists and maintenance technicians, among other skilled trades. Manufacturers are also looking for welders, but also for workers outside of production, including biomedical engineers, dispatchers, and truck drivers. An overview of current manufacturing issues and statistics is included. **Availability:** Print; Online.

29237 ■ *"Green Manufacturer Scouts Sites in Greater Cincinnati"* **in Business Courier (Vol. 27, July 23, 2010, No. 12, pp. 1)**

Pub: Business Courier

Ed: Dan Monk. **Description:** CresaPartners is searching for a manufacturing facility in Cincinnati, Ohio. The company is set to tour about ten sites in the area. **Availability:** Print; Online.

29238 ■ *"GreenTech Gears Up for Production"* **in Memphis Business Journal (Vol. 33, April 6, 2012, No. 52, pp. 1)**

Pub: Baltimore Business Journal

Contact: Rhonda Pringle, President

E-mail: rpringle@bizjournals.com

Description: GreenTech Automotive has broken ground for construction of a new production facility in Tunica, Tennessee. The company will focus its manufacturing operations in the new facility. **Availability:** Print; Online.

29239 ■ *"Growth in Fits and Starts"* **in Canadian Business (Vol. 83, July 20, 2010, No. 11-12, pp. 18)**

Description: US home sales and manufacturing indicators have dropped and fears of a double-dip recession are widespread. However, a chief economist says that this is endemic to what can be seen after a recession caused by a financial crisis. In Canada, consumer optimism is rising and anxiety over losing one's job is waning. **Availability:** Print; Online.

29240 ■ *"GTI Licenses TMC to Cannon Boiler Works"* **in Contractor (Vol. 56, December 2009, No. 12, pp. 6)**

Description: Gas Technology Institute has licensed Cannon Boiler Works Inc. to use its transport membrane condenser technology. The technology can be applied to elevated-temperature industrial processes

such as boilers. It allows the capture and beneficial use of latent waste heat and water vapor from exhaust/flue gas. **Availability:** Online.

29241 ■ *"Halls Give Hospital Drive $11 Million Infusion"* **in The Business Journal-Serving Metropolitan Kansas City (Vol. 26, July 18, 2008)**

Description: Don Hall, chairman of Hallmark Cards Inc., and eight family members have announced that they will give $11 million to Children's Mercy Hospitals and Clinics for its $800 million expansion plan. Hall Family Foundation president Bill Hall that contributions such as that for Children's Mercy reflect the charitable interests of the foundation's board and founders. The possible impacts of the Hall's donation are analyzed.

29242 ■ *"H&M Offers a Dress for Less"* **in Canadian Business (Vol. 83, September 14, 2010, No. 15, pp. 20)**

Pub: Rogers Media Inc.

Contact: Neil Spivak, Chief Executive Officer

Ed: Laura Cameron. **Description:** Swedish clothing company H&M has implemented loss leader strategy by pricing some dresses at extremely low prices. The economy has forced retailers to keep prices down despite the increasing cost of manufacturing, partly due to Chinese labor becoming more expensive. How the trend will affect apparel companies is discussed. **Availability:** Print; Online.

29243 ■ *"Harvesting the Royal Oak"* **in Barron's (Vol. 92, September 17, 2012, No. 38, pp. 18)**

Description: The Royal Oak wrist watch made by Audemars Piguet of Switzerland was considered revolutionary during its creation in the 1970s, but enjoys wide popularity 40 years later. The all-steel sports watch pays attention to detail and has enabled its manufacturer to survive. **Availability:** Print; Online.

29244 ■ *"Hayes Lemmerz Reports Some Good News Despite Losses"* **in Crain's Detroit Business (Vol. 24, April 14, 2008, No. 15, pp. 4)**

Pub: Crain Communications Inc.

Contact: Barry Asin, President

Ed: Nancy Kaffer. **Description:** Hayes Lemmerz International Inc., a wheel manufacturer from Northville that has reported a positive free cash flow for the first time in years, a narrowed net loss in the fourth quarter and significant restructuring of the company's debt. **Availability:** Print; Online.

29245 ■ *"Helping Customers Fight Pet Waste"* **in Pet Product News (Vol. 64, November 2010, No. 11, pp. 52)**

Ed: Sandy Robins. **Description:** Pet cleaning products manufacturers have been enjoying high sales figures by paying attention to changing pet ownership trends and environmental awareness. Meanwhile, the inclusion of user-friendly features in these products has also been boosted by the social role of pets and the media attention to pet waste. How manufacturers have been responding to this demand is explored. **Availability:** Print; Online.

29246 ■ *"Hey, You Can't Do That"* **in Green Industry Pro (Vol. 23, September 2011)**

Ed: Rod Dickens. **Description:** Manufacturers of landscape equipment are making better use of energy resources, such as the use of fuel-injection systems instead of carburetors, lightweight materials, better lubricants, advanced battery technology, and innovative engine designs. **Availability:** Online.

29247 ■ *"High-Yield Turns Into Road Kill"* **in Barron's (Vol. 88, July 7, 2008, No. 27, pp. M7)**

Pub: Dow Jones & Company Inc.

Contact: Almar Latour, Chief Executive Officer

Ed: Emily Barrett. **Description:** High-yield bonds have returned to the brink of collapse after profits have recovered from the shock brought about by the collapse of Bear Stearns. The high-yield bond market could decline again due to weakness in the automotive sector, particularly in Ford and General Motors. **Availability:** Online.

29248 ■ *"How CoolBrands' Thrills Turned to Chills"* in *Globe & Mail (January 25, 2007, pp. B1)*

Ed: Keith McArthur. **Description:** The key reasons behind the sudden share price fall of ice cream giant CoolBrands International Inc. are discussed. **Availability:** Print; Online.

29249 ■ *"How to Find a Factory to Manufacture Your Product"* in *Business News Daily (February 21, 2023)*

URL(s): www.businessnewsdaily.com/8820-how-to -find-factory.html

Ed: Bennett Conlin. **Released:** February 21, 2023. **Description:** Specifies how to find the right factory to manufacture the goods you sell in your small business. **Availability:** Online.

29250 ■ *"How Much Profit is Enough?"* in *Automotive News (Vol. 86, October 31, 2011, No. 6488, pp. 12)*

Pub: Crain Communications Inc.

Contact: Barry Asin, President

Description: Workers at the big three automobile companies are unhappy about the issues of class wealth, like the high compensations offered to CEOs. **Availability:** Print; Online.

29251 ■ *"How Our Picks Beat The Bear"* in *Barron's (Vol. 88, July 14, 2008, No. 28, pp. 18)*

Pub: Dow Jones & Company Inc.

Contact: Almar Latour, Chief Executive Officer

Ed: Andrew Bary. **Description:** Performance of the stocks that Barron's covered in the first half of 2008 is discussed; some of the worst picks and most rewarding pans have been in the financial sector while the best plays were in the energy, materials, and the transportation sectors. **Availability:** Online.

29252 ■ *"Husky Proceeds on Heavy-Oil Expansion"* in *Globe & Mail (March 21, 2006, pp. B1)*

Ed: Patrick Brethour. **Description:** Canadian energy giant Husky Energy Inc. has started its $90 million engineering effort to determine the cost of the $2.3 billion heavy-oil up gradation expansion plan. Details of the project are elaborated upon. **Availability:** Online.

29253 ■ *"Hyundai Enters Minivan Market"* in *Globe & Mail (February 15, 2006, pp. B7)*

Ed: Greg Keenan. **Description:** The reasons behind the launch of minivan by Hyundai Auto Canada Inc. are presented. **Availability:** Online.

29254 ■ *"Imports Frothing Up Beer Market"* in *Globe & Mail (February 16, 2006, pp. B4)*

Ed: Andy Hoffman. **Description:** The reasons behind the rise in market share of beer imports, in Canada, are presented. **Availability:** Online.

29255 ■ *"Industrial Vacancies Hit High"* in *Crain's Chicago Business (Apr. 21, 2008)*

Pub: Crain Communications Inc.

Contact: Barry Asin, President

Ed: Alby Gallun. **Description:** Hitting its highest level in four years in the first quarter is the Chicago-area industrial vacancy rate, a sign that the slumping economy is depressing demand for warehouse and manufacturing space. **Availability:** Online.

29256 ■ *"Innovation Adoption and Diffusion in Business-to-Business Marketing"* in *Journal of Business & Industrial Marketing (Vol. 29, May 2014, No. 4, pp. 324-331)*

Pub: Emerald Group Publishing Limited

Contact: Erika Valenti, President

Description: Evaluation of the innovation adoption and diffusion approach that links it with the key theoretical fields within business-to-business marketing is explored. A conceptual discussion is presented with the aim to develop an integrative conceptual

framework and concludes that the proposed theoretical approaches could provide support in establishing a more matter-of-fact view of adoption and diffusion in the industrial sector. **Availability:** Download; Online; PDF.

29257 ■ *"Intermodal Makes Suppliers Look to Rack Up Big Sales to Distributors"* in *The Business Journal-Serving Metropolitan Kansas City (August 15, 2008)*

Pub: American City Business Journals, Inc.

Contact: Mike Olivieri, Executive Vice President

Ed: James Dornbrook. **Description:** Suppliers of shelving units, conveyor systems and other equipment used in distribution facilities are expecting new business opportunities along with the planned intermodal projects in the Kansas City area. Suppliers have already observed that small distributors have started to relocate to the city because of the intermodal projects. Demand for shelves and lifts have also increased. **Availability:** Online.

29258 ■ *"logen in Talks to Build Ethanol Plant in Canada"* in *Globe & Mail (March 21, 2007, pp. B7)*

Ed: Shawn McCarthy. **Description:** Ottawa based logen Corp. is planning to construct a cellulosic ethanol plant in Saskatchewan region. The company will be investing an estimated $500 million for this purpose. **Availability:** Print; Online.

29259 ■ *"It May Be Cheaper to Manufacture At Home"* in *Harvard Business Review (Vol. 88, October 2010, No. 10, pp. 84)*

Pub: Harvard Business Publishing

Contact: Diane Belcher, Managing Director

Ed: Suzanne de Treville, Lenos Trigeorgis. **Price:** $8.95, PDF. **Description:** Using a real options framework rather than a discounted cash flow model to assess and value supply chain processes is examined. This enables companies to assess costs for a variety of situations, not just ideal or normal circumstances, which can make the difference between domestic and foreign manufacturing decisions. **Availability:** Online; PDF.

29260 ■ *"It's Time To Swim"* in *Canadian Business (Vol. 81, March 3, 2008, No. 3, pp. 37)*

Description: Canadian manufacturers should consider Asian markets such as India and the United Arab Emirates as the U.S. economic downturn continues. Canada's shortage in skilled labor is also expected to negatively affect manufacturing industries. Ontario's plans to assist manufacturers are also presented. **Availability:** Print; PDF; Download; Online.

29261 ■ *"ITT Places Its Bet With Defense Buy: Selling Equipment to Army Pays Off"* in *Crain's New York Business (Vol. 24, January 6, 2008)*

Pub: Crain Communications, Inc.

Contact: Jessica Botos, Manager, Marketing

E-mail: jessica.botos@crainsnewyork.com

Description: ITT Corp.'s revenue has jumped by 20 percent in each of the past three years due to demand for the company's radio sets and night-vision goggles. The firm has acquired EDO Corp., which specializes in battlefield communications systems, in an attempt to expand its defense-industry division. **Availability:** Online.

29262 ■ *"Jacksonville Doing Well In Growing Economy"* in *Orlando Business Journal (Vol. 30, June 27, 2014, No. 53, pp. 8)*

Pub: American City Business Journals, Inc.

Contact: Mike Olivieri, Executive Vice President

Released: June 27, 2014. **Description:** Jerry Mallot is the president of JaxUSA Partnership, the economic development arm of the Jax Chambers. According to Mallot, Northeast Florida's strongest selling points for business site or relocation there include advanced manufacturing, financial services, aviation and aerospace technology, life sciences, logistics and information technology.

29263 ■ *"Japan-Brand Shortages Will Linger Into '12"* in *Automotive News (Vol. 86, October 31, 2011, No. 6488, pp. 1)*

Pub: Crain Communications Inc.

Contact: Barry Asin, President

Ed: Amy Wilson, Mark Rechtin. **Description:** Floods in Thailand and the tsunami in Japan have caused shortages of Japanese-brand vehicle parts. These shortages are expected to linger into 2012. **Availability:** Online.

29264 ■ *"Jet Sales Put Bombardier Back in Black"* in *Globe & Mail (March 30, 2006, pp. B1)*

Ed: Bertrand Morotte. **Description:** The details on Bombardier Inc., which posted 20 percent rise in shares following $86 million profit for fourth quarter 2005, are presented. **Availability:** Online.

29265 ■ *"Jobs Data Show A Slow Leak"* in *Barron's (Vol. 88, July 7, 2008, No. 27, pp. 34)*

Pub: Dow Jones & Company Inc.

Contact: Almar Latour, Chief Executive Officer

Ed: Gene Epstein. **Description:** In June 2008, the United States manufacturing sector showed an expansion, with the purchasing managers' index rising to 50.2 from 49.6; the unemployment rate in the US, which stayed steady at 5.5 percent in June 2008 is also discussed. Statistical data included. **Availability:** Online.

29266 ■ *"Keeping the Vehicle On the Road--A Survey On On-Road Lane Detection Systems"* in *ACM Computing Surveys (Vol. 46, Spring 2014, No. 1, pp. 2)*

Pub: Association for Computing Machinery - University of Wyoming

Contact: Ed Seidel, President

E-mail: uwpres@uwyo.edu

Description: The development of wireless sensor networks, such as researchers Advanced Driver Assistance Systems (ADAS) requires the ability to analyze the road scene in the same as a human. Road scene analysis is an essential, complex, and challenging task and it consists of: road detection and obstacle detection. The detection of the road borders, the estimation of the road geometry, and the localization of the vehicle are essential tasks in this context since they are required for the lateral and longitudinal control of the vehicle. A comprehensive review of vision-based road detection systems vision in automobiles and trucks is examined. **Availability:** Online.

29267 ■ *"Keltic Gets Nod to Build N.S. Petrochemical Plant"* in *Globe & Mail (March 15, 2007, pp. B9)*

Ed: Shawn McCarthy. **Description:** The government of Nova Scotia has awarded clearance to Keltic Inc. for the construction of new petrochemical plant in Goldboro region. Complete details in this context are discussed. **Availability:** Online.

29268 ■ *"Kerkorian Shakes Up Chrysler Race"* in *Globe & Mail (April 6, 2007, pp. B1)*

Ed: Greg Keenan. **Description:** The bid of Kirk Kerkorian's Tracinda Corp. to acquire Daimler-Chrysler AG for $4.5 billion is discussed. **Availability:** Online.

29269 ■ *"Kinetico Exec Going Global to Increase Growth Flow"* in *Crain's Cleveland Business (Vol. 28, October 1, 2007, No. 39, pp. 5)*

Pub: Crain Communications Inc.

Contact: K. C. Crain, President

Ed: David Bennett. **Description:** Shamus Hurley, the new CEO and president of Kinetico Inc., a manufacturer of water filtering and softening equipment for residential, commercial and municipal use, plans to expand the company to target markets overseas. **Availability:** Online.

29270 ■ *The King of Vodka: The Story of Pyotr Smirnov and the Upheaval of an Empire*

Pub: HarperCollins Publishers L.L.C.

Contact: Brian Murray, President

Ed: Linda Himelstein. **Released:** November 30, 2010. **Price:** $15.99, paperback. **Description:** Biography of Pyotr Smirnov and how his determination took him from serf to the head of Smirnov Vodka. Smirnov's marketing techniques are defined and show how he expanded the drink worldwide. **Availability:** E-book; Print; Online.

29271 ■ "Kohler Building Earns LEED Silver Certification" in Contractor (Vol. 56, September 2009, No. 9, pp. 12)

Description: United States Green Building Council has awarded Kohler Co. with the Silver Leadership in Energy and Environmental Design Status. The award has highlighted the company's work to transform its building into a more environmentally efficient structure. A description of the facility is also provided. **Availability:** Print; Online.

29272 ■ "Kraft Taps Cheese Head; Jordan Charged With Fixing Foodmaker's Signature Product" in Crain's Chicago Business (April 14, 2008)
Pub: Crain Communications Inc.
Contact: Barry Asin, President

Ed: David Sterrett. **Description:** Kraft Foods Inc. has assigned Rhonda Jordan, a company veteran, to take charge of the cheese and dairy division which has been losing market shares to cheaper store-brand cheese among cost-sensitive shoppers as Kraft and its competitors raise prices to offset soaring dairy costs. **Availability:** Online.

29273 ■ "Lancaster Firm Helps Tidy Navy Aircraft Carriers" in Business First of Buffalo (Vol. 30, February 7, 2014, No. 21, pp. 4)
Pub: American City Business Journals, Inc.
Contact: Mike Olivieri, Executive Vice President

Released: February 7, 2014. **Price:** $140, Digital & Print; $115, Digital only. **Description:** Performance Advantage Company sells aluminum took racking systems for use by fire trucks, SWAT teams and departments of public works. The Lancaster, New York-based firm also manufactures clamps and racks for the U.S. Navy, which uses them in aircraft carriers. **Availability:** Print; Online.

29274 ■ "Laurent Beaudoin Interview: Deja Vu" in Canadian Business (Vol. 81, July 22, 2008, No. 12-13, pp. 38)
Pub: Rogers Media Inc.
Contact: Neil Spivak, Chief Executive Officer

Ed: Joe Castaldo. **Description:** Laurent Beaudoin has retired as chief executive officer for Bombardier Inc.'s, a manufacturer of regional and business aircraft, but kept a role in the firm as a non-executive chairman. Beaudoin first resigned from the company in 1999, but had to return in 2004 to address challenging situations faced by the company. Beaudoin's views on management and the company are presented. **Availability:** Online.

29275 ■ "Lawyers Sued Over Lapsed Lacrosse Patent" in Crain's Detroit Business (Vol. 25, June 8, 2009, No. 23, pp. 5)
Pub: Crain Communications Inc.
Contact: Barry Asin, President

Ed: Chad Halcom. **Description:** Warrior Sports Inc., a manufacturer of lacrosse equipment located in Warren, Michigan is suing the law firm Dickinson Wright PLLC and two of its intellectual property lawyers over patent rights to lacrosse equipment. **Availability:** Print; Online.

29276 ■ "Lead-Free Products must Meet Requirements" in Contractor (Vol. 56, September 2009, No. 9, pp. 30)

Ed: Robert Gottermeier. **Description:** United States Environmental Protection Agency's adoption of the Safe Drinking Water Act is aimed at lowering lead extraction levels from plumbing products. Manufacturers have since deleaded brass and bronze potable water products. Meanwhile, California and Vermont have passed a law limiting lead content for potable water conveying plumbing products. **Availability:** Print; Online.

29277 ■ The Leadership Challenge: How to Make Extraordinary Things Happen in Organizations
Pub: Jossey-Bass

Ed: James M. Kouzes, Barry Z. Posner. **Released:** 7th edition. **Price:** $34.95, hardcover; $34.95, hardcover. **Description:** According to research by the authors, people can make extraordinary things happen by liberating the leader within everyone around them. This handbook gives practical tips to aspire leaders in retail, manufacturing, government, community, church and school settings. **Availability:** E-book; Print.

29278 ■ "Lean Machine: Health Care Follows Auto's Lead, Gears Up for Efficiency" in Crain's Detroit Business (Vol. 26, Jan. 11, 2010)
Pub: Crain Communications Inc.
Contact: Barry Asin, President

Ed: Jay Greene. **Description:** Reducing waste and becoming more efficient is a goal of many businesses involved in the health care industry. These firms are looking to the local manufacturing sector, comparing themselves in specifically to the auto industry, for ways in which to become more efficient. **Availability:** Print; Online.

29279 ■ "Learn New Ideas from Experienced Menu Makers" in Nation's Restaurant News (Vol. 45, June 27, 2011, No. 13, pp. 82)
Pub: Informa USA, Inc.
Contact: Stephen A. Carter, Chief Executive Officer

Ed: Nancy Kruse. **Released:** June 27, 2011. **Description:** National Restaurant Association Restaurant, Hotel-Motel Show featured the Food Truck Spot, a firm committed to all aspects of mobile catering, foodtruck manufacturers, leasers of fully equipped truck and a food-truck franchising group.

29280 ■ Lethal Logic: Exploding the Myths that Paralyze American Gun Policy
Pub: Potomac Books Inc.

Ed: Dennis A, Henigan. **Released:** June 01, 2009. **Price:** $34.95, hardcover. **Description:** Marketing tactics being used by gun manufacturers regarding possible new gun control laws are examined. **Availability:** E-book; Print; PDF.

29281 ■ "Lining Up at the Ethanol Trough (Ethanol Production in Canada)" in Globe & Mail (January 25, 2007, pp. B2)

Ed: Eric Reguly. **Description:** The future of ethanol production in Canada is discussed; alternate fuel market is expected to reach 35 billion gallons by 2017. **Availability:** Online.

29282 ■ "Linking Human Capital to Competitive Advantages: Flexibility in a Manufacturing Firm's Supply Chain" in Human Resource Management (Vol. 49, September-October 2010, No. 5)
Pub: John Wiley & Sons, Inc.
Contact: Christina Van Tassell, Executive Vice President Chief Financial Officer

Ed: Yan Jin, Margaret M. Hopkins, Jenell L.S. Wittmer. **Released:** September 01, 2010. **Description:** A study was conducted to confirm the links among human capital, firm flexibility, and firm performance. The study also examines the emerging role of flexibility for a company's performance. A total of 201 senior supply chain management professionals from several manufacturing companies were included in the study.

29283 ■ "Live & Learn: Ian Delaney" in Canadian Business (Vol. 81, Summer 2008, No. 9, pp. 168)
Pub: Rogers Media Inc.
Contact: Neil Spivak, Chief Executive Officer

Ed: Joe Castaldo. **Description:** Interview with Ian Delaney who is the executive chairman of chemical company Sherritt International Corp.; Delaney previously worked as chief executive for a holding company owned by Peter Munk. Details of his beliefs, profession and family life are discussed. **Availability:** Online.

29284 ■ "Local Industrial Vacancies Climb" in Crain's Chicago Business (Vol. 31, November 17, 2008, No. 46, pp. 18)
Pub: Crain Communications Inc.
Contact: Barry Asin, President

Ed: Eddie Baeb. **Description:** Demand for local industrial real estate has declined dramatically as companies that use warehouse and factory space struggle to survive in an ailing economy. According to a report by Colliers Bennett & Kahnweiler Inc., a commercial real estate brokerage, the regional vacancy rate has risen to 9.86 percent in the third quarter, the fourth straight increase and the highest in the past 14 years. **Availability:** Online.

29285 ■ "The Lost Opportunity for a Canadian Steel Giant" in Globe & Mail (April 23, 2007, pp. B1)

Ed: Greg Keenan. **Description:** The efforts of Algoma Steel Inc. to create a Canadian steel manufacturer that could survive the global trends of consolidation in the steel industry are described. The company's efforts to acquire Stelco Inc., Ivaco Inc. and Slater Steel Inc. are discussed. **Availability:** Print; Online.

29286 ■ "Lynn Johnson, President: Dowland-Bach" in Alaska Business Monthly (Vol. 27, October 2011, No. 10, pp. 11)
Pub: Alaska Business Publishing Company Inc.
Contact: Charles Bell, Vice President, Sales and Marketing
E-mail: cbell@akbizmag.com

Ed: Peg Stomierowski. **Description:** Profile of Lynn C. Johnson cofounder of Dowland-Bach Corporation, a manufacturing and distribution company is presented. The firms primary products are wellhead control and chemical injection systems for corrosion control, UL industrial control panels, and specialty stainless steel sheet metal fabrication. **Availability:** Print; Online.

29287 ■ "Made in San Francisco: Manufacturing a Comeback" in San Francisco Business Times (Vol. 28, February 14, 2014, No. 30, pp. 4)
Pub: American City Business Journals, Inc.
Contact: Mike Olivieri, Executive Vice President

Released: February 14, 2014. **Price:** $4, print. **Description:** Reports show that San Francisco, California's manufacturing industry is making a comeback due to the rise in new entrepreneurs. However, some observers believe that the increasing costs of production could limit the sector's growth. San Francisco currently supports more than 4,000 manufacturing jobs. **Availability:** Print; Online.

29288 ■ "Manufacturers Become Part of Coalition" in Contractor (Vol. 56, July 2009, No. 7, pp. 40)

Description: Bradford White Water Heaters, Rheem Water Heating, Rinnai America Corp., and A.O. Smith Water Heaters have joined the Consortium for Energy Efficiency in the Coalition for Energy Star Water Heaters. The coalition seeks to increase the awareness of Energy Star water heaters. **Availability:** Print; Online.

29289 ■ "Manufacturing Behind the Great Wall: What Works, What Doesn't" in Canadian Electronics (Vol. 23, February 2008, No. 1, pp. 6)

Description: Electronic component producers are increasingly transitioning their manufacturing operations to China in order to take advantage of the growing Chinese manufacturing industry. It is believed that manufacturers have to carefully consider whether their run sizes are appropriate for Chinese manufacturing before moving their operations. **Availability:** PDF.

29290 ■ "Manufacturing Boom Leads to Local Warehouse Leasing Fury" in Houston Business Journal (Vol. 44, April 11, 2014, No. 49, pp. 10A)
Pub: American City Business Journals, Inc.
Contact: Mike Olivieri, Executive Vice President

Released: Weekly. **Price:** $4, introductory 4-week offer(Digital only). **Description:** The growth of Houston, Texas manufacturing sector has resulted in companies' investment in local warehouse space. Siemens AG and Emerson Electric Company have leased new warehouse space in the area. Meanwhile, other energy companies have also contributed to the decline of industrial vacancy rates. **Availability:** Print; Online.

29291 ■ *"Manufacturing Skills Fading Away"* in Memphis Business Journal (Vol. 34, July 20, 2012, No. 14, pp. 1)

Pub: Baltimore Business Journal

Contact: Rhonda Pringle, President

E-mail: rpringle@bizjournals.com

Ed: Michael Sheffield. **Description:** Chemical manufacturers in Memphis, Tennessee are seen to face a shortage of skilled workers. A large portion of employees are nearing retirement age. **Availability:** Print; Online.

29292 ■ *"Market Takes Shape for Emissions Credits"* in Globe & Mail (April 16, 2007, pp. B3)

Ed: Shawn McCarthy. **Description:** The effort of Canadian companies to prepare for emissions trading after the government imposes climate change regulations is discussed. **Availability:** Online.

29293 ■ *"Marketer Bets Big on U.S.'s Growing Canine Obsession"* in Advertising Age (Vol. 79, April 14, 2008, No. 15, pp. 14)

Pub: Crain Communications, Inc.

Contact: Jessica Botos, Manager, Marketing

E-mail: jessica.botos@crainsnewyork.com

Ed: Emily Bryson York. **Description:** Overview of FreshPet, a New Jersey company that began marketing two brands of refrigerated dog food-Deli Fresh and FreshPet Select-which are made from fresh ingredients such as beef, rice and carrots. The company projects continued success due to the amount of money consumers spend on their pets as well as fears derived from the 2007 recalls that inspired consumers to look for smaller, independent manufacturers that are less likely to source ingredients from China. **Availability:** Online.

29294 ■ *"Markets Defy the Doomsayers"* in Barron's (Vol. 88, March 24, 2008, No. 12, pp. M5)

Pub: Dow Jones & Company Inc.

Contact: Almar Latour, Chief Executive Officer

Ed: Leslie P. Norton. **Description:** US stock markets registered strong gains, with the Dow Jones Industrial Average rising 3.43 percent on the week to close at 12,361.32, in a rally that may be seen as short-covering. Shares of Hansen Natural are poised for further drops with a slowdown in the energy drink market. **Availability:** Online.

29295 ■ *"Medical Device Makers Brace for Excise Tax"* in Memphis Business Journal (Vol. 34, July 20, 2012, No. 14, pp. 1)

Pub: Baltimore Business Journal

Contact: Rhonda Pringle, President

E-mail: rpringle@bizjournals.com

Ed: Michael Sheffield. **Description:** The US Government's plan to increase excise tax is seen to impact medical device manufacturers. The tax is expected to raise as much as $60 billion over the next 10 years. **Availability:** Print; Online.

29296 ■ *"Memphis Area Manufacturing Companies"* in Memphis Business Journal (No. 35, March 14, 2014, No. 49, pp. 10)

Pub: American City Business Journals, Inc.

Contact: Mike Olivieri, Executive Vice President

Released: Weekly. **Price:** $25, all 25 Companies. **Description:** The top 25 manufacturing firms in Memphis, Tennessee are ranked by local full-time employees. Smith and Nephew Inc. got the top spot, while UTC-Carrier Corporation ranked second. **Availability:** Print; Download; Online.

29297 ■ *"Mercury (1939-2010)"* in Canadian Business (Vol. 83, June 15, 2010, No. 10, pp. 27)

Ed: Steve Maich. **Released:** 2018. **Description:** Ford's Mercury brand of cars began in 1939 and it was designed by Ford to attract a wealthier clientele. Mercury was mentioned in a 1949 song by K.C. Douglas and was driven in the movie, "Rebel Without a Cause". However, the brand was too expensive for the mass market and not exclusive enough through the years, so Ford Motor Company decided to discontinue the brand in 2010. **Availability:** Print; Online.

29298 ■ *"Minority Auto Suppliers Get Help Diversifying"* in Crain's Detroit Business (Vol. 26, January 11, 2010, No. 2, pp. 3)

Pub: Crain Communications Inc.

Contact: Barry Asin, President

Ed: Sherri Welch. **Description:** Displaced minority auto suppliers are being given assistance by the Kauffman's Foundation Urban Entrepreneur Partnership Detroit program, a three-year effort to assist 150 of the region's suppliers into more diversified businesses. **Availability:** Online.

29299 ■ *"A Model Machine for Titanium"* in Modern Machine Shop (Vol. 84, October 2011, No. 5, pp. 84)

Pub: Gardner Business Media Inc.

Contact: Rick Kline, Jr., President

E-mail: rkline2@gardnerweb.com

Released: September 15, 2011. **Description:** Researchers have developed a machine tool that controls vibration in order to mill titanium more productively. In-depth information on the machine tool as well as understanding the processes involved in milling titanium is covered. **Availability:** Online.

29300 ■ *"Monogram Foods Eyes Acquisition: Midwest Manufacturer Target of Latest Expansion"* in Memphis Business Journal (Vol. 34, August 10, 2012, No. 17, pp. 1)

Pub: Baltimore Business Journal

Contact: Rhonda Pringle, President

E-mail: rpringle@bizjournals.com

Description: Monogram Food Solutions, a Memphis-based food company is raising $12.5 million for the acquisition of an undisclosed company or companies. The acquistion is expected to generate $50 million revenue, add 200 new employees for Monogram, and strengthen its manufacturing arm. **Availability:** Print; Online.

29301 ■ *"Monogram Foods Lands Another Acquisition In Quest for Growth Goals"* in Memphis Business Journal (Vol. 34, September 14, 2012, No. 22, pp. 1)

Pub: Baltimore Business Journal

Contact: Rhonda Pringle, President

E-mail: rpringle@bizjournals.com

Ed: Michael Sheffield. **Description:** Memphis, Tennessee-based Monogram Food Solutions has announced a deal to acquire Enjoy and Hickory Best Beef Jerky brands from Colton, California-based Enjoy Foods International. The move follows the acquisition of Bristol, Indiana-based Hinsdale Farms, which manufactures corn dogs.

29302 ■ *"Montana's Manufacturing Industry"* in Montana Business Quarterly (Vol. 49, Spring 2011, No. 1, pp. 29)

Pub: University of Montana Bureau of Business and Economic Research

Contact: Patrick Barkey, Director

E-mail: patrick.barkey@business.umt.edu

Ed: Todd A. Morgan, Charles E. Keegan, III, Colin B. Sorenson. **Released:** Quarterly. **Description:** Manufacturing remains a vital part of Montana's economy despite the recession and decline in the production of wood products. Statistical data included. **Availability:** Online.

29303 ■ *"The More Incredible Egg"* in Entrepreneur (June 2014)

Pub: Entrepreneur Media Inc.

Contact: Dan Bova, Director

E-mail: dbova@entrepreneur.com

Description: San Francisco, California-based startup Hampton Creek has developed a plant-based alternative to eggs. The startup touts it as a healthier, more humane and environment-friendly egg alternative. The company used several varieties of the yellow pea and discovered that its properties mimic egg emulsion. Hampton Creek's first food product was Beyond Eggs, a powder that allows food manufacturers to eliminate eggs from food products. It also developed Just Mayo, an egg-free mayonnaise substitute, and is developing Eat the Dough, an egg-free substitute for cookie dough. **Availability:** Print; Online.

29304 ■ *"Morgan Hill Attracts Manufacturing to South County"* in Silicon Valley/San Jose Business Journal (Vol. 30, September 21, 2012, No. 26, pp. 1)

Pub: Baltimore Business Journal

Contact: Rhonda Pringle, President

E-mail: rpringle@bizjournals.com

Description: The Grow Morgan Hill Fund offers $2 million in loans to qualifying businesses off of an initial $500,000 city investment. The fund is a way for the city of Morgan Hill, California to help local businesses expand int he absence of redevelopment agencies. **Availability:** Print; Online.

29305 ■ *"Mosaid Grants First Wireless Patent License To Matsushita"* in Canadian Electronics (Vol. 23, June-July 2008, No. 5, pp. 1)

Pub: Annex Buisness Media

Contact: Mike Fredericks, President

Description: Matsushita Electric Industrial Co. Ltd. has been granted a six-and-a-half-year license by Mosaid Technologies Inc. to manufacture the latter's products. The patent portfolio license agreement covers Mosaid's Wi-Fi, Wi-Max, CDMA-enabled notebook computers and other products.

29306 ■ *"Motors and Motion Control"* in Canadian Electronics (Vol. 23, February 2008, No. 1, pp. 23)

Description: A new version of MicroMo Electronics Inc.'s Smoovy Series 0303.B has been added to MicroMo's DC motor product line. United Electronic Industries, on the other hand, has introduced the new UEIPAC series of programmable automation controllers that can offer solutions to various applications such as unmanned vehicle controllers. Features and functions of other new motors and motion control devices are given.

29307 ■ *"Mover and Sheika"* in Conde Nast Portfolio (Vol. 2, June 2008, No. 6, pp. 104)

Ed: John Arlidge. **Description:** Profile of Princess Sheika Lubna who is the first female foreign trade minister in the Middle East, the United Arab Emirates biggest business envoy, paving the way for billions in new investment, and also a manufacturer of her own perfume line. **Availability:** Online.

29308 ■ *"Myths of Deleveraging"* in Barron's (Vol. 90, August 23, 2010, No. 34, pp. M14)

Pub: Barron's Editorial & Corporate Headquarters

Ed: Gene Epstein. **Description:** The opposite is true against reports about deleveraging or the decrease in credit since inflation-adjusted-investment factories and equipment rose 7.8 percent in the first quarter of 2010. On consumer deleveraging, sales of homes through credit is weak but there is a trend towards more realistic homeownership and consumer spending on durable goods rose 8.8 percent. **Availability:** Online.

29309 ■ *"Navistar, Cat Talk Truck Deal"* in Crain's Chicago Business (Vol. 31, March 24, 2008, No. 12, pp. 1)

Pub: Crain Communications Inc.

Contact: Barry Asin, President

Ed: Bob Tita. **Description:** Caterpillar Inc. and Navistar International Corp. are negotiating a partnership in which Navistar would build Cat-branded trucks with engines supplied by the Peoria-based equipment manufacturer, Caterpillar. **Availability:** Online.

29310 ■ *"New Developments in Cat's Play"* in *Pet Product News (Vol. 66, September 2012, No. 9, pp. 1)*
Description: Developments in toys for cats have been characterized by items that bring out a cat's natural instincts, toxin-free composition, and durability, among other trends. Meanwhile, consumers are encouraged to try these toys so follow-up purchases can be made. Ways in which manufacturers have addressed the demand for these toys is also discussed. **Availability:** Online.

29311 ■ *"New Ethanol Plant, Planned for Nevada, IA, Will Use Corn Stover"* in *Farm Industry News (June 27, 2011)*
Pub: Informa Business Media, Inc.
Contact: Charlie McCurdy, President
Ed: Lynn Grooms. **Description:** DuPont Danisco Cellulosic Ethanol (DDCE) will buy land next to the Lincolnway Energy corn-based ethanol plant in Nevada, Iowa in order to produce ethanol from corn stover at the location. **Availability:** Online.

29312 ■ *"The New Frontier"* in *Crain's Detroit Business (Vol. 26, January 18, 2010, No. 3, pp. S025)*
Description: Due to the changing consumer preference resulting from new fuel-efficiency standards, concern about climate change and higher gasoline prices, Detroit car designers are beginning to shift focus onto smaller vehicles. **Availability:** Print; Online.

29313 ■ *"New Life for Porsche's VW Dreams"* in *Barron's (Vol. 89, July 6, 2009, No. 27, pp. 9)*
Pub: Dow Jones & Company Inc.
Contact: Almar Latour, Chief Executive Officer
Ed: Vito J. Racanelli. **Description:** Porsche and Volkswagen moved closer to a merger after the Qatar Investment Authority offered to take a stake in Porsche. The QIA could take up to a 30 percent stake in Porsche and purchase all Volkswagen calls for up to $6 billion. **Availability:** Online.

29314 ■ *"Nexen, OPTI Boost Oil Sands Spending"* in *Globe & Mail (February 18, 2006, pp. B5)*
Ed: Dave Ebner. **Description:** The reasons behind the decision of Nexen Inc. and OPTI Canada Inc., to allocate 10 percent more funding on oil sands, are presented. **Availability:** Print; Online.

29315 ■ *"NKC Keeps Pace with Auto Industry"* in *Memphis Business Journal (Vol. 34, September 14, 2012, No. 22, pp. 1)*
Pub: Baltimore Business Journal
Contact: Rhonda Pringle, President
E-mail: rpringle@bizjournals.com
Ed: Michael Sheffield. **Description:** Memphis, Tennessee-based NKC of American Inc. has been expecting sales to increase to about $60 million for 2012 after its revenue dropped to about $20 million during the peak of the recession in 2008-2009. NKC's growth is being driven by new contracts with automotive manufacturers. **Availability:** Print; Online.

29316 ■ *"No Frills - And No Dodge"* in *Crain's Detroit Business (Vol. 24, September 22, 2008, No. 38, pp. 3)*
Pub: Crain Communications Inc.
Contact: Barry Asin, President
Ed: Bradford Wernle. **Description:** Chrysler LLC is in the middle of a business plan known as Project Genesis, a five-year strategy in which the company will reduce the dealer count by combining its Jeep, Chrysler and Dodge brands under one rooftop wherever possible. Not every dealer will be able to arrange this deal because of the investment required to expand stores in which have low-overhead; many of these stores feel that low-overhead structures are more likely to survive difficult times than the larger stores in which the Genesis consolidation plan intends to implement. **Availability:** Online.

29317 ■ *"No End to the Nightmare; America's Car Industry"* in *The Economist (Vol. 390, January 3, 2009, No. 8612, pp. 46)*
Description: Detroit's struggling auto industry and the government loan package is discussed as well as the United Auto Worker union, which is loathed by Senate Republicans. **Availability:** Print; Online.

29318 ■ *"Nonstop Round Baler Earns Top International Award for Krone"* in *Farm Industry News (November 18, 2011)*
Pub: Informa Business Media, Inc.
Contact: Charlie McCurdy, President
Ed: Karen McMahon. **Description:** The new Ultima baler from Krone can make and net a bale in 40 seconds without stopping, thus producing 90 bales an hour. The new baler, still in test stage, won top honors at the Agritechnica farm equipment show in Hannover, Germany. **Availability:** Online.

29319 ■ *"Nuclear Plans May Stall on Uranium Shortage"* in *Globe & Mail (March 22, 2007, pp. B4)*
Ed: Shawn McCarthy. **Description:** The poor investments in uranium production and enrichment despite growing demand for it for nuclear energy is discussed. **Availability:** Online.

29320 ■ *"No. 300: My Job Is To Solve Every Kind of Crisis"* in *Inc. (Vol. 36, September 2014, No. 7, pp. 72)*
Pub: Mansueto Ventures L.L.C.
Contact: Stephanie Mehta, Chief Executive Officer
Released: September 2014. **Description:** Saima Chowdhury started her integrated sourcing company in New York City after receiving an MBA from Wharton School. Noi Solutions helps retailers manufacture goods in Bangladesh while helping Bangladeshi factories market their capabilities to retailers. Chowdhury discusses the challenges and has learned to remain calm during any crisis. **Availability:** Print; Online.

29321 ■ *"Nvidia Shares Clobbered After Gloomy Warning"* in *Barron's (Vol. 88, July 7, 2008, No. 27, pp. 25)*
Pub: Dow Jones & Company Inc.
Contact: Almar Latour, Chief Executive Officer
Ed: Eric J. Savitz. **Description:** Shares of graphics chip manufacturer Nvidia suffered a 30 percent drop in its share price after the company warned that revenue and gross margin forecasts for the quarter ending July 27, 2008 will be below expectations. Stan Glasgow, chief operating officer of Sony Electronics, believes the US economic slowdown will not affect demand for the company's products. Statistical data included. **Availability:** Online.

29322 ■ *"Nvidia's Picture Brighter Than Stock Price Indicates"* in *Barron's (Vol. 88, March 24, 2008, No. 12, pp. 46)*
Pub: Dow Jones & Company Inc.
Contact: Almar Latour, Chief Executive Officer
Ed: Eric J. Savitz. **Description:** Shares of graphics chip maker Nvidia, priced at $18.52 each, do not indicate the company's strong position in the graphics chip market. The company's shares have dropped due to fears of slower demand for PCs, but the company is not as exposed to broader economic forces. **Availability:** Online.

29323 ■ *"NYPA Grants Aid Area Companies"* in *Business First of Buffalo (Vol. 30, January 10, 2014, No. 17, pp. 6)*
Pub: American City Business Journals, Inc.
Contact: Mike Olivieri, Executive Vice President
Released: Weekly. **Price:** $140, One-Year Print & Digital; $115, One-Year Digital. **Description:** New York Power Authority (NYPA) trustees have approved more than $3.5 million in financial aid to Western New York enterprises. The NYPA and Empire State Development have also funded a package that includes low cost hydropower and $7 million in capital grants and tax credits. The Western New York area manufacturers that were granted aid are also presented. **Availability:** Print; Online.

29324 ■ *"The Ode: S. M. Whitney Co. (1868 – 2010)"* in *Canadian Business (Vol. 83, October 12, 2010, No. 17, pp. 27)*
Pub: Rogers Media Inc.
Contact: Neil Spivak, Chief Executive Officer
Ed: Angelina Chapin. **Released:** October 12, 2010. **Description:** A history of S.M. Whitney Company is presented. The cotton company was opened in 1868. The cotton is sold to textile manufacturers after crops have been picked, ginned and baled. The company closed down in 2010 after chief executive officer Barry Whitney decided to sell his last bale of cotton. **Availability:** Print; Online.

29325 ■ *"Old Ford Plant to Sign New Tenants"* in *Business Courier (Vol. 27, August 13, 2010, No. 15, pp. 1)*
Pub: Business Courier
Ed: Dan Monk. **Description:** Ohio Realty Advisors LLC, a company handling the marketing of the 1.9 million-square-foot former Ford Batavia plant is on the brink of landing one distribution and three manufacturing firms as tenants. These tenants are slated to occupy about 20 percent of the facility and generate as many as 250 jobs in Ohio. **Availability:** Print; Online.

29326 ■ *"Ontario Keeps Bleeding Jobs as Michelin Closes Tire Plant"* in *Globe & Mail (February 3, 2006, pp. B1)*
Description: The reasons behind facility shutdown and workforce reduction by Michelin SA, in Ontario, are presented. **Availability:** Online.

29327 ■ *"Optimum Nutrition, Maximum Profit"* in *Pet Product News (Vol. 66, September 2012, No. 9, pp. S1)*
Description: How pet food manufacturers have expanded brand lines to address pet owners' demand for fresh, balanced superfood diets that provide optimum pet nutrtion and foster rapid digestion among pets is explored. Retailers have been maximizing profits by guiding pet owners in selecting he appropriate superfood brands for their pets. **Availability:** Online.

29328 ■ *"Options Abound in Winter Wares"* in *Pet Product News (Vol. 64, November 2010, No. 11, pp. 1)*
Ed: Maggie M. Shein. **Description:** Pet supply manufacturers emphasize creating top-notch construction and functional design in creating winter clothing for pets. Meanwhile, retailers and pet owners seek human-inspired style, quality, and versatility for pets' winter clothing. How retailers generate successful sales of pets' winter clothing outside of traditional brand marketing is also examined. **Availability:** Online.

29329 ■ *"Outlook 2008 (9 Sectors to Watch): Metals"* in *Canadian Business (Vol. 81, December 19, 2007, No. 1, pp. 46)*
Pub: Rogers Media Inc.
Contact: Neil Spivak, Chief Executive Officer
Ed: John Gray. **Description:** Forecasts on the Canadian metal industries for 2008 are discussed. Details on mine production and the rise in prices are also presented. **Availability:** Print; Online.

29330 ■ *"Packaging Firm Wraps Up Remake: Overseas Plants Help Firm Fatten Margins"* in *Crain's New York Business (January 6, 2008)*
Pub: Crain Communications, Inc.
Contact: Jessica Botos, Manager, Marketing
E-mail: jessica.botos@crainsnewyork.com
Description: Sealed Air Corp., a packaging manufacturer, has seen its share price fall nearly 20 percent over the past two years, making it one of the worst performers in the packaging sector. **Availability:** Online.

29331 ■ *"Parent Firm's Global Reach, Stricter Air Quality Rules Have Stock Smiling"* in *Crain's Cleveland Business (October 15, 2007)*
Pub: Crain Communications Inc.
Contact: K. C. Crain, President

Ed: David Bennett. **Description:** Since Stock Equipment Co., a firm that makes industrial pollution control equipment, was acquired by Schenck Process Group, a diversified global manufacturer based in Germany, the company's orders from abroad have been on the rise. The purchase has opened the doors to regions such as Eastern and Central Europe, Latin America and Australia. **Availability:** Online.

29332 ■ "A Parts Maker Primed for Takeoff" in Barron's (Vol. 92, August 25, 2012, No. 35, pp. 39)
Pub: Dow Jones & Company Inc.
Contact: Almar Latour, Chief Executive Officer

Ed: David Englander. **Description:** The stocks of machinery maker Curtiss-Wright could gain value due to the manufacturing company's healthy commercial business. The company's stock prices have fallen to $29.27/share due to concerns about reductions in defense spending, but could be worth $40/share. **Availability:** Online.

29333 ■ "Parts, Tooling Manufacturer Machinists Inc. Opts to Expand in South Park" in Puget Sound Business Journal (Vol. 34, February 21, 2014, No. 45, pp. 6)
Pub: American City Business Journals, Inc.
Contact: Mike Olivieri, Executive Vice President

Description: Seattle, Washington-based Machinists Inc. announced an expansion with a seventh building in South Park. The new 20,000-square-foot building will increase the company's footprint to 115,000-square-feet when fully outfitted. The machine manufacturer shares insight into its decision to stay in Seattle rather than relocate is offered. **Availability:** Online.

29334 ■ "Perry Ellis and G-III Apparel--Out of Fashion, but Still in Style" in Barron's (Vol. 88, March 17, 2008, No. 11, pp. 48)
Pub: Dow Jones & Company Inc.
Contact: Almar Latour, Chief Executive Officer

Ed: Robin Goldwyn Blumenthal. **Description:** Shares of Perry Ellis International and G-III Apparel Group have taken some beating in the market despite good growth earnings prospects. Perry Ellis sees earnings growth of 8 to 11 percent for fiscal 2009, while G-III Apparel expects earnings growth of 25 percent. **Availability:** Online.

29335 ■ "Pet Food Bank 'Shares the Love" in Pet Product News (Vol. 64, December 2010, No. 12, pp. 6)

Description: Winston-Salem, North Carolina-based nonprofit Share the Love Pet Food Bank has donated 60,000 pounds of pet food since its establishment in 2009. It has been linking pet food manufacturers and rescue groups to supply unsold pet food to needy animals. The nonprofit intends to reach out to more animal welfare groups by building more warehouses. **Availability:** Online.

29336 ■ "A Pioneer of Paying With Plastic" in Crain's Chicago Business (Vol. 31, April 28, 2008, No. 17, pp. 39)
Pub: Crain Communications Inc.
Contact: Barry Asin, President

Ed: Phuong Ly. **Description:** Profile of Perfect Plastic Printing Corp., a family-owned company which manufactures credit cards, bank cards and gift cards and whose sales hit $50.1 million last year, a 16 percent jump from 2006. **Availability:** Online.

29337 ■ "Portability and Durability Are Key When It Comes to Pet Containment" in Pet Product News (Vol. 66, September 2012, No. 9, pp. 64)

Ed: Wendy Bedwell-Wilson. **Description:** Containment products that have been offered by pet supply manufacturers are marked by features such as portability and durability. Some of these products include crates, partitions, and adjustable pens to cordon off dog and ensure their safety within the household premises. **Availability:** Online.

29338 ■ "Precision Fertilizer Spreading Shown at Agritechnica" in Farm Industry News (November 23, 2011)
Pub: Informa Business Media, Inc.
Contact: Charlie McCurdy, President

Ed: Karen McMahon. **Description:** Rauch, the German firm, introduced a new system that precisely spreads fertilizer on crops. The new product was shown at Agritechnica. **Availability:** Online.

29339 ■ "Pricey Oil, High Dollar Wipe Out Jobs" in Globe & Mail (February 11, 2006, pp. B6)

Ed: Heather Scoffield. **Description:** The impact of higher oil prices and dollar value, on manufacturing jobs in Canada, is discussed. **Availability:** Online.

29340 ■ "Priority: In Memoriam" in Inc. (December 2007, pp. 25-26, 28, 30)

Ed: Ryan McCarthy. **Description:** Profiles of entrepreneurs who died in 2007; these individuals helped to create some major business trends in the last fifty years, from the advent of socially responsible business to development of quality manufacturing. **Availability:** Online.

29341 ■ "PSC Decision Could Help Bolster a Solar Market Supernova" in Tampa Bay Business Journal (Vol. 29, November 6, 2009, No. 46, pp. 1)
Pub: Tampa Bay Business Journal
Contact: Ian Anderson, President
E-mail: ianderson@bizjournals.com

Ed: Michael Hinman. **Description:** Florida's Public Service Commission (PSC) decision on a power purchase agreement that could add 25 megawatts of solar energy on Tampa Electric Company's offerings is presented. The decision could support the growing market for suppliers and marketers of renewable energy such as Jabil Circuit Inc., which manufactures photovoltaic modules. Details of the agreement are discussed. **Availability:** Print; Online.

29342 ■ "Putting 'Extra' in Extra-Silky Shampoo" in Crain's Chicago Business (Vol. 31, April 28, 2008, No. 17, pp. 37)
Pub: Crain Communications Inc.
Contact: Barry Asin, President

Ed: Phuong Ly. **Description:** Profile of HallStar Co., a Chicago-based company which develops and manufactures specialty chemicals to upgrade existing products such as hair dye, lotion and deodorant. HallStar has seen its annual earnings rise more than 30 percent since 2002. **Availability:** Online.

29343 ■ "Q&A Interview With Perrin Beatty" in Canadian Business (Vol. 80, October 8, 2007, No. 20, pp. 13)

Description: Perrin Beatty, president and chief executive officer of the Canadian Chamber of Commerce, talks about his move from the Canadian Manufacturers and Exporters to his current organization. He also discusses the state of Canada's economy, as well as the need for leadership.

29344 ■ "Q&A: The CAPP's Greg Stringham" in Canadian Business (Vol. 81, February 12, 2008, No. 3, pp. 8)
Pub: Rogers Media Inc.
Contact: Neil Spivak, Chief Executive Officer

Ed: Michelle Magnan. **Description:** Canadian Association of Petroleum Producers' Greg Stringham thinks that the new royalty plan will result in companies pulling out their investments for Alberta's conventional oil and gas sector. Stringham adds that Alberta is losing its competitive advantage and companies must study their cost profiles to retrieve that advantage. The effects of the royalty system on Alberta's economy are examined further. **Availability:** Print; Online.

29345 ■ "The Quest for a Smart Prosthetic" in Canadian Business (Vol. 83, October 12, 2010, No. 17, pp. 26)
Pub: Rogers Media Inc.
Contact: Neil Spivak, Chief Executive Officer

Ed: Jacqueline Nelson. **Description:** Information about a two-year research project led by Southern Methodist University (SMU) and funded by the Defense Advance Research Projects Agency (DARPA) is provided. The agency aims to create a 'smart prosthetic' which will improve the lives of military amputees. The planned prosthetic will use a sensor that can carry nerve signals through synthetic channels. **Availability:** Print; Online.

29346 ■ "A Questionable Chemical Romance" in Barron's (Vol. 88, July 14, 2008, No. 28, pp. 28)
Pub: Dow Jones & Company Inc.
Contact: Almar Latour, Chief Executive Officer

Ed: Andrew Bary. **Description:** Dow Chemical paid $78-a-share for the surprise takeover of Rohm & Haas. The acquisition is reducing Dow Chemical's financial flexibility at a time when chemical companies are being affected by high costs and a weak U.S. economy. **Availability:** Online.

29347 ■ "R&R Launches Upscale Spoony's and Low Fat Dragon's Den" in Ice Cream Reporter (Vol. 23, August 20, 2010, No. 9, pp. 3)

Description: European ice cream manufacturer R&R has acquired French ice cream maker Rolland and will position itself as an upscale challenger to brands like Ben & Jerry's. **Availability:** Print; Online.

29348 ■ "RavenBrick Ready to Manufacture Its High-Tech Windows" in Denver Business Journal (Vol. 64, September 7, 2012, No. 16, pp. 1)
Pub: Baltimore Business Journal
Contact: Rhonda Pringle, President
E-mail: rpringle@bizjournals.com

Description: RavenBrick LLC is set to build a new manufacturing plant in Denver, Colorado. The company manufactures auto-darkening window films. RavenBrick has raised a total of $13.5 million in new investment capital. **Availability:** Print; Online.

29349 ■ "Recovery on Tap for 2010?" in Orlando Business Journal (Vol. 26, January 1, 2010, No. 31, pp. 1)
Pub: Orlando Business Journal
Contact: Julie Swyers, Director
E-mail: jswyers@bizjournals.com

Ed: Melanie Stawicki Azam, Richard Bilbao, Christopher Boyd, Anjali Fluker. **Description:** Economic forecasts for Central Florida's leading business sectors in 2010 are presented. These sectors include housing, film and TV, sports business, law, restaurants, aviation, tourism and hospitality, banking and finance, commercial real estate, retail, health care, insurance, higher education, and manufacturing. According to some local executives, Central Florida's economy will slowly recover in 2010. **Availability:** Online.

29350 ■ "Region to Be Named Innovation Hub" in Business Courier (Vol. 27, July 2, 2010, No. 9, pp. 1)
Pub: Business Courier

Ed: Dan Monk. **Description:** The selection of Cincinnati's consumer-marketing cluster as a 'Hub of Innovation' by the Ohio Department of Development could boost Cincinnati's chances of receiving $100 million in grants from Ohio's Third Frontier program and other funding sources. Implications of the University of Cincinnati's designation as a Center of Excellence in Advanced Transportation and Aerospace are also discussed. **Availability:** Print; Online.

29351 ■ "Region Wins as GE Puts Plants Close to R&D" in Business Review Albany (Vol. 41, July 4, 2014, No. 15, pp. 8)
Pub: American City Business Journals, Inc.
Contact: Mike Olivieri, Executive Vice President

Description: General Electric Company (GE) invested over $400 million into the expansion of its health care, battery and renewable energy businesses in the Albany, New York region. The company's local growth secured about 7,000 private-sector jobs in the area and strengthened the relationship between GE research and manufacturing. **Availability:** Print; Online.

29352 ■ *"Rep Contracts: Simple, Clear, Fair"* **in Agency Sales Magazine (Vol. 39, September-October 2009, No. 9, pp. 3)**
Description: Things that a manufacturer and a sales representative needs to strive for when creating an Agreement for Representation includes an agreement that is simple and complete, one that covers all the needs of both parties and is fair, equitable, and balanced. Sales representatives need to make more sales calls and find new opportunities during this recession.

29353 ■ *"Rep Vs. Direct: Always an Interesting Story"* **in Agency Sales Magazine (Vol. 39, July 2009, No. 7, pp. 3)**
Description: Manufacturers benefit from outsourcing their field sales to professional sales representatives in the areas of multi-line selling and customer knowledge and relationship. Some misperceptions about sales reps include the belief that they are an additional 'channel' in sales. **Availability:** Online.

29354 ■ *"Report: McD's Pepsi Score Best With Young Hispanics"* **in Brandweek (Vol. 49, April 21, 2008, No. 16, pp. 8)**
Description: According to a new report, in order to reach Hispanic Gen Yers, marketing strategists need to understand this demographic's "bi-dentity," something which has proved an elusive task to many marketers. Another trend is the emergence of Latinas who have careers, as opposed to just jobs. There is an opportunity to tap this new, young and empowered female market with innovative messaging. Statistical data included. **Availability:** Online.

29355 ■ *"Reports of Banks' Revival were Greatly Exaggerated"* **in Barron's (Vol. 88, July 7, 2008, No. 27, pp. L14)**
Pub: Dow Jones & Company Inc.
Contact: Almar Latour, Chief Executive Officer
Ed: Jack Willoughby. **Description:** Performance of mutual funds improved for the second quarter of 2008 compared to the previous quarter, registering an average gain of 0.13 percent; funds focusing on natural resources rose the highest, their value rising by an average of 24.50 percent. **Availability:** Online.

29356 ■ *"Reps Have Needs Too!"* **in Agency Sales Magazine (Vol. 39, December 2009, No. 11, pp. 16)**
Description: There is common information that a sales representatives needs to know prior to choosing a manufacturer to represent. Both parties must keep promises made to customers and prospects. Reps also need the support from the manufacturers and to clear matters regarding their commission. Interviewing tips for representatives to get this vital information are presented. **Availability:** Online.

29357 ■ *"Reps Vs. Factory Direct Sales Force..Which Way to Go?"* **in Agency Sales Magazine (Vol. 39, September-October 2009, No. 9, pp. 28)**
Description: Hiring independent manufacturers' sales representative is a cost-effective alternative to a direct sales force. Sales reps have predictable sales costs that go up and down with sales, stronger local relationships and better market intelligence. **Availability:** Print; Online.

29358 ■ *"A Reverse-Innovation Playbook: Insights From a Company That Developed Products For Emerging Markets and Then Brought Them Back Home"* **in Harvard Business Review (Vol. 90, April 2012, No. 4, pp. 120)**
Pub: Harvard Business Review Press
Contact: Moderna V. Pfizer, Contact
Ed: Vijay Govindarajan. **Price:** $8.95, hardcover. **Description:** An overview is presented on the organizational change implemented by Harman International Industries Inc. to create products for emerging markets and ensure that they would be

accepted in already established middle markets. Components include setting radical goals, selecting team leaders with no competing interests, and leveraging global resources. **Availability:** PDF; Online.

29359 ■ *"Revisiting Rep Coping Strategies"* **in Agency Sales Magazine (Vol. 39, December 2009, No. 11, pp. 32)**
Description: Independent manufacturer's representatives should become a well-rounded and complete businessman with continued education. The new type of representative is a problem solver and the resource for answering questions. Employing the concept of synergistic selling is also important to salespeople. **Availability:** Online.

29360 ■ *"RipCode Founder Starts Private Equity Firm Vspeed Capital"* **in Dallas Business Journal (Vol. 35, September 9, 2012, No. 51, pp. 1)**
Pub: Baltimore Business Journal
Contact: Rhonda Pringle, President
E-mail: rpringle@bizjournals.com
Ed: Jeff Bounds. **Description:** Brendon Mills, founder of Genband Inc., cofounds Vspeed Capital LLC, a new private equity firm. The company has joined forces with Galatyn Private Equity to make its first purchase, that of Fortress Solutions Ltd. Vspeed plans to acquire companies in the manufacturing and distribution sectors, and double its revenue in the next 24 months. **Availability:** Print; Online.

29361 ■ *"Robai Aims to Commercialize Robot Arm for Manufacturers; Eyes Series A Funding"* **in Boston Business Journal (Vol. 34, July 4, 2014, No. 22, pp. 5)**
Pub: American City Business Journals, Inc.
Contact: Mike Olivieri, Executive Vice President
Released: June 25, 2014. **Description:** Robai aims to raise $5 million in funding to help commercialize a lightweight and easy to use robot arm, called Cyton. The robot arm operates much like a human arm with multiple ranges of motion. It weighs under five pounds, can be programmed in 15 minutes, has the ability to reach around obstacles, and is meant to do repetitive, mundane tasks for contract manufacturing companies. **Availability:** Print; Online.

29362 ■ *"The Role of Leadership In Successful International Mergers and Acquisitions: Why Renault-Nissan Succeeded and DaimlerChrysler-Mitsubishi Failed"* **in Human Resource Management (Vol. 51,May-June 2012, No. 3, pp. 433-456)**
Pub: John Wiley & Sons, Inc.
Contact: Christina Van Tassell, Executive Vice President Chief Financial Officer
Ed: Carol Gill. **Released:** May 25, 2012. **Description:** The effects of national and organizational culture on the performance of Nissan and Mitsubishi after their mergers with Renault and DaimlerChrysler respectively are examined. Japanese national culture was found to influence organizational culture and human resource management practices, while leadership affected the success of their turnaround efforts.

29363 ■ *"Ross: There's Still Money In the Auto Industry"* **in Crain's Detroit Business (Vol. 24, January 28, 2008, No. 4, pp. 12)**
Pub: Crain Communications Inc.
Contact: Barry Asin, President
Ed: Brent Snavely. **Description:** Wilbur Ross, chairman and CEO of WL Ross and Company LLC, a private equity firm, predicts U.S. vehicle sales will fall by about 750,000 in 2008, but continues to look for supplier bargains. **Availability:** Online.

29364 ■ *"Royal Dutch's Grip Firm on Shell"* **in Globe & Mail (March 19, 2007, pp. B1)**
Ed: David Ebner. **Description:** The proposed acquisition of Shell Canada Ltd. by Royal Dutch Shell PLC for $8.7 billion is discussed. **Availability:** Print; Online.

29365 ■ *"Russia: Uncle Volodya's Flagging Christmas Spirit"* **in The Economist (Vol. 390, January 3, 2009, No. 8612, pp. 22)**
Description: Overview of Russia's struggling economy as well as unpopular government decisions such as raising import duties on used foreign vehicles so as to protect Russian carmakers. **Availability:** Print; Online.

29366 ■ *"Russian Renaissance"* **in Chicago Tribune (September 22, 2008)**
Pub: Tribune News Service
Contact: Jack Barry, Vice President, Operations
E-mail: jbarry@tribpub.com
Ed: Alex Rodriguez. **Description:** Winemakers from Russia are returning to the craft and quality of wine-making now that they are free from Soviet restraints. **Availability:** Print; Online.

29367 ■ *"Rust Belt No More: The Demise of Manufacturing"* **in Crain's Chicago Business (Vol. 31, March 31, 2008, No. 13, pp. 52)**
Pub: Crain Communications Inc.
Contact: Barry Asin, President
Ed: Sarah A. Klein. **Description:** Discusses the history of manufacturing in the Chicago area as well as the history of manufacturer International Harvester Co. **Availability:** Online.

29368 ■ *"S.A. Chasing Tesla, Other Auto-Industry Firms"* **in San Antonio Business Journal (Vol. 28, April 4, 2014, No. 8, pp. 7)**
Pub: American City Business Journals, Inc.
Contact: Mike Olivieri, Executive Vice President
Price: $4, Introductory 4-Week Offer(Digital & Print). **Description:** San Antonio, Texas has joined cities trying to land the $5 billion battery plant of Tesla Motors that could employ 6,500 workers. San Antonio's drive to establish a major auto-industry cluster in the region would be boosted by Tesla's choosing the city as the site for manufacturing batteries. The benefits from the Texas-Mexico Automotive SuperCluster initiative are also explored. **Availability:** Print; Online.

29369 ■ *"Sale of Owings Mills Solo Cup Plant Pending"* **in Boston Business Journal (Vol. 29, June 17, 2011, No. 6, pp. 1)**
Pub: Boston Business Journal
Contact: Carolyn M. Jones, President
E-mail: cmjones@bizjournals.com
Ed: Daniel J. Sernovitz. **Released:** Weekly; X. **Price:** $4, Print. **Description:** Baltimore developers Vanguard Equities Inc. and Greenberg Gibbons Commercial have contracted to buy the Solo Cup Company facility in Owing Mills and are now considering several plans for the property. Sale should be completed by September 2011 but no proposed sale terms are disclosed. **Availability:** Print; Online.

29370 ■ *"Sales of What's Under Feet Add Up Fast"* **in Pet Product News (Vol. 66, September 2012, No. 9, pp. S8)**
Description: Pet supplies retailers and manufacturers have been emphasizing the type of substances in creating new approaches to developing environment-friendly natural litters and beddings for small mammals and cats. Some of these approaches are highlighted, along with marketing strategies retailers have implemented. **Availability:** Print; Online.

29371 ■ *"San Jose Hopes to Build on Uptick in Manufacturing"* **in Silicon Valley/San Jose Business Journal (Vol. 30, July 13, 2012, No. 16, pp. 1)**
Pub: Baltimore Business Journal
Contact: Rhonda Pringle, President
E-mail: rpringle@bizjournals.com
Description: San Jose, California-based manufacturing companies that cater to high-technology companies and startups have been experiencing an uptick in business. The San Jose metropolitan area is the country's second-largest specialized manufacturing market and the city has rolled out its efforts to help support this growth. **Availability:** Print; Online.

29372 ■ *"The Second Most Fuel-Efficient Tractor of the Decade: John Deere 8320R"* in *Farm Industry News (November 10, 2011)*
Pub: Informa Business Media, Inc.
Contact: Charlie McCurdy, President
Description: John Deere's 8320R Tractor was ranked second in the Farm Industry News listing of the top 40 most fuel-efficient tractors of the decade, following the winner, John Deere's 8295R PTO tractor. **Availability:** Online.

29373 ■ *"Selling Michigan; R&D Pushed as Reason For Chinese To Locate In State"* in *Crain's Detroit Business (Vol. 24, January 14, 2008)*
Pub: Crain Communications Inc.
Contact: Barry Asin, President
Ed: Marti Benedetti. **Description:** Southeast Michigan Economic Development organizations are working to develop relationships with Chinese manufacturers so they will locate their automotive research and development operations in the state.

29374 ■ *"Seven Things Great Employers Do (That Others Don't); Unusual, Innovative, and Proven Tactics To Create Productive and Profitable Working Environments"* in *Gallup Business Journal (April 15, 2014)*
Pub: Gallup, Inc.
Contact: Jon Clifton, Chief Executive Officer
Price: $8.95. **Description:** Seven unusual, innovative, and proven tactics that create productive and profitable working environments are examined through researching 32 companies. These firms represented many industries, including healthcare, financial services, hospitality, manufacturing, and retail throughout the world. **Availability:** Print; PDF; Online.

29375 ■ *"Seven Tips for Continuous Improvement"* in *American Printer (Vol. 120, July 1, 2011, No. 7)*
Description: Seven tips are given to help any graphic arts or printing company improve by integrating lean manufacturing into operations. **Availability:** Online.

29376 ■ *"Sharp Restarts Toner Manufacturing: Production Moved from Japan to Serve China Market"* in *Memphis Business Journal (Vol. 34, May 11, 2012, No. 4, pp. 1)*
Pub: Baltimore Business Journal
Contact: Rhonda Pringle, President
E-mail: rpringle@bizjournals.com
Ed: Michael Sheffield. **Description:** Sharp Manufacturing Company of America has decided to reopen its ink toner production plant in Memphis, Tennessee because of cheaper material, labor and freight costs. The company's move was also attributed to local economic growth and the government support they received after a 2008 tornado hit the area surrounding the area. **Availability:** Print; Online.

29377 ■ *"Shedding Light on Innovation"* in *Rental Product News (Vol. 33, June 2011)*
Description: Light tower manufacturers have introduced numerous new products that feature alternative power sources, LED lighting and a second generation of performance and value. **Availability:** Online.

29378 ■ *"Shell Profits Top $2 Billion as Oil Sands Output Surges"* in *Globe & Mail (January 26, 2006, pp. B6)*
Description: The reasons behind posting of $2 billion profits for 2005, by Shell Canada Ltd. are presented. **Availability:** Online.

29379 ■ *"Sherwin-Williams Workers Forgo Travel for Virtual Trade Show"* in *Crain's Cleveland Business (Vol. 28, October 15, 2007, No. 41, pp. 4)*
Pub: Crain Communications Inc.
Contact: K. C. Crain, President

Ed: John Booth. **Description:** Overview of Cyber-Coating 2007, a cutting-edge virtual three-dimensional trade show that exhibitors such as Sherwin-Williams Co.'s Chemical Coatings Division will take part in by chatting verbally or via text messages in order to exchange information and listen to pitches just like they would on an actual trade show floor. **Availability:** Online.

29380 ■ *"Size Does Matter"* in *International Journal of Globalisation and Small Business (Vol. 4, September 21, 2010, No. 1, pp. 61)*
Ed: Julia Connell, Ranjit Voola. **Description:** Examination of how members of an Australian-based manufacturing and engineering cluster share knowledge through networking as a means to improve competitive advantage. **Availability:** Online.

29381 ■ *"Sizing Up Bentley"* in *Barron's (Vol. 92, September 17, 2012, No. 38, pp. 16)*
Description: The energy efficiencies of cars produced by Bentley Motors have shown little improvement over time. The company needs to invest in improving the fuel efficiencies of its vehicles to attract new customers and remain competitive. **Availability:** Online.

29382 ■ *"Slimmed-Down Supplier TI Automotive Relaunches"* in *Crain's Detroit Business (Vol. 26, January 11, 2010, No. 2, pp. 14)*
Pub: Crain Communications Inc.
Contact: Barry Asin, President
Ed: Robert Sherefkin. **Description:** TI Automotive Ltd., one of the world's largest suppliers of fuel storage and delivery systems, has reorganized the company by splitting it into five global divisions and is relaunching its brand which is now more focused on new technology. **Availability:** Print; Online.

29383 ■ *"Slimmer Interiors Make Small Cars Seem Big"* in *Automotive News (Vol. 86, October 31, 2011, No. 6488, pp. 16)*
Pub: Crain Communications Inc.
Contact: Barry Asin, President
Ed: David Sedgwick. **Description:** Cost-conscious buyers want luxury car amenities in their smaller vehicles, so automakers are rethinking interiors. Style, efficiency and value could be the next trend in vehicles. **Availability:** Print; Online.

29384 ■ *"Small is the New Big in Autos"* in *Globe & Mail (February 16, 2006, pp. B3)*
Ed: Greg Keenan. **Description:** The reasons behind the introduction of subcompact cars by companies such as Ford Motor Co. are presented. The automobiles were unveiled at Canadian International Auto Show in Toronto.

29385 ■ *"Solar Gaining Power in Tennessee"* in *Memphis Business Journal (Vol. 34, June 15, 2012, No. 9, pp. 1)*
Pub: Baltimore Business Journal
Contact: Rhonda Pringle, President
E-mail: rpringle@bizjournals.com
Ed: Michael Sheffield. **Description:** Tennessee's solar energy industry has grown, the Tennessee Solar Institute has reported. Solar energy use, manufacture and employment in the state have increase in the past four years. **Availability:** Print; Online.

29386 ■ *"Solectria Renewables Supplies Solar Stations for Solar Farm in New England"* in *Professional Close-Up (October 2, 2012)*
Description: Solectria Renewables LLC reported that its Megawatt Solar Stations (MSS) will be used for the 5MW True North solar farm in Salisbury, Massachusetts. Solectria is an American PV inverter manufacturer. Details of the project are given. **Availability:** PDF; Online.

29387 ■ *"Solon Wire to Ramp Up Plant"* in *Memphis Business Journal (Vol. 33, March 23, 2012, No. 50, pp. 1)*
Pub: Baltimore Business Journal
Contact: Rhonda Pringle, President

E-mail: rpringle@bizjournals.com
Description: Solon Wire Company is set to reopen a production facility, following its acquisition of Bluff City Steel Industries. Solon will begin manufacturing steel wires again by the end of March 2012. **Availability:** Print; Online.

29388 ■ *"Some Relief Possible Following Painful Week"* in *Barron's (Vol. 88, July 14, 2008, No. 28, pp. M3)*
Pub: Dow Jones & Company Inc.
Contact: Almar Latour, Chief Executive Officer
Ed: Kopin Tan. **Description:** Dow Chemical is offering a 74 percent premium to acquire Rohm & Haas' coatings and electronics materials operations. Frontline amassed a 5.6 percent stake in rival Overseas Shipholding Group and a merger between the two would create a giant global fleet with pricing power. Highlights of the U.S. stock market during the week that ended in July 11, 2008 are discussed. Statistical data included. **Availability:** Online.

29389 ■ *"Sources"* in *Canadian Electronics (Vol. 23, August 2008, No. 5, pp. 12)*
Description: Directory of electronic manufacturers, distributors and representatives in Canada is provided. The list presents distributors and representatives under each manufacturer.

29390 ■ *"Spam's Biggest Fan"* in *Barron's (Vol. 92, August 25, 2012, No. 35, pp. 42)*
Pub: Dow Jones & Company Inc.
Contact: Almar Latour, Chief Executive Officer
Ed: Lawrence C. Strauss. **Description:** Jeffrey Ettinger, chief executive officer of meat packing and packaged food firm Hormel Foods, is credited with expanding the company's product offerings. Ettinger, who took over in 2006, involves himself in almost every aspect of the company's business. **Availability:** Online.

29391 ■ *"Spectre of Iran War Spooks Oil Markets"* in *Globe & Mail (March 28, 2007, pp. B1)*
Ed: Shawn McCarthy. **Description:** The increase in the price of crude oil by $5 a barrel to reach $68 in the United States following speculation over war against Iran, is discussed. **Availability:** Online.

29392 ■ *"State Democrats Push for Changes to Plant Security Law"* in *Chemical Week (Vol. 172, July 19, 2010, No. 17, pp. 8)*
Description: Legislation has been introduced to revise the existing U.S. Chemical Facility Anti-Terrorism Standards (CFATS) that would include a requirement for facilities to use inherently safer technology (IST). The bill would eliminate the current law's exemption of water treatment plants and certain port facilities and preserve the states' authority to establish stronger security standards. **Availability:** PDF; Online.

29393 ■ *"Steeling for Battle"* in *Crain's Chicago Business (Vol. 31, April 21, 2008, No. 16, pp. 3)*
Pub: Crain Communications Inc.
Contact: Barry Asin, President
Ed: Bob Tita. **Description:** Discusses contract negotiations between the United Steelworkers union and ArcelorMittal USA Inc., the nation's largest steelmaker, and U.S. Steel Corp., the third-largest; the union sees these negotiations as the best chance in two decades to regain lost ground but industry experts predict the companies will try to reduce benefits, demand a separate, lower wage scale for new hires and look for relief from the rising costs for retirees' health insurance coverage. **Availability:** Online.

29394 ■ *"Steeling Themselves: Price Hikes Testing The Mettle of Scrap Dealers"* in *Baltimore Business Journal (Vol. 30, July 6, 2012, No. 9, pp. 1)*
Ed: James Bach. **Description:** Members of Maryland's steel sector have been seeking to revive the Sparrows Point steel plant. The plan also involves saving 2,000 jobs. Comments from executives included. **Availability:** Print; Online.

29395 ■ *"Steering Toward Profitability"* in *Black Enterprise (Vol. 41, December 2010, No. 5, pp. 72)*
Pub: Earl G. Graves Ltd.
Contact: Earl Graves, Jr., President
Ed: Alan Hughes. **Description:** Systems Electro Coating LLC had to make quick adjustments when auto manufacturers were in a slump. The minority father-daughter team discuss their strategies during the auto industry collapse.

29396 ■ *"Stock Car Racing"* in *Canadian Business (Vol. 81, September 15, 2008, No. 14-15, pp. 29)*
Description: Some analysts predict a Chapter 11-style tune-up making GM and Ford a speculative turnaround stock. However, the price of oil could make or break the shares of the Big Three U.S. automobile manufacturers and if oil goes up too high then a speculative stock to watch is an electric car company called Zenn Motor Co. **Availability:** Online.

29397 ■ *"A Stock Worth Trading Down To"* in *Barron's (Vol. 88, July 14, 2008, No. 28, pp. 36)*
Pub: Dow Jones & Company Inc.
Contact: Almar Latour, Chief Executive Officer
Ed: Alexander Eule. **Description:** Shares of Ralcorp Holdings are cheap at around $49.95 after slipping 20 percent prior to their acquisition of Post cereals from Kraft. Some analysts believe its shares could climb over 60 percent to $80 as value-seeking consumers buy more private label products. **Availability:** Print; Online.

29398 ■ *"The Story of a Complex Project, Seen From a Bridge"* in *Business Review Albany (Vol. 41, June 27, 2014, No. 14, pp. 7)*
Pub: American City Business Journals, Inc.
Contact: Mike Olivieri, Executive Vice President
Released: Weekly. **Price:** $4, introductory 4-week offer(Digital only). **Description:** The bridge connecting the manufacturing and technology development buildings at GlobalFoundries in Malta, NY allows employees to transport computer chip-containing wafers without the risk of contamination. The connector is a cleanroom and has its own air conditioning system and foundation vibration control. **Availability:** Print; Online.

29399 ■ *Strategic Design Thinking: Innovation in Products, Services, Experiences and Beyond*
Ed: Natalie W. Nixon. **Released:** 2016. **Description:** This book guides the reader on how to use process instead of solution to design a product that will meet your customer's needs.

29400 ■ *"Succeed With the Right Equipment"* in *Pet Product News (Vol. 64, November 2010, No. 11, pp. 42)*
Ed: Sandi Cain. **Description:** Grooming shop owners have been focusing on obtaining ergonomic, durable, and efficient products such as restraints, tables, and tubs. These products enhance the way grooming tasks are conducted. Ways pet supply manufacturers have responded to this trend are examined. **Availability:** Online.

29401 ■ *"Supplements Mix Nutrition With Convenience"* in *Pet Product News (Vol. 64, November 2010, No. 11, pp. 44)*
Ed: Karen Shugart. **Description:** Pet supply manufacturers have been making supplements and enhanced foods that improve mineral consumption, boost bone density, and sharpen appetite in herps. Customers seem to enjoy the convenience as particular herps demands are being addressed by these offerings. Features of other supplements and enhanced foods for herps are described. **Availability:** Print; Online.

29402 ■ *"Suppliers May Follow Fiat: Local Group Says Italian Firms are Inquiring"* in *Crain's Detroit Business (Vol. 25, June 15, 2009, No. 24, pp. 1)*
Pub: Crain Communications Inc.
Contact: Barry Asin, President

Ed: Ryan Beene. **Description:** Italian suppliers to Fiat SpA are looking toward Detroit after the formation of Chrysler Group LLC, the Chrysler-Fiat partnership created from Chrysler's bankruptcy. The Italian American Alliance for Business and Technology is aware of two Italy-based powertrain component suppliers that are considering a move to Detroit. **Availability:** Online.

29403 ■ *"Supply-Chain Collaboration, Image of Industry are OESA Chief's Top Tasks; Q&A Julie Fream, Original Equipment Suppliers Association"* in *Crain's Detroit Business (Vol. 30, January 6, 2014, No. 1, pp. 4)*
Pub: Crain Communications Inc.
Contact: Barry Asin, President
Description: Julie Fream is the new CEO of the Original Equipment Suppliers Assocation. Fream is a former Visteon Corporation executive and has held numerous positions in automotive manufacturing, sales and marketing. She is committed to holding transparency and collaboration within the industry. **Availability:** Online.

29404 ■ *"The 'Supply Side' of the Auto Industry"* in *Montly Labor Review (Vol. 133, September 2010, No. 9, pp. 72)*
Pub: U.S. Department of Labor Bureau of Labor Statistics
Contact: Amrit Kohli, Director
E-mail: kohli.amrit@bls.gov
Description: Restructuring and geographic change in the automobile industry is discussed. **Availability:** PDF; Online.

29405 ■ *"Survey: Confident Parts Makers Plan to Expand, Hire"* in *Crain's Detroit Business (Vol. 30, August 18, 2014, No. 33, pp. 5)*
Pub: Crain Communications Inc.
Contact: Barry Asin, President
Description: North American automotive suppliers are increasing capital expenditure, hiring new workers, and raising funds for possible mergers and acquisitions. Automotive manufacturing suppliers are forecasting a rebound in new vehicle sales. Statistical data included. **Availability:** Online.

29406 ■ *"Suzlon S88-Powered Wind Farm in Minnesota Secures Long-Term Financing"* in *PR Newswire (September 21, 2011)*
Pub: PR Newswire Association LLC.
Description: Suzlon Energy Limited is the world's fifth largest manufacturer of wind turbines. Owners of the Grant County Wind Farm in Minnesota have secured a long-term financing deal for the ten Suzlon S88 2.1 MW wind turbines that generate enough electricity to power 7,000 homes.

29407 ■ *"Syracuse Gear Manufacturer Buys Buffalo Company"* in *Business First of Buffalo (Vol. 30, January 24, 2014, No. 19, pp. 3)*
Pub: American City Business Journals, Inc.
Contact: Mike Olivieri, Executive Vice President
Released: Weekly. **Price:** $140, One-Year Print & Digital; $115, One-Year Digital. **Description:** Niagara Gear Corporation of Buffalo, New York was acquired by Gear Motions Inc., in a deal that could make Gear Motions the largest precision gear manufacturer for the commercial and industrial compressor market. Niagara Gear will supply larger ground and cut spur and helical gears to existing customers as part of the sale. **Availability:** Print; Online.

29408 ■ *"Taylor Tests Land Grant Program"* in *Austin Business Journal (Vol. 31, June 3, 2011, No. 13, pp. 1)*
Pub: Austin Business Journal
Contact: Rachel McGrath, Director
E-mail: rmcgrath@bizjournals.com
Ed: Vicky Garza. **Description:** Taylor Economic Development Corporation implemented a land grant program called Build On Our Lot to lure businesses to Taylor City, Austin, Texas. They are targeting small

businesses, especially those in the renewable energy, advanced manufacturing, technical services and food products. Program details are included. **Availability:** Print; Online.

29409 ■ *"Tesla Eyes Two Sites for New Battery-Pack Plant"* in *San Antonio Business Journal (Vol. 28, May 16, 2014, No. 14, pp. 8)*
Pub: American City Business Journals, Inc.
Contact: Mike Olivieri, Executive Vice President
Released: Weekly. **Price:** $4, introductory 4-week offer(Digital only). **Description:** The City of San Antonio, Texas is competing with other cities in five states to land the contract for the $5 million battery-pack plant of Texla Motors. Bill Avila of Bracewell & Giuliani LLPO law firm believes that San Antonio has an edge over some of the cities competing for the Tesla manufacturing plant because of its successful recruitment of Toyota in 2003. **Availability:** Print; Online.

29410 ■ *"Thai Ice Cream Cremo Expanding to Middle East"* in *Ice Cream Reporter (Vol. 23, September 20, 2010, No. 10, pp. 3)*
Description: Thai-based frozen dessert manufacturer Chomthana, maker of Cremo brand ice cream, is expanding into the Middle East. **Availability:** Print; Online.

29411 ■ *"This Just In: TechTown, Partners Get $1M to Start Tech Exchange"* in *Crain's Detroit Business (Vol. 25, June 1, 2009, No. 22, pp. 1)*
Pub: Crain Communications Inc.
Contact: Barry Asin, President
Ed: Daniel Duggan. **Description:** Three veterans of the auto industry have partnered to create, Revitalizing Michigan, a nonprofit dedicated to help manufacturers improve their processes. The firm is seeking federal, state and private grants to fund the mission. **Availability:** Print; Online.

29412 ■ *"Timken's Bearings Rolling in China, India"* in *Crain's Cleveland Business (Vol. 28, October 29, 2007, No. 43, pp. 14)*
Pub: Crain Communications Inc.
Contact: K. C. Crain, President
Ed: David Bennett. **Description:** Canton-based Timken Co., a manufacturer of bearings and specialty metals, is seeing growing demand for its line of tapered roller bearings, which allow rail users to carry heavy car loads. The company is finding significant growth in China and India due to their rapidly growing rail markets. **Availability:** PDF; Online.

29413 ■ *"To Be or Not To Be an S Corporation"* in *Modern Machine Shop (Vol. 84, September 2011, No. 4, pp. 38)*
Pub: Gardner Business Media Inc.
Contact: Rick Kline, Jr., President
E-mail: rkline2@gardnerweb.com
Ed: Irving L. Blackman. **Description:** The definitions of both C corporations and S corporations are defined to help any machine shop discover which best suits the owner's business plan. **Availability:** Online.

29414 ■ *"Tony Armand, Shock Doctor CEO"* in *Business Journal (Vol. 31, March 21, 2014, No. 43, pp. 6)*
Pub: American City Business Journals, Inc.
Contact: Mike Olivieri, Executive Vice President
Released: March 21, 2014. **Price:** $4, print. **Description:** Tony Armand, CEO of Shock Doctor Inc., discusses the company's acquisition by private equity firm Bregal Partners. Armand believes the deal will give the sports protective equipment manufacturer a strong financial partner that will help with the executive strategy. **Availability:** Print; Online.

29415 ■ *"Toolmakers' New Tack: Firms' Goal -- Advance Wind-Turbine Technology"* in *Crain's Detroit Business (Vol. 25, June 8, 2009,)*
Pub: Crain Communications Inc.
Contact: Barry Asin, President

Ed: Ryan Beene, Amy Lane. **Description:** MAG Industrial Automation Systems LLC and Dowding Machining Inc. have partnered to advance wind-turbine technology. The goal is to cut costs of wind energy to the same level as carbon-based fuel. **Availability:** Print; Online.

29416 ■ *"Top Design Award for Massey Ferguson 7624 Dyna-VT" in Farm Industry News (November 14, 2011)*
Pub: Informa Business Media, Inc.
Contact: Charlie McCurdy, President

Description: Massey Ferguson won top honors for its MF 7624 Dyna-VT as the Golden Tractor for Design award in the 2012 Tractor of the Year competition. The award is presented annually by journalists from 22 leading farming magazines in Europe and manufacturers have to be nominated to enter. **Availability:** Online.

29417 ■ *"Toyota Marks Record Profit Sales" in Globe & Mail (February 7, 2007, pp. B10)*

Description: The record quarterly sales and earnings reported by Japanese automaker Toyota Motor Corp. are discussed. The company sold 2.16 million vehicles during the quarter while registering 426.8 billion yen in profits. **Availability:** Print; Online.

29418 ■ *"Toyota Revs Up Plans for Ontario Plant" in Globe & Mail (February 7, 2006, pp. B1)*

Description: The production output and workforce addition proposals of Toyota Motor Corp., at Ontario plant, are presented. **Availability:** Online.

29419 ■ *"Toyota Tops GM in Global Sales" in Globe & Mail (April 24, 2007, pp. B1)*
Ed: Greg Keenan. **Description:** The success of Toyota Motor Corp. in surpassing General Motors Corp. in its global sales is discussed. **Availability:** Online.

29420 ■ *"The Trouble With $150,000 Wine" in Barron's (Vol. 88, July 7, 2008, No. 27, pp. 33)*
Pub: Dow Jones & Company Inc.
Contact: Almar Latour, Chief Executive Officer

Ed: Jay Palmer. **Description:** Review of the book, "The Billionaire's Vinegar: The Mystery of the World's Most Expensive Bottle of Wine," which discusses vintners along with the marketing and distribution of wine as well as the winemaking industry as a whole. **Availability:** Online.

29421 ■ *"Turning Drivers Into Geeks; Auto Dealers Debate Need for Technology Specialists to Bring Buyers Up to Speed" in Crain's Detroit Business (Vol. 30, January 6, 2014, No. 1, pp. 3)*
Pub: Crain Communications Inc.
Contact: Barry Asin, President

Description: Dealers at the 2014 North American International Auto Show discuss the need for technology specialists to educate sales staff as well as customers on the new high-tech items manufactured on today's automobiles and trucks. **Availability:** Print; Online.

29422 ■ *"Unexpected Guest: Caterpillar-Bucyrus Deal Came Out of Nowhere" in Business Journal-Milwaukee (Vol. 28, November 19, 2010, No. 7, pp. A1)*
Pub: The Business Journal
Contact: Heather Ladage, President
E-mail: hladage@bizjournals.com

Ed: Rich Rovito. **Description:** Caterpillar has agreed to purchase Bucyrus for $92 per share. The deal, which is subjected to a $200 million termination fee, is expected to close in mid-2011. **Availability:** Print; Online.

29423 ■ *"An Unfair Knock on Nokia" in Barron's (Vol. 88, March 10, 2008, No. 10, pp. 36)*
Pub: Dow Jones & Company Inc.
Contact: Almar Latour, Chief Executive Officer

Ed: Mark Veverka. **Description:** Discusses the decision by the brokerage house Exane to recommend a Sell on Nokia shares, presumably due to higher inventories, which is unfounded. The news that the company's inventories are rising is not an indicator of falling demand for its products. The company is also benefiting from solid management and rising market share. **Availability:** Online.

29424 ■ *"Unilever Acquiring EVGA's Ice Cream Brands in Greece" in Ice Cream Reporter (Vol. 23, October 20, 2010, No. 11, pp. 1)*

Description: Unilever will acquire the ice cream brands and distribution network of the Greek frozen dessert manufacturer EVGA. **Availability:** Print; Online.

29425 ■ *"Unilever's CMO Finally Gets Down To Business" in Advertising Age (Vol. 79, July 7, 2008, No. 26, pp. 11)*
Description: Overview of Unilever's chief marketing officer Simon Clift's strategy for promoting its products; now that the company has restructured, Clift is able to focus all of his energy on the challenges of the new-media climate that marketers are having to face. **Availability:** Print; Online.

29426 ■ *"Union, Heal Thyself" in Canadian Business (Vol. 81, July 21, 2008, No. 11, pp. 9)*
Description: General Motors Corp. was offered by the federal government a $250 million fund after the company declared plans to close its facility in Ontario. The government move is geared towards supporting the workers who have refused to support the automotive company. Details of the labor contract between General Motors and the Canadian Auto Workers are presented. **Availability:** Print; Online.

29427 ■ *"Upsurge" in Puget Sound Business Journal (Vol. 33, July 13, 2012, No. 12, pp. 1)*
Description: Kent, Washington-based Flow International Corporation posted a record of $254 million in annual sales for fiscal 2012 and it is expected to reach about $300 million by 2014. Flow is being lifted by a global manufacturing revival and by its machines' ability to handle the carbon-fiber composites used in aerospace. Insights on Flow's water jet cutting tools are also given.

29428 ■ *"VASCO DIGIPASS GO3 in Combination With IDENTIKEY Enhances the Security of Business Intelligence Solution Developed by CDS for General Motors Brazil" in News Bites US (March 29, 2012)*
Description: VASCO Data Security International Inc. will provide Condominio de Corporativas, a vendor and business solutions integrator, its DIGIPASS GO 3 authentication solution along with IDENTIKEY Authentacation Server to provide security to the BI Retail Program developed for General Motors Brazil. VASCO is a leading software security firm specializing in authentication products. **Availability:** Print; Online.

29429 ■ *"Veteran-Owned Business 3E Services Gains Recognition in 2011 and Welcomes 2012 With New Offerings" in Marketwired (January 10, 2012)*
Pub: Comtex News Network Inc.
Contact: Kan Devnani, President

Description: 3E Services Inc. specializes in the selling, repairing, and remanufacturing of electrical components. It is a veteran-owned busiens located in Tucker, Georgia near Atlanta.The Washington Post recognized 3E as an exemplary veteran-owned business. David Loftin, president and founder, learned his skills as a US Navy nuclear electrician and attributes that training to his firm's growth and success. **Availability:** Print; Online.

29430 ■ *"Volvo: Logistics Agreement to Reduce Environmental Impact" in Ecology, Environment & Conservation Business (July 19, 2014, pp. 28)*
Pub: NewsRX LLC.
Contact: Kalani Rosell, Contact

Description: Scandinavian Logistics Partners AB (Scanlog) will sell surplus capacity in rail transport from Belgium to Sweden to the Volvo Group. The partnership benefits both costs and environmental impact. The Volvo group is committed to optimizing transport of their manufactured cars and trucks. **Availability:** Online.

29431 ■ *"A Week of the Worst Kind of Selling" in Barron's (Vol. 88, June 30, 2008, No. 26, pp. M3)*
Pub: Dow Jones & Company Inc.
Contact: Almar Latour, Chief Executive Officer

Ed: Kopin Tan. **Description:** In the week that ended in June 27, 2008 the selloff in the U.S. stock market was brought on by mounting bank losses and the spread of economic slowdown on top of high oil prices. The 31 percent decrease in the share price of Ingersoll-Rand since October 2007 may have factored in most of its risks. The company has completed its acquisition of Trane to morph into a refrigeration-equipment company. **Availability:** Online.

29432 ■ *"Wenzel Downhole Tools Ltd. Announces First Quarter Results for 2007" in Marketwired (May 14, 2007)*
Pub: Comtex News Network Inc.
Contact: Kan Devnani, President

Description: Wenzel Downhole Tools Ltd., a manufacturer, renter, and seller of drilling tools used in gas and oil exploration, announced its financial results for the first quarter ended March 31, 2007 which includes achieved revenues of $14.5 million. Statistical data included. **Availability:** Print; Online.

29433 ■ *"What Do Your ISO Procedures Say?" in Modern Machine Shop (Vol. 84, September 2011, No. 4, pp. 34)*
Pub: Gardner Business Media Inc.
Contact: Rick Kline, Jr., President
E-mail: rkline2@gardnerweb.com
Ed: Wayne Chaneski. **Released:** August 24, 2011. **Description:** ISO 9000 certification can be time-consuming and costly, but it is a necessary step in developing a quality management system that meets both current and potential customer needs. **Availability:** Print; Online.

29434 ■ *"What Is In Your Company Library?" in Modern Machine Shop (Vol. 84, October 2011, No. 5, pp. 60)*
Pub: Gardner Business Media Inc.
Contact: Rick Kline, Jr., President
E-mail: rkline2@gardnerweb.com
Ed: Mike Lynch. **Released:** September 15, 2011. **Description:** A good company library in any machine shop can help keep employees productive. Safety as well as information are critical to complete any task in a shop. **Availability:** Print; Online.

29435 ■ *"What's Working Now: In Providing Jobs for North Carolinians" in Business North Carolina (Vol. 28, February 2008, No. 2, pp. 16)*
Pub: Business North Carolina
Contact: Peggy Knaack, Manager
E-mail: pknaack@businessnc.com
Ed: Edward Martin, Frank Maley. **Description:** Individuals previously employed in the furniture, tobacco, or textile manufacturing sectors have gone back to school to be trained in new sectors in the area such as life sciences, finances and other emerging sectors. **Availability:** Online.

29436 ■ *"When R&D Spending Is Not Enough: The Critical Role of Culture When You Really Want to Innovate" in Human Resource Management (Vol. 49, July-August 2010, No. 4, pp. 767-792)*
Pub: John Wiley & Sons, Inc.
Contact: Christina Van Tassell, Executive Vice President Chief Financial Officer

Ed: Sheng Wang, Rebecca M. Guidice, Judith W. Tansky, Zhong-Ming Wang. **Released:** July 19, 2010. **Description:** A study was conducted to examine the effect of contextual contingencies on innovation. Findings indicate that Chinese manufacturers with cultures emphasizing innovation and teamwork more effectively utilize financial resources in the innovation process. Results also show that a culture emphasizing outcomes and stability leads to lower levels innovation irrespective of investments. **Availability:** Print; PDF; Online.

29437 ■ *"Where the Money Is" in Conde Nast Portfolio (Vol. 2, June 2008, No. 6, pp. 113)*
Description: Revenue generated from treatments for common brain disorders that are currently on the market are listed. **Availability:** Online.

29438 ■ *"Where Pet Nutrition Meets Love" in Pet Product News (Vol. 66, September 2012, No. 9, pp. S14)*
Description: Michael Landa, coowner of Nulo Pet Products, discusses the role of his company in reducing pet obesity through the manufacture of high-protein foods. Aside from explaining his interest in pet obesity, Landa also describes how the company differentiates itself from competitors. **Availability:** Online.

29439 ■ *"Why Change?" in Canadian Business (Vol. 80, October 8, 2007, No. 20, pp. 9)*
Description: The need for economic change in Canada is discussed. Despite the country's economic growth and low unemployment rate, economic reform is needed in order to maximize its economic potential in the future. Other reasons for the need to further develop its economy, such as the rise of manufacturing and service industries in Asia and the emergence of regional trade pacts in South America are also tackled.

29440 ■ *"Why the Ethanol King Loves Driving his SUV" in Globe & Mail (January 29, 2007, pp. B17)*
Ed: Gordon Pitts. **Description:** Ken Field, chairman of Canada's leading ethanol manufacturer Green-Field Ethanol, talks about the cars he drives, the commercial use of cellulose, ethanol's performance as an alternative to gasoline and about the plans of his firm to go public. **Availability:** Online.

29441 ■ *Why GM Matters: Inside the Race to Transform an American Icon*
Ed: William Holstein. **Price:** $26, Hardback. **Description:** A timely examination of General Motors Corporation and the problems it is facing. **Availability:** Audio.

29442 ■ *"Why Intel Should Dump Its Flash-Memory Business" in Barron's (Vol. 88, March 10, 2008, No. 10, pp. 35)*
Pub: Dow Jones & Company Inc.
Contact: Almar Latour, Chief Executive Officer
Ed: Eric J. Savitz. **Description:** Intel Corp. must sell its NAND flash-memory business as soon as it possibly can to the highest bidder to focus on its PC processor business and take advantage of other business opportunities. Apple should consider a buyback of 10 percent of the company's shares to lift its stock. **Availability:** Online.

29443 ■ *"Why Nestle Should Sell Alcon" in Barron's (Vol. 88, March 17, 2008, No. 11, pp. M12)*
Pub: Dow Jones & Company Inc.
Contact: Almar Latour, Chief Executive Officer
Ed: Sean Walters. **Description:** Nestle should sell Alcon because Nestle can't afford to be complacent as its peers have made changes to their portfolios to boost competitiveness. Nestle's stake in Alcon and L'Oreal have been ignored by investors and Nestle could realize better value by strengthening its nutrition division through acquisitions. **Availability:** Online.

29444 ■ *"Wing and a Prayer" in Canadian Business (Vol. 81, November 10, 2008, No. 19, pp. 70)*
Ed: Sean Silcoff. **Released:** January 09, 2016. **Description:** The 61st Annual National Business Aviation Association convention in Orlando, Florida

saw unabashed display of wealth and privilege, but the U.S. market meltdown and possible economic crash has raised questions on the industry's future. Statistical details included. **Availability:** Print; Online.

29445 ■ *"With Algoma Steel Gone, Is Stelco Next?" in Globe & Mail (April 16, 2007, pp. B1)*
Ed: Greg Keenan. **Description:** Speculation in Canadian steel industry over possible sale of Stelco Inc. too after the sale of Algoma Steel Inc. to Essar Global Ltd. is discussed. **Availability:** Online.

29446 ■ *"Worry No. 1 at Auto Show: Recession" in Crain's Detroit Business (Vol. 24, January 21, 2008, No. 3, pp. 1)*
Pub: Crain Communications Inc.
Contact: Barry Asin, President
Ed: Brent Snavely. **Description:** Recession fears clouded activity at the 2008 Annual North American International Auto Show. Automakers are expecting to see a drop in sales due to slow holiday retail spending as well as fallout from the subprime lending crisis. **Availability:** Online.

29447 ■ *"Xerox Diverts Waste from Landfills" in Canadian Electronics (Vol. 23, February 2008, No. 1, pp. 1)*
Description: Xerox Corporation revealed that it was able to divert more than two billion pounds of electronic waste from landfills through waste-free initiatives. The company's program, which was launched in 1991, covers waste avoidance in imaging supplies and parts reuse. Environmental priorities are also integrated into manufacturing operations. **Availability:** Print; Online; PDF.

29448 ■ *"Xstrata and CAW Get Tentative Deal" in Globe & Mail (February 2, 2007, pp. B3)*
Description: The agreement between Xstrata PLC and Canadian Auto Workers union over wage hike is discussed. **Availability:** Print; Online.

STATISTICAL SOURCES

29449 ■ *RMA Annual Statement Studies*
Pub: Risk Management Association
Contact: Nancy Foster, President
Released: Annual. **Description:** Contains composite balance sheets and income statements for more than 360 industries, including the accounting, auditing, and bookkeeping industries. Also contains five years of comparative historical data for discerning trends. Includes 16 commonly used ratios, computed for most of the size groupings for nearly every industry.

TRADE PERIODICALS

29450 ■ *Compoundings*
Pub: Independent Lubricant Manufacturers Association
Contact: Michael Damiani, President
URL(s): ilma.org/advocacy
Released: 11/year **Description:** Presents timely technical and marketing news about the lubricant manufacturing industry. Covers trends, new products, legislative, and regulatory information. Also focuses on Association members and events. **Availability:** Print; Online.

29451 ■ *Human Factors and Ergonomics in Manufacturing & Service Industries*
Pub: Wiley Periodicals Inc.
Contact: Brian Napack, Chief Executive Officer
URL(s): onlinelibrary.wiley.com/journal/15206564
Ed: Paul Salmon. **Released:** Bimonthly **Price:** $2,115, Institutions for online only Canada and US, India. **Description:** International journal focusing on the discovery, integration, application, and translation of scientific knowledge within the field of human factors and ergonomics (HFE). **Availability:** Print; Download; PDF; Online.

29452 ■ *Industrial Laser Solutions*
URL(s): www.industrial-lasers.com

Facebook: www.facebook.com/industriallasersolutions
Linkedin: www.linkedin.com/showcase/industrial-laser-solutions
X (Twitter): twitter.com/ILS_for_Mfg
Price: Free. **Description:** Devoted exclusively to the increased productivity and profitability of industrial lasers. Offers current information on the application of lasers in material processing, lasers on the production line, new systems and products, technical and economic analyses, company information, business news and more.

29453 ■ *Manufacturers' Mart*
Pub: Manufacturers' Mart Publications
URL(s): www.manufacturersmart.com/about.html
Released: Monthly **Description:** Publication for manufacturing and production engineers. **Availability:** Print.

29454 ■ *Manufacturing and Technology News*
Pub: Publishers & Producers
Released: Weekly **Description:** Relates breaking news on manufacturing programs and policies, electronic commerce, new manufacturing technologies, and techniques. Carries guest editorials. Recurring features include letters to the editor, interviews, news of research, reports of meetings, book reviews, and notices of publications available. **Availability:** Online.

29455 ■ *SEMA News*
Pub: Specialty Equipment Market Association
Contact: Mike Spagnola, President
URL(s): www.sema.org/news-media/magazine
Released: Monthly **Description:** Covers the automotive speciality, performance equipment, and accessory sectors. Recurring features include news of government and legislative actions, new products, international markets, and member and Association activities. **Availability:** Print; Online.

29456 ■ *Teamwork*
Pub: Dartnell Corporation
URL(s): www.dartnellcorp.com/newsletters/teamwork.php
Released: Monthly **Price:** $179, Individuals online only. **Description:** Focuses on successful teamwork in manufacturing and corporate businesses. Recurring features include columns titled What Would You Do?, Test Yourself and See, and Teamwork in Action. **Availability:** Online.

VIDEO/AUDIO MEDIA

29457 ■ *Manufacturing Control in the Small Plant*
Released: 19??. **Description:** Part of an integrated course for anyone involved in the management and operation of a small company, or a small division of a large company. **Availability:** 3/4 U.

29458 ■ *This Is Small Business: How to Manufacture Your Own Product*
URL(s): www.smallbusiness.amazon/podcast-episodes/ep-20-how-to-manufacture-your-own-product
Ed: Andrea Marquez. **Released:** March 28, 2023. **Description:** Podcast discusses manufacturing your own product, how to protect your business in doing that, and its pros and cons.

TRADE SHOWS AND CONVENTIONS

29459 ■ **Canadian Manufacturing Technology Show**
Siemens Canada Ltd.
  1577 N Service Rd. E
  Oakville, ON, Canada L6H 0H6
URL: http://new.siemens.com/ca/en.html
Contact: Faisal Kazi, Chief Executive Officer
URL(s): www.cmts.ca

Frequency: Annual. **Description:** Exhibits related to manufacturing, including components and supplies. **Audience:** Manufacturing industry professionals. **Principal Exhibits:** Exhibits related to manufacturing, including components and supplies. **Telecommunication Services:** cmts@sme.org.

29460 ■ International Manufacturing Technology Show (IMTS)
Association for Manufacturing Technology (AMT)
7901 Jones Branch Dr., Ste. 900
McLean, VA 22102-4206
Ph: (703)893-2900
Free: 800-524-0475
Fax: (703)893-1151
Co. E-mail: amt@amtonline.org
URL: http://www.amtonline.org/home
Contact: Douglas K. Woods, President
URL(s): www.imts.com/show/abouttheshow.cfm
Facebook: www.facebook.com/IMTS.show
Frequency: Biennial. **Audience:** Industry professionals. Dates and Locations: 2026 Sep 14-19, McCormick Place, Chicago, IL. **Telecommunication Services:** imts2024@xpressreg.net.

29461 ■ North American Manufacturing Research Conference
North American Manufacturing Research Institution of SME (NAMRI-SME)
1000 Town Ctr., Ste. 1910
Southfield, MI 48075
Co. E-mail: publications@sme.org
URL: http://www.sme.org/namri
URL(s): namrc.sme.org/?_ga=2.190073579.15287 26158.1715922898-810918125.1715922697
Frequency: Annual. **Description:** Collocated with ASME Manufacturing Science and Engineering Conference. **Audience:** Researchers from leading companies, government laboratories, academic institutions and industrial think tanks. **Principal Exhibits:** Collocated with ASME Manufacturing Science and Engineering Conference. **Telecommunication Services:** namri@sme.org.

29462 ■ Re/focus Sustainability & Recycling Summit
URL(s): events.plasticsindustry.org/2021Refocus
Frequency: Annual. **Description:** Recycling topic seminars for those in plastic manufacturing industry. **Principal Exhibits:** Recycling topic seminars for those in plastic manufacturing industry.

29463 ■ Silicone Expo
URL(s): www.silicone-expo.com
Frequency: Annual. **Description:** Manufacturing trade show with booths featuring silicone products, elastomers, resins, fluids, and gels. Also provides conferences in manufacturing and application. **Principal Exhibits:** Manufacturing trade show with booths featuring silicone products, elastomers, resins, fluids, and gels. Also provides conferences in manufacturing and application.

29464 ■ South-tec
Ellison Technologies
9828 Arlee Ave.
Santa Fe Springs, CA 90670
Ph: (569)949-8311
Free: 888-207-2787
Fax: (569)949-8049
Co. E-mail: support@ellisontechnologies.com
URL: http://www.ellisontechnologies.com
Contact: Becky DeGeorge, Contact
URL(s): www.southteconline.com
Frequency: Annual. **Description:** Exhibits related to manufacturing equipment, supplies and services. **Audience:** Industry professionals. **Principal Exhibits:** Exhibits related to manufacturing equipment, supplies and services.

CONSULTANTS

29465 ■ Business Industrial Network (BIN)
9205 W Russell Rd.
Las Vegas, NV 89148
Ph: (702)625-7715

Co. E-mail: bin2018@bin95.com
URL: http://bin95.com
Contact: Don Fitchett, President
Facebook: www.facebook.com/BusinessIndustrialNe twork
Linkedin: www.linkedin.com/company/business-indus trial-network
X (Twitter): x.com/indtraining
YouTube: www.youtube.com/user/bin952
Pinterest: www.pinterest.com/plctech
Description: Provider of industrial training such as PLC training, industrial training software and video training courses, and much more. **Scope:** Provider of industrial training such as PLC training, industrial training software and video training courses, and much more. **Founded:** 1995. **Publications:** "Total Productive Maintenance definition as married to TPM"; "Recession survival tips for Manufacturing Industry"; "Converting AB PLC DH485 to USB"; "How to Reduce Data Errors on Infrared Surveys"; "CMMS Systems Integration"; "Supply Chain Management with RFID Systems"; "Slip and fall safety around chip machine"; "Equipment Failure and the Cost of that Failure"; "PID Controller Design, Model based control tuning"; "Safety Relay Circuits"; "M2M Device Networking"; "How a photoelectric sensor saved my job"; "OEE - Automated Data Collection". **Training:** Maintenance Process Management; CMMS Made Easy; Plant Construction Management; Energy Management; Advanced Microsoft Project for Maintenance, Apr, 2010; Maintenance Planning and Scheduling, Mar, 2010; Maintenance Storerooms, Apr, 2010; Microsoft Project for Maintenance, Apr, 2010; Shutdowns, Turnarounds, and Outages, Mar, 2010; A Maintenance and Engineering Training Seminar, Feb, 2009; PLC Troubleshooting Training Seminars.

29466 ■ Business Process Consulting Group (BPCG)
166 Willowleaf Dr.
Littleton, CO 80127-3574
Ph: (720)981-1111
URL: http://theprocessconsultant.com
Linkedin: www.linkedin.com/in/ianjames theprocessconsultant
X (Twitter): twitter.com/fixesprocess
Description: A provider of training, consulting services, kaizen and software solutions in flow and lean manufacturing and Kanban techniques, as they apply to the factory and the office. Consultants have implemented the flow methodologies in factories and offices throughout the world. **Scope:** A provider of training, consulting services, kaizen and software solutions in flow and lean manufacturing and Kanban techniques, as they apply to the factory and the office. Consultants have implemented the flow methodologies in factories and offices throughout the world. **Founded:** 1999. **Publications:** "Leaning Out Health Care: A How-To Manual for the Optimization of Health Care Processes"; "Flow White Paper"; "Flow Processing in at Medical Device Manufacturer"; "Operational Savings Choices"; "Sky Radio™; Soundtrack - Gerard Leone"; "Advanced Manufacturing Magazine: When to Train your Employees," Nov, 2002. **Special Services:** Administrative Flow™; Flow Processing Advantage®.

29467 ■ GDC Total Business Solutions (GDC-TBS)
403 Gilead Rd., Ste. L
Huntersville, NC 28078
Ph: (704)274-2050
Fax: (704)274-2051
Co. E-mail: info@gdc-tbs.com
URL: http://www.gdctotalbusinesssolutions.wor dpress.com
Contact: Curtis Walker, Contact
Facebook: www.facebook.com/GDC.TBS
Linkedin: www.linkedin.com/company/gdc-total-busi ness-solutions/about
X (Twitter): x.com/gdc_tbs
Description: Firm provides organizations with lean conversion, six-sigma and professional skills training and implementations and services include financial or operational restructuring, strategic planning and much more. **Scope:** Firm provides organizations with

lean conversion, six-sigma and professional skills training and implementations and services include financial or operational restructuring, strategic planning and much more. **Founded:** 1999. **Publications:** "A Simplified Solution to Better Costing Activity Based Quoting: GDC s Solution to Costing for Small Manufacturers"; "Benchmarking: A Practical Guide for Smaller Manufacturers"; "Making Improvements to Your Company Get Employees Involved"; "Project Management: A Necessary Skill for Manufacturers"; "Effective Change: Sustain Lean Improvements by Building Business Maturity"; "Lean in Healthcare"; "Creating a Lean Culture"; "Never Double Dip With the Wrong End of Your Chopsticks And Other Lessons in Lean Operations". **Training:** Business Operating System; Strategic Planning/SWOT; Leading Through Change; Structured Team Problem Solving; Leadership/Management Training.

29468 ■ Hewitt Development Enterprises (HDE)
1717 N Bayshore Dr., Ste. 2154
Miami, FL 33132
Ph: (305)372-0941
Fax: (305)372-0941
Co. E-mail: info@hewittdevelopment.com
URL: http://www.hewittdevelopment.com
Contact: Robert G. Hewitt, Contact
E-mail: bob@hewittdevelopment.com
Description: Firm specializes in strategic planning, profit enhancement, startup businesses, interim and crisis management, turnarounds, production planning, just-in-time inventory and project management, serves senior management and acquirers of distressed businesses. **Scope:** Firm specializes in strategic planning, profit enhancement, startup businesses, interim and crisis management, turnarounds, production planning, just-in-time inventory and project management, serves senior management and acquirers of distressed businesses. **Founded:** 1985.

29469 ■ Institute for Management Excellence
Trabuco Canyon, CA 92679
Ph: (949)667-1012
URL: http://www.itstime.com
Contact: Barbara Taylor, Executive Director
Description: Consulting firm and training focuses on improving productivity, using practices and creative techniques. **Scope:** Consulting firm and training focuses on improving productivity, using practices and creative techniques. **Founded:** 1995. **Publications:** "Income Without a Job," 2008; "The Other Side of Midnight, 2000: An Executive Guide to the Year 2000 Problem"; "Concordance to the Michael Teachings"; "Handbook of Small Business Advertising"; "The Personality Game"; "How to Market Yourself for Success". **Training:** The Personality Game; Power Path Seminars; Productivity Plus; Sexual Harassment and Discrimination Prevention; Worker's Comp Cost Reduction; Americans with Disabilities Act; In Search of Identify: Clarifying Corporate Culture.

29470 ■ Japan Business Consultants Ltd.
1140 Morehead Ct.
Ann Arbor, MI 48103
Description: Firm specializes in Japanese quality control methods including total quality management, quality function deployment, and hoshin management and serves automotive, computer, aerospace, chemical, finance, consumer products and service. **Scope:** Firm specializes in Japanese quality control methods including total quality management, quality function deployment, and hoshin management and serves automotive, computer, aerospace, chemical, finance, consumer products and service. **Founded:** 1983. **Publications:** "Quality Infrastructure Improvement: Using QFD to Manage Project Priorities and Project Management Resources"; "The Next Generation Explosive Ordnance Disposal (EOD) Robotic Controlled Vehicle: Using QFD to Define the Operational Analysis"; "QFD to Direct Value Engineering in the Design of a Brake System"; "QFD Killed My Pet"; "Gemba Research in the Japanese Cellular Phone Market"; "Strategy Deployment for SMEs"; "Consumer Encounters and Idea Development and Concept Optimization"; "Task Deployment: Managing the Hu-

man Side of QFD". **Training:** Total Quality Management; QFD for Product Developments; QFD for Service Organizations; QFD for Healthcare Organizations. **Special Services:** QFD Red Belt®; QFD Gold Belt®; QFD Green Belt®.

29471 ■ Northwest Trade Adjustment Assistance Center (NWTAAC)
1200 Westlake Ave. N, Ste. 604
  Seattle, WA 98109
Ph: (206)622-2730
Free: 800-667-8087
Fax: (206)622-1105
Co. E-mail: nwtaac@nwtaac.org
URL: http://nwtaac.org
Contact: David Holbert, Executive Director
E-mail: david@nwtaac.org
Description: Provider of up to 75 percent cost paid technical assistance to help manufacturers improve their competitive position relative to imported products. areas of expertise include website design, ISO 9000 certification, new market identification, new product introduction, business plans, marketing plans and more. **Scope:** Provider of up to 75 percent cost paid technical assistance to help manufacturers improve their competitive position relative to imported products. areas of expertise include website design, ISO 9000 certification, new market identification, new product introduction, business plans, marketing plans and more. **Founded:** 1979.

FRANCHISES AND BUSINESS OPPORTUNITIES

29472 ■ The Gutter Guys
2547 Fire Rd., Unit. E-5
  Egg Harbor Township, NJ 08234
Ph: (609)646-1400
URL: http://thegutterguys.com
Contact: Bill Bradley, Owner
Description: Firm provides gutter cleaning services and also provides gutter doors and repair services. **Financial Assistance:** Yes

29473 ■ Old Hippy Wood Products Inc.
2415 80 Ave.
  Edmonton, AB, Canada T6P 1N3
Ph: (780)448-1163
Free: 888-464-9700
URL: http://www.oldhippy.com
Facebook: www.facebook.com/oldhippywoodpro
  ducts
X (Twitter): x.com/OldHippy1990
Instagram: www.instagram.com/oldhippywoodpro
  ducts
Description: Distributor of wood products such as wood tops, fronts, gables, drawer boxes, shelves and cabinet frames. **Founded:** 1990. **Franchised:** 1990. **Equity Capital Needed:** $350,000-$850,000. **Training:** Initial training and ongoing support provided.

RESEARCH CENTERS

29474 ■ California State Polytechnic University, Pomona - Don B. Huntley College of Agriculture - Apparel Technology & Research Center (ATRC)
3801 West Temple Ave.
  Pomona, CA 91768
URL: http://www.cpp.edu/agri/apparel-technology
  -research-center

Description: Integral unit of College of Agriculture, California State Polytechnic University Pomona. Offers consulting and technical assistance. **Scope:** Apparel and textile market research, strategic analysis and apparel technology transfer. **Founded:** 1992.

29475 ■ Grand Valley State University - The Michigan Small Business Development Center (SBDC)
50 Front Ave., SW
  Grand Rapids, MI 49504
Ph: (231)929-5060
Co. E-mail: sbdcmichigan@gvsu.edu
URL: http://michigansbdc.org
Contact: J. D. Collins, Executive Director
E-mail: colljaso@gvsu.edu
Facebook: www.facebook.com/MichiganSBDC
Linkedin: www.linkedin.com/company/michigan-sbdc
X (Twitter): x.com/MichiganSBDC
Instagram: www.instagram.com/michigansbdc
YouTube: www.youtube.com/channel/
  UCFFAuIAXZFvRBHrQpuiLCCA
Description: Provides a full-range of services for a variety of small businesses including: counseling; training; programs for a variety of needs, from how to get started, to financing; effective selling and e-commerce as well as how to develop business plans. Also provides research help and advocacy. **Scope:** Manufacturing, financing, and international business information (particularly the export process) for small businesses. Resources for the export process includes determining and detailing international feasibility, foreign market entry plans, and responding to international inquiries. **Founded:** 1983. **Publications:** *Changing the Face of the American Economy--A Resource Guide for the Michigan Woman Business Owner* (Biennial).

29476 ■ National Center for Manufacturing Sciences (NCMS)
3025 Boardwalk St.
  Ann Arbor, MI 48108
Free: 800-222-6267
Fax: (734)995-1150
Co. E-mail: contact@ncms.org
URL: http://www.ncms.org
Contact: C. Alan Ferguson, Chairman
Facebook: www.facebook.com/NCMSmanufacturing
X (Twitter): x.com/ncmsmfg
Description: Aims to further the global competitiveness of North American manufacturers through collaboration, innovation, and advanced technologies. **Scope:** Fundamental manufacturing sciences, process technology and capabilities, behavior of materials during manufacturing, machine mechanics and components, precision manufacturing, sensor and control techniques. **Founded:** 1986. **Publications:** *SOLV-DB®* - *Solvents Database*; *NCMS at a Glance*. **Educational Activities:** CTMA Annual Partners Meeting (Annual).

29477 ■ North American Manufacturing Research Institution of SME (NAMRI-SME)
1000 Town Ctr., Ste. 1910
  Southfield, MI 48075
Co. E-mail: publications@sme.org
URL: http://www.sme.org/namri
URL(s): www.sme.org/education/manufacturing
  -research
Description: Nonprofit research arm of the Society of Manufacturing Engineers (SME). Supports individuals in manufacturing research and technology development. Stimulates research, writing, publication,

and dissemination of new manufacturing technology; works to coordinate efforts and cooperate with counterpart organizations worldwide; provides a forum for the active community of researchers whose work contributes in furthering manufacturing technology and productivity. **Scope:** Manufacturing research and technology development. Provides researchers and industry practitioners with a means of exchanging ideas and sharing findings with leading researchers in the field of manufacturing. **Founded:** 1932. **Publications:** *Proceedings of the North American Manufacturing Research Institution of the Society of Manufacturing Engineers* (Annual). **Educational Activities:** NAMRI/SME Annual Meeting (Annual); North American Manufacturing Research Conference (Annual), Collocated with ASME Manufacturing Science and Engineering Conference. **Awards:** NAMRI/SME Outstanding Paper Award (Annual); NAMRI/SME S.M. Wu Research Implementation Award (Annual). **Geographic Preference:** National.

29478 ■ Ohio State University - Engineering Research Center for Net Shape Manufacturing (ERC/NSM)
201 W 19th Ave.
  Columbus, OH 43210
URL: http://mae.osu.edu/research-labs-and-centers
Description: Integral unit of Ohio State University. Offers continuing education courses. **Scope:** Manufacturing processes, specifically the manufacture of discrete parts to net or near-net dimensions, sheet forming, precision forging, tube/sheet hydroforming, machining, die/mold manufacturing. **Founded:** 1986. **Publications:** *Technical papers and presentations.*

29479 ■ Rochester Institute of Technology - Center for Integrated Manufacturing Studies (CIMS)
One Lomb Memorial Dr.
  Rochester, NY 14623
URL: http://www.rtma.org/manufacturing-innovation
Contact: Dr. Nabil Nasr, Director
E-mail: nzneie@rit.edu
Description: Center provides dynamic collaboration of technical experts as well as academic, industry and government resources. Offers extension services for small businesses. **Scope:** Researches on electronics, imaging, supplier integration, remanufacturing, ergonomics and simulation. Areas of study include total quality management, cycle time reduction, life cycle costs, product and process development, concurrent engineering, and integration theory. **Founded:** 1992. **Educational Activities:** CIMS Training programs.

29480 ■ Tennessee Technological University - Center for Manufacturing Research (CMR)
1 William L Jones Dr.
  Cookeville, TN 38505
URL: http://www.tntech.edu/engineering/research/
  cmr
Contact: Dr. Ying Zhang, Director
E-mail: yzhang@tntech.edu
Description: Integral unit of College of Engineering, Tennessee Technological University. Offers material testing, seminars, workshops, and short courses. **Scope:** Control of processes and equipment; next generation materials and manufacturing processes; integrated product/process realization; and pervasive simulation and modeling. **Founded:** 1985. **Publications:** *CMR Annual report* (Annual); *Executive Summary* (Annual); *CMR Research reports.* **Educational Activities:** Center for Manufacturing Research Conferences; Industrial Study-Work Program.

START-UP INFORMATION

29481 ■ *The Marketing Plan Handbook*

Ed: Robert W. Bly. **Released:** 2015. **Description:** A beginner's guide to understanding customers and their needs to help form a solid marketing plan for your business. Designed to help your small business outpace your competitors, this book will help you understand the market for your products and develop steps to achieve success. Comes with assignments and examples.

ASSOCIATIONS AND OTHER ORGANIZATIONS

29482 ■ Media & Content Marketing Association (MCMA)

405 N Stanwick Rd.
Moorestown, NJ 08057
Co. E-mail: help@the-mcma.org
URL: http://www.the-macma.org/privacy_updated

Description: Fulfillment executives, direct mail marketing management, publishing, circulation, and fundraising executives. Educates, updates, and maintains high standards of service in operations management and customer service. Offers monthly luncheon Programs, Annual Fulfillment Day in New York; sponsors three seminars per year. Maintains job advisory service. **Founded:** 1948. **Awards:** Fulfillment Hall of Fame Award (Annual); Fulfillment Manager of the Year (Annual); MCMA Hall of Fame (Annual); MCMA Manager of the Year Award (Annual); MCMA Lee C. Williams Award (Annual). **Geographic Preference:** National.

REFERENCE WORKS

29483 ■ *"3 Market Research Tips for Small Business"* in Small Business Computing.com

Ed: Maryalene LaPonsie. **Description:** Discusses why market research is a valuable growth tool for businesses of every size and every budget. Offers three ways to conduct low-cost market research. **Availability:** Online.

29484 ■ *"5-Step Guide on How to Do Market Research for Your Business"* in Small Business Rainmaker Blog (November 3, 2020)

Released: November 03, 2020. **Description:** Provides details on proven market research methods for entrepreneurs using a 5-step approach. **Availability:** Online.

29485 ■ *"7 of the Best Market Research Tools for Small Businesses"* in Groupon Merchant (January 24, 2020)

Ed: Sarah Stasik. **Released:** January 24, 2020. **Description:** Offers information on seven of the best market research tools for small businesses to find solutions that allow you to approach marketing and other processes with the right understanding of your target audience. **Availability:** Online.

29486 ■ *"7 Popular Marketing Techniques for Small Businesses"* in Investopedia (June 16, 2020)

Ed: Andrew Beattie. **Released:** June 16, 2020. **Description:** Offers 7 tangible marketing methods to attract and maintain a customer base. **Availability:** Online.

29487 ■ *Business-to-Business Marketing 2023*

Released: 6th edition. **Description:** Delves into the world of business-to-business marketing by presenting and examining tactics, surveys, and trends of the industry. **Availability:** Online.

29488 ■ *"Conducting Market Research"* in Entrepreneur Press

Description: Details what is involved in the crucial marketing research step of the product development cycle. **Availability:** Online.

29489 ■ *Entrepreneur's Showcase: Market Research for Small Businesses and the Woman Entrepreneur's Guide to Financing a Business*

Pub: Gale, part of Cengage Group
Contact: Paul Gazzolo, General Manager Senior Vice President
URL(s): www.gale.com/ebooks/9781933884080/en trepreneurs-showcase-market-research-for-small -businesses-and-the-woman-entrepreneurs-guide -to-financing-a-business
Description: Published by Know!Books Press. Provides information on multiple aspects of entrepreneurship, focusing on market research for small business as well as on more gender-specific topics involved in starting a business. **Availability:** E-book.

29490 ■ *The Groundbreaking Impact of Technology on Brand Market Research for Small Businesses*

Ed: Bhavika Sharma. **Description:** Describes how the use of technology is especially critical to startups and small businesses as it helps them avoid risks and pitfalls. **Availability:** Online.

29491 ■ *"How to Attract Clients for Your Residential and Office Cleaning Business"* in Chron (March 12, 2019)

Ed: Tracey Sandilands. **Released:** March 12, 2019. **Description:** Provides information on effectively marketing home and office cleaning services to attract clients. **Availability:** Online.

29492 ■ *"How to Conduct Primary Market Research for Your Small Business"* in FindLaw (October 7, 2019)

Released: October 07, 2019. **Description:** Discusses the difference between primary and secondary market research and how to use each to efficiently hone in on your target market. **Availability:** Online.

29493 ■ *"How to Conduct Thorough Market Research for Your Startup or Small Business"* SalesForce Resource Center

Description: Discusses the importance of market research as well as steps involved in doing thorough research including costs and analysis information. **Availability:** Online.

29494 ■ *"How to Do Market Research for Small Business: 8 Affordable Market Research Techniques"* in ActiveCampaign (December 15, 2017)

Ed: Benyamin Elias. **Released:** December 15, 2017. **Description:** Covers how to do market research for small business using eight affordable market research techniques. **Availability:** Online.

29495 ■ *"How to Do Market Research for Your Small Business"* in Fit Small Business (October 23, 2019)

Ed: Kiah Treece. **Released:** October 23, 2019. **Description:** Discusses the importance of learning what their market wants for both new and existing businesses. Explains how market research works, offers five steps to complete market research, and provides the top eleven market research tips from professionals. **Availability:** Online.

29496 ■ *"Jim Kukral Answers the Question: What is Marketing?"* in Small Business Trends(December 6, 2022)

URL(s): smallbiztrends.com/2022/12/what-is-marke ting.html
Ed: Holly Chavez. **Released:** December 06, 2022. **Description:** A transcript and a link to a full interview about marketing. Defines what marketing actually is and how to step away from your brand to see what your customers see. **Availability:** Online.

29497 ■ *"Market Research Guide for Business Owners"* in Business News Daily (August 31, 2020)

Ed: Adam Uzialko. **Released:** August 31, 2020. **Description:** Provides information on how to test the viability of new business ideas, products, and features using market research. **Availability:** Online.

29498 ■ *Marketing for Dummies*

Pub: John Wiley & Sons, Inc.
Contact: Christina Van Tassell, Executive Vice President Chief Financial Officer
URL(s): www.wiley.com/en-us/Marketing+For+Dum-mies%2C+6th+Edition-p-9781119894896
Ed: Jeanette Maw McMurtry. **Released:** 4th edition. **Price:** $18, e-book; $29.99, paperback. **Description:** All you needed to know about marketing for your company. This edition includes topics such as using digital engagement, social media campaigns, and tapping into the influencer market. **Availability:** E-book; Print.

29499 ■ *"Small Business Tips: How to Do Market Research"* in Guardian Small Business Network (August 13, 2015)

Ed: Emily Wight. **Released:** August 13, 2015. **Description:** Discusses how market research will help you understand your customers, familiarize yourself with your competition, and get to know what people are prepared to pay for your product or service. **Availability:** Online.

STATISTICAL SOURCES

29500 ■ *Black Consumers: Digital Trends & Impact of COVID-19 One Year Later - US - April 2021*
URL(s): store.mintel.com/report/black-consumers-digital-trends-impact-of-covid-19-one-year-later-us-april-2021
Price: $4,366.35. **Description:** Downloadable report detailing the purchase power of the Black consumer and the relationship to digital products and services. Report includes an executive summary, interactive databook, PowerPoint presentation, infographic overview, report PDF, and previous years data. **Availability:** PDF.

29501 ■ *Hispanics: Digital Trends & Impact of COVID-19 One Year Later - US - April 2021*
URL(s): store.mintel.com/report/hispanics-digital-trends-impact-of-covid-19-one-year-later-us-april-2021
Price: $4,366.35. **Description:** Downloadable report discussing the impact the COVID-19 pandemic has had on the Hispanic community and their shopping habits. Provides data on Hispanics' approach to technology and attitudes about digital products. Report includes an executive summary, interactive databook, PowerPoint presentation, infographic overview, report PDF, and previous years data. **Availability:** PDF.

29502 ■ *Market Research Industry in the US - Market Research Report*
URL(s): www.ibisworld.com/united-states/market-research-reports/market-research-industry/
Price: $925. **Description:** Downloadable report analyzing the current and future trends in the market research industry. **Availability:** Download.

29503 ■ *U.S. Key Elements of Ecommerce Market Report 2021*
URL(s): store.mintel.com/report/us-key-elements-of-ecommerce
Price: $4,366.35. **Description:** Downloadable report providing data on the online shopping habits of US consumers. Report includes an executive summary, interactive databook, PowerPoint presentation, infographic overview, report PDF, and previous years data. **Availability:** PDF.

29504 ■ *US Hispanics: Online Shopping Behaviors Market Report 2021*
URL(s): store.mintel.com/report/us-hispanics-online-shopping-behaviors-us-market-report
Price: $4,366.35. **Description:** Downloadable report providing data on the online shopping habits of Hispanics living in the US. Report includes an executive summary, interactive databook, PowerPoint presentation, infographic overview, report PDF, and previous years data. **Availability:** PDF.

29505 ■ *US Retail and eCommerce & the Impact of COVID-19 - One Year Later 2021*
URL(s): store.mintel.com/report/us-state-of-retail-ecommerce-impact-of-covid-19-one-year-later-market-report
Price: $4,366.35. **Description:** Downloadable report featuring analysis of the impact COVID-19 has had on the retail and eCommerce industries. Report includes an executive summary, interactive databook, PowerPoint presentation, infographic overview, report PDF, and previous years data. **Availability:** PDF.

TRADE SHOWS AND CONVENTIONS

29506 ■ Email Innovations Summit
URL(s): emailinnovationssummit.com
Frequency: Annual. **Description:** Workshops and talks about new email marketing trends and developments. **Principal Exhibits:** Workshops and talks about new email marketing trends and developments.

29507 ■ LeadsCon
URL(s): www.leadscon.com
Facebook: www.facebook.com/leadscon
Linkedin: www.linkedin.com/groups/1810842
X (Twitter): twitter.com/leadscon
Description: Talks and workshops focused on generating leads and market strategies for small businesses. **Principal Exhibits:** Talks and workshops focused on generating leads and market strategies for small businesses.

CONSULTANTS

29508 ■ National Business Research Institute Inc. (NBRI)
2701 Dallas Pwy., Ste. 650
Plano, TX 75093
Ph: (972)612-5070
Free: 800-756-6168
Co. E-mail: info@nbrii.com
URL: http://www.nbrii.com
Contact: Jan G. West, President
Facebook: www.facebook.com/WhyNBRI
Linkedin: www.linkedin.com/company/national-business-research-institute
X (Twitter): x.com/nbri
Description: Firm provides consulting services in survey research and consulting solutions for research, benchmarking, analytics, synergy, action, financial and related services. **Scope:** Firm provides consulting services in survey research and consulting solutions for research, benchmarking, analytics, synergy, action, financial and related services. **Founded:** 1982. **Publications:** "Get Our New E-Book, How To Conduct A Survey, Free"; "The Importance Of Customer Surveys"; "Survey Root Cause Analysis"; "The Winning Employee-Customer Link".

PUBLISHERS

29509 ■ *ClickZ*
URL(s): www.clickz.com
Facebook: www.facebook.com/ClickZ
Linkedin: www.linkedin.com/company/clickz-com
X (Twitter): twitter.com/ClickZ
Description: Provides online marketing tools, insights, research, and reference. **Availability:** Online.

INTERNET DATABASES

29510 ■ *African Americans in Business and Entrepreneurship: A Resource Guide*
URL(s): guides.loc.gov/african-americans-in-business
Description: A guide providing key topics on the history of African Americans in various business industries. **Availability:** Online.

29511 ■ *Influencer Marketing: A Research Guide*
URL(s): guides.loc.gov/influencer-marketing
Description: Provides links to online reports and books about using social media as a marketing tool. **Availability:** Online.

EDUCATIONAL PROGRAMS

29512 ■ **Elevate Your Social Media Marketing and Presence for Engagement and Growth**
URL(s): cwewbc.ecenterdirect.com/events/977226
Description: This online class offered by the Center for Women and Enterprise explores how best to use the tools of social media to effectively market your small business. **Audience:** Women who are small-business owners. **Principal Exhibits:** This online class offered by the Center for Women and Enterprise explores how best to use the tools of social media to effectively market your small business.

29513 ■ **How to Land Your First Client, Part 1**
URL(s): cwewbc.ecenterdirect.com/events/977256
Frequency: Continuous. **Description:** Online course offered by the Center for Women & Enterprise about content development for marketing your business. **Principal Exhibits:** Online course offered by the Center for Women & Enterprise about content development for marketing your business.

29514 ■ **Kickstart Your Social Media Blueprint with TikTok and IG Reels, Part I**
URL(s): cwewbc.ecenterdirect.com/events/977312
Description: This online workshop offered by the Center for Women and Enterprise provides information on how to use TikTok and Instagram Reels to market your small business and develop and solid social media presence. **Audience:** Women small business owners. **Principal Exhibits:** This online workshop offered by the Center for Women and Enterprise provides information on how to use TikTok and Instagram Reels to market your small business and develop and solid social media presence.

REFERENCE WORKS

29515 ■ *"4 Analytics Categories to Track to Improve Your Marketing Strategy"* in Forbes (October 22, 2020)
Ed: Serenity Gibbons. **Released:** October 22, 2020. **Description:** Discusses the use of four categories of data analytics and how each category can each be broken down to help you improve your marketing strategy with precision. **Availability:** Online.

29516 ■ *"5 Tips to Protect Your Brand on Social Media"* in Legal Zoom (March 16, 2023)
URL(s): www.legalzoom.com/articles/5-tips-to-protect-your-brand-on-social-media
Ed: Kylie Ora Lobell. **Released:** March 16, 2023. **Description:** Using social media sites for marketing your company can be a great way to reach your customers, but sometimes things can go wrong and bad press can take place. Be sure follow the steps given to protect your brand and avoid disaster. **Availability:** Online.

29517 ■ *"7 Facebook Tips for Small & Medium-Sized Businesses"* in Business 2 Community (October 1, 2021)
URL(s): www.business2community.com/small-business/7-facebook-tips-for-small-medium-sized-businesses-02433957

Ed: Haiden Hibbert. **Released:** October 01, 2021. **Description:** Tips on how to market your small to medium-sized business using Facebook. **Availability:** Online.

29518 ■ *"8 Pricing Strategies for Your Digital Product"* in Entrepreneur (October 18, 2016)
Ed: Eric Siu. **Released:** October 18, 2016. **Description:** Discusses how pricing can be used as a marketing strategy to generate interest, drive sales, and attract customers. **Availability:** Online.

29519 ■ *"10 Ways to Tailor Your Marketing Strategy to Your Business"* in Small Business Trends (August 15, 2020)
Ed: Annie Pilon. **Released:** August 15, 2020. **Description:** Provides tips on how to carefully consider what options are best suited for your products, services, and customers so you can create a marketing strategy that is completely tailored to your business. **Availability:** Online.

29520 ■ *"16 Awesome Marketing Strategies for Small Businesses"* in buildfire
Ed: Ian Blair. **Description:** Discusses sixteen different marketing strategies that have a proven history of success for small businesses. **Availability:** Online.

29521 ■ *"Clairol Taps Hair Color Influencers for First Ad Campaign in Five Years"* in Bizwomen (March 24, 2023)
URL(s): www.bizjournals.com/bizwomen/news/latest-news/2023/03/clairol-assembles-slate-of-hair-color-influencers.html
Ed: Anne Stych. **Released:** March 24, 2023. **Description:** Clairol has tapped into the social media influencer market and launched a new ad for it's brand. **Availability:** Online.

29522 ■ *"Constant Contact Launches Marketing Podcast for Small Business"* in Small Business Trends (March 10, 2023)
URL(s): smallbiztrends.com/2023/03/constant-contact-launches-small-business-marketing-podcast.html
Ed: Joshua Sophy. **Released:** March 10, 2023. **Description:** The email marketing and online marketing tools company, Constant Contact, launched a small business podcast, which discusses marketing strategies. **Availability:** Online.

29523 ■ *"Digital Marketing in 2020 - 7 Reasons Why Small Businesses Need It"* in Marketo Blog.
Ed: Anita Sambol. **Description:** A detailed guide on why small business owners should invest in digital marketing. **Availability:** Online.

29524 ■ *"Does Your Business Really Need a Facebook Page?"* in Legal Zoom (March 22, 2023)
URL(s): www.legalzoom.com/articles/does-your-business-really-need-a-facebook-page

Ed: Bilal Kaiser. **Released:** March 22, 2023. **Description:** Discusses the merits of having a Facebook page dedicated to your small business as part of your marketing plan. **Availability:** Online.

29525 ■ *"Email Marketing: Still the Most Powerful Tool to Take Your Business to the Next Level"* in Forbes (October 26, 2020)
Released: October 26, 2020. **Description:** Discusses the continued power of email marketing and how its return-on-investment remains the highest of all marketing channels. **Availability:** Online.

29526 ■ *"Get the Picture: 8 Instagram Tips for Small Businesses"* in Legal Zoom (March 21, 2023)
URL(s): www.legalzoom.com/articles/get-the-picture-8-instagram-tips-for-small-businesses
Ed: Michelle Kaminsky, Esq. **Released:** March 21, 2023. **Description:** Instagram is a very popular social media tool for small businesses to use. Get the right picture of your product and you could attract a lot of new customers and get old customers through your door as well. **Availability:** Online.

29527 ■ *Improve Small Business Marketing Strategy with Social Media*
Ed: Michael Tasner. **Description:** Provides detailed steps to utilize social media recruiting for your small business and target audience, and offers tips on how to monetize it. **Availability:** Online.

29528 ■ *"The Ingredients of a Marketing Plan"* in Entrepreneur
Description: Outlines the key ingredients of a marketing plan to provide a clear direction for your marketing efforts for the coming year. **Availability:** Online.

29529 ■ *"Jim Kukral Answers the Question: What is Marketing?"* in Small Business Trends(December 6, 2022)
URL(s): smallbiztrends.com/2022/12/what-is-marketing.html
Ed: Holly Chavez. **Released:** December 06, 2022. **Description:** A transcript and a link to a full interview about marketing. Defines what marketing actually is and how to step away from your brand to see what your customers see. **Availability:** Online.

29530 ■ *"Local Marketing Strategies for Success"* in Business News Daily (August 17, 2020)
Ed: Adam Uzialko. **Released:** August 17, 2020. **Description:** Local marketing is an essential element of a large marketing strategy for small businesses. This article offers local marketing strategies. **Availability:** Online.

29531 ■ *"Small Business Marketing on a Budget: 5 Low-Cost High-Impact Strategies"* in Benchmark One
Ed: Jonathan Herrick. **Description:** Provides information on how small businesses with limited resources and effectively market their producs/services and grow sales. **Availability:** Online.

29532 ■ *"Social Media & Your Business: Getting Started" in Legal Zoom (March 23, 2023)*
URL(s): www.legalzoom.com/articles/social-media -your-business-getting-started
Ed: Bilal Kaiser. **Released:** March 23, 2023. **Description:** Using social media as part of your marketing is a smart move because of the number of people on these sites that you can reach. Gives tips on what to do to set these accounts up and how to manage them. **Availability:** Online.

29533 ■ *"Upgrade Your Pricing Strategy to Match Consumer Behavior" in Harvard Business Review (May 28, 2020)*
Ed: David Hardisty, Thomas Allard, Dale Griffin. **Released:** May 28, 2020. **Description:** Provides hacks that marketing managers can use to nudge consumers to purchase higher quality goods and services. **Availability:** Online.

29534 ■ *"Want to Target Generation Z? You Need a Snapchat Marketing Strategy" in Forbes (October 23, 2020)*
Ed: Amine Rahal. **Released:** October 23, 2020. **Description:** Makes the case for integrating Snapchat advertising into your social media marketing strategy, especially for businesses and e-commerce stores targeting young Americans. **Availability:** Online.

29535 ■ *"Why It Is Essential to Put Strategy Before Tactics" in Duct Tape Marketing podcast*
Ed: John Jantsch. **Description:** Discusses what marketing is and what it is not as well as the need to develop a marketing strategy before thinking about tactics. **Availability:** Online.

VIDEO/AUDIO MEDIA

29536 ■ *7 Deadly Marketing Mistakes*
URL(s): ducttapemarketing.com/the-7-deadly-marke ting-mistakes-podcast
Ed: John Jantsch. **Released:** July 12, 2023. **Description:** Podcast outlines seven marketing mistakes: lacking a clear vision, trying to please everyone, mimicking the competition, wasting marketing resources, competing only on price, succumbing to the idea of the week, and lacking measurable success criteria.

29537 ■ *BS-Free Service Business Show: Mindful Marketing: Andréa Jones Shares Her Social Media Evolution*
URL(s): bsfreebusiness.com/mindful-marketing
Ed: Maggie Patterson. **Released:** April 08, 2024. **Description:** Podcast discusses navigating social media with a mindful marketing strategist. .

29538 ■ *BS-Free Service Business Show: Your Guide to Marketing a Service Based Business*
URL(s): insidescoop.libsyn.com/your-guide-to-marke ting-a-service-based-business
Ed: Maggie Patterson. **Released:** December 04, 2023. **Description:** Podcast offers a guide on marketing a service-based business, even if marketing isn't your forte.

29539 ■ *Finding Your Niche Market*
URL(s): www.startuphustlepodcast.com/finding-your -niche-market
Ed: Andrew Morgans. **Released:** October 31, 2023. **Description:** Podcast discusses finding your niche market, pivoting business strategy, and reinventing business models.

29540 ■ *HBR Ideacast: The Ins and Outs of the Influencer Industry*
URL(s): hbr.org/podcast/2023/02/the-ins-and-outs-of -the-influencer-industry
Ed: Alison Beard. **Released:** February 28, 2023. **Description:** Podcast offers advice for developing better influencer marketing strategies.

29541 ■ *How to Build Your Business Without Social Media with Rebecca Tracey*
URL(s): makinggoodpodcast.com/episodes/214
Ed: Lauren Tilden. **Released:** January 09, 2024. **Description:** Podcast discusses how to build a business without social media.

29542 ■ *How to Build Your Startup's Waitlist*
URL(s): www.startuphustlepodcast.com/how-to-buil d-your-startups-waitlist
Ed: Matt Watson. **Released:** January 04, 2023. **Description:** Podcast discusses the role a waitlist plays in generating buzz for your offerings and the secrets of strategic product/service launches. .

29543 ■ *How to Get Rapid Visibility*
URL(s): bizchix.com/353-how-to-get-rapid-visibility
Released: January 17, 2019. **Description:** Discusses an underutilized visibility strategy: leveraging your personal network. Also covers local speaking, live video, and workshops to build visibility.

29544 ■ *How I Built This: Advice Line with Maureen Kelly of Tarte Cosmetics*
URL(s): wondery.com/shows/how-i-built-this/episode/ 10386-advice-line-with-maureen-kelly-of-tarte -cosmetics
Ed: Guy Raz. **Released:** June 10, 2024. **Description:** Podcast answers questions from three early-stage founders about marketing strategies.

29545 ■ *How Two Sisters Scaled Vintage Lockers into a Thriving Global Brand with Mustard Made Founders Becca and Jess Stern*
URL(s): theceoschool.co/?s=245
Ed: Suneera Madhani. **Released:** June 12, 2023. **Description:** Podcast discusses scaling a business, establishing a brand, and fostering a resilient team in a highly competitive market.

29546 ■ *Impact of Community*
URL(s): ducttapemarketing.com/the-impact-of -community
Ed: John Jantsch. **Released:** August 23, 2023. **Description:** Podcast discusses the importance of community as acquisition channel, brand differentiator, feedback source, retention lever, and catalyst for change.

29547 ■ *The Knowledge Project: The Marketing Expert: A Masterclass in Strategic Positioning*
URL(s): fs.blog/knowleddge-project-podcast/april -dunford-2
Ed: Shane Parrish. **Released:** August 20, 2024. **Description:** Podcast discusses the framework behind market leadership. Includes market definition, competitive positioning, and strategic narrative.

29548 ■ *Navigating the Crowded Market Space*
URL(s): www.startuphustlepodcast.com/navigating -the-crowded-market-space
Ed: Matt Watson. **Released:** January 12, 2024. **Description:** Podcast discusses the online dating app landscape and describes hurdles in a highly competitive industry.

29549 ■ *Optimizing Product Launches for Growth*
URL(s): www.startuphustlepodcast.com/optimizing -product-launches-for-growth
Ed: Matt Watson. **Released:** December 14, 2023. **Description:** Podcast discusses optimal product launches.

29550 ■ *Strategies for Successful Product Launches*
URL(s): ducttapemarketing.com/strategies-for -successful-product-launches
Ed: John Jantsch. **Released:** June 01, 2023. **Description:** Podcast outlines product strategies with Mary Sheehan. Covers strategic readiness, understanding the market, and developing impactful messages.

29551 ■ *This Is Small Business: How to Build Your Marketing Strategy*
URL(s): www.smallbusiness.amazon/podcast-episo des/ep-55-how-to-build-your-marketing-strategy

Ed: Andrea Marquez. **Released:** April 30, 2024. **Description:** Podcast discusses how to find a target audience, how marketing approach may change as businesses grow, and how to use realistic goal setting and data analysis.

29552 ■ *This Is Small Business: How to Expand to Other Markets*
URL(s): www.smallbusiness.amazon/podcast-episo des/eo-41-how-to-expand-to-other-markets
Ed: Andrea Marquez. **Released:** November 28, 2023. **Description:** Podcast explores the challenges of entering a new market, even internationally, and how to switch your marketing strategy to accommodate that.

29553 ■ *This Is Small Business: How to Find the Right Customer for Your Product*
URL(s): www.smallbusiness.amazon/podcast-episo des/ep-40-how-to-find-the-right-customer-for-your -product
Ed: Andrea Marquez. **Released:** November 14, 2023. **Description:** Podcast explains how to use customer research as a marketing tool and the importance of timing when targeting customers.

29554 ■ *Video Marketing Made Easy*
URL(s): omny.fm/shows/startup-hustle/video-marke ting-made-easy
Released: September 11, 2023. **Description:** Discusses the evolution of content marketing, the importance of video, the impact of AI, and successful business content frequency. Features Vikram Chalana, CEO of Plctory.

TRADE SHOWS AND CONVENTIONS

29555 ■ Email Innovations Summit
URL(s): emailinnovationssummit.com

Frequency: Annual. **Description:** Workshops and talks about new email marketing trends and developments. **Principal Exhibits:** Workshops and talks about new email marketing trends and developments.

PUBLICATIONS

29556 ■ *"Marketing Strategies in Family Firms" in Journal of Small Business Strategy (April 13, 2021)*
URL(s): libjournals.mtsu.edu/index.php/jsbs/article/ view/2010

Ed: Manuel Alonso Dos Santos, Orlando Llanos Contreras, Raj V. Mahto. **Released:** April 13, 2021. **Description:** Explores why family firms do not apply marketing theories and branding concepts. **Availability:** PDF.

PUBLISHERS

29557 ■ *"Website promotion from scratch, where to start" in Geekers Magazine (September 20, 2021)*
URL(s): www.geekersmagazine.com/website-promo tion-from-scratch-where-to-start

Ed: Leon Howard. **Released:** September 20, 2021. **Description:** Discusses popular tactics small companies use for online marketing using social media.

START-UP INFORMATION

29558 ■ *"9 Strategies to BUILD and GROW Your Author Platform: A Step-by-Step Book Marketing Plan to Get More Exposure and Sales"*

Released: May 04, 2016. **Description:** A nine-step formula for marketing self-published books is presented. The author has sold over 103,000 books using this method since 2008 and continues to grow her customer base through email and followers. **Availability:** Print.

29559 ■ *Entrepreneurship*
Pub: John Wiley & Sons, Inc.
Contact: Christina Van Tassell, Executive Vice President Chief Financial Officer

Ed: William D. Bygrave, Andrew Zacharakis. **Released:** Fourth edition. **Price:** $75.95, paperback. **Description:** Information for starting a new business is shared, focusing on marketing and financing a product or service. **Availability:** Print.

29560 ■ *Going Solo: Developing a Home-Based Consulting Business from the Ground Up*

Description: Ways to turn specialized knowledge into a home-based successful consulting firm, focusing on targeting client needs, business plans, and growth.

29561 ■ *"How to Open and Operate a Financially Successful Florist and Floral Business Online and Off"*
Pub: Atlantic Publishing Co.
Contact: Dr. Heather L. Johnson, Contact

Released: Revised second edition. **Description:** A concise and easy to follow guide for opening a retail florist or floral business online or a traditional brick and mortar store. Knowledge shared includes: cost control systems, retail math and competitive pricing, legal concerns, tax reporting requirements and reporting, profit and loss statements, management skills, sales advertising, and marketing techniques, customer service, direct sales, internal marketing ideas, and more. **Availability:** CD-ROM; Print; Online.

29562 ■ *How to Start a Home-Based Mail Order Business*

Ed: Georganne Fiumara. **Released:** June 01, 2011. **Price:** Paperback. **Description:** Step-by-step guide for starting and growing a home-based mail order business. Information about equipment, pricing, online marketing, are included along with worksheets and checklists for planning. **Availability:** Print; Online.

29563 ■ *"The Self Starting Entrepreneurs Handbook"*
Pub: CreateSpace

Released: September 24, 2014. **Price:** $17.99; $11.03, paperback. **Description:** Information for starting a business is provided. Advice is given for writing a business plan, naming your new business, obtaining a business license if required, and building a marketing strategy for entrepreneurs. **Availability:** Print.

29564 ■ *Small Business for Dummies*
Pub: John Wiley & Sons, Inc.
Contact: Christina Van Tassell, Executive Vice President Chief Financial Officer

Ed: Eric Tyson, Jim Schell. **Released:** 5th Edition. **Price:** $24.99, paperback; $16.99, E-book. **Description:** Guidebook for anyone wanting to start or grow a small business; topics include information financing, budgeting, marketing, management and more. **Availability:** E-book; Print.

29565 ■ *"Starting Up All Over Again: Alex Bogusky Backs Bootcamp for Advertising Startup" in Denver Business Journal (Vol. 65, February 7, 2014, No. 39, pp. 8)*
Pub: American City Business Journals, Inc.
Contact: Mike Olivieri, Executive Vice President

Released: February 7, 2014. **Description:** Once called the Elvis of advertising, Alex Bogusky is now launching a new startup named 'Boomtown' with an aim to cultivate a new generation of advertising, marketing, design, and media related tech companies. The end goal of boomtown will be to figure out the trend in which media as well as the relationship between brands and people is going.

ASSOCIATIONS AND OTHER ORGANIZATIONS

29566 ■ **American Academy of Professional Coders (AAPC)**
2233 S Presidents Dr., Ste. F
  Salt Lake City, UT 84120
Ph: (801)236-2200
Free: 800-626-2633
Fax: (801)236-2258
Co. E-mail: info@aapc.com
URL: http://www.aapc.com
Contact: Colleen Gianatasio, President
E-mail: colleen.gianatasio@aapcnab.com
Facebook: www.facebook.com/AAPCFan
Linkedin: www.linkedin.com/company/aapc
X (Twitter): x.com/aapcstaff
Instagram: www.instagram.com/aapc_official
YouTube: www.youtube.com/c/AAPCHealthCare

Description: Works to elevate the standards of medical coding by providing ongoing education, certification, networking and recognition. Promotes high standards of physician and outpatient facility coding through education and certification. **Founded:** 1988. **Educational Activities:** HEALTHCON (Annual). **Geographic Preference:** National.

29567 ■ **American Marketing Association (AMA)**
American Marketing Association (AMA)
  130 E Randolph St., 22nd Fl.
  Chicago, IL 60601
Ph: (312)542-9000

Free: 800-262-1150
Co. E-mail: customersupport@ama.org
URL: http://www.ama.org
Contact: Bennie F. Johnson, Chief Executive Officer
Facebook: www.facebook.com/AmericanMarketing
Linkedin: www.linkedin.com/company/american
  -marketing-association
X (Twitter): x.com/ama_marketing

Description: Serves as a professional society of marketing and market research executives, sales and promotion managers, advertising specialists, academics, and others interested in marketing. Fosters research; sponsors seminars, conferences, and student marketing clubs; provides educational placement service and doctoral consortium. **Founded:** 1937. **Publications:** *Journal of International Marketing (JIM)* (Quarterly); *Journal of Public Policy & Marketing (JPP&M)* (Quarterly); *Marketing Health Services* (Quarterly); *Journal of Marketing Research (JMR)* (Bimonthly); *Marketing News: Reporting on the Marketing Profession* (Monthly); *AMA Conference Proceedings*; *Marketing Academics at AMA* (Bimonthly); *Marketing Matters* (Biweekly); *Journal of Marketing* (Bimonthly); *Marketing Management* (Bimonthly); *Marketing Executive Report* (Monthly); *Services Marketing Today* (Bimonthly); *Marketing News--Directory of Professional Courses for Marketing Issue*; *American Marketing Association--The M Guide Services Directory* (Annual); *International Membership Directory and Marketing Services Guide* (Annual); *Marketing News--Software Directory* (Annual); *Marketing Insights* (Quarterly). **Educational Activities:** AMA International Collegiate Conference (Annual); AMA Research and Strategy Summit; AMA Summer Academic Conference (Annual); Winter Academic Conference (Annual). **Awards:** AMA Explor Award (Annual); AMA/Irwin/McGraw-Hill Distinguished Marketing Educator Award (Annual); Shelby D. Hunt/Harold H. Maynard Award (Annual); Weitz-Winer-O'Dell Award (Annual); Charles Coolidge Parlin Marketing Research Award (Annual); AMA/Marketing Science Institute/H. Paul Root Award (Annual). **Geographic Preference:** National; Local.

29568 ■ **American Marketing Association Foundation (AMAF)**
130 E Randolph St., 22nd Fl.
  Chicago, IL 60601
Free: 800-262-1150
Co. E-mail: foundation@ama.org
URL: http://www.ama.org/about-ama-foundation
Contact: Jeremy Van Ek, Chief Executive Officer (Acting) Chief Operating Officer
Facebook: www.facebook.com/AmericanMarketing
Linkedin: www.linkedin.com/company/american
  -marketing-association
X (Twitter): x.com/AMA_Marketing

Description: Recognizes visionary leaders who have made an impact in the industry and in their communities. Presents awards to influential marketing students, academics, and professionals. **Awards:** Richard A. Hammill Scholarship Fund (Annual); Robert J. Lavidge Global Marketing Research Award (Annual); Valuing Diversity PhD Scholarship (Annual);

Erin Anderson Award for an Emerging Female Marketing Scholar and Mentor (Annual); Leonard L. Berry Marketing Book Award (Annual); S. Tamar Cavusgil Award (Annual); Paul E. Green Award (Annual); John A. Howard/AMA Doctoral Dissertation Award (Annual); Thomas C. Kinnear/Journal of Public Policy and Marketing Award (Annual); The Vijay Mahajan Award for Career Contributions to Marketing Strategy (Annual); AMA Foundation Nonprofit Marketer of the Year (Annual); Sheth Foundation/Journal of Marketing Award (Annual); Louis W. Stern Award (Annual); Hans B. Thorelli Award (Annual).

29569 ■ AMIN Worldwide [The Advertising and Marketing Independent Network (AMIN)]
3587 Northshore Dr.
  Wayzata, MN 55391
Ph: (613)473-4124
Co. E-mail: contact@aminworldwide.com
URL: http://www.aminworldwide.com
Contact: Ali Sizemore Mahaffy, President
Facebook: www.facebook.com/AMINWorldwide
Linkedin: www.linkedin.com/company/aminworldwide
YouTube: www.youtube.com/channel/UC7S7jayioY9J
  6HBEfrlIdjA
Description: Represents independent marketing agencies. **Founded:** 1932. **Geographic Preference:** Multinational.

29570 ■ ANA Business Marketing
155 E 44th St.
  New York, NY 10017
Ph: (212)697-5950
URL: http://www.marketing.org
Contact: Elizabeth Bamonte, President
URL(s): anab2b.nyc
Linkedin: www.linkedin.com/company/ana
  -businessmarketing-nyc
Description: The primary repository of the best in business-to-business marketing information and resources. **Founded:** 1922. **Publications:** The Business to Business Marketer (Quarterly); Business Marketing Association--Membership Directory (Annual); Tuesday Marketing Notes (Weekly). **Awards:** ANA B2 Awards (Annual). **Geographic Preference:** Multinational.

29571 ■ Center for Exhibition Industry Research (CEIR)
12700 Pk. Central Dr., Ste. 308
  Dallas, TX 75251
Ph: (972)687-9242
Fax: (972)692-6020
Co. E-mail: info@ceir.org
URL: http://www.ceir.org
Contact: Cathy Breden, CMP, CAE, Chief Executive Officer
Facebook: www.facebook.com/CEIRHQ
X (Twitter): x.com/ceir_hq
YouTube: www.youtube.com/user/CEIRHQ
Description: Promotes the growth and value of exhibitions and other face-to-face marketing events by delivering research-based knowledge tools. Consists of exhibition organizers, service providers, exhibitors, CVBs, and facilities. **Founded:** 1978. **Geographic Preference:** National.

29572 ■ CMO Council [Chief Marketing Officer Council]
1494 Hamilton Way
  San Jose, CA 95125
Ph: (408)677-5300
URL: http://www.cmocouncil.org
Contact: Donovan Neale-May, Executive Director
E-mail: donovan@cmocouncil.org
X (Twitter): x.com/CMO_Council
YouTube: www.youtube.com/user/cmocouncil
Description: Fosters thought leadership and knowledge exchange, business support, and networking among marketing leaders and executives around the world. **Geographic Preference:** Multinational.

29573 ■ Direct Marketing Association of Detroit (DMAD) - Resource Library
PO Box 2515
  Southfield, MI 48037
Ph: (313)462-9325

Co. E-mail: info@dmadetroit.org
URL: http://dmadetroit.org
Contact: Charlie Kondek, President
Facebook: www.facebook.com/dmadetroit
Instagram: www.instagram.com/dmadetroit
Description: Promotes excellence in the direct marketing industry in Michigan. Facilitates networking; provides referrals. **Scope:** Marketing. **Founded:** 1959. **Holdings:** Figures not available. **Publications:** Direct Marketing Association of Detroit Response (Monthly); Direct Marketing Association of Detroit-- Membership Directory. **Awards:** Direct Marketing Association of Detroit Target Award (Annual). **Geographic Preference:** Local.

29574 ■ Internet Marketing Association (IMA)
638 Camino De Los Mares, Ste. H130-612
  San Clemente, CA 92673
Ph: (949)443-9300
Fax: (949)443-2215
Co. E-mail: info@imanetwork.org
URL: http://imanetwork.org
Contact: Sinan Kanatsiz, Founder Chairman
Facebook: www.facebook.com/IMAnetwork
Linkedin: www.linkedin.com/company/internetmarke
  tingassociation
X (Twitter): x.com/IMA_Network
YouTube: www.youtube.com/user/IMAnetworking
Description: Promotes the internet marketing industry; offers training and networking opportunities for members. **Founded:** 2001.

29575 ■ Professionels en Produits Promotionnels du Canada (PPPC) [Promotional Products Professionals of Canada]
386 Broadway, Ste. 503
  Winnipeg, MB, Canada R3C 3R6
Ph: (514)489-5359
Free: 866-450-7722
Fax: (877)947-9767
Co. E-mail: info@pppc.ca
URL: http://pppc.ca
Contact: Jonathan N. Strauss, President
E-mail: jonathan@pppc.ca
Facebook: www.facebook.com/PPPC.ca
Linkedin: www.linkedin.com/company/promotional
  -product-professionals-of-canada-pppc-
X (Twitter): x.com/pppcinc
Instagram: www.instagram.com/pppcinc
YouTube: www.youtube.com/user/pppcinc
Description: Studies, promotes, fosters, and develops the economic interests of the participants in the promotional products industry of Canada. **Founded:** 1956. **Publications:** The Image News (Quarterly); E-Image News (Monthly); The Idea Book (Annual); Images (Semiannual); promoVantage (Semiannual); promoXpert (Semiannual). **Educational Activities:** National Convention (Annual); Traveling Optimum Promotional Show (TOPS). **Awards:** PPPC Image Award (Annual). **Geographic Preference:** National.

29576 ■ Women's Regional Publications of America (WRPA)
c/o J. M. Gaffney
  San Antonio Woman, 8603 Botts Ln.
  San Antonio, TX 78217
Ph: (210)826-5375
URL: http://www.womensregionalpublications.org
Contact: J. M. Gaffney, Publisher
E-mail: info@sawoman.com
Description: Provides a forum where publishers of women's publications and business directories share information and resources. Increases the visibility, authority, influence and status of women's business for the purpose of promoting growth and support of women. Educates the general public about the need to support women-owned businesses, including equal opportunity employers and contractors. **Founded:** 1986. **Geographic Preference:** National.

EDUCATIONAL PROGRAMS

29577 ■ Advertising Research (Onsite)
URL(s): www.burkeinstitute.com/Schedules/outline
  .cfm?p=1&sid=504

Description: This seminar provides a practical and a comprehensive framework for classifying various advertising research methods. **Audience:** Print and broadcast advertising professionals. **Principal Exhibits:** This seminar provides a practical and a comprehensive framework for classifying various advertising research methods.

29578 ■ AMA Successful Product Management (Onsite)
American Management Association (AMA)
  1601 Broadway
  New York, NY 10019
Ph: (212)586-8100
Free: 800-262-9699
Fax: (212)903-8168
Co. E-mail: customerservice@amanet.org
URL: http://www.amanet.org
Contact: Manny Avramidis, President
URL(s): www.amanet.org/training/seminars/onsite/
  Successful-Product-Management.aspx
Description: Covers duties, finance, marketing techniques, new product development, and advertising. **Audience:** Product managers and brand marketers and directors. **Principal Exhibits:** Covers duties, finance, marketing techniques, new product development, and advertising.

29579 ■ AMA's Advanced Course in Strategic Marketing (Onsite)
American Management Association (AMA)
  1601 Broadway
  New York, NY 10019
Ph: (212)586-8100
Free: 800-262-9699
Fax: (212)903-8168
Co. E-mail: customerservice@amanet.org
URL: http://www.amanet.org
Contact: Manny Avramidis, President
URL(s): www.amanet.org/training/seminars/onsite/a
  dvanced-course-in-strategic-marketing.aspx
Price: $2,345, Non-members; $2,095, Members AMA; $1,984, Members GSA. **Description:** Three-day seminar focusing on strategic marketing tools to increase the spending of customers and acquire new ones. **Audience:** Anyone whose business would benefit from strategic marketing, including experienced marketing managers, directors and vice presidents of marketing, as well as executives and managers in finance, operations, customer service, R&D and other departments. **Principal Exhibits:** Three-day seminar focusing on strategic marketing tools to increase the spending of customers and acquire new ones.

29580 ■ Applications of Marketing Research (Onsite)
Seminar Information Service Inc. (SIS)
  250 El Camino Real., Ste. 112
  Tustin, CA 92780
Ph: (714)508-0340
Free: 877-736-4636
Fax: (714)734-8027
Co. E-mail: info@seminarinformation.com
URL: http://www.seminarinformation.com
Contact: Catherine Bellizzi, President
URL(s): www.seminarinformation.com
Description: Learn which research techniques are used (and misused) for providing management with practical information to make decisions in several specific areas including new and current products, promotion, claim justification, demand analysis, positioning and segmentation. **Audience:** Marketing researchers, professionals. **Principal Exhibits:** Learn which research techniques are used (and misused) for providing management with practical information to make decisions in several specific areas including new and current products, promotion, claim justification, demand analysis, positioning and segmentation.

29581 ■ Comprehensive Email Marketing Strategies Seminar (Onsite)
Seminar Information Service Inc. (SIS)
  250 El Camino Real., Ste. 112
  Tustin, CA 92780
Ph: (714)508-0340

Free: 877-736-4636
Fax: (714)734-8027
Co. E-mail: info@seminarinformation.com
URL: http://www.seminarinformation.com
Contact: Catherine Bellizzi, President
URL(s): www.seminarinformation.com/qqbumg/
comprehensive-email-marketing-strategies-seminar

Description: Learn how to meet your acquisition and retention objectives through the power of email; comply with changing regulations; crank up response using the latest best practices; reach your target every time; determine true campaign ROI by analyzing the measurements of success that matter; and identify what's working and what isn't through testing and improve campaign performance. **Audience:** Professionals. **Principal Exhibits:** Learn how to meet your acquisition and retention objectives through the power of email; comply with changing regulations; crank up response using the latest best practices; reach your target every time; determine true campaign ROI by analyzing the measurements of success that matter; and identify what's working and what isn't through testing and improve campaign performance.

29582 ■ Consultative Selling Skills Training
URL(s): www.bakercommunications.com/Consultative-Selling-Skills.htm

Description: This hands-on, exercise-driven workshop teaches skills that boost sales and profitability through an increased understanding and implementation of the need/satisfaction sales process. Cloud-based training also available. **Audience:** Industry professionals. **Principal Exhibits:** This hands-on, exercise-driven workshop teaches skills that boost sales and profitability through an increased understanding and implementation of the need/satisfaction sales process. Cloud-based training also available.

29583 ■ Content That Drives Sales Across Pinterest and Instagram, Session #1
URL(s): cwewbc.ecenterdirect.com/events/977106

Description: Online class offered by the Center for Women and Enterprise teaching how to create effective content for your small business to be used on social media. **Principal Exhibits:** Online class offered by the Center for Women and Enterprise teaching how to create effective content for your small business to be used on social media.

29584 ■ Content That Drives Sales Across Pinterest and Instragram, Session #2
Description: Online course offered by the Center for Women and Enterprise that shows how to create content and marketing for your small business using Pinterest. **Principal Exhibits:** Online course offered by the Center for Women and Enterprise that shows how to create content and marketing for your small business using Pinterest.

29585 ■ Data Analysis for Marketing Research: The Fundamentals (Onsite)
URL(s): www.burkeinstitute.com

Description: Participants will learn how to summarize basic trends and relationships in marketing research. **Audience:** Research analysts, consultants, marketing specialists and project managers . **Principal Exhibits:** Participants will learn how to summarize basic trends and relationships in marketing research.

29586 ■ Designing Effective Questionnaires: A Step By Step Workshop
Burke Inc.
  500 W 7th St.
  Cincinnati, OH 45203
Free: 800-688-2674
Co. E-mail: info@burke.com
URL: http://www.burke.com
URL(s): www.burkeinstitute.com/SeminarDescription/Detail/RM03

Description: Participants will learn how to phrase questions and design questionnaires that are responsive to management's information needs. **Audience:** Industry professionals. **Principal Exhibits:** Partici-

pants will learn how to phrase questions and design questionnaires that are responsive to management's information needs.

29587 ■ EEI Communications Intensive Introduction to Copyediting (Onsite)
URL(s): www.eeicom.com

Description: Covers basic editorial marks, style, spelling and grammar, and other details of copywriting and editing. **Audience:** Writers, editors, designers, proofreaders, and publication specialists. **Principal Exhibits:** Covers basic editorial marks, style, spelling and grammar, and other details of copywriting and editing. **Telecommunication Services:** train@eeicom.com.

29588 ■ Focus Group Moderator Training (Onsite)
Seminar Information Service Inc. (SIS)
  250 El Camino Real., Ste. 112
  Tustin, CA 92780
Ph: (714)508-0340
Free: 877-736-4636
Fax: (714)734-8027
Co. E-mail: info@seminarinformation.com
URL: http://www.seminarinformation.com
Contact: Catherine Bellizzi, President
URL(s): www.seminarinformation.com/details.cfm?qc=qqahrb

Description: Learn through hands-on experiences: how to moderate a focus group by participating in a series of skill-building workshops and personal feedback sessions; to assess their development by watching multiple videotapes of themselves moderating group sessions; and how to consult with clients from design to final results presentation. **Audience:** Marketing managers, marketing researchers . **Principal Exhibits:** Learn through hands-on experiences: how to moderate a focus group by participating in a series of skill-building workshops and personal feedback sessions; to assess their development by watching multiple videotapes of themselves moderating group sessions; and how to consult with clients from design to final results presentation. Dates and Locations: Cincinnati, OH.

29589 ■ Focus Group Moderator Training (Onsite)
URL(s). www.burkeinstitute.com

Description: A four-day seminar that teaches how to moderate a focus group by participating in a series of skill-building workshops and personal feedback sessions. **Audience:** Market researh analysts, managers, engineers, and professionals. **Principal Exhibits:** A four-day seminar that teaches how to moderate a foous group by partioipating in a ceries of okill building workshops and personal feedback sessions.

29590 ■ Fundamentals of Marketing: Your Action Plan for Success
American Management Association (AMA)
  1601 Broadway
  New York, NY 10019
Ph: (212)586-8100
Free: 800-262-9699
Fax: (212)903-8168
Co. E-mail: customerservice@amanet.org
URL: http://www.amanet.org
Contact: Manny Avramidis, President
URL(s): www.amanet.org/training/seminars/Fundamentals-of-Marketing-Your-Action-Plan-for-Success.aspx
Facebook: www.facebook.com/AmericanManagementAssn
Linkedin: www.linkedin.com/company/american-management-association
X (Twitter): twitter.com/amanet
Instagram: www.instagram.com/americanmanagementassociation
YouTube: www.youtube.com/user/AmericanManagement

Price: $2,095, Non-members; $1,895, Members; $1,795, General Services Administration (GSA). **Frequency:** Continuous. **Description:** Three-day seminar for new marketing professionals and product managers; covers marketing tools, skills, and techniques. Held in Chicago, IL; New York, NY; San

Francisco, CA; Washington, DC; and Arlington, VA. Also available live online. **Audience:** Newly-appointed marketers, product, brand, and advertising managers, business professionals and executives who need a clearer understanding of marketing's role in generating profits. **Principal Exhibits:** Three-day seminar for new marketing professionals and product managers; covers marketing tools, skills, and techniques. Held in Chicago, IL; New York, NY; San Francisco, CA; Washington, DC; and Arlington, VA. Also available live online. **Telecommunication Services:** customerservice@amanet.org.

29591 ■ Fundamentals of Marketing: Your Action Plan for Success
Canadian Management Centre (CMC)
  150 King St. W Ste. 271
  Toronto, ON, Canada M5H 1J9
Ph: (416)214-5678
Free: 877-262-2519
Fax: (416)214-6047
Co. E-mail: cmcinfo@cmcoutperform.com
URL: http://cmcoutperform.com
Contact: Chris Peacock, Director

Description: Three-day seminar for new marketing professionals and product managers; covers marketing tools, skills, and techniques. **Audience:** Individuals new to marketing and those who work closely with marketing department; Professionals and managers who seek a better understanding of marketing objectives, strategies and plans. **Principal Exhibits:** Three-day seminar for new marketing professionals and product managers; covers marketing tools, skills, and techniques.

29592 ■ How to Write a Killer Marketing Plan (Onsite)
URL(s): www.amanet.org

Description: Develop a successful marketing plan from financials to research to media method. **Audience:** New marketers, mid- to senior-level marketers, brand managers, directors, VPs and CMOs. **Principal Exhibits:** Develop a successful marketing plan from financials to research to media method.

29593 ■ Linking Customer, Employee and Process Data to Drive Profitability (Onsite)
Seminar Information Service Inc. (SIS)
  250 El Camino Real., Ste. 112
  Tustin, CA 92780
Ph: (714)508-0340
Free: 877-736-4636
Fax: (714)734-8027
Co. E-mail: info@seminarinformation.com
URL: http://www.seminarinformation.com
Contact: Catherine Bellizzi, President
URL(s): www.seminarinformation.com

Description: Learn the origins of the rational for linkage research and analysis, and why linkage research and analysis is an area of critical importance to marketers and marketing researchers. **Audience:** Industry professionals. **Principal Exhibits:** Learn the origins of the rational for linkage research and analysis, and why linkage research and analysis is an area of critical importance to marketers and marketing researchers.

29594 ■ Market Research: How To Get The Right Data to Make the Right Decisions (Onsite)
Seminar Information Service Inc. (SIS)
  250 El Camino Real., Ste. 112
  Tustin, CA 92780
Ph: (714)508-0340
Free: 877-736-4636
Fax: (714)734-8027
Co. E-mail: info@seminarinformation.com
URL: http://www.seminarinformation.com
Contact: Catherine Bellizzi, President
URL(s): www.seminarinformation.com

Description: Learn how to use market research to determine your company's competitive position and enhance performance. **Audience:** Industry professionals. **Principal Exhibits:** Learn how to use market research to determine your company's competitive position and enhance performance.

29595 ■ Market Segmentation and Positioning Research (Onsite)

Seminar Information Service Inc. (SIS)
250 El Camino Real., Ste. 112
Tustin, CA 92780
Ph: (714)508-0340
Free: 877-736-4636
Fax: (714)734-8027
Co. E-mail: info@seminarinformation.com
URL: http://www.seminarinformation.com
Contact: Catherine Bellizzi, President
URL(s): www.seminarinformation.com/details.cfm?qc=qqahzf

Description: Learn how to segment your markets and select the best target markets for your products and services, including how to design marketing research studies from start to finish to segment markets and which commercial data sources are available to help you segment your markets. **Audience:** Product and marketing researchers, and managers. **Principal Exhibits:** Learn how to segment your markets and select the best target markets for your products and services, including how to design marketing research studies from start to finish to segment markets and which commercial data sources are available to help you segment your markets.

29596 ■ Measuring and Maximizing Marketing ROI (Onsite)

Seminar Information Service Inc. (SIS)
250 El Camino Real., Ste. 112
Tustin, CA 92780
Ph: (714)508-0340
Free: 877-736-4636
Fax: (714)734-8027
Co. E-mail: info@seminarinformation.com
URL: http://www.seminarinformation.com
Contact: Catherine Bellizzi, President
URL(s): www.seminarinformation.com

Description: Learn how to use marketing ROI results to general more competitive corporate-wide product and service strategies, including the challenges, opportunities and roadblocks of marketing ROI today and how leading companies track and access marketing ROI. **Audience:** Marketers at all levels including marketing VPs, directors and managers . **Principal Exhibits:** Learn how to use marketing ROI results to general more competitive corporate-wide product and service strategies, including the challenges, opportunities and roadblocks of marketing ROI today and how leading companies track and access marketing ROI.

29597 ■ New Product Research: Laying the Foundation for New Product Success (Onsite)

Seminar Information Service Inc. (SIS)
250 El Camino Real., Ste. 112
Tustin, CA 92780
Ph: (714)508-0340
Free: 877-736-4636
Fax: (714)734-8027
Co. E-mail: info@seminarinformation.com
URL: http://www.seminarinformation.com
Contact: Catherine Bellizzi, President
URL(s): www.seminarinformation.com/qqapap/new-product-research-laying-the-foundation-for-new-product

Price: $2,195. **Description:** Learn how to design and implement marketing research studies to guide the total product development and evaluation process. **Audience:** Marketing researchers, and staff members . **Principal Exhibits:** Learn how to design and implement marketing research studies to guide the total product development and evaluation process.

29598 ■ Next Generation Qualitative Tools: Social Media, Online Communities & Virtual Research Platforms (Onsite)

Seminar Information Service Inc. (SIS)
250 El Camino Real., Ste. 112
Tustin, CA 92780
Ph: (714)508-0340
Free: 877-736-4636

Fax: (714)734-8027
Co. E-mail: info@seminarinformation.com
URL: http://www.seminarinformation.com
Contact: Catherine Bellizzi, President
URL(s): www.seminarinformation.com/qqbtgc/next-generation-qualitative-tools-social-media-online

Description: Learn how social media is being used by qualitative research professionals to support data and enhance the ability to reach their target audience, and more. **Audience:** Marketing research practitioners, qualitative research consultants, and end users. **Principal Exhibits:** Learn how social media is being used by qualitative research professionals to support data and enhance the ability to reach their target audience, and more.

29599 ■ Online Marketing and Search Engine Optimization

URL(s): www.eeicom.com

Description: Covers how to increase traffic to your online site to market your products and services using the Web, including creating and implementation of your plan, setting a budget, redesigning Web site for search engine optimization, tips and tricks, promotion hints, tips, and advice, and how to measure your Internet marketing results. **Audience:** Marketing professionals. **Principal Exhibits:** Covers how to increase traffic to your online site to market your products and services using the Web, including creating and implementation of your plan, setting a budget, redesigning Web site for search engine optimization, tips and tricks, promotion hints, tips, and advice, and how to measure your Internet marketing results.

29600 ■ Online Research Best Practices and Innovations (Onsite)

Seminar Information Service Inc. (SIS)
250 El Camino Real., Ste. 112
Tustin, CA 92780
Ph: (714)508-0340
Free: 877-736-4636
Fax: (714)734-8027
Co. E-mail: info@seminarinformation.com
URL: http://www.seminarinformation.com
Contact: Catherine Bellizzi, President
URL(s): www.seminarinformation.com

Description: Get up to date with the most recent developments relating to Web surveys and other online marketing research, and learn when to consider online qualitative research, including in-depth interviews, bulletin board sessions and online focus groups. **Audience:** Anyone responsible for conducting online research, professionals. **Principal Exhibits:** Get up to date with the most recent developments relating to Web surveys and other online marketing research, and learn when to consider online qualitative research, including in-depth interviews, bulletin board sessions and online focus groups.

29601 ■ Online Research Best Practices and Innovations (Onsite)

URL(s): www.burkeinstitute.com/blog/?p=328

Description: To help participants get up to date with the most recent developments relating to Web surveys and other online marketing. **Audience:** Research analysts, consultants, marketing specialists, project managers, researchers and moderators . **Principal Exhibits:** To help participants get up to date with the most recent developments relating to Web surveys and other online marketing.

29602 ■ Planning and Developing New Products (Onsite)

Seminar Information Service Inc. (SIS)
250 El Camino Real., Ste. 112
Tustin, CA 92780
Ph: (714)508-0340
Free: 877-736-4636
Fax: (714)734-8027
Co. E-mail: info@seminarinformation.com
URL: http://www.seminarinformation.com
Contact: Catherine Bellizzi, President
URL(s): www.seminarinformation.com

Description: Covers how to take your new product from concept to profitability. **Audience:** Product managers . **Principal Exhibits:** Covers how to take your new product from concept to profitability.

29603 ■ Practical Marketing Research (Onsite)

URL(s): www.burkeinstitute.com

Description: A user-oriented discussion of traditional and contemporary methods for research practitioners. **Audience:** Marketing researchers, marketing analysts and research managers. **Principal Exhibits:** A user-oriented discussion of traditional and contemporary methods for research practitioners.

29604 ■ Practical Multivariate Analysis (Onsite)

URL(s): www.burkeinstitute.com/seminars/index.cfm?pgid=5&sid=DA10

Description: Extends participants' understanding of data analysis beyond "Tools and Techniques of Data Analysis.". **Audience:** Project managers, marketing research managers and research analysts. **Principal Exhibits:** Extends participants' understanding of data analysis beyond "Tools and Techniques of Data Analysis.".

29605 ■ Pricing Strategies: Capturing and Sustaining a Competitive Advantage (Onsite)

Seminar Information Service Inc. (SIS)
250 El Camino Real., Ste. 112
Tustin, CA 92780
Ph: (714)508-0340
Free: 877-736-4636
Fax: (714)734-8027
Co. E-mail: info@seminarinformation.com
URL: http://www.seminarinformation.com
Contact: Catherine Bellizzi, President
URL(s): www.seminarinformation.com

Price: 1,995.00. **Description:** Gain unique tools and proven tactics to better assess your current pricing position and develop a pricing strategy that will increase your company's 'wallet share' and long-term customer loyalty. **Audience:** Industry professionals. **Principal Exhibits:** Gain unique tools and proven tactics to better assess your current pricing position and develop a pricing strategy that will increase your company's 'wallet share' and long-term customer loyalty.

29606 ■ Social Media Made Simple

URL(s): cwewbc.ecenterdirect.com/events/977280

Description: This online course gives an introduction on how to use various social media sites to market your small business. **Audience:** Women small business owners. **Principal Exhibits:** This online course gives an introduction on how to use various social media sites to market your small business.

29607 ■ Social Media Marketing (Onsite)

Seminar Information Service Inc. (SIS)
250 El Camino Real., Ste. 112
Tustin, CA 92780
Ph: (714)508-0340
Free: 877-736-4636
Fax: (714)734-8027
Co. E-mail: info@seminarinformation.com
URL: http://www.seminarinformation.com
Contact: Catherine Bellizzi, President
URL(s): www.seminarinformation.com

Description: Learn how you can obtain social marketing success for your organization. **Audience:** Social media marketing professionals. **Principal Exhibits:** Learn how you can obtain social marketing success for your organization.

29608 ■ Specialized Moderator Skills for Qualitative Research Applications (Onsite)

URL(s): www.burkeinstitute.com

Description: A four-day workshop designed for the active focus moderator. **Audience:** Product managers, research analysts, and executive directors . **Principal Exhibits:** A four-day workshop designed for the active focus moderator.

29609 ■ Strategy Execution: Getting it Done (Onsite)

URL(s): cmcoutperform.com

Description: Learn techniques to help ensure that costly and risky organizational or corporate strategy initiatives succeed. **Audience:** Industry professionals. **Principal Exhibits:** Learn techniques to help ensure that costly and risky organizational or corporate strategy initiatives succeed.

29610 ■ Tools and Techniques of Data Analysis

Burke Inc.
500 W 7th St.
Cincinnati, OH 45203
Free: 800-688-2674
Co. E-mail: info@burke.com
URL: http://www.burke.com
URL(s): www.burkeinstitute.com/SeminarDescription/Detail/DA02

Description: A comprehensive seminar that packs everything participants want to know about data analysis in marketing research into flowcharts and real world experience. **Audience:** Research analysts, consultants, marketing specialists, and project managers, professionals. **Principal Exhibits:** A comprehensive seminar that packs everything participants want to know about data analysis in marketing research into flowcharts and real world experience.

29611 ■ Tools & Techniques of Data Analysis (Onsite)

Seminar Information Service Inc. (SIS)
250 El Camino Real., Ste. 112
Tustin, CA 92780
Ph: (714)508-0340
Free: 877-736-4636
Fax: (714)734-8027
Co. E-mail: info@seminarinformation.com
URL: http://www.seminarinformation.com
Contact: Catherine Bellizzi, President
URL(s): www.seminarinformation.com/details.cfm?qc=qqahua

Description: Includes everything participants want to know about data analysis in marketing research using a series of specially developed how-to flowcharts and real world examples, including how to plan, execute, analyze, interpret, and communicate the results of an analysis plan to answer management's questions. **Audience:** Marketing research analysts. **Principal Exhibits:** Includes everything participants want to know about data analysis in marketing research using a series of specially developed how-to flowcharts and real world examples, including how to plan, execute, analyze, interpret, and communicate the results of an analysis plan to answer management's questions.

29612 ■ Web Marketing: Design. Navigation. Analytics. Understanding the Big Picture (Onsite)

Seminar Information Service Inc. (SIS)
250 El Camino Real., Ste. 112
Tustin, CA 92780
Ph: (714)508-0340
Free: 877-736-4636
Fax: (714)734-8027
Co. E-mail: info@seminarinformation.com
URL: http://www.seminarinformation.com
Contact: Catherine Bellizzi, President
URL(s): www.seminarinformation.com

Description: Both the marketer and the programmer learn how to get the creative and technical sides of website development working together achieving the best results. **Audience:** Professionals. **Principal Exhibits:** Both the marketer and the programmer learn how to get the creative and technical sides of website development working together achieving the best results.

29613 ■ Writing and Presenting Actionable Marketing Research Reports (Onsite)

URL(s): www.burkeinstitute.com/Schedules/index.cfm?sid=C01

Description: A three-day seminar to teach participants what decision-makers want from a marketing research study and how to apply the findings. **Audi-**ence: Research analysts, consultants, marketing specialists, project managers, researchers and moderators . **Principal Exhibits:** A three-day seminar to teach participants what decision-makers want from a marketing research study and how to apply the findings.

REFERENCE WORKS

29614 ■ 4 Ways AI Is Helping Small Businesses in Sales & Marketing

Ed: Usman Khalil. **Released:** April 03, 2020. **Description:** Discusses how small businesses can utilize artificial intelligence (AI) to help them run their businesses more efficiently, to simplify tasks, to reduce risks and human errors, and to safe on costs. Presents 4 ways in which small businesses are leveraging AI for sales and marketing. **Availability:** Online.

29615 ■ "The 5 Keys to Successful Marketing" in Massage Magazine (January 10, 2019)

Ed: Savanna Bell. **Released:** January 10, 2019. **Description:** Provides an overview of how to market your massage therapy business, providing five keys to successful marketing. **Availability:** Online.

29616 ■ "5 Marketing Missteps That Make Cash Flow and Business Growth Stumble" in Entrepreneur (January 25, 2018)

Ed: Shaun Buck. **Released:** January 25, 2018. **Description:** Discusses the fact that mistakes that many entrepreneurs make are often made with marketing, sales, and business growth and these mistakes are causing cash flow issues. Discusses the success and growth that comes from creating marketing assets and business systems and processes. **Availability:** Online.

29617 ■ "5 Tips to Attract New Online Customers" in Legal Zoom (March 9, 2023)

URL(s): www.legalzoom.com/articles/5-tips-to-attract-new-online-customers
Ed: Sandra Beckwith. **Released:** March 09, 2023. **Availability:** Online.

29618 ■ "5 Tips to Protect Your Brand on Social Media" in Legal Zoom (March 16, 2023)

URL(s): www.legalzoom.com/articles/5-tips-to-protect-your-brand-on-social-media
Ed: Kylie Ora Lobell. **Released:** March 16, 2023. **Description:** Using social media sites for marketing your company can be a great way to reach your customers, but sometimes things can go wrong and bad press can take place. Be sure follow the steps given to protect your brand and avoid disaster. **Availability:** Online.

29619 ■ "5 Ways to Use Video Marketing to Strengthen Your Small Business Branding" in Insider (Feb. 26, 2021)

URL(s): www.businessinsider.com/how-to-use-video-marketing-to-expand-small-business-branding-2021-2
Ed: Kimberly Zhang. **Released:** February 26, 2021. **Description:** Video marketing can take your small business brand to new levels. This article provides tips on how to master video marketing. **Availability:** Online.

29620 ■ "6 Effective Yoga Marketing Tips to Take Your Studio to the Next Level" in Glofox blog (April 2, 2019)

Ed: Eamonn Curley. **Released:** April 02, 2019. **Description:** Whether you're a yoga teacher, opening a yoga studio or own an existing business, your marketing plan is crucial to growing your business. This article will go through 6 effective tips to help you grow your studio today. **Availability:** Online.

29621 ■ "6 Tips for Growing a Waste Management Business" in Fundbox Blog (April 27, 2017)

Ed: Rieva Lesonsky. **Released:** April 27, 2017. **Description:** Discusses the variety of opportunities in the waste management industry as well as how to grow a waste management business. **Availability:** Online.

29622 ■ "6 Ways Artificial Intelligence Can Transform Your Small Business" in business.com (April 10, 2020)

Released: April 10, 2020. **Description:** Discusses how you can leverage artificial intelligence (AI) to better serve your business and your customers. **Availability:** Online.

29623 ■ 7 AI Tools for Small Businesses Marketing

Ed: Yonge Chen. **Released:** February 14, 2020. **Description:** Artificial Intelligence (AI) resources are indispensable tools for establishing your marketing presence. This article discusses some of the most popular AI-based tools that small-scale businesses can use for marketing purposes. **Availability:** Online.

29624 ■ 8 Ideas on How to Get Landscaping Customers

Description: Provides techniques to utilize to gain landscaping customers to help you build a profitable landscape business. **Availability:** Online.

29625 ■ "10 B2B Marketing Strategies to Grow Your Presence" in The Blueprint (September 23, 2020)

Ed: John Rampton. **Released:** September 23, 2020. **Description:** Discusses how business-to-business marketing has changed in the digital age, defines why B2B marketing strategies have to be different than business-to-consumer strategies, discusses what to consider before developing your B2B strategy and the best strategies to use for your business. **Availability:** Online.

29626 ■ 10 Easy Ways to Get Started with Marketing AI (Artificial Intelligence)

Ed: Bridget Johnston. **Released:** September 26, 2019. **Description:** Implementing an AI strategy is becoming a standard for brands, online retailers and agencies. This article discusses how to get started with the right AI marketing solution for your small business so that you can reap the benefits. **Availability:** Online.

29627 ■ 10 Unconventional Ways to Get More Moving Leads

Ed: Jason Rothman. **Released:** August 09, 2017. **Description:** This article looks at unconventional moving ideas can bring in tons of leads and moving clients to your business. **Availability:** Online.

29628 ■ 13 B2B E-commerce Brands Unveil the Secrets to Scalable Online Success

Ed: Tracey Wallace. **Description:** Discusses business-to-business e-commerce and benefits of selling online, e-commerce misconceptions, and e-commerce marketing. **Availability:** Online.

29629 ■ 25 Dead Simple Landscape Marketing Ideas to Increase New Lawn Care Customers and Sales

Ed: Joy Gendusa. **Released:** August 03, 2020. **Description:** From lawn care flyers to social media landscape advertising, there are dozens of landscaping marketing strategies. This article provides a list of 25 proven landscape advertising ideas that you can use to promote your small business. **Availability:** Online.

29630 ■ 31 Days to Greeting Card Marketing Mastery

Price: $17.95, paperback. **Description:** The use of simple greeting cards for marketing and increasing sales is explained. **Availability:** Print.

29631 ■ "33 FIVERR Power Tips: Featuring Prove Ways to Boost Your Sales and Quit Your Job"

Description: Thirty-three proven methods to increase sales, include directions for setting up an automated buyer email collection system, using a new list to direct market buyers, a system for creating events to boost sales and ways to maximize customer satisfaction.

29632 ■ 101 Internet Businesses You Can Start from Home: How to Choose and Build Your Own Successful E-Business
Pub: Maximum Press

Ed: Susan Sweeney. **Released:** Third edition. **Description:** Guide for starting and growing an Internet business; information for developing a business plan, risk levels, and promotional techniques are included.

29633 ■ "352 Media Group Opens New Tampa Web Design and Digital Marketing Office" in Entertainment Close-Up (May 2, 2011)
Pub: Close-Up Media Inc.
Contact: Caroline S. Moore, President
E-mail: cms@closeupmedia.com

Description: 352 Media Group opened its newest office in Tampa, Florida in May 2011. The firm is noted for its achievements in Web design and digital marketing. **Availability:** Print; Online.

29634 ■ "529.com Wins Outstanding Achievement in Web Development" in Investment Weekly (November 14, 2009, pp. 152)
Pub: Investment Weekly News

Description: Web Marketing Association's 2009 WebAward for Financial Services Standard of Excellence and Investment Standard of Excellence was won by 529.com, the website from Upromise Investments, Inc., the leading administrator of 529 college savings plans. **Availability:** Online.

29635 ■ "1914 Proved to Be Key Year for Chevy" in Automotive News (Vol. 86, October 31, 2011, No. 6488, pp. S18)
Pub: Crain Communications Inc.
Contact: Barry Asin, President

Ed: Jamie LaReau. **Description:** Chevy Bow Tie emblem was born in 1914, creating the brand's image that has carried through to current days. **Availability:** Print; Online.

29636 ■ "Abacast, Citadel Strike Radio Ad Deal" in Business Journal Portland (Vol. 27, December 31, 2010, No. 44, pp. 3)
Pub: Portland Business Journal
Contact: Andy Giegerich, Managing Editor
E-mail: agiegerich@bizjournals.com

Fd: Frik Siemers. **Description:** Software firm Abacast Inc. has partnered with Citadel Media to aid the latter's advertising sales. Citadel provides radio networks and syndicated programs to 4,200 affiliate stations. **Availability:** Print; Online.

29637 ■ "Acsys Interactive Announces Crowdsourcing Comes to the Hospital Industry" in Marketwired (August 23, 2010)
Pub: Comtex News Network Inc.
Contact: Kan Devnani, President

Description: Hospital marketers are obtaining data through crowdsourcing as strategy to gain ideas and feedback. The Hospital Industry Crowdsourced Survey of Digital, Integrated and Emerging Marketing is the first initiative among hospitals. **Availability:** Print; Online.

29638 ■ "Adidas' Brand Ambitions" in Business Journal Portland (Vol. 27, December 10, 2010, No. 41, pp. 1)
Pub: Portland Business Journal
Contact: Andy Giegerich, Managing Editor
E-mail: agiegerich@bizjournals.com

Ed: Erik Siemers. **Description:** Adidas AG, the second-largest sporting goods brand in the world, hopes to increase global revenue by 50 percent by 2015. The German company, which reported $14.5 billion sales, plans to improve its U.S. market. The U.S. is Adidas' largest, but also the most underperforming market for the firm. **Availability:** Print; Online.

29639 ■ Advanced Selling for Dummies
Released: 2011. **Description:** This book explores topics such as: visualizing success (includes exercises), investing and reinvesting in your own success,

harnessing media and multi-media outlets, calculating risks that stretch your limits, creating lasting relationships, finding balance to avoid burnout and more. This guide is for salespeople who have already read 'Selling for Dummies' and now want forward-thinking, advanced strategies for recharging and reenergizing their careers and their lives. Blogging, Internet leads and virtual assistants are also discussed. **Availability:** emobi; Online; Electronic publishing.

29640 ■ "Africa Rising" in Harvard Business Review (Vol. 86, September 2008, No. 9, pp. 36)
Pub: Harvard Business Review Press
Contact: Moderna V. Pfizer, Contact

Ed: Vijay Mahajan. **Description:** Review of the book entitled, "Africa Rising: How 900 Million African Consumers Offer More Than You Think" provides advice for marketing to those on the African continent. **Availability:** Print; Online.

29641 ■ "The Agency Model Is Bent But Not Broken" in Advertising Age (Vol. 79, July 7, 2008, No. 26, pp. 17)
Pub: Crain Communications, Inc.
Contact: Jessica Botos, Manager, Marketing
E-mail: jessica.botos@crainsnewyork.com

Ed: Stephen Fajen. **Description:** In the new-media environment, advertising agencies must change the way in which they do business and receive payment. **Availability:** Online.

29642 ■ "The Agency-Selection Process Needs Fixing Now" in Advertising Age (Vol. 79, July 7, 2008, No. 26, pp. 18)
Pub: Crain Communications, Inc.
Contact: Jessica Botos, Manager, Marketing
E-mail: jessica.botos@crainsnewyork.com

Ed: Avi Dan. **Description:** Marketers are facing increased challenges in this sagging economic climate and must realize the importance of choosing the correct advertising agency for their company in order to benefit from a more-stable relationship that yields better business results. Advice for marketers regarding the best way to choose an agency is included. **Availability:** Online.

29643 ■ AI Academy Experts Discuss AI for Small Business and Content Marketing
Ed: Gianna Mannarino. **Released:** October 19, 2020. **Description:** Experts from the AI Academy provide an inside look into the AI opportunities for content marketers and small businesses. **Availability:** Online.

29644 ■ AI for Marketing: A CMO's Guide
Released: November 2020. **Description:** A guide that covers how to use artificial intelligence for copywriting, for creativity, and for machine learning to guide your marketing strategy. **Availability:** Online.

29645 ■ "Allied Brands Loses Baskin-Robbins Franchise Down Under" in Ice Cream Reporter (Vol. 23, November 20, 2010, No. 12, pp. 2)
Description: Dunkin Brands, worldwide franchisor of Baskin-Robbins, terminated the master franchise agreement for Australia held by the food marketer Allied Brands Services. **Availability:** Print; Online.

29646 ■ "Alternative Energy Calls for Alternative Marketing" in Indoor Comfort Marketing (Vol. 70, June 2011, No. 6, pp. 8)
Pub: Spray Technology & Marketing
Contact: Ava Caridad, Director, Editorial
E-mail: acaridad@spraytm.com

Ed: Richard Rutigliano. **Released:** June 01, 2011. **Description:** Advice for marketing solar energy products and services is given. **Availability:** Print; Online.

29647 ■ "Amazing Apple Does It Again" in Barron's (Vol. 92, September 15, 2012, No. 38, pp. 26)
Pub: Dow Jones & Company Inc.
Contact: Almar Latour, Chief Executive Officer

Ed: Tiernan Ray. **Description:** The introduction of the Apple iPhone 5 lacked the flair of previous product introductions by the company. New chief executive officer Tim Cook has been criticized for this lack of flair for marketing, although pre-orders for the iPhone 5 remain high. **Availability:** Online.

29648 ■ "Ampm Focus Has BP Working Overtime" in Crain's Chicago Business (April 28, 2008)
Pub: Crain Communications Inc.
Contact: Barry Asin, President

Ed: John T. Slania. **Description:** Britian's oil giant BP PLC is opening its ampm convenience stores in the Chicago market and has already begun converting most of its 78 Chicago-area gas stations to ampms. The company has also started to franchise the stores to independent operators. BP is promoting the brand with both traditional and unconventional marketing techniques such s real or simulated 3D snacks embedded in bus shelter ads and an in-store Guitar Hero contest featuring finalists from a recent contest at the House of Blues. **Availability:** Online.

29649 ■ "Are Offline Pushes Important to E-Commerce?" in DM News (Vol. 31, September 14, 2009, No. 23, pp. 10)
Pub: Haymarket Media Inc.
Contact: Kevin Costello, Chief Executive Officer

Description: With the importance of Internet marketing and the popularity of ecommerce increasing experts debate the relevance of more traditional channels of advertising. **Availability:** Online.

29650 ■ "Are You Ignoring Trends That Could Shake Up Your Business?" in Harvard Business Review (Vol. 88, July-August 2010, No. 7-8, pp. 124)
Pub: Harvard Business Publishing
Contact: Diane Belcher, Managing Director

Ed: Elie Ofek, Luc Wathieu. **Price:** $8.95, PDF. **Description:** Ways for firms to capitalize on trends that might otherwise negatively affect their business are spotlighted. These include using certain aspects of the trend to augment traditional product/service offerings, and combining the trend with the offerings to transcend its traditional category. **Availability:** Online; PDF.

29651 ■ "Are You Ready for a Transformation?" in Women Entrepreneur (November 28, 2008)
Description: Marlene J. Waldock, an expert in women's empowerment and reinvention, discusses brand modification and what a business owner should consider before attempting to change or modify their brand. **Availability:** Online.

29652 ■ "Artscape Looks for Last Big Donations" in Baltimore Business Journal (Vol. 32, July 11, 2014, No. 10, pp. 4)
Pub: American City Business Journals, Inc.
Contact: Mike Olivieri, Executive Vice President

Released: Weekly. **Price:** $4, introductory 4-week offer(Digital only). **Description:** Kathy Hornig, festivals director for Baltimore's Office of Promotion and the Arts, discusses last-minute efforts to raise the final $100,000 in donations for Artscape from mobile marketers and festival goers. The event, to be held July 18-23, 2014 in Baltimore, will focus on dance and movement. **Availability:** Print; Online.

29653 ■ "As Traditional Web Site Adoption Slows, Facebook and Other Social Networks Become Key Platforms for Home-Based Business Promotional and Commercial Activity Online" in Marketing Weekly News (June 16, 2012)
Description: Websites have provided an inexpensive means for businesses to market their products and services. However, home-based businesses are using social networking, email marketing, search engine optimization, search engine marketing, Website optimization for mobile devices, banner advertisements, and the use of ecommerce platforms such as eBay, Craigs list, and Amazon. **Availability:** Print; Online.

29654 ■ *"Automaker Foundations Run Leaner"* in *Crain's Detroit Business (Vol. 26, January 11, 2010, No. 2, pp. 1)*
Pub: Crain Communications Inc.
Contact: Barry Asin, President
Ed: Sherri Welch. **Description:** Overview of the Detroit automobile industry includes restoring profitability, smarter marketing strategies and philanthropy. Each company comprising the Big 3 is examined, as is their vision for the future. **Availability:** Print; Online.

29655 ■ *"avVaa World Health Care Products Rolls Out Internet Marketing Program"* in *Health and Beauty Close-Up (September 18, 2009)*
Description: avVaa World Health Care Products, Inc., a biotechnology company, manufacturer and distributor of nationally branded therapeutic, natural health care and skin products, has signed an agreement with Online Performance Marketing to launch of an Internet marketing campaign in order to broaden its presence online. The impact of advertising on the Internet to generate an increase in sales is explored. **Availability:** Online.

29656 ■ *B2B Marketing: 10 Key Differences from Consumer Marketing*
Description: Details the importance of good quality market intelligence and close attention to target markets for business-to-business marketers. Provides ten key differences between B2B and consumer marketing. **Availability:** Online.

29657 ■ *"B2B Marketing: How to Grow Your Business"* in *Evinex (November 2, 2020)*
Ed: Carlos Trillo. **Released:** November 02, 2020. **Description:** Discusses business-to-business marketing strategies and fundamentals to help generate growth and increase your sales. **Availability:** Online.

29658 ■ *"B2B vs. B2C Marketing: What's the Difference in Marketing to the Business Market?"* in *Catalyst (January 3, 2019)*
Ed: Doug Fairbrother. **Released:** January 03, 2019. **Description:** Discusses how marketing to the business world is different than marketing to consumers. Provides information on the major differences and how to put the best strategies into action. **Availability:** Online.

29659 ■ *"Bakugan Battle Brawlers From Spin Master: A Marketing 50 Case Study"* in *Advertising Age (Vol. 79, November 17, 2008, No. 43, pp. S2)*
Pub: Crain Communications, Inc.
Contact: Jessica Botos, Manager, Marketing
E-mail: jessica.botos@crainsnewyork.com
Ed: Kate Fitzgerald. **Description:** Spin Master toys has a new hit, Bakugan Battle Brawlers, an interactive game board with 106 characters that battle with one another in tournaments. Bakugan tournaments are being held at Toys "R" Us stores. **Availability:** Online.

29660 ■ *"Balancing Risk and Return in a Customer Portfolio"* in *Journal of Marketing (Vol. 75, May 2011, No. 3, pp. 1)*
Pub: American Marketing Association
Contact: Bennie F. Johnson, Chief Executive Officer
Ed: Crina O. Tarasi, Ruth N. Bolton, Michael D. Hutt, Beth A. Walker. **Released:** Volume: 75 issue: 3. **Description:** A framework for reducing the vulnerability and volatility of cash flows in customer portfolios is presented. The efficient portfolios of firms are identified and tested against their current portfolios and hypothetical profit maximization portfolios. **Availability:** PDF.

29661 ■ *"Baltimore Grand Prix Week Schedule Filling Up With Galas, Nonprofit Fundraisers"* in *Baltimore Business Journal (Vol. 29, July 22, 2011, No. 11, pp. 1)*
Pub: Boston Business Journal
Contact: Carolyn M. Jones, President
E-mail: cmjones@bizjournals.com

Ed: Alexander Jackson. **Description:** Baltimore, Maryland-based businesses and nonprofit groups have been planning their own events to coincide with the Baltimore Grand Prix during the Labor Day weekend. They also plan to partner with others in hopes of drumming up new business, raising money or to peddle their brands.

29662 ■ *"Baltimore Ravens Back to Business as NFL Lockout Ends"* in *Baltimore Business Journal (Vol. 29, July 29, 2011, No. 12, pp. 1)*
Pub: Boston Business Journal
Contact: Carolyn M. Jones, President
E-mail: cmjones@bizjournals.com
Ed: Scott Dance. **Description:** The Baltimore Ravens football team has been marketing open sponsorship packages following the end of the National Football League lockout. Team officials are working to get corporate logos and slogans on radio and television commercials and online advertisements. **Availability:** Print; Online.

29663 ■ *"BayTSP, NTT Data Corp. Enter Into Reseller Pact to Market Online IP Monitoring"* in *Professional Services Close-Up (Sept. 11, 2009)*
Description: Due to incredible interest from distributors and content owners across Asia, NTT Data Corp. will resell BayTSP's online intellectual property monitoring, enforcement, business intelligence and monetization services in Japan.

29664 ■ *"BBB Reworks Logo, Grading System"* in *Crain's Cleveland Business (Vol. 28, October 8, 2007, No. 40, pp. 5)*
Pub: Crain Communications Inc.
Contact: K. C. Crain, President
Ed: John Booth. **Description:** During the next year, the Better Business Bureau will adopt a grading system that will establish performance minimums that will make it tougher for some types of businesses to become accredited, this nationwide rebranding effort is part of a campaign to sharpen the Better Business Bureau's image. **Availability:** Online.

29665 ■ *"Because Kids Need To Be Heard: Tina Wells: Buzz Marketing Group: Voorhees, New Jersey"* in *Inc. (Volume 32, December 2010)*
Pub: Mansueto Ventures L.L.C.
Contact: Stephanie Mehta, Chief Executive Officer
Ed: Tamara Schweitzer. **Released:** December 01, 2010. **Description:** Profile of Tina Wells, founder and CEO of Buzz Marketing Group, who writes a tween book series called Mackenzie Blue to reach young girls. **Availability:** Online.

29666 ■ *"Beep Fruit Drink Makes Comeback: Prodded by Fans, a Maritime Dairy Brings Back Retro Drink Beep"* in *Canadian Business (Vol. 85, August 13, 2012, No. 13, pp. 9)*
Ed: Matthew McClearn. **Description:** Farmers Co-Operative Dairy temporarily resumed production of the Beep fruit drink in response to customers' call to bring back the product that the company has been selling since 1962. As part of the relaunch, the company replicated the original 1960s packaging and used social media to connect with customers. **Availability:** Print; Online.

29667 ■ *"Being All a-Twitter"* in *Canadian Business (Vol. 81, December 8, 2008, No. 21, pp. 22)*
Description: Marketing experts suggest that advertising strategies have to change along with new online social media. Companies are advised to find ways to incorporate social software because workers and customers are expected to continue its use. **Availability:** Print; Online.

29668 ■ *"Best of the Best: 20 Business-to-Business Examples to Check Out"* in *Disruptive Advertising (March 17, 2020)*
Ed: Cydney Hatch. **Released:** March 17, 2020. **Description:** Lists twenty examples of business-to-business companies who do a great job of targeting

precise audiences, creating meaningful and engaging content, and optimizing efforts for business and social media. **Availability:** Online.

29669 ■ *Best Cannabis Marketing Guide*
Description: A detailed cannabis marketing guide that shows how to successfully market your cannabis business online and offline.

29670 ■ *"The Best Organic Marketing Strategies for Small Business"* in *TechRadar (Jan. 6, 2022)*
URL(s): www.techradar.com/features/the-best-organic-marketing-strategies-for-small-business
Ed: Paul Maplesden. **Released:** January 06, 2022. **Description:** Explores how splitting your small business marketing strategies into two approaches--organic marketing and paid promotion--is an effective approach. **Availability:** Online.

29671 ■ *"The Best Text Message Marketing Services of 2023"* in *Business News Daily (March 22, 2023)*
URL(s): www.businessnewsdaily.com/15044-best-text-message-marketing-solutions.html
Ed: Max Freedman. **Released:** March 22, 2023. **Description:** Text message marketing is gaining popularity since it lets small businesses be able to send out communications directly to customers. This article discusses the best services available. **Availability:** Online.

29672 ■ *"Better ROI Or Your Money Back, Says Buzz Agency"* in *Advertising Age (Vol. 79, July 14, 2008, No. 7, pp. 1)*
Pub: Crain Communications Inc.
Contact: Jessica Botos, Manager, Marketing
E-mail: jessica.botos@crainsnewyork.com
Ed: Michael Bush. **Description:** Word-of-mouth marketing is discussed as well as the impact on the advertising industry. Although many firms specializing in this form of marketing have opened over the past few years, many marketers are reluctant to try this route. **Availability:** Online.

29673 ■ *"Better Than New Runs on Tried-and-True Model"* in *Bellingham Business Journal (Vol. February 2010, pp. 16)*
Pub: Sound Publishing Inc.
Contact: Josh O'Connor, President
Ed: Ashley Mitchell. **Description:** Profile of family owned Better Than New clothing store that sells overstock items from department stores and clothing manufacturers. The stores location makes it easy to miss and its only advertising is a large sign posted outside. This is the sixth store owned by the couple, Keijeo and Sirba Halmekanqas.

29674 ■ *"Bioheat - Alternative for Fueling Equipment"* in *Indoor Comfort Marketing (Vol. 70, May 2011, No. 5, pp. 14)*
Description: Profile of Worley and Obetz, supplier of biofuels used as an alternative for fueling industry equipment. **Availability:** Print; Online.

29675 ■ *"BK Menu Gives Casual Dining Reason to Worry"* in *Advertising Age (Vol. 79, November 17, 2008, No. 43, pp. 12)*
Pub: Crain Communications, Inc.
Contact: Jessica Botos, Manager, Marketing
E-mail: jessica.botos@crainsnewyork.com
Ed: Emily Bryson York. **Description:** Burger King is beginning to compete with such casual dining restaurants as Applebees and the Cheesecake Factory with new premium menu items, including thicker burgers and ribs; statistical data regarding the casual dining segment which continues to fall and Burger King, whose sales continue to rise is included. **Availability:** Online.

29676 ■ *"Blue Bell Touts Non-Shrinkage"* in *Ice Cream Reporter (Vol. 21, July 20, 2008, No. 8, pp. 1)*
Description: Blue Bell Ice Cream is promoting its decision to keep their ice cream products in a full half-gallon container rather than downsizing the pack-

age. Thirty-second television ads contrast the move by other ice cream makers to offer less for the same money. **Availability:** Online.

29677 ■ *Blue Book Marketing Research Services Directory*

Contact: Cheryl Bechard, Contact
E-mail: cheryl.bechard@mra-net.org
URL(s): bluebook.marketingresearch.orgbluebook
.insightsassociation.org; www.bluebook.org; ol
d.marketingresearch.org/blue-book-0
Released: Annual; Latest edition 2015. **Price:** $299, Members online and print; $399, Nonmembers online only; $200, Members online only; Free; $170, Nonmembers; $100, Members. **Description:** Covers over 1,200 marketing research companies and field interviewing services. Includes separate geographical listings for firms with one-way mirror facilities, focus group moderators and facilities, central telephone facilities, and permanent shopping mall locations. **Entries include:** Company name, address, phone, names of executives, services, facilities, special interviewing capabilities. **Arrangement:** Geographical; business type. **Indexes:** Geographic and by specialty. **Availability:** Print; PDF; Online.

29678 ■ *"Blue Cross to Put Kiosk in Mall" in News & Observer (November 9, 2010)*

Pub: News and Observer
Contact: Bill Church, Editor
Ed: Alan M. Wolf. **Description:** Blue Cross and Blue Shield of North Carolina has placed a kiosk in Durham's Streets of Southpoint in order to market its health insurance. **Availability:** Online.

29679 ■ *"Blue Hill Tavern to Host Baltimore's First Cupcake Camp" in Daily Record (August 10, 2011)*

Pub: BridgeTower Media
Contact: Adam Reinebach, President
Ed: Rachel Bernstein. **Description:** Cities joining the trend to host cupcake camps are listed. The camps are open to all individuals wishing to share and eat cupcakes in an open environment.

29680 ■ *"Bonnaroo 2012: Food Truck Oasis Returns With 9 Delicious Trucks" in International Business Times (June 4, 2012)*

Pub: International Business Times
Contact: Michael Learmonth, Editor
Ed: Amanda Remling. **Description:** Manchester, Tennessee is the location for the Bonnaroo 2012 food truck event. The nine food trucks will be features offering their fares include: Eatbox, Gastropod, Good You, Gypsy Queen, Petro's Chili & Chips, Pot Kettle Black, Roti Rolls, Savory And Sweet, Tex's Tacos. **Availability:** Online.

29681 ■ *"Book Yourself Solid: The Fastest, Easiest, and Most Reliable System for Getting More Clients Than You Can Handle"*

Pub: John Wiley & Sons, Inc.
Contact: Christina Van Tassell, Executive Vice President Chief Financial Officer
Released: 3rd edition. **Price:** $22, paperback; $14.99, E-book. **Description:** Self-promotion is essential for successful selling. Strategies, techniques, and skills necessary for success are presented, covering social media marketing strategies for service professionals; pricing models and sales strategies to simplify selling; new networking and outreach plans that take only minutes a day; and new product launches ideas and tactics. **Availability:** E-book; Print.

29682 ■ *Bookkeeping Practices for Digital Marketers*

URL(s): bookkeepwithus.com/bookkeeping-practices
-for-digital-marketers
Ed: Chris Groote. **Description:** Explores the value of professional bookkeeping; includes bookkeeping practices. **Availability:** Online.

29683 ■ *Bradford's International Directory of Marketing Research Agencies*

Pub: Business Research Services, Inc.
URL(s): www.sba8a.com/brs.htm

Description: Covers over 2,300 marketing research agencies worldwide. Includes domestic and international demographic data and professional association contacts. **Entries include:** Company name, address, phone, name and title of contact, date founded, number of employees, description of products or services, e-mail, URL. **Arrangement:** Geographical. **Indexes:** Alphabetical by company. **Availability:** Print. **Type:** Directory.

29684 ■ *"Branching Out: Towards a Trait-based Understanding of Fungal Ecology" in Canadian Business (Vol. 79, July 17, 2006, No. 14-15, pp. 41)*

Availability: Print; Online.

29685 ■ *"Brand Police Keep the Lines Distinct at GM" in Automotive News (Vol. 86, October 31, 2011, No. 6488, pp. 3)*

Pub: Crain Communications Inc.
Contact: Barry Asin, President
Ed: Mike Colias. **Description:** Joel Ewanick, marketing chief at General Motors, is working to keep General Motor's four brands distinct within their brands. **Availability:** Online.

29686 ■ *"Brand Storytelling Becomes a Booming Business" in Entrepreneur (April 2012)*

Pub: Entrepreneur Media Inc.
Contact: Dan Bova, Director
E-mail: dbova@entrepreneur.com
Ed: Paula Andruss. **Description:** San Francisco-based Story House Creative engages in helping small businesses connect with their audience in communicating their brand identity. Web content, bios and tag lines are some of the marketing materials Story House Creative creates for its clients. The company also does search engine optimization, video, design, and copywriting. The Brandery, another brand-building company, helps startups promote their business. Eight to ten Brandery mentors are assigned to assist each startup client. Meanwhile, Brand Journalists is a Tennessee-based company focusing on corporate storytelling. It offers Web and blog content, human stories reporting and ghostwriting services. **Availability:** Print; Online.

29687 ■ *"Branding Your Way" in Canadian Business (Vol. 80, February 12, 2007, No. 4, pp. 31)*

Description: The trend in involving consumers in brand marketing by seeking their views through contests or inviting them to produce and submit commercials through Internet is discussed. **Availability:** Online.

29688 ■ *"Brands' Mass Appeal" in ADWEEK (Vol. 51, June 14, 2010, No. 24)*

Ed: Brian Morrissey. **Description:** Engineering/science crowdsourced projects tend to result from posting and/or publishing interim results as well as from other talents building upon those results to produce even better results. However, the author does not see the same results in the creative world. **Availability:** Online.

29689 ■ *"Brewing Up a Brand" in Canadian Business (Vol. 80, February 26, 2007, No. 5, pp. 68)*

Description: The marketing strategies adopted by Molson Coors Brewing Company, to improve customer loyalty to the Coors Light brand, are presented. **Availability:** Online.

29690 ■ *"Bridging the Academic-Practitioner Divide in Marketing Decision Models" in Journal of Marketing (Vol. 75, July 2011, No. 4, pp. 196)*

Pub: American Marketing Association
Contact: Bennie F. Johnson, Chief Executive Officer
Ed: Gary L. Lilien. **Description:** A study to determine the reason for the relatively low level of practical use of the many marketing models is presented. Changing the incentive and reward systems for marketing academics, practitioners, and intermediaries can

bring about adoption and implementation improvements. Those changes could be beneficial by bridging the academic-practitioner divide. **Availability:** PDF.

29691 ■ *"Brite-Strike Tactical Launches New Internet Marketing Initiatives" in Marketwired (September 15, 2009)*

Pub: Comtex News Network Inc.
Contact: Kan Devnani, President

Description: Brite-Strike Tactical Illumination Products, Inc. has enlisted the expertise of Internet marketing guru Thomas J. McCarthy to help revamp the company's Internet campaign. An outline of the Internet marketing strategy is provided. **Availability:** Print; Online.

29692 ■ *"The Buck Stops Here" in Canadian Business (Vol. 81, November 10, 2008, No. 19, pp. 25)*

Ed: Sarka Halas. **Description:** Reputation strategist Leslie Gaines-Ross says that minimizing the damage followed by the identification of what went wrong are the first steps that companies need to take when trying to salvage their reputation. Gaines-Ross states that it is up to the CEO to ensure the company's speedy recovery and they need to be at the forefront of the process. **Availability:** Online.

29693 ■ *Business Black Belt: Develop the Strength, Flexibility and Agility to Run Your Company*

Price: $15.99. **Description:** Manual offering insights that will enable anyone to become successful in small business. Seventy short chapters included topics such as attitude, management, marketing, selling, employees, money, MBAs, lawyers, consultants, and investors. **Availability:** Print.

29694 ■ *Business-to-Business Marketing 2023*

Released: 6th edition. **Description:** Delves into the world of business-to-business marketing by presenting and examining tactics, surveys, and trends of the industry. **Availability:** Online.

29695 ■ *Business Warrior: Strategy for Entrepreneurs*

Price: $9.99. **Description:** Advice to help entrepreneurs understand competitive strategies in order to succeed, focusing on sales, marketing, and personnel management. **Availability:** Print; Download; PDF.

29696 ■ *"BusinessOnLine Launches New Web-Based Search Engine Optimization Tool: First Link Checker for Google" in Marketwired (October 19, 2009)*

Pub: Comtex News Network Inc.
Contact: Kan Devnani, President

Description: First Link Checker, a complimentary new search engine optimization tool that helps site owners optimize their on-page links by understanding which of those links are actually being counted in Google's relevancy algorithm, was developed by BusinessOnLine, a rapidly growing Internet marketing agency. This tool will make it easy for the average web master to ensure that their internal link structure is optimized. **Availability:** Print.

29697 ■ *"Buy the Pants, Save the Planet?" in Globe & Mail (February 5, 2007, pp. B1)*

Description: The marketing campaign of the clothing company Diesel S.p.A. is discussed. The company has based its latest collection of T-shirt designs on the problem of global warming. **Availability:** Online.

29698 ■ *Buyology: Truth and Lies About Why We Buy*

Pub: Doubleday

Ed: Martin Lindstrom. **Released:** February 02, 2010. **Price:** $15, paperback. **Description:** Marketers study brain scans to determine how consumers rate Nokia, Coke, and Ford products. **Availability:** Print.

29699 ■ *"Calendar" in Crain's Detroit Business (Vol. 24, March 10, 2008, No. 10, pp. 21)*
Pub: Crain Communications Inc.
Contact: Barry Asin, President
Description: Listing of events in the Detroit area include conferences addressing entrepreneurialism, economic development, and women business ownership. **Availability:** Print; Online.

29700 ■ *"Campaigner Survey: 46 Percent of Small Businesses Use Email Marketing" in Wireless News (November 21, 2009)*
Description: Almost half (46 percent) of small businesses surveyed by Campaigner's 2009 State of Small Business Online Marketing, say that they rely on email marketing to help them find new customers, keep existing ones and grow their businesses. The survey also found that 36 percent of small businesses plan to begin using email marketing over the next year. The trend to utilize Internet marketing tools is allowing small businesses to grow faster and generate higher revenues than those that are not using these mediums. **Availability:** Print; Online.

29701 ■ *"Canadian Hydronics Businesses Promote 'Beautiful Heat" in Indoor Comfort Marketing (Vol. 70, September 2011, No. 9, pp. 20)*
Pub: Spray Technology & Marketing
Contact: Ava Caridad, Director, Editorial
E-mail: acaridad@spraytm.com
Released: September 01, 2011. **Description:** Canadian hydronics companies are promoting their systems as beautiful heat. Hydronics is the use of water as the heat-transfer medium in heating and cooling system. **Availability:** Print; Online.

29702 ■ *"Capturing Generation Y: Ready, Set, Transform" in Credit Union Times (Vol. 21, July 14, 2010, No. 27, pp. 20)*
Ed: Senthil Kumar. **Description:** The financial services sector recognizes that Generation Y will have a definite impact on the way business is conducted in the future. The mindset of Generation Y is social and companies need to use networking tools such as Facebook in order to reach this demographic. **Availability:** Online.

29703 ■ *"Casinos In Pitch Battle" in Philadelphia Business Journal (Vol. 28, July 20, 2012, No. 23, pp. 1)*
Pub: Baltimore Business Journal
Contact: Rhonda Pringle, President
E-mail: rpringle@bizjournals.com
Description: The extent to which casinos in Philadelphia, Pennsylvania have invested in marketing and rebranding effortsin the Philadelphia-Atlantic City markets is explored. These efforts are part of the goal of the casinos to compete for customers considering that casinos contribute about $6 billion in taxes to Pennsylvania. Statistics pertaining to casinos and their advertising expenditures are presented. **Availability:** Print; Online.

29704 ■ *"Celebrate Holiday Spirit With Sparkling Sales" in Pet Product News (Vol. 66, September 2012, No. 9, pp. 48)*
Ed: Cheryl Reeves. **Description:** Pet supplies retailers can increase frequency of holiday sales, from Halloween through New Year's, by integrating creative marketing strategies into merchandise and incentives that elicit customer attention. The impression of fun should also be emphasized on customers. Guidelines for presenting displays and organizing special store-related events are also provided. **Availability:** Print; Online.

29705 ■ *"The CEO of Williams-Sonoma on Blending Instinct with Analysis" in Harvard Business Review (Vol. 92, September 2014, No. 9, pp. 41)*
Pub: Harvard Business Publishing
Contact: Diane Belcher, Managing Director

Price: $8.95. **Description:** At Williams-Sonoma Inc., analytics are used to provide customers with experiences that best match their preferences, based on browsing history and/or previous purchases. This data is also used to inform designers, vendors, and distributors of supply and demand patterns. **Availability:** Online; PDF.

29706 ■ *"The Changing Face of the U.S. Consumer" in Advertising Age (Vol. 79, July 7, 2008, No. 26, pp. 1)*
Pub: Advertising Age
Contact: Dan Peres, President
Ed: Peter Francese. **Description:** It is essential for marketers to examine demographic shifts when looking at ways in which to market brands. The average head-of-households is aging and marketers must not continue to ignore them. Statistical data included. **Availability:** Print; Online.

29707 ■ *"Charlotte Pipe Launches Satirical Campaign" in Contractor (Vol. 57, January 2010, No. 1, pp. 6)*
Description: Charlotte Pipe and Foundry Co. launched an advertising campaign that uses social media and humor to make a point about how it can be nearly impossible to determine if imported cast iron pipes and fittings meet the same quality standards as what is made in the U.S. The campaign features 'pipe whisperers' and also spoofs pipe sniffing dogs. **Availability:** Print; Online.

29708 ■ *"Chesapeake Beach Resort and Spa Announces Dream Waterfront Wedding Giveaway" in Benzinga.com (October 29, 2011)*
Description: Chesapeake Beach Resort and Spa will give away a Dream Waterfront Wedding to a lucky bride and groom in order to promote their resort as a wedding venue. **Availability:** Print; Online.

29709 ■ *"Chew On This: Soul Fans to 'Chews' Games' First Play" in Philadelphia Business Journal (Vol. 30, September 30, 2011, No. 33, pp. 3)*
Pub: Philadelphia Business Journal
Contact: Sierra Quinn, Director
E-mail: squinn@bizjournals.com
Ed: John George. **Description:** Arena football team Philadelphia Soul extended its marketing partnership with Just Born Inc. The team's fans will enter a contest where the winner will be allowed to select the team's first play during a home game. **Availability:** Online.

29710 ■ *"Citadel EFT (CDFT) Contracts With New Search Engine Optimization (SEO) and Banner Ad Web Marketing Companies" in Internet Wire (August 8, 2012)*
Pub: Comtex News Network Inc.
Contact: Kan Devnani, President
Description: Citafel EFT Inc. provides credit card terminals, online, mail order and retail credit card processing services. The firm has contracted with two Web marketing companies to increase its awareness on the Internet. **Availability:** Print; Online.

29711 ■ *"ClickFuel Unveils Internet Marketing Tools for Small Businesses" in Marketwired (October 19, 2009)*
Pub: Comtex News Network Inc.
Contact: Kan Devnani, President
Description: ClickFuel, a firm that manages, designs and tracks marketing campaigns has unveiled a full software suite of affordable services and technology solutions designed to empower small business owners and help them promote and grow their businesses through targeted Internet marketing campaigns. **Availability:** Online.

29712 ■ *"Cloud Computing for a Crowd" in CIO (Vol. 24, October 2, 2010, No. 1, pp. 16)*
Pub: CIO
Ed: Stephanie Overby. **Description:** Information about a project which aimed to implement a cloud-based crowdsourcing platform and innovation-management process is provided. Chubb Group of

Insurance Companies wanted to mine revenue-generating ideas from its 10,400 employees and hundreds of thousands of external agents. The company hosted its first innovation event using its new system in October 2008. **Availability:** Online.

29713 ■ *"The CMO of Consequence" in Business Strategy Review (Vol. 21, Autumn 2010, No. 3, pp. 42)*
Ed: D. Eric Boyd, Rajesh K. Chandy, Marcus Cunha, Jr. **Released:** September 29, 2010. **Description:** Do chief marketing officers matter? Some say that CMOs have limited effect on corporate performance and don't add significant value to the firm. The authors agree that the job in many firms is in great peril, but their research has uncovered why the contributions of some CMOs are invaluable. **Availability:** Print; PDF; Online.

29714 ■ *"CMO Nicholson Exits Pepsi as Share Declines" in Advertising Age (Vol. 79, July 7, 2008, No. 26, pp. 4)*
Pub: Crain Communications, Inc.
Contact: Jessica Botos, Manager, Marketing
E-mail: jessica.botos@crainsnewyork.com
Ed: Natalie Zmuda. **Description:** Cie Nicholson, the chief marketing officer at Pepsi-Cola UK, is leaving the company at a time when its market share is down; the brand, which was known for its dynamic marketing, has diverted much of its attention from its core brands and shifted attention to the ailing Gatorade brand as well as Sobe Life Water and Amp. **Availability:** Online.

29715 ■ *"Coin Toss? A Real Cartoon Caper" in Barron's (Vol. 92, September 17, 2012, No. 38, pp. 17)*
Description: An estimated $20,000 worth of coins bearing the likeness of cartoon character SpongeBob SquarePants are missing, according to Ira Bodenstein, the bankruptcy trustee of commodities futures broker Peregrine Financial. The coins were used by the company as a marketing tool and could rise in value if found and auctioned. **Availability:** Online.

29716 ■ *"Come Together: A Thematic Collection of Times Articles, Essays, Maps and More About Creating Community" in Pet Product News (Vol. 64, December 2010, No. 12, pp. 28)*
Ed: Lizett Bond. **Description:** Pet supply retailers have posted improved sales and improved customer service by bundling their offerings. Bundling pertains to grouping related items such as collars and leashes into a single unit for marketing purposes. Aside from providing convenience and enhanced product information to customers, bundling has facilitated more efficient purchases. **Availability:** Online.

29717 ■ *"A Comment on 'Balancing Risk and Return in a Customer Portfolio" in Journal of Marketing (Vol. 75, May 2011, No. 3, pp. 18)*
Description: Issues regarding the use of approaches to managing customer portfolios are described. These are related to assumptions in modern financial portfolio theory and return and risk. **Availability:** Online.

29718 ■ *The Complete Guide to Google Adwords: Secrets, Techniques, and Strategies You Can Learn to Make Millions*
Pub: Atlantic Publishing Co.
Contact: Dr. Heather L. Johnson, Contact
Released: 2012. **Description:** Google AdWords, when it launched in 2002 signaled a fundamental shift in what the Internet was for so many individuals and companies. Learning and understanding how Google AdWords operates and how it can be optimized for maximum exposure, boosting click through rates, conversions, placement, and selection of the right keywords, can be the key to a successful online business. **Availability:** Print; Online.

29719 ■ *"Conference Calendar" in Marketing to Women (Vol. 21, April 2008, No. 4, pp. 7)*
Description: Listing of current conferences and events concerning women, marketing and business. **Availability:** Print; PDF; Download; Online.

29720 ■ *"Constant Contact Launches Marketing Podcast for Small Business"* in *Small Business Trends (March 10, 2023)*
URL(s): smallbiztrends.com/2023/03/constant-contac t-launches-small-business-marketing-podcast.html
Ed: Joshua Sophy. **Released:** March 10, 2023. **Description:** The email marketing and online marketing tools company, Constant Contact, launched a small business podcast, which discusses marketing strategies. **Availability:** Online.

29721 ■ *Consumer Behavior*
Ed: Leon G. Schiffman, Joseph Wisenblit. **Released:** Fifth Edition. **Price:** $276.20, cloth; $112.99, adobe reader. **Description:** Consumer behavior is central to the planning, development and implementation of marketing strategies. **Availability:** Print; Online; PDF.

29722 ■ *"Contagious: Why Things Catch On"*
Pub: Simon & Schuster, Inc.
Contact: Jonathan Karp, President
Released: March 2013. **Price:** $26, after_pricingtext. **Description:** Wharton marketing professor, Jonah Berger, reveals the science of successful word-of-mouth and social media marketing that provides greater results than traditional advertising. **Availability:** Print.

29723 ■ *Content Rich: Writing Your Way to Wealth on the Web*
Released: 1st Edition. **Description:** A definitive search engine optimization (SEO) copywriting guide for search engine rankings and sales conversion. It includes topics not covered in other books on the subject and targets the small to medium sized business looking for ways to maximize online marketing activities as well as designers and Web developers seeking to incorporate more SEO techniques into design and content.

29724 ■ *"Convenience Store Deal for Cardtronics"* in *American Banker (Vol. 174, July 28, 2009, No. 143, pp. 12)*
Pub: SourceMedia LLC
Contact: Gemma Postlethwaite, Chief Executive Officer
Description: Royal Buying Group, Inc., a convenience store marketing company, has agreed to recommend automated teller machine services from Cardtronics, to its clients.

29725 ■ *"Conversations with Customers"* in *Business Journal Serving Greater Tampa Bay (Vol. 31, December 31, 2010, No. 1, pp. 1)*
Pub: Tampa Bay Business Journal
Contact: Ian Anderson, President
E-mail: ianderson@bizjournals.com
Description: Tampa Bay, Florida-based businesses have been using social media to interact with customers. Forty percent of businesses have been found to have at least one social media platform to reach customers and prospects. **Availability:** Print; Online.

29726 ■ *"Conversations Need to Yield Actions Measured in Dollars"* in *Advertising Age (Vol. 79, July 7, 2008, No. 26, pp. 18)*
Pub: Crain Communications, Inc.
Contact: Jessica Botos, Manager, Marketing
E-mail: jessica.botos@crainsnewyork.com
Ed: Jonathan Salem Baskin. **Description:** New ways in which to market to consumers are discussed. **Availability:** Online.

29727 ■ *"Convert New Customers to Long Term Accounts"* in *Indoor Comfort Marketing (Vol. 70, February 2011, No. 2, pp. 22)*
Description: Marketing to new customers and suggestions for retaining them is covered. **Availability:** Online.

29728 ■ *"The Copyright Evolution"* in *Information Today (Vol. 28, November 2011, No. 10, pp. 1)*
Pub: Information Today Inc.
Contact: Thomas H. Hogan, President

Ed: Nancy Davis Kho. **Description:** For information professionals, issues surrounding copyright compliance have traditionally been on the consumption side. However, today, content consumption is only half the program because blogging, tweeting, and commenting is a vital part of more standard duties for workers as corporations aim to create authentic communications with customers.

29729 ■ *"Corporate Event Management Best Practices: 2020 Guide"* in *The Bizzabo Blog (January 9, 2020)*
Released: January 09, 2020. **Description:** Details best practices that lead to a strong corporate event management strategy. **Availability:** Online.

29730 ■ *"Counting on Cornhole: Popular Bean Bag Game Brings Crowds to Bars"* in *Baltimore Business Journal (Vol. 29, July 15, 2011, No. 10, pp. 1)*
Pub: Boston Business Journal
Contact: Carolyn M. Jones, President
E-mail: cmjones@bizjournals.com
Ed: Alexander Jackson. **Description:** Cornhole game is being used by bars to spur business as the games hikes beer and food sales on slow weekdays. The game is played with two cornhole boards facing each other and is played with one or two people on one team who try to place a bag on the board. **Availability:** Print; Online.

29731 ■ *"Covario Recognized for Second Year in a Row as OMMA Award Finalist for Online Advertising Creativity in Both SEO and SEM"* in *Internet Wire (August 29, 2012)*
Pub: Comtex News Network Inc.
Contact: Kan Devnani, President
Description: Leading independent search marketing agency, Covario, providing search engine optimization (SEO) and search engine marketing (SEM) for companies was chosen as a finalist for the MediaPost Onlien Media, Marketing and Advertising award. This is Covario's second year to be recognized for this award. **Availability:** Print; Online.

29732 ■ *"Crain's Makes Ad Sales, Custom Marketing Appointments"* in *Crain's Chicago Business (Vol. 34, October 24, 2011, No. 42, pp. 13)*
Pub: Crain Communications Inc.
Contact: Barry Asin, President
Description: Crain's Chicago Business announced key appointments in its sales department: David Denor has been named first director of custom marketing services and Kate Van Etten will succeed Denor as advertising director. **Availability:** Online.

29733 ■ *"Cross Atlantic Commodities Launches National Internet Marketing Programs"* in *Manufacturing Close-Up (September 8, 2009)*
Description: Profile of the Internet campaign recently launched by Cross Atlantic Commodities, Inc., a manufacturer of specialty beauty and health products. **Availability:** Print; Online.

29734 ■ *Crossing the Chasm: Marketing and Selling Disruptive Products to Mainstream Customers*
Pub: HarperCollins Publishers L.L.C.
Contact: Brian Murray, President
Ed: Geoffrey A. Moore. **Released:** 3rd edition. **Price:** $21.99, paperback; $11.99, e-book. **Description:** A guide for marketing in high-technology industries, focusing on the Internet. **Availability:** E-book; Print.

29735 ■ *"Crowdsourcing their Way into One Big Mess"* in *Brandweek (Vol. 51, October 25, 2010, No. 38, pp. 26)*
Description: The Gap, was counting on crowdsourcing to provide feedback for its new logo, but it did not prove positive for the retailer. However, a massive outcry of negative opinion, via crowdsourcing, may not always equal valid, constructive criticism. **Availability:** Online.

29736 ■ *"Cyber Thanksgiving Online Shopping a Growing Tradition"* in *Marketing Weekly News (December 12, 2009, pp. 137)*
Pub: Investment Weekly News
Description: According to e-commerce analysts, Thanksgiving Day is becoming increasingly important to retailers in terms of online sales. Internet marketers are realizing that consumers are already searching for Black Friday sales and if they find deals on the products they are looking for, they are highly likely to make their purchase on Thanksgiving Day instead of waiting. **Availability:** Online.

29737 ■ *"A Day Late and a Dollar Short"* in *Indoor Comfort Marketing (Vol. 70, March 2011, No. 3, pp. 30)*
Description: A discussion involving futures options and fuel oil prices is presented. **Availability:** Online.

29738 ■ *"Decoding Demand Opportunities"* in *Business Strategy Review (Vol. 21, Spring 2010, No. 1, pp. 64)*
Ed: Erich Joachimsthaler, Markus Pfeiffer. **Released:** February 09, 2010. **Description:** Classic marketing techniques, such as the use of focus groups or ethnographies, miss the enormous opportunities that can be leveraged once companies commit to understanding consumers in the context of life experiences. **Availability:** Print; PDF; Online.

29739 ■ *"Defend Your Research: Commercials Make Us Like TV More"* in *Harvard Business Review (Vol. 88, October 2010, No. 10, pp. 36)*
Pub: Harvard Business Publishing
Contact: Diane Belcher, Managing Director
Ed: Leif Nelson. **Price:** $6, PDF. **Description:** Research indicates that people prefer commercial interruption over uninterrupted shows due to the break creating a reactivation of the initial pleasure when beginning a desirable activity. **Availability:** Online; PDF.

29740 ■ *"Denali Asks Consumers to Name Next Moose Tracks Flavor"* in *Ice Cream Reporter (Vol. 23, August 20, 2010, No. 9, pp. 4)*
Description: Denali Flavors based in Michigan is inviting consumer to name its newest Moose Tracks version of ice cream flavors. **Availability:** Print; Online.

29741 ■ *The Designer's Guide to Marketing and Pricing: How to Win Clients and What to Charge Them*
Released: First edition. **Description:** Guide to running a creative services business teaches designers how to be more effective, attract new clients, wages, and how to accurately estimate a project.

29742 ■ *"Designing Solutions Around Customer Network Identity Goals"* in *Journal of Marketing (Vol. 75, March 2011, No. 2, pp. 36)*
Pub: American Marketing Association
Contact: Bennie F. Johnson, Chief Executive Officer
Ed: Amber M. Epp, Linda L. Price. **Price:** $36. **Description:** The role relational and collective goals in creating customer solutions is investigated using in-depth interviews with 21 families. Findings revealed four integration processes in customer networks, namely, offerings formed around individual coalitions, concurrent participation, alternate participation, and offerings formed around priority goals.

29743 ■ *"Designing Women? Apparel Apparatchic at Kmart"* in *Barron's (Vol. 88, March 17, 2008, No. 11, pp. 16)*
Pub: Dow Jones & Company Inc.
Contact: Almar Latour, Chief Executive Officer
Ed: Robin Goldwyn Blumenthal. **Description:** Kmart began a nationwide search for women to represent the company in a national advertising campaign. Contestants need to upload their photos to Kmart's website and winners will be chosen by a panel of

celebrity judges. The contest aims to reverse preconceived negative notions about the store's quality and service. **Availability:** Online.

29744 ■ *"Deskside Story: As the Latest Buzzword Suggests, PR Firms Are Happy To Drop By"* in Inc. (December 2007, pp. 70, 73)
Ed: Nitasha Tiku. **Description:** Setting up a meeting between a company's CEO and a journalist is known as deskside and is becoming popular again whereby a publicist offers clients deskside visits, briefings and alerts to help promote public relations for a company. **Availability:** Print; Online.

29745 ■ *"Destination Wedding Giveaway: A Custom Instagram Book"* in Benzinga.com (October 29, 2011)
Pub: Benzinga.com
Contact: Jason Raznick, Founder
Description: Eden Condominiums in Perdido Key, Florida will award a beach wedding to a couple in 2012. The event is a marketing tool to draw attention brides as a perfect wedding venue. **Availability:** Print; Online.

29746 ■ *Digital Marketing for Dummies*
Pub: John Wiley & Sons, Inc.
Contact: Christina Van Tassell, Executive Vice President Chief Financial Officer
URL(s): www.wiley.com/en-us/Digital+Marketing+All+In+One+For+Dummies%2C+2nd+Edition-p-9781119932369
Ed: Stephanie Diamond. **Released:** 2nd edition. **Price:** $24, e-book; $39.99, paperback. **Description:** Learn about the newest trends in digital marketing and help your brand succeed. **Availability:** E-book; Print.

29747 ■ *"Digital Marketing: Integrating Strategy and Tactics with Values, A Guidebook for Executives, Managers, and Students"*
Pub: Routledge, Taylor & Francis Group
Released: First edition. **Price:** $59.95, Paperback-$47.96; $190, Hardback - $152; $29.98, e-book. **Description:** Guidebook filled with information on the latest digital marketing tactics and strategic insights to help small businesses generate sustainable growth and achieve competitive advantage through digital integration. A five-step program: mindset, model, strategy, implementation, and sustainability is explained. **Availability:** E-book; Print.

29748 ■ *"Digital Marketing Trends for Gyms in 2019"* in Glofox blog (July 26, 2019)
Ed: Jenny Weller. **Released:** July 26, 2019. **Description:** As digital trends evolve, marketers and small business owners should be aware so they can quickly adapt to emerging technologies to grow their business. This article discusses twelve digital marketing trends for gym and fitness business owners. **Availability:** Online.

29749 ■ *"Direct to Your Mailbox"* in Silicon Valley/San Jose Business Journal (Vol. 30, August 10, 2012, No. 20, pp. 1)
Pub: Baltimore Business Journal
Contact: Rhonda Pringle, President
E-mail: rpringle@bizjournals.com
Description: Silicon Valley has a growing group of subscription e-commerce companies that give an opportunity for consumers to discover new products and to get a surprise box of goodies in the mail each month. Meanwhile, these companies provide merchandisers a new ay to market to shoppers. **Availability:** Print; Online.

29750 ■ *"Discovery Networks"* in Brandweek (Vol. 49, April 21, 2008, No. 16, pp. SR9)
Description: Provides contact information for sales and marketing personnel for the Discovery networks as well as a listing of the station's top programming and an analysis of the current season and the target audience for those programs running in the current season. The networks flagship station returned to the top 10 in 2007, averaging 1.28 million viewers.

29751 ■ *"Disruptive Innovators: Commonground is Transforming the Advertising Landscape by Living at the Intersection of Culture, Creativity, Content, and Technology"* in Black Enterprise (Vol. 44, June 2014, No. 10, pp. 82)
Pub: Earl G. Graves Ltd.
Contact: Earl Graves, Jr., President
Description: Profile of partners, Sherman Wright and Ahmad Islam, who started the Chicago-based Commonground Marketing. The firm is an integrated, multicultural and general market advertising company. The partners met while on vacation in Cancun, Mexico.

29752 ■ *"Diving Into Internet Marketing"* in American Agent and Broker (Vol. 81, December 2009, No. 12, pp. 24)
Ed: Steve Anderson. **Description:** Internet marketing is becoming an essential tool for most businesses; advice is provided regarding the social networking opportunities available for marketing one's product or service on the Internet. **Availability:** Online.

29753 ■ *"Do Social Deal Sites Really Work? A Theme Park Chain Considers Whether the Boost In Ticket Sales Is Worth the Trouble"* in Harvard Business Review (Vol. 90, May 2012, No. 5, pp. 139)
Pub: Harvard Business Review Press
Contact: Moderna V. Pfizer, Contact
Ed: Marco Bertini, Luc Wathieu, Betsy Page Sigman, Michael I. Norton. **Price:** $8.95. **Description:** A fictitious group-purchasing promotion scenario is presented, with contributors providing advice. At issue is whether deal-type promotions compromise the customer experience to the point where it offsets any marketing benefit from the deal. While one approach is to more effectively manage the traffic generated from deals, the other is to more closely target promotions to optimize outcomes. **Availability:** Online; PDF.

29754 ■ *"Does Your Business Really Need a Facebook Page?"* in Legal Zoom (March 22, 2023)
URL(s): www.legalzoom.com/articles/does-your-business-really-need-a-facebook-page
Ed: Bilal Kaiser. **Released:** March 22, 2023. **Description:** Discusses the merits of having a Facebook page dedicated to your small business as part of your marketing plan. **Availability:** Online.

29755 ■ *"Dollar General Selects GSI Commerce to Launch Its eCommerce Business"* in Benzinga.com (October 29, 2011)
Pub: Benzinga.com
Contact: Jason Raznick, Founder
Description: Dollar General Corporation chose GSI Commerce, a leading provider of ecommerce and interactive marketing solutions, to launch its online initiative. GSI Commerce is an eBay Inc. company. **Availability:** Online.

29756 ■ *"Down on the Boardwalk"* in Retail Merchandiser (Vol. 51, September-October 2011, No. 5, pp. 56)
Description: Classic board game, Monopoly, continues to be the most recognized game brand while staying fresh by entering new markets and gaming platforms for all walks of life. Monopoly is available in over 100 countries, translated into 43 languages and played by more than 1 billion people since its introduction, and the game is tailored to each geographic market it enters. **Availability:** Online.

29757 ■ *"Doyle: Domino's New Pizza Seasoned with Straight Talk"* in Crain's Detroit Business (Vol. 26, January 11, 2010, No. 2, pp. 8)
Pub: Crain Communications Inc.
Contact: Barry Asin, President

Ed: Nathan Skid. **Description:** Interview with J. Patrick Doyle, the CEO of Domino's Pizza, Inc.; the company has launched a new marketing campaign that focuses on its bold new vision. **Availability:** Online.

29758 ■ *"Dozens 'Come Alive' in Downtown Chicago"* in Green Industry Pro (July 2011)
Ed: Gregg Wartgow. **Description:** Highlights from the Come Alive Outside training event held in Chicago, Illinois July 14-15, 2011 are shared. Nearly 80 people representing 38 landscape companies attended the event that helps contractors review their services and find ways to sell them in new and various ways. **Availability:** Online.

29759 ■ *Duct Tape Marketing: The World's Most Practical Small Business Marketing Guide*
Pub: Thomas Nelson, Inc.
Contact: Thomas Nelson, Publisher
Ed: John Jantsch. **Released:** 2007. **Description:** Small business owners are provided the tools and tactics necessary to market and grow a business.

29760 ■ *"Eagles Add Sponsors to Nest"* in Orlando Business Journal (Vol. 28, August 24, 2012, No. 28, pp. 1)
Pub: Baltimore Business Journal
Contact: Rhonda Pringle, President
E-mail: rpringle@bizjournals.com
Description: New and for-renewal sponsorship deals are being secured by the Philadelphia Eagles football team with marketing partners are described. Compared with some National Football League teams having more than 100 deals, the Eagles restrict their corporate sponsors to 46 in an attempt to generate more value for limited supply. **Availability:** Print; Online.

29761 ■ *"Eagles Measure Suite Success"* in Philadelphia Business Journal (Vol. 30, September 9, 2011, No. 30, pp. 1)
Pub: Philadelphia Business Journal
Contact: Sierra Quinn, Director
E-mail: squinn@bizjournals.com
Ed: John George. **Description:** Philadelphia Eagles have a new software program that helps suite holders keep track of how their suite is being used and whether they are getting a return on their investment. The software allows suite holders to better utilize and distribute their tickets. **Availability:** Online.

29762 ■ *EBay Income: How ANYONE of Any Age, Location, and/or Background Can Build a Highly Profitable Online Business with eBay*
Pub: Atlantic Publishing Co.
Contact: Dr. Heather L. Johnson, Contact
Description: A complete overview of eBay is given and guides any small company through the entire process of creating the auction and auction strategies, photography, writing copy, text and formatting, multiple sales, programming tricks, PayPal, accounting, creating marketing, merchandising, managing email lists, advertising plans, taxes and sales tax, best time to list items and for how long, sniping programs, international customers, opening a storefront, electronic commerce, buy-it now pricing, keywords, Google marketing and eBay secrets.

29763 ■ *"Eclectic Reading"* in Business Strategy Review (Vol. 23, Spring 2012, No. 1, pp. 68)
Released: March 06, 2012. **Description:** If ever a field of study was both science and art, marketing seems to fit the bill. Which may be why Nader Tavassoli has a keen interest in diverse subjects: branding, consumer cognition, communication effectiveness, consumer behavior across culturesand several others. What keeps his mind open to a constant flow of new possibilities? As you'll see by his suggested top ten list of books to read, Tavassoli believes strongly in delving into the arts and sciences. **Availability:** Print; PDF; Online.

29764 ■ "Eco-Preneuring" in Small Business Opportunities (Feb. 6, 2012)
Pub: Harris Publishing, Inc.
Contact: Janet Chase, Contact
Description: Iceland Naturally is a joint marketing effort among tourism and business interests hoping to increase demand for Icelandic products including frozen seafood, bottled water, agriculture, and tourism in North America.

29765 ■ "The Effect of 3-D Product Visualization on the Strength of Brand Attitude" in International Journal of Advertising (Vol. 31, May 2012, No. 2, pp. 377)
Description: Research investigates the effect of 3-D product visualization on attitude accessibility and attitude confidence in advertising, two non-evaluative dimensions of attitudes that have not been studied in previous research. The experiment analyzed two versions of a Website (3-D vs 2-D), in which the capacity to interact with the product has been manipulated. **Availability:** PDF; Online.

29766 ■ "The Effectiveness of Advertising That Leverages Sponsorship and Cause-Related Marketing: A Contingency Model" in International Journal of Advertising (Vol. 31, May 2012, No. 2, pp. 317)
Description: Consumers are more likely to have ambivalent attitudes towards cause-related marketing (CRM) than sponsorship. Whereas consumers share similar positive perceptions of CRM and sponsorship, and attribute the motives behind them to altruism, their negative perceptions and attributions of CRM are more accessible than those of sponsorship. **Availability:** Print; Online.

29767 ■ "Elanco Challenges Bayer's Advantage, K9 Advantix Ad Claims" in Pet Product News (Vol. 64, November 2010, No. 11, pp. 11)
Description: Elanco Animal Health has disputed Bayer Animal Health's print and Web advertising claims involving its flea, tick, and mosquito control products Advantage and K9 Advantix. The National Advertising Division of the Council of Better Business Bureaus recommended the discontinuation of ads, while Bayer Animal Health reiterated its commitment to self-regulation. **Availability:** Online.

29768 ■ Electronic Commerce
Ed: Gary P. Schneider, Bryant Chrzan, Charles McCormick. **Released:** 12th edition. **Price:** $29.49, e-book. **Description:** E-commerce can open the door to more opportunities than ever before for small business. Packed with real-world examples and cases, the book delivers comprehensive coverage of emerging online technologies and trends and their influence on the electronic marketplace. It details how the landscape of online commerce is evolving, reflecting changes in the economy and how business and society are responding to those changes. Balancing technological issues with the strategic business aspects of successful e-commerce, the new edition includes expanded coverage of international issues, social networking, mobile commerce, Web 2.0 technologies, and updates on spam, phishing, and identity theft. **Availability:** Print.

29769 ■ "Emack & Bolio's Founder Blames Brookline Store Closure on Rising Rents" in Ice Cream Reporter (Vol. 23, October 20, 2010, No. 11, pp. 8)
Released: Weekly. **Description:** Emack & Bolio's is engaging in scent marketing using various odors to help boost sales by attracting consumers with scents appropriate to their products. **Availability:** Print; Online.

29770 ■ Emerging Business Online: Global Markets and the Power of B2B Internet Marketing
Pub: FT Press
Ed: Lara Fawzy, Lucas Dworski. **Released:** First edition. **Price:** $39.99, Members, watermarked. **Description:** An introduction into ebocube (emerging busi-

ness online), a comprehensive proven business model for Internet B2B marketing in emerging markets. **Availability:** E-book; Print; Online; PDF; Electronic publishing.

29771 ■ "The Emerging Capital Market for Nonprofits" in Harvard Business Review (Vol. 88, October 2010, No. 10, pp. 110)
Pub: Harvard Business Publishing
Contact: Diane Belcher, Managing Director
Ed: Robert S. Kaplan, Allen S. Grossman. **Price:** $8.95, PDF. **Description:** Demonstration of how nonprofits can use intermediaries to grow their organizational structures, giving them improved scale and impact is offered. Some intermediaries play a mutual-fund role and conduct due diligence, while others act as venture capital funds and implement strategy. **Availability:** Online; PDF.

29772 ■ "Emotional Brand Attachment and Brand Personality: The Relative Importance of the Actual and the Ideal Self" in Journal of Marketing (Vol. 75, July 2011, No. 4, pp. 35)
Pub: American Marketing Association
Contact: Bennie F. Johnson, Chief Executive Officer
Ed: Bettin Nyffeneger, Lucia Malar, Harley Krohmer, Wayne D. Hoyer. **Description:** A study on whether the brand's personality should match the consumer's actual self or ideal self is presented. Actual self-congruence is found to have the most impact on emotional brand attachment. **Availability:** PDF.

29773 ■ "The Employee Brand: Is Yours an All-Star?" in Business Horizons (September-October 2007, pp. 423)
Pub: Elsevier Technology Publications
Contact: Kumsal Bayazit, Chief Executive Officer
Ed: W. Glynn Mangold, Sandra Jeanquart Miles. **Description:** Employees can influence the brand image either positively or negatively. The typology presented provides guidelines on how employees can reflect a company's brand image. Classifications of organizations into all-star rookies, injured reserves, or strike-out kings are also discussed. **Availability:** Online.

29774 ■ "Bartering Takes Businesses Back to Basics" in Buffalo News (July 9, 2010)
Pub: The Buffalo News, Inc.
Contact: Tom Wiley, President
E-mail: twiley@buffnews.com
Ed: Dino Grandoni. **Description:** Bartering clubs can help small businesses reach new customers and to expand their business. **Availability:** Print; Online.

29775 ■ "Equity Crowdfunding Platform Initial Crowd Offering, Inc. Closes Equity Financing with Third-Party Investor" in GlobeNewswire (July 18, 2012)
Description: Initial Crowd Offering Inc. closed third-party equity financing round hat provided capital to finish development of its equity crowdfunding portal to the Website. A private angel investor provided development costs to promote the firm's marketing program. Discussion on equity crowdfunding is included. **Availability:** Print; PDF; Online.

29776 ■ "Event Postponement and Cancellation Guide" Cvent (May 15, 2020)
Ed: Anna Linthicum. **Released:** May 15, 2020. **Description:** Provides details on making decisions about cancelling or postponing planned events, especially during uncertain times. Discusses best practices, cancellation insurance, and using event cancellations and postponements as opportunities. **Availability:** Online.

29777 ■ "The Evolution of Self-Regulation in Food Advertising: an Analysis of CARU Cases from 2000-2012" in International Journal of Advertising (Vol. 31, May 2012, No. 2, pp. 257)
Price: $42.50. **Description:** The FTC envisions the Children's Advertising Review Unit (CARU) and the Children's Food and Beverage Advertising Initiative playing lead roles in self-regulatory efforts to address advertising's contribution to childhood obesity. Peeler

(2009) notes that CARU's decisions provide comprehensive guidance to advertisers. Limited research has investigated those decisions. This study examines CARU case reports from 2000 to 2010 involving food marketers from a longitudinal perspective. **Availability:** Print; Online.

29778 ■ "Evolutionary Psychology in the Business Sciences"
Pub: Springer Publishing Co.
Contact: Bernhard Springer, Founder
Released: First edition. **Description:** All individuals operating in the business sphere share a common biological heritage, including consumers, employers, employees, entrepreneurs, or financial traders, to name a few. The evolutionary behavioral sciences and specific business contexts including marketing, consumer behavior, advertising, innovation and creativity and invention, intertemporal choice, negotiations, competition and cooperation in organizational settings, sex differences in workplace patterns, executive leadership, business ethics, store and office design, behavioral decision making, and electronic communications and commerce are all addressed. **Availability:** E-book; Print.

29779 ■ "Ex-Medical Student Stages Career In Event Planning: Barcelona Owner Makes Inroads with Luxury Car Dealerships" in Los Angeles Business Journal (Vol. 34, June 18, 2012, No. 25, pp. 10)
Pub: CBJ L.P.
Contact: Terri Cunningham, Contact
Description: Barcelona Enterprises started as a company designing menus for restaurants, organizing food shows, to planning receptions for luxury car dealers. The firm will be launching the first Las Vegas Chocolate Festival & Pastry Show in July 2012. Presently, the company runs 24 wine and food festivals, organizes events for an upscale dog shampoo maker, and sports car dealerships. **Availability:** Print; Online.

29780 ■ "Executive Decision: XM Mulls Betting the Bank in Competitive Game of Subscriber Growth" in Globe & Mail (March 18, 2006, pp. B3)
Ed: Grant Robertson. **Description:** Canadian Satellite Radio Inc., XM Canada, president and Chief Operating Officer Stephen Tapp feel that establishing a profile in satellite radio to attract subscribers is a very big challenge. His views on the Canadian radio market are detailed. **Availability:** Print; Online.

29781 ■ "Facebook: A Promotional Budget's Best Friend" in Women Entrepreneur (February 1, 2009)
Description: Facebook began as a social networking website but has become a valuable marketing tool for all types of businesses, organizations and causes. Tips are provided for creating a Facebook account and growing one's network on Facebook. **Availability:** Online.

29782 ■ Facebook Marketing: Leveraging Facebook's Features for Your Marketing Campaigns
Pub: Que Publishing
Ed: Justin R. Levy. **Released:** Third edition. **Price:** $18.21, e-book; $16.18, paperback. **Description:** Detailed steps are given in order to develop, use, and create awareness for any business. The book provides detailed instructions, along with case studies from known brands, for launching marketing campaigns on Facebook. **Availability:** E-book; Print.

29783 ■ "Far Out: Satellite Radio Finds New Way to Tally Listeners" in Globe & Mail (March 14, 2007, pp. B14)
Description: The marketing strategy adopted by satellite radio broadcasting firm XM Satellite Radio Inc. in Canada for increasing its subscriber based is discussed. **Availability:** Online.

29784 ■ *"The Fitness Marketing Guide for the Modern Fitness Founder"* in Glofox blog (March 20, 2019)

Ed: Eamonn Curley. **Released:** March 20, 2019. **Description:** Acquiring customers is the most important part of running a fitness business. To grow you need to make sure your message is getting out to potential clients. This article shares a range of strategies you can use to acquire new clients and grow your fitness business. **Availability:** Online.

29785 ■ *"Five Distinct Divisions, One Collective Focus"* in Green Industry Pro (Vol. 23, October 2011)

Ed: Gregg Wartgow. **Description:** Profile of ACLS Inc., an amalgamation of All Commercial Landscape Service (commercial maintenance), All Custom Landscape Service (design/build), Fresno Tree Service, Certified Water Consulting (irrigation), and Tractor Service (disking and flailing services on everything from one-acre lots to hundreds of acres of open land). The firm discusses its rebranding effort in order to increase sales. **Availability:** Online.

29786 ■ *"For Tax Preparation Agencies, Inbound Consumer Calls Trend Higher in January than April"* in Marketing Weekly News (May 5, 2012)

Pub: NewsRX LLC.

Contact: Kalani Rosell, Contact

Description: According to Marchex Institute, caller activity is highest in January, no April when tax deadlines loom. Online advertising campaigns for tax preparers should be optimized at the beginning of the year when peak calls occurred during the week of January 9, 2012. **Availability:** Online.

29787 ■ *"Fort Lauderdale Hotel's Service, Facilities Honored at 'Bride's Choice' by WeddingWire"* in Internet Wire (February 10, 2012)

Pub: Comtex News Network Inc.

Contact: Kan Devnani, President

Description: Harbor Beach Marriott Resort & Spa was awarded the WeddingWire's Bride's Choice Awards for excellence in quality, service, responsiveness and professionalism. More than 200,000 wedding professionals are members of WeddingWire, which brings couples and wedding professionals together in an all-in-one marketing platform. **Availability:** Print; Online.

29788 ■ The Four Steps to the Epiphany: Successful Strategies for Products that Win

Pub: John Wiley & Sons, Inc.

Contact: Christina Van Tassell, Executive Vice President Chief Financial Officer

URL(s): www.wiley.com/en-us/The+Four+Steps+to +the+Epiphany%3A+Successful+Strategies+for +Products+that+Win-p-9781119690351

Ed: Steve Blank. **Released:** March 2020. **Price:** $24, e-book; $40, hardcover. **Description:** Helps entrepreneurs starting new businesses understand the four-step Customer Development process, which helps target what is necessary to achieve sales and marketing for your product. **Availability:** E-book; Print.

29789 ■ *"A Framework for Conceptual Contributions in Marketing"* in Journal of Marketing (Vol. 75, July 2011, No. 4, pp. 136)

Pub: American Marketing Association

Contact: Bennie F. Johnson, Chief Executive Officer

Ed: Deborah J. MacInnis. **Description:** A look at a new framework for thinking about conceptualization in marketing is presented. Conceptual advances are essential to the vitality of the marketing discipline but recent writings indicate that advancement is slowing. The types of conceptual contributions are described, including their similarities and difference, and their importance to the field of marketing. **Availability:** PDF.

29790 ■ *"Free Speech Vs. Privacy in Data Mining"* in Information Today (Vol. 28, September 2011, No. 8, pp. 22)

Pub: Information Today Inc.

Contact: Thomas H. Hogan, President

Ed: George H. Pike. **Description:** The U.S. Constitution does not explicitly guarantee the right of privacy. Organizations and businesses that require obtaining and disseminating information can be caught in the middle of privacy rights. The long-term impact on data mining, Internet marketing, and Internet privacy issues are examined.

29791 ■ Free: The Future of a Radical Price

Description: A new trend shows companies using giveaways as a means to attract business and increase profits.

29792 ■ *"Friendly Ice Cream Corporation"* in Ice Cream Reporter (Vol. 23, August 20, 2010, No. 9, pp. 8)

Description: Friendly Ice Cream Corporation appointed Andrea M. McKenna as vice president of marketing and chief marketing officer. **Availability:** Print; Online.

29793 ■ From Concept To Consumer: How to Turn Ideas Into Money

Ed: Phil Baker. **Released:** 1st edition. **Price:** $27.99, paperback. **Description:** Renowned product developer Phil Baker explains how a great idea accounts for only 5 percent of all the factors of success and why the majority of success is dependent upon a myriad of other factors, including the time it takes to get to market, price, marketing and distribution. By being their own best competition, a small company can stay one step ahead of competitors. **Availability:** Print.

29794 ■ *"From Craft Biz To Wholesale Giant"* in Women Entrepreneur (January 19, 2009)

Description: Advice is given on how to turn a small craft business into a full-time venture; tips to help one transition from a part-time designer to a full-time wholesaler and brand are also included.

29795 ■ *"Funds 'Friend' Facebook"* in Barron's (Vol. 89, July 27, 2009, No. 30, pp. 30)

Pub: Dow Jones & Company Inc.

Contact: Almar Latour, Chief Executive Officer

Ed: Leslie P. Norton. **Description:** Mutual-fund companies are the latest entrants to the "social media" space and several companies have already set up Facebook and Twitter pages. The use of this technology pose special challenges for compliance and regulators especially since the Financial Industry Regulatory Authority reminds companies that advertising, sales and literature are governed by regulations. **Availability:** Online.

29796 ■ *"Funeral Directors Get Creative As Boomers Near Great Beyond"* in Advertising Age (Vol. 79, October 13, 2008, No. 38, pp. 30)

Pub: Crain Communications, Inc.

Contact: Jessica Botos, Manager, Marketing

E-mail: jessica.botos@crainsnewyork.com

Ed: Lenore Skenazy. **Description:** Despite the downturn in the economy, the funeral business is thriving due to the number of baby boomers who realize the importance of making preparations for their death. Marketers are getting creative in their approach and many companies have taken into consideration the need for a more environmental friendly way to dispose of bodies and thus have created innovative businesses that reflect this need. **Availability:** Online.

29797 ■ The Future of AI Marketing for Small Businesses

Released: January 07, 2020. **Description:** Discusses how small businesses can stay ahead and use AI with martech tools in advertising, deciphering in-house analytics, forecasting, lead gen, and more. **Availability:** Online.

29798 ■ *"The Future of Work"* in Black Enterprise (Vol. 41, August 2010, No. 1, pp. 65)

Pub: Earl G. Graves Ltd.

Contact: Earl Graves, Jr., President

Ed: Annya M. Lott. **Description:** Technology, globalization, and outsourcing will continue to shape the future of work. Social media is a means for small companies to market goods and services. **Availability:** Online.

29799 ■ *"FutureDash Launches IndieGoGo Crowdfunding Campaign for the EnergyBuddy Home Energy Monitoring System"* in Benzinga.com (June 21, 2012)

Pub: Benzinga.com

Contact: Jason Raznick, Founder

Ed: Aaron Wise. **Description:** FutureDash launched its campaign on IndieGoGo to promote its home energy monitoring system called EnergyBuddy. The system monitors the amount of electricity being used in the home or building. Information and control is available through an iPhone, iPad, Android smartphone or computer screen or anywhere on a secure Internet connection. **Availability:** Online.

29800 ■ *"Gain the 'Come Alive Outside' Selling Edge"* in Green Industry Pro (July 2011)

Ed: Jim Paluch. **Description:** Marketing the 'Come Alive Outside' slogan can help landscapers to increase their market share by identifying and applying these elements to each customer as well as their workers. **Availability:** Online.

29801 ■ Get Clients Now!: A 28-Day Marketing Program for Professionals, Consultants, and Coaches

Pub: American Management Association

Contact: Manny Avramidis, President

Ed: C.J. Hayden. **Availability:** Print.

29802 ■ *"Get the Picture: 8 Instagram Tips for Small Businesses"* in Legal Zoom (March 21, 2023)

URL(s): www.legalzoom.com/articles/get-the-picture -8-instagram-tips-for-small-businesses

Ed: Michelle Kaminsky, Esq. **Released:** March 21, 2023. **Description:** Instagram is a very popular social media tool for small businesses to use. Get the right picture of your product and you could attract a lot of new customers and get old customers through your door as well. **Availability:** Online.

29803 ■ *"Getting the Bioheat Word Out"* in Indoor Comfort Marketing (Vol. 70, September 2011, No. 9, pp. 32)

Description: Ways to market advanced liquid fuels to the public are outlined. **Availability:** Print; Online.

29804 ■ *"Girls Will Gossip: Psst! Buzz About Target"* in Barron's (Vol. 89, July 27, 2009, No. 30, pp. 15)

Pub: Dow Jones & Company Inc.

Contact: Almar Latour, Chief Executive Officer

Ed: Katherine Cheng. **Description:** Target rebutted the rumor that they will disassociate themselves from a line of clothing inspired by the television show 'Gossip Girl'. Target's spokesman says that the retailer intends to remain closely identified with the show. Target's sales should benefit from the hotly anticipated clothing line. **Availability:** Online.

29805 ■ *"The Globe: How to Conquer New Markets With Old Skills"* in Harvard Business Review (Vol. 88, November 2010, No. 11, pp. 118)

Pub: Harvard Business Publishing

Contact: Diane Belcher, Managing Director

Ed: Mauro F. Guillen, Esteban Garcia-Canal. **Price:** $8.95, PDF. **Description:** Exploration of business-networking factors that have helped lead to the success of Spain's multinational companies is provided. These include development of political skills, access to capabilities and resources, globalization partnerships, and speed of implementation. **Availability:** Online; PDF.

29806 ■ *"The Globe: Let Emerging Market Customers Be Your Teachers" in Harvard Business Review (Vol. 88, December 2010, No. 12, pp. 115)*
Pub: Harvard Business Publishing
Contact: Diane Belcher, Managing Director
Ed: Guillermo D'Andrea, David Marcotte, Gwen Dixon Morrison. **Price:** $8.95, PDF. **Description:** Examination of effective strategies for emerging markets is presented. These include helping educate customers as well as selling to them, adapting to customers' habits, and focusing brands appropriately. Magazine Luiza, a chain store in Brazil, is used to illustrate these points. **Availability:** Online; PDF.

29807 ■ *"GM Canada Revved Up Over Camaro" in Globe & Mail (February 17, 2006, pp. B4)*
Ed: Greg Keenan. **Description:** General Manager of General Motors Canada is planning to start the production of company's muscle car Camaro in Canadian facility. The car was exhibited at Canadian International Auto Show held in Toronto. **Availability:** Online.

29808 ■ *"Golfsmith Goes On Offensive" in Austin Business Journal (Vol. 32, April 27, 2012, No. 8, pp. A1)*
Pub: American City Business Journals, Inc.
Contact: Mike Olivieri, Executive Vice President
Ed: Sandra Zaragoza. **Description:** Golfsmith International Holdings Inc. is targeting existing golfers with its marketing campaign as it attempts to increase its market share. The company aims to attract golfers by providing the right solutions to improving their games. **Availability:** Online.

29809 ■ *"Google Places a Call to Bargain Hunters" in Advertising Age (Vol. 79, September 29, 2008, No. 36, pp. 13)*
Pub: Crain Communications, Inc.
Contact: Jessica Botos, Manager, Marketing
E-mail: jessica.botos@crainsnewyork.com
Ed: Abbey Klaassen. **Description:** Google highlighted application developers who have created tools for its Android mobile phone in the device's unveiling; applications such as ShopSavvy and CompareEverywhere help shoppers to find bargains by allowing them to compare prices in their local areas and across the web. **Availability:** Online.

29810 ■ *Greening Your Small Business: How to Improve Your Bottom Line, Grow Your Brand, Satisfy Your Customers and Save the Planet*
Price: $19.95. **Description:** A definitive resource for anyone who wants their small business to be cutting-edge, competitive, profitable, and eco-conscious. Stories from small business owners address every aspect of going green, from basics such as recycling waste, energy efficiency, and reducing information technology footprint, to more in-depth concerns such as green marketing and communications, green business travel, and green employee benefits.

29811 ■ *"Grey Power: On Target" in Canadian Business (Vol. 81, July 22, 2008, No. 12-13, pp. 45)*
Pub: Rogers Media Inc.
Contact: Neil Spivak, Chief Executive Officer
Ed: Calvin Leung. **Description:** Companies such as LavalifePRIME, a dating website devoted to singles 45 and older, discuss the value of marketing and services aimed at Canada's older consumers. One-third of Canada's 33 million people are 50-plus, controlling 77 percent of the countries wealth. **Availability:** Print; Online.

29812 ■ *"'Groundhog Day' B&B Likely Will Be Converted Into One In Real Life" in Chicago Tribune (October 21, 2008)*
Pub: Tribune News Service
Contact: Jack Barry, Vice President, Operations
E-mail: jbarry@tribpub.com

Ed: Carolyn Starks. **Description:** Everton Martin and Karla Stewart Martin have purchased the Victorian house that was featured as a bed-and-breakfast in the 1993 hit move "Groundhog Day"; the couple was initially unaware of the structure's celebrity status when they purchased it with the hope of fulfilling their dream of owning a bed-and-breakfast. **Availability:** Print; Online.

29813 ■ *Groundswell: Winning in a World Transformed by Social Technologies*
Pub: Harvard Business Review Press
Contact: Moderna V. Pfizer, Contact
Ed: Charlene Li, Josh Bernoff. **Released:** June 09, 2011. **Price:** $22, paperback/softbound. **Description:** Individuals are using online social technologies such as blogs, social networking sites, YouTube, and podcasts to discuss products and companies, write their own news, and find their own deals. When consumers you've never met are rating your company's products in public forums with which you have no experience or influence, your company is vulnerable. This book teaches the tools and data necessary to turn this treat into an opportunity. **Availability:** E-book; Print.

29814 ■ *Guerrilla Marketing Goes Green: Winning Strategies to Improve Your Profits and Your Planet*
Pub: John Wiley & Sons, Inc.
Contact: Christina Van Tassell, Executive Vice President Chief Financial Officer
Ed: Jay Conrad Levinson, Shel Horowitz, Jay Conrad Levinson. **Released:** 2010. **Description:** The latest tips on green marketing and sustainable business strategies are shared. **Availability:** E-book; Print; Electronic publishing; Online.

29815 ■ *"Half of Canadian Firms to Boost Marketing Budgets" in Globe & Mail (January 22, 2007, pp. B1)*
Ed: Keith McArthur. **Description:** The advertising and marketing spending plans of different companies are presented. **Availability:** Online.

29816 ■ *"Handbook of Research on Marketing and Social Corporate Responsibility"*
Pub: Edward Elgar Publishing Inc.
Contact: Edward Elgar, Founder Chairman
Released: 2016. **Description:** Corporate Social Responsibility (CSR) is crucial for both small and large companies to promote growth. The complex relationship between marketing and social responsibility, with a focus on marketing as a driver for CSR initiatives is examined.

29817 ■ *"Hanson's to Widen Marketing Window; Company Plans Mall Kiosks, to Attend Events" in Crain's Detroit Business (Vol. 28, May 28, 2012, No. 22, pp. 3)*
Pub: Crain Communications, Inc.
Contact: Barry Asin, President
Ed: Sherri Welch. **Description:** Hanson's Window and Construction Company is expanding its presence through the use of kiosks installed at malls as well as attending local events in order to increase awareness of their firm. Las year Hanson spent nearly $9.2 million on marketing their vinyl replacement windows, siding and roofing for homes. **Availability:** Print; Online.

29818 ■ *"Happy Trails: RV Franchiser Gives Road Traveling Enthusiasts a Lift" in Black Enterprise (Vol. 38, July 2008, No. 12, pp. 47)*
Pub: Earl G. Graves Ltd.
Contact: Earl Graves, Jr., President
Ed: Tamara E. Holmes. **Description:** Overview of Bates International Motor Home Rental Systems Inc., a growing franchise that gives RV owners the chance to rent out their big-ticket purchases to others when they are not using them; Sandra Williams Bate launched the company as a franchise in July 1997 and now has a fleet of 30 franchises across the country. She expects the company to reach 2.2 million for 2008 due to a marketing initiative that will expand the company's presence.

29819 ■ *"Harness the Internet to Boost Equipment Sales" in Indoor Comfort Marketing (Vol. 70, July 2011, No. 7, pp. 24)*
Description: Advice is given to increase HVAC/R equipment sales using the Internet. **Availability:** Online.

29820 ■ *"The Harris Teeter Grocery Chain Has Started a New Ice Cream Club for Shoppers" in Ice Cream Reporter (Vol. 21, July 20, 2008)*
Description: Store loyalty cards are being issued to Harris Teeter customers to purchase any variety of Ben & Jerry's, Haagen-Dazs, Dove, Starbucks, Ciao Bella, Clemmy's, Purely Decadent, So Delicious, Harris Teeter Naturals, HT Traders, Hunter Farms or Denali Ice Cream. One point is earned for every dollar spent, 30 total points earns a $5 electronic coupon towards the next purchase. **Availability:** Print; Online.

29821 ■ *"HBC Enlists IBM to Help Dress Up Its On-Line Shopping" in Globe & Mail (February 7, 2006, pp. B3)*
Description: The details of management contract between Hudson's Bay Co. and International Business Machines Corp. are presented. **Availability:** Print; Online.

29822 ■ *"Headwinds From the New Sod Slow Aer Lingus" in Barron's (Vol. 88, March 10, 2008, No. 10, pp. M6)*
Pub: Dow Jones & Company Inc.
Contact: Almar Latour, Chief Executive Officer
Ed: Sean Walters, Arindam Nag. **Description:** Aer Lingus faces a drop in its share prices with a falling US market, higher jet fuel prices, and lower long-haul passenger load factors. British media companies Johnston Press and Yell Group are suffering from weaker ad revenue and heavier debt payments due to the credit crunch. **Availability:** Online.

29823 ■ *"Helping Customers Fight Pet Waste" in Pet Product News (Vol. 64, November 2010, No. 11, pp. 52)*
Ed: Sandy Robins. **Description:** Pet cleaning products manufacturers have been enjoying high sales figures by paying attention to changing pet ownership trends and environmental awareness. Meanwhile, the inclusion of user-friendly features in these products has also been boosted by the social role of pets and the media attention to pet waste. How manufacturers have been responding to this demand is explored. **Availability:** Print; Online.

29824 ■ *"Hitting the Green" in Canadian Business (Vol. 81, July 22, 2008, No. 12-13, pp. 34)*
Description: RBC is sponsoring the Canadian Open golf tournament, which is the second-oldest event in the PGA Tour. RBC is expected to receive television exposure on CBS and the Golf Channel. Additional information relating to the sponsorship is presented. **Availability:** Print; Online.

29825 ■ *"Hostess Names $10,000 Grand Prize Winner of its 'CupCake Jackpot' Promotion" in Entertainment Close-Up (August 19, 2011)*
Pub: Close-Up Media Inc.
Contact: Caroline S. Moore, President
E-mail: cms@closeupmedia.com
Description: Tricia Botbyl was the grand prize winner of the Hostess 'CupCake Jackpot' promotion that asked consumers to 'spin' online to win $10,000. Consumers were asked to vote for their favorite Hostess Brand cupcake flavor. **Availability:** Online.

29826 ■ *"Hot to Use Instagram Stories for Your Fitness Business" in Glofox blog (July 13, 2019)*
Ed: Jenny Weller. **Released:** July 13, 2019. **Description:** Instagram Stories give businesses the opportunity to increase their visibility. This article details why you should include Instagram stories in your social media and marketing strategy and ways you can use it to grow your business. **Availability:** Online.

29827 ■ *"Hotels Up the Ante in Bid to Lure Visitors"* in *Sacramento Business Journal (Vol. 29, June 1, 2012, No. 14, pp. 1)*

Pub: Baltimore Business Journal
Contact: Rhonda Pringle, President
E-mail: rpringle@bizjournals.com

Description: Hotel owners in Sacramento, California will spend more on marketing the region to convention planners and tourists. The Sacramento Tourism Marketing District is set to replace a 10-year-old marketing business improvement district on July 1, 2012. It is believed that convention and travel business is an economic driver in the city. **Availability:** Print; Online.

29828 ■ *"How AI Tools at Mailchimp Could Help Market Smaller Businesses"* in *Adweek (November 13, 2020)*

Ed: Patrick Kulp. **Released:** November 13, 2020. **Description:** A new pair of marketing tools from Mailchimp aims to make machine learning capabilities more accessible to companies that don't necessarily have the resources for a big data science division or expensive tech. This article discusses those tools and how they can benefit your small business. **Availability:** Online.

29829 ■ *"How Artificial Intelligence Can Help Small Businesses"* in *Bplans Blog*

Ed: Nicole Walters. **Description:** Discusses how artificial intelligence is becoming more accessible and more affordable for small businesses and how you can incorporate machine intelligence to make your company more efficient and improve your bottom line. **Availability:** Online.

29830 ■ *"How to Attract Clients for Your Residential and Office Cleaning Business"* in *Chron (March 12, 2019)*

Ed: Tracey Sandilands. **Released:** March 12, 2019. **Description:** Provides information on effectively marketing home and office cleaning services to attract clients. **Availability:** Online.

29831 ■ *"How to Boost Your Small Business Marketing Efforts With AI"* in *Forbes (June 28, 2019)*

Ed: Stephanie Wells. **Released:** June 28, 2019. **Description:** As a small business owner, getting the most out of your marketing is important. This article discusses how small businesses can utilize artificial intelligence (AI) to boost marketing efforts. **Availability:** Online.

29832 ■ *"How to Brand-Crash the Olympics"* in *Canadian Business (Vol. 85, August 13, 2012, No. 13, pp. 18)*

Ed: Jeff Beer. **Description:** Several ways of taking advantage of the marketing opportunities in the 2012 London Olympics without having to spend millions in sponsorship fees are recommended. A few suggestions include securing advertising placements just outside of the brand exclusion zones, establishing presence on the Web and sponsoring an individual athlete.

29833 ■ *"How to get Commercial Cleaning Clients without Appearing Desperate"* in *Marketing Systems by Design (July 3, 2019)*

Ed: Jean Hanson. **Released:** July 03, 2019. **Description:** Details information on how to gain commercial cleaning clients for your cleaning business. **Availability:** Online.

29834 ■ *"How to Create a Landscaping Business Website"* in *GoDaddy (May 19, 2020)*

Ed: Jayson DeMers. **Released:** March 19, 2020. **Description:** Discusses why having a website for your landscaping business is important from visibility and information to lead generation. Includes information on what to include on your website, characteristics of a successful website, and how to create your website. **Availability:** Online.

29835 ■ *"How Detroit Built Its Marquee Auto Show"* in *Crain's Detroit Business (Vol. 30, January 6, 2014, No. 1, pp. 17)*

Pub: Crain Communications Inc.
Contact: Barry Asin, President

Description: Detroit-area automobile dealers and business leaders, along with staff from the Detroit Auto Dealers Association, promoted Detroit as the premier North American International Auto Show event, upstaging New York. Few would have considered cold and snowy Detroit as a January destination, but they succeeded in their marketing campaign and the show has continued to grow since. **Availability:** Online.

29836 ■ *"How to Develop an Active Sales Program"* in *Green Industry Pro (Vol. 23, September 2011)*

Ed: Gregg Wartgow. **Description:** Craig den Hartog, owner of Emerald Magic Lawn Care located in Holtsville, New York, describes the various marketing tactics he has developed to increase sales in the current economic environment. Statistical data included. **Availability:** Online.

29837 ■ *"How Do You Measure Your PR's Return On Investment?"* in *Puget Sound Business Journal (Vol. 34, March 21, 2014, No. 49, pp. 9)*

Pub: American City Business Journals, Inc.
Contact: Mike Olivieri, Executive Vice President

Description: The process of measuring public relations and its return on investment (ROI) is difficult because not all expenditures are directed towards media relations and public image. Public relations covers leadership programs, speaking engagements, and word of mouth campaigns. The possibility of linking PR efforts towards bottom line marketing as a goal is discussed. **Availability:** Online.

29838 ■ *"How to Dominate in Residential Maintenance"* in *Green Industry Pro (Vol. 23, October 2011)*

Ed: Gregg Wartgow. **Description:** Lawn care services were ranked among the most expendable consumer expenditures, according to the National Retail Federation data accumulated in early 2011. This makes it critical for any landscape firm to target sales efforts toward higher-income households and higher-value homes. **Availability:** Online.

29839 ■ *"How to Get More Clients for Your Cleaning Business"* in *insureon Small Business Blog (January 6, 2020)*

Released: January 06, 2020. **Description:** Provides information on tactics to use to attract and keep clients for your cleaning business. **Availability:** Online.

29840 ■ *"How Good Advice 'Online' Can Attract Customers"* in *Indoor Comfort Marketing (Vol. 70, August 2011, No. 8, pp. 20)*

Pub: Spray Technology & Marketing
Contact: Ava Caridad, Director, Editorial
E-mail: acaridad@spraytm.com

Ed: Richard Rutigilano. **Description:** Online marketing tips for heating and cooling small businesses are explained.

29841 ■ *"How I Did It: Best Buy's CEO On Learning to Love Social Media"* in *Harvard Business Review (Vol. 88, December 2010, No. 12, pp. 43)*

Pub: Harvard Business Publishing
Contact: Diane Belcher, Managing Director

Ed: Brian J. Dunn. **Price:** $8.95, PDF. **Description:** Effective utilization of online social networks to enhance brand identity, connect with consumers, and address bad publicity scenarios is examined. **Availability:** Online; PDF.

29842 ■ *"How I Did It: Zappos's CEO on Going to Extremes for Customers"* in *Harvard Business Review (Vol. 88, July-August 2010, No. 7-8, pp. 41)*

Pub: Harvard Business Publishing
Contact: Diane Belcher, Managing Director

Ed: Tony Hsieh. **Price:** $8.95, PDF. **Description:** Footwear firm Zappos.com Inc. improved corporate performance through enhanced customer service. Enhancements include highly visible phone numbers, avoidance of scripts, and viewing call centers as marketing departments. **Availability:** Online; PDF.

29843 ■ *"How to Improve Your Mobile Marketing"* in *Contractor (Vol. 56, October 2009, No. 10, pp. 54)*

Ed: Matt Michel. **Description:** Plumbers can improve their mobile advertising by making their logos as large as possible and positioning their logo on top of the truck so people can see it over traffic. They should also make the phone numbers small because people only take note of these when the truck is parked. **Availability:** Online.

29844 ■ *How to Make Big Money in Your Own Small Business: Unexpected Rules Every Small Business Owner Needs to Know*

Ed: Jeffrey J. Fox, Jeffrey J. Fox. **Released:** May 12, 2004. **Price:** $16.95; C$24.95; $16.95; C$24.95; $16.95; C$24.95. **Description:** Former sales and marketing pro offers advice on growing a small business. **Availability:** Print.

29845 ■ *How to Make Money with Social Media: An Insider's Guide to Using New and Emerging Media to Grow Your Business*

Ed: Jamie Turner, Reshma Shah, PhD. **Released:** 2nd edition. **Description:** Marketers, executives, entrepreneurs are shown more effective ways to utilize Internet social media to make money. This guide brings together both practical strategies and proven execution techniques for driving maximum value from social media marketing. **Availability:** E-book; Print.

29846 ■ *"How to Manage Successful Crowdsourcing Projects"* in *oWook (September 29, 2010)*

Ed: Lukas Biewald. **Released:** September 29, 2010. **Description:** The advantages, challenges and pitfalls faced when using crowdsourcing to improve a business are outlined. Crowdsourcing helps to eliminate the need to rely on an internal workforce and the need to forecast task volume. **Availability:** Online.

29847 ■ *How to Market Your Business*

Description: 2009. eBook. Published by Kogan Page. Covers market research, advertising, promotion, selling techniques, product launches, and use of the internet - everything you need to ensure your product reaches your market successfully.

29848 ■ *"How Marketers Can Tap the Web"* in *Sales and Marketing Management (November 12, 2009)*

Description: Internet marketing strategies require careful planning and tools in order to track success. Businesses are utilizing this trend to attract new clients as well as keep customers they already have satisfied. Advice on website development and design is provided. **Availability:** Online.

29849 ■ *"How to Run a Promotion without Running from the Law"* in *Legal Zoom (March 28, 2023)*

URL(s): www.legalzoom.com/articles/how-to-run-a-promotion-without-running-from-the-law

Ed: Bilal Kaiser. **Released:** March 28, 2023. **Description:** If you are planning on running a sweepstakes or an online contest for your small business, follow these tips so that you make sure your business is in compliance with the law. You will also need to be mindful of data privacy issues. **Availability:** Online.

29850 ■ *How to Start a Home-Based Landscaping Business*

Ed: Owen E. Dell. **Released:** 7th edition. **Price:** $21.95, paperback(£14.95); $9.99, e-book(£6.95); $18.95; Electronic Book. **Description:** Guide to starting and running a home-based landscaping business. **Availability:** E-book; Print.

29851 ■ *How to Start a Home-Based Senior Care Business: Develop a Winning Business Plan*

Ed: James L. Ferry. **Released:** Second edition. **Price:** paperback; softback; Electronic Book. **Description:** Everything needed to know in order to start and run a profitable, ethical, and satisfying senior care business from your home. Information covers writing a good business plan, marketing services to families, creating a fee structure, and developing a network of trusted caregivers and service providers. **Availability:** E-book; Print.

29852 ■ *"How To Find More Customers and Clients with Webinars, Seminars and Workshops"*

Pub: CreateSpace

Released: September 27, 2014. **Price:** $2.34, kindle. **Description:** Steps to present successful Webinars, seminars and workshops to market your products at conferences and trade shows are highlighted. A checklist is also provided. **Availability:** Print.

29853 ■ *How to Use the Internet to Advertise, Promote, and Market Your Business or Web Site: With Little or No Money*

Pub: Atlantic Publishing Co.

Contact: Dr. Heather L. Johnson, Contact

Ed: Bruce C. Brown. **Released:** Revised third edition. **Description:** Information is given to help build, promote, and make money from your Website or brick and mortar store using the Internet, with minimal costs.

29854 ■ *How to Write a Great Business Plan for Your Small Business in 60 Minutes or Less*

Pub: Atlantic Publishing Co.

Contact: Dr. Heather L. Johnson, Contact

Ed: Sharon L. Fullen. **Released:** 2013. **Description:** A good business plan outlines goals and works as a company's resume to obtain funding, credit from suppliers, management of the operations and finances, promotion and marketing, and more. **Availability:** CD-ROM; E-book; Print; Online.

29855 ■ *"Hyundai Enters Minivan Market"* in *Globe & Mail* (February 15, 2006, pp. B7)

Ed: Greg Keenan. **Description:** The reasons behind the launch of minivan by Hyundai Auto Canada Inc. are presented. **Availability:** Online.

29856 ■ *"I Hear You're Interested In A..."* in *Inc.* (January 2008, pp. 40-43)

Ed: Leah Hoffmann. **Description:** Four tips to help any small business generate sales leads online are examined. **Availability:** Online.

29857 ■ *I Love You More Than My Dog*

Pub: Portfolio

Contact: Adrian Zackheim, President

Ed: Jeanne Bliss. **Released:** October 15, 2009. **Price:** $14.99, E-book. **Description:** Ways to win passionate, loyal and vocal customers in order to build a small business is outlined. **Availability:** E-book; Print.

29858 ■ *"An Ice Boost in Revenue; Wings Score With Expanded Corporate Sales"* in *Crain's Detroit Business* (Vol. 25, June 1, 2009, No. 22)

Pub: Crain Communications Inc.

Contact: Barry Asin, President

Ed: Bill Shea. **Description:** Stanley Cup finals always boost business for the Detroit area, even during a recession. The Red Wings corporate office reported corporate sponsorship revenue luxury suite rentals, Legends Club seats and advertising were up 40 percent this year over 2008. **Availability:** Print; Online.

29859 ■ *"Iconic Boise Skateboard Shop to Close"* in *Idaho Business Review* (August 19, 2014)

Pub: BridgeTower Media

Contact: Adam Reinebach, President

Description: Lori Wright and Lori Ambur have owned Newt & Harold's for over 30 years. The partners are closing the firm that sold skateboards and snowboards. Wright focused on the marketing and inventory aspects of the retail shop, while Ambur ran the organizational and financial end. Wright and Ambur say they are leaving retail because the industry has faced so many changes since they first opened, particularly competing with online stores.

29860 ■ *"Ideas at Work: Sparkling Innovation"* in *Business Strategy Review* (Vol. 21, Summer 2010, No. 2, pp. 07)

Ed: Julian Birkinshaw, Peter Robbins. **Released:** June 24, 2010. **Description:** GlaxoSmithKline faced a situation common to large global organizations: how to allocate marketing resources to smaller, regional brands. The company's approach to worldwide marketing that led to the development of a unique and productive network is outlined. **Availability:** Print; PDF; Online.

29861 ■ *"If the Opportunity is There, Move Boldly"* in *Indoor Comfort Marketing* (Vol. 70, March 2011, No. 3)

Pub: Spray Technology & Marketing

Contact: Ava Caridad, Director, Editorial

E-mail: acaridad@spraytm.com

Ed: Richard Rutigliano. **Released:** March 01, 2011. **Description:** Suggestions are offered to help improve air conditioning sales. **Availability:** Print; Online.

29862 ■ *"The Impact of Incomplete Typeface Logos on Perceptions of the Firms"* in *Journal of Marketing* (Vol. 75, July 2011, No. 4, pp. 86)

Description: A study of the influence of incomplete typeface logos on consumer perceptions of the company is presented. The findings suggest that companies should avoid incomplete typeface logos if perceptions of trustworthiness are critical or if consumers are likely to have a prevention focus. **Availability:** PDF; Online.

29863 ■ *"In the Wake of Pet-Food Crisis, Iams Sales Plummet Nearly 17 Percent"* in *Advertising Age* (Vol. 78, May 14, 2007, No. 18, pp. 3)

Pub: Crain Communications, Inc.

Contact: Jessica Botos, Manager, Marketing

E-mail: jessica.botos@crainsnewyork.com

Ed: Jack Neff. **Description:** Although the massive U.S. pet-food recall impacted more than 100 brands, Procter & Gamble Co.'s Iams lost more sales and market share than any other industry player. According to Information Resources Inc. data, the brand's sales dropped 16.5 percent in the eight-week period ended April 22. Many analysts feel that the company could have handled the crisis in a better manner. **Availability:** Online.

29864 ■ *"Indulgent Parsimony: an Enduring Marketing Approach"* in *Strategy and Leadership* (Vol. 39, March-April 2011, No. 2, pp. 36)

Pub: Emerald Group Publishing Limited

Contact: Erika Valenti, President

Ed: Kenneth Alan Grossberg. **Description:** Indulgent parsimony (IP), a marketing strategy employed on consumers that are affected by recession, is found to be a relevant and appropriate approach that can help encourage buying. IP involves the selling of cheaper goods and services that allow consumers experience comfort and relief from stress. **Availability:** Download; Online.

29865 ■ *"Info Junkie: Karen Eng"* in *Crain's Chicago Business* (Vol. 34, October 24, 2011, No. 42, pp. 35)

Pub: Crain Communications Inc.

Contact: Barry Asin, President

Ed: Christina Le Beau. **Description:** Greg Colando, president of Flor Inc., an eco-friendly carpet company located I Chicago discusses his marketing program to increase sales. **Availability:** Online.

29866 ■ *"Infomercial King on TeleBrands, Going Broke, Making Millions"* in *Philadelphia Business Journal* (Vol. 33, July 11, 2014, No. 22, pp. 3)

Pub: American City Business Journals, Inc.

Contact: Mike Olivieri, Executive Vice President

Released: Weekly. **Price:** $4, Introductory 4-week offer(Digital only). **Description:** Ajit "A.J." Khubani is CEO of TeleBrands, the Fairfield, New Jersey company that brings to the American mainstream market novelty products by using infomercials, including AmberVision sunglasses and PedEgg. Though the marketing/advertising firm is worth $1 billion, Khubani's entrepreneurship career has gone through ups and downs and he has been close to bankruptcy three times. **Availability:** Print; Online.

29867 ■ *"InnoCentive Announces Next Generation Crowdsourcing Platform"* in *Marketwired* (June 15, 2010)

Pub: Comtex News Network Inc.

Contact: Kan Devnani, President

Description: InnoCentive, Inc., a world leader in open innovation, is launching InnoCentive@Work3, a third generation of its @Work enterprise platform for collaborative-driven innovation for companies. The product will help clients solve critical business and technical issues by tapping information both inside and outside of a company. **Availability:** Online.

29868 ■ *"Innovate or Stagnate: How Doing Things Differently Helps Business"* in *South Florida Business Journal* (Vol. 34, January 10, 2014, No. 25, pp. 10)

Pub: American City Business Journals, Inc.

Contact: Mike Olivieri, Executive Vice President

Released: Weekly. **Price:** $8, Introductory 4-week offer(Digital & Print). **Description:** Business enterprises can drive growth by focusing on innovations. Companies are advised to consider radical ideas, invent different ways of working and avoid bureaucracy. Peter Drucker, a management consultant, believes that business has two functions: marketing and innovation. **Availability:** Print; Online.

29869 ■ *"Innovation Adoption and Diffusion in Business-to-Business Marketing"* in *Journal of Business & Industrial Marketing* (Vol. 29, May 2014, No. 4, pp. 324-331)

Pub: Emerald Group Publishing Limited

Contact: Erika Valenti, President

Description: Evaluation of the innovation adoption and diffusion approach that links it with the key theoretical fields within business-to-business marketing is explored. A conceptual discussion is presented with the aim to develop an integrative conceptual framework and concludes that the proposed theoretical approaches could provide support in establishing a more matter-of-fact view of adoption and diffusion in the industrial sector. **Availability:** Download; Online; PDF.

29870 ■ *"Innovation Can Be Imperative for Those in Hands-On Trades"* in *Crain's Cleveland Business* (Vol. 28, November 12, 2007, No. 45)

Pub: Crain Communications Inc.

Contact: K. C. Crain, President

Ed: Harriet Tramer. **Description:** Discusses the importance of networking and innovative marketing concerning those in art and restoration trades. **Availability:** Online.

29871 ■ *"Inside Intel's Effectiveness System for Web Marketing"* in *Advertising Age* (Vol. 81, January 25, 2010, No. 4, pp. 4)

Pub: Crain Communications, Inc.

Contact: Jessica Botos, Manager, Marketing

E-mail: jessica.botos@crainsnewyork.com

Ed: Beth Snyder Bulik. **Description:** Overview of Intel's internally developed program called Value Point System in which the company is using in order to evaluate and measure online marketing effectiveness. **Availability:** Online.

29872 ■ *Instant Income: Strategies That Bring in the Cash*
Pub: McGraw-Hill Professional

Ed: Janet Switzer. **Released:** First Edition. **Price:** $24. **Description:** Book covers small business advertising techniques, marketing, joint ventures, and sales. **Availability:** Print.

29873 ■ *"Insurers No Longer Paying Premium for Advertising" in Brandweek (Vol. 49, April 21, 2008, No. 16, pp. SR3)*

Description: Insurance companies are cutting their advertising budgets after years of accelerated double-digit growth in spending due to the economic downturn, five years of record-breaking ad spend and a need to cut expenditures as claims costs rise and a competitive market keeps premiums in place. Statistical data included. **Availability:** Print; Online.

29874 ■ *"Intentional Networking: Your Guide to Word of Mouth Marketing Greatness"*
Pub: CreateSpace

Released: October 28, 2014. **Price:** $10.55, kindle; paperback ; $7.84, paperback. **Description:** Business owners and salespeople know the power of word of mouth marketing to increase sales. Networking, email communications, social media and referrals are techniques to help build revenue. **Availability:** Print.

29875 ■ *"Internet Marketing 2.0: Closing the Online Chat Gap" in Agent's Sales Journal (November 2009, pp. 14)*

Ed: Jeff Denenholz. **Description:** Advice regarding the implementation of an Internet marketing strategy for insurance agencies includes how and why to incorporate a chat feature in which a sales agent can communicate in real-time with potential or existing customers. It is important to understand if appropriate response mechanisms are in place to convert leads into actual sales. **Availability:** Print; Online.

29876 ■ *"Into the Light: Making Our Way Through the Economic Tunnel" in Agency Sales Magazine (Vol. 39, August 2009, No. 8, pp. 26)*

Description: Ways in which to avoid business stagnation brought about by the economic downturn is presented. Being different, being a puzzle solver, and knowing the competition are among the things marketing personnel should do in order to wade through the economic downturn. Marketing via direct mail and the Internet also recommended. **Availability:** Online.

29877 ■ *"Inventive Doctor New Venture Partner" in Houston Business Journal (Vol. 40, January 29, 2010, No. 38, pp. A2)*
Pub: Houston Business Journal
Contact: Bob Charlet, President
E-mail: bcharlet@bizjournals.com

Ed: Ford Gunter. **Description:** Dr. Billy Cohn, a surgeon from Houston, Texas has been named as venture partner for venture firm Sante Ventures LLC of Austin, Texas. Cohn will be responsible for seeing marketable developing technologies in the medical industry. The motivation for Cohn's naming as venture partner is his development of a minimally invasive therapy for end-stage renal disease. **Availability:** Print; Online.

29878 ■ *"Israeli Spam Law May Have Global Impact" in Information Today (Vol. 26, February 2009, No. 2, pp. 28)*
Pub: Information Today Inc.
Contact: Thomas H. Hogan, President

Ed: David Mirchin. **Description:** Israels new law, called Amendment 40 of the Communications Law, will regulate commercial solicitations including those sent without permission via email, fax, automatic phone dialing systems, or short messaging technologies. **Availability:** PDF; Online.

29879 ■ *It's Not Who You Know - It's Who Knows You!: The Small Business Guide to Raising Your Profits by Raising Your Profile*
Pub: John Wiley & Sons, Inc.

Contact: Christina Van Tassell, Executive Vice President Chief Financial Officer

Ed: David Arvin. **Released:** 2nd edition. **Price:** $8.69, hardcover. **Description:** When it comes to promoting a small business or a brand, it is essential to know how valuable high-profile attention can be. But for most small companies, the cost of hiring an outside firm to increase attention can be too expensive. **Availability:** Print; Online.

29880 ■ *"Jab, Jab, Jab, Right Hook: How to Tell Your Story in a Noisy Social World"*
Pub: Harper Business
Contact: Hollis Heimbouch, Senior Vice President Publisher

Released: November 26, 2013. **Price:** $23.99, hardcover. **Description:** Author and social media expert shares advice on ways to connect with customers and beat the competition. Social media strategies for marketers and managers need to convert Internet traffic to sales. Communication is the key to online sales that are adapted to high quality social media platforms and mobile devices. **Availability:** E-book; Print.

29881 ■ *"Jacksonville-based Interline Expanding in Janitorial-Sanitation Market" in Florida Times-Union (May 10, 2011)*
Pub: Florida Times-Union

Ed: Mark Basch. **Description:** Interline Brands Inc., located in Jacksonville, Florida, aims to grow its business with two recent acquisitions of firms that distribute janitorial and sanitation products. Interline markets and distributes maintenance, repair and operations products. **Availability:** Online.

29882 ■ *"Jim Kukral Answers the Question: What is Marketing?" in Small Business Trends(December 6, 2022)*
URL(s): smallbiztrends.com/2022/12/what-is-marketing.html

Ed: Holly Chavez. **Released:** December 06, 2022. **Description:** A transcript and a link to a full interview about marketing. Defines what marketing actually is and how to step away from your brand to see what your customers see. **Availability:** Online.

29883 ■ *"Jo-Ann Launches Quilt Your Colors Contest to Celebrate National Sewing Month" in Marketwired (September 10, 2010)*
Pub: Comtex News Network Inc.
Contact: Kan Devnani, President

Description: Jo-Ann Fabric and Craft Stores featured a contest to create a quilt in order to promote National Sewing Month.

29884 ■ *"Just 10% of Retail Businesses Use AI" in Small Business Trends (December 17, 2019)*

Released: December 17, 2019. **Description:** Research shows that many small businesses are reluctant to implement artificial intelligence (AI) or machine learning (ML) solutions into their workflow. This article discusses how to use these technologies to make your business smarter. **Availability:** Online.

29885 ■ *"Keep Customers Out of the Yellow Pages" in Contractor (Vol. 56, November 2009, No. 11, pp. 47)*

Ed: Matt Michel. **Description:** Mechanical contractors should keep customers away from the Yellow Pages where they could find their competition by putting stickers on the water heater or the front of the directory. Giving out magnets to customers and putting the company name on sink rings and invoices are other suggestions. **Availability:** Print; Online.

29886 ■ *The King of Madison Avenue: David Ogilvy and the Making of Modern Advertising*
Pub: Palgrave Macmillan

Ed: Kenneth Roman. **Released:** 2010. **Price:** $18, Paperback; $9.99, e-book. **Description:** The rise and fall of David Ogilvy, once the leader on Madison Avenue, is discussed. **Availability:** E-book; Print.

29887 ■ *The King of Vodka: The Story of Pyotr Smirnov and the Upheaval of an Empire*
Pub: HarperCollins Publishers L.L.C.
Contact: Brian Murray, President

Ed: Linda Himelstein. **Released:** November 30, 2010. **Price:** $15.99, paperback. **Description:** Biography of Pyotr Smirnov and how his determination took him from serf to the head of Smirnov Vodka. Smirnov's marketing techniques are defined and show how he expanded the drink worldwide. **Availability:** E-book; Print; Online.

29888 ■ *"Kokanee Films World's Longest Beer Commercial: Ready for a 90-Minute Feature Starring the Cast of Kokanee?" in Canadian Business (Vol. 85, July 16, 2012, No. 11-12, pp. 11)*

Ed: Jeff Beer. **Description:** Labatt Brewing Company and advertising agency Grip Ltd. produced a feature-length commercial for the Kokanee beer entitled, "The Movie Out Here", which centers on the reunion of friends in a ski town. As part of the marketing campaign, consumers can submit suggestions for props and set locations, audition for parts and vote online for the soundtrack. **Availability:** Online.

29889 ■ *"Kuno Creative to Present the Three Steps of a Successful B2B Social Media Campaign" in Business Tech & Wireless (August 25, 2011)*
Pub: Close-Up Media Inc.
Contact: Caroline S. Moore, President
E-mail: cms@closeupmedia.com

Released: August 24, 2011. **Description:** Kuno Creative, an inbound marketing agency, will host Three Steps of a Successful B2B Social Media Campaign. The firm is a provider of Website development, branding, marketing strategy, public relations, Internet marketing, and inbound marketing. **Availability:** Print; Online.

29890 ■ *"LatinWorks Cozies Up to Chevy in Detroit" in Austin Business Journal (Vol. 31, August 12, 2011, No. 23, pp. A1)*
Pub: Austin Business Journal
Contact: Rachel McGrath, Director
E-mail: rmcgrath@bizjournals.com

Ed: Sandra Zaragoza. **Description:** Hispanic marketing agency LatinWorks opened an office in Detroit to better serve its client Chevrolet and to potentially secure more contracts from its parent company General Motors, whose offices are located nearby. **Availability:** Print; Online.

29891 ■ *"Lavante, Inc. Joins Intersynthesis, Holistic Internet Marketing Company" in Marketwired (November 5, 2009)*
Pub: Comtex News Network Inc.
Contact: Kan Devnani, President

Description: Lavante, Inc., the leading provider of on-demand vendor information and profit recovery audit solutions for Fortune 1000 companies has chosen Intersynthesis, a new holistic Internet marketing firm, as a provider of pay for performance services. Lavante believes that Intersynthesis' expertise and knowledge combined with their ability to develop integrated strategies, will help them fuel more growth. **Availability:** Print; Online.

29892 ■ *"Leading Ohio Internet Marketing Firm Announces Growth in September" in Marketing Weekly News (September 26, 2009, pp. 24)*
Pub: Investment Weekly News

Description: Despite a poor economy, Webbed Marketing, a leading social media marketing and search engine optimization firm in the Midwest, has added five additional professionals to its fast-growing team. The company continues to win new business, provide more services and hire talented employees. **Availability:** Online.

29893 ■ *Lethal Logic: Exploding the Myths that Paralyze American Gun Policy*
Pub: Potomac Books Inc.

Ed: Dennis A, Henigan. **Released:** June 01, 2009. **Price:** $34.95, hardcover. **Description:** Marketing tactics being used by gun manufacturers regarding possible new gun control laws are examined. **Availability:** E-book; Print; PDF.

29894 ■ "Lights, Camera, Action: Tools for Creating Video Blogs" in Inc. (Volume 32, December 2010, No. 10, pp. 57)
Pub: Mansueto Ventures L.L.C.
Contact: Stephanie Mehta, Chief Executive Officer
Ed: John Brandon. **Description:** A video blog is a good way to spread company news, talk about products, and stand out among traditional company blogs. New editing software can create two- to four-minute blogs using a webcam and either Windows Live Essentials, Apple iLife 2011, Powerdirector 9 Ultra, or Adobe Visual Communicator 3. **Availability:** Online.

29895 ■ "Little Cheer in Holiday Forecast for Champagne" in Advertising Age (Vol. 88, November 17, 2008, No. 43, pp. 6)
Pub: Crain Communications, Inc.
Contact: Jessica Botos, Manager, Marketing
E-mail: jessica.botos@crainsnewyork.com
Ed: Jeremy Mullman. **Description:** Due to a weak economy that has forced consumers to trade down from the most expensive alcoholic beverages as well as a weak U.S. dollar that has driven already lofty Champagne prices higher, makers of the French sparkling wine are anticipating a brutally slow holiday season. **Availability:** Online.

29896 ■ "LivingSocial's New 'Glue'" in Washington Business Journal (Vol. 33, May 2, 2014, No. 2, pp. 10)
Pub: American City Business Journals, Inc.
Contact: Mike Olivieri, Executive Vice President
Description: LivingSocial Inc. CFO, John Bax, shares his views on the confluence of forces that shaped the company's first quarter results. Bax reports the company is pouring resources into the creation of a new retail merchant solution platform to help market products and services. Bax named the project Glue because it is geared to encouraging customer loyalty to merchants along with repeat business. **Availability:** Print; Online.

29897 ■ "Loblaw's Apparel Guru No Average Joe" in Globe & Mail (March 13, 2006, pp. B1)
Ed: Marina Strauss. **Description:** The details on Loblaw Companies Ltd., which unveiled Joe Fresh Style line of clothing, are presented. **Availability:** Online.

29898 ■ "Lobster Mania Hits China: They Just Had to Get Used to the Claws" in Canadian Business (Vol. 85, July 16, 2012, No. 11-12, pp. 10)
Ed: Joe Castaldo. **Description:** Canadian lobster exports to China have tripled to almost $30 million annually since 2010 as a result of marketing efforts by Maritimes governments including pitching lobster to cooking shows and organizing training sessions for Chinese chefs. Canadian exporters must decide whether their lobster is a premium product or a commodity product to solidify its image in China. **Availability:** Print; Online.

29899 ■ "Local Firm Snaps up 91 Area Pizza Huts" in Orlando Business Journal (Vol. 26, January 8, 2010, No. 32, pp. 1)
Pub: Orlando Business Journal
Contact: Julie Swyers, Director
E-mail: jswyers@bizjournals.com
Ed: Alexis Muellner, Anjali Fluker. **Description:** Orlando, Florida-based CFL Pizza LLC bought the 91 Orlando-area Pizza Hut restaurants for $35 million from parent company Yum! Brands Inc. CFL Pizza plans to distribute parts of the business to Central Florida vendors and the first business up for grabs is the advertising budget. **Availability:** Print; Online.

29900 ■ "A Look at 2020 Food Trends" in FoodTruckOperator.com (February 20, 2020).
Ed: Christine Potts. **Released:** February 20, 2020.

29901 ■ "A Love of Likes: What's a Facebook Nod Worth to a Business? Serious Sales Growth, Say Some" in Boston Business Journal (Vol. 31, July 8, 2011, No. 24, pp. 1)
Pub: Boston Business Journal
Contact: Carolyn M. Jones, President
E-mail: cmjones@bizjournals.com
Ed: Lisa Van der Pool. **Description:** An increasing number of companies in Boston, Massachusetts have been keen on getting Facebook 'likes' from people. Business owners realize that Facebook 'likes' could generate sales and based on some studies, equate to specific dollar values.

29902 ■ Low-Budget Online Marketing for Small Business
Pub: Self-Counsel Press Inc.
Contact: Diana Douglas, Governor
Ed: Holly Berkley. **Released:** 3rd edition. **Price:** C$21.95; $20.95; $20.95; C$21.95; C$12.99; C$21.95. **Description:** Low-budget advertising campaigns are presented to help market any small business. **Availability:** CD-ROM; Print; Download; Electronic publishing; PDF.

29903 ■ "Lux Coffees, Breads Push Chains to React" in Advertising Age (Vol. 77, June 26, 2006, No. 26, pp. S14)
Pub: Crain Communications, Inc.
Contact: Jessica Botos, Manager, Marketing
E-mail: jessica.botos@crainsnewyork.com
Ed: Kate MacArthur. **Description:** Fast-food giants such as McDonald's, Burger King, Dunkin' Donuts and Subway have adjusted their menus in order to become more competitive with gourmet coffee shops and bakeries like Panera Bread and Starbucks which have taken a large share in the market. Statistical data included. **Availability:** Online.

29904 ■ "Macy's Seeks Balance in All Things Ad-Related" in Crain's Chicago Business (Vol. 31, March 31, 2008, No. 13, pp. 19)
Pub: Crain Communications Inc.
Contact: Barry Asin, President
Ed: Natalie Zmuda. **Description:** Macy's Inc. is seeking to balance its national television campaign with locally tailored promotions and products. **Availability:** Online.

29905 ■ Managing Economies, Trade and International Business
Pub: Palgrave Macmillan
Released: 1st edition. **Price:** $89, e-book; $115, Hardcover; $110, softcover. **Description:** An in-depth look at the areas that affect and influence international business, exploring specific issues businesses face in terms of economic development, trade law, and international marketing and management. **Availability:** E-book; Print.

29906 ■ "Managing Yourself: What's Your Personal Social Media Strategy?" in Harvard Business Review (Vol. 88, November 2010, No. 11, pp. 127)
Pub: Harvard Business Publishing
Contact: Diane Belcher, Managing Director
Ed: Soumitra Dutta. **Price:** $8.95, PDF. **Description:** Identification of four distinct sectors and how they interrelate to social media is given. The sectors are personal and private; professional and private; personal and public; and professional and public. Appropriate topics and types of social media are discussed for each. **Availability:** Online; PDF.

29907 ■ "Market and Technology Orientations for Service Delivery Innovation: the Link of Innovative Competence" in Journal of Business & Industrial Marketing (Vol. 29, July 2014, No. 6)
Pub: Emerald Group Publishing Limited
Contact: Erika Valenti, President
Description: A study to formulate an alternative method of predicting service delivery innovation based on market and technology orientations and innovative competence is examined. Five hypotheses were proposed and tested using the Partial Least

Square (PLS) analysis. It was observed that proactive market orientation and technology orientation regulate exploratory and exploitative innovative competences, while exploitative competence influences service delivery innovation. **Availability:** Download; Online.

29908 ■ "Marketer Bets Big on U.S.'s Growing Canine Obsession" in Advertising Age (Vol. 79, April 14, 2008, No. 15, pp. 14)
Pub: Crain Communications, Inc.
Contact: Jessica Botos, Manager, Marketing
E-mail: jessica.botos@crainsnewyork.com
Ed: Emily Bryson York. **Description:** Overview of FreshPet, a New Jersey company that began marketing two brands of refrigerated dog food-Deli Fresh and FreshPet Select-which are made from fresh ingredients such as beef, rice and carrots. The company projects continued success due to the amount of money consumers spend on their pets as well as fears derived from the 2007 recalls that inspired consumers to look for smaller, independent manufacturers that are less likely to source ingredients from China. **Availability:** Online.

29909 ■ "Marketers Push for Mobile Tuesday as the New Black Friday" in Advertising Age (Vol. 79, December 1, 2008, No. 44, pp. 21)
Pub: Crain Communications, Inc.
Contact: Jessica Botos, Manager, Marketing
E-mail: jessica.botos@crainsnewyork.com
Ed: Natalie Zmuda. **Description:** Marketers are using an innovative approach in an attempt to stimulate business on the Tuesday following Thanksgiving by utilizing consumer's cell phones to alert them of sales or present them with coupons for this typically slow retail business day; with this campaign both advertisers and retailers are hoping to start Mobile Tuesday, another profitable shopping day in line with Black Friday and Cyber Monday. **Availability:** Online.

29910 ■ "Marketing in the Digital World: Here's How to Craft a Smart Online Strategy" in Black Enterprise (Vol. 40, July 2010, No. 12, pp. 47)
Pub: Earl G. Graves Ltd.
Contact: Earl Graves, Jr., President
Ed: Sonya A. Donaldson. **Description:** Social media is an integral part of any small business plan in addressing marketing, sales, and branding strategies.

29911 ■ Marketing for Dummies
Pub: John Wiley & Sons, Inc.
Contact: Christina Van Tassell, Executive Vice President Chief Financial Officer
URL(s): www.wiley.com/en-us/Marketing+For+Dummies%2C+6th+Edition-p-9781119894896
Ed: Jeanette Maw McMurtry. **Released:** 4th edition. **Price:** $18, e-book; $29.99, paperback. **Description:** All you needed to know about marketing for your company. This edition includes topics such as using digital engagement, social media campaigns, and tapping into the influencer market. **Availability:** E-book; Print.

29912 ■ Marketing for Entrepreneurs
Pub: FT Press
Ed: Jurgen Wolff. **Released:** 1st edition. **Description:** This text identifies marketing as the entire process of researching, creating, distributing and selling a product or service. It isn't about theory and metrics, rather it is a practical guide that starts with the basics of all marketing aspects. **Availability:** Print.

29913 ■ "Marketing is Everything, But Timing Helps" in Idaho Business Review (September 9, 2014)
Pub: BridgeTower Media
Contact: Adam Reinebach, President
Description: Profile of Ladd Family Pharmacy, founded by husband and wife Kip and Elaine, who borrowed money from Idaho Banking Company to start their pharmacy. The firm has expanded from three workers in 2008 to 22 to date and reported $6.2 million in revenue for 2013.

29914 ■ *"Marketing the Modern Estate-Planning Practice" in WealthManagement.com (May 9, 2017)*
Ed: Craig R. Hersch. **Released:** May 09, 2017. **Description:** Provides detailed information on how to market your estate planning business. Discusses traditional marketing, ineffective marketing, identification of target market, client value creation, and detailed marketing options. **Availability:** Online.

29915 ■ *"Marketing at the Olympics Is No Longer Worth It: An Exercise in Olympic Vanity" in Canadian Business (Vol. 85, August 13, 2012, No. 13, pp. 15)*
Ed: Bruce Philp. **Description:** The cost and return on investment of sponsoring the 2012 London Olympics is examined. Given the high price of official sponsorship in the Olympics, marketers should realize the value of the television advertising audience. **Availability:** Online.

29916 ■ *Marketing Outrageously Redux: How to Increase Your Revenue by Staggering Amounts*
Pub: Bard Press
Contact: Ray Bard, Founder
Ed: Jon Spoelstra, Mark Cuban. **Released:** February 16, 2011. **Description:** Creative marketing strategies are defined. The book shows how considering marketing problems as outrageously but consistently can benefit any small business. The author talks about his own experience when there were not adequate funds for marketing and advertising and the outrageous approach he created to promote sports teams. **Availability:** Print; Electronic publishing.

29917 ■ *"Marketing Scholarship 2.0" in Journal of Marketing (Vol. 75, July 2011, No. 4, pp. 225)*
Pub: American Marketing Association
Contact: Bennie F. Johnson, Chief Executive Officer
Ed: Richard J. Lutz. **Released:** Volume: 75 issue: 4. **Description:** A study of the implications of changing environment and newer collaborative models for marketing knowledge production and dissemination is presented. Crowdsourcing has become a frequently employed strategy in industry. Academic researchers should collaborate more as well as the academe and industry, to make sure that important problems are being investigated. **Availability:** PDF.

29918 ■ *Marketing Without Money for Small and Midsize Businesses: 300 FREE and Cheap Ways to Increase Your Sales*
Price: $11.25. **Description:** Three hundred practical low-cost or no-cost strategies to increase sales, focusing on free advertising, free marketing assistance, and free referrals to the Internet. **Availability:** Print; Online.

29919 ■ *Marketing that Works: How Entrepreneurial Marketing Can Add Sustainable Value to Any Sized Company*
Pub: Wharton School Publishing
Ed: Leonard M. Lodish, Howard Morgan, Shellye Archambeau. **Released:** 2nd edition. **Price:** $57.49, book plus e-book bundle price; $99.98, book plus e-book bundle list price; $39.99, book; $49.99, e-book(water marked). **Description:** Entrepreneurial marketing techniques are shared in order to help a new company position and target products and services. **Availability:** E-book; Print; Electronic publishing; PDF.

29920 ■ *Marketing Works: Unlock Big Company Strategies for Small Business*
Description: Marketing strategies for any small business are outlined. **Availability:** Print.

29921 ■ *"Marketing: You Are On the Air: Radio and TV Producers Are Looking For Shows Starring Smart CEOs" in Inc. (December 2007, pp. 67-69)*
Ed: Sarah Goldstein. **Description:** Many successful entrepreneurs are being hired to host television and radio shows in order to share business expertise. **Availability:** Print; Online.

29922 ■ *"Mars Advertising's Orbit Grows as Other Ad Segments Fall" in Crain's Detroit Business (Vol. 25, June 1, 2009, No. 22, pp. 10)*
Pub: Crain Communications Inc.
Contact: Barry Asin, President
Ed: Bill Shea. **Description:** An electrical fire burned at Mars Advertising's headquarters in Southfield, Michigan. The company talks about its plans for regrouping and rebuilding. The family firm specializes in in-store marketing that targets consumers already in the buying mode. **Availability:** Print; Online.

29923 ■ *"Maryland Casinos Face Atlantic City's $150M Might" in Baltimore Business Journal (Vol. 30, June 1, 2012, No. 4, pp. 1)*
Pub: American City Business Journals, Inc.
Contact: Mike Olivieri, Executive Vice President
Ed: Gary Haber. **Description:** Atlantic City has launched a campaign to attract visitors from the East Coast. The campaign is part of the city's $150 million marketing plan, which markets the city not for its casinos but as a shopping destination. Executive comments included. **Availability:** Online.

29924 ■ *"Maximize Your Marketing Results In a Down Economy" in Franchising World (Vol. 42, November 2010, No. 11, pp. 45)*
Pub: International Franchise Association
Contact: Matthew Haller, President
E-mail: mhaller@franchise.org
Ed: Loren Rakich. **Description:** Strategies to help any franchisee to maximize their marketing efforts in a slow economy are outlined. **Availability:** Online.

29925 ■ *"MBlox, Which Sends Coupons to Phones and Tables, Raises $43.5M" in Atlanta Business Chronicle (July 11, 2014, pp. 12A)*
Pub: American City Business Journals, Inc.
Contact: Mike Olivieri, Executive Vice President
Released: Weekly. **Price:** $4, introductory 4-week offer(Digital only). **Description:** mBlox, the mobile technology firm that sends coupons to hphones and tablets has managed to successfully raise $43.5 million to undertake global expansion. **Availability:** Print; Online.

29926 ■ *"Media Terminology" in MarketingMagazine (Vol. 115, September 27, 2010, No. 13, pp. 80)*
Pub: Rogers Media Inc.
Contact: Neil Spivak, Chief Executive Officer
Description: Media terminology is provided. **Availability:** Print; PDF; Online.

29927 ■ *"Medicine Men" in Canadian Business (Vol. 80, February 12, 2007, No. 4, pp. 19)*
Description: The effort of HPI Health Products' owners Dong Pedersen and Kent Pedersen to popularize their pain reliever product 'Lakota' is discussed. **Availability:** Online.

29928 ■ *"Men May Wear the Pants in the Family, But Women Retain the Power of the Purse" in Marketing to Women (Vol. 22, August 2009, No. 8)*
Description: Nearly 8 in 10 women say that their opinion holds the most sway in the families' financial decisions. Significant factors that influence women's $100 or more purchases include Online reviews, the opinion of spouse or significant other and expert recommendations. Statistical data included. **Availability:** Print; Online.

29929 ■ *"Men and Menu: A Switch in the Kitchen" in Barron's (Vol. 88, March 24, 2008, No. 12, pp. 17)*
Pub: Dow Jones & Company Inc.
Contact: Almar Latour, Chief Executive Officer
Ed: Robin Goldwyn Blumenthal. **Description:** Men are doing more kitchen duties, with 18 percent of meals at home being made by men in 2007 compared to 11 percent four years previously. Young wives, however, choose to forgo work and stay at home. **Availability:** Online.

29930 ■ *"Message to the Masses"*
Pub: BK Royston Publishing
Contact: Julia A. Royston, Publisher
E-mail: julia@bkroystonpublishing.com
Description: Information is offered to help explore ways to get your message to your audience so they not only hear your words, they understand their meaning. Marketing tips for using social media, blogs, the elevator pitch and more are featured. **Availability:** Video; CD-ROM; E-book; Print; Audio.

29931 ■ *"Messaging Apps: What the New Face of Social Media Means for Brands" in New Generation Latino Consortium (December 2010)*
Ed: Gary Fackler. **Description:** Latina bloggers carve out a new niche in social media that helps preserve their unique cultural identities. **Availability:** Online.

29932 ■ *"Microsoft's Diversity Program Clicks Into High Speed" in Hispanic Business (Vol. 30, July-August 2008, No. 7-8, pp. 54)*
Ed: Derek Reveron. **Description:** Microsoft's diversity hiring and vendor diversity program to capture more Hispanic consumer and business-to-business market is described. One of the main goals of these programs is to hire more Hispanic executives and managers who will help the company develop and market products and services that will appeal and benefit Hispanic consumers.

29933 ■ *"MillerCoors Needs the Quickie Mart" in Crain's Chicago Business (Vol. 32, November 16, 2009, No. 46, pp. 2)*
Pub: Crain Communications Inc.
Contact: Barry Asin, President
Ed: David Sterrett. **Description:** Power Marts convenience store owner Sam Odeh says that Chicago-based MillerCoors LLC has done a poor job at promoting its brand, keeping its signs up to date and stocking the shelves at his stores. He complains that the company's service has been awful and the marketing pathetic. Convenience stores accounted for more than $14 billion in beer sales in the past year. **Availability:** Online.

29934 ■ *"Mini Melts Offers 'Win an Ice Cream Business' Contest" in Ice Cream Reporter (Vol. 23, October 20, 2010, No. 11, pp. 3)*
Description: Mini Melts USA launched a promotional program offering contestants the opportunity to win a Mini Melts ice cream business. The business is not a franchise and there are not royalty fees. **Availability:** Print; Online.

29935 ■ *"Missing Ingredients In Cause-Related Advertising: The Right Formula of Execution Style and Cause Framing" in International Journal of Advertising (Vol. 31, May 2012, No. 2, pp. 231)*
Description: In traditional cause-related marketing (CRM) campaigns, marketers focus on a promoted product and ads containing CRM messesage only in small print at the bottom. Some recent marketers have choses to highlight the cause, with the product taking a lesser role in the advertising copy. The purpose of this research is to compare these two execution styles. **Availability:** Download; PDF; Online.

29936 ■ *"Mobile Discounts: A Matter of Distance and Time" in Harvard Business Review (Vol. 92, May 2014, No. 5, pp. 30)*
Pub: Harvard Business Publishing
Contact: Diane Belcher, Managing Director
Price: $6. **Description:** Geolocation via smartphone enables companies to offer consumers real-time incentives and discounts. Research shows that time and distance are key factors in a customers' receptiveness for these promotions: same day and close proximity increase the odds of a sales purchase. **Availability:** Online; PDF.

29937 ■ *"Mobile Marketing Grows With Size of Cell Phone Screens" in Crain's Detroit Business (Vol. 24, January 14, 2008, No. 2, pp. 13)*
Pub: Crain Communications Inc.
Contact: Barry Asin, President

Ed: Bill Shea. **Description:** Experts are predicting increased marketing for cell phones with the inception of larger screens and improved technology.

29938 ■ *"More Leading Retailers Using Omniture Conversion Solutions to Boost Sales and Ecommerce Performance"* in *Marketwired (September 22, 2009)*
Pub: Comtex News Network Inc.
Contact: Kan Devnani, President

Description: Many retailers are utilizing Omniture conversion solutions to improve the performance of their ecommerce businesses; recent enhancements to Omniture Merchandising and Omniture Recommendations help clients drive increased conversion to their Internet ventures.

29939 ■ *"Natural Pet Product Merchandiser Roundtable: Functional Foods and Treats"* in *Pet Product News (Vol. 64, December 2010, No. 12, pp. S1)*
Released: January 18, 2013. **Description:** Executives and business owners from the pet supplies industries deliberate on the role of functional foods in the retail sector. Functional foods pertain to foods with specified health benefits. Insight into marketing functional foods and convincing pet owners to make the transition to these products is examined. **Availability:** Online.

29940 ■ *"Neighborhood Awaits Its 'Very Sexy Building"* in *Dallas Business Journal (Vol. 37, June 27, 2014, No. 42, pp. 12)*
Pub: American City Business Journals, Inc.
Contact: Mike Olivieri, Executive Vice President

Released: Weekly. **Price:** $4, introductory 4-week offer(Digital only). **Description:** Crescent Real Estate Holdings LLC chairman and CEO, John Goff, described the upcoming 20-story, $225 million office and retail tower in Uptown Dallas as a 'sexy addition' to the neighborhood. Goff believes the location offers companies a unique marketing advantage. **Availability:** Print; Online.

29941 ■ *"Net Savings Link Announces SpyderShare Inc. Contract for Development of Search Engine Optimization (S.E.O.) Program"* in *Internet Wire (February 21, 2012)*
Pub: Comtex News Network Inc.
Contact: Kan Devnani, President

Description: Net Savings Link provides electronically deliverable sales incentives for the business market along with improved Web based savings programs for consumers has partnered with SpyderShare Inc. to enhance the firm's presence on the Internet. Details of the partnership are included. **Availability:** Print; Online.

29942 ■ *"Networking Web Sites: a Two-Edge Sword"* in *Contractor (Vol. 56, October 2009, No. 10, pp. 52)*
Ed: H. Kent Craig. **Description:** People need to be careful about the information that they share on social networking Web sites. They should realize that future bosses, coworkers, and those that might want to hire them might read those information. Posting on these sites can cost career opportunities and respect. **Availability:** Print; Online.

29943 ■ *"A New Day is Dawning"* in *Indoor Comfort Marketing (Vol. 70, August 2011, No. 8, pp. 18)*
Description: New trends in the HVAC/R industry regarding biofuels and bioheat are explored. **Availability:** Online.

29944 ■ *"A New Globe - In Print and Online"* in *Marketing to Women (Vol. 22, August 2009, No. 8, pp. 3)*
Description: Seventeen magazine is unifying its print and Online editions with complementary content, a strategy that seems to be working as every aspect of Seventeen drives the reader to another component. **Availability:** Online.

29945 ■ *"New Ideas Urged for 'Superman' Reuse"* in *Providence Business News (Vol. 28, March 10, 2014, No. 49, pp. 1)*
Pub: American City Business Journals, Inc.
Contact: Mike Olivieri, Executive Vice President

Released: March 08, 2014. **Description:** High Rock Development is requesting help from the public to architecturally renovate the 'Superman Building', the tallest building in Providence, Rhode Island. High Rock, the owner of the building, started a lobbying and marketing campaign in February 2014 to garner support. **Availability:** Print; Online.

29946 ■ *"New iPhone Also Brings New Way of Mobile Marketing"* in *Advertising Age (Vol. 79, June 16, 2008, No. 24, pp. 23)*
Pub: Crain Communications, Inc.
Contact: Jessica Botos, Manager, Marketing
E-mail: jessica.botos@crainsnewyork.com

Ed: Abbey Klaassen. **Description:** Currently there are two kinds of applications for the iPhone and other mobile devices: native applications that allow for richer experiences and take advantage of features that are built into a phone and web applications, those that allow access to the web through specific platforms. Marketers are interested in creating useful experiences for customers and opening up the platforms which will allow them to do this. **Availability:** Online.

29947 ■ *"New Recession-Proof Internet Marketing Package Allows Businesses to Ramp Up Web Traffic and Profits"* in *PR Newswire (January 25, 2010)*
Pub: PR Newswire Association LLC.

Description: Profile of Reel Web Design, a leading marketing firm in New York City that caters to small to medium sized businesses with smaller budgets that need substantial return on investment; Reel Web Design offers video production and submission, web design and maintenance and press release writing among additional services. **Availability:** Online.

29948 ■ *"New Sony HD Ads Tout Digital"* in *Brandweek (Vol. 49, April 21, 2008, No. 16, pp. 5)*
Description: Looking to promote Sony Electronics' digital imaging products, the company has launched another campaign effort known as HDNA, a play on the words high-definition and DNA; originally Sony focused the HDNA campaign on their televisions, the new ads will include still and video cameras as well and marketing efforts will consist of advertising in print, Online, television spots and publicity at various venues across the country. **Availability:** Online.

29949 ■ *"The Next Great Canadian Idea: Peripiteia Generator"* in *Canadian Business (Vol. 81, July 21, 2008, No. 11, pp. 45)*
Pub: Rogers Media Inc.
Contact: Neil Spivak, Chief Executive Officer

Ed: Sharda Prashad. **Description:** Thane Heins has invented a generator that produces energy in an isolated system which contradicts the law of conservation of energy. Perepiteia generator is referred to as a 'perpetual motion machine.' Other inventions slated for the Canadian invention competition include Rob Matthies' batteries and Frank Naumann's Smart Trap. **Availability:** Online.

29950 ■ *Niche and Grow Rich*
Description: Consultants share insight to entrepreneurs wishing to find a profitable niche market. Authors write that good niche businesses are easy to start and easy to defend from competitors. They also report that finding a successful niche can attract and maintain good customers who are willing to pay more for unique goods and services.

29951 ■ *"No, Those Casino Rama Ads Aren't Running in NYC"* in *Globe & Mail (March 15, 2006, pp. B1)*
Ed: Keith McArthur. **Description:** The reason Casino Rama did not advertise on New York Cabs is discussed. **Availability:** Online.

29952 ■ *"'Nobody Knows What To Do' To Make Money on the Web"* in *Barron's (Vol. 88, March 17, 2008, No. 11, pp. 40)*
Pub: Dow Jones & Company Inc.
Contact: Almar Latour, Chief Executive Officer

Ed: Mark Veverka. **Description:** Attendees of the South by Southwest Interactive conference failed to get an insight on how to make money on the Web from former Walt Disney CEO Michael Eisner when Eisner said there's no proven business model for financing projects. Eisner said he finances his projects with the help of his connections to get product-placement deals. **Availability:** Online.

29953 ■ *"Noodles Founder Becomes Colorado's Chief Marketing Officer"* in *Denver Business Journal (Vol. 64, August 24, 2012, No. 14, pp. 1)*
Pub: Baltimore Business Journal
Contact: Rhonda Pringle, President
E-mail: rpringle@bizjournals.com

Description: Governor John Hickenlooper has hired Aaron Kennedy to become the first chief marketing officer of the state of Colorado. The founder of restaurant, Noodles & Company will begin his job on August 6, 2012 of creating a state brand to attract more entrepreneurs and businesses entreprises to invest in Colorado. **Availability:** Print; Online.

29954 ■ *"Nortel Makes Customers Stars in New Campaign"* in *Brandweek (Vol. 49, April 21, 2008, No. 16, pp. 8)*
Description: Nortel has launched a new television advertising campaign in which the business-to-business communications technology provider cast senior executives in 30-second TV case studies that show how Nortel's technology helped their businesses innovate. **Availability:** Online.

29955 ■ *"Norvax University Health Insurance Sales Training and Online Marketing Conference"* in *Marketwired (January 27, 2010)*
Pub: Comtex News Network Inc.
Contact: Kan Devnani, President

Description: Overview of the Norvax University Marketing and Sales Success Conference Tour which includes insurance sales training seminars, proven and innovative online marketing techniques and a host of additional information and networking opportunities. **Availability:** Print; Online.

29956 ■ *"Not Sales, But a Secret Sauce"* in *Memphis Business Journal (Vol. 35, March 14, 2014, No. 49, pp. 15)*
Pub: American City Business Journals, Inc.
Contact: Mike Olivieri, Executive Vice President

Released: Weekly. **Price:** $4, introductory 4-week offer(Digital only). **Description:** Farmhouse Marketing LLC creative director, Ben Fent, says businesses should focus on connections instead of sales. He added that businesses should use more visual language in selling. Fant also stated that the key to making a sale is making people see the benefit of a product. **Availability:** Print; Online.

29957 ■ *"Nowspeed and OneSource to Conduct Webinar: How to Develop Social Media Content That Gets Results"* in *Marketwired (December 14, 2009)*
Pub: Comtex News Network Inc.
Contact: Kan Devnani, President

Description: OneSource, a leading provider of global business information, and Nowspeed, an Internet marketing agency, will conduct a webinar titled "How to Develop Social Media Content That Gets Results" in order to provide marketers insight into how to develop and optimize effective social media content to get consumer results that translate into purchases and lead generation. **Availability:** Print; Mailing list; Online.

29958 ■ *Obsessive Branding Disorder: The Illusion of Business and the Business of Illusion*
Pub: PublicAffairs
Contact: Jaime Leifer, Director

Ed: Lucas Conley. **Released:** 2008. **Description:** The implications of brand-centric marketing shows how defenseless consumers are against advertising because they are assaulted with 3,000 to 5,000 ads and branding stratagems that subtly dictate all aspects of their lives. **Availability:** Print; Online.

29959 ▪ "Offer Your Own Authentic Truth" in South Florida Business Journal (Vol. 34, July 25, 2014, No. 53, pp. 13)
Pub: American City Business Journals, Inc.
Contact: Mike Olivieri, Executive Vice President
Released: Weekly. **Price:** $8, introductory 4-week offer(Digital only). **Description:** Turkel Brands CEO, Bruce Turkel, was born in Miami Beach, Florida and has a bachelor's degree in design at the University of Florida. Turkel was a respected advertising agency owner and executive creative director before he began blogging on marketing and branding. He shares three tips for building a brand and creating a positive public image. **Availability:** Print; Online.

29960 ▪ "Old Spice Guy (Feb.-July 2010)" in Canadian Business (Vol. 83, August 17, 2010, No. 13-14, pp. 23)
Pub: Rogers Media Inc.
Contact: Neil Spivak, Chief Executive Officer
Ed: Andrew Potter. **Description:** Old Spice Guy was played by ex-football player and actor Isaiah Mustafa who made the debut in the ad for Old Spice Red Zone body wash that was broadcast during Super Bowl XLIV in February 2010. Old Spice Guy has become one of social marketing success but was cancelled in July when online viewership started to wane. **Availability:** Print; Online.

29961 ▪ "Olympic Challenge: The Skinny on Sponsors" in Barron's (Vol. 92, July 23, 2012, No. 30, pp. 13)
Pub: Dow Jones & Company Inc.
Contact: Almar Latour, Chief Executive Officer
Ed: Jacqueline Doherty. **Description:** Sponsorship of the Olympics by Coca-Cola and McDonald's has been criticized due to the nature of their products. Representatives of the two companies, however, claim that their products are also enjoyed by athletes and can still remain part of a healthy lifestyle. **Availability:** Print; Online.

29962 ▪ "On Comcast, Sarge, Wheels and the Big Price" in Philadelphia Business Journal (Vol. 32, February 7, 2014, No. 52, pp. 4)
Pub: American City Business Journals, Inc.
Contact: Mike Olivieri, Executive Vice President
Released: Weekly. **Price:** $4, introductory 4-week offer(Digital & Print). **Description:** In an interview with David Montgomery, president and CEO of the Philadelphia Phillies team, he shares his views on the upcoming baseball season, the tremendous fan support the team is receiving, and the marketability of the team, with a special focus on their association with Comcast SportsNet as a broadcast producer. He also disclosed the league's plans for spending the new incoming TV money and said they will try to deliver the best product using the available resources. **Availability:** Print; Online.

29963 ▪ "On Managerial Relevance" in Journal of Marketing (Vol. 75, July 2011, No. 4, pp. 211)
Pub: American Marketing Association
Contact: Bennie F. Johnson, Chief Executive Officer
Ed: Bernard J. Jaworski. **Description:** A study to define and clarify managerial relevance, in order to act as a catalyst for debate, disagreement and future scholarship, is presented. The role of chief marketing officer (CMO) is examined to identify areas of inquiry that are both novel and high managerially relevant. The analysis reveals the seven core tasks necessary to perform the CMO role. **Availability:** PDF.

29964 ▪ "On Your Marks, American Airlines, Now Vote! Contest Creating Possibilities and Opportunities for Delray Beach Wedding Planner" in Benzinga.com (2011)
Pub: Benzinga.com
Contact: Jason Raznick, Founder

Description: Wedding planner, Aviva Samuels, owner of Kiss the Planner boutique wedding and event planning agency in Florida, says that winning this contest would help her increase her knowledge base and provide in-depth, personal experience offering more destination wedding destinations.

29965 ▪ "The One Thing You Must Get Right When Building a Brand" in Harvard Business Review (Vol. 88, December 2010, No. 12, pp. 80)
Pub: Harvard Business Publishing
Contact: Diane Belcher, Managing Director
Ed: Patrick Barwise, Sean Meehan. **Price:** $8.95, PDF. **Description:** Four uses for new media include: communicating a clearly defined customer promise, creating trust via delivering on the promise, regularly improving on the promise, and innovating past what is familiar. **Availability:** Online; PDF.

29966 ▪ "Online Marketing and Promotion of Canadian Films via Social Media Tools: Telefilm Launches New Initiative to Foster Innovative Distribution Strategies" in CNW Group (January 27, 2010)
Pub: Comtex News Network Inc.
Contact: Kan Devnani, President
Description: Telefilm Canada announced the launch of a pilot initiative aimed at encouraging the integration of online marketing and the use of social media tools into means of distribution ahead of a films' theatrical release. During this pilot phase Web-Cine 360 will target French-language feature films. **Availability:** Online.

29967 ▪ "Options Abound in Winter Wares" in Pet Product News (Vol. 64, November 2010, No. 11, pp. 1)
Ed: Maggie M. Shein. **Description:** Pet supply manufacturers emphasize creating top-notch construction and functional design in creating winter clothing for pets. Meanwhile, retailers and pet owners seek human-inspired style, quality, and versatility for pets' winter clothing. How retailers generate successful sales of pets' winter clothing outside of traditional brand marketing is also examined. **Availability:** Online.

29968 ▪ "Oreos, Mercedes Join Super Bowl Ad Lineup; 90 Percent of Inventory Sold" in Advertising Age (Vol. 83, October 8, 2012, No. 36, pp. 3)
Description: Mercedes-Benz and Oreo cookes, along with Coca-Cola and Best Buy, announced marketing plans to advertise during Super Bowl XLVII. **Availability:** Print; Online.

29969 ▪ "Organic Dog Food Options" in Pet Product News (Vol. 66, September 2012, No. 9, pp. 54)
Ed: Keith Loria. **Description:** How pet supplies manufacturers have responded to dog owners' demand for natural and organic dog food is discussed. This demand has been generated by increasing health-consciousness, leading to greater tendency to look more closely at food ingredients. Reasons why the switch to organic dog food should be done are presented, along with marketing tips for organic dog food products. **Availability:** Print; Online.

29970 ▪ "Overheating Taking Place? Pay Attention to Details.." in Indoor Comfort Marketing (Vol. 70, March 2011, No. 3)
Description: Boiler facts are outlined to help the small HVAC company when servicing customers. **Availability:** PDF; Online.

29971 ▪ "Overseas Marketing Key to Success of Chicago Spire" in Commercial Property News (March 17, 2008)
Description: New construction of the Chicago Spire, a condominium project located on Lake Michigan's shore, is being marketed to would-be clients in Asia where Chicago is viewed as an emerging world city. **Availability:** Online.

29972 ▪ Oversubscribed: How to Get People Lining up to Do Business with You
Pub: John Wiley & Sons, Inc.
Contact: Christina Van Tassell, Executive Vice President Chief Financial Officer
URL(s): www.wiley.com/en-us/Oversubscribed%3A +How+To+Get+People+Lining+Up+To+Do+Business+With+You%2C+2nd+Edition-p-97808 57088253
Ed: Daniel Priestley. **Released:** 2nd edition. **Price:** $13, e-book; $22, paperback. **Description:** Discusses the principles used to achieve popularity with customers. **Availability:** E-book; Print.

29973 ▪ "Paper Tigers" in Conde Nast Portfolio (Vol. 2, June 2008, No. 6, pp. 84)
Ed: Roger Lowenstein. **Description:** Newspapers are losing their advertisers and readers and circulation today is equal to that of 1950, a time when the U.S. population was half its present size. **Availability:** Print; Online.

29974 ▪ "Partnering for Success" in Art Business News (Vol. 36, October 2009, No. 10, pp. 4)
Description: In such a volatile economy many savvy artists and gallery owners are turning to out-of-the-box partnerships for continued success; these partnerships are also pervading the Internet, especially with such social media networks as Facebook and Twitter where artists and businesses can develop a loyal following. **Availability:** PDF; Online.

29975 ▪ "People; E-Commerce, Online Games, Mobile Apps" in Advertising Age (Vol. 80, October 19, 2009, No. 35, pp. 14)
Pub: Crain Communications, Inc.
Contact: Jessica Botos, Manager, Marketing
E-mail: jessica.botos@crainsnewyork.com
Ed: Nat Ives. **Description:** Profile of People Magazine and the ways in which the publisher is moving its magazine forward by exploring new concepts in a time of declining newsstand sales and advertising pages; among the strategies are e-commerce such as the brand People Style Watch in which consumers are able highlight clothing and jewelry and then connect to retailers' sites and a channel on Taxi TV, the network of video-touch screens in New Your City taxis. **Availability:** Online.

29976 ▪ "The Performer: Soulpepper Theatre Company's Albert Shultz" in Canadian Business (Vol. 83, August 17, 2010, No. 13-14, pp. 71)
Pub: Rogers Media Inc.
Contact: Neil Spivak, Chief Executive Officer
Ed: Steve Maich. **Description:** Soulpepper Theater Company founder and actor/director Albert Schultz shares the key ingredient to his success both artistically and commercially. Schultz believes his success was a combination of passion and persistence, as well as team building. He believes his entrepreneurial impulse came when he began thinking of making opportunities instead of taking them.

29977 ▪ "Pick A Name, Not Just Any Name" in Women Entrepreneur (December 17, 2008)
Description: Craft business owners must choose a name that sounds personal since customers who buy hand-made products want to feel that they are buying from an individual rather than an institution. Tips for choosing a name are provided.

29978 ▪ "The Picture Perfect Guide on How to Make a Fitness Video Strategy" in Glofox blog (April 17, 2019)
Ed: Eamonn Curley. **Released:** April 17, 2019. **Description:** Discusses the effective combination of fitness and video, tips on creating great video, and how you can distribute your video content effectively on organic and paid platforms. **Availability:** Online.

29979 ▪ "Picture Perfect: Startup Ships Camera Products After Kickstarter Campaign" in Austin Business Journal (Vol. 34, June 6, 2014, No. 16, pp. A12)
Pub: American City Business Journals, Inc.
Contact: Mike Olivieri, Executive Vice President

Released: Weekly. **Description:** The nearly three-year-old Austin camera technology startup Cinetics of Texas LLC has begun shipping its latest modular product the Axis360. The shipping began after a successful Kickstarter marketing campaign whereby Cinetics founder and CEO, Justin Jensen, raised more than $1.1 million. All products of Cinetics are built and tested in Austin, Texas. **Availability:** Print; Online.

29980 ■ *"Pink Label: Victoria's Sales Secret"* in *Advertising Age (Vol. 79, July 7, 2008, No. 26, pp. 4)*
Pub: Crain Communications, Inc.
Contact: Jessica Botos, Manager, Marketing
E-mail: jessica.botos@crainsnewyork.com
Ed: Natalie Zmuda. **Description:** Victoria Secret's Pink label accounted for roughly 17 percent of the retailer's total sales last year. The company is launching a Collegiate Collection which will be promoted by a campus tour program. **Availability:** Print; Online.

29981 ■ *"Play By Play: These Video Products Can Add New Life to a Stagnant Website"* in *Black Enterprise (Vol. 41, December 2010, No. 5)*
Pub: Earl G. Graves Ltd.
Contact: Earl Graves, Jr., President
Ed: Marcia Wade Talbert. **Description:** Web Visible, provider of online marketing products and services, cites video capability as the fastest-growing Website feature for small business advertisers. Profiles of various devices for adding video to a Website are included. **Availability:** Online.

29982 ■ *"Please Pass the Mayo"* in *Crain's Chicago Business (Vol. 31, April 28, 2008, No. 17, pp. 32)*
Pub: Crain Communications Inc.
Contact: Barry Asin, President
Ed: Samantha Stainburn. **Description:** Fort Dearborn Co. has come a long way since it started as on one-press print shop; the family-owned company was struggling to keep up with the technology of making consumer product labels for curvy bottles of products like V8 V-Fusion juice and in 2006 sold off to Genstar Capital LLC which has pushed for acquisitions; last year, Fort Derborn bought its biggest competitor, Renaissance Mark Inc., doubling its size and adding spirit and wine makers to its client roster. **Availability:** Online.

29983 ■ *"Poisoning Relationships: Perceived Unfairness in Channels of Distribution"* in *Journal of Marketing (Vol. 75, May 2011, No. 3, pp. 99)*
Pub: American Marketing Association
Contact: Bennie F. Johnson, Chief Executive Officer
Ed: Stephen A. Samaha, Robert W. Palmatier, Rajiv P. Dant. **Released:** Volume: 75 issue: 3. **Description:** The effects of perceived unfairness on the relationships among members of distribution channels are examined. Perceived unfairness is found to directly damage relationships, aggravate the negative effects of conflict and opportunism, and undermine the benefits of the contract. **Availability:** PDF.

29984 ■ *"Politics & Pros: D.C. Considering Sports-Based Marketing Campaign"* in *Washington Business Journal (Vol. 31, July 13, 2012, No. 12, pp. 1)*
Description: Events D.C. is mulling over a targeted marketing campaign at boosting the sports reputation of Washington, D.C. Aside from making presentations to city stakeholders, Events D.C. has organized a growing number of sport-related events. Other actions that have been done by Events D.C. to further its goal of pushing a sports-based marketing campaign are discussed. **Availability:** Print; Online.

29985 ■ *"Potential for Water Pumping in Africa"* in *Canadian Business (Vol. 79, October 23, 2006, No. 21, pp. 162)*
Description: EastCoast Energy Corp.'s business venture of opening a natural gas company based in Tanzania and marketing of natural gas to expanding markets in East Africa is discussed. **Availability:** Print; Online.

29986 ■ *"The Power of Habit: Why We Do What We Do in Life and Business"*
Description: Marketers study the habits of individuals in order to develop creative marketing campaigns. Studies are presented showing how habits work and where, exactly, they reside in our brains. The right habits are crucial to our success. **Availability:** Print; Online.

29987 ■ *Predictably Irrational: The Hidden Forces That Shape Our Decisions*
Pub: HarperCollins Publishers L.L.C.
Contact: Brian Murray, President
Ed: Dan Ariely. **Released:** April 27, 2014. **Price:** $16.99, trade pb. **Description:** Behaviorists are bringing the economics profession around to realizing that human beings are impulsive, shortsighted and procrastinating in behavior. Economists are using this information to market products to consumers. **Availability:** E-book; Print.

29988 ■ *"The Price Is Right: Turning a Profit in the Event Planning Business"* in *Entrepreneur*
Ed: Cheryl Kimball. **Description:** Details how to get started in the event planning industry as well as explains how to determine what to charge clients to turn a profit. **Availability:** Online.

29989 ■ *"Pro Livestock Launches Most Comprehensive Virtual Sales Barn for Livestock and Breed Stock"* in *Benzinga.com (October 29, 2011)*
Description: Pro Livestock Marketing launched the first online sales portal for livestock and breed stock. The firm has designed a virtual sales barn allowing individuals to purchase and sell cattle, swine, sheep, goats, horses, rodeo stock, show animals, specialty animals, semen and embryos globally. It is like an eBay for livestock and will help ranchers and farmers grow. **Availability:** Print; PDF; Online.

29990 ■ *"Professional Grooming Marketplace: Cash In On Green Products and Services"* in *Pet Product News (Vol. 66, September 2012, No. 9, pp. 84)*
Ed: Lizett Bond. **Description:** Pet grooming salons can build customer reputation by providing sustainable and environment-friendly products and services. Energy efficiency and electricity conservation can also be focused upon as pet grooming salons aspire for green marketing goals. **Availability:** Online.

29991 ■ *Professional Services Marketing: How the Best Firms Build Premier Brands, Thriving Lead Generation Engines, and Cultures of Business Development Success*
Pub: John Wiley & Sons, Inc.
Contact: Christina Van Tassell, Executive Vice President Chief Financial Officer
Ed: Mike Schultz, John E. Doerr, Lee Frederiksen. **Released:** Second edition. **Price:** $29.95, hardcover; $19.99, E-Book. **Description:** Research based on best practices and processes for the professional services industry is presented. The book covers five key areas: creating a custom marketing and growth strategy, establishing a brand, implementing a marketing communications program, developing a lead strategy, and winning new clients. **Availability:** E-book; Print.

29992 ■ *"Progress Means Business"* in *Pet Product News (Vol. 66, September 2012, No. 9, pp. 88)*
Description: Pet supplies retailers are encouraged to promote devices featuring technologies that will assist herp hobbyists to properly monitor temperature, humidity and UVB in tanks with improved control and precision. Customer connction should also be taken into consideration by retailers to generate more sales. Other marketing tips for promoting sophisticated monitoring devices for herp tanks are given. **Availability:** Online.

29993 ■ *"Promotional Marketing: How to Create, Implement & Integrate Campaigns That Really Work"*
Pub: Kogan Page
Released: Sixth edition. **Description:** Promotional marketing helps companies stay ahead of competition to gain new customers and keep existing ones. The guide includes new developments in the field of marketing, examining the use of digital media such as mobile devices and phones, interactive television, and Web-based advertising, as well as ways to research and evaluate promotional marketing campaigns. **Availability:** Online; PDF.

29994 ■ *"Promotions Create a Path to Better Profit"* in *Pet Product News (Vol. 64, December 2010, No. 12, pp. 1)*
Ed: Joan Hustace Walker. **Description:** Pet store retailers can boost small mammal sales by launching creative marketing and promotions such as social networking and adoption days.

29995 ■ *"PSC Decision Could Help Bolster a Solar Market Supernova"* in *Tampa Bay Business Journal (Vol. 29, November 6, 2009, No. 46, pp. 1)*
Pub: Tampa Bay Business Journal
Contact: Ian Anderson, President
E-mail: ianderson@bizjournals.com
Ed: Michael Hinman. **Description:** Florida's Public Service Commission (PSC) decision on a power purchase agreement that could add 25 megawatts of solar energy on Tampa Electric Company's offerings is presented. The decision could support the growing market for suppliers and marketers of renewable energy such as Jabil Circuit Inc., which manufactures photovoltaic modules. Details of the agreement are discussed. **Availability:** Print; Online.

29996 ■ *"Psychological Ownership: A Social Marketing Advertising Message Appeal? Not for Women"* in *International Journal of Advertising (Vol. 31, May 2012, No. 2, pp. 291)*
Description: An assessment of psychological ownership as a potential persuasive advertising message appeal in the social marketing effort is examined. Psychological ownership is a feeling of possession; it occurs when individuals feel that something is their even though they cannot hold legal tide to it. **Availability:** PDF; Online.

29997 ■ *"Put Power in Your Direct Mail Campaigns"* in *Contractor (Vol. 56, September 2009, No. 9, pp. 64)*
Ed: Matt Michel. **Description:** Advice on how members of the United States plumbing industry should manage direct mail marketing campaigns is offered. Determining the purpose of a campaign is recommended. Focusing on a single message, product or service is also encouraged. **Availability:** Print; Online.

29998 ■ *"Quantivo Empowers Online Media Companies to Immediately Expand Audiences and Grow Online Profits"* in *Marketwired (November 18, 2009)*
Pub: Comtex News Network Inc.
Contact: Kan Devnani, President
Description: Quantivo, the leader in on-demand Behavioral Analytics, has launched a new solution that includes 22 of the most critical Internet audience behavior insights as out-of-the-box reports; Internet marketers need to understand their audience, what they want and how often to offer it to them in order to gain successful branding and campaigns online. **Availability:** Online.

29999 ■ *"Radio"* in *MarketingMagazine (Vol. 115, September 27, 2010, No. 13, pp. 24)*
Pub: Rogers Media Inc.
Contact: Neil Spivak, Chief Executive Officer
Description: Market data in the radio broadcasting industry in Canada is outlined. **Availability:** Print; Online.

30000 ■ "ReachLocal Plans to Double DFW Space, is Hunting for 150K Square Feet" in Dallas Business Journal (Vol. 35, March 23, 2012, No. 28, pp. 1)

Pub: Baltimore Business Journal
Contact: Rhonda Pringle, President
E-mail: rpringle@bizjournals.com

Description: Online marketing firm ReachLocal Inc. is planning to double its presence in North Texas. The company is considering building up to 150,000-square-feet of space in the area. Construction plans are included. **Availability:** Print; Online.

30001 ■ "The Real Estate Success Formula: 19 Proven Strategies to Making Money in Real Estate"

Pub: CreateSpace

Released: September 28, 2014. **Price:** $19.99, paperback; $1.07, kindle; $99, paperback. **Description:** Nineteen proven strategies for selling real estate are provided by husband and wife real estate team. The book teaches how to buy, hold and sell houses quickly without using your money or your credit. Tactics for marketing, systematizing and managing your real estate business are outlined. **Availability:** Print.

30002 ■ "Real-Life Coursework for Real-Life Business People" in Women In Business (Vol. 63, Summer 2011, No. 2, pp. 22)

Pub: American Business Women's Association
Contact: Rene Street, Executive Director

Ed: Leigh Elmore. **Released:** June 22, 2011. **Description:** American Business Women's Association National Women's Leadership Conference provides members with academic business training courses. Members can take a variety of MBA-level courses that are taught by University of Kansas School of Business professors. Courses include marketing, management, leadership and communication and decision making. **Availability:** Print; Online.

30003 ■ "Real Luxury: How Luxury Brands Can Create Value for the Long Term"

Pub: Palgrave Macmillan
Contact: Beth Farrow, Editor
E-mail: beth.farrow@palgrave.com

Released: First edition. **Description:** An examination of luxury brands from the economic, sociological, and psychological perspectives is discussed. The challenges faced by the luxury sector are explored.

30004 ■ Reality Check: The Irreverent Guide to Outsmarting, Outmanaging, and Outmarketing Your Competition

Pub: Penguin Publishing Group

Ed: Guy Kawasaki. **Released:** February 22, 2011. **Price:** $13.34, paperback; $4.99, e-book; $19.89, hardcover; $20.43, audio. **Description:** Marketing guru and entrepreneur, Guy Kawasaki, provides a compilation of his blog posts on all aspects of starting and operating a business. **Availability:** E-book; Print.

30005 ■ "Recruiting Diversifies" in Advertising Age (Vol. 83, October 8, 2012, No. 36, pp. 25)

Description: Heidrick & Struggles launches a data and analytics practice that fills the void as marketing becomes more data-driven. H&S specializes in recruiting and filling CEO and other senior-level positions for human resource departments of large firms. **Availability:** Print; Online.

30006 ■ "A Refresher Course: California Tortilla Unveils New Logo, Colors, Store Design" in Washington Business Journal (Vol. 31, June 8, 2012, No. 7, pp. 1)

Pub: Baltimore Business Journal
Contact: Rhonda Pringle, President
E-mail: rpringle@bizjournals.com

Description: California Tortilla restaurants have updated its brand with a new logo, color scheme and store design. The company has spent $250,000 on the new marketing effort. **Availability:** Print.

30007 ■ "Region to Be Named Innovation Hub" in Business Courier (Vol. 27, July 2, 2010, No. 9, pp. 1)

Pub: Business Courier

Ed: Dan Monk. **Description:** The selection of Cincinnati's consumer-marketing cluster as a 'Hub of Innovation' by the Ohio Department of Development could boost Cincinnati's chances of receiving $100 million in grants from Ohio's Third Frontier program and other funding sources. Implications of the University of Cincinnati's designation as a Center of Excellence in Advanced Transportation and Aerospace are also discussed. **Availability:** Print; Online.

30008 ■ "Reinventing Marketing to Manage the Environmental Imperative" in Journal of Marketing (Vol. 75, July 2011, No. 4, pp. 132)

Pub: American Marketing Association
Contact: Bennie F. Johnson, Chief Executive Officer

Ed: Philip Kotler. **Description:** Marketers must now examine their theory and practices due to the growing recognition of finite resources and high environmental costs. Companies also need to balance more carefully their growth goals with the need to purse sustainability. Insights on the rise of demarketing and social marketing are also given. **Availability:** PDF.

30009 ■ "Reinventing the Rings" in Business Strategy Review (Vol. 23, Spring 2012, No. 1, pp. 75)

Released: March 06, 2012. **Description:** Over the last three decades, the Olympic Games has undergone a dramatic reversal of fortune. And yet, until now, the story has remained largely untold. Michael Payne provided the inside story in this article originally published in Spring 2005. Payne worked for the Olympic Movement for over 21 years and was involved in 15 Winter and Summer Olympic Games. In 1989 he became the IOC's first marketing director and in 2003 the first director of global broadcast and media rights. He authored 'Olympic Turnaround' and now acts as an adviser to the Olympic host cities and potential host cities. **Availability:** Print; PDF; Online.

30010 ■ "Relationship Marketing Strategy: an Operant Resource Perspective" in Journal of Business & Industrial Marketing (Vol. 29, May 2014, No. 4, pp. 275-283)

Pub: Emerald Group Publishing Limited
Contact: Erika Valenti, President

Description: Successful relationship marketing (RM) strategies are examined. Relationship marketing literature and operant resources positively influencing the RM success are identified.

30011 ■ "Relax! 5 Marketing Ideas for Massage Therapists" in Outbound Engine (January 13, 2020)

Ed: Taylor Landis. **Released:** January 13, 2020. **Description:** As stress levels increase with our face-paced lives, services such as massage therapy are needed more than ever. Coming up with marketing ideas and thinking creatively to ensure your business stands out. This article provides 5 marketing ideas to improve your visibility. **Availability:** Online.

30012 ■ "Report: McD's Pepsi Score Best With Young Hispanics" in Brandweek (Vol. 49, April 21, 2008, No. 16, pp. 8)

Description: According to a new report, in order to reach Hispanic Gen Yers, marketing strategists need to understand this demographic's "bi-dentity," something which has proved an elusive task to many marketers. Another trend is the emergence of Latinas who have careers, as opposed to just jobs. There is an opportunity to tap this new, young and empowered female market with innovative messaging. Statistical data included. **Availability:** Online.

30013 ■ "Reportlinker.com Adds Report: GeoWeb and Local Internet Markets: 2008 Edition" in Entertainment Close-Up (September 11, 2009)

Description: Reportlinker.com is adding a new market research report that is available in its catalogue: GeoWeb and Local Internet Markets - 2008 Edition; highlights include the outlook for consumer mapping services and an examination of monetizing services and an analysis the development outlook for geospacial Internet market, also referred to as the Geoweb. **Availability:** Online.

30014 ■ "Research and Markets Adds Report: Cyprus: Convergence, Broadband and Internet Market" in Wireless News (September 4, 2009)

Description: Overview of a new report by Research and Markets entitled, "Cyprus Convergence, Broadband and Internet Market - Overview, Statistics and Forecasts." Highlights include information regarding broadband accounts which now account for the majority of household Internet connections. **Availability:** Print; Online.

30015 ■ "Research and Markets Adds Report: The U.S. Mobile Web Market" in Entertainment Close-Up (December 10, 2009)

Description: Highlights of the new Research and Markets report "The U.S. Mobile Web Market: Taking Advantage of the iPhone Phenomenon" include: mobile Internet marketing strategies; the growth of mobile web usage; the growth of revenue in the mobile web market; and a look at Internet business communications, social media and networking. **Availability:** Print; Online.

30016 ■ "Restaurants Dish Up Meal Deals To Attract Customers" in Crain's Detroit Business (Vol. 24, October 6, 2008, No. 40, pp. 1)

Pub: Crain Communications Inc.
Contact: Barry Asin, President

Ed: Nathan Skid. **Description:** Restaurateurs are devising many creative and rewarding incentives to get customers to frequent their establishments during this economic crisis. Innovative ways in which even higher-end establishments are drawing in business are discussed. **Availability:** Online.

30017 ■ "The Return of the Infomercial" in Canadian Business (Vol. 83, September 14, 2010, No. 15, pp. 19)

Pub: Rogers Media Inc.
Contact: Neil Spivak, Chief Executive Officer

Ed: James Cowan. **Description:** Infomercials or direct response ads have helped some products succeed in the marketplace. The success of infomercials is due to the cheap advertising rates, expansion into retail stores and the products' oddball appeal. Insights into the popularity of infomercial products on the Internet and on television are given. **Availability:** Online.

30018 ■ "Rise Interactive, Internet Marketing Agency, Now Offers Social Media Services" in Marketwired (November 4, 2009)

Pub: Comtex News Network Inc.
Contact: Kan Devnani, President

Description: Profile of Rise Interactive, a full-service Internet marketing agency which has recently added social media to its list of offerings; the agency touts that its newest service gives their clients the power to have ongoing communication with current and potential customers on the sites they are most actively visiting. **Availability:** Print; Online.

30019 ■ "The Rise of Pompei" in Retail Merchandiser (Vol. 51, September-October 2011, No. 5, pp. 13)

Description: Soho creative consulting group follows its C3 philosophy to create an invigorated brand experience that transforms customers from consumers to empowered buyers. Pompei AD is a leading creative consultancy that specializes in design and branding for retail, museum, hospitality, and other sectors. **Availability:** Print; Online.

30020 ■ "ROIonline Announces Streaming Video Products" in Marketing Weekly News (December 5, 2009, pp. 155)

Pub: Investment Weekly News

Description: ROIonline LLC, an Internet marketing firm serving business-to-business and the industrial marketplace, has added streaming video options to the Internet solutions it offers its clients; due to the huge increase of broadband connections, videos are now commonplace on the Internet and can often convey a company's message in a must more efficient, concise and effective way that will engage a website's visitor thus delivering a high return on a company's investment. **Availability:** Print; Mailing list; Online.

30021 ■ "The Role of Advertising in Consumer Emotion Management" in International Journal of Advertising (Vol. 31, May 2012, No. 2, pp. 339)
Description: Consumer research has demonstrated that emotions play an important role in the decision-making process. Individuals may use consumption or purchasing as a way to manage their emotions. This research develops a model to help explain the process by which individuals engage in consumption to manage their emotions, and examines the efficacy of an advertisement for a hedonic product that uses affect-laden language in marketing to stimulate such a process. **Availability:** Print; Online; Download.

30022 ■ "Rule of the Masses: Reinventing Fashion Via Crowdsourcing" in WWD (Vol. 200, July 26, 2010, No. 17, pp. 1)
Pub: Conde Nast Publications
Contact: Agnes Chu, President

Ed: Cate T. Corcoran. **Description:** Large apparel brands and retailers are crowdsourcing as a way to increase customer loyalty and to build their businesses. **Availability:** PDF; Download; Online.

30023 ■ "Sage Advice" in Canadian Business (Vol. 80, October 22, 2007, No. 21, pp. 70)
Description: Seymour Schulich, one of Canada's richest men and generous philanthropist, wrote the book, "Get Smarter: Life and Business Lessons". The business book sold more than 50,000 copies and now sits on Canada's bestseller's list. Its popularity is attributed to the marketing efforts of the entrepreneur and author. **Availability:** Print; Online.

30024 ■ "St. Louis Digital Marketing Agency Publishes Free SEO Audit Tool" in Internet Wire (February 16, 2012)
Pub: Comtex News Network Inc.
Contact: Kan Devnani, President

Description: Evolve Digital Labs has created a document to help with Search Engine Optimization. The Saint Louis digital marketing firm's 'SEO Guide for Beginners' offers comprehensive information on thetopic of search engine operations, on-site component of Web pages, and strategies for improving visibility in search engine result pages (SERPs). **Availability:** Online.

30025 ■ "Sales of What's Under Feet Add Up Fast" in Pet Product News (Vol. 66, September 2012, No. 9, pp. S8)
Description: Pet supplies retailers and manufacturers have been emphasizing the type of substances in creating new approaches to developing environment-friendly natural litters and beddings for small mammals and cats. Some of these approaches are highlighted, along with marketing strategies retailers have implemented. **Availability:** Print; Online.

30026 ■ Scorecasting: The Hidden Influences Behind How Sports Are Played and Games Are Won
Released: January 25, 2011. **Price:** $1.25, hardcover; $12.75, Paperback. **Description:** Behavioral economist and veteran writer partner to write about research and studies revealing the hidden forces that shape how basketball, baseball, football and hockey games are played, won and lost. **Availability:** audiobook; E-book; Print.

30027 ■ "Search and Discover New Opportunities" in DM News (Vol. 31, December 14, 2009, No. 29, pp. 13)
Pub: Haymarket Media Inc.
Contact: Kevin Costello, Chief Executive Officer

Ed: Chantal Tode. **Description:** Although other digital strategies are gaining traction in Internet marketing, search marketing continues to dominate this advertising forum. Companies like American Greetings, which markets e-card brands online, are utilizing social networking sites and affiliates to generate a higher demand for their products. **Availability:** Print; Online.

30028 ■ "Search Engine Optimization is Becoming a Must for Businesses, But Unethical Companies Can Hurt Worse than Help" in Idaho Business Review (August 3, 2012)
Ed: Sean Olson. **Description:** Search engine optimization increases presence on the Internet for any small business wishing to market a service or product. It is critical to choose an ethical company that has experience in creating Web sites that will get noticed. **Availability:** Print; Online.

30029 ■ Secrets of Power Marketing
Pub: Stoddart Publishing Company, Ltd.

Ed: George Torok, Peter Urs Bender. **Description:** How-to marketing book provides information for putting personal into any marketing plan. The book also offers marketing strategies build around perceptions, relationships, the media, leverage and database marketing. **Availability:** Print.

30030 ■ "Seed Funding: Monsanto Plants Millions in Image Advertising" in Saint Louis Business Journal (Vol. 31, July 29, 2011, No. 49, pp. 1)
Pub: Saint Louis Business Journal
Contact: Robert Bobroff, President
E-mail: rbobroff@bizjournals.com

Ed: Kelsey Volkman. **Description:** Monsanto kicked off a new campaign, 'St. Louis Grown' to show its commitment to the St. Louis, Missouri region after spending millions of dollars in recent years on national advertising campaigns. Monsanto had a marketing budget totaling $839 million in 2010 for both brand and corporate marketing. **Availability:** Print; Online.

30031 ■ "Sell a Movement Within a Smoothie" in Canadian Business (Vol. 87, July 2014, No. 7, pp. 58)
Description: Vega is a nutritional and fitness supplement maker based in Vancouver, British Columbia that has Increased Its sales sevenfold from 2008 to 2013, earning the 9th spot in the 2014 Profit 500 ranking of fastest growing companies in Canada. The firm's strategy is to promote its flagship product Vega One using an in-store bicycle-powered blender. **Availability:** Online.

30032 ■ Selling the Invisible: A Field Guide to Modern Marketing
Ed: Harry Beckwith. **Released:** March 20, 2012. **Price:** $16, paperback, ($21.00 in canada); $13.98, audiobook abridged library($16.99 in canada); $16.98, audiobook abridged($19.75 in canada); $9.98, audiobook abridged($12.98 in canada); $9.99, electronic book($9.99 in canada). **Description:** Tips for marketing and selling intangibles such as health care, entertainment, tourism, legal services, and more are provided. **Availability:** audiobook; E-book; Print.

30033 ■ Selling Online: Canada's Bestselling Guide to Becoming a Successful E-Commerce Merchant
Description: Helps individuals build online retail enterprises; this updated version includes current tools, information and success strategies, how to launch an online storefront, security, marketing strategies, and mistakes to avoid. **Availability:** Online.

30034 ■ "Selling to Other Businesses: 8 Sales Promotion Methods for a B2B Market" in business.com (April 28, 2020)
Released: April 28, 2020. **Description:** Discusses the fact that selling to businesses is different than selling to individual customers and provides promotional tactics small businesses can use for B2B products. **Availability:** Online.

30035 ■ The Seven Principles of WOM and Buzz Marketing: Crossing the Tipping Point
Pub: Springer Science + Business Media LLC.
Ed: Panos Mourdoukoulas, George J. Siomkos. **Released:** First edition. **Description:** An examination into the reasons for some word-of-mouth marketing campaigns being effective while other fail, with a discussion about which group of consumers should be targeted, and how to turn a word-of-mouth campaign into buzz.

30036 ■ "Should I or Shouldn't I?" in Indoor Comfort Marketing (Vol. 70, February 2011, No. 2, pp. 30)
Description: Investment tips are shared for investing in futures options. **Availability:** Print; Online.

30037 ■ Should Your Small Business Invest in AI?
Ed: Jonathan Herrick. **Description:** Artificial intelligence (AI) can help your small business in a number of ways including virtual assistants, machine learning, marketing strategy, accounting, customer support, chatbots, speech recognition, marketing, and sales. This article discusses how you can use AI in some of these areas. **Availability:** Online.

30038 ■ "Silverpop Recognised for Email Marketing Innovations by Econsultancy" in Marketing Weekly News (January 23, 2010, pp. 124)
Pub: Investment Weekly News
Description: Econsultancy, a respected source of insight and advice on digital marketing and e-commerce, recognized Silverpop, the world's only provider of both marketing automation solutions and email marketing specifically tailored to the unique needs of B2C and B2B marketers at Econsultancy's 2009 Innovation Awards. **Availability:** Online.

30039 ■ "Slimmed-Down Supplier TI Automotive Relaunches" in Crain's Detroit Business (Vol. 26, January 11, 2010, No. 2, pp. 14)
Pub: Crain Communications Inc.
Contact: Barry Asin, President
Ed: Robert Sherefkin. **Description:** TI Automotive Ltd., one of the world's largest suppliers of fuel storage and delivery systems, has reorganized the company by splitting it into five global divisions and is relaunching its brand which is now more focused on new technology. **Availability:** Print; Online.

30040 ■ "Small Budget, Big Impact" in Small Business Opportunities (Summer 2010)
Pub: Harris Publishing, Inc.
Contact: Janet Chase, Contact
Description: Ways to use social media to get in from of a target audience for small businesses are examined. **Availability:** Online.

30041 ■ The Small Business Bible: Everything You Need to Know to Succeed in Your Small Business
Pub: John Wiley & Sons, Inc.
Contact: Christina Van Tassell, Executive Vice President Chief Financial Officer
Ed: Steven D. Strauss. **Released:** Third edition. **Price:** $22.95, paperback; $14.99, E-book. **Description:** Comprehensive guide to starting and running a successful small business. Topics include bookkeeping and financial management, marketing, publicity, and advertising. **Availability:** E-book; Print.

30042 ■ Small Business Marketing for Dummies
Pub: John Wiley & Sons, Inc.
Contact: Christina Van Tassell, Executive Vice President Chief Financial Officer
Ed: Paul Lancaster. **Released:** December 2013. **Description:** Marketing strategies for every type of small business. **Availability:** E-book; Print; Online.

30043 ■ Small Business Marketing Strategies Need Rethinking
URL(s): www.yahoo.com/now/small-business-marketing-strategies-rethinking-200500272.html

Released: May 09, 2021. **Description:** Explores how and why small businesses need to adapt and rethink their marketing strategies. **Availability:** Online.

30044 ■ *"Small Dutch Islands Saba, Statia Content With Low-Key Niche" in Travel Weekly (Vol. 69, August 16, 2010, No. 33, pp. 22)*
Pub: NorthStar Travel Media

Ed: Gay Nagle Myers. **Description:** Small Caribbean islands market and promote their region for tourism by never competing with the bigger destinations. Saba and Statia are the two smallest islands in the Caribbean and rely on repeat guests, word-of-mouth recommendations and travel agents willing to promote them. **Availability:** Print; Online.

30045 ■ *"Small is the New Big in Autos" in Globe & Mail (February 16, 2006, pp. B3)*
Ed: Greg Keenan. **Description:** The reasons behind the introduction of subcompact cars by companies such as Ford Motor Co. are presented. The automobiles were unveiled at Canadian International Auto Show in Toronto.

30046 ■ *The Social Media Bible: Tactics, Tools, and Strategies for Business Success*
Pub: John Wiley & Sons, Inc.
Contact: Christina Van Tassell, Executive Vice President Chief Financial Officer
Ed: Lon Safko. **Released:** Third edition. **Price:** $29.95, paperback; $19.99, E-Book. **Description:** Information is given to build or transform a business into social media, where customers, employees, and prospects connect, collaborate, and champion products and services in order to increase sales and to beat the competition. **Availability:** E-book; Print.

30047 ■ *"Social Media, E-Mail Remain Challenging for Employers" in Workforce Management (Vol. 88, December 14, 2009, No. 13, pp. 4)*
Pub: Crain Communications Inc.
Contact: Barry Asin, President
Ed: Ed Frauenheim. **Description:** Examining the impact of Internet social networking and the workplace; due to the power of these new technologies, it is important that companies begin to set clear policies regarding Internet use and employee privacy. **Availability:** Online.

30048 ■ *Social Media For Small Business: Marketing Strategies for Business Owners*
Pub: John Wiley & Sons, Inc.
Contact: Christina Van Tassell, Executive Vice President Chief Financial Officer
URL(s): www.wiley.com/en-us/Social+Media+For +Small+Business%3A+Marketing+Strategies+for +Business+Owners-p-9780730390329
Ed: Franziska Iseli. **Released:** March 2021. **Price:** $12, e-book; $19.99, paperback. **Description:** Social media has grown into the de facto way to reach customers with marketing. This guide shows how to attract customers with the various social media platforms available. Case studies are given. **Availability:** E-book; Print.

30049 ■ *"Social Media By the Numbers: Social-Media Marketing Is All the Rage" in Inc. (Vol. 33, November 2011, No. 9, pp. 70)*
Pub: Inc. Magazine
Ed: J.J. McCorvey, Issie Lapowsky. **Description:** Six strategies to help small businesses use social media sites such as Facebook and Twitter to promote their companies are presented. **Availability:** Online.

30050 ■ *"Social Media & Your Business: Getting Started" in Legal Zoom (March 23, 2023)*
URL(s): www.legalzoom.com/articles/social-media -your-business-getting-started
Ed: Bilal Kaiser. **Released:** March 23, 2023. **Description:** Using social media as part of your marketing is a smart move because of the number of people on these sites that you can reach. Gives tips on what to do to set these accounts up and how to manage them. **Availability:** Online.

30051 ■ *"Social Networking: Growing Pains" in Canadian Business (Vol. 81, July 22, 2008, No. 12-13, pp. 35)*
Pub: Rogers Media Inc.
Contact: Neil Spivak, Chief Executive Officer
Ed: Alex Mlynek. **Description:** Laughing Stock Vineyards' Cynthia Enns and David Enns plan to target young buyers by using social media. The Enns however, are concerned that targeting younger buyers may affect Laughing Stock's image as a premium brand. Additional information regarding the company's future plans is presented. **Availability:** Print; Online.

30052 ■ *"Social Networks in the Workplace: The Risk and Opportunity of Business 2.0" in Strategy & Leadership (Vol. 38, July-August 2010, No. 4, pp. 50-53)*
Pub: Emerald Inc.
Ed: Daniel Burrus. **Description:** The opinions of futurist Daniel Burrus on a novel trend called 'Business 2.0', which involves the use of social networking applications as business tools, are presented. His suggestion that personal social networking technology can be used by businesses to improve collaboration, problem solving, and leadership communications to achieve continuous value innovation is discussed. **Availability:** Online.

30053 ■ *"A Software Company's Whimsical Widgets Were an Instant Hit. But Its Core Product Was Getting Overshadowed" in Inc. (January 2008)*
Ed: Alex Salkever. **Description:** A widget designed as a marketing tool tuned into a hit on Facebook. Should ChipIn shift its focus?. **Availability:** Online.

30054 ■ *"Sorrell Digs Deep to Snag TNS" in Advertising Age (Vol. 79, July 14, 2008, No. 7, pp. 1)*
Pub: Crain Communications, Inc.
Contact: Jessica Botos, Manager, Marketing
E-mail: jessica.botos@crainsnewyork.com
Ed: Michael Bush. **Description:** Martin Sorrell's strategic vision for expansion in order to become the largest ad-agency holding company in the world is discussed. **Availability:** Online.

30055 ■ *"Sponsorships, Booths Available for Business Showcase" in Bellingham Business Journal (February 2010, pp. 3)*
Pub: Sound Publishing Inc.
Contact: Josh O'Connor, President
Ed: Lance Henderson. **Description:** Third Annual Spring Business Showcase still have space available for vendors and sponsors. The event gives local businesses the opportunity to increase their visibility and provides a means to increase sales and build relationships.

30056 ■ *Start Your Own Fashion Accessories Business*
Pub: Entrepreneur Media Inc.
Contact: Dan Bova, Director
E-mail: dbova@entrepreneur.com
Ed: Eileen Figure Sandlin. **Released:** Second edition. **Description:** Entrepreneurs wishing to start a fashion accessories business will find important information for setting up a home workshop and office, exploring the market, managing finances, publicizing and advertising the business and more.

30057 ■ *"State of the Unions" in Canadian Business (Vol. 81, December 8, 2008, No. 21, pp. 23)*
Pub: Mondaq Ltd.
Contact: Tim Harty, Chief Executive Officer
Ed: Sharda Prashad. **Description:** Companies planning on joint ventures should look for partners they can trust and respect and are also competent. Joint venture deals aim to bring existing products to a a new market or in acquiring a foreign product for an existing market. **Availability:** Print.

30058 ■ *"Staying Social Complements Retail Goals" in Pet Product News (Vol. 66, September 2012, No. 9, pp. 34)*
Description: Pet supplies retailers can take advantage of social media to brand the store and its products and facilitate dialogue with consumers. As these retail goals are realized, profits can be attained. Strategies that can enable pet supplies retailers to create business networks through social media marketing are also presented. **Availability:** Online.

30059 ■ *Steal These Ideas!: Marketing Secrets That Will Make You a Star*
Ed: Steve Cone. **Released:** 2nd Edition. **Price:** $24.95, hardcover; $16.99. **Description:** The book shares information to successfully market any product or service. **Availability:** E-book; Print.

30060 ■ *"Steering a Steady Course Through Turbulent Waters" in Providence Business News (Vol. 29, June 2, 2014, No. 9, pp. 22)*
Pub: American City Business Journals, Inc.
Contact: Mike Olivieri, Executive Vice President
URL(s): pbn.com/steering-a-steady-course-through -turbulent-waters97424
Description: Barbara Haynes, Cumulus Broadcasting Market Manager, continues to remain clear sighted amid changing ownership, competition and technology propelling radio through dramatic transformation. Some of the elements that have driven her to success include resilience and dedication to community service.

30061 ■ *"Study: New Moms Build A Lot of Brand Buzz" in Brandweek (Vol. 49, April 21, 2008, No. 16, pp. 7)*
Description: According to a new survey which sampled 1,721 pregnant women and new moms, this demographic is having 109 word-of-mouth conversations per week concerning products, services and brands. Two-thirds of these conversations directly involve brand recommendations. The Internet is driving these word-of-mouth, or W-O-M, conversations among this segment, beating out magazines, television and other forms of media. **Availability:** Online.

30062 ■ *"Stung by Recession, Hemmer Regroups with New Strategy" in Business Courier (Vol. 27, June 4, 2010, No. 5, pp. 1)*
Pub: Business Courier
Ed: Lucy May. **Description:** Paul Hemmer Companies reduced its work force and outsourced operations such as marketing and architecture, in order for the commercial and construction firm to survive the recession. Hammer's total core revenue in 2009 dropped to less than $30 million forcing the closure of its Chicago office. **Availability:** PDF; Online.

30063 ■ *"Sweet Tea From McDonald's: A Marketing 50 Case Study" in Advertising Age (Vol. 79, November 17, 2008, No. 43, pp. 4)*
Pub: Crain Communications, Inc.
Contact: Jessica Botos, Manager, Marketing
E-mail: jessica.botos@crainsnewyork.com
Ed: Emily Bryson York. **Description:** McDonald's launch of iced coffee and sweat tea, which were promoted via price cuts over the summer, helped to boost sales at the fast-food chain. **Availability:** Online.

30064 ■ *"Sweeten Your Bottom Line: How To Bring In Dollars When Times Are Tough" in Small Business Opportunities (November 2007)*
Description: Adding a new product or promoting a product in a new way can help any small business during hard economic times. **Availability:** Online.

30065 ■ *"Sylvie Collection Offers a Feminine Perspective and Voice in Male Dominated Bridal Industry" in Benzinga.com (October 29, 2011)*
Description: Bridal jewelry designer Sylvie Levine has created over 1,000 customizable styles of engagement rings and wedding bands and is reach-

ing out to prospective new brides through a new Website, interactive social media campaign and monthly trunk show appearances. **Availability:** Online.

30066 ■ *"Symbility Solutions Joins Motion Computing Partner Program"* in *Marketwired* (May 14, 2007)
Pub: Comtex News Network Inc.
Contact: Kan Devnani, President
Description: Symbility Solutions Inc., a wholly owned subsidiary of Automated Benefits Corp., announced an agreement with Alliance Partner of Motion Computing, a leader in wireless communications and mobile computing, in which both companies will invest in a sales and marketing strategy that focuses specifically on the insurance market. **Availability:** Print; Online.

30067 ■ *"Talent Shows"* in *Canadian Business* (Vol. 81, December 24, 2007, No. 1, pp. 14)
Description: Canadian companies are increasingly turning to marketing to promote themselves as employers, as concerns on employee recruitment increase with the nearing retirement age of the baby boomers. Details on skills shortage, the potential advantage for the immigrant workforce, and employee retention are discussed. **Availability:** Online.

30068 ■ *"Tap Into Food Truck Trend to Rev Up Sales, Build Buzz"* in *Nation's Restaurant News* (Vol. 45, February 7, 2011, No. 3, pp. 18)
Ed: Brian Sacks. **Description:** Food truck trend is growing, particularly in New York City, Philadelphia, Washington DC, and Los Angeles, California. Man entrepreneurs are using a mobile food component to market their food before opening a restaurant. **Availability:** Print; Online.

30069 ■ *"Targeted Personal Trainer Business Strategies Build Clients, Income, Business and Success"* in *Marketing Weekly News* (August 4, 2012)
Description: Various business strategies can help personal trainers build their business include getting certified, creating postcards or flyers, and partnering with other fitness professionals. **Availability:** Print; PDF; Online.

30070 ■ *"Technically Speaking"* in *Black Enterprise* (Vol. 38, February 2008, No. 7, pp. 64)
Pub: Earl G. Graves Ltd.
Contact: Earl Graves, Jr., President
Ed: Sonia Alleyne. **Description:** Marketing manager for Texas Instruments discusses the Strategic Marketing of Technology Products course offered at the California Institute of Technology. The course helps turn products into profits.

30071 ■ *"Teksapiens, A Leading SEO Company, Offers Free SEO Consulting Services to Dallas Businesses"* in *Wireless News* (March 29, 2012)
Description: Dallas-based Web design firm, Teksapiens, offers free search engine optimization to Dallas businesss signing up at DallasBestSEO.com. The free service provides tips to outperform competition when marketing on the Internet. **Availability:** Print; Online.

30072 ■ *"That Was a B2B Ad? How the Pandemic Forced Business Marketers to Pivot Forever"* in *The Drum* (September 22, 2020)
Ed: Kenneth Hein. **Released:** September 22, 2020. **Description:** Discusses how the business-to-business market is becoming increasingly indistinguishable from consumer marketing. **Availability:** Online.

30073 ■ *"This Week: McD's Eyes Ad Plan, Shifts Breakfast Biz"* in *Crain's Chicago Business* (Vol. 30, February 2007, No. 6, pp. 1)
Description: McDonald's is moving its national breakfast ad account from DDB Chicago to Arnold Worldwide of Boston and Moroch of Dallas in an at-

tempt to change its marketing strategy. It is also doing a study to keep abreast of consumer trends. **Availability:** Print; Online.

30074 ■ *"Three Megatrends to Help Your Business Compete in 2014"* in *South Florida Business Journal* (Vol. 34, January 3, 2014, No. 24, pp. 10)
Pub: American City Business Journals, Inc.
Contact: Mike Olivieri, Executive Vice President
Released: Weekly. **Price:** $8, Introductory 4-week offer(Digital & Print). **Description:** Businesses can improve their competitive edge in 2014 by adapting several mega small business trends in marketing and communications. Brands can use brand bridging to get customers attention, use wearable technology to increase their value, and adapt environmental sustainability and corporate social responsibility to keep their customers. **Availability:** Print; Online.

30075 ■ *"Three Ways to Improve the Prospect's Experience"* in *South Florida Business Journal* (Vol. 35, September 12, 2014, No. 7, pp. 12)
Pub: American City Business Journals, Inc.
Contact: Mike Olivieri, Executive Vice President
Description: Advice on how marketers should get prospective buyers' attention by using Websites is given. Website readability on mobile devices and cell phones should be improved. Marketers should also offer a maximum of two landing pages to increase sales. **Availability:** Online.

30076 ■ *"Three Ways to Power Up Mobile Marketing"* in *South Florida Business Journal* (Vol. 34, July 18, 2014, No. 52, pp. 12)
Pub: American City Business Journals, Inc.
Contact: Mike Olivieri, Executive Vice President
Released: Weekly. **Price:** $8, introductory 4-week offer(Digital only). **Description:** A number of strategies that companies can apply to prepare for the future reality of mobile marketing are provided. Companies are encouraged to start the change to accommodate the new mobile world as mobile traffic data is projected to increase in record numbers and mobile connected devices will reach over 10 billion by 2007. **Availability:** Print; Online.

30077 ■ *"Tigers Put to Test: Can Team Win Back Fans, Advertisers?"* in *Crain's Detroit Business* (Vol. 24, October 6, 2008, No. 40, pp. 1)
Pub: Crain Communications Inc.
Contact: Barry Asin, President
Ed: Bill Shea. **Description:** Despite the enormous amount of money the Detroit Tigers' owner Mike Illitch spent on player salaries, a record $137.6 million this season, the team finished in last-place; ticket sales and advertising dollars for next season are expected to fall dramatically. Additional speculation regarding the future of the ball team is included. **Availability:** Online.

30078 ■ *"Time to Tweet: Banks and Fun, Benefits in Social Media"* in *Philadelphia Business Journal* (Vol. 31, February 24, 2012, No. 2, pp. 1)
Pub: Baltimore Business Journal
Contact: Rhonda Pringle, President
E-mail: rpringle@bizjournals.com
Description: Pennsylvania-based banks have benefited from the use of social media to market their services. TD Bank used Twitter to respond to customer complaints. Citizens Bank uses Twitter to provide customers with financial tips. **Availability:** Print.

30079 ■ *"Tips to Improve Your Direct Mail Results"* in *Contractor* (Vol. 57, January 2010, No. 1, pp. 55)
Ed: Matt Michel. **Description:** Plumbers can improve their direct mail efforts by buying quality lists and writing good headlines. The mail should also tell a story and urge its readers to action. **Availability:** Print; Online.

30080 ■ *"Titan to Become New York's Largest Provider of Phone Kiosk Advertising"* in *Marketing Weekly News* (September 11, 2010, pp. 150)
Pub: VerticalNews
Description: Titan will acquire from Verizon 1,900 payphones at 1,300 phone kiosk locations in New York City, New York. This transaction will triple the firm's inventory of New York Phone Kiosk media to over 5,000 advertising faces. Details are included. **Availability:** Print; Online.

30081 ■ *"TiVo, Domino's Team to Offer Pizza Ordering by DVR"* in *Advertising Age* (Vol. 79, November 17, 2008, No. 43, pp. 48)
Pub: Crain Communications, Inc.
Contact: Jessica Botos, Manager, Marketing
E-mail: jessica.botos@crainsnewyork.com
Ed: Brian Steinberg. **Description:** Domino's Pizza and TiVo are teaming up to make it possible for customers to order from the restaurant straight from their DVR. The companies see that this kind of interactive television and consumer experience will only serve to generate more sales as the customer can be exposed to a fuller range of menu selections and will not have to interrupt their viewing, while workers can spend more time making the product. **Availability:** Online.

30082 ■ *"To Catch Up, Colgate May Ratchet Up Its Ad Spending"* in *Advertising Age* (Vol. 81, December 6, 2010, No. 43, pp. 1)
Pub: Crain Communications, Inc.
Contact: Jessica Botos, Manager, Marketing
E-mail: jessica.botos@crainsnewyork.com
Ed: Jack Neff. **Description:** Colgate-Palmolive Company has been losing market share in the categories of toothpaste, deodorant, body wash, dish soap and pet food. **Availability:** Online.

30083 ■ *"Too Much Information?"* in *Black Enterprise* (Vol. 37, December 2006, No. 5, pp. 59)
Pub: Earl G. Graves Ltd.
Contact: Earl Graves, Jr., President
Ed: James C. Johnson. **Description:** African American business owners often face the dilemma of whether or not to divulge their minority status when soliciting new customers and financial institutions. The quality of the products or services is always the key factor and race should never define one's business; however, it is appropriate to market oneself as a minority- or women-owned business, especially if the company is in an industry where those clients are offered top-tier contracts. **Availability:** Online.

30084 ■ *"The Top Mistakes of Social Media Marketing"* in *Agency Sales Magazine* (Vol. 39, November 2009, No. 9, pp. 42)
Description: One common mistake in social media marketing is having more than one image on the Internet because this ruins a business' credibility. Marketers need to put out messages that are useful to their readers and to keep messages consistent. **Availability:** Online.

30085 ■ *"Top Tips for a Killer Facebook Ad Campaign, for Your Gym or Studio'* in *Glofox blog* (April 18, 2017)
Ed: Eamonn Curley. **Released:** April 18, 2017. **Description:** This article describes everything you need to know to create a Facebook Ad Campaign that generates high quality leads for your fitness business. **Availability:** Online.

30086 ■ *"The Trouble With $150,000 Wine"* in *Barron's* (Vol. 88, July 7, 2008, No. 27, pp. 33)
Pub: Dow Jones & Company Inc.
Contact: Almar Latour, Chief Executive Officer
Ed: Jay Palmer. **Description:** Review of the book, "The Billionaire's Vinegar: The Mystery of the World's Most Expensive Bottle of Wine," which discusses vintners along with the marketing and distribution of wine as well as the winemaking industry as a whole. **Availability:** Online.

30087 ■ *"Troy Complex has New Brand, New Leases"* in Crain's Detroit Business (Vol. 24, April 14, 2008, No. 15, pp. 32)
Pub: Crain Communications Inc.
Contact: Barry Asin, President
Ed: Daniel Duggan. **Description:** Discusses the re-branding of the 1.2 million-square-foot collection of office buildings in Troy purchased by New York-based Emmes Co. The firm has also pledged more than $6 million in upgrades, hired a new leasing company and completed 67,000 square feet of leasing with another 100,000 in negotiations. **Availability:** Print; Online.

30088 ■ *"Try a Little Social Media"* in American Printer (Vol. 128, June 1, 2011, No. 6)
Description: Social media helps keep Ussery Printing on customers radar. Jim David, VP of marketing for the firm, states that 350 people following them on Facebook are from the local area. **Availability:** Print; Mailing list; Online.

30089 ■ *"Tweet Me, Friend Me, Make Me Buy"* in (Vol. 90, July-August 2012, No. 7-8, pp. 88)
Pub: Harvard Business Review Press
Contact: Moderna V. Pfizer, Contact
Ed: Barbara Giamanco, Kent Gregoire. **Price:** $8.95, PDF and hardcover black and white. **Description:** Sales representatives can make the most out of social media through training on communication skills such as tone, etiquette, and consistency. The most valuable aspects of social media are lead qualification, front-end prospecting, and maintaining post-deal relationships. **Availability:** Print; PDF; Online.

30090 ■ *"The Ultimate Guide to B2B Marketing in 2020"* in HubSpot (December 16, 2019)
Ed: Allie Decker. **Released:** December 16, 2019. **Description:** Provides tips and strategies to understand your B2B audience, round out your buyer personas, and effectively use B2B marketing strategies that reach them. **Availability:** Online.

30091 ■ *"Ultimate Guide to Google AdWords: How to Access 100 Million People in 10 Minutes"*
Pub: Entrepreneur Media Inc.
Contact: Dan Bova, Director
E-mail: dbova@entrepreneur.com
Released: 5th edition. **Price:** $24.95, paperback. **Description:** The Google AdWords experts and analytics specialist present the techniques, tools, and tricks for using Google AdWords. The experts help small businesses to write advertising and Web site copy design, work in difficult markets, advertise, increase search engine presence, bid strategies for online auctions, financial budgeting and more. **Availability:** Print.

30092 ■ *"The Ultimate Guide to Push Notifications for Fitness Businesses"* in Glofox blog (July 29, 2019)
Ed: Eamonn Curley. **Released:** July 29, 2019. **Description:** Push notifications, brief messages or alerts sent through a mobile app, can enhance your fitness business. This article details how push notifications can be used to take your fitness business to the next level. **Availability:** Online.

30093 ■ *"Ultra Low Sulfur Diesel: The Promise and the Reality"* in Indoor Comfort Marketing (Vol. 70, July 2011, No. 7, pp. 22)
Description: Impacts of ultra low sulfur diesel are examined.

30094 ■ *"Under Armour Wants to Equip Athletes, Too"* in Boston Business Journal (Vol. 29, July 8, 2011, No. 9, pp. 1)
Pub: Boston Business Journal
Contact: Carolyn M. Jones, President
E-mail: cmjones@bizjournals.com
Ed: Ryan Sharrow. **Description:** Baltimore sportswear maker Under Armour advances plans to enter into the equipment field, aiming to strengthen its hold on football, basketball and lacrosse markets where it

already has a strong market share. The company is now cooking up licensing deals to bolster the firm's presence among athletes. **Availability:** Print; Online.

30095 ■ *"Under Armour's Founder On Learning to Leverage Celebrity Endorsements"* in Harvard Business Review (Vol. 90, May 2012, No. 5, pp. 45)
Pub: Harvard Business Review Press
Contact: Moderna V. Pfizer, Contact
Ed: Kevin Plank. **Description:** Using his athletic apparel company Under Armour as an illustration, the author identifies two key points in effective utilization of endorsement advertising: balancing freebies with fair-price contracts, and offering stock opportunities so that celebrities can be personally engaged with growth.

30096 ■ *"Understanding Clients Her Key To Shaping Message"* in Providence Business News (Vol. 29, July 7, 2014, No. 14, pp. 10)
Pub: American City Business Journals, Inc.
Contact: Mike Olivieri, Executive Vice President
Released: July 05, 2014. **Description:** Kerry Chaffer, a partner at HCC Marketing, attributes her firm's success to their ability to understand clients, their business and the market. Chaffer discusses HCC's expertise in marketing community banks and commends engagement by local banks and their communities. **Availability:** Print; Online.

30097 ■ *"Unfilled Hotels Go All Out for Business Meetings"* in Crain's Detroit Business (Vol. 25, June 8, 2009, No. 23, pp. 9)
Pub: Crain Communications Inc.
Contact: Barry Asin, President
Ed: Daniel Duggan. **Description:** Hotels in Michigan are offering discounts to companies holding business meetings at their properties. Details of competition and plans are included. **Availability:** Print; Online.

30098 ■ *"Unilever's CMO Finally Gets Down To Business"* in Advertising Age (Vol. 79, July 7, 2008, No. 26, pp. 11)
Description: Overview of Unilever's chief marketing officer Simon Clift's strategy for promoting its products; now that the company has restructured, Clift is able to focus all of his energy on the challenges of the new-media climate that marketers are having to face. **Availability:** Print; Online.

30099 ■ *"U.S. Retailer Eyes 'Tween' Market"* in Globe & Mail (January 30, 2007, pp. B1)
Ed: Marina Strauss. **Description:** The decision of Tween Brands Inc. (Too Incorporated) to open 100 new stores in Canada as part of its expansion is discussed. The company's focus on targeting girls for its products is detailed. **Availability:** Online.

30100 ■ *"Unleashing the Power of Marketing"* in Harvard Business Review (Vol. 88, October 2010, No. 10, pp. 90)
Pub: Harvard Business Publishing
Contact: Diane Belcher, Managing Director
Ed: Beth Comstock, Ranjay Gulati, Stephen Liguori. **Price:** $8.95, PDF. **Description:** Chronicle of the development of General Electric's marketing framework that focused on three key factors: Principles, people and process. GE determined that successful marketing fulfills four functions: instigating, innovating, implementing, and integrating. **Availability:** Online; PDF.

30101 ■ *"Unused Coupons Still Pay Off"* in Harvard Business Review (Vol. 90, May 2012, No. 5, pp. 32)
Pub: Harvard Business Review Press
Contact: Moderna V. Pfizer, Contact
Ed: Rajkumar Venkatesan, Paul Farris. **Price:** $6, hardcopy and PDF. **Description:** Unredeemed coupons have been found to create a sales lift for retailers as they increase awareness of a retailer or a brand even when consumers do not use them. Redemption rates should still be monitored however to assess campaign effectiveness. **Availability:** Print; Online.

30102 ■ *"Up Close With: Learfield Sports CEO Greg Brown"* in San Antonio Business Journal (Vol. 28, February 28, 2014, No. 3, pp. 7)
Pub: American City Business Journals, Inc.
Contact: Mike Olivieri, Executive Vice President
Released: Weekly. **Price:** $4, Introductory 4-week offer(Digital only). **Description:** Learfield Sports chief executive officer, Greg Brown, says the sports marketing company stands to benefit from having a college program in San Antonio, Texas. He also said that the company has been developing relationships with the University of Texas San Antonio. Brown added that Learfield will aggressively market the University. **Availability:** Print; Online.

30103 ■ *"Use Social Media to Enhance Brand, Business"* in Contractor (Vol. 56, December 2009, No. 12, pp. 14)
Ed: Elton Rivas. **Description:** Advice on how plumbing contractors should use online social networks to increase sales is presented including such issues as clearly defining goals and target audience. An additional advantage to this medium is that advertisements can easily be shared with other users.

30104 ■ *"Verizon's Big Gamble Comes Down to the Wire"* in Globe & Mail (February 3, 2007, pp. B1)
Ed: Catherine McLean. **Description:** The launch of a new broadband service by Verizon Communications Inc. based on fiber optic cable technology is discussed. The company has spent $23 billion for introducing the new service. **Availability:** Online.

30105 ■ *"The View From the Front Row"* in Philadelphia Business Journal (Vol. 32, January 31, 2014, No. 51, pp. 6)
Pub: American City Business Journals, Inc.
Contact: Mike Olivieri, Executive Vice President
Released: Weekly. **Price:** $4, introductory 4-week offer(Digital & Print). **Description:** Eric Smallwood, senior vice president of Front Row Analytics, reveals that the company conducts full-season sponsorship marketing analysis for the Seattle Seahawks. He mentions that a 30-second Super Bowl commercial could cost $4 million. Information about his favorite Super Bowl commercials is revealed. **Availability:** Print; Online.

30106 ■ *"Virtus.com Wins 'Best of Industry' WebAward for Excellence in Financial Services"* in Investment Weekly News (October 24, 2009, pp. 227)
Pub: Investment Weekly News
Description: Web Marketing Association honored Virtus.com, the Website of Virtus Investment Partners, Inc., for Outstanding Achievement in Web Development and Acsys Interactive was awarded the Financial Services Standard of Excellence Award for developing the site. The site was part of a rebranding effort and is a one-stop portal for both financial advisors and their investors. **Availability:** Online.

30107 ■ *"Vistaprint Survey Indicates that Online Marketing Taking Hold Among Small Businesses"* in Marketwired (December 10, 2009)
Pub: Comtex News Network Inc.
Contact: Kan Devnani, President
Description: According to a comprehensive survey from Vistaprint N.V., small businesses are very likely to increase their use of Internet marketing strategies such as paid and organic search, email marketing, social media networking and custom websites over the next year. Trends continue to show that more small businesses are indeed adapting to the changing marketplace and are more willing to diversify their marketing strategies than ever before. **Availability:** Print; Online.

30108 ■ *"Vote Count Chocula in 2014"* in Canadian Business (Vol. 87, July 2014, No. 7, pp. 28)
Released: July 2014. **Description:** The current state of political marketing is criticized for exploiting the weaknesses of both the press and the electorate and

is compared to brand marketing. The soul of brand marketing is perpetual accountability and marketers are expected to make sure that consumers are not disappointed.

30109 ▪ *"Warning Lights Flashing for Air Canada: Carty's Back"* in Globe & Mail (February 22, 2006, pp. B1)

Ed: Brent Jang. **Description:** Air Canada's rival, Donald Carty, former chief executive officer at American Airlines and new chairman of Toronto based Regco Holdings Inc., launches Porter Airlines Inc. out of Toronto City Center Airport this fall.

30110 ▪ *"Web-Based Marketing Excites, Challenges Small Business Use"* in Colorado Springs Business Journal (January 20, 2010)

Pub: BridgeTower Media

Contact: Adam Reinebach, President

Ed: Becky Hurley. **Description:** Business-to-business and consumer-direct firms alike are using the fast-changing Web technologies to increase sales, leads and track consumer behavior but once a company commits to an Online marketing plan, experts believe, they must be prepared to consistently tweak and overhaul content and distribution vehicles in order to keep up. **Availability:** Online.

30111 ▪ *"Website Triples Traffic in Three Weeks Using Press Releases"* in PR Newswire (January 5, 2010)

Pub: PR Newswire Association LLC.

Description: Irbtrax, an Internet marketing firm, concluded a comprehensive study revealing that online press release submission services offer measurable Website traffic-building results. **Availability:** Online.

30112 ▪ *"Well-Heeled Startup Plots Course for a Run at Garmin"* in Business Journal Portland (Vol. 27, November 12, 2010, No. 37, pp. 1)

Pub: Portland Business Journal

Contact: Andy Giegerich, Managing Editor

E-mail: agiegerich@bizjournals.com

Description: Oh! Shoes LLC expects to receive about $1.5 million in funding from angel investors, while marketing a new line of high heel shoes that are comfortable, healthy, and attractive. The new line of shoes will use the technology of athletic footwear while having the look of an Italian designer. Oh! Shoes hopes to generate $35 million in sales by 2014. **Availability:** Print; Online.

30113 ▪ *"What to Do in an Economic Upswing Before It's too Late"* in Agency Sales Magazine (Vol. 39, November 2009, No. 10, pp. 36)

Description: Some marketing suggestions for businesses as the economy recovers are presented. These include not waiting for the economy to change and telling your brand's story. Showing people what you can do for them and changing doubters into believers is also advised. **Availability:** Online.

30114 ▪ *"What Is B2B?"* in Business News Daily (June 23, 2020)

Ed: Adam Uzialko. **Released:** June 23, 2020. **Description:** A guide including all you need to know about businesses that primarily provide goods or services to other companies. Includes information on how to develop a marketing plan for a B2B company and information for digital B2B companies. **Availability:** Online.

30115 ▪ *"What Is the Best Way to Promote My New Company?"* in Legal Zoom (March 9, 2023)

URL(s): www.legalzoom.com/articles/what-is-the-best-way-to-promote-my-new-company

Ed: Kylie Ora Lobell. **Released:** March 09, 2023. **Description:** There are several really good options for getting the word out about your new business including hiring an advertising company to handle the details or by using social media and other online options yourself. **Availability:** Online.

30116 ▪ *"What Makes a Great Tweet"* in Harvard Business Review (Vol. 90, May 2012, No. 5, pp. 36)

Pub: Harvard Business Review Press

Contact: Moderna V. Pfizer, Contact

Ed: Kurt Luther, Michael Bernstein, Paul Andre. **Price:** $6, PDF. **Description:** A chart uses readership approval percentages to identify the most effective uses of Twitter. Best tweets include amusing random thoughts and self promotion; worst include complaints and presence maintenance. **Availability:** Online; PDF.

30117 ▪ *"What Marketers Misunderstand about Online Reviews: Managers Must Analyze What's Really Driving Buying Decisions - and Adjust Their Strategies Accordingly"* in Harvard Business Review (Vol. 92, January-February 2014, No. 1-2, pp. 23)

Pub: Harvard Business Press

Contact: Gabriela Allmi, Regional Manager

E-mail: gabriela.allmi@hbsp.harvard.edu

Price: $6, hardcopy black and white. **Description:** Companies may overestimate the influence of online reviews, as consumers do not turn to reviews for certain products and services (for example, habitual low-involvement purchases such as groceries). Others' opinions matter more for purchases such as independent restaurants and electronics. **Availability:** Print; PDF; Online.

30118 ▪ *"What's In Your Toolbox"* in Women In Business (Vol. 61, August-September 2009, No. 4, pp. 7)

Pub: American Business Women's Association

Contact: Rene Street, Executive Director

Ed: Mimi Kopulos. **Description:** Business owners are increasingly turning to using social networking websites, such as Facebook, LinkedIn and Twitter, to promote their companies. The number of adult social media users has increased from 8 percent in 2005 to 35 percent in 2009. **Availability:** Online.

30119 ▪ *"What's Your Social Media Strategy?"* in Black Enterprise (Vol. 41, November 2010, No. 4, pp. 75)

Pub: Earl G. Graves Ltd.

Contact: Earl Graves, Jr., President

Ed: Denise A. Campbell. **Description:** Advice for using social media sites such as Twitter, Facebook and LinkedIn as a professional networking tool is given. **Availability:** Online.

30120 ▪ *"A Whiteboard that Peels and Sticks"* in Inc. (Volume 32, December 2010, No. 10, pp. 58)

Pub: Inc. Magazine

Ed: Issie Lapwosky. **Description:** Profile of an affordable adhesive whiteboard that can be restuck multiple times; the whiteboard was created by three college friends. The students share insight in the contacts they used in order to promote the sale of their invention. **Availability:** Online.

30121 ▪ *"Why Digital Marketing Is Important for Small Business"* by Digital Marketing Institute (Nov. 3, 2021)

URL(s): digitalmarketinginstitute.com/blog/why-digital-marketing-is-important-for-small-business

Released: November 03, 2021. **Description:** Discusses the benefits of stepping outside of traditional marketing and incorporating digital marketing to help grow your small business. **Availability:** Online.

30122 ▪ *"Why Is Social Responsibility Important in Marketing?"* in Investopedia (Dec. 9, 2021)

URL(s): www.investopedia.com/ask/answers/042215/why-social-responsibility-important-marketing.asp

Released: December 09, 2021. **Description:** Explains how social responsibility in marketing works, including examples. Discusses how you can gain small business customers by demonstrating your business' social commitment. **Availability:** Online.

30123 ▪ *"Why Marketing Slogans Matter"* in Canadian Business (Vol. 85, June 11, 2012, No. 10, pp. 18)

Ed: Bruce Philp. **Description:** Slogans earn their meaning in popular culture through dramatic beginnings and repetition over the years so marketers should consider whether the brand can earn it before replacing the tag lines. People in the branding business should not use the tag line exercise as a substitute for creating a strategy. **Availability:** Online.

30124 ▪ *"Why Press Releases Are More Important Than Ever"* in Legal Zoom (March 22, 2023)

URL(s): www.legalzoom.com/articles/why-press-releases-are-more-important-than-ever

Ed: Miranda Tan. **Released:** March 22, 2023. **Description:** Discusses the merits of using old-fashioned press releases to convey important information about your company. **Availability:** Online.

30125 ▪ *"Why You Aren't Buying Venezuelan Chocolate "* in Harvard Business Review (Vol. 88, December 2010, No. 12, pp. 25)

Pub: Harvard Business Publishing

Contact: Diane Belcher, Managing Director

Ed: Rohit Deshpande. **Price:** $6, PDF. **Description:** The concept of provenance paradox is defined as the preconceived notions consumers have about the country of origin of a given product, which can pose significant difficulties for emerging markets. Five strategies are presented for combating this problem, including building on historic events that have informed cultural perspectives. **Availability:** Online; PDF.

30126 ▪ *"Why You Need a New-Media 'Ringmaster'"* in Harvard Business Review (Vol. 88, December 2010, No. 12, pp. 78)

Pub: Harvard Business Publishing

Contact: Diane Belcher, Managing Director

Ed: Patrick Spenner. **Price:** $8.95, PDF. **Description:** The concept of ringmaster is applied to brand marketing. This concept includes integrative thinking, lean collaboration skills, and high-speed decision cycles. **Availability:** Online; PDF.

30127 ▪ *"Will Mobile's Massive Growth Ever Equal Real Revenue?"* in Advertising Age (Vol. 83, October 1, 2012, No. 35, pp. 18)

Pub: Crain Communications Inc.

Contact: Barry Asin, President

Ed: Jason Del Rey. **Description:** Media companies are concerned over the return on investment when advertising on mobile applications. Firms lament that these ads are worth less to a small business than offline marketing programs. **Availability:** Online.

30128 ▪ *"Winning With Women"* in Marketing to Women (Vol. 22, August 2009, No. 8, pp. 6)

Description: Women shoppers are buying more utilitarian categories despite the overall fall in consumer electronics sales. Among the top five purchases women will defer in the next three months are personal consumer electronics, such as MP3 players and digital cameras, as well as home entertainment items. **Availability:** Online.

30129 ▪ *"With Traffic Jam in Super Bowl, Can Any Auto Brand Really Win?"* in Advertising Age (Vol. 81, December 6, 2010, No. 43, pp. 1)

Pub: Crain Communications, Inc.

Contact: Jessica Botos, Manager, Marketing

E-mail: jessica.botos@crainsnewyork.com

Ed: Rupal Parekh. **Description:** Car marketers are doubling down for Super Bowl XLV in Arlington, Texas and asking their ad agencies to craft commercials unique enough to break through the clutter and to capture viewers' attention. **Availability:** Online.

30130 ▪ *"Women Clicking to Earn Virtual Dollars"* in Sales and Marketing Management (November 11, 2009)

Ed: Stacy Straczynski. **Description:** According to a new report from Internet marketing firm Q Interactive, women are increasingly playing social media games where they are able to click on an ad or sign up for a promotion to earn virtual currency. Research is showing that this kind of marketing may be a potent tool, especially for e-commerce and online stores. **Availability:** Print; Online.

30131 ■ *"Women Prefer Cookbooks Over Word-Of-Mouth for Recipe Suggestions"* in *Marketing to Women (Vol. 23, November 2010, No. 11, pp. 6)*
Pub: EPM Communications Inc.
Contact: Ira Mayer, Chief Executive Officer
Description: Sixty-five percent of women surveyed enjoy a sit-down dinner at least five times a week according to Martha Steward Omni-media. Cookbooks, recipe Websites, food-focused magazines, and TV cooking shows are their primary source for new recipes. **Availability:** Print; Online.

30132 ■ *"WordStream Announces a Pair of Firsts for SEO & PPC Keyword Research Tools"* in *Marketwired (November 10, 2009)*
Pub: Comtex News Network Inc.
Contact: Kan Devnani, President
Description: WordStream, Inc., a provider of pay-per-click (PPC) and search engine optimization (SEO) solutions for continuously expanding and optimizing search marketing efforts has released two new features in their flagship Keyword Management solution; these tools will allow marketers to analyze data from paid search, organic search and estimated totals from keyword suggestion tools side-by-side. **Availability:** Print; Online.

30133 ■ *"Wrigley's Newest Taste: Wolfberry"* in *Crain's Chicago Business (Vol. 31, March 31, 2008, No. 13, pp. 1)*
Pub: Crain Communications Inc.
Contact: Barry Asin, President
Ed: David Sterrett. **Description:** Wm. Wrigley Jr. Co. has introduced a gum line in China that touts the medicinal advantages of aloe vera to improve skin and wolfberry to boost energy In an attempt to keep the company positioned as the top candy firm in China. **Availability:** Online.

30134 ■ *"Young Adults, Childless May Help Fuel Post-Recession Rebound"* in *Pet Product News (Vol. 64, November 2010, No. 11, pp. 4)*
Ed: David Lummis. **Description:** Pet industry retailers and marketers are encouraged to tap into the young adult and childless couple sectors to boost consumer traffic and sales to pre-recession levels. Among young adult owners, pet ownership increased from 40 percent in 2003 to 49 percent in 2009. Meanwhile, the childless couple sector represented 63 percent of all dog/cat owners in 2009. **Availability:** Online.

30135 ■ *Your First Year in Real Estate: Making the Transition from Total Novice to Successful Professional*
Released: Second edition. **Price:** $22, paperback; $9.99, e-book. **Description:** Zeller helps new realtors to select the right company, develop mentor and client relationships, using the Internet and social networking to stay ahead of competition, to set and reach career goals, to stay current in the market, and more. **Availability:** E-book; Print.

30136 ■ *"Your Guide to Starting an Affiliate Business Sitting in Your Home"* in *Home Business (June 21, 2022)*
URL(s): homebusinessmag.com/business-start-up/how-to-guides/guide-starting-affiliate-business-sitting-home/
Released: June 21, 2022. **Description:** Affiliate businesses are a good choice if you are looking for a home-based business to run and have your own website. Tips on marketing, increasing readership, and what your initial investment will be are discussed. **Availability:** Online.

30137 ■ *"YouTube Handles are Here – What it Means for Your Business"* in *Small Business Trends (October 19, 2022)*
URL(s): smallbiztrends.com/2022/10/youtube-handles.html

Ed: Gabrielle Pickard-Whitehead. **Released:** October 19, 2022. **Description:** YouTube introduced "handles" which will be unique to each creator, including your small business if it has its own channel. Further details about how the handles work are discussed. **Availability:** Online.

30138 ■ *"Zions Offers Step-by-Step Small Business Guidance"* in *Idaho Business Review (September 1, 2014)*
Pub: BridgeTower Media
Contact: Adam Reinebach, President
Description: Zions bank provides small business guidance to clients through its Zions Bank Idaho Business Resource Center. The program helps entrepreneurs learn the basic rules of running a small business. Free courses teach the essentials of finance, marketing and selling, .

TRADE PERIODICALS

30139 ■ *Journal of Global Marketing*
Pub: Taylor And Francis Group
Contact: Annie Callanan, Chief Executive Officer
URL(s): www.tandfonline.com/journals/wglo20
Released: 5/year **Price:** $1,899, Institutions for print And online; $331, Individuals for print and online; $1,557, Institutions for online only; $291, Individuals for online only. **Description:** Provides valuable marketing information for CEOs, management at all levels, marketing professionals of all types, educators, and students. **Availability:** Print; Download; PDF; Online.

30140 ■ *Journal of International Consumer Marketing*
Pub: Taylor And Francis Group
Contact: Annie Callanan, Chief Executive Officer
URL(s): www.tandfonline.com/journals/wicm20
Ed: Erdener Kaynak. **Released:** 5/year **Price:** $1,879, Institutions for print and online; $331, Individuals for print and online; $291, for online only; $1,541, Institutions for online. **Description:** Examines consumer and organizational buyer behavior. **Availability:** Print; Download; PDF; Online.

30141 ■ *Journal of Relationship Marketing*
Pub: Taylor And Francis Group
Contact: Annie Callanan, Chief Executive Officer
URL(s): www.tandfonline.com/journals/wjrm20
Ed: David Bejou, PhD. **Released:** Quarterly **Price:** $1,165, Institutions for print & online; $255, Individuals for print & online; $223, Individuals for online only; $955, Institutions for online only. **Description:** Journal on marketing. **Availability:** Print; Download; PDF; Online.

30142 ■ *Meetings & Conventions*
Pub: Northstar Travel Media
Contact: Robert G. Sullivan, President
URL(s): www.meetings-conventions.com
Released: Monthly **Description:** Magazine focusing on meetings, conferences and trade show. **Availability:** Print; Online.

30143 ■ *Online Media News*
Pub: Worldwide Videotex
URL(s): wvpubs.com/publications
Released: Annual **Price:** $185, for hardcopy; $165, for outside North America e-file; $200, for within north America hard copy. **Description:** Provides coverage of the projects, products, and developments of the commercial applications of CD-ROM, CD-I, and all the other optical storage devices used in computing. Concentrates on information relating to successful marketing strategies. **Availability:** Print; PDF.

VIDEO/AUDIO MEDIA

30144 ■ *7 Marketing Mistakes to Avoid*
URL(s): www.makinggoodpodcast.com/episodes/106
Ed: Lauren Tilden. **Released:** February 22, 2022. **Description:** Podcast discusses 7 marketing mistakes commonly made by small businesses.

30145 ■ *Adapting Your Marketing Strategy in the Creator Age with Kipp Bodnar*
URL(s): www.eofire.com/podcast/kippbodnar
Ed: Jon Lee Dumas. **Released:** March 08, 2024. **Description:** Podcast suggests aligning with creators for more effective marketing.

30146 ■ *Analytics without Overwhelm with Aby Blum Sudds*
URL(s): www.makinggoodpodcast.com/episodes/192
Ed: Lauren Tilden. **Released:** August 22, 2023. **Description:** Podcast discusses how to avoid being overwhelmed by analytics, kinds of data to notice, and the benefit of tracking analytics.

30147 ■ *The Art of Social Impact Storytelling with Tamika Bickham*
URL(s): www.awarepreneurs.com/podcast/324-social-impact-storytelling
Ed: Paul Zelizer. **Released:** February 27, 2024. **Description:** Podcast discusses social impact storytelling and entrepreneurship.

30148 ■ *The Best Small Business Show: Boost Your Video Presence*
URL(s): richgee.libsyn.com/284-boost-your-video-presence
Ed: Rich Gee. **Released:** February 27, 2023. **Description:** Podcast discusses how to increase your video presence.

30149 ■ *The Best Small Business Show: Enhancing Your Lead Generation*
URL(s): richgee.libsyn.com/309-enhancing-your-lead-generation
Ed: Rich Gee. **Released:** August 21, 2023. **Description:** Podcast discusses better lead generation.

30150 ■ *Building a High Tech Marketing Agency*
URL(s): www.startuphustlepodcast.com/building-a-high-tech-marketing-agency
Ed: Matt Watson. **Released:** November 27, 2023. **Description:** Podcast discusses building a high-tech marketing agency, especially for home services companies.

30151 ■ *Entrepreneurial Thought Leaders: Marketing for Entrepreneurs*
URL(s): ecorner.stanford.edu/podcasts/lynda-kate-smith-mparticle-marketing-for-entrepreneurs
Ed: Ravi Belani. **Released:** October 13, 2021. **Description:** Podcast suggests fundamental marketing lessons with real-world examples in technology entrepreneurship.

30152 ■ *Hot to Not be Invisible (10 Ways to Get Discovered)*
URL(s): www.makinggoodpodcast.com/episodes/249
Ed: Lauren Tilden. **Released:** July 23, 2024. **Description:** Podcast offers 10 ways to get discovered by ideal customers and how to decide which ones make sense for you.

30153 ■ *The How of Business: Email Marketing*
URL(s): www.thehowofbusiness.com/415-email-marketing
Ed: Henry Lopez. **Released:** March 08, 2022. **Description:** Podcast discusses email marketing, from how to build an email list to tips on formatting an effective message.

30154 ■ *How I Built This: Advice Line with Andrew Abraham of Orgain*
URL(s): wondery.com/shows/how-i-built-this/episode/10386-advice-line-with-andrew-abraham-of-orgain
Ed: Guy Raz. **Released:** May 16, 2024. **Description:** Podcast answers questions from early-stage founders about strategically positioning their products. .

30155 ■ *How I Built This: Advice Line with Gary Erickson of Clif Bar*
URL(s): wondery.com/shows/how-i-built-this/episode/10386-advice-line-with-gary-erickson-of-clif-bar

Ed: Guy Raz. **Released:** May 09, 2024. **Description:** Podcast answers questions from early-stage founders about expanding a customer base.

30156 ■ *How I Built This: Advice Line: Reaching New Customers*

URL(s): wondery.com/shows/how-i-built-this/episode/10386-advice-line-reaching-new-customers

Ed: Guy Raz. **Released:** October 03, 2024. **Description:** Podcast offers advice to early-stage founders about finding new customers.

30157 ■ *Make Marketing Simple with These 7 Marketing Priniples*

URL(s): www.makinggoodpodcast.com/episodes/246

Ed: Lauren Tilden. **Description:** Podcast offers seven principles to create a marketing approach that feels good and works for you.

30158 ■ *Marketing for Beginners (Let's Start from Scratch)*

URL(s): www.makinggoodpodcast.com/episodes/156

Ed: Lauren Tilden. **Released:** January 10, 2023. **Description:** Podcast discusses why marketing is important, activities that fall under marketing, and tactical exercises to drive results.

30159 ■ *Mastering the Art of Word of Mouth Marketing with Joe Blackburn*

URL(s): www.eofire.com/podcast/joeblackburn

Ed: Jon Lee Dumas. **Released:** August 15, 2024. **Description:** Podcast offers strategies for word-of-mouth marketing through building and maintaining client relationships.

30160 ■ *Planet Money Summer School: MBA 4: Marketing and the Ultimate Hose Nozzle*

URL(s): www.npr.org/2023/08/02/1191666159/mba-4-marketing-and-the-ultimate-hose-nozzle

Ed: Robert Smith. **Released:** August 02, 2023. **Description:** Discusses perfecting your pitch and following up with marketing: where to spread the message and how to make it unforgettable.

30161 ■ *The Secret Key to Magnetic Content that Makes Sales*

URL(s): www.makinggoodpodcast.com/episodes/236

Ed: Lauren Tilden. **Released:** May 16, 2024. **Description:** Podcast discloses the secret key to magnetic content.

30162 ■ *Side Hustle to Small Business: How Bonnie Conrad Went from Furniture Builder to Marketer*

URL(s): www.hiscox.com/side-hustle-to-small-business/bonnie-conrad-inn8ly-podcast-season-4

Ed: Sanjay Parekh. **Released:** October 23, 2024. **Description:** Podcast offers a conversation with a furniture-maker-turned-marketer.

30163 ■ *Small Biz 101: Strategic Steps to Marketing Success*

URL(s): scatteredtostreamlined.com/strategic-steps-to-marketing-success-sb025

Ed: Connie Whitesell. **Released:** April 10, 2024. **Description:** Podcast discusses marketing challenges, including how to market without many contacts, creating a compelling lead magnet, and prioritizing a marketing list.

30164 ■ *The Ultimate Win-Win? Partnerships + Collaborations with Erika Rodriguez*

URL(s): www.makinggoodpodcast.com/episodes/218

Ed: Lauren Tilden. **Released:** January 30, 2024. **Description:** Podcast discusses partnership marketing, when two businesses create a campaign or promotion that benefits both parties, whether it's a giveaway or offer.

30165 ■ *Want More Engagement? Start Here.*

URL(s): www.makinggoodpodcast.com/episodes/227

Ed: Lauren Tilden. **Released:** March 19, 2024. **Description:** Podcast defines engagement, explains why it matters, and suggests how to improve it. .

30166 ■ *What to Do About Marketing Overwhelm*

URL(s): www.makinggoodpodcast.com/episodes/117

Ed: Lauren Tilden. **Released:** May 10, 2022. **Description:** Podcast discusses how to avoid being overwhelmed by marketing.

30167 ■ *Working with Affiliates at Scale*

URL(s): www.startuphustlepodcast.com/working-with-affiliates-at-scale

Ed: Matt Watson. **Released:** January 16, 2024. **Description:** Podcast discusses working with affiliates at scale and offers different approaches for affiliate marketing.

30168 ■ *Your Guide to Experiential Marketing - 10 Insider Tips and Tricks for a Successful Brand Roadshow with Ray Sheehan*

URL(s): www.eofire.com/podcast/raysheehan

Released: June 05, 2023. **Description:** Podcast offers marketing tips.

TRADE SHOWS AND CONVENTIONS

30169 ■ Business Opportunity Expo

New York and New Jersey Minority Supplier Development Council (NY & NJ MSDC)
65 W 36th St., Ste. 702
New York, NY 10018
Ph: (212)502-5663
Fax: (212)502-5807
Co. E-mail: council@nynjmsdc.org
URL: http://nynjmsdc.org
Contact: Terrence Clark, President
E-mail: terrence.clark@nynjmsdc.org
URL(s): nynjmsdc.org/calendar

Frequency: Annual. **Description:** Marketing and business information, supplies, and services. **Audience:** Business industry professionals. **Principal Exhibits:** Marketing and business information, supplies, and services.

30170 ■ Direct Marketing to Business - Fall

URL(s): thedma.org

Description: Direct marketing information and services. **Audience:** Business industry professionals. **Principal Exhibits:** Direct marketing information and services.

30171 ■ Email Innovations Summit

URL(s): emailinnovationssummit.com

Frequency: Annual. **Description:** Workshops and talks about new email marketing trends and developments. **Principal Exhibits:** Workshops and talks about new email marketing trends and developments.

30172 ■ FMI Midwinter Executive Conference

Mars
Usman Abad Karachi, Garden West Karachi
Karachi, Sindh 00876, Pakistan
Ph: 92 021 7644263
Fax: 92 021 2237799
Co. E-mail: hanif_mars@hotmail.com
Contact: Hanif Abdullah, Managing Director
URL(s): www.fmi.org/midwinter-conference

Frequency: Annual. **Description:** For senior-level executives in the food retail industry. **Audience:** Industry professionals. **Principal Exhibits:** For senior-level executives in the food retail industry. Dates and Locations: 2025 Jan 30-Feb 02 JW Marriott Marco Island, Marco Island, FL; 2026 Jan 21-24 San Diego, CA; 2027 Jan 20-23 San Diego, CA. **Telecommunication Services:** pcollins@fmi.org.

30173 ■ LeadsCon

URL(s): www.leadscon.com
Facebook: www.facebook.com/leadscon
Linkedin: www.linkedin.com/groups/1810842
X (Twitter): twitter.com/leadscon

Description: Talks and workshops focused on generating leads and market strategies for small businesses. **Principal Exhibits:** Talks and workshops focused on generating leads and market strategies for small businesses.

30174 ■ Pubcon Fullstack Marketing Conference

URL(s): www.pubcon.com

Facebook: www.facebook.com/PubCon
X (Twitter): twitter.com/pubcon
Instagram: www.instagram.com/pubcon
Pinterest: www.pinterest.com/pubcon/_created

Price: $199, Pre-registered; $250, Onsite. **Frequency:** Annual. **Description:** Networking and talks for professional digital marketers. **Principal Exhibits:** Networking and talks for professional digital marketers.

CONSULTANTS

30175 ■ 22squared Inc.

100 N Tampa St., Ste. 2500
Tampa, FL 33602
Ph: (813)202-1200
URL: http://www.22squared.com
Contact: Amanda Ferber, Chief Operating Officer
Facebook: www.facebook.com/22Squared
Linkedin: www.linkedin.com/company/22squaredinc
Instagram: www.instagram.com/22squared

Description: Provider of advertising solutions. It serves consumers and business owners. **Scope:** Provider of advertising solutions. It serves consumers and business owners. **Founded:** 1922.

30176 ■ Alden & Associates Marketing Research (AA-MR)

703 S Pacific Coast Hwy.
Redondo Beach, CA 90277-4226
Ph: (310)544-6282
Free: 800-742-6076
Fax: (310)544-6285
URL: http://www.aa-mr.com
Contact: Scott Alden, President
E-mail: scott.alden@aa-mr.com

Description: Provider of market research and aviation services. **Founded:** 1976.

30177 ■ Alexander Business Investment Consultants Inc.

409 Granville St., Ste. 1617
Vancouver, BC, Canada V6C 1T2
Ph: (604)688-1956
Co. E-mail: abic@abicanada.com
URL: http://www.abicanada.com

Description: Firm provides marketing consulting services. **Scope:** Firm provides marketing consulting services. **Founded:** 1998.

30178 ■ Arnold Sanow, MBA, CSP

2810 Glade Vale Way
Vienna, VA 22181
Ph: (703)255-3133
Co. E-mail: speaker@arnoldsanow.com
URL: http://www.arnoldsanow.com/meet-arnold
Contact: Arnold Sanow, Contact

Description: Firm is engaged in developing business and marketing strategies for companies, organizations, and individuals through speaking, training and consulting and focuses on providing practical, how-to, entertaining and non-boring keynotes, seminars, workshops, facilitations, retreats, coaching and consultation on communication and interpersonal issues. **Scope:** Firm is engaged in developing business and marketing strategies for companies, organizations, and individuals through speaking, training and consulting and focuses on providing practical, how-to, entertaining and non-boring keynotes, seminars, workshops, facilitations, retreats, coaching and consultation on communication and interpersonal issues. **Founded:** 1985. **Publications:** "How I Overcame My Fear of Public Speaking"; "Check Out Your Rule Book"; "Your Attitude - Deadly or Dazzling"; "Customer Advisory Boards"; "Marketing Audit"; "Perception is Reality"; "Winning Presentation Skills"; "Pump up Your Persuasive Powers"; "Rev Up Your rapport"; "Rudeness Wrecks Relationships"; "Sales Presentations Come Alive!"; "Master Emotional Control"; "7 Steps to Mastering Any Negotiation"; "8 Keys to Sales Success"; "8 Ways to Handle Bullies at Work". **Training:** 150 year Getting Business to Come to You; Keeping Customers for Life; Entrepreneur Boot Company; Boost Your Communication IQ; Keeping Customers for Life at el3 Building a WOW Customer Experience; Get Along with Anyone,

Anywhere, Anytime at el3 Build Rapport, Relationships and Connect with Customers and Co-workers; Communicate Like A Pro -Boost Your Communication IQ; Winning Presentation Skills - Put Power, Punch and Pizzazz into Your Presentations; Reducing and Resolving Conflicts It Starts with You; Entrepreneur Boot Camp at el3 Secrets of Successful Entrepreneurs; Managing Chaos; Don't Just Survive at el3 Thrive; Developing a Winning Marketing Plan and Strategy; Marketing Boot Camp Tools, Techniques and Strategies to Boost Your Bottom Line; Team building and Leadership techniques and Strategies in these Changing Times.

30179 ■ Aventi Group L.L.C.

350 Townsend, Ste. 781
  San Francisco, CA 94107
Ph: (415)890-5434
Co. E-mail: info@aventigroup.com
URL: http://aventigroup.com
Contact: Jeff Thompson, President
Facebook: www.facebook.com/aventigroup
Linkedin: www.linkedin.com/company/aventi-group
YouTube: www.youtube.com/channel/
  UCNScBnq7JFw-NmVInRNTSmA

Description: Aventi Group is an executive marketing consulting firm that specializes in accelerating revenue for technology companies. Services include strategic planning, business development, and marketing services. **Scope:** Aventi Group is an executive marketing consulting firm that specializes in accelerating revenue for technology companies. Services include strategic planning, business development, and marketing services. **Founded:** 2008. **Publications:** "Is Traditional Email Marketing Dead?"; "Advice to a CMO on Day One"; "Do you know your prospect's impending event?"; "Are you building solutions for your customer or your org chart?"; "Where's Your Product Marketing Manager?"; "Four Steps to Better Customer Presentations"; "10 Reasons Why Cold Calling Is A Total Waste". **Training:** Social Media WorkShop, Nov, 2009; Launching New Offerings in a Social World: What to consider when incorporating Social Media in your Go-To-Market Planning!.

30180 ■ BIA/Kelsey

14901 Bogle Dr., Ste. 101
  Chantilly, VA 20151
Ph: (703)818-2425
Co. E-mail: info@bia.com
URL: http://www.bia.com
Contact: Tom Buono, Chief Executive Officer
Facebook: www.facebook.com/biakelsey
Linkedin: www.linkedin.com/company/biaadvisorysrvs
X (Twitter): x.com/BIAAdvisorySvcs
YouTube: www.youtube.com/user/BIAmediacenter

Description: Publishes market and industry reports for the communications industry. Does not accept unsolicited manuscripts. Reaches market through commission representatives, direct mail, reviews and listings and distributors. **Scope:** A provider of research and fact-based analysis focusing on local advertising and electronic commerce. **Founded:** 1983. **Publications:** "Penetration of Online Media Surpasses Traditional Media for First Time Among Small-Business Advertisers," Aug, 2009; "Rapid Adoption of Advanced Mobile Devices Driving Increased Mobile Local Search Activity, According to The Kelsey Group," Nov, 2008; "Online Consumer Generated Reviews Have Significant Impact on Offline Purchase Behavior," Nov, 2007. **Training:** Drilling Down on Local: Marketplaces, The Westin Seattle, Seattle, Washington, Apr, 2008; The Future of Local Search in Europe, London, Jun, 2007; DDC2006?Directory Driven Commerce Conference, Hyatt Century Plaza, LA, Sep, 2006; Drilling Down on Local: Targeting the On-Demand Marketplace, 2005.

30181 ■ Bitner Group, Inc.

6750 N Andrews Ave., Ste. 200
  Fort Lauderdale, FL 33309
Ph: (954)730-7730
Co. E-mail: info@bitnergroup.com
URL: http://bitnergroup.com
Contact: Gary E. Bitner, President
E-mail: gary@bitnergroup.com

Facebook: www.facebook.com/bitnergroup
Linkedin: www.linkedin.com/company/bitner-group
X (Twitter): x.com/bitnergroup
Instagram: www.instagram.com/bitnergroup
YouTube: www.youtube.com/channel/UCOa7l
  4QJPhMpnDQhAvxBFGw

Description: Provider of media relations, social media management and production of videos and printed materials. **Scope:** A public relations, advertising and marketing consultancy. Serves industries including: travel, technology, telecommunications, financial services, consumer products, health-care, government, automotive, real estate and retail. **Founded:** 2003.

30182 ■ Business Development Advisors Inc. (BDA)

2300 N Barrington Rd., Ste. 400
  Hoffman Estates, IL 60195
Ph: (847)897-1121
Fax: (847)620-0613
Co. E-mail: info@bdail.com
URL: http://www.bdail.com

Description: Provider of business owners and executives with the expertise to integrate business organization and operations knowledge, proven offline sales process and proven online web usability to increase sales and profitability in today global business marketplace. **Scope:** Provider of business owners and executives with the expertise to integrate business organization and operations knowledge, proven offline sales process and proven online web usability to increase sales and profitability in today global business marketplace.

30183 ■ Business Improvement Architects (BIA)

633 Lakelands Ave.
  Innisfil, ON, Canada L9S 4E5
Co. E-mail: info@bia.ca
URL: http://bia.ca
Contact: Rowena Lamy, Consultant
E-mail: rlamy@bia.ca
Facebook: www.facebook.com/BusinessImprovemen
  tArchitects
Linkedin: www.linkedin.com/company/business
  -improvement-architects

Description: Provider of the following services, strategic planning, leadership development, innovation and project and quality management. Specialize in strategic planning, change management, leadership assessment and development of skills. **Scope:** Provider of the following services, strategic planning, leadership development, innovation and project and quality management. Specialize in strategic planning, change management, leadership assessment and development of skills. **Founded:** 1989. **Publications:** "Avoiding Pit falls to Innovation"; "Create a New Dimension of Performance with Innovation"; "The Power of Appreciation in Leadership"; "Why It Makes Sense To Have a Strategic Enterprise Office"; "Burning Rubber at the Start of Your Project"; "Accounting for Quality"; "How Pareto Charts Can Help You Improve the Quality of Business Processes"; "Managing Resistance to Change". **Training:** The Innovation Process From Vision to Reality, San Diego, Oct, 2007; Critical Thinking, Kuala Lump or, Sep, 2007; Critical Thinking, Brunei, Sep, 2007; Delivering Project Assurance, Auckland, Jun, 2007; From Crisis to Control: A New Era in Strategic Project Management, Prague, May, 2007; What Project Leaders Need to Know to Help Them Sleep Better At Night, London, May, 2007; Innovation Process. From Vision To Reality, Orlando, Apr, 2007. **Special Services:** Project Planning Tool™.

30184 ■ BusinessMedia

180 Brodie Dr., Ste. 5
  Richmond Hill, ON, Canada L4B 3K8
Ph: (905)760-1977
Co. E-mail: info@businessmedia.ca
URL: http://www.businessmedia.ca
Facebook: www.facebook.com/BusinessMedia.ca
X (Twitter): x.com/BusinessMedia2

Description: A full service multimedia company specializing in business media strategies, design, project management and dynamic internet application development. **Founded:** 1997. **Publications:** "The Importance of Updating your Website Design Part Three," Nov, 2010.

30185 ■ Capstone Communications Group

15 Wilson St.
  Markham, ON, Canada L3P 1M9
Ph: (905)472-2330
Co. E-mail: services1@capstonecomm.com
URL: http://www.capstonecomm.com
Contact: Keith Thirgood, Principal

Description: Provider of marketing, design, copy writing, consulting and advertising solutions. **Scope:** Provider of marketing, design, copy writing, consulting and advertising solutions. **Publications:** "Guide to finding the best keywords for your site"; "Seeking Help: Ideas on how to get out from under"; "Get your visitors to voluntarily give you their contact information"; "Where is 'King Content'"; "Is Blogging the Next Great Thing"; "Nice Guys Finish First: How the right kind of volunteering can help grow your business"; "Why should a business have a website"; "Too Dull, Too Sharp"; "Dialing for Dollars: Is fax marketing for you"; "Getting Paid to Promote Yourself"; "Why should a business have a website"; "Cave Paintings, Baseball and Connecting: There's no such thing as a captive audience"; "Marketing vs. Selling: What's the difference and why should you care"; "Selling Services"; "A New Opportunity"; "Improve Your Website"; "How to Price Right"; "A Questionnaire for Businesses"; "Web Report Card: How this site has been performing"; "At The Speed Of Light". **Training:** Your Image Your Message Your Market; Emotional Marketing; Developing a Marketing Mindset; Target Marketing; How to Create Marketing Materials That Work; Facing the Challenge of the Blank Page-A Design Workshop for Non-Designers, How to Create Web Sites that Work; The Service Sellers Masters Course; The Net writing Masters Course; The Pricing Masters Course; The Info Product Masters Course; The Net Auction Masters Course; The Affiliate Masters Course.

30186 ■ Cicco & Associates Inc.

221 Rainprint Sq.
  Murrysville, PA 15668
Contact: John A. Cicco, Jr., President

Description: Provider of marketing and management consulting services to smaller businesses and marketing and research consulting to larger corporations wishing to market to the U.S. small-business market. **Scope:** Provider of marketing and management consulting services to smaller businesses and marketing and research consulting to larger corporations wishing to market to the U.S. small-business market. **Training:** Corporate Executive Briefing on Marketing to Small Business; The Simple Secret to Marketing Success; Japanese Management: Made in the USA.

30187 ■ Comer & Associates L.L.C. (CA)

5255 Holmes Pl.
  Boulder, CO 80303
Ph: (303)786-7986
URL: http://www.comerassociates.com
Contact: Gerald Comer, Contact

Description: Specialize in developing markets and businesses. Marketing support includes developing and writing strategic and tactical business plans, developing and writing focused, effective market plans, researching market potential and competition, implementing targeted marketing tactics to achieve company objectives, conducting customer surveys to determine satisfaction and attitudes toward client. **Scope:** Specialize in developing markets and businesses. Marketing support includes developing and writing strategic and tactical business plans, developing and writing focused, effective market plans, researching market potential and competition, implementing targeted marketing tactics to achieve company objectives, conducting customer surveys to determine satisfaction and attitudes toward client. **Training:** Developing a Strategic Market Plan; Market

Research: Defining Your Opportunity; Management and Leadership Effectiveness; Team Building; Developing a Business Plan; How to Close; Using Questions to Sell; Sales System Elements and Checklist; Working With Independent Reps; Features vs. Benefits; Overcoming Objections; Sales Force Automation.

30188 ■ Creative Company Inc.
PO Box 446
Newberg, OR 97132
Ph: (503)883-4433
Co. E-mail: optimize@creativeco.com
URL: http://www.creativeco.com
Contact: Jennifer Larsen Morrow, President
E-mail: jlmorrow@creativeco.com
Facebook: www.facebook.com/pages/McMinnville
-OR/Creative-Company-Inc/58557673552
X (Twitter): x.com/optimizemybrand
YouTube: www.youtube.com/user/optimizemybrand
Pinterest: www.pinterest.com/creativecoinc
Description: Provider of marketing, brand programs, websites, marketing strategy, online branding and more. **Scope:** Provider of marketing, brand programs, websites, marketing strategy, online branding and more. **Founded:** 1978. **Publications:** "Generational Marketing"; "Apply Branding to Bring Power to Your Marketing"; "Brand Your Business".

30189 ■ Crossmedia451 Inc.
Chicago, IL
Co. E-mail: crossmedia451@gmail.com
URL: http://crossmedia451.net
Contact: Laura Gale, Founder
Description: Digital marketing and business development firm that works with businesses to raise brand awareness, increase customer engagement, and increase sales. **Scope:** Digital marketing and business development firm that works with businesses to raise brand awareness, increase customer engagement, and increase sales.

30190 ■ Crouser & Associates Inc.
235 Dutch Rd.
Charleston, WV 25302
Contact: Thomas P. Crouser, President
E-mail: tom@crouser.com
Description: Provider of management, accounting, pricing, personnel, and marketing for smaller organizations and market research for companies selling to small press printers. **Scope:** Provider of management, accounting, pricing, personnel, and marketing for smaller organizations and market research for companies selling to small press printers. **Publications:** "Dead Printer Working: A Printer's Financial Survival Guide"; "Prospering: Putting Your Business to Work for You and Your Family". **Training:** Power Pricing - Pricing Small Press Printing; Family Business Families in Small Press Printing Businesses; Getting Jobs Out - Production Management in the Small Press Shop. **Special Services:** CPrint®.

30191 ■ Customer Perspectives
875-A Island Dr.
Alameda, CA 94502
Free: 800-339-2861
Co. E-mail: info@customerperspectives.com
URL: http://www.customerperspectives.com
Contact: Judi Hess, Founder
Facebook: www.facebook.com/CustomerPerspec
tivesMysteryShopping
Linkedin: www.linkedin.com/company/customer
-perspectives
X (Twitter): x.com/JancynShops
Description: Firm provides mystery and secret shopping, customer service telephone evaluations, customer experience measurement, call center evaluations, training need and manager assessments, and competitor comparisons. **Scope:** A market research consultancy specializing in mystery shopping. **Founded:** 1983. **Special Services:** Customer Perspectives™.

30192 ■ D.E.I. Management Group Inc.
888 7th Ave., 9th Fl.
New York, NY 10106
Contact: Stephan Schiffman, Chief Executive Officer

Description: Firm offers counsel and training in productivity and goal setting in the corporate setting as well as selling skills and serves telecommunication, financial services, banking services, real-estate and manufacturing. **Scope:** Firm offers counsel and training in productivity and goal setting in the corporate setting as well as selling skills and serves telecommunication, financial services, banking services, real-estate and manufacturing. **Publications:** "Just Plain Tired," Jun, 2006; "The Sales Manager and the Sale," May, 2006; "The Collaborative Sale," Mar, 2006; "Ten MUSTS For a Successful Speech," Mar, 2006; "Five Stages of the Sales Career," Mar, 2006. **Special Services:** Prospect Management System.

30193 ■ Derivative Integrated Solutions
1090 Homer St., Ste. 300
Vancouver, BC, Canada V6B 2W9
Ph: (604)805-1456
Co. E-mail: info@derivative.solutions
URL: http://www.derivative.solutions
Facebook: www.facebook.com/derivative.solutions
X (Twitter): twitter.com/derivative2015
Description: Firm offers business consultancy solutions.

30194 ■ Don Phin, Esq.
114 C. Ave., No. 200
Coronado, CA 92118
Ph: (619)852-4580
URL: http://www.donphin.com
Contact: Don Phin, Contact
E-mail: don@donphin.com
Linkedin: www.linkedin.com/in/donphin
X (Twitter): x.com/donphin12
YouTube: www.youtube.com/donphin
Description: Firm is engaged in consulting services on training, coaching and mentoring for the individuals and small businesses. **Scope:** Firm is engaged in consulting services on training, coaching and mentoring for the individuals and small businesses. **Founded:** 1983. **Publications:** "Doing Business Right!"; "HR That Works!"; "Lawsuit Free! How to Prevent Employee Lawsuits"; "Building Powerful Employment Relationships!"; "Victims, Villains and Heroes: Managing Emotions in The Workplace". **Training:** Doing Business Right!; HR That Works!; Building Powerful Employment Relationships; Lawsuit Free!.

30195 ■ Elizabeth Capen
415 Madison Ave., 17th Fl.
New York, NY 10017
Ph: (212)644-2222
Co. E-mail: ecapen@lansco.com
URL: http://www.lansco.com
Contact: Elizabeth Capen, Contact
E-mail: ecapen@lansco.com
Description: Focuses on strategic marketing planning and positioning. Identifies effective marketing tools, plans and reviews advertising and collateral materials, writes business plans and performs secondary research and competitive analysis. Industries served services, small businesses and entrepreneurial ventures in northeastern and middle Atlantic regions. **Scope:** Focuses on strategic marketing planning and positioning. Identifies effective marketing tools, plans and reviews advertising and collateral materials, writes business plans and performs secondary research and competitive analysis. Industries served services, small businesses and entrepreneurial ventures in northeastern and middle Atlantic regions. **Training:** Handling Issues of Growth; Using Published Information as a Marketing Tool.

30196 ■ Endorphin Advisors
Troy Innovation Garage
24 Fourth St.
Troy, NY 12180
Ph: (518)351-2240
Co. E-mail: info@endorphinadvisors.com
URL: http://www.endorphindigital.com
Contact: Erik Bunaes, President
Description: Full-service strategy and digital marketing consulting firm. **Founded:** 2005.

30197 ■ The Farnsworth Group (TFG)
6640 Intech Blvd., No. 100
Indianapolis, IN 46278
Co. E-mail: results@thefarnsworthgroup.com
URL: http://www.thefarnsworthgroup.com
Contact: Grant Farnsworth, President
E-mail: gfarnsworth@thefarnsworthgroup.com
Linkedin: www.linkedin.com/company/the-farnsworth
-group
Description: Firm is engaged in providing research-based marketing consulting company and serves the home improvement, construction and building materials industries and services for manufacturers include product development and much more. **Scope:** Firm is engaged in providing research-based marketing consulting company and serves the home improvement, construction and building materials industries and services for manufacturers include product development and much more. **Founded:** 1989. **Publications:** "Research Guides Hyde Tool's Re-branding," Jun, 2011.

30198 ■ Freese & Associates Inc. (F&A)
16105 Lucky Bell Ln.
Newbury, OH 44065
Ph: (440)487-4509
URL: http://www.freeseinc.com
Contact: Thomas L. Freese, Principal
E-mail: tfreese@freeseinc.com
Description: Provider of supply chain management and logistics consulting services such as customer service, material management, transportation, and much more. **Scope:** Provider of supply chain management and logistics consulting services such as customer service, material management, transportation, and much more. **Founded:** 1987. **Publications:** "Building Relationships is Key to Motivation," Distribution Center Management, Apr, 2006; "Getting Maximum Results from Performance Reviews," WERC Sheet, Oct, 2003; "SCM: Making the Vision a Reality," Supply Chain Management Review, Oct, 2003; "Contents Under Pressure," DC Velocity, Aug, 2003; "When Considering Outsourcing, It's Really a Financial Decision," Inventory Management Report, Mar, 2003. **Training:** WERC/CAWS Warehousing in China Conference, Sep, 2008; CSCMP Annual Conference, Denver, Oct, 2008; Keys to Retaining and Motivating Your Associates, Dallas, Mar, 2006; The Value and Challenges of Supply Chain Management, Dubai, Feb, 2006; Best Practices in Logistics in China, Jun, 2005; Keys to Motivating Associates, Dallas, May, 2005; The Goal and the Way of International Cooperation in Logistics, Jenobuk, Apr, 2005.

30199 ■ The Handler Group Inc.
425 W End Ave.
New York, NY 10024
Contact: Mark L. Handler, Chief Executive Officer
Description: Provider of marketing, communication planning and design services, specializing in development of internal and external business communications. Develops corporate identity, corporate literature, employee communications, sales promotion materials, consumer product packaging and information, brochures, annual reports and presentation materials. Industries served: Cable/television, technology software, business information, hospitality and banking. **Scope:** Provider of marketing, communication planning and design services, specializing in development of internal and external business communications. Develops corporate identity, corporate literature, employee communications, sales promotion materials, consumer product packaging and information, brochures, annual reports and presentation materials. Industries served: Cable/television, technology software, business information, hospitality and banking.

30200 ■ Help Business Services Inc.
417 Dartmouth Ave.
Swarthmore, PA 19081
Contact: John R. Kaufman, President
Description: Distributor of secondary marketing information like competitor intelligence to manufacturers, marketing service firms, and consultants and questions researched using electronic and hard copy

databases, business and consumer publications, directories, government materials, published surveys and reports, as well as contact with associations and serves the private industry as well as government agencies worldwide. **Scope:** Distributor of secondary marketing information like competitor intelligence to manufacturers, marketing service firms, and consultants and questions researched using electronic and hard copy databases, business and consumer publications, directories, government materials, published surveys and reports, as well as contact with associations and serves the private industry as well as government agencies worldwide.

30201 ■ Holcomb Gallagher Adams Advertising Inc. [300m]

4000 Horizons Dr.
  Columbus, OH 43220
Co. E-mail: info@300m.co
URL: http://300m.co

Description: Consults in strategic marketing planning, and new business, brand equity, creative strategy, and media strategy development. Industries served: Consumer goods and services, manufacturing, retail, business-to-business products and services, education, travel, and tourism. **Scope:** Consults in strategic marketing planning, and new business, brand equity, creative strategy, and media strategy development. Industries served: Consumer goods and services, manufacturing, retail, business-to-business products and services, education, travel, and tourism. **Founded:** 1993.

30202 ■ Ilium Associates Inc.

10900 NE 8th St., Ste. 1495
  Bellevue, WA 98004
Ph: (425)646-6525
Free: 800-874-6525
Fax: (425)646-6522
Co. E-mail: ilium@ilium.com
UHL: http://www.ilium.com
Contact: Carolyn Andersen, President

Description: Firm provides communication and marketing consulting services and graphic designs.

30203 ■ In Plain English

14501 Antigone Dr.
  Gaithersburg, MD 20878-2484
Ph: (301)340-2821
Free: 800-274-9645
Fax: (301)279-0115
URL: http://www.inplainenglish.com

Description: Management consultants helping government and business research, design, write and produce user oriented management information for human resources, employee benefits, business process, corporate and marketing needs. Services include: GSA mob is schedule for consulting to the government; employee benefit communications, plain English business writing workshops for print and electronic media; communicating strategy and tactics; marketing research, business planning and communications; readability testing; usability testing and monitoring strategy. **Scope:** Management consultants helping government and businesses research, design, write and produce user oriented management information for human resources, employee benefits, business process, corporate and marketing needs. Services include: GSA mob is schedule for consulting to the government; employee benefit communications, plain English business writing workshops for print and electronic media; communicating strategy and tactics; marketing research, business planning and communications; readability testing; usability testing and monitoring strategy. **Founded:** 1977. **Publications:** "The Benefits Communication"; "The Employee Benefits Communication ToolKit," Commerce Clearinghouse; "Benefits Communication," Business and Legal Reports. **Training:** Plain English Writing Training; Summary Plan Description Compliance workshops; Re-Humanizing the Corporation, Human Resources and Employee Benefits Communication Workshop; 21 Writing Tips for the 21st Century; Make the Write Impression; Writing to Inform and Instruct; The Dreaded Nuts and Bolts; Writing to

Persuade; Writing Policy and Procedure Manuals In Plain English; Writing for Accountants and Auditors In Plain English. **Special Services:** In Plain English®.

30204 ■ Institute of Business Forecasting and Planning (IBF)

350 N Blvd.
  Great Neck, NY 11021
Ph: (516)504-7576
Fax: (516)498-2029
Co. E-mail: info@ibf.org
URL: http://www.ibf.org
Contact: Andrew Scuoler, Contact
E-mail: andrews@ibf.org
Facebook: www.facebook.com/DemandPlanning
Linkedin: www.linkedin.com/company/institute-of
  -business-forecasting-and-planning
X (Twitter): x.com/demandplanning

Description: Provider of forecasting and planning services, supply chain management and demand planning performance services. Offers consulting services in the areas of direct response marketing and business forecasting. **Scope:** Provider of forecasting and planning services, supply chain management and demand planning performance services. Offers consulting services in the areas of direct response marketing and business forecasting. **Founded:** 1981. **Publications:** "Practical Guide to Business Forecasting," 2005; "Regression Analysis Modeling and Forecasting," 2003; "Bibliography on Forecasting and Planning," 1995; "Ivy League Business School Far Behind the Time," The Journal of Business Forecasting, 1992; "The Role of Judgment in Business Forecasting," Industrial Management, Nov, 1992; "Conference Sales and Operations Planning: The How-To Handbook"; "Conference Sales and Operations Planning: A Visual Introduction". **Training:** Introduction to Business Forecasting and Planning: A Hands-On Workshop, Atlanta, GA, May, 2009; Statistical Forecasting: A Hands-On Workshop, London, UK, May, 2009; Demand Planning and Forecasting: Best Practices Conference, Las Vegas, Nevada, Apr, 2009; Statistical Forecasting: A Hands-On Workshop, Seattle, WA, Mar, 2009; Supply Chain Forecasting and Planning Conference, Phoenix, AZ, Feb, 2009. **Educational Activities:** Business Forecasting: Best Practices Conference (Annual).

30205 ■ JB Associates

3807 W Sierra Hwy., Ste. 6
  Acton, CA 93510
Contact: Jason Brown, Secretary

Description: Firm provides domestic and international marketing expertise, including strategic market and sales planning, product marketing, sales channel development, evaluation of representative and distributor networks, semiconductor marketing and distribution management and skilled in foreign languages. **Scope:** Firm provides domestic and international marketing expertise, including strategic market and sales planning, product marketing, sales channel development, evaluation of representative and distributor networks, semiconductor marketing and distribution management and skilled in foreign languages.

30206 ■ Jeffrey Lant Associates, Inc. (JLA)

50 Follen St., No. 507
  Cambridge, MA 02138
Ph: (617)547-6372
Co. E-mail: drlant@drjeffreylant.com
URL: http://www.drjeffreylant.com

Description: Publishes technical assistance books for nonprofit organizations, consultants, independent professionals and small and home-based businesses. Offers audio cassettes, workshops and consultation services. Also publish twice the monthly Worlgram newsletter. Reaches market through commission representatives, direct mail, telephone sales and the Internet. Accept unsolicited manuscripts. **Founded:** 1997. **Publications:** "E-mail El Dorado," JLA Publications, 1998; "Web Wealth: How to Turn the World Wide Web Into a Cash Hose for Your Business. Whatever You're Selling," 1997; "Multi-Level Money," JLA Publications, 1994; "No More Cold Calls," JLA

Publications, 1997; "Cash Copy"; "How to make at least $100000 a year"; "E-Money". **Training:** Business and personal development, including Establishing and Operating Your Successful Consulting Business; Successfully Promoting Your Small Business and Professional Practice; Succeeding in Your Mail Order Business; Successfully Raising Money for Your Nonprofit Organization from Foundations, Corporations and Individuals; Money Making Marketing: Finding the People Who Need What You're Selling and Making Sure They Buy It; Getting Corporations, Foundations, and Individuals to Give You the Money Your Nonprofit Organization Needs.

30207 ■ Kelley Chunn & Associates (KCA)

PO Box 190871
  Boston, MA 02119
Ph: (617)427-0046
Co. E-mail: kcassociates106@gmail.com
URL: http://www.kelleychunn.com
Contact: Kelley C. Chunn, Contact
Facebook: www.facebook.com/kcaforsocialchange
X (Twitter): x.com/KelleyChunn
Pinterest: www.pinterest.com/kc4info

Description: A consulting firm that specializes in multicultural and cause-related public relations and marketing. It offers cause-related marketing, strategic planning, community relations, corporate communications, guerrilla marketing, event planning and management, public affairs, media relations and training. **Founded:** 1991. **Publications:** "The Tipping point of social marketing Color Magazine"; "Community Voices, Bay State Banner"; "Education: Inner City Slickers", 2006. **Training:** Crisis communications; Guerrilla marketing; Ethnic marketing.

30208 ■ Krantz Marketing Services L.L.C.

Trenton, NJ 08625
Ph: (908)326-3518
URL: http://enterprisenj.com/company/krantz-marke
  ting-services-llc-duml

Description: Offers strategic planning for digital marketing and e-business, public relations, advertising, marketing, research, management consulting, telemarketing and sales and management training for clients in business-to-business and professional services. **Scope:** Offers strategic planning for digital marketing and e-business, public relations, advertising, marketing, research, management consulting, telemarketing and sales and management training for clients in business-to-business and professional services. **Founded:** 1980. **Training:** Sales Management; Market Planning; Pricing; Entrepreneurial Marketing; High Technology Marketing - Creating Differentiation in Product and Service Marketing.

30209 ■ Liberty Business Strategies Ltd.

329 S 16th
  Philadelphia, PA 19102
Ph: (267)858-4021
Co. E-mail: info@libertystrategies.com
URL: http://libertystrategies.com
Contact: Emmy Miller, President
Linkedin: www.linkedin.com/company/525207
X (Twitter): x.com/LibertyBusiness

Description: Management consulting firm provides executive coaching, strategic alignment, succession planning such as healthcare, consumer products, technology, and much more. **Scope:** Management consulting firm provides executive coaching, strategic alignment, succession planning such as healthcare, consumer products, technology, and much more. **Founded:** 1980. **Training:** Winning with Talent, Morison Annual Conference, Jul, 2009.

30210 ■ LoudBird LLC

456 N 1200 W
  Salt Lake City, UT 84116
URL: http://loudbirdmarketing.com
Contact: Clair Jones, Founder
Facebook: www.facebook.com/loudbirdmarketing
Instagram: www.instagram.com/loudbirdmarketing
YouTube: www.youtube.com/channel/UCAY2Kp
  ttXmBb-5QBl1TJjFg
Pinterest: www.pinterest.com/loudbirdmarketing

Description: Small business marketing agency whose services include branding, SEO, websites, content, social media, copywriting, advertising, and training.

30211 ■ Lucchesi Business Consulting, L.L.C. (LBC)
Raleigh, NC
Ph: (984)200-3197
URL: http://lbcsuccess.com
Contact: Donna Lucchesi, Owner
Description: Firm provides business and marketing consulting services. **Scope:** Firm provides business and marketing consulting services. **Founded:** 2004.

30212 ■ Market Focus, Inc.
2307 Fenton Pkwy. No. 134
San Diego, CA 92108
Free: 800-708-9715
Co. E-mail: sales@emarketfocus.com
URL: http://www.emarketfocus.com
Contact: Chris Carter, Contact
Facebook: www.facebook.com/marketfocusinc
Description: Provider of custom qualitative and quantitative market research designed to answer key questions and then offers ideas that generate results. Provides counsel in marketing research and planning and marketing programs, particularly for financial service organizations, banking, insurance, electronics, publishing and industrial organizations. **Founded:** 1992. **Publications:** "Surviving in Hard Times," NJ Contractor. **Training:** Charting a Course for Future Company Growth; Marketing Planning; Construction Marketing in the 90's; Marketing and The CFO.

30213 ■ Marketing Resource Group Inc.
215 S Washington Sq., Ste. F
Lansing, MI 48933
Ph: (517)372-4400
URL: http://www.mrgmi.com
Contact: Jenell Leonard, Owner
E-mail: jleonard@mrgmi.com
Facebook: www.facebook.com/marketingresourcegroup
Linkedin: www.linkedin.com/company/marketing-resource-group
X (Twitter): x.com/MRGMichigan
Instagram: www.instagram.com/marketingresourcegroup
Description: Provides customized sales skills and field training systems for salespeople, sales managers, executives and non-selling staff and curriculums developed and branded for in-house program to be used with future trainees and new hires and offers pre-screening of sales candidates and strategic consulting. **Founded:** 1995. **Training:** Basic Sales Skills; Consultative Selling; Relationship Selling; Networking to Maximize Your Business; Six Critical Steps for Every Sales Call; Selling Skills for the Non-Sales Professional; Effective Sales Management; Maximizing Revenue.

30214 ■ Matterhorn Business Solutions
5319 3rd St. SE, Ste. 763
Calgary, AB, Canada T2H 1J7
Ph: (403)991-8863
Co. E-mail: info@matterhornsolutions.ca
URL: http://matterhornsolutions.ca
Contact: David Howse, Director, Marketing Manager, Marketing Consultant
E-mail: david@matterhornsolutions.ca
Facebook: www.facebook.com/yycsem
Linkedin: www.linkedin.com/company/matterhorn-business-solutions-inc.
X (Twitter): x.com/yycsem
YouTube: www.youtube.com/channel/UCPVDSlmJHvUK4rRP0JLtTrA
Description: A full-service marketing solutions provider that provides small and mid-market businesses with a wide range of services such as web design, PPC, and social media marketing and SEO implementations. **Scope:** A full-service marketing solutions provider that provides small and mid-market businesses with a wide range of services such as web design, PPC, and social media marketing and SEO implementations. **Founded:** 2008.

30215 ■ Medical Imaging Consultants Inc. (MIC)
1037 US Hwy. 46, Ste. G-2
Clifton, NJ 07013-2445
Ph: (973)574-8000
Free: 800-589-5685
Fax: (973)574-8001
Co. E-mail: info@micinfo.com
URL: http://www.micinfo.com
Contact: Philip A. Femano, President
Description: Provider of professional support services in radiology management and comprehensive continuing education programs for radiologic technologists such as professional educators, life scientists, biomedical engineers, and much more. **Scope:** Provider of professional support services in radiology management and comprehensive continuing education programs for radiologic technologists such as professional educators, life scientists, biomedical engineers, and much more. **Founded:** 1991. **Training:** Sectional Anatomy and Imaging Strategies; CT Cross-Trainer; CT Registry Review Program; MR Cross Trainer; MRI Registry Review Program; Digital Mammography Essentials for Technologists; Radiology Trends for Technologists.

30216 ■ Mefford, Knutson & Associates Inc. (MKA)
6437 Lyndale Ave. S
Richfield, MN 55423
Co. E-mail: info@mkcconsulting.com
URL: http://mkaconsulting.com
Contact: Jeanette Mefford, Co-Founder
Description: Provider of consulting services to home health and related sectors. **Scope:** Provider of consulting services to home health and related sectors. **Founded:** 1990.

30217 ■ OF+ Consulting
London, United Kingdom
URL: http://ofplus.com
Contact: Simon Wright, Founder
E-mail: simon@ofplus.com
Description: Helps food and drink companies develop and market their products.

30218 ■ Olmstead & Associates (OA)
111 W Port Plz., 6 Fl., Ste. 600
Saint Louis, MO 63146
Ph: (314)241-5665
Fax: (314)666 9805
Co. E-mail: info@olmsteadassoc.com
URL: http://www.olmsteadassoc.com
Contact: Dr. John W. Olmstead, President
E-mail: jolmstead@olmsteadassoc.com
Description: A practice management, marketing and technology consulting firm that works with law and other professional service firms ranging in size from 100 professionals to firms with solo practitioners. Assists with implementing change and improving operational and financial performance, management, leadership, client development and marketing. **Scope:** A practice management, marketing and technology consulting firm that works with law and other professional service firms ranging in size from 100 professionals to firms with solo practitioners. Assists with implementing change and improving operational and financial performance, management, leadership, client development and marketing. **Founded:** 1984. **Publications:** "Marketing The Small Law Firm," Sep, 2008; "How To Use Secondary Research To Manage Your Firm," Sep, 2008; "How to Use Current E-Business Web Sites To Improve Law Firm Profits," Sep, 2008; "Year End Client Satisfaction Surveys: Out-Think and Out-Service Your Competitors," Sep, 2008; "Developing A Focused Marketing Strategy," Sep, 2008; "Law Office Management & Marketing Checklist"; "Leadership Interpersonal Characteristics of Attorney Members of a State Bar Association"; "People and Technology"; "Marketing Legal Services"; "Financial Management with Integrated Accounting Software"; "The Development of Responsive Management in Law Firms, Corporate and Governmental Law Departments"; "How to Practice Successful Management Strategies for the Twenty-First Century"; "How to Reinvent Your Law Practice in Order to Prosper in the 21st Century"; "Seven Communication Styles That Can Improve Law Firm Performance And Enhance Firm Profitability"; "Trapped In An Insurance Defense Practice? Two Strategic Approaches"; "Office Conflict: Are You Coach or Referee?"; "How Effective Law Firm Leadership Practices Can Help You Acquire and Keep Your Clients"; "Cutting The Pie-Determining Partner Compensation"; "Protecting Your Firm Against Loss Of Key Employees"; "Coach Your Firm Staff for Better Performance"; "Seven Communication Styles That Can Improve Law Firm Performance"; "Using A Firm Retreat To Plan For The Next Decade"; "Planning For Computerized Litigation Document Management". **Training:** Fundamentals of Business Planning, Sep, 2008; Interpersonal Communications Skills For the Lawyer, Sep, 2008; Cutting the Pie: Determining Partner Compensation, Mar, 2008; How to Build and Manage a Successful Practice, St. Louis, Oct, 2007; Escaping Career Burnout: Ways to Balance Your Personal and Professional Life, St. Charles, Sep, 2007; Build & Manage A Successful Practice, May, 2007; Characteristics of Successful Law Firms, Sep, 2006; Tips for Balancing Your Personal and Professional Life, Jun, 2005; Getting New Business, Apr, 2001; Reinventing the Law Practice, Mar, 2000; Taking Care of Business While You Practice Law; The Small Law Office: Prescription for Survival; Getting New Business; Reinventing Your Practice.

30219 ■ Prosper Business Development
400 W Wilson Bridge, Ste. 200
Worthington, OH 43085
Ph: (614)846-0146
Fax: (614)846-0156
Co. E-mail: info@goprosper.com
URL: http://www.goprosper.com
Contact: Gary Drenik, Chief Executive Officer
E-mail: gary@goprosper.com
Description: Provider of marketing productivity, business development and online information retrieval solutions. **Scope:** Provides business development and marketing productivity services with unique capabilities and expertise in marketplace and competitive intelligence, strategic alliances and integrated marketing systems. **Founded:** 1990. **Publications:** "Energy's Challenge to Change"; "Managing the Efficacy of E-Commerce in China". **Special Services:** Consumer Intentions and Actions™; Simultaneous Media Usage Study™.

30220 ■ RG Digital Marketing
171 E Liberty St.
Toronto, ON, Canada M6K 3P6
Co. E-mail: hello@rahulghosh.ca
URL: http://rahulghosh.ca
Facebook: www.facebook.com/digitalmarketingtoronto
Description: A boutique digital marketing agency that works with local business owners and startups to help them generate more sales and increase top of the line revenue. **Scope:** A boutique digital marketing agency that works with local business owners and startups to help them generate more sales and increase top of the line revenue.

30221 ■ Sales and Marketing Communications Associates Inc.
2835 W Juneau Ave.
Milwaukee, WI 53208-2922
Contact: Shelia Payton, Contact
Description: A full-service marketing, public relations, focus group research and advertising company that provides clients with everything from results-oriented ideas to finished programs and materials. **Scope:** A full-service marketing, public relations, focus group research and advertising company that provides clients with everything from results-oriented ideas to finished programs and materials. **Training:** Owning and Operating a Successful Small Business; An Entrepreneur's Guide to Marketing; Getting the Message Across: Effective Business Communications; Planning Your Way to Business Success; To Be or Not To Be(A Business Owner).

30222 ■ The Sanderson Group Inc.

515 E 85 St., Ste. 4E
New York, NY 10028
Contact: Robin Sanderon, Chief Executive Officer
E-mail: robin@thesandersongroup.com

Description: Full-service marketing firm is engaged in providing traditional, digital and tailored marketing solutions, the company offers consulting, communications, lead generation, brand identity, events and promotions, and strategic planning services and serves both large corporations, small- and medium-sized businesses.

30223 ■ Shannon Staffing Inc.

1590-B Coshocton Ave.
Mount Vernon, OH 43050
Ph: (740)397-2040
Co. E-mail: mountvernon@shannonstaffing.com
URL: http://www.shannonstaffing.com
Facebook: www.facebook.com/shannonstaffing
Linkedin: www.linkedin.com/company/shannon-staffing-inc.
X (Twitter): x.com/shannonstaffing

Description: Provides human resources recruiting and outplacement counseling services to industries and public sector organizations. **Founded:** 1985. **Publications:** "Powells Rules for Picking People". **Training:** Time Management workshop.

30224 ■ Steve Moeller's American Business Vision L.L.C.

Tustin, CA
Ph: (530)652-4081
Co. E-mail: steve@stevemoeller.com
URL: http://www.stevemoeller.com

Description: Firm works with product sponsors and broker-dealers to design programs, training material, and presentations that provide value to the advisors and visibility to your organization, their services include strategic planning, training wholesalers, creating or customizing training material, creating customized, private-labeled training programs for advisors. **Scope:** Firm works with product sponsors and broker-dealers to design programs, training material, and presentations that provide value to the advisors and visibility to your organization, their services include strategic planning, training wholesalers, creating or customizing training material, creating customized, private-labeled training programs for advisors. **Founded:** 1989. **Publications:** "Effort-Less Marketing". **Training:** Attract and Serve Wealthy Investors with Vision Coaching; Effort-Less Marketing for Financial Advisors; Design a Win-Win Business Model; Convert Traditional Accounts to Fee-Based Business; Position Yourself as a Client-Centered Advisor.

30225 ■ Taste Profit Marketing, LLC

54 Pleasant St., Unit 9
Concord, NH 03301
Ph: (617)833-2417
Co. E-mail: info@tasteprofit.com
URL: http://tasteprofit.com
Contact: Noah Munro, Founder
Facebook: www.facebook.com/TasteProfitMarketing
Linkedin: www.linkedin.com/company/taste-profit
X (Twitter): x.com/tasteprofit
Instagram: www.instagram.com/tasteprofit

Description: Helps food entrepreneurs grow profitable food businesses and become better marketing managers. Services include website development, eCommerce development, branding, email automation, SEO, food photography, graphic design, blogging, and marketing planning. **Founded:** 2015.

30226 ■ Westlife Consultants and Advisors

4 Robert Speck Pkwy.
Mississauga, ON, Canada L4Z, CA
URL: http://www.westlifeconsultants.com
Contact: Syed N. Hussain, President
E-mail: shussain@westlifeconsultants.com

Linkedin: www.linkedin.com/company/westlife-consultants-&-advisors

Description: Provider of entrepreneurs and businesses with a highly commercial and global perspectives on the international business development ideas under consideration. **Scope:** Provider of entrepreneurs and businesses with a highly commercial and global perspectives on the international business development ideas under consideration. **Founded:** 1992. **Publications:** "Innovative Management"; "Team Building and Leadership"; "Financial Planning"; "Estate Planning"; "Risk Management"; "Export/Import Trade Finance Mechanics"; "Marketing and Sales Management"; "What Your Banker Needs to Know"; "Building A Successful Financial Plan".

30227 ■ William Blades L.L.C.

5405 S Abbey
Mesa, AZ 85212
Ph: (480)556-1467
Co. E-mail: bill@billblades.com
URL: http://www.billblades.com
Contact: William Blades, Contact
E-mail: bill@billblades.com

Description: Firm provides consulting services in sales, sales management, marketing, leadership, corporate culture, and much more. **Scope:** Firm provides consulting services in sales, sales management, marketing, leadership, corporate culture, and much more. **Founded:** 1988. **Publications:** "Selling-The Mother of All Enterprise"; "Leadership Defined"; "Why Do We Make Change So Hard"; "10 Crucial Steps for Sales Management Success"; "In Sales, it's all About Accountability"; "Conversations Of Success"; "Celebrate Selling"; "Vision: Help Your Mind"; "Leadership Defined"; "Managing to Improve: 10 Areas of Emphasis for Workplace Leaders"; "Creativity: Let the Juices Flow In the Workplace"; "Get Bill Blades Philosophy on Boot Camps"; "Great Leadership Grows From a Mixed Bag"; "Self Improvement - The Million Dollar Equation". **Training:** Sales Leadership Culture Creativity; Sales and Management; Coaching for Executives and Sales Managers; Sales and Marketing Action Plans.

30228 ■ Xerox Business Research Group

201 Merritt 7
Norwalk, CT 06851-1056
Free: 800-835-6100
URL: http://www.xerox.com/en-us
Contact: Steve Bandrowczak, President
Linkedin: www.linkedin.com/company/xerox
X (Twitter): x.com/Xerox
Instagram: www.instagram.com/xerox

Description: A full service firm specializing in business to business marketing research related to medical technology and other high tech industries. Areas of expertise include conjoint analysis, customer satisfaction, market segmentation and image tracking. **Scope:** A full service firm specializing in business to business marketing research related to medical technology and other high tech industries. Areas of expertise include conjoint analysis, customer satisfaction, market segmentation and image tracking. **Founded:** 1986. **Special Services:** Customer Experience Measurement and Tracking Systems; Monitron Brand Image Tracking™; Horizon Prophecy Polls™; Concourse Prospect Dialogs™; MAPS Brand Charting™.

PUBLICATIONS

30229 ■ "How to Claim a Google Business Profile" in Business 2 Community (October 22, 2021)

URL(s): www.business2community.com/small-business/how-to-claim-a-google-business-profile-02437585

Ed: Haiden Hibbert. **Description:** Discusses why a small business should set up a Google Business profile and then gives step-by-step instructions on how to complete the process. **Availability:** Online.

INTERNET DATABASES

30230 ■ *Marketing Industry: A Resource Guide*

URL(s): guides.loc.gov/marketing-industry

Description: Provides links to online resources covering the topics of marketing, public relations, and advertising. Users can obtain links to books, academic journals, trade publications, marketing associations, agencies, rankings and awards, brands and advertisements, manufacturers and wholesalers, regulations and ethics, and subscription databases. **Availability:** Online.

LIBRARIES

30231 ■ Boston Public Library - Kirstein Business Library & Innovation Center

700 Boylston St.
Boston, MA 02116
Ph: (617)536-5400
Co. E-mail: businessref@bpl.org
URL: http://www.bpl.org/kbl
Facebook: www.facebook.com/KirsteinBusiness
Linkedin: www.linkedin.com/company/kblic
X (Twitter): x.com/bplkirstein

Scope: Business administration; small business. **Services:** Copying is available through the library's interlibrary loan department; reference faxing up to three pages. **Founded:** 1930. **Holdings:** Mergent Manuals (1935 to present in print; 1909-1997 in microfiche); Commercial and Financial Chronicle, 1957-1987; Bank and Quotation Record, 1928-1987; Standard and Poor's Daily Stock Price Record: New York and American Stock Exchanges, 1962 to present; over-the-counter stocks, 1968 to present; domestic and foreign trade directories; city directories; telephone directories for New England and U.S. cities with populations over 100,000 for New England cities and towns; Standard Stock Market Service, 1921-1922; Standard Stock Offerings, 1925-1939; National Stock Summary, 1927 to present; Standard & Poor's Stock Guide, 1943 to present; New York and American Stock Exchange companies Annual and 10K reports on microfiche (1987-1996); Wall Street Journal on microfilm (latest 10 years); Wall Street Transcript on microfilm (latest 5 years); D-U-N-S Business Identification Service (November 1973-1995).

30232 ■ Carnegie Library of Pittsburgh Downtown & Business

612 Smithfield St.
Pittsburgh, PA 15222
Ph: (412)281-7141
URL: http://www.carnegielibrary.org/clp_location/downtown-business
Contact: Andrew Medlar, President

Scope: Local history. **Services:** Library open to the public. **Founded:** 1924. **Holdings:** Books; magazines; CD-ROMs; videos.

30233 ■ Chicago Public Library Central Library - Business/Science/Technology Division

400 S State St.
Chicago, IL 60605
URL: http://www.chipublib.org/resources/science-technology

Scope: Small business; marketing; technology; sciences; computer science; careers and environmental information. **Services:** Interlibrary loan; library open to the public. **Founded:** 1977. **Holdings:** Figures not available.

30234 ■ University of Kentucky - Business & Economics Information Center

105 Main Bldg.
  Lexington, KY 40506-0132
URL: http://gatton.uky.edu

Description: Center that provides various programs involving business strategies and ideas about the economy. **Scope:** Business, economics, business management, marketing, finance, accounting. **Services:** Library open to the public for reference use only. **Founded:** 1993.

RESEARCH CENTERS

30235 ■ Wayne State College - Nebraska Business Development Center (NBDC)

1111 Main St.
  Wayne, NE 68787
Ph: (402)375-7575
Fax: (402)375-7574
Co. E-mail: nbdc@wsc.edu
URL: http://www.wsc.edu/info/20372/partnerships/
  114/nebraska_business_development_center

Contact: Loren Kucera, Director
E-mail: lokucer1@wsc.edu

Description: A cooperative program of the U.S. Small Business Administration and Wayne State College. Offers consulting services. **Scope:** Management education, market research, marketing plans, strategic planning, financial planning, cash flow budgeting, capital budgeting, loan packaging, and rural development. **Founded:** 1977. **Publications:** *NBDC Brochure*; *NBDC Business Calendar* (Annual). **Educational Activities:** NBDC Continuing education program.

START-UP INFORMATION

30236 ■ *"Breaking Barriers" in Baltimore Business Journal (Vol. 30, June 29, 2012, No. 8, pp. 1)*
Ed: Jack Lambert. **Description:** Many Hispanic entrepreneurs have been struggling to start businesses in Baltimore, Maryland. Many necessary documents are available only in English. Hispanic businesses are seen to spark future economic growth in Baltimore. **Availability:** Print; Online.

ASSOCIATIONS AND OTHER ORGANIZATIONS

30237 ■ **African American Entrepreneurs Association (AAEA)**
601 Innovation Way
Daytona Beach, FL 32114
Ph: (386)234-2014
Free: 800-671-1397
Fax: (386)675-0605
Co. E-mail: info@aaeassociation.org
URL: http://www.aaeassociation.org
Contact: Leslie F. Giscombe, MBA, Chief Executive Officer
Description: Seeks to develop and create economic development through entrepreneurship within the underserved African American community through education, mentoring, workshops, group economics, and micro-financing opportunities. **Founded:** 2018.

30238 ■ **Airport Minority Advisory Council (AMAC)**
45 L St. SW
Washington, DC 20024
Ph: (703)414-2622
Co. E-mail: info@amac-org.com
URL: http://www.amac-org.com
Contact: Simeon Terry, Vice Chairman of the Board
Facebook: www.facebook.com/AirportMinorityA dvisoryCouncil
Linkedin: www.linkedin.com/company/airport-minority -advisory-council
X (Twitter): x.com/AMAC_ORG
Instagram: www.instagram.com/amac_org
YouTube: www.youtube.com/channel/UCKDJh --0mbVOvNltAz9vSiQ
Description: Advocates for equal opportunity for minorities and women in airport contracting and employment. **Founded:** 1984. **Publications:** *AMAC-ESP Informational Brochure*. **Educational Activities:** Annual Airport Business Diversity Conference (Annual). **Awards:** Airport AEC Award (Annual); Airport Concessions Innovation and Inclusion Award (Annual); AMAC Award of the Organization (Annual); AMAC Hall of Fame Award (Annual). **Geographic Preference:** National.

30239 ■ **American Tamil Entrepreneurs Association (ATEA)**
691 S Milpitas Blvd.
Milpitas, CA 95035
Co. E-mail: contact@ateausa.org
URL: http://ateausa.org
Contact: Prabhakar Murugiah, President
Facebook: www.facebook.com/ateausa
Linkedin: www.linkedin.com/company/ateausa
X (Twitter): x.com/ateausa
YouTube: www.youtube.com/channel/UCKwZI0 _HrqN00Nv1lySmYIA
Description: Fosters entrepreneurship among members of Tamil community in the United States. Offers entrepreneurial events, networking opportunities, and mentorship programs. **Founded:** 2016.

30240 ■ **Arab American Business Women's Council (AABWC)**
22952 Outer Dr.
Dearborn, MI 48124
Ph: (313)277-1986
Co. E-mail: info@aawbc.org
URL: http://www.aawbc.org
Contact: Taharah Saad, President
E-mail: tsaad@aawbc.org
Facebook: www.facebook.com/aawbcorg
Linkedin: www.linkedin.com/company/arab-american -women's-business-council
X (Twitter): x.com/aawbc
Instagram: www.instagram.com/aawbc
YouTube: www.youtube.com/channel/ UCpwOZRakfrgL4bT7FY-HeNg
Description: Aims to bring together Arab American business women of diverse disciplines and industries. Addresses the needs of Arab American women professionals and business owners. Assists members by providing mentorships, internships, scholarships and professional development programs. **Founded:** 2007. **Geographic Preference:** National.

30241 ■ **Asian American Journalists Association (AAJA)**
5 3rd St., Ste. 1108
San Francisco, CA 94103
Ph: (202)729-8383
Co. E-mail: support@aaja.org
URL: http://www.aaja.org
Contact: Michelle Lee, President
Facebook: www.facebook.com/AAJAHQ
Linkedin: www.linkedin.com/company/aaja
X (Twitter): x.com/aaja
Instagram: www.instagram.com/aajaofficial
Description: A professional membership association working toward the visibility and inclusion of Asian Americans and Pacific Islander (AAPI) journalists in newsroom leadership and toward equitable and accurate coverage of AAPIs and AAPI issues. **Founded:** 1981. **Publications:** *Directory of Asian American Journalists*. **Educational Activities:** Journalism Opportunities Conference (Annual). **Awards:** AAJA National Journalism Awards (Annual); AAJA Special Recognition Award (Annual); AAJA Lifetime Achievement Award (Annual); Dr. Suzanne Ahn Award (Irregular). **Geographic Preference:** National.

30242 ■ **Asian Women in Business (AWIB) - Library**
125 Lafayette St.
New York, NY 10013
Co. E-mail: info@awib-sc.org
URL: http://www.awib-sc.org
Instagram: www.instagram.com/ asianwomeninbusiness
Description: Asian-American women in business. Seeks to enable Asian-American women to achieve their entrepreneurial potential. Serves as a clearinghouse on issues affecting small business owners; provides technical assistance and other support to members; sponsors business and entrepreneurial education courses. **Scope:** Women; business; Asian American. **Services:** Library open to the public for reference use. **Founded:** 1995. **Holdings:** Articles. **Awards:** AWIB Entrepreneurial Leadership Award (Annual). **Geographic Preference:** National; Regional.

30243 ■ **Association of African Entrepreneurs-USA, Inc. (AAE-USA)**
Milwaukee, WI 53233
Co. E-mail: info@aaeusa.org
URL: http://www.aaeusa.org
Description: Works to create the voice of change and a membership platform for dialogue about entrepreneurship and social impact investment among the African Diaspora and entrepreneurs living in the USA.

30244 ■ **Atlanta Business League (ABL)**
931 Martin Luther King Jr., Dr. NW
Atlanta, GA 30314
Ph: (404)584-8126
Fax: (404)584-0445
URL: http://atlantabusinessleague.org
Contact: Leona Barr-Davenport, President
Facebook: www.facebook.com/Atlan taBusinessLeague
Linkedin: www.linkedin.com/company/2884258
X (Twitter): x.com/ABL1933
Instagram: www.instagram.com/abl1933
YouTube: www.youtube.com/user/ABLTV1933
Geographic Preference: Local.

30245 ■ **Backstage Capital**
6121 Sunset Blvd.
Los Angeles, CA 90028
URL: http://backstagecapital.com
Contact: Arlan Hamilton, Founder Managing Partner
X (Twitter): x.com/Backstage_Cap
Description: Invests in startups owned by people of color, women, and the LGBT community. **Founded:** 2015.

30246 ■ **BaMa**
1425 Justin Rd., Ste. 300
Lewisville, TX 75077-2182
Contact: Stephen Bentley, Director

Description: Seeks to bridge the investment gap in minority-led startups as well as startups targeting minority-driven markets by educating investors and introducing them to candidate startups.

30247 ■ Base Ventures
Berkeley, CA
Co. E-mail: hello@base.ventures
URL: http://www.base.ventures
Contact: Erik Moore, Managing Director Co-Founder
Linkedin: www.linkedin.com/company/baseventures
X (Twitter): x.com/basevc
Description: Venture capital and private equity fund investing in technology companies. **Founded:** 2013.

30248 ■ Black Business Association (BBA)
PO Box 43159
Los Angeles, CA 90043
Ph: (323)291-9334
Fax: (323)291-7820
Co. E-mail: mail@bbala.org
URL: http://www.bbala.org
Contact: Sarah R. Harris, President
Facebook: www.facebook.com/
BlackBusinessAssociation
Linkedin: www.linkedin.com/in/black-business
-association-3790a0b9
X (Twitter): x.com/BBANews
Instagram: www.instagram.com/
blackbusinessassociation
YouTube: www.youtube.com/user/
BlackBusinessAssoc
Description: Represents the interests of black-owned business entrepreneurs. **Founded:** 1970. **Geographic Preference:** Local.

30249 ■ Black Business and Professional Association (BBPA)
180 Elm St.
Toronto, ON, Canada M5T 3M4
Ph: (416)504-4097
Co. E-mail: info@bbpa.org
URL: http://bbpa.org
Contact: Camille Stewart Edwards, Treasurer
Facebook: www.facebook.com/thebbpa
X (Twitter): x.com/thebbpa
Instagram: www.instagram.com/thebbpa
YouTube: www.youtube.com/channel/UCOnNI7
_YWYyyW85KkJwvTtw
Description: Canadian businesspeople and professionals of African descent. Seeks to end discrimination in business, employment, education, housing, policing, political representation, and immigration. Provides assistance to young adults attempting to enter business or the professions. Serves as a unified voice speaking for members on business and economic issues. Facilitates networking among members; conducts community outreach programs; sponsors social activities. Makes available continuing professional education programs for members. **Founded:** 1983. **Awards:** Beverley Mascoll Scholarship (Annual); BBPA Specialty Scholarships - LGBTQ Scholarship (Annual); BBPA Specialty Scholarships - Skilled Trades Scholarship (Annual); BBPA Future Leaders Scholarships (Annual); Xero Scholarship (Annual); Kindred Foundation Scholarship (Annual); Canadian Public Relations Society Foundation Scholarship (Annual); Ned and Myrna Blair Scholarship (Annual); APW African Canadian Youth Scholarship (Annual); Connor, Clark & Lunn Financial Group Scholarship (Annual); TD Bank Scholarships (Annual); Christeen Ross Julien Scholarship (Annual); Dr. Anderson Abbott Scholarship (Annual); Mejuri Scholarship Fund (Annual); Denham Jolly Scholarship (Annual); Hon. Lincoln Alexander Scholarship (Annual); Robert K. Brown Scholarships (Annual); Herb Carnegie Scholarship (Annual); Fraser Milner Casgrain LLP Scholarships (Annual); Harry Gairey Scholarship (Annual); Canadian Medical Foundation Bursary for Black Medical Students (Annual); Toronto Community Housing/Leaders of Tomorrow Scholarships (Annual); Lucille May Gopie Scholarships (Annual); Guntley-Lorimer Science and Arts Scholarships (Annual); Al Hamilton Scholarship (Annual); Hon. Michaelle Jean Scholarship (Annual); Harry Jerome Legacy Scholarship (Annual); Minerva Scholarships

(Annual); Royal Bank Scholarships (Annual); Portia White Scholarship (Annual); BBPA First Generation Scholarships (Annual); Robert Sutherland/Harry Jerome Entrance Award (Annual). **Geographic Preference:** National.

30250 ■ Black Career Women's Network (BCWN)
Cincinnati, OH
Ph: (513)729-9724
URL: http://bcwnetwork.com
Contact: Sherry Sims, Chief Executive Officer
Facebook: www.facebook.com/BCWNetwork
Linkedin: www.linkedin.com/company/bcwnetwork
X (Twitter): x.com/bcwnetwork
Instagram: www.instagram.com/bcwnetwork
Description: A national career development organization dedicated to fostering the professional growth of black women. **Founded:** 2012.

30251 ■ Black Connect
27251 Wesley Chapel Blvd., Ste. B14, No. 747
Wesley Chapel, FL 33544
Ph: (813)405-5918
Co. E-mail: info@blackconnect.org
URL: http://www.blackconnect.org
Contact: Angela Majette, President
Description: Strives to eliminate racial wealth gap in America by increasing the number and success rate of Black-owned businesses. Provides business-related educational programs, activities, events, and financial assistance to Black individuals, entrepreneurs, and business owners. **Founded:** 2019.

30252 ■ Black Entrepreneurs
PO Box 775295
Saint Louis, MO 63177-5295
Ph: (314)585-6010
Co. E-mail: be@blackentrepreneursinc.org
URL: http://blackentrepreneursinc.org
Contact: Jared S. Jenkins, President
Description: Seeks to cultivate and promote the entrepreneurial spirit of the Black community. Offers study abroad opportunities to future entrepreneurs who are pursuing either an undergraduate and/or graduate degree. **Founded:** 2014.

30253 ■ Black Innovation Alliance (BIA)
1954 Airport Rd., No.1107
Atlanta, GA 30341
Ph: (404)399-9506
Co. E-mail: info@blackinnovationalliance.com
URL: http://blackinnovationalliance.com
Contact: Hermione Malone, President
Facebook: www.facebook.com/buildwithbia
Linkedin: www.linkedin.com/company/buildwithbia
X (Twitter): x.com/buildwithbia
Instagram: www.instagram.com/buildwithbia
Description: Coalition of innovator support organizations focused on creating pathways to black prosperity and empowerment. Seeks to close "the racial wealth gap through the direct support of Black-led innovator support organizations in service to Black entrepreneurs, tech founders and creative technologists.". **Founded:** 2020.

30254 ■ Black Women Business Owners of America (BWBO)
36 E Cameron St., No. 15
Tulsa, OK 74103
Ph: (539)302-2686
Co. E-mail: info@bwboamerica.com
URL: http://www.bwboamerica.com
Contact: Tashia Sumpter, President
Facebook: www.facebook.com/bwboamerica
Linkedin: www.linkedin.com/company/bwboamerica
Instagram: www.instagram.com/bwbo_america
Description: Supports African American women business owners, entrepreneurs, and startup founders across the United States by providing tools, resources, and knowledge needed to grow successful businesses. **Founded:** 2018.

30255 ■ Capital Region Minority Supplier Development Council (CRMSDC)
10750 Columbia Pke., Ste. 200
Silver Spring, MD 20901

Ph: (301)593-5860
Co. E-mail: crmsdc@crmsdc.org
URL: http://crmsdc2.wpengine.com
Contact: Sharon R. Pinder, President
E-mail: sharon.pinder@crmsdc.org
Facebook: www.facebook.com/CRMSDC
Linkedin: www.linkedin.com/company/capi
talregionmsdc
X (Twitter): x.com/crmsdc
Instagram: www.instagram.com/crmsdc
YouTube: www.youtube.com/channel/UCRuQ-5o8jf
d_o43jXwnmuzg
Description: Provides a direct link between corporate America and minority-owned businesses. Increases procurement and business opportunities for minority businesses of all sizes. **Founded:** 1972. **Geographic Preference:** Regional.

30256 ■ The Caribbean American Chamber of Commerce & Industry Inc. (CACCI)
2121 Caton Ave.
Brooklyn, NY 11226
Co. E-mail: caccimembership@outlook.com
URL: http://www.caribbeantradecenter.com
Contact: Harry J. Fouche, Chairman (Acting)
Description: Provides small business assistance in New York City. Promotes trade and tourism in the Caribbean. **Founded:** 1985. **Geographic Preference:** National.

30257 ■ ColorComm: Women of Color in Communications
Washington, DC
Co. E-mail: membership@colorcommnetwork.com
URL: http://www.colorcommnetwork.com
Contact: Natalie Boden, Chief Executive Officer
Facebook: www.facebook.com/ColorComm
Linkedin: www.linkedin.com/company/colorcomm-inc
Instagram: www.instagram.com/colorcomm
Description: Supports professional women of color in all areas of communications, including public relations, corporate communications, advertising, media relations, and political communications. Seeks to foster a strong network of leaders by creating mentors/mentees, business relationships, and friendships. **Founded:** 2011.

30258 ■ Council for Supplier Diversity (CSD)
10679 Westview Pky.
San Diego, CA 92126
Ph: (858)537-2281
Fax: (858)537-2286
Co. E-mail: info@supplierdiversitysd.org
URL: http://councilforsupplierdiversity.org
Contact: Ronald B. Garnett, President
Facebook: www.facebook.com/
CouncilforSupplierDiversity
Linkedin: www.linkedin.com/company/
councilforsupplierdiversity
X (Twitter): twitter.com/CouncilforSD
Description: Provides a direct link between corporate America and minority-owned businesses. Increases procurement and business opportunities for minority businesses of all sizes. **Founded:** 1999. **Geographic Preference:** Local.

30259 ■ CSRA Business League Inc.
821 12th St.
Augusta, GA 30901
Ph: (706)722-0994
Fax: (706)722-3115
Co. E-mail: administrativeassistant@business-league
.org
URL: http://business-league.org
Contact: Ellis B. Albright, President
Facebook: www.facebook.com/CsraBusinessLeague
Description: Firm offers networking events and virtual seminars. Black-owned. **Founded:** 1970.

30260 ■ Cuban American National Council (CNC)
1223 SW 4th St.
Miami, FL 33135
Ph: (305)642-3484
Fax: (305)642-9122
URL: http://cnc.org
Contact: Gabriela Musiet, President

E-mail: gmusiet@cnc.org
Facebook: www.facebook.com/CNCorg
X (Twitter): x.com/cncorg
YouTube: www.youtube.com/user/cncutube
Description: Aims to identify the socioeconomic needs of the Cuban population in the US. and to offer needed human services. Services those in need through research and human services while advocating on behalf of Hispanics and other minority groups. **Founded:** 1972. **Publications:** *The Council Letter* (Quarterly). **Geographic Preference:** National.

30261 ■ Detroit Chinese Business Association (DCBA)
3250 W Big Beaver Rd., Ste. 430
  Troy, MI 48084
URL: http://dcba.com
Contact: Andrew L. Gutman, President
Facebook: www.facebook.com/Detroi
tChineseBusinessAssociation
X (Twitter): x.com/DetroitCBA
Instagram: www.instagram.com/dcba_michigan
Description: Fosters beneficial business relationship between Chinese and American business. Serves as a catalyst to promote entrepreneurship within the Chinese American community. **Founded:** 1995. **Publications:** *DCBA Online* (Monthly). **Geographic Preference:** Local.

30262 ■ digitalundivided
261 Madison Ave., Fl., 9, Ste. 1040
  New York, NY 10016
Co. E-mail: talk@digitalundivided.com
URL: http://digitalundivided.com
Contact: Rodrigo Zavala, President
Facebook: www.facebook.com/digitalundivided
Linkedin: www.linkedin.com/company/digitalundivided
X (Twitter): x.com/digundiv
Instagram: www.instagram.com/digitalundivided
Description: Assists Black and Latino women entrepreneurs with venture funding and providing opportunities via innovation and technology. **Founded:** 2012.

30263 ■ Diversity Information Resources, Inc. (DIR)
2300 Kennedy St. NE, Ste. 230
  Minneapolis, MN 55413
Ph: (612)781-6819
Co. E-mail: info@diversityinforesources.com
URL: http://www.diversityinforesources.com
Contact: Leslie Bonds, President
E-mail: lbonds@diversityinforesources.com
Facebook: www.facebook.com/DiversityInforma
tionResources
X (Twitter): x.com/diversity411
YouTube: www.youtube.com/channel/UCFikCMXHK
2fca1zBDygfyOw
Pinterest: www.pinterest.com/dirmarketing
Description: Promotes businesses with minority, women, veteran, service-disabled veteran and HUB-Zone ownership. Compiles and publishes minority and women-owned business directories to acquaint major corporations and government purchasing agents with the products and services of minority and women-owned firms. Sponsors national supplier diversity seminars. **Founded:** 1968. **Publications:** *Purchasing People in Major Corporations* (Annual); *Supplier Diversity Contacts* (Annual); *National Minority and Women-Owned Business Directory* (Annual); *The Business of Supplier Diversity: A Handbook of Essential Contacts and Information for Navigating the Industry* (Annual); *TRY US National Women-Owned Business Directory*; *Guide to Obtaining Minority Business Directories*. **Geographic Preference:** National.

30264 ■ Dreamit Ventures
33 Irving Pl., 10th Fl.
  New York, NY 10003
Co. E-mail: info@dreamit.com
URL: http://www.dreamit.com
Contact: Brittany Gillow, Director
Facebook: www.facebook.com/dreamitventures
Linkedin: www.linkedin.com/company/dreamit-ven
tures
X (Twitter): x.com/dreamit
YouTube: www.youtube.com/user/DreamItVentures

Description: Business incubator supporting entrepreneurs by providing seed, early venture, and late stage venture investing. **Founded:** 2008.

30265 ■ The Executive Leadership Council (ELC)
1301 K St. NW, Ste. 210 W
  Washington, DC 20005
Ph: (202)655-2952
Co. E-mail: elcinfo@elcinfo.com
URL: http://www.elcinfo.com
Contact: Michael C. Hyter, President
Facebook: www.facebook.com/elcinfo
Linkedin: www.linkedin.com/company/elcinfo
X (Twitter): x.com/elcinfo
Instagram: www.instagram.com/elcinfo
YouTube: www.youtube.com/user/elcinfo1
Description: Provides senior African-American corporate executives with a network and leadership forum that adds perspective and direction to the achievement of excellence in business, economic and public policies for the African-American community and its corporations, and the community at large. Conducts educational and research programs. **Founded:** 1986. **Publications:** *Contact* (Quarterly). **Educational Activities:** CEO Game Changer Conference; The Executive Leadership Council Recognition Dinner (Annual). **Awards:** Executive Leadership Foundation Achievement Award (Annual); Executive Leadership Foundation Corporate Award (Annual); Alvaro L. Martins Heritage Award (Annual). **Geographic Preference:** National.

30266 ■ Filipino Chamber of Commerce
PO Box 1572
  Honolulu, HI 96806
Ph: (808)755-9229
Co. E-mail: filipinochamber@gmail.com
URL: http://filipinochamber.org
Contact: Rose Galanto, President
Description: Supports Filipino-based businesses and events. Organizes activities and events to provide networking opportunities. Publishes a newsletter and directory.

30267 ■ Ford Minority Dealers Association (FMDA)
PO Box 760386
  Southfield, MI 48075
Ph: (248)557-2500
Free: 866-559-1732
URL: http://fordmda.com
Contact: Dr. A. V. Fleming, Executive Director
E-mail: deedee0914@aol.com
Description: Minority-owned car dealerships. Promotes professional standards of minority dealerships. Strives to increase the number of minority dealerships. **Founded:** 1980. **Geographic Preference:** National.

30268 ■ Founders First Capital Partners (FFCP)
9920 Pacific Heights Blvd., Ste. 430
  San Diego, CA 92121
Ph: (858)264-4102
Co. E-mail: info@f1stcp.com
URL: http://foundersfirstcapitalpartners.com
Contact: Kim T. Folsom, Chief Executive Officer
Facebook: www.facebook.com/f1stcp
Linkedin: www.linkedin.com/company/founders-firs
t-capital-partners
X (Twitter): x.com/f1stcp
Instagram: www.instagram.com/f1stcp
YouTube: www.youtube.com/channel/UCa
dqC8UNVFH0c_6NBdkE-hA
Description: Venture capital firm providing support to startup companies owned by minorities, women, and military veterans. **Founded:** 2015.

30269 ■ Funding Circle Limited (FCL)
85 2nd St., Ste. 400
  San Francisco, CA 94105
Co. E-mail: loanquestions@fundingcircle.com
URL: http://fundingcircle.com/us
Contact: Lisa Jacobs, Chief Executive Officer
Facebook: www.facebook.com/FundingCircleUS
X (Twitter): twitter.com/FundingCircleUS

YouTube: www.youtube.com/channel/UCOD52xlde
5wG8qMJNN_9YaA
Description: A small business loans platform, matching small businesses who want to borrow with investors who want to lend in the U.K., U.S., Germany, and the Netherlands. **Founded:** 2010.

30270 ■ Harlem Capital Partners (HCP)
1180 Ave. Of The Americas, 8Th Fl.
  New York, NY 10036
Co. E-mail: info@harlem.capital
URL: http://harlem.capital
Contact: Melody Hahm, Director
E-mail: melody@harlem.capital
X (Twitter): x.com/HarlemCapital
Description: Venture capital firm focusing on minority-owned startup companies. **Founded:** 2015.

30271 ■ Humble Ventures
Washington, DC
URL: http://humble.vc
Contact: Ajit Verghese, Co-Founder
X (Twitter): x.com/humbleventures
Description: Venture capital firm focusing on startup businesses owned by women and minority groups.

30272 ■ Investment Company Institute (ICI) - Library
1401 H St. NW, Ste. 1200
  Washington, DC 20005
Ph: (202)326-5800
Co. E-mail: memberservices@ici.org
URL: http://www.ici.org
Contact: Eric J. Pan, President
Facebook: www.facebook.com/ici.org
X (Twitter): x.com/ici
YouTube: www.youtube.com/user/ICIVideo
Description: Represents open-end and closed-end investment companies registered under Investment Company Act of 1940; investment advisers to, and underwriters of, such companies; unit investment trust sponsors; interested others. **Scope:** Legislation, taxation, regulation, economic research marketing, small business, public information. **Founded:** 1940. **Holdings:** Figures not available. **Publications:** *The Investment Compant Service Directory* (Annual); *Trends in Mutual Fund Activity* (Monthly); *National Association of Investment Companies--Membership Directory* (Annual); *ICI Membership Directory* (Semi-annual). **Educational Activities:** Annual General Membership Meeting (GMM) (Annual). **Geographic Preference:** National.

30273 ■ Latin Business Association (LBA)
888 S Figueroa St., Ste. 1730
  Los Angeles, CA 90017
Ph: (213)628-8510
Co. E-mail: membership@lbausa.com
URL: http://lbausa.com
Contact: Ruben Guerra, Chairman of the Board
E-mail: rguerra@lbausa.com
Facebook: www.facebook.com/LBAUSA
X (Twitter): x.com/LBA
Description: Latino business owners and corporations. Assists Latino business owners to develop their businesses. **Founded:** 1975. **Publications:** *Latin Business Association Business Journal* (Weekly); *Latin Business Association Business Newsletter* (Monthly). **Awards:** LBA Sol Business Awards - Business of the Year; LBA Sol Business Awards - Corporation of the Year; LBA Sol Business Awards - Advocate of the Year (Annual). **Geographic Preference:** National.

30274 ■ MaC Venture Capital
6255 Sunset Blvd.
  Los Angeles, CA 90028
URL: http://macventurecapital.com
Contact: Adrian Fenty, Managing Partner
Linkedin: www.linkedin.com/company/mac-venture
-capital
X (Twitter): x.com/MaCVentureCap
Instagram: www.instagram.com/macventurecap
Description: Early stage venture capital firm investing in minority-owned tech companies. **Founded:** 2019.

30275 ■ Midwest Minority Supplier Development Council (MMSDC)

111 3rd Ave. S, Ste. 375
  Minneapolis, MN 55401-2579
Contact: Heather N. Olson, President

Description: Provides a direct link between corporate America and minority-owned businesses. Increases procurement and business opportunities for minority businesses of all sizes. **Founded:** 1975. **Geographic Preference:** State.

30276 ■ Milton S. Eisenhower Foundation

1875 Connecticut Ave. NW, Ste. 410
  Washington, DC 20009
Ph: (202)234-8104
Fax: (202)234-8484
Co. E-mail: info@eisenhowerfoundation.org
URL: http://www.eisenhowerfoundation.org/aboutus/mission.html
Contact: Alan Curtis, President

Description: Dedicated to youth investment and economic development in the inner city by reducing the school dropout rate, crime, welfare dependency, drug abuse, unemployment, and family instability. Works as a "mediating institution" to finance, technically assist, and evaluate minority nonprofit organizations. **Founded:** 1981. **Geographic Preference:** National.

30277 ■ Minority Cannabis Business Association (MCBA)

805 SW Broadway, Ste. 2400
  Portland, OR 97205
Ph: (202)681-2889
Co. E-mail: info@minoritycannabis.org
URL: http://minoritycannabis.org
Contact: Kaliko Castille, President
Facebook: www.facebook.com/MCBA.org
X (Twitter): x.com/MinCannBusAssoc
Instagram: www.instagram.com/minoritycannabis

Description: Seeks to serve the specific needs of minority cannabis entrepreneurs, workers, and patients/consumers across the United States. Advocates for the creation and fair enforcement of sensible policies. Aims to act as an economic accelerator and creator of opportunity, and to improve critical social and health measures of all communities. **Founded:** 2015.

30278 ■ Minority Christian Women Entrepreneurs Network (MCWEN)

10 E N Ave., Ste. 5
  Baltimore, MD 21202
Ph: (443)203-8741
Co. E-mail: mcwenetwork@gmail.com
URL: http://www.mcwen.org
Contact: Andrena Sawyer, Executive Director
Facebook: www.facebook.com/MCWENetwork
Linkedin: www.linkedin.com/company/mcwen
X (Twitter): x.com/mcwe_network
Instagram: www.instagram.com/mcwe_network

Description: Christian organization for women of color who have an interest in entrepreneurship and business ownership. **Founded:** 2019.

30279 ■ National 8(a) Association

1200 G St. NW, Ste. 800
  Washington, DC 20005
Ph: (202)286-0557
Co. E-mail: info@national8aassociation.org
URL: http://www.national8aassociation.org
Facebook: www.facebook.com/National8a
Linkedin: www.linkedin.com/company/national-8-a-association
X (Twitter): x.com/national_8a

Description: Provides education and guidance for 8(a) businesses -- a classification based on the Small Business Administration (SBA) 8(a) Business Development Program for businesses that are owned and controlled at least 51% by socially and economically disadvantaged individuals. Seeks to educate and promote members, to advocate favorable legislation policies, and to serve and support the effectiveness and continuance of the 8(a) program. **Founded:** 2000.

30280 ■ National Association of Black Accountants, Inc. (NABA)

7474 Greenway Center Dr., Ste. 1120
  Greenbelt, MD 20770
Ph: (301)474-6222
Co. E-mail: customerservice@nabainc.org
URL: http://nabainc.org
Contact: Guylaine Saint Juste, President
Facebook: www.facebook.com/NABAInc
Linkedin: www.linkedin.com/company/nabainc
X (Twitter): x.com/nabainc
YouTube: www.youtube.com/user/NABAInc

Description: Represents minority students and professionals currently working, or interested in the fields of accounting, finance, technology, consulting or general business. Seeks, promotes, develops, and represents the interests of current and future minority business professionals. **Founded:** 1969. **Publications:** *Achieve* (Semiannual); *Spectrum* (Semiannual); *Spectrum* (Semiannual); *National Association of Black Accountants--News Plus* (Quarterly). **Educational Activities:** NABA National Convention & Expo (Annual). **Awards:** NABA National Scholarship Program (Annual). **Geographic Preference:** National; Local.

30281 ■ National Association of Black Journalists (NABJ)

1100 Knight Hall, Ste. 3101
  College Park, MD 20742
Ph: (301)405-0248
Co. E-mail: contact@nabj.org
URL: http://nabjonline.org
Contact: Dorothy Tucker, President
Facebook: www.facebook.com/NABJOfficial
Linkedin: www.linkedin.com/company/national-association-of-black-journalists-nabj
X (Twitter): x.com/NABJ
Instagram: www.instagram.com/nabjofficial
YouTube: www.youtube.com/user/NABJOfficial

Description: Offers innovative training, career advancement opportunities and advocacy initiatives for Black journalists and media professionals worldwide. **Founded:** 1975. **Publications:** *NABJ Update*. **Awards:** Ida B. Wells Award (Annual); NABJ Hall of Fame (Annual); NABJ Special Honors Awards (Annual); NABJ Salute to Excellence Awards (Annual); NABJ Special Honors (Annual). **Geographic Preference:** National.

30282 ■ National Association of Black Owned Broadcasters (NABOB) [National Black Owned Broadcasters Association]

1001 Conn. Ave., NW, Ste. 504
  Washington, DC 20036
Ph: (202)463-8970
Co. E-mail: info@usbcnetwork.com
URL: http://nabob.org
Contact: Jim Winston, President
E-mail: jwinston@nabob.org

Description: Black broadcast station owners; black formatted stations not owned or controlled by blacks; organizations having an interest in the black consumer market or black broadcast industry; individuals interested in becoming owners; and communications schools, departments and professional groups and associations. Works with the Office of Federal Procurement Policy to determine which government contracting major advertisers and advertising agencies are complying with government initiatives to increase the amount of advertising dollars received by minority-owned firms. Conducts lobbying activities; provides legal representation for the protection of minority ownership policies. Sponsors annual Communications Awards Dinner each March. Publishes to improve and increase the opportunities for success for black and minority owners in the broadcast industry. **Founded:** 1976. **Publications:** *Black Owned Station Directory* (Quarterly); *NABOB News*. **Geographic Preference:** National.

30283 ■ National Association of Black Women in Construction, Inc. (NABWIC)

c/o Ann McNeill, Founder
  6600 NW 27th Ave. No. 208
  Haverhill, FL 33417

URL: http://nabwic.org

Description: Promotes the advancement of black women in the construction industry. Supports aspiring construction executives. Provides advocacy, mentorship and professional development for its members. **Founded:** 1991. **Geographic Preference:** National.

30284 ■ National Association of Hispanic Publications, Inc. (NAHP)

National Press Bldg.
  529 14th St. NW, Ste. 923
  Washington, DC 20045
URL: http://nahp.org
Contact: Álvaro Gurdián, President
Facebook: www.facebook.com/NAHPofficial

Description: Promotes adherence to high standards of ethical and professional standards by members; advocates continuing professional development of Hispanic journalists and publishers. Provides technical assistance to members in areas including writing and editing skills, circulation and distribution methods, attracting advertisers, obtaining financing, design and layout, and graphic arts. Conducts public service programs including voter registration drives. **Founded:** 1982. **Publications:** *The Hispanic Press* (Quarterly). **Educational Activities:** NAHP Annual Convention (Annual). **Geographic Preference:** National.

30285 ■ National Association of Minority Automobile Dealers (NAMAD)

9475 Lottsford Rd., Ste. 150
  Largo, MD 20774
Ph: (301)306-1614
Fax: (301)306-1493
URL: http://namad.org
Contact: Fernando Varela, Chairman
Facebook: www.facebook.com/namadusa
YouTube: www.youtube.com/user/NAMADVIDEOS

Description: To better the business conditions of its members on an ongoing basis. Serves as a confidential spokesperson for dealers. Offers business analysis, financial counseling, and short- and long-term management planning. Conducts research programs; compiles statistics. **Founded:** 1980. **Publications:** *NAMAD Newsletter*. **Geographic Preference:** National.

30286 ■ National Association of Minority Companies Inc. (NAMCO)

848 N Rainbow Blvd., Ste. 5041
  Las Vegas, NV 89107
Free: 877-848-1008
Fax: (855)210-3729
Co. E-mail: info@namcodiversity.org
URL: http://www.namcodiversity.org
Contact: Rodney Thompson, President

Description: Works to promote access to funding and contracts for diverse businesses. Promotes leadership opportunities for members. Assists members with business plans, lending and financial management, procurement and contracting, marketing, and other business development needs. Provides internships to students and recent graduates.

30287 ■ National Association of Minority Contractors (NAMC)

The Barr Bldg. 910 17st St., NW, Ste. 413
  Washington, DC 20006
Ph: (202)296-1600
Co. E-mail: info@namcnational.org
URL: http://namcnational.org
Contact: Wendell R. Stemley, President
X (Twitter): x.com/namcnational

Description: Minority construction contractors and major corporations wishing to do business with minority contractors. Identifies procurement opportunities; provides specialized training; acts as national advocate for minority construction contractors. Holds workshops and seminars; compiles statistics. **Founded:** 1969. **Publications:** *Legislative Bulletin*; *Procurement Bulletin* (Periodic). **Educational Activities:** NAMC Annual National Conference (Annual). **Geographic Preference:** National.

30288 ■ National Association of Negro Business and Professional Women's Clubs, Inc. (NANBPWC)
1806 New Hampshire Ave. NW
   Washington, DC 20009
Ph: (202)483-4206
Fax: (202)462-7253
Co. E-mail: info@nanbpwc.org
URL: http://nanbpwc.org
Contact: Robin Waley, Executive Director
E-mail: executivedirector@nanbpwc.com
Facebook: www.facebook.com/NANBPWC
X (Twitter): x.com/NANBPWC
Instagram: www.instagram.com/nanbpwc
Description: African American women actively engaged in a business or a profession who are committed to rendering service through club programs and activities. Seeks to direct the interest of business and professional women toward united action for improved social and civic conditions, and to provide enriching and ennobling experiences that will encourage freedom, dignity, self-respect, and self-reliance. Offers information and help regarding education, employment, health, housing, legislation, and problems of the aged and the disabled. Sponsors educational assistance program, which includes local and national scholarships. Conducts consumer education and prison reform programs. Maintains youth department clubs. Provides placement services; operates speakers' bureau; compiles statistics. **Founded:** 1935. **Awards:** Dr. Julianne Malveaux Scholarship (Annual); The Dr. Blanca Moore-Velez Woman of Substance Scholarship (Annual); NANBPWC National Scholarship (Annual). **Geographic Preference:** National.

30289 ■ National Black Chamber of Commerce (NBCC)
601 Pennsylvania Ave. NW, Ste. 900, S Bldg.
   Washington, DC 20004
Ph: (202)220 3060
Co. E-mail: info@nationalbcc.org
URL: http://www.nationalbcc.org
Contact: Charles H. DeBow, III, President
Facebook: www.facebook.com/NationalBCC
X (Twitter): x.com/NationalBCC
YouTube: www.youtube.com/user/Nationalbcc
Description: Represents Black owned businesses. Seeks to empower and sustain African American communities through entrepreneurship and capitalistic activity. Provides advocacy, training and education to Black communities. **Founded:** 1993. **Publications:** *The Small Business Resource Guide.* **Geographic Preference:** Multinational; Local.

30290 ■ National Black MBA Association, Inc. (NBMBAA)
400 W Peachtree St. NW, Ste. 203
   Atlanta, GA 30308
Ph: (404)260-5444
Co. E-mail: help@nbmbaa.org
URL: http://nbmbaa.org
Contact: Joe Handy, President
Facebook: www.facebook.com/theblackmba
Linkedin: www.linkedin.com/company/theblackmba
X (Twitter): x.com/nbmbaahq
Instagram: www.instagram.com/theblackmba
Description: Creates educational opportunities to form professional and economic growth of African-Americans. Develops partnerships among its members and provides educational programs on business. **Founded:** 1970. **Geographic Preference:** Local.

30291 ■ National Black MBA Association Inc. - Chicago Chapter
PO Box 8513
   Chicago, IL 60680
Ph: (312)458-9161
Co. E-mail: partnerships@ccnbmbaa.org
URL: http://www.chicagochapternbmbaa.org
Contact: Stacy Crook, President
E-mail: scrook@ccnbmbaa.org
URL(s): nbmbaa.org/nbmbaa-chicago-chapter
Facebook: www.facebook.com/groups/
   chicagoblackmba

Linkedin: www.linkedin.com/company/national-black
   -mba-association-chicago-chapter
X (Twitter): x.com/chicagoblackmba
Instagram: www.instagram.com/nbmbaa
   _chicagochapter
Description: Creates educational opportunities to form professional and economic growth of African-Americans. Develops partnerships to its members and provides educational programs to increase the awareness on business field. **Founded:** 1970. **Publications:** *National Black MBA Association-Newsletter; Black MBA* (Semiannual). **Educational Activities:** NBMBAA Annual Conference and Exposition (Annual). **Awards:** CEIBS scholarship (Annual). **Geographic Preference:** Local; National.

30292 ■ National Hispanic Business Group (NHBG)
115 Broadway., 5th Fl.
   New York, NY 10006
Ph: (212)265-2664
Fax: (212)265-2675
Co. E-mail: info@nhbg.org
URL: http://www.nhbg.org
Contact: Marcelo D. Reggiardo, Chairman
E-mail: mreggiardo@alianzacorp.com
Description: Serves as a platform for Hispanic entrepreneurs to promote their businesses. Provides opportunities and partnerships to spur the growth of Hispanic business enterprises. **Founded:** 1985. **Geographic Preference:** National.

30293 ■ National Hispanic Business Women Association (NHBWA)
2020 N Broadway, Ste. 100
   Santa Ana, CA 92706
Contact: Patty Homo, Contact
Description: Seeks to empower and encourage Hispanic women and business owners to develop and increase their business by sponsoring educational seminars and speakers, offering mutual support, and promoting the sharing of information, business referrals, and networking. **Founded:** 1997.

30294 ■ National Hispanic Corporate Council (NHCC)
1050 Connecticut Ave. NW 5th Fl.
   Washington, DC 20036
Ph: (202)772-1100
Fax: (202)772-3101
Co. E-mail: membership@nhcchq.org
URL: http://www.nhcchq.org
Contact: Eduardo Arabu, Executive Director
E-mail: earabu@nhcchq.org
Facebook: www.facebook.com/NHCCHQ
Linkedin: www.linkedin.com/company/national
   -hispanic-corporation-council
X (Twitter): x.com/NHCCorg
YouTube: www.youtube.com/channel/UCx
   4UxOyCW714Z_o3ikvvAlw
Description: Aims to provide its member companies a multi-layered approach and resources to effectively maximize the diversity of the Hispanic market. **Scope:** Hispanic market; language; household trends; corporate America; consumer trends. **Founded:** 1985. **Publications:** *NHCC News* (Quarterly). **Educational Activities:** NHCC Annual Summit (Annual). **Geographic Preference:** National.

30295 ■ National Hispanic Media Coalition (NHMC)
12825 Philadelphia St.
   Whittier, CA 90601
Ph: (626)792-6462
Co. E-mail: info@nhmc.org
URL: http://www.nhmc.org
Contact: Brenda Victoria Castillo, President
Facebook: www.facebook.com/nhmc.org
X (Twitter): x.com/nhmc
Instagram: www.instagram.com/nhmc_org
YouTube: www.youtube.com/user/nhmcorg
Description: Promotes the employment and image of Hispanic Americans in radio, television, and film. **Founded:** 1986. **Publications:** *Positive Images* (Annual). **Awards:** NHMC Impact Awards (Annual). **Geographic Preference:** National.

30296 ■ National Latina Business Women Association (NLBWA)
1107 Fair Oaks Ave.
   South Pasadena, CA 91030
Co. E-mail: info@nlbwa-la.org
URL: http://www.nlbwa-la.org
Contact: Wendy Estrada, President
Facebook: www.facebook.com/NLBWALA
X (Twitter): x.com/NLBWALA
Instagram: www.instagram.com/nlbwala
YouTube: www.youtube.com/channel/UCN5W
   -t4KyLooVD6G_VLZumg
Description: Strives to promote, develop, and support the growth of Latina business owners and professionals. Seeks to create networking and mentoring opportunities for members. **Founded:** 2003. **Geographic Preference:** National.

30297 ■ National Minority Business Council (NMBC)
1120 Avenue of the Americas, Ste. 4179
   New York, NY 10036
Ph: (347)289-7620
Co. E-mail: info@nmbc.org
URL: http://www.nmbc.org
Contact: John F. Robinson, President
Facebook: www.facebook.com/NMBCinc
Linkedin: www.linkedin.com/company/nmbc1972
X (Twitter): x.com/nmbcny
YouTube: www.youtube.com/user/usnmbc
Description: Represents minority businesses in all areas of industry and commerce. Seeks to increase profitability by developing marketing, sales, and management skills in minority businesses. **Founded:** 1972. **Publications:** *NMBC Business Report; NMBC Business Report* (Biennial); *Business Directory; Corporate Purchasing Directory* (Annual). **Awards:** NMBC Luncheon Award. **Geographic Preference:** National.

30298 ■ National Minority Supplier Development Council (NMSDC)
1359 Broadway, 10th Fl., Ste. 1000
   New York, NY 10018
Ph: (212)944-2430
URL: http://nmsdc.org
Contact: Adrienne Trimble, Chief Executive Officer
Facebook: www.facebook.com/nmsdchq
Linkedin: www.linkedin.com/company/nmsdchq
X (Twitter): x.com/nmsdchq
Instagram: www.instagram.com/nmsdchq
YouTube: www.youtube.com/user/NMSDC
Description: Provides a direct link between its 3,500 corporate members and minority-owned businesses (Black, Hispanic, Asian and Native American) and increases procurement and business opportunities for minority businesses of all sizes. **Founded:** 1972. **Publications:** *Minority Business Information Center; Minority Supplier News* (Quarterly); *National Minority Supplier Development Council--Annual Report* (Annual). **Educational Activities:** Business Opportunity Fair (Annual). **Awards:** NMSDC Corporation of the Year (Annual). **Geographic Preference:** National.

30299 ■ National Sales Network (NSN)
3575 Piedmont Rd. NE, Bldg. 15, Ste. 1510
   Atlanta, GA 30305
Ph: (770)551-2734
Co. E-mail: admin@salesnetwork.org
URL: http://www.salesnetwork.org
Contact: Anthony Tuggle, President
Facebook: www.facebook.com/nsnhq
Linkedin: www.linkedin.com/company/national-sales
   -network-headquarters
X (Twitter): x.com/nsnhq
Instagram: www.instagram.com/NSNHQ
YouTube: www.youtube.com/user/SalesNetwork1992
Description: Strives to meet the professional and developmental needs of Black sales and sales management professionals and individuals who want to improve their professional sales skills. **Founded:** 1996.

30300 ■ Pipeline Angels
1321 Upland Dr., Ste. 5167
   Houston, TX 77043
Co. E-mail: info@pipelineangels.com

URL: http://pipelineangels.com
Contact: Natalia Oberti Noguera, Chief Executive Officer
Facebook: www.facebook.com/PipelineAngels
Linkedin: www.linkedin.com/company/pipeline-angels
X (Twitter): x.com/PipelineAngels
Instagram: www.instagram.com/pipelineangels
YouTube: www.youtube.com/c/Pipelineangels
Pinterest: www.pinterest.com/pipelineangels

Description: Angel investment funding for women and non-binary femme social entrepreneurs. Offer angel investment bootcamp, networking, and educational opportunities. **Founded:** 2011.

30301 ▪ Precursor Ventures

580 Pacific Ave.
  San Francisco, CA 94133
Co. E-mail: hello@precursorvc.com
URL: http://precursorvc.com
Contact: Charles Hudson, Managing Partner
Facebook: www.facebook.com/precursorvc
X (Twitter): x.com/PrecursorVC

Description: Venture capital firm providing funding to technology startups. **Founded:** 2015.

30302 ▪ Professional Women of Color Network (PWOCN)

Seattle, WA
Ph: (206)659-6356
Co. E-mail: info@pwocn.org
URL: http://www.pwocn.org
Contact: Meko L. Lawson, Chief Executive Officer
Facebook: www.facebook.com/PWOCN
X (Twitter): x.com/pwocn

Description: Seeks to create a business resource for all professional women of color. Facilitates and encourages strategic business relationships amongst all women of color. Fosters the professional advancement of all women of color. **Founded:** 2002. **Geographic Preference:** National.

30303 ▪ Prospanica [The Association of Hispanic MBAs & Business Professionals]

11700 Preston Rd., Ste. 660-354
  Dallas, TX 75230
Free: 866-276-2140
Co. E-mail: info@prospanica.org
URL: http://prospanica.org
Contact: Thomas Savino, Chief Executive Officer
E-mail: tsavino@nshmba.org
Facebook: www.facebook.com/ProspanicaNational
Linkedin: www.linkedin.com/company/prospanicafkanshmba
X (Twitter): x.com/Prospanica
Instagram: www.instagram.com/prospanicanational
YouTube: www.youtube.com/channel/UCbG7LZJxFtw0IAwBCFzcd-g

Description: Hispanic MBA professional business network dedicated to economic and philanthropic advancement. **Founded:** 1988. **Educational Activities:** Prospanica Conference & Career Expo (Annual). **Awards:** Prospanica Foundation Scholarships (Annual); Brillante Awards in Corporate / Government Excellence Category; Brillante Awards in Educational Excellence Category (Annual); Brillante Awards (Annual); NSHMBA Brillante Awards in Founder Category; NSHMBA Brillante Awards in Government Category; NSHMBA Brillante Awards in Military Category; Brillante Awards in Community Service Excellence Category (Annual). **Geographic Preference:** National.

30304 ▪ Racial Equity Institute LLC (REI)

Greensboro, NC
Ph: (336)582-0351
URL: http://racialequityinstitute.org
Facebook: www.facebook.com/racialequityinstitute
Linkedin: www.linkedin.com/company/the-racial-equity-institute/mycompany
X (Twitter): x.com/RacialEquityREI

Description: An alliance of trainers, organizers, and institutional leaders working to create racially equitable organizations.

30305 ▪ Southwest Minority Supplier Development Council (SMSDC)

PO Box 151267
  Austin, TX 78715
Ph: (512)386-8766
Fax: (512)386-8988
Co. E-mail: smsdc@smsdc.org
URL: http://www.smsdc.org
Contact: Karen Box, President
Facebook: www.facebook.com/SMSDCTX
Linkedin: www.linkedin.com/company/smsdctx
X (Twitter): x.com/SMSDC_TX
Instagram: www.instagram.com/nmsdchq

Description: Provides a direct link between corporate America and minority-owned businesses. Increases procurement and business opportunities for minority businesses of all sizes. **Founded:** 1999. **Geographic Preference:** Local.

30306 ▪ StartOut

4 Embarcadero Ctr., Ste. 1400
  San Francisco, CA 94111
Ph: (415)275-2446
Co. E-mail: info@startout.org
Facebook: www.facebook.com/StartOut
Linkedin: www.linkedin.com/company/startout

Description: Offers education, networking, mentorship, and access to capital in order to foster entrepreneurs and business leaders in the LGBTQ+ community. **Founded:** 2009.

30307 ▪ U.S. Black Chambers, Inc. (USBC)

1701 K St. NW, Ste. 1150
  Washington, DC 20006
Ph: (202)463-8722
Co. E-mail: info@usblackchambers.org
URL: http://usblackchambers.org
Contact: Ron Busby, President
Facebook: www.facebook.com/usblackchambers
Linkedin: www.linkedin.com/company/u-s-black-chamber-inc-
X (Twitter): x.com/usblackchambers
Instagram: www.instagram.com/usblackchambers
YouTube: www.youtube.com/channel/UC9WE7fR_NFVCHYv0j6MitLg

Description: Seeks to support African American Chambers of Commerce throughout the United States by providing advocacy, access to capital, contracting opportunities, entrepreneur and business management training, and growth and development resources. **Founded:** 2000.

30308 ▪ U.S. Department of Commerce - Minority Business Development Agency (MBDA)

1401 Constitution Ave. NW
  Washington, DC 20230
Ph: (202)482-2332
URL: http://www.mbda.gov
Contact: Richard M. Nixon, President
Facebook: www.facebook.com/USMBDA
Linkedin: www.linkedin.com/company/usmbda
X (Twitter): x.com/USMBDA
Instagram: www.instagram.com/usmbda
YouTube: www.youtube.com/channel/UCc8oT_4PDPOVnaQQQ7zBs5w

Description: Maintains contact with major corporations to identify business opportunities for minority-owned enterprises, and they utilize other federal, state, and local government agencies to identify contract opportunities and sources of financing to expand the minority business community. **Founded:** 1969. **Publications:** *North Carolina Minority Purchasing Guide.*

30309 ▪ United States Hispanic Chamber of Commerce (USHCC)

750 17th St. NW, Ste. 825
  Washington, DC 20006
Ph: (202)842-1212
Fax: (202)842-3221
Co. E-mail: info@ushcc.com
URL: http://ushcc.com
Contact: Ramiro Cavazos, President
Facebook: www.facebook.com/USHCC
X (Twitter): x.com/USHCC
Instagram: www.instagram.com/theushcc

YouTube: www.youtube.com/user/USHCCTV

Description: Promotes a positive image of Hispanics and encourages corporate involvement with Hispanic firms. Conducts business-related workshops, conferences, and management training; reports on business achievements and vendor programs of major corporations; compiles statistics. **Founded:** 1979. **Educational Activities:** USHCC National Convention. **Awards:** USHCC Chamber of the Year Awards (Annual). **Geographic Preference:** National.

CHAMBERS OF COMMERCE

30310 ▪ Asian/Pacific Islander American Chamber of Commerce and Entrepreneurship (ACE)

1300 Pennsylvania Ave. NW, Ste. 700
  Washington, DC 20004
Ph: (202)204-2579
Co. E-mail: info@nationalace.org
URL: http://www.nationalace.org
Contact: Chiling Tong, President
Facebook: www.facebook.com/nationalace
Linkedin: www.linkedin.com/company/national-ace
X (Twitter): x.com/nationalace
Instagram: www.instagram.com/national.ace

Description: Seeks to promote the business interests of Asian Americans and Pacific Islanders throughout the United States. **Founded:** 2012.

30311 ▪ The Black Business Alliance (BBA)

1201 Boston Post Rd.
  Milford, CT 06460
Free: 877-459-0002
Co. E-mail: info@bbusinessalliance.org
URL: http://www.bbusinessalliance.org
Contact: Anne-Marie Knight, Executive Director
E-mail: annemarie@bbusinessalliance.org
Facebook: www.facebook.com/ctbbaorg
Linkedin: www.linkedin.com/company/ctbbaorg

Description: Seeks to empower and promote small and medium-sized Black and minority businesses by addressing the gap in access to funding, educational resources, and capacity building. **Founded:** 2016.

30312 ▪ Minority Chamber of Commerce

1111 Brickell Ave.
  Miami, FL 33131
Ph: (305)419-4810
Co. E-mail: info@minoritychamber.net
URL: http://minoritychamber.net

Description: Supports minority-owned businesses in the U.S. by striving to empower business owners and individuals, provide technical assistance to members, advocate for members' rights, promote a better relationship between business and government, facilitate trade and investment worldwide, and promote commercial, economic, business educational, and humanitarian relations on a global scale. **Founded:** 2000.

EDUCATIONAL PROGRAMS

30313 ▪ WBENC Allyship Program

URL(s): www.wbenc.org/programs/wbenc-allyship-program

Frequency: Irregular. **Description:** Program designed to cultivate inclusion and learn to become better allies to diverse individuals and groups. **Principal Exhibits:** Program designed to cultivate inclusion and learn to become better allies to diverse individuals and groups.

30314 ▪ WBENC Women & Pride

URL(s): www.wbenc.org/programs/women-and-pride

Frequency: Irregular. **Description:** A program to help provide support and development for LGBTQ+ entrepreneurs and corporate professionals. **Principal Exhibits:** A program to help provide support and development for LGBTQ+ entrepreneurs and corporate professionals.

30315 ▪ Women of Color Program

URL(s): www.wbenc.org/programs/women-of-color-program

Frequency: Irregular. **Description:** Outreach and development for women of color entrepreneurs. **Principal Exhibits:** Outreach and development for women of color entrepreneurs.

REFERENCE WORKS

30316 ▪ *"9 Grants for Black Women Entrepreneurs"* by Now Corp.
URL(s): nowcorp.com/grants
Description: Discusses the fastest-growing group of small business owners -- black women. Provides information on grants that are specifically for black women entrepreneurs. **Availability:** Online.

30317 ▪ *"10 Minority Grant Opportunities for Small Business in 2022"* in Merchant Maverick (Nov. 30, 2021)
URL(s): www.merchantmaverick.com/business-grants-minorities
Released: November 30, 2021. **Description:** Provides information on ten minority grant opportunities for minority-owned small businesses. **Availability:** Online.

30318 ▪ *"11+ Small Business Grants for Minorities"* by Now Corp.
URL(s): nowcorp.com/minority-business-grants/
Description: Provides details on nine minority small business grants that can help secure working capital. **Availability:** Online.

30319 ▪ *"50 Best Companies for Diversity"* in Black Enterprise (Vol. 38, July 2008, No. 12, pp. 12)
Pub: Earl G. Graves Ltd.
Contact: Earl Graves, Jr., President
Description: Maintaining excellence in a company's diversity efforts requires critical challenges such as recruiting, retaining and developing talent in the oxecutive pipeline. Top young and diverse emerging executives in corporate America are featured. **Availability:** Online.

30320 ▪ *"AG Warns Slots MBE Plan Risky"* in Boston Business Journal (Vol. 29, May 27, 2011, No. 3, pp. 1)
Description: Attorney General Doug Gansler states that the law extending the minority business program on slots parlors contracting through 2018 could be open to lawsuits. He recommended that the state should conduct a study proving that minority- and women-owned businesses do not get a fair share in the gaming industry before it signs the bill to avoid lawsuits from majority-owned firms. **Availability:** Print; Online.

30321 ▪ *"The AHA Moment"* in Hispanic Business (December 2010)
Description: An interview with Gisela Girard on how competitive market conditions push buttons. Girard stepped down from her 18-month position as chairwoman the Association of Hispanic Advertising Agencies. She has more than 20 years of experience in advertising and research marketing. **Availability:** Print; Online.

30322 ▪ *"As Technology Changes, So Must African American Business"* in Black Enterprise (Vol. 41, August 2010, No. 1, pp. 61)
Pub: Earl G. Graves Ltd.
Contact: Earl Graves, Jr., President
Ed: Sonya A. Donaldson. **Description:** Social media is essential to compete in today's business environment, especially for African American firms. **Availability:** Online.

30323 ▪ *"AT&T Spend Nears $2 Billion in California With Minority, Women and Disabled Veteran-Owned Businesses in 2011"* in Engineering Business Journal (March 21, 2012)
Description: AT&T reported $2 billion working with diverse suppliers in 2011, representing a consistent annual increase working with minority, women and

disabled veteran owned businesses in California. AT&T prides itself on its 44 years leading the way by including minority, women and disabled veteran owned businesses to its supply chain. **Availability:** Print; Online.

30324 ▪ *"Baltimore's Hispanic Businesses Try to Drum Up Cash to Battle Crime Spree"* in Baltimore Business Journal (Vol. 28, September 3, 2010, No. 17)
Pub: Baltimore Business Journal
Contact: Rhonda Pringle, President
E-mail: rpringle@bizjournals.com
Ed: Scott Dance. **Description:** Hispanic businesses in Baltimore, Maryland have been raising funds to pay off-duty police officers to patrol a few blocks of Broadway in Fells Point to help curb crime. Efforts to make the area a Latin Town have failed owing to muggings, prostitution and drug dealing. Comments from small business owners are also given. **Availability:** Print; Online.

30325 ▪ *"Black Business Owners Are Up 38% in U.S. From Pre-Covid Levels"* in Bloomberg (September 15, 2021)
URL(s): www.bloomberg.com/news/articles/2021-09-15/black-business-owners-are-up-38-in-u-s-from-pre-covid-levels
Released: September 15, 2021. **Description:** Discusses how Black business owners are surging after Covid. **Availability:** Online.

30326 ▪ *"Black-Owned Businesses See Largest Surge in 25 Years Amidst Pandemic, Social Uprisings"* in The Black Wall Street Times (July 14, 2021)
Ed: Erika Stone. **Released:** July 14, 2021. **Description:** Black-owned businesses are flourishing in the post-Covid times. Black entrepreneurs decided to take uncertain times and turn it around to create new businesses and create new jobs within the community.

30327 ▪ *"Black-Woman Owned Tech Company Introduces First Two-Part Charging System Portable Device"* in Minority Business Entrepreneur (February 2, 2022)
URL(s): mbemag.com/articles/black-woman-owned-tech-company-introduces-first-two-part-charging-system-portable-device/
Ed: Gaby M. Rojas. **Description:** Sparkee has announced its new charging device, Sparkee puck, on Kickstarter. This black-woman-owned tech company designed a small device that doesn't take up much room while it charges your electronic devices. **Availability:** Online.

30328 ▪ *"Breaking with Tradition, Foundations Seek Out Diverse Asset Managers"* in Crain's Chicago Business (October 15, 2021)
Ed: Steve Hendershot. **Released:** October 15, 2021. **Description:** Within the investment industry, a development to increase diversity in management is taking hold.

30329 ▪ *"Building Black-Owned Bigger"* in Crain's Chicago Business (November 11, 2021)
URL(s): www.chicagobusiness.com/equity/chicagos-black-owned-businesses-look-scale
Ed: Cassandra West. **Released:** November 12, 2021. **Description:** Profiling several black-owned businesses and their successes. Also discusses how black-owned businesses are growing revenue, creating jobs, and entering high-growth sectors. **Availability:** Online.

30330 ▪ *"Business Financing Tips for Hispanic Small Business Owners"* in Legal Zoom (February 13, 2023)
URL(s): www.legalzoom.com/articles/business-financing-tips-for-hispanic-small-business-owners
Ed: Patricia Guadalupe. **Released:** February 13, 2023. **Description:** A discussion about business planning and financing for Hispanic small business owners, with helpful links. **Availability:** Online.

30331 ▪ *"Calendar"* in Crain's Detroit Business (Vol. 24, March 10, 2008, No. 10, pp. 21)
Pub: Crain Communications Inc.
Contact: Barry Asin, President
Description: Listing of events in the Detroit area include conferences addressing entrepreneurialism, economic development, and women business ownership. **Availability:** Print; Online.

30332 ▪ *"Celebrate Success. Embrace Innovation"* in Black Enterprise (Vol. 37, February 2007, No. 7, pp. 145)
Description: 2007 Women of Power Summit provides networking opportunities, empowerment sessions, and nightly entertainment. More than 500 executive women of color are expected to attend this inspiring summit in Phoenix, February 7-10. **Availability:** Print; Online.

30333 ▪ *"CEO Forecast: With Cloudy Economy, Executives Turn to Government Contracting"* in Hispanic Business (January-February 2009, pp. 34, 36)
Ed: Jessica Haro, Richard Kaplan. **Description:** As economic uncertainty fogs the future, executives turn to government contracts in order to boost business. Revenue sources, health care challenges, environmental consulting and remediation services, as well as technological strides are discussed. **Availability:** Print; Online.

30334 ▪ *"Cincinnati's Minority Business Accelerator Welcomes First Hispanic Firms"* in Business Courier (Vol. 27, August 13, 2010, No. 15, pp. 1)
Pub: Business Courier
Ed: Lucy May. **Description:** The Minority Business Accelerator (MBA) initiative of the Cincinnati USA Regional Chamber in Ohio has included Hispanic-owned firms Best Upon Request and Vivian Llambi and Associates Inc. to its portfolio. Vivian Llambi and Associates is a design, landscape architecture and civil engineering specialist. Prior to these firms' membership, MBA was limited to black-owned companies. **Availability:** Print; Online.

30335 ▪ *"City Seeks More Minorities"* in Austin Business Journal (Vol. 28, November 7, 2008, No. 34, pp. A1)
Pub: Austin Business Journal
Contact: Rachel McGrath, Director
E-mail: rmcgrath@bizjournals.com
Ed: Jean Kwon. **Description:** Austin, Texas is planning to increase the participation of minority- and women-owned businesses in government contracts. Contractors are required to show 'good faith' to comply with the specified goals. The city is planning to effect the changes in the construction and professional services sector. **Availability:** Print; Online.

30336 ▪ *"Complete Discovery Source, Inc. (CDS) Receives Minority Owned Business Certification"* in Marketwired (December 14, 2010)
Pub: Comtex News Network Inc.
Contact: Kan Devnani, President
Description: Complete Discovery Source Inc. (CDS) was granted Minority-Owned Business Enterprise status by the New York State Department of Economic Development. The certification provides CDS, an end-to-end eDiscovery services provider, with access to contracting opportunities with 130 government agencies throughout New York state. **Availability:** Print; Online.

30337 ▪ *"Conference To Aid Minority Business Ties"* in Tulsa World (July 24, 2012)
Description: Preview of the 34th Annual Oklahoma Minority Supplier Development Council Business Conference and Opportunity Fair is presented. The event will be held in downtown Tulsa, OK and brings together corporate, government and minority representatives. Business opportunities for minority suppliers will also be presented. **Availability:** Online.

30338 ■ *"Coronavirus Pandemic Upends the Dry Cleaning Industry" in NPR.org (March 31, 2021)*
URL(s): www.npr.org/2021/03/31/982953808/coronavirus-pandemic-upends-the-dry-cleaning-industry
Released: March 21, 2021. **Description:** Discusses the effects the COVID-19 pandemic has had on the dry cleaning business and the Korean American's who own these businesses. **Availability:** Online.

30339 ■ *"Detroit Hosts Conferences on Green Building, IT, Finance" in Crain's Detroit Business (Vol. 25, June 1, 2009, No. 22, pp. 9)*
Pub: Crain Communications Inc.
Contact: Barry Asin, President
Ed: Tom Henderson. **Description:** Detroit will host three conferences in June 2009, one features green technology, one information technology and the third will gather black bankers and financial experts from across the nation. **Availability:** Online.

30340 ■ *"DIA Contract Sets a Record for Denver Minority, Woman-Owned Business" in Denver Business Journal (Vol. 65, February 21, 2014, No. 41)*
Pub: American City Business Journals, Inc.
Contact: Mike Olivieri, Executive Vice President
Released: Weekly. **Description:** The City of Denver, Colorado has awarded a $39.6 million contract to Burgess Services Inc. to construct a transit and hotel project near the Denver International Airport. Burgess Services is owned by Denise Burgess. This is the largest public contract awarded to a woman0 or minority-owned business in the city's history. **Availability:** Print; Online.

30341 ■ *"Diversity in Business Awards: Minority Businessperson of the Year and Diversity Corporation of the Year Finalists" in ColoradoBiz (Vol. 30, July 2012, No. 7, pp. 32)*
Description: Finalists for the ColoradoBiz 18th annual award presentation are profiled. The journal acknowledges minority businesses and businesspeople as well as firms that have been committed to hiring, contracting, and customer/community service to minorities.

30342 ■ *Diversity, Equity, and Inclusion in the Workplace in 2022: Best Practices*
Pub: UpCity, Inc.
URL(s): upcity.com/experts/diversity-equity-and-inclusion-in-the-workplace/
Ed: Rebecca Lubecki. **Released:** June 10, 2022. **Description:** Provides information on how entrepreneurs and small-to-midsize businesses can get started with incorporation of diversity, equity, and inclusion initiatives. **Availability:** Online.

30343 ■ *"DMW Gets MBE Certification" in Wireless News (July 29, 2012)*
Description: Towson, Maryland's Daft McCune Walker (DMW) received the Minority Business Enterprise (MBE) Certification from the State of Maryland for Engineering, Surveying, Environmental and CAD services. The firm is a multidisciplinary consulting organization and is woman-owned. **Availability:** Print; Online.

30344 ■ *"DNERO & Bits of Stock Team Up to Offer Wealth-Building Rewards to Hispanic Market" in Minority Business Entrepreneur (March 7, 2022)*
URL(s): mbemag.com/articles/dnero-bits-of-stock-team-up-to-offer-wealth-building-rewards-to-hispanic-market/
Ed: Gaby M. Rojas. **Description:** DNERO and bits of Stock have created a partnership that will allow DNERO users to earn Stock Rewards, which will equal fractional shares of stock. **Availability:** Online.

30345 ■ *"Edible Endeavors" in Black Enterprise (March 1, 2008)*
Pub: Earl G. Graves Ltd.
Contact: Earl Graves, Jr., President

Ed: Carolyn M. Brown. **Description:** Profile of Jacqueline Frazer, woman entrepreneur who turned her love for cooking into a catering business. She is chef and owner of Command Performance in New York City. The firm works with more than 50 clients annually and generates annual revenues of about $350,000. **Availability:** Online.

30346 ■ *"FCC Adopts New Media Ownership Rules" in Black Enterprise (Vol. 38, March 1, 2008, No. 8, pp. 26)*
Pub: Earl G. Graves Ltd.
Contact: Earl Graves, Jr., President
Ed: Joyce Jones. **Description:** Federal Communications Commission approved a ruling that lifts a ban on newspaper and/or broadcast cross ownership. Because of declining sales in newspaper advertising and readership the ban will allow companies to share local news gathering costs across multiple media platforms. **Availability:** Online.

30347 ■ *"Fighting for Civil Rights Tourism" in Memphis Business Journal (Vol. 33, March 2, 2012, No. 47, pp. 1)*
Pub: Baltimore Business Journal
Contact: Rhonda Pringle, President
E-mail: rpringle@bizjournals.com
Ed: Michael Sheffield. **Description:** Memphis, Tennessee-based National Civil Rights Museum will complete its $27 million renovation in late 2013. It faces competition from Smithsonian Institution's National Museum of African-American History and Culture in Washington DC and the National Center for Civil and Human Rights in Atlanta, Georgia. **Availability:** Print; Online.

30348 ■ *"Filling the Business Gap" in Hispanic Business (December 2010)*
Description: New York group seeks to increase state diversity supplier spending to help create jobs and boost the economy. According to a recent study, six out of 10 small business owners will increase capital spending but delay hiring in 2011. However, potential job creation is good among businesses owned by women and minorities. **Availability:** Print; Online.

30349 ■ *"Gabrielle Union Providing $75K in Business Grants to Black Women Owned Companies" in Small Business Trends (March 14, 2023)*
URL(s): smallbiztrends.com/2023/03/75k-in-business-grants-to-black-women-owned-companies.html
Ed: Gabrielle Pickard-Whitehead. **Released:** March 14, 2023. **Description:** Black women-owned companies are eligible for business grants from actress and entrepreneur Gabrielle Union. **Availability:** Online.

30350 ■ *"Gen Z-Led Executive Communications and Strategic Engagement Agency Launches in DC" in Minority Business Entrepreneur (March 17, 2023)*
URL(s): mbemag.com/articles/gen-z-led-executive-communications-and-strategic-engagement-agency-launches-in-dc/
Ed: Gaby M. Rojas. **Description:** One of the first Black, Queer, and Gen Z-led agencies was launched by Words Normalize Behavior, which is a company dedicated to communications, coalition-building, and advice. **Availability:** Online.

30351 ■ *"Get On the Shelf: Selling Your Product In Retail Stores" in Black Enterprise (Vol. 44, February 2014, No. 6, pp. 18)*
Pub: Earl G. Graves Ltd.
Contact: Earl Graves, Jr., President
Description: Profile of Arsha and Charles Jones, Washington DC natives, who are selling their Capital City Mumbo Sauce to local retailers as well as big box retailers. The husband and wife team share tips for getting your product into retail establishments.

30352 ■ *"Go Green Or Go Home" in Black Enterprise (Vol. 41, August 2010, No. 1, pp. 53)*
Pub: Earl G. Graves Ltd.
Contact: Earl Graves, Jr., President

Ed: Robinson M. Tennille. **Description:** The green economy has become an essential part of every business, however, small business owners need to learn how to participate, including minority owned entrepreneurs. **Availability:** Online.

30353 ■ *"Happy Trails: RV Franchiser Gives Road Traveling Enthusiasts a Lift" in Black Enterprise (Vol. 38, July 2008, No. 12, pp. 47)*
Pub: Earl G. Graves Ltd.
Contact: Earl Graves, Jr., President
Ed: Tamara E. Holmes. **Description:** Overview of Bates International Motor Home Rental Systems Inc., a growing franchise that gives RV owners the chance to rent out their big-ticket purchases to others when they are not using them; Sandra Williams Bate launched the company as a franchise in July 1997 and now has a fleet of 30 franchises across the country. She expects the company to reach 2.2 million for 2008 due to a marketing initiative that will expand the company's presence.

30354 ■ *"Hispanic Business 100 Influentials" in Hispanic Business (October 2009, pp. 22)*
Description: Profiles of the top one hundred influential Hispanics in business and government are presented. **Availability:** Online.

30355 ■ *How Diversity, Equity, and Inclusion Can Help Corporate America Thrive*
URL(s): nala.org/how-diversity-equity-and-inclusion-can-help-corporate-american-thrive/2022/
Ed: Roderick Parker. **Released:** nala.org/how-diversity-equity-and-inclusion-can-help-corporate-american-thrive/2022/. **Description:** Discusses the importance of including diversity, equity, and inclusion in your small business goals. **Availability:** Online.

30356 ■ *How to Get Diversity and Inclusion Right in 2022*
URL(s): www.zenefits.com/workest/how-to-get-diversity-and-inclusion-right-in-2022/
Ed: Dan Marzullo. **Released:** April 24, 2022. **Description:** Discusses the pros of having a diverse and inclusive workplace and provides suggestions on how to start incorporating representation into your workplace. **Availability:** Online.

30357 ■ *"How Hispanic Small Businesses Are Using Supplier Diversity Programs to Secure Contracts" in Legal Zoom (February 17, 2023)*
URL(s): www.legalzoom.com/articles/how-hispanic-small-businesses-are-using-supplier-diversity-programs-to-secure-contracts
Ed: Lauren Schenkman. **Released:** February 17, 2023. **Description:** Discusses the positive impact supplier diversity programs are having within the Hispanic community and their businesses. **Availability:** Online.

30358 ■ *"How to Start a Minority-Owned Business" in NerdWallet (Oct. 22, 2020)*
URL(s): www.nerdwallet.com/article/small-business/how-to-start-a-minority-owned-business
Released: October 22, 2020. **Description:** A guide to starting a minority-owned business; includes resources for minority entrepreneurs to help start and grow your business. **Availability:** Online.

30359 ■ *"Investment Firms Unite: Coalition Fights New Tax Law" in Black Enterprise (Vol. 38, December 2007, No. 5, pp. 52)*
Description: Minorities working in private equity, real estate and investment management firms have united to form the Access to Capital Coalition to oppose legislation that they feel would adversely affect their ability to attract investments and executives. Details of the group are included. **Availability:** Print; Online.

30360 ■ *"Investment Needs to Come From Our Community" in Crain's Chicago Business (November 12, 2021)*
Ed: Cassandra West. **Released:** November 12, 2021. **Description:** Examines some of Chicago's small minority-owned businesses and how they can benefit from the local community investing in them.

30361 ■ *"Largest Indianapolis-Area Minority-Owned Businesses" in Indianapolis Business Journal (Vol. 33, July 2, 2012, No. 18, pp. 14A)*

Description: A listing of the largest minority owned businesses in the Indianapolis, Indiana area. They are ranked by number of employees and number of area locations. **Availability:** Online.

30362 ■ *"The Latest Grant Opportunities for Women- and Minority-Owned Small Businesses" in Small Business Trends(February 28, 2023)*

URL(s): smallbiztrends.com/2023/02/latest-small-business-grants-for-women-and-minority-owned-businesses.html

Ed: Annie Pilon. **Released:** February 28, 2023. **Description:** Information about grants available to women- and minority-owned small businesses is given. **Availability:** Online.

30363 ■ *"LISC and Uber Eats Announce Black Restaurant Fund " in Minority Business Entrepreneur (February 2, 2022)*

URL(s): mbemag.com/articles/lisc-and-uber-eats-announce-black-restaurant-fund/

Ed: Gaby M. Rojas. **Description:** The Local Initiatives Support Corporation (LISC) and Uber Eats formed a collaboration that will allow Black restaurant owners acquire financing. These loans do not have fixed repayment terms but will instead focus on allowing the borrower to start paying back after targeted revenue growth is achieved. **Availability:** Online.

30364 ■ *"Maryland Nonprofits May Lose Minority Business Enterprise Status" in Baltimore Business Journal (Vol. 29, September 2, 2011, No. 17, pp. 1)*

Pub: Boston Business Journal

Contact: Carolyn M. Jones, President

E-mail: cmjones@bizjournals.com

Ed: Scott Dance. **Description:** A business group has been pushing to bar nonprofits from Maryland's Minority Business program. Nonprofits have been found to take a large portion of state contracts intended for women- and minority-owned businesses. The group is also crafting proposed legislation to remove nonprofits from the program. **Availability:** Online.

30365 ■ *"Maryland Ready to Defend Slots Minority Policy" in Boston Business Journal (Vol. 29, July 8, 2011, No. 9, pp. 3)*

Pub: Boston Business Journal

Contact: Carolyn M. Jones, President

E-mail: cmjones@bizjournals.com

Ed: Scott Dance. **Description:** The legality of Maryland's minority inclusion policy may be put under scrutiny once the lawsuit filed by rejected slots developer Baltimore City Entertainment Group on July 5, 2011 is heard in court. The lawsuit aims to stop the bidding process on a proposed casino in Baltimore because the minority policy amounts to reverse discrimination. **Availability:** Print; Online.

30366 ■ *"MicroTech Is Fastest Growing Private Company in Washington Area on Deloitte Technology Fast 500" in Hispanic Business (July-August 2009, pp. 20, 22)*

Ed: Suzanne Heibel. **Description:** Profile of Tony Jimenez, former lieutenant colonel in the Army and CEO and founder of Virginia-based information technology firm, Micro Tech LLC. Jimenez was named Latinos in Information Science and Technology Association's CEO of the Year for 2008.

30367 ■ *"Minority Auto Suppliers Get Help Diversifying" in Crain's Detroit Business (Vol. 26, January 11, 2010, No. 2, pp. 3)*

Pub: Crain Communications Inc.

Contact: Barry Asin, President

Ed: Sherri Welch. **Description:** Displaced minority auto suppliers are being given assistance by the Kauffman's Foundation Urban Entrepreneur Partner-ship Detroit program, a three-year effort to assist 150 of the region's suppliers into more diversified businesses. **Availability:** Online.

30368 ■ *"Minority Entrepreneurs Must Make Growth a Priority" in Crain's Chicago Business (November 12, 2021)*

URL(s): www.chicagobusiness.com/equity/minority-entrepreneurs-must-make-growth-priority

Released: November 12, 2021. **Description:** While small businesses are important, now is the time for minority-owned companies to branch out of their comfort zone and redevelop as midsize to large businesses. Doing so will create more jobs and help develop communities. **Availability:** Online.

30369 ■ *Minority Women Entrepreneurs: How Outsider Status Can Lead to Better Business Practices*

Ed: Mary Godwyn, Donna Stoddard. **Released:** September 08, 2017. **Description:** Minority women in the US start businesses at a faster rate then non-minority men and women. This book explores their success and how they use their outside status to develop business practices that benefit not only their company, but their communities. **Availability:** E-book.

30370 ■ *National Minority and Women-Owned Business Directory*

Pub: Diversity Information Resources, Inc.

Contact: Leslie Bonds, President

E-mail: lbonds@diversityinforesources.com

URL(s): www.diversityinforesources.com/Products/ProductDetail/89

Ed: Leslie Bonds. **Released:** Annual **Price:** $220, Individuals. **Description:** Covers information regarding minority and women-owned business directories to acquaint major corporations and government purchasing agents with the products and services of minority and women-owned firms. Covers approximately 7000 minority-owned firms. **Entries include:** Company name, address, phone, fax, e-mail, Web site, number of employees, year established, products or services, certification status, minority identification, annual sales, NAICS code. **Arrangement:** Classified by product or service, then geographical and alphabetical. **Indexes:** Commodity, keyword. **Availability:** Online.

30371 ■ *"On the Green: Sheila Johnson Adds $35 Million Golf Resort To Her Expanding Portfolio" in Black Enterprise (January 2008)*

Pub: Earl G. Graves Ltd.

Contact: Earl Graves, Jr., President

Ed: Donna M. Owens. **Description:** Profile of Sheila Johnson, CEO of Salamander Hospitality LLC, made history when she purchased the Innisbrook Resort and Golf Club, making her the first African American woman to own this type of property. The resort includes four championship golf courses, six swimming pools, four restaurants, eleven tennis courts, three conference halls, and a nature preserve. **Availability:** Online.

30372 ■ *Originate, Motivate, Innovate: 7 Steps for Building a Billion Dollar Network*

Pub: John Wiley & Sons, Inc.

Contact: Christina Van Tassell, Executive Vice President Chief Financial Officer

URL(s): www.wiley.com/en-us/Originate%2C+Motivate%2C+Innovate%3A+7+Steps+for+Building+a+Billion+Dollar+Network-p-9781119900542

Ed: Shelly Omilade Bell. **Released:** May 2023. **Price:** $26, hardcover. **Description:** Discusses business funding for women of color in a white male-dominated field. **Availability:** Print.

30373 ■ *"Plenty of Businesses Are Ready to 'Up Their Game" in Crain's Chicago Business (November 12, 2021)*

Ed: Mott Smith. **Released:** November 12, 2021. **Description:** Examines how providing the right tools to minority-owned businesses can really make a difference in their success. Tools can include mentorship, operating support, and investment opportunities. **Availability:** Online.

30374 ■ *"Power Partnerships" in Business Courier (Vol. 27, October 22, 2010, No. 25, pp. 1)*

Description: The $400 million Harrah's casino and the $47 million redevelopment and expansion of Washington Park are project aimed at boosting the economy in downtown Cincinnati, Ohio. These projects will be done in cooperation with the National Association for the Advancement of Colored People. Insights into the role of minority-owned businesses in regional economic development are explored. **Availability:** Print; Online.

30375 ■ *"Private Equity Struggles with Its Diversity Problem" in Crain's Chicago Business (October 15, 2021)*

URL(s): www.chicagobusiness.com/equity/private-equity-struggles-its-diversity-problem

Ed: Steve Hendershot. **Released:** October 15, 2021. **Description:** Discusses the issues of low diversity rates within the C-suite of private equity firms.

30376 ■ *Profit First for Minority Business Enterprises*

Ed: Susanne Mariga. **Released:** May 25, 2021. **Description:** Explains the Profit First systems to help entrepreneurs succeed in their chosen business path. **Availability:** Print.

30377 ■ *Race and Entrepreneurial Success: Black-, Asian-, and White-Owned Businesses in the United States*

Pub: The MIT Press

Ed: Robert W. Fairlie, Alicia M. Robb. **Released:** 2008. **Description:** Trends in minority small business ownership are explored, focusing on the importance of human capital, financial capital, and family business background in successful business ownership. **Availability:** E-book; Print; PDF.

30378 ■ *"The Racial Divide and the Class Struggle in the United States" in WorkingUSA (Vol. 11, September 2008, No. 3, pp. 311)*

Description: An examination of questions of race that continue to play such a prominent role in contemporary society is presented, focusing on the undermining of potential solidarity and strength of the working class movement, what sustains racists attitudes, practices and institutions, especially in the face of trends in world economic development. **Availability:** PDF; Online.

30379 ■ *"Rebrand, Rebuild, and Recharge Your Business: How This BE 100s CEO Got a New Lease On Life With a Frozen Yogurt Café" in Black Enterprise (Vol. 44, March 2014, No. 7, pp. 11)*

Pub: Earl G. Graves Ltd.

Contact: Earl Graves, Jr., President

Description: Profile of Rumia Ambrose-Burbank, chief executive of one of the country's largest minority-owned businesses. Her Troy, Michigan-based firm ranks number 51 on the magazine's 100 Industrial/Service companies and focuses on the maintenance, repair, and operations (MRO) supply side. Ambrose-Burbank opened Sol De Frio, in 2013, a self-serve frozen yogurt dessert shop.

30380 ■ *The Rhythm of Success: How an Immigrant Produced His Own American Dream*

Pub: Penguin Publishing Group

Ed: Emilio Estefan. **Description:** Emilio Estefan, husband to singer Gloria Estefan and founder of the Latin pop legend Miami Sound Machine, is the classic example of the American dream. He shares his guiding principles that entrepreneurs need to start and grow a business. **Availability:** E-book; Print.

30381 ■ *"The Road Warrior: Pamela Rodgers Kept Rodgers Chevrolet On Course Despite Numerous Obstacles" in Black Enterprise (Vol. 44, June 2014, No. 10, pp. 76)*

Pub: Earl G. Graves Ltd.

Contact: Earl Graves, Jr., President

Description: Profile of Pamela Rodgers, who built her company into one of General Motor's flagship franchises and ranked among the largest black-owned dealerships. Rodgers addresses the importance of customer service in order to grow her business. She is a 30-year veteran with her Chevrolet dealership located in the Detroit area.

30382 ■ *"Small-Business Grants for Minorities: 10 Opportunities"* in NerdWallet (Nov. 4, 2021)
URL(s): www.nerdwallet.com/article/small-business/small-business-grants-minorities
Released: November 04, 2021. **Description:** Provides information on small-business grants and other financing resources for minority-owned businesses. **Availability:** Online.

30383 ■ *"Small Business Investment Company Reforms Proposed by SBA to Address Diversity"* in Small Business Trends (October 25, 2022)
URL(s): smallbiztrends.com/2022/10/small-business-investment-company-reforms.html
Ed: Gabrielle Pickard-Whitehead. **Released:** October 25, 2022. **Description:** The Small Business Administration (SBA) proposed new reforms to help reduce financial barriers that many small businesses from underserved communities experience. The new reforms also aim to diversify the Small Business Investment Company (SBIC) program. **Availability:** Online.

30384 ■ *"Small Businesses Have Surged in Black Communities. Was It the Stimulus?"* in The New York Times (May 24,2021)
Ed: Quoctrung Bui. **Released:** May 24, 2021. **Description:** Discusses the data that tracked a surge in new businesses within Black communities.

30385 ■ *"Social Media News: TikTok Supporting Black Business Owners, Snapchat Available on Chrome"* in Small Business Trends (August 19, 2022)
URL(s): smallbiztrends.com/2022/08/social-media-news-roundup-august-19-2022.html
Ed: Michael Guta. **Released:** August 19, 2022. **Description:** Learning how to make TikTok videos is proving to be advantageous for many small business owners as it helps drive up engagement for your company and your brand. TikTok is also supporting Black business owners by accepting applications for their Support Black Businesses accelerator program. **Availability:** Online.

30386 ■ *"Start 2022 with a Bang with These Grants"* in Small Business News (Dec. 31, 2021)
URL(s): smallbiztrends.com/2021/12/in-the-news-start-2022-with-a-bang-with-these-grants.html
Released: December 31, 2021. **Description:** Discusses grants that are available to small businesses in many cities throughout the United States. Includes information about requirements for businesses affected by the pandemic as well as women and minority-owed businesses. **Availability:** Online.

30387 ■ *"Start Up Boom in the Pandemic Is Growing Stronger"* in New York Times (August 19, 2021)
URL(s): www.nytimes.com/2021/08/19/business/startup-business-creation-pandemic.html
Ed: Ben Casselman. **Released:** August 19, 2021. **Description:** Explores the concept of Covid-era startups, which were started by necessity by those who were laid off or lost a job through over means during the pandemic. Boosted by stimulus checks, many people were able to fund a new small business in order to follow passions and new opportunities. Studies showed that women and Black and Hispanic entrepreneurs led the way in pandemic start-ups. **Availability:** Online.

30388 ■ *"Starting and Scaling a Small Business as a Minority Entrepreneur"* in Sahan Journal (Nov. 1, 2021)
Released: November 01, 2021. **Description:** Provides information to support first-time entrepreneurs to launch a successful business. **Availability:** Online.

30389 ■ *"The State of Minority Entrepreneurship in America"* in Next Avenue (Nov. 9, 2021)
URL(s): www.nextavenue.org/minority-entrepreneurship-in-america
Released: November 09, 2021. **Description:** Details how minority entrepreneurs can tap into trends to launch businesses. **Availability:** Online.

30390 ■ *"Steering Toward Profitability"* in Black Enterprise (Vol. 41, December 2010, No. 5, pp. 72)
Pub: Earl G. Graves Ltd.
Contact: Earl Graves, Jr., President
Ed: Alan Hughes. **Description:** Systems Electro Coating LLC had to make quick adjustments when auto manufacturers were in a slump. The minority father-daughter team discuss their strategies during the auto industry collapse.

30391 ■ *"Still Stretching"* in Business Courier (Vol. 24, December 28, 2008, No. 37, pp. 1)
Description: Minority-owned businesses have experienced growth in 2007 as Cincinnati and Hamilton County used a workforce development and economic inclusion policy. Kroger Co., for example, has been inducted to the Billion Dollar Roundtable in 2007 for attaining $1 billion in annual spending with suppliers that are minority- owned. The need for more progress within the minority-owned enterprises is discussed. **Availability:** Online.

30392 ■ *"Still Unprepared For Natural Disasters: Blacks More Likely to be Affected and Less Prepared"* in Black Enterprise (Vol. 38, January 2008, No. 6, pp. 28)
Pub: Earl G. Graves Ltd.
Contact: Earl Graves, Jr., President
Ed: Alexis McCombs. **Description:** According to a study conducted by the American Red Cross, 19 percent of African Americans are not prepared for a natural disaster, compared to 10 percent of white Americans. **Availability:** Online.

30393 ■ *"Strivers and High Fliers"* in Dallas Business Journal (Vol. 37, February 7, 2014, No. 22, pp. 4)
Pub: American City Business Journals, Inc.
Contact: Mike Olivieri, Executive Vice President
Released: February 08, 2014. **Price:** $4, print. **Description:** The winners of the 2014 Minority Business Leader Award in Dallas, Texas, all share significant entrepreneurial traits like taking the lessons they learned as a child in their careers. Each of the award winners have achieved success using very particular and personal sets of benchmarks. **Availability:** Print; Online.

30394 ■ *"Supermercado El Rancho Chain Grows Along with Hispanic Population"* in Dallas Business Journal (Vol. 35, July 13, 2012, No. 44, pp. 1)
Pub: Baltimore Business Journal
Contact: Rhonda Pringle, President
E-mail: rpringle@bizjournals.com
Ed: Matt Joyce. **Description:** Garland, Texas-based Supermercado El Rancho has grown rapidly with its take on the Hispanic grocery market and is planning to open 12 stores in six years. La Bodega Meat Inc., the chain's affiliate distribution company, is planning a $13.1 million renovation and double the size of its warehouse to accommodate the plans for more stores.

30395 ■ *"Too Much Information?"* in Black Enterprise (Vol. 37, December 2006, No. 5, pp. 59)
Pub: Earl G. Graves Ltd.
Contact: Earl Graves, Jr., President
Ed: James C. Johnson. **Description:** African American business owners often face the dilemma of whether or not to divulge their minority status when soliciting new customers and financial institutions. The quality of the products or services is always the key factor and race should never define one's business; however, it is appropriate to market oneself as

a minority- or women-owned business, especially if the company is in an industry where those clients are offered top-tier contracts. **Availability:** Online.

30396 ■ *"Top Women In Tech: Whether It's Mobile or Engineering, These Mavens Are Making an Impact on Today's Tech Scene"* in Black Enterprise (Vol. 44, February 2014, No. 6, pp. 29)
Pub: Earl G. Graves Ltd.
Contact: Earl Graves, Jr., President
Description: There are fewer women than men in technology, science, engineering, and mathematics professions. As part of the magazine's Women of Power coverage, three successful minority women in their fields are profiled.

30397 ■ *"Transitioning From Hobbyist to Entrepreneur: Teen Designer Creates Custom and Handmade Jewelry for the Everyday Diva"* in Black Enterprise (Vol. 44, March 2014, No. 7, pp. 14)
Pub: Earl G. Graves Ltd.
Contact: Earl Graves, Jr., President
Description: Profile of Jaya Kiere Johnson, who states that every one of her jewelry creations represents a generation of black female entrepreneurship in her life, from her mother to her great-grandmother. The young entrepreneur tells how she was inspired while designing and creating handmade jewelry in high school.

30398 ■ *"Two Local Firms Make Inc. List: Minority Business"* in Indianapolis Business Journal (Vol. 31, August 30, 2010, No. 26, pp. 13A)
Description: Smart IT staffing agency and Entap Inc., an IT outsourcing firm were among the top ten fastest growing black-owned businesses in the U.S. by Inc. magazine. **Availability:** Print; Online.

30399 ■ *"Union Pacific Railroad Receives Minority Business Exchange Award of Excellence"* in News Bites US (July 7, 2012)
Description: Union Pacific Railroad was given the Award of Excellence at the 2012 Iowa Minority Business Exchange held in Des Moines, Iowa. The award is part of the Wisconsin Iowa and Central Illinois Minority Supplier Development Council. Union Pacific has a history of purchasing from minority- and women-owned businesses. **Availability:** Print; Online.

30400 ■ *"U.S. to Spend $10 Billion to Boost Small Businesses"* in The Wall Street Journal (Jan. 8, 2022)
URL(s): www.wsj.com/articles/u-s-to-spend-10-billion-to-boost-small-businesses-11641637801
Released: January 08, 2022. **Description:** Discusses a treasury department program that aims to target small, minority-owned businesses and ensure that they have access to the financing they seek. **Availability:** Online.

30401 ■ *"Unveiling the Secrets Behind Hispanic Business' 100 Fastest-Growing Companies"* in Hispanic Business (Vol. 30, July-August 2008, No. 7-8, pp. 22)
Ed: Michael Bowker. **Description:** CEO's of the five fastest growing Hispanic-owned companies discuss the success of their companies; most of them attribute their success to good investment and diversification, effective innovations and seeing growth opportunities where others see roadblocks. **Availability:** Online.

30402 ■ *"USHCC Applauds 10 Best U.S. Corporations for Veteran-Owned Businesses for 2012"* in Economics Week (April 20, 2012, pp. 153)
Description: The United States Hispanic Chamber of Commerce honored the 2012 National Veteran-Owned Business Association and its 10 Best US Corporations for veteran-owned businesses. The list includes large corporations that engage three million veteran-owned businese as suppliers. The Hispanic

Chamber promotes economic growth and development of Hispanic entrepreneurs in the US. **Availability:** Print; Online.

30403 ■ *"Wal-Mart Sharpens Focus on Roxbury" in Boston Business Journal (Vol. 31, July 8, 2011, No. 24, pp. 1)*
Pub: Boston Business Journal
Contact: Carolyn M. Jones, President
E-mail: cmjones@bizjournals.com

Ed: Mary Moore. **Price:** $4. **Description:** Wal-Mart Stores is boosting its search for a possible location in the Roxbury section of Boston, Massachusetts. The search is focused on underserved communities in terms of jobs and access to reasonably-priced merchandise. The extent Boston's African American community has clashed with Mayor Thomas M. Memino over the accommodations of the retailer in Roxbury is discussed. **Availability:** Print; Online.

30404 ■ *"We Do: Copreneurs Simultaneously Build Happy Marriages and Thriving Enterprises" in Black Enterprise (Vol. 38, February 1, 2008)*
Pub: Earl G. Graves Ltd.
Contact: Earl Graves, Jr., President

Ed: Krissah Williams. **Description:** Of the 2.7 million businesses in the U.S. that are equally owned by male-female partnerships, about 79,000 are black-owned. One couple shares their experiences of working and growing their business together.

30405 ■ *"We Must Put an End to 'Male, Pale, and Stale' Corporate Boards" in Black Enterprise (Vol. 45, July-August 2014, No. 1, pp. 10)*
Pub: Earl G. Graves Ltd.
Contact: Earl Graves, Jr., President

Description: Corporate governance behavior is addressed. With a surplus of black executive talent with impeccable professional credentials and reputations, publicly traded companies continue to ignore African Americans in the boardroom. **Availability:** Online.

30406 ■ *"What's Needed Are More Seats at the Table" in Crain's Chicago Business (November 12, 2021)*
Ed: Charles Smith. **Released:** November 12, 2021. **Description:** Discusses how Chicago's Black business leaders are working to reduce the wealth gap within the Black community. **Availability:** Online.

30407 ■ *"Woman-Owned Firm 3D Strategic Management to Operate New Location of Orlando Business Center" in Orlando Business Journal (November 10, 2021)*
URL(s): www.bizjournals.com/orlando/news/2021/11/10/3d-strategic-management-to-operate-minority-center.html
Ed: Anjali Fluker. **Released:** November 10, 2021. **Description:** A business development training center is under new management. Discussion of the woman-owned firm and their goals for this project are given. **Availability:** Online.

30408 ■ *Women Entrepreneurs in The Global Marketplace*
Pub: Edward Elgar Publishing Inc.
Contact: Edward Elgar, Founder Chairman

Ed: Andrea E. Smith-Hunter. **Released:** 2013. **Description:** Focus is on women entrepreneurs; information includes human capital, network structures and financial capital, with comparative analysis across racial lines.

30409 ■ *"Women of Power Summit" in Black Enterprise (Vol. 38, February 2008, No. 7, pp. 163)*
Description: Third annual Women of Power Summit, hosted by State Farm, will host over 700 executive women of color offering empowerment sessions, tips for networking, along with entertainment. **Availability:** Online.

STATISTICAL SOURCES

30410 ■ *Diversity and Inclusion (D&I)*
Price: $5,800. **Description:** Covers the global diversity and inclusion market with projections to 2027. Provides a market overview, focus on select players, market trends and drivers, a global market perspective, and market analysis. **Availability:** PDF.

30411 ■ *A Foundation for Trust with Diversity, Equity, and Inclusion*
URL(s): www.marketresearch.com/IDC-v2477/Foundation-Trust-Diversity-Equity-Inclusion-30379623/
Price: $4,500. **Description:** Doing business with and working for a diverse and inclusive company that strives to value the well-being of individuals and society at large is a forefront topic for consideration and effecting change. Report covers market developments and dynamics, perspectives, trends, business outcomes, technology investment, the future of work, data analytics, and related reserach. **Availability:** Download.

TRADE PERIODICALS

30412 ■ *Black Enterprise*
Pub: Black Enterprise
Contact: Earl G. Graves, Jr., President
URL(s): www.blackenterprise.com/about
Facebook: www.facebook.com/BLACKENTERPRISE
Linkedin: www.linkedin.com/company/black-enterprise
YouTube: www.youtube.com/user/BEMultiMedia
Released: Monthly **Description:** Black-oriented business magazine. **Availability:** Print; Online.

30413 ■ *The Columbus Times*
Pub: Columbus Times
Contact: Petra Ophelia Gertjegerdes, Publisher Managing Editor
E-mail: petra@columbustimes.com
URL(s): www.columbustimes.com/main-news.html
Released: Weekly **Price:** $2.50, Individuals for single copy; $182, for Yearly (52 weeks)-local; $234, for Non local. **Description:** Black community newspaper. **Availability:** Print.

30414 ■ *Minority Business Entrepreneur*
Contact: Barbara Oliver, Editor
E-mail: boliver@mbemag.com
URL(s): www.mbemag.com
Facebook: www.facebook.com/mbemag
X (Twitter): twitter.com/MBEMag
Ed: Barbara Oliver. **Released:** Quarterly **Price:** $28, for 1 year print and online; $20, for 1 year prtint; $14, for 1 year print; $40, for 2 year print and online; $33, for 2 years print; $22, for 2 years online only. **Description:** Business magazine for ethnic minority and women business owners. **Availability:** Print; Online.

30415 ■ *Multicultural Marketing News (MMN)*
Pub: Multicultural Marketing Resources Inc.
Contact: Lisa Skriloff, President
E-mail: lisa@multicultural.com
URL(s): multicultural.com/newsletter-category/multicultural-marketing-news
Released: Monthly **Description:** Covers minority- and women-owned businesses and corporations that sell to them. Provides story ideas, diverse resources for journalists, and contacts for marketing executives. Recurring features include a calendar of events, business profiles, and a feature on a trend in multicultural marketing. **Availability:** Online.

VIDEO/AUDIO MEDIA

30416 ■ *Building a Community*
URL(s): omny.fm/shows/startup-hustle/building-a-community
Ed: Lauren Conway. **Released:** September 08, 2023. **Description:** Podcast discusses the challenges and benefits of an inclusive community, how to get it involved in your business, and offering a place of diversity. .

30417 ■ *Small Business Sessions: Why Business Owners Should Embrace Diversity and Inclusion*
URL(s): www.enterprisenation.com/learn-something-small-business-session-podcast-cynthia-v-davis-diversifying-group
Ed: Dan Martin. **Released:** December 13, 2023. **Description:** Podcast defines diversity, explains why it's important for small businesses, and suggests what more needs to be done to support female entrepreneurs. .

30418 ■ *Supporting the Growth of Black Businesses with Karla Causey*
URL(s): www.awarepreneurs.com/podcast/329-black-businesses
Ed: Paul Zelizer. **Released:** April 09, 2024. **Description:** Podcast discusses how to support minority-owned businesses in New Mexico.

30419 ■ *Supporting Social Entrepreneurship in Indian Country with Cecelia Pacheco*
URL(s): www.awarepreneurs.com/podcast/native-american-entrepreneurship
Ed: Paul Zelizer. **Released:** January 23, 2024. **Description:** Podcast discusses entrepreneurship in indigenous communities.

30420 ■ *Tackling the Racial Wealth Gap*
URL(s): www.startuphustlepodcast.com/tackling-the-racial-wealth-gap
Ed: Lauren Conaway. **Released:** December 20, 2023. **Description:** Podcast discusses actionable insights in addressing racial wealth disparities and explores initiates to support black-owned businesses in Kansas City.

30421 ■ *Tackling Wealth Inequities*
URL(s): omny.fm/shows/startup-hustle/tackling-wealth-inequities
Ed: Lauren Conway. **Released:** September 20, 2023. **Description:** Podcast asks why venture capital and the investor landscape needs to shift focus. Explores bridging the gaps and barriers for historically excluded founders and why profit and social impact aren't mutually exclusive. Features Nassir Criss, Principal at Sixty8 Capital.

30422 ■ *Textured Hair, Crowdfunding and Beauty Tech Innovation*
URL(s): www.startuphustlepodcast.com/textured-hair-crowdfuding-and-beauty-tech-innovation
Ed: Lauren Conway. **Released:** October 25, 2023. **Description:** Podcast explores how curly hair challenges have shaped the beauty industry.

30423 ■ *This Is Small Business: How Culture Can Lead to Unique Business Opportunities*
URL(s): www.smallbusiness.amazon/podcast-episodes/ep-68-how-culture-can-lead-to-unique-business-opportunities
Ed: Andrea Marquez. **Released:** September 17, 2024. **Description:** Podcast discusses the importance of staying connected to your roots, building a community around your brand, and how empowering Hispanic-owned businesses benefits everyone.

30424 ■ *This Is Small Business: Miguel Connects with His Community to Grow His Brand*
URL(s): www.smallbusiness.amazon/podcast-episodes/ep-28-miguel-connects-wiht-his-community-to-grow-his-brand
Ed: Andrea Marquez. **Released:** May 23, 2023. **Description:** Podcast discusses the importance of representation and what it means to be a Latinx entrepreneur.

TRADE SHOWS AND CONVENTIONS

30425 ■ **NABA National Convention & Expo**
National Association of Black Accountants, Inc. (NABA)
7474 Greenway Center Dr., Ste. 1120
Greenbelt, MD 20770

Ph: (301)474-6222
Co. E-mail: customerservice@nabainc.org
URL: http://nabainc.org
Contact: Guylaine Saint Juste, President
URL(s): nabainc.org/2024-convention-expo
Frequency: Annual. **Description:** Exhibits relating to accounting. **Audience:** Accounting professionals. **Principal Exhibits:** Exhibits relating to accounting. **Telecommunication Services:** info@nabainc.org.

CONSULTANTS

30426 ■ Avita & Associates
5257 NE MLK, Ste. 201
  Portland, OR 97211
Ph: (503)998-9560
Co. E-mail: info@avitabiz.com
URL: http://www.avitabiz.com
Contact: Kedma Ough, Director
Description: Women-owned economic development firm dedicated to serving the interests of women, minorities, and persons with disabilities. Offers consulting and financial services.

30427 ■ Black Business Investment Fund (BBIF)
301 E Pine St., Ste. 175
  Orlando, FL 32801
Ph: (407)649-4780
Co. E-mail: info@bbif.com
URL: http://bbif.com
Contact: Inez Long, President
Facebook: www.facebook.com/bbifflorida
Linkedin: www.linkedin.com/company/bbifflorida
X (Twitter): x.com/bbifflorida
Description: Firm offers business clients a complete business support and growth service package. Primary goal is to provide Black and underserved small business owners with the know-how to successfully operate and manage their business. Provides technical assistance as well as direct, facilitated and guaranteed loans. **Scope:** Firm offers business clients a complete business support and growth service package. Primary goal is to provide Black and underserved small business owners with the know-how to successfully operate and manage their business. Provides technical assistance as well as direct, facilitated and guaranteed loans. **Founded:** 1987. **Training:** BBIF Business Community Outreach Seminar, Apopka, Apr, 2006.

30428 ■ The Nova Collective
1819 W Grand Ave., Ste. 203
  Chicago, IL 60622
Free: 866-383-4463
Co. E-mail: connect@thenovacollective.com
URL: http://www.thenovacollective.com
Facebook: www.facebook.com/thenovacollective
Linkedin: www.linkedin.com/company/thenovacollective
X (Twitter): x.com/findnova
Instagram: www.instagram.com/findnova
Description: Works to make the world a more inclusive place by helping businesses build and sustain diversity, equity, and inclusion (DEI) programs with real impact.

30429 ■ Redwood Enterprise LLC
Washington, DC
Ph: (205)546-7485
Co. E-mail: info@redwoodenterprise.com
URL: http://www.redwoodenterprise.com
Contact: Rene Redwood, Chief Executive Officer
X (Twitter): x.com/reneredwood
Description: Partners with clients to promote access and equal opportunity for individuals to reach their full potential, and organizations to accomplish their mission.

30430 ■ She+ Geeks Out, LLC
68 Harrison Ave. No 605
  Boston, MA 02111
Co. E-mail: hello@shegeeksout.com
URL: http://www.shegeeksout.com
Contact: Akyanna Smith-Gonzalez, Program
  Manager
Linkedin: www.linkedin.com/company/she-geeks-out

X (Twitter): x.com/shegeeksout
Instagram: www.instagram.com/shegeeksout
Description: Works to abolish inequity in the workplace. Supports businesses in their diversity, equity, and inclusion efforts by providing them with the knowledge, skills, and tools to create an inclusive environment. **Founded:** 2015.

30431 ■ True North EDI
2005 Dauphine St.
  New Orleans, LA 70116
Co. E-mail: info@truenorthedi.com
Facebook: www.facebook.com/truenorthedi
Description: A professional development firm that operates within the diversity, equity, and inclusion space. Supports professional communities in the design and development of practices, policies, and cultures where historically marginalized individuals and communities can thrive through workshops, coaching, and consulting. **Founded:** 2018.

PUBLICATIONS

30432 ■ *Atlanta Tribune*
URL(s): atlantatribune.com
Facebook: www.facebook.com/atltribune/
Linkedin: www.linkedin.com/company/atlanta-tribune
  -the-magazine/
X (Twitter): twitter.com/atlantatribune
YouTube: www.youtube.com/user/AtlantaTribune
Released: Monthly. **Description:** Business lifestyle publication and Black Atlanta's source for relevant, thought-provoking news and information on business and generational wealth-building. **Availability:** Online. **Telecommunication Services:** editorial@atlantatribune.com.

30433 ■ *Black Business News*
URL(s): www.bbala.org/bb-news-group
Released: Monthly. **Description:** A national monthly magazine published by the Black Business Association. **Availability:** Online.

30434 ■ *Black Enterprise*
URL(s): www.blackenterprise.com
Released: 1970. **Description:** Business, investing, and wealth-building resource for African Americans. Provides essential business information and advice to professionals, corporate executives, entrepreneurs, and decision makers. **Availability:** Online.

30435 ■ *Black EOE Journal*
URL(s): blackeoejournal.com
Facebook: www.facebook.com/BlackEOEJournal/
Linkedin: ww.linkedin.com/company/blackeoejournal/
X (Twitter): twitter.com/blackeoejournal
Instagram: www.instagram.com/blackeoejournal/
Released: Quarterly. **Price:** $18, Two-year; 4-issues. **Description:** African-American career and business resource whose mission is to inform, educate, and employ while providing equal opportunity within business-to-business connections and corporate American to create a more diverse and inclusive work environment. **Availability:** Print.

30436 ■ *BlackBusiness.org Blog*
URL(s): www.blackbusiness.com
Description: Online publication and newsletter that empowers Black entrepreneurs by promoting relevant news, success stories, and other valuable information to stimulate entrepreneurship in African-American communities. **Availability:** Online.

30437 ■ *DiversityInc*
URL(s): www.diversityinc.com
Released: Bimonthly. **Description:** Bi-monthly magazine and website that includes information on diversity management. **Availability:** Online.

30438 ■ *Entrepreneurs of Color Magazine*
URL(s): www.blackhistoryent.net/eocmag
Released: Monthly. **Description:** Monthly magazine that spotlights entrepreneurs and business owners of African descent. Works to educate entrepreneurs and business professionals.

30439 ■ *MBE Magazine*
URL(s): mbemag.com

Facebook: www.facebook.com/mbemag
X (Twitter): twitter.com/MBEmag
Instagram: www.instagram.com/mbemagazine/
Released: Quarterly. **Description:** Publication promoting the success of minority- and women-owned businesses and diversity programs. Provides business management resources with articles addressing business challenges, trends, and research, which enables diverse business owners to sustain and build upon their business success. **Availability:** Print.

30440 ■ *Minority & Multicultural Business News*
URL(s): mbnusa.biz
Facebook: www.facebook.com/MBNUSA/
X (Twitter): twitter.com/mbnusa
YouTube: www.youtube.com/channel/UCfuQYZPj
  dXeRb-0w6JSeQwg
Released: 1988. **Description:** Print and digital publication supporting the national minority supplier development initiative. **Availability:** Print; Online.

30441 ■ *The Network Journal (TNJ)*
URL(s): tnj.com
Released: Quarterly. **Description:** Black business magazine dedicated to educating and empowering its readers by providing news and commentary on issues that affect the growth of business and the advancement of professionals in the workplace. **Availability:** Print; Online. **Telecommunication Services:** tnjeditors@tnj.com.

30442 ■ *"Weigh in: 9 ways your store can better support BIPOC-owned brands" in Natural Foods Merchandiser (September 14, 2021)*
URL(s): www.newhope.com/natural-foods-merchan
  diser
Ed: Melaina Juntti. **Released:** September 14, 2021. **Description:** Tips and resources on how to support BIPOC-owned brands by including their products in retail spaces.

30443 ■ *"Young Latino Business Owners Getting Helping Hand Amid Hispanic Heritage Month" in Business 2 Community (October 6, 2021)*
URL(s): www.business2community.com/small-busi
  ness/young-latino-business-owners-getting-helping
  -hand-amid-hispanic-heritage-month-02434741
Ed: Merilee Kern. **Released:** October 06, 2021. **Description:** Discusses two business leaders who help facilitate young entrepreneurs of Hispanic heritage by hosting summits and other events in order to give a boost to that particular community of small businesses. **Availability:** Online.

INTERNET DATABASES

30444 ■ *African Americans in Business and Entrepreneurship: A Resource Guide*
URL(s): guides.loc.gov/african-americans-in-business
Description: A guide providing key topics on the history of African Americans in various business industries. **Availability:** Online.

RESEARCH CENTERS

30445 ■ University of Illinois at Chicago - Center for Urban Economic Development (CUED)
412 S Peoria St., MC 348
  Chicago, IL 60607
Co. E-mail: cued@uic.edu
URL: http://cued.uic.edu
Contact: Dr. Nik Theodore, Director
E-mail: theodore@uic.edu
Description: Integral unit of College of Urban Planning and Public Affairs, University of Illinois at Chicago. Offers program evaluations and technical assistance; research services to community organizations. **Scope:** Economic development, labor market research, technical assistance to community organizations and governments, immigration, globalization of the economy. **Founded:** 1978. **Publications:** *CUED Manuals*; *CUED Technical Reports*.

START-UP INFORMATION

30446 ■ *"Culinary School Puts a Food Truck on the Road" in St. Louis Post-Dispatch (March 21, 2012)*

Ed: Joe Bonwich. **Description:** Le Food Truck is a teach tool to help students learn about the fast-growing food truck market. Tony Hedger, instructor at L'Ecole Culinaire, a career college located in Laude, Missouri, coordinated the new program. The school also operates the Presentation Room, a restaurant used as part of the classroom. **Availability:** Print; Online.

30447 ■ *"Faces: Q&A With Katie Johnson, Co-Owner of Bloomy's Roast Beef Food Truck" in Saint Paul Pioneer Press (June 13, 2012)*

Ed: Kathie Jenkins. **Description:** Profile of Katie Johnson, 29 year old co-owner of Bloomy's Roast Beef food truck. Johnson discusses how her and her friend Ryan planned and started their food truck business and why they chose roast beef for their menu. **Availability:** Print; Online.

30448 ■ *"The Food Truck Handbook: Start, Grow, and Succeed in the Mobile Food Business"*

Pub: John Wiley & Sons, Inc.

Contact: Christina Van Tassell, Executive Vice President Chief Financial Officer

Released: March 2012. **Price:** $19.95, paperback; $12.99, e-book. **Description:** Food truck businesses have grown so much in popularity, there are actually food truck competitions and was once a television show featuring them. A practical, step-by-step handbook is offered to help an entrepreneur start a mobile food delivery service. Information includes tips on choosing vending locations, opening and closing checklists; creation of a business plan with budget and finding vendor services, daily operation issues; common operating mistakes; and insight into delivery high quality food. **Availability:** E-book; Print.

30449 ■ *"Radio Producer Launches Food Truck, New Show" in Dickinson Press (April 18, 2012)*

Description: Jason Spiess left his radio job to open The Rolling Stove mobile food truck in Dickinson, North Dakota. He will broadcast a new radio show from the food truck called, 'Talkin' Bakken' while serving breakfast and barbecue. He's using a 1973 Indian Winnebago that he bought from Craigslist.com and converted it into a barbecue smoker. **Availability:** Online.

30450 ■ *"Street Bistro Brings Food Truck Treats to Bangor" in Bangor Daily News (June 26, 2012)*

Ed: Emily Burnham. **Description:** Chef Kim Smith launched her food truck, Street Bistro in Bangor, Maine. Smith took a year off after closing her two restaurants called Unbridled Bistro and Bennett's Market. Smith and her husband purchased a Snap-On truck and redesigned it into a kitchen. Menu items range from French to Tex-Mex to Thai to American. **Availability:** Video; Online.

ASSOCIATIONS AND OTHER ORGANIZATIONS

30451 ■ **American Mobile Retail Association (AMRA)**
1993 Ford Step Van
Los Angeles, CA
Ph: (213)785-4783
Co. E-mail: info@americanmra.com
URL: http://www.americanmra.com

Description: Provides support, assistance, and education to mobile retailers across the United States. Seeks to inform the public and city officials of the positive benefits mobile retail businesses have on local economies, and to lift outdated restrictions on mobile retail vending. **Founded:** 2011.

30452 ■ **MMA Global Inc. (MMA)**
41 E 11 St., 11th Fl.
New York, NY 10003
Ph: (646)257-4515
Co. E-mail: mma@mmaglobal.com
URL: http://www.mmaglobal.com
Facebook: www.facebook.com/mmaglobal
Linkedin: www.linkedin.com/company/mma-global
X (Twitter): x.com/#!/mmaglobal
Instagram: www.instagram.com/mmaglobal

Description: Represents agencies, advertisers, hand held device manufacturers, wireless operators and service providers, retailers, software and services providers, and any company focused on the potential of marketing via the mobile channel. Strives to stimulate the growth of mobile marketing and its associated technologies. Establishes standards and practices for sustainable growth. **Founded:** 2003. **Publications:** *International Journal of Mobile Marketing* (Semiannual). **Awards:** MMA Best Use of Mobile Marketing Awards - Cross Media Integration; MMA Best Use of Mobile Marketing Awards - Direct Response (Annual); MMA Best Use of Mobile Marketing Awards - Product/Services Launch (Annual); MMA Best Use of Mobile Marketing Awards - Promotion; MMA Best Use of Mobile Marketing Awards - Relationship Building; MMA Best Use of Mobile Marketing Awards - Branding (Annual); MMA Outstanding Individual Achievement in Mobile Marketing (Annual). **Geographic Preference:** Multinational.

INCUBATORS/RESEARCH AND TECHNOLOGY PARKS

30453 ■ **Plug and Play - Mobility**
440 N Wolfe Rd.
Sunnyvale, CA 94085
URL: http://www.plugandplaytechcenter.com/industries/mobility

Description: An accelerator for startups in the mobility tech industry. Provides support with venture and angel partners, mentorship, a data center, office space, and networking opportunities. The program focuses on autonomous transport, connectivity, shared economy, electrification, industry 4.0, smart city and infrastructure, hardware and sensors, last mile logistics, VR and AR, and edge computing and data analytics.

REFERENCE WORKS

30454 ■ *7 Best Mobile Business Ideas With Real Life Examples*

URL(s): longtailpro.com/mobile-business-ideas/

Description: Technology has made the dream of location independent careers a very real possibility for many people. This article describes what a mobile business is and provides information about mobile businesses that are grounded in reality. **Availability:** Online.

30455 ■ *"7 Mobile Business Ideas To Meet Customers' Post-Pandemic Needs" in Forbes (Aug. 13, 2021)*

URL(s): www.forbes.com/sites/square/2021/08/13/7-mobile-business-ideas-to-meet-customers-post-pandemic-needs/?sh=36e66824472d

Released: August 13, 2021. **Description:** While the pandemic has forced many shops to close their doors, it has also created opportunities for entrepreneurs. Mobile businesses are uniquely equipped to bring their goods and services to their customers. This article brings forth 7 popular mobile business ideas. **Availability:** Online.

30456 ■ *"10 Mobile Business Ideas You Can Take on the Road" by U.S. Chamber of Commerce (Feb. 4, 2021)*

URL(s): www.uschamber.com/co/start/business-ideas/mobile-business-ideas

Ed: Andrea Forstadt. **Released:** February 04, 2021. **Description:** Discusses things to know before starting a mobile business, including permit requirements, local codes, ordinances and limitations on truck-based businesses. **Availability:** Online.

30457 ■ *"16 Money-Making Mobile Business Ideas" in The Balance Small Business (Nov. 20, 2019)*

URL(s): www.thebalancesmb.com/money-making-mobile-business-ideas-4126148

Ed: Alyssa Gregory. **Released:** November 20, 2019. **Description:** Mobile businesses allow owners and employees to travel to different locations to provide your products and services to your customers. This article discusses 16 types of mobile businesses that may work for you. **Availability:** Online.

30458 ■ *"17 Mobile Business Ideas to Get Your Company-on-Wheels Rolling" in NerdWallet (Oct. 22, 2020)*

URL(s): www.nerdwallet.com/article/small-business/mobile-business-ideas

Ed: Sally Lauckner. **Released:** October 22, 2020. **Description:** For small business owners who desire flexibility and mobility, the options in mobile business are broad and varied. This article provides information on 17 lucrative mobile business ideas. **Availability:** Online.

30459 ■ "49 Clever Mobile Business Ideas You Can Start in 2022" in Starter Story (Jan. 20, 2022)
URL(s): www.starterstory.com/mobile-business-ideas
Released: January 20, 2022. **Description:** Provides a detailed list of 49 low-capital, profitable mobile business ideas. **Availability:** Online.

30460 ■ "50 Mobile Business Ideas to Keep You Moving in a Profitable Direction" in Small Business Trends (Apr 4, 2017)
URL(s): smallbiztrends.com/2017/04/mobile-business -ideas.html
Ed: Annie Pilon. **Released:** April 04, 2017. **Description:** Mobile businesses have become more viable than ever in today's market. This article provides 50 different mobile small business ideas for entrepreneurs to explore. **Availability:** Online.

30461 ■ "Avoid the Stress of Traffic and Pollution with House Call Doctor Los Angeles" in Ecology, Environment & Conservation Business (May 24, 2014)
Pub: NewsRX LLC.
Contact: Kalani Rosell, Contact
Description: Record levels of air pollution in the Los Angeles, California area pose serious risks to those suffering from illness or injury. Michael Farzam and his team at House Call Doctor Los Angeles provides telephone medicine for those unable or unwilling to visit a physician in person. The mobile doctor in Los Angeles offers individuals throughout the area with concierge care without leaving home. **Availability:** Online.

30462 ■ "Bank of America Fights To Keep Top Spot in Mobile Banking" in Charlotte Business Journal (Vol. 27, June 15, 2012, No. 13, pp. 1)
Pub: American City Business Journals, Inc.
Contact: Mike Olivieri, Executive Vice President
Released: Weekly. **Price:** $20, Introductory 12-week offer(Digital & Print). **Description:** Bank of America has been fighting to maintain its lead in mobile banking services. Financial institutions, payment processors and e-commerce firms have started offering mobile banking services. **Availability:** Print; Online.

30463 ■ "Beyond the Food Truck: 10 Unique Mobile Businesses" in Entrepreneur (June 6, 2013)
URL(s): www.entrepreneur.com/slideshow/226734
Ed: Kathleen Davis. **Released:** June 06, 2013. **Description:** The costs associated with setting up a brick-and-mortar retail location can be daunting for first-time entrepreneurs. This article discusses the differences between mobile and brick-and-mortar businesses and provides examples of unique mobile business ideas that go well-beyond the food truck. **Availability:** Online.

30464 ■ "Bonnaroo 2012: Food Truck Oasis Returns With 9 Delicious Trucks" in International Business Times (June 4, 2012)
Pub: International Business Times
Contact: Michael Learmonth, Editor
Ed: Amanda Remling. **Description:** Manchester, Tennessee is the location for the Bonnaroo 2012 food truck event. The nine food trucks will be features offering their fares include: Eatbox, Gastropod, Good You, Gypsy Queen, Petro's Chili & Chips, Pot Kettle Black, Roti Rolls, Savory And Sweet, Tex's Tacos. **Availability:** Online.

30465 ■ "Choosing a Location for Your Retail Business: Pros and Cons of Brick and Mortar vs. Online" in business.com (Apr 8, 2020)
URL(s): www.business.com/articles/picking-your -business-location-pros-cons/

Released: April 08, 2020. **Description:** Discusses the advantages and disadvantages of online vs. brick-and-mortar retail businesses for entrepreneurs. **Availability:** Online.

30466 ■ "Conducting Effective Reference Checks For Your Food Truck" in Mobile-Cuisine.com (2020)
Ed: Richard Myrick. **Description:** Provides steps on successfully hiring food truck staff members. **Availability:** Online.

30467 ■ The Costs and Benefits of Running a Mobile Business
URL(s): completecontroller.com/the-costs-and-benefi ts-of-running-a-mobile-business/
Released: February 02, 2021. **Description:** Mobile businesses are completely situated within a vehicle and services can be provided anywhere. This article discusses the wide variety of mobile business types as well as advantages of running a mobile business. Also includes tips to consider before you start your mobile business. **Availability:** Online.

30468 ■ "Everything You Need to Know About Owning a Mobile Business" in Million Mile Secrets (May 3, 2019)
URL(s): millionmilesecrets.com/guides/everything -you-need-to-know-about-owning-a-mobile-busi ness-the-closest-thing-to-true-freedom/
Ed: Meghan Hunter. **Released:** May 03, 2019. **Description:** Many popular small businesses are mobile businesses. This article discusses what a mobile business is, costs involved for start-up and maintenance, insurance, etc. **Availability:** Online.

30469 ■ "First Food Truck Festival Features Enticing Fare, Frustrating Waits" in Saint Paul Pioneer Press (August 6, 2012)
Pub: McClatchy-Tribune Regional News
Ed: Megan Boldt. **Description:** The first Minnesota Food Truck Fest was held in downtown Minneapolis, Minnesota. Despite best intentions, attendees were left waiting in long lines and two vendors ran out of food in two hours. Fourteen food vendors and 25 craft beer trucks were representing this trend in food service. **Availability:** Print; Online.

30470 ■ "Food Truck Group Backs Proposed Regulations" in Buffalo News (January 18, 2012)
Ed: Aaron Besecker. **Description:** Food truck operators in the city of Buffalo, New York have accepted the newly created rules governing their operations in the city, despite the higher-than-expected $1,000 permit fee. An attorney for the Western New York Food Truck Association stated that the proposed rules would be acceptable to the membership. **Availability:** Print; Online.

30471 ■ "Food Truck Weddings Gain Popularity, Buck Tradition" in Tampa Tribune (June 24, 2012)
Ed: Jeff Houck. **Description:** A new trend crossing the nation is the use of a food truck for feeding guests as weddding receptions. Food trucks allow the bride and groom to provide a more casual atmosphere for their wedding party and is less expensive than a formal dinner. **Availability:** Print; Online.

30472 ■ "Food Trucks Savor Rebirth in City" in Providence Business News (Vol. 27, April 16, 2012, No. 2, pp. 1)
Description: Providence, Rhode Island has been experiencing the growth of the food truck business as the trucks and their devoted followers become regular fixtures in the city. Food trucks have a strong presence in the West Coast and have proliferated across the U.S. in recent years. Insights into Providence's food truck community are also given. **Availability:** Online.

30473 ■ "Fuel Costs Curb Food Truck Trend" in Tampa Tribune (March 26, 2012)
Ed: Jeff Houck. **Description:** Owner of Maggie on the Move food truck, Margaret Loflin, has had to raise the cost of drinks served in order to cover the

increased cost of gasoline to run her business. She also added smaller, less costly items to her menu. Her husband has gone back to a part-time job in he hopes of keeping their food truck running. **Availability:** Print; Online.

30474 ■ "How Mobile Devices Can Be Used in Food Truck Hiring" in Mobile-Cuisine.com (September, 23, 2020)
Ed: Richard Myrick. **Released:** September 23, 2020. **Description:** Details how to utilize mobile devices in your recruiting and hiring processes. **Availability:** Online.

30475 ■ "How to Start a Mobile Business" in The Zebra (July 12, 2021)
URL(s): www.thezebra.com/resources/personal-fi nance/how-to-start-a-mobile-business/
Released: July 12, 2021. **Description:** Many business owners are taking their product on the road. This article discusses a variety of aspects of mobile business, including flexibility and low startup costs. Also discusses risks involved in running a mobile business. **Availability:** Online.

30476 ■ "How to Start a Mobile Business - On the Way to Small Business Success" in Next (Aug. 14, 2018)
URL(s): www.nextinsurance.com/blog/how-to-start-a -mobile-business/
Released: August 14, 2018. **Description:** Discusses the complexities involved in starting a mobile business. **Availability:** Online.

30477 ■ "Hunhu Healthcare Gets Some Mayo Help" in Business Journal (Vol. 32, August 29, 2014, No. 14, pp. 4)
Pub: American City Business Journals, Inc.
Contact: Mike Olivieri, Executive Vice President
Description: Hunhu Healthcare Inc. has signed a licensing agreement with Mayo Clinic to develop mobile and Web applications that will enable patients to communicate with the company's network using social networking tools. The firm is expected to charge a monthly fee for the service. **Availability:** Print; Online.

30478 ■ Make Money As a Freelance Writer: 7 Simple Steps to Start Your Freelance Writing Business and Earn Your First $1,000
Ed: Sally Miller, Gina Horkey. **Released:** April 19, 2018. **Price:** $9.99, Paperback. **Description:** A how-to guide for turning your writing hobby into a freelance business. **Availability:** Print.

30479 ■ "Meals on Wheels; Chicago Puts the Brakes on Upwardly Mobile Food Truck Operators" in Wall Street Journal (August 7, 2012, pp. A12)
Pub: Dow Jones & Company Inc.
Contact: Almar Latour, Chief Executive Officer
Description: Details on the City of Chicago's move to regulate mobile food truck operators is presented. **Availability:** Online.

30480 ■ "Mercyhurst Rolls Out Culinary Cab Food Truck" in Erie Times-News (June 19, 2012)
Ed: Erica Erwin. **Description:** Mercyhurst University's food service company launched a Culinary Cab, or food truck, offering a variety of food choices to the campus community. Details of Parkhurst Dining Services plan for the mobile restaurant are outlined.

30481 ■ "Mobile Discounts: A Matter of Distance and Time" in Harvard Business Review (Vol. 92, May 2014, No. 5, pp. 30)
Pub: Harvard Business Publishing
Contact: Diane Belcher, Managing Director
Price: $6. **Description:** Geolocation via smartphone enables companies to offer consumers real-time incentives and discounts. Research shows that time and distance are key factors in a customers' receptiveness for these promotions: same day and close proximity increase the odds of a sales purchase. **Availability:** Online; PDF.

30482 ■ *"No. 82: a Few Good Apps"* in Inc. *(Vol. 36, September 2014, No. 7, pp. 103)*
Pub: Mansueto Ventures L.L.C.
Contact: Stephanie Mehta, Chief Executive Officer
Description: Alan S. Knitowski, former U.S. Army Captain, and his Austin, Texas-based mobile-focused development company is profiled. Phunware, creates apps for clients like ESPN, Cisco, Noscar, WWE, and NBC Sports. The firm won awards for its MythBusters app. **Availability:** Online.

30483 ■ *"One of the First Food Trucks in Montreal"* in America's Intelligence Wire *(May 31, 2012)*
Description: Food Trucks in Montreal launched its grand opening June 1, 2012. La Mangeoire offers five types of sandwiches and will serve food at festivals and locations permitted by the city during the summer. **Availability:** Online.

30484 ■ *"PayDragon Brings Mobile Payment App to Food-Truck Vendors"* in PaymentsSource *(April 16, 2012)*
Pub: SourceMedia LLC
Contact: Gemma Postlethwaite, Chief Executive Officer
Ed: David Heun. **Description:** PayDragon is a new App for food truck vendors to collect payments. It is also used by other small merchants. Paperlinks, developed this unit to provide a fast technology that enables consumers to securely order and pay for food with credit and debit cards using email, which elimiantes these steps for the vendors. **Availability:** Print; Online.

30485 ■ *"Practical Tips for Starting and Managing a Mobile Business"* in PowerHomeBiz.com *(Sept. 16, 2021)*
URL(s): www.powerhomebiz.com/business-ideas/ practical-tips-for-starting-and-managing-a-mobile busineso.htm
Ed: Derek Goodman. **Released:** September 16, 2021. **Description:** With a good business plan and knowledge of ongoing costs, a mobile business can be just as profitable as brick-and-mortar companies. Provides details on what to consider before you launch your company. **Availability:** Online.

30486 ■ *"Rice & Roll Onigiri Food Truck to Tour Los Angeles Area"* in Entertainment Close-Up *(July 30, 2012)*
Description: Rice & Roll Onigiri food truck service is entering the US market, offering Japanese stuffed rice balls in a variety of flavors and fillings. Asian cuisine is popular in restaurants and markets. The ten locations to visit Rice & Roll in California are listed.

30487 ■ *"Riverview Food Truck Event Draws Huge Crowds"* in Tampa Tribune *(January 25, 2012)*
Ed: Lois Kindle. **Description:** Brandon, Florida's first food truck rally offered sampling dishes to attendees. Over 6,000 people tasted food from 14 trucks serving gourmet and specialty foods. **Availability:** Print; Online.

30488 ■ *"Sabra Food Truck Gives Canadians a New Reason to Take a Dip This Summer"* in America's Intelligence Wire *(August 1, 2012)*
Description: Sabra Canada Inc. is taking its food truck on tour of Canada's largest cities, offering people an opportunity to sample their hummus and dips. A schedule of the various stops is provided. **Availability:** Online.

30489 ■ *Start Your Own Freelance Writing Business: The Complete Guide to Starting and Scaling from Scratch*
Ed: Laura Pennington Briggs. **Released:** July 16, 2019. **Price:** $13.49, Paperback; $9.99, E-Book. **Description:** A helpful guide for those seeking to pursue a freelance writing career. **Availability:** E-book; Print.

30490 ■ *"State Reverses Food Truck Order"* in Cape Cod Times *(May 15, 2012)*
Ed: Patrick Cassidy. **Description:** Massachusetts Department of Transportation is developing a plan that will allow food truck owners to operate under a new pilot program. Owners must obtain a license to operate through the Transportation Department's legal division. License requirements will be modeled on present license applications and some modifications may be necessary. Insurance issues must be addressed. **Availability:** Online.

30491 ■ *"Three Ways to Power Up Mobile Marketing"* in South Florida Business Journal *(Vol. 34, July 18, 2014, No. 52, pp. 12)*
Pub: American City Business Journals, Inc.
Contact: Mike Olivieri, Executive Vice President
Released: Weekly. **Price:** $8, introductory 4-week offer(Digital only). **Description:** A number of strategies that companies can apply to prepare for the future reality of mobile marketing are provided. Companies are encouraged to start the change to accommodate the new mobile world as mobile traffic data is projected to increase in record numbers and mobile connected devices will reach over 10 billion by 2007. **Availability:** Print; Online.

30492 ■ *"Top 10 In-demand Profitable Mobile Business Ideas You Can Start in 2022"* in StartupTalky*
URL(s): ctartuptalky.com/now mobilo buoinooo idoao/
Released: January 06, 2022. **Description:** Many mobile businesses are being opened based on current customer demands. This article looks at top ideas for mobile business. **Availability:** Online.

TRADE PERIODICALS

30493 ■ *Urgent Communications: Technical Information for Paging, Trunking and Private Wireless Networks*
Contact: Greg Herring, President
E-mail: gregg.herring@penton.com
URL(s): urgentcomm.com
Facebook: www.facebook.com/UrgentCommunica tions
Linkedin: www.linkedin.com/company/iwce%27s -urgent-communications
X (Twitter): twitter.com/UrgentComm
Ed: Donny Jackson. **Description:** Technical magazine for the mobile communications industry. **Availability:** Print; Online.

VIDEO/AUDIO MEDIA

30494 ■ *"Dining Notes: The Salty Fig is Jacksonville's Newest Food Truck"* in Florida Times-Union *(July 13, 2012)*
Ed: Gary T. Mills. **Description:** Jeff and John Stanford has selected locations throughout the city of Jacksonville, Florida to operate the food truck operation called, The Salty Fig. The brothers serve New

American Southern style food along with a bar drink menu. The Salty Fig is named after the trees the boys enjoyed at their grandparent's home. **Availability:** Online.

FRANCHISES AND BUSINESS OPPORTUNITIES

30495 ■ **Fast-teks On-site Computer Services**
17425 Bridge Hill Ct., Ste. 200
Tampa, FL 33647
Ph: (908)824-9222
Free: 800-262-1671
Co. E-mail: corporate@fastteks.com
URL: http://www.fastteks.com
Description: Onsite computer repair services. **Founded:** 2003. **Franchised:** 2004. **Financial Assistance:** Yes **Training:** Offers 2 days training at headquarters and 2 days onsite with ongoing support provided.

30496 ■ **Kidokinetics**
Broward, Miami-Dade
Weston, FL 33326
Ph: (954)385-8511
Co. E-mail: sef@kidokinetics.com
URL: http://kidokinetics.com
Contact: Terri Braun, Founder
Facebook: www.facebook.com/kidokinetics
X (Twitter): x.com/kidokinetics
Instagram: www.instagram.com/kidokineticssefl
Pinterest: www.pinterest.com/kidokinetics
Description: Firm provides sports and fitness programs for children. **Founded:** 1995. **Equity Capital Needed:** $42,900 to $57,000. **Franchise Fee:** $30,000. **Royalty Fee:** 7%. **Training:** Yes.

30497 ■ **Pop-A-Lock Franchise System**
Lafayette, LA
Free: 800-767-2562
URL: http://www.popalock.com
Contact: Tony McKeon, President
Facebook: www.facebook.com/popalock
Linkedin: www.linkedin.com/company/pop-a-lock
X (Twitter): x.com/popalook
Description: Mobile locksmith/car unlocking service. There is no build-out required with quick to market/ revenue generation. Your employees provide our mobile tech services to commercial and residential customers and national accounts. **Founded:** 1991. **Training:** Offers new franchisee business training, employee advanced technical training including state-of-the-art dispatch service. Provides ongoing technical updates, public relations and marketing, business analysis, and National Accounts Support-mentor program.

PUBLICATIONS

30498 ■ *Handbook of Research in Mobile Business: Technical, Methodological, and Social Perspectives*
701 E Chocolate Ave.
Hershey, PA 17033
Ph: (717)533-8845
Free: 866-342-6657
Fax: (717)533-8661
Co. E-mail: cust@igi-global.com
URL: http://www.igi-global.com
Contact: Jan Travers, Director
URL(s): www.igi-global.com/book/handbook-research -mobile-business-second/439
Released: Latest 2nd edition. **Price:** $37.50, Individuals for on demand (individual chapters); $320, Individuals for hardcover and e-book; $265, Individuals for hardcover; $265, Individuals for e-book. **Description:** Published by IGI Global. Provides research and scientific findings in the constantly expanding field of mobile business. **Availability:** E-book; Print.

ASSOCIATIONS AND OTHER ORGANIZATIONS

30499 ■ American Association for Access, Equity and Diversity (AAAED)
1701 Pennsylvania Ave. NW, Ste. 206
  Washington, DC 20006
Ph: (202)349-9855
Free: 866-562-2233
Fax: (202)355-1399
Co. E-mail: aaaaexecdir@gmail.com
URL: http://www.aaaed.org/aaaed/default.asp
Contact: Annette D. Butler, President
Facebook: www.facebook.com/theaaaed
X (Twitter): x.com/theaaaed
Instagram: www.instagram.com/theaaaed

Description: Purposes are: to foster the implementation of affirmative action and equal opportunity in employment and in education nationwide; to provide formal liaison with federal, state, and local agencies involved with equal opportunity compliance in employment and education. Is developing speakers' bureau and training program. **Founded:** 1974. **Publications:** *American Association for Access, Equity, and Diversity-Membership directory*; *American Association for Access, Equity and Diversity Newsletter* (Monthly). **Awards:** Cesar Estrada Chavez Award (Annual); AAAA President's Award (Annual); Rosa Parks Award (Annual). **Geographic Preference:** National.

30500 ■ American Indian Sciences and Engineering Society (AISES)
6321 Riverside Plz. Ln. NW, Unit A
  Albuquerque, NM 87120
Ph: (505)765-1052
Co. E-mail: info@aises.org
URL: http://www.aises.org
Contact: Sarah EchoHawk, Chief Executive Officer
Facebook: www.facebook.com/aises.org
Linkedin: www.linkedin.com/company/aiseshq
X (Twitter): x.com/AISES
Instagram: www.instagram.com/aises_hq
YouTube: www.youtube.com/user/aiseshq

Description: A national nonprofit organization focused on increasing the representation of Indigenous peoples of North America and the Pacific Islands in science, technology, engineering, and math (STEM) studies and careers. **Founded:** 1977.

30501 ■ American Society of Association Executives (ASAE)
1575 I St. NW
  Washington, DC 20005
Ph: (202)626-2723
Free: 888-950-2723
Fax: (202)371-8315
Co. E-mail: socmed@asaecenter.org
URL: http://www.asaecenter.org
Contact: Jennifer Baker, Director
E-mail: jbaker@asaecenter.org
Facebook: www.facebook.com/ASAEfan

Linkedin: www.linkedin.com/company/asae-the-center-for-association-leadership
X (Twitter): x.com/ASAEcenter
Instagram: www.instagram.com/asaecenter
YouTube: www.youtube.com/user/asaecenter

Description: An organization for association management, representing both organizations and individual association professionals. Works to help association professionals achieve previously unimaginable levels of performance by nurturing a community of smart, creative, and interesting people.

30502 ■ Association of Latino Professionals for America (ALPFA)
1717 W 6th St., Ste. 410
  Austin, TX 78703
Free: 855-MYA-LPFA
Co. E-mail: info@national.alpfa.org
URL: http://www.alpfa.org
Contact: Ann Marquez, Chief Executive Officer
E-mail: ann.l.marquez@national.alpfa.org
Facebook: www.facebook.com/ALPFA
Linkedin: www.linkedin.com/company/alpfa
X (Twitter): x.com/ALPFA
Instagram: www.instagram.com/alpfa
YouTube: www.youtube.com/alpfa

Description: Seeks to develop Latino men and women as leaders of character for the nation, in every sector of the global economy. ALPFA chapters offer professional development and career-building opportunities. **Founded:** 1972. **Awards:** ALPFA Scholarships (Annual). **Geographic Preference:** National.

30503 ■ Association for Multicultural Counseling and Development (AMCD)
6101 Stevenson Ave.
  Alexandria, VA 22304
URL: http://www.multiculturalcounselingdevelopment.org
Contact: Asha Dickerson, President
Facebook: www.facebook.com/MulticulturalCounselingandDevelopment
Linkedin: www.linkedin.com/company/association-for-multicultural-counseling-and-development
X (Twitter): x.com/AMCD2018
Instagram: www.instagram.com/amcd.profdevelopment

Description: Strives to increase ethnic and racial empathy and understanding in counseling, and to enhance understanding of cultural diversity. **Founded:** 1985.

30504 ■ Coqual
75 Rockefeller Plz., Ste. 2200C
  New York, NY 10019
Ph: (212)315-2333
Co. E-mail: info@coqual.org
URL: http://coqual.org
Contact: Lanaya Irvin, Chief Executive Officer
Facebook: www.facebook.com/Coqual
Linkedin: www.linkedin.com/company/coqual
X (Twitter): x.com/Coqual_

Description: A global, nonprofit think tank and advisory group that works to address bias and uncover barriers to advancement for underrepresented populations in the workplace. **Founded:** 2004.

30505 ■ Ethnic and Multicultural Information Exchange Round Table of the American Library Association (EMIERT)
225 N Michigan Ave., Ste.1300
  Chicago, IL 60601
Free: 800-545-5433
Fax: (312)280-3256
Co. E-mail: diversity@ala.org
URL: http://www.ala.org/emiert/emiertpeople
Contact: Dr. Andrea Jamison, Chairman
Facebook: www.facebook.com/AmericanLibraryAssociation
X (Twitter): x.com/ALA_EMIERT

Description: A round table of the ALA. Exchanges information about minority materials and library services for minority groups in the U. S. Conducts educational programs with a focus on multicultural librarianship. **Founded:** 1972. **Publications:** *Directory of Ethnic & Multicultural Publishers, Distributors and Resource Organizations, 5th Ed.* (Periodic); *Directory of Ethnic & Multicultural Publishers, Distributors and Resource Organizations, 5th Edition* (Periodic); *EMIE Bulletin* (Quarterly). **Awards:** The Coretta Scott King Book Awards (Annual); David Cohen/EMIERT Multicultural Award (Biennial); The GALE/EMIERT Multicultural Award; EMIERT Distinguished Librarian Award (Annual). **Geographic Preference:** National.

30506 ■ HeartMath Institute (HMI) - Research Library
14700 West Park Ave.
  Boulder Creek, CA 95006
Ph: (831)338-8500
Free: 800-711-6221
Fax: (831)338-8504
Co. E-mail: info@heartmath.org
URL: http://www.heartmath.org
Contact: Sara Childre, President
Facebook: www.facebook.com/HeartMathInstitute
Linkedin: www.linkedin.com/company/institute-of-heartmath
X (Twitter): x.com/HeartMathInst
YouTube: www.youtube.com/user/HeartMathInstitute

Description: Works to create a cultural shift in how organizations view people, and how people view each other and themselves. Validates the intelligence of the heart. Conducts biomedical research programs on the sources of stress, including work with post-cardiac patients, people interested in emotional management, educators serving child populations of at risk, learning disabled, at risk for violence, and in all sectors of society. **Scope:** Emotional physiology, heart-brain interactions, intuition, and the physiology of learning, performance and health. **Founded:** 1991. **Holdings:** Books; articles; monographs; Ebooks. **Publications:** *Science of the Heart*; *HeartMath Report* (Annual); *IHM Newsletters* (Quarterly). **Geographic Preference:** National.

30507 ■ Hispanic Public Relations Association (HPRA)
PO Box 86760
  Los Angeles, CA 90086
Ph: (917)880-8702
Co. E-mail: info@hprausa.org
URL: http://hprausa.org
Contact: Sonia Diaz, President
Facebook: www.facebook.com/HPRAusa
Linkedin: www.linkedin.com/company/hispanic-public
  -relations-association
X (Twitter): x.com/HPRAusa
Instagram: www.instagram.com/hpra_national
Description: Hispanic professionals in public relations. Promotes a positive image of Hispanics in the media. **Founded:** 1984. **Awards:** HPRA National Scholarship Program (Annual). **Geographic Preference:** National.

30508 ■ International MultiCultural Institute (IMCI)
595 6th St.
  Brooklyn, NY 11215
Ph: (718)832-8625
URL: http://imciglobal.org
Contact: Margaret Regan, Chairman
E-mail: mregan@imciglobal.org
Description: Seeks to work with individuals, organizations, and communities in creating a society that is strengthened and empowered by its diversity. Leads efforts to increase communication, understanding, and respect among diverse groups and addresses important issues of multiculturalism facing society today. **Scope:** A non-profit organization specializing in the areas of workforce diversity, human resource management, multicultural education and cross-cultural conflict resolution. Offers consulting programs in policy review and benchmarking; strengthening recruitment and retention programs; promoting cross-cultural communication; leading crisis interventions; and networking with affinity groups. **Founded:** 1983. **Publications:** Aims to work with individuals, organizations, and communities to facilitate personal and systemic change in order to build an inclusive society that is strengthened and empowered by its diversity. **Educational Activities:** iMCI Conferences. **Geographic Preference:** Multinational.

30509 ■ Kapor Center
2148 Broadway
  Oakland, CA 94612
Ph: (510)488-6600
URL: http://www.kaporcenter.org
Contact: Allison Scott, Chief Executive Officer
Facebook: www.facebook.com/KaporCenter
Linkedin: www.linkedin.com/company/kapor-center
X (Twitter): x.com/KaporCenter
Instagram: www.instagram.com/kaporcenter
YouTube: www.youtube.com/user/KaporCenter
Description: Works to remove barriers to science, technology, engineering, and math (STEM) education and tech careers for underrepresented people of color.

30510 ■ Muslim Entrepreneur Association (MEA) [Muslim Entrepreneurs Association]
8450 257th St.
  Floral Park, NY 11001
Ph: (516)308-6498
Co. E-mail: infomuslimstartups@gmail.com
URL: http://muslimstartups.co
Contact: Abdul Rahman, Contact
E-mail: abdul.rahman@mea-community.com
Instagram: www.instagram.com/mea_network
YouTube: www.youtube.com/channel/
  UCb9Gu90KunkdKZ6vIqVErmw
Description: Supports entrepreneurs in the Muslim community around the world through networking, capital fundraising, philanthropy, and professional events.

30511 ■ National Action Council for Minorities in Engineering (NACME)
1 N Broadway, Ste. 601
  White Plains, NY 10601-2318
Ph: (703)879-4010
Co. E-mail: scholarships@nacme.org

URL: http://www.nacme.org
Contact: Michele Lezama, President
Facebook: www.facebook.com/Nacme.org
X (Twitter): x.com/nacme
Instagram: www.instagram.com/nacme_org
Description: Leads the national effort to increase access to careers in engineering and other science-based disciplines. Conducts research and public policy analysis, develops and operates national demonstration programs at precollege and university levels, and disseminates information through publications, conferences and electronic media. Serves as a privately funded source of scholarships for minority students in engineering. **Founded:** 1974. **Publications:** *NACME Now* (Quarterly); *The Sky's Not the Limit*; *Financial Aid Unscrambled: A Guide for Minority Engineering Students* (Biennial). **Awards:** Alfred P. Sloan Foundation - Sloan Indigenous Graduate Partnership (SIGP) (Annual); Reginald H. Jones Distinguished Service Award (Annual); Alfred P. Sloan Foundation Graduate Scholarships - Sloan Minority Ph.D. Program (MPHD) (Annual). **Geographic Preference:** National; Local.

30512 ■ National Association of Black Professional Organizers (NABPO)
PO Box 723021
  Atlanta, GA 31139
Co. E-mail: nabporganizers@gmail.com
URL: http://nabpo.org
Contact: Takilla Combs, President
E-mail: president@nabpo.org
Facebook: www.facebook.com/nabpo
Linkedin: www.linkedin.com/company/nabpo
Instagram: www.instagram.com/nabpo_inc
Description: Works to provide education and support to professional organizers of all ethnic backgrounds. **Founded:** 2017.

30513 ■ National Association for Equity, Diversity & Inclusion (NAEDI)
Description: A member organization dedicated to improving the state of equity, diversity, and inclusion in workspaces so that marginalized and underrepresented individuals can thrive.

30514 ■ National Diversity Council (NDC)
1301 Regents Pk. Dr., Ste. 210
  Houston, TX 77058
Ph: (281)975-0626
Co. E-mail: info@ndcindex.org
URL: http://ndc.nationaldiversitycouncil.org
Contact: Angeles M. Valenciano, Chief Executive Officer
Facebook: www.facebook.com/nationaldiversi
  tycouncil
Linkedin: www.linkedin.com/company/national-diversi
  ty-council
X (Twitter): x.com/NDC_Diversity
Instagram: www.instagram.com/nationaldiversi
  tycouncil
YouTube: www.youtube.com/user/NDCPromotions
Description: Individuals and corporations at the national, regional, and state level. Seeks to bring together the private, public, and non-profit sectors to promote the benefits of a multicultural workplace environment. Serves as the umbrella organization for statewide and regional affiliates. **Founded:** 2008.

30515 ■ National Economic Association (NEA)
URL: http://neaecon.org
Contact: Valerie Wilson, President
Linkedin: www.linkedin.com/company/national-eco
  nomic-association/
X (Twitter): twitter.com/neaecon
Description: Concerned with encouraging blacks to enter the economics profession. Conducts research on the economic problems of the black community. **Founded:** 1969.

30516 ■ National Urban League (NUL)
80 Pine St., 9th Fl.
  New York, NY 10005
Ph: (212)558-5300
Co. E-mail: legal@nulshare.org
URL: http://nul.org

Contact: Marc Morial, President
Facebook: www.facebook.com/NatUrbanLeague
Linkedin: www.linkedin.com/company/national-urban
  -league
X (Twitter): x.com/naturbanleague
Instagram: www.instagram.com/naturbanleague
YouTube: www.youtube.com/user/IAmEmpowere
  dVideo
Description: Community service agency of civic, professional, business, labor, and religious leaders with a staff of trained social workers and other professionals. Aims to eliminate racial segregation and discrimination in the U.S. and to achieve parity for blacks and other minorities in every phase of American life. Works to eliminate institutional racism and to provide direct service to minorities in the areas of employment, housing, education, social welfare, health, family planning, mental disabilities, law and consumer affairs, youth and student affairs, labor affairs, veterans' affairs, and community and minority business development. Maintains research department in Washington, DC. **Founded:** 1910. **Publications:** *The Urban League News* (Quarterly); *The Urban League Review* (Semiannual). **Educational Activities:** National Urban League Conference (Annual). **Awards:** NUL Equal Opportunity Day Awards (Annual). **Geographic Preference:** National.

30517 ■ Native Hawaiian Organizations Association (NHOA)
3375 Koapaka St., Ste. B200
  Honolulu, HI 96819
Co. E-mail: daphne@nhoassociation.org
URL: http://www.nhoassociation.org
Contact: Lani Dawson, President
Facebook: www.facebook.com/nhoassociation
X (Twitter): x.com/nhoassociation
Description: Provides support and advocacy for Native Hawaiian Organizations (NHOs), which are non-profit organizations authorized by the U.S. Small Business Administration to participate in the 8(a) Business Development program. **Founded:** 2007.

30518 ■ OutLEADERSHIP (OL)
135 W 26th St.
  New York, NY 10001
Co. E-mail: info@outleadership.com
URL: http://outleadership.com
Contact: Todd Sears, Chief Executive Officer
Facebook: www.facebook.com/OutLeadership
Linkedin: www.linkedin.com/company/out-leadership
X (Twitter): x.com/outleadership
Instagram: www.instagram.com/outleadership
Description: A global LGBTQ+ business network trusted by CEOs and multinational companies to drive equality forward. **Founded:** 2010.

30519 ■ Racial Equity Institute LLC (REI)
Greensboro, NC
Ph: (336)582-0351
URL: http://racialequityinstitute.org
Facebook: www.facebook.com/racialequityinstitute
Linkedin: www.linkedin.com/company/the-racial-equi
  ty-institute/mycompany
X (Twitter): x.com/RacialEquityREI
Description: An alliance of trainers, organizers, and institutional leaders working to create racially equitable organizations.

30520 ■ Seramount
2445 M St. NW
  Washington, DC 20037
Ph: (202)747-1005
Co. E-mail: hello@seramount.com
URL: http://seramount.com
Contact: Subha Barry, President
Facebook: www.facebook.com/seramount
X (Twitter): x.com/seramount
Description: Helps companies create strategies and solutions needed to navigate the ever-changing landscape of diversity, equity, and inclusion (DEI) in the workplace. **Founded:** 1979.

30521 ■ We Are All Human (WAAH)
348w 57th St., ste. 169
  New York, NY 10013
Co. E-mail: info@weareallhuman.org

URL: http://www.weareallhuman.org
Contact: Claudia Romo Edelman, Founder
Facebook: www.facebook.com/weareallhumanorg
Linkedin: www.linkedin.com/company/weareallhuman
X (Twitter): x.com/WAAH_Foundation
Instagram: www.instagram.com/weareallhumanorg
YouTube: www.youtube.com/channel/
UCeXfBROaErGce-af1E_jwYw
Description: Brings people together to rediscover our common humanity by advancing equity, diversity and inclusion. **Founded:** 2018.

EDUCATIONAL PROGRAMS

30522 ■ Diversity Awareness (Onsite)

Seminar Information Service Inc. (SIS)
250 El Camino Real., Ste. 112
Tustin, CA 92780
Ph: (714)508-0340
Free: 877-736-4636
Fax: (714)734-8027
Co. E-mail: info@seminarinformation.com
URL: http://www.seminarinformation.com
Contact: Catherine Bellizzi, President
URL(s): www.seminarinformation.com

Description: Increase understanding of all aspects of diversity and begin the process of dialogue and working together productively. **Audience:** Diversity managers, consultants, and all persons with responsibility for training. **Principal Exhibits:** Increase understanding of all aspects of diversity and begin the process of dialogue and working together productively.

30523 ■ Training Difficult Issues in Diversity (Onsite)

Seminar Information Service Inc. (SIS)
250 El Camino Real., Ste. 112
Tustin, CA 92780
Ph: (714)508-0340
Free: 877-736-4636
Fax: (714)734-8027
Co. E-mail: info@seminarinformation.com
URL: http://www.seminarinformation.com
Contact: Catherine Bellizzi, President
URL(s): www.seminarinformation.com

Description: Provides trainers with a step-by-step curriculum for delivering training and education on the tougher issues, including racism, privilege, religion, sexual orientation, gender identity, and oppression. Explore training techniques and models that get diversity messages across. **Audience:** Diversity managers and consultants. **Principal Exhibits:** Provides trainers with a step-by-step curriculum for delivering training and education on the tougher issues, including racism, privilege, religion, sexual orientation, gender identity, and oppression. Explore training techniques and models that get diversity messages across.

REFERENCE WORKS

30524 ■ "4 Visa Programs That Can Help Employers Solve Their Workforce Needs" in U.S. Chamber of Commerce (Nov. 12, 2021)

URL(s): www.uschamber.com/immigration/4-visa-programs-that-can-help-employers-solve-their-workforce-needs

Ed: Jon Baselice. **Released:** November 12, 2021. **Description:** Provides information on four non-immigrant visa programs small business leaders should know about as they look to fill open positions. **Availability:** Online.

30525 ■ 5 Powerful Ways to Take REAL Action on DEI

URL(s): www.ccl.org/articles/leading-effectively-articles/5-powerful-ways-to-take-real-action-on-dei-diversity-equity-inclusion/

Released: September 01, 2022. **Description:** Discusses DEI (Diversity, Equity & Inclusion) training and why EDI (Equity, Diversity & Inclusion) is recommended, with a focus on equity first. **Availability:** Online.

30526 ■ "7 Tips for Hiring a More Diverse Workforce" in U.S. Chamber of Commerce (June 9, 2020)

URL(s): www.uschamber.com/co/run/human-resources/hiring-diverse-workforce

Ed: Sean Ludwig. **Released:** June 09, 2020. **Description:** Offers seven tips for hiring a more diverse workforce. **Availability:** Online.

30527 ■ 10 Everyday Actions to Make the Workplace More Inclusive for Women

URL(s): www.kornferry.com/insights/featured-topics/diversity-equity-inclusion/10-everyday-actions-to-make-the-workplace-more-inclusive-for-women

Released: April 04, 2022. **Description:** Proposes ten everyday actions of inclusion that you can take to ensure that your workplace is more inclusive for women. **Availability:** Online.

30528 ■ 11 Diversity, Equity & Inclusion Resources for Small Businesses

URL(s): www.wordstream.com/blog/ws/2022/05/31/diversity-equity-inclusion-resources

Ed: Kristen McCormick. **Released:** July 28, 2022. **Description:** Provides eleven diversity, equity, and inclusion (DEI) resources to incorporate true accessibility and inclusivity into your small business marketing and business strategy. **Availability:** Online.

30529 ■ "Accessibility Is an Opportunity, Not an Obstacle" in Associations Now (May 9, 2022)

URL(s): associationsnow.com/article/accessibility-is-an-opportunity-not-an-obstacle/

Ed: Lisa Boylan. **Released:** May 09, 2022. **Description:** Discusses the importance of disability access as part of diversity, equity, and inclusion (DEI) programs within your small business. **Availability:** Online.

30530 ■ "Accounting Lags Behind: Profession Trails Others in Recruiting and Retaining Minorities" in Philadelphia Business Journal (Vol. 28, June 29, 2012, No. 20, pp. 1)

Pub: Baltimore Business Journal
Contact: Rhonda Pringle, President
E-mail: rpringle@bizjournals.com

Description: Accounting firms in the US had a low number of ethnic minorities in their talent pool, particularly African Americans and Hispanic accountants. A survey by the Pennsylvania Institute of CPAs found that 71 percent of their members do not believe their organization has a diversity recruitment and retention strategy in place. **Availability:** Print; Online.

30531 ■ Aleria Opens Groundbreaking One-Year Inclusion Program for Small Businesses

URL(s): www.yahoo.com/now/aleria-opens-groundbreaking-one-inclusion-203750594.html

Released: September 27, 2022. **Description:** Offers information on the Inclusion for Small Business program offered by Aleria, a program for business leaders who are searching for meaningful ways to improve their diversity, equity, and inclusion (DEI) practices. **Availability:** Online.

30532 ■ "All Things Being Equitable" in Associations now (May 9, 2022)

URL(s): associationsnow.com/article/all-things-being-equitable/

Ed: Mark Athitakis. **Released:** May 09, 2022. **Description:** Presents information on addressing diversity, equity, and inclusion (DEI) not only within your current workforce, but addressing DEI for potential employees. **Availability:** Online.

30533 ■ "American Water's Ed Vallejo Chosen for 2012 Minority Business Leader Awards" in Manufacturing Close-Up (July 30, 2012)

Description: Ed Vallejo, vice presient of investor relations at American Water, has been awarded the 2012 Minority Business Leader Award from the Philadelphia Business Journal. Vallejo is responsible for developing investor relations strategies for the publicly traded water and wastewater utility firm. He also serves as the company's liaison with financial analyst and investor communities. **Availability:** Online.

30534 ■ "Another Determinant of Entrepreneurship: The Belief in Witchcraft and Entrepreneurship" in International Journal of Entrepreneurship and Small Business (Vol. 10, July 6, 2010)

Ed: Felix Pauligard Ntep, Wilton Wilton. **Description:** Interviews were carried out with entrepreneurs of Douala, Cameroon. These entrepreneurs believe that witchcraft existed and could bring harm to them or their enterprises. **Availability:** Download; PDF; Online.

30535 ■ "Ask Inc.: Managing and Real Estate to Build Value" in Inc. (December 2007, pp. 83-84)

Ed: Ari Weinzweig. **Price:** $8.95. **Description:** Questions regarding knowledge management in the case of a retiring CFO, issues involved in opening a satellite office for a New York realtor, and information for hiring a multicultural workforce are all discussed. **Availability:** PDF; Online.

30536 ■ "Assess Your DEI Maturity to Determine What's Next" in Associations Now (May 9, 2022)

URL(s): associationsnow.com/article/assess-your-dei-maturity-to-determine-whats-next/

Ed: Rasheeda Childress. **Released:** May 09, 2022. **Description:** Has your small business has already incorporated diversity, equity, and inclusion (DEI) practices? If so, this article explores how to assess your DEI maturity level and how to figure out where you're at so you can get where you want to go. **Availability:** Online.

30537 ■ "Be a Better Manager: Live Abroad" in Harvard Business Review (Vol. 88, September 2010, No. 9, pp. 24)

Pub: Harvard Business Publishing
Contact: Diane Belcher, Managing Director

Ed: William W. Maddux, Adam D. Galinsky, Carmit T. Tadmor. **Price:** $6, PDF. **Description:** Interrelationship between international experience and entrepreneurship is discussed. Individuals with international experience are likelier to be promoted and to develop new products and businesses. **Availability:** Online; PDF.

30538 ■ The Big Payback: The History of the Business of Hip-Hop

Ed: Dan Charnas. **Released:** November 01, 2011. **Price:** $17, paperback; $13.99. **Description:** The complete history of hip-hop music is presented, by following the money and the relationship between artist and merchant. In its promise of economic security and creative control for black artist-entrepreneurs, it is the culmination of dreams of black nationalists and civil rights leaders. **Availability:** E-book; Print.

30539 ■ "Bond Hill Cinema Site To See New Life" in Business Courier (Vol. 27, October 29, 2010, No. 26, pp. 1)

Pub: Business Courier

Ed: Dan Monk. **Description:** Avondale, Ohio's Corinthian Baptist Church will redevelop the 30-acre former Showcase Cinema property to a mixed-use site that could feature a college, senior home, and retail. Corinthian Baptist, which is one of the largest African-American churches in the region, is also planning to relocate the church. **Availability:** Print; Online.

30540 ■ "Border Boletin: UA to Take Lie-Detector Kiosk to Poland" in Arizona Daily Star (September 14, 2010)

Pub: Arizona Daily Star
Contact: John D'Orlando, President
E-mail: jdorlando@tucson.com

Ed: Brady McCombs. **Description:** University of Arizona's National Center for Border Security and Immigration Research will send a team to Warsaw, Poland to show border guards from 27 European Union countries the center's Avatar Kiosk. The Avatar technology is designed for use at border ports and airports to assist Customs officers detect individuals who are lying. **Availability:** Print; Online.

30541 ■ Build Diversity, Equity and Inclusion in the Workplace
URL(s): www.kornferry.com/insights/featured-topics/diversity-equity-inclusion/build-diversity-equity-and-inclusion-in-the-workplace
Released: August 17, 2022. **Description:** Presents information on why businesses should embed diversity, equity, and inclusion (DEI) into their culture, purpose and practices. Also discusses the dimensions of DEI maturity. **Availability:** Online.

30542 ■ Building a More Diverse and Inclusive Culture
URL(s): www.kornferry.com/insights/featured-topics/diversity-equity-inclusion/building-a-more-diverse-and-inclusive-culture
Released: August 22, 2022. **Description:** Presents a real-life example of how one company worked to accelerate diversity programming. **Availability:** Online.

30543 ■ Building the Perfect Scorecard to Achieve DE&I Goals
URL(s): www.kornferry.com/insights/featured-topics/diversity-equity-inclusion/building-the-perfect-scorecard-to-achieve-d-e-and-i-goals
Released: February 14, 2022. **Description:** Provides a 10-step blueprint that your small business can use to design a scorecard grounded in diversity, equity, and inclusion (DEI) metrics to help you achieve your diversity and inclusion goals. **Availability:** Online.

30544 ■ "Building a Workforce" in Business Journal Milwaukee (Vol. 29, July 27, 2012, No. 44, pp. 1)
Ed: Rich Kirchen. **Description:** Governor Scott Walker's 'Wisconsin Working' initiative head Tim Sullivan announced that he will recommend the encouragement of immigration to meet current and future employment needs of the state. Sullivan believes immigration could help address the worker skills shortage that affected many southeaster Wisconsin businesses. **Availability:** Print; Online.

30545 ■ "The Business Case for Diversity May Be Backfiring, a New Study Shows" in Forbes (June 20, 2022)
URL(s): www.forbes.com/sites/kimelsesser/2022/06/20/the-business-case-for-diversity-is-backfiring/?sh=78132829351d
Ed: Kim Elsesser. **Released:** June 20, 2022. **Description:** Offers information on why using diversity, equity, and inclusion (DEI) as a link to corporate profits may backfire. **Availability:** Online.

30546 ■ "A Business Guide to Diversity, Equity, and Inclusion" in U.S. Chamber of Commerce (Sept. 14, 2021)
URL(s): www.uschamber.com/diversity/business-guide-to-diversity-equity-and-inclusion
Released: September 14, 2021. **Description:** A guide to how diversity, equity, and inclusion (DEI) can benefit your small business. Includes ways to increase diversity at your company. **Availability:** Online.

30547 ■ "Campaign Launches to Educate Hispanics on Tax Preparation" in Economics Week (February 3, 2012, pp. 35)
Pub: NewsRX LLC.
Contact: Kalani Rosell, Contact

Description: Hispanic Access Foundation has partnered with H&R Block to offer a program to help Hispanics file their taxes while avoiding fraud and misinformation. The campaign is called, 'Preparate Para Un Futuro Mejor' (Prepare Yourself for a Better Future) and will help fill the void for tax preparation education for Hispanics. **Availability:** Online.

30548 ■ "The CEO Poll: Split on Migrant Workers" in Canadian Business (Vol. 83, September 14, 2010, No. 15, pp. 23)
Pub: Rogers Media Inc.
Contact: Neil Spivak, Chief Executive Officer

Ed: Jacqueline Nelson. **Description:** A survey of Canadian CEOs shows that 49 percent of the respondents believe it was wrong to suspend the immigration programs and companies should be allowed to hire the most skilled workers regardless of citizenship. However, 42 percent believe the suspension was right because employment of Canadians must take precedence. **Availability:** Print; Online.

30549 ■ "The CEO's Role in DEI Success" in Associations Now (May 9, 2022)
URL(s): associationsnow.com/article/the-ceos-role-in-dei-success/
Ed: Lisa Boylan. **Released:** May 09, 2022. **Description:** Describes the type of leadership needed from a CEO to successfully advance diversity, equity, and inclusion (DEI) in your business. **Availability:** Online.

30550 ■ "The Color of Success: ELC Focuses On Making Diversity Work" in Black Enterprise (Vol. 41, December 2010, No. 5, pp. 59)
Pub: Earl G. Graves Ltd.
Contact: Earl Graves, Jr., President

Ed: Sonia Alleyne. **Description:** CEOs and top ELC members at the annual recognition conference held in New York in October 2010 shared their perspective on corporate inclusion and advice for C-suite aspirants. **Availability:** Online.

30551 ■ "A Comparison of Adverse Impact Levels Based on Top-Down, Multisource, and Assessment Center Data: Promoting Diversity and Reducing Legal Challenges" in Human Resource Management (Vol. 51, May-June 2012, No. 3, pp. 313-341)
Pub: John Wiley & Sons, Inc.
Contact: Christina Van Tassell, Executive Vice President Chief Financial Officer

Ed: H. John Bernardin, Robert Konopaske, Christine M. Hagan. **Released:** May 25, 2012. **Description:** Levels of adverse impact against minorities and women were compared based on promotional decision methods. Results indicate significant effects for race and minority status in favor of white people but not for gender. **Availability:** Print; PDF; Online.

30552 ■ "Culturally Incongruent Messages In International Advertising" in International Journal of Advertising (Vol. 31, May 2012, No. 2, pp. 355)
Description: Research into the effect of culturally incongruent messages in international advertising on consumer responses is presented. The results of an experiment suggest that the type of cultural values (terminal vs instrumental)and ethnic background of models (foreign vs local) significantly moderate the effectof message congruency on attitude towards the advertisement, and such effect is mediated by the number of counter-arguments. **Availability:** Print; Online.

30553 ■ "Data Deep Dive: Supporting and Hiring Individuals with Disabilities and Neurodivergence" in U.S. Chamber of Commerce (Aug. 25, 2022)
URL(s): www.uschamber.com/workforce/data-deep-dive-supporting-and-hiring-individuals-with-disabilities-and-neurodivergence
Ed: Stephanie Ferguson. **Released:** August 25, 2022. **Description:** Discusses how businesses can give themselves a competitive edge when it comes to hiring by demonstrating their commitment to diversity, equity, and inclusion (DEI). **Availability:** Online.

30554 ■ "DEI Gets Real" in Harvard Business Review (Jan-Feb 2022)
URL(s): hbr.org/2022/01/dei-gets-real

Ed: Dagny Dukach. **Released:** 2022. **Description:** Discusses what it will take for small businesses to make diversity, equity, and inclusion (DEI) a reality within their business. **Availability:** Online.

30555 ■ "Disruptive Innovators: Commonground is Transforming the Advertising Landscape by Living at the Intersection of Culture, Creativity, Content, and Technology" in Black Enterprise (Vol. 44, June 2014, No. 10, pp. 82)
Pub: Earl G. Graves Ltd.
Contact: Earl Graves, Jr., President

Description: Profile of partners, Sherman Wright and Ahmad Islam, who started the Chicago-based Commonground Marketing. The firm is an integrated, multicultural and general market advertising company. The partners met while on vacation in Cancun, Mexico.

30556 ■ "Diversity in Business Awards: Minority Businessperson of the Year and Diversity Corporation of the Year Finalists" in ColoradoBiz (Vol. 30, July 2012, No. 7, pp. 32)
Description: Finalists for the ColoradoBiz 18th annual award presentation are profiled. The journal acknowledges minority businesses and businesspeople as well as firms that have been committed to hiring, contracting, and customer/community service to minorities.

30557 ■ The Diversity Code: Unlock the Secrets to Making Differences Work in the Real World
Pub: HarperCollins Leadership
Contact: Donald Miller, Chief Executive Officer

Ed: Michelle T. Johnson. **Released:** January 24, 2019. **Description:** The most diligent compliance with laws and regulations can't foster true work place diversity. The best organizations have become genuine cross-cultural communities that believe equality in reconciling difference and valuing them. The book promotes understanding by answering many of the toughest questions that professionals and their employers are afraid to ask. **Availability:** Print.

30558 ■ Diversity, Equity, and Inclusion in the Workplace in 2022: Best Practices
Pub: UpCity, Inc.
URL(s): upcity.com/experts/diversity-equity-and-inclusion-in-the-workplace/
Ed: Rebecca Lubecki. **Released:** June 10, 2022. **Description:** Provides information on how entrepreneurs and small-to-midsize businesses can get started with incorporation of diversity, equity, and inclusion initiatives. **Availability:** Online.

30559 ■ "Diversity Knocks" in Canadian Business (Vol. 83, October 12, 2010, No. 17, pp. 62)
Ed: Angelina Chapin. **Released:** October 12, 2010. **Description:** Canadian companies have a global edge because of their multicultural workforce. However, most of these organizations do not take advantage and avoid doing business abroad. Canadian firms could leverage their multicultural staff with language skills and knowledge of local customs. **Availability:** Print; Online.

30560 ■ "Eclectic Reading" in Business Strategy Review (Vol. 23, Spring 2012, No. 1, pp. 68)
Released: March 06, 2012. **Description:** If ever a field of study was both science and art, marketing seems to fit the bill. Which may be why Nader Tavassoli has a keen interest in diverse subjects: branding, consumer cognition, communication effectiveness, consumer behavior across culturesand several others. What keeps his mind open to a constant flow of new possibilities? As you'll see by his suggested top ten list of books to read, Tavassoli believes strongly in delving into the arts and sciences. **Availability:** Print; PDF; Online.

30561 ■ *"Emerging Equals" in Business Strategy Review (Vol. 25, Summer 2014, No. 2, pp. 38)*

Released: June 02, 2014. **Description:** What role can and should businesses play in challenging gender inequality in emerging economies? . **Availability:** Print; PDF; Online.

30562 ■ *"Employer Guide to Tax Credits for Hiring Employees With Disabilities" in U.S. Chamber of Commerce (Aug. 25, 2022)*

URL(s): www.uschamber.com/workforce/employer-guide-to-tax-credits-for-hiring-employees-with-disabilities

Ed: Jenna Shrove. **Released:** August 25, 2022. **Description:** Provides tax credit information for businesses that hire employees with disabilities. **Availability:** Online.

30563 ■ *"Engage Employees to Embed DEI Across Your Association" in Assocations Now (May 9, 2022)*

URL(s): associationsnow.com/article/engage-employees-to-embed-dei-across-your-association/

Ed: Rasheeda Childress. **Released:** May 09, 2022. **Description:** Discusses the importance of getting buy-in from all staff members as you roll out initiatives aimed at addressing diversity, equity, and inclusion (DEI) within your small business. **Availability:** Online.

30564 ■ *"An Equitable Workforce" in Business Journal Portland (Vol. 31, May 2, 2014, No. 9, pp. 10)*

Pub: American City Business Journals, Inc.

Contact: Mike Olivieri, Executive Vice President

Description: Bank of America has awarded the Urban League of Portland a $200,000 unrestricted grant as part of its Neighborhood Builders program. Urban League has been working to revive its workforce development program to tackle unemployment among African Americans in Portland, Oregon. Details of the Urban League's plans are also presented. **Availability:** Online.

30565 ■ *"Expatriate Knowledge Transfer, Subsidiary Absorptive Capacity, and Subsidiary Performance" in Academy of Management Journal (Vol. 55, August 1, 2012, No. 4, pp. 927)*

Pub: Academy of Management

Contact: Sharon Alvarez, President

Ed: Yi-Ying Chang, Yaping Gong, Mike W. Peng. **Description:** The influence of expatriate competencies in knowledge transfer on the performance of subsidiary companies is examined. Results suggest that the success of knowledge transfer and subsidiary performance rely on the expatriates' ability and motivation to transfer knowledge as well as on the action taken by multinational corporations to develop subsidiary absorptive capacity. **Availability:** Electronic publishing; Download; PDF; Online.

30566 ■ *"Filling the Business Gap" in Hispanic Business (December 2010)*

Description: New York group seeks to increase state diversity supplier spending to help create jobs and boost the economy. According to a recent study, six out of 10 small business owners will increase capital spending but delay hiring in 2011. However, potential job creation is good among businesses owned by women and minorities. **Availability:** Print; Online.

30567 ■ *"Finding Your Place in the World: Global Diversity Has Become a Corporate Catchphrase" in Black Enterprise (November 2007)*

Pub: Earl G. Graves Ltd.

Contact: Earl Graves, Jr., President

Ed: Wendy Harris. **Description:** Does the inclusion of workers from other countries mean exclusion of African American workers in the U.S.?. **Availability:** Online.

30568 ■ *"Foreign Flavor of U.S. Innovation: Report Makes New Case for Immigration Reform" in Silicon Valley/San Jose Business Journal (Vol. 30, July 20, 2012, No. 17, pp. 1)*

Pub: Baltimore Business Journal

Contact: Rhonda Pringle, President

E-mail: rpringle@bizjournals.com

Released: Weekly. **Description:** The results of a recent study show that 76 percent of the patents created at the top 10 patent-producing universities include at least one foreign-born invetor. Findings also indicate that immigrants are three times more likely and US-born individuals to file a patent. Information about H1-B Visas is also provided. **Availability:** Print; Online.

30569 ■ *"Future of Diversity: Cultural Inclusion Is a Business Imperative" in Black Enterprise (Vol. 41, August 2010, No. 1, pp. 75)*

Pub: Earl G. Graves Ltd.

Contact: Earl Graves, Jr., President

Ed: Annya M. Lott. **Description:** As globalization continues to make the world a smaller place, workforce diversity will be imperative to any small company in order to be sustainable.

30570 ■ *"Global Business Speaks English: Why You Need a Language Strategy Now" in Harvard Business Review (Vol. 90, May 2012, No. 5, pp. 116)*

Pub: Harvard Business Review Press

Contact: Moderna V. Pfizer, Contact

Ed: Tsedal Neeley. **Price:** $8.95. **Description:** English is rapidly becoming the language of businesses regardless of where they are located. To improve efficiency, the author advocates implementing an English-only policy. However, this must be conducted with sufficient training and support, and appropriate cultural sensitivity. **Availability:** PDF; Online.

30571 ■ *"The Globe: A Cautionary Tale for Emerging Market Giants" in Harvard Business Review (Vol. 88, September 2010, No. 9, pp. 99)*

Pub: Harvard Business Publishing

Contact: Diane Belcher, Managing Director

Ed: J. Stewart Black, Allen J. Morrison. **Price:** $8.95. **Description:** Key factors that negatively affected Japan corporate growth and organizational effectiveness include: devotion to established path, isolated domestic markets, homogenous executive teams, and a non-contentious labor force. Solutions include leadership development programs, multicultural input, and cross-cultural training. **Availability:** Online; PDF.

30572 ■ *How Diversity, Equity, and Inclusion Can Help Corporate America Thrive*

URL(s): nala.org/how-diversity-equity-and-inclusion-can-help-corporate-american-thrive/2022/

Ed: Roderick Parker. **Released:** nala.org/how-diversity-equity-and-inclusion-can-help-corporate-american-thrive/2022/. **Description:** Discusses the importance of including diversity, equity, and inclusion in your small business goals. **Availability:** Online.

30573 ■ *How to Get Diversity and Inclusion Right in 2022*

URL(s): www.zenefits.com/workest/how-to-get-diversity-and-inclusion-right-in-2022/

Ed: Dan Marzullo. **Released:** April 24, 2022. **Description:** Discusses the pros of having a diverse and inclusive workplace and provides suggestions on how to start incorporating representation into your workplace. **Availability:** Online.

30574 ■ *"How Metrics Can Improve the Quality of Your DEI Initiatives" in Associations Now (May 9, 2022)*

URL(s): associationsnow.com/article/how-metrics-can-improve-the-quality-of-your-dei-initiatives/

Ed: Rasheeda Childress. **Released:** May 09, 2022. **Description:** Discusses the importance of using metrics to take stock of gains (or losses) that you are making with diversity, equity, and inclusion (DEI). **Availability:** Online.

30575 ■ *"Immigration: Give Us Your Skilled" in Canadian Business (Vol. 80, October 8, 2007, No. 20, pp. 78)*

Pub: Rogers Media Inc.

Contact: Neil Spivak, Chief Executive Officer

Ed: Zena Olijnyk. **Description:** Demand for skilled workers in Canada is discussed. Despite a strong demand, as evidenced by shortages in both skilled and unskilled labor, the country's immigration policy is affecting the recruitment process. Peter Veress, founder and president of Vermax Group, believes the country is wasting opportunities to take advantage of its attractiveness as a destination for foreign workers. **Availability:** Online.

30576 ■ *"The Importance of Mixing Equity, Diversity, and Inclusion into Your Company's DNA" in U.S. Chamber of Commerce (Oct. 26, 2021)*

URL(s): www.uschamber.com/diversity/the-importance-of-mixing-equity-diversity-and-inclusion-into-your-companys-dna

Ed: Marcus Ashe. **Released:** October 26, 2021. **Description:** Discusses the importance of asking the question: "What has our organization done to truly support Equity, Diversity, and Inclusion within our walls and in our communities?". **Availability:** Online.

30577 ■ *Inclusive Sustainability*

URL(s): www.kornferry.com/insights/featured-topics/diversity-equity-inclusion/inclusive-sustainability-download-pdf

Released: January 20, 2022. **Description:** A downloadable paper that discusses why the environment, social, and governance spotlight should be on diversity, equity, and inclusion. **Availability:** Download.

30578 ■ *"Investment Firms Unite: Coalition Fights New Tax Law" in Black Enterprise (Vol. 38, December 2007, No. 5, pp. 52)*

Description: Minorities working in private equity, real estate and investment management firms have united to form the Access to Capital Coalition to oppose legislation that they feel would adversely affect their ability to attract investments and executives. Details of the group are included. **Availability:** Print; Online.

30579 ■ *"It's Not the How or the What but the Who: Succeed by Surrounding Yourself with the Best"*

Pub: Harvard Business Review Press

Contact: Moderna V. Pfizer, Contact

Released: June 03, 2014. **Price:** $32, Hardcover/Hardcopy. **Description:** Surrounding yourself with the best matters in every aspect of life and can mean the difference between success and failure. The author draws upon years of experience in global executive search and talent development, as well as the latest management and psychology research, to help improve the choices management makes about employees and mentors, business partners and friends, top corporate leaders and elected officials. **Availability:** E-book; Print.

30580 ■ *The Journey Forward: DE&I in the Workplace*

URL(s): www.kornferry.com/insights/featured-topics/diversity-equity-inclusion/the-journey-forward-dei-in-the-workplace

Released: July 21, 2022. **Description:** Presents key insights that business leaders need to build a more diverse, equitable, and inclusive workforce. **Availability:** Online.

30581 ■ *"The Language of DEI and the Terms Every Business Owner Should Know" in U.S. Chamber of Commerce (April 6, 2021)*

URL(s): www.uschamber.com/co/start/strategy/diversity-equity-inclusion-terms-to-know

Ed: Emily Heaslip. **Released:** April 06, 2021. **Description:** Breaks down the language of diversity, equity, and inclusion (DEI) so that small business owners have an understanding of what these terms mean and how they differ from one another so that you may work toward more inclusive hiring practices. **Availability:** Online.

30582 ■ *"LatinWorks Cozies Up to Chevy in Detroit" in Austin Business Journal (Vol. 31, August 12, 2011, No. 23, pp. A1)*

Pub: Austin Business Journal

Contact: Rachel McGrath, Director

E-mail: rmcgrath@bizjournals.com

Ed: Sandra Zaragoza. **Description:** Hispanic marketing agency LatinWorks opened an office in Detroit to better serve its client Chevrolet and to potentially secure more contracts from its parent company General Motors, whose offices are located nearby. **Availability:** Print; Online.

30583 ■ *"Looking for Diversity? How to Build a More Inclusive Small Business" in U.S. Chamber of Commerce (July 20, 2020)*

URL(s): www.uschamber.com/co/start/strategy/how-to-create-inclusive-business

Ed: Emily Heaslip. **Released:** July 20, 2020. **Description:** Offers information on how to build diversity, equity, and inclusion (DEI) practices into your small business culture and customer service. **Availability:** Online.

30584 ■ *"Lowering Retirement System Barriers for Women" in Employee Benefit News (Vol. 25, December 1, 2011, No. 15)*

Pub: SourceMedia LLC

Contact: Gemma Postlethwaite, Chief Executive Officer

Ed: Mary Nell Billings. **Description:** Challenges faced by small business for lowering retirement benefits barriers for women and minorities, which is difficult to put into practice, is discussed.

30585 ■ *"Managing Member Pushback to DEI Initiatives" in Associations Now (May 9, 2022)*

URL(s): associationsnow.com/article/managing-member-pushback-to-del-Initiatives/

Ed: Lisa Boylan. **Released:** May 09, 2022. **Description:** Discusses how to manage pushback on diversity, equity, and inclusion (DEI) initiatives within your small business. **Availability:** Online.

30586 ■ *Managing the Older Worker: How to Prepare for the New Organizational Order*

Pub: Harvard Business Press

Contact: Gabriela Allmi, Regional Manager

E-mail: gabriela.allmi@hbsp.harvard.edu

Ed: Peter Cappelli, Bill Novelli. **Description:** Your organization needs older workers more than ever: They transfer knowledge between generations, transmit your company's values to new hires, make excellent mentors for younger employees, and provide a 'just in time' workforce for special projects. **Availability:** Print; Audio.

30587 ■ *"The Many Dimensions of DEI" in Associations Now (May 9, 2022)*

URL(s): associationsnow.com/article/the-many-dimensions-of-dei/

Ed: Lisa Boylan. **Released:** May 09, 2022. **Description:** Discusses the complexities involved in diversity, equity, and inclusion (DEI), including nuances and distinctions that are sometimes overlooked when implementing DEI plans within your small business. **Availability:** Online.

30588 ■ *"Messaging Apps: What the New Face of Social Media Means for Brands" in New Generation Latino Consortium (December 2010)*

Ed: Gary Fackler. **Description:** Latina bloggers carve out a new niche in social media that helps preserve their unique cultural identities. **Availability:** Online.

30589 ■ *Neurodiversity in the Workplace: An Untapped Superpower*

URL(s): www.kornferry.com/insights/featured-topics/diversity-equity-inclusion/neurodiversity-in-the-workplace-an-untapped-superpower

Released: October 06, 2022. **Description:** Explains neurodiversity and offers information on the benefits of neurodiversity in the workplace and how neurodiverse employees can help your small business thrive. **Availability:** Online.

30590 ■ *"New Data Shows Small Businesses Are Embracing Diversity, Equity & Inclusion in the Workplace" in Business Wire (July 20, 2022)*

URL(s): martechseries.com/mts-insights/new-data-shows-small-businesses-are-embracing-diversity-equity-inclusion-in-the-workplace/

Released: July 20, 2022. **Description:** Presents information on how small business owners are making diversity, equity, and inclusion (DEI) a priority for their employees and customers. **Availability:** Online.

30591 ■ *"New Generation Deans Lead Atlanta Area Business Schools Into the Future" in Atlanta Business Chronicle (July 25, 2014, pp. 3A)*

Pub: American City Business Journals, Inc.

Contact: Mike Olivieri, Executive Vice President

Released: Weekly. **Price:** $4, introductory 4-week offer(Digital only). **Description:** An interview with five business school deans from Georgia share their views on the future of business education, changing business education needs, and other issues affecting the Atlanta area business schools. The growing demands for greater global competences, good communication skills across various cultures, and other challenges faced by the students and employers are discussed. Other topics include the role of women in the corporate world. **Availability:** Print; Online.

30592 ■ *"No Place Like Home? An Identity Strain Perspective On Repatriate Turnover" in Academy of Management Journal (Vol. 55, April 1, 2012, No. 2, pp. 399)*

Pub: Academy of Management

Contact: Sharon Alvarez, President

Ed: Maria L. Kraimer, Margaret A. Shaffer, David A. Harrison, Hong Ren. **Description:** Identity theory is invoked to investigate why employees returning from an international assignment may leave their organizations. Identity strain is attributed to the relation between prior job embeddedness during expatriation and strength of one's identity as an international employee of repatriation. Implications on international role transitions and turnover mechanisms are discussed. **Availability:** Electronic publishing; Download; PDF; Online.

30593 ■ *Non-Standard Employment under Globalization: Flexible Work and Social Security in the Newly Industrializing Countries*

Pub: Palgrave Macmillan

Ed: Koichi Usami. **Released:** First edition. **Description:** Expansion of non-standard employment under globalization is being recognized in all of the newly industrialized countries. The book examines deregulation of labor markets, social protection for nonstandard workers, and social security reforms in accordance with the transformation of employment.

30594 ■ *"The One Thing That's Holding Back Your Wellness Program" in Employee Benefit News (Vol. 25, December 1, 2011, No. 15, pp. 8)*

Pub: SourceMedia LLC

Contact: Gemma Postlethwaite, Chief Executive Officer

Description: A 13-year study shows that women who sat for more than six hours a day were 94 percent more likely to die during the study period. Most women sit at their desks an average of 7.7 hours while at work.

30595 ■ *"Overseas Overtures" in Business Journal-Portland (Vol. 24, October 26, 2007, No. 35, pp. 1)*

Pub: Portland Business Journal

Contact: Andy Giegerich, Managing Editor

E-mail: agiegerich@bizjournals.com

Ed: Robin J. Mood. **Description:** Oregon has a workforce shortage, specifically for the health care industry. Recruiting agencies, such as the International Recruiting Network Inc., answers the high demand for workforce by recruiting foreign employees. The difficulties recruiting companies experience with regards to foreign labor laws are investigated. **Availability:** Print; Online.

30596 ■ *"Post-Pandemic Rise in the Adoption of DEI Initiatives But Hiring Is a Different Story" in Incfile blog (July 20, 2022)*

URL(s): www.incfile.com/blog/rise-in-dei-initiatives-post-pandemic

Ed: Wendi Williams. **Released:** July 20, 2022. **Description:** Discusses results of Incfile's 2022 survey of small business owners related to how they are incorporating diversity, equity and inclusion (DEI) into their business practices and where they need to improve. **Availability:** Online.

30597 ■ *Profiting from Diversity: The Business Advantages and the Obstacles to Achieving Diversity*

Pub: Palgrave Macmillan

Released: First edition. **Description:** Although the benefits of diversity in small business are often discussed, specific ways in which organizations can profit from diversity and some of the obstacles faced are defined.

30598 ■ *"The Racial Divide and the Class Struggle in the United States" in WorkingUSA (Vol. 11, September 2008, No. 3, pp. 311)*

Description: An examination of questions of race that continue to play such a prominent role in contemporary society is presented, focusing on the undermining of potential solidarity and strength of the working class movement, what sustains racists attitudes, practices and institutions, especially in the face of trends in world economic development. **Availability:** PDF; Online.

30599 ■ *"Resources Roundup: Diversity, Equity, and Inclusion" in Associations Now (May 9, 2022)*

URL(s): associationsnow.com/article/resources-roundup-diversity-equity-and-inclusion/

Ed: Samantha Whitehorne. **Released:** May 09, 2022. **Description:** Discusses the importance of conscious inclusion strategies and other resources that will help small businesses apply diversity, equity, and inclusion (DEI) policies within their company. **Availability:** Online.

30600 ■ *"The Role of Leadership In Successful International Mergers and Acquisitions: Why Renault-Nissan Succeeded and DaimlerChrysler-Mitsubishi Failed" in Human Resource Management (Vol. 51,May-June 2012, No. 3, pp. 433-456)*

Pub: John Wiley & Sons, Inc.

Contact: Christina Van Tassell, Executive Vice President Chief Financial Officer

Ed: Carol Gill. **Released:** May 25, 2012. **Description:** The effects of national and organizational culture on the performance of Nissan and Mitsubishi after their mergers with Renault and DaimlerChrysler respectively are examined. Japanese national culture was found to influence organizational culture and human resource management practices, while leadership affected the success of their turnaround efforts.

30601 ■ *Scaling DE&I Through Supplier Diversity*

URL(s): www.kornferry.com/insights/featured-topics/diversity-equity-inclusion/scaling-dei-through-supplier-diversity

Released: September 09, 2022. **Description:** Includes information on how to improve your diversity, equity, and inclusion (DEI) efforts by focusing on supplier diversity. **Availability:** Online.

30602 ■ *"Scepticism Towards DTC Advertising: A Comparative Study of Korean and Caucasian Americans"* in *International Journal of Advertising (Vol. 31, February 2012, No. 1, pp. 147)*

Ed: Jisu Huh, Denise E. DeLorme, Leonard N. Reid. **Description:** Studies of cultural and subcultural differences among consumers are important for advancing knowledge on direct-to-consumer prescription drug advertising (DTCA). This study investigates and compares scepticism towards DTCA between Korean and Caucasian Americans and the relationship of cultural values (collectivism vs individualism) and acculturation to DTCA secpticism. The results of the research is provided.

30603 ■ *"Six Things for Employers to Consider When Hiring Individuals With Disabilities"* in *U.S. Chamber of Commerce (Aug. 25, 2022)*

URL(s): www.uschamber.com/workforce/six-things -for-employers-to-consider-when-hiring-individuals -with-disabilities

Ed: Jenna Shrove. **Released:** August 25, 2022. **Availability:** Online.

30604 ■ *"Speaking In Tongues: Rosetta Stone's TOTALE Adds 'Social' To Language Learning"* in *Black Enterprise (Vol. 41, September 2010, No. 2)*

Pub: Earl G. Graves Ltd.

Contact: Earl Graves, Jr., President

Ed: Sonya A. Donaldson. **Description:** As small businesses become more globalized, it is necessary to learn new languages in order to compete. Rosetta Stone's TOTALe is profiled. **Availability:** Online.

30605 ■ *"Sustain Your Focus on DEI"* in *Associations Now (May 9, 2022)*

URL(s): associationsnow.com/article/sustain-your -focus-on-dei/

Ed: Mark Athitakis. **Released:** May 09, 2022. **Description:** Explores the importance of a business' diversity statement and why companies must establish metrics around diversity, equity, and inclusion (DEI) goals. **Availability:** Online.

30606 ■ *"Sustained DEI Efforts Take All Hands on Deck"* in *Associations Now (May 9, 2022)*

URL(s): associationsnow.com/article/sustained-dei -efforts-take-all-hands-on-deck/

Ed: Rasheeda Childress. **Released:** May 09, 2022. **Description:** Discusses the importance of and how-to's related to operating long-term diversity, equity, and inclusion (DEI) programs within your small business. **Availability:** Online.

30607 ■ *"Taking Charge of Who's in Charge"* in *Associations Now (May 9, 2022)*

URL(s): associationsnow.com/article/taking-charge-of -whos-in-charge/

Ed: Mark Athitakis. **Released:** May 09, 2022. **Description:** Discusses the importance of establishing specific leadership roles for diversity, equity, and inclusion (DEI) within your small business. **Availability:** Online.

30608 ■ *"Talent Shows"* in *Canadian Business (Vol. 81, December 24, 2007, No. 1, pp. 14)*

Description: Canadian companies are increasingly turning to marketing to promote themselves as employers, as concerns on employee recruitment increase with the nearing retirement age of the baby boomers. Details on skills shortage, the potential advantage for the immigrant workforce, and employee retention are discussed. **Availability:** Online.

30609 ■ *"Tao of Downfall: the Failures of High-profile Entrepreneurs in the Chinese Economic Reform"* in *International Journal of Entrepreneurship and Small Business (Vol. 11, August 31, 2010, No. 2, pp. 121)*

Ed: Wenxian Zhang, Ilan Alon. **Description:** Through historical reviews and case studies, this research seeks to understand why some initially successful entrepreneurs failed in the economic boom of past decades. Among various factors contributing to their downfall are a unique political and business environment, fragile financial systems, traditional cultural influences and personal characteristics. **Availability:** Online.

30610 ■ *"USHCC Applauds 10 Best U.S. Corporations for Veteran-Owned Businesses for 2012"* in *Economics Week (April 20, 2012, pp. 153)*

Description: The United States Hispanic Chamber of Commerce honored the 2012 National Veteran-Owned Business Association and its 10 Best US Corporations for veteran-owned businesses. The list includes large corporations that engage three million veteran-owned businesse as suppliers. The Hispanic Chamber promotes economic growth and development of Hispanic entrepreneurs in the US. **Availability:** Print; Online.

30611 ■ *"The View from the Field: Six Leaders Offer Their Perspectives On Sales Success"* in *(Vol. 90, July-August 2012, No. 7-8, pp. 101)*

Pub: Harvard Business Review Press

Contact: Moderna V. Pfizer, Contact

Ed: Jim Koch, James Farley, Susan Silbermann, Duncan Mac Naughton, Phil Guido, Suresh Goklaney. **Price:** $8.95. **Description:** Six business leaders provide their perspectives on successful selling. Common themes include engaging customers and seeking their input, personalizing their services, ensuring accountability, implementing community outreach, being mindful of cultural and regulatory issues, providing unique offerings, incorporating experiential learning, and properly identifying a customer's needs. **Availability:** Online; PDF.

30612 ■ *"Voices From the Front Lines: Four Leaders on the Cross-Border Challenges They've Faced"* in *Harvard Business Review (Vol. 92, September 2014, No. 9, pp. 77)*

Pub: Harvard Business Publishing

Contact: Diane Belcher, Managing Director

Price: $8.95. **Description:** Points presented include building cultural sensitivity into organizations, employing varying talent to respond to market specifics, creating standard human resource practices worldwide, and emphasizing the importance of emerging markets. **Availability:** Online; PDF.

30613 ■ *"Wanted: African American Professional for Hire"* in *Black Enterprise (Vol. 37, November 2006, No. 4, pp. 93)*

Pub: Earl G. Graves Ltd.

Contact: Earl Graves, Jr., President

Ed: Joe Watson. **Description:** Excerpt from the book, Without Excuses: Unleash the Power of Diversity to Build Your Business, speaks to the lack of diversity in the corporate arena and why executives, recruiters, and HR professionals claim they are unable to find qualified individuals of different races when hiring. **Availability:** Online.

30614 ■ *"What Employees Worldwide Have in Common"* in *Gallup Management Journal (September 22, 2011)*

Description: According to a Gallup study, workplace conditions are strongly tied to personal wellbeing, regardless of geographic region. The employee study covered 116 countries. **Availability:** Print; Online.

30615 ■ *"What Is DEI and How Can It Benefit Your Small Business?"* in *America's Small Business Development Center blog (April 4, 2022)*

URL(s): americassbdc.org/75625-2/

Released: April 04, 2022. **Description:** Provides information on how diversity, equity, and inclusion (DEI) are vital to creating and maintaining a successful workplace. **Availability:** Online.

30616 ■ *"What It Takes to Be an Effective Leader"* in *Black Enterprise (Vol. 41, December 2010, No. 5, pp. 62)*

Pub: Earl G. Graves Ltd.

Contact: Earl Graves, Jr., President

Ed: Sonia Alleyne. **Description:** Redia Anderson and Lenora Billings-Harris have partnered to write the book, 'Trailblazers: How Top Business Leaders Are Accelerating Results Through Inclusion and Diversity'. The book offers insight into best practices demonstrated by some of the most influential chief diversity officers in business. **Availability:** Online.

30617 ■ *What Leading Businesses Do Differently to Increase Diversity and Inclusion*

URL(s): news.sap.com/2022/06/deib-what-leading -businesses-do-differently/

Ed: Jacqueline Prause. **Released:** June 09, 2022. **Description:** Presents information on how employers are investing more effort and resources to move beyond talking about diversity, equity, and inclusion (DEI) to implementation. **Availability:** Online.

30618 ■ *"What's Your Language Strategy? It Should Bind Your Company's Global Talent Management and Vision"* in *Harvard Business Review (Vol. 92, September 2014, No. 9, pp. 70)*

Pub: Harvard Business Publishing

Contact: Diane Belcher, Managing Director

Price: $8.95. **Description:** Cultural awareness and language skills should be built into organizations to promote talent that is equally effective locally and globally. This will bridge gaps between non-native and native language speakers, fostering collaboration and increase competitiveness. **Availability:** Online; PDF.

30619 ■ *When Inclusive Language Leaves Us at a Loss for Words*

URL(s): www.kornferry.com/insights/featured-topics/ diversity-equity-inclusion/when-inclusive-language -leaves-us-at-a-loss-for-words

Released: August 08, 2022. **Description:** Discusses the ever-evolving nature of inclusive language and how it takes the right knowledge, mindset, and effort to ensure no one in your business is left behind. **Availability:** Online.

30620 ■ *Why Diversity, Equity and Inclusion Are a Business Priority*

URL(s): www.metacareers.com/life/why-diversity-equi ty-inclusion-are-a-business-priority

Released: July 13, 2022. **Description:** Discusses why diversity, equity, and inclusion (DEI) are a priority for a company like Meta. Profiles employees who share a commitment to DEI and a commitment to supporting small businesses in their communities. **Availability:** Online.

30621 ■ *"Why 'I'm Sorry' Doesn't Always Translate"* in *(Vol. 90, June 2012, No. 6, pp. 26)*

Pub: Harvard Business Review Press

Contact: Moderna V. Pfizer, Contact

Ed: Jeanne Brett, Peter H. Kim, Tetsushi Okumura, William W. Maddux. **Description:** Studies indicate that Americans associate an apology with culpability and personal responsibility, while Japan and other countries with group-oriented cultures view an apology as an acknowledgement that a transgression has occurred and that it is unfortunate. Implications for the role of the apology in negotiations and establishing trust are presented.

30622 ■ *"Why Make Diversity So Hard to Achieve?"* in *(Vol. 90, June 2012, No. 6, pp. 40)*

Pub: Harvard Business Review Press

Contact: Moderna V. Pfizer, Contact

Ed: John H. Rice. **Price:** $6, PDF and hardcover black and white. **Description:** Four obstacles to workplace diversity are identified: distributing the responsibility for improving diversity; managing activities rather than outcomes; focusing on correcting the culture rather than on promotion rates; and prioritizing minority candidates for diversity department positions without enabling them to transcend problems they themselves may be facing. **Availability:** Print; PDF; Online.

30623 ■ *"Why My Company Prioritizes Hiring Employees with Disabilities" in U.S. Chamber of Commerce (Sept. 14, 2022)*
URL(s): www.uschamber.com/workforce/why-my
-company-prioritizes-hiring-employees-with-disabili
ties
Ed: Kristen Barnfield. **Released:** September 14, 2022. **Description:** Addresses outdated, ill-informed misperceptions of people with disabilities in the workplace and provides information on diversity, equity, and inclusion practices. **Availability:** Online.

STATISTICAL SOURCES

30624 ■ *Diversity and Inclusion (D&I)*
Price: $5,800. **Description:** Covers the global diversity and inclusion market with projections to 2027. Provides a market overview, focus on select players, market trends and drivers, a global market perspective, and market analysis. **Availability:** PDF.

30625 ■ *A Foundation for Trust with Diversity, Equity, and Inclusion*
URL(s): www.marketresearch.com/IDC-v2477/Foun
dation-Trust-Diversity-Equity-Inclusion-30379623/
Price: $4,500. **Description:** Doing business with and working for a diverse and inclusive company that strives to value the well-being of individuals and society at large is a forefront topic for consideration and effecting change. Report covers market developments and dynamics, perspectives, trends, business outcomes, technology investment, the future of work, data analytics, and related reserach. **Availability:** Download.

TRADE PERIODICALS

30626 ■ *The Columbus Times*
Pub: Columbus Times
Contact: Petra Ophelia Gertjegerdes, Publisher
  Managing Editor
E-mail: petra@columbustimes.com
URL(s): www.columbustimes.com/main-news.html
Released: Weekly **Price:** $2.50, Individuals for single copy; $182, for Yearly (52 weeks)-local; $234, for Non local. **Description:** Black community newspaper. **Availability:** Print.

30627 ■ *Insight into Diversity: The EEO Recruitment Publication*
Pub: INSIGHT Into Diversity
Contact: Lenore Pearlstein, Publisher
E-mail: lpearlstein@insightintodiversity.com
URL(s): www.insightintodiversity.com
Facebook: www.facebook.com/insightintodiversity
Linkedin: www.linkedin.com/company/insight-into
-diversity
X (Twitter): x.com/INSIGHT_News
Ed: Alexandra Vollman. **Released:** Monthly **Description:** Journal for business, academia, non-profit organizations and the government to use in recruiting females, Native Americans, minorities, veterans, and persons with disabilities. **Availability:** Print; PDF; Online.

VIDEO/AUDIO MEDIA

30628 ■ *Capital + Support: Helping Native Entrepreneurs Thrive with Garry McBerryhill*
URL(s): www.awarepreneurs.com/podcast/299-native
-entrepreneurs
Ed: Paul Zelizer. **Released:** July 24, 2023. **Description:** Podcast offers advice on empowering indigenous entrepreneurs.

TRADE SHOWS AND CONVENTIONS

30629 ■ NBMBAA Annual Conference and Exposition
National Black MBA Association Inc. - Chicago
  Chapter
  PO Box 8513
  Chicago, IL 60680
Ph: (312)458-9161
Co. E-mail: partnerships@ccnbmbaa.org
URL: http://www.chicagochapternbmbaa.org
Contact: Stacy Crook, President
E-mail: scrook@ccnbmbaa.org
URL(s): nbmbaaconference.org
Frequency: Annual. **Description:** Topics including career, education, entrepreneurship, lifestyle and leadership. **Audience:** Business professionals, students, faculty, and advisors. **Principal Exhibits:** Topics including career, education, entrepreneurship, lifestyle and leadership. **Telecommunication Services:** conference@nbmbaa.org.

CONSULTANTS

30630 ■ Becoming Better Together, LLC (BBT)
2222 Cold Canyon Rd.
  Calabasas, CA 91302
Contact: Jennifer Mayer-Sandoval, Chief Executive
  Officer
Description: A collective of consultants and coaches that work with individuals and small businesses to create diverse, equitable, and inclusive cultures.

30631 ■ Big 2Go (B2G)
Bloomfield, NJ 07003
URL: http://big2go.com
Linkedin: www.linkedin.com/company/big-inspirations
-2go-llc-big2go
Instagram: www.instagram.com/biginspirations2go
Description: Helps leaders, teams, and organizations foster well-being at work. Specializes in managing stress and burnout, leader development, team retreats, and diversity, equity and inclusion.

30632 ■ Collective
Brooklyn, NY 11201
Co. E-mail: team@hello-collective.com
URL: http://www.hello-collective.com
Contact: C. S. Nas, Chief Executive Officer
Facebook: www.facebook.com/CollectiveDEI
Linkedin: www.linkedin.com/company/collectivedei
X (Twitter): x.com/CollectiveDEI
Instagram: www.instagram.com/collectivedei
Description: Partners with teams and organizations who want to build a culture that attracts, engages, and retains underrepresented talent. **Founded:** 2017.

30633 ■ CommunityConnective, LLC
7015 N Wolcott Ave., Apt. 2
  Chicago, IL 60626
Ph: (312)488-9395
URL: http://communityconnective.com
Contact: Heidi Massey, Founder
E-mail: heidi@communityconnective.com
Facebook: www.facebook.com/communityconnective
X (Twitter): x.com/HeidiEKMassey
Description: Works to build connections for small businesses and non-profits. Provides consulting in the following areas: anti-racism training, marketing & technology, and training & facilitation.

30634 ■ Construct The Present (CTP)
1631 NE Broadway St.824
  Portland, OR 97232
Ph: (971)500-5000
Co. E-mail: support@constructthepresent.com
URL: http://constructthepresent.com
Contact: Alexis Braly James, Chief Executive Officer
Facebook: www.facebook.com/ctppdx
Linkedin: www.linkedin.com/company/construct-the
-present
Instagram: www.instagram.com/ctp_consulting

Description: Experienced equity, diversity, and inclusion consultants committed to working with small businesses that are committed to building a better future. **Founded:** 2015.

30635 ■ CourtSide Consulting
PO Box 6176
  Broomfield, CO 80021
Ph: (720)740-8704
URL: http://www.courtsidehr.com
Contact: Courtney Berg, Owner

Description: Works with small businesses as a human resources support system. Specializes in establishing and improving on diversity, equity, and inclusion initiatives.

30636 ■ Culture Cipher Consulting
88 Quincy St., Apt. 4
  Brooklyn, NY 11238
URL: http://culturecipher.org
Contact: Nadia Ramadan Jones, Owner
E-mail: nadia@culturecipher.org

Description: A boutique consulting firm that focuses on building inclusive environments for small businesses. Collaborates with companies to create talent, equity, and inclusion programs and advise on how best to execute them.

30637 ■ Culture Solutions Group
1610 Little Raven St., Unit PH3
  Denver, CO 80202
Ph: (970)390-9420
Co. E-mail: info@culturesolutionsgroup.com
URL: http://culturesolutionsgroup.com
Contact: Caroline Fisher, Principal
Facebook: www.facebook.com/culturesolutionsgroup
Linkedin: www.linkedin.com/company/culture-solu
tions-group
X (Twitter): x.com/CSG_Culture
Description: Works to transform business culture through targeted training, facilitation, and leadership development.

30638 ■ DEI & You Consulting
Chaussee de Louvain 273
  1410 Waterloo, Belgium
Co. E-mail: contact@daiandyou.com
URL: http://deiandyou.com
Contact: Dolores Crazover, Chief Executive Officer
Facebook: www.facebook.com/DEIandYouConsulting
Linkedin: www.linkedin.com/company/dei-you-consul
ting
X (Twitter): x.com/ConsultingDei
Instagram: www.instagram.com/dei_and_youconsul
ting
Description: Helps companies foster a more diverse, equitable, and inclusive climate. **Founded:** 2021.

30639 ■ Diverse & Engaged
624 Broad St., Ste. 240
  Newark, NJ 07102
Ph: (973)755-6700
Co. E-mail: contact@diverseandengaged.com
URL: http://www.diverseandengaged.com
Contact: Dee Marshall, Chief Executive Officer
Linkedin: www.linkedin.com/diverseandengaged

Description: Provides strategy, programs and initiatives to engage, support and develop diverse populations.

30640 ■ Diversity Services Group
622 Third Ave., 7th Fl.
  New York, NY 10017
Ph: (212)683-0045
URL: http://diversity-services.com

Description: Helps companies design and hire an effective and diverse workforce with a focus on meeting the needs of their client organizations. **Founded:** 1996.

30641 ■ EMBOLDEN Action LLC
Dallas, TX
Ph: (972)626-8628
URL: http://www.emboldenaction.com
Contact: Reeshemah Davis, Founder Consultant

Description: A change management consulting business specializing in diversity, equity, and inclusion strategy development, systems change, leadership development, and executive coaching.

30642 ■ Equity & Results Consulting LLC
6115 Margarido Dr.
　Kingston, NY 12401-6619
URL: http://www.equityandresults.com
Contact: Elodie Baquerot Lavery, Leader Member
Description: Works with companies to create racially equitable processes and cultures.

30643 ■ Human Resource Solutions, Inc.
501 W 123Rd. St., No. 10-D
　New York, NY 10027-5009
Contact: Gerald Olivero, Chief Executive Officer
Description: Organizational performance improvement firm provides consulting services in executive coaching, process consulting, team building, organization development, management training, strategic planning retreats, quality and productivity enhancement and conflict resolution. Industries served manufacturing, retail, communications, computers and government. **Scope:** Organizational performance improvement firm provides consulting services in executive coaching, process consulting, team building, organization development, management training, strategic planning retreats, quality and productivity enhancement and conflict resolution. Industries served manufacturing, retail, communications, computers and government. **Publications:** "Executive coaching as a transfer of training tool: Effects on productivity in a public agency," Public Personnel Management, 1997.

30644 ■ ITEC Inc.
5835 Callaghan, Ste. 360
　San Antonio, TX 78228
Contact: Judith Rae Gates, President
Description: Designs materials and conducts workshops for companies and agencies with culturally diverse workforces. Sees diversity as a positive factor in creativity and high productivity, specializes in supervisory/managerial development, as well as maintenance, mechanic and support staff empowerment. **Scope:** Designs materials and conducts workshops for companies and agencies with culturally diverse workforces. Sees diversity as a positive factor in creativity and high productivity, specializes in supervisory/managerial development, as well as maintenance, mechanic and support staff empowerment. **Training:** The Challenge of Leadership; Managing Diversity via Empowerment; Basic Leadership Skills for Women; The Challenge of Team Building; Conflict Management; Controlling and Eliminating Employee Absenteeism; Managing Stress and Preventing Burnout; Managing Performance; Making Meetings Work; Taming and Training the Pen; No-Limit Secretary; Managing Organizational Change; Effective Problem Solving and Decision Making.

30645 ■ Kochman Mavrelis Associates Inc. (KMA)
PO Box 3549
　Oak Park, IL 60302
Ph: (708)383-9235
Free: 888-562-4070
Co. E-mail: info@kmadiversity.com
URL: http://www.kmadiversity.com
Contact: Jean Mavrelis, Chief Executive Officer
E-mail: jean.mavrelis@kmadiversity.com
Facebook: www.facebook.com/kmadiversity
Linkedin: www.linkedin.com/company/kochman
　-mavrelis-associates
X (Twitter): x.com/kmadiversity
Description: Firm provides guidance through various stages of growth and understanding that leads to effective management of cultural differences and allows people to identify the patterns of cultural difference, social experiences, issues, and concerns of a socially and culturally diverse workforce. **Scope:** Firm provides guidance through various stages of growth and understanding that leads to effective management of cultural differences and allows people to identify the patterns of cultural difference, social experiences, issues, and concerns of a socially and

culturally diverse workforce. **Founded:** 1986. **Publications:** "Opening Pathways to Tolerance: School Leadership in an Age of Diversity," Dec, 1997; "Corporate Tribalism: White Men/White Women and Cultural Diversity at Work"; "Black and White Styles in Conflict"; "We Hold These Truths to Be Self-Evident...An Interdisciplinary Analysis of the Roots of Racism and Slavery in America".

30646 ■ Lee Grossman Associates
9030 Forestview Rd.
　Evanston, IL 60203
Ph: (847)679-6796
URL: http://ablocal.com/us/evanston-il/LX399
　1365-lee-grossman-associates
Description: Offers counsel in managing change, personnel issues and organization development. **Scope:** Offers counsel in managing change, personnel issues and organization development. **Founded:** 1974. **Publications:** "The Change Agent," American Management Association; "Fat Paper, Diets for Trimming Paperwork," McGraw Hill. **Training:** Making Affirmative Action Work.

30647 ■ New Dynamics Associates
72 Shore Dr.
　Laconia, NH 03246
Contact: Carol Pierce, Owner
Description: Provider of organization development consulting to a variety of organizations, specializing in the management of diversity and working in flat inclusive structures. **Scope:** Provider of organization development consulting to a variety of organizations, specializing in the management of diversity and working in flat inclusive structures. **Publications:** "A Male/Female Continuum: Paths to Colleagueship"; "Sexual Orientation and Identity"; "The Power Equity Group"; "Definitions for Multicultural Dialogue". **Training:** Sexual Orientation and Identity; Journeys of Race and Culture; Gender Men, Women, and Colleagueship; Valuing Multicultural Diversity.

30648 ■ The Nova Collective
1819 W Grand Ave., Ste. 203
　Chicago, IL 60622
Free: 866-383-4463
Co. E-mail: connect@thenovacollective.com
URL: http://www.thenovacollective.com
Facebook: www.facebook.com/thenovacollective
Linkedin: www.linkedin.com/company/thenovacollective
X (Twitter): x.com/findnova
Instagram: www.instagram.com/findnova
Description: Works to make the world a more inclusive place by helping businesses build and sustain diversity, equity, and inclusion (DEI) programs with real impact.

30649 ■ Pope Consulting
11800 Conrey Rd., Ste. 240
　Cincinnati, OH 45249-1067
Free: 833-364-7673
Co. E-mail: info@popeconsulting.com
URL: http://popeconsulting.com
Contact: Merlin Pope, III, President
Facebook: www.facebook.com/popeconsultingdni
Linkedin: www.linkedin.com/company/pope
　-&-associates
Description: Provider of services like training, assessment, consultancy to firms. **Scope:** Provider of services like training, assessment, consultancy to firms. **Founded:** 1983. **Publications:** Provides management consulting services. **Training:** Managing Personnel Diversity; Diversity SOS: Skills for Ongoing Success; Diversity Learning Lab; Understanding Gender Dynamics; ConsultingPairs.

30650 ■ Red Lotus Consulting (RLC)
Boston, MA
Co. E-mail: s.rae.redlotusconsulting@gmail.com
URL: http://www.red-lotus-consulting.com
Contact: S. Rae Peoples, Founder
Description: Works to support your organization's commitment to equity, justice, and inclusion.

30651 ■ Redwood Enterprise LLC
Washington, DC

Ph: (205)546-7485
Co. E-mail: info@redwoodenterprise.com
URL: http://www.redwoodenterprise.com
Contact: Rene Redwood, Chief Executive Officer
X (Twitter): x.com/reneredwood
Description: Partners with clients to promote access and equal opportunity for individuals to reach their full potential, and organizations to accomplish their mission.

30652 ■ SAIR Collective
129 Ruskin Dr.
　Chapel Hill, NC 27516
Co. E-mail: connect@saircollective.com
URL: http://www.saircollective.com
Contact: Corey Williams, Founder
Facebook: www.facebook.com/saircollective
Linkedin: www.linkedin.com/company/sair-collective
X (Twitter): x.com/saircollective
Instagram: www.instagram.com/saircollective
Description: A diverse group of humans with a wide range of identities who seek to disrupt cycles of harmful beliefs and dismantle the hierarchy of human worth. Works to help individuals and organizations see, value, and include people with diverse identities. **Founded:** 2021.

30653 ■ She+ Geeks Out, LLC
68 Harrison Ave. No 605
　Boston, MA 02111
Co. E-mail: hello@shegeeksout.com
URL: http://www.shegeeksout.com
Contact: Akyanna Smith-Gonzalez, Program
　Manager
Linkedin: www.linkedin.com/company/she-geeks-out
X (Twitter): x.com/shegeeksout
Instagram: www.instagram.com/shegeeksout
Description: Works to abolish inequity in the workplace. Supports businesses in their diversity, equity, and inclusion efforts by providing them with the knowledge, skills, and tools to create an inclusive environment. **Founded:** 2015.

30654 ■ True North EDI
2005 Dauphine St.
　New Orleans, LA 70116
Co. E-mail: info@truenorthedi.com
Facebook: www.facebook.com/truenorthedi
Description: A professional development firm that operates within the diversity, equity, and inclusion space. Supports professional communities in the design and development of practices, policies, and cultures where historically marginalized individuals and communities can thrive through workshops, coaching, and consulting. **Founded:** 2018.

30655 ■ Two Brown Girls
PO Box 15858
　Washington, DC 20003
Ph: (641)715-3900
Co. E-mail: info@2brwngirls.com
URL: http://2brwngirls.com
Contact: Nicole Newman, Co-Founder
Description: Helps organizations transform at the individual, group and institutional levels. We work with organizations to build their capacity to live out their mission and professed values in ways that enliven and excite them.

30656 ■ YJLaurent Consulting
Washington, DC
Ph: (617)453-8348
Co. E-mail: yasmine@yjlconsulting.com
URL: http://yjlconsulting.com
Contact: Yasmine Laurent, Consultant
Description: Consulting firm offering integrated talent management solutions through a diversity, equity and inclusion lens.

RESEARCH CENTERS

30657 ■ Intercultural Communication Institute (ICI) - Research Library
Portland, OR 97225
Co. E-mail: info@interculturallibrary.org
URL: http://interculturallibrary.org

Contact: Dr. Janet M. Bennett, Contact
Facebook: www.facebook.com/ICIcommunity

Description: Independent, nonprofit organization.
Scope: Intercultural communication, international
education; diversity; counseling; conflict, negotiation
and mediation. **Services:** Copying; Library open to
the public. **Founded:** 1986. **Holdings:** 8600 books;
542 reports; 2445 archives; 1 microfiche.

30658 ■ International MultiCultural Institute (IMCI)
595 6th St.
 Brooklyn, NY 11215
Ph: (718)832-8625
URL: http://imciglobal.org
Contact: Margaret Regan, Chairman
E-mail: mregan@imciglobal.org

Description: Seeks to work with individuals, organizations, and communities in creating a society that is
strengthened and empowered by its diversity. Leads
efforts to increase communication, understanding,
and respect among diverse groups and addresses
important issues of multiculturalism facing society
today. **Scope:** A non-profit organization specializing
in the areas of workforce diversity, human resource
management, multicultural education and cross-
cultural conflict resolution. Offers consulting programs

in policy review and benchmarking; strengthening
recruitment and retention programs; promoting cross-
cultural communication; leading crisis interventions;
and networking with affinity groups. **Founded:** 1983.
Publications: Aims to work with individuals, organizations, and communities to facilitate personal and
systemic change in order to build an inclusive society
that is strengthened and empowered by its diversity.
Educational Activities: iMCI Conferences. **Geographic Preference:** Multinational.

30659 ■ Medical College of Wisconsin - Center for the Study of Bioethics
8701 Watertown Plank Rd.
 Milwaukee, WI 53226
Ph: (414)955-8498
Fax: (414)955-0042
Co. E-mail: bioethics@mcw.edu
URL: http://www.mcw.edu/departments/center-for
 -bioethics-and-medical-humanities
Contact: Kristen Tym, MA, Program Manager
E-mail: ktym@mcw.edu
X (Twitter): x.com/MCW_Bioethics

Description: Integral unit of Health Policy Institute,
Medical College of Wisconsin. **Scope:** Strive to distill
the underlying philosophical, legal, and cultural assumptions and implications of bioethical issues and
to recommend a process of consensus building and

policy formation. **Founded:** 1982. **Publications:**
Medical Ethics Committee Network Newsletter
(Quarterly). **Educational Activities:** Ethics Grand
Rounds (Monthly), Teaching on topics related to the
current issues in bioethics.

30660 ■ University of Houston College of Liberal Arts and Social Sciences - African American Studies Program (AAS)
3553 Cullen Blvd. Rm. 629
 Houston, TX 77204-3303
Ph: (713)743-2811
Co. E-mail: jcougar@uh.edu
URL: http://uh.edu/class/aas
Contact: Dr. James L. Conyers, Director
E-mail: jconyers@uh.edu
Facebook: www.facebook.com/AASCoogs

Description: Integral unit of College of Liberal Arts
and Social Sciences, University of Houston. **Scope:**
Public policy-related issues and topics focused on
African Americans in Houston, Texas, and throughout
the U.S. **Founded:** 1969. **Publications:** *Ujima* (Biennial). **Educational Activities:** Instruction emphasizing cultural and historical heritage of Africans and
black Americans, Analyzing and critically examining
sociological, psychological, economic, and political
aspects of the black community, as it exists in the
U.S. and Africa.

ASSOCIATIONS AND OTHER ORGANIZATIONS

30661 ■ **Association of Network Marketing Professionals (ANMP)**
13330 Noel Rd., Ste. 1602
Dallas, TX 75240
Co. E-mail: info@anmp.com
URL: http://www.anmp.com
Contact: Garrett McGrath, President
Facebook: www.facebook.com/NetworkMarke tingPros
Description: Supports network marketing professionals worldwide by providing education, resources, and advocacy. **Founded:** 2004.

REFERENCE WORKS

30662 ■ *Steal These Ideas!: Marketing Secrets That Will Make You a Star*
Ed: Steve Cone. **Released:** 2nd Edition. **Price:** $24.95, hardcover; $16.99. **Description:** The book shares information to successfully market any product or service. **Availability:** E-book; Print.

CONSULTANTS

30663 ■ **Eastern Point Consulting Group Inc.**
75 Oak St.
Newton, MA 02465
Ph: (617)965-4141
URL: http://www.eastpt.com
Contact: Katherine Herzog, President
Description: Firm specializes in bringing practical solutions to complex challenges and provides consulting and training in managing diversity, comprehensive sexual-harassment policies and programs, organizational development, benchmarks 360-degree skills assessment, executive coaching, strategic human resource planning, team building, leadership development for women, mentoring programs, and gender issues in the workplace. **Scope:** Firm specializes in bringing practical solutions to complex challenges and provides consulting and training in managing diversity, comprehensive sexual-harassment policies and programs, organizational development, benchmarks 360-degree skills assessment, executive coaching, strategic human resource planning, team building, leadership development for women, mentoring programs, and gender issues in the workplace. **Training:** Leadership Development for Women.

LIBRARIES

30664 ■ **Alticor Inc. Corporate Library**
40600 Ann Arbor Rd. E, Ste. 201
Plymouth, MI 48170
Contact: Milind Pant, President
Scope: Chemistry; direct selling; business; e-commerce. **Services:** Interlibrary loan; copying; SDI; library not open to the public. **Founded:** 1970. **Holdings:** Figures not available.

START-UP INFORMATION

30665 ■ *"After $4M Funding, ThisClicks CEO Talks What's Next"* in Business Journal (Vol. 31, January 10, 2014, No. 33, pp. 7)
Pub: American City Business Journals, Inc.
Contact: Mike Olivieri, Executive Vice President
Released: Weekly. **Price:** $4, Introductory 4-week offer(Digital & Print). **Description:** Chad Halvorson, CEO of technology startup ThisClicks, describes the fundraising process for the Roseville, Minnesota-based company. He discusses the factors driving the startup's growth and the firm's new products. **Availability:** Print; Online.

30666 ■ *"Wheel Genius"* in Entrepreneur (June 2014)
Pub: Entrepreneur Media Inc.
Contact: Dan Bova, Director
E-mail: dbova@entrepreneur.com
Description: Electric car startup, Kenguru, has developed a hatchback that aims to improve mobility for wheelchair users, who enter the vehicle using a rear-opening tailgate and automatic ramp. The Kenguru, which is Hungarian for kangaroo, uses motorcycle-style handlebars instead of steering wheels. The 1,000-pound car has an estimated range of 60 miles and can travel up to 35 miles per hour. The Kenguru could sell for about $25,000. Founder Stacy Zoern partnered with Budapest, Hungary-based Istvan Kissaroslaki in developing the new car. **Availability:** Print; Online.

30667 ■ *Your Million-Dollar Idea: From Concept to Marketplace*
Description: Self-taught entrepreneur provides a 12-step plan to make a new product or service a profitable reality.

ASSOCIATIONS AND OTHER ORGANIZATIONS

30668 ■ **Product Development and Management Association (PDMA)**
1000 Westgate Dr., Ste. 252
  Saint Paul, MN 55114
Ph: (651)290-6280
Fax: (651)290-2266
Co. E-mail: pdma@pdma.org
URL: http://www.pdma.org
Contact: Steve Stucky, President
Facebook: www.facebook.com/PDMAINTL
X (Twitter): x.com/PDMAIntl
Description: Promotes improved product innovation management by drawing upon member's resources. Encourages research designed to make product innovation management more effective and efficient; Provides forum for the exchange of ideas and findings among universities, industry, government and related sectors. **Founded:** 1976. **Publications:** *Journal of Product Innovation Management (JPIM)* (Bimonthly); *Visions: PDMA Practitioner Magazine*

(Quarterly); *Member Directory*. **Awards:** Outstanding Corporate Innovator Award (OCI) (Annual). **Geographic Preference:** Multinational.

EDUCATIONAL PROGRAMS

30669 ■ **New Product Research: Laying the Foundation for New Product Success (Onsite)**
Seminar Information Service Inc. (SIS)
  250 El Camino Real., Ste. 112
  Tustin, CA 92780
Ph: (714)508-0340
Free: 877-736-4636
Fax: (714)734-8027
Co. E-mail: info@seminarinformation.com
URL: http://www.seminarinformation.com
Contact: Catherine Bellizzi, President
URL(s): www.seminarinformation.com/qqapap/new
  -product-research-laying-the-foundation-for-new-pro
  duct
Price: $2,195. **Description:** Learn how to design and implement marketing research studies to guide the total product development and evaluation process. **Audience:** Marketing researchers, and staff members . **Principal Exhibits:** Learn how to design and implement marketing research studies to guide the total product development and evaluation process.

REFERENCE WORKS

30670 ■ *"3Par: Storing Up Value"* in Barron's (Vol. 90, August 30, 2010, No. 35, pp. 30)
Pub: Barron's Editorial & Corporate Headquarters
Ed: Mark Veverka. **Description:** Dell and Hewlett Packard are both bidding for data storage company 3Par. The acquisition would help Dell and Hewlett Packard provide customers with a one-stop shop as customers move to a private cloud in the Internet. **Availability:** Online.

30671 ■ *"7-Eleven Considers Private Label Ice Cream"* in Ice Cream Reporter (Vol. 22, December 20, 2008, No. 1, pp. 1)
Description: 7-Eleven is considering the introduction of a private label of snack foods, including ice cream desserts. **Availability:** Print; Online.

30672 ■ *"2011 FinOvation Awards"* in Farm Industry News (January 19, 2011)
Pub: Informa Business Media, Inc.
Contact: Charlie McCurdy, President
Ed: Karen McMahon, Jodie Wehrspann. **Description:** The 2011 FinOvation Award winners are announced, covering new products that growers need for corn and soybean crops. Winners range from small turbines and a fuel-efficient pickup to a Class 10 combine and drought-tolerant hybrids. **Availability:** Online.

30673 ■ *"Acsys Interactive Announces Crowdsourcing Comes to the Hospital Industry"* in Marketwired (August 23, 2010)
Pub: Comtex News Network Inc.
Contact: Kan Devnani, President
Description: Hospital marketers are obtaining data through crowdsourcing as strategy to gain ideas and feedback. The Hospital Industry Crowdsourced Survey of Digital, Integrated and Emerging Marketing is the first initiative among hospitals. **Availability:** Print; Online.

30674 ■ *"Advancing the Ball"* in Inside Healthcare (Vol. 6, December 2010, No. 7, pp. 31)
Description: Profile of Medicalodges an elder-care specialty company that provides both patient care and technology development. President and CEO of the firm believes that hiring good employees is key to growth for any small business. **Availability:** Online.

30675 ■ *"ALA: Hot Topics for Librarianship"* in Information Today (Vol. 28, September 2011, No. 8, pp. 17)
Pub: Information Today Inc.
Contact: Thomas H. Hogan, President
Ed: Barbara Brynko. **Description:** Highlights from the American Library Association Annual Conference and Exhibition are listed. Thousands of attendees sought out services, displays, demos, new product rollouts, and freebies. Emerging technology for librarians, staff development, gray literature, interlibrary loans, and next-generation interfaces were among the topics discussed.

30676 ■ *"Alternative Fuels Take Center Stage at Houston Auto Show"* in Houston Business Journal (Vol. 44, January 31, 2014, No. 39, pp. 8)
Pub: American City Business Journals, Inc.
Contact: Mike Olivieri, Executive Vice President
Released: January 31, 2014. **Price:** $4, Introductory 4-Week Offer(Digital & Print). **Description:** An energy summit was held at the Houston Auto Show in Texas on January 22, 2014, where energy executives discussed new technology and initiatives. They considered the market for electric and natural gas-fueled vehicles as well as other options including hydrogen, fuel cells, and biofuels. **Availability:** Print; Online.

30677 ■ *"Are You Ready for a Transformation?"* in Women Entrepreneur (November 28, 2008)
Description: Marlene J. Waldock, an expert in women's empowerment and reinvention, discusses brand modification and what a business owner should consider before attempting to change or modify their brand. **Availability:** Online.

30678 ■ *"The Art of Rapid, Hands-On Execution Innovation"* in Strategy and Leadership (Vol. 39, March-April 2011, No. 2, pp. 28)
Pub: Emerald Group Publishing Limited
Contact: Erika Valenti, President

Ed: Anssi Tuulenmaki, Liisa Valikangas. **Description:** A model of 'rapid execution innovation' that can be used to increase the chances of achieving innovations that develop into successful new business models is introduced. The model involves company experiments that inspire the radical rethinking business opportunities, and by continuing these experiments until the idea evolves into a product. **Availability:** Download; Online.

30679 ■ *"As Windows 8 Looms, Tech Investors Hold Their Breath"* in Barron's (Vol. 92, July 23, 2012, No. 30, pp. 22)
Pub: Dow Jones & Company Inc.
Contact: Almar Latour, Chief Executive Officer

Ed: Tiernan Ray. **Description:** Launch of the Microsoft Windows 8 operating system could affect the stock prices of Microsoft and Intel. The effects of the software's introduction on the market share of personal computers remains uncertain. **Availability:** Online.

30680 ■ *"Auxilium Drug's New Use: Putting the Squeeze On Cellulite"* in Philadelphia Business Journal (Vol. 30, September 16, 2011, No. 31, pp. 1)
Pub: Philadelphia Business Journal
Contact: Sierra Quinn, Director
E-mail: squinn@bizjournals.com

Ed: John George. **Description:** Auxilium Pharmaceuticals and BioSpecifics Technologies are getting on with their plans of finding new uses for their drug Xiaflex, a possible treatment for cellulite. The two firms have dismissed their pending litigations and mapped out an amended licensing agreement for their search for the potential uses of the drug. **Availability:** Online.

30681 ■ *"Baskin-Robbins"* in Ice Cream Reporter (Vol. 23, November 20, 2010, No. 12, pp. 7)
Description: Baskin-Robbins is reintroducing its popular Turkey Ice Cream Cake for the holiday. **Availability:** Online.

30682 ■ *"Be a Better Manager: Live Abroad"* in Harvard Business Review (Vol. 88, September 2010, No. 9, pp. 24)
Pub: Harvard Business Publishing
Contact: Diane Belcher, Managing Director

Ed: William W. Maddux, Adam D. Galinsky, Carmit T. Tadmor. **Price:** $6, PDF. **Description:** Interrelationship between international experience and entrepreneurship is discussed. Individuals with international experience are likelier to be promoted and to develop new products and businesses. **Availability:** Online; PDF.

30683 ■ *"Better Made's Better Idea: Diversify Despite Rising Costs"* in Crain's Detroit Business (Vol. 24, September 22, 2008, No. 38, pp. 18)
Pub: Crain Communications Inc.
Contact: Barry Asin, President

Ed: Nathan Skid. **Description:** Better Made Snack Foods Inc. is planning to expand its product lines and market reach as well as boost manufacturing capability during a time in which the company is being buffeted by rising commodity and fuel costs. The company feels that diversification is the key to maintain sales and growth. **Availability:** Online.

30684 ■ *"A Big Dream That 'Was Going Nowhere"* in Globe & Mail (February 4, 2006, pp. B4)
Description: The reasons behind the decision of Bombardier Inc. to terminate its plans to develop jet airplanes are presented. **Availability:** Online.

30685 ■ *"Biodiesel Poised to Regain Growth"* in Farm Industry News (January 21, 2011)
Pub: Informa Business Media, Inc.
Contact: Charlie McCurdy, President

Ed: Lynn Grooms. **Description:** According to Gary Haer, vice president of sales and marketing for Renewable Energy Group, the biodiesel industry is

positioned to regain growth in 2011 with the reinstatement of the biodiesel blendersa tax credit of $1 per gallon. **Availability:** Print; Online.

30686 ■ *"BK Menu Gives Casual Dining Reason to Worry"* in Advertising Age (Vol. 79, November 17, 2008, No. 43, pp. 12)
Pub: Crain Communications, Inc.
Contact: Jessica Botos, Manager, Marketing
E-mail: jessica.botos@crainsnewyork.com

Ed: Emily Bryson York. **Description:** Burger King is beginning to compete with such casual dining restaurants as Applebees and the Cheesecake Factory with new premium menu items, including thicker burgers and ribs; statistical data regarding the casual dining segment which continues to fall and Burger King, whose sales continue to rise is included. **Availability:** Online.

30687 ■ *"BlackBerry 10 Unlikely to Save RIM. RIM Has Few Options. Staying the Course Isn't One of Them"* in Canadian Business (Vol. 85, July 16, 2012, No. 11-12, pp. 12)
Ed: Joe Castaldo. **Description:** Research in Motion (RIM) plans to launch a new line of Blackberry 10 Smartphones in 2012 as part of a strategy to stay in business despite expected operating loss in the first quarter and strong competition. Other options for RIM include a sale, opening its network to offer added security and data compression services, or reinventing itself as a niche handset provider. **Availability:** Print; Online.

30688 ■ *"Blue Cross to Put Kiosk in Mall"* in News & Observer (November 9, 2010)
Pub: News and Observer
Contact: Bill Church, Editor

Ed: Alan M. Wolf. **Description:** Blue Cross and Blue Shield of North Carolina has placed a kiosk in Durham's Streets of Southpoint in order to market its health insurance. **Availability:** Online.

30689 ■ *"Book Yourself Solid: The Fastest, Easiest, and Most Reliable System for Getting More Clients Than You Can Handle"*
Pub: John Wiley & Sons, Inc.
Contact: Christina Van Tassell, Executive Vice President Chief Financial Officer

Released: 3rd edition. **Price:** $22, paperback; $14.99, E-book. **Description:** Self-promotion is essential for successful selling. Strategies, techniques, and skills necessary for success are presented, covering social media marketing strategies for service professionals; pricing models and sales strategies to simplify selling; new networking and outreach plans that take only minutes a day; and new product launches ideas and tactics. **Availability:** E-book; Print.

30690 ■ *Borrowing Brilliance: The Six Steps to Business Innovation by Building on the Ideas of Others*
Released: October 05, 2010. **Price:** $16, paperback; $9.99, e-book. **Description:** The author builds the case that cherry-picking the ideas of others is a vital part of the research and development process for any small firm. **Availability:** E-book; Print.

30691 ■ *"Branding Spree"* in Pet Product News (Vol. 66, September 2012, No. 9, pp. 40)
Ed: Michael Ventre. **Description:** The extent to which pet security firm PetSafe has continued to diversify into new product categories to realize growth opportunities is explored. An arm of Radio Systems Corporation, PetSafe has been known for manufacturing products such as wireless fences and electronic pet collars. **Availability:** Print; Online.

30692 ■ *"Brands' Mass Appeal"* in ADWEEK (Vol. 51, June 14, 2010, No. 24)
Ed: Brian Morrissey. **Description:** Engineering/science crowdsourced projects tend to result from posting and/or publishing interim results as well as from other talents building upon those results to produce even better results. However, the author does not see the same results in the creative world. **Availability:** Online.

30693 ■ *"Business Diary"* in Crain's Detroit Business (Vol. 24, October 6, 2008, No. 40, pp. 23)
Pub: Crain Communications Inc.
Contact: Barry Asin, President

Description: Detailed listing of acquisitions, expansions, new products, new services, business contracts and startups from the Detroit area is provided. **Availability:** Print; Online.

30694 ■ *"Celebrate Innovation, No Matter Where It Occurs"* in Harvard Business Review (Vol. 90, April 2012, No. 4, pp. 36)
Pub: Harvard Business Review Press
Contact: Moderna V. Pfizer, Contact

Ed: Nitin Nohria. **Price:** $6, hardcover. **Description:** Yoga is used to illustrate the global success of a given concept not originally construed as a product or service. Although yoga emerged in ancient India, it is now practiced worldwide and is at the center of many businesses and disciplines, from the health care industry to clothing and accessories. **Availability:** PDF; Online.

30695 ■ *"A Chinese Approach to Management: A Generation of Entrepreneurs Is Writing Its Own Rules"* in Harvard Business Review (Vol. 92, September 2014, No. 9, pp. 103)
Pub: Harvard Business Publishing
Contact: Diane Belcher, Managing Director

Price: $8.95. **Description:** The Chinese approach to management include simple structures for organizations, quick development of products, responsiveness to local values and needs, and investment in source firms and vendors. Manufacturing and engineering operations are typically co-located. **Availability:** Online; PDF.

30696 ■ *"Chopping Option Added to Calmer Corn Head Kits"* in Farm Industry News (January 16, 2011)
Pub: Informa Business Media, Inc.
Contact: Charlie McCurdy, President

Ed: Karen McMahon. **Description:** New equipment for combines, called the BT Chopper option for Calmer Corn Heads, will chop and crust BT corn stalks into confetti-sized pieces for easier decomposition in the field.

30697 ■ *"Chuck's Big Chance"* in Barron's (Vol. 89, July 13, 2009, No. 28, pp. L3)
Pub: Dow Jones & Company Inc.
Contact: Almar Latour, Chief Executive Officer

Ed: Leslie P. Norton. **Description:** Charles Schwab is cutting prices and rolling out new products to lure customers and the company is well positioned to benefit from Wall Street's misery. Their shares are trading at just 17 times earnings, which should be at least at a multiple of 20. **Availability:** Online.

30698 ■ *"Cloud Computing for a Crowd"* in CIO (Vol. 24, October 2, 2010, No. 1, pp. 16)
Pub: CIO

Ed: Stephanie Overby. **Description:** Information about a project which aimed to implement a cloud-based crowdsourcing platform and innovation-management process is provided. Chubb Group of Insurance Companies wanted to mine revenue-generating ideas from its 10,400 employees and hundreds of thousands of external agents. The company hosted its first innovation event using its new system in October 2008. **Availability:** Online.

30699 ■ *"The Code-Cracker: Prominent Researcher at Miami Part of Federal Effort to Solve Protein Structures"* in Business Courier (Vol. 24, January 10, 2008, No. 40, pp. 1)
Pub: American City Business Journals, Inc.
Contact: Mike Olivieri, Executive Vice President

Ed: James Ritchie. **Description:** Michael Kennedy, a professor in the chemistry and biochemistry department at the Miami University, is a part of the Protein Structure Initiative, a project that is aimed at forming a catalog of three-dimensional protein structures. The initiative is a project of the Northeast Structural

Genomics consortium, of which the Miami University is a member. The impacts of the research on drug development are discussed. **Availability:** Print; Online.

30700 ■ *"Cold Stone Creamery Offers New Eight-Layer Ice Cream Cakes"* in *Ice Cream Reporter (Vol. 23, October 20, 2010, No. 11, pp. 2)*

Description: Cold Stone Creamery is introducing a new line of eight-layer ice cream cakes, which are crafted with three layers of ice cream, three layers of cake and two mid-layers of mix-ins and finished with frosting and a creative design. **Availability:** Print; Online.

30701 ■ *"Cold Stone in Licensing Agreement with Turin Chocolates"* in *Ice Cream Reporter (Vol. 22, December 20, 2008, No. 1, pp. 2)*

Description: Cold Stone Creamery and Turin Chocolatier are teaming up to offer a new line of chocolate truffles under the Cold Stone label. The treats will feature four the most popular Cold Stone flavors: Coffee Lovers Only, Chocolate Devotion, Our Strawberry Blonde, and Peanut Butter Cup Perfection. **Availability:** Print; Online.

30702 ■ *"Column: To Win, Create What's Scarce"* in *Harvard Business Review (Vol. 88, November 2010, No. 11, pp. 46)*

Pub: Harvard Business Publishing

Contact: Diane Belcher, Managing Director

Ed: Seth Godin. **Price:** $6, PDF. **Description:** It is recommended to identify what is scarce yet valuable and applying this principle to business in order to be successful. **Availability:** Online; PDF.

30703 ■ *"Coming Soon: Electric Tractors"* in *Farm Industry News (November 21, 2011)*

Pub: Informa Business Media, Inc.

Contact: Charlie McCurdy, President

Ed: Jodie Wehrspann. **Description:** The agricultural industry is taking another look at electric farm vehicles. John Deere Product Engineering Center said that farmers can expect to see more diesel-electric systems in farm tractors, sprayers, and implements. **Availability:** Online.

30704 ■ *"Coming Through When It Matters Most: How Great Teams Do Their Best Work Under Pressure"* in *Harvard Business Review (Vol. 90, April 2012, No. 4, pp. 82)*

Pub: Harvard Business Review Press

Contact: Moderna V. Pfizer, Contact

Ed: Heidi K. Gardner. **Price:** $8.95, hardcover. **Description:** Teamwork can be enhanced by measuring each member's contribution more deliberately, and by examining every new item of information. This way, teams avoid performance pressure that constricts creativity and innovation. **Availability:** PDF; Online.

30705 ■ *"Company Severs Ties with Chiquita, Starts Own Brand"* in *Business Journal-Serving Phoenix and the Valley of the Sun (October 4, 2007)*

Pub: Phoenix Business Journal

Contact: Alex McAlister, Director

E-mail: amcalister@bizjournals.com

Ed: Mike Sunnucks. **Description:** Melones International is ending a deal with Chiquita Brands International Inc. Melones will now distribute its produce in the U.S. under its own brand, called Plain Jane. Alejandro N. Canelos Jr., head of the firm, stated their relationship with Chiquita was good, but wants to promote the Plain Jane brand name. **Availability:** Print; Online.

30706 ■ *"Crowdsourcing the Law"* in *LJN's Legal Tech Newsletter (October 1, 2010)*

Pub: Minnesota State Bar Association

Contact: Jennifer Thompson, President

Ed: Robert J. Ambrogi. **Released:** August 01, 2010. **Description:** Spindle Law strives to make legal research faster and smarter using crowdsourcing as one means to reach users. **Availability:** Print; Online.

30707 ■ *"Crowdsourcing their Way into One Big Mess"* in *Brandweek (Vol. 51, October 25, 2010, No. 38, pp. 26)*

Description: The Gap, was counting on crowdsourcing to provide feedback for its new logo, but it did not prove positive for the retailer. However, a massive outcry of negative opinion, via crowdsourcing, may not always equal valid, constructive criticism. **Availability:** Online.

30708 ■ *"Death of the PC"* in *Canadian Business (Vol. 83, October 12, 2010, No. 17, pp. 44)*

Description: The future of the personal computer (PC) is looking bleak as consumers are relying more on new mobile devices instead of their PC. A 'Wall Street Journal' article published in September 2010 reported that the iPad had cannibalized sales of laptops by as much as 50 percent. The emergence of tablet computers running alternative operating systems is also explained. **Availability:** Print; Online.

30709 ■ *"Digital Power Management and the PMBus"* in *Canadian Electronics (Vol. 23, June-July 2008, No. 4, pp. 8)*

Pub: Annex Buisness Media

Contact: Mike Fredericks, President

Ed: Torbjorn Holmberg. **Description:** PMBus is an interface that can be applied to a variety of devices including power management devices. Information on digital power management products using this interface are also provided. **Availability:** Print; Online.

30710 ■ *"Disney's High Hopes for Duffy"* in *Canadian Business (Vol. 83, October 12, 2010, No. 17, pp. 14)*

Pub: Rogers Media Inc.

Contact: Neil Spivak, Chief Executive Officer

Ed: James Cowan. **Description:** The reintroduction of Duffy is expected to create a new, exclusive product line that distinguishes Disney's parks and stores from competitors. Duffy, a teddy bear, was first introduced at a Disney World store in Florida in 2002. The character was incorporated into the Disney mythology when its popularity grew in Japan. **Availability:** Online.

30711 ■ *"The Doctor Is In"* in *Canadian Business (Vol. 80, February 12, 2007, No. 4, pp. 38)*

Description: The research at McMaster University to make a pill having imaging devices to takes pictures of any possible cancerous cells in the human body is discussed. **Availability:** Online.

30712 ■ *"Does America Really Need Manufacturing? Yes, When Production Is Closely Tied to Innovation"* in *Harvard Business Review (Vol. 90, March 2012, No. 3, pp. 94)*

Pub: Harvard Business Review Press

Contact: Moderna V. Pfizer, Contact

Ed: Gary P. Pisano, Willy C. Shih. **Price:** $8.95. **Description:** A framework is presented for assessing when manufacturing and research and development are crucial to innovation and therefore should be kept in close proximity to each other. The framework denotes the degree to which product design data can be separated from manufacturing, and the opportunities to improve manufacturing. **Availability:** Online; PDF.

30713 ■ *"Dog Marketplace: Pet Waste Products Pick Up Sales"* in *Pet Product News (Vol. 66, September 2012, No. 9, pp. 58)*

Ed: Sandi Cain. **Description:** Pet supplies manufacturers are developing dog waste pickup bags and other convenient cleanup tools characterized by environment-friendliness and fashion. The demand for these cleanup tools has been motivated by dog owners' desire to minimize their and their dogs' environmental footprints. **Availability:** Online.

30714 ■ *"DuPont's Pioneer Hi-Bred, Evogene to Develop Rust-Resistant Soybean Varieties"* in *Farm Industry News (November 22, 2011)*

Pub: Informa Business Media, Inc.

Contact: Charlie McCurdy, President

Ed: Karen McMahon. **Description:** DuPont and Evogene have signed a new contract to work together to develop resistance in soybeans to rust. Financial terms of the agreement were not disclosed. **Availability:** Online.

30715 ■ *"Ecovative Moves Beyond Packaging"* in *Business Review Albany (Vol. 41, August 1, 2014, No. 19, pp. 12)*

Description: Ecovative Design of Green Island, NY has started making new packaging materials to add to its biodegradable product line, including the Myco Board, a material similar to particleboard. Clients range from computer manufacturers to furniture retailers. **Availability:** Print; Online.

30716 ■ *Electronic Commerce*

Ed: Gary P. Schneider, Bryant Chrzan, Charles McCormick. **Released:** 12th edition. **Price:** $29.49, e-book. **Description:** E-commerce can open the door to more opportunities than ever before for small business. Packed with real-world examples and cases, the book delivers comprehensive coverage of emerging online technologies and trends and their influence on the electronic marketplace. It details how the landscape of online commerce is evolving, reflecting changes in the economy and how business and society are responding to those changes. Balancing technological issues with the strategic business aspects of successful e-commerce, the new edition includes expanded coverage of international issues, social networking, mobile commerce, Web 2.0 technologies, and updates on spam, phishing, and identity theft. **Availability:** Print.

30717 ■ *"Electronics Assembly"* in *Canadian Electronics (Vol. 23, February 2008, No. 1, pp. 12)*

Description: I&J Fisnar Inc. has launched a new system of bench top dispensing robots while Vitronics Soltec and KIC have introduced a new reflow soldering machine. Teknek, on the other hand, has announced a new product, called the CM10, which an be used in cleaning large format substrates. Other new products and their description are presented. **Availability:** Print; Online.

30718 ■ *"Enriching the Ecosystem: A Four-Point Plan for Linking Innovation, Enterprises, and Jobs"* in *Harvard Business Review (Vol. 90, March 2012, No. 3, pp. 140)*

Pub: Harvard Business Review Press

Contact: Moderna V. Pfizer, Contact

Ed: Rosabeth Moss Kanter. **Price:** $8.95, hardcopy black and white. **Description:** The four goals for enriching the ecosystem include: linking venture creation and knowledge creation to speed up the idea-to-enterprise transition; revitalizing small-, medium-, and large-sized firms via partnerships; improving matches between education and employment opportunities; and bringing together leaders across different sectors to create regional strategies. **Availability:** Print; PDF; Online.

30719 ■ *"Executive Decision: To Make Inroads Against RIM, Palm Steals Its Strategy"* in *Globe & Mail (March 25, 2006, pp. B3)*

Ed: Simon Avery. **Description:** The Palm Inc., global leader in portable device manufacturing, is looking forward to improve its sales of Palm Treos, a wireless portable device that connects to internet and email. Palm is also planning to build partnerships, under the efficient management of Michael Moskowitz, general manager and vice-president of Palm Inc., with the other companies to increase the sales of its wireless devices.

30720 ■ *"Facilitating and Rewarding Creativity During New Product Development"* in *Journal of Marketing (Vol. 75, July 2011, No. 4, pp. 53)*

Pub: American Marketing Association

Contact: Bennie F. Johnson, Chief Executive Officer

Ed: James E. Burroughs, Darren W. Dahl, C. Page Moreau, Amitava Chattopadhay, Gerald J. Gorn. **Description:** A study to determine the effects of rewards to creativity in the process of new product development is presented. The findings show that the effect of rewards can be made positive if combined with appropriate creativity training. **Availability:** PDF.

30721 ■ "Feeding the Elephants While Searching for Greener Pastures" in Inc. (Volume 32, December 2010, No. 10, pp. 34)
Pub: Mansueto Ventures L.L.C.
Contact: Stephanie Mehta, Chief Executive Officer
Ed: April Joyner. **Released:** December 2010. **Description:** Innovation is the future for small business. A new book, Inside Real Innovation: How the Right Approach Can Move Ideas from R&D to Market - And Get the Economy Moving helps to break down the process by which innovation occurs. **Availability:** Print.

30722 ■ "FinOvation 2009" in Farm Industry News (Vol. 42, January 1, 2009, No. 1)
Ed: Karen McMahon, Mark Moore, David Hest. **Description:** New and innovative products and technologies are presented.

30723 ■ "'Focusing On the Moment'" in Dallas Business Journal (Vol. 37, June 27, 2014, No. 42, pp. 4)
Pub: American City Business Journals, Inc.
Contact: Mike Olivieri, Executive Vice President
Description: Southwest Airlines chairman, president, and CEO Gary Kelly, believes the key to the carrier's growth in 2014 will be to 'focus on the moment' and ensure that new projects and strategies implemented successfully. Kelly discusses the potential impact of the repeal of the Wright Amendment on October 13, as well as Southwest's merger with AirTran and the launch of nonstop flights from New York and Washington DC. **Availability:** Print; Online.

30724 ■ "Foods for Thought" in Pet Product News (Vol. 64, December 2010, No. 12, pp. 16)
Ed: Maddy Heleine. **Description:** Manufacturers have been focused on developing species-specific fish foods due to consumer tendency to assess the benefits of the food they feed their fish. As retailers stock species-specific fish foods, manufacturers have provided in-store items and strategies to assist in efficiently selling these food products. Trends in fish food packaging and ingredients are also discussed. **Availability:** Online.

30725 ■ "For Apple, It's Showtime Again" in Barron's (Vol. 90, August 30, 2010, No. 35, pp. 29)
Pub: Barron's Editorial & Corporate Headquarters
Ed: Eric J. Savitz. **Description:** Speculations on what Apple Inc. will unveil at its product launch event are presented. These products include a possible new iPhone Nano, a new update to its Apple TV, and possibly a deal with the Beatles to distribute their songs over iTunes. **Availability:** Online.

30726 ■ From Concept To Consumer: How to Turn Ideas Into Money
Ed: Phil Baker. **Released:** 1st edition. **Price:** $27.99, paperback. **Description:** Renowned product developer Phil Baker explains how a great idea accounts for only 5 percent of all the factors of success and why the majority of success is dependent upon a myriad of other factors, including the time it takes to get to market, price, marketing and distribution. By being their own best competition, a small company can stay one step ahead of competitors. **Availability:** Print.

30727 ■ "FutureDash Launches IndieGoGo Crowdfunding Campaign for the EnergyBuddy Home Energy Monitoring System" in Benzinga.com (June 21, 2012)
Pub: Benzinga.com
Contact: Jason Raznick, Founder

Ed: Aaron Wise. **Description:** FutureDash launched its campaign on IndieGoGo to promote its home energy monitoring system called EnergyBuddy. The system monitors the amount of electricity being used in the home or building. Information and control is available through an iPhone, iPad, Android smartphone or computer screen or anywhere on a secure Internet connection. **Availability:** Online.

30728 ■ "Gadget Makers Aim for New Chapter in Reading" in Crain's Cleveland Business (Vol. 28, October 22, 2007, No. 42, pp. 20)
Pub: Crain Communications Inc.
Contact: K. C. Crain, President
Ed: Jennifer McKevitt. **Description:** Although e-books and e-audiobooks are becoming more popular, e-readers, devices that display digital books, still haven't caught on with the public. Experts feel that consumers, many of whom have to look at a computer screen all day for work, still like the feel of a real book in their hands. **Availability:** Online.

30729 ■ "Game On: When Work Becomes Play" in Canadian Business (Vol. 80, February 12, 2007, No. 4, pp. 15)
Description: The plan of president of TransGaming Vikas Gupta to create innovative software programs for games that can be played in different operating systems is discussed. **Availability:** Online.

30730 ■ "German Firm Ifm Electronic to Open Second Local Unit" in Philadelphia Business Journal (Vol. 28, July 20, 2012, No. 23, pp. 1)
Pub: Baltimore Business Journal
Contact: Rhonda Pringle, President
E-mail: rpringle@bizjournals.com
Description: German electronic control and sensor manufacturer, ifm electronic gmbh, has established ifm prover USA in January 2012, its second subsidiary in Exton, Pennsylvania after ifm efector Inc. Ifm prover will relocate in July 2012 to a new 36,000 square foot building that features a product development area and multiple laboraties for testing and quality control. **Availability:** Print; Online.

30731 ■ "Getting Inventive With..Ed Spellman" in Crain's Cleveland Business (Vol. 28, October 22, 2007, No. 42, pp. 18)
Pub: Crain Communications Inc.
Contact: K. C. Crain, President
Ed: Kimberly Bonvissuto. **Description:** Profile featuring Ed Spellman, a mechanical engineer who decided to quit his job at Invacare Corp., a medical equipment manufacturer and distributor, in order to devote his full attention to promoting his numerous inventions, including the DV-Grip, a vehicle mount for portable DVD players. **Availability:** Online.

30732 ■ "Getting the Word Out" in Modern Machine Shop (Vol. 84, September 2011, No. 4, pp. 16)
Pub: Gardner Business Media Inc.
Contact: Rick Kline, Jr., President
E-mail: rkline2@gardnerweb.com
Ed: Derek Korn. **Description:** Many times machine shops create devices to streamline their own machining processes and find these devices can be used by other shops, thus developing a marketable product. Tips for this process are outlined. **Availability:** Print; Online.

30733 ■ "GM Canada Revved Up Over Camaro" in Globe & Mail (February 17, 2006, pp. B4)
Ed: Greg Keenan. **Description:** General Manager of General Motors Canada is planning to start the production of company's muscle car Camaro in Canadian facility. The car was exhibited at Canadian International Auto Show held in Toronto. **Availability:** Online.

30734 ■ "Good Companies Launch More New Products" in Harvard Business Review (Vol. 90, April 2012, No. 4, pp. 28)
Pub: Harvard Business Review Press
Contact: Moderna V. Pfizer, Contact

Ed: Xueming Luo, Shuili Du. **Description:** Because corporate social responsibility enhances relationships with outside stakeholders, it gives companies access to a large range of knowledge sources, enabling firms to keep up with innovations and shifts in market preferences.

30735 ■ "GSK Creating Pathways From Academia to Industry" in Philadelphia Business Journal (Vol. 33, March 7, 2014, No. 4, pp. 8)
Pub: American City Business Journals, Inc.
Contact: Mike Olivieri, Executive Vice President
Released: Weekly. **Price:** $4, introductory 4-week offer(Digital & Print). **Description:** The Discovery Fast Track Challenge program of GlaxoSmithKline will expand in 2014 to include scientists in North America and Europe. Scientists will be asked to submit information about their innovative drug research proposals and the winner could be offered a deal with the Discovery Partnerships with Academia team. **Availability:** Print; Online.

30736 ■ "HBR Case Study: Play It Safe or Take a Stand?" in Harvard Business Review (Vol. 88, November 2010, No. 11, pp. 139)
Pub: Harvard Business Publishing
Contact: Diane Belcher, Managing Director
Ed: Trish Gorman Clifford, Jay Barney. **Price:** $8.95, PDF. **Description:** A fictitious leadership scenario is presented, with contributors providing comments and recommendations. A female executive ponders whether to assert a point of view on a new venture. Both experts agree that after providing careful analysis of pros and cons, the executive should come to a well-informed conclusion. **Availability:** Online; PDF.

30737 ■ "Helping Apple Go Wearable" in Austin Business Journal (Vol. 34, July 4, 2014, No. 20, pp. 13)
Pub: American City Business Journals, Inc.
Contact: Mike Olivieri, Executive Vice President
Released: July 04, 2014. **Price:** $4, introductory 4-week offer(Digital only). **Description:** Andrew Hamra, CEO and designer at Red Street Ventures will launch the Runnur Hands Free iPad Clip and Carry Case across the U.S. in July 2014 following the success of his flagship product the Hands Free Carry-All. Hamra builds and designs the products and controls startup costs by outsourcing most of the production to China's Xiamen Uptex Industrial Company Ltd. **Availability:** Print; Online.

30738 ■ "Hey, You Can't Do That" in Green Industry Pro (Vol. 23, September 2011)
Ed: Rod Dickens. **Description:** Manufacturers of landscape equipment are making better use of energy resources, such as the use of fuel-injection systems instead of carburetors, lightweight materials, better lubricants, advanced battery technology, and innovative engine designs. **Availability:** Online.

30739 ■ "Hope Grows for a Muscular Dystrophy Drug" in Barron's (Vol. 92, August 25, 2012, No. 35, pp. 35)
Pub: Dow Jones & Company Inc.
Contact: Almar Latour, Chief Executive Officer
Ed: Andrew Bary. **Description:** The stocks of biotechnology firm Sarepta Therapeutics could gain value if trials for eterpirsen, a drug being developed for Duchenne muscular dystrophy, are successful. The company's stock prices could rise from $10/share to as high as $26/share. **Availability:** Online.

30740 ■ "How to Manage Successful Crowdsourcing Projects" in eWeek (September 29, 2010)
Ed: Lukas Biewald. **Released:** September 29, 2010. **Description:** The advantages, challenges and pitfalls faced when using crowdsourcing to improve a business are outlined. Crowdsourcing helps to eliminate the need to rely on an internal workforce and the need to forecast task volume. **Availability:** Online.

30741 ■ *"How to Play the Tech Mergers"* in *Barron's (Vol. 90, August 30, 2010, No. 35, pp. 18)*
Pub: Barron's Editorial & Corporate Headquarters
Ed: Tiernan Ray. **Description:** The intense bidding by Hewlett-Packard and Dell for 3Par was foreseen in a previous Barron's cover story and 3Par's stock has nearly tripled since reported. Other possible acquisition targets in the tech industry include Brocade Communication Systems, NetApp, Xyratex, and Isilon Systems. **Availability:** Online.

30742 ■ *"IBR Breakfast Series: Idaho's Dairy Industry Quietly Grows"* in *Idaho Business Review (August 15, 2014)*
Pub: BridgeTower Media
Contact: Adam Reinebach, President
Description: Several dairy industry members were called to a breakfast to discuss the past, present and future of the Idaho dairy farms and products. The impact of technology changes and rising foreign market demands as well as creating more and different products was addressed.

30743 ■ *"In a Twist, Pretzel Vendors Will Be Selling Pizza: Wetzels to Launch Blaze Fast-Fire'd Concept with Two SoCal Locations"* in *Los Angeles Business Journal (Vol. 34, June 4, 2012, No. 23, pp. 12)*
Pub: CBJ L.P.
Contact: Terri Cunningham, Contact
Ed: Bethany Firnhaber. **Description:** Rick and Elise Wetzel, cofounders of Wetzel's Pretzels is launching its new restaurants featuring fast-casual pizza. The concept is of an assembly line process where customers can make 11-inch personalized pizzas with toppings like artichokes, gorgonzola cheese, roasted red peppers and arugula. The pizzas bake in two minutes. **Availability:** Online.

30744 ■ *"IndieCompanyDk Offers Eco-Friendly Furniture That Stands Out"* in *Ecology, Environment & Conservation Business (September 6, 2014, pp. 39)*
Pub: NewsRX LLC.
Contact: Kalani Rosell, Contact
Description: A new manufacturer of eco-friendly furniture and interiors, IndieCompanyDk, is offering a new concept in sustainable furniture design, using exclusive and affordable smooth designs, which maintain the natural and raw look of quality reclaimed materials. **Availability:** Online.

30745 ■ *"InnoCentive Announces Next Generation Crowdsourcing Platform"* in *Marketwired (June 15, 2010)*
Pub: Comtex News Network Inc.
Contact: Kan Devnani, President
Description: InnoCentive, Inc., a world leader in open innovation, is launching InnoCentive@Work3, a third generation of its @Work enterprise platform for collaborative-driven innovation for companies. The product will help clients solve critical business and technical issues by tapping information both inside and outside of a company. **Availability:** Online.

30746 ■ *"Innovating Low-Cost Business Models"* in *Strategy and Leadership (Vol. 39, March-April 2011, No. 2, pp. 43)*
Pub: Emerald Group Publishing Limited
Contact: Erika Valenti, President
Ed: Nicolas Kachaner, Zhenya Lindgardt, David Michael. **Description:** A process that can be used to implement low-cost innovation is presented. The process can be used to address the competitive challenges presented by multinationals' practice of presenting applications and price points that are intended for developing markets into developed markets. The process involves targeting large, and low-income segments of the market.

30747 ■ *"Innovation in 3D: NextFab"* in *Philadelphia Business Journal (Vol. 28, January 22, 2010, No. 49, pp. 1)*
Pub: Philadelphia Business Journal
Contact: Sierra Quinn, Director

E-mail: squinn@bizjournals.com
Ed: Peter Key. **Description:** NextFab Studio LLC is set to offer product development services using 3D technology. The company has developed a three-dimensional printer which fabricates objects usually made of plastic. **Availability:** Online.

30748 ■ *"The Internet Of You"* in *Canadian Business (Vol. 87, July 2014, No. 7, pp. 43)*
Description: Wearable computers like smart watches, fitness trackers, and bracelets like Nymi are starting to break down the barrier between human beings and the digital world. The Nymi is a wrist-worn device developed by Bionym that allows the wearer to be instantly recognizable to any wireless device. **Availability:** Online.

30749 ■ *"Inventive Doctor New Venture Partner"* in *Houston Business Journal (Vol. 40, January 29, 2010, No. 38, pp. A2)*
Pub: Houston Business Journal
Contact: Bob Charlet, President
E-mail: bcharlet@bizjournals.com
Ed: Ford Gunter. **Description:** Dr. Billy Cohn, a surgeon from Houston, Texas has been named as venture partner for venture firm Sante Ventures LLC of Austin, Texas. Cohn will be responsible for seeing marketable developing technologies in the medical industry. The motivation for Cohn's naming as venture partner is his development of a minimally invasive therapy for end-stage renal disease. **Availability:** Print; Online.

30750 ■ *"It's New or Improved, But Does It Work?"* in *Contractor (Vol. 57, January 2010, No. 1, pp. 22)*
Ed: Al Schwartz. **Description:** There is a place for skepticism in the HVAC and plumbing industry as not all new products that are specified may not always perform. The tradesman has the responsibility of integrating new technology into the field. **Availability:** Print; Online.

30751 ■ *"Janitorial Equipment and Supplies US Market"* in *PR Newswire (October 24, 2011)*
Description: United States demand for janitorial equipment and supplies (excluding chemical products) is predicted to rise 2.4 percent per year to $7.6 billion in 2013. New product development will lead to increased sales of higher-value goods in the industry. **Availability:** Print; Online.

30752 ■ *"Kaiser Permanente's Innovation on the Front Lines"* in *Harvard Business Review (Vol. 88, September 2010, No. 9, pp. 92)*
Pub: Harvard Business Publishing
Contact: Diane Belcher, Managing Director
Ed: Lew McCreary. **Price:** $8.95. **Description:** Kaiser Permanente's human-centered model for organizational effectiveness emphasizes the roles of patients and providers as collaborators driving quality improvement and innovation. **Availability:** Online; PDF.

30753 ■ *"Kosher Ice Cream Features Traditional Jewish Ingredients"* in *Ice Cream Reporter (Vol. 23, August 20, 2010, No. 9, pp. 5)*
Description: Chozen Ice Cream is offering traditional Jewish dessert and snack foods using tradition Jewish ingredients to name items: regelach, coconut-almond macaroon, and chocolate matzo. **Availability:** Print; Online.

30754 ■ *"Lee's Launches With Focus on Liqueur-based Ice Creams"* in *Ice Cream Reporter (Vol. 23, August 20, 2010, No. 9, pp. 6)*
Description: Lee's Cream Liqueur Ice Cream Parlors launched their grand opening in Old Town Scottsdale in July, featuring premium liqueurs to create adult-only ice creams that can be served on their own or blended into exotic drinks. **Availability:** Print; Online.

30755 ■ *"Leica Beefs Up Steering Options, Steering Display Features"* in *Farm Industry News (January 10, 2011)*
Pub: Informa Business Media, Inc.
Contact: Charlie McCurdy, President
Ed: David Hest. **Description:** Leica Geosystems is offering a new hydraulic steering kit for older tractors, along with new steering patterns and other features on its Leica mojo3C and mojoMINI displays. **Availability:** Online.

30756 ■ *"Life's Work: James Dyson"* in *Harvard Business Review (Vol. 88, July-August 2010, No. 7-8, pp. 172)*
Pub: Harvard Business Publishing
Contact: Diane Belcher, Managing Director
Ed: Alison Beard. **Price:** $8.95. **Description:** The founder of appliance company Dyson Ltd. discusses the role of making mistakes in learning and innovation, and emphasizes the importance of hands-on involvement to make a company successful. **Availability:** Online; PDF.

30757 ■ *"Little Guy is Taking On Potent Competition"* in *Philadelphia Business Journal (Vol 32, January 10, 2014, No. 48, pp. 4)*
Pub: American City Business Journals, Inc.
Contact: Mike Olivieri, Executive Vice President
Released: Weekly. **Price:** $4, introductory 4-week offer(Digital & Print). **Description:** Auxilium Pharmaceuticals has introduced the erectile dysfunction drug Stendra, which it licensed from Vivus Inc. in a $300 million deal. Auxilium CEO, Adrian Adams, says Stendra has some advantages over competing products. **Availability:** Print; Online.

30758 ■ *"Local Company Seeks Patent For Armored Trucks"* in *Crain's Detroit Business (Vol. 24, February 4, 2008, No. 5, pp. 10)*
Pub: Crain Communications Inc.
Contact: Barry Asin, President
Description: Profile of James LeBlanc Sr., mechanical engineer and defense contractor, discusses his eleven utility patents pending for a set of vehicles and subsystems that would work as countermeasures to explosively formed projectiles. **Availability:** Print; Online.

30759 ■ *"Local Startup Hits Big Leagues"* in *Austin Business JournalInc. (Vol. 28, December 19, 2008, No. 40, pp. 1)*
Description: Qcue LLC, an Austin, Texas-based company founded in 2007 is developing a software system that can be used by Major League Baseball teams to change the prices of their single-game tickets based on variables affecting demand. The company recently completed a trial with the San Francisco Giants in 2008. **Availability:** Print; Online.

30760 ■ *"Managing Yourself: How to Save Good Ideas"* in *Harvard Business Review (Vol. 88, October 2010, No. 10, pp. 129)*
Pub: Harvard Business Publishing
Contact: Diane Belcher, Managing Director
Ed: Jeff Kehoe. **Price:** $8.95, PDF. **Description:** Harvard Business School Professor John P. Kotter identifies situations that may hinder the development and implementation of ideas, and discusses effective ways to counter them. **Availability:** Online; PDF.

30761 ■ *"Marketer Bets Big on U.S.'s Growing Canine Obsession"* in *Advertising Age (Vol. 79, April 14, 2008, No. 15, pp. 14)*
Pub: Crain Communications, Inc.
Contact: Jessica Botos, Manager, Marketing
E-mail: jessica.botos@crainsnewyork.com
Ed: Emily Bryson York. **Description:** Overview of FreshPet, a New Jersey company that began marketing two brands of refrigerated dog food-Deli Fresh and FreshPet Select-which are made from fresh ingredients such as beef, rice and carrots. The company projects continued success due to the amount of money consumers spend on their pets as well as fears derived from the 2007 recalls that

inspired consumers to look for smaller, independent manufacturers that are less likely to source ingredients from China. **Availability:** Online.

30762 ■ "Medtronic Heading to Foreign Markets" in Memphis Business Journal (Vol. 34, September 28, 2012, No. 24, pp. 1)
Pub: Baltimore Business Journal
Contact: Rhonda Pringle, President
E-mail: rpringle@bizjournals.com

Description: Medtronics Inc.'s Spinal and Biologics Division will launch a new spinal surgery system in 2012. The spinal fusion procedure has not yet been approved by international surgical governing bodies, but the company is already rolling it out in different countries. The new service uses the company's various surgical systems and implants. **Availability:** Print; Online.

30763 ■ "MFG Wind Launched at AWEA WindPower 2012 Conference and Exhibition" in Marketing Weekly News (June 23, 2012, pp. 169)
Description: American Wind Energy Association's Conference & Exhibition was held in Atlanta, Georgia. The Molded Fiber Glass Companies (MFG) introduced MFG Wind, a new brand that stands for comprehensive wind-focused set of capabilities that it is bringing to the marketplace.

30764 ■ "Microsoft's Diversity Program Clicks into High Speed" in Hispanic Business (Vol. 30, July-August 2008, No. 7-8, pp. 54)
Ed: Derek Reveron. **Description:** Microsoft's diversity hiring and vendor diversity program to capture more Hispanic consumer and business-to-business market is described. One of the main goals of these programs is to hire more Hispanic executives and managers who will help the company develop and market products and services that will appeal and benefit Hispanic consumers.

30765 ■ "MIR Growing With Help From Former Pfizer Workers" in Crain's Detroit Business (Vol. 24, January 28, 2008, No. 4, pp. 33)
Pub: Crain Communications Inc.
Contact: Barry Asin, President

Ed: Tom Henderson. **Description:** Molecular Imaging Research Inc. helps fund research at its parent firm, Molecular Therapeutics Inc. The company provides imaging services and other in vivo and in vitro services to help pharmaceutical companies test new compounds. **Availability:** Print; Online.

30766 ■ "A Model Machine for Titanium" in Modern Machine Shop (Vol. 84, October 2011, No. 5, pp. 84)
Pub: Gardner Business Media Inc.
Contact: Rick Kline, Jr., President
E-mail: rkline2@gardnerweb.com

Released: September 15, 2011. **Description:** Researchers have developed a machine tool that controls vibration in order to mill titanium more productively. In-depth information on the machine tool as well as understanding the processes involved in milling titanium is covered. **Availability:** Online.

30767 ■ "Monsanto's Next Single-Bag Refuge Product Approved" in Farm Industry News (December 5, 2011)
Pub: Informa Business Media, Inc.
Contact: Charlie McCurdy, President

Description: Monsanto's refuge-in-a-bag (RIB) product was approved for commercialization in 2012. The Genuity VT Double Pro RIB Complete is a blend of 95 percent Genuity VT Double Pro and 5 percent refuge (non-Bt) seed and provides above-ground pest control and not corn rootworm protection. **Availability:** Print; Online.

30768 ■ "The More Incredible Egg" in Entrepreneur (June 2014)
Pub: Entrepreneur Media Inc.
Contact: Dan Bova, Director
E-mail: dbova@entrepreneur.com

Description: San Francisco, California-based startup Hampton Creek has developed a plant-based alternative to eggs. The startup touts it as a healthier, more humane and environment-friendly egg alternative. The company used several varieties of the yellow pea and discovered that its properties mimic egg emulsion. Hampton Creek's first food product was Beyond Eggs, a powder that allows food manufacturers to eliminate eggs from food products. It also developed Just Mayo, an egg-free mayonnaise substitute, and is developing Eat the Dough, an egg-free substitute for cookie dough. **Availability:** Print; Online.

30769 ■ "Motors and Motion Control" in Canadian Electronics (Vol. 23, February 2008, No. 1, pp. 23)
Description: A new version of MicroMo Electronics Inc.'s Smoovy Series 0303.B has been added to MicroMo's DC motor product line. United Electronic Industries, on the other hand, has introduced the new UEIPAC series of programmable automation controllers that can offer solutions to various applications such as unmanned vehicle controllers. Features and functions of other new motors and motion control devices are given.

30770 ■ "Necessity Mother of This Startup" in Providence Business News (Vol. 28, January 6, 2014, No. 40, pp. 1)
Pub: American City Business Journals, Inc.
Contact: Mike Olivieri, Executive Vice President
URL(s): pbn.com/necessity-mother-of-this-startup9
4159

Description: Kailas Narendran, founder of kiinde LLC, invented a device that can quickly thaw breast milk to precisely the right temperature for feeding a baby without losing nutrients. Innovative products for mothers and babies are now being sold by kiine throughout the U.S., Canada and South Korea. New product development is discussed by Narendran. **Availability:** Online.

30771 ■ "The New Alchemists" in Canadian Business (Vol. 81, October 27, 2008, No. 18, pp. 22)
Description: Ethanol industry expects second-generation ethanol or cellulosic biofuels to provide ecologically friendly technologies than the ethanol made from food crops. Government and industries are investing on producing cellulosic biofuels. **Availability:** Print; Online.

30772 ■ "New Backers, New Products at Halo" in Business Journal (Vol. 32, July 18, 2014, No. 8, pp. 5)
Pub: American City Business Journals, Inc.
Contact: Mike Olivieri, Executive Vice President
Released: Weekly. **Price:** $4, introductory 4-week offer(Digital only). **Description:** Minnetonka, Minnesota-based Halo Innovations Inc. announced the launch of its first baby bassinet. The product launch follows a recapitalization that allowed new backers, including Balance Point Capital Partners, to buy the stakes of long-time investors. The risk of suffocation in having babies sleep with parents is also discussed. **Availability:** Print; Online.

30773 ■ "New Crop Protection Products from Monsanto, Valent, DuPont, FMC, BASF" in Farm Industry News (December 17, 2010)
Pub: Informa Business Media, Inc.
Contact: Charlie McCurdy, President

Ed: Mark Moore. **Price:** $4, Print and Online; Special Offers only for 4 weeks. **Description:** Glyphosate-dominated herbicides are declining because a more diversified market for corn and soybeans is available. New crop care includes old chemistries, new formulations and unique combinations of both giving farmers more choices to protect the yield potential of their corn and soybean crops. Profiles of new products are included. **Availability:** Print; Online.

30774 ■ "New Ethanol Plant, Planned for Nevada, IA, Will Use Corn Stover" in Farm Industry News (June 27, 2011)
Pub: Informa Business Media, Inc.
Contact: Charlie McCurdy, President

Ed: Lynn Grooms. **Description:** DuPont Danisco Cellulosic Ethanol (DDCE) will buy land next to the Lincolnway Energy corn-based ethanol plant in Nevada, Iowa in order to produce ethanol from corn stover at the location. **Availability:** Online.

30775 ■ "New Pet Product Launches IndieGoGo Crowdfunding to Remain American Made" in Benzinga.com (June 11, 2012)
Pub: Benzinga.com
Contact: Jason Raznick, Founder

Ed: Aaron Wise. **Description:** The Supercollar (r) is a new dog collar and leash combination launched on an Indiegogo crowdfunding campaign in order to raise fund to help the firm keep their business in America. The firm is striving to design and manufacture the Supercollar here in the US in order to create and save American jobs. The Supercollar's technology is also discussed. **Availability:** Print; Online.

30776 ■ "New Recipes Added to IAMS Naturals Pet Food Line" in MMR (Vol. 28, August 1, 2011, No. 11, pp. 17)
Description: Procter & Gamble Company's IAMS brand has created a new pet food line called IAMS Naturals for pet owners wishing to feed their pets natural, wholesome food. IAMS Sensitive Naturals has ocean fish and its first ingredient for dogs with sensitivities. IAMS Simple & Natural features chicken with no fillers. **Availability:** Print; Online.

30777 ■ "New Sony HD Ads Tout Digital" in Brandweek (Vol. 49, April 21, 2008, No. 16, pp. 5)
Description: Looking to promote Sony Electronics' digital imaging products, the company has launched another campaign effort known as HDNA, a play on the words high-definition and DNA; originally Sony focused the HDNA campaign on their televisions, the new ads will include still and video cameras as well and marketing efforts will consist of advertising in print, Online, television spots and publicity at various venues across the country. **Availability:** Online.

30778 ■ "New Sprint Phone Whets Appetite for Applications, Brings Revenue for Handmark" in The Business Journal-Serving Metropolitan Kansas City (Vol. 26, July 25, 2008)
Description: Firms supporting the applications of the new Samsung Instinct, which was introduced by Sprint Nextel Corp. in June 2008, have reported usage rates increase for their products. Handmark, whose mobile services Pocket Express comes loaded with Instinct, has redirected employees to meet the rising demand for the services. Other views and information on Instinct, are presented. **Availability:** Print; Online.

30779 ■ "New Yetter Stubble Solution Prevents Tire, Track Damage" in Farm Industry News (November 21, 2011)
Pub: Informa Business Media, Inc.
Contact: Charlie McCurdy, President

Description: The new Yetter 5000 Stalk Devastator helps prevent premature tire and track wear and damage caused by crop stubble. **Availability:** Print; Online.

30780 ■ "Nonstop Round Baler Earns Top International Award for Krone" in Farm Industry News (November 18, 2011)
Pub: Informa Business Media, Inc.
Contact: Charlie McCurdy, President

Ed: Karen McMahon. **Description:** The new Ultima baler from Krone can make and net a bale in 40 seconds without stopping, thus producing 90 bales an hour. The new baler, still in test stage, won top honors at the Agritechnica farm equipment show in Hannover, Germany. **Availability:** Online.

30781 ■ "Our Gadget of the Week: Eye Candy From Dell" in Barron's (Vol. 89, July 27, 2009, No. 30, pp. 26)
Description: Zeo Sleep Coach has a lightweight headband with built-in sensors which measures the user's brain waves and records their sleep patterns.

The device details the time the users spends in deep sleep, light sleep and the restorative REM (rapid eye movement) sleep mode. Users can get lifestyle change recommendations from a website to improve their sleep. **Availability:** Online.

30782 ■ *"Patently (Un)Clear" in Business Strategy Review (Vol. 21, Spring 2010, No. 1, pp. 28)*
Ed: Markus Reitzig, Stefan Wagner. **Released:** 2010. **Description:** After developing a great product or process, it's important to protect it. The benefits of using internal patent lawyers versus outsourcing the task are examined. **Availability:** Print; PDF; Online.

30783 ■ *"Patient Monitoring Tool Nears Testing Phase" in Pittsburgh Business Times (Vol. 33, February 7, 2014, No. 30, pp. 5)*
Pub: American City Business Journals, Inc.
Contact: Mike Olivieri, Executive Vice President
Description: Aided with a $500,000 investment, Wellbridge Health Inc. and its partner, Philadelphia-based Biotelemetry Inc., will launch an interactive and easy to use patient monitoring tool. Wellbridge CEO, Mary Del Brady, reports that this device will allow for a real-time monitoring of a patient's condition. **Availability:** Online.

30784 ■ *"Perry's Goes Organic" in Ice Cream Reporter (Vol. 22, December 20, 2008, No. 1, pp. 1)*
Description: Family-owned Perry's Ice Cream is starting a new line of organic ice cream in both vanilla and chocolate flavors. All Perry's products are made with milk and cream from local dairy farmers. **Availability:** Print; Online.

30785 ■ *"Faster To Dissolve, Faster To Work" in Philadelphia Business Journal (Vol. 33, March 14, 2014, No. 5, pp. 8)*
Pub: American City Business Journals, Inc.
Contact: Mike Olivieri, Executive Vice President
Released: Weekly. **Price:** $4, introductory 4-week offer(Digital & Print). **Description:** The U.S. Food and Drug Administration approved Iroko Pharmaceutical's anti-inflammatory drug Tivorbex. The company's technology reformulates a braded drug's active ingredient as submicron particles 20 times smaller than their original size. Iroko also applies the technology to drugs used in oncology. **Availability:** Print; Online.

30786 ■ *"Pink Label: Victoria's Sales Secret" in Advertising Age (Vol. 79, July 7, 2008, No. 26, pp. 4)*
Pub: Crain Communications, Inc.
Contact: Jessica Botos, Manager, Marketing
E-mail: jessica.botos@crainsnewyork.com
Ed: Natalie Zmuda. **Description:** Victoria Secret's Pink label accounted for roughly 17 percent of the retailer's total sales last year. The company is launching a Collegiate Collection which will be promoted by a campus tour program. **Availability:** Print; Online.

30787 ■ *"Pioneer Unveils Drought-Tolerant Hybrids" in Farm Industry News (January 6, 2011)*
Pub: Informa Business Media, Inc.
Contact: Charlie McCurdy, President
Ed: Mark Moore. **Description:** Eight new drought-tolerant hybrids are now available across five genetic platforms from Pioneer. The new hybrids, marketed under the Optimum AQUAmax brand name (previously announced as Drought Tolerant 1 Hybrids), contain a collection of native corn traits that improve water access and utilization. **Availability:** Print; Online.

30788 ■ *"Pioneering Strategies for Entrepreneurial Success" in Business Horizons (Vol. 51, January-February 2008, No. 1, pp. 21)*
Pub: Elsevier Advanced Technology Publications
Ed: Candida G. Brush. **Price:** $8.95, hardcopy black and white. **Description:** Entrepreneurs are known for new products, services, processes, markets and industries. In order to achieve success, they have to develop a clear vision, creatively manage finances, and use social skills to persuade others to commit to the venture. Pioneering strategies and their implementation are examined. **Availability:** Print; PDF; Online.

30789 ■ *"Plumbing, Heating Products Shine at Greenbuild Expo" in Contractor (Vol. 56, December 2009, No. 12, pp. 1)*
Ed: Robert P. Mader. **Description:** Greenbuild Show held in Phoenix, Arizona has showcased the latest in plumbing and heating products. Zurn displayed its EcoVantage line of fixtures and valves during the event. Meanwhile, Sloan Valve offered its washdown 1-pint/flush Alphine urinal. **Availability:** Online.

30790 ■ *"Portland Home Is First in U.S. to Use Variable Speed Inverter Technology" in Contractor (Vol. 56, December 2009, No. 12, pp. 5)*
Description: Daikin Altherma heat pump with inverter drive has been installed in a Portland, Oregon home. The heat pump provides a high coefficient of performance while delivering hydronic and domestic hot water functionality. Other product features and dimensions are also supplied. **Availability:** Print; Online.

30791 ■ *"Powering Intelligent Commerce: eCommera Rebrands as OrderDynamics, Helping Retailers Activate Commerce from First Interaction to Fulfillment" in Computer Business Week (August 28, 2014, pp. 20)*
Pub: NewsRX LLC.
Contact: Kalani Rosell, Contact
Description: OrderDynamics, a new global brand created by eCommera, is profiled. The firm will continue to provide an integrated suite of software-as-a-service (SaaS) big data products and service that power intelligent commerce for retailers and brands around the world. Details of the integration of the new brand are included. **Availability:** Online.

30792 ■ *"Preceptis Gets Gopher Angels' Biggest-Ever Investment" in Business Journal (Vol. 31, January 31, 2014, No. 36, pp. 8)*
Pub: American City Business Journals, Inc.
Contact: Mike Olivieri, Executive Vice President
Description: Preceptis Medical Inc. has secured $1.2 million in funding from Gopher Angels. The funding will help Preceptis to finance ongoing clinical studies and general operating expenses. The company develops surgical tools for pediatric ear-tube surgery. **Availability:** Print; Online.

30793 ■ *"Precision Fertilizer Spreading Shown at Agritechnica" in Farm Industry News (November 23, 2011)*
Pub: Informa Business Media, Inc.
Contact: Charlie McCurdy, President
Ed: Karen McMahon. **Description:** Rauch, the German firm, introduced a new system that precisely spreads fertilizer on crops. The new product was shown at Agritechnica. **Availability:** Online.

30794 ■ *"Presidential Address: Innovation in Retrospect and Prospect" in Canadian Journal of Electronics (Vol. 43, November 2010, No. 4)*
Pub: Journal of the Canadian Economics Association
Ed: James A. Brander. **Description:** Has innovation slowed in recent decades? While there has been progress in information and communications technology, the recent record of innovation in agriculture, energy, transportation and healthcare sectors is cause for concern. **Availability:** PDF; Online.

30795 ■ *"Press Release: New Corn Hybrid from Seed Consultants" in Farm Industry News (January 6, 2011)*
Description: Seed Consultants Inc. is releasing its first proprietary corn line called SC 1101. The product was developed, bred, and tested for the eastern Corn Belt diseases, soils, and growing conditions.

30796 ■ *"Press Release: Trimble Introduces CFX-750 Display" in Farm Industry News (January 4, 2011)*
Description: Trimble is offering a touch screen display called the CFX-750. The new 8-inch full-color display allows farmers to choose the specific guidance, steering and precision agriculture capabilities that best fit their farm's particular needs. The display can be upgraded as business needs change, including the addition of GLONASS capabilities, or the addition of section and rate control for crop inputs such as seed, chemicals and fertilizer. **Availability:** Print; Online.

30797 ■ *"Probability Processing Chip: Lyric Semiconductor" in Inc. (Volume 32, December 2010, No. 10, pp. 52)*
Pub: Inc. Magazine
Ed: Christine Lagorio. **Description:** Lyric Semiconductor, a start up located in Cambridge, Massachusetts, has developed a computer chip that also uses values that fall between zero and one, resulting in a chip that can process information using probabilities, considering many possible answers that find the best fit. **Availability:** Online.

30798 ■ *"Putting 'Extra' in Extra-Silky Shampoo" in Crain's Chicago Business (Vol. 31, April 28, 2008, No. 17, pp. 37)*
Pub: Crain Communications Inc.
Contact: Barry Asin, President
Ed: Phuong Ly. **Description:** Profile of HallStar Co., a Chicago-based company which develops and manufactures specialty chemicals to upgrade existing products such as hair dye, lotion and deodorant. HallStar has seen its annual earnings rise more than 30 percent since 2002. **Availability:** Online.

30799 ■ *"The Quest for a Smart Prosthetic" in Canadian Business (Vol. 83, October 12, 2010, No. 17, pp. 26)*
Pub: Rogers Media Inc.
Contact: Neil Spivak, Chief Executive Officer
Ed: Jacqueline Nelson. **Description:** Information about a two-year research project led by Southern Methodist University (SMU) and funded by the Defense Advance Research Projects Agency (DARPA) is provided. The agency aims to create a 'smart prosthetic' which will improve the lives of military amputees. The planned prosthetic will use a sensor that can carry nerve signals through synthetic channels. **Availability:** Print; Online.

30800 ■ *"Red Velvet Cupcake Bites" in CandyIndustry (Vol. 176, September 2011, No. 9, pp. RC4)*
Pub: BNP Media
Contact: Harper Henderson, Owner Co-Chief Executive Officer
Description: Taste of Nature's Cookie Dough Bites has launched a new candy called, Red Velvet Cupcake Bites. The new product will feature a cupcake center covered in red frosting; ingredients are listed.

30801 ■ *"Retail Doesn't Cross Borders: Here's Why and What To Do About It" in Harvard Business Review (Vol. 90, April 2012, No. 4, pp. 104)*
Pub: Harvard Business Review Press
Contact: Moderna V. Pfizer, Contact
Ed: Marcel Corstjens, Rajiv Lal. **Description:** Globalization poses challenges for retailers, such as competing directly with well established local businesses. To succeed, retailers should enter markets at the right time, focus not on synergies but on differentiation, and introduce new and innovative products and services.

30802 ■ *"Retailers Tap into War-Room Creativity of Employees" in Globe & Mail (March 12, 2007, pp. B1)*
Ed: Marina Strauss. **Description:** The methods adopted by Canadian Tire Corporation Ltd. to utilize the creative abilities of its employees for innovation during new product development are discussed. **Availability:** Print; Online.

30803 ■ *"A Reverse-Innovation Playbook: Insights From a Company That Developed Products For Emerging Markets and Then Brought Them Back Home"* in *Harvard Business Review (Vol. 90, April 2012, No. 4, pp. 120)*

Pub: Harvard Business Review Press

Contact: Moderna V. Pfizer, Contact

Ed: Vijay Govindarajan. **Price:** $8.95, hardcover. **Description:** An overview is presented on the organizational change implemented by Harman International Industries Inc. to create products for emerging markets and ensure that they would be accepted in already established middle markets. Components include setting radical goals, selecting team leaders with no competing interests, and leveraging global resources. **Availability:** PDF; Online.

30804 ■ *"Robai Aims to Commercialize Robot Arm for Manufacturers; Eyes Series A Funding"* in *Boston Business Journal (Vol. 34, July 4, 2014, No. 22, pp. 5)*

Pub: American City Business Journals, Inc.

Contact: Mike Olivieri, Executive Vice President

Released: June 25, 2014. **Description:** Robai aims to raise $5 million in funding to help commercialize a lightweight and easy to use robot arm, called Cyton. The robot arm operates much like a human arm with multiple ranges of motion. It weighs under five pounds, can be programmed in 15 minutes, has the ability to reach around obstacles, and is meant to do repetitive, mundane tasks for contract manufacturing companies. **Availability:** Print; Online.

30805 ■ *"Rule of the Masses: Reinventing Fashion Via Crowdsourcing"* in *WWD (Vol. 200, July 26, 2010, No. 17, pp. 1)*

Pub: Conde Nast Publications

Contact: Agnes Chu, President

Ed: Cate T. Corcoran. **Description:** Large apparel brands and retailers are crowdsourcing as a way to increase customer loyalty and to build their businesses. **Availability:** PDF; Download; Online.

30806 ■ *"SCS Renewables Helps Hook Up Solar Deals"* in *Silicon Valley/San Jose Business Journal (Vol. 30, July 13, 2012, No. 16, pp. 1)*

Pub: Baltimore Business Journal

Contact: Rhonda Pringle, President

E-mail: rpringle@bizjournals.com

Description: Campbell, California-based SCS Renewables Inc. has launched a new system that will provide a standardized overview of a solar project's characteristics and match it with a bank or other interested investor. SCS executives believe their technology enables the process of funding solar projects to become simple and faster. **Availability:** Print; Online.

30807 ■ *"Sinai Doctor's Research May Lead to Rival Plavix Drug"* in *Baltimore Business Journal (Vol. 28, July 16, 2010, No. 10, pp. 1)*

Pub: Baltimore Business Journal

Contact: Rhonda Pringle, President

E-mail: rpringle@bizjournals.com

Ed: Emily Mullin. **Description:** Paul Gurbel, Sinai Hospital Center for Thrombosis Research director, is seeking an FDA approval of Brilinta, a drug which he helped create and test. Gurbel says that the approval could bring the drug to market as early as December 2010. The drug is expected to rival Bristol-Myers' Plavix, which generated almost $6.2 billion in 2009. **Availability:** Print; Online.

30808 ■ *"The Sky's the Limit"* in *Retail Merchandiser (Vol. 51, July-August 2011, No. 4, pp. 64)*

Description: Mars Retail Group (MRG) is the licensing division handling M&M's Brand Candies. Since taking over the brand they have expanded from 12 licensees to 50 licensees with new offerings. **Availability:** Online.

30809 ■ *"Stop the Innovation Wars"* in *Harvard Business Review (Vol. 88, July-August 2010, No. 7-8, pp. 76)*

Pub: Harvard Business Publishing

Contact: Diane Belcher, Managing Director

Ed: Vijay Govindarajan, Chris Trimble. **Price:** $8.95, PDF. **Description:** Methods for managing conflicts between partners during the innovation initiative process are highlighted. These include dividing the labor, assembling a dedicated team, and mitigating likelihood for any potential conflict. **Availability:** Online; PDF.

30810 ■ *"Strange Brew"* in *Canadian Business (Vol. 85, June 11, 2012, No. 10, pp. 52)*

Ed: Paul Brent. **Description:** Molson Coors is launching the Coors Light Iced T beer in summer 2012 as part of its effort to improve weak sales in North America. The new product is aimed at female drinkers and is part of an effort to win back sales from wine and spirits. **Availability:** Print; Online.

30811 ■ *"Stronger Corn? Take It Off Steroids, Make It All Female"* in *Farm Industry News (December 5, 2011)*

Pub: Informa Business Media, Inc.

Contact: Charlie McCurdy, President

Ed: Brian Wallheimer. **Description:** Purdue University researcher found that higher improvements in corn crops, and possibly other crops, were yielded when steroids were discontinued. **Availability:** Print; Online.

30812 ■ *"Study: New Moms Build A Lot of Brand Buzz"* in *Brandweek (Vol. 49, April 21, 2008, No. 16, pp. 7)*

Description: According to a new survey which sampled 1,721 pregnant women and new moms, this demographic is having 109 word-of-mouth conversations per week concerning products, services and brands. Two-thirds of these conversations directly involve brand recommendations. The Internet is driving these word-of-mouth, or W-O-M, conversations among this segment, beating out magazines, television and other forms of media. **Availability:** Online.

30813 ■ *"Sweet Tea From McDonald's: A Marketing 50 Case Study"* in *Advertising Age (Vol. 79, November 17, 2008, No. 43, pp. 4)*

Pub: Crain Communications, Inc.

Contact: Jessica Botos, Manager, Marketing

E-mail: jessica.botos@crainsnewyork.com

Ed: Emily Bryson York. **Description:** McDonald's launch of iced coffee and sweat tea, which were promoted via price cuts over the summer, helped to boost sales at the fast-food chain. **Availability:** Online.

30814 ■ *"Taking a Leap With Mobile Wi-Fi"* in *Austin Business Journal (Vol. 34, July 25, 2014, No. 23, pp. 10)*

Pub: American City Business Journals, Inc.

Contact: Mike Olivieri, Executive Vice President

Released: July 25, 2014. **Price:** $4, introductory 4-week offer(Digital only). **Description:** Austin-based semi-conductor design company Nitero Inc.'s recent release of its Wi-Fi chip, Nietero's key rival Wilocity Ltd.'s acquisition by a tech giant, pushing demand for semiconductors; thus spurring growth for Nitero. It's Wi-Fi's system for mobile platforms will enable users to do more things on their Smartphones, thus converging more devices into one. **Availability:** Print; Online.

30815 ■ *"Tale of a Gun"* in *Canadian Business (Vol. 80, February 26, 2007, No. 5, pp. 37)*

Description: The technology behind automated ballistic identification systems, which can be used to analyze fired ammunition components and link them to crime guns and suspects, developed by Canadian companies is presented. **Availability:** Online.

30816 ■ *"TomTom GO910: On the Road Again"* in *Black Enterprise (Vol. 37, January 2007, No. 6, pp. 52)*

Pub: Earl G. Graves Ltd.

Contact: Earl Graves, Jr., President

Ed: Stephanie Young. **Description:** TomTom GO 910 is a GPS navigator that offers detailed maps of the U.S., Canada, and Europe. Consumers view their routes by a customizable LCD screen showing everything from the quickest to the shortest routes available or how to avoid toll roads. Business travelers may find this product invaluable as it also functions as a cell phone and connects to a variety of other multi-media devices. **Availability:** Online.

30817 ■ *Trade-Off: The Ever-Present Tension Between Quality and Conscience*

Released: August 17, 2010. **Price:** $15. **Description:** The tension between fidelity (the quality of a consumer's experience) and convenience (the ease of getting and paying for a product) are shown to be the forces that determine the success or failure of new products and services in the marketplace.

30818 ■ *"UM-Dearborn to Launch Program for Entrepreneurs"* in *Crain's Detroit Business (Vol. 24, April 14, 2008, No. 15, pp. 7)*

Pub: Crain Communications Inc.

Contact: Barry Asin, President

Ed: Chad Halcom. **Description:** Starting this fall the University of Michigan-Dearborn will begin its Product Realization and Technology Commercialization Program for entrepreneurs and innovators with lab-tested, high-technology products. Ultimately, 20 businesses will each work with the university in creating a customer base, commercializing a new high-tech product or process and connecting with venture capitalists who may invest in the new companies. **Availability:** Online.

30819 ■ *"Unbreakable: Computer Software"* in *Canadian Business (Vol. 79, October 9, 2006, No. 20, pp. 111)*

Pub: Rogers Media Inc.

Contact: Neil Spivak, Chief Executive Officer

Ed: Robert Hercz. **Description:** The features and functions of Neutrino, an embedded operating system developed by QNX Software Systems are discussed. **Availability:** Online.

30820 ■ *"Under Armour Hopes to Stomp on Nike with Basketball Shoe"* in *Baltimore Business Journal (Vol. 28, October 22, 2010, No. 24, pp. 1)*

Pub: Baltimore Business Journal

Contact: Rhonda Pringle, President

E-mail: rpringle@bizjournals.com

Ed: Erik Siemers. **Description:** Uner Armour Inc. will release its Micro G line of four basketball sneakers on October 23, 2010. The company's executives mentioned that Under Armour's goal is to appeal to customers, and not to chip away at Nike Inc.'s supremacy in basketball shoes. The new sneakers will range from $80 to $110. **Availability:** Print; Online.

30821 ■ *"Under Armour Wants to Equip Athletes, Too"* in *Boston Business Journal (Vol. 29, July 8, 2011, No. 9, pp. 1)*

Pub: Boston Business Journal

Contact: Carolyn M. Jones, President

E-mail: cmjones@bizjournals.com

Ed: Ryan Sharrow. **Description:** Baltimore sportswear maker Under Armour advances plans to enter into the equipment field, aiming to strengthen its hold on football, basketball and lacrosse markets where it already has a strong market share. The company is now cooking up licensing deals to bolster the firm's presence among athletes. **Availability:** Print; Online.

30822 ■ *"U.S. Competitiveness and the Chinese Challenge"* in *Harvard Business Review (Vol. 90, March 2012, No. 3, pp. 40)*

Pub: Harvard Business Review Press

Contact: Moderna V. Pfizer, Contact

Ed: Xu Xiaonian. **Price:** $6, hardcover. **Description:** Although China's shift from cntral planningto market-oriented policies has boosted innovation, intellectual property rights and original research are still insufficiently valued. The U.S. has the edge on China in this respect; it remains for the U.S. to restore confidence in its innovation and creativity. **Availability:** PDF; Online.

30823 ■ *"Unleashing the Power of Marketing"* *in Harvard Business Review (Vol. 88, October 2010, No. 10, pp. 90)*
Pub: Harvard Business Publishing
Contact: Diane Belcher, Managing Director
Ed: Beth Comstock, Ranjay Gulati, Stephen Liguori. **Price:** $8.95, PDF. **Description:** Chronicle of the development of General Electric's marketing framework that focused on three key factors: Principles, people and process. GE determined that successful marketing fulfills four functions: instigating, innovating, implementing, and integrating. **Availability:** Online; PDF.

30824 ■ *"US Hygiene Adds Bed Bug Fix to Its Line of Highly Effective Cleaning and Pest Control Products"* *in Benzinga.com (October 29, 2011)*
Pub: Benzinga.com
Contact: Jason Raznick, Founder
Description: US Hygiene LLC introduced its newest product called Bed Bug Fix, which is a naturally-derived, nontoxic insecticide that kills a multitude of bugs including bed bugs and dust mites. The product is safe to use around children, plants and pets. **Availability:** Print; Online.

30825 ■ *"uTest Discusses the Evolution of Crowdsourcing Models at CrowdConf 2010"* *in Marketwired (October 1, 2010)*
Pub: Comtex News Network Inc.
Contact: Kan Devnani, President
Description: World's largest software testing marketplace, uTest, announces its first conference dedicated to the emerging field of crowdsourcing along with the future of distributed work. A panel of experts will discuss common misconceptions about crowdsourcing using real-world examples. **Availability:** Print; Mailing list; Online.

30826 ■ *"VC-Heavy, Revenue-Light Sensicore Sold to GE Division"* *in Crain's Detroit Business (Vol. 24, April 14, 2008, No. 15, pp. 28)*
Pub: Crain Communications Inc.
Contact: Barry Asin, President
Ed: Tom Henderson. **Description:** General Electric has acquired Sensicore Inc., which although one of Michigan's most successful companies in raising venture capital was unable to generate significant revenue from its handheld water-testing devices. GE is capable of penetrating a larger market than a private company and will be able to take the devices to the municipal marketplace. **Availability:** Online.

30827 ■ *"Vitabath: Sweet Smell of Success"* *in Retail Merchandiser (Vol. 51, September-October 2011, No. 5, pp. 82)*
Pub: Phoenix Media Corp.
Description: After taking over at Vitabath, Rich Brands developed new scents and products and while discovering new channels to distribute these items. **Availability:** PDF; Online.

30828 ■ *"Wabtec Delivering Strategic Plan for Long-term Growth"* *in Pittsburgh Business Times (Vol. 33, July 11, 2014, No. 52, pp. 10)*
Pub: American City Business Journals, Inc.
Contact: Mike Olivieri, Executive Vice President
Released: July 2014. **Description:** Raymond Betler, new CEO of Wabtec Corporation, the only company with a 13-year streak of annual stock price increase on US exchanges is profiled. Betler attributes the company's growth to four corporate strategies, including to grow internationally, focus on new product development, expand after-market opportunities, and pursue acquisitions. **Availability:** Print; Online.

30829 ■ *"Wall Street Is No Friend to Radical Innovation"* *in Harvard Business Review (Vol. 88, July-August 2010, No. 7-8, pp. 28)*
Pub: Harvard Business Publishing
Contact: Diane Belcher, Managing Director
Ed: Julia Kirby. **Price:** $6, PDF. **Description:** Research indicates that investors are skittish about backing a business that proposes significant changes to its product or service status quo. **Availability:** Online; PDF.

30830 ■ *"Watson May Study New Field"* *in Business Review Albany (Vol. 41, July 18, 2014, No. 17, pp. 10)*
Description: IBM Corporation has extended its Watson computer system's cognitive capacities to the Cloud. Rensselaer Polytechnic Institute has been training Watson to be a data advisor. It is also using the system to study human thought and cognition. **Availability:** Print; Online.

30831 ■ *"Wealth and Jobs: the Broken Link"* *in Harvard Business Review (Vol. 88, November 2010, No. 11, pp. 44)*
Pub: Harvard Business Publishing
Contact: Diane Belcher, Managing Director
Ed: Nitin Nohria. **Price:** $6, PDF. **Description:** Rebuilding the link between business and job creation to shore up the middle class is advocated. A blend of government policies and business strategies that foster entrepreneurship and innovation are essential. **Availability:** Online; PDF.

30832 ■ *"Well-Heeled Startup Plots Course for a Run at Garmin"* *in Business Journal Portland (Vol. 27, November 12, 2010, No. 37, pp. 1)*
Pub: Portland Business Journal
Contact: Andy Giegerich, Managing Editor
E-mail: agiegerich@bizjournals.com
Description: Oh! Shoes LLC expects to receive about $1.5 million in funding from angel investors, while marketing a new line of high heel shoes that are comfortable, healthy, and attractive. The new line of shoes will use the technology of athletic footwear while having the look of an Italian designer. Oh! Shoes hopes to generate $35 million in sales by 2014. **Availability:** Print; Online.

30833 ■ *"Where Good Ideas Come From: The Natural History of Innovation"* *in Business Owner (Vol. 35, July-August 2011, No. 4, pp. 6)*
Description: A history of ideas, concepts, innovations and technologies that have created a successful small business environment are explored. **Availability:** Print; Online.

30834 ■ *"A Whiteboard that Peels and Sticks"* *in Inc. (Volume 32, December 2010, No. 10, pp. 58)*
Pub: Inc. Magazine
Ed: Issie Lapwosky. **Description:** Profile of an affordable adhesive whiteboard that can be restuck multiple times; the whiteboard was created by three college friends. The students share insight in the contacts they used in order to promote the sale of their invention. **Availability:** Online.

30835 ■ *"Why Entrepreneurs Matter More Than Innovators"* *in Gallup Management Journal (November 22, 2011)*
Ed: Jim Clifton. **Released:** November 22, 2011. **Description:** In the race to create good jobs, leaders are not paying enough attention to cultivating talented entrepreneurs, rather they invest too much attention on innovation. **Availability:** Print; Online.

30836 ■ *"Why Life Science Needs Its Own Silicon Valley: Human Genomics Won't Reach Its Full Potential Until It Has a Sizable Industry Cluster"* *in Harvard Business Review (Vol. 90, July-August 2012, No. 7-8, pp. 25)*
Pub: Harvard Business Review Press
Contact: Moderna V. Pfizer, Contact

Ed: Fariborz Ghadar, John Sviokla, Dietrich A. Stephan. **Price:** $6, PDF and hardcover black and white. **Description:** The creation of an industry cluster will be key to advancing human genomics research. High degrees of specialization via multiple contributors will be needed to generate significant innovations; an accessible, coherent data source will also be necessary. **Availability:** Print; PDF; Online.

30837 ■ *"With Whom Do You Trade? Defensive Innovation and the Skill-Bias"* *in Canadian Journal of Electronics (Vol. 43, November 2010)*
Pub: Journal of the Canadian Economics Association
Ed: Pushan Dutt, Daniel Traca. **Released:** Vol. 43, No. 4. **Price:** $5. **Description:** Examination into whether increased trade with ineffective protection of intellectual property has contributed to the skill-deepening of the 1980s. An index of effective protection of intellectual property at the country level, combining data on protection of patents and rule of law are presented. An industry-specific version of this index is given using as weights each country's trade share in the total trade of the industry. A decline is seen in this trade-weighted index, owing to a rise in trade with countries with low effective protection of intellectual property, which explains 29 percent of the rise within-industry skill-intensity. **Availability:** Print; Online; Download.

VIDEO/AUDIO MEDIA

30838 ■ *Getting to Product Market Fit, Harvard MBA vs Startup Experience*
URL(s): www.startuphustlepodcast.com/getting-to -product-market-fit-harvard-mba-vs-startup -experience
Ed: Matt Watson. **Released:** April 24, 2024. **Description:** Podcast discusses product-market fit and entrepreneurial challenges.

30839 ■ *The How of Business: Henrik Johansson - Product Development*
URL(s): www.thehowofbusiness.com/452-henrik -johansson-product-development
Ed: Henry Lopez. **Released:** December 19, 2022. **Description:** Podcast discusses the challenges facing product inventors/developers and common misconceptions about the product development process.

30840 ■ *The How of Business: Kristina Schlegel - Make Bake*
URL(s): www.thehowofbusiness.com/455-kristina -schlegel-starting-make-bake
Ed: Henry Lopez. **Released:** January 16, 2023. **Description:** Podcast discusses the origins of Make Bake, a CPG (consumer packaged goods) baking brand.

30841 ■ *How I Built This: Advice Line with Boston Beer Company*
URL(s): wondery.com/shows/how-i-built-this/episode/ 10386-advice-line-with-jim-koch-of-boston-beer -company
Ed: Guy Raz. **Released:** August 08, 2024. **Description:** Podcast answers questions about finding product-market fit.

30842 ■ *How I Built This: What It Really Takes to Build a Food Business: Part 1*
URL(s): wondery.com/shows/how-i-built-this/episode/ 10386-what-it-really-takes-to-build-a-food-business -part-1
Ed: Guy Raz. **Released:** October 18, 2024. **Description:** Podcast explains how to go from a tasty idea to a spot on the grocery store shelf.

30843 ■ *How I Built This: What It Really Takes to Build a Food Business: Part 2*
URL(s): wondery.com/shows/how-i-built-this/episode/ 10386-what-it-really-takes-to-build-a-food-business -part-2

Ed: Guy Raz. **Released:** October 25, 2024. **Description:** Podcast share how three founds grew their brands, handled challenging moments, and offer strategic advice.

30844 ■ *The Knowledge Project: Shreyas Doshi: Better Teams, Better Products*

URL(s): fs.blog/knowleddge-project-podcast/shreyas -doshi

Ed: Shane Parrish. **Released:** September 05, 2023. **Description:** Podcast discusses the connection between building a solid team and building a better product.

30845 ■ *The Value of Product Teams*

URL(s): www.startuphustlepodcast.com/the-value-of -product-teams

Ed: Matt Watson. **Released:** March 12, 2024. **Description:** Podcast discusses common problems tech companies face in product development. .

CONSULTANTS

30846 ■ Aurora Management Partners Inc.

1201 Peachtree St., Ste. 1570
 Atlanta, GA 30361
Ph: (704)377-6010
Co. E-mail: info@auroramp.com
URL: http://www.auroramp.com
Contact: David Baker, CTP, Managing Partner
Linkedin: www.linkedin.com/company/aurora -management-partners/about

Description: Specializes in turnaround management and reorganization consulting, the company develops strategic initiatives, organize and analyze solutions, deal with creditor issues, review organizational structures and develop time frames for decision making. **Founded:** 2000. **Publications:** "TMA Turnaround of the Year Award, Small Company, Honorable Mention," Nov, 2005; "Back From The Brink - Bland Farms," Progressive Farmer, Oct, 2004; "New Breed of Turnaround Managers," Catalyst Magazine, Aug, 2004; "Key Performance Drivers - Bland Farms," The Produce News, Apr, 2004; "Corporate Governance: Averting Crisis's Before They Happen," ABJ journal, Feb, 2004.

30847 ■ ByrneMRG Corp.

5459 Rinker Cir.
 Doylestown, PA 18902
Ph: (215)630-7411
Co. E-mail: info@byrnemrg.com
URL: http://www.byrnemrg.com
Contact: Patrick Boyle, Founder Consultant
E-mail: pjboyle@byrnemrg.com

Description: Services: Management consulting. **Scope:** Services: Management consulting. **Founded:** 1972. **Publications:** "Implementing Solutions to Everyday Issues".

30848 ■ Comer & Associates L.L.C. (CA)

5255 Holmes Pl.
 Boulder, CO 80303
Ph: (303)786-7986
URL: http://www.comerassociates.com
Contact: Gerald Comer, Contact

Description: Specialize in developing markets and businesses. Marketing support includes developing and writing strategic and tactical business plans, developing and writing focused, effective market plans, researching market potential and competition, implementing targeted marketing tactics to achieve company objectives, conducting customer surveys to determine satisfaction and attitudes toward client. **Scope:** Specialize in developing markets and businesses. Marketing support includes developing and writing strategic and tactical business plans, developing and writing focused, effective market plans, researching market potential and competition, implementing targeted marketing tactics to achieve company objectives, conducting customer surveys to determine satisfaction and attitudes toward client. **Training:** Developing a Strategic Market Plan; Market Research: Defining Your Opportunity; Management and Leadership Effectiveness; Team Building; Developing a Business Plan; How to Close; Using Ques-

tions to Sell; Sales System Elements and Checklist; Working With Independent Reps; Features vs. Benefits; Overcoming Objections; Sales Force Automation.

30849 ■ Global Technology Transfer L.L.C.

1500 Dixie Hwy.
 Park Hills, KY 41011
Contact: Anthony R. Zembrodt, Sr., Member

Description: Firm specializes in product development, quality assurance, new product development, and total quality management focusing on household chemical specialties, especially air fresheners. Utilizes latest technology from global resources. Specializes in enhancement products for home and automobile. **Scope:** Firm specializes in product development, quality assurance, new product development, and total quality management focusing on household chemical specialties, especially air fresheners. Utilizes latest technology from global resources. Specializes in enhancement products for home and automobile.

30850 ■ Hewitt Development Enterprises (HDE)

1717 N Bayshore Dr., Ste. 2154
 Miami, FL 33132
Ph: (305)372-0941
Fax: (305)372-0941
Co. E-mail: info@hewittdevelopment.com
URL: http://www.hewittdevelopment.com
Contact: Robert G. Hewitt, Contact
E-mail: bob@hewittdevelopment.com

Description: Firm specializes in strategic planning, profit enhancement, startup businesses, interim and crisis management, turnarounds, production planning, just-in-time inventory and project management, serves senior management and acquirers of distressed businesses. **Scope:** Firm specializes in strategic planning, profit enhancement, startup businesses, interim and crisis management, turnarounds, production planning, just-in-time inventory and project management, serves senior management and acquirers of distressed businesses. **Founded:** 1985.

30851 ■ Interminds & Federer Resources Inc.

PO Box 438
 Pasadena, CA 91102
Ph: (512)261-0761
Co. E-mail: yesyoucan@interminds.com
URL: http://www.interminds.com

Description: Firm specializes in feasibility studies, startup businesses, small business management, mergers and acquisitions, joint ventures, divestitures, interim and crisis management, turnarounds, production planning, team building, appraisals, and valuations. **Scope:** Firm specializes in feasibility studies, startup businesses, small business management, mergers and acquisitions, joint ventures, divestitures, interim and crisis management, turnarounds, production planning, team building, appraisals, and valuations. **Founded:** 1985. **Publications:** "Yes You Can: How To Be A Success No Matter Who You Are Or Where You're From".

30852 ■ Intuition Design Inc.

508 Second St.
 Chesapeake City, MD 21915
Ph: (410)885-2513
Co. E-mail: rob@intuitiondesign.com
URL: http://intuitiondesign.com

Description: Provider of cost-effective product development services. The firm excels in identifying problems, evaluating concepts, and providing practical product solutions. **Scope:** Provider of cost-effective product development services. The firm excels in identifying problems, evaluating concepts, and providing practical product solutions.

30853 ■ Mako Design + Invent

5120 Burnet Rd., Bldg. 2
 Austin, TX 78756
Ph: (512)888-2822
Free: 888-806-6256
Co. E-mail: info@makodesign.com
URL: http://www.makodesign.com
Contact: Kevin Mako, President

Facebook: www.facebook.com/MakoInvent
Linkedin: www.linkedin.com/company/makodesign
X (Twitter): x.com/MakoInvent
Instagram: www.instagram.com/makoinvent
YouTube: www.youtube.com/c/Makoinvent
Pinterest: www.pinterest.com/makoinvent

Description: A product development firm that provides design, prototype, manufacturing, and sales services for both startups and corporations. **Scope:** A product development firm that provides design, prototype, manufacturing, and sales services for both startups and corporations.

30854 ■ Medical Imaging Consultants Inc. (MIC)

1037 US Hwy. 46, Ste. G-2
 Clifton, NJ 07013-2445
Ph: (973)574-8000
Free: 800-589-5685
Fax: (973)574-8001
Co. E-mail: info@micinfo.com
URL: http://www.micinfo.com
Contact: Philip A. Femano, President

Description: Provider of professional support services in radiology management and comprehensive continuing education programs for radiologic technologists such as professional educators, life scientists, biomedical engineers, and much more. **Scope:** Provider of professional support services in radiology management and comprehensive continuing education programs for radiologic technologists such as professional educators, life scientists, biomedical engineers, and much more. **Founded:** 1991. **Training:** Sectional Anatomy and Imaging Strategies; CT Cross-Trainer; CT Registry Review Program; MR Cross Trainer; MRI Registry Review Program; Digital Mammography Essentials for Technologists; Radiology Trends for Technologists.

30855 ■ Mefford, Knutson & Associates Inc. (MKA)

6437 Lyndale Ave. S
 Richfield, MN 55423
Co. E-mail: info@mkcconsulting.com
URL: http://mkaconsulting.com
Contact: Jeanette Mefford, Co-Founder

Description: Provider of consulting services to home health and related sectors. **Scope:** Provider of consulting services to home health and related sectors. **Founded:** 1990.

RESEARCH CENTERS

30856 ■ Ball State University - Center for Organizational Resources (CORe)

Applied Technology Bldg.
 2000 W University Ave.
 Muncie, IN 47306
Ph: (765)285-5645
Co. E-mail: core@bsu.edu
URL: http://www.bsu.edu/academics/centersandinsti tutes/core
Contact: Dr. Chris Davison, Contact
E-mail: cbdavison@bsu.edu

Description: Integral unit of the School of Extended Education, Ball State University. Offers contract consulting. **Scope:** Development of existing businesses, including corporate training, executive development, adult literacy, technology transfer, strategic planning, human resource development, needs assessment, creativity, program evaluation, consultant selection, computer software, new product development, sales training, marketing strategy development, hospitality training, and customer service strategy development.

30857 ■ Canadian Innovation Centre (CIC)

Waterloo Research & Technology Park Accelerator Centre
 295 Hagey Blvd., Ste. 15
 Waterloo, ON, Canada N2L 6R5
Ph: (519)885-5870
Fax: (519)513-2421
Co. E-mail: info@innovationcentre.ca
URL: http://innovationcentre.ca
Contact: Josie Graham, Chief Executive Officer

E-mail: jgraham@innovationcentre.ca
Linkedin: www.linkedin.com/company/canadian
-innovation-centre
X (Twitter): x.com/innovationctre

Description: Offers Invention Assistance Program, which assesses all aspects of an invention and aids in its development. **Scope:** Privately incorporated organization associated with University of Waterloo. Offers Invention Assistance Program, which assesses all aspects of an invention and aids in its development. Provides market research assistance to small, medium, and large companies. **Founded:** 1980. **Publications:** "Getting Going on Innovation part 3 in a series of 4: How a Gating System Can Boost Your Innovation Success," 2008; "Aligning the stages of the commercialization process"; "Overestimating the importance of licensing in fostering the Entrepreneurial University"; "Creating a New Model for Technology Commercialization in the Canadian Context"; "The role of Incubators and Contract research Organizations in growing new biotechnology companies"; "The role of Incubators within a University Environment"; "How the Inno-Gate System Can Boost Your Rates of Innovation Success"; "How entrepreneurs-in-residence increase seed investment rates"; "Technology incubators: Facilitating technology transfer or creating regional wealth"; "Pitchers Bible," Oct, 2007; "Making the Pitch - A Guide," Oct, 2006; "What should I include in my pitch? - A Guide," Oct, 2006. **Training:** Big Companies Can't Innovate; Innovation Awareness Seminar, Mar, 2008; First Steps Seminar, Jun, 2006; Government Assistance: Financing and Risk Solutions in Trying Times; First Steps for Innovators, 2006; Services for Innovation Partners; Innovation Workshop, Jun, 2006; Increasing the Rate of Commercialization of technological innovation: the catalytic role of the commerce agent, Jul, 2006; CFA Workshop; The Role of Universities and Colleges in Creating Canada's Wealth, Feb, 2005; Increasing the commercialization yield of Canada's innovation Efforts by Establishing Customer Pull, Jan, 2005; BCIP Presentation, Nov, 2004. **Geographic Preference:** National.

30858 ■ IIT Research Institute (IITRI)

10 W 35th St.
   Chicago, IL 60616
Ph: (312)567-4487
URL: http://iitri.org
Contact: Dr. David L. McCormick, President
Facebook: www.facebook.com/pages/IIT-Research
-Institute/104022946301792
X (Twitter): x.com/IITRI_Chicago

Description: Provider of GLP compliant pre-clinical toxicology, efficacy, PK and ADME evaluation services to the pharmaceutical, biotech, veterinary, agrichemical and nutriceuticals industries. **Scope:** Provider of GLP compliant pre-clinical toxicology, efficacy, PK and ADME evaluation services to the pharmaceutical, biotech, veterinary, agrichemical and nutriceuticals industries. **Founded:** 1936. **Publications:** Provider of basic research for government agencies and academic researchers. **Geographic Preference:** National.

30859 ■ Institute for the Future (IFTF)

201 Hamilton Ave.
   Palo Alto, CA 94301
Ph: (650)854-6322
Fax: (650)854-7850
Co. E-mail: info@iftf.org
URL: http://www.iftf.org
Contact: Marina Gorbis, Executive Director
Facebook: www.facebook.com/InstituteForTheFuture
Linkedin: www.linkedin.com/company/institute-for-the
-future
X (Twitter): x.com/iftf

Description: Independent, nonprofit research group serving companies and organizations around the world by providing methodologies and toolsets that offer "coherent views of transformative possibilities across all sectors that together support a more sustainable future.". **Scope:** Forecasting and planning techniques, development and assessment of new information technology, strategic planning assistance, policy analysis, and market outlooks for

new products and next-generation technologies. Areas of special interest include long-range planning and forecasting, emerging technologies, health care, domestic and global development, and education and training. The Institute assists organizations in planning their long-term future, with staff expertise in business, communications, economics, engineering, health care, history, law, mathematics, physics, psychology, sociology, statistics, and systems analysis. **Founded:** 1968. **Publications:** *Ten-Year Forecast* (Annual); *INSTITUTE FOR THE FUTURE (IFTF)*. **Educational Activities:** IFTF Annual Conference (Annual).

30860 ■ Iowa State University of Science and Technology College of Engineering - Center for Industrial Research and Service (CIRAS)

Economic Development Core Facility
   1805 Collaboration Pl., Ste. 2300
   Ames, IA 50010
Ph: (515)294-3420
Co. E-mail: ciras@iastate.edu
URL: http://www.ciras.iastate.edu
Contact: Leah M. Barton, Assistant Director
E-mail: bartonl@iastate.edu
Linkedin: www.linkedin.com/company/ciras-iowasta
   teuniversity
X (Twitter): x.com/ciras_isu
YouTube: www.youtube.com/channel/
   UCJDRwpBeTkCEsotoZTfY8bw

Description: Integral unit of University Extension at Iowa State University of Science and Technology. Consults with industry on special problems; information retrieval available to industry and professional groups within the state; statewide University Center program for Iowa businesses. Offers workshops, briefings, and specialized extension courses for various phases of industry in the state. **Scope:** Problem areas of business, manufacturing, technology transfer, productivity, new product design, manufacturing processes, marketing, and related topics. Acts as a problem-handling facility and a clearinghouse for efforts to help Iowa's industry grow through studies highlighting not only production and management problems but also markets and profit potential of possible new developments. **Founded:** 1963. **Publications:** *CIRASNews* (Quarterly).

30861 ■ Pennsylvania State University - Institute for the Study of Business Markets (ISBM)

Business Bldg.
   University Park, PA 16802
Ph: (814)863-2782
Co. E-mail: isbm@psu.edu
URL: http://isbm.org
Contact: Stefan Wuyts, Director

Description: Integral unit of Pennsylvania State University. Offers business marketing research support; doctoral dissertation support; short courses and conferences. **Scope:** Business-to-business marketing and sales, including studies on new products, market structure and operations, eBusiness, market communications, channels relationships, buying strategies and operations, public policy, and customer value. Acts as the United States partner of the International Marketing and Purchasing Group, which is studying relationships between members of international distribution channels. Collaborates with marketing professionals nationally and internationally. **Founded:** 1983. **Publications:** *ISBM Insights*; *Marketplace: The ISBM Review Newsletter* (Semiannual); *ISBM Working papers*. **Educational Activities:** ISBM Joint educational programs, With Pennsylvania State Executive Programs.; ISBM Special-interest consortia; ISBM Academic Conference (Biennial), Held in the same city location as AMA, this academic meeting brings the top business-to-business researchers together to present their most recent research.; ISBM Members Meetings. **Awards:** ISBM Business Marketing Doctoral Award Support Competition (Annual).

30862 ■ University of Missouri, St. Louis College of Business Administration - Center for Business and Industrial Studies (CBIS)

c/o L. Douglas Smith, 220 Express Scripts Hall
   1 University Blvd.
   Saint Louis, MO 63121-4400

Ph: (314)516-6108
Co. E-mail: ldsmith@umsl.edu
URL: http://www.umsl.edu/divisions/business/ncbis/in
   dex.html
Contact: L. Douglas Smith, Director
E-mail: ldsmith@umsl.edu

Description: Research and service unit of the College of Business Administration, University of Missouri - St. Louis. **Scope:** Managerial problems, including risk management, planning, business development, job analysis/job evaluation, design and evaluation of incentive systems, inventory management and control, competition, market concentration, market demographics, market penetration, market segmentation, buyer behavior, marketing research designs for new product development and product positioning, measurement of promotional effectiveness, and design and administration of surveys. Specific projects include development of computer software for operations in public transit systems and forecasting models for losses on loan portfolios of financial institutions. **Founded:** 1983.

30863 ■ University of North Dakota - Center for Innovation (CFI)

4200 James Ray Dr.
   Grand Forks, ND 58202
Ph: (701)777-3132
Fax: (701)777-2339
Co. E-mail: info@innovators.net
URL: http://www.innovators.net
Contact: Amy Whitney, Director
Facebook: www.facebook.com/centerforinnovation
Linkedin: www.linkedin.com/company/center-for
-innovation
X (Twitter): x.com/ndinnovators
YouTube: www.youtube.com/channel/UC
   5dHMwGsDEBCW1Hwt3i-Z7g

Description: Provides technical and business support services to entrepreneurs, inventors, and small manufacturers. Assists specifically with the product evaluation process, the patenting process, and technology transfer. **Scope:** Offers market and demographic research, business plan development, financial forecasts, and manufacturing services to entrepreneurs, particularly manufacturing technology start-up enterprises. Provides assistance to innovators, entrepreneurs, and researchers to launch new ventures, commercialize new technologies, and secure access to capital from private and public sources. **Founded:** 1984. **Publications:** The Business Plan: A State-Of-The-Art Guide; "The Marketing Plan: Step-By-Step"; "The Ultimate Business Planner"; "Campus Entrepreneurship: A Changing Curriculum for Changing Times"; "Financing Startup Ventures"; "The Business Plan: A State-of-the-Art Guide"; "The Marketing Plan: Step-by-Step". **Educational Activities:** Center for Innovation Conferences and workshops, Seed and Angel Capital, Entrepreneur Startups, Business Planning, Market Feasibility.

30864 ■ Virginia Polytechnic Institute and State University - Center for High Performance Manufacturing (CHPM)

1145 Perry St.
   Blacksburg, VA 24061
Ph: (540)231-6201
Fax: (540)231-3322
URL: http://www.ise.vt.edu/about/facilities/centers/
   chpm.html
Contact: Dinesh Verma, Executive Director

Description: Integral unit of Virginia Polytechnic Institute and State University. **Scope:** Flexible automation and lean manufacturing, production and information technologies, rapid prototyping and rapid tooling, manufacturing logistics and supply chain management, low-cost composite manufacturing. **Founded:** 2001. **Educational Activities:** CHPM Biannual Meeting (Biennial).

Nonmanufacturing

REFERENCE WORKS

30865 ■ *"ACE Aims High With Spinoff of Repair Unit" in Globe & Mail (January 31, 2007, pp. B15)*
Description: The decision of ACE Aviation Holdings Inc. to sell its aircraft maintenance division and add workforce at its El Salvador plant is discussed. **Availability:** Online.

30866 ■ *Adoption Resource Book*
Pub: HarperCollins Publishers L.L.C.
Contact: Brian Murray, President
URL(s): www.harpercollins.com/products/the-adoption-resource-book-4th-edition-lois-gilman?variant=32117479079970
Price: $19.99, Individuals for paperback. **Description:** Publication includes list of public and private adoption agencies, support groups, and services. **Entries include:** Agency name, address, phone, special requirements. Principal content of the publication is a discussion of adoption procedures and requirements, including adoption of foreign children and open adoption. **Arrangement:** Geographical. **Availability:** Print.

30867 ■ *"Alberta Star Begins Phase 2 Drilling On Its Eldorado & Contact Lake IOCG & Uranium Projects" in Canadian Corporate News (May 16, 2007)*
Description: Profile of Alberta Star Development Corp., a Canadian mineral exploration company that identifies, acquires, and finances advanced stage exploration projects in Canada, and its current undertaking of its 2007 drill program in which the company intends to begin accelerating its uranium and poly-metallic exploration and drilling activities on all of its drill targets for 2007 now that it has been granted its permits. **Availability:** Online.

30868 ■ *"Bitumen Oilsands: Slick Science" in Canadian Business (Vol. 81, September 15, 2008, No. 14-15, pp. 55)*
Pub: Rogers Media Inc.
Contact: Neil Spivak, Chief Executive Officer
Ed: Andrew Nikiforuk. **Description:** N-Solv Corp's John Nenniger has discovered a better alternative to steam-assisted gravity drainage methods for extracting bitumen. Nenniger's technique also relies on gravity but replaces steam with propane, which leaves behind impurities like asphaltenes and heavy metals that are too dirty to burn. **Availability:** Print; Mailing list; Online.

30869 ■ *"The CEO Poll: Fuel for Thought II Canadian Business Leaders on Energy Policy" in Canadian Business (Vol. 81, September 15, 2008, No. 14-15, pp. 12)*
Pub: Rogers Media Inc.
Contact: Neil Spivak, Chief Executive Officer
Ed: Joe Castaldo. **Description:** Most Canadian business leaders worry about the unreliability of the oil supply but feel that Canada is in a better position to benefit from the energy supply crisis than other

countries. Many respondents also highlighted the need to invest in renewable energy sources. **Availability:** Online.

30870 ■ *"CN Aims for Regional Pacts to Halt Labor Row" in Globe & Mail (April 17, 2007, pp. B2)*
Ed: Brent Jang. **Description:** The decision of Canadian National Railway Co. to settle labor dispute with regional unions is discussed. **Availability:** Print; Online.

30871 ■ *"eResearch Issues Initiating Report on Aldershot Resources Ltd." in Marketwired (May 14, 2007)*
Pub: Comtex News Network Inc.
Contact: Kan Devnani, President
Description: Overview of Bob Weir and Michael Wood's Initiating Report on Aldershot Resources Ltd., a junior Canadian-based uranium exploration company with prospective projects in Canada, Zambia, Australia, and a base metals project in Chile. **Availability:** Print; Online.

30872 ■ *"Goldfingers" in Canadian Business (Vol. 81, Summer 2008, No. 9, pp. 31)*
Description: Large players in the mining industry are looking for junior mining companies in Canada to be acquired. The U.S. recession and subprime mortgage crisis have made it easier for giant miners to acquire small mining companies than to conduct the operations themselves. Junior miners are those that lack cash flow and expertise to build and operate mine. **Availability:** Online.

30873 ■ *"Life After Cod" in Globe & Mail (March 18, 2006, pp. B1)*
Pub: The Globe & Mail Inc.
Ed: Gordon Pitts. **Description:** Canadian fishing industry is under threat because of Chinese processing competition, high energy costs, rise of powerful retailers and the rise of Canadian dollar value. Fishing industry of Canada is analyzed. **Availability:** Print; PDF; Online.

30874 ■ *"Lundin Deal Leaves Nickel Market Thin" in Globe & Mail (April 5, 2007, pp. B4)*
Ed: Andy Hoffman. **Description:** The likely acquisition of Rio Narcea Gold Mines Ltd. by Lundin Mining Corp. and the decreasing number of nickel mining companies on the list of Toronto Stock Exchange are discussed. **Availability:** Online.

30875 ■ *National Agricultural Aviation Association--Membership Directory*
Pub: National Agricultural Aviation Association
Contact: Jim Perrin, President
URL(s): www.agaviation.org/membership/#advantages
Ed: Andrew D. Moore. **Released:** Annual **Description:** Covers nearly 1300 executives, pilots, and supplier companies engaged primarily in aerial application. **Entries include:** For chapter and supplier company members--Name, spouse's name, company name, address, phone. **Arrangement:** Classified by

type of membership; chapter members are then geographical; supplier company members are then by product. **Availability:** Print.

30876 ■ *National Council of Acoustical Consultants--Directory*
Pub: National Council of Acoustical Consultants
Contact: Eric Reuter, President
URL(s): ncac.com/resources-directory
Description: Covers 125 acoustical consulting firms, primarily in the United States. **Entries include:** Company name, address, phone, name of principal executive, list of services. **Arrangement:** Alphabetical. **Availability:** Print.

30877 ■ *North American Drama Therapy Association--Membership List*
Pub: North American Drama Therapy Association
Contact: Sherry Diamond, President
E-mail: president@nadta.org
URL(s): www.nadta.org/benefits-of-membership
Description: Covers about 400 registered drama therapists and NADT members. **Entries include:** Name, address, membership category. **Arrangement:** Separate alphabetical sections for registered drama therapists and regular members. **Indexes:** Geographical. **Availability:** Online.

30878 ■ *"Not in Your Backyard?" in Canadian Business (Vol. 80, March 12, 2007, No. 6, pp. 44)*
Description: The threat of losing residential property rights of persons whose land has rightful stakes from miners due to availability of minerals at the place is discussed. **Availability:** Print; Online.

30879 ■ *"Playfair Receives Drill Permit for Risby, Yukon Tungsten Deposit" in Marketwired (May 16, 2007)*
Pub: Comtex News Network Inc.
Contact: Kan Devnani, President
Description: Playfair Mining announced that it has received a 5 year Class III land use permit from the Mineral Resources Branch, Yukon which will allow the company to carry out a drill program during the upcoming drill season on the company-owned Risby, Yukon tungsten deposit. Statistical data included. **Availability:** Online.

30880 ■ *"Reports of Banks' Revival were Greatly Exaggerated" in Barron's (Vol. 88, July 7, 2008, No. 27, pp. L14)*
Pub: Dow Jones & Company Inc.
Contact: Almar Latour, Chief Executive Officer
Ed: Jack Willoughby. **Description:** Performance of mutual funds improved for the second quarter of 2008 compared to the previous quarter, registering an average gain of 0.13 percent; funds focusing on natural resources rose the highest, their value rising by an average of 24.50 percent. **Availability:** Online.

30881 ■ *"Rimfire Minerals Corporation: Jake Gold Project-Drilling Planned for 2007" in Marketwired (May 16, 2007)*
Pub: Comtex News Network Inc.
Contact: Kan Devnani, President

Description: Rimfire Minerals Corporation and Island Arc Exploration Corporation formed a partnership to explore the Jake Property, a high-grade gold prospect with previously unrecognized potential to host economic gold mineralization, located 13 kilometers west of Clearwater, British Columbia. **Availability:** Print; Online.

30882 ■ *"The Search for Big Oil" in Canadian Business (Vol. 80, April 9, 2007, No. 8, pp. 10)*

Description: The continuing effort of Canmex Minerals Corp. to explore for oil in Somalia despite the failure of several other companies is discussed. **Availability:** Print; Online.

30883 ■ *"Shell Venture Aims at 'Oil Rocks'" in Globe & Mail (March 22, 2006, pp. B1)*

Ed: Patrick Brethour. **Description:** Royal Dutch Shell PLC is all set to launch its Alberta's operations in bitumen deposits trapped in limestone. Details of the new venture are analyzed. **Availability:** Online.

30884 ■ *"Ship Shape" in Hawaii Business (Vol. 53, January 2008, No. 7, pp. 46)*

Ed: David K. Choo. **Description:** Ship Maintenance LLC is in charge of repairing and maintaining the U.S. Navy ships at Pearl Harbor's Middle Noch, having renewed a five-year contract with the navy. Cleaning a ship is a difficult process, which involves degreasing and removal of sensitive items such as guns and missiles. The awards given to Ship Maintenance are also discussed. **Availability:** Online.

30885 ■ *"Uranerz Acquires Additional Uranium Property Adjoining Nichols Ranch" in Marketwired (May 14, 2007)*

Pub: Comtex News Network Inc.

Contact: Kan Devnani, President

Description: Uranerz Energy Corporation announced the successful leasing of the fee mineral lands that appear to host the "nose" of the oxidation-reduction geochemical front and has the potential for increasing the known uranium mineralization at the Nichols Ranch project which lies west of and adjacent to Uranerz's Nichols Ranch ISR uranium project. **Availability:** Print; Online.

30886 ■ *"Uranium Energy Corp Provides an Update on Its Goliad Operations" in Canadian Corporate News (May 16, 2007)*

Description: Complaints against Uranium Energy Corp. and its Goliad Project in South Texas have been dismissed. The Railroad Commission of Texas (RRC), the regulatory authority which oversees mineral exploration in Texas, concluded that Uranium Energy Corp.'s drilling activities on the Goliad Project have not contaminated certain water wells or the related aquifer. **Availability:** Print; Online.

Nontraditional Financing

START-UP INFORMATION

30887 ■ *"3rd Annual 'OneMedForum NY 2012', July 11th-12th, to Spotlight JOBS Act, Crowdfunding, and Promising Areas for Healthcare Investment" in Investment Weekly (June 23, 2012)*
Description: Third annual forum presented by OneMed provided sessions for understanding the changes in regulation due to the new JOBS Act, which will create opportunities for investors and entrepreneurs. Experts in healthcare and life science investments will be featured. Details of the event are covered. **Availability:** Online.

30888 ■ *"Begslist.org Launches Crowdfunding On Its Website" in Computer Business Week (August 2, 2012)*
Description: Donation Website called Begslist has added crowdfunding to its site. Crowdfunding and begging are popular among small startups wishing to procure funding for their new companies. **Availability:** Online.

30889 ■ *"Crowdfunding Becomes Relevant for Medical Start-Ups as TCB Medical Launches Campaign On Idiegogo to Bring Life-Saving Epinephrine Key to Market" in PR Newswire (July 31, 2012)*
Pub: PR Newswire Association LLC.
Ed: Hilton Head. **Description:** Startup company, TCB Medical Devices, is hoping to raise money through crowdfunding to launch its life-saving Epinephrine Key to the marketplace. According to allergist, Thomas C. Beller, MD, epinephrine provides safe and effective relief to allergy sufferers. **Availability:** Online.

30890 ■ *"CrowdFunding Made Simple Conference at University of Utah Ignites Ecosystem of Entrepreneurs and Investors" in Economics Week (June 29, 2012)*
Description: The first national conference on crowdfunding was held at the University of Utah Guest House and Conference Center May 31 through June 1, 2012. The event, CrowdFunding Made Simple, gathered entrepreneurs, business owners, professional service providers, investors, government officials and students to provide understanding and potential of crowdfunding, including information on the Jumpstart Our Business Startups (JOBS) Act. **Availability:** Print; Online.

30891 ■ *"CrowdFunding Platform, START.ac, Announces It Is Expanding Its International Scope From the US, Canada and the UK to 36 Countries Including Australia, India, Israel, Italy and Africa" in Benzinga.com (July 11, 2012)*
Pub: Benzinga.com
Contact: Jason Raznick, Founder
Ed: Aaron Wise. **Description:** START.ac is expanding its CrowdFunding site to include 36 countries and increasing its scope to include business startups,

teen projects, as well as medical products. START.ac projects are in the fundraising stage at this point, with 23 percent located outside the United States. **Availability:** Online.

30892 ■ *"Crowdfunding Site Targets Jan. Launch" in Crain's Detroit Business (July 9, 2012)*
Pub: Crain Communications Inc.
Contact: Barry Asin, President
Ed: Meghana Keshavan. **Description:** Michigan based RelayFund Inc. incorporates social media with fundraising private equity form small businesses. Before the JOBS Act legislation, it was difficult for small firms to raise money. Crowdfunding connects groups of investors with small startup businesses. **Availability:** Print; Online.

30893 ■ *"Equity 'Crowdfunding' Platform, RelayFund, Launched by Michigan Investor Group" in Economics Week (July 20, 2012)*
Description: RelayFund was launched by a group of Michigan venture capitalists, entrepreneurs, and investment bankers to link small investors with startup firms under the new JOBS (Jumpstart Our Business Startups) Act. Crowdfunding is money raised for charities, projects or pre-selling products or services and allows online micro investments for startup companies.

30894 ■ *"Kickstarter Funds the Future; Crowdfunding Services Such as Kickstarter Have Been Hailed as a New Way To Get Started In Business and Cut Out the Traditional Money Men" in Telegraph Online (August 24, 2012)*
Pub: Telegraph Media Group Limited
Contact: Nick Hugh, Chief Executive Officer
Ed: Monty Munford. **Description:** More than 530 crowdfunding sites are expected to his the net by the end of the year. Crowdfunding helps companies raise money from investors for specific projects. A musician was able to raise over $1 million to fund a new record. **Availability:** Online.

30895 ■ *"Legal Matters: 'Crowdfunding' a Boon for Entrepreneurs, If They Clear Regulatory Hurdles" in Finance and Commerce (July 17, 2012)*
Pub: BridgeTower Media
Contact: Adam Reinebach, President
Ed: Dan Heilman. **Description:** Part of the Jumpstart Our Business Startups Act (JOBS) is crowdfunding, which allows the funding of a company by selling small parts of equity to a group of investors. Kickstarter, a Website for raising funds for business entities, is primarily used for film and book projects. Most businesses cannot adopt Kickstarter's model because of the legality of receiving investor funds without offering security.

30896 ■ *"MicroVentures: New Crowdfunding Game Makes Startups the Stars, Prepares Players for a New Kind of Investing" in Health & Beauty Close-Up (July 31, 2012)*
Description: MicroVentures created the MicroVentures Investor Challenge as a game on Facebook.

The game features real startups such as AirBnB, Etsy, and Pinterest and players invest in these firms. The game has real startups face off in six weekly rounds and the players act as venture capitalists. One startup and one investor will win the game. **Availability:** Print; Online.

30897 ■ *"New Angel Group Aims To Keep Cash Local" in Puget Sound Business Journal (Vol. 35, September 26, 2014, No. 23, pp. 5)*
Pub: American City Business Journals, Inc.
Contact: Mike Olivieri, Executive Vice President
Description: Seattle Angel Fund head and angel investor, Susan Preston, shares her views about the need for another angel fund in Seattle, Washington. Preston says there are not many actual funds in the city, while there are so many young, aspiring and great companies in the area. She also believes Washington will lose companies when funding comes from out of state investors. **Availability:** Online.

30898 ■ *"PeoplesVC Becomes the 1st Stock-Based Crowdfunding Site to Open Its Doors to Investors" in Investment Weekly (June 23, 2012)*
Description: Peoples VC is the first equity-based crowdfunding site to invite public investors to set up individual crowdfunding investment accounts. Equity-based crowdfunding allows funders to receive stock in return for their investment into companies. In the past, this process was only available to venture capitalists and accredited investors. **Availability:** Print; Online.

30899 ■ *Raising Capital*
Released: Third edition. **Price:** $34.95, Paperback/E-book. **Description:** Corporate attorney provides a comprehensive guide using in-depth, practical advice on raising money to start and grow a business. A 115-page appendix contains samples of financing agreements, forms and questionnaires. **Availability:** E-book; Print.

30900 ■ *"SEC, NASAA Tell Small Businesses: Wait To Join the 'Crowd': Crowdfunding Is 'Not Yet Legal Until the Commission Appoints Rules', Says SEC's Kim" in Investment Advisor (Vol. 3, August 2012, No. 8, pp. 13)*
Ed: Melanie Waddell. **Description:** Securities and Exchange Commission along with state regulators have advised small businesses and entrepreneurs to wait until the SEC has produced rules governing crowdfunding practices. Until that happens, federal and state securities laws prohibit publicly accessible Internet securities offerings. An overview of crowdfunding and the JOBS Act is included. **Availability:** Online.

30901 ■ *"Three Common Computer Repair Franchise Funding Sources Revealed by SP Home Run Inc." in Investment Weekly News (May 12, 2012)*
Description: SP Home Run discusses three popular sources for initial funding capital when starting a computer repair franchise: family, friends, and fools.

It is advised that if money could become a problem within any relationship it is best to avoid that type of funding source. **Availability:** Online.

REFERENCE WORKS

30902 ■ *3 Alternative Ways to Fund Your Startup*
URL(s): www.netsuite.com/portal/business-bench-mark-brainyard/industries/articles/entrepreneur/alternative-funding-startup.shtml
Ed: Kris Blackman. **Released:** August 18, 2021. **Description:** Not all businesses are great fits for traditional funding methods. This article explores three alternative funding routes for growing businesses. **Availability:** Online.

30903 ■ *"4 Reasons Small Businesses Need Nonbank Lenders More Than Ever"* in *Entrepreneur (Aug. 30, 2021)*
URL(s): www.entrepreneur.com/article/379711
Ed: Chris Hurn. **Released:** August 30, 2021. **Description:** Discussion of how non-bank lenders are increasingly taking market share from traditional banks, especially in small business lending. **Availability:** Online.

30904 ■ *"The 5 Best Non-Traditional Funding Tactics for Your Small Business"* in *Yelp Business Blog (June 14, 2019)*
URL(s): blog.yelp.com/businesses/the-5-best-non-traditional-funding-tactics-for-your-small-business/
Ed: John Carroll. **Released:** June 14, 2019. **Description:** Provides information on the five most accessible non-traditional funding sources for small businesses. **Availability:** Online.

30905 ■ *7 Sources of Start-up Financing*
URL(s): www.bdc.ca/en/articles-tools/start-buy-business/start-business/start-up-financing-sources
Description: Discusses the importance of diversifying your source for small business financing. Provides an overview of seven common sources for startup financing. **Availability:** Online.

30906 ■ *"8 Alternative Funding Options for Small Businesses"* in *Bplans*
URL(s): articles.bplans.com/top-alternative-funding-options/
Ed: Makenna Crocker. **Description:** Explains what alternative funding is and provides details on a variety of methods you can use to seek funding for your small business. **Availability:** Online.

30907 ■ *"14 Types of Alternative Financing for Small Businesses"* in *Merchant Maverick Blog (July 13, 2021)*
URL(s): www.merchantmaverick.com/types-alternative-financing-small-business/
Ed: Shannon Vissers. **Released:** July 13, 2021. **Description:** Provides information on more easily accessible alternative lending methods than a traditional bank for your small business. **Availability:** Online.

30908 ■ *"Alternate Financing Options For Startups"* in *Inc42 (Aug. 29, 2020)*
URL(s): inc42.com/resources/alternate-financing-options-for-startups/
Ed: Siddharth Jaiswal. **Released:** August 29, 2020. **Description:** Provides information on avenues of funding that small business startups can explore. **Availability:** Online.

30909 ■ *"Alternative Financing for a Small Business"* in *Chron*
URL(s): smallbusiness.chron.com/alternative-financing-small-business-664.html
Ed: Joe Taylor, Jr. **Description:** Alternative financing for small businesses can help companies whose owners have exhausted traditional small business loans, personal credit cards, and angel investors. This article describes alternative financing options for your small business. **Availability:** Online.

30910 ■ *"Alternative Lending: Best Lenders and Loan Options"* in *Fundera (Dec. 20, 2021)*
URL(s): www.fundera.com/business-loans/guides/alternative-lending
Ed: Katie Campbell. **Released:** December 20, 2021. **Description:** Breaks down five of the top alternative lenders, the most common types of alternative loans, and the possible advantages and disadvantages of alternative vs. traditional bank lending. **Availability:** Online.

30911 ■ *"Angel Investors Across Texas Collaborate"* in *Austin Business Journal (Vol. 31, May 20, 2011, No. 11, pp. 1)*
Pub: Austin Business Journal
Contact: Rachel McGrath, Director
E-mail: rmcgrath@bizjournals.com
Ed: Christopher Calnan. **Description:** Texas' twelve angel investing groups are going to launch the umbrella organization Alliance of Texas Angel Networks (ATAN) to support more syndicated deals and boost investments in Texas. In 2010, these investing groups infused more than $24 million to startups in 61 deals. **Availability:** Print; Online.

30912 ■ *Beyond Venture Capital: 4 Alternative Financing Strategies*
URL(s): newsroom.cnb.com/en/business/finances/alternative-financing-strategies.html
Released: September 30, 2019. **Description:** Discusses the use of venture capital funding as well as alternative funding options for your small business. **Availability:** Online.

30913 ■ *Business Incubator: The Ultimate Step-By-Step Guide*
Ed: Gerardus Blokdyk. **Released:** May 20, 2018. **Price:** $70.24, Paperback; $40.99, E-book. **Description:** A business incubator self-assessment tool, which will also answer many questions regarding the industry. **Availability:** E-book; Print.

30914 ■ *"Can You Say $1 Million? A Language-Learning Start-Up Is Hoping That Investors Can"* in *Inc. (Vol. 33, November 2011, No. 9, pp. 116)*
Pub: Inc. Magazine
Ed: April Joyner. **Description:** Startup, Verbling is a video platform that links language learners and native speakers around the world. The firm is working to raise money to hire engineers in order to build the product and redesign their Website. **Availability:** Online.

30915 ■ *"Chasing Credit"* in *Canadian Business (Vol. 81, November 10, 2008, No. 19, pp. 59)*
Pub: Rogers Media Inc.
Contact: Neil Spivak, Chief Executive Officer
Ed: Joe Castaldo. **Description:** Small and medium sized companies are dealing with tightening credit because they appear riskier than usual. Some of these businesses are turning to private investors, but this is not easy since many have invested everything in the stock market. The sector is expected to weaken with the broader Canadian market in the next six months from October 2008. **Availability:** Online.

30916 ■ *"Crowdfunding Author Thinks Google Will Beat Facebook to the Punch on InvestP2P Acquisition"* in *GlobeNewswire (July 17, 2012)*
Pub: Comtex News Network Inc.
Contact: Kan Devnani, President
Description: Author, Mark Kanter, explores the potentials of crowdfunding Websites, especially InvestP2P (aka: peer to peer lending) in his new book, "Street Smart CEO". Invest P2P has social networking tools built into its system. Kanter predicts Google to acquire InvestP2P. **Availability:** Online.

30917 ■ *"Equity Crowdfunding Platform Initial Crowd Offering, Inc. Closes Equity Financing with Third-Party Investor"* in *GlobeNewswire (July 18, 2012)*
Description: Initial Crowd Offering Inc. closed third-party equity financing round hat provided capital to finish development of its equity crowdfunding portal

to the Website. A private angel investor provided development costs to promote the firm's marketing program. Discussion on equity crowdfunding is included. **Availability:** Print; PDF; Online.

30918 ■ *"The Funding Is Out There!: Access the Cash You Need to Impact Your Business"*
Pub: Morgan James Publishing L.L.C.
Contact: Amber Parrott, Director
Released: June 01, 2014. **Price:** $15.95, paperback; $9.99, e-book. **Description:** Thirty in-depth case studies are presented to show what actual business owners have done to acquire funding for their companies. Most small and medium sized businesses are unaware of the financing sources available to them. **Availability:** E-book; Print.

30919 ■ *"GSK Creating Pathways From Academia to Industry"* in *Philadelphia Business Journal (Vol. 33, March 7, 2014, No. 4, pp. 8)*
Pub: American City Business Journals, Inc.
Contact: Mike Olivieri, Executive Vice President
Released: Weekly. **Price:** $4, introductory 4-week offer(Digital & Print). **Description:** The Discovery Fast Track Challenge program of GlaxoSmithKline will expand in 2014 to include scientists in North America and Europe. Scientists will be asked to submit information about their innovative drug research proposals and the winner could be offered a deal with the Discovery Partnerships with Academia team. **Availability:** Print; Online.

30920 ■ *"How To Get a Loan the Web 2.0 Way"* in *Black Enterprise (Vol. 41, December 2010, No. 5, pp. 23)*
Pub: Earl G. Graves Ltd.
Contact: Earl Graves, Jr., President
Ed: John Simons. **Description:** People are turning to online peer-to-peer network for personal loans as banks are lending less money. **Availability:** Online.

30921 ■ *"Initial Crowd Offering, Inc. Announces Launch of Equity Crowdfunding Intermediary Site"* in *GlobeNewswire (June 21, 2012)*
Pub: Comtex News Network Inc.
Contact: Kan Devnani, President
Description: Initial Crowd Offering is the IPO for small and emerging businesses and is the most current process to invest and raise capital. The site allows direct, real-time investments in exchange for equity ownership. **Availability:** Print; PDF; Online.

30922 ■ *"Investment Bank Dinan & Company Launches ConfidentCrowd Exclusive Crowdfunding Portal for FINRA Broker-Dealers"* in *Investment Weekly (June 9, 2012, pp. 458)*
Description: ConfidentCrowd is a newly developed portal created by Dinan & Company to provide exclusive use of FINRA-registered broker-dealers to participate as members in order to screen firms seeking funding. This process will eleviate risk in equity-based crowdfunding. **Availability:** Online.

30923 ■ *"Jumpstarting Your Business Through Non-Traditional Funding"* in *SBA.gov*
URL(s): www.sba.gov/offices/district/nd/fargo/resources/jumpstarting-your-business-through-non-traditional-funding
Ed: Michael Gallagher. **Description:** Discusses the Jobs Act legislation that aims to make it easier for small businesses to access capital. **Availability:** Online.

30924 ■ *"Meet University of Texas' New Business Mind"* in *Austin Business Journal (Vol. 31, May 13, 2011, No. 10, pp. A1)*
Pub: Austin Business Journal
Contact: Rachel McGrath, Director
E-mail: rmcgrath@bizjournals.com
Ed: Sandra Zaragoza. **Description:** University of Texas (UT) chief commercialization officer, Dr. Richard Miller, has opened a satellite office in Silicon Valley, California in the hopes of luring Californian

investors to the science and technology at UT. The satellite office is just one of Miller's efforts to reshape and widen the commercialization of UT-Austin. Insights into Miller's long-term view approach to commercialization are also covered. **Availability:** Online.

30925 ■ *"Microlending Seen as Having a Major Impact" in Business Journal Serving Greater Tampa Bay (Vol. 30, November 26, 2010, No. 49, pp. 1)*
Pub: Tampa Bay Business Journal
Contact: Ian Anderson, President
E-mail: ianderson@bizjournals.com

Ed: Margie Manning. **Description:** There are several organizations that are planning to offer microlending services in Tampa Bay, Florida. These include the Children's Board of Hillsborough County, and OUR Microlending Florida LLC. Organizations that are already offering these services in the area include the Small Business Administration and the Tampa Bay Black Business Investment Corp. **Availability:** Print; Online.

30926 ■ *"New Economy Initiative Gains Partners" in Crain's Detroit Business (Vol. 25, June 1, 2009, No. 22, pp. M014)*
Pub: Crain Communications Inc.
Contact: Barry Asin, President

Ed: Sherri Begin Welch. **Description:** New Economy Initiative is a $100 million philanthropic initiative that focuses on regional economic development. Recent grants awarded to Michigan companies are outlined. **Availability:** Print; Online.

30927 ■ *"New Pet Product Launches IndieGoGo Crowdfunding to Remain American Made" in Benzinga.com (June 11, 2012)*
Pub: Benzinga.com
Contact: Jason Raznick, Founder

Ed: Aaron Wise. **Description:** The Supercollar (r) is a new dog collar and leash combination launched on an Indiegogo crowdfunding campaign in order to raise fund to help the firm keep their business in America. The firm is striving to design and manufacture the Supercollar here in the US in order to create and save American jobs. The Supercollar's technology is also discussed. **Availability:** Print; Online.

30928 ■ *Non-Traditional Financing for Your Small Business*
URL(s): businessmodelinstitute.com/non-traditional -financing-for-your-small-business/

Ed: Sara Mackey. **Description:** Alternative and non-traditional funding has become a necessity when considering a small business model. This article explores available alternative business financing options. **Availability:** Online.

30929 ■ *Raising Capital*
Pub: HarperCollins Leadership
Contact: Donald Miller, Chief Executive Officer

Ed: Andrew J. Sherman. **Released:** 2nd edition. **Availability:** Print.

30930 ■ *"Savvy Solutions" in Black Enterprise (Vol. 41, December 2010, No. 5, pp. 42)*
Pub: Earl G. Graves Ltd.
Contact: Earl Graves, Jr., President

Ed: Tennille M. Robinson. **Description:** Individual asks for advice in launching a graphic design business, particularly grants available in a slow economy.

30931 ■ *"Savvy Solutions" in Black Enterprise (Vol. 41, November 2010, No. 4, pp. 42)*
Description: Society of Children's Book Writers and Illustrators offers members many benefits, including directories of agencies looking for new writers of books. **Availability:** Online.

30932 ■ *"SEC FAQs About Crowdfunding Intermediaries" in Mondaq Business Briefing (June 11, 2012)*
Pub: Mondaq Ltd.
Contact: Tim Harty, Chief Executive Officer

Ed: Yelena Barychev, Christin R. Cerullo, Francis E. Dehel, Melissa Palat Murawsky, Michael E. Plunkett. **Description:** Guide for implementing crowdfunding intermediary provisions of Title III of the JOBS Act is provided. Operating restrictions and legal obligations are outlined. **Availability:** Print; Online.

30933 ■ *"Seminar on Crowdfunding Set for Aug. 1" in Gazette (July 25, 2012)*
URL(s): gazette.com/seminar-on-crowdfunding-se t-for-aug.-1/article/142192#!

Description: Senator Michael Bennet is co-hosting a seminar with Epicentral Coworking on crowdfunding featuring two panels with local entrepreneurs and business owners, legal experts, and representatives from investment firms. The seminar will be held August 1, 2012. **Availability:** Print; Online.

30934 ■ *"Small Business Financing Options That Bypass Traditional Banks" in Business News Daily (Jan. 3, 2022)*
URL(s): www.businessnewsdaily.com/1733-small -business-financing-options-.html

Ed: Sean Peek. **Released:** January 03, 2022. **Description:** Article provides information for small business owners who are seeking information on alternatives to traditional bank loans. **Availability:** Online.

30935 ■ *"Small Business Guide to Alternative Lending" in business.com (Feb. 1, 2022)*
URL(s): www.business.com/articles/alternative-len ding-for-small-business/

Ed: Donna Fuscaldo. **Released:** February 01, 2022. **Description:** A guide that introduces the concept of alternative lending and explains some of the most common types of alternative loans. It also presents some of the major players in the space to help you find the right lender for your business. **Availability:** Online.

30936 ■ *Traditional and Non-Traditional Small Business Lending Options*
URL(s): gudcapital.com/small-business-lending/
Description: Describes a variety of small business loan products. **Availability:** Online.

30937 ■ *"Truffles & Trifles' Marci Arthur Plans YouTube Channel, Cookbook" in Orlando Business Journal (Vol. 30, May 2, 2014, No. 45, pp. 3)*
Pub: American City Business Journals, Inc.
Contact: Mike Olivieri, Executive Vice President

Released: Weekly. **Price:** $8, introductory 4-week offer(Digital & Print). **Description:** Marci Arthur, founder of Truffles & Trifles Cooking School, plans to create a YouTube channel and publish a cookbook. Arthur believes that the survival of her business can be attributed to the devotion and integrity of her employees. Reports show that the school has been receiving donations from sponsors such as Wolf Appliances and Sub-Zero. **Availability:** Print; Online.

30938 ■ *"Where New Economy Initiative Grants Have Gone" in Crain's Detroit Business (Vol. 25, June 1, 2009, No. 22, pp. M014)*
Pub: Crain Communications Inc.
Contact: Barry Asin, President

Ed: Sherri Begin Welch. **Description:** Listing of grants totaling $20.5 million focusing on talent development, attraction and retention; innovation and entrepreneurship; and shifting to a culture that values learning, work and innovation, is presented. **Availability:** Online; PDF.

VIDEO/AUDIO MEDIA

30939 ■ *How to Get Funder After the Banks Have Told You No with Brett Denton: An EOFire Classeic from 2021*
URL(s): www.eofire.com/podcast/brettdenton

Ed: Jon Lee Dumas. **Released:** September 11, 2024. **Description:** Podcast explains how to prepare for business financing.

ASSOCIATIONS AND OTHER ORGANIZATIONS

30940 ■ Association of Occupational Health Professionals in Healthcare (AOHP)
125 Warrendale Bayne Rd., Ste. 375
  Warrendale, PA 15086
Free: 800-362-4347
Fax: (724)935-1560
Co. E-mail: info@aohp.org
URL: http://www.aohp.org
Contact: Annie Wiest, Executive Director
E-mail: a.wiest@kamo-ms.com
Facebook: www.facebook.com/Association-of
  -Occupational-Health-Professionals-in-Healthcare
  -AOHP-128269079138
Linkedin: www.linkedin.com/company/association-of
  -occupational-health-professionals-in-healthcare
X (Twitter): x.com/AOHP_Org

Description: Occupational health professionals. Promotes the health and safety of workers in healthcare. Provides occupational health education and networking opportunities. **Founded:** 1981. **Publications:** *Journal of the Association of Occupational Health Professionals in Healthcare* (Quarterly). **Awards:** Ann Stinson President's Award for Association Excellence (Annual); AOHP Business Recognition Award (Annual); AOHP Honorary Membership Award (Annual); Joyce Safian Scholarship Award (Annual); AOHP National Award for Extraordinary Member (Annual); Sandra Bobbitt Continuing Education Scholarship (Annual); Julie Schmid Research Scholarship (Occasionally). **Geographic Preference:** National.

REFERENCE WORKS

30941 ■ *"5 Occupational Safety and Health Trends to Watch in 2020"* in The Link (December 11, 2019)
Released: December 11, 2019. **Description:** Workforce demographics, employee expectations, and other influences continually change training methods and tools used to improve workplace safety. Five trends that have an influence on this field are discussed. **Availability:** Online.

30942 ■ *"7 Things You Need to Remember About Workplace Safety"* in Bplans
Ed: Katrina Otuonye. **Description:** Offers steps to follow to ensure your small business follows employee safety rules and laws. **Availability:** Online.

30943 ■ *"7 Tips for Managing Safety for a Small Business"* in BasicSafe (February 24, 2016)
Ed: Don Brown. **Released:** February 24, 2016. **Description:** Offers seven tips for small business owners to ensure you are keeping your workers safe. **Availability:** Online.

30944 ■ *"10 Things About OSHA Small Businesses Must Know"* in Small Business Trends (October 9, 2019)
Ed: Rob Starr. **Released:** October 08, 2019. **Description:** Details ten rules small business owners need to follow under OSHA so your workplace is safe for employees. **Availability:** Online.

30945 ■ *"12 Workplace Safety Tips Every Employee Should Know in 2021"* in Connecteam (October 26, 2020)
Ed: Denis Yankovsky. **Released:** October 26, 2020. **Description:** Discusses the importance of OSHA regulations as well as the role personal responsibility plays in workplace safety. Outlines 12 steps to follow to ensure a safe workplace. **Availability:** Online.

30946 ■ *"Creating a Safety Culture in a Small Business Environment"* in OH&S (July 7, 2020)
Ed: Jennifer Dawson. **Released:** July 07, 2020. **Description:** Discusses safety rules of small businesses reopening in the age of "the new normal" in a world with a pandemic. **Availability:** Online.

30947 ■ *"Safety in 2020: Here's What the Stats Show"* in BeSafe Technologies (December 4, 2019)
Released: December 04, 2019. **Description:** Workplace safety doesn't just mean an absence of violence or major accidents. It includes having a safe working environment. This article discusses the types of challenges that exist to workplace safety and possible solutions technology might provide. **Availability:** Online.

30948 ■ *"The Top Occupational Safety and Health Issues for 2020: An Employer's Guide"* in EHS Daily Advisor (December 16, 2019)
Ed: Guy Burdick. **Released:** December 16, 2019. **Description:** Discusses OSHA issues including the aging workforce, shifting employment relationships like contingent or "gig" employment, and uncertainty about how best to manage new technologies like artificial intelligence, robotics, and 3D printing entering the workplace. **Availability:** Online.

30949 ■ *"What Companies Are Required to Meet OSHA Regulations?"* in Chron (July 7, 2020)
Released: July 07, 2020. **Description:** Discusses the OSHA Act of 1970, providing employees with hazard-free work environments as well as exclusions. **Availability:** Online.

30950 ■ *"What OSHA Regulations Apply to Small Business?"* in allBusiness
Description: Provides details on OSHA workplace requirements for small businesses. **Availability:** Online.

RESEARCH CENTERS

30951 ■ National Institute for Occupational Safety and Health - Small Business Assistance and Outreach Cross-Sector Program
4676 Columbia Pky., C-14
  Cincinnati, OH 45226
URL: http://www.cdc.gov/niosh/programs/sbao/projec
  ts.html
Contact: Rick Niemeier, Contact
Description: Mission is to minimize and eliminate occupational illnesses, injuries, and hazardous exposures in small enterprises through a focused program of research, prevention efforts, and public health activities. **Scope:** Reductions in occupational illnesses, injuries and hazardous exposures in small businesses.

Office Automation

START-UP INFORMATION

30952 ■ *"Leading Digital: Turning Technology into Business Transformation"*
Pub: Harvard Business Review Press
Contact: Moderna V. Pfizer, Contact

Released: October 14, 2014. **Price:** $32, Hardcover/Hardcopy. **Description:** Mobile technology, analytics, social media, sensors, and cloud computing have changed the entire business environment in every industry. A guide to help any small startup business in any industry gain strategic advantage using digital, including where to invest in digital technologies and how to lead the transformation. The guide teaches how to engage better with customers, digitally enhance operations, create a digital vision, and govern digital activities. **Availability:** E-book; Print.

REFERENCE WORKS

30953 ■ *"7 Trends Affecting the Security Technology Business"* in IP SecurityWatch.com (March 2012)
Ed: Geoff Kohl. **Description:** Scott Harkins, president of Honeywell Security Products for the Americas, outlines the seven trends affecting the security technology business. He covers smart phones and tablets, home automation, interctive services, integration beyond security systems, cloud services, standards, and apps. **Availability:** Online.

30954 ■ *"Agfa To Debut New: M-Press Leopard"* in American Printer (Vol. 128, June 1, 2011, No. 6)
Description: M-Press Leopard is a new version of the machine that offers advanced ink jet technology at a lower price point. Agfa Graphics introduced the new version that allows for new applications that require more manual handling. **Availability:** Print; Online.

30955 ■ *"Crouser Releases Offline UV Coating Price Report"* in American Printer (Vol. 128, June 1, 2011, No. 6)
Description: Crouser and Associates will offer the 'Pricing Off-Line UV Coating' report that provides background information on all three types of protective printing coatings and price guidance. The report will also offer comparisons of four popular types of offline equipment.

30956 ■ *"Death of the PC"* in Canadian Business (Vol. 83, October 12, 2010, No. 17, pp. 44)
Description: The future of the personal computer (PC) is looking bleak as consumers are relying more on new mobile devices instead of their PC. A 'Wall Street Journal' article published in September 2010 reported that the iPad had cannibalized sales of laptops by as much as 50 percent. The emergence of tablet computers running alternative operating systems is also explained. **Availability:** Print; Online.

30957 ■ *"Digital Marketing: Integrating Strategy and Tactics with Values, A Guidebook for Executives, Managers, and Students"*
Pub: Routledge, Taylor & Francis Group
Released: First edition. **Price:** $59.95, Paperback-$47.96; $190, Hardback - $152; $29.98, e-book. **Description:** Guidebook filled with information on the latest digital marketing tactics and strategic insights to help small businesses generate sustainable growth and achieve competitive advantage through digital integration. A five-step program: mindset, model, strategy, implementation, and sustainability is explained. **Availability:** E-book; Print.

30958 ■ *"For Apple, It's Showtime Again"* in Barron's (Vol. 90, August 30, 2010, No. 35, pp. 29)
Pub: Barron's Editorial & Corporate Headquarters
Ed: Eric J. Savitz. **Description:** Speculations on what Apple Inc. will unveil at its product launch event are presented. These products include a possible new iPhone Nano, a new update to its Apple TV, and possibly a deal with the Beatles to distribute their songs over iTunes. **Availability:** Online.

30959 ■ *Greening Your Small Business: How to Improve Your Bottom Line, Grow Your Brand, Satisfy Your Customers and Save the Planet*
Price: $19.95. **Description:** A definitive resource for anyone who wants their small business to be cutting-edge, competitive, profitable, and eco-conscious. Stories from small business owners address every aspect of going green, from basics such as recycling waste, energy efficiency, and reducing information technology footprint, to more in-depth concerns such as green marketing and communications, green business travel, and green employee benefits.

30960 ■ *"Horse Race: Putting the App in Apple"* in Inc. (Vol. 30, November 2008, No. 11)
Pub: Mansueto Ventures L.L.C.
Contact: Stephanie Mehta, Chief Executive Officer
Ed: Nitasha Tiku. **Description:** Aftermarket companies are scrambling to develop games and widgets for Apple's iPhone. Apple launched a kit for developers interested in creating iPhone-specific software along with the App Store, and an iTunes spinoff. Profiles of various software programs that may be used on the iPhone are given. **Availability:** Online.

30961 ■ *"How To Make the Most of Digital Music"* in Birmingham Business Journal (Vol. 31, May 23, 2014, No. 21, pp. 10)
Pub: American City Business Journals, Inc.
Contact: Mike Olivieri, Executive Vice President
Price: $4, print. **Description:** Advice to help small businesses in the use of digital technology is given. Businesses should include more information on their Web pages. The use of social media should not be over used. **Availability:** Print; Online.

30962 ■ *"James Donnelly on Keeping His Company's Edge: 'We Have Documented Best Practice for Everything'"* in South Florida Business Journal (Vol. 34, May 23, 2014, No. 44, pp. 15)
Pub: American City Business Journals, Inc.
Contact: Mike Olivieri, Executive Vice President
Description: James Donnelly, CEO of Castle Group, a community management firm specializing in homeowners and condominium associations, believes that organizational culture is an important driver of business success. He reveals that the company keeps its edge by maintaining the best office technology and the best employees. His views about the importance of customer satisfaction are stressed. **Availability:** Print; Online.

30963 ■ *"Leading the Way"* in Business Strategy Review (Vol. 23, Spring 2012, No. 1, pp. 10)
Description: The ability to persevere in the face of what may seem impossible odds is the story of Ursula Burns, who began her career as an engineering intern at Xerox and rose to become CEO of the company in 2009. Burns talked with Pearl Doherty about her career at Xerox. **Availability:** Online.

30964 ■ *"Lights, Camera, Action: Tools for Creating Video Blogs"* in Inc. (Volume 32, December 2010, No. 10, pp. 57)
Pub: Mansueto Ventures L.L.C.
Contact: Stephanie Mehta, Chief Executive Officer
Ed: John Brandon. **Description:** A video blog is a good way to spread company news, talk about products, and stand out among traditional company blogs. New editing software can create two- to four-minute blogs using a webcam and either Windows Live Essentials, Apple iLife 2011, Powerdirector 9 Ultra, or Adobe Visual Communicator 3. **Availability:** Online.

30965 ■ *"Look, No Hands!"* in Inc. (Vol. 33, September 2011, No. 7, pp. 52)
Description: The Jabra Freeway, a small Bluetooth speakerphone clips to a car visor and allows the user to place, answer and ignore calls by speaking commands. **Availability:** Print; Online.

30966 ■ *"Macroeconomic Policy and U.S. Competitiveness: A Reformed Fiscal Policy Is Vital To Renewing America's Productivity"* in Harvard Business Review (Vol. 90, March 2012, No. 3, pp. 112)
Pub: Harvard Business Review Press
Contact: Moderna V. Pfizer, Contact
Ed: Matthew Weinzierl, Richard H.K. Vietor. **Description:** Improving productivity requires increasing physical capital (such as equipment or technology), raising human capital, or using both of these types of capital more efficiently. The authors promote a plan that blends cuts in defense and health care spending, adjustments to Social Security, and carbon and gas taxes.

30967 ■ *Mobile Office: The Essential Small Business Guide to Office Technology*

Released: September 1, 2009. **Price:** $6.95. **Description:** Essential pocket guide for startup businesses and entrepreneurs which provides information to create a mobile office in order to maximize business potential while using current technologies.

30968 ■ *"MyWireless.org Commends Arizona Congressman Trent Franks for Committing to Wireless Tax Relief for American Consumers and Businesses"* in PR Newswire (September 21, 2012)

Pub: PR Newswire Association LLC.

Description: MyWireless.org presented Congressman Trent Franks from Arizona with the 2012 Wireless Consumer Hero Award for his work on wireless tax relief for American consumers and businesses. Franks' 'Wireless Tax Fairness Act' (HR 1002) promotes access to wireless networks as a key ingredient of millions of Americans' livelihoods, whether phone, broadband Internet necessary to run a small business. **Availability:** Print; Online.

30969 ■ *"Not Your Father's Whiteboard"* in Inc. (Vol. 33, November 2011, No. 9, pp. 50)

Pub: Inc. Magazine

Ed: Adam Baer. **Description:** Sharp's new interactive whiteboard is really a 70-inch touch screen monitor with software for importing presentations from any Windows 7 computer. **Availability:** Online.

30970 ■ *"Play By Play: These Video Products Can Add New Life to a Stagnant Website"* in Black Enterprise (Vol. 41, December 2010, No. 5)

Pub: Earl G. Graves Ltd.

Contact: Earl Graves, Jr., President

Ed: Marcia Wade Talbert. **Description:** Web Visible, provider of online marketing products and services, cites video capability as the fastest-growing Website feature for small business advertisers. Profiles of various devices for adding video to a Website are included. **Availability:** Online.

30971 ■ *"Port of Call"* in Entrepreneur (Vol. 35, November 2007, No. 11, pp. 66)

Ed: Amanda C. Kooser. **Released:** July 01, 2016. **Description:** List of the latest USB (universal serial bus) devices for upgrading technology for a small business is presented. **Availability:** Online.

30972 ■ *"Power Ranger"* in Inc. (November 2007, pp. 131)

Ed: Nitasha Tiku. **Description:** Surveyor software is designed to power down computers when not in use, in order to save energy. **Availability:** Online.

30973 ■ *"The Pre-Tail Revolution"* in Canadian Business (Vol. 87, October 2014, No. 10, pp. 10)

Description: A number of products that succeeded in security support from crowdfunding platforms, Kickstarter and Indiegogo, and those that failed are presented. Included are the do-it-yourself computer kit Kano, Bluetooth speakers Edge.sound, three-dimensional printer The Micro, Coolest Cooler the insect control device BugASalt, hexacopter Hexo+, and the Ubuntu Edge. **Availability:** Print; Online.

30974 ■ *"Presidential Address: Innovation in Retrospect and Prospect"* in Canadian Journal of Electronics (Vol. 43, November 2010, No. 4)

Pub: Journal of the Canadian Economics Association

Ed: James A. Brander. **Description:** Has innovation slowed in recent decades? While there has been progress in information and communications technology, the recent record of innovation in agriculture, energy, transportation and healthcare sectors is cause for concern. **Availability:** PDF; Online.

30975 ■ *"PrintCity Shares Guide for Carbon Footprinting"* in American Printer (Vol. 128, June 1, 2011, No. 6)

Description: PrintCity Alliance published its new report, 'Carbon Footprint & Energy Reduction for Graphic Industry Value Chain.' The report aims to help improve the environmental performance of printers, converters, publishers, brand owners and their suppliers. **Availability:** Online.

30976 ■ *Reading Financial Reports for Dummies*

Pub: John Wiley & Sons, Inc.

Contact: Christina Van Tassell, Executive Vice President Chief Financial Officer

URL(s): www.amazon.com/gp/product/1119871360/ref=as_li_tl?ie=UTF8&tag=wiley01-20

Ed: Lita Epstein. **Released:** 4th Edition. **Price:** $27. 18, paperback; $18, e-book. **Description:** The fourth edition contains more new and updated information. This book is meant as a guide to help the reader interpret and understand financial reports, annual reports, balance sheets, income statements, statements of cash flow and consolidated statements. Real-world examples are given. . **Availability:** E-book; Print.

30977 ■ *"RIM Opts to Be Less Open"* in Canadian Business (Vol. 83, October 12, 2010, No. 17, pp. 13)

Pub: Rogers Media Inc.

Contact: Neil Spivak, Chief Executive Officer

Ed: Joe Castaldo. **Description:** RIM is planning to stop releasing quarterly subscriber updates. However, some analysts are skeptical about the change due to the previous drop in company subscribers. The company also decided to stop reporting the average selling price of the BlackBerry, which analysts have also scrutinized. **Availability:** Online.

30978 ■ *"Samsung's Metamorphosis in Austin"* in Austin Business Journal (Vol. 31, May 20, 2011, No. 11, pp. 1)

Pub: Austin Business Journal

Contact: Rachel McGrath, Director

E-mail: rmcgrath@bizjournals.com

Ed: Christopher Calnan. **Description:** Samsung Austin Semiconductor LP, a developer of semiconductors for smartphones and tablet computers, plans to diversify its offerings to include niche products: flash memory devices and microprocessing devices. In light of this strategy, Samsung Austin will be hiring 300 engineers as part of a $3.6 billion expansion of its plant. **Availability:** Print; Online.

30979 ■ *"Social Networks in the Workplace: The Risk and Opportunity of Business 2.0"* in Strategy & Leadership (Vol. 38, July-August 2010, No. 4, pp. 50-53)

Pub: Emerald Inc.

Ed: Daniel Burrus. **Description:** The opinions of futurist Daniel Burrus on a novel trend called 'Business 2.0', which involves the use of social networking applications as business tools, are presented. His suggestion that personal social networking technology can be used by businesses to improve collaboration, problem solving, and leadership communications to achieve continuous value innovation is discussed. **Availability:** Online.

30980 ■ *"A Souped-Up Digital Pen"* in Inc. (Vol. 33, November 2011, No. 9, pp. 50)

Pub: Inc. Magazine

Ed: Adam Baer. **Description:** Wacom's Inkling is a digital pen designed to record drawings and can save layers of sketches and add or remove them at a later date. Animation of these drawings can also be played. Files can be saved on the receiver which has a 2GB memory and they can then be transferred to a computer. **Availability:** Online.

30981 ■ *"A Stylish New Labelmaker"* in Inc. (Vol. 33, October 2011, No. 8, pp. 48)

Pub: Inc. Magazine

Ed: John Brandon. **Description:** Epson's first labelmaker, the LabelWorks LW-400 offers many design options and has a full QWERTY keyboard that allows users to create and print labels in various sizes. **Availability:** Online.

30982 ■ *"Suited for Success"* in Retail Merchandiser (Vol. 51, July-August 2011, No. 4, pp. 6)

Description: MyBestFit is a size-matching body scanner that helps consumers find the perfect size clothing for themselves, giving brick and mortar retailers an edge on ecommerce competitors. **Availability:** Online.

30983 ■ *"Thinking Strategically About Technology"* in Franchising World (Vol. 42, August 2010, No. 8, pp. 9)

Pub: International Franchise Association

Contact: Matthew Haller, President

E-mail: mhaller@franchise.org

Ed: Bruce Franson. **Released:** 2010. **Description:** Nearly 25 percent of companies waste money from their technology budget. Most of the budget is spent on non-strategic software. Ways to spend money on technology for any franchise are examined. **Availability:** Online.

30984 ■ *"Time For a Change at Canon?"* in Barron's (Vol. 92, July 23, 2012, No. 30, pp. 17)

Pub: Dow Jones & Company Inc.

Contact: Almar Latour, Chief Executive Officer

Ed: Neil A. Martin. **Description:** Stocks of Japanese imaging equipment maker Canon could lose value unless the company undergoes changes in operations and governance. Prices of the company's American Depositary Receipts could fall 20 percent from $37.22 per share within 12 months. **Availability:** Online.

30985 ■ *"Travel Tech: 4 Gadgets for Running Your Business on the Fly"* in Entrepreneur (May 2014)

Pub: Entrepreneur Media Inc.

Contact: Dan Bova, Director

E-mail: dbova@entrepreneur.com

Description: The Goal Zero Sherpa 100 Power Pack includes two USB ports, a 12-volt plug and a proprietary laptop port that can fill a MacBook Air's battery faster on a single charge. The Nomad ChargeKey is lightweight, flexible and allows users to connect their spent smartphones to any full-size USB outlet. The Jawbone Era Bluetooth headset features a sleek carrying case that also functions as a battery-powered charger. The Belkin WeMo Insight Switch is a mobile wall plug that connects to a Wi-Fi and links to smartphones through an application. **Availability:** Online.

30986 ■ *"Understanding Geeks: A Field Guide To Your Tech Staff"* in Inc. (December 2007, pp. 62-63)

Ed: Adam Bluestein. **Description:** Guide to demystify managing the information technology staff of any small business is presented, including a list of do's and don'ts and a glossary of technical terms. **Availability:** Online.

30987 ■ *"UTM Appliances Protect Small Businesses/Hotspots/Branch Offices"* in Product News Network (March 7, 2012)

Pub: Thomas Publishing Company

Contact: Tony Uphoff, President

E-mail: tuphoff@thomaspublishing.com

Description: Five 1GbE ports, WatchGuard(R) XTM 25 and XTM 26 are profiled. All deliver intrusion prevention, spam-blocking, and gateway anti-virus functionality. Borth models profiled integrate VPN, HTTPS inspection and VoIP support along with options for Application Control and other WatchGuard security services already available. Details are included. **Availability:** Online.

30988 ■ *"Vision Statement: Tired of PowerPoint? Try This Instead" in Harvard Business Review (Vol. 88, September 2010, No. 9, pp. 30)*
Pub: Harvard Business Publishing
Contact: Diane Belcher, Managing Director
Ed: Daniel McGinn, Stephanie Crowley. **Price:** $6, PDF. **Description:** Usefulness of graphic recording, also known as storyboarding or visual facilitation, during client meetings is illustrated. **Availability:** Online; PDF.

TRADE PERIODICALS

30989 ■ *Software: Practice and Experience*
Pub: John Wiley & Sons Ltd.
Contact: Matthew Kissner, Chief Executive Officer
URL(s): onlinelibrary.wiley.com/journal/1097024x
Facebook: www.facebook.com/SoftwareJournal
Ed: Rami Bahsoon, Prof. Rajkumar Buyya, Prof. Agostino Poggi, Satish Srirama, Prof. Daniel Lemire.
Released: Monthly **Price:** $9,707, Institutions for print and online; $8,644, Institutions for online only; $9,016, Institutions for print only. **Description:** Refereed journal focused on software systems and applications. **Availability:** Print; PDF; Download; Online.

CONSULTANTS

30990 ■ **Advanced Network Consulting (ANC)**
12627 Gabbett Dr.
La Mirada, CA 90638
Ph: (562)903-3992
Co. E-mail: solutions@ancsite.com
Contact: Christopher Lee Staples, Contact
Facebook: www.facebook.com/ancsite
Linkedin: www.linkedin.com/company/advanced-network-consulting
Description: Network technology consulting firm offering services such as network assessment, internet protocol telephony and more. **Founded:** 2003.

30991 ■ **Agility Computer Network Services L.L.C.**
211 W Wacker
Chicago, IL 60606
Ph: (312)587-9894
Free: 877-244-5489
Co. E-mail: sales@agilitynetworks.com
URL: http://agilitynetworks.com
Contact: Chandler P. Denney, Contact
Linkedin: www.linkedin.com/company/agility-networks
X (Twitter): x.com/agilitynetworks
Description: Provides network services for businesses and offers on-site and off-site managed services, IT consulting, network design, and other related services. **Founded:** 1994.

30992 ■ **Alexander Associates**
38 Hilton Ave.
Falmouth, MA 02543
Contact: Kenneth A. Alexander, President
Description: Provider of computer technology expertise for industrial operations worldwide. Offers outsourced development and application support for a broad spectrum of commercial and not-for-profit entities in Insurance, Health-care, Bio-tech, Communications, Government. **Scope:** Provider of computer technology expertise for industrial operations worldwide. Offers outsourced development and application support for a broad spectrum of commercial and not-for-profit entities in Insurance, Health-care, Bio-tech, Communications, Government.

30993 ■ **Bell Techlogics**
4400 W 96th St.
Indianapolis, IN 46268
Ph: (317)333-7777
Free: 866-782-2355
Fax: (888)890-9494
Co. E-mail: bellservice@belltechlogix.com
URL: http://belltechlogix.com
Contact: Ron S. Frankenfield, Chief Executive Officer

Facebook: www.facebook.com/belltechlogixinc
Linkedin: www.linkedin.com/company/bell-techlogix-inc-
X (Twitter): x.com/BellTechlogixHQ
Description: The company operates as an information technology managed services and solutions company and focuses on global and mid-market enterprises and educational institutions and installs, configures, maintains and supports the local and wide area network technologies and also offers connectivity services that include secure internet and intranet communication solutions, virus scanning and firewall protections. **Founded:** 1978. **Training:** Virtualization and Disaster Recovery, 2008.

30994 ■ **Business Logic Incorporated**
62 William St., 5th Fl.
New York, NY 10005
Ph: (212)505-9555
Fax: (212)725-4808
Co. E-mail: info@blogicnyc.com
URL: http://www.blogicnyc.com
Contact: Marjorie Zien, Chief Executive Officer
Description: Firm specializes in custom software solutions, software application development, information systems and technology. **Scope:** Firm specializes in custom software solutions, software application development, information systems and technology.

30995 ■ **Champion Networks L.L.C.**
TWO MONUMENT SQ.
Portland, ME 04101
Contact: Michael J. Pearce, Contact
Description: Firm specializes in network integration, total wide area network solutions and network services. **Scope:** Firm specializes in network integration, total wide area network solutions and network services.

30996 ■ **Computer Connections Inc.**
1241-2 E Dixon Blvd.
Shelby, NC 28152
Ph: (704)482-0057
Free: 844-369-3993
URL: http://painlesspc.net
Contact: David Rockwell, Manager
X (Twitter): x.com/CCSalesShelby
Instagram: www.instagram.com/ccsalesshelby
Description: Provider of IT services. **Scope:** Provider of IT services. **Founded:** 1996.

30997 ■ **Creative Associates International Inc.**
5301 Wisconsin Ave. NW, Ste. 700
Washington, DC 20015
Ph: (202)966-5804
Co. E-mail: communications@creativedc.com
URL: http://www.creativeassociatesinternational.com
Contact: Leland Kruvant, President
Description: Provider of IT services. **Scope:** Supports public, private and non-governmental institutions that are makers and managers of change and transition. It builds the individual and organizational means to join forces for progress through education, information and communication. **Founded:** 1977. **Publications:** "Tool 4 - Textbook Analysis of Equity". **Training:** The Principles of the Abrahamic Faiths: Traditions that Advance Education; Creative Edge Literacy Network: A Guide to integrated Post-Literacy Methodology.

30998 ■ **Electronic Solutions Co. (ESC)**
PO Box 2501
Cinnaminson, NJ 08077-4901
Ph: (856)733-0008
URL: http://www.electronicsolutionsco.com
Contact: Mario Leone, Founder Senior Partner
Description: Provider of engineering and technical support for home automation manufacturers, dealers, and installers, products design and build services for highly customizable home management systems. **Scope:** Provider of engineering and technical support for home automation manufacturers, dealers, and installers, products design and build services for highly customizable home management systems. **Founded:** 1994. **Training:** Lighting Control System

Design; Advanced Custom System Controllers; Technical Aspects of Whole House Systems; Communication Protocols: The Good, The Bad and The Ugly. **Special Services:** ESC Home Management System.

30999 ■ **EM Microelectronic-US Inc.**
The Swatch Group Ltd.
703 Waterford Way, Ste. 450
Miami, FL 33126
Ph: 41 32 343-6811
Fax: 41 32 343-6911
Co. E-mail: corporate.communications@swatchgroup.com
URL: http://www.swatchgroup.com
Description: Firm is engaged in designing low-power, low-voltage, mixed-signal ASICs and ASSPs with non-volatile memory, as well as optoelectronics where PDICs, XOEICs are used in CD and DVD drive applications. **Scope:** Firm is engaged in designing low-power, low-voltage, mixed-signal ASICs and ASSPs with non-volatile memory, as well as optoelectronics where PDICs, XOEICs are used in CD and DVD drive applications.

31000 ■ **EssentialNet Solutions**
2301 W Eau Gallie Blvd., Ste. 4
Melbourne, FL 32935
Ph: (321)259-3242
Fax: (888)205-7518
Co. E-mail: sales@ensusa.com
URL: http://www.ensusa.com
Contact: David R. Soper, President
Description: Firm specializes in simultaneous internet web and email access via LAN, their capabilities include requirements analysis, computer system setup, network design and installation, software development, training and support. **Scope:** Firm specializes in simultaneous internet web and email access via LAN, their capabilities include requirements analysis, computer system setup, network design and installation, software development, training and support. **Founded:** 1996. **Training:** Network Design & Implementation; Managed Services & Support; Collection of your Personal Information; Use of your Personal Information. **Special Services:** SAAZ.

31001 ■ **Gimbel Associates**
71 Longview Dr.
Churchville, PA 18966
Description: Help organizations create, utilize, analyze and manage information. Specializes in helping small businesses select and install microcomputers and integrate microcomputer based applications into their organizations. **Scope:** Help organizations create, utilize, analyze and manage information. Specializes in helping small businesses select and install microcomputers and integrate microcomputer based applications into their organizations. **Training:** How to Become a Successful Consultant in Your Own Field; How to Computerize Your Small Business. **Special Services:** Fringe98; Fringe for DOS; EPAY2000.

31002 ■ **Glades Crop Care, Inc. (GCC)**
560 Center St.
Jupiter, FL 33458
Ph: (561)746-3740
URL: http://www.gladescropcare.com
Contact: Dr. H. Charles Mellinger, Consultant
E-mail: cmellinger@gladescropcare.com
Description: Firm provides scouting and consulting, contract research, pesticide and food safety education services for a variety of crops including vegetables, citrus, sugarcane, turf, rice, and more. **Founded:** 1972. **Publications:** "IPM Adoption Evaluated: A Strong Foundation for a Safe, Profitable Crop"; "Ring spot Damage to Florida Citrus Fruit Caused by Thrips Feeling Injury"; "Aspects of Biologically Based Pest Management in Commercial Pepper Production"; "Potential Use of Beauveria bassiana for Biological Control of Thrips in Peppers"; "Measuring Integrated Pest Management Adoption in South Florida Vegetable Crops," 1998. **Training:** Getting the Most for Your Money: An Effective Weed Control Program.

31003 ■ GlobalNET Corp.

6100 Corporate Dr., Ste. 270
Houston, TX 77036-3493
Contact: Hanh Dang, President

Description: Installation, configuration and technical support of local and wide area networks. Installs multi-user and multi-platform systems which perform accounting, client/server database, word processing, spreadsheet and computer aide design tasks in a variety of industries. **Scope:** Specializes in the installation, configuration, and technical support of local (LAN) and wide (WAN) Area Networks. Installs Multi-User and Multi-Platform systems (i.e. DOS, OS2, Windows NT, UNIX, Next-Step, and Macintosh) which perform Accounting, client/server Database, Word Processing, Spreadsheet, and Computer Aide Design (CAD) tasks in a variety of industries.

31004 ■ GSC Associates Inc.

2727 Xanthia Ct.
Denver, CO 80238-2611
Ph: (720)453-8045
Co. E-mail: info@gscassociates.com
URL: http://www.gscassociates.com
Contact: Dr. George Carson, Contact
E-mail: carson@gscassociates.com

Description: Firm provides systems engineering, computer graphics, and much more. **Scope:** Computer design consultants and systems integrators. Specializes in innovation in systems engineering and in research and development. **Founded:** 1981. **Publications:** "Collaboration in Regional Civilian and Military Transportation Planning," Jun, 2007; "A Measurement and Monitoring System for Tracking and Visualizing Collaboration Metrics in Real-time and for Later Analysis," Jun, 2005; "UML and Human Performance Modeling," Mar, 2005; "Graphics Networking and Distributed Computing"; "X3H3 standards report"; "Introduction to the computer graphics reference model". **Training:** VRML Conformance Testing Workshop, Aug, 1990. **Special Services:** GraphPorter; MetaPICT; T-CALS; FAX2PICT; PICT2FAX.

31005 ■ IMC

399 Sackett Point Rd.
North Haven, CT 06473
Ph: (203)248-5324
Co. E-mail: support@imcinternet.net
URL: http://www.imcinternet.net
Contact: Craig Becker, Member

Description: Specializes in the development of total office solutions for business which includes office networking, client/server technologies, Internet access and computer sales. **Scope:** Specializes in the development of total office solutions for business which includes office networking, client/server technologies, Internet access and computer sales. **Founded:** 1994.

31006 ■ Integrated Security Technologies (IST)

520 Herndon Pky., Ste. C
Herndon, VA 20170-6218
Contact: Alexander Oppenhimer, President
Instagram: www.instagram.com/ISTIncOfficial

Description: Firm provides engineered solutions to government, education, healthcare markets and offers various services including security management, physical security detection, video surveillance, and more. **Publications:** "American University Wins High Marks for New Security System"; "All American Upgrade"; "IST named 77th on SDM's Top 100 System Integrators".

31007 ■ KCS Computer Technology Inc. (KCS)

9524 Franklin Ave.
Franklin Park, IL 60131
Ph: (847)288-9820
Co. E-mail: sales@kcstech.com
URL: http://www.kcstech.com
Contact: Kenneth Kollar, President
Linkedin: www.linkedin.com/company/kcs-computer
-technology-inc

Description: Full-service information technology firm offers a wide range of services including IT consulting, network installation, maintenance, and also a retailer of desktops, servers, notebooks, and other related products. **Founded:** 1993.

31008 ■ LAN Solutions

San Francisco, CA
Ph: (650)261-1300
Co. E-mail: info@lansol.com
URL: http://www.lansol.com

Description: Firm provides a wide range of computer and network information technology support services, it offers various services including IT support, consulting, installation and troubleshooting, among others. **Founded:** 1989.

31009 ■ Mountain Realty Inc.

590 Main St.
Young Harris, GA 30582
Ph: (706)379-0903
Free: 800-201-5526
Fax: (706)749-7867
URL: http://ssg-i.com

Description: Specializes in custom applications and systems development for micro and mid range business systems. Industries served: manufacturing, retail, construction, and general office automation. **Scope:** Specializes in custom applications and systems development for micro and mid range business systems. Industries served: manufacturing, retail, construction, and general office automation. **Founded:** 1971.

31010 ■ Paladin Consultants L.L.C.

11 Beech Ct.
Chatham, NJ 07928
Ph: (973)635-0080
Fax: (973)701-8151
Co. E-mail: info@paladn.com
URL: http://www.paladn.com

Description: Firm provides IT consulting, database design, custom software, web and much more services. **Scope:** Firm provides IT consulting, database design, custom software, web and much more services. **Publications:** "Database Design"; "Technical Complexities of Database Design"; "VB Custom Programming"; ".NET (DOTNET) Programming And Development"; "Client Server Northern New Jersey Morristown SQL Server New York Client Server Consulting Services"; "User-Defined Functions"; "Rozenshte in Method"; "Case expressions".

31011 ■ Perceptive Technology Corp.

1701 Tawakoni Ln.
Plano, TX 75075-6731
Contact: Suzanne Witcher, Bookkeeper

Description: Services include business web site design and hosting, internet connectivity, web server co location, intranet design, LAN or WAN design and consulting. **Scope:** Services include business web site design and hosting, internet connectivity, web server co location, intranet design, LAN or WAN design and consulting.

31012 ■ R & S Design Computer Services Inc.

10 W Front St.
Media, PA 19063
Ph: (610)565-5523
Fax: (610)480-8398
Co. E-mail: info@rsdesign.com
URL: http://rsdesign.com
Contact: Robert Strain, Contact
Facebook: www.facebook.com/rsdesigncompu
terservices

Description: Provider of technology solutions offer sale, installation, and configuration of PC software for business and home users, they also offer training for a wide variety of software applications, maintenance and repair of hardware and network systems. **Scope:** Provider of technology solutions offer sale, installation, and configuration of PC software for business and home users, they also offer training for a wide variety of software applications, maintenance and repair of hardware and network systems. **Founded:** 1987. **Training:** Quick Postings and Processes, Jan,

2012; Analysis Reports, Jan, 2012; Intro to Church Office, Feb, 2012; Stewardship Library of Reports, Feb, 2012; Intermediate Reporting in Church Office, Mar, 2012; Tuition, Mar, 2102; Communicating in Church Office, Apr, 2012; Financial Reports, Apr, 2012. **Special Services:** Parish Data Software.

31013 ■ S & S Office Solutions Inc. (SSOS)

3480 Johnson Ferry Rd.
Roswell, GA 30075-5214
Contact: Jeffrey W. Stone, Chief Executive Officer

Description: Provider of IT services such as designs, retails, maintenance and cabling solutions for business, retail stores and restaurants.

31014 ■ SBA Computers Inc.

620 E State St.
O Fallon, IL 62269
Contact: Richard W. Scaiefe, President

Description: Provider of web site and domain hosting. Offers domain registration services. **Scope:** Provider of web site and domain hosting. Offers domain registration services.

31015 ■ Simplified Technology Co. (STC)

39180 Liberty St., Ste. 101
Fremont, CA 94538
Ph: (510)794-5520
Co. E-mail: sales@simplifiedtechnology.com
URL: http://www.simplifiedtechnology.com
Contact: Gregory Curtis Carvalho, Contact

Description: Firm provides networking, software development, security, and much more services related to strategic planning and tactical operations. **Founded:** 1994. **Special Services:** MRO's Maximo and Datastream's Maintenance Package 2 (MP2).

31016 ■ SON Systems International Inc.

619 Cricklewood Rd., Ste. 100
West Chester, PA 19380
Contact: Eric C. Burling, President

Description: Provider of corporate performance management, business intelligence services and solutions.

31017 ■ Thomas R. Egan Consulting Inc.

440 6th Ave.
Pleasant Grove, AL 35127
Contact: Thomas R. Egan, Contact

Description: Firm provides consultation and design services, installation and service, maintenance for several network platforms. **Scope:** Firm provides consultation and design services, installation and service, maintenance for several network platforms.

31018 ■ Verbit & Co.

152 Union Ave.
Bala Cynwyd, PA 19004
Contact: Alan C. Verbit, Owner

Description: Management consulting firm to assist executives and managers fulfill their mission and to assure that adequate planning of day-to-day operations occurs, that controls sufficient to safeguard valuable resources and that results of decisions reviewed in sufficient time to effect continuing action. **Scope:** Management consulting firm to assist executives and managers fulfill their mission and to assure that adequate planning of day-to-day operations occurs, that controls sufficient to safeguard valuable resources and that results of decisions reviewed in sufficient time to effect continuing action. **Training:** Integrating Manufacturing Management Systems with Business Systems; Negotiating Information Systems Agreements with Suppliers.

31019 ■ Zentek Computer Consulting

Bellaire, TX
Ph: (713)667-8228
Co. E-mail: zentek@acm.org
URL: http://www.zentek.us

Description: Provider of computer management and support for small businesses. Specializes in supporting and training physicians, attorneys, and executives. Also offers software and networking support and Anti-virus and data backup support. **Scope:** Provider of computer management and support for small businesses. Specializes in supporting and training physicians, attorneys, and executives. Also offers software and networking support and Anti-virus and data backup support.

LIBRARIES

31020 ■ Bluegrass Community & Technical College Learning Resource Center (BCTC)
470 Cooper Dr.
  Lexington, KY 40506-0235
URL: http://bluegrass.kctcs.edu/index.aspx
Contact: Kathleen Richardson, Librarian, Technical Services
E-mail: kathleen.richardson@kctcs.edu

Scope: Associated health technologies, computer information systems, business technology, undergraduate general education, and technical degree/certificate programs. **Services:** Interlibrary loan; copying; library open to the public. **Founded:** 2005. **Holdings:** Figures not available. **Preferred Investment Size:** Lexington Community College and Central Kentucky Technical College.

31021 ■ Chicago Public Library Central Library - Business/Science/Technology Division
400 S State St.
  Chicago, IL 60605
URL: http://www.chipublib.org/resources/science-technology

Scope: Small business; marketing; technology; sciences; computer science; careers and environmental information. **Services:** Interlibrary loan; library open to the public. **Founded:** 1977. **Holdings:** Figures not available.

31022 ■ York Technical College - Anne Springs Close Library
452 S Anderson Rd.
  Rock Hill, SC 29730
Ph: (803)327-8025
Co. E-mail: library@yorktech.edu
URL: http://www.yorktech.edu/learning-commons

Scope: Engineering technology. **Founded:** 1964. **Holdings:** Books; e-books; journals; articles.

ASSOCIATIONS AND OTHER ORGANIZATIONS

31023 ■ International Association of Lighting Designers (IALD)
242 N York St., Ste. 514
Elmhurst, IL 60126
Ph: (312)527-3677
Fax: (312)527-3680
Co. E-mail: iald@iald.org
URL: http://www.iald.org
Contact: Kelly Ashmore, Director
E-mail: kelly@iald.org
Instagram: www.instagram.com/iald
YouTube: www.youtube.com/theiald

Description: Represents professionals, educators, students, and others working in the field of lighting design worldwide. Promotes the benefits of quality lighting design and emphasizes the impact of lighting on architectural design and environmental quality. Furthers professional standards of lighting designers and seeks to increase their function in the interior design industry. **Founded:** 1969. **Publications:** *Reflections* (Monthly); *Why Hire an IALD Lighting Designer*; *International Association of Lighting Designers--Membership Directory*. **Educational Activities:** LIGHTFAIR International (LFI) (Biennial). **Awards:** Thomas M. Lemons Scholarship (Annual); IALD Award (Annual); IALD International Lighting Design Awards (Annual). **Geographic Preference:** National.

31024 ■ Planning and Visual Education Partnership (PAVE)
8570 Stirling Rd., Ste. 102-227
Hollywood, FL 33024
Ph: (954)551-9144
Co. E-mail: info@paveglobal.org
URL: http://www.paveglobal.org
Contact: Jerry Fox, President
Facebook: www.facebook.com/PAVEorg
Linkedin: www.linkedin.com/company/paveglobal
X (Twitter): x.com/PAVEorg
Instagram: www.instagram.com/pave_connects

Description: Retail executives, visual merchandisers, store planners, architects. Provides training and networking opportunities. Holds annual design competition; donates proceeds of shows toward financial aid for students. **Founded:** 1992. **Educational Activities:** PAVE Gala (Annual). **Awards:** PAVE Student Design Competition (Annual). **Geographic Preference:** National.

REFERENCE WORKS

31025 ■ "7 Factors of Great Office Design" in Harvard Business Review (May 20, 2016)
Ed: Peter Bacevice, Liz Burrow, Mat Triebner. **Released:** May 20, 2016. **Description:** Discusses the importance of office design and how outfitting your workspace is a major capital investment and is a pillar in ensuring that your workspace works for both form and function. **Availability:** Online.

31026 ■ "13 Effective Office Design Ideas for a Small Business" in Autonomous (Mar 28, 2021)
URL(s): www.autonomous.ai/ourblog/13-effective-office-design-ideas-for-small-business
Released: March 28, 2021. **Description:** Provides fourteen small business office design ideas to assist you in setting up what works best for your small business. **Availability:** Online.

31027 ■ 15 Reasons Why the Office Matters
Ed: Allan Smith. **Description:** The importance of the workplace and all that it offers has become clear: An office is more than just a place to work. The workplace drives innovation and growth and fosters culture and sense of community, while providing the tools and resources people need to be truly productive. This article includes 15 reasons why the workplace matters. **Availability:** Online.

31028 ■ 16 Tips for a Happy and Productive Office Environment
URL(s): www.bondcollective.com/blog/office-environment/
Description: Describes how to set up and run the best possible workspace for your small business. **Availability:** Online.

31029 ■ "Baltimore's Co-Working Spaces Introduces New Kind of Cubicle Culture" in Baltimore Business Journal (Vol. 29, August 19, 2011, No. 15, pp. 1)
Pub: Boston Business Journal
Contact: Carolyn M. Jones, President
E-mail: cmjones@bizjournals.com
Ed: Alexander Jackson. **Description:** Beehive Baltimore offers a co-working space where independent freelancers and entrepreneurs can work. There are two other companies that provide the same service and the value of these services to these professional is that it provides them with an office that is both convenient and affordable aside from letting them network with peers.

31030 ■ The Best Video Conferencing Equipment for 2022
URL(s): blog.webex.com/collaboration-devices/best-video-conferencing-equipment/
Ed: Derek Stevens. **Released:** January 26, 2022. **Description:** The need for high-quality video conferencing has become more important than ever with hybrid work. This article provides things to consider as you evaluate the best video conferencing equipment for your home and office. **Availability:** Online.

31031 ■ "Coworking Spaces Can Be Ideal for Entrepreneurs" in The Balance Small Business (January 2, 2020)
Ed: Susan Ward. **Released:** January 02, 2020. **Description:** Discusses the advantages of utilizing coworking spaces for small business entrepreneurs. **Availability:** Online.

31032 ■ Creative Office Solutions for Small Businesses
URL(s): commonsensebusinesssolutions.com/creative-office-solutions-for-small-businesses/
Ed: Ross Wiffler. **Released:** March 02, 2020. **Description:** Provides information on finding workplace office solutions that will allow you to operate efficiently. **Availability:** Online.

31033 ■ "CSE: Contractors Are Always Responsible" in Contractor (Vol. 56, November 2009, No. 11, pp. 34)
Ed: Dave Yates. **Description:** Plumbing contractors should purchase a long snorkel hose, a tripod with manual-crank hoist, and a sump pump in order to prevent accidents associated with Confined Space Entry. Liability issues surrounding confined space entry prevention and accidents are discussed. **Availability:** Print; Online.

31034 ■ Dilbert and the Cubicle vs the Open Office
Ed: Tamara Sheehan. **Description:** Discusses advantages and disadvantages of using both cubicles and having an open office space. **Availability:** Online.

31035 ■ "The Dynamic DUO" in Canadian Electronics (Vol. 23, February 2008, No. 1, pp. 24)
Description: Citronics Corporation not only aims to proved a good working environment for its employees, it also values the opinions of its personnel. Citronics had its employees test different workbenches before finally purchasing thirty-five of Lista's Align adjustable height workstation, which combines flexibility with aesthetics. The design of the Alin workbench is described. **Availability:** Print; Online.

31036 ■ "For Apple, It's Showtime Again" in Barron's (Vol. 90, August 30, 2010, No. 35, pp. 29)
Pub: Barron's Editorial & Corporate Headquarters
Ed: Eric J. Savitz. **Description:** Speculations on what Apple Inc. will unveil at its product launch event are presented. These products include a possible new iPhone Nano, a new update to its Apple TV, and possibly a deal with the Beatles to distribute their songs over iTunes. **Availability:** Online.

31037 ■ "How to Choose the Best Workspace for Your Startup?" in Small Business Trends (Sept. 18, 2019)
URL(s): smallbiztrends.com/2019/09/startup-workspace.html
Ed: Larry Alton. **Released:** September 18, 2019. **Description:** Discusses the importance of your physical work environment, describes basic types of offices and workspaces, and provides five tips on choosing the right startup workspace. **Availability:** Online.

31038 ■ "How to Create a Workspace That Improves Productivity" in Business News Daily (January 10, 2020)
Ed: Jennifer Post. **Released:** January 10, 2020. **Description:** Discusses how productivity can be improved by the structure and setting of your office.

This article discusses how to lay out your office furniture and equipment and how to improve the flow in your office space to increase productivity. **Availability:** Online.

31039 ■ *"How Creative Workspace Design Encourages Productivity"* in Mindspace (September 3, 2019)

Released: September 03, 2019. **Description:** Studies have shown that design-led organizations significantly outperform those that are not design-led, over the long term. This article will help you discover how your agency can integrate design thinking principles to catapult creativity and innovation. **Availability:** Online.

31040 ■ *"How to Design a Workspace That Improves Productivity"* in business.com (Jan. 7, 2020)

URL(s): www.business.com/articles/workspace -design-for-productivity/

Ed: Katharine Paljug. **Released:** January 07, 2020. **Description:** Discusses the importance of the design of your workplace and provides tips on improving the quality of work your employees can do by arranging their workspaces. **Availability:** Online.

31041 ■ How to Design Your Office for Improved Productivity and Purpose

Ed: Betty Ernst. **Description:** Office design is about creating a space that facilitates productive and purposeful work while leaving room for creativity, customization, and personalization. This article discusses why office design is important and how to design your office for productivity and purpose. **Availability:** Online.

31042 ■ *"How to Design Your Office for Improved Productivity and Purpose"* in WeWork (October 10, 2019)

Ed: Kristen Hickes. **Released:** October 10, 2019. **Description:** To create a space that helps your employees do their best work, follow the five research-backed tips in this article for designing an office that improves productivity. **Availability:** Online.

31043 ■ How to Make Big Money in Your Own Small Business: Unexpected Rules Every Small Business Owner Needs to Know

Ed: Jeffrey J. Fox, Jeffrey J. Fox. **Released:** May 12, 2004. **Price:** $16.95; C$24.95; $16.95; C$24.95; $16.95; C$24.95. **Description:** Former sales and marketing pro offers advice on growing a small business. **Availability:** Print.

31044 ■ How to Organize Your Small Business Office/Workspace

URL(s): www.eqbsystems.com/organize-small-busi ness-officesworkspaces/

Ed: Alicia Butler Pierre. **Description:** Discusses how to organize your small business with a Work Space Logistics (WSL) plan that considers the proper placement of staff, furniture, and equipment. **Availability:** Online.

31045 ■ *"How to Outfit Your Startup with Technology"* in Small Business Trends (May 30, 2019)

URL(s): smallbiztrends.com/2019/05/small-business -technology.html

Ed: Annie Pilon. **Released:** May 30, 2019. **Description:** Discusses the importance of properly outfitting your startup with appropriate technology and provides things to consider. **Availability:** Online.

31046 ■ *"How to Set Up an Effective Home Office"* in Women Entrepreneur (August 22, 2008)

Description: Checklist provides ways in which one can arrange their home office to provide the greatest efficiency which will allow maximum productivity and as a result the greater chance of success. **Availability:** Online.

31047 ■ *"How to Set Up Your Physical Office"* in The Hartford Business Owner's Playbook

Description: Ensuring that both personal workspaces and entire offices are equipped with efficient equipment, include comfortable work areas, and are conducive to promoting productivity is key to a good work environment. This article details things to consider as you set up your office environment. **Availability:** Online.

31048 ■ *"Intel Joins Movement to Turn Cube Farms Into Wide-Open Spaces"* in Sacramento Business Journal (Vol. 28, May 27, 2011, No. 13, pp. 1)

Pub: Sacramento Business Journal
Contact: Stephanie Fretwell, Director
E-mail: sfretwell@bizjournals.com

Ed: Melanie Turner. **Description:** Intel Corporation has remodeled its facility in Folsom, California. The renovation has required some workers to give up their cubicles. Comments from executives are included.

31049 ■ *"Open Office Design of Today Focuses on Choice and Collaboration"* in Buildings (September 24, 2019)

URL(s): www.buildings.com/news/industry-news/ar ticleid/22110/title/open-office-design-collaboration

Ed: Valerie Dennis Craven. **Released:** September 24, 2019. **Description:** The history of the open office plan is discussed and how this concept has shifted over the years. A one-size-fits-all approach to office design is not working well, and office designers are encouraging managers to communicate what types of work needs to be done during the day so a variety of spaces can be created and implemented. **Availability:** Online.

31050 ■ *"Outfitting your Office to Support the Return to Office"* in Owl Labs (Apr 27, 2021)

URL(s): resources.owllabs.com/blog/outfitting-your -office-to-support-the-return-to-office

Ed: Katherine Boyarsky. **Released:** April 27, 2021. **Description:** Discusses the future of the workplace and the flexibility that will be needed. Provides tips on how to create hybrid workspaces to support your flexible small business employees. **Availability:** Online.

31051 ■ *"The Science of Serendipity in the Workplace"* in The Wall Street Journal (April 30, 2013)

Ed: Rachel Emma Silverman. **Released:** April 30, 2013. **Description:** To encourage interaction and innovation, companies are using smaller spaces, games, and comfort to boost productivity. This article details how to effectively set up your business space to produce results. **Availability:** Online.

31052 ■ Should Startups Think Differently About Workspace?

URL(s): www.coxblue.com/startups-think-differently -workspace/

Ed: Chelsea Segal. **Description:** Discusses how to find the most effective workspace layout for your small business. **Availability:** Online.

31053 ■ *"Succeed With the Right Equipment"* in Pet Product News (Vol. 64, November 2010, No. 11, pp. 42)

Ed: Sandi Cain. **Description:** Grooming shop owners have been focusing on obtaining ergonomic, durable, and efficient products such as restraints, tables, and tubs. These products enhance the way grooming tasks are conducted. Ways pet supply manufacturers have responded to this trend are examined. **Availability:** Online.

31054 ■ *"What Is In Your Company Library?"* in Modern Machine Shop (Vol. 84, October 2011, No. 5, pp. 60)

Pub: Gardner Business Media Inc.
Contact: Rick Kline, Jr., President
E-mail: rkline2@gardnerweb.com

Ed: Mike Lynch. **Released:** September 15, 2011. **Description:** A good company library in any machine shop can help keep employees productive. Safety as well as information are critical to complete any task in a shop. **Availability:** Print; Online.

31055 ■ *"A Whiteboard that Peels and Sticks"* in Inc. (Volume 32, December 2010, No. 10, pp. 58)

Pub: Inc. Magazine

Ed: Issie Lapwosky. **Description:** Profile of an affordable adhesive whiteboard that can be restuck multiple times; the whiteboard was created by three college friends. The students share insight in the contacts they used in order to promote the sale of their invention. **Availability:** Online.

CONSULTANTS

31056 ■ Advanced Network Consulting (ANC)
12627 Gabbett Dr.
La Mirada, CA 90638
Ph: (562)903-3992
Co. E-mail: solutions@ancsite.com
Contact: Christopher Lee Staples, Contact
Facebook: www.facebook.com/ancsite
Linkedin: www.linkedin.com/company/advanced-ne twork-consulting

Description: Network technology consulting firm offering services such as network assessment, internet protocol telephony and more. **Founded:** 2003.

31057 ■ Agility Computer Network Services L.L.C.
211 W Wacker
Chicago, IL 60606
Ph: (312)587-9894
Free: 877-244-5489
Co. E-mail: sales@agilitynetworks.com
URL: http://agilitynetworks.com
Contact: Chandler P. Denney, Contact
Linkedin: www.linkedin.com/company/agility-networks
X (Twitter): x.com/agilitynetworks

Description: Provides network services for businesses and offers on-site and off-site managed services, IT consulting, network design, and other related services. **Founded:** 1994.

31058 ■ AIM Associates
100 Fair St.
Petaluma, CA 94952-2515
Ph: (707)763-3300
Co. E-mail: info@aimgreen.com
URL: http://www.aimgreen.com
Contact: George Beeler, Contact

Description: Firm provides consulting, integrated design team management, architectural and engineering services for offices. **Founded:** 1982.

31059 ■ Architectural Alliance
400 Clifton Ave.
Minneapolis, MN 55403
Ph: (612)874-4100
Co. E-mail: info@alliiance.us
URL: http://www.alliiance.us
Contact: Eric Peterson, President
E-mail: epeterson@alliiance.us
Facebook: www.facebook.com/Alliiance-127 264233985200
Linkedin: www.linkedin.com/company/alliiance
X (Twitter): x.com/_Alliiance_
Instagram: www.instagram.com/alliiance_
YouTube: www.youtube.com/channel/UC 5Wnnxea9v0Eje_XB4MGvKw
Pinterest: www.pinterest.com/alliiance

Description: Firm provides architectural and interior design, and solutions for academic, aviation, civic, lifestyle and workplace environments. **Scope:** Firm provides architectural and interior design, and solutions for academic, aviation, civic, lifestyle and workplace environments. **Founded:** 1970.

31060 ■ Array Healthcare Facilities Solutions
1 W Elm St., Ste. 500
Conshohocken, PA 19428
Ph: (610)270-0599

URL: http://array-architects.com
Contact: Kent Doss, Senior Vice President
E-mail: kdoss@array-architects.com
Description: Firm provides health care designing services. **Founded:** 2005. **Publications:** "Drawing a Meaning from a Mission," Oct, 2009; "Constructive Thinking," Sep, 2009; "A Patient Centered ED," Aug, 2009.

31061 ■ BBLM Architects PC
924 Cherry St., Fl. 1
  Philadelphia, PA 19107
Ph: (215)625-2500
Co. E-mail: contact@bblm.com
URL: http://www.bblm.com
Contact: David Chadwick, Business Manager
Description: Firm provides architectural and interior designing services. **Founded:** 1986.

31062 ■ Bell Techlogics
4400 W 96th St.
  Indianapolis, IN 46268
Ph: (317)333-7777
Free: 866-782-2355
Fax: (888)890-9494
Co. E-mail: bellservice@belltechlogix.com
URL: http://belltechlogix.com
Contact: Ron S. Frankenfield, Chief Executive Officer
Facebook: www.facebook.com/belltechlogixinc
Linkedin: www.linkedin.com/company/bell-techlogix -inc-
X (Twitter): x.com/BellTechlogixHQ
Description: The company operates as an information technology managed services and solutions company and focuses on global and mid-market enterprises and educational institutions and installs, configures, maintains and supports the local and wide area network technologies and also offers connectivity services that include secure internet and intranet communication solutions, virus scanning and firewall protections. **Founded:** 1978. **Training:** Virtualization and Disaster Recovery, 2008.

31063 ■ Cambridge Seven Associates Inc.
1050 Massachusetts Ave.
  Cambridge, MA 02138
Ph: (617)492-7000
Fax: (617)492-7007
Co. E-mail: resumes@cambridgeseven.com
URL: http://www.cambridgeseven.com
Contact: Gary Johnson, President
Facebook: www.facebook.com/cambridgeseven
X (Twitter): x.com/cambridgeseven
Description: Consulting firm offering services in architecture, planning graphic, exhibit, habitat and interior design. **Scope:** Consulting firm offering services in architecture, planning graphic, exhibit, habitat and interior design. **Founded:** 1962. **Publications:** "On Strip, Hard Rock has a touch of interactivity," Oct, 2009; "Architectural follies surprise contest jurors," Sep, 2009; "Buck Center for Health and Fitness opens doors," Sep, 2009; "Die-hard fans hail The Hall at Patriot Place," Aug, 2009; "Mentors - Where are They When You Need Them," Aug, 2009; "Boston may soon have a history museum," Aug, 2009. **Training:** Where We Learn seminar.

31064 ■ Cassway/Albert Ltd.
1528 Walnut St., Ste. 1100
  Philadelphia, PA 19102
Contact: Robert L. Cassway, President
Description: Consultants in architecture, landscape architecture, urban planning, interior design and space planning. **Scope:** Consultants in architecture, landscape architecture, urban planning, interior design and space planning.

31065 ■ C.E. Marquardt Lighting Design
13498 SE Wiese Rd.
  Boring, OR 97009
Ph: (503)658-5505
Fax: (503)658-6800
URL: http://www.lightingservicesinc.com
Description: Architectural lighting design firm offering services in both interior and exterior lighting. Services include custom control design, ceiling and

skylight design, computer mock ups, scale models and lighting art. **Scope:** Architectural lighting design firm offering services in both interior and exterior lighting. Services include custom control design, ceiling and skylight design, computer mock ups, scale models and lighting art.

31066 ■ Champion Networks L.L.C.
TWO MONUMENT SQ.
  Portland, ME 04101
Contact: Michael J. Pearce, Contact
Description: Firm specializes in network integration, total wide area network solutions and network services. **Scope:** Firm specializes in network integration, total wide area network solutions and network services.

31067 ■ Cole & Goyette Architects & Planners Inc.
540 Franklin St.
  Cambridge, MA 02139
Ph: (617)491-5662
URL: http://www.doriscolearchitect.com
Contact: Doris Cole, Founder
E-mail: d.cole@verizon.net
Description: Firm provides architecture and planning, interior design and design review for educational, commercial, residential and governmental clients. **Scope:** Firm provides architecture and planning, interior design and design review for educational, commercial, residential and governmental clients. **Founded:** 1981.

31068 ■ Computer Connections Inc.
1241-2 E Dixon Blvd.
  Shelby, NC 28152
Ph: (704)482-0057
Free: 844-369-3993
URL: http://painlesspc.net
Contact: David Rockwell, Manager
X (Twitter): x.com/CCSalesShelby
Instagram: www.instagram.com/ccsalesshelby
Description: Provider of IT services. **Scope:** Provider of IT services. **Founded:** 1996.

31069 ■ Creative Organizing
1023 Forest Ave.
  Boulder, CO 80304
Contact: Karina Black, Contact
Description: Provider of creative solutions for paper management, filing systems and space planning development. **Scope:** Provider of creative solutions for paper management, filing systems and space planning development. **Founded:** 1983. **Publications:** "File Anything in Your Home and Find it Again!," Kamal Publications, 1996; "Traumatic Brain Injury, the Silent Epidemic," 2004; "Mild Traumatic Brain Injury: Lost and Found," 2004; "Traumatic Brain Injury". **Special Services:** Creative Organizing™.

31070 ■ Design Collective Inc. (DCI)
151 E Nationwide Blvd.
  Columbus, OH 43215
Ph: (614)464-2880
URL: http://dcollective.com
Contact: Brent Lacount, Principal
E-mail: blacount@dcollective.com
Linkedin: www.linkedin.com/company/design-collective-incorporated
Instagram: www.instagram.com/dcollective_
YouTube: www.youtube.com/channel/UCUaykYRsic -xnpzVXNHV8cQ
Description: Provider of interior design services. **Scope:** Firm offers expertise in interior design to clients in the commercial trade industry. **Founded:** 1969.

31071 ■ EF Marburger Fine Flooring
9999 Allisonville Rd.
  Fishers, IN 46038
Ph: (317)841-7250
Co. E-mail: info@efmarburger.com
URL: http://www.efmarburger.com
Contact: Kelly Marburger Novak, President
E-mail: kmarburger@efmarburger.com
Facebook: www.facebook.com/efmarburger
X (Twitter): x.com/efmarburger

Instagram: www.instagram.com/efmarburgerflooring
YouTube: www.youtube.com/channel/UCRGNbVCpb -LFKK1SExOzzEw
Pinterest: www.pinterest.com/efmarburger
Description: Offers counsel to architects, designers, interior decorators and institutions, on the proper type of carpeting to be used in commercial applications. Furnishes sound absorbing and sound loss transmission data on carpet wall coverings. Also offers counsel on acoustical absorption and sound transmission factors on other types of acoustical products. **Scope:** Offers counsel to architects, designers, interior decorators and institutions, on the proper type of carpeting to be used in commercial applications. Furnishes sound absorbing and sound loss transmission data on carpet wall coverings. Also offers counsel on acoustical absorption and sound transmission factors on other types of acoustical products. **Founded:** 1913. **Training:** Use of Glass in Your Kitchen and Bath Designs.

31072 ■ Engineered Lighting Products, Inc. (ELP)
10768 Lower Azusa Rd.
  El Monte, CA 91731
Ph: (626)579-0943
Fax: (626)579-6803
Co. E-mail: contact@elplighting.com
URL: http://www.elplighting.com
Contact: Ralph Swarens, President
Facebook: www.facebook.com/ELP-Lighting-1029 51813106114
X (Twitter): x.com/ELPLighting
YouTube: www.youtube.com/user/ELPLighting/videos
Description: Manufacturer for superior interior and exterior lighting fixtures for commercial, residential and industrial projects. **Scope:** Manufacturer for superior interior and exterior lighting fixtures for commercial, residential and industrial projects. **Founded:** 1985.

31073 ■ Error Analysis Inc.
5173 Waring Rd., Ste. 157
  San Diego, CA 92120
Ph: (619)464-4427
Co. E-mail: info@erroranalysis.com
URL: http://www.erroranalysis.com
Contact: Dr. Joseph Cohen, Consultant
E-mail: joe@erroranalysis.com
Description: Research and consulting in the fields of human factors, safety and accident reconstruction. Provides consulting and expert witness services to attorneys, the insurance industry and businesses throughout the world. **Scope:** Research and consulting in the fields of human factors, safety and accident reconstruction. Provides consulting and expert witness services to attorneys, the insurance industry and businesses throughout the world. **Publications:** "Participation on voluntary committees for standards and codes by forensic practitioners: A win-win combination,"2011; "Ergonomics in Design,"2011; "Stairway falls: An ergonomics analysis of 80 cases," Professional Safety, 2009; "The practice of forensic human factors/ergonomics and related safety professions," Lawyers & Judges Publishing Company, 2009. **Training:** The role of a just culture, American Society of Safety Engineers, Costa Mesa, TCA, Jan, 2009; Common trends in slip and falls, Las Vegas, NV, Sep, 2008; Safety; Risk Management; Premises and Product Liability.

31074 ■ EssentialNet Solutions
2301 W Eau Gallie Blvd., Ste. 4
  Melbourne, FL 32935
Ph: (321)259-3242
Fax: (888)205-7518
Co. E-mail: sales@ensusa.com
URL: http://www.ensusa.com
Contact: David R. Soper, President
Description: Firm specializes in simultaneous internet web and email access via LAN, their capabilities include requirements analysis, computer system setup, network design and installation, software development, training and support. **Scope:** Firm specializes in simultaneous internet web and email access via LAN, their capabilities include require-

ments analysis, computer system setup, network design and installation, software development, training and support. **Founded:** 1996. **Training:** Network Design & Implementation; Managed Services & Support; Collection of your Personal Information; Use of your Personal Information. **Special Services:** SAAZ.

31075 ■ Gary Steffy Lighting Design Inc. (GSLD)
2900 S State St., Ste. 12
  Ann Arbor, MI 48104-6772
Ph: (734)747-6630
Free: 800-537-1230
Co. E-mail: grs@gsld.net
URL: http://www.gsld.net
Contact: Gary Steffy, President
E-mail: grs@gsld.net

Description: Firm is engaged in lighting design and consultant for architectural and daylighting. **Founded:** 1982. **Publications:** "Architectural Lighting Design". **Training:** Office Lighting; Lighting for Electronic Offices; Lighting Design; Historic Lighting.

31076 ■ GlobalNET Corp.
6100 Corporate Dr., Ste. 270
  Houston, TX 77036-3493
Contact: Hanh Dang, President

Description: Installation, configuration and technical support of local and wide area networks. Installs multi-user and multi-platform systems which perform accounting, client/server database, word processing, spreadsheet and computer aide design tasks in a variety of industries. **Scope:** Specializes in the installation, configuration, and technical support of local (LAN) and wide (WAN) Area Networks. Installs Multi-User and Multi-Platform systems (i.e. DOS, OS2, Windows NT, UNIX, Next-Step, and Macintosh) which perform Accounting, client/server Database, Word Processing, Spreadsheet, and Computer Aide Design (CAD) tasks in a variety of industries.

31077 ■ Humanics ErgoSystems Inc.
10202 La Costa Dr.
  Austin, TX 78747-1103
Ph: (818)345-3746
Co. E-mail: ergoquestions@gmail.com
URL: http://www.humanics-es.com
Contact: Rani Lueder, Principal Founder
E-mail: rani@humanics-es.com

Description: Firm is engaged in ergonomics consulting services such as occupational ergonomics, research and design of products and places for adults children and people with disabilities. **Scope:** Firm is engaged in ergonomics consulting services such as occupational ergonomics, research and design of products and places for adults children and people with disabilities. **Founded:** 1982. **Publications:** "The Future of Ergonomics in Children's Education," IEA 2009; "Ergonomics for Children; designing products and places for toddlers to teens," 2007; "Are Children just Little Adults? Child growth, development and age-related risk," Dec, 2003; "Rethinking Sitting," Oct, 2003; "Revisiting Ergonomics," May, 2003. **Training:** Teaching elder design, Las Vegas, Jul, 2008; Ergonomic considerations in seated work activities, University of California, Los Angeles, Jun, 2008; Rethinking back support: Sacral, lumbar or live backs, Dec, 2007; Adjunct Faculty, Human Factors and Design, 2006; Zen sitting and Western seating, 2005; Behavioral ergonomics, Oct, 2005; Sitting & seating in Zenmonasteries, Sep, 2005; Walking in their shoe.

31078 ■ Illuminated Concepts Inc.
23011 Moulton Pwy., Ste. D7
  Laguna Hills, CA 92653
Ph: (949)455-9914
Co. E-mail: info@oclights.com
URL: http://www.oclights.com
Contact: Charles M. Evans, Contact
Facebook: www.facebook.com/oclights4u
X (Twitter): x.com/oclights4u
Instagram: www.instagram.com/illuminatedconcep
  tsinc
YouTube: www.youtube.com/user/
  LEDLANDSCAPELIGHTS
Pinterest: www.pinterest.com/oclights

Description: Provider of extensive design and installation services for interior and exterior lighting and specializing in low voltage lighting, and fiber optic systems. **Scope:** Provider of extensive design and installation services for interior and exterior lighting and specializing in low voltage lighting, and fiber optic systems. **Founded:** 1988.

31079 ■ IMC
399 Sackett Point Rd.
  North Haven, CT 06473
Ph: (203)248-5324
Co. E-mail: support@imcinternet.net
URL: http://www.imcinternet.net
Contact: Craig Becker, Member

Description: Specializes in the development of total office solutions for business which includes office networking, client/server technologies, Internet access and computer sales. **Scope:** Specializes in the development of total office solutions for business which includes office networking, client/server technologies, Internet access and computer sales. **Founded:** 1994.

31080 ■ Integrated Security Technologies (IST)
520 Herndon Pky., Ste. C
  Herndon, VA 20170-6218
Contact: Alexander Oppenhimer, President
Instagram: www.instagram.com/ISTIncOfficial

Description: Firm provides engineered solutions to government, education, healthcare markets and offers various services including security management, physical security detection, video surveillance, and more. **Publications:** "American University Wins High Marks for New Security System"; "All American Upgrade"; "IST named 77th on SDM's Top 100 System Integrators".

31081 ■ Jacobs Schneider Interior Design
1012 E 75th St.
  Indianapolis, IN 46240
Ph: (317)251-0312
Fax: (317)251-0339
URL: http://www.jacobs-schneider.com
Contact: Janie Jacobs, Contact
E-mail: jjacobs@jacobs-schneider.com

Description: Interior design consulting firm provide a truly custom design, executed with skill and to fulfill the client's expectations creating timeless interiors. **Scope:** Interior design consulting firm provide a truly custom design, executed with skill and to fulfill the client's expectations creating timeless interiors.

31082 ■ KCS Computer Technology Inc. (KCS)
9524 Franklin Ave.
  Franklin Park, IL 60131
Ph: (847)288-9820
Co. E-mail: sales@kcstech.com
URL: http://www.kcstech.com
Contact: Kenneth Kollar, President
Linkedin: www.linkedin.com/company/kcs-computer
  -technology-inc

Description: Full-service information technology firm offers a wide range of services including IT consulting, network installation, maintenance, and also a retailer of desktops, servers, notebooks, and other related products. **Founded:** 1993.

31083 ■ Lam Partners Inc.
84 Sherman St.
  Cambridge, MA 02140
Ph: (617)354-4502
Co. E-mail: info@lampartners.com
URL: http://www.lampartners.com
Contact: Steve Iski, Director
Facebook: www.facebook.com/pages/category/Archi
  tectural-Designer/Lam-Partners-279154772128072
Instagram: www.instagram.com/lam_partners
Pinterest: www.pinterest.com/lampartners

Description: Firm provides architectural lighting consulting services all phases of lighting designs including artificial and day lighting, lighting for urban and custom fixture designs. **Scope:** Firm provides architectural lighting consulting services all phases of

lighting designs including artificial and day lighting, lighting for urban and custom fixture designs. **Founded:** 1961.

31084 ■ LAN Solutions
San Francisco, CA
Ph: (650)261-1300
Co. E-mail: info@lansol.com
URL: http://www.lansol.com

Description: Firm provides a wide range of computer and network information technology support services, it offers various services including IT support, consulting, installation and troubleshooting, among others. **Founded:** 1989.

31085 ■ Lighting Design Collaborative (LDC)
1216 Arch St., Ste. 3A
  Philadelphia, PA 19107
Ph: (215)569-2115
URL: http://www.lightingdesigncollaborative.com
Contact: John Sarkioglu, Principal
E-mail: jsarkioglu@ldc-us.com

Description: Provider of lighting design and energy consulting services for financial institutions, malls, theaters and also energy efficient aesthetic architectural, and landscape. **Scope:** Provider of lighting design and energy consulting services for financial institutions, malls, theaters and also energy efficient aesthetic architectural, and landscape. **Founded:** 1978.

31086 ■ The Luminations Group L.L.C.
Hillsborough, NJ
Ph: (908)281-9027
Fax: (908)349-3270
Co. E-mail: info@luminationsgroup.com
URL: http://luminationsgroup.com
Contact: Helene Cotton, Leader
Facebook: www.facebook.com/LuminationsGroup
X (Twitter): x.com/LuminationsGrp

Description: Strategic consulting firm offers business solutions and marketing services and experienced in commercial, retail, institutional, and residential projects. **Founded:** 2003. **Special Services:** FleXforce®; Namestrom®; FleXforce®.

31087 ■ Marshall Craft Associates Inc. (MCA)
2031 Clipper Pk. Rd., Ste. 105
  Baltimore, MD 21211
Ph: (410)532-3131
Co. E-mail: info@mca.design
URL: http://mca.design
Contact: Stephen Bates, President
E-mail: sbates@mca.design
Facebook: www.facebook.com/MarshallCraf
  tAssociates
Linkedin: www.linkedin.com/company/marshall-craf
  t-associates
Instagram: www.instagram.com/marshallcraft_mca

Description: Specializes in architecture, interior design, and planning. Offers professional services to health-care, academic, corporate and government clients. **Scope:** Specializes in architecture, interior design, and planning. Offers professional services to health-care, academic, corporate and government clients. **Founded:** 1986.

31088 ■ Mitchell B. Kohn Lighting Design
2256 Linden Ave.
  Highland Park, IL 60035
Ph: (847)433-0840
Co. E-mail: mitchell@mbklightingdesign.com
URL: http://mbklightingdesign.com
Contact: Mitchell B. Kohn, President
E-mail: mitchell@mbklightingdesign.com

Description: Firm provides interior illumination design for corporate, commercial, institutional, and selective residential environments such as hospitality, exterior, and much more. **Scope:** Firm provides interior illumination design for corporate, commercial, institutional, and selective residential environments such as hospitality, exterior, and much more. **Publications:** "Lighting Today's Office Environment," Professional Lighting Design Magazine, 2002; "Lighting Focus," 1998; "Lighting Considered," Apr, 1997; "Task Lighting for Offices," Apr, 1994; "Effective Lighting for Open Plan Offices," Facilities Magazine, Feb, 1992;

"Task Lighting is a Key to Productivity," Consulting-Specifying Magazine, Nov, 1990; "Lighting Design and Vdts," Electrical Business Magazine, Mar, 1990; "Office Lighting for the 1990S," Commerce Magazine, Nov, 1989; "Lighting Offices Containing Vdts," Lighting Design and Application Magazine, Dec, 1988. **Training:** NEOCON, Chicago, 1999; Light Fair International, San Francisco, 1996; IIDACEU accredited seminars, 2004; IBD Chicago, Office Lighting Seminar, 1993.

31089 ■ MJS Lighting Consultants
Houston, TX
Ph: (832)266-8592
URL: http://www.mjslight.com
Contact: Michael John Smith, Principal
Description: Firm provides lighting design including architectural interior, exterior, landscape, roadway, and industrial illumination and their services include consultation, design of custom luminaries and architectural details, specification writing, digital visualization, and final adjustment. **Founded:** 1982.

31090 ■ Nelson Worldwide
201 E 4th St., Ste. 1700
   Cincinnati, OH 45202
Ph: (513)241-3000
Co. E-mail: nelson@upspringpr.com
URL: http://www.nelsonworldwide.com
Contact: John Nelson, Jr., Chief Executive Officer
Facebook: www.facebook.com/NELSONWorldwide
Linkedin: www.linkedin.com/company/nelsonworldwide
X (Twitter): x.com/NELSONworldwide
Instagram: www.instagram.com/nelsonworldwide
Description: Firm provides architecture, graphic and interior Designer service. **Scope:** Offers interior design, architectural, graphic communications, graphic design, brand consulting and new media development services. **Founded:** 1980. **Training:** Futureshop: Inspiring Your Next Design.

31091 ■ Organize Your Space
CA
Ph: (216)235-8376
URL: http://www.organizeyourspace.com
Description: Office and home organization specialists with emphasis on space planning and paper control and storage. Other areas of specialization include filing systems, accounting systems, super bills and office furniture. Also offers expertise in medical or dental, legal and color-coded filing systems. **Scope:** Office and home organization specialists with emphasis on space planning and paper control and storage. Other areas of specialization include filing systems, accounting systems, super bills and office furniture. Also offers expertise in medical or dental, legal and color-coded filing systems. **Founded:** 1982. **Publications:** "De-Clutter, De-Stress and Design Your Office Space". **Training:** Quick Start Office Systems; Quick Start Plus Office Systems; Total Office Makeover Plan.

31092 ■ Peckham Guyton Albers and Viets Inc. (PGAV)
200 N Broadway, Ste. 1000
   Saint Louis, MO 63102
Ph: (314)231-7318
URL: http://www.pgav.com
Facebook: www.facebook.com/PGAVDestinations
Linkedin: www.linkedin.com/company/pgav-destinations
X (Twitter): x.com/PGAVDestination
Instagram: www.instagram.com/pgavdestinations
Description: Provider of planning, architecture, design and destination consulting. **Scope:** Provides programming, planning and urban design, architecture, engineering, interior design, space planning, graphics, landscape architecture, energy engineering, construction documents, feasibility studies, zoning and codes analysis, development studies, computer aided design, computer based specifications, cost estimating, construction management and value engineering. Projects include the design of civic, criminal justice, educational, library, recreational, governmental/public, healthcare facilities and multi-family housing. Also experienced in historic

preservation and restoration. Industries served: Governmental organizations, criminal justice, public administration, corporate administration, education and recreation. **Founded:** 1965. **Training:** Consensus Building in the Planning of Public Facilities; Juvenile Detention and Adult Detention Facilities. **Educational Activities:** ASTC Conference (Annual).

31093 ■ Perceptive Technology Corp.
1701 Tawakoni Ln.
   Plano, TX 75075-6731
Contact: Suzanne Witcher, Bookkeeper
Description: Services include business web site design and hosting, internet connectivity, web server co location, intranet design, LAN or WAN design and consulting. **Scope:** Services include business web site design and hosting, internet connectivity, web server co location, intranet design, LAN or WAN design and consulting.

31094 ■ Plantkeeper Inc.
PO Box 226142
   Dallas, TX 75222
Ph: (214)752-5750
URL: http://www.plantkeeperinc.com
Facebook: www.facebook.com/plantkeeperinc
Description: Firm provides interior tropical plants designing and maintenance services. **Scope:** Firm provides interior tropical plants designing and maintenance services. **Founded:** 1977.

31095 ■ R & S Design Computer Services Inc.
10 W Front St.
   Media, PA 19063
Ph: (610)565-5523
Fax: (610)480-8398
Co. E-mail: info@rsdesign.com
URL: http://rsdesign.com
Contact: Robert Strain, Contact
Facebook: www.facebook.com/rsdesigncomputerservices
Description: Provider of technology solutions offer sale, installation, and configuration of PC software for business and home users, they also offer training for a wide variety of software applications, maintenance and repair of hardware and network systems. **Scope:** Provider of technology solutions offer sale, installation, and configuration of PC software for business and home users, they also offer training for a wide variety of software applications, maintenance and repair of hardware and network systems. **Founded:** 1987. **Training:** Quick Postings and Processes, Jan, 2012; Analysis Reports, Jan, 2012; Intro to Church Office, Feb, 2012; Stewardship Library of Reports, Feb, 2012; Intermediate Reporting in Church Office, Mar, 2012; Tuition, Mar, 2102; Communicating in Church Office, Apr, 2012; Financial Reports, Apr, 2012. **Special Services:** Parish Data Software.

31096 ■ RMJM
NY
Co. E-mail: info@rmjm.com
URL: http://www.rmjm.com
Linkedin: www.linkedin.com/company/rmjm
X (Twitter): x.com/RMJM_
Instagram: www.instagram.com/rmjmofficial
Description: Firm provides services such as architecture, engineering, and much more. **Scope:** Firm provides services such as architecture, engineering, and much more. **Founded:** 1956.

31097 ■ Robert Newell Lighting Design (RNLD)
654 N Ave. W
   Westfield, NJ 07090
Ph: (908)654-9304
Co. E-mail: robert.newell@robertnewelllightingdesign.com
URL: http://www.robertnewelllightingdesign.com
Contact: Robert Newell, Principal
E-mail: robert.newell@robertnewelllightingdesign.com
Facebook: www.facebook.com/RobertNewellLightingDesign
Pinterest: www.pinterest.com/rnlighting

Description: Full-service architectural lighting design firm manufactures track, accent, display and LED lighting systems. **Scope:** Full-service architectural lighting design firm manufactures track, accent, display and LED lighting systems. **Founded:** 1984. **Training:** LED's.

31098 ■ S & S Office Solutions Inc. (SSOS)
3480 Johnson Ferry Rd.
   Roswell, GA 30075-5214
Contact: Jeffrey W. Stone, Chief Executive Officer
Description: Provider of IT services such as designs, retails, maintenance and cabling solutions for business, retail stores and restaurants.

31099 ■ SBA Computers Inc.
620 E State St.
   O Fallon, IL 62269
Contact: Richard W. Scaiefe, President
Description: Provider of web site and domain hosting. Offers domain registration services. **Scope:** Provider of web site and domain hosting. Offers domain registration services.

31100 ■ Scott M. Watson Inc.
15200 Shady Grove Rd., Ste. 350
   Rockville, MD 20850
Ph: (301)869-8800
Fax: (301)869-8802
URL: http://www.lightingservicesinc.com
Description: Lighting design consultant for new and renovated commercial, institutional and high-end residential projects. Particular expertise provided in lighting layouts, fixture specifications, control groupings, dimmer specifications, shop drawing review, punch-out and focus of installations. **Scope:** Lighting design consultant for new and renovated commercial, institutional and high-end residential projects. Particular expertise provided in lighting layouts, fixture specifications, control groupings, dimmer specifications, shop drawing review, punch-out and focus of installations.

31101 ■ Simplified Technology Co. (STC)
39180 Liberty St., Ste. 101
   Fremont, CA 94538
Ph: (510)794-5520
Co. E-mail: sales@simplifiedtechnology.com
URL: http://www.simplifiedtechnology.com
Contact: Gregory Curtis Carvalho, Contact
Description: Firm provides networking, software development, security, and much more services related to strategic planning and tactical operations. **Founded:** 1994. **Special Services:** MRO's Maximo and Datastream's Maintenance Package 2 (MP2).

31102 ■ Spacial Design
San Anselmo, CA 94960
Ph: (415)457-3195
URL: http://spacialdesign.com
Contact: Susan Lund, Contact
E-mail: susan.lund@mac.com
Description: Firm engages in designing and remodeling. **Founded:** 1979. **Training:** Kitchen Planning, Sonoma Valley Adult School, Oct, 2006; So you'd love a new kitchen?; Where do you begin?; What should you expect from the design and your budget?.

31103 ■ Symmes Maini & McKee Associates (SMMA)
1000 Massachusetts Ave.
   Cambridge, MA 02138
Ph: (617)547-5400
URL: http://www.smma.com
Contact: Ara Krafian, President
E-mail: akrafian@smma.com
Linkedin: www.linkedin.com/company/smma-symmes-maini-&-mckee-associates
X (Twitter): x.com/smma_design
Instagram: www.instagram.com/smma_design
Description: Firm provides balanced architecture, engineering, interiors, and site designs to afford clients for mechanical, electrical, plumbing and fire protection planning, programming and design services, energy and building performance solutions, and much more services. **Founded:** 1955.

31104 ■ T. Kondos Associates

300 E 33rd St., Ste. 5B
New York, NY 10016
Ph: (917)912-5321
Co. E-mail: tkondos@tkondos.com
URL: http://www.tkondos.com
Facebook: www.facebook.com/tkondosassociates
Instagram: www.instagram.com/tkondos
Description: Firm provides full-service architectural lighting designs for product development, budgeting, production, and equipment specifications, lighting for both domestic and international projects using the latest technology.

31105 ■ Thomas R. Egan Consulting Inc.

440 6th Ave.
Pleasant Grove, AL 35127
Contact: Thomas R. Egan, Contact
Description: Firm provides consultation and design services, installation and service, maintenance for several network platforms. **Scope:** Firm provides consultation and design services, installation and service, maintenance for several network platforms.

FRANCHISES AND BUSINESS OPPORTUNITIES

31106 ■ California Closet Company Inc. (CC)

FirstService Brands
1414 Harbour Way S, Ste. 1750
Richmond, CA 94804
Free: 866-366-0420
Fax: (601)549-7973
URL: http://www.fsvbrands.com
Contact: Carolyn Musher, Vice President, Sales
URL(s): www.fsvbrands.com/our_companies/california_closets.html
Facebook: www.facebook.com/CaliforniaClosets
X (Twitter): x.com/caclosets
Instagram: www.instagram.com/caclosets
Pinterest: www.pinterest.com/caclosets
Description: Custom closet design, manufacture, and installation. **Founded:** 1978. **Financial Assistance:** Yes **Training:** Includes training at headquarters, franchisee's location and ongoing support.

RESEARCH CENTERS

31107 ■ New Jersey Institute of Technology (NJIT) - Center for Building Knowledge (CBK)

335 Campbell Hall
323 Martin Luther King Blvd.
Newark, NJ 07102-1982
Ph: (973)596-3097
Fax: (973)596-8443
Co. E-mail: cbk@njit.edu
URL: http://research.njit.edu/cbk
Contact: Deane Evans, Executive Director
E-mail: deane.evans@njit.edu
Description: Integral unit of New Jersey Institute of Technology. **Scope:** The relationship between the built environment and the institutions, policies and trends that shape it, emphasizing building types and environments related to housing, education, health and aging, and developmental disabilities planning. The center also studies ways to optimize the use of available resources to create more effective and efficient environments to better serve users' needs, cost effective methods and approaches to translate research concepts into practice through programs, policies and actions devoted to improving new and existing facilities and related social conditions. **Founded:** 1985.

31108 ■ Rensselaer Polytechnic Institute - Lighting Research Center (LRC)

21 Union St.
Troy, NY 12180
Ph: (518)276-7100
Fax: (518)276-7199
Co. E-mail: lrc@rpi.edu
URL: http://www.lrc.rpi.edu
Contact: Nadarajah Narendran, Director, Research Professor
E-mail: narenn2@rpi.edu
Description: Integral unit of Rensselaer Polytechnic Institute. **Scope:** Lighting systems, including studies in vision, visibility, daylighting, efficient lighting technologies, architecture, building systems interactions, control systems, design tools, glass science, lighting economics, technology transfer, vision, transportation lighting, light and health, and human responses to lighting, including productivity, mood, and perception of brightness and spaciousness. **Founded:** 1988. **Publications:** *Delta Portfolios*; *Design books, evaluations*; *NLPIP Lighting Answers* (Periodic); *NLPIP Specifier Reports*. **Educational Activities:** LRC Industrial partners program; LRC Utility Personnel Training Seminars.

ASSOCIATIONS AND OTHER ORGANIZATIONS

31109 ■ International Association of Outsourcing Professionals (IAOP)
2600 S Rd., Ste. 44-240
 Poughkeepsie, NY 12601
Ph: (845)452-0600
Fax: (845)452-6988
Co. E-mail: info@iaop.org
URL: http://www.iaop.org
Contact: Debi Hamill, Chief Executive Officer
Facebook: www.facebook.com/IAOP1
Instagram: www.instagram.com/iaopinpics

Description: Promotes outsourcing as a management practice, as a profession and as an industry. Strives to lead the effort to transform the world of business through outsourcing. Helps organizations to increase outsourcing success rate, improve outsourcing Return on Investment (ROI) and expand outsourcing opportunities across the organization. **Scope:** A research and training firm dedicated to advancing outsourcing as a management discipline. **Founded:** 2005. **Publications:** "The Outsourcing Revolution: Why It Makes Sense and How to Do It Right". **Awards:** IAOP Leadership Hall of Fame (Annual). **Geographic Preference:** Multinational.

31110 ■ Outsourcing Institute (OI)
480 Forest Ave.
 Locust Valley, NY 11560
Ph: (516)279-6850
Co. E-mail: info@outsourcing.com
URL: http://www.outsourcing.com
Contact: Daniel Goodstein, President
Linkedin: www.linkedin.com/company/the-outsourcing-institute
X (Twitter): x.com/OutsourcingInst

Description: Represents corporations making use of outside resources and services. Serves as a clearinghouse on the strategic use of outside resources. Conducts research, executive events, publications and educational programs. **Scope:** A professional association and executive network with a mission to provide information exchange and services on outsourcing and related sourcing strategies. **Founded:** 1993. **Publications:** Buyer's Guide (Annual). **Geographic Preference:** Multinational.

EDUCATIONAL PROGRAMS

31111 ■ Auditing Outsourced Operations (Onsite)
Seminar Information Service Inc. (SIS)
 250 El Camino Real., Ste. 112
 Tustin, CA 92780
Ph: (714)508-0340
Free: 877-736-4636
Fax: (714)734-8027
Co. E-mail: info@seminarinformation.com
URL: http://www.seminarinformation.com
Contact: Catherine Bellizzi, President
URL(s): www.seminarinformation.com

Description: Explore the prime risk factors present in outsourcing arrangements. You will identify the key areas you must cover to ensure your audits protect your organization's interest, including audit procedures, maintaining and enforcing your right to audit with guaranteed access, and creating contracts that focus on delivery, ROI, and performance metrics. **Audience:** Audit directors and managers, Internal, external and IT auditors; contract, IT Information Security, and Operations managers. **Principal Exhibits:** Explore the prime risk factors present in outsourcing arrangements. You will identify the key areas you must cover to ensure your audits protect your organization's interest, including audit procedures, maintaining and enforcing your right to audit with guaranteed access, and creating contracts that focus on delivery, ROI, and performance metrics.

REFERENCE WORKS

31112 ■ "20 Advantages and Disadvantages of Outsourcing from Your Small Business" in Small Business Trends (March 11, 2021)
Pub: Small Business Trends, LLC
Contact: Anita Campbell, Chief Executive Officer
URL(s): smallbiztrends.com/2017/02/advantages-and-disadvantages-of-outsourcing.html
Ed: Nash Riggins. **Released:** March 11, 2021. **Description:** The pros and cons of outsourcing staff is discussed. This includes using freelancers instead of using in-office employees. **Availability:** Online.

31113 ■ "Beaumont Outsources Purchasing as Route to Supply Cost Savings" in Crain's Detroit Business (Vol. 25, June 1, 2009, No. 22)
Pub: Crain Communications Inc.
Contact: Barry Asin, President
Ed: Jay Greene. **Description:** William Beaumont Hospitals in Royal Oak have begun outsourcing the purchasing of supplies in order to cut costs. So far, Beaumont is the only hospital in southeast Michigan to outsource its purchasing department. Other hospitals employ their own purchasing supply workers. **Availability:** Online.

31114 ■ "A Change Would Do You Good" in Canadian Business (Vol. 80, November 19, 2007, No. 23, pp. 15)
Description: Western Glove Works will be manufacturing clothing offshore, including Sheryl Crow's jeans collection, in countries such as China and the Philippines. The company decided to operate offshore after 86 years of existence due to the high price of manufacturing jeans in Canada. Western Glove's focus on producing celebrity-endorsed goods is discussed. **Availability:** Print; Online.

31115 ■ "The China Syndrome" in Canadian Business (Vol. 79, July 17, 2006, No. 14-15, pp. 25)
Pub: Rogers Media Inc.
Contact: Neil Spivak, Chief Executive Officer

Ed: Peter Diekmeyer. **Description:** Contrasting pace of growth in China and India are presented. Reasons for the slow pace of growth of Canadian companies like CAE Inc. and Magna in India are also discussed. **Availability:** Online.

31116 ■ "Choosing the United States: In Contests to Attract High-Value Business Activities, the U.S. Is Losing out More than It Should" in Harvard Business Review (Vol. 90, March 2012, No. 3, pp. 80)
Pub: Harvard Business Review Press
Contact: Moderna V. Pfizer, Contact
Ed: Jan W. Rivkin, Michael E. Porter. **Price:** $8.95. **Description:** Weaknesses in the US business environment have contributed to decisions to outsource work, or have influenced foreign-firm decisions not to locate bases in US. This in turn has compromised US competitiveness. However, signs are that managers are reevaluating outsourcing and are beginning to bring business back to the US. **Availability:** Online; PDF.

31117 ■ "Closed Minds and Open Skies" in Barron's (Vol. 88, March 10, 2008, No. 10, pp. 50)
Pub: Dow Jones & Company Inc.
Contact: Almar Latour, Chief Executive Officer
Ed: Thomas G. Donlan. **Description:** American politicians have closed minds when it comes to fair trade. The American government must not interfere with the country's manufacturing industries or worry about outsourcing defense contracts to European aerospace company Airbus. **Availability:** Online.

31118 ■ "Debt-Collection Agency to Lay Off 368 in Hampton Center" in Virginian-Pilot (December 4, 2010)
Pub: The Virginian-Pilot
Contact: Kevin Goyette, Director
E-mail: kgoyette@dailypress.com
Ed: Tom Shean. **Description:** NCO Financial Systems Inc., provider of debt-collection and outsourcing services will permanently lay off 368 workers at its Hampton call center in 2011. **Availability:** Print; Online.

31119 ■ "The Future Of Outsourcing—And How To Outsource The Right Way" in Forbes(October 21, 2022)
URL(s): www.forbes.com/sites/forbesbusinesscouncil/2022/10/21/the-future-of-outsourcing-and-how-to-outsource-the-right-way/?sh=19f4a04c72e5
Ed: Stephen King. **Released:** October 21, 2022. **Description:** The concept of outsourcing work is discussed. Various functions within a company can be effectively streamlined with the use of outsourcing certain tasks, such as IT work, accounting, or marketing. With more and more people working within a hybrid environment, outsourcing various aspects of day-to-day work is becoming the new normal. **Availability:** Online.

31120 ■ *"The Future of Work" in Black Enterprise (Vol. 41, August 2010, No. 1, pp. 65)*

Pub: Earl G. Graves Ltd.

Contact: Earl Graves, Jr., President

Ed: Annya M. Lott. **Description:** Technology, globalization, and outsourcing will continue to shape the future of work. Social media is a means for small companies to market goods and services. **Availability:** Online.

31121 ■ *"Helping Apple Go Wearable" in Austin Business Journal (Vol. 34, July 4, 2014, No. 20, pp. 13)*

Pub: American City Business Journals, Inc.

Contact: Mike Olivieri, Executive Vice President

Released: July 04, 2014. **Price:** $4, introductory 4-week offer(Digital only). **Description:** Andrew Hamra, CEO and designer at Red Street Ventures will launch the Runnur Hands Free iPad Clip and Carry Case across the U.S. in July 2014 following the success of his flagship product the Hands Free Carry-All. Hamra builds and designs the products and controls startup costs by outsourcing most of the production to China's Xiamen Uptex Industrial Company Ltd. **Availability:** Print; Online.

31122 ■ *How to Start a Bankruptcy Forms Processing Service*

Released: First edition. **Description:** Due to the increase in bankruptcy filings, attorneys are outsourcing related jobs in order to reduce overhead.

31123 ■ *"The Incentive Bubble: Outsourcing Pay Decisions To Financial Markets Has Skewed Compensation and, With It, American Capitalism" in Harvard Business Review (Vol. 90, March 2012, No. 3, pp. 124)*

Pub: Harvard Business Review Press

Contact: Moderna V. Pfizer, Contact

Ed: Mihir A. Desai. **Price:** $8.95. **Description:** Basing incentive contracts and executive compensation on financial markets actually rewards luck rather than performance, and can promote dangerous risk taking. This has led to America's two main crises of capitalism: growing income inequality and governance failures. Boards of directors must focus on perfor-

mance rather than stocks, and endowments and foundations must focus on incentives for long-term growth. **Availability:** Online; PDF.

31124 ■ *"It's Time To Swim" in Canadian Business (Vol. 81, March 3, 2008, No. 3, pp. 37)*

Description: Canadian manufacturers should consider Asian markets such as India and the United Arab Emirates as the U.S. economic downturn continues. Canada's shortage in skilled labor is also expected to negatively affect manufacturing industries. Ontario's plans to assist manufacturers are also presented. **Availability:** Print; PDF; Download; Online.

31125 ■ *"Knox County Schools Debate Outsourcing Janitorial Services" in (March 29, 2011)*

Description: Custodial services of Knox County Schools in Tennessee may be outsourced in move to save money for the school district. Details of the proposed program are included. **Availability:** Print; Online.

31126 ■ *"Nobel Prize Winners Provide Insight on Outsourcing, Contract Work" in Workforce Management (Vol. 88, November 16, 2009, No. 12, pp. 11)*

Pub: Crain Communications Inc.

Contact: Barry Asin, President

Ed: Jeremy Smerd. **Description:** Insights into such workforce management issues as bonuses, employee contracts and outsourcing has been recognized by the Nobel Prize winners in economics whose research sheds a light on the way economic decisions are made outside markets. **Availability:** Online.

31127 ■ *"Overseas Overtures" in Business Journal-Portland (Vol. 24, October 26, 2007, No. 35, pp. 1)*

Pub: Portland Business Journal

Contact: Andy Giegerich, Managing Editor

E-mail: agiegerich@bizjournals.com

Ed: Robin J. Mood. **Description:** Oregon has a workforce shortage, specifically for the health care industry. Recruiting agencies, such as the International Recruiting Network Inc., answers the high demand for workforce by recruiting foreign employ-

ees. The difficulties recruiting companies experience with regards to foreign labor laws are investigated. **Availability:** Print; Online.

31128 ■ *"Patently (Un)Clear" in Business Strategy Review (Vol. 21, Spring 2010, No. 1, pp. 28)*

Ed: Markus Reitzig, Stefan Wagner. **Released:** 2010. **Description:** After developing a great product or process, it's important to protect it. The benefits of using internal patent lawyers versus outsourcing the task are examined. **Availability:** Print; PDF; Online.

31129 ■ *"Rep Vs. Direct: Always an Interesting Story" in Agency Sales Magazine (Vol. 39, July 2009, No. 7, pp. 3)*

Description: Manufacturers benefit from outsourcing their field sales to professional sales representatives in the areas of multi-line selling and customer knowledge and relationship. Some misperceptions about sales reps include the belief that they are an additional 'channel' in sales. **Availability:** Online.

31130 ■ *"Research: Mind the Gap" in Business Strategy Review (Vol. 21, Summer 2010, No. 2, pp. 84)*

Ed: Georgina Peters. **Released:** September 01, 2017. **Description:** Isabel Fernandez-Mateo's cumulative gender disadvantage in contract employment is presented. **Availability:** Print; PDF; Online.

31131 ■ *"Stung by Recession, Hemmer Regroups with New Strategy" in Business Courier (Vol. 27, June 4, 2010, No. 5, pp. 1)*

Pub: Business Courier

Ed: Lucy May. **Description:** Paul Hemmer Companies reduced its work force and outsourced operations such as marketing and architecture, in order for the commercial and construction firm to survive the recession. Hammer's total core revenue in 2009 dropped to less than $30 million forcing the closure of its Chicago office. **Availability:** PDF; Online.

31132 ■ *"Two Local Firms Make Inc. List: Minority Business" in Indianapolis Business Journal (Vol. 31, August 30, 2010, No. 26, pp. 13A)*

Description: Smart IT staffing agency and Entap Inc., an IT outsourcing firm were among the top ten fastest growing black-owned businesses in the U.S. by Inc. magazine. **Availability:** Print; Online.

ASSOCIATIONS AND OTHER ORGANIZATIONS

31133 ■ **National Association of Part-Time and Temporary Employees (NAPTE) - Library**
5800 Barton, Ste. 201
 Shawnee, KS 66203
Ph: (913)962-7740
Free: 800-846-3018
Fax: (913)631-0489
Co. E-mail: napte-champion@worldnet.att.net
URL: http://www.members.tripod.com/~napte
URL(s): napte.tripod.com
Description: Promotes the economic and social interests of persons working on a part-time, contingent, or temporary basis through research, advocacy, and member services. Offers short-term portable health insurance. **Scope:** Economic; career development; public policy. **Founded:** 1994. **Subscriptions:** journals Books; reports; magazines. **Geographic Preference:** National.

REFERENCE WORKS

31134 ■ *"Does the Gig Economy Have a Future in Grocery Stores?" in Grocery Dive (November 7, 2019)*
URL(s): www.grocerydive.com/news/does-the-gig
 -economy-have-a-future-in-grocery-stores/566797/
Ed: Jeff Wells. **Released:** November 07, 2019.
Description: The gig economy has entered the grocery business by filling jobs for workers who shop for customers and deliver the goods. This type of work is expanding in the market as e-commerce demand accelerates, and traditional grocers have taken notice and started to provide their own on-demand labor. **Availability:** Online.

31135 ■ *"Side Income: Is It a Hobby or a Business?" in Money Under 30 (March 12, 2019)*
URL(s): www.moneyunder30.com/side-income-hobby
 -or-a-business
Ed: Amber Gilstrap. **Released:** March 12, 2019.
Description: A practical discussion of how to determine if your hobby that you love is actually a business. The IRS has some guidelines and questions, and if you meet certain criteria, you can then deduct expenses and report it to the IRS. **Availability:** Online.

31136 ■ *"The Temp Economy and the Future of Work" in U.S. News & World Report (August 10, 2018)*
URL(s): www.usnews.com/news/the-report/articles/20
 18-08-10/the-temp-economy-and-the-future-of-work
Ed: Gabrielle Levy. **Description:** Over the years, companies have shifted to using machines and computers and with that came a reduced work staff. Instead of full-time employees, many companies have opted to use independent contractors. Historian Louis Hyman explores the gig economy and if it is sustainable. **Availability:** Online.

RESEARCH CENTERS

31137 ■ **New Ways to Work [New Ways]**
1012 West Beverly Blvd. No.377
 Montebello, CA 90640
Ph: (707)824-4000
Co. E-mail: coyn@newwaystowork.org
URL: http://www.newwaystowork.org
Contact: Che Casul, Chief Executive Officer
Facebook: www.facebook.com/newwaystoworkfb
X (Twitter): x.com/NewWays2Work
Description: Helps communities build systems that connect schools, community organizations and businesses, and improve the services, educational programs and support the community provides for its youth. Engages and supports local communities in the invention and renewal of connected, comprehensive youth-serving systems. **Scope:** Focuses on improving the lives of the nations youth. helps communities build systems that connect schools, community organizations and businesses. Creates the environment and guides a process that brings the right people together with customized tools for powerful learning and dramatic change. **Founded:** 1972. **Publications:** "A Guide to Career Development Opportunities in California's High Schools". **Training:** Career pathways; building local intermediary organizations; strengthening youth councils; increasing youth involvement; creating quality work-based learning systems; All Youth-One Systems. **Educational Activities:** New Ways to Work Workshops, To educate employers and employees in work time options and policy issues. **Geographic Preference:** National.

Partnerships/Mergers

START-UP INFORMATION

31138 ■ *"Angel Investing Network Launches"* **in Washington Business Journal (Vol. 31, August 31, 2012, No. 19, pp. 1)**
Pub: Baltimore Business Journal
Contact: Rhonda Pringle, President
E-mail: rpringle@bizjournals.com

Description: Dan Mindus, investment director for Virginia's CIT GAP Funds, is launching a network of angel investors, venture capitalists and entrepreneurs. The network, which is expected to have 45 to 50 investors, is in the final stages of formation and could be a source of funds for startups in Washington, DC. **Availability:** Print; Online.

31139 ■ *"Faces: Q&A With Katie Johnson, Co-Owner of Bloomy's Roast Beef Food Truck"* **in Saint Paul Pioneer Press (June 13, 2012)**
Ed: Kathie Jenkins. **Description:** Profile of Katie Johnson, 29 year old co-owner of Bloomy's Roast Beef food truck. Johnson discusses how her and her friend Ryan planned and started their food truck business and why they chose roast beef for their menu. **Availability:** Print; Online.

31140 ■ *"The Introvert's Guide to Entrepreneurship: How to Become a Successful Entrepreneur as an Introvert"*
Pub: CreateSpace

Released: October 17, 2014. **Price:** $4.27, kindle; $12.99, paperback . **Description:** The five main strengths and the five harmful weaknesses for an introvert wishing to become an entrepreneur are listed. Three key strategies to help an introvert run his new company are examined. Five key attributes of a good business partner are considered. Management tips are also shared for introverted leaders. **Availability:** Print.

31141 ■ *"JOBS Act Spurring Bio IPOs"* **in Philadelphia Business Journal (Vol. 33, May 2, 2014, No. 12, pp. 4)**
Pub: American City Business Journals, Inc.
Contact: Mike Olivieri, Executive Vice President

Released: Weekly. **Price:** $4, Introductory 4-week offer(Digital only). **Description:** The Jumpstart Our Business Startups Act has important provisions that are helping many early-stage biotechnology companies in their initial public offerings. Trevena Inc. of King of Prussia, Pennsylvania benefited from the extra time to educate the investment community and from the exemptions on the regulatory requirements. **Availability:** Print; Online.

31142 ■ *"Katharine Grayson: Three Questions with John Brownlee, CEO of Vidscrip.com"* **in Business Journal (Vol. 32, June 27, 2014, No. 5, pp. 6)**
Pub: American City Business Journals, Inc.
Contact: Mike Olivieri, Executive Vice President

Description: John Brownlee, CEO of vidscrip.com, discusses the Minneapolis, Minnesota startup's deal with Partners HealthCare and what it means for the business. Partners HealthCare is using the vidscrip technology to create educational videos for patients. **Availability:** Print; Online.

31143 ■ *"Kickstarter Funds the Future; Crowdfunding Services Such as Kickstarter Have Been Hailed as a New Way To Get Started In Business and Cut Out the Traditional Money Men"* **in Telegraph Online (August 24, 2012)**
Pub: Telegraph Media Group Limited
Contact: Nick Hugh, Chief Executive Officer

Ed: Monty Munford. **Description:** More than 530 crowdfunding services are expected to his the net by the end of the year. Crowdfunding helps companies raise money from investors for specific projects. A musician was able to raise over $1 million to fund a new record. **Availability:** Online.

31144 ■ *Partnership: Small Business Start-Up Kit*
Released: Second edition. **Description:** Guidebook detailing partnership law by state covering the formation and use of partnerships as a business form. Information on filing requirements, property laws, legal liability, standards, and the new Revised Uniform Partnership Act is covered.

31145 ■ *"So What Is Crowdfunding Anyway? New Legislation by Obama and Congress Relaxes Solicitation by Startups"* **in Accounting Today (August 6, 2012)**
Ed: Jim Brendel. **Description:** An introduction to crowdfunding provides a concise description to the process in which a group of investors partner to fund small business and startups. Rules from the SEC regarding crowdfunding are expected to be in place by the end of the year. **Availability:** Print; Online.

31146 ■ *"The Startup of Something Big"* **in Philadelphia Business Journal (Vol. 33, July 11, 2014, No. 22, pp. 4)**
Pub: American City Business Journals, Inc.
Contact: Mike Olivieri, Executive Vice President

Released: Weekly. **Price:** $4, Introductory 4-week offer(Digital only). **Description:** Philadelphia is slowly emerging as America's leading innovation district. The South Bank Campus is the city's game changer as University of Pennsylvania and Drexel University, along with others are seeking to harness the merging of innovation and academic pursuits that ultimately translate into new business development. **Availability:** Print; Online.

31147 ■ *The Toilet Paper Entrepreneur: The Tell-It-Like-It-Is Guide to Cleaning Up In Business, Even If You Are At the End of Your Roll*
Pub: Obsidian Launch L.L.C.
Contact: Kelsey Ayres, President

Ed: Mike Michalowicz. **Description:** The founder of three multimillion-dollar companies, including Obsidian Launch, a company that partners with first-time entrepreneurs to grow their concepts into industry leaders. **Availability:** Print; Online.

31148 ■ *"Upscale Consignment Shop Opens In Brandon"* **in Tampa Tribune (January 25, 2012)**
Ed: Yvette C. Hammett. **Description:** Agape Chic Consignment Boutique opened February 4, 2012. The owners, Dena Ham and Stacy Ulrey Regan became friends working on their children's school PTA. Their business partnership hopes that people walking into their new shop will feel as if they are walking into an upscale boutique. The store offers designer labels in sizes 2-20. **Availability:** Print; Online.

EDUCATIONAL PROGRAMS

31149 ■ **AMA's Course on Mergers and Acquisitions (Onsite)**
American Management Association (AMA)
  1601 Broadway
  New York, NY 10019
Ph: (212)586-8100
Free: 800-262-9699
Fax: (212)903-8168
Co. E-mail: customerservice@amanet.org
URL: http://www.amanet.org
Contact: Manny Avramidis, President
URL(s): www.amanet.org/training/seminars/onsite/
  Course-on-Mergers-and-Acquisitions.aspx

Description: Covers organizational, financial, planning, tax, and risk aspects of mergers and acquisitions. **Audience:** CEOs and CFOs, owners of companies, presidents, vice presidents of finance, treasurers, controllers, corporate planning directors, financial planners and analysts, directors of new business development, directors of mergers and acquisitions and accountants. **Principal Exhibits:** Covers organizational, financial, planning, tax, and risk aspects of mergers and acquisitions.

REFERENCE WORKS

31150 ■ *"3 Key Growth Elements for Small Security Integrators"* **in Security Distributing & Marketing (Vol. 42, July 2012, No. 7, pp. 108)**
Description: Local and regional integrators facing a choice between expansion and annihilation by global organizations face an uphill battle. Facing down giants requires critical use of key market principles including niche identity, co-branding, and planning for modest growth. **Availability:** Print; Online.

31151 ■ *"3M Teams Up with Graphic Design Company Wrapmate"* **in Twin Cities Business (September 25, 2019)**
URL(s): tcbmag.com/news/articles/2019/september/
  3m-teams-up-with-graphic-design-company
  -wrapmate

Ed: Amanda Ostuni. **Released:** September 25, 2019. **Description:** A new partnership between 3M and a California-based design company named Wrapmate is providing businesses a new way to create vehicle graphics. **Availability:** Online.

31152 ■ *"3Par: Storing Up Value" in Barron's (Vol. 90, August 30, 2010, No. 35, pp. 30)*
Pub: Barron's Editorial & Corporate Headquarters
Ed: Mark Veverka. **Description:** Dell and Hewlett Packard are both bidding for data storage company 3Par. The acquisition would help Dell and Hewlett Packard provide customers with a one-stop shop as customers move to a private cloud in the Internet. **Availability:** Online.

31153 ■ *"5 Steps to Filing Partnership Taxes" in Legal Zoom (February 28, 2023)*
URL(s): www.legalzoom.com/articles/5-steps-to-filing -partnership-taxes
Ed: Jane Haskins, Esq. **Released:** February 28, 2023. **Description:** Follow these steps for filing partnership taxes and avoid making some costly mistakes in the process. **Availability:** Online.

31154 ■ *"11 Minutes That Rocked the Sneaker World" in Business Journal Portland (Vol. 30, February 14, 2014, No. 50, pp. 8)*
Pub: American City Business Journals, Inc.
Contact: Mike Olivieri, Executive Vice President
Released: Weekly. **Price:** $4, Introductory 4-week offer(Digital & Print). **Description:** The sale of the Nike Air Yeezy 2, the latest shoes from a partnership with artist Kanye West, sparked a social media debate on the importance of limited edition shoes for the Nike brand. The shoes sold out in 11 minutes and made their way to eBay for as much as $10,000. **Availability:** Print; Online.

31155 ■ *"113D Filings: Investors Report to the SEC" in Barron's (Vol. 88, March 24, 2008, No. 12, pp. M13)*
Pub: Dow Jones & Company Inc.
Contact: Almar Latour, Chief Executive Officer
Released: April 02, 2016. **Description:** HealthCor Management called as problematic the plan of Magellan Health Services to use its high cash balances for acquisitions. Carlson Capital discussed with Energy Partners possible changes in the latter's board. Investor Carl Icahn suggested that Enzon Pharmaceuticals consider selling itself or divest some of its assets. **Availability:** Print; Online.

31156 ■ *"$100M Merger Stalled" in Philadelphia Business Journal (Vol. 31, February 17, 2012, No. 1, pp. 1)*
Description: The $100 million merger between Origlio Beverage and All Star Beverage has been delayed by lawsuits. The merger will create an entity to distribute Yuengling Beer. But Yuengling and Son Inc. has sued All Star for breach of contract.

31157 ■ *"$560 Million Acquisition in Storage for CubeSmart" in Orlando Business Journal (Vol. 28, September 7, 2012, No. 30, pp. 1)*
Pub: Baltimore Business Journal
Contact: Rhonda Pringle, President
E-mail: rpringle@bizjournals.com
Description: CubeSmart has completed its $560 million acquisition of 22 storage facilities in late August 2012, making it one of the leading self-storage companies in the US. In light of this growth, an overview of CubeSmart is explored. **Availability:** Print; Online.

31158 ■ *"2014 Promises Tech IPO Frenzy" in San Francisco Business Times (Vol. 28, January 3, 2014, No. 24, pp. 6)*
Pub: American City Business Journals, Inc.
Contact: Mike Olivieri, Executive Vice President
Released: Weekly. **Price:** $4, Introductory 4-week offer(Digital & Print). **Description:** Bay Area-based venture-backed technology companies are expected to fill 2014 with initial public offerings (IPOs) and fuel more venture capital funding in the region. The U.S. IPO market has recorded more than 220 pricings and

was the strongest since the dot-com bubble of 2000. California-based technology companies that valued at $1 billion or more are also profiled. **Availability:** Print; Online.

31159 ■ *"2015 Corporate Counsel Legal Pricing Guide - Mergers & Acquisitions" in Economics & Business Week (August 16, 2014, pp. 3)*
Pub: NewsRX LLC.
Contact: Kalani Rosell, Contact
Description: Research and Markets has added the 2015 Corporate Counsel Legal Pricing Guide - Mergers & Acquisitions to its report. The guide details how the mergers and acquisitions market for law firms has increased since the downturn in 2008-2009 due mostly to an improved economy, increased corporate liquidity and sometimes corporate tax policies of certain countries. **Availability:** Print; Online.

31160 ■ *"Abacast, Citadel Strike Radio Ad Deal" in Business Journal Portland (Vol. 27, December 31, 2010, No. 44, pp. 3)*
Pub: Portland Business Journal
Contact: Andy Giegerich, Managing Editor
E-mail: agiegerich@bizjournals.com
Ed: Erik Siemers. **Description:** Software firm Abacast Inc. has partnered with Citadel Media to aid the latter's advertising sales. Citadel provides radio networks and syndicated programs to 4,200 affiliate stations. **Availability:** Print; Online.

31161 ■ *"Abaddon Acquires Pukaskwa Uranium Properties in NW Ontario" in Canadian Corporate News (May 16, 2007)*
Description: Rubicon Minerals Corp. has entered into an Option Agreement with Consolidated Abaddon Resources Inc. for the acquisition of Pukaskwa uranium properties and plans to conduct an extensive exploration program to prove out the resource and geological potential of the area. Statistical data included. **Availability:** Online.

31162 ■ *"Acacia Subsidiary Acquires Patents Related to Shared Memory for Multimedia Processing from a Major Corporation" in Economics & Business Week (April 26, 2014, pp. 5)*
Pub: NewsRX LLC.
Contact: Kalani Rosell, Contact
Description: Acacia Research Corporation that a subsidiary has acquired U.S. patents and foreign counterparts related to the use of shared memory in multimedia processing systems such as mobile phones, tablets and other consumer electronic devices. **Availability:** Online.

31163 ■ *"Acciona Windpower to Supply 3-Megawatt Turbines to Prince Edward Island Energy" in Professional Close-Up (September 11, 2012)*
Description: Acciona Windpower and Prince Edward Island Energy Corporation (PEIEC) have partnered to supply turbines for the Hermanville & Clear Springs Wind Project that will provide 10 Acciona Windpower AW3000/116 wind turbine generators with capacity of 3 megawatts and a rotor diameter of 116 meters. Acciona will operate and maintain the turbines for the first 15 years.

31164 ■ *"Accounting Firm Weaver is Still Pursuing Growth Via Mergers" in San Antonio Business Journal (Vol. 25, January 6, 2012, No. 50, pp. 1)*
Pub: Baltimore Business Journal
Contact: Rhonda Pringle, President
E-mail: rpringle@bizjournals.com
Description: Fort Worth, Texas-based Weaver LLP has worked out a merger to absorb the San Antonio-based John R. Hannah & Company LLP. The merger deal is Weaver's third in San Antonio area after it absorbed Polansky McNutt Perry & Company in 2008 and Edelman Arnold in 2009. Insights into the accounting firm's plan for Hannah are also provided. **Availability:** Print; Online.

31165 ■ *"ACE Expands M&A Practice" in Economics & Business Week (March 22, 2014, pp. 2)*
Pub: NewsRX LLC.
Contact: Kalani Rosell, Contact
Description: ACE Group announced an expansion of its mergers and acquisitions practice focusing on insurance solutions for private equity firms, their portfolio companies as well as their M&A transactions. **Availability:** Online.

31166 ■ *"ACON Investments Acquires Igloo Products Corporation" in Economics & Business Week (April 19, 2014, pp. 6)*
Pub: NewsRX LLC.
Contact: Kalani Rosell, Contact
Description: ACON Investments LLC has acquired Igloo Products Corporation, the top cooler manufacturer in the world. Details of the acquisition are included. **Availability:** Online.

31167 ■ *"Acquisition to Give Mylan Tax Benefits, Boost Sales" in Pittsburgh Business Times (Vol. 33, July 18, 2014, No. 53, pp. 3)*
Pub: American City Business Journals, Inc.
Contact: Mike Olivieri, Executive Vice President
Released: Weekly. **Price:** $4, introductory 4-week offer(Digital & Print). **Description:** Mylan Inc.'s acquisition of Abbot's foreign specialty and branded generic drug business is a win situation for the company. The acquisition will help Mylan expand and diversify in the largest markets outside the U.S. as well as prove beneficial in growth through enhanced financial flexibility and a more competitive global tax structure. **Availability:** Print; Online.

31168 ■ *"Adrian Ellis Wears No Cape, But His Firm Protects Execs From Bad Guys" in Orlando Business Journal (Vol. 30, March 14, 2014, No. 38, pp. 3)*
Pub: American City Business Journals, Inc.
Contact: Mike Olivieri, Executive Vice President
Released: Weekly. **Description:** Infinity Protection Service chief executive officer, Adrian Ellis, says his experience in providing security details led to the formation of the company. He added that some of the company's clients are high-profile individuals who may have received threats. Ellis also stated that the company is planning to expand in the U.S. through mergers and acquisitions. **Availability:** Print; Online.

31169 ■ *"Alcoa: 'Going Where No Materials Scientist Has Gone Before" in Pittsburgh Business Times (Vol. 33, July 18, 2014, No. 53, pp. 5)*
Pub: American City Business Journals, Inc.
Contact: Mike Olivieri, Executive Vice President
Released: Weekly. **Price:** $4, introductory 4-week offer(Digital & Print). **Description:** Alcoa Inc. has signed a $1.1 billion supply agreement with Pratt & Whitney to build the forging for aluminum jet-engine fan blades as well as other parts made with aluminum lithium. This partnership brings together Alcoa's proprietary alloys and unique manufacturing processes with Pratt & Whitney's design, thus forging an aluminum fan blade that is lighter and enables better fuel efficiency. **Availability:** Print; Online.

31170 ■ *"Alcoa's Quebec Deal Keeps Smelters Running" in Pittsburgh Business Times (Vol. 33, February 28, 2014, No. 33, pp. 3)*
Pub: American City Business Journals, Inc.
Contact: Mike Olivieri, Executive Vice President
Released: Weekly. **Price:** $4, Introductory 4-week offer(Digital & Print). **Description:** Alcoa Inc. has renewed its power supply contract with the Quebec provincial government for three of its smelters in 2014. The aluminum company is investing $250 million in the smelters over the next five years to support growth in the automotive manufacturing industry. **Availability:** Print; Online.

31171 ▪ *"All About The Benjamins"* **in** *Canadian Business (Vol. 81, September 29, 2008, No. 16, pp. 92)*

Description: Discusses real estate developer Royal Indian Raj International Corp., a company that planned to build a $3 billion "smart city" near the Bangalore airport; to this day nothing has ever been built. The company was incorporated in 1999 by Manoj C. Benjamin one investor, Bill Zack, has been sued by the developer for libel due to his website that calls the company a scam. Benjamin has had a previous case of fraud issued against him as well as a string of liabilities and lawsuits. **Availability:** Online.

31172 ▪ *"Altegrity Acquires John D. Cohen, Inc."* **in** *(November 19, 2009, pp. 14)*

Pub: Investment Weekly News

Description: John D. Cohen, Inc., a contract provider of national security policy guidance and counsel to the federal government, was acquired by Altegrity, Inc., a global screening and security solutions provider; the company will become part of US Investigations Services, LLC and operate under the auspices of Altegrity's new business, Altegrity Security Consulting. **Availability:** Print; Online.

31173 ▪ *"Amcon Distributing Expands Into Northwest Arkansas"* **in** *Arkansas Business (Vol. 26, November 9, 2009, No. 45, pp. 13)*

Pub: Arkansas Business Publishing Group

Contact: Mitch Bettis, President

Description: Amcon Distributing Co., a consumer products company, has bought the convenience store distribution assets of Discount Distributors from its parent, Harps Food Stores Inc., significantly increasing its wholesale distribution presence in the northwest Arkansas market. The acquisition will be funded through Amcon's existing credit facilities. **Availability:** Online.

31174 ▪ *"Amistee Air Duct Acquires Ducts R Us, Looks at 2nd Competitor"* **in** *Crain's Detroit Business (Vol. 35, September 1, 2014, No. 35, pp. 5)*

Pub: Crain Communications Inc.

Contact: Barry Asin, President

Description: Details of the Novi-based Amistee Air Duct Cleaning & Insulation firm's acquisition of their competitor Ducts R Us Air Duct Cleaning of Clinton Township, Michigan. Co-owners of Amistee revealed the plan to acquire another competitor in Southeast Michigan. Details of the deal are included. **Availability:** Online.

31175 ▪ *"And Now, Goodbye: Consumer Response To Sponsor Exit"* **in** *International Journal of Advertising (Vol. 31, February 2012, No. 1, pp. 39)*

Ed: Julie A. Ruth, Yuliya Strizhakova. **Description:** While most sponsorship research focuses on the initiation and maintenance of properties and the brands that sponsor them, little is known about how brands fare when they terminate sponsorship relationships. **Availability:** Download; PDF; Online.

31176 ▪ *"Angel Investors Across Texas Collaborate"* **in** *Austin Business Journal (Vol. 31, May 20, 2011, No. 11, pp. 1)*

Pub: Austin Business Journal

Contact: Rachel McGrath, Director

E-mail: rmcgrath@bizjournals.com

Ed: Christopher Calnan. **Description:** Texas' twelve angel investing groups are going to launch the umbrella organization Alliance of Texas Angel Networks (ATAN) to support more syndicated deals and boost investments in Texas. In 2010, these investing groups infused more than $24 million to startups in 61 deals. **Availability:** Print; Online.

31177 ▪ *"Angiotech to Buy Top Medical Devices Company"* **in** *Globe & Mail (February 1, 2006, pp. B1)*

Description: The details on Angiotech Pharmaceuticals Inc.'s acquisition of American Medical Instruments Holdings Inc. are presented. **Availability:** Online.

31178 ▪ *"Architecture Panel Pushes Bozzuto"* **in** *Baltimore Business Journal (Vol. 31, March 21, 2014, No. 47, pp. 4)*

Pub: American City Business Journals, Inc.

Contact: Mike Olivieri, Executive Vice President

Released: Weekly. **Price:** $4, introductory 4-week offer(Digital & Print). **Description:** The Bozzuto Group along with the Solstice Partners LLC, is developing its most ambitious $80 million Locust Point apartment project in Baltimore. Notorious for getting pretty tough with architects, the members of the city's Urban Design and Architecture Panel are highly focused on getting the building right. Designed in a unique S-shape, this building was approved by the UDARP panelists and they are planning to refine the details with the concerned architect within a week's time. **Availability:** Print; Online.

31179 ▪ *"Area Small Businesses Enjoy Benefits of Bartering Group"* **in** *News-Herald (August 22, 2010)*

Pub: The News Herald

Contact: Tricia Ambrose, Executive Editor

E-mail: tambrose@news-herald.com

Ed: Brandon C. Baker. **Description:** ITEX is a publicly traded firm that spurs cashless, business-to-business transactions within its own marketplace. Details of the bartering of goods and services within the company are outlined. **Availability:** Online.

31180 ▪ *"As Capital Gains Tax Hike Looms, Baltimore's Merger Activity Percolates"* **in** *Baltimore Business Journal (Vol. 28, August 27, 2010, No. 16, pp. 1)*

Pub: Baltimore Business Journal

Contact: Rhonda Pringle, President

E-mail: rpringle@bizjournals.com

Ed: Scott Dance. **Description:** Concerns for higher capital gains taxes in 2011 have been provoking buyers and sellers to engage in mergers and acquisitions activity, which is expected to gain momentum before the end of 2010. Companies that had saved cash during the recession have been taking advantage of the buyer's market. Other trends in local and national mergers and acquisitions activity are presented. **Availability:** Print.

31181 ▪ *"As Comic Book Industry Grows, Smaller Publishers Learn to Adapt"* **in** *The New York Times (May 8, 2019)*

URL(s): www.nytimes.com/2019/05/08/business/lion -forge-oni-merger.html

Released: May 08, 2019. **Description:** With DC Comics and Marvel dominating the comic scene, smaller independent publishers are getting creative in order to compete. Some are merging, while others are doing direct-to-consumer sales. **Availability:** Online.

31182 ▪ *"Austin Group-Buying Site Hones In on Hispanics"* **in** *Austin Business Journal (Vol. 31, July 1, 2011, No. 17, pp. 1)*

Pub: Austin Business Journal

Contact: Rachel McGrath, Director

E-mail: rmcgrath@bizjournals.com

Ed: Vicky Garza. **Description:** Descuentl Libre is a new group-buying site from Austin, Texas that targets the Hispanic market, offering discounts of practical items and family-friendly activities. The Hispanic market constitutes 17 percent of the U.S. population and spends $23 billion yearly online. **Availability:** Online.

31183 ▪ *"Austin Realtors Cozy Up To Trulia"* **in** *Austin Business Journal (Vol. 34, May 9, 2014, No. 12, pp. 6)*

Pub: American City Business Journals, Inc.

Contact: Mike Olivieri, Executive Vice President

Released: Weekly. **Price:** $4, Introductory 4-week offer(Digital & Print). **Description:** Austin Board of Realtors (ABOR) MLS Advisory Committee chairman Lisa Messana explains the organization's decision to share data exclusively with Trulia.com. She describes member response to the announcement to end ABOR's data license agreement with ListHub. **Availability:** Print; Online.

31184 ▪ *"AV Concept Expands Into Green Energy Storage"* **in** *Wireless News (January 25, 2010)*

Description: Electronics distributor and manufacturer AV Concept Holdings Limited announced a marketing partnership with Boston-Power, a provider of lithium-ion batteries, with a focus in the Chinese and Korean markets. **Availability:** Online.

31185 ▪ *"Baking Up a Bigger Lance"* **in** *Charlotte Business Journal (Vol. 25, December 3, 2010, No. 37, pp. 1)*

Pub: Charlotte Business Journal

Contact: Robert Morris, Editor

E-mail: rmorris@bizjournals.com

Ed: Ken Elkins. **Description:** Events that led to the merger between Charlotte, North Carolina-based snack food manufacturer Lance Inc. and Pennsylvania-based pretzel maker Snyder's of Hanover Inc. are discussed. The merger is expected to help Lance in posting a 70 percent increase in revenue, which reached $900 million in 2009. How the merger would affect Snyder's of Hanover is also described. **Availability:** Print; Online.

31186 ▪ *"Baldwin Connelly Partnership Splits"* **in** *Business Journal Serving Greater Tampa Bay (Vol. 30, November 19, 2010, No. 48, pp. 1)*

Pub: Tampa Bay Business Journal

Contact: Ian Anderson, President

E-mail: ianderson@bizjournals.com

Description: The fast-growing insurance brokerage Baldwin Connelly is now breaking up after five years. Two different entrepreneurial visions have developed within the organization and founders Lowry Baldwin and John Connell will not take separate tracks. Staffing levels in the firm are expected to remain the same. **Availability:** Print; Online.

31187 ▪ *"Bank Buys May Heat Up In Birmingham"* **in** *Birmingham Business Journal (Vol. 31, May 9, 2014, No. 19, pp. 8)*

Pub: American City Business Journals, Inc.

Contact: Mike Olivieri, Executive Vice President

Released: Weekly. **Price:** $4, introductory 4-week offer(Digital & Print). **Description:** The banking industry in Birmingham, Alabama is poised for more mergers and acquisitions in the next two years as bank failures drop and potential sellers look for protection from increasing regulations. Experts suggest Birmingham is an attractive market for potential buyers because of its rich history as a top financial center and its stable economic environment. **Availability:** Print; Online.

31188 ▪ *"The Bankrate Double Play, Bankrate Is Having Its Best Quarter Yet"* **in** *Barron's (Vol. 88, March 24, 2008, No. 12, pp. 27)*

Pub: Dow Jones & Company Inc.

Contact: Almar Latour, Chief Executive Officer

Ed: Neil A. Martin. **Description:** Shares of Bankrate may rise as much as 25 percent from their level of $45.08 a share due to a strong cash flow and balance sheet. The company's Internet business remains strong despite weakness in the online advertising industry and is a potential takeover target. **Availability:** Online.

31189 ▪ *"Barbarians Set Bar Low With Lowly Canadian Telco"* **in** *Globe & Mail (March 31, 2007, pp. B1)*

Ed: Derek DeCloet. **Description:** The efforts of the private equity fund Kohlberg, Kravis, Roberts and Co. to acquire the Canadian telecommunications firm BCE are described. **Availability:** Online.

31190 ▪ *"Bartering Trades on Talents"* **in** *Reading Eagle (June 20, 2010)*

Description: Bartering is not just a way of trading goods and services, it can be an essential tool for small business to survive in a bad economy.

31191 ■ *"BCE Mulls Radical Changes With Industry Under Pressure"* in *Globe & Mail (March 30, 2007, pp. B1)*

Ed: Andrew Willis, Jacquie McNish, Catherine McLean. **Description:** An account on the expansion plans of BCE Inc., which plans to acquire TELUS Corp., is presented. **Availability:** Online.

31192 ■ *"The Bear Stearns-JPMorgan Deal - Rhymes with Steal - Of A Lifetime"* in *Barron's (Vol. 88, March 24, 2008, No. 12, pp. 24)*

Pub: Dow Jones & Company Inc.

Contact: Almar Latour, Chief Executive Officer

Ed: Andrew Bary. **Description:** JPMorgan Chase's impending acquisition of Bear Stearns for $2.50 a share is a huge steal for the former. JPMorgan is set to acquire a company with a potential annual earnings of $1 billion while the Federal Reserve funds Bear's illiquid assets by providing $30 billion in nonrecourse loans. **Availability:** Online.

31193 ■ *"Beat the Buck: Bartering Tips from In-The-Know Authors"* in *(June 23, 2010)*

Pub: The Telegraph

Contact: Don Cherry, District Manager

E-mail: dcherry@thetelegraph.com

Description: The Art of Barter is a new book to help small businesses learn this art form in order to expand customer base and reserve cash flow. **Availability:** Online.

31194 ■ *"Because 10 Million Zumba Lovers Can't Be Wrong"* in *Inc. (Volume 32, December 2010, No. 10, pp. 106)*

Pub: Mansueto Ventures L.L.C.

Contact: Stephanie Mehta, Chief Executive Officer

Ed: Christine Lagorio. **Released:** December 01, 2010. **Description:** Profile of partners, Alberto Perez, Alberto Perlman, and Alberto Aghion, founders of Zumba, a form of dance used for fitness. **Availability:** Online.

31195 ■ *"Benefits of Bartering"* in *Mail Tribune (November 22, 2010)*

Ed: Damian Mann. **Description:** Various people discuss the use of bartering for their small companies in order to improve business. **Availability:** Online.

31196 ■ *"Bethesda Firm Aims to Revitalize Hat Chain Lids"* in *Washington Business Journal (March 15, 2019)*

URL(s): www.bizjournals.com/washington/news/20 19/03/15/bethesda-firm-aims-to-revitalize-hat-chain -lids.html

Ed: Katishi Maake. **Released:** March 15, 2019. **Description:** Ames Watson LLC acquired Lids Sports Group and is looking to have the chain sell more than just hats. This is due in part to consolidating Lids with Fanzz, a sports apparel retailer, which will offer customers a larger selection of items to choose from. **Availability:** Online.

31197 ■ *"Beware this Chinese Export"* in *Barron's (Vol. 90, August 30, 2010, No. 35, pp. 21)*

Pub: Barron's Editorial & Corporate Headquarters

Ed: Bill Alpert, Leslie P. Norton. **Description:** A look at 158 China reverse-merger stocks in the U.S. reveal that the median underperformed the index of U.S. listed Chinese companies by 75 percent in their first three years. These reverse merger stocks also lagged the Russell 2000 index of small cap stocks by 66 percent. **Availability:** Online.

31198 ■ *"Beyond Microsoft and Yahoo!: Some M&A Prospects"* in *Barron's (Vol. 88, March 17, 2008, No. 11, pp. 39)*

Pub: Dow Jones & Company Inc.

Contact: Almar Latour, Chief Executive Officer

Ed: Eric J. Savitz. **Description:** Weak quarterly earnings report for Yahoo! could pressure the company's board to cut a deal with Microsoft. Electronic Arts is expected to win its hostile $26-a-share bid for Take-Two Interactive Software. Potential targets and buyers for mergers and acquisitions are mentioned. **Availability:** Online.

31199 ■ *"Beyond Zipcar: Collaborative Consumption"* in *Harvard Business Review (Vol. 88, October 2010, No. 10, pp. 30)*

Pub: Harvard Business Publishing

Contact: Diane Belcher, Managing Director

Ed: Rachel Botsman, Roo Rogers. **Price:** $6, PDF. **Description:** Description of the rise of collaborative consumption, the sharing or redistributing of products, rather than the purchasing thereof is discussed. **Availability:** Online; PDF.

31200 ■ *"Bienvenido, Mercadito"* in *Washington Business Journal (Vol. 33, September 12, 2014, No. 21, pp. 8)*

Pub: American City Business Journals, Inc.

Contact: Mike Olivieri, Executive Vice President

Released: Weekly. **Price:** $4, introductory 4-week offer(Digital & Print). **Description:** Restaurateur, Alfredo Sandoval, partnered with brothers Felipe and Patricio to open Mercadito, an upscale casual Mexican restaurant at the Marriott Marquis Hotel in Washington DC. The restaurant is geared to attract customers between 25 and 40 years of age. **Availability:** Print; Online.

31201 ■ *"Big Bling: Signet Acquires Zales Corporation"* in *Dallas Business Journal (Vol. 37, June 6, 2014, No. 39, pp. 6)*

Pub: American City Business Journals, Inc.

Contact: Mike Olivieri, Executive Vice President

Released: June 06, 2014. **Price:** $4, print. **Description:** Signet Jewelers of Bermuda acquired Zale Corporation in a $1.4 billion deal or $21 per share in cash following the approval by a majority of stockholders of the Irving, Texas-based company. The acquisition will increase Signet's earnings by a high single-digit percentage in the first fiscal year of the merger. **Availability:** Print; Online.

31202 ■ *"Big Deals With More To Come"* in *Business Journal Portland (Vol. 30, January 24, 2014, No. 47, pp. 14)*

Pub: American City Business Journals, Inc.

Contact: Mike Olivieri, Executive Vice President

Released: January 24, 2014. **Price:** $4, Introductory 4-Week Offer(Digital & Print). **Description:** D.A. Davidson & Company investment banking head, Brad Gevurtz, describes the local mergers and acquisitions (M&A) market in Portland, Oregon in 2013. Gevurtz says 2014 will be a good year for M&A because corporations have a lot of cash and lenders are lending. **Availability:** Print; Online.

31203 ■ *"Big Gains Brewing at Anheuser-Busch InBev"* in *Barron's (Vol. 90, August 30, 2010, No. 35, pp. 34)*

Pub: Barron's Editorial & Corporate Headquarters

Ed: Christopher C. Williams. **Description:** Anheuser-Busch InBev is realizing cost synergies and it posted better than expected returns two years after the merger that formed the company. One analyst believes its American depositary receipt could be worth as much as 72 in a year. **Availability:** Online.

31204 ■ *The Big Payback: The History of the Business of Hip-Hop*

Ed: Dan Charnas. **Released:** November 01, 2011. **Price:** $17, paperback; $13.99. **Description:** The complete history of hip-hop music is presented, by following the money and the relationship between artist and merchant. In its promise of economic security and creative control for black artist-entrepreneurs, it is the culmination of dreams of black nationalists and civil rights leaders. **Availability:** E-book; Print.

31205 ■ *"Big Trouble at Sony Ericsson"* in *Barron's (Vol. 88, March 24, 2008, No. 12, pp. M9)*

Pub: Dow Jones & Company Inc.

Contact: Almar Latour, Chief Executive Officer

Ed: Angelo Franchini. **Description:** Sony Ericsson is facing trouble as it warned that its sales and net income before taxes will fall by nearly half for the first quarter of 2008. The joint venture of Sony and Erics-

son has a global mobile phone market share of nine percent as of 2007, fourth largest in the world. **Availability:** Online.

31206 ■ *"Biotechs Are Using Back Door to Go Public"* in *Boston Business Journal (Vol. 31, May 27, 2011, No. 18, pp. 1)*

Pub: Boston Business Journal

Contact: Carolyn M. Jones, President

E-mail: cmjones@bizjournals.com

Ed: Julie M. Donnelly. **Description:** Members of Massachusetts' biotechnology sector have been engaging in reverse mergers as an alternative to initial public offerings. Reverse mergers provide access to institutional investors and hedge funds. **Availability:** Print; Online.

31207 ■ *"Blackstone Set to Sell Stake"* in *Globe & Mail (March 17, 2007, pp. B6)*

Description: The plan of Blackstone Group to sell 10 percent of its stake to raise $4 billion and its proposal to go for initial public offering is discussed.

31208 ■ *"Blackstone's Outlook Still Tough"* in *Barron's (Vol. 88, March 17, 2008, No. 11, pp. 19)*

Pub: Dow Jones & Company Inc.

Contact: Almar Latour, Chief Executive Officer

Ed: Andrew Bary. **Description:** Earnings for the Blackstone Group may not recover soon since the company's specialty in big leveraged buyouts is floundering and may not recover until 2009. The company earns lucrative incentive fees on its funds but those fees went negative in the fourth quarter of 2007 and there could be more fee reversals in the future. **Availability:** Online.

31209 ■ *"Boeing Partnership to Preserve Thousands of Acres of Threatened Wetlands in South Carolina"* in *Ecology, Environment & Conservation Business (August 2, 2014, pp. 3)*

Pub: NewsRX LLC.

Contact: Kalani Rosell, Contact

Description: U.S. Army Corps of Engineers approved Boeing's comprehensive wetlands mitigation plan to preserve about 4,000 acres of land, including more than 2,000 acres of wetlands near the Francis Marion National Forest in South Carolina Lowcountry. Boeing worked in partnership with federal, state and local agencies and conservation organizations to identify the tracts for preservation in order to achieve conservation goals of regional and national significance. **Availability:** Online.

31210 ■ *"BofA Will Reach the Top with Countrywide Deal"* in *Business North Carolina (Vol. 28, March 2008, No. 3, pp. 36)*

Description: Bank of America, headquartered in Charlotte, North Carolina, will add Countrywide to its let of credits. Countrywide is the largest U.S. mortgage lender. Statistical data included.

31211 ■ *"Bonds v. Stocks: Who's Right About Recession?"* in *Barron's (Vol. 90, August 23, 2010, No. 34, pp. M3)*

Pub: Barron's Editorial & Corporate Headquarters

Ed: Kopin Tan. **Description:** The future of treasury securities and stocks should the U.S. enter or avoid a recession are discussed. The back to school business climate and BHP Billiton's bid for Potash Corporation of Saskatchewan are also discussed. **Availability:** Online.

31212 ■ *"Boom and Bust in the Book Biz"* in *Canadian Business (Vol. 83, August 17, 2010, No. 13-14, pp. 16)*

Pub: Rogers Media Inc.

Contact: Neil Spivak, Chief Executive Officer

Ed: Jordan Timm. **Description:** Electronic book marketplace is booming with Amazon.com's e-book sales for the Kindle e-reader exceeding the hardcover sales. Kobo Inc. has registered early success with its Kobo e-reader and has partnered with Hong Kong telecom giant on an e-book store. **Availability:** Print; Online.

31213 ■ *"Border Boletin: UA to Take Lie-Detector Kiosk to Poland"* in *Arizona Daily Star (September 14, 2010)*
Pub: Arizona Daily Star
Contact: John D'Orlando, President
E-mail: jdorlando@tucson.com

Ed: Brady McCombs. **Description:** University of Arizona's National Center for Border Security and Immigration Research will send a team to Warsaw, Poland to show border guards from 27 European Union countries the center's Avatar Kiosk. The Avatar technology is designed for use at border ports and airports to assist Customs officers detect individuals who are lying. **Availability:** Print; Online.

31214 ■ *"Branded Entertainment: Dealmaking Strategies & Techniques for Industry Professionals"*
Pub: J. Ross Publishing Inc.
Contact: Stephen Buda, President

Released: October 01, 2014. **Price:** $39.95, hardcover, plus shipping charge extra. FL sale tax $3.36. **Description:** Branded entertainment, also known as branded content or advertainment, is an entertainment-based method that is funded by and complementary to a brand's marketing strategy. These projects are usually a partnership between brands, television or radio producers, and broadcasters. **Availability:** E-book; Print; Download.

31215 ■ *"Brazil's New King of Food"* in *Barron's (Vol. 89, July 13, 2009, No. 28, pp. 28)*
Pub: Dow Jones & Company Inc.
Contact: Almar Latour, Chief Executive Officer

Ed: Kenneth Rapoza. **Description:** Perdigao and Sadia's merger has resulted in the creation of Brasil Foods and the shares of Brasil Foods provides a play on both Brazil's newly energized consumer economy and its role as a major commodities exporter. Brasil Foods shares could climb as much as 36 percent. **Availability:** Online.

31216 ■ *"Breaking Up: How Will It Affect Your Residence Permit?"* in *Canadian Business (Vol. 80, March 12, 2007, No. 6, pp. 34)*

Description: The need for business partners to draft a shareholder agreement in the beginning of their business to make it easier to break their relationship in case of disputes later is discussed. **Availability:** Online.

31217 ■ *"Bridging the Talent Gap Through Partnership and Innovation"* in *Canadian Business (Vol. 81, October 27, 2008, No. 18, pp. 88)*

Description: Research revealed that North America is short by more than 60,000 qualified networking professionals. Businesses, educators and communities are collaborating in order to address the shortfall. **Availability:** Print; Online.

31218 ■ *"Briefly: Physician Groups Unite"* in *Crain's Detroit Business (Vol. 25, June 15, 2009, No. 24, pp. 18)*
Pub: Crain Communications Inc.
Contact: Barry Asin, President

Ed: Tom Henderson, Jay Greene. **Description:** Details of the merger between Planning Alternatives Ltd. and Oakland Wealth Management are highlighted. The two investment advisory firms will have a combined staff of 12 and will maintain two offices. **Availability:** Online.

31219 ■ *"Business Diary"* in *Crain's Detroit Business (Vol. 24, October 6, 2008, No. 40, pp. 23)*
Pub: Crain Communications Inc.
Contact: Barry Asin, President

Description: Detailed listing of acquisitions, expansions, new products, new services, business contracts and startups from the Detroit area is provided. **Availability:** Print; Online.

31220 ■ *"Business Without Borders: All For One, None for All?"* in *Canadian Business (Vol. 83, October 12, 2010, No. 17, pp. 60)*
Pub: Rogers Media Inc.
Contact: Neil Spivak, Chief Executive Officer

Ed: Michael McCullogh. **Description:** The effect of the growth of Canada's overseas provincial trade offices on Canadian trade is discussed. Economic development commissions in the country have devised a single 'Consider Canada' campaign to pitch foreign investors. It is hoped that large cities will gain from banding together rather than competing against one another. **Availability:** Print; Online.

31221 ■ *"Buyout Rumors Have Rackspace Back in the News"* in *San Antonio Business Journal (Vol. 28, September 12, 2014, No. 31, pp. 6)*
Pub: American City Business Journals, Inc.
Contact: Mike Olivieri, Executive Vice President

Description: Louisiana-based CenturyLink Inc. has offered to buyout San Antonio, Texas-based Rackspace Hosting in order to boost its Internet and cloud services. The latest stock market valuation of Rackspace was at $5.33 billion. The potential impact of the CenturyLink and Rackspace merger deal on the managed hosting services market is also analyzed. **Availability:** Online.

31222 ■ *"CADD Microsystems Launches the CADD Community, Partners with Global eTraining to Provide Online, On-Demand Training for Autodesk Software"* in *Computer Business Week (August 28, 2014, pp. 24)*
Pub: NewsRX LLC.
Contact: Kalani Rosell, Contact

Description: A new online customer-only portal the integrates on-demand training, applications and extension, videos and additional value-added content for customers only was developed by CADD Microsystems. The Autodesk Platinum Partner calls this training program, CADD Community. **Availability:** Online.

31223 ■ *"Cameco to Supply Reactors With Recycled Nukem Warheads"* in *Canadian Business (Vol. 85, August 13, 2012, No. 13, pp. 10)*

Ed: Richard Warnica. **Description:** Cameco Corporation has acquired Nukem Energy gmbH from private equity firm Advent International for $136 million as part of the Canadian mining company's plan to double annual uranium production to 40 million pounds by 2018. Such agreement gives Cameco access to some of the last of the uranium supply in the Megatons to Megawatt deal between Russia and the U.S. which expires in 2013. **Availability:** Print; Online.

31224 ■ *"Canada Joins TPP Free Trade Talks"* in *Canadian Business (Vol. 85, August 13, 2012, No. 13, pp. 7)*

Ed: Tim Shufelt. **Description:** The decision of the Canadian government to join the Trans-Pacific Partnership (TPP) has potential economic benefits in terms of trading with China and the U.S.Failure of the World Trade Ogranization's Doha Round and the admission of the U.S. to the TPP prompted Canada to join the trade agreement. **Availability:** Print; Online.

31225 ■ *"The Canadians Are Coming!"* in *Canadian Business (Vol. 80, October 22, 2007, No. 21, pp. 15)*

Description: Toronto-Dominion Bank declared its acquisition of the New Jersey-based Commerce Bancorp for C$8.5 billion. Royal Bank of Canada has scooped up Trinidad-based Financial Group for C$2.2 billion. Details of the foreign acquisitions, as well as the impact of high Canadian dollars on the mergers are discussed. **Availability:** Online.

31226 ■ *"Capital Position: M&I Acquisition Opens the Door for Rivals to Gain Market Share"* in *Business Journal-Milwaukee (Vol. 28, December 24, 2010, No. 12, pp. A1)*
Pub: The Business Journal
Contact: Heather Ladage, President

E-mail: hladage@bizjournals.com

Ed: Rich Kirchen. **Description:** Canada-based BMO Financial Group has purchased Marshall and Isley Corporation (M and I), which dominated lending among Wisconsin businesses for decades. The sale of M and I will enable other banks to recruit M and I's customers but BMO Financial remains a stronger competitor since it possesses a more potent capital position. **Availability:** Print; Online.

31227 ■ *"Capitalizing On Our Intellectual Capital"* in *Harvard Business Review (Vol. 90, May 2012, No. 5, pp. 42)*
Pub: Harvard Business Review Press
Contact: Moderna V. Pfizer, Contact

Ed: Iqbal Quadir. **Price:** $6, hardcopy and PDF. **Description:** By managing education as an export, the US can benefit not only from revenue received from tuition, but also from the relationships forged with foreign students. The students will import the networks and technologies they used while in the US and their education levels will help create global growth. **Availability:** Print; Online; PDF.

31228 ■ *"Cash-Heavy Biovail on the Prowl for Deals"* in *Globe & Mail (March 24, 2006, pp. B1)*

Ed: Leonard Zehr. **Description:** Biovail Corp. posted 48 percent rise in profits for 2005. The business growth plans of the company through acquisitions are presented. **Availability:** Online.

31229 ■ *"CBC Eyes Partners for TV Downloads"* in *Globe & Mail (February 9, 2006, pp. B1)*

Description: The details on Canadian Broadcasting Corp.'s distribution agreement with Google Inc. and Apple Computer Inc. are presented. **Availability:** Online.

31230 ■ *"CE2 Carbon Capital and Dogwood Carbon Solutions Partner with Missouri Landowners to Generate High Quality Carbon Offsets from 300,000 Acres of Forest"* in *Nanotechnolgy Business Journal (January 25, 2010)*
Pub: Investment Weekly News

Description: Dogwood Carbon Solutions, a developer of agriculture and forestry based conservation projects, has partnered with CE2 Carbon Capital, one of the largest investors and owners of U.S. carbon commodities and carbon emissions reduction projects, to develop high-quality carbon offsets from over 30,000 acres of privately-owned non-industrial forest in the Ozark mountain region of Arkansas and Missouri. **Availability:** Print; Online.

31231 ■ *"Centurion Signs Egypt Deal With Shell"* in *Globe & Mail (March 21, 2006, pp. B5)*

Ed: Dave Ebner. **Description:** Centurion Energy International Inc., a Calgary-based natural gas producer in Egypt, has signed contract with Royal Dutch Shell PLC to explore about 320,000 hectares of land in Egypt. Details of the agreement are presented. **Availability:** Online.

31232 ■ *"CEOs Keep Bringing Home the Perks"* in *Baltimore Business Journal (Vol. 30, May 18, 2012, No. 2, pp. 1)*
Pub: American City Business Journals, Inc.
Contact: Mike Olivieri, Executive Vice President

Ed: Gary Haber. **Description:** According to the annual proxy statement of Baltimore-based Stanley Black & Decker, executive chairman Nolan D. Archibald received a $12.3 million compensation package in 2011. According to the company, Archibald's perks are part of his employment agreement which was duly approved by the shareholders during the merger of Stanley Works and Black & Decker. **Availability:** Print; Online.

31233 ■ *"Chafee Eyes Tax On Travel Sites"* in *Providence Business News (Vol. 28, March 24, 2014, No. 51, pp. 1)*
Pub: American City Business Journals, Inc.
Contact: Mike Olivieri, Executive Vice President

URL(s): pbn.com/chafee-eyes-tax-on-travel-sites9 5903
Description: Rhode Island Governor, Lincoln D. Chafee's 2015 budget will include new tax rules for travel Websites. State officials claim the new regulations will deal with a loophole that has allowed travel Websites to pay less in taxes. Many hotels enter into partnerships with travel Websites in order to sell rooms in bulk. **Availability:** Online. **Telecommunication Services:** Anderson@pbn.com.

31234 ■ *"Challenges Await Quad in Going Public"* in Milwaukee Business Journal (Vol. 27, January 29, 2010, No. 18, pp. A1)
Pub: The Business Journal
Contact: Heather Ladage, President
E-mail: hladage@bizjournals.com

Ed: Rich Rovito. **Description:** Sussex, Wisconsin-based Quad/Graphics Inc.'s impending acquisition of rival Canadian World Color Press Inc. will transform it into a publicly held entity for the first time. Quad has operated as a private company for nearly 40 years and will need to adjust to changes, such as the way management shares information with Quad/Graphics' employees. Details of the merger are included. **Availability:** Print; Online.

31235 ■ *"The Change Foundation Awards Northumberland Community Partnership $3 Million Project To Improve Seniors' Healthcare Transitions and Use Patient Input to Drive Redesign"* in CNW Group (June 5, 2012)
Pub: Comtex News Network Inc.
Contact: Kan Devnani, President

Description: The Change Foundation has awarded the Northumberland Community Partnership with its $3 million project PATH-Partners Advancing Transitions in Healthcare for Ontario patients. The program brings together 12 health and social care organizations with patients and caregivers to identify healthcare transition issues in Central East Ontario, Canada. It will work with service providers to redesign care and to improve experiences. **Availability:** Online.

31236 ■ *"Chew On This: Soul Fans to 'Chews' Games' First Play"* in Philadelphia Business Journal (Vol. 30, September 30, 2011, No. 33, pp. 3)
Pub: Philadelphia Business Journal
Contact: Sierra Quinn, Director
E-mail: squinn@bizjournals.com

Ed: John George. **Description:** Arena football team Philadelphia Soul extended its marketing partnership with Just Born Inc. The team's fans will enter a contest where the winner will be allowed to select the team's first play during a home game. **Availability:** Online.

31237 ■ *"Chicago Senior Care Acquires The Clare at Water Tower"* in Investment Weekly News (April 29, 2012, pp. 168)
Pub: PR Newswire Association LLC.

Description: Senior Care Development LLC, Fundamental Advisors LP, and Life Care Companies LLC partnered to create Chicago Senior Care LLC (CSC) and won the bid for purchasing The Clare at Water Tower, a senior housing community. **Availability:** Online.

31238 ■ *"China Vs the World: Whose Technology Is It?"* in Harvard Business Review (Vol. 88, December 2010, No. 12, pp. 94)
Pub: Harvard Business Publishing
Contact: Diane Belcher, Managing Director

Ed: Thomas M. Hout, Pankaj Ghemawat. **Price:** $8.95, PDF. **Description:** Examination of the regulation the Chinese government is implementing that require foreign corporations wishing to do business in the country to give up their new technologies. These regulations avoid World Trade Organization technology transfer provisions and complicate the convergence of socialism and capitalism. **Availability:** Online; PDF.

31239 ■ *"China's ZTE in Hunt for Partners"* in Globe & Mail (February 27, 2006, pp. B1)
Ed: Gordon Pitts. **Description:** The business growth plans of ZTE Corp. in Canada, through partnership, are presented. **Availability:** Online.

31240 ■ *"Chinese Coal Giant Shifts Focus with ECA Pact"* in Pittsburgh Business Times (Vol. 33, January 10, 2014, No. 26, pp. 3)
Pub: American City Business Journals, Inc.
Contact: Mike Olivieri, Executive Vice President

Description: China Shenhua Energy Company has signed a deal with Energy Corporation of America (ECA) for a joint venture with its U.S. subsidiary, Shenhua America Holdings Corporation, to drill 25 wells in Greene County, Pennsylvania. Shenhua will initially provide $90 million to cover the costs of drilling and production for the wells in ECA-owned land. **Availability:** Online.

31241 ■ *"CIBC Spends $1.1 Billion on Caribbean Expansion"* in Globe & Mail (March 14, 2006, pp. B1)
Ed: Sinclair Stewart. **Description:** Canadian Imperial Bank of Commerce (CIBC), the fifth-largest bank of Canada, is planning to spend $1.1billion to buy major share of Barbados-based First Caribbean International Bank. The details of the acquisition plan are presented. **Availability:** Print; Online.

31242 ■ *"Citadel EFT (CDFT) Contracts With New Search Engine Optimization (SEO) and Banner Ad Web Marketing Companies"* in Internet Wire (August 8, 2012)
Pub: Comtex News Network Inc.
Contact: Kan Devnani, President

Description: Citafel EFT Inc. provides credit card terminals, online, mail order and retail credit card processing services. The firm has contracted with two Web marketing companies to increase its awareness on the Internet. **Availability:** Print; Online.

31243 ■ *"Clarence Firm Gets OK To Make Tobacco Products"* in Business First of Buffalo (Vol. 30, March 14, 2014, No. 26, pp. 3)
Pub: American City Business Journals, Inc.
Contact: Mike Olivieri, Executive Vice President

Released: March 14, 2014. **Price:** $4, Introductory 4-Week Offer(Digital & Print). **Description:** Clarence, New York-based 22nd Century Group Inc.'s subsidiary Goodrich Tobacco Company, has received approval from the Alcohol and Tobacco Tax Trade Bureau to produce tobacco products. The approval came after 22nd Century purchased the assets of North Carolina-based Nasco Products LLC, which holds a similar permit. Details of the deal are included. **Availability:** Print; Online.

31244 ■ *"Clean-Tech Focus Sparks Growth"* in Philadelphia Business Journal (Vol. 28, January 15, 2010, No. 48, pp. 1)
Pub: Philadelphia Business Journal
Contact: Sierra Quinn, Director
E-mail: squinn@bizjournals.com

Ed: Peter Key. **Description:** Keystone Redevelopment Group and economic development organization Ben Franklin Technology Partners of Southeastern Pennsylvania have partnered in supporting the growth of new alternative energy and clean technology companies. Keystone has also been developing the Bridge Business Center. **Availability:** Online.

31245 ■ *"Clearwire Struggling, Banks on Deals with Competitors"* in Puget Sound Business Journal (Vol. 33, August 24, 2012, No. 18, pp. 1)
Pub: Baltimore Business Journal
Contact: Rhonda Pringle, President
E-mail: rpringle@bizjournals.com

Ed: Emily Parkhurst, Alyson Raletz. **Description:** Clearwire Corporation's chief executive, Erik Prusch, is planning to lease the wireless spectrum of the company to major mobile providers that run out of their own supply. At issue is whether the Bellevue, Washington-based telecommunication company can

manage its $4 billion debt and maximize the value of its technology while managing its partners all at the same time. **Availability:** Print; Online.

31246 ■ *"Closures Pop Cork on Wine Bar Sector Consolidation"* in Houston Business Journal (Vol. 40, January 22, 2010, No. 37, pp. A2)
Pub: Houston Business Journal
Contact: Bob Charlet, President
E-mail: bcharlet@bizjournals.com

Ed: Allison Wollam. **Description:** Wine bar market in Houston, Texas is in the midst of a major shift and heads toward further consolidation due to the closure of pioneering wine bars that opened in the past decade. The Corkscrew owner, Andrew Adams, has blamed the creation of competitive establishments to the closure which helped wear out his concept. **Availability:** Print; Online.

31247 ■ *"Co-Working a Hit in Seattle Market"* in Puget Sound Business Journal (Vol. 34, March 14, 2014, No. 48, pp. 8)
Pub: American City Business Journals, Inc.
Contact: Mike Olivieri, Executive Vice President

Released: Weekly. **Price:** $4, introductory 4-week offer(Digital & Print). **Description:** Companies in Seattle, Washington are learning about the new trend in co-working. The city's co-working industry continues to grow, which is why competitors have established a trade group. Co-working is the process of sharing office space within business centers. Regus, which manages 21 business centers in the city, plans to introduce private booths called WorkBoxes. **Availability:** Print; Online.

31248 ■ *"Coinstar, Inc. and Seattle's Best Coffee Sign Exclusive Agreement to Roll Out Thousands of the New Rubi Kiosks in Grocery, Drug and Mass Channels"* in Marketing Weekly News (June 23 2012, pp. 77)
Pub: PR Newswire Association LLC.

Description: Seattles' Best Coffee, a firm of Starbucks Corporation, has partnered with Coinstar Inc. to install coffee kiosks in grocery, drug and mass merchant retailers featuring Seattle's Best coffee drinks. Rubi kiosk is the third automated kiosk owned by Coinstar. Details of the deal are included.

31249 ■ *"Cold Stone in Licensing Agreement with Turin Chocolates"* in Ice Cream Reporter (Vol. 22, December 20, 2008, No. 1, pp. 2)
Description: Cold Stone Creamery and Turin Chocolatier are teaming up to offer a new line of chocolate truffles under the Cold Stone label. The treats will feature four the most popular Cold Stone flavors: Coffee Lovers Only, Chocolate Devotion, Our Strawberry Blonde, and Peanut Butter Cup Perfection. **Availability:** Print; Online.

31250 ■ *"Colliers Shifts Its Brokerage Home"* in Charlotte Business Journal (Vol. 25, November 5, 2010, No. 33, pp. 1)
Pub: Charlotte Business Journal
Contact: Robert Morris, Editor
E-mail: rmorris@bizjournals.com

Ed: Will Boye. **Description:** Colliers International signed a long-term affiliate agreement with commercial real estate firm Clarus Properties, in a move that would allow Colliers to resume business in Charlotte, North Carolina. Colliers also hired well known brokers Brad Grow and Brent Royall. **Availability:** Print; Online.

31251 ■ *"Company Severs Ties with Chiquita, Starts Own Brand"* in Business Journal-Serving Phoenix and the Valley of the Sun (October 4, 2007)
Pub: Phoenix Business Journal
Contact: Alex McAlister, Director
E-mail: amcalister@bizjournals.com

Ed: Mike Sunnucks. **Description:** Melones International is ending a deal with Chiquita Brands International Inc. Melones will now distribute its produce in the U.S. under its own brand, called Plain Jane. Alejandro N. Canelos Jr., head of the firm, stated their relationship with Chiquita was good, but wants to promote the Plain Jane brand name. **Availability:** Print; Online.

31252 ■ *"Competition Qualms Overblown: Inco"* in *Globe & Mail (February 15, 2006, pp. B1)*
Ed: Wendy Stueck. **Description:** Inco Ltd. plans the acquisition of Falconbridge Ltd., for $12.5 billion. The advantages of the acquisition for Inco Ltd. are presented. **Availability:** Online.

31253 ■ *"Consulting Firm Goes Shopping"* in *Crain's Chicago Business (Vol. 31, April 28, 2008, No. 17, pp. 45)*
Pub: Crain Communications Inc.
Contact: Barry Asin, President
Ed: Phuong Ly. **Description:** Clark & Wamberg LLC was created last year after the merger of Clark Inc. to a Dutch insurance conglomerate. Clark Inc. was a life insurance and benefits consultancy which had been on a downslide, returning just 5.6 percent a year to shareholders. In contrast Clark & Wamberg posted first-year revenue of $106.8 million, fueled by business from its executive compensation and health care clients. **Availability:** Online.

31254 ■ *"Copyright Clearance Center (CCC) Partnered with cSubs"* in *Information Today (Vol. 28, November 2011, No. 10, pp. 14)*
Description: Copyright Clearance Center (CCC) partnered with cSubs to integrate CCC's point-of-content licensing solution RightsLink Basic directly into cSubs' workflow. The partnership will allow cSubs' customers a user-friendly process for obtaining permissions. Csubs is a corporate subscription management service for books, newspapers, and econtent. **Availability:** Online.

31255 ■ *"Cornerstone Seeks Investors for Hedge Fund"* in *Baltimore Business Journal (Vol. 32, June 20, 2014, No. 7, pp. 10)*
Pub: American City Business Journals, Inc.
Contact: Mike Olivieri, Executive Vice President
Description: Cornerstone Advisory LLP is looking for investors to create a hedge fund that ties returns to various indices, real estate or commodity prices. Cornerstone hopes to raise between $30 million to $50 million and are planning a fall launch for the fund. They have hired New York law firm Thompson Hine LLP to draft the subscription agreement and Nebras-kaEs Gimini Fund Services LLC to run as third party administrator. **Availability:** Print; Online.

31256 ■ *"The Coup Is Over, the Execution Begins"* in *Canadian Business (Vol. 85, June 11, 2012, No. 10, pp. 9)*
Ed: Matthew McClearn. **Description:** U.S. activist investor Bill Ackman of Pershing Square Capital Management faces the challenge of satisfying the high expectations he set when he acquired Canadian Pacific (CP) Railway and all of Pershing's nominees were elected to the CP board. Ackman promises that CP would reach an operating ratio of 65 percent by 2015. **Availability:** Online.

31257 ■ *"Crouching Tigers Spring to Life"* in *Globe & Mail (April 14, 2007, pp. B1)*
Ed: Grant Robertson. **Description:** The prospects of the acquisition of BCE Inc, by Canadian pension funds are discussed. The effect of the growth of these pension funds on the Canadian economy is described. **Availability:** Online.

31258 ■ *"Crowdfunding Author Thinks Google Will Beat Facebook to the Punch on InvestP2P Acquisition"* in *GlobeNewswire (July 17, 2012)*
Pub: Comtex News Network Inc.
Contact: Kan Devnani, President
Description: Author, Mark Kanter, explores the potentials of crowdfunding Websites, especially InvestP2P (aka: peer to peer lending) in his new book, "Street Smart CEO." Invest P2P has social networking tools built into its system. Kanter predicts Google to acquire InvestP2P.

31259 ■ *"CRTC Signals CHUM Deal Will Get Nod"* in *Globe & Mail (May 2, 2007, pp. B3)*
Ed: Grant Robertson. **Description:** The likely approval of Canadian Radio-Television and Telecommunications Commission to the proposed acquisition of CHUM Ltd. by CTVglobemedia Inc. is discussed. **Availability:** Print; Online.

31260 ■ *"CTV's CHUM Proposal Gets Chilly Reception"* in *Globe & Mail (May 1, 2007, pp. B1)*
Ed: Grant Robertson. **Description:** The possible violation of broadcast regulations in case of acquisition of CHUM Ltd. by CTV Inc. for $1.4 billion is discussed. **Availability:** Online.

31261 ■ *"Dallas Law Firms Play Big Role in State's M&A Deals"* in *Dallas Business Journal (Vol. 37, July 18, 2014, No. 45, pp. 9)*
Pub: American City Business Journals, Inc.
Contact: Mike Olivieri, Executive Vice President
Released: June 18, 2014. **Price:** $4, Introductory 4-Week Offer(Digital & Print). **Description:** Law firms in Dallas, Texas have played a crucial role in several mergers and acquisitions in the state, which has been the highest in 2014. the pace of mergers and acquisitions is expected to stay the same or improve during the second half of 2014. **Availability:** Print; Online.

31262 ■ *"Danaher to Acquire Tectronix for $2.8 Billion"* in *Canadian Electronics (Vol. 22, November-December 2007, No. 7, pp. 1)*
Description: Leading supplier of measurement, test and monitoring equipment Tektronix will be acquired by Danaher Corporation for $2.8 billion. Tektronix products are expected to complement Danaher's test equipment sector. The impacts of the deal on Tektronix shareholders and Danaher's operations are discussed. **Availability:** Print; Online.

31263 ■ *"David Maus Debuting New Dealership"* in *Orlando Business Journal (Vol. 26, February 5, 2010, No. 36, pp. 1)*
Pub: Orlando Business Journal
Contact: Julie Swyers, Director
E-mail: jswyers@bizjournals.com
Ed: Anjali Fluker. **Description:** Automotive dealers David Maus Automotive Group and Van Tuyl Automotive Investment Group will launch David Maus Chevrolet in Sanford, Florida in fall 2010. The 12-acre site of the Chevy dealership will be located adjacent to the David Maus Toyota dealership. The new store is expected to generate nearly 125 new jobs. **Availability:** Print; Online.

31264 ■ *"Davis Family Expands Cable Empire"* in *St. Louis Business Journal (Vol. 32, June 15, 2012, No. 43, pp. 1)*
Pub: Baltimore Business Journal
Contact: Rhonda Pringle, President
E-mail: rpringle@bizjournals.com
Description: Missouri-based Fidelity Communications has become a standout in the $98 billion cable industry through low-profile management of the Davis family, with the help of John Colbert. Fidelity has made five acquisitions since 1992 and has grown its subscriber base to more than 115,000 customers or revenue generating units. **Availability:** Print; Online.

31265 ■ *"Deal Braces Cramer for Growth Run"* in *The Business Journal-Serving Metropolitan Kansas City (Vol. 26, July 4, 2008, No. 43, pp. 1)*
Description: Gardner, Kansas-based Cramer Products Inc. bought 100 percent of the stocks of Louisville, Kentucky-based Active Ankle Inc. from 26 private investors increasing its revenue by 20 percent. The latter is the second largest vendor of Cramer. Other details of the merger are presented. **Availability:** Print; Online.

31266 ■ *"Dealer Gets a Lift with Acquisitions at Year's End"* in *Crain's Detroit Business (Vol. 26, January 11, 2010, No. 2, pp. 3)*
Pub: Crain Communications Inc.
Contact: Barry Asin, President

Ed: Ryan Beene. **Description:** Alta Equipment Co., a forklift dealer, closed 2009 with a string of acquisitions expecting to double the firm's employee headcount and triple its annual revenue. Alta Lift Truck Services, Inc., as the company was known before the acquisitions, was founded in 1984 as Michigan's dealer for forklift manufacturer Yale Materials Handling Corp. **Availability:** Print; Online.

31267 ■ *"Death Spiral"* in *Business Journal Serving Greater Tampa Bay (Vol. 30, October 29, 2010, No. 45, pp. 1)*
Pub: Tampa Bay Business Journal
Contact: Ian Anderson, President
E-mail: ianderson@bizjournals.com
Description: Bay Cities Bank has started working on the loan portfolio of its acquisition, Progress Bank of Florida. Regulators closed Progress Bank in October 2010 after capital collapsed due to charge-offs and increases in the provision for future loan losses. **Availability:** Print; Online.

31268 ■ *"Defense Mobile Joins Forces with RadioShack to launch New Military Focuses Mobile Service this Fall"* in *Defense & Aerospace Business (September 10, 2014, pp. 7)*
Pub: NewsRX LLC.
Contact: Kalani Rosell, Contact
Description: RadioShack and Defense Mobile Corporation have partnered for RadioShack to be the exclusive national retailer for Defense Mobile's new nationwide 4G LTE mobile services. Defense Mobile was launched by veterans and supported by a 100 percent veteran-staffed Member Service organization and its mobile services are designed to benefit, honor and reward active U.S. military and veterans for their commitment and service. **Availability:** Online.

31269 ■ *"Desmarais Makes Move into U.S."* in *Globe & Mail (February 2, 2007, pp. B1)*
Ed: Andrew Willis. **Description:** The decision of Desmarais family, which runs Great-West Lifeco Inc., to acquire Putnam Investment Trust for $4.6 billion to enter the United States market, is discussed. **Availability:** Online.

31270 ■ *"Digital Duplication"* in *Crain's Cleveland Business (Vol. 28, October 1, 2007, No. 39, pp. 3)*
Pub: Crain Communications Inc.
Contact: K. C. Crain, President
Ed: David Bennett. **Description:** Profile of the business plan of eBlueprint Holdings LLC, a reprographics company that found success by converting customers' paper blueprints to an electronic format; the company plans to expand into other geographic markets by acquiring solid reprographics companies and converting their computer systems so that customers' blueprints can be managed electronically. **Availability:** Online.

31271 ■ *"Dish Network to Buy EchoStar's Broadcast Satellite Business"* in *The Wall Street Journal (May 20, 2019)*
URL(s): www.wsj.com/articles/dish-network-buys-echostar-broadcast-satellite-business-11558 348751
Ed: Patrick Thomas. **Released:** May 20, 2019. **Description:** Dish Network has reached an agreement to purchase EschoStar Corp.'s broadcast satellite-service business for about $800 million in stock. Dish already depends on EchoStar to operate most of its satellites, and the deal also includes various real estate. **Availability:** Online.

31272 ■ *"Dish's Charlie Ergen Sees Nothing Good in Comcast-Time Warner Merger"* in *Denver Business Journal (Vol. 65, February 21, 2014, No. 41)*
Pub: American City Business Journals, Inc.
Contact: Mike Olivieri, Executive Vice President
Released: Weekly. **Description:** The co-founder and CEO of Dish Network, Charlie Ergen, is against the proposed $45.2 billion merger of Comcast and Time Warner. Ergen feels that his satellite TV company

and others in the broadband and TV industries will be put in an unfair situation if the two companies are allowed to combine. **Availability:** Print; Online.

31273 ■ *"Disruptive Innovators: Commonground is Transforming the Advertising Landscape by Living at the Intersection of Culture, Creativity, Content, and Technology"* in Black Enterprise (Vol. 44, June 2014, No. 10, pp. 82)
Pub: Earl G. Graves Ltd.
Contact: Earl Graves, Jr., President
Description: Profile of partners, Sherman Wright and Ahmad Islam, who started the Chicago-based Commonground Marketing. The firm is an integrated, multicultural and general market advertising company. The partners met while on vacation in Cancun, Mexico.

31274 ■ *"DocuSign Raises $85 Million for Electronic Signatures"* in San Francisco Business Times (Vol. 28, March 7, 2014, No. 33, pp. 6)
Pub: American City Business Journals, Inc.
Contact: Mike Olivieri, Executive Vice President
Released: Weekly. **Description:** DocuSign, the market leader in electronic signatures, reported that it was able to raise another $85 million in capital. The company is expected to file an initial public offering in 2014 or 2015. CFO, Mike Dinsdale, shares that the firm also wants to expand internationally. **Availability:** Print; Online.

31275 ■ *"Dow Champions Innovative Energy Solutions for Auto Industry at NAIAS"* in Business of Global Warming (January 25, 2010, pp. 7)
Description: This year's North American International Auto Show in Detroit will host the "Electric Avenue" exhibit sponsored by the Dow Chemical Company. The display will showcase the latest in innovative energy solutions from Dow as well as electric vehicles and the technology supporting them. This marks the first time a non-automotive manufacturer is part of the main floor of the show. **Availability:** Print; PDF; Online.

31276 ■ *"Downtown Bank Got High Marks for Irwin Purchase, Is Looking For More"* in Business Courier (Vol. 27, September 3, 2010, No. 18, pp. 1)
Pub: Business Courier
Ed: Steve Watkins. **Price:** $4, Introductory 4-Week Offer(Digital & Print). **Description:** First Financial Bancorp is looking to acquire more troubled banks following its purchase of Irwin Union Bank. The bank has reported a $383 million bargain purchase gain during the third quarter of 2009. **Availability:** Print; Online.

31277 ■ *"Driving With No Brakes: How a Bunch of Hooligans Built the Best Travel Company in the World"*
Pub: Grand Circle Corp.
Ed: Alan Lewis, Harriet Lewis. **Released:** 2010. **Description:** Inspirational book about how two courageous leaders built a remarkable company that can thrive in change and succeed in an unpredictable world. Important lessons for any business leader trying to create value in the 21st Century are included. **Availability:** Print.

31278 ■ *"DuPont's Pioneer Hi-Bred, Evogene to Develop Rust-Resistant Soybean Varieties"* in Farm Industry News (November 22, 2011)
Pub: Informa Business Media, Inc.
Contact: Charlie McCurdy, President
Ed: Karen McMahon. **Description:** DuPont and Evogene have signed a new contract to work together to develop resistance in soybeans to rust. Financial terms of the agreement were not disclosed. **Availability:** Online.

31279 ■ *The Economics of Integrity: From Dairy Farmers to Toyota, How Wealth Is Built on Trust and What That Means for Our Future*
Ed: Anna Bernasek. **Released:** February 23, 2010. **Price:** $3.99. **Description:** Integrity is built over time

and the importance of trust in starting and building business relationships is stressed. **Availability:** E-book.

31280 ■ *"Eight Bucks an Hour"* in South Florida Business Journal (Vol. 34, July 11, 2014, No. 51, pp. 13)
Pub: American City Business Journals, Inc.
Contact: Mike Olivieri, Executive Vice President
Released: Weekly. **Price:** $8, introductory 4-week offer(Digital only). **Description:** Tips on ways to improve entrepreneurial selling behavior are listed. A number of potential activities that entrepreneurs can and should be doing to build business include cold calling, attending networking events, and creating business alliances. **Availability:** Print; Online.

31281 ■ *"Empty Office Blues"* in Business Journal Portland (Vol. 26, December 4, 2009, No. 39, pp. 1)
Pub: Portland Business Journal
Contact: Andy Giegerich, Managing Editor
E-mail: agiegerich@bizjournals.com
Ed: Wendy Culverwell. **Description:** Portland's office vacancy rates could reach almost 15 percent by the end of 2010 due to job reductions and mergers. **Availability:** Print; Online.

31282 ■ *"Endeca Gears Up for Likely IPO Bid"* in Boston Business Journal (Vol. 31, July 1, 2011, No. 23, pp. 1)
Pub: Boston Business Journal
Contact: Carolyn M. Jones, President
E-mail: cmjones@bizjournals.com
Ed: Kyle Alspach. **Released:** Weekly. **Price:** $4. **Description:** Endeca Inc. is readying itself for its plans to register as a public company. The search engine technology leader is enjoying continued growth with revenue up by 30 percent in 2010 while its expansion trend makes it an unlikely candidate for an acquisition. **Availability:** Print; Online.

31283 ■ *"Bartering Takes Businesses Back to Basics"* in Buffalo News (July 9, 2010)
Pub: The Buffalo News, Inc.
Contact: Tom Wiley, President
E-mail: twiley@buffnews.com
Ed: Dino Grandoni. **Description:** Bartering clubs can help small businesses reach new customers and to expand their business. **Availability:** Print; Online.

31284 ■ *"Enriching the Ecosystem: A Four-Point Plan for Linking Innovation, Enterprises, and Jobs"* in Harvard Business Review (Vol. 90, March 2012, No. 3, pp. 140)
Pub: Harvard Business Review Press
Contact: Moderna V. Pfizer, Contact
Ed: Rosabeth Moss Kanter. **Price:** $8.95, hardcopy black and white. **Description:** The four goals for enriching the ecosystem include: linking venture creation and knowledge creation to speed up the idea-to-enterprise transition; revitalizing small-, medium-, and large-sized firms via partnerships; improving matches between education and employment opportunities; and bringing together leaders across different sectors to create regional strategies. **Availability:** Print; PDF; Online.

31285 ■ *"EPAM May End the IPO Dry Spell"* in Philadelphia Business Journal (Vol. 31, February 3, 2012, No. 51, pp. 1)
Pub: Baltimore Business Journal
Contact: Rhonda Pringle, President
E-mail: rpringle@bizjournals.com
Description: EPAM SystemsInc. has launched its initial public offering. The company is the first Philadelphia, Pennsylvania-based firm to go public in more than a year. **Availability:** Print; Online.

31286 ■ *"eResearch Issues Initiating Report on Aldershot Resources Ltd."* in Marketwired (May 14, 2007)
Pub: Comtex News Network Inc.
Contact: Kan Devnani, President
Description: Overview of Bob Weir and Michael Wood's Initiating Report on Aldershot Resources Ltd., a junior Canadian-based uranium exploration com-

pany with prospective projects in Canada, Zambia, Australia, and a base metals project in Chile. **Availability:** Print; Online.

31287 ■ *"ESolar Partners With Penglai on Landmark Solar Thermal Agreement for China"* in Business of Global Warming (January 25, 2010, pp. 8)
Description: Penglai Electric, a privately-owned Chinese electrical power equipment manufacturer, and eSolar, a global provider of cost-effective and reliable solar power plants, announced a master licensing agreement in which eSolar will build at least 2 gigawatts of solar thermal power plants in China over the next 10 years. **Availability:** Print; Online.

31288 ■ *"Executive Decision: To Make Inroads Against RIM, Palm Steals Its Strategy"* in Globe & Mail (March 25, 2006, pp. B3)
Ed: Simon Avery. **Description:** The Palm Inc., global leader in portable device manufacturing, is looking forward to improve its sales of Palm Treos, a wireless portable device that connects to internet and email. Palm is also planning to build partnerships, under the efficient management of Michael Moskowitz, general manager and vice-president of Palm Inc., with the other companies to increase the sales of its wireless devices.

31289 ■ *"Expanding Middleby's Food Processing Biz"* in Crain's Chicago Business (Vol. 31, April 21, 2008, No. 16, pp. 6)
Pub: Crain Communications Inc.
Contact: Barry Asin, President
Ed: David Sterrett. **Description:** Profile of the executive vice-president of the food processing company, Middleby Corp, whose business plan is to develop new products, begin looking for acquisitions and simplify operations in order to expand the firm. **Availability:** Online.

31290 ■ *"Facebook IPO Buyers Deserved To Lose"* in Canadian Business (Vol. 85, July 16, 2012, No. 11-12, pp. 16)
Ed: Andrew Hallam. **Description:** Investors buying into an overhyped initial public offering (IPO) like Facebook, which opened with a price/earnings ratio exceeding 100 times earnings, are overpaying for uncertain promise. Studies found that the most profitable IPO are those unpopular businesses which are not overpriced. **Availability:** Print; Online.

31291 ■ *"The Facebook IPO Hype Meter"* in Canadian Business (Vol. 85, June 11, 2012, No. 10, pp. 74)
Ed: Joe Castaldo. **Description:** Comparison of the Facebook frenzy with other notable initial public offerings (IPO) based on market capitalization divided by profit indicated that an overpriced IPO such as that of Facebook does not equate to poor returns in the short-term. Studies found that IPOs that debut at more reasonable prices get better returns in the long term. **Availability:** Online.

31292 ■ *"FCC Adopts New Media Ownership Rules"* in Black Enterprise (Vol. 38, March 1, 2008, No. 8, pp. 26)
Pub: Earl G. Graves Ltd.
Contact: Earl Graves, Jr., President
Ed: Joyce Jones. **Description:** Federal Communications Commission approved a ruling that lifts a ban on newspaper and/or broadcast cross ownership. Because of declining sales in newspaper advertising and readership the ban will allow companies to share local news gathering costs across multiple media platforms. **Availability:** Online.

31293 ■ *"Fieldbrook Foods Acquired By Private Equity Firm"* in Ice Cream Reporter (Vol. 23, October 20, 2010, No. 11, pp. 1)
Description: Fieldbrook Foods Corporation, manufacturer of frozen novelty and ice cream products was acquired by Chicago-based private equity firm

Arbor Investments. Arbor partnered with Herman 'Bing' Graffunder, a long-term dairy industry partner, in its acquisition of Fieldbrook. **Availability:** Print; Online.

31294 ■ *"Fifth Third Spinoff Eyes More Space"* in Business Courier (Vol. 27, July 16, 2010, No. 11, pp. 1)

Pub: Business Courier

Ed: Dan Monk, Steve Watkins. **Description:** Electronic-funds transfer company Fifth Third Solutions (FTPS), a spinoff of Fifth Third Bancorp, is seeking as much as 200,000 square feet of new office space in Ohio. The bank's sale of 51 percent ownership stake to Boston-based Advent International Corporation has paved the way for the growth of FTPS. How real estate brokers' plans have responded to FTPS' growth mode is discussed. **Availability:** Print; Online.

31295 ■ *"Finally, New Life For Old IBM Offices"* in Austin Business Journal (Vol. 34, June 6, 2014, No. 16, pp. A4)

Pub: American City Business Journals, Inc.

Contact: Mike Olivieri, Executive Vice President

Released: Weekly. **Price:** $4, introductory 4-week offer(Digital only). **Description:** Two nondescript, 1970s-style industrial buildings, occupied in the 1970s by IBM Corporation, were purchased by an Austin-based contracting and construction management company. Burt-Watts Industries, from Powell Austin Properties Ltd., a local family. The company spent $3 million to renovate all the spaces into attractive, contemporary offices. Tommy Burt, co-founder of Burt-Watts was helped in this endeavor by Clay Little, partner in NoackLittle Architecture & Interiors. **Availability:** Print; Online.

31296 ■ *Financing Your Small Business*

Released: First edition. **Description:** Tips for raising venture capital, dealing with bank officials, and initiating public offerings of stock shares for small business.

31297 ■ *"Finding Competitive Advantage in Adversity"* in Harvard Business Review (Vol. 88, November 2010, No. 11, pp. 102)

Pub: Harvard Business Publishing

Contact: Diane Belcher, Managing Director

Ed: Bhaskar Chakravorti. **Price:** $8.95, PDF. **Description:** Four opportunities in adversity are identified and applied to business scenarios. These are matching unmet needs with unneeded resources, seeking collaboration from unlikely partners, developing small/appropriate solutions to large/complex issues, and focusing on the platform as well as the product. **Availability:** Online; PDF.

31298 ■ *"First, the Merger: Then, The Culture Clash. How To Fix the Little Things That Can Tear a Company Apart"* in Inc. (January 2008)

Ed: Elaine Appleton Grant. **Description:** Ways three CEOs handled the culture classes that followed after company mergers; companies profiled include Fuel Outdoor, an outdoor advertising company; Nelson, an interior design and architecture firm; and Beber Silverstein, an ad agency. **Availability:** Online.

31299 ■ *"First Solar Signs Power Purchase Agreements with Pacific Gas and Electric Company for 72 Megawatts"* in Benzinga.com (September 11, 2012)

Pub: Benzinga.com

Contact: Jason Raznick, Founder

Ed: Paul Quintaro. **Description:** First Solar has signed power purchase agreements with Pacific Gas and Electric Company for 72 megawatts of solar electricity to be generated at two photovoltaic power plants in central California. Details of the projects are included. **Availability:** PDF; Online.

31300 ■ *"Florida Hospital, UCF Affiliation in Danger?"* in Orlando Business Journal (Vol. 29, September 21, 2012, No. 29, pp. 1)

Pub: Baltimore Business Journal

Contact: Rhonda Pringle, President

E-mail: rpringle@bizjournals.com

Description: Florida Hospital is said to be considering the possibility of terminating its affiliation agreement with the University of Central Florida's (UCF) College of Medicine that ends June 30, 2018. Two of the reasons for the move include UCF's plans for a teaching hospital and a new graduate medical education program that could place Florida Hospital into competition with UCF. **Availability:** Print; Online.

31301 ■ *"Florida's Housing Gloom May Add To Woes of National City"* in Crain's Cleveland Business (Vol. 28, October 29, 2007, No. 43, pp. 1)

Pub: Crain Communications Inc.

Contact: K. C. Crain, President

Ed: Shawn A. Turner. **Description:** Already suffering by bad loans in the troubled mortgage market, National City Corp. is attempting to diversify its geographic presence beyond the slow-growth industrial Midwest by acquiring two Florida firms. Analysts worry that the acquisitions may end up making National City vulnerable to a takeover if the housing slump continues and credit quality becomes more of an issue for the bank. **Availability:** Online.

31302 ■ *"'Focusing On the Moment"* in Dallas Business Journal (Vol. 37, June 27, 2014, No. 42, pp. 4)

Pub: American City Business Journals, Inc.

Contact: Mike Olivieri, Executive Vice President

Description: Southwest Airlines chairman, president, and CEO Gary Kelly, believes the key to the carrier's growth in 2014 will be to 'focus on the moment' and ensure that new projects are launched and strategies implemented successfully. Kelly discusses the potential impact of the repeal of the Wright Amendment on October 13, as well as Southwest's merger with AirTran and the launch of nonstop flights from New York and Washington DC. **Availability:** Print; Online.

31303 ■ *"For Allegiance Capital, Oil and Gas are Hot"* in Dallas Business Journal (Vol. 37, May 30, 2014, No. 38, pp. 8)

Pub: American City Business Journals, Inc.

Contact: Mike Olivieri, Executive Vice President

Released: Weekly. **Price:** $4, introductory 4-week offer(Digital & Print). **Description:** Allegiance Capital Corporation has completed four merger and acquisition deals involving oil and gas companies totaling $350 million, as of May 30, 2014. Company founder and chairman, David Mahmood, says it is the right time to sell oil and gas companies because prices are at their peak. **Availability:** Print; Online.

31304 ■ *"For Giving Us a Way To Say Yes To Solar: Lynn Jurich and Edward Fenster"* in Inc. (Volume 32, December 2010, No. 10, pp. 110)

Pub: Mansueto Ventures L.L.C.

Contact: Stephanie Mehta, Chief Executive Officer

Ed: Leigh Buchanan. **Released:** December 01, 2010. **Description:** Profile of entrepreneurs Lynn Jurich and Edward Fenster, cofounders of SunRun. The firm installs solar panels at little or no cost and homeowners sign 20-year contracts to buy power at a fixed price. **Availability:** Online.

31305 ■ *"Fraser and Neave Acquires King's Creameries"* in Ice Cream Reporter (Vol. 23, November 20, 2010, No. 12, pp. 1)

Description: Fraser and Neave Ltd., a Singapore-based consumer products marketer, has entered a conditional agreement to acquire all outstanding shares of King's Creameries, the leading manufacturer and distributor of frozen desserts. **Availability:** Print; Online.

31306 ■ *"Free File Alliance & IRS Launch 10th Year of Free Online Tax Preparation Services for Millions of Americans"* in Economics Week (February 3, 2012, pp. 82)

Pub: PR Newswire Association LLC.

Description: A coalition of tax software companies have partnered with the Internal Revenue Service to offer the 212 IRS Free File progam. The Free File Alliance offers low-to-moderate income taxpayers free access to online commercial tax preparation software. Details of the program are included. **Availability:** Online.

31307 ■ *"Friedland's Next Frontier: Drilling for Oil in Iraq"* in Globe & Mail (April 20, 2007, pp. B1)

Ed: Wendy Stueck. **Description:** The decision of the Canadian oil and gas company Ivanhoe Energy Inc. to partner with the Japanese oil and gas firm INPEX Corp. for the development of heavy oil fields in north central Iraq is discussed. **Availability:** Print; Online.

31308 ■ *"From Malls to Steel Plants"* in Crain's Chicago Business (Vol. 31, April 28, 2008, No. 17, pp. 30)

Pub: Crain Communications Inc.

Contact: Barry Asin, President

Ed: Samantha Stainburn. **Description:** Profile of the company Graycor Inc. which started out as a sand-blasting and concrete-breaking firm but has grown into four businesses due to innovation and acquisitions. Graycor's businesses include: Graycor Industrial Constructors Inc., which builds and renovates power plants and steel mills; Graycor Construction Co., which erects stores, medical centers and office buildings; Graycor Blasting Co., which uses explosives and blasts tunnels for industrial cleaning, and Graycor International Inc., which provides construction services in Mexico. **Availability:** Online.

31309 ■ *"Funders Fuel Explosion of Biotech Activity"* in Puget Sound Business Journal (Vol. 35, July 11, 2014, No. 12, pp. 3A)

Pub: American City Business Journals, Inc.

Contact: Mike Olivieri, Executive Vice President

Description: Washington's life sciences industry is experiencing problems due to a lack of support from state lawmakers, but the industry is receiving capital through initial public offerings, partnerships and venture equity. Joel Marcus of Alexandria Real Estate Equities claims that capital flows are at their highest levels since the dot-com bubble. **Availability:** Online.

31310 ■ *"Future of Convention and Visitors Bureau In Question"* in Houston Business Journal (Vol. 44, April 4, 2014, No. 48, pp. 10)

Pub: American City Business Journals, Inc.

Contact: Mike Olivieri, Executive Vice President

Released: Weekly. **Price:** $4, introductory 4-week offer(Digital & Print). **Description:** Greater Houston Convention and Visitors Bureau (GHCVB) chairwoman Sonia Garza-Monarchi shares her views about the merger talks with Houston First Corporation. Garza-Monarchi says the current proposal is for the continuing existence of the GHCVB board, which approves its own budget and business plan. She also says the members and the board just want an open and fair merger process. **Availability:** Print; Online.

31311 ■ *"Futures Shock for the CME"* in Crain's Chicago Business (Vol. 31, November 10, 2008, No. 45, pp. 8)

Pub: Crain Communications Inc.

Contact: Barry Asin, President

Ed: Ann Saphir. **Description:** Chicago-based CME Group Inc., the largest futures exchange operator in the U.S., is facing a potentially radically altered regulatory landscape as Congress weighs sweeping reform of financial oversight. The possible merger of the CFTC and the Securities and Exchange Commission are among CME's concerns. Other details of possible regulatory measures are provided. **Availability:** Online.

31312 ■ *"Gannett Looks to Spare Journalists' Jobs after Big Newspaper Merger"* in The Wall Street Journal (November 19, 2019)

URL(s): www.wsj.com/articles/gannett-looks-to-spare-journalists-jobs-after-big-newspaper-merger-11574197800

Ed: Lukas I. Alpert. **Released:** November 19, 2019. **Description:** CEO Paul Bascobert of Gannett Media Corp., vowed to avoid big layoffs of journalists when Gannett Co. and GateHouse Media merge. However, there will be cuts to eliminate duplicate jobs and functions from regional printing, distribution, and copy-editing. **Availability:** Online.

31313 ■ *"Geico and the USO of Metropolitan Washington Have Teamed Up to Provide Military Troops with a New 'Home Away From Home" in Best's Review (Vol. 113, September 2012, No. 5, pp. 13)*
Description: Geico and the USO of Metropolitan Washington have partnered to provide military troops and their families an area in the USO airport lounge at Ronald Reagan Washington National Airport with wireless Internet access, seating area with large-screen TV, assistance with travel-related questions, and a snack bar. **Availability:** Online.

31314 ■ *"GeoEye CEO Sees Investors In His Future: Matt O'Connell Eyeing Intel Startup Post-Sale" in Washington Business Journal (Vol. 31, September 14, 2012, No. 21, pp. 1)*
Pub: Baltimore Business Journal
Contact: Rhonda Pringle, President
E-mail: rpringle@bizjournals.com
Description: GeoEye Inc. chief executive officer, Matt O'Connell, plans to start a new technology venture in Northern Virginia like the one that supports intelligence gathering once DigitalGlobe Inc. has completed the acquisition of his company in 2013. He will work in an advisory role for DigitalGlobal following the acquisition and will not be involved in satellite imagery security for competitive reasons. **Availability:** Print; Online.

31315 ■ *"Getting Emotional Over Microsoft's Minecraft" in Puget Sound Business Journal (Vol. 35, September 19, 2014, No. 22, pp. 7)*
Pub: American City Business Journals, Inc.
Contact: Mike Olivieri, Executive Vice President
Description: Microsoft's acquisition of Minecraft maker Mojan AB is helps to promote STEM education. Microsoft will purchase the company for $2.5 billion. Minecraft game creator, Markus Persson, will not be joining the new Microsoft team. **Availability:** Online.

31316 ■ *"Giant Garages Could Rise Up in Downtown Cincinnati" in Business Courier (Vol. 27, October 22, 2010, No. 25, pp. 1)*
Pub: Business Courier
Ed: Dan Monk. **Description:** More than 2,500 new parking spaces could rise up to the eastern edge of downtown Cincinnati, Ohio as public and private investors collect resources for new garage projects. These projects are expected to accommodate almost 1,500 monthly parkers who will lose access at Broadway Commons due to the construction of Harrah's casino. **Availability:** Print; Mailing list; Online.

31317 ■ *"GIV Mobile Announces New Partnership with American Forests, the Oldest National Nonprofit Conservation Organization in the Country" in Ecology, Environment & Conservation Business (January 25, 2014, pp. 34)*
Pub: PR Newswire Association LLC.
Description: GIV Mobile has partnered with American Forests to restore and protect urban and rural forests in the nation. GIV is the first consumer conscious wireless network and operates on the 4G network of T-Mobile USA cellular service. **Availability:** Online.

31318 ■ *"Global Steel Makers Circle Stelco" in Globe & Mail (April 19, 2007, pp. B3)*
Ed: Greg Keenan. **Description:** The details of the take over bids offered to Stelco Inc. are presented. Due to these bids the shares of Stelco Inc rose up to 70 percent. **Availability:** Online.

31319 ■ *"The Globe: How to Conquer New Markets With Old Skills" in Harvard Business Review (Vol. 88, November 2010, No. 11, pp. 118)*
Pub: Harvard Business Publishing
Contact: Diane Belcher, Managing Director

Ed: Mauro F. Guillen, Esteban Garcia-Canal. **Price:** $8.95, PDF. **Description:** Exploration of business-networking factors that have helped lead to the success of Spain's multinational companies is provided. These include development of political skills, access to capabilities and resources, globalization partnerships, and speed of implementation. **Availability:** Online; PDF.

31320 ■ *"GM's Mortgage Unit Deal Brings in $9 Billion" in Globe & Mail (March 24, 2006, pp. B3)*
Ed: Shawn McCarthy. **Description:** General Motors Corp. sells General Motors Acceptance Corp.'s commercial real estate division to Kohlberg Kravis Roberts & Co. Five Mile Capital Partners LLC and Goldman Sachs Capital Partners. The reasons behind the deal are presented. **Availability:** Print; Online.

31321 ■ *"GNC Reaches 'A Pivotal Moment'" in Pittsburgh Business Times (Vol. 34, August 15, 2014, No. 4, pp. 4)*
Pub: American City Business Journals, Inc.
Contact: Mike Olivieri, Executive Vice President
Released: Weekly. **Price:** $4, introductory 4-week offer(Digital & Print). **Description:** Goldman analyst, Stephen Tanal, states Michael Archbold is taking over as CEO of GNC Holdings Inc. at a pivotal moment as the company shifts from heavy dependence on promotions to sustaining sales growth beyond 2015. Analysts discuss the recent problems faced by the vitamin, health and fitness retailer and the implications of a possible merger between GNC and Archbolds' former company, the Vitamin Shoppe Inc. **Availability:** Print; Online.

31322 ■ *"Goldfingers" in Canadian Business (Vol. 81, Summer 2008, No. 9, pp. 31)*
Description: Large players in the mining industry are looking for junior mining companies in Canada to be acquired. The U.S. recession and subprime mortgage crisis have made it easier for giant miners to acquire small mining companies than to conduct the operations themselves. Junior miners are those that lack cash flow and expertise to build and operate mine. **Availability:** Online.

31323 ■ *"Goodwill Haunts Local Companies" in Crain's Chicago Business (Apr. 28, 2008)*
Pub: Crain Communications Inc.
Contact: Barry Asin, President
Ed: Ann Saphir. **Description:** Many companies are having to face the reality that they overpaid for acquisitions made in better economic times; investors often dismiss such one-time charges as mere accounting adjustments but writeoffs related to past acquisitions can signal future problems because they mean the expected profits that justified the purchase have not materialized. Writeoffs are particularly worrisome for firms with a lot of debt and whose banks require them to have enough assets to back up their borrowings. **Availability:** Online.

31324 ■ *"Graphic Tech Acquires First U.S. :M-Press Tiger with Inline Screen Printing" in American Printer (Vol. 128, June 1, 2011, No. 6)*
Description: Graphic Tech located in California bought M-Press Tiger, the first in North America with an inline screen printing unit. **Availability:** Online.

31325 ■ *"Greenhouse Announces Reverse Merger With Custom Q, Inc." in Investment Weekly (January 30, 2010, pp. 338)*
Pub: Investment Weekly News
Description: In accordance with an Agreement and Plan of Share Exchange, GreenHouse Holdings, Inc., an innovative green solutions provider, has gone public via a reverse merger with Custom Q, Inc. **Availability:** Print; Online.

31326 ■ *"GSK Creating Pathways From Academia to Industry" in Philadelphia Business Journal (Vol. 33, March 7, 2014, No. 4, pp. 8)*
Pub: American City Business Journals, Inc.
Contact: Mike Olivieri, Executive Vice President

Released: Weekly. **Price:** $4, introductory 4-week offer(Digital & Print). **Description:** The Discovery Fast Track Challenge program of GlaxoSmithKline will expand in 2014 to include scientists in North America and Europe. Scientists will be asked to submit information about their innovative drug research proposals and the winner could be offered a deal with the Discovery Partnerships with Academia team. **Availability:** Print; Online.

31327 ■ *"Hain Celestial Acquires Greek Gods Yogurt" in Ice Cream Reporter (Vol. 23, July 20, 2010, No. 8, pp. 1)*
Description: Hain Celestial Group acquired The Greek Gods LLC. Hain Celestial is a natural and organic products company and Greek Gods makes all natural, Greek-style yogurt and ice cream. **Availability:** Print; Online.

31328 ■ *"Happy About Joint-Venturing: The 8 Key Critical Factors of Success*
Pub: Happy About
Contact: Ric Vatner, Chief Executive Officer
Ed: Valerie Orsoni-Vauthey. **Price:** $19.95, paperback,(with 15% discount only ($16.96); $14.95, eBook,(with 20% discount only $11.95). **Description:** An overview of joint venturing is presented. **Availability:** E-book; Print; PDF.

31329 ■ *"Harleysville Eyes Growth After Nationwide Deal" in Philadelphia Business Journal (Vol. 30, October 7, 2011, No. 34, pp. 1)*
Pub: Philadelphia Business Journal
Contact: Sierra Quinn, Director
E-mail: squinn@bizjournals.com
Ed: Jeff Blumenthal. **Price:** $4, introductory 4-week offer(Digital & Print). **Description:** Harleysville Group announced growth plans after the company was sold to Columbus, Ohio-based Nationwide Mutual Insurance Company for about $1.63 billion. Nationwide gained an independent agency platform in 32 states with the Harleysville deal. **Availability:** Print; Online.

31330 ■ *"Has Microsoft Found a Way to Get at Yahoo?" in Advertising Age (Vol. 79, July 7, 2008, No. 26, pp. 4)*
Pub: Crain Communications, Inc.
Contact: Jessica Botos, Manager, Marketing
E-mail: jessica.botos@crainsnewyork.com
Ed: Abbey Klaassen. **Description:** Microsoft's attempt to acquire Yahoo's search business is discussed as is Yahoo's plans for the future at a time when the company's shares have fallen dangerously low. **Availability:** Print; Online.

31331 ■ *"Hatching Twitter: A True Story of Money, Power, Friendship, and Betrayal"*
Pub: Portfolio Hardcover
Contact: Adrian Zackheim, President
Released: September 05, 2013. **Price:** $18, paperback; $2.18, paperback(100 used from $2.18); $4.28, paperback(55 new from $4.28); $4.39, kindle; $12.99, hardcover; $1.96, hardcover(73 used from $1.96); $8.59, hardcover(9 new from $8.59); $17.50, hardcover(2 collectible from $17.50). **Description:** The first full coverage story covering the four founders of Twitter: Evan Williams, Biz Stone, Jack Dorsey, and Noah Glass, who went from ordinary engineers to wealthy celebrities and entrepreneurs. The story explores their pursuits for money, influence, publicity, and control as Twitter grew larger and more powerful. **Availability:** E-book; Print; Audio.

31332 ■ *"HBC Sells Credit Card Division" in Globe & Mail (February 8, 2006, pp. B1)*
Description: The details on General Electric Co.'s acquisition of Hudson's Bay Co.'s credit card division, for $370 million, are presented. **Availability:** Print; Online.

31333 ■ *"Health Care of the Future" in Business Journal Serving Greater Tampa Bay (Vol. 30, November 19, 2010, No. 48, pp. 1)*
Pub: Tampa Bay Business Journal
Contact: Ian Anderson, President
E-mail: ianderson@bizjournals.com

Description: Information about accountable care organizations (ACO), which are integrated care systems with doctors and hospitals working closely together to handle patient care, is provided. The Patient Protection and Affordable Care Act paved the way for ACOs as Medicare demonstration projects. **Availability:** Online.

31334 ■ *"Healthy Fast Food Acquires Rights to U-Swirl Yogurt" in Ice Cream Reporter (Vol. 21, October 20, 2008, No. 11, pp. 5)*
Description: Healthy Fast Food Inc. will acquire worldwide rights to U-Swirl Frozen Yogurt; the firm will use the new acquisition to create a yogurt superstore in a cafe setting concept for its operations. **Availability:** Print; Online.

31335 ■ *"The Heat Is On" in Crain's Chicago Business (Vol. 31, April 28, 2008, No. 17, pp. 4)*
Pub: Crain Communications Inc.
Contact: Barry Asin, President

Ed: Steve Daniels. **Description:** Discusses Nicor Inc., a natural-gas utility serving 2 million customers in Chicago's suburbs, and its potential acquirers; shares of the company have dropped 17 percent this year making Nicor the second-worst among 31 utilities in an index tracked by Standrd & Poor's. Statistical data included.

31336 ■ *"Hedge Funds Prevail In Merger" in Baltimore Business Journal (Vol. 31, March 21, 2014, No. 47, pp. 8)*
Pub: American City Business Journals, Inc.
Contact: Mike Olivieri, Executive Vice President
Released: Weekly. **Price:** $4, introductory 4-week offer(Digital & Print). **Description:** Contrary to expectations of the retail experts, after five months of internal strife, Jos. A Bank accepted Men's Wearhouse's offer and closed this hot deal. Men's Wearhouse purchased the Jos. A. Bank Clothiers Inc. for $1.8 billion and is planning to continue both brands. However, this will result in the Greater Baltimore area losing one more corporate headquarters. As the two companies combine operations, Jos. A. Banks stores will close, thus cutting more jobs. **Availability:** Print; Online.

31337 ■ *"High Touch Expands, Purchases Dallas Firms" in Wichita Business Journal (Vol. 27, February 3, 2012, No. 5, pp. 1)*
Pub: Baltimore Business Journal
Contact: Rhonda Pringle, President
E-mail: rpringle@bizjournals.com
Description: Wichita, Kansas-based High Touch Inc. has finalized the acquisitions of the Dallas, Texas-based UniCom Data and Dallas Data Center, after a similar purchase of Newbase LLC at the start of the year. High Touch believes the acquisitions helped the company further expand its regional presence and services. **Availability:** Print; Online.

31338 ■ *"History Partners with Tour Guide Associations to Promote Members" in Breaking Travel News (November 8, 2019)*
URL(s): www.breakingtravelnews.com/news/article/history-partners-with-tour-guide-associations-to-promote-members/
Released: November 08, 2019. **Description:** The entertainment channel, History, has partnered with the World Federation of Tourist Guide Association and the European Federation of Tourist Guide Associations in an effort to promote their tourist guide members around the world. The partnership will also make sure that tourist guides are promoted and protected. **Availability:** Online.

31339 ■ *"Home Developers Buy 9 Acres in Lakewood" in Dallas Business Journal (Vol. 35, August 10, 2012, No. 48, pp. 1)*
Pub: Baltimore Business Journal
Contact: Rhonda Pringle, President
E-mail: rpringle@bizjournals.com

Ed: Candace Carlisle. **Description:** Megatel Homes, together with Centurion American Development Group, has purchased a 9.4 acre land in Lakewood, Dallas for $35 million. Centurion plans to begin real

estate development of 59 single-family home lots in the next three months, while Megatel plans construction to build Tudor style homes. The infill land is considered a prime investment for its desireable location.

31340 ■ *"Hong Kong's Boom in IPOs" in Barron's (Vol. 89, July 13, 2009, No. 28, pp. M7)*
Pub: Dow Jones & Company Inc.
Contact: Almar Latour, Chief Executive Officer
Ed: Nick Lord. **Description:** Hong Kong's IPO (initial public offering) market is booming with 13 Chinese IPOs already on the market for the year as July 2009. One of them is Bawang International which raised $214 million after generating $9 billion in order which makes it 42 times oversubscribed. **Availability:** Online.

31341 ■ *"Hospital Communication Goes Mobile" in Providence Business News (Vol. 29, July 7, 2014, No. 14, pp. 12)*
Pub: American City Business Journals, Inc.
Contact: Mike Olivieri, Executive Vice President
Released: July 05, 2014. **Description:** Software company, Care Thread, has designed a mobile health records application that allows providers to share patient e-medical records over a secure network. Care Thread signed a contract for the system with Eastern Connecticut Health Network and Boston's Brigham and Women's Hospital as well as a deal with health care management firm Beacon Partners Inc. to sell and implement the app across the U.S. **Availability:** Print; Online.

31342 ■ *"Houston Doctors Buy In to Medical Timeshares" in Houston Business Journal (Vol. 40, December 11, 2009, No. 31, pp. 1)*
Pub: Houston Business Journal
Contact: Bob Charlet, President
E-mail: bcharlet@bizjournals.com
Ed: Mary Ann Azevedo. **Description:** Memorial Hermann Hospital System has leased to doctors three examination rooms and medical office space in the Memorial Hermann Medical Plaza in line with its new timeshare concept. The concept was designed to bring primary care physicians to its Texas Medical Center campus. **Availability:** Print; Online.

31343 ■ *"How to Dissolve a Business Partnership" in Legal Zoom (February 28, 2023)*
URL(s): www.legalzoom.com/articles/how-to-dissolve-a-business-partnership
Ed: Marcia Layton Turner. **Released:** February 28, 2023. **Description:** Dissolving a business partnership can be a tricky process since it can involve hurt feelings with the partner. Follow the steps given to keep the process smooth. **Availability:** Online.

31344 ■ *"How I Did It: Jack Ma, Alibaba.com" in Inc. (January 2008, pp. 94-102)*
Ed: Rebecca Fannin. **Description:** Profile of Jack Ma, who started as a guide and interpreter for Western tourists in Hangzhou. Ma used the Internet to build Alibaba.com, China's largest business-to-business site and one of the hottest IPOs in years. **Availability:** Online.

31345 ■ *"How I Did It: Timberland's CEO On Standing Up to 65,000 Angry Activists" in Harvard Business Review (Vol. 88, September 2010, No. 9, pp. 39)*
Pub: Harvard Business Publishing
Contact: Diane Belcher, Managing Director
Ed: Jeff Swartz. **Price:** $8.95, PDF. **Description:** Timberland Company avoided a potential boycott by taking a two-way approach. It addressed a supplier issue that posed a threat to the environment, and launched an email campaign to keep Greenpeace activists informed of the development of a new supplier agreement. **Availability:** Online; PDF.

31346 ■ *"How One Company Joins Corporate Public Relations and Community Engagement" in Denver Business Journal (Vol. 65, January 17, 2014, No. 36, pp. A6)*
Pub: American City Business Journals, Inc.
Contact: Mike Olivieri, Executive Vice President

Description: Denver, Colorado-based Barefoot PR was formed by Cori Streetman and Sarah Hogan in 2010 to change corporate views on philanthropy. The partners made a commitment to make community investment the driving force of business. Insights on the next-generation of community relations consultants are also given. **Availability:** Online.

31347 ■ *"How to Play the Tech Mergers" in Barron's (Vol. 90, August 30, 2010, No. 35, pp. 18)*
Pub: Barron's Editorial & Corporate Headquarters
Ed: Tiernan Ray. **Description:** The intense bidding by Hewlett-Packard and Dell for 3Par was foreseen in a previous Barron's cover story and 3Par's stock has nearly tripled since reported. Other possible acquisition targets in the tech industry include Brocade Communication Systems, NetApp, Xyratex, and Isilon Systems. **Availability:** Online.

31348 ■ *"How Tender Green Turns Top Chefs Into Fast-Food Cooks: a Quick-Serve Chain Lures Kitchen Starts by Treating Them Like Entrepreneurs" in Inc. (Vol. 36, March 2014, No. 2, pp. 28)*
Pub: Mansueto Ventures L.L.C.
Contact: Stephanie Mehta, Chief Executive Officer
Released: March 2014. **Description:** Chefs Erik Oberholtzer, David Dressier and Matt Lyman launched Tender Greens, a series of quick-service restaurants serving fresh organic dishes made from local produce, cheeses and meats. The three partners set out to hire fine-dining chefs to run each location. The used their entrepreneurial skills to inspire great chefs into entrepreneur type control by allowing them to run their restaurant individually, including operations, culture and menu items. Tender Greens has grown to 12 locations with an estimated $40 million annual revenue. Their business vision and strategy is examined. **Availability:** Print; Online.

31349 ■ *"How to... Harness Green Power" in The Caterer (July 20, 2012, No. 325)*
Pub: LNRS Data Services Limited
Contact: Mark Vickers Kelsey, Director

Description: Roger and Emma Stevens discuss their success as at winning the Considerate Hoteliers Association's award for Best Green Marketing Initiative. The couple discusses their restaurant and its partnership with tow nearby guesthouses. **Availability:** Online.

31350 ■ *"How To Win In Emerging Markets: Lessons From Japan" in Harvard Business Review (Vol. 90, May 2012, No. 5, pp. 126)*
Pub: Harvard Business Review Press
Contact: Moderna V. Pfizer, Contact
Ed: Shigeki Ichii, Susumu Hattori, David Michael. **Price:** $8.95. **Description:** Corporate Japan's four challenges in engaging emerging markets are an aversion to mergers and acquisitions, an aversion to low- and middle-end segments, lack of organizational or financial commitments to emerging markets, and a shortage of executive talent placed in emerging markets. By addressing these weaknesses, Japan can succeed in global expansion. **Availability:** Online; PDF.

31351 ■ *"How and When Should You Take on a Business Partner?" in Legal Zoom (February 15, 2023)*
URL(s): www.legalzoom.com/articles/how-and-when-should-you-take-on-a-business-partner
Ed: Marcia Layton Turner. **Released:** February 15, 2023. **Description:** Discusses the questions around taking on a business partner for your small business. **Availability:** Online.

31352 ■ *"How Yamana CEO First Struck Gold With Desert Sun" in Globe & Mail (February 27, 2006, pp. B3)*
Ed: Andrew Willis. **Description:** The role of chief executive officer Peter Marronne of Yamana Gold Inc. in the acquisition of Desert Sun Mining Corp. is discussed. **Availability:** Online.

31353 ■ *"Humana Seeks Higher Stake in Memphis Market" in Memphis Business Journal (Vol. 33, February 17, 2012, No. 45, pp. 1)*

Pub: Baltimore Business Journal

Contact: Rhonda Pringle, President

E-mail: rpringle@bizjournals.com

Ed: Christopher Sheffield. **Description:** Humana of Tennessee has been hoping to get a bigger share of the West Tennessee insurance market through its new three-year contract with Baptist Memorial Health Care Corporation. Louisville, Kentucky-based Humana Inc. has a business relationship with Baptist that stretches back more than two decades. **Availability:** Print; Online.

31354 ■ *"Iconic Boise Skateboard Shop to Close" in Idaho Business Review (August 19, 2014)*

Pub: BridgeTower Media

Contact: Adam Reinebach, President

Description: Lori Wright and Lori Ambur have owned Newt & Harold's for over 30 years. The partners are closing the firm that sold skateboards and snowboards. Wright focused on the marketing and inventory aspects of the retail shop, while Ambur ran the organizational and financial end. Wright and Ambur say they are leaving retail because the industry has faced so many changes since they first opened, particularly competing with online stores.

31355 ■ *"If They Build It, Will Customers Come?" in Business Journal Portland (Vol. 30, February 7, 2014, No. 49, pp. 7)*

Pub: American City Business Journals, Inc.

Contact: Mike Olivieri, Executive Vice President

Price: $4, Introductory 4-week offer(Digital & Print). **Description:** The Portland Trail Blazers partnered with Levy Restaurants to open a 10,000-square-foot restaurant at Moda Center in Oregon in spring 2014. GBD Architects and Lorentz Brunn Construction were enlisted for the project. **Availability:** Print; Online.

31356 ■ *"IGT Expands Partnership with Olympic Entertainment Group" in Travel & Leisure Close-Up (October 8, 2012)*

Description: International Game Technology is partnering with Olympic Jarve and Olympic Ulemiste properties by providing IGT Cloud solution. IGT is a provider of gaming systems technology which will increase the gambling experience for Olympic game players. **Availability:** Print; Online.

31357 ■ *"Ihilani's New Day" in Pacific Business News (Vol. 26, August 22, 2014, No. 26, pp. 14)*

Pub: American City Business Journals, Inc.

Contact: Mike Olivieri, Executive Vice President

Description: JW Marriott Ihilani Resort and Spa is likely to be rebranded in 2014 as the Four Seasons Hotels and Resorts, making it the chain's fifth largest property in Hawaii. The implications of the hotel's renovation and rebranding for West Oahu's leisure and business travel sectors are discussed. **Availability:** Online.

31358 ■ *I'm on LinkedIn - Now What?*

Pub: Happy About

Contact: Ric Vatner, Chief Executive Officer

Ed: Jason Alba. **Released:** Fourth edition. **Price:** $19.95, paperback; $14.95; $9.99. **Description:** Designed to help get the most out of LinkedIn, the popular business networking site and follows the first edition and includes the latest and great approaches using LinkedIn. With over 32 million members there is a lot of potential to find and develop relationships to help in your business and personal life, but many professionals find themselves wondering what to do once they sign up. This book explains the different benefits of the system and recommends best practices (including LinkedIn Groups) so that you get the most out of LinkedIn. **Availability:** E-book; Print; PDF; DVD; Electronic publishing; Download; Online.

31359 ■ *"Image Consultants" in Entrepreneur (June 2014)*

Pub: Entrepreneur Media Inc.

Contact: Dan Bova, Director

E-mail: dbova@entrepreneur.com

Description: The ASAP54 mobile application, created by a company of the same name, uses visual recognition technology to help users determine the name of the designer or retailer of a clothing item using photographs. The company has compiled a database consisting of more than 1 million products from its retail partners. It claims an average of 5 percent commission on purchases completed through the application. Other useful wearable gadgets include Nymi, which authenticates identities based on cardiac rhythms, and Netatmo, a bracelet that measures daily sun exposure. **Availability:** Online.

31360 ■ *"The Impact of Acquisitions On the Productivity of Inventors at Semiconductor Firms: A Synthesis of Knowledge-Based and Incentive-Based Perspective" in Academy of Management Journal (Vol. 50, No. 5, October 1, 2007, pp. 1133)*

Pub: Academy of Management

Contact: Sharon Alvarez, President

Ed: Rahul Kapoor, Kwanghui Lim. **Description:** Study examined the relation between knowledge-based and incentive-based outlook in explaining the impact of acquisitions on the productivity of inventors at acquired semiconductor firms. Results showed a definite relation between the two perspectives. **Availability:** Electronic publishing; Download; PDF; Online.

31361 ■ *"In My Shoes: A Memoir"*

Pub: Portfolio Hardcover

Contact: Adrian Zackheim, President

Released: October 01, 2013. **Price:** $3.48, kindle; $32.80, hardcover; $0.25, hardcover(49 used from $0.25); $25.60, hardcover (6 new from $25.60); $8.86, paperback; $1.55, paperback(93 used from $1.55); $4.01, paperback(49 new from $4.01). **Description:** Profile of Tamara Mellon, woman entrepreneur who built Jimmy Choo into a premier name in the global fashion industry. She addresses her family life, her battles with anxiety and depression, as well as time spend in rehabilitation. She shares her entire life story from her work as a young editor at Vogue to her partnership with shoemaker, Jimmy Choo to her public relationships. She confides what it was like working with an obstinate business partner but also her ability to understand what customers want. **Availability:** E-book; Print; Audio.

31362 ■ *"Inco Takeover Faces Foreign Hurdles" in Globe & Mail (February 13, 2006, pp. B1)*

Ed: Paul Waldie. **Description:** The issues that impact Inco Ltd.'s acquisition of Falconbridge Ltd., for $12.5 billion, are presented. Inco Ltd. is awaiting foreign regulatory approval in the United States and Europe. **Availability:** Print; Online.

31363 ■ *"Inco's Takeover Offer Extended Four Months" in Globe & Mail (February 22, 2006, pp. B1)*

Description: United States and Europe competition authorities wanted more time to investigate Inco Ltd.'s takeover of Falconbridge Ltd. and compelling Inco to extend its $12.5 billion offer for the third time. **Availability:** Online.

31364 ■ *"Indian Buyer Gives Life to Algoma Expansion" in Globe & Mail (April 17, 2007, pp. B1)*

Ed: Greg Keenan. **Description:** The proposed capacity expansion of Algoma Steel Inc. after its acquisition by Essar Global Ltd. is discussed. **Availability:** Online.

31365 ■ *"Ingrian and Channel Management International Sign Distribution Agreement" in Canadian Corporate News (May 16, 2007)*

Description: Channel Management International (CMI), a Canadian channel management and distribution company, and Ingrian Networks, Inc., the leading provider of data privacy solutions, announced a Canadian distribution agreement to resell Ingrian encryption solutions to the Canadian market. **Availability:** Online.

31366 ■ *"Initial Crowd Offering, Inc. Announces Launch of Equity Crowdfunding Intermediary Site" in GlobeNewswire (June 21, 2012)*

Pub: Comtex News Network Inc.

Contact: Kan Devnani, President

Description: Initial Crowd Offering is the IPO for small and emerging businesses and is the most current process to invest and raise capital. The site allows direct, real-time investments in exchange for equity ownership. **Availability:** Print; PDF; Online.

31367 ■ *"Inland Snaps Up Rival REITs" in Crain's Chicago Business (Vol. 31, November 17, 2008, No. 46, pp. 3)*

Pub: Crain Communications Inc.

Contact: Barry Asin, President

Ed: Alby Gallun. **Description:** Discusses Inland American Real Estate Trust Inc., a real estate investment trust that is napping up depressed shares of publicly traded competitors, a possible first step toward taking over these companies; however, with hotel and retail properties accounting for approximately 70 percent of its portfolio, the company could soon face its own difficulties. **Availability:** Online.

31368 ■ *"Inmet Selling Nunavut Mining Properties" in Globe & Mail (February 15, 2006, pp. B6)*

Ed: Allan Robinson. **Description:** The details on Wolfden Resources Inc.'s acquisition of mining assets of Inmet Mining Corp. are presented. **Availability:** Online.

31369 ■ *"Innovation Adoption and Diffusion in Business-to-Business Marketing" in Journal of Business & Industrial Marketing (Vol. 29, May 2014, No. 4, pp. 324-331)*

Pub: Emerald Group Publishing Limited

Contact: Erika Valenti, President

Description: Evaluation of the innovation adoption and diffusion approach that links it with the key theoretical fields within business-to-business marketing is explored. A conceptual discussion is presented with the aim to develop an integrative conceptual framework and concludes that the proposed theoretical approaches could provide support in establishing a more matter-of-fact view of adoption and diffusion in the industrial sector. **Availability:** Download; Online; PDF.

31370 ■ *"Instant Income: Strategies That Bring in the Cash*

Pub: McGraw-Hill Professional

Ed: Janet Switzer. **Released:** First Edition. **Price:** $24. **Description:** Book covers small business advertising techniques, marketing, joint ventures, and sales. **Availability:** Print.

31371 ■ *"Intrawest Puts Itself on Market" in Globe & Mail (March 1, 2006, pp. B1)*

Ed: Elizabeth Church. **Description:** The reasons behind the decision of Intrawest Corp. to go for sale or seek partnerships are presented. The company appointed Goldman Sachs & Co. to meet the purpose. **Availability:** Online.

31372 ■ *"Inventive Doctor New Venture Partner" in Houston Business Journal (Vol. 40, January 29, 2010, No. 38, pp. A2)*

Pub: Houston Business Journal

Contact: Bob Charlet, President

E-mail: bcharlet@bizjournals.com

Ed: Ford Gunter. **Description:** Dr. Billy Cohn, a surgeon from Houston, Texas has been named as venture partner for venture firm Sante Ventures LLC of Austin, Texas. Cohn will be responsible for seeing marketable developing technologies in the medical industry. The motivation for Cohn's naming as venture partner is his development of a minimally invasive therapy for end-stage renal disease. **Availability:** Print; Online.

31373 ■ *"Investment Bank Predicts Shakeup in Farm Equipment Industry"* in *Farm Industry News (November 16, 2011)*
Pub: Informa Business Media, Inc.
Contact: Charlie McCurdy, President

Ed: Jodie Wehrspann. **Description:** Farming can expect to see more mergers and acquisitions in the agricultural equipment industry, as it appears to be in the early stages of growth over the next few years. **Availability:** Online.

31374 ■ *"Investment Firms Unite: Coalition Fights New Tax Law"* in *Black Enterprise (Vol. 38, December 2007, No. 5, pp. 52)*
Description: Minorities working in private equity, real estate and investment management firms have united to form the Access to Capital Coalition to oppose legislation that they feel would adversely affect their ability to attract investments and executives. Details of the group are included. **Availability:** Print; Online.

31375 ■ *"Investment Funds: Friends with Money"* in *Canadian Business (Vol. 81, May 22, 2008, No. 9, pp. 22)*
Pub: Rogers Media Inc.
Contact: Neil Spivak, Chief Executive Officer

Ed: Jeff Stanford. **Description:** Two of the most well connected managers in Canadian capital markets Rob Farquharson and Brian Gibson will launch Panoply Capital Asset Management in June. The investment management company aims to raise a billion dollars from institutions and high-net worth individuals. **Availability:** Print; Online.

31376 ■ *"Investment In Israel Is Investment in the Future of Georgia"* in *Atlanta Business Chronicle (May 30, 2014, pp. 22A)*
Pub: American City Business Journals, Inc.
Contact: Mike Olivieri, Executive Vice President

Description: Georgia Governor Nathan Deal will travel to Israel to lead an economic and trade mission and consolidate Georgia's trade ties with Israel. Israel and the State of Georgia are already collaborating in the fields of health information technology, agrotechnology, homeland security, defense, aerospace and cybersecurity, and microelectronics and nanotechnology. The proposed visit by the Governor will build on this particular partnership from which both parties will benefit. **Availability:** Print; Online.

31377 ■ *"IPOs: Can You Keep a Secret?"* in *Silicon Valley/San Jose Business Journal (Vol. 30, August 31, 2012, No. 23, pp. 1)*
Pub: Baltimore Business Journal
Contact: Rhonda Pringle, President
E-mail: rpringle@bizjournals.com

Description: Many business enterprises have been keeping their initial public offering (IPO) filings confidential through a new rule under the JOBS Act. The rule permits companies with less than $1 billion in revenue to keep their IPO filings confidential until 21 days before going public. As keeping IPO filings secret offer many advantages, drawbacks of this action are also discussed. **Availability:** Print; Online.

31378 ■ *"It's Good To Be King"* in *South Florida Business Journal (Vol. 35, August 29, 2014, No. 5, pp. 12)*
Released: December 01, 2013. **Description:** The $11.4 billion deal that will create a new holding company for Burger King Worldwide and Tim Hortons will be based in Oakville, Ontario, Canada and was met with public outrage. Burger King declares that the merger with the Canadian coffee and doughnut franchise chain was about global growth, not a strategy to avoid millions of dollars in corporate income tax payments to the U.S. government. **Availability:** Print; Online.

31379 ■ *"It's Not the How or the What but the Who: Succeed by Surrounding Yourself with the Best"*
Pub: Harvard Business Review Press
Contact: Moderna V. Pfizer, Contact

Released: June 03, 2014. **Price:** $32, Hardcover/ Hardcopy. **Description:** Surrounding yourself with the best matters in every aspect of life and can mean the difference between success and failure. The author draws upon years of experience in global executive search and talent development, as well as the latest management and psychology research, to help improve the choices management makes about employees and mentors, business partners and friends, top corporate leaders and elected officials. **Availability:** E-book; Print.

31380 ■ *"ITT Places Its Bet With Defense Buy: Selling Equipment to Army Pays Off"* in *Crain's New York Business (Vol. 24, January 6, 2008)*
Pub: Crain Communications, Inc.
Contact: Jessica Botos, Manager, Marketing
E-mail: jessica.botos@crainsnewyork.com

Description: ITT Corp.'s revenue has jumped by 20 percent in each of the past three years due to demand for the company's radio sets and night-vision goggles. The firm has acquired EDO Corp., which specializes in battlefield communications systems, in an attempt to expand its defense-industry division. **Availability:** Online.

31381 ■ *"Jamieson Eyes $175 Million Trust IPO"* in *Globe & Mail (March 7, 2006, pp. B1)*
Ed: Sinclair Stewart, Leonard Zehr. **Description:** The reasons behind $175 million initial public offering plans of Jamieson Laboratories Ltd. are presented. **Availability:** Print; Online.

31382 ■ *"JK Lasser's New Rules for Estate, Retirement, and Tax Planning"*
Pub: John Wiley & Sons, Inc.
Contact: Christina Van Tassell, Executive Vice President Chief Financial Officer

Released: 6th Edition. **Price:** $24.95, paperback; $16.99, E-book. **Description:** The authoritative guide to estate, retirement and tax planning is fully updated and reflects the new changes and legal updates. Estate planning section covers: planning, taxation, investing, wills, executors, trusts, life insurance, retirement planning, Social Security, business planning, succession, asset protection and family limited partnerships. **Availability:** E-book; Print.

31383 ■ *"Jo-Ann Fabric and Craft Stores Joins ArtFire.com to Offer Free Online Craft Marketplace"* in *Marketwired (January 26, 2010)*
Pub: Comtex News Network Inc.
Contact: Kan Devnani, President

Description: Jo-Ann Fabric and Craft Stores has entered into a partnership with ArtFire.com which will provide sewers and crafters all the tools they need in order to make and sell their products from an online venue. **Availability:** Print; Online.

31384 ■ *"A Jobs Compact for America's Future: Badly Needed Investments In Human Capital Are Not Being Made. What We Can Do - Together - To Jump-Start the Process?"* in *Harvard Business Review (Vol. 90, March 2012, No. 3, pp. 64)*
Pub: Harvard Business Review Press
Contact: Moderna V. Pfizer, Contact

Ed: Thomas A. Kochan. **Price:** $8.95. **Description:** Obstacles to strengthening US human capital are a lack of focus on obtaining both high wages and high productivity, and a lack of value placed on human capital as a competitive advantage. Business schools are well positioned to address these obstacles via curricula, programs, and partnerships. **Availability:** Online; PDF.

31385 ■ *"Juicy Couture (1997-2014) Couldn't Evolve When Its Cachet Dried Up"* in *Canadian Business (Vol. 87, July 2014, No. 7, pp. 16)*
Description: Fashion brand Juicy Couture was started by Pamela Skaist-Ley and Gela Nash-Taylor in Los Angeles, California in 1997 and was acquired by Fifth & Pacific Companies in 2003. Fifth & Pacific put Juicy Couture up for sale in fall 2013, with

Authentic Brands Group owning the rights to the brand name for $195 million. The last of the Canadian outlets will close June 30, 2014. **Availability:** Online.

31386 ■ *"KBA, Graphic Art System Partner on Cold Foil"* in *American Printer (Vol. 128, June 1, 2011, No. 6)*
Description: KBA North America has partnered with Graphic Art System to retrofit and equip presses with cold foil machines. **Availability:** Online.

31387 ■ *"Keeping Railcars 'Busy At All Times' At TTX"* in *Crain's Chicago Business (Vol. 31, April 28, 2008, No. 17, pp. 6)*
Pub: Crain Communications Inc.
Contact: Barry Asin, President

Ed: Bob Tita. **Description:** Profile of the president of Chicago railcar pool operator TTX Co. and his business plan for the company which includes improving fleet management and car purchasing through better use of data on railroad demand. **Availability:** Online.

31388 ■ *"Kerkorian Shakes Up Chrysler Race"* in *Globe & Mail (April 6, 2007, pp. B1)*
Ed: Greg Keenan. **Description:** The bid of Kirk Kerkorian's Tracinda Corp. to acquire Daimler-Chrysler AG for $4.5 billion is discussed. **Availability:** Online.

31389 ■ *"Kinderhook Acquires Chemtron Corp."* in *Waste Today (August 23, 2019)*
URL(s): www.wastetodaymagazine.com/article/kin derhook-acquires-chemtron-corp/
Ed: Adam Redling. **Released:** August 23, 2019. **Description:** The hazardous and non-hazardous waste management provider, Chemtron, was acquired by Kinderhook Industries LLC. **Availability:** Online.

31390 ■ *"Kinnser: Sales In Overdrive"* in *Austin Business Journal (Vol. 32, March 30, 2012, No. 4, pp. 1)*
Pub: American City Business Journals, Inc.
Contact: Mike Olivieri, Executive Vice President

Ed: Christopher Calnan. **Description:** Kinnser Software Inc.'s receipt of fresh capitalization is seen to enable the company to pursue its acquisition strategy. The company is planning to grow organically. It is also planning to double the number of its employees. **Availability:** Online.

31391 ■ *"Kinross Holds Firm on Offer for Bema"* in *Globe & Mail (January 20, 2007, pp. B5)*
Ed: Andy Hoffman. **Description:** The acquisition of Bema Gold Corp. by Kinross Gold Corp. is discussed. **Availability:** Online.

31392 ■ *"Kodak Offers Cloud-Based Operating Option"* in *American Printer (Vol. 128, June 1, 2011, No. 6)*
Description: Kodak partnered with VMware to offer its first Virtual Operating Environment option for Kodak Unified Workflow Solutions. The new feature enables cost savings, increased efficiency and failover protection. **Availability:** Online.

31393 ■ *"Kratos Announces Buy of Critical Infrastructure Security Business"* in *M & A Navigator (January 3, 2012)*
Description: Kratos Defense & Security Solutions Inc., a US national security firm, purchased a competitor for USD $20 million. The acquisition will help expand its critical infrastructure security business. **Availability:** Print.

31394 ■ *"Labatt to Swallow Lakeport"* in *Globe & Mail (February 2, 2007, pp. B1)*
Ed: Keith McArthur. **Description:** The decision of Labatt Brewing Company Ltd. to acquire Lakeport Brewing Income Fund for $201.4 million is discussed. **Availability:** Print; Online.

31395 ■ *"Last Call?"* in *Puget Sound Business Journal (Vol. .35, August 8, 2014, No. 16, pp. 12)*
Pub: American City Business Journals, Inc.
Contact: Mike Olivieri, Executive Vice President

Description: T-Mobile US cellular phone service is targeted for acquisition by large firms, but so far no deals have materialized. Analysts believe a deal will emerge soon as T-Mobile's parent company is seeking suitable bidders. The impact of a merger on Puget Sound's economy is viewed. **Availability:** Online.

31396 ■ *"The Leaders Who Make M&A Work"* in Harvard Business Review (Vol. 92, September 2014, No. 9, pp. 28)
Pub: Harvard Business Publishing
Contact: Diane Belcher, Managing Director
Price: $6. **Description:** Leadership capabilities for both acquiring and targeting firms are predictors of merger and acquisition success. Capabilities for acquirers include motivation, influence, adaptability, and integrity; those for targets include providing direction. **Availability:** Online; PDF.

31397 ■ *"A League of Their Own"* in St. Louis Business Journal (Vol. 32, May 4, 2012, No. 37, pp. 1)
Pub: Baltimore Business Journal
Contact: Rhonda Pringle, President
E-mail: rpringle@bizjournals.com
Description: Entrepreneurs Brian and Carol Matthews, Jim McKelvey and Rick Holton Jr. have partnered to create Cultivation Capital. The venture capital fund will target technology firms. **Availability:** Print; Online.

31398 ■ *Let's Buy a Company: How to Accelerate Growth Through Acquisitions*
Description: Advice for negotiating terms and pricing as well as other aspects of mergers and acquisitions in small companies. **Availability:** Print.

31399 ■ *"Liberty Media Pushes to Close on Sirius XM While Cable Deals Wait"* in Denver Business Journal (Vol. 65, February 28, 2014, No. 42)
Pub: American City Business Journals, Inc.
Contact: Mike Olivieri, Executive Vice President
Released: Weekly. **Description:** Liberty Media Corporation CEO, Greg Maffei, notes that various cable TV mergers are on hold while everyone awaits the decision if Comcast and Time Warner will be allowed to go through with their $45.2 billion merger. Liberty Media had supported Charter Communications plans to buy Time Warner for cash and stock. That deal was pushed aside when Comcast came along with a larger, all-stock offer. **Availability:** Print; Online.

31400 ■ *"Loans Are Plentiful for Small Businesses"* in South Florida Business Journal (Vol. 35, September 12, 2014, No. 7, pp. 16)
Pub: American City Business Journals, Inc.
Contact: Mike Olivieri, Executive Vice President
Description: Banks have relaxed requirements for small business loans in South Florida. Total bank loans increased by 11.4 percent in 2014. It has also become easier for small businesses to secure credit for acquisitions and mergers and growth. **Availability:** Online.

31401 ■ *"Local TV Hits Media Radar Screen"* in Business Courier (Vol. 27, July 2, 2010, No. 9, pp. 1)
Pub: Business Courier
Ed: Dan Monk. **Description:** Fort Wright, Kentucky-based broadcasting company Local TV LLC has acquired 18 television stations since its founding in 2007, potentially boosting its chances of becoming a media empire. In the last twelve months that ended in March 2010, Local TV LLC has posted total revenues of $415 million. How Local TV LLC has entered into cost-sharing deals with other stations is also discussed. **Availability:** Print; Online.

31402 ■ *"Loss of Rutgers Name Causing a Stir for Law School"* in Philadelphia Business Journal (Vol. 28, April 20, 2012, No. 10, pp. 1)
Pub: Baltimore Business Journal
Contact: Rhonda Pringle, President
E-mail: rpringle@bizjournals.com

Description: The plan to merge Rutgers University-Camden with Rowan University is being opposed by those from Rutgers who feel they will have problems recruiting students if they lose the Rutgers brand. Rowan on the other hand, is more known in the South Jersey area only. **Availability:** Print; Online.

31403 ■ *"The Lost Opportunity for a Canadian Steel Giant"* in Globe & Mail (April 23, 2007, pp. B1)
Ed: Greg Keenan. **Description:** The efforts of Algoma Steel Inc. to create a Canadian steel manufacturer that could survive the global trends of consolidation in the steel industry are described. The company's efforts to acquire Stelco Inc., Ivaco Inc. and Slater Steel Inc. are discussed. **Availability:** Print; Online.

31404 ■ *"Lundin Deal Leaves Nickel Market Thin"* in Globe & Mail (April 5, 2007, pp. B4)
Ed: Andy Hoffman. **Description:** The likely acquisition of Rio Narcea Gold Mines Ltd. by Lundin Mining Corp. and the decreasing number of nickel mining companies on the list of Toronto Stock Exchange are discussed. **Availability:** Online.

31405 ■ *"Madison Partner Eyes Overton: French Quarter Suites May Become Luxury Hotel"* in Memphis Business Journal (Vol. 34, April 27, 2012, No. 2, pp. 1)
Pub: Baltimore Business Journal
Contact: Rhonda Pringle, President
E-mail: rpringle@bizjournals.com
Description: Former hotel executive Mohammad Hakimian and a group of investors are planning to purchase and redevelop the French Quarter Suites into a hotel. Loeb Properties Inc. is planning to invest $19.2 million in the project. **Availability:** Print; Online.

31406 ■ *"Magpower May Build Solar Panels in Pflugerville"* in Austin Business Journal (Vol. 31, May 13, 2011, No. 10, pp. A1)
Pub: Austin Business Journal
Contact: Rachel McGrath, Director
E-mail: rmcgrath@bizjournals.com
Ed: Christopher Calnan. **Description:** RRE Austin Solar LLC CEO Doven Mehta has revealed plans to partner with Portugal-based Magpower SA, only if Austin energy buys electricity from planned solar energy farm in Pflugerville. Austin Energy has received 100 bids from 35 companies to supply 200 megawatts of solar- and wind-generated electricity. **Availability:** Print; Online.

31407 ■ *"M&A Weakness Takes Toll on Phila. Law Firms"* in Philadelphia Business Journal (Vol. 28, August 10, 2012, No. 26, pp. 1)
Pub: Baltimore Business Journal
Contact: Rhonda Pringle, President
E-mail: rpringle@bizjournals.com
Released: Weekly. **Price:** $4, introductory 4-week offer(Digital & Print). **Description:** Slowdown in mergers and acquisitions impact law firms in Philadelphia, Pennsylvania. Data show that M&A activity involving the US has decreased by 35 percent int he first half of 2012. With the number of deals decreasing, local firms have become cautious about hiring transactional lawyers in terms of selecting those from high revenue areas such as intellectual property. **Availability:** Print; Online.

31408 ■ *"M&T On the March?"* in Baltimore Business Journal (Vol. 28, November 12, 2010, No. 27, pp. 1)
Pub: Baltimore Business Journal
Contact: Rhonda Pringle, President
E-mail: rpringle@bizjournals.com
Ed: Gary Haber. **Description:** Information on the growth of M&T Bank, as well as its expansion plans are presented. M&T recently acquired Wilmington Trust and took over $500 million in deposits from the failed K Bank. Analysts believe that M&T would continue its expansion through Washington DC and Richmond, Virginia, especially after a bank executive acknowledged that the markets in those areas are attractive. **Availability:** Print; Online.

31409 ■ *"Manufacturers Become Part of Coalition"* in Contractor (Vol. 56, July 2009, No. 7, pp. 40)
Description: Bradford White Water Heaters, Rheem Water Heating, Rinnai America Corp., and A.O. Smith Water Heaters have joined the Consortium for Energy Efficiency in the Coalition for Energy Star Water Heaters. The coalition seeks to increase the awareness of Energy Star water heaters. **Availability:** Print; Online.

31410 ■ *"Market Resource Set for Expansion: Supply Chain Firm to Add Up to 700 Employees"* in Memphis Business Journal (Vol. 34, May 11, 2012, No. 4, pp. 1)
Pub: Baltimore Business Journal
Contact: Rhonda Pringle, President
E-mail: rpringle@bizjournals.com
Description: Market Resource Packaging LLC is planning to expand its operation in Memphis, Tennessee under the new ownership of IAM Acquisition. The supply chain services company plans to increase its distribution space from 260,000 square feet to 1 million square feet in three years and to grow its employees from 300 to 1,000 in 18 months. **Availability:** Print; Online.

31411 ■ *"Maybe We're Exploiting China"* in Canadian Business (Vol. 85, September 17, 2012, No. 14, pp. 4)
Ed: Duncan Hood. **Description:** The proposed deal by China National Offshore Oil Corp. (CNOOC) to acquire Canada's Nexen for $27.50 a share is met with uncertainty by the public. The U.S. is believed to be opposing the deal because it would no longer have quite as much power to set oil prices in Canada. **Availability:** Online.

31412 ■ *"Mazel Tov: L'Chaim Gets a Deal to Expand with Southern Wine"* in South Florida Business Journal (Vol. 33, September 7, 2012, No. 6, pp. 1)
Pub: Baltimore Business Journal
Contact: Rhonda Pringle, President
E-mail: rpringle@bizjournals.com
Description: L'Chaim Kosher Vodka could triple its sales in 2012. The company won a deal to expand with Southern Wine and Spirits, which is the largest distributor of wine and spirits in the United States. The Distilled Spirits Council of the United States reported that vodka drives 31 percent of all spirit sales.

31413 ■ *"Meadowbrook To Acquire ProCentury in $272.6 Million Deal"* in Crain's Detroit Business (Vol. 24, February 21, 2008, No. 8, pp. 4)
Pub: Crain Communications Inc.
Contact: Barry Asin, President
Ed: Jay Greene. **Description:** Meadowbrook Insurance Group, based in Southfield, Michigan reports its proposed acquisition of ProCentury Corporation based in Columbus, Ohio. Meadowbrook provides risk-management to agencies, professional and trade associations and small-to-midsize businesses. **Availability:** Print; Online.

31414 ■ *"Medicaid Insurers See Growth in Small Biz Market"* in Boston Business Journal (Vol. 31, July 15, 2011, No. 25, pp. 1)
Pub: Boston Business Journal
Contact: Carolyn M. Jones, President
E-mail: cmjones@bizjournals.com
Ed: Julie M. Donnelly. **Description:** BMC HealthNet Plan announced plans to launch small business products to serve small businesses that are priced out of rising premium rates at large Massachusetts insurers. BMC joined competitors CeltiCare Health Plan and Neighborhood Health Plan in augmenting its core business. **Availability:** Print; Online.

31415 ■ *"Meet Houston's Top Legal Dealmakers"* in Austin Business Journal (Vol. 34, June 27, 2014, No. 19, pp. A15)
Pub: American City Business Journals, Inc.
Contact: Mike Olivieri, Executive Vice President

Description: Austin-based law firm, Vinson & Elkins LLP emerged at the biggest player in Texas in the 12-month period between second quarter 2013 through first quarter 2014 when it comes to mergers and acquisitions. The firm handled 68 deals worth a total of $61.8 billion. **Availability:** Print; Online.

31416 ■ "Melnyk Loses Round in Battle for Hemosol" in Globe & Mail (January 24, 2007, pp. B3)

Ed: Leonard Zehr. **Description:** Biovail Corp. chairman Eugene Melnyk's loosing of the case against Catalyst Capital Group Inc. over the acquisition of Hemosol Corp. is discussed. **Availability:** Online.

31417 ■ "Merger Expected to Bring New Player to TV Market" in Providence Business News (Vol. 28, March 31, 2014, No. 52, pp. 1)

Pub: American City Business Journals, Inc.

Contact: Mike Olivieri, Executive Vice President

URL(s): pbn.com/merger-expected-to-bring-new -player-to-tv-market96073

Description: The proposed merger of Media General and Providence, Rhode Island-based LIN Media LLC has the potential to change the TV landscape in the state. The two media companies' TV stations overlap in five markets and ownership at one of the stations is expected to change due to federal regulations regarding TV station ownership. The two TV stations are outlined.

31418 ■ Mergers and Acquisitions from A to Z

Pub: HarperCollins Leadership

Contact: Donald Miller, Chief Executive Officer

Released: 2nd edition. **Price:** $19.99, Paperback. **Description:** Guide for the entire process of mergers and acquisitions, including taxes, accounting, laws, and projected financial gain. **Availability:** E-book; Print.

31419 ■ "Merrill Lynch in Talks to Buy BlackRock Stake" in Globe & Mail (February 13, 2006, pp. B4)

Description: Financial services firm Merrill Lynch and Co. Inc. is planning to acquire money managing company BlackRock Inc. for 8 million dollars. Sources report that this deal would create 1-trillion dollar huge fund management venture. **Availability:** Online.

31420 ■ "Methodist Sees Dwindling Transplant Organs" in Memphis Business Journal (Vol. 34, June 29, 2012, No. 11, pp. 1)

Pub: Baltimore Business Journal

Contact: Rhonda Pringle, President

E-mail: rpringle@bizjournals.com

Ed: Cole Epley. **Description:** The Methodist University Hospital Transplant Institute opposes the national organ policies established by the United Network for Organ Sharing as it would impact their liver transplant program negatively. Mid-South Transplant Foundation refuses to go forward with a merger with Tennessee Donor Services as favored by the Methodist program. **Availability:** Print; Online.

31421 ■ "Micro-Finance Agencies and SMEs: Model of Explication of Tacit Knowledge" in International Journal of Entrepreneurship and Small Business (Vol. 11, August 3, 2010)

Ed: Patricia A. Rowe, Michael J. Christie, Frank Hoy. **Description:** Institutional preparedness of economic development agencies for developing small and medium-sized enterprises (SMEs) is discussed. The cases presented illustrate variations in the microfinance lender agency-enterprise development of processes for sharing vision and interdependence. **Availability:** Online.

31422 ■ "Microsoft Partners With Good Technology to Provide Enterprise-Class Security for Business Customers on Windows Phone Devices" in Benzinga.com (February 27, 2012)

Pub: PR Newswire Association LLC.

Description: Microsoft has partnered with Good Technology in order to provide its Windows Phone 7.5 Preferred Partner Solution for secured encrypted mobile mail services. Details of the strategic partnership are outlined.

31423 ■ "Microsoft's Big Gamble" in Canadian Business (Vol. 81, March 3, 2008, No. 3, pp. 13)

Description: Microsoft Corp. is taking a big risk in buying Yahoo, as it is expected to pay more than $31 a share to finalize the acquisition. The deal would be seven and a half times bigger than any other that Microsoft has entered before, an execution of such deal is also anticipated to become a challenge for Microsoft. Recommendations on how Microsoft should handle the integration of the two businesses are given. **Availability:** Print; Online.

31424 ■ "Minor-League Baseball's Sliders Plan Stock Offering" in Crain's Detroit Business (Vol. 25, June 15, 2009, No. 24, pp. 3)

Pub: Crain Communications Inc.

Contact: Barry Asin, President

Ed: Bill Shea. **Description:** New minor-league baseball team is raising funds to build a new stadium in Waterford Township, Michigan because banks are unwilling to provide loans for the project. Owners of the Midwest Sliders in Ypsilanti, Michigan are waiting for the federal Securities and Exchange Commission to approve a Regulation A public offering. **Availability:** Print; Online.

31425 ■ "Monogram Foods Eyes Acquisition: Midwest Manufacturer Target of Latest Expansion" in Memphis Business Journal (Vol. 34, August 10, 2012, No. 17, pp. 1)

Pub: Baltimore Business Journal

Contact: Rhonda Pringle, President

E-mail: rpringle@bizjournals.com

Description: Monogram Food Solutions, a Memphis-based food company is raising $12.5 million for the acquisition of an undisclosed company or companies. The acquistion is expected to generate $50 million revenue, add 200 new employees for Monogram, and strengthen its manufacturing arm. **Availability:** Print; Online.

31426 ■ "Monogram Foods Lands Another Acquisition In Quest for Growth Goals" in Memphis Business Journal (Vol. 34, September 14, 2012, No. 22, pp. 1)

Pub: Baltimore Business Journal

Contact: Rhonda Pringle, President

E-mail: rpringle@bizjournals.com

Ed: Michael Sheffield. **Description:** Memphis, Tennessee-based Monogram Food Solutions has announced a deal to acquire Enjoy and Hickory Best Beef Jerky brands from Colton, California-based Enjoy Foods International. The move follows the acquisition of Bristol, Indiana-based Hinsdale Farms, which manufactures corn dogs.

31427 ■ "Move Marks KKR's Latest Push into Retail" in Globe & Mail (March 13, 2007, pp. B17)

Ed: Heather Burke. **Description:** Investment giant Kohlberg Kravis Roberts and Co. has finalized a deal to acquire retail store chain Dollar General Corp. for an estimated 6.9 billion dollars. The company will be entering lucrative retail market by this acquisition.

31428 ■ "Much Work Still To Be Done on Meadows Deal" in Pittsburgh Business Times (Vol. 33, May 16, 2014, No. 44, pp. 3)

Pub: American City Business Journals, Inc.

Contact: Mike Olivieri, Executive Vice President

Released: Weekly. **Price:** $4, introductory 4-week offer(Digital only). **Description:** Real estate investment trust, Gaming and Leisure Properties Inc., is acquiring the Meadows Racetrack & Casino in Washington, Pennsylvania from Cannery Casino & Resorts LLC in a $465 million deal. The process of finding an operator and getting the license transfers approved will be the next critical step following the deal. **Availability:** Print; Online.

31429 ■ "MyReviewsNow.net Announces New Affiliate Partner Gift Baskets Overseas" in M2 EquityBites (EQB) (June 22, 2012)

Description: MyReviewsNow.net has partnered with Gift Baskets Overseas in order to offer gift baskets to be shipped overseas. Gift Baskets Oversease works with local florists and shippers worldwide. No financial details were disclosed. **Availability:** Online.

31430 ■ "Navigating Dog Trainer Partnerships" in Pet Product News (Vol. 66, September 2012, No. 9, pp. 47)

Ed: Steven Appelbaum. **Description:** Benefits and disadvantages of partnerships between pet supplies retailers and dog trainers are discussed. With the proper approach to partnering with dog trainers who are duly specialized in dog behavior modification, pet supplies retailers can realize improved business and stronger customer loyalty. Tips on cross-promoting pet-related services are also provided. **Availability:** Online.

31431 ■ "Navistar, Cat Talk Truck Deal" in Crain's Chicago Business (Vol. 31, March 24, 2008, No. 12, pp. 1)

Pub: Crain Communications Inc.

Contact: Barry Asin, President

Ed: Bob Tita. **Description:** Caterpillar Inc. and Navistar International Corp. are negotiating a partnership in which Navistar would provide Cat-branded trucks with engines supplied by the Peoria-based equipment manufacturer, Caterpillar. **Availability:** Online.

31432 ■ "Nestle Acquires Waggin' Train Dog Treat Company" in Pet Product News (Vol. 64, November 2010, No. 11, pp. 7)

Description: Vevey, Switzerland-based Nestle has acquired South Carolina-based dog treat firm Waggin' Train LLC from private equity firm VMG Partners in September 2010. Waggin' Train LLC, which will be operated as a wholly owned subsidiary, is expected to fill a gap in Nestle's dog treat product portfolio. **Availability:** Online.

31433 ■ "Net Savings Link Announces SpyderShare Inc. Contract for Development of Search Engine Optimization (S.E.O.) Program" in Internet Wire (February 21, 2012)

Pub: Comtex News Network Inc.

Contact: Kan Devnani, President

Description: Net Savings Link provides electronically deliverable sales incentives for the business market along with improved Web based savings programs for consumers has partnered with SpyderShare Inc. to enhance the firm's presence on the Internet. Details of the partnership are included. **Availability:** Print; Online.

31434 ■ "NetSpend and Family Dollar Announce New Prepaid Card Agreement" in GlobeNewswire (May 10, 2012)

Pub: Comtex News Network Inc.

Contact: Kan Devnani, President

Description: Partnership between Family Dollar and NetSpend will offer customers a NetSpend Visa(R) Prepaid Debit Card to be used at Family Dollar's 7,200 locations. NetSpend is a leading provider of general-purpose reloadable (GPR) prepaid debit cards and other related financial services. **Availability:** Print; Online.

31435 ■ "Neuromed Strikes Major Merck Deal" in Globe & Mail (March 21, 2006, pp. B1)

Ed: Leonard Zehr. **Description:** Neuromed Pharmaceuticals Ltd., a spin off of British Columbia University, has struck a drug research deal valued at up to $500 million (U.S) with giant Merck &Co. Inc., the biggest collaboration in Canada. Details of the deal are presented. **Availability:** Online.

31436 ■ "A New Alliance For Global Change" in Harvard Business Review (Vol. 88, September 2010, No. 9, pp. 56)

Pub: Harvard Business Publishing

Contact: Diane Belcher, Managing Director

Ed: Bill Drayton, Valeria Budinich. **Price:** $8.95, PDF. **Description:** Collaboration between social organizations and for-profit firms through the development of hybrid value chains to target complex global issues is promoted. While social organizations offer links to communities and consumers, firms provide financing and scale expertise. **Availability:** Online; PDF.

31437 ■ *"New Beat for Marley's Daughter: Offspring of Reggae Royalty Opens Vintage Clothing Shop with Pal"* in *Los Angeles Business Journal (Vol. 34, March 12, 2012, No. 11, pp. 3)*

Pub: CBJ L.P.

Contact: Laura Garrett, Vice President Publisher

E-mail: garrett@ocbj.com

Ed: Bethany Firnhaber. **Description:** Karen Marley, daughter of famous reggae musician Bob Marley, explains her passion for vintage clothing. Karen and her fried Monique Aquino have partnered to open a resale consignment store in Los Angeles selling designer and vintage clothing. **Availability:** Online.

31438 ■ *"New Brewpub Includes a Manapua Shop"* in *Pacific Business News (Vol. 52, March 14, 2014, No. 3, pp. 6)*

Pub: American City Business Journals, Inc.

Contact: Mike Olivieri, Executive Vice President

Released: March 14, 2014. **Price:** $4, Introductory 4-Week Offer(Digital & Print). **Description:** Hoku Brewing Company is set to open a brewery restaurant in Hawaii. The new restaurant will be built on the site of the former Aloha Beer Company restaurant. The project is a joint venture between Hoku and restaurateur Dave Campbell. **Availability:** Print; Online.

31439 ■ *"A New Cloud-Based Phone System Is Installed Remotely for North Carolina Senior Care Council"* in *Information Technology Business (June 19, 2012)*

Description: North Carolina Senior Care Council (NcSCC) has partnered with VoxNet to provide long-term care for Cloud-based PBX to help NcSCC manage their system that assists seniors. **Availability:** Online.

31440 ■ *"New Economy Initiative Gains Partners"* in *Crain's Detroit Business (Vol. 25, June 1, 2009, No. 22, pp. M014)*

Pub: Crain Communications Inc.

Contact: Barry Asin, President

Ed: Sherri Begin Welch. **Description:** New Economy Initiative is a $100 million philanthropic initiative that focuses on regional economic development. Recent grants awarded to Michigan companies are outlined. **Availability:** Print; Online.

31441 ■ *"A New Flavor for Second Street: Lamberts Chef Backs New Restaurant"* in *Austin Business JournalInc. (Vol. 28, January 2, 2009)*

Description: Chef Larry McGuire has teamed up with the Icon Group to develop the La Condesa restaurant and the Malverde lounge in the Second Street district. The La Condesa restaurant will be a Mexico City-inspired restaurant, while the Malverde lounge atop the La Condesa will host DJs and live music. **Availability:** Print; Online.

31442 ■ *"The New Janus CEO of Battle-Hardened Money Manager Plots Comeback"* in *Denver Business Journal (Vol. 64, August 31, 2012, No. 15, pp. 1)*

Pub: Baltimore Business Journal

Contact: Rhonda Pringle, President

E-mail: rpringle@bizjournals.com

Description: Richard Well, chief executive officer of Janus Capital Group Inc., discusses the strategic plans of the mutual fund company. He touches on the firm's alliance with Dai-chi Life Insurance Company Ltd., the future of equity markets, and the company's intelligent diversification strategy. **Availability:** Print; Online.

31443 ■ *"New Life for Porsche's VW Dreams"* in *Barron's (Vol. 89, July 6, 2009, No. 27, pp. 9)*

Pub: Dow Jones & Company Inc.

Contact: Almar Latour, Chief Executive Officer

Ed: Vito J. Racanelli. **Description:** Porsche and Volkswagen moved closer to a merger after the Qatar Investment Authority offered to take a stake in Porsche. The QIA could take up to a 30 percent stake in Porsche and purchase all Volkswagen calls for up to $6 billion. **Availability:** Online.

31444 ■ *"New Owners Take Over at Leather District Restaurants"* in *Boston Business Journal (Vol. 33, January 31, 2014, No. 53, pp. 4)*

Pub: American City Business Journals, Inc.

Contact: Mike Olivieri, Executive Vice President

Released: Weekly. **Description:** Restaurateur Anthony Botta of Boston, Massachusetts partnered with Mark Tosi of Pastene Companies to acquire Les Zygomates and Sorriso restaurants at the Leather District owned by Ian Just. Robert Fathman was hired as the executive chef of both restaurants. **Availability:** Print; Online.

31445 ■ *"New Stem Cell Research Awareness Org Launched in Austin"* in *Austin Business Journal (Vol. 31, June 3, 2011, No. 13, pp. 1)*

Pub: Austin Business Journal

Contact: Rachel McGrath, Director

E-mail: rmcgrath@bizjournals.com

Ed: Sandra Zaragoza. **Description:** MedRebels Foundation was launched in February 2011 with the goal of providing millions of dollars for research funding, education and advocacy for adult stem cell-focused medicine. The foundation, whose major contributor is SpineSmith LP, is a collaboration of other adult stem cell-related companies and nonprofit partners. It hopes to raise $200,000 by the end of 2011. **Availability:** Print; Online.

31446 ■ *"New Texas South-International Alliance Seeking to Net Foreign Firms for South Texas"* in *San Antonio Business Journal (Vol. 26, June 22, 2012, No. 21, pp. 1)*

Pub: Baltimore Business Journal

Contact: Rhonda Pringle, President

E-mail: rpringle@bizjournals.com

Description: The city of San Antonio, Texas is partnering with Brownsville, Corpus Christi, Edinburg, Laredo, and San Marcos, to form the Texas South-International Alliance. The alliance is aimed at attracting more International economic development opportunities and investment to South Texas. **Availability:** Print; Online.

31447 ■ *"New York Developer Revives Adams Morgan Hotel Project"* in *Washington Business Journal (Vol. 31, July 6, 2012, No. 11, pp. 1)*

Pub: Baltimore Business Journal

Contact: Rhonda Pringle, President

E-mail: rpringle@bizjournals.com

Description: Real estate developer Brian Friedman brought on Andrew Zobler of Sydell Group LLC as a development partner for the Adams Morgan boutique hotel project. A previous plan for a $100 million property was shelved due to neighborhood opposition. **Availability:** Print; Online.

31448 ■ *"New Zealand Natural Co-Branding with Mrs. Fields"* in *Ice Cream Reporter (Vol. 23, November 20, 2010, No. 12, pp. 2)*

Description: Mrs. Fields has partnered with a New Zealand firm to co-brand ice cream and cookies in Australian markets. **Availability:** Print; Online.

31449 ■ *"No More Ivory Towers: Local Colleges and Universities are Here to Help Your Business"* in *Orlando Business Journal (Vol. 30, February 28, 2014, No. 36, pp. 4)*

Pub: American City Business Journals, Inc.

Contact: Mike Olivieri, Executive Vice President

Released: Weekly. **Price:** $8, Introductory 4-week offer(Digital & Print). **Description:** A number of school leaders in Central Florida share their views on partnering with the business community, boosting science and technology graduates, benefits of a private college, economic development efforts and fixing the higher education construction gridlock. Local universities and colleges have a combined economic impact of $15 billion each year. **Availability:** Print; Online.

31450 ■ *The Nokia Revolution: The Story of an Extraordinary Company That Transformed an Industry*

Description: Profile of Nokia, the world's largest wireless communications company. Nokia started in 1865 in rural Finland and merged its rubber company and a cabling firm to form the corporation around 1965. The firm's corporate strategy in the mobile communications industry is highlighted. **Availability:** E-book; Print.

31451 ■ *"Nonprofit NAIC Acquires Software Developer as For-Profit Arm"* in *Crain's Detroit Business (Vol. 25, June 22, 2009, No. 25, pp. 10)*

Pub: Crain Communications Inc.

Contact: Barry Asin, President

Ed: Sherri Begin Welch. **Description:** Details of National Association of Investors Corporation's acquisition of a Massachusetts investment software developer in order to offer more products to investment clubs and individual investors nationwide. **Availability:** Online.

31452 ■ *"Nortel Romances Chinese Rival Huawei"* in *Globe & Mail (February 2, 2006, pp. B1)*

Description: The reasons behind Nortel Networks Corp.'s joint venture with Huawei Technologies Company Ltd. are presented. **Availability:** Online.

31453 ■ *"Norwegian Cruise Line Adds to Fleet with $3B Prestige Deal"* in *South Florida Business Journal (Vol. 35, September 5, 2014, No. 6, pp. 6)*

Pub: American City Business Journals, Inc.

Contact: Mike Olivieri, Executive Vice President

Released: Weekly. **Price:** $8, introductory 4-week offer(Digital only). **Description:** Norwegian Cruise Line Holdings has agreed to purchase Prestige Cruises International for $3 billion. Norwegian will finance the acquisition with debt and by selling 20.3 million shares of its common stock. The deal will add five ships to Norwegian's 13-ship fleet. **Availability:** Print; Online.

31454 ■ *"NStar Feels the Heat"* in *Cape Cod Times (September 30, 2011)*

Pub: Cape Cod Media Group

Contact: Anne Brennan, Executive Editor

E-mail: abrennan@capecodonline.com

Ed: Patrick Cassidy. **Description:** Massachusetts energy officials wish to delay a merger between NStar and Northeast Utilities until it is clear how the partnership would meet the state's green energy goals. Governor Deval Patrick supports the proposed Nantucket Sound wind farm. **Availability:** Online.

31455 ■ *"NSU Seeks Private Partners For New $80M Research Building"* in *South Florida Business Journal (Vol. 34, February 21, 2014, No. 31, pp. 4)*

Pub: American City Business Journals, Inc.

Contact: Mike Olivieri, Executive Vice President

Released: Weekly. **Price:** $8, Introductory 4-week offer(Digital & Print). **Description:** The $80 million Center for Collaborative Research at Nova Southeastern University hopes to become the largest incubator and wet laboratory space in Broward County, Florida. The center had its groundbreaking on February 13, 2014, and will be open for lease to private companies when it is ready in 22 months. **Availability:** Print; Online.

31456 ■ *"Nymex Dissidents Rattle Sabers"* in *Crain's Chicago Business (Vol. 31, April 21, 2008, No. 16, pp. 2)*
Pub: Crain Communications Inc.
Contact: Barry Asin, President

Ed: Ann Saphir. **Description:** Two groups of New York Mercantile Exchange members say they have more than enough votes to stop CME Group Inc.'s $10 billion deal to acquire the oil and metals exchange and they are threatening a proxy fight if the Chicago exchange doesn't raise its offer. **Availability:** Online.

31457 ■ *"The Ode: CoolBrands (1986 - 2010)"* in *Canadian Business (Vol. 83, September 14, 2010, No. 15, pp. 25)*
Pub: Rogers Media Inc.
Contact: Neil Spivak, Chief Executive Officer

Ed: Joe Castaldo. **Description:** CoolBrands International Inc.'s merger with Swisher International Inc., a US hygiene products and services company, has formally erased the last traces of the former ice cream company. CoolBrands began as a frozen yogurt stand in 1986 and flourished across the world. How the string of acquisitions and poor corporate governance led to its demise are cited. **Availability:** Online.

31458 ■ *"Of Paper Towels and Health Insurance"* in *Philadelphia Business Journal (Vol. 28, May 11, 2012, No. 13, pp. 1)*
Pub: Baltimore Business Journal
Contact: Rhonda Pringle, President
E-mail: rpringle@bizjournals.com

Description: Health insurance companies are using different strategies to take advantage of the demand growth in health coverage in markets such as Philadelphia. Horizon Blue Cross lue Shield of New Jersey, for example, is creating a retail center where customers can get information from specially trained staff about insurance, health and wellness. IBC, on the other hand, has partnered with AAA Mid-Atlantic to market its plan option to AAA members. **Availability:** Print; Online.

31459 ■ *"Offer for Sears Canada 'Inadequate"* in *Globe & Mail (February 10, 2006, pp. B4)*
Description: The financial feasibility of Sears Holdings Corp.'s proposed acquisition of Sears Canada Inc., for $835 million, is discussed. **Availability:** Online.

31460 ■ *"Oil Markets: A Nasty Russian Tale"* in *Canadian Business (Vol. 81, March 3, 2008, No. 3, pp. 85)*
Pub: Rogers Media Inc.
Contact: Neil Spivak, Chief Executive Officer

Ed: Andrew Nikiforuk. **Description:** Billionaires Alex Shnaider and Michael Shtaif entered a partnership for an oil venture which ended in a slew of litigations. Cases of breach of contract, injurious falsehood and other related lawsuits were filed against Shnaider. Details of the lawsuits and the other parties involved in the disputes are presented. **Availability:** Online.

31461 ■ *"Old Friends Make Old Buildings Successful Restaurants"* in *Crain's Detroit Business (Vol. 24, February 4, 2008, No. 5, pp. 14)*
Pub: Crain Communications Inc.
Contact: Barry Asin, President

Ed: Brent Snavely. **Description:** Profiles of Jon Carlson and Gregory Lobdell, founders of ten new restaurants in Ann Arbor, Royal Oak, and Traverse City, Michigan, and their plans to add four more in the near future. **Availability:** Online.

31462 ■ *"Oliver Russell Acquiring Social Good Network"* in *Idaho Business Review (August 29, 2014)*
Pub: BridgeTower Media
Contact: Adam Reinebach, President

Description: Oliver Russell, owner of a Boise advertising firm, is acquiring the assets of startup Social Good Network, an online fundraising firm that was turned down for additional funding beyond its seed funding. Details of the deal and future plans are discussed.

31463 ■ *"Olympus is Urged to Revise Board"* in *Wall Street Journal Eastern Edition (November 28, 2011, pp. B3)*
Pub: Dow Jones & Company Inc.
Contact: Almar Latour, Chief Executive Officer

Ed: Phred Dvorak. **Description:** Koji Miyata, once a director on the board of troubled Japanese photographic equipment company, is urging the company to reorganize its board, saying the present group should resign their board seats but keep their management positions. The company has come under scrutiny for its accounting practices and costly acquisitions. **Availability:** Online.

31464 ■ *"OMERS Joins Bid for U.K. Port Giant"* in *Globe & Mail (March 28, 2006, pp. B1)*
Ed: Paul Waldie. **Description:** The plans of Ontario Municipal Employees Retirement Board to partner with Goldman Sachs Group Inc., in order to acquire Associated British Ports PLC, are presented. **Availability:** Online.

31465 ■ *"Other Players Want In On Ellis-St. Peter's Deal"* in *Business Review Albany (Vol. 41, July 4, 2014, No. 15, pp. 9)*
Pub: American City Business Journals, Inc.
Contact: Mike Olivieri, Executive Vice President

Released: Weekly. **Price:** $4, introductory 4-week offer(Digital only). **Description:** Other hospital systems and smaller health care providers expressed interest in joining the partnership between Ellis Medicine and St. Peter's Health Partners in Albany, New York. The partnership aims to transform a scattered health care industry into regional networks while allowing companies to maintain independent operations. **Availability:** Print; Online.

31466 ■ *"Ottawa to Push for Gas Deal Between Petrocan, Gazprom"* in *Globe & Mail (February 13, 2006, pp. B1)*
Ed: Greame Smith. **Description:** Jim Flaherty, finance minister of Canada is negotiating a 1.3 billion dollar deal between state owned Petro-Canada and Russia's OAO Gazprom. This once again highlighted the country's increasing dependence on Russia for its energy requirements. **Availability:** Online.

31467 ■ *"Out of This World"* in *Black Enterprise (November 2007)*
Pub: Earl G. Graves Ltd.
Contact: Earl Graves, Jr., President

Ed: Anthony Calypso. **Description:** Profile of Noah Samara, CEO of WorldSpace Inc. who raised $1 billion to help create the technological architecture for satellite radio. **Availability:** Online.

31468 ■ *"The Overlicensed Society"* in *Harvard Business Review (Vol. 90, April 2012, No. 4, pp. 38)*
Pub: Harvard Business Review Press
Contact: Moderna V. Pfizer, Contact

Ed: Robert E. Litan. **Price:** $6, hardcover. **Description:** The author argues that certification and licensing requirements are hindering professionals who might otherwise be able to find positions and provide services inexpensively. To key areas are healthcare and law. Federal mutual recognition agreements may be one method of addressing both practice and consumer protection issues. **Availability:** PDF; Online.

31469 ■ *"Panera Breadwinner Tries on Tattu Designer Jeans"* in *Houston Business Journal (Vol. 40, December 18, 2009, No. 32, pp. 1)*
Pub: Houston Business Journal
Contact: Bob Charlet, President
E-mail: bcharlet@bizjournals.com

Ed: Allison Wollam. **Description:** Chuck Cain, the franchisee who introduced Panera Bread to Houston, Texas has partnered with tax accountant Jim Jacobsen to introduce custom-make Tattu Jeans. As more Tattu Jeans outlets are being planned, Cain is using entrepreneurial lessons learned from Panera Bread in the new venture. Both Panera Bread and Tattu Jeans were opened by Cain during economic downturns. **Availability:** Print; Online.

31470 ■ *"Parent Firm's Global Reach, Stricter Air Quality Rules Have Stock Smiling"* in *Crain's Cleveland Business (October 15, 2007)*
Pub: Crain Communications Inc.
Contact: K. C. Crain, President

Ed: David Bennett. **Description:** Since Stock Equipment Co., a firm that makes industrial pollution control equipment, was acquired by Schenck Process Group, a diversified global manufacturer based in Germany, the company's orders from abroad have been on the rise. The purchase has opened the doors to regions such as Eastern and Central Europe, Latin America and Australia. **Availability:** Online.

31471 ■ *"Partnering for Success"* in *Art Business News (Vol. 36, October 2009, No. 10, pp. 4)*
Description: In such a volatile economy many savvy artists and gallery owners are turning to out-of-the-box partnerships for continued success; these partnerships are also pervading the Internet, especially with such social media networks as Facebook and Twitter where artists and businesses can develop a loyal following. **Availability:** PDF; Online.

31472 ■ *"Paterson Plots Comeback With Internet IPO"* in *Globe & Mail (February 20, 2006, pp. B1)*
Ed: Grant Robertson. **Description:** The initial public offering plans of chief executive officer Scott Paterson of JumpTV.com are presented. **Availability:** Online.

31473 ■ *"Patient Monitoring Tool Nears Testing Phase"* in *Pittsburgh Business Times (Vol. 33, February 7, 2014, No. 30, pp. 5)*
Pub: American City Business Journals, Inc.
Contact: Mike Olivieri, Executive Vice President

Description: Aided with a $500,000 investment, Wellbridge Health Inc. and its partner, Philadelphia-based Biotelemetry Inc., will launch an interactive and easy to use patient monitoring tool. Wellbridge CEO, Mary Del Brady, reports that this device will allow for a real-time monitoring of a patient's condition. **Availability:** Online.

31474 ■ *"PC Connection Acquires Cloud Software Provider"* in *New Hampshire Business Review (Vol. 33, March 25, 2011, No. 6, pp. 8)*
Description: Merrimack-based PC Connection Inc. acquired ValCom Technology, a provider of cloud-based IT service management software. Details of the deal are included. **Availability:** Print; Online.

31475 ■ *"The Perils of Partnering in Developing Markets: How a Health Care Provider Addresses the Risks That Come With Globalization"* in *Harvard Business Review (Vol. 90, June 2012, No. 6, pp23)*
Pub: Harvard Business Review Press
Contact: Moderna V. Pfizer, Contact

Ed: Steven J. Thompson. **Price:** $6. **Description:** Effective evaluation of international risk includes assessing the opportunity; ramping up processes, operations, and metrics; and establishing long-term functionality. Warning signs for each stage are also presented. **Availability:** Online; PDF.

31476 ■ *"Planned Rice MLP Latest In Series of Spinoffs"* in *Pittsburgh Business Times (Vol. 34, August 15, 2014, No. 4, pp. 6)*
Pub: American City Business Journals, Inc.
Contact: Mike Olivieri, Executive Vice President

Released: Weekly. **Price:** $4, introductory 4-week offer(Digital & Print). **Description:** Companies such as Rice Energy Inc., EQT Corporation and Consol

Energy, are separating their midstream businesses from exploration and production by forming master limited partnerships (MLPs) to gain tax benefits and a higher valuation on midstream assets. However, Kinder Morgan Inc. plans to reorganize and reacquire its three separate MLPs in an effort to streamline the company and remove its distribution incentive rights. **Availability:** Print; Online.

31477 ■ *"Please Pass the Mayo" in Crain's Chicago Business (Vol. 31, April 28, 2008, No. 17, pp. 32)*

Pub: Crain Communications Inc.

Contact: Barry Asin, President

Ed: Samantha Stainburn. **Description:** Fort Dearborn Co. has come a long way since it started as on one-press print shop; the family-owned company was struggling to keep up with the technology of making consumer product labels for curvy bottles of products like V8 V-Fusion juice and in 2006 sold off to Genstar Capital LLC which has pushed for acquisitions; last year, Fort Derborn bought its biggest competitor, Renaissance Mark Inc., doubling its size and adding spirit and wine makers to its client roster. **Availability:** Online.

31478 ■ *"Points of Law: Unbundling Corporate Legal Services to Unlock Value" in (Vol. 90, July-August 2012, No. 7-8, pp. 126)*

Pub: Harvard Business Review Press

Contact: Moderna V. Pfizer, Contact

Ed: Danny Ertel, Mark Gordon. **Price:** $8.95. **Description:** Maintaining the relationship between law firms and corporate legal departments requires aligning incentives between in-house counsel and law firm, and allocating work to the providers who are best-positioned to address it. **Availability:** Online; PDF.

31479 ■ *"Poor Economy Inspires Rich Alternatives In a Modern, and Tax-Free, Twist on Bartering" in Houston Chronicle (June 7, 2010)*

Pub: Houston Chronicle

Ed: Michael Rubinkam. **Description:** Time banking helps individuals and firms receive goods or services by depositing time dollars into a bank reserved for receipt of goods and services.

31480 ■ *"Power Partnerships" in Business Courier (Vol. 27, October 22, 2010, No. 25, pp. 1)*

Description: The $400 million Harrah's casino and the $47 million redevelopment and expansion of Washington Park are project aimed at boosting the economy in downtown Cincinnati, Ohio. These projects will be done in cooperation with the National Association for the Advancement of Colored People. Insights into the role of minority-owned businesses in regional economic development are explored. **Availability:** Print; Online.

31481 ■ *"Pre-Deal Trades More Common in Canada, Study Finds" in Globe & Mail (March 23, 2007, pp. B5)*

Ed: John Kipphoff, Joe Schneider. **Description:** The results of the study conducted by Measuredmarkets Inc. to examine the impact of merger activity on insider trading of the companies are presented. **Availability:** Print; Online.

31482 ■ *"Precision Crop Control with Valley Irrigation/CropMetrics Partnership" in Farm Industry News (January 6, 2011)*

Pub: Informa Business Media, Inc.

Contact: Charlie McCurdy, President

Ed: Karen McMahon. **Description:** Irrigation systems have become a precision farming tool since partnering with agronomic software systems to apply products across the field by prescription. Valley Irrigation and CropMetrics have partnered in order to variably control water, fertilizer and other crop management products through a center pivot irrigation system. **Availability:** Print; Online.

31483 ■ *"Private Equity Firm Links First Arizona Deal" in Business Journal-Serving Phoenix and the Valley of the Sun (November 2, 2007)*

Description: Pacific Investment Partners and Your Source Financial launched a $10 million fund and signed their first deal. The two companies acquires a minority stake in Dreambrands Inc. for $3 million. Dreambrands is using the capital to market its personal lubricant product Carrageenana.

31484 ■ *"Private Equity Firms Focus on Failing Banks" in Baltimore Business Journal (Vol. 28, July 16, 2010, No. 10, pp. 1)*

Pub: Baltimore Business Journal

Contact: Rhonda Pringle, President

E-mail: rpringle@bizjournals.com

Ed: Gary Haber. **Description:** Four deals in which assets of failed banks were acquired by private equity firms have been approved by the Federal Deposit Insurance Corporation in the past couple of years. Bay Bank FSK, for example, purchased Bay National Bank's assets in July 2010. Forecasts on more private equity acquisitions in the community banking industry are given. **Availability:** Print; Online.

31485 ■ *"Private Health-Care Services Growing in Canada" in Canadian Business (Vol. 85, June 11, 2012, No. 10, pp. 10)*

Ed: Laura Cameron. **Description:** Some public-private partnerships in Canada include the acquisition of clinics by Centric Health Corporation and the partnership between Westbank First National and Johns Hopkins Hospital. Private healthcare providers have operated by dividing their funding among government contracts, clients not covered by Medicare and patients paying out of pocket and non-insured services. **Availability:** Print; Online.

31486 ■ *"Proposed Triangle Redo in Motion" in Crain's Cleveland Business (Vol. 28, October 15, 2007, No. 41, pp. 1)*

Pub: Crain Communications Inc.

Contact: K. C. Crain, President

Ed: Stan Bullard. **Description:** Zaremba Homes and MRN Ltd. are partnering to redevelop the so-called Triangle section of University Circle. The proposed project will include a total of 434 new rental and for-sale residential suites and as much as 227,000 square feet of retail and restaurant space. **Availability:** Online.

31487 ■ *"Putting Down Roots" in Entrepreneur (August 2014)*

Released: October 28, 2016. **Description:** Entrepreneur Justin Hartfield and partner Doug Francis created Weedmaps.com, an online portal for marijuana dispensaries, after California legalized the sale of medical marijuana. Hartfield is looking forward to a billion-dollar business once the federal prohibition of marijuana is ended. Local dispensaries pay a monthly subscription of $420 to appear on the site while doctors pay $295 to be featured on the site. Harfield is seeking partnerships with laboratories that will provide marijuana testing and other services. **Availability:** Online.

31488 ■ *"A Questionable Chemical Romance" in Barron's (Vol. 88, July 14, 2008, No. 28, pp. 28)*

Pub: Dow Jones & Company Inc.

Contact: Almar Latour, Chief Executive Officer

Ed: Andrew Bary. **Description:** Dow Chemical paid $78-a-share for the surprise takeover of Rohm & Haas. The acquisition is reducing Dow Chemical's financial flexibility at a time when chemical companies are being affected by high costs and a weak U.S. economy. **Availability:** Online.

31489 ■ *"Ralcorp Investigated for Rejecting ConAgra Bid" in Saint Louis Business Journal (Vol. 32, September 16, 2011, No. 3, pp. 1)*

Pub: Saint Louis Business Journal

Contact: Robert Bobroff, President

E-mail: rbobroff@bizjournals.com

Ed: Evan Binns. **Description:** New York-based Levi & Korsinsky started investigating Ralcorp Holidngs Inc. after it rejected ConAgra Foods Inc.'s third and latest takeover bid of $5.17 billion. The investigation would determine whether Ralcorp's directors had acted on behalf of shareholders' best interest. **Availability:** Print; Online.

31490 ■ *"R&R Launches Upscale Spoony's and Low Fat Dragon's Den" in Ice Cream Reporter (Vol. 23, August 20, 2010, No. 9, pp. 3)*

Description: European ice cream manufacturer R&R has acquired French ice cream maker Rolland and will position itself as an upscale challenger to brands like Ben & Jerry's. **Availability:** Print; Online.

31491 ■ *"Regal Venture Puts Imax Back in the Spotlight" in Globe & Mail (March 13, 2007, pp. B5)*

Ed: Shirley Won. **Description:** Imax Corp. has signed new contract with cinema hall operating giant Regal Entertainment Corp. for constructing two more giant screen theaters. Share prices of Imax Corp. have increased sharply after this announcement. **Availability:** Online.

31492 ■ *"Regent's Signal, Once Powerful, Fading From Local Scene" in Business Courier (Vol. 27, June 4, 2010, No. 5, pp. 1)*

Pub: Business Courier

Ed: Dan Monk. **Description:** Los Angeles, California-based Oaktree Capital Management bought former Regent Communications Inc. from Chapter 11 bankruptcy and transformed it into Townsquare Media Inc., a privately held firm. Regent's corporate presence has faded fast in Cincinnati, Ohio as its operations wind down. Insights on Regent's failed business model are also given. **Availability:** PDF; Online.

31493 ■ *"Research, Treatment to Expand" in Philadelphia Business Journal (Vol. 28, June 22, 2012, No. 19, pp. 1)*

Pub: Baltimore Business Journal

Contact: Rhonda Pringle, President

E-mail: rpringle@bizjournals.com

Description: Fox Chase Cancer Center and Temple University Health System have been planning several projects once their merger is completed. Their plans include the construction of a unit for cancer patients on the third floor of the Founder's Building at Jeanes Hospital and a granting mechanism to fund research collaborations. **Availability:** Print; Online.

31494 ■ *"Revenge of the Scorned Protege" in Canadian Business (Vol. 85, September 17, 2012, No. 14, pp. 48)*

Ed: Joanna Pachner. **Released:** September 17, 2012. **Description:** The prospect of a merger between Canadian distributor Alliance Films and international television and independent films distributor Entertainment One Group is expected to control the Canadian market and could rationalize competition in Great Britain. Entertainment One's offerings to broadcasters and other partners will be added with Alliance's 11,000 movie titles.

31495 ■ *"RIM Reinforces Claim as Top Dog by Expanding BlackBerry Service" in Globe & Mail (March 11, 2006, pp. B3)*

Ed: Simon Avery. **Description:** The plans of Research in Motion Ltd. to enhance the features of BlackBerry, through acquisition of Ascendent Systems, are presented. **Availability:** Online.

31496 ■ *"Rimfire Minerals Corporation: Jake Gold Project-Drilling Planned for 2007" in Marketwired (May 16, 2007)*

Pub: Comtex News Network Inc.

Contact: Kan Devnani, President

Description: Rimfire Minerals Corporation and Island Arc Exploration Corporation formed a partnership to explore the Jake Property, a high-grade gold prospect with previously unrecognized potential to host economic gold mineralization, located 13 kilometers west of Clearwater, British Columbia. **Availability:** Print; Online.

31497 ■ "The Role of Leadership In Successful International Mergers and Acquisitions: Why Renault-Nissan Succeeded and DaimlerChrysler-Mitsubishi Failed" in Human Resource Management (Vol. 51,May-June 2012, No. 3, pp. 433-456)

Pub: John Wiley & Sons, Inc.

Contact: Christina Van Tassell, Executive Vice President Chief Financial Officer

Ed: Carol Gill. **Released:** May 25, 2012. **Description:** The effects of national and organizational culture on the performance of Nissan and Mitsubishi after their mergers with Renault and DaimlerChrysler respectively are examined. Japanese national culture was found to influence organizational culture and human resource management practices, while leadership affected the success of their turnaround efforts.

31498 ■ "Roll Your Own" in Business North Carolina (Vol. 28, March 2008, No. 3, pp. 66)

Description: Profile of U.S. Flue-Cured Tobacco Growers who process tobacco and make cigarettes. Details of the program are outlined. **Availability:** Online.

31499 ■ "Rose Pest Solutions Acquires Indiana Pest Control" in PCTonline (November 18, 2019)

URL(s): www.pctonline.com/article/rose-acquires-indiana-pest-control/

Ed: Brad Harbison. **Released:** November 18, 2019. **Description:** Troy, Michigan-based Rose Pest Solutions announced it acquired Indiana Pest Control. Both companies offer similar services in residential and commercial pest management along with wildlife control, but clients in Indiana will now benefit from Rose's canine bed bug inspections and professional fumigation. **Availability:** Online.

31500 ■ "Royal Dutch's Grip Firm on Shell" in Globe & Mail (March 19, 2007, pp. B1)

Ed: David Ebner. **Description:** The proposed acquisition of Shell Canada Ltd. by Royal Dutch Shell PLC for $8.7 billion is discussed. **Availability:** Print; Online.

31501 ■ "San Antonio's Alamo Iron Works Is On the Prowl for Acquisitions" in San Antonio Business Journal (Vol. 26, August 3, 2012, No. 27, pp. 1)

Pub: Baltimore Business Journal

Contact: Rhonda Pringle, President

E-mail: rpringle@bizjournals.com

Description: Alamo Iron Works is preparing for acquisitions two years after emerging from Chapter 11 bankruptc reorganization. The company is in talks to purchase other firms to strengthen its share in the Texas steel market and serve the state's energy industry.

31502 ■ The Savvy Gal's Guide to Online Networking: Or What Would Jane Austen Do?

Pub: Booklocker.com Inc.

Ed: Diane K. Danielson, Lindsey Pollak. **Description:** It is a truth universally acknowledged that a woman in search of a fabulous career must be in want of networking opportunities. Or so Jane Austen would say if she were writing, or more likely, blogging today. So begins the must-read guide to networking in the 21st Century. Authors and networking experts share the nuts, bolts and savvy secrets that businesswomen need in order to use technology to build professional relationships. **Availability:** Print; Online; PDF.

31503 ■ "Scanning Dell's Shopping List" in Barron's (Vol. 89, July 13, 2009, No. 28, pp. 24)

Pub: Dow Jones & Company Inc.

Contact: Almar Latour, Chief Executive Officer

Ed: Mark Veverka. **Description:** It is believed that Dell will be looking for companies to acquire since they poached an experienced mergers-and-acquisitions executive. In addition Dell's CEO is

reportedly telling people he plans to go shopping. Dell executives have also stated an interest in data storage. **Availability:** Online.

31504 ■ "School for Tech Skills" in San Antonio Business Journal (Vol. 28, September 5, 2014, No. 30, pp. 4)

Pub: American City Business Journals, Inc.

Contact: Mike Olivieri, Executive Vice President

Released: Weekly. **Price:** $4, introductory 4-week offer(Digital & Print). **Description:** The Alamo Academies program is a nonprofit partnership between Alamo Colleges, local high schools, local industry groups and the City of San Antonio, Texas aimed at creating skilled workers. The program has been recognized by the Texas Higher Education Coordinating Board for meeting the state's goal of reducing the skills gap in the workforce. **Availability:** Print; Online.

31505 ■ "Sears and H&R Block Offer New Tax Preparation Options and Savings Through Tax Season" in Benzinga.com (January 30, 2012)

Description: Individuals preparing their own tax forms can file using www.sears.com/hrblock and receive a 15 percent discount on the purchase of Basic, Deluxe, and Premium H&R Block online editions. H&R Block at Sears also offers free 1040EZ filing online and in Sears stores. Customers filing on the site can also import previous year's tax data from TurboTax and TaxAct Online.

31506 ■ "Sears' Lampert Solid in Game of Valuation Chicken" in Globe & Mail (February 25, 2006, pp. B2)

Ed: Eric Reguly. **Description:** The feasibility of share value of Sears Canada Inc., following Sears Holdings Corp.'s acquisition, is discussed. **Availability:** Online.

31507 ■ "Sedo Keeps Trucking in Good Times and Bad" in Crain's Chicago Business (Vol. 31, April 28, 2008, No. 17, pp. 35)

Description: Discusses Seko Worldwide Inc., an Itasca-based freight forwarder, and its complicated road to growth and expansion on a global scale. **Availability:** Print; Online.

31508 ■ "Sense of Discovery" in Business Journal Portland (Vol. 27, November 19, 2010, No. 38, pp. 1)

Pub: Portland Business Journal

Contact: Andy Giegerich, Managing Editor

E-mail: agiegerich@bizjournals.com

Description: Tigard, Oregon-based Exterro Inc. CEO Bobby Balachandran announced plans to go public without the help of an institutional investor. Balachandran believes Exterro could grow to a $100 million legal compliance software company in the span of three years. Insights on Exterro's growth as market leader in the $1 billion legal governance software market are also given. **Availability:** Print; Online.

31509 ■ "Sheet Metal Union Locals Join Forces: Could Help Local Contractors Compete for Bay Area Jobs" in Sacramento Business Journal (Vol. 29, June 29, 2012, No. 18, pp. 1)

Pub: Baltimore Business Journal

Contact: Rhonda Pringle, President

E-mail: rpringle@bizjournals.com

Description: The Sacramento Local 162 and Local 104 of Sheet Metal Workers International Association in California's Bay Area have merged, leading to an action that is expected to help local contractors compete for jobs in the area. Aside from improving efficiency in operations, the merger could also prevent duplication of services. Other potential benefits of the merger are discussed. **Availability:** Print; Online.

31510 ■ "A Signaling Theory of Acquisition Premiums: Evidence From IPO Targets" in Academy of Management Journal (Vol. 55, June 1, 2012, No. 3, pp. 667)

Pub: Academy of Management

Contact: Sharon Alvarez, President

Ed: Jeffrey J. Reuer, Tony W. Tong, Cheng-Wei Wu. **Description:** The value of acquisition premiums that newly public targets capture in post-initial public offering (IPO) acquisitions is investigated. Results reveal greater benefits from signals such as interorganizational relationships for IPO targets selling their firms to acquirers from different industries. Associations with prominent alliance partners, venture capitalists and underwriters can also enhance the gains for acquisition targets. **Availability:** Electronic publishing; Download; PDF; Online.

31511 ■ "Size Does Matter" in International Journal of Globalisation and Small Business (Vol. 4, September 21, 2010, No. 1, pp. 61)

Ed: Julia Connell, Ranjit Voola. **Description:** Examination of how members of an Australian-based manufacturing and engineering cluster share knowledge through networking as a means to improve competitive advantage. **Availability:** Online.

31512 ■ "Sky Harvest Windpower Corp. - Operational Update" in Investment Weekly News (March 10, 2012, pp. 744)

Pub: PR Newswire Association LLC.

Description: Sky Harvest Windpower Corporation is rebranding its focus on gas and power activities both nationally and internationally. The firm's Canadian projects are outlined as well as its commitment to purse the Green Options Partners Program in 2012. **Availability:** Online.

31513 ■ "Small Firms Punch Ticket for Growth" in Houston Business Journal (Vol. 40, January 29, 2010, No. 38, pp. 1)

Pub: Houston Business Journal

Contact: Bob Charlet, President

E-mail: bcharlet@bizjournals.com

Ed: Allison Wollam. **Description:** Independent ticket agencies anticipate growth as American and Canadian authorities approved a merger between Ticketmaster and concert promoter Live Nation. Expansion of service offerings and acquisition of venues have also been done by independent ticket agencies in light of the merger. Details of the merger are included. **Availability:** Print; Online.

31514 ■ "Software's Last Hurrah" in Canadian Business (Vol. 81, December 24, 2007, No. 1, pp. 27)

Description: Canada's software industry could be facing a challenge with IBM's acquisition of Cognos, which was the country's last major independent business intelligence company and was also IBM's largest acquisition ever. Next in line to Cognos in terms of prominence is Open Text Corporation, which could also be a possible candidate for acquisition, as analysts predict. **Availability:** Print; Online.

31515 ■ "Solon Wire to Ramp Up Plant" in Memphis Business Journal (Vol. 33, March 23, 2012, No. 50, pp. 1)

Pub: Baltimore Business Journal

Contact: Rhonda Pringle, President

E-mail: rpringle@bizjournals.com

Description: Solon Wire Company is set to reopen a production facility, following its acquisition of Bluff City Steel Industries. Solon will begin manufacturing steel wires again by the end of March 2012. **Availability:** Print; Online.

31516 ■ "Some Relief Possible Following Painful Week" in Barron's (Vol. 88, July 14, 2008, No. 28, pp. M3)

Pub: Dow Jones & Company Inc.

Contact: Almar Latour, Chief Executive Officer

Ed: Kopin Tan. **Description:** Dow Chemical is offering a 74 percent premium to acquire Rohm & Haas' coatings and electronics materials operations. Frontline amassed a 5.6 percent stake in rival Overseas Shipholding Group and a merger between the two would create a giant global fleet with pricing power. Highlights of the U.S. stock market during the week that ended in July 11, 2008 are discussed. Statistical data included. **Availability:** Online.

31517 ■ *"Sorrell Digs Deep to Snag TNS"* in *Advertising Age (Vol. 79, July 14, 2008, No. 7, pp. 1)*

Pub: Crain Communications, Inc.
Contact: Jessica Botos, Manager, Marketing
E-mail: jessica.botos@crainsnewyork.com

Ed: Michael Bush. **Description:** Martin Sorrell's strategic vision for expansion in order to become the largest ad-agency holding company in the world is discussed. **Availability:** Online.

31518 ■ *"Southwest Expected to Forego Subsidy Eventually"* in *Wichita Business Journal (Vol. 27, February 3, 2012, No. 5, pp. 1)*

Description: Southwest Airlines has taken over Air-Tran Airways service from Wichita to Atlanta and it would be using the subsidies that AirTran received as part of the Kansas-backed Affordable Airfares program. However, Southwest will only use the subsidies for two years since these are not part of its usual business model. Insights on the Afordable Airfares program are also given. **Availability:** Print; Online.

31519 ■ *"Southwest Expected to Up ICT Passenger Counts by Nearly 30 Percent: Taking Off"* in *Wichita Business Journal (Vol. 27, January 20, 2012, No. 3, pp. 1)*

Pub: Baltimore Business Journal
Contact: Rhonda Pringle, President
E-mail: rpringle@bizjournals.com

Ed: Daniel McCoy. **Description:** Passenger numbers at Wichita Mid-Continent Airport are expected to rise with the entry of Southwest Airlines. The airline will start serving the area uponn completion of its merger with AirTran Airways. **Availability:** Print; Online.

31520 ■ *"'Stalking Horse' Bidder Keeping Plextronics Here"* in *Pittsburgh Business Times (Vol. 33, March 28, 2014, No. 37, pp. 6)*

Pub: American City Business Journals, Inc.
Contact: Mike Olivieri, Executive Vice President

Released: March 28, 2014. **Price:** $4, Introductory 4-week offer(Digital & Print). **Description:** Chemical company Solvay American has acquired solar and lighting company Plextronics Inc. of Pittsburgh, Pennsylvania. Solvay's research and innovation department is seen as a better fit for Plextronics because it is developing a new technology. **Availability:** Print; Online.

31521 ■ *"State of the Unions"* in *Canadian Business (Vol. 81, December 8, 2008, No. 21, pp. 23)*

Pub: Mondaq Ltd.
Contact: Tim Harty, Chief Executive Officer

Ed: Sharda Prashad. **Description:** Companies planning on joint ventures should look for partners they can trust and respect and are also competent. Joint venture deals aim to bring existing products to a a new market or in acquiring a foreign product for an existing market. **Availability:** Print.

31522 ■ *"Steeling Themselves: Price Hikes Testing The Mettle of Scrap Dealers"* in *Baltimore Business Journal (Vol. 30, July 6, 2012, No. 9, pp. 1)*

Ed: James Bach. **Description:** Members of Maryland's steel sector have been seeking to revive the Sparrows Point steel plant. The plan also involves saving 2,000 jobs. Comments from executives included. **Availability:** Print; Online.

31523 ■ *"Stikemans' Ascent, Its Legacy, and Its Future"* in *Globe & Mail (January 29, 2007, pp. B2)*

Description: Pierre Raymond, chairman of legal firm Stikeman Elliott LLP, talks about his strategies to handle competition, his challenges, and about Canada's present mergers and acquisition scenario. Stikeman achieved the first place in 2006 M&A legal rankings. **Availability:** Online.

31524 ■ *"STMicroelectronics"* in *Canadian Electronics (Vol. 23, February 2008, No. 1, pp. 1)*

Description: STMicroelectronics, a semiconductor maker, revealed that it plans to acquire Genesis Microchip Inc. Genesis develops image and video processing systems. It was reported that the acquisition has been approved by Genesis' Board of Directors. It is expected that Genesis will enhance STMicroelectronics' technological capabilities. **Availability:** Online.

31525 ■ *"A Stock Worth Trading Down To"* in *Barron's (Vol. 88, July 14, 2008, No. 28, pp. 36)*

Pub: Dow Jones & Company Inc.
Contact: Almar Latour, Chief Executive Officer

Ed: Alexander Eule. **Description:** Shares of Ralcorp Holdings are cheap at around $49.95 after slipping 20 percent prior to their acquisition of Post cereals from Kraft. Some analysts believe its shares could climb over 60 percent to $80 as value-seeking consumers buy more private label products. **Availability:** Print; Online.

31526 ■ *"The Story Of Diane Greene"* in *Barron's (Vol. 88, July 14, 2008, No. 28, pp. 31)*

Pub: Dow Jones & Company Inc.
Contact: Almar Latour, Chief Executive Officer

Ed: Mark Veverka. **Description:** Discusses the ousting of Diane Greene as a chief executive of VMWare, a developer of virtualization software, after the firm went public; in this case Greene, a brilliant engineer, should not be negatively impacted by the decision because it is common for companies to bring in new executive leadership that is more operations oriented after the company goes public. **Availability:** Online.

31527 ■ *"Strategy Migration In a Changing Climate"* in *Harvard Business Review (Vol. 92, May 2014, No. 5, pp. 42)*

Pub: Harvard Business Publishing
Contact: Diane Belcher, Managing Director

Price: $6. **Description:** The CEO of World Wildlife Fund discusses the importance of ensuring reliable source supplies and mitigating reputational and financial risk in promoting corporate sustainability. Forging alliances to achieve goals is also key. **Availability:** Online; PDF.

31528 ■ *"A Strong, Aligned Board of Directors Is Ideal"* in *South Florida Business Journal (Vol. 35, August 1, 2014, No. 1, pp. 8)*

Pub: American City Business Journals, Inc.
Contact: Mike Olivieri, Executive Vice President

Released: Weekly. **Price:** $8, introductory 4-week offer(Digital only). **Description:** The advantages of an informed and congruent board of directors to a company are described. The board of directors should provide the company with a strategic business perspective, access to prospective investors, and potential strategic business partners to help a firm achieve its vision and goals. **Availability:** Print; Online.

31529 ■ *"Subprime Mess Hits Huntington"* in *Business First-Columbus (November 26, 2007, pp. A1)*

Pub: Business First
Contact: Nick Fortine, President
E-mail: nfortine@bizjournals.com

Ed: Adrian Burns. **Description:** Huntington Bancshares Inc. picked up a $1.5 billion exposure to the country's subprime mortgage mess. It caused the bank to set aside $450 million to cover increases in loan losses. When Huntington acquired Sky Financial, it absorbed a 17-year relationship Sky had with Franklin Credit Corporation, which is a subprime lender and servicer. **Availability:** Print; Online.

31530 ■ *"Sudbury Waits With Future Up in the Air"* in *Globe & Mail (February 22, 2006, pp. B1)*

Ed: Wendy Stueck. **Description:** The takeover of Falconbridge Ltd., by Inco Ltd Sudbury, is in the process with uncertainty. The transaction has been a long overdue. **Availability:** Online.

31531 ■ *"SunBank Plans Expansion Via Wal-Mart"* in *Business Journal-Serving Phoenix and the Valley of the Sun (Vol. 10, November 8, 2007)*

Pub: Phoenix Business Journal
Contact: Alex McAlister, Director
E-mail: amcalister@bizjournals.com

Ed: Chris Casacchia. **Description:** SunBank plans to install 12 to 14 branches in Wal-Mart stores in Arizona and hire 100 bankers by the end of 2008. Wal-Mart also offers financial products at other stores through partnerships with other banks. **Availability:** Print; Online.

31532 ■ *"Suppliers May Follow Fiat: Local Group Says Italian Firms are Inquiring"* in *Crain's Detroit Business (Vol. 25, June 15, 2009, No. 24, pp. 1)*

Pub: Crain Communications Inc.
Contact: Barry Asin, President

Ed: Ryan Beene. **Description:** Italian suppliers to Fiat SpA are looking toward Detroit after the formation of Chrysler Group LLC, the Chrysler-Fiat partnership created from Chrysler's bankruptcy. The Italian American Alliance for Business and Technology is aware of two Italy-based powertrain component suppliers that are considering a move to Detroit. **Availability:** Online.

31533 ■ *"Surge in the South"* in *Canadian Business (Vol. 85, June 11, 2012, No. 10, pp. 48)*

Ed: Jeff Beer. **Description:** Canada should get involved as a trading partner in the emerging markets as South-South trade, which is between these markets, is projected to grow between 2012 and 2030 from 13 percent of global trade to 26 percent. Canadian firms can join the South-South trade by setting up operations in an emeging market and use it as a base for trade or by acting as facilitator between trade partners. **Availability:** Online.

31534 ■ *"Swope: Breakup Won't Delay East Village"* in *The Business Journal-Serving Metropolitan Kansas City (Vol. 26, August 22, 2008, No. 50, pp. 1)*

Pub: American City Business Journals, Inc.
Contact: Mike Olivieri, Executive Vice President

Ed: Rob Roberts. **Description:** Swope Community Builders said that the Kansas City Redevelopment Project will not be delayed by the breakup of their partnership with Sherman Associates Inc. Swopes will be the sole master developer of the project. **Availability:** Online.

31535 ■ *"Symbility Solutions Joins Motion Computing Partner Program"* in *Marketwired (May 14, 2007)*

Pub: Comtex News Network Inc.
Contact: Kan Devnani, President

Description: Symbility Solutions Inc., a wholly owned subsidiary of Automated Benefits Corp., announced an agreement with Alliance Partner of Motion Computing, a leader in wireless communications and mobile computing, in which both companies will invest in a sales and marketing strategy that focuses specifically on the insurance market. **Availability:** Print; Online.

31536 ■ *"Synthesis: From Lone Hero to a Culture of Leadership"* in *Harvard Business Review (Vol. 88, November 2010, No. 11, pp. 146)*

Pub: Harvard Business Publishing
Contact: Diane Belcher, Managing Director

Ed: Charles J. Palus, John B. McGuire. **Released:** November 30, 2010. **Description:** Review of the book, 'Working Together: Why Great Partnerships Succeed', is given. **Availability:** Print; Online.

31537 ■ *"Syracuse Gear Manufacturer Buys Buffalo Company"* in *Business First of Buffalo (Vol. 30, January 24, 2014, No. 19, pp. 3)*

Pub: American City Business Journals, Inc.
Contact: Mike Olivieri, Executive Vice President

Released: Weekly. **Price:** $140, One-Year Print & Digital; $115, One-Year Digital. **Description:** Niagara Gear Corporation of Buffalo, New York was acquired by Gear Motions Inc., in a deal that could make Gear Motions the largest precision gear manufacturer for the commercial and industrial compressor market. Niagara Gear will supply larger ground and cut spur and helical gears to existing customers as part of the sale. **Availability:** Print; Online.

31538 ■ *"Taking a Leap With Mobile Wi-Fi" in Austin Business Journal (Vol. 34, July 25, 2014, No. 23, pp. 10)*
Pub: American City Business Journals, Inc.
Contact: Mike Olivieri, Executive Vice President

Released: July 25, 2014. **Price:** $4, introductory 4-week offer(Digital only). **Description:** Austin-based semi-conductor design company Nitero Inc.'s recent release of its Wi-Fi chip, Nietero's key rival Wilocity Ltd.'s acquisition by a tech giant, pushing demand for semiconductors; thus spurring growth for Nitero. It's Wi-Fi's system for mobile platforms will enable users to do more things on their Smartphones, thus converging more devices into one. **Availability:** Print; Online.

31539 ■ *"Taking the Over-the-Counter Route to U.S." in Barron's (Vol. 88, July 7, 2008, No. 27, pp. 24)*
Pub: Dow Jones & Company Inc.
Contact: Almar Latour, Chief Executive Officer

Ed: Eric Uhlfelder. **Description:** Many multinational companies have left the New York Stock Exchange and allowed their shares to trade over-the-counter. The companies have taken advantage of a 2007 SEC rule allowing publicly listed foreign companies to change trading venues if less than 5 percent of global trading volume in the past 12 months occurred in the US. **Availability:** Online.

31540 ■ *"Target to Power New Toys 'R' Us Online Business" in Reuters (October 8, 2019)*
URL(s): www.reuters.com/article/us-target-toys-r-us/target-to-power-new-toys-r-us-online-business-idUSKBN1WN1GG

Released: October 08, 2019. **Description:** Target announced a partnership with Tru Kids, which is the parent of the Toys 'R' Us brand, in order to run their toy website, ToysRUs.com. Consumers have the option to complete their purchase at Target.com. **Availability:** Online.

31541 ■ *"Targeted Personal Trainer Business Strategies Build Clients, Income, Business and Success" in Marketing Weekly News (August 4, 2012)*
Description: Various business strategies can help personal trainers build their business include getting certified, creating postcards or flyers, and partnering with other fitness professionals. **Availability:** Print; PDF; Online.

31542 ■ *"Tastee-Freez Celebrates 60th Anniversary" in Ice Cream Reporter (Vol. 23, July 20, 2010, No. 8, pp. 2)*
Description: Tastee-Freez founders, Leo Moranz (inventor) and Harry Axene, an inventor partnered to market the soft-serve pump and freezer for serving frozen treats back in 1950. **Availability:** Print; Online.

31543 ■ *"Tasti D-Lite Has Franchise Agreement for Australia" in Ice Cream Reporter (Vol. 23, November 20, 2010, No. 12, pp. 3)*
Description: Tasti D-Lite signed an international master franchise agreement with Friezer Australia Pty. Ltd. and will open 30 units throughout Australia over the next five years. **Availability:** Print; Online.

31544 ■ *"Tax Services Firm Ryan Prepares for Growth" in Dallas Business Journal (Vol. 35, June 29, 2012, No. 42, pp. 1)*
Pub: Baltimore Business Journal
Contact: Rhonda Pringle, President
E-mail: rpringle@bizjournals.com

Ed: Candace Carlisle. **Description:** Ryan LLC is seen to grow with three pending acquisitions. The tax services firm has opened offices in Australia and Singapore. **Availability:** Print; Online.

31545 ■ *"Teachers, U.S. Fund Providence Made Moves On BCE Buyout" in Globe & Mail (April 10, 2007, pp. B17)*
Ed: Boyd Erman, Sinclair Stewart, Jacquie McNish. **Description:** The Ontario Teachers' Pension Plan, the largest shareholder of telecommunications firm BCE Inc., has called for a partnership with buyout firm Providence Equity Partners Inc. in order to acquire BCE Inc. **Availability:** Online.

31546 ■ *"Teaching Sales: Great Sales Professionals are Scarce and Getting Scarcer. Why Aren't Universities Working Harder to Create More?" in (Vol. 90, July-August 2012, No. 7-8, pp. 94)*
Pub: Harvard Business Review Press
Contact: Moderna V. Pfizer, Contact

Ed: Suzanne Fogel, David Hoffmeister, Richard Rocco, Daniel P. Strunk. **Price:** $8.95, PDF and hardcover black and white. **Description:** Partnerships between industry and business schools can improve the quality of new sales education programs, increasing access to funding and talent. Industry input to school curricula and scholarly research informing business decisions will produce mutual benefits. **Availability:** Print; PDF; Online.

31547 ■ *"TELUS Says No Thanks to Joining BCE Fray" in Globe & Mail (April 24, 2007, pp. B1)*
Ed: Eric Reguly, Catherine McLean. **Description:** The causes of the refusal of TELUS Corp. to try and acquire BCE Inc. are discussed. The prospects of the acquisition of TELUS Corp. by private equity funds are discussed, besides the availability of cash with private equity funds. **Availability:** Online.

31548 ■ *"This Just In: TechTown, Partners Get $1M to Start Tech Exchange" in Crain's Detroit Business (Vol. 25, June 1, 2009, No. 22, pp. 1)*
Pub: Crain Communications Inc.
Contact: Barry Asin, President

Ed: Daniel Duggan. **Description:** Three veterans of the auto industry have partnered to create, Revitalizing Michigan, a nonprofit dedicated to help manufacturers improve their processes. The firm is seeking federal, state and private grants to fund the mission. **Availability:** Print; Online.

31549 ■ *"Tiny Telecom Big Prize in Bell Aliant Bid Battle" in Globe & Mail (April 4, 2007, pp. B1)*
Ed: Catherine McLean. **Description:** The competition between Bell Aliant Regional Communications Income Fund of BCE Inc. and Bragg Communications Inc. to bid for acquiring Amtelecom Income Fund is discussed. **Availability:** Online.

31550 ■ *"TiVo, Domino's Team to Offer Pizza Ordering by DVR" in Advertising Age (Vol. 79, November 17, 2008, No. 43, pp. 48)*
Pub: Crain Communications Inc.
Contact: Jessica Botos, Manager, Marketing
E-mail: jessica.botos@crainsnewyork.com

Ed: Brian Steinberg. **Description:** Domino's Pizza and TiVo are teaming up to make it possible for customers to order from the restaurant straight from their DVR. The companies see that this kind of interactive television and consumer experience will only serve to generate more sales as the customer can be exposed to a fuller range of menu selections and will not have to interrupt their viewing, while workers can spend more time making the product. **Availability:** Online.

31551 ■ *"Tony Armand, Shock Doctor CEO" in Business Journal (Vol. 31, March 21, 2014, No. 43, pp. 6)*
Pub: American City Business Journals, Inc.
Contact: Mike Olivieri, Executive Vice President

Released: March 21, 2014. **Price:** $4, print. **Description:** Tony Armand, CEO of Shock Doctor Inc., discusses the company's acquisition by private equity firm Bregal Partners. Armand believes the deal will give the sports protective equipment manufacturer a strong financial partner that will help with the executive strategy. **Availability:** Print; Online.

31552 ■ *"Toolmakers' New Tack: Firms' Goal -- Advance Wind-Turbine Technology" in Crain's Detroit Business (Vol. 25, June 8, 2009,)*
Pub: Crain Communications Inc.
Contact: Barry Asin, President

Ed: Ryan Beene, Amy Lane. **Description:** MAG Industrial Automation Systems LLC and Dowding Machining Inc. have partnered to advance wind-turbine technology. The goal is to cut costs of wind energy to the same level as carbon-based fuel. **Availability:** Print; Online.

31553 ■ *"Top Law Firms Join Forces" in Business Journal Portland (Vol. 27, December 3, 2010, No. 40, pp. 1)*
Pub: Portland Business Journal
Contact: Andy Giegerich, Managing Editor
E-mail: agiegerich@bizjournals.com

Description: Law Firms Powell PC and Roberts Kaplan LLP will forge a collaboration, whereby 17 Roberts Kaplan attorneys will join the Portland, Oregon-based office of Lane Powell. The collaboration is expected to strengthen the law firms' grip on Portland's banking clients. **Availability:** Print; Online.

31554 ■ *"Toys R Us Is Coming Back But with a Different Approach" in NPR (July 18, 2019)*
URL(s): www.npr.org/2019/07/18/743157480/toys-r-us-is-coming-back-but-with-a-different-approach

Ed: Dani Matias. **Released:** July 18, 2019. **Description:** The iconic chain of stores, Toys R Us, is coming back and relaunched in the US, but with a different twist from its old business model. Tru Kids Brand, the parent company, announced that Toys R Us will come back with smaller stores that will feature toy demonstrations and open play areas. This is in partnership with b8ta, which owns similar stores. **Availability:** Online.

31555 ■ *"Transcontinental to Exchange Assets with Quad/Graphics" in American Printer (Vol. 128, August 1, 2011, No. 8)*
Description: Transcontinental Inc. and Quad/Graphics Inc. entered into an agreement where Transcontinental will indirectly acquire all shares of Quad Graphics Canada Inc. **Availability:** Print; Online.

31556 ■ *"Trust Buyouts Not My Fault, Flaherty Says" in Globe & Mail (April 3, 2007, pp. B1)*
Ed: Tara Perkins, Doug Saunders, Steven Chase. **Description:** The causes of the acquisition of Canadian firms by foreign investors are discussed by the Canadian Finance Minister Jim Flaherty. **Availability:** Online.

31557 ■ *"Trust Tax Under Fire as Drain on Revenue" in Globe & Mail (April 9, 2007, pp. B1)*
Ed: Steven Chase. **Description:** The economic aspects of the implementation of the trust levy by the Canadian government are discussed. The acquisition of Canadian income trusts by Canadian and international financial institutions is described. **Availability:** Online.

31558 ■ *"U-Swirl To Open in Salt Lake City Metro Market" in Ice Cream Reporter (Vol. 23, November 20, 2010, No. 12, pp. 4)*
Description: Healthy Fast Food Inc., parent company to U-SWIRL International Inc., the owner and franchisor of U-SWIRL Frozen Yogurt cafes signed a franchising area development agreement for the Salt Lake City metropolitan area with Regents Management and will open 5 cafes over a five year period. **Availability:** Print; Online.

31559 ■ *"Under Fire, Sabia Triggers Battle for BCE"* in Globe & Mail (April 14, 2007, pp. B1)
Ed: Boyd Erman. **Description:** The announcement of negotiations for the sale of BCE Inc. by its chief executive officer Michael Sabia is discussed. The efforts of Ontario Teachers Pension Plan to submit its proposal for the sale are described. **Availability:** Online.

31560 ■ *"Unilever Acquiring Danish Operations of Diplom-Is Ice Cream"* in Ice Cream Reporter (Vol. 23, August 20, 2010, No. 9, pp. 1)
Description: Unilever will acquire Danish operations of the ice cream company Diplom-Is from Norwegian dairy group Tine. **Availability:** Print; Online.

31561 ■ *"Unilever Acquiring EVGA's Ice Cream Brands in Greece"* in Ice Cream Reporter (Vol. 23, October 20, 2010, No. 11, pp. 1)
Description: Unilever will acquire the ice cream brands and distribution network of the Greek frozen dessert manufacturer EVGA. **Availability:** Print; Online.

31562 ■ *"U.S. Buyer Rescues KCP From Trust Tax Burden"* in Globe & Mail (April 3, 2007, pp. B1)
Ed: Richard Blackwell. **Description:** The economic aspects of the buyout of KCP Income Fund by Caxton-Iseman Capital Inc. are discussed. **Availability:** Online.

31563 ■ *"United Way Offers Free Tax Assistance for Local Low-Income Families"* in The Blade (January 6, 2012)
Pub: Block Communications Inc.
URL(s): www.toledoblade.com
Ed: Kate Giammarise. **Description:** United Way of Greater Toledo, Ohio is offering free income tax preparation for households earning under $50,000 in 2011. United Way has partnered with the Lucas County Commissioner, Tina Skeldon Wozniak; Lucas County Treasurer, Wade Kapszukiewicz; and other social service agencies to help low-income workers in their region. **Availability:** Online.

31564 ■ *"University of Texas Deans Serious about Biz"* in Austin Business Journal (Vol. 31, May 20, 2011, No. 11, pp. 1)
Pub: Austin Business Journal
Contact: Rachel McGrath, Director
E-mail: rmcgrath@bizjournals.com
Ed: Sandra Zaragoza. **Description:** Dean Thomas Gilligan of the University of Texas, McCombs School of Business and engineering school Dean Gregory Fenves have partnered to develop a joint engineering and business degree. Their partnership has resulted in an undergraduate course on initiating startups. **Availability:** Print; Online.

31565 ■ *"Up In the Air"* in The Business Journal-Serving Greater Tampa Bay (Vol. 28, July 18, 2008, No. 30, pp. 1)
Description: Views and information on Busch Gardens and on its future, are presented. The park's 3,769 employees worry for their future, after tourism industry experts have expressed concerns on possible tax cuts and other cost reductions. The future of the park, which ranks number 19 as the most visited park in the world, is expected to have a major impact on the tourism industry. **Availability:** Online.

31566 ■ *"Uranerz Acquires Additional Uranium Property Adjoining Nichols Ranch"* in Marketwired (May 14, 2007)
Pub: Comtex News Network Inc.
Contact: Kan Devnani, President
Description: Uranerz Energy Corporation announced the successful leasing of the fee mineral lands that appear to host the "nose" of the oxidation-reduction geochemical front and has the potential for increasing the known uranium mineralization at the Nichols Ranch project which lies west of and adjacent to Uranerz's Nichols Ranch ISR uranium project. **Availability:** Print; Online.

31567 ■ *"Valener Announces that Gaz Metro has Achieved a Key Step in Acquiring CVPS"* in CNW Group (September 30, 2011)
Pub: CNW Group Ltd.
Description: Valener Inc., which owns about 29 percent of Gaz Metro Ltd. Partnership, announced that Gaz Metro welcomes the sale of Central Vermont Public Service Corporation (CVPS). Valener owns an indirect interest of 24.5 percent in the wind power projects jointly developed by Beaupre Eole General Partnership and Boralex Inc. on private lands in Quebec. Details of the deal are included. **Availability:** Print; Online.

31568 ■ *"VC-Heavy, Revenue-Light Sensicore Sold to GE Division"* in Crain's Detroit Business (Vol. 24, April 14, 2008, No. 15, pp. 28)
Pub: Crain Communications Inc.
Contact: Barry Asin, President
Ed: Tom Henderson. **Description:** General Electric has acquired Sensicore Inc., which although one of Michigan's most successful companies in raising venture capital was unable to generate significant revenue from its handheld water-testing devices. GE is capable of penetrating a larger market than a private company and will be able to take the devices to the municipal marketplace. **Availability:** Online.

31569 ■ *"Venture: Nonprofit Aims to Spur New Companies"* in South Florida Business Journal (Vol. 34, April 18, 2014, No. 39, pp. 8)
Pub: American City Business Journals, Inc.
Contact: Mike Olivieri, Executive Vice President
Released: Weekly. **Price:** $8, Introductory 4-week offer(Digital & Print). **Description:** The Scripps Research Institute has created the Scripps Advance group with an aim to turn early-stage research from its scientists in Jupiter, Florida and La Jolla, California into companies and to obtain venture capital funding to support clinical trials. Johnson and Johnson Innovation has become its first collaborator. The terms of the collaboration are also presented. **Availability:** Print; Online.

31570 ■ *"Volvo: Logistics Agreement to Reduce Environmental Impact"* in Ecology, Environment & Conservation Business (July 19, 2014, pp. 28)
Pub: NewsRX LLC.
Contact: Kalani Rosell, Contact
Description: Scandinavian Logistics Partners AB (Scanlog) will sell surplus capacity in rail transport from Belgium to Sweden to the Volvo Group. The partnership benefits both costs and environmental impact. The Volvo group is committed to optimizing transport of their manufactured cars and trucks. **Availability:** Online.

31571 ■ *"Want Leverage? Multi-Unit Franchisees Deliver Substantial Savings"* in Franchising World (Vol. 42, October 2010, No. 10, pp. 39)
Pub: International Franchise Association
Contact: Matthew Haller, President
E-mail: mhaller@franchise.org
Ed: Aziz Hashim. **Description:** Many retail franchises selling the same product are able to buy in bulk. Volume-buying can save money for any franchise. **Availability:** Online.

31572 ■ *"Water Treatment Player Zenon Goes to GE"* in Globe & Mail (March 15, 2006, pp. B1)
Ed: Leonard Zehr. **Description:** General Electric Co. acquires Ontario-based company, Zenon Environmental Inc., a technology giant in purifying water in northern Canada. **Availability:** Online.

31573 ■ *"Wayne, Oakland Counties Create Own 'Medical Corridor"* in Crain's Detroit Business (Vol. 24, October 6, 2008, No. 40, pp. 8)
Pub: Crain Communications Inc.
Contact: Barry Asin, President

Ed: Jay Greene. **Description:** Woodward Medical Corridor that runs along Woodward Avenue and currently encompasses twelve hospitals and is rapidly growing with additional physician offices, advanced oncology centers and new hospitals. Beaumont Hospital is building a $160 million proton-beam therapy cancer center on its Royal Oak campus in a joint venture with Procure Treatment Centers of Bloomington Ind. That is expected to open in 2010 and will employ approximately 145 new workers. **Availability:** Online.

31574 ■ *"A Week of the Worst Kind of Selling"* in Barron's (Vol. 88, June 30, 2008, No. 26, pp. M3)
Pub: Dow Jones & Company Inc.
Contact: Almar Latour, Chief Executive Officer
Ed: Kopin Tan. **Description:** In the week that ended in June 27, 2008 the selloff in the U.S. stock market was brought on by mounting bank losses and the spread of economic slowdown on top of high oil prices. The 31 percent decrease in the share price of Ingersoll-Rand since October 2007 may have factored in most of its risks. The company has completed its acquisition of Trane to morph into a refrigeration-equipment company. **Availability:** Online.

31575 ■ *"West Sacramento Food Shipper Changes Hands"* in Sacramento Business Journal (Vol. 31, May 30, 2014, No. 3)
Pub: American City Business Journals, Inc.
Contact: Mike Olivieri, Executive Vice President
Released: Weekly. **Price:** $4, Introductory 4-week offer(Digital & Print). **Description:** United Natural Foods Inc. (UNFI) is acquiring Tony's Fine Foods in a $195 million deal that brings together two companies native to Sacramento, California. Tony's is the leading distributor of perishable food products since 1934 and will operate as a wholly-owned subsidiary of UNFI as part of the deal. **Availability:** Print; Online.

31576 ■ *"What's In a Relationship? The Case of Commercial Lending"* in Business Horizons (Vol. 51, March-April 2008, No. 2, pp. 93)
Pub: Elsevier Advanced Technology Publications
Ed: Gregory F. Udell. **Description:** Academic literature on relationship lending and banking to small and medium enterprises is analyzed. This practice is best suited to some SME types but creates special challenges for bank managers. Relationship lending may also be better delivered by community banks. **Availability:** PDF; Online.

31577 ■ *"When Anything (And Everything) Goes"* in Globe & Mail (January 20, 2007, pp. B4)
Ed: Elizabeth Church. **Description:** The forecast on acquisition of different real estate firms is presented. **Availability:** Online.

31578 ■ *"Why Intel Should Dump Its Flash-Memory Business"* in Barron's (Vol. 88, March 10, 2008, No. 10, pp. 35)
Pub: Dow Jones & Company Inc.
Contact: Almar Latour, Chief Executive Officer
Ed: Eric J. Savitz. **Description:** Intel Corp. must sell its NAND flash-memory business as soon as it possibly can to the highest bidder to focus on its PC processor business and take advantage of other business opportunities. Apple should consider a buyback of 10 percent of the company's shares to lift its stock. **Availability:** Online.

31579 ■ *"Why Life Science Needs Its Own Silicon Valley: Human Genomics Won't Reach Its Full Potential Until It Has a Sizable Industry Cluster"* in Harvard Business Review (Vol. 90, July-August 2012, pp. 25)
Pub: Harvard Business Review Press
Contact: Moderna V. Pfizer, Contact
Ed: Fariborz Ghadar, John Sviokla, Dietrich A. Stephan. **Price:** $6, PDF and hardcover black and white. **Description:** The creation of an industry cluster will be key to advancing human genomics research. High degrees of specialization via multiple

contributors will be needed to generate significant innovations; an accessible, coherent data source will also be necessary. **Availability:** Print; PDF; Online.

31580 ■ *"Why Nestle Should Sell Alcon"* in *Barron's (Vol. 88, March 17, 2008, No. 11, pp. M12)*

Pub: Dow Jones & Company Inc.

Contact: Almar Latour, Chief Executive Officer

Ed: Sean Walters. **Description:** Nestle should sell Alcon because Nestle can't afford to be complacent as its peers have made changes to their portfolios to boost competitiveness. Nestle's stake in Alcon and L'Oreal have been ignored by investors and Nestle could realize better value by strengthening its nutrition division through acquisitions. **Availability:** Online.

31581 ■ *Wikinomics: How Mass Collaboration Changes Everything*

Pub: Penguin Publishing Group

Ed: Don Tapscott, Anthony D. Williams, Anthony D. Williams. **Released:** September 28, 2010. **Price:** $16.93, paperback; $8.99, e-book; $12.77, audio; $17, paperback; $13.99. **Description:** Research and information about the every changing world of the Internet is provided to help small businesses. **Availability:** E-book; Print; Electronic publishing.

31582 ■ *"With Algoma Steel Gone, Is Stelco Next?"* in *Globe & Mail (April 16, 2007, pp. B1)*

Ed: Greg Keenan. **Description:** Speculation in Canadian steel industry over possible sale of Stelco Inc. too after the sale of Algoma Steel Inc. to Essar Global Ltd. is discussed. **Availability:** Online.

31583 ■ *Working Together: Why Great Partnerships Succeed*

Pub: Harper Business

Contact: Hollis Heimbouch, Senior Vice President Publisher

Ed: Michael D. Eisner, Aaron Cohen. **Released:** September 14, 2010. **Price:** $13.59, trade paperback. **Description:** Michael D. Eisner, former CEO of the Walt Disney Company interviews corporate partners from various industries, including Bill and Melinda Gates and Warren Buffet and Charlie Munger. Why certain business partnerships succeed in the corporate world is discussed. **Availability:** E-book; Print; Download; Audio.

31584 ■ *"World Watch: Where Michigan Does Business"* in *Crain's Detroit Business (Vol. 30, October 13, 2014, No. 41, pp. 22)*

Pub: Crain Communications Inc.

Contact: Barry Asin, President

Description: Canada is Michigan's closest trading partner. Canada's most significant industries include chemicals, minerals, wood/paper products, food products, transportation equipment, petroleum and natural gas. Canada is also the largest energy supplier to the United States, thus helping Canada's petroleum sector grow. Major export partners of Canada include: U.S. (74.5 percent), China (4.3 percent) and the United Kingdom (4.1 percent). Major exports include motor vehicles and parts, aircraft, telecommunication equipment, chemicals, crude petroleum and natural gas. **Availability:** Online.

31585 ■ *"Xstrata's Takeover Bid Comes Up Short in Shareholders' Eyes"* in *Globe & Mail (March 27, 2007, pp. B16)*

Ed: Andy Hoffman. **Description:** The share holders of LionOre Mining International have expressed dissatisfaction over $4.6 billion take over by Xstrata PLC. Share holders are demanding more prices for share value. **Availability:** Online.

31586 ■ *"The Yahoo Family Tree"* in *Conde Nast Portfolio (Vol. 2, June 2008, No. 6, pp. 34)*

Pub: Conde Nast Publications

Contact: Agnes Chu, President

Ed: Blaise Zerega. **Description:** Yahoo, founded in 1994 by Stanford students Jerry Yang and David Filo, is still an Internet powerhouse. The company's history is also outlined as well as the reasons in which Microsoft desperately wants to acquire the firm. **Availability:** Print.

31587 ■ *"Year In Review: Houston-Area IPOs Included Nation's Largest"* in *Houston Business Journal (Vol. 44, January 3, 2014, No. 35, pp. 5)*

Pub: American City Business Journals, Inc.

Contact: Mike Olivieri, Executive Vice President

Released: January 03, 2014. **Description:** A list of the initial public offerings (IPOs) held in Houston, Texas, during 2013 is presented. Houston-based Frank's International NV's IPO raised $712 million in August at $22 share price and Cheniere Energy Partners LP Holdings LLC raised $677 million at $20 share price in December. Both companies were included among the nation's largest IPOs. **Availability:** Print; Online.

31588 ■ *"Younger, Permenter Build New Real Estate Firm in Dallas"* in *Dallas Business Journal (Vol. 35, May 18, 2012, No. 36, pp. 1)*

Pub: Baltimore Business Journal

Contact: Rhonda Pringle, President

E-mail: rpringle@bizjournals.com

Ed: Candace Carlisle. **Description:** Former Grubb and Ellis brokers Moody Younger and Kathy Permenter have started Younger Partners Commercial LLC, a new commercial real estate firm based in Dallas. The idea for Younger Partners came about after Grubb and Ellis was acquired by BGC Partners Inc. The firm plans to concentrate on office leasing and corporate service. **Availability:** Print; Online.

31589 ■ *"Zucker's HBC Shakeup Imminent"* in *Globe & Mail (February 20, 2006, pp. B3)*

Ed: Marina Strauss. **Description:** The plans of investor Jerry Zucker to revamp Hudson's Bay Co., upon its acquisition, are presented. **Availability:** Online.

VIDEO/AUDIO MEDIA

31590 ■ *The How of Business: David Siegel - Avoiding Partnership Disputes*

URL(s): www.thehowofbusiness.com/431-david-siegel-partnership-disputes

Ed: Henry Lopez. **Released:** July 18, 2022. **Description:** Podcast discusses partnership agreements, avoiding disputes, and being adequately capitalized to avoid disputes. Also highlights common mistakes and how to extricate yourself from a bad partnership.

31591 ■ *The How of Business: Pat Flynn & Matt Gartland - Entrepreneurships & Partnerships*

URL(s): www.thehowofbusiness.com/462-flynn-gartland-entrepreneurship-partnership

Ed: Henry Lopez. **Released:** March 06, 2023. **Description:** Podcast explains how two entrepreneurs make their partnership work.

31592 ■ *The How of Business: Prepare for Successful Partnership*

URL(s): www.thehowofbusiness.com/465-prepare-for-business-partnerships

Ed: Henry Lopez. **Released:** March 27, 2023. **Description:** Podcast offers considerations for a business partnership, including discussing various situations with the prospective partner and executing a comprehensive legal agreement.

31593 ■ *How to Monetize Partnerships*

URL(s): www.startuphustlepodcast.com/how-to-monetize-partnerships

Ed: Matt Watson. **Released:** October 09, 2023. **Description:** Podcast discusses white-label partnerships, integration partnerships, and content and referral partnerships.

31594 ■ *Main Street Business Insights: Kaycee McCoy, Pawsnickety Pets*

URL(s): mainstreet.org/resources/knowledge-hub/podcast/kaycee-mccoy-pawsnickety-pets

Ed: Matt Wagner. **Released:** October 16, 2024. **Description:** Podcast offers a conversation with the co-owners of an all-natural and organic pet supply business.

31595 ■ *Side Hustle to Small Business: Succeeding in Business after Leaving a Partnership*

URL(s): www.hiscox.com/side-hustle-to-small-business/jennifer-stewart-gateway-productivity-podcast-season-3

Ed: Sanjay Parekh. **Released:** October 11, 2023. **Description:** Podcast discusses leaving a partnership.

31596 ■ *This Is Small Business: Danyel Manages a Momentous Merger*

URL(s): www.smallbusiness.amazon/podcast-episodes/ep-27-danyel-manages-a-momentous-merger

Ed: Andrea Marquez. **Released:** May 16, 2023. **Description:** Podcast discusses preparing and managing a business merger.

31597 ■ *This Is Small Business: Meghan Parts Ways with Her Business Partner*

URL(s): www.smallbusiness.amazon/podcast-episodes/ep-21-meghan-parts-ways-with-her-business-partner

Ed: Andrea Marquez. **Released:** April 04, 2023. **Description:** Podcast discusses parting ways with a business partner and the legal considerations that go along with it. .

31598 ■ *This Is Small Business: Pros and Cons of a Business Partnership*

URL(s): www.smallbusiness.amazon/podcast-episodes/ep-22-pros-and-cons-of-a-business-partnership

Ed: Andrea Marquez. **Released:** April 21, 2021. **Description:** Podcast discusses the pros and cons of business partnership.

CONSULTANTS

31599 ■ *Air Comm Corp. (ACC)*

1575 W 124th Ave., Ste. 210

Westminster, CO 80234

Ph: (303)440-4075

Co. E-mail: info@aircommcorp.com

URL: http://www.aircommcorp.com

Contact: Kim A. Spero, Contact

Facebook: www.facebook.com/Air-Comm-Corporation-111186934536946

Linkedin: www.linkedin.com/company/air-comm-corporation

X (Twitter): x.com/AirCommCorp

Instagram: www.instagram.com/aircommcorp

Description: Firm engages in manufacturing bleed air heaters and vapor-cycle air conditioners. **Founded:** 1987.

31600 ■ *ARDITO Information and Research Inc.*

910 Foulk Rd., Ste. 200

Wilmington, DE 19803

Description: A full-service information and research firm. Provides information in areas of financial data, published research, demographic data, industry-specific publications, competitor data, marketing and sales trends, new product developments, government relations, bibliographies. Industries served are pharmaceutical, health, publishing and environment and business. **Scope:** A full-service information and research firm. Provides information in areas of financial data, published research, demographic data, industry-specific publications, competitor data, marketing and sales trends, new product developments, government relations, bibliographies. Industries served are pharmaceutical, health, publishing and environment and business. **Publications:** "The Swine flu pandemic: Authoritative information versus community gossip," Searcher, Oct, 2009; "The Medical blogosphere: How social networking platforms are changing medical searching," Searcher, May, 2009; "Social Networking and Video Web Sites:

MySpace and YouTube Meet the Copyright Cops," Searcher, May, 2007; "Copyright Clearance Center raises transactional fees," Information Today, Jul, 2004.

31601 ■ The Argus Group
5950 Canoga Ave., Ste. 515
Woodland Hills, CA 91367
Ph: (818)999-3300
URL: http://www.arguslending.com
Contact: Charles E. Bercy, President
E-mail: cbercy@arguslending.com
Description: Provider of real estate loans and construction and rehabilitation services for multi-family residential, commercial and industrial properties, and much more. **Scope:** Provider of real estate loans and construction and rehabilitation services for multi-family residential, commercial and industrial properties, and much more. **Founded:** 1990.

31602 ■ Associated Management Systems Inc.
2995 Woodside Rd., Ste. 400-188
Woodside, CA 94062
Contact: Adil Khan, Chief Executive Officer
Description: Consulting firm is engaged in entrepreneurial and professional expertise includes corporate management, investment banking, finance, strategic planning, risk evaluation, due diligence studies and management audits and also assists with mergers and acquisitions and provides management for turnaround situations and undertakes project packaging, plant relocations, capital restructuring and funding. **Scope:** Consulting firm is engaged in entrepreneurial and professional expertise includes corporate management, investment banking, finance, strategic planning, risk evaluation, due diligence studies and management audits and also assists with mergers and acquisitions and provides management for turnaround situations and undertakes project packaging, plant relocations, capital restructuring and funding.

31603 ■ Atlantic Management Company, Inc.
One New Hampshire Ave., Ste. 125
Portsmouth, NH 03801
Ph: (603)436-8009
URL: http://www.atlantic-mgmt.com
Contact: John P. Murphy, President
Description: Firm provides valuation and financial advisory services such as business valuation, litigation support, and much more. **Scope:** Firm provides valuation and financial advisory services such as business valuation, litigation support, and much more. **Founded:** 1968. **Publications:** "Business Succession Strategies," 2006; "Selling a Company," 2006; "Case Study on Business Valuation and Industry Intelligence," 2006; "Lock, Stock, and Barrel: A Well Connected Hedge Firm Buys Bushmaster Firearms," Maine biz, May, 2006; "Buying A Company," 2006; "ESOP Questions & Answers," 2006; "Tips for Lawyers When Working with Appraisers," New Hampshire Bar Review, Oct, 2005; "A Win All Around," Worcester Telegram and Gazette, Mar, 2005. **Training:** Current Techniques For Successful Business Transition, Keeley the Katerer Banquet Center, Sep, 2009; Maximizing the Value of Your ESOP in Challenging Times, Mar, 2009; Business Succession Planning & ESOPs - Creating a Buyer for the Closely-Held Company, Sep, 2008; Business Valuation II, Boston Tax Institute, Jun, 2008; Business Valuation I, Boston Tax Institute, Jun, 2008; Now That You've Built It, What Do You Want To Do With It?, May, 2008; Human Resource and Fiduciary Issues for New and Established ESOPs, Mar, 2008; Now That You've Built It; Feb, 2008; A Journey to Employee Ownership: The Future Is In Your Hands, Oct, 2007; Advanced Limited Liability Issues, Jun, 2007.

31604 ■ Bain & Company, Inc.
Bain & Company, Inc.
131 Dartmouth St.
Boston, MA 02116
Ph: (617)572-2000
Fax: (617)572-2427
Co. E-mail: paris.marketing@bain.com
URL: http://www.bain.com

Contact: Orit Gadiesh, Chairperson
Facebook: www.facebook.com/bainandcompany
Linkedin: www.linkedin.com/company/bain-an d-company
X (Twitter): twitter.com/BainAlerts
Instagram: www.instagram.com/bainandcompany
YouTube: www.youtube.com/user/bainandcompany
Description: Global management consulting firm which focuses on helping clients improve their financial performance through a wide variety of consulting services. Client base represents virtually all economic sectors manufacturing, wholesaling, retailing, transportation, services, and more. **Founded:** 1973. **Publications:** "Bain Insights.".

31605 ■ Biomedical Management Resources (BMR)
4131 Fortuna Way
Salt Lake City, UT 84124
Contact: Ping Fong, Jr., Contact
E-mail: pfongbmr@gmail.com
Description: Provides business development, interim management and executive search services. Assists companies in strategic alliances, corporate partnering, business acquisition. Demonstrated success in identifying recruiting and placing key managers in difficult to hire positions. **Scope:** Provides business development, interim management and executive search services. Assists companies in strategic alliances, corporate partnering, business acquisition. Demonstrated success in identifying recruiting and placing key managers in difficult to hire positions.

31606 ■ Business Centre
4327 W Calle Don Clemente
Tucson, AZ 85746
Ph: (520)529-1808
Fax: (520)577-0570
URL: http://businesscentre.net
Contact: Keith McLeod, CBI, SAC, BBS, Principal
E-mail: keith@businesscentre.net
Description: Firm is engaged in mergers and acquisitions, business brokerage, business exit strategies, profitability, and growth consulting services. **Scope:** Firm is engaged in mergers and acquisitions, business brokerage, business exit strategies, profitability, and growth consulting services. **Publications:** "Value-Based Leadership: Buying or Selling a Business"; "TEN STEPS TO CREATE A SIX FIGURE INCOME AND MORE". **Training:** Buyer Paradigm Program.

31607 ■ Business Marketing Consultants (BMC)
CA
URL: http://www.bizmark.net
Contact: Stephen J. Kerr, Founder Regional Manager Vice President
E-mail: stephen@belagemedias.com
Description: Boutique investment banking firm specializes in mergers and acquisition advisory, financial consulting, business plan execution, business valuation and strategic relationship services, motion picture financing, and private capital fundraising initiatives. **Founded:** 1989. **Publications:** "Becoming a super sales sleuth!"; "Do you know your mq?"; "Making money/making books"; "Need to know vs. Want to know"; "Publish for Profit"; "Ten Things To Do Before Selling Any Publishing Company"; "How to buy a printing company scoring your acquisition"; "Nine Things To Do In 1989 To Sell Your Printing Company In 1990"; "How To Sell Your Printing Company For The Right Price, Right Now!"; "e-valuation"; "Exit Strategy: Optimizing The Value Of Your Internet Business"; "Ecommerce -Survival Of The Fittest". **Training:** Exit Strategy timing the sale of your business for MAXIMUM value; Ways to raise money for your publishing company; How to Write a Winning Business Plan; Exit Strategy; Sources of Capital; Buying, Selling & Valuing a Christian Bookstore; How to Buy, Sell & Value a Book Publishing Company; Strategies In Financial Management.

31608 ■ The Business Place Ltd.
30 Eglinton Ave. W, Ste. 710
Mississauga, ON, Canada L5R 3E7
Ph: (905)366-7323

Fax: (905)366-7329
URL: http://thebusinessplace.com
Description: Firm provides buying and selling of businesses, arranging bank financing, venture capital loans/investments, mergers and acquisitions. **Scope:** Firm provides buying and selling of businesses, arranging bank financing, venture capital loans/investments, mergers and acquisitions. **Founded:** 1986.

31609 ■ Business Team (BT)
1475 S Bascom Ave., Ste. 113
Campbell, CA 95008
Ph: (408)246-1102
Fax: (408)246-2219
Co. E-mail: sanjose@business-team.com
URL: http://www.business-team.com
Contact: Armstrong Wong, Officer
E-mail: armstrong@business-team.com
Description: A business brokerage firm that specializes in merger, acquisition, and divestiture services for privately held, mid-sized companies. The company's value-added services include business valuation, pre-marketing consultation, and exit strategy planning. **Founded:** 1981. **Training:** Business Valuation Enhancing the Value of Your Company.

31610 ■ Cole, Warren and Long Inc.
2 Penn Center Plz., Ste. 1020
Philadelphia, PA 19102
Contact: Ronald Colclough, President
Description: Firm provides management guidance to commercial, industrial and government organizations specializing in the areas of organization studies, executive searches, acquisitions and mergers, compensation programs, audits and improvement seminars and conducts marketing, economic and systems studies counsels on profit improvement, manpower control, operations, and systems integration. **Scope:** Firm provides management guidance to commercial, industrial and government organizations specializing in the areas of organization studies, executive searches, acquisitions and mergers, compensation programs, audits and improvement seminars and conducts marketing, economic and systems studies counsels on profit improvement, manpower control, operations, and systems integration.

31611 ■ Devries & Associates, P.C.
3145 Broadway
Kansas City, MO 64111
Ph: (816)561-2555
Fax: (816)561-3939
URL: http://www.devries-law-kc.com
Contact: Coulter F. deVries, Director
Description: Investment banking/financial consulting firm which helps companies solve financial problems and achieve growth and diversification goals. Helps established companies raise capital and assists new and developing companies secure venture capital and create public markets for their stocks. **Scope:** Investment banking/financial consulting firm which helps companies solve financial problems and achieve growth and diversification goals. Helps established companies raise capital and assists new and developing companies secure venture capital and create public markets for their stocks. **Founded:** 1984.

31612 ■ Haas Wheat & Partners L.P.
300 Cres. Ct., Ste. 1700
Dallas, TX 75201-7857
Contact: Robert B. Haas, Contact
Description: Business consulting firm offering expertise with mergers and acquisitions and financial investment in the United States. **Scope:** Business consulting firm offering expertise with mergers and acquisitions and financial investment in the United States.

31613 ■ Jacalyn E. S. Bennett & Co.
45 Water St.
Newburyport, MA 01950
Ph: (978)462-1966
Fax: (978)463-2062
Co. E-mail: info@bennettcompany.com
URL: http://www.bennettcompany.com

Contact: Jacalyn Bennett, President
Description: Manufacture and distributor of lingerie, sleepwear, and related product categories and also provides product development services such as trend and research development, textile and trim development, and much more. **Founded:** 1989.

31614 ■ KGI Advisors Inc.
12300 Wilshire Blvd., Ste. 300
　Los Angeles, CA 90025
Ph: (310)829-0255
URL: http://www.kginc.com
Contact: Steven J. Green, President
E-mail: sgreen@kginc.com
Description: Provider of services in turn around and crisis management, value creation and investment banking and serves manufacturing, service, technology, retail, distribution and real estate industries. **Scope:** Provider of services in turn around and crisis management, value creation and investment banking and serves manufacturing, service, technology, retail, distribution and real estate industries. **Founded:** 1984. **Publications:** "Avoiding the Lose-Lose Paradigm," Apr, 2012; "Kibel Green Hits a Home Run for Defense Manufacturer," Feb, 2012; "Kibel Green Advises on $320M Restructuring," Dec, 2011; "Kibel Green helps Arlie & Co. Beat-the-Clock," Aug, 2011; "Where's My Bail Out? - Restructuring Debts and Eliminating Personal Guarantees," Jul, 2011; "Kibel Green Completes $191M Real Estate Restructuring," Jun, 2011; " Working Wonders for a Small Equipment Distributor," Apr, 2011; "The 2010 Letter - Reflections from the President," Feb, 2011; "Winning the Loan Restructuring Battle," Aug, 2010; "Show Me the Money," May, 2010; "Shopping Center Owners Act Now or Lose Your Shirt," Apr, 2009; "Kibel Green Helps Save Media Company," Mar, 2009; "The Role of the Chief Restructuring Officer," Jan, 2009; "The Growth Paradox Effectively Resizing to Drive Profits," Dec, 2008. **Special Services:** The Kibel Green System™.

31615 ■ McTevia & Associates
1331 S Brandywine Cir.
　Fort Myers, FL 33919
Contact: James V. McTevia, Manager
E-mail: jmctevia@mctevialc.com
Description: Firm is engaged in reorganization programs for businesses with serious financial problems. Services include debt restructuring, bankruptcy trustees, liquidations, management reorganization and acquisitions and mergers. **Scope:** Firm is engaged in reorganization programs for businesses with serious financial problems. Services include debt restructuring, bankruptcy trustees, liquidations, management reorganization and acquisitions and mergers. **Publications:** "Survival in The Face of Change," Jun, 2006; "Tips for Picking An Outside Adviser," Sep, 2005; "Out-of Court Problem Solving and Restructuring: Guide to a Successful Outcome," May, 2005; "Small Business: The Basics of Business Problem Solving," Mar, 2005; "Annual Business Check," Jan, 2005; "When Bad Things Happen To Good Family Businesses," Business Direct Weekly, Dec, 2001. **Training:** Alternative Methods of Financing for Underperforming Companies, Jun, 2009; Preventing or Structuring a Reorganization without Court Supervision, May, 2008; Business and Professions in Transition - Unlocking Your Business Potential, Jun, 2007; Professions in Transition, Oct, 2007; Preventing or Structuring a Reorganization without Court Supervision, Novi, Jun, 2006; Guiding the Customer in Preventing or Structuring a Reorganization Without Court Supervision, Atlanta, Jun, 2005.

31616 ■ Mertz Associates Inc.
N1629 County Rd. P
　Rubicon, WI 53078
URL: http://www.mertz.com
Contact: Linda Mertz, Chief Executive Officer
E-mail: lnda@mertz.com
Description: Firm provides strategic consulting services such as strategic assessments, acquisition strategies, and exit options. **Scope:** Firm provides strategic consulting services such as strategic as-

sessments, acquisition strategies, and exit options. **Publications:** "Why Successful Companies are Launching Acquisition Searches Now"; "On the Block"; "Selling Troubled Divisions and Companies"; "Don't Fear the D Word"; "M and A Multiples: A Key to Value Or a Distraction"; "Savvy CPA Levels the Playing Field"; "M and A Trends Strategic Focus Drives Success".

31617 ■ Rehmann, Robson and Co.
5800 Gratiot Rd., Ste. 201
　Saginaw, MI 48638
Ph: (989)799-9580
Free: 866-799-9580
Fax: (989)799-0227
Co. E-mail: info@rehmann.com
URL: http://www.rehmann.com
Contact: Randall Rupp, Chief Executive Officer
E-mail: randy.rupp@rehmann.com
Linkedin: www.linkedin.com/company/rehmann
Description: Provider of financial, tax, accounting, assurance, business consulting, wealth management and corporate investigative services. **Founded:** 1941. **Publications:** "Manufacturing Monitor "; "Bwg Magazine"; "Bwd Magazine".

31618 ■ Robbinex Inc.
8 Christie St.
　Grimsby, ON, Canada L3M 4H4
Ph: (289)235-7552
Free: 888-762-2463
Co. E-mail: robbinex@robbinex.com
URL: http://www.robbinex.com
Contact: Doug Robbins, President
Facebook: www.facebook.com/robbinexinc
Linkedin: www.linkedin.com/company/robbinex-inc-
X (Twitter): x.com/robbinexinc
Instagram: www.instagram.com/robbinex
Description: Business consultants specializing in the merger and acquisition area and financial planning for small to medium size companies. Other services include business financing, crisis management, acquisition search, business valuations, joint ventures and venture capital, resolution of partnership problems, implementation of franchise programs and general assistance in site selection. **Scope:** Business consultants specializing in the merger and acquisition area and financial planning for small to medium size companies. Other services include business financing, crisis management, acquisition search, business valuations, joint ventures and venture capital, resolution of partnership problems, implementation of franchise programs and general assistance in site selection. **Founded:** 1974. **Training:** Creating Transitional Strategies; How to Start a Small Business; Growing Through Acquisition: How to Buy a Business; How to Successfully Manage Medium to Small Businesses; Expansion Through Acquisition; Growth Through Franchising; How to Borrow Money from a Bank; Syndicating Equity; Global Expansion: Are You Missing the Boat; Business succession planning: What's the hurry. **Special Services:** Robbinex®.

31619 ■ Siebrand-Wilton Associates Inc. (S-WA)
PO Box 193
　Rocky Hill, NJ 08553-0193
URL: http://www.s-wa.com
Contact: John S. Sturges, Principal
Description: Firm provides nationwide human resources consulting support and also offers executive coaching and counseling, benefit plan design, and other related services. **Founded:** 1986. **Publications:** "Should Government or Business Try to Save Medicare," HR News; "Executive Temping," HR Horizons; "When is an Employee Truly an Employee," HR Magazine; "Examining Your Insurance Carrier," HR Magazine.

31620 ■ Value Creation Group Inc.
7820 Scotia Dr., Ste. 2000
　Dallas, TX 75248-3115
Ph: (972)980-7407
Co. E-mail: assistyou@valuecreationgroup.com
URL: http://www.valuecreationgroup.com
Contact: John Antos, Contact

E-mail: assistyou@valuecreationgroup.com
Description: Consulting firm provides process management, continuous improvement, performance management, cost accounting, forecasting, budgeting and training services. **Scope:** Consulting firm provides process management, continuous improvement, performance management, cost accounting, forecasting, budgeting and training services. **Founded:** 1984. **Publications:** "Handbook of Process Management Based Predictive Accounting," Aicpa 2002; "Cost Management for Today's Manufacturing Environment and Activity Based Management for Service Environments, Government Entities and Nonprofit Organizations"; "Risks and Opportunities in International Finance and Treasury"; "Driving Value Using Activity Based Budgeting"; "Process Based Accounting Leveraging Processes to Predict Results"; "Handbook of Supply Chain Management"; "Economic Value Management Applications and Techniques"; "The Change Handbook": "Group Methods for Creating the Future"; "Why Value Management and Performance Measurement Through U.S. Binoculars," Journal of Strategic Performance Measurement; "Real Options, Intangibles Measurement and the Benefits of Human Capital Investment to Power the Organization," Journal of Strategic Performance Measurement. **Training:** Activity Based Management; Predictive Accounting; Performance measures; ABM for Manufacturing; ABM for Service Organizations; Finance and Accounting for Non-Financial Executives; Return on Investment/Capital Expenditure Evaluation; Planning and Cost Control; The Next Step Intermediate Finance and Accounting for Non-financial Managers; Activity-Based Budgeting; Friendly Finance for Fund Raisers; Strategic Outsourcing.

31621 ■ Vencon Management Inc. (VMI)
301 W 53rd St.
　New York, NY 10019
Contact: Irwin Barash, Chief Executive Officer
Description: Venture capital firm and management consultants to corporations and entrepreneurs. Specializes in the areas of mergers and acquisitions evaluation and negotiation and the preparation of marketing and business plans. Assists small or new businesses in expansion plans and financing. **Scope:** Venture capital firm and management consultants to corporations and entrepreneurs. Specializes in the areas of mergers and acquisitions evaluation and negotiation and the preparation of marketing and business plans. Assists small or new businesses in expansion plans and financing. **Training:** Heegaard Knot Diagrams, Sep, 2009; Issues in finite Approximation, Oct, 2009. **Preferred Investment Size:** $500,000 to $3,000,000. **Industry Preferences:** Communications, computer software, Internet specific, semiconductors and other electronics, biotechnology, medical and health.

RESEARCH CENTERS

31622 ■ Babson College - Arthur M. Blank Center for Entrepreneurship
231 Forest St.
　Babson Park, MA 02457
URL: http://www.babson.edu/academics/centers-and-institutes/the-arthur-m-blank-center-for-entrepreneurship
Contact: Debi Kleiman, Executive Director
E-mail: dkleiman@babson.edu
URL(s): www.babson.edu/entrepreneurship-center/about
Description: Business accelerator providing tailored resources and guidance for new businesses. **Scope:** Entrepreneurship and new and growing businesses, including studies in venture capital, starting and financing new value-creating ventures, family businesses, franchises, and harvesting enterprises through IPO's, merger or sale, and family succession. **Founded:** 1998. **Publications:** *Babson Entrepreneurial Review; Frontiers of Entrepreneurship Research* (Annual). **Educational Activities:** Babson College Entrepreneurship Research Conference (Annual). **Awards:** Academy of Distinguished Entrepreneurs (Irregular).

ASSOCIATIONS AND OTHER ORGANIZATIONS

31623 ■ American Payroll Association (APA)
660 N Main Ave., Ste. 100
San Antonio, TX 78205
Ph: (210)224-6406
Fax: (210)224-6038
URL: http://www.americanpayroll.org
Contact: Dan Maddux, Executive Director
Facebook: www.facebook.com/
AmericanPayrollAssociation
X (Twitter): x.com/PayNews
Instagram: www.instagram.com/americanpayroll
YouTube: www.youtube.com/user/PayNewsNetwork

Description: Works to increase member's skills and professionalism through education and mutual support. Represents the interest of members before legislative bodies. Conducts training courses. Administers the certified payroll professional program of recognition. **Founded:** 1982. **Publications:** Creates opportunities and forge a community by providing the education, skills, and resources necessary for payroll professionals to become successful. **Training:** Standard Foundation of Payroll Administration; Implementing Payroll Best Practices; Payroll System Selection and Implementation; Accounts Payable or Disbursements Preparing for Year-End and 2009; Canadian Payrolls Preparing for Year-End and 2009; Government/Public Sector Preparing for Year-End and 2009; Payroll Issues For Multi-State Employers. **Educational Activities:** Educational Institutions Payroll Conference (EIPC) (Annual). **Awards:** Payroll Education Grants (Annual). **Geographic Preference:** State.

REFERENCE WORKS

31624 ■ *"3 Tips to Help Small Business Owners Calculate Payroll Taxes" in Hiscox Blog*
Description: Details necessary steps in calculating taxes and withholdings for employees for small business owners. **Availability:** Online.

31625 ■ *"6 Common IRS Tax Penalties on Small Business Owners" in allBusiness*
Description: Discusses the complexities involved in small business tax reporting. Details six common tax penalties that small businesses or small business owners are charged with. **Availability:** Online.

31626 ■ *"Are You Micromanaging Your Company's Financial Tasks?" in allBusiness*
Ed: Rieva Lesonsky. **Description:** Provides information on the benefits of utilizing technology and/or outsourcing certain business operation tasks so that you can concentrate on working on the business you've invested so much time and money into building. The article goes into detail about micromanaging payroll and how to best use your time. **Availability:** Online.

31627 ■ *"Best Payroll Software for Small Businesses" in NerdWallet (April 9, 2018)*
Ed: Steve Nicastro. **Released:** April 09, 2018. **Description:** Offers comparisons of five different payroll software options for small businesses. **Availability:** Online.

31628 ■ *"How Do I Do My Own Payroll and Payroll Taxes?" in The Balance Small Business (May 24, 2020)*
Ed: Jean Murray. **Released:** May 24, 2020. **Description:** An employer's checklist detailing basic steps involved in the payroll process including things to think about before you hire employees, what is involved in paying employees, and what happens after you've paid employees. **Availability:** Online.

31629 ■ *"How to Manage Your Small Business Payroll Taxes the Easy Way" in Sage Advice Blog (Nov. 8, 2021)*
URL(s): www.sage.com/en-us/blog/how-to-manage
-your-small-business-payroll-taxes-the-easy-way/
Released: November 08, 2021. **Description:** Discusses the complexities involved in small business payroll taxes, helps small business owners understand payroll taxes, and provides resources to ensure that you stay on track. **Availability:** Online.

31630 ■ *"How to Pay Yourself from Your Small Business" in Legal Zoom (February 10, 2023)*
URL(s): www.legalzoom.com/articles/how-to-pay
-yourself-from-your-small-business
Ed: Jane Haskins, Esq. **Released:** February 10, 2023. **Description:** Getting a small business off the ground is not easy and it can even come with a financial cost to your personal funds. However, consider the given ideas in this article and see if there is a better way so you can pay yourself from money earned through all your hard work. **Availability:** Online.

31631 ■ *"How to Withhold Payroll Taxes for Your Small Business" in SurePayroll (March 14, 2018)*
Ed: Ross Matthews. **Released:** March 14, 2018. **Description:** Walks through the basics of federal income tax, Medicare and Social Security taxes, and state and local taxes for small businesses. **Availability:** Online.

31632 ■ *I Just Started My Small Business—Do I Need Payroll Software?*
URL(s): articles.bplans.com/i-just-started-my-small
-business-do-i-need-payroll-software/
Ed: Jenna Lee. **Description:** Discusses the advantages of utilizing payroll software for your small business and what to look for in a good payroll service. **Availability:** Online.

31633 ■ *"Payroll Deductions: The Ultimate Guide for Business Owners" in NerdWallet (Feb. 4, 2021)*
URL(s): www.nerdwallet.com/article/small-business/
payroll-deductions

Ed: Randa Kriss. **Released:** February 04, 2021. **Description:** Explains everything small business owners need to know about payroll deductions, including which are required by law. **Availability:** Online.

31634 ■ *Payroll Tax Basics for Small Business Owners*
URL(s): www.allbusiness.com/payroll-tax-basics-for
-small-business-owners-2553-1.html
Description: Provides the basics of handling payroll taxes for your small business. **Availability:** Online.

31635 ■ *Payroll Tax Penalties Small Businesses Should Know About*
URL(s): www.zenefits.com/workest/payroll-tax-penal
ties-small-businesses-should-know-about/
Ed: Grace Ferguson. **Released:** May 07, 2021. **Description:** Explains penalties your small business might face for failing to comply with payroll tax laws. Includes waivers and technology for avoiding them. **Availability:** Online.

31636 ■ *"Payroll Tax for Small Business" in Mile IQ Blog (May 8, 2021)*
URL(s): mileiq.com/blog-en-us/payroll-tax-small
-business
Ed: Manasa Reddigari. **Released:** May 08, 2021. **Description:** Includes details on what payroll taxes cover and how to collect and submit them for your small business. **Availability:** Online.

31637 ■ *Payroll Tax: What It Is, How to Calculate It*
URL(s): bench.co/blog/accounting/calculate-payroll
-tax/?blog=e6
Ed: Jennifer Dunn. **Released:** August 19, 2020. **Description:** Every small business that has employees is required to pay payroll taxes. This guide shows how to calculate employer payroll taxes as well as how much employee tax to remit to the government. **Availability:** Online.

31638 ■ *Payroll Taxes: A Small Business Employer's Guide*
URL(s): web.blockadvisors.com/payroll-tax/
Released: July 26, 2021. **Description:** Explains what payroll taxes are, how they're calculated, and other duties involved in managing payroll taxes for your small business. **Availability:** Online.

31639 ■ *"Payroll Taxes for Small Businesses: The Basics" in Human Interest Blog (March 26, 2017)*
Ed: Cyndia Zwahlen. **Released:** March 26, 2017. **Description:** Provides information on payroll taxes for small business owners. Provides a tax glossary as well as information on federal and state payroll taxes, employer payroll tax responsibilities, employee payroll tax responsibilities, payroll tax payment schedule and deadlines, how to report payroll taxes, and what to do if you can't pay your payroll taxes. **Availability:** Online.

31640 ■ *"Payroll Taxes Take up to 5 Hours Per Pay Period for Small Business Owners" in Small Business Trends (Jan. 12, 2020)*
URL(s): smallbiztrends.com/2020/01/payroll-tax-statistics.html
Ed: Michael Guta. **Released:** January 12, 2020. **Description:** Provides payroll tax statistics, how to automate payroll, and how to choose the tool that will work best for your small business. **Availability:** Online.

31641 ■ *"The Perils and Pitfalls of S Corporations" in allBusiness*
Ed: Amanda Han. **Description:** Provides in-depth information on one of the most commonly used business structures for small to mid-sized business owners, the S Corporation. Covers strategies as well as common costly mistakes. **Availability:** Online.

31642 ■ *"A Small Business Owner's Guide to Managing Payroll Taxes" in Biz2Credit (January 23, 2020)*
Ed: Nico Robben. **Released:** January 23, 2020. **Description:** A guide to small business payroll taxes including what they are, what paperwork to know about, your responsibilities as a business owner, and some of the best apps and services that you can use to manage these taxes simply and easily. **Availability:** Online.

31643 ■ *"Small Business Tax Obligations: Payroll Taxes" in Investopedia (June 25, 2019)*
Ed: Chizoba Morah. **Released:** June 25, 2019. **Description:** Focuses on the small business owner's obligations with regard to payroll taxes. **Availability:** Online.

31644 ■ *"Thanks, But No: Small Businesses Shun Payroll Tax Deferral" (September 5, 2020), Associated Press.*
Released: September 05, 2020. **Description:** Discusses deferred payroll taxes allowed by President Trump and the wariness of small business owners to take advantage of this due to the unwanted financial hit that could come as a result. **Availability:** Online.

31645 ■ *"Understanding Payroll Tax Payment and Filing Requirements" in Wolders Kluwer website*
Ed: Mike Enright. **Description:** Details proper handling of payroll tax responsibilities for small business including: reporting and payment of federal and state taxes to the appropriate tax agencies; proper reporting of income, amounts withheld, and amounts paid on behalf of employees and contractors; and maintenance of required federal and state records. **Availability:** Online.

31646 ■ *"What Are Payroll Taxes?" in Business News Daily (Nov. 10, 2021)*
URL(s): www.businessnewsdaily.com/2228-payroll-taxes-bndmp.html
Ed: Sean Peek. **Released:** November 10, 2021. **Description:** Explains what payroll taxes are, how they work, how to manage them for your small business, and what happens if you don't pay your payroll taxes. **Availability:** Online.

31647 ■ *"What Is Payroll Tax and How Much Does it Cost?" in Xero*
Description: Takes a look at what federal and state payroll taxes need to be paid and the rules and exceptions that apply. **Availability:** Online.

31648 ■ *"What You Need to Know about the Federal Overtime Rules" in Business News Daily (March 17, 2023)*
URL(s): www.businessnewsdaily.com/9110-federal-overtime-rules.html
Ed: Max Freedman. **Released:** March 17, 2023. **Description:** Every small business owner should be well acquainted with the Fair Labor Standards Act (FLSA) in order to remain compliant in federal overtime law. **Availability:** Online.

REFERENCE WORKS

31649 ■ *"5 Strategies of 'Psychological Pricing"* in Entrepreneur (July 21, 2016)
Ed: Pius Boachie. **Released:** July 21, 2016. **Description:** Discusses the use of psychological pricing and five pricing strategies entrepreneurs can adopt to have an impact on consumers. **Availability:** Online.

31650 ■ *"8 Pricing Strategies for Your Digital Product"* in Entrepreneur (October 18, 2016)
Ed: Eric Siu. **Released:** October 18, 2016. **Description:** Discusses how pricing can be used as a marketing strategy to generate interest, drive sales, and attract customers. **Availability:** Online.

31651 ■ *"How to Choose a Pricing Strategy for Your Small Business"* in Intuit Quickbooks (June 20, 2019)
Ed: Chris Scott. **Released:** June 20, 2019. **Description:** Whether your business is just getting started or you're ready to begin advertising to drive sales, this is the time to learn what role pricing plays in the big picture. **Availability:** Online.

31652 ■ *"How to Price Your Small Business Products or Services"* excerpt in dummies
Ed: Barbara Findlay Schenck. **Description:** Discusses how pricing your small business products and services properly is one of the most important business decision to be made as it centers on the relationship between perceived value or quality and the price customers are willing to pay. **Availability:** Online.

31653 ■ *"How to Start a Consulting Business: Determining Your Rates"* in Entrepreneur (March 10, 2020)
Ed: Terry Rice. **Released:** March 10, 2020. **Description:** Discusses factors involved in setting rates as a consultant. **Availability:** Online.

31654 ■ *"Pricing Strategies for Small Business"* in The Balance Small Business (February 12, 2020)
Ed: Darrell Zahorsky. **Released:** February 12, 2020. **Description:** Discusses how the pricing strategy for your small business sets the standard for your product or service in the marketplace and how pricing is an important dimension in your bottom line and in your competitive edge. **Availability:** Online.

31655 ■ *"Pricing Strategies for a Strong Bottom Line"* in Small Business Trends (May 26, 2020)
Ed: Robb Starr. **Released:** May 26, 2020. **Description:** Provides steps detailing how to create a strategic pricing model for your small business. **Availability:** Online.

31656 ■ *"Strategies and Formulas for Pricing Services at Your Small Business"* in Patriot (November 5, 2019)
Ed: Amanda Cameron. **Released:** November 05, 2019. **Description:** Discusses why pricing can be so difficult and provides strategies for pricing services to ensure that your small business is profitable. **Availability:** Online.

31657 ■ *"Upgrade Your Pricing Strategy to Match Consumer Behavior"* in Harvard Business Review (May 28, 2020)
Ed: David Hardisty, Thomas Allard, Dale Griffin. **Released:** May 28, 2020. **Description:** Provides hacks that marketing managers can use to nudge consumers to purchase higher quality goods and services. **Availability:** Online.

31658 ■ *"Use Perceived Value to Determine Your Food Truck Menu Prices"* in Mobile-Cuisine.com (October 16, 2017)
Ed: Richard Myrick. **Released:** October 16, 2017. **Description:** Provides details on using the perceived value of your food truck dishes and setting appropriate menu prices. **Availability:** Online.

31659 ■ *"Why Some Prices Are More Right Than Others"* in Entrepreneur (September 15, 2016)
Ed: Craig Simpson. **Released:** September 15, 2016. **Description:** Discusses how setting the right price can have a powerful effect on the success of your direct marketing campaigns. Includes factors that determine what your most attractive price is. **Availability:** Online.

VIDEO/AUDIO MEDIA

31660 ■ *The Best Small Business Show: Pricing Your Company Out of Business - When to Stop Raising Prices*
URL(s): richgee.libsyn.com/293-pricing-your-company-out-of-business-when-to-stop-raising-prices
Ed: Rich Gee. **Released:** May 02, 2023.

31661 ■ *The Best Small Business Show: Raise Your Rates without Losing Customers*
URL(s): richgee.libsyn.com/249-raise-your-rates-without-losing-customers
Ed: Rich Gee. **Released:** July 27, 2022. **Description:** Podcast explains how to raise rates without losing clients.

31662 ■ *BS-Free Service Business Show: Practical Pricing for Service Business Owners*
URL(s): insidescoop.libsyn.com/practical-pricing-for-service-business-owners
Ed: Maggie Patterson. **Released:** October 02, 2023. **Description:** Podcast offers a practical approach to pricing for service businesses.

31663 ■ *HBR Ideacast: Algorithms Won't Solve All Your Pricing Problems*
URL(s): hbr.org/podcast/2021/10/when-pricing-algorithms-hurt-customer-relationships
Ed: Alison Beard. **Released:** October 19, 2021. **Description:** Podcast explains how relying on artificial intelligence and machine learning can damage the customer relationship. Offers steps to alleviate it, including guardrails, overrides, and better communication tactics.

31664 ■ *The How of Business: Pricing Fundamentals*
URL(s): www.thehowofbusiness.com/498-pricing-fundamentals
Ed: Henry Lopez. **Released:** November 13, 2023. **Description:** Podcast outlines the fundamentals of pricing products/services in a profitable small business.

31665 ■ *Marketplace: For Indigenous Artists, Pricing Is a Tricky Proposition*
URL(s): www.marketplace.org/2023/08/28/santa-fe-indian-market-indigenous-artists-inflation
Ed: Savannah Maher. **Released:** August 28, 2023. **Description:** Podcast discusses the difficulty of factoring inflation in pricing art.

31666 ■ *Marketplace: In the Face of High Inflation, This Couple's Plant Keeps Growing*
URL(s): www.marketplace.org/2023/06/22/in-the-face-of-high-inflation-this-couples-plant-keeps-growing
Ed: Livi Burdette. **Released:** June 22, 2023. **Description:** Podcast discusses the need to raise prices in inflation.

31667 ■ *Profit First Nation: Your Price Controls Your Profit*
URL(s): www.profitfirstnation.com/episodes/ep-143-your-price-controls-your-profit
Ed: Danielle Mulvey. **Released:** October 24, 2023. **Description:** Podcast discusses the role of pricing on customer experience and profitability.

31668 ■ *Startups for the Rest of Us: Building a Recurring, Annual Price Increase into Your SaaS*
URL(s): www.startupsfortherestofus.com/episodes/episode-646-building-a-recurring-annual-price-increase-into-your-saas
Ed: Rob Walling. **Released:** January 20, 2023. **Description:** Podcast discusses the pros and cons of an annual price increase and how to communicate it to leads and customers.

31669 ■ *Think Business with Tyler: Increase Profits with Pricing Strategy Tips from James Wilton*
URL(s): thinktyler.com/podcast_episode/pricing-strategy-james-wilton
Ed: Tyler Martin. **Released:** October 07, 2024. **Description:** Podcast discusses the nuances of pricing strategy and the advantages of tiered pricing.

Public Administration

ASSOCIATIONS AND OTHER ORGANIZATIONS

31670 ■ Alliance for Nonprofit Management
89 South St. Ste. 700
Boston, MA 02111
Free: 800-397-2034
Co. E-mail: info@allianceonline.org
URL: http://allianceonlinecommunity.org
Facebook: www.facebook.com/AllianceForNonprofitManagement
Linkedin: www.linkedin.com/company/alliance-for-nonprofit-management
X (Twitter): x.com/AllianceforNPM
Description: Member organizations and individuals devoted to building the capacity of non-profit organizations in order to increase their effectiveness. **Founded:** 1997. **Publications:** *Pulse!* (Bimonthly); *Alliance for Nonprofit Management--Membership Directory.* **Awards:** Terry McAdam Book Award (Annual). **Geographic Preference:** National.

31671 ■ American Federation of State County and Municipal Employees (AFSCME)
1625 L St. NW
Washington, DC 20036-5687
Ph: (202)429-1000
Fax: (202)429-1293
Co. E-mail: afscmepa@afscme.org
URL: http://www.afscme.org
Contact: Lee Saunders, President
Facebook: www.facebook.com/AFSCME
X (Twitter): x.com/AFSCME
Instagram: www.instagram.com/afscme
YouTube: www.youtube.com/user/afscme
Description: Represents service and health care workers in the public and private sectors. Organizes for social and economic justice in the workplace and through political action and legislative advocacy. **Founded:** 1936. **Publications:** *AFSCME Works: The Magazine of the American Federation of State, County and Municipal Employees, AFL-CIO* (Quarterly); *Public Employee* (8/year). **Geographic Preference:** National.

31672 ■ American Society for Public Administration (ASPA)
1730 Rhode Island Ave. NW, Ste. 500
Washington, DC 20036
Ph: (202)393-7878
Fax: (202)638-4952
Co. E-mail: info@aspanet.org
URL: http://www.aspanet.org
Contact: Paul Danczyk, President
Facebook: www.facebook.com/ASPANational
X (Twitter): x.com/ASPANational
Description: Promotes excellence in public service, including government, non-profit and private sectors, and academic community. **Founded:** 1939. **Publications:** *Section for Women in Public Administration-- Membership Directory* (Biennial); *Public Administration Review (PAR)* (Bimonthly); *PA Times* (Quarterly). **Educational Activities:** ASPA Annual Conference

(Annual). **Awards:** Louis Brownlow Award (Annual); Laverne Burchfield Award (Annual); Marshall E. Dimock Award (Annual); William E. Mosher and Frederick C. Mosher Award (Annual); NASPAA/ASPA Distinguished Researcher Award (Irregular); ASPA Equal Opportunity/Affirmative Action Exemplary Practice Award (Annual); Donald C. Stone Service to ASPA Award (Irregular); Dwight Waldo Award (Annual); James E. Webb Award (Irregular). **Geographic Preference:** Multinational.

31673 ■ Association of Metropolitan Planning Organizations (AMPO)
444 N Capitol St. NW, Ste. 532
Washington, DC 20001
Ph: (202)624-3680
URL: http://ampo.org
Contact: Ronald Chicka, President
Facebook: www.facebook.com/AssocMPOs
X (Twitter): x.com/Assoc_MPOs
Instagram: www.instagram.com/assoc_mpos
Description: Promotes planning, programming and coordination of federal highway and transit investments. Provides training, forum, conferences for transportation policy development. **Founded:** 1994. **Publications:** *ITS* (Quarterly); *aMPO eMAIL* (Biweekly); *Metros* (Quarterly); *Profiles of Metropolitan Planning Organizations* (Annual). **Awards:** Award for Outstanding Overall Achievement for a TMA MPO (Annual); Award for Outstanding Overall Achievement for a non-TMA MPO (Annual); The Ronald F. Kirby Lifetime Achievement Award (Irregular). **Geographic Preference:** National.

31674 ■ National Academy of Public Administration (NAPA)
1600 K St. NW Ste. 400
Washington, DC 20006
Ph: (202)347-3190
Co. E-mail: feedback@napawash.org
URL: http://napawash.org
Contact: Teresa W. Gerton, President
Facebook: www.facebook.com/napawash
Linkedin: www.linkedin.com/company/national-academy-of-public-administration
X (Twitter): x.com/napawash
YouTube: www.youtube.com/channel/UCrBcegZJjqMZmhum2oi8RoQ
Description: Works to respond to specific requests from public agencies and non-governmental organizations. Promotes discourse on emerging trends in governance through standing panels and external funding. Assists federal agencies, congressional committees, state and local governments, civic organizations, and institutions overseas through problem solving, objective research, rigorous analysis, information sharing, development strategies for change, and connecting people and ideas. Promotes forward-looking ideas and of analyzing successes and failures of government reform. **Founded:** 1967. **Awards:** Louis Brownlow Book Award (Annual); Rosslyn Kleeman Keeper of the Flame Award (Annual); Herbert Roback Scholarship (Annual); National Public Service Award (Annual). **Geographic Preference:** Multinational.

31675 ■ National Forum for Black Public Administrators (NFBPA)
200 Massachusetts Ave. NW, Ste. 700
Washington, DC 20001
Ph: (202)408-9300
Fax: (844)236-6154
Co. E-mail: nfbpa2@gmail.com
URL: http://www.nfbpa.org/home
Contact: Darnell Brown, President
Facebook: www.facebook.com/BPA83
X (Twitter): x.com/NFBPA1
YouTube: www.youtube.com/user/NFBPA2011
Description: Black city and county managers and assistant managers; chief administrative officers; agency directors; bureau and division heads; corporate executives; students. Works to promote, strengthen, and expand the role of blacks in public administration. Seeks to focus the influence of black administrators toward building and maintaining viable communities. Develops specialized training programs for managers and executives. Provides national public administrative leadership resource and skills bank. Works to further communication among black public, private, and academic institutions. Addresses issues that affect the administrative capacity of black managers. **Founded:** 1983. **Publications:** *The Forum Magazine* (Quarterly). **Educational Activities:** National Forum for Black Public Administrators FORUM (Annual). **Awards:** CIGNA Undergraduate Scholarship (Annual); Johnnie L. Cochran, Jr./MWH Scholarships (Annual); Marks of Excellence Award (Annual); NFBPA Hall of Fame Award (Annual); Steven D. Ford Memorial Award (Annual); NFBPA Future Colleagues Scholarships (Annual); RA Consulting Service/Maria Riley Scholarships (Annual). **Geographic Preference:** National.

31676 ■ National Notary Association (NNA)
9350 De Soto Ave.
Chatsworth, CA 91311
Free: 800-876-6827
URL: http://www.nationalnotary.org
Contact: Thomas A. Heymann, President
Facebook: www.facebook.com/nationalnotary
Linkedin: www.linkedin.com/company/national-notary-association
X (Twitter): x.com/nationalnotary
Instagram: www.instagram.com/NationalNotary
YouTube: www.youtube.com/c/NationalnotaryOrg
Description: Notaries public (officers empowered to witness the signing of documents, identify the signers, take acknowledgments, and administer oaths). Works to teach notaries public in the US. their duties, powers, limitations, liabilities, and obligations. Keeps members informed of changes in notary law; offers various services, supplies, and insurance plans to members. **Founded:** 1957. **Publications:** *The National Notary* (Bimonthly); *Notary Seal and Certificate Verification Manual.* **Awards:** Notary of the Year Award (Annual); March Fong Eu Achievement Award (Annual). **Geographic Preference:** National.

31677 ■ Network of Schools of Public Policy, Affairs, and Administration (NASPAA)
1029 Vermont Ave. NW Ste. 1100
  Washington, DC 20005-3517
Ph: (202)628-8965
Fax: (202)626-4978
Co. E-mail: info@nbsims.org
URL: http://www.naspaa.org
Contact: Laurel McFarland, Executive Director
E-mail: mcfarland@naspaa.org
Facebook: www.facebook.com/naspaaglobal
Linkedin: www.linkedin.com/company/national
  -association-of-schools-of-public-affairs-and-a
  dministration
X (Twitter): x.com/naspaa
Instagram: www.instagram.com/naspaaglobal
YouTube: www.youtube.com/channel/
  UCxZklrbLpBTRF6AKxFz575Q
Description: Fosters goals and standards of educational excellence and represents the concerns and interests of member institutions in the formulation and support of national policies for education in public affairs/public administration. Accredits master's degree program in public affairs and administration. Cooperates with governmental organizations, professional associations, and national public interest groups to improve the quality of public management. **Founded:** 1970. **Publications:** *Public Enterprise* (Irregular); *Programs in Public Affairs and Administration* (Biennial); *Journal of Public Affairs Education (JPAE)* (Quarterly). **Awards:** NASPAA Dissertation Award (Annual); ASPA/NASPAA Distinguished Research Award (Biennial); Elmer B. Staats Public Service Career Award (Irregular); Leslie A. Whittington Excellence in Teaching Award (Annual); Alfred M. Zuck Public Courage Award (Periodic); Journal of Public Affairs Education Outstanding Article Award (Annual). **Geographic Preference:** National.

31678 ■ Section for Women in Public Administration (SWPA)
1730 Rhode Island Ave. NW, Ste. 500
  Washington, DC 20036
Ph: (202)393-7878
Fax: (202)638-4952
Co. E-mail: swpasection@gmail.com
URL: http://www.swpaaspa.org
Contact: Helisse Levine, Chairman
Facebook: www.facebook.com/aspaswpa
Linkedin: www.linkedin.com/company/swpa
X (Twitter): x.com/swpaaspa
Instagram: www.instagram.com/swpa_women
Description: Established by the American Society for Public Administration to initiate action programs appropriate to the needs and concerns of women in public administration. Promotes equal educational and employment opportunities for women in public service, and full participation and recognition of women in all areas of government. Develops strategies for implementation of ASPA policies of interest to women in public administration; recommends qualified women to elective and appointive ASPA governmental leadership positions; acts as forum for communication among professional and laypeople interested in the professional development of women in public administration. **Founded:** 1971. **Awards:** Joan Fiss Bishop Leadership Award (Annual); Dr. Rita Mae Kelly Distinguished Research Award (Annual). **Geographic Preference:** National.

31679 ■ Southern Public Administration Education Foundation (SPAEF)
619 Hillen Rd.
  Towson, MD 21286
Ph: (717)689-6126
URL: http://spaef.org
Description: Represents researchers and scholars in the public administration and public management fields. Produces publications and sponsors educational programs. **Founded:** 1977. **Publications:** *Journal of Health and Human Services Administration (JHHSA)* (Quarterly); *Public Administration Quarterly (PAQ)* (Quarterly); *Journal of Power and Ethics: An Interdisciplinary Review* (Quarterly); *German Policy Studies (GPS)* (3/year); *Global Virtue Ethics Review (GVER)* (Quarterly); *Public Administration*

& Management: An Interactive Journal (3/year); *International Journal of Economic Development (IJED)* (Semiannual).

REFERENCE WORKS

31680 ■ "1914 Proved to Be Key Year for Chevy" in Automotive News (Vol. 86, October 31, 2011, No. 6488, pp. S18)
Pub: Crain Communications Inc.
Contact: Barry Asin, President
Ed: Jamie LaReau. **Description:** Chevy Bow Tie emblem was born in 1914, creating the brand's image that has carried through to current days. **Availability:** Print; Online.

31681 ■ "Adidas' Brand Ambitions" in Business Journal Portland (Vol. 27, December 10, 2010, No. 41, pp. 1)
Pub: Portland Business Journal
Contact: Andy Giegerich, Managing Editor
E-mail: agiegerich@bizjournals.com
Ed: Erik Siemers. **Description:** Adidas AG, the second-largest sporting goods brand in the world, hopes to increase global revenue by 50 percent by 2015. The German company, which reported $14.5 billion sales, plans to improve its U.S. market. The U.S. is Adidas' largest, but also the most underperforming market for the firm. **Availability:** Print; Online.

31682 ■ "Baltimore Developer Caves Valley Partners Bids for $750M Social Security Project - County Tract Pitched for Data Center" in Baltimore Business Journal (Vol. 28, July 23, 2010, No. 11, pp. 1)
Pub: Baltimore Business Journal
Contact: Rhonda Pringle, President
E-mail: rpringle@bizjournals.com
Ed: Scott Dance. **Description:** One hundred acres of land in Woodlawn, Maryland is set to be sold for use in the construction of a data center for the U.S. Social Security Administration. Baltimore County has submitted a bid for the $750M construction project. **Availability:** Print.

31683 ■ "California Water Treatment Facility Turns to Solar Power" in Chemical Business Newsbase (September 11, 2012)
Description: Ramona, California municipal water district providing water, sewer, recycled water, fire protection, emergency medical services, and park services to the community has commissioned a 530KWp solar energy installation. Enfinity America Corporation developed and financed the solar panels and EPC services were provided by manufacturer Siliken. **Availability:** Print; Online.

31684 ■ "Cincinnati Business Committee's Tom Williams: Future is Now" in Business Courier (Vol. 27, August 13, 2010, No. 15, pp. 1)
Pub: Business Courier
Ed: Lucy May. **Description:** Tom Williams, chairman of the Cincinnati Business Committee (CBC), maintains that politicians and business leaders must cooperate to ensure the competitiveness of the city for the 21st Century. Under Williams' leadership, the CBC has put emphasis on initiatives related to government efficiency, economic development, and public education. Williams' views on a proposed inland port are given. **Availability:** Print; Online.

31685 ■ "Cincinnati Consults Executives on Police Chief Hire" in Business Courier (Vol. 27, August 27, 2010, No. 17, pp. 1)
Pub: Business Courier
Ed: Dan Monk, Lucy May. **Description:** The City of Cincinnati, Ohio has begun a selection process for the new police chief by consulting the city's business executives. The city charter amendment known as Issue 5 has removed civil service protection from the chief's post and enables City Manager Milton Dohoney to hire a chief from outside the department. **Availability:** Print; Online.

31686 ■ "City-Owned Buildings Get an Injection of Solar Power" in America's Intelligence Wire (September 11, 2012)
Description: City of Toronto, Ontario, Canada and Toronto Hydro-Electric System Ltd. have launched the first phase of a program that will outfit city-owned buildings with over 8,800 solar photovoltaic (PV) panels. Construction begins at MimicoArena, York Mills Arena, and Goulding Park Community Centre/Arena. Details of the project are included. **Availability:** Online.

31687 ■ "Developers Give Big to Stephanie Rawlings-Blake Bid for Mayor" in Baltimore Business Journal (Vol. 29, August 26, 2011, No. 16, pp. 1)
Pub: Boston Business Journal
Contact: Carolyn M. Jones, President
E-mail: cmjones@bizjournals.com
Ed: Scott Dance. **Description:** Mayor Stephanie Rawlings-Blake received thousands of dollars in her political campaign from companies of real estate developers who are vying to build key development projects in Baltimore, Maryland. Rawlings-Blake created a major fundraising advantage over other mayoral candidates with the help of those contributions. **Availability:** Online.

31688 ■ "Governor Candidates Differ on Oregon's Green Streak" in Business Journal Portland (Vol. 27, October 22, 2010, No. 34, pp. 1)
Pub: Portland Business Journal
Contact: Andy Giegerich, Managing Editor
E-mail: agiegerich@bizjournals.com
Ed: Andy Giegerich. **Description:** The views of Oregon gubernatorial candidates Chris Dudley and John Kitzhaber on the state's economy and on environmental policies are presented. Both Dudley, who is a Republican, and his Democratic challenger believe that biomass could help drive the state's economy. Both candidates also pledged changes in Oregon's business energy tax credit (BETC) program.

31689 ■ "Hotel Woes Reflect Area Struggle" in Business Journal Serving Greater Tampa Bay (Vol. 30, December 3, 2010, No. 50, pp. 1)
Pub: Tampa Bay Business Journal
Contact: Ian Anderson, President
E-mail: ianderson@bizjournals.com
Ed: Mark Holan. **Description:** Quality Inn and Suites in East Tampa, Florida has struggled against the sluggish economy but remained open to guests despite facing a foreclosure. The hotel project is the center of East Tampa's redevelopment plans and public officials defend the $650,000 investment in public amenities near the building. **Availability:** Print; Online.

31690 ■ "Lawyers Lock Up Cops as Clients" in Sacramento Business Journal (Vol. 28, April 8, 2011, No. 6, pp. 1)
Pub: Sacramento Business Journal
Contact: Stephanie Fretwell, Director
E-mail: sfretwell@bizjournals.com
Ed: Kathy Robertson. **Released:** Weekly. **Price:** $4. **Description:** Sacramento-based law firm Mastagni, Holstedt and Chiurazzi has grown its client base by specializing in law enforcement labor issues. The firm represents 80,000 public sector correctional officers in the US. The firm has been experiencing an increase in new business as public sector employers face huge budget deficits. **Availability:** Online.

31691 ■ "Lotteries Scratch Their Way to Billions" in Saint Louis Business Journal (Vol. 31, August 19, 2011, No. 52, pp. 1)
Pub: Saint Louis Business Journal
Contact: Robert Bobroff, President
E-mail: rbobroff@bizjournals.com
Ed: Kelsey Volkmann. **Description:** Missouri Lottery reported $1 billion in sales in 2011. A six-fold increase in the lottery's advertising budget is seen to drive the revenue increase; a 4.5 percent rise in its scratch-off tickets and new sponsorships has also contributed to the development. **Availability:** Print; Online.

31692 ■ *"Md. Pension System Tries to Recoup $73M from Actuary"* in *Baltimore Business Journal (Vol. 28, June 11, 2010, No. 5, pp. 1)*
Pub: Baltimore Business Journal
Contact: Rhonda Pringle, President
E-mail: rpringle@bizjournals.com

Ed: Gary Haber. **Description:** Maryland State Retirement and Pension System has won nearly $73 million in administrative ruling against Milliman Inc. over pension loss miscalculations. However, Milliman filed two court cases seeking to reverse the decision and to recoup to the state any money a court orders. **Availability:** Print; Online.

31693 ■ *"New APS AZ Sun Launches"* in *Manufacturing Close-Up (September 19, 2012)*
Description: Permit process has begun to construct the Hyder II Solar Power Plant located in Hyder, Arizona. The project is a partnership between Arizona Public Service and McCarthy Building Companies. The Arizona Sun Program is adding 200 MW of solar photovoltaic power plants across Arizona by 2015. **Availability:** Print; Online.

31694 ■ *"Philadelphia Tourism Push Rising in Fall"* in *Philadelphia Business Journal (Vol. 30, August 26, 2011, No. 28, pp. 1)*
Pub: Philadelphia Business Journal
Contact: Sierra Quinn, Director
E-mail: squinn@bizjournals.com

Ed: Peter Van Allen. **Description:** Philadelphia is offering events for tourists this fall despite massive cuts for tourism promotion. Governor Tim Corbet slashed $5.5 million in funding for the state's tourism-promotion agencies which received $32 million in 2009. The agencies were forced to cooperate and fend for themselves using the hotel taxes that sustain them. **Availability:** Online.

31695 ■ *"Smart Businesses See Value, and Profit, in Promoting Women"* in *Crain's Chicago Business (Vol. 30, February 2007, No. 6, pp. 30)*
Description: Despite U.S. corporations making little progress in advancing women to leadership positions over the past ten years, enlightened corporate decision makers understand that gender diversity is good business as the highest percentages of women officers yielded, on average, a 34 percent higher total return to shareholders and a 35.1 percent higher return on equity than those firms with the lowest percentages of women officers, according to a 2004 Catalyst study of Fortune 500 companies. **Availability:** Online.

31696 ■ *"State Center Lease Deal High for Md."* in *Baltimore Business Journal (Vol. 28, August 6, 2010, No. 13, pp. 1)*
Pub: Baltimore Business Journal
Contact: Rhonda Pringle, President
E-mail: rpringle@bizjournals.com

Ed: Daniel J. Sernovitz. **Description:** The proposed $1.5 billion State Center development project in Midtown Baltimore might cause the State of Maryland to pay the most expensive rental rates in the city. The state will have to pay an effective rental rate of $34 per square foot, including expenses, on the leasing. Other details of the redevelopment project are discussed. **Availability:** Print; Online.

31697 ■ *"University Place Building Gets an Anchor Tenant: Groundbreaking 2.0"* in *Philadelphia Business Journal (Vol. 30, September 23, 2011, No. 32, pp. 1)*
Pub: Philadelphia Business Journal
Contact: Sierra Quinn, Director
E-mail: squinn@bizjournals.com

Ed: Natalie Kostelni. **Description:** University Place Associates, the developer of 2.0 University Place in West Philadelphia, Pennsylvania, will break ground on a five-story, 97,000-square-foot office building in December 2011. The decision follows the Citizenship and Immigration Services signing of a 15-year lease as anchor tenant. **Availability:** Online.

31698 ■ *"VA Seeking Bidders for Fort Howard"* in *Baltimore Business Journal (Vol. 28, June 25, 2010, No. 7, pp. 1)*
Pub: Baltimore Business Journal
Contact: Rhonda Pringle, President
E-mail: rpringle@bizjournals.com

Ed: Daniel J. Servnoitz. **Description:** The Veterans Affairs Maryland Health Care Systems has requested proposals from developers to build a retirement community at Fort Howard in Baltimore County. The historic site, which has about 36 mostly vacant buildings, could become the home to hundreds of war veterans. Details of the proposed development are discussed. **Availability:** Print; Online.

31699 ■ *"Vision for Camden in Better Focus"* in *Philadelphia Business Journal (Vol. 30, September 30, 2011, No. 33, pp. 1)*
Pub: Philadelphia Business Journal
Contact: Sierra Quinn, Director
E-mail: squinn@bizjournals.com

Ed: Natalie Kostelni. **Description:** More than $500 million worth of projects aimed at redeveloping the downtown and waterfront areas of Camden, New Jersey are being planned. These include the construction of residential, commercial, and education buildings. **Availability:** Online.

31700 ■ *"Walker Seeks More Business Participation"* in *Business Journal-Milwaukee (Vol. 28, December 10, 2010, No. 10, pp. A1)*
Pub: The Business Journal
Contact: Heather Ladage, President
E-mail: hladage@bizjournals.com

Ed: Rich Kirchen. **Description:** Wisconsin governor Scott Walker is seeking the aid of Milwaukee business leaders to participate in resolving the challenges posed by the economic crisis. Walker is aiming to create 250,000 jobs. He is also planning to call a special session of the legislature to enact strategies to jumpstart the economy. **Availability:** Print; Online.

TRADE PERIODICALS

31701 ■ *American City and County*
Pub: Informa USA Inc.
Contact: Gareth Wright, Director
URL(s): www.americancityandcounty.com
Facebook: www.facebook.com/AmericanCityCountyMag
Linkedin: www.linkedin.com/company/americancity&county
X (Twitter): twitter.com/AmerCityCounty
Ed: Derek Prall. **Released:** Monthly **Description:** Municipal and county administration magazine. **Availability:** Print; Online.

31702 ■ *The American Review of Public Administration (ARPA)*
Pub: SAGE Publications
Contact: Tracey Ozmina, President
URL(s): journals.sagepub.com/home/arp
Ed: Stephanie P. Newbold. **Released:** 8/year **Price:** $254, Institutions for single print issue; us.sagepub.com/en-us/nam/journal/American-review-public-administration; $2,071, Institutions for backfile lease, combined plus backfile (current volume print & all online content); $1,789, Institutions for ackfile lease, e-access plus backfile (all online content); $3,808, Institutions for backfile purchase, e-access (content through 1998); $26, Individuals for single print issue; $1,883, Institutions for print and online; $1,601, Institutions for online only; $159, Individuals for print only; $1,845, Institutions for print only. **Description:** Scholarly, peer-reviewed journals covering public administration and public affairs. Published in Association between SAGE and the American Society for Public Administration, Section on Public Administration Research. **Availability:** Print; PDF; Download; Online.

31703 ■ *Canadian Public Administration (CPA)*
Pub: L'Institut d'Administration Publique du Canada
Contact: Suzanne Patterson, Director, Finance
E-mail: spatterson@ipac.ca

URL(s): www.ipac.ca/iPAC_EN/iPAC_EN/Programs/CPA_Journal/CPA.aspxonlinelibrary.wiley.com/journal/17547121
X (Twitter): twitter.com/CdnPublicAdm

Ed: Evert A. Lindquist. **Released:** Quarterly **Price:** $603, Institutions for online only US, Canada; $648, Institutions for online India. **Description:** Peer-reviewed journal printing refereed articles by administrative practitioners and academics for university teachers and public servants in federal, provincial, and municipal government (English and French). **Availability:** Print; Download; PDF; Online.

31704 ■ *Demokratzatsiya: The Journal of Post-Soviet Democratization*
Pub: George Washington University Institute for European, Russian and Eurasian Studies
Contact: Dr. Marlene Laruelle, Director
E-mail: laruelle@gwu.edu
URL(s): demokratizatsiya.pub
Facebook: www.facebook.com/demokjournal
X (Twitter): twitter.com/demokjournal

Released: Quarterly; Quarterly; spring, summer, fall and winter. **Price:** $175, Institutions for domestic print only 1 Year; $191, Institutions for foreign print only 1 Year; $62, Individuals for online only 1 Year; $175, Institutions for online only 1 Year; $65, Individuals for domestic print & online only 1 Year; $210, Institutions for domestic print & online only 1 Year; $81, Individuals for foreign print & online only 1 Year; $226, Institutions for foreign print & online only 1 Year; $350, Institutions for domestic print only 2 Year; $382, Institutions for foreign print only 2 Year; $124, Individuals for online only 2 Year; $350, Institutions for online only 2 Year; $130, Individuals for domestic print & online only 2 Year; $420, Institutions for domestic print & online only 2 Year; $162, Individuals for foreign print & online only 2 Year; $452, Institutions for foreign print & online only 2 Year; $525, Institutions for domestic print only 3 Year; $573, Institutions for foreign print only 3 Year; $186, Individuals for online only 3 Year; $525, Institutions for online only 3 Year; $195, Individuals for domestic print & online only 3 Year; $630, Institutions for domestic print & online only 3 Year; $243, Individuals for foreign print & online only 3 Year; $678, Institutions for foreign print & online only 3 Year; $25, Single issue for domestic print; $29, Single issue for foreign print. **Description:** Journal covering past and current political, economical, social, and legal changes and developments in the Soviet Union and its successor states. **Availability:** Print; Online.

31705 ■ *Illinois Issues*
Pub: University of Illinois
URL(s): www.nprillinois.org/illinois

Description: Magazine focusing on public affairs and state and local government. **Availability:** Print.

31706 ■ *Journal of Policy Analysis and Management (JPAM)*
Pub: John Wiley & Sons, Inc.
Contact: Christina Van Tassell, Executive Vice President Chief Financial Officer
URL(s): onlinelibrary.wiley.com/journal/15206688www.appam.org/news/jpam
X (Twitter): x.com/JPAM_DC

Ed: Erdal Tekin. **Released:** Quarterly **Price:** $2,185, Institutions for online only US Canada India; $2,453, Institutions for print & online only US Canada India; $2,279, Institutions for print only US Canada India; $561, Individuals for print only US Canada India. **Description:** Journal focusing on issues and practices in policy analysis and public management. Published by Wiley on behalf of the Association for Public Policy Analysis and Management. **Availability:** Print; Download; PDF; Online.

31707 ■ *Missouri Municipal Review*
Pub: Missouri Municipal League
Contact: Richard Sheets, Executive Director
E-mail: rsheets@mocities.com
URL(s): www.mocities.com/Web/Web/News/MML-Review-Magazine/MML-Review-Magazine.aspx

Ed: Laura Holloway. **Released:** Bimonthly **Price:** $30, Single issue for calendar year. **Description:** Magazine for local officials actively engaged in the procurement of products and services, policy-making, and local government administration. **Availability:** Print; Online.

31708 ■ *Municipal World*
Pub: Municipal World Inc.
Contact: Susan M. Gardner, Chief Executive Officer
URL(s): www.municipalworld.com/themagazine
Facebook: www.facebook.com/MunicipalWorld
Linkedin: www.linkedin.com/company/municipalworld
X (Twitter): x.com/MunicipalWorld
YouTube: www.youtube.com/user/MunicipalWorld
Released: Monthly **Price:** $99.95, for one year; $66.95, for print. **Description:** Magazine in the interest of good local government, covering municipal law, planning, technology, economic development and administration. **Availability:** Print; Online.

31709 ■ *PA Times*
Pub: American Society for Public Administration
Contact: Paul Danczyk, President
URL(s): www.aspanet.org/ASPA/ASPA/PA-TIMES/PA-TIMES.aspx
Released: Quarterly; online is published twice-weekly. **Description:** Public administration newspaper (tabloid). **Availability:** Print; Online.

31710 ■ *Public Administration Abstracts*
Pub: EBSCO Information Services
Contact: Tim Collins, Chief Executive Officer
URL(s): www.ebsco.com/products/research-databases/public-administration-abstracts
Description: Journal containing abstracts on public administration. **Availability:** Download; Online. **Type:** Bibliographic.

31711 ■ *Public Administration Review (PAR)*
Pub: John Wiley & Sons, Inc.
Contact: Christina Van Tassell, Executive Vice President Chief Financial Officer
URL(s): www.publicadministrationreview.comonlinelibrary.wiley.com/journal/15406210
Facebook: www.facebook.com/PAReview
Linkedin: www.linkedin.com/in/pareview
X (Twitter): x.com/PAReview
Ed: Richard Feiock, Gregg G. Van Ryzin. **Released:** Bimonthly **Price:** $864, Institutions for print + online US, Canada; $1,672, Institutions for print + online, India; $769, Institutions for online US, Canada; $803, Institutions for print US, Canada; $1,489, Institutions for online India; $1,554, Institutions for print, India; $769, Institutions for online US, Canada, India; $864, Institutions for print and online US, Canada; $803, Institutions for print US, Canada, India; $1,672, Institutions for print and online India; $1,554, Institutions for print India. **Description:** Public administration journal. **Availability:** Print; Download; PDF; Online.

31712 ■ *Public Management (PM)*
Pub: International City/County Management Association
Contact: Marc A. Ott, Chief Executive Officer
URL(s): icma.org/page/about-public-management-pm-magazine
Released: Monthly; latest issue April 2024. **Price:** $50, for online only 12 issues (one year); $60, U.S. for print and online 12 issues (one year); $155, Other countries for print and online 12 issues (one year); $25, Members for print and online. **Description:** Magazine for local government administrators. **Availability:** Print; Online.

TRADE SHOWS AND CONVENTIONS

31713 ■ **Maryland Municipal League Convention**
Maryland Municipal League (MML)
1212 W St.
Annapolis, MD 21401
Ph: (410)295-9100
Free: 800-492-7121

Co. E-mail: mml@mdmunicipal.org
URL: http://www.mdmunicipal.org
Contact: Scott A. Hancock, Executive Director
E-mail: scotth@mdmunicipal.org
URL(s): www.mdmunicipal.org/list.aspx?MID=40
Frequency: Annual. **Description:** Office equipment, public works equipment, insurance companies, consulting firms, recreation equipment, computers, engineering firms, police equipment, and code publishers. **Audience:** City and town officials. **Principal Exhibits:** Office equipment, public works equipment, insurance companies, consulting firms, recreation equipment, computers, engineering firms, police equipment, and code publishers.

31714 ■ **New Jersey League of Municipalities Annual Conference**
New Jersey State League of Municipalities (NJLM)
222 W State St.
Trenton, NJ 08608
Ph: (609)695-3481
Fax: (609)695-0151
URL: http://www.njlm.org
Contact: Michael F. Cerra, Executive Director
E-mail: mcerra@njlm.org
URL(s): conference.njlm.org/about.html
Frequency: Annual. **Audience:** Technical and professional employees. **Telecommunication Services:** klawrence@njlm.org.

CONSULTANTS

31715 ■ **National Center for Public Policy Research (NCPPR)**
2005 Massachusetts Ave. NW
Washington, DC 20036
Ph: (202)507-6398
Co. E-mail: info@nationalcenter.org
URL: http://nationalcenter.org
Contact: David A. Ridenour, President
E-mail: dridenour@nationalcenter.org
Facebook: www.facebook.com/NCPPR
X (Twitter): x.com/NationalCenter
YouTube: www.youtube.com/channel/UCFrgtYxKOBuDqXavBuK0FFA
Description: Educates the public about public policy issues. Conducts research; distributes national policy analysis papers, memorandums, brochures, newsletters, article reprints, and other materials to the public, libraries, and the media. **Scope:** A communications and research nonprofit organization offering advice and information on international affairs and United States domestic affairs. Sponsors Project 21. Gives special emphasis an environmental and regulatory issues and civil rights issues. **Founded:** 1982. **Publications:** "National Policy Analysis"; "Legal Briefs"; "White Paper: National Policy Analysis 523"; "Shattered Dreams: One Hundred Stories of Government Abuse"; "Shattered Lives: 100 Victims of Government Health Care". **Awards:** National Center for Public Policy Research Paid Internships. **Geographic Preference:** National.

31716 ■ **North Carolina Fair Share CDC**
3509 Haworth Dr., Ste. 303
Raleigh, NC 27609
Contact: Akiba H. Byrd, Sr., Contact
Description: Social services firm consults on community organizing and lobbying for health issues. **Scope:** Social services firm consults on community organizing and lobbying for health issues.

31717 ■ **Practice Development Counsel**
New York, NY
Ph: (212)593-1549
URL: http://www.pdcounsel.com
Contact: Phyllis Weiss Haserot, President
E-mail: pwhaserot@pdcounsel.com
Description: Firm is engaged in business development, organizational consulting and coaching. **Founded:** 1983. **Publications:** "The Rainmaking Machine: Marketing Planning, Strategy and Management For Law Firms"; "The Marketer's Handbook of Tips and Checklists"; "Venturesome Questions: The Law Firms Guide to Developing a New Business Venture"; "Navigating the Whitewater of Internal

Politics"; "Changing Attitudes on Firm Flexibility"; "Transition Planning: A Looming Challenge"; "Don't You Think the Solution Is to Bring In a Good Rainmaker?"; "Aligning Firm Culture with the Needs of the Times"; "What New Partners Need to Know"; "Dangers of Lack of Diversity"; "Learn to Respect Emotion in Business"; "What New Partners Need to Know"; "Taking Responsibility: Implementing Personal Marketing Plans"; "How to Change Unwritten Rules"; "Mentoring and Networking Converge"; "Integrating a New Practice into the Firm"; "Using Conflict Resolution Skills for Marketing Success"; "Sports Team Models for Law Firm Management". **Training:** Managing Work Expectations; Effective Coaching Skills; Service Quality; End-Running the Resistance Professionals Have to Getting Client Input; Ancillary Business Activities; Marketing for Professional Firms; Marketing Ethics; Business Development Training; Trends in Professional Services Marketing; Client Relationship Management; Collaborative Culture; Reaching Consensus; Conflict Resolution; Work life Balance; Generational Issues; Preparing New Partners; Becoming the Employer of Choice; A Marketing Approach to Recruiting; Implementing Workplace Flexibility; The Business Case for Flexible Work Arrangements.

31718 ■ **Public Sector Consultants Inc. (PSC)**
230 N Washington Sq., Ste. 300
Lansing, MI 48933
Ph: (517)484-4954
Fax: (517)484-6549
Co. E-mail: psc@publicsectorconsultants.com
URL: http://publicsectorconsultants.com
Contact: Jonathon Beard, Director
E-mail: jbeard@publicsectorconsultants.com
Facebook: www.facebook.com/PublicSectorConsultants
X (Twitter): x.com/pscmichigan
YouTube: www.youtube.com/channel/UCjoEsgFvA7ks_46qrf-pYqQ
Description: Offers policy research expertise, specializing in opinion polling, public relations, conference planning, and legislative and economic analysis. Industries served: Associations, education, environment, health-care, and public finance. **Scope:** Offers policy research expertise, specializing in opinion polling, public relations, conference planning, and legislative and economic analysis. Industries served: Associations, education, environment, health-care, and public finance. **Founded:** 1980. **Publications:** "The New Landscape of Civic Business: How Business Leadership Is Influencing Civic Progress in Our Metropolitan Regions Today," Feb, 2012; "Saginaw Bay Watershed and Area of Concern," Mar, 2012; "Michigan Public School Employees Retirement System: Major Changes in Recent Years and More Changes to Come," May, 2012; "Saginaw River/Bay Area of Concern: Restoration Plan for the Habitat and Populations BUIs," Sep, 2012; "Proposal 3: Key Questions and Answers," Sep, 2012; "Final Report of the Michigan State Park and Recreation Blue Ribbon Panel," Oct, 2012; "The Impact of Reducing PIP Coverage in Michigan," Sep, 2011; "Michigan Sales Tax Collection and the Internet: A Need for Fairness," Sep, 2011; "Ingham Community Voices Final Evaluation Report," Nov, 2008; "First Class Schools Analysis," Aug, 2008; "Opportunities for Achieving Efficiency in the Aging, Community Mental Health, Local Public Health, and Substance Abuse Coordinating Agency Networks," Aug, 2008; "Saginaw River Bay Area of Concern," Jun, 2008; "Portage Lake Watershed Forever Plan," May, 2008; "Smoke Free Workplaces," Apr, 2008; "Protecting and Restoring the Upper Looking Glass River," Feb, 2008; "Market Structures and the 21st Century Energy Plan," Sep, 2007; "The Growing Crisis of Aging Dams," Apr, 2007; "Financing Community Health Workers Why and How," Jan, 2007; "Hastings Area: Inter local Approaches to Growth Management," Jan, 2007; "Michigan's Part 201 Environmental Remediation Program Review," Jan, 2007.

RESEARCH CENTERS

31719 ■ **California State University, Long Beach College of Health and Human Services - Graduate Center for Public Policy and Administration (GCPPA)**
1250 Bellflower Blvd. SSPA 228
Long Beach, CA 90840

URL: http://www.csulb.edu/college-of-health-human
-services/public-policy-and-administration
Contact: Dr. David C. Powell, Contact
E-mail: david.powell@csulb.edu
Description: Integral unit of California State University, Long Beach. **Scope:** Seeks to develop increased competency and perspective of administrative process of government. **Founded:** 1973.

31720 ■ Carleton University - Carleton Research Unit on Innovation, Science, and Environment (CRUISE)
Carleton University 1125 Colonel By Dr.
  Ottawa, ON, Canada K1S 5B6
URL: http://research.carleton.ca/2014/04/carleton
-university-partners-with-un-climate-and-clean-air
-coalition
Contact: Rafik Goubran, Vice President
Description: Integral unit of Carleton University. Offers consulting services. **Scope:** Involves in program evaluation and scientific and technical activities; science and technical indicators, technology diffusion and standards; local level industrial agglomeration or "clustering"; energy and environment policies, including carbon emissions; and information technologies. **Founded:** 1997. **Publications:** *CRUISE Journal* (Annual).

31721 ■ Citizens Budget Commission (CBC)
240 West 35th St., Ste. 302
  New York, NY 10001
Ph: (212)279-2605
Co. E-mail: info@cbcny.org
URL: http://cbcny.org
Contact: Andrew S. Rein, President
Facebook: www.facebook.com/CitizensBudgetCommission
Linkedin: www.linkedin.com/company/citizens-budget-commission
X (Twitter): x.com/cbcny
Description: Independent, nonprofit, nonpartisan civic research organization. **Scope:** Management of New York City and New York State's fiscal affairs and service delivery. Specific studies include reviews of city and state expense budgets, tax policy, public services, capital budget, and state-city financial relationships. **Founded:** 1932. **Publications:** *CBC Research Reports.* **Awards:** Citizens Budget Commission Medal for High Civic Service (Annual); Citizens Budget Commission Prize for Public Service Innovation (Annual).

31722 ■ Cornell University - International Studies in Planning Concentration
106 W Sibley Hall
  Ithaca, NY 14853
Ph: (607)255-4613
Fax: (607)255-1971
Co. E-mail: crpinfo@cornell.edu
URL: http://aap.cornell.edu/academics/crp/graduate/
  planning/mrp/concentrations/international-studies
Contact: Prof. Sophie Oldfield, Chairman
E-mail: sophie.oldfield@cornell.edu
Description: Integral unit of Department of City and Regional Planning, Cornell University, affiliated with the Center for International Studies. **Scope:** Analysis of the regional and spatial dimensions of development issues with a focus—although by no means exclusive—on the Third World, including political economy of regional and national development; planning and the global economy; critical development theory; project planning and administration; political ecology and international environmental planning; community economic development; gender and development; infrastructure; and NGOs and social movements. Areas of research include Latin America, Caribbean, Africa, Europe, and Southeast Asia. **Founded:** 1972.

31723 ■ Council on Foreign Relations (CFR) - Library
58 E 68th St.
  New York, NY 10065
Ph: (212)434-9400
Fax: (212)434-9800
Co. E-mail: corporate@cfr.org
URL: http://www.cfr.org

Contact: Michael Froman, President
E-mail: president@cfr.org
Facebook: www.facebook.com/councilonforeignrelations
Linkedin: www.linkedin.com/company/council-on-foreign-relations
X (Twitter): x.com/CFR_org
Instagram: www.instagram.com/cfr_org
YouTube: www.youtube.com/user/cfr
Description: Individuals with specialized knowledge of and interest in international affairs. Studies the international aspects of American political, economic, and strategic problems; research projects are carried out by professional staff advised by study groups of selected leaders in education, public service, business, and the media. **Scope:** Long-range foreign policy problems, including area, political, economic, and strategic studies. Administers International Affairs, Military, State Department, and Murrow press fellowship programs. **Founded:** 1921. **Holdings:** Figures not available. **Publications:** *Foreign Affairs* (6/year); *Membership Roster; CFR Annual Report* (Annual). **Awards:** CFR Volunteer Internships (Annual); CFR Military Fellowships (Annual); CFR Stanton Nuclear Security Fellowship (Annual); International Affairs Fellowship in Japan (IAF) (Annual); CFR National Intelligence Fellowship (Annual); Edward R. Murrow Press Fellowship (Annual); CFR International Affairs Fellowship (IAF) (Annual); International Affairs Fellowships in Nuclear Security (IAF-NS) (Annual). **Geographic Preference:** National.

31724 ■ Florida State University - Florida Center for Public Management (FCPM)
227 N Bronough St., Ste. 4600
  Tallahassee, FL 32301
Ph: (850)644-6460
Co. E-mail: its-help@fsu.edu
URL: http://fcpm.fsu.edu
Contact: Linda Jimenez-Lopez, Director
E-mail: ljimenez@fsu.edu
Facebook: www.facebook.com/FSUCPM
Instagram: www.instagram.com/fsucpm
YouTube: www.youtube.com/channel/UCWCyhUBfBJ
  1DxEA2WFk6__w
Description: Research service activity at Florida State University. Offers conference planning. **Scope:** Studies state, county, and city government management, planning, and budgeting. **Founded:** 1979.

31725 ■ George Washington University - Elliott School of International Affairs - Institute for International Science and Technology Policy (IISTP)
1957 E ST NW Lindner Commons
  Washington, DC 20052
Co. E-mail: iistp@gwu.edu
URL: http://iistp.elliott.gwu.edu
Contact: Nicholas Vonortas, Director, Economics Professor
E-mail: vonortas@gwu.edu
X (Twitter): x.com/iistp_gw
Description: Integral unit of George Washington University, under control of Elliott School of International Affairs. **Scope:** Interdisciplinary research and policy analysis. Program includes such disciplines as public administration, political science, economics, international affairs, and environmental resources for application to science and technology policy, international science policy, technology transfer, research and development policy, risk analysis and management, regulatory process, institutional analysis, public perception assessment, space policy, environmental quality, economics of technology, networks and information and telecommunications policy. **Founded:** 1968.

31726 ■ Harvard University - A. Alfred Taubman Center for State and Local Government
Harvard Kennedy School of Government
  79 JFK St.
  Cambridge, MA 02138
Ph: (617)495-2199
Fax: (617)496-1722
Co. E-mail: taubman@harvard.edu

URL: http://www.hks.harvard.edu/centers/taubman
Contact: Jeffrey Liebman, Director
E-mail: jeffrey_liebman@hks.harvard.edu
Facebook: www.facebook.com/TaubmanCenter
Linkedin: www.linkedin.com/company/taubman-center-for-state-and-local-government
X (Twitter): x.com/TaubmanCenter
Description: Integral unit of John F. Kennedy School of Government at Harvard University. **Scope:** Politics, public management, and public finance in state and local government, land use policy, transportation, community development and growth management, strategic uses of new technology, education, and governance. Publishes journal articles, policy briefs, and working papers. **Founded:** 1988.

31727 ■ Murray State University - Bureau of Business and Economic Research (BBER)
105 Business Bldg.
  Murray, KY 42071
Ph: (270)809-4433
URL: http://www.murraystate.edu/about/Offices/
  InformationSystems/DepartmentalPhoneListings
  .aspx
Description: Integral unit of Murray State University. **Scope:** Business development, economic planning, economic impact analysis, socio-economic issues for Western Kentucky and neighboring states. **Publications:** *Business and Public Affairs Journal* (Periodic); *BBER Research reports; State of the Economy in Western Kentucky* (Semiannual); *Western Kentucky Quarterly Economic Report* (Quarterly). **Educational Activities:** BBER Seminars, For local civic and educational organizations.

31728 ■ Ohio University - Voinovich School of Leadership & Public Affairs - Institute for Local Government Administration and Rural Development (ILGARD)
Schoonover Center 247A
  Athens, OH 45701
URL: http://www.ohio.edu/applied-ethics/resources/o
  ther-institutes
Description: Integral unit of Center for Public and Environmental Affairs at Ohio University. Research and development arm of Governor's Office of Appalachia. Training programs and technical assistance: for local government and non-profits. **Scope:** Provides state and local officials in Ohio (with primary focus in Southeast Ohio) with research and technical assistance in economic development, public policy and administration, and survey research and geographic information systems, including aid in linking local and regional officials with state and national resource persons. Partners with primary economic development and capital access partners in the public and private sector, providing sophisticated business assistance for both start-up and existing businesses. **Founded:** 1981. **Publications:** *Educational Access; Employment and Business Opportunities for Low Income Populations in SE Ohio; Environmental Risk.* **Educational Activities:** Business Assistance and Capital Access, Offer exemplary teaching programs.; ILGARD Environmental remediation, Offer exemplary teaching programs.; ILGARD Facilitation and evaluation, Offer exemplary teaching programs.; ILGARD Public administration and policy innovation and research, Offer exemplary teaching programs.; ILGARD Survey analysis, Offer exemplary teaching programs.; ILGARD Value-added research, Offer exemplary teaching programs.

31729 ■ Oklahoma State University - Center for Local Government Technology (CLGT)
1201 S Innovation Way Dr.
  Stillwater, OK 74074
Ph: (405)744-6049
Co. E-mail: clgt@okstate.edu
URL: http://clgt.okstate.edu
Contact: Gary Snyder, Director
E-mail: gary.snyder@okstate.edu
Description: Integral unit of Oklahoma State University, operating under the Dean of College of Engineering, Architecture and Technology as a public service program. **Scope:** Provides technical assistance and educational programs at state, county, and municipal government levels relating to engineering, manage-

ment technology, and accounting, including county officer training, computer applications in small city and county government, vehicle fleet management, tax procedures, productivity in local government, and street, road, and bridge maintenance. **Founded:** 1974. **Publications:** *CLGT Manuals*; *CLGT Newsletters* (Quarterly); *Project Journals*; *Technical Fact Sheets*. **Educational Activities:** CLGT Seminars, Offer exemplary teaching programs.; CLGT Workshops, Offer exemplary teaching and training programs.; Equipment Maintenance Management Conference, Offer exemplary teaching and training programs.; Road and Street Conference, Offer exemplary teaching and training programs.

31730 ■ Queen's University at Kingston School of Policy Studies - Institute of Intergovernmental Relations (IIGR)

Robert Sutherland Hall, Rm. 412
138 Union St.
Kingston, ON, Canada K7L 3N6
Ph: (613)533-2080
Co. E-mail: iigr@queensu.ca
URL: http://www.queensu.ca/iigr/home
Contact: Christian Leuprecht, Director
E-mail: christian.leuprecht@queensu.ca
Facebook: www.facebook.com/IIGR.QU
X (Twitter): x.com/iigr_queensu
Description: Distributes books on international relations. Reaches market through direct mail. Distributor of titles related to international relations. **Scope:** Political, financial, and administrative intergovernmental relations and policymaking in federal systems, with particular emphasis on Canada, including self-generated projects and contract research. Specific research themes and projects include an examination of the Canadian federation, constitutional reform, the relationship between Quebec and its Confederation partners, the relationship between the structure of the Canadian federal system and the design and implementation of public policy (especially in the economic sphere), impact of the global economy on Canadian federalism, federalism and political theory, the structure of central institutions, the conduct of intergovernmental relations, and fiscal federalism and federal-provincial financial relations. **Founded:** 1965. **Publications:** *IIGR Annual Reports* (Annual); *Bibliographies on Federalism*; *Canada: The State of the Federation* (Annual); *IIGR Monographs*; *Reflections Series*; *Research Paper Series*. **Educational Activities:** IIGR Institute's Advisory Council, Offer exemplary teaching programs.; IIGR Kenneth R. MacGregor Lectureship in Intergovernmental Relations, Offer exemplary teaching programs.; IIGR Seminars, Offer exemplary teaching programs.; Institute of Intergovernmental Relations (Biennial), Offer exemplary teaching and training programs.

31731 ■ University of California, Berkeley - Institute of Governmental Studies (IGS) - Library

109 Philosophy Hall
Berkeley, CA 94720-2370
Ph: (510)642-1473
Co. E-mail: igs@berkeley.edu
URL: http://igs.berkeley.edu
Contact: Christine Trost, Executive Director
E-mail: ctrost@berkeley.edu
Facebook: www.facebook.com/berkeleyigs
Linkedin: www.linkedin.com/company/institute-of-governmental-studies
X (Twitter): x.com/BerkeleyIGS
YouTube: www.youtube.com/channel/UCcG1QNUH_cqO9dtodcA4fXA
Description: Publishes on public policy. **Scope:** American national, state, and local government and politics, public policy, public organization and administration, urban-metropolitan problems, federalism and intergovernmental relations, comparative methodology, and technology and government. **Services:** Interlibrary loan; copying; library open to the public. **Founded:** 1919. **Holdings:** 400,000 volumes. **Sub-**

scriptions: 1200 journals and other serials. **Publications:** *Public Affairs Report* (Annual); *IGS Monographs*; *IGS Research Reports*. **Educational Activities:** IGS Conferences (Annual), Offer exemplary teaching and training programs.; Institute of Governmental Studies Lectures, Offer exemplary teaching programs.; Institute of Governmental Studies Seminars, Teaching on topics related to government policies and social issues.; Institute of Governmental Studies Workshops, Offer exemplary teaching and training programs. **Awards:** IGS John Gardner Fellowship (Annual).

31732 ■ University of Delaware - Institute for Public Administration (IPA)

261 Academy St., University of Delaware
Newark, DE 19716
Ph: (302)831-8971
Fax: (302)831-3488
Co. E-mail: ipa@udel.edu
URL: http://www.bidenschool.udel.edu/ipa
Facebook: www.facebook.com/DelawareIPA
X (Twitter): x.com/DelawareIPA
Description: Integral unit of College of Human Services, Education and Public Policy of the University of Delaware. **Scope:** Integral unit of University of Delaware. Research, education, and public service program areas include civic education, conflict resolution, health care policy, land use planning, organizational development, school leadership, state and local management, water resources management, and women's leadership. **Founded:** 1973. **Publications:** *IPA Reports*. **Educational Activities:** Policy Forums (Annual); IPA Training Workshops, Certificate Programs. **Awards:** IPA Internship Program; Institute for Public Administration Legislative Fellows Program (Annual).

31733 ■ University of Georgia - Carl Vinson Institute of Government

201 North Milledge Ave.
Athens, GA 30602
Ph: (706)542-2736
Fax: (706)542-9301
Co. E-mail: vinsoninstitute@uga.edu
URL: http://www.cvlog.uga.edu
Facebook: www.facebook.com/VinsonInstitute
Linkedin: www.linkedin.com/company/carl-vinson-institute-of-government
X (Twitter): x.com/cviog_uga
Description: Publishes for government officials about government laws and management. Reaches market through direct mail. Does not accept unsolicited manuscripts. **Scope:** Government, public administration, public finance, public personnel administration, science and technology policy, public law, and organizational development. **Founded:** 1927. **Publications:** *Books and reports* (7/year); *Project Reports*; *State and Local Government Review (SLGR)* (Quarterly). **Educational Activities:** Carl Vinson Institute of Government Workshops.

31734 ■ University of Maryland at College Park - Institute for Governmental Service and Research (IGSR)

8400 Baltimore Ave., Ste. 100
College Park, MD 20740-2438
Ph: (301)405-4905
Fax: (301)314-9258
Co. E-mail: igsr@umd.edu
URL: http://www.igsr.umd.edu
Contact: Dr. Cheryll Alipio, Principal
E-mail: calipio@umd.edu
Linkedin: www.linkedin.com/company/igsr
X (Twitter): x.com/IGSRatUMD
Description: Integral unit of University of Maryland at College Park. **Scope:** Strategic planning, fiscal issues, land use and annexation, program evaluation, personnel management, and other related governmental areas. **Founded:** 1947. **Publications:** *Compensation Survey of Maryland Local Govern-*

ments (Occasionally); *Did You Know* (Occasionally); *Handbook for Maryland Municipal Officials* (Annual); *Home Rule Options in Maryland Counties* (5/year); *Maryland Government Report* (Annual); *Outreach Newsletter* (5/year).

31735 ■ University of Minnesota, Duluth College of Liberal Arts - Center for Community and Regional Research (CCRR)

1049 University Dr.
Duluth, MN 55812
URL: http://cahss.d.umn.edu/centers-facilities/ccrr
Description: Integral unit of University of Minnesota, Duluth. **Scope:** The primary focus of the Center is community-based education at UMD, providing faculty and students in the social and natural sciences and related fields the opportunity to work with local and regional community organizations. With this focus, students apply research skills and principles of social engagement and analysis, UMD faculty receive funding for projects in which they apply their expert knowledge and skills in a real-world local context, and local organizations, communities and agencies benefit through research on issues central to them.

31736 ■ University of North Florida - College of Arts and Sciences - Department of Sociology, Anthropology, and Social Work - Center for Community Initiatives (CCI)

1 UNF Dr. Bldg. 1/1901
Jacksonville, FL 32224
Ph: (904)620-2463
Fax: (904)620-4415
Co. E-mail: unf-alumni@unf.edu
URL: http://www.unf.edu/coas/cci
Contact: Dr. Jeffry A. Will, Director
E-mail: jwill@unf.edu
Description: Research activity at Department of Sociology, Anthropology, and Social Work, College of Arts and Sciences, University of North Florida. **Scope:** Community, local, state and federal programs affecting community life in Northeast Florida.

31737 ■ University of South Dakota College of Arts & Sciences - Government Research Bureau (GRB)

414 E Clark St.
Vermillion, SD 57069
Ph: (605)677-6663
Fax: (605)677-6968
Co. E-mail: grb@usd.edu
URL: http://www.usd.edu/Academics/Colleges-and-Schools/college-of-arts-sciences/Government-Research-Bureau
Contact: John Dudley, Contact
E-mail: john.dudley@usd.edu
Description: Integral unit of College of Arts and Sciences, University of South Dakota. Clearinghouse for information on governmental administration; consultation services for governmental officials. **Scope:** Governmental problems, including studies of state and local government, public administration, political party organization, political behavior, governmental finance, and miscellaneous governmental problems connected with South Dakota. Provides research training for students of the University. **Founded:** 1939. **Publications:** *Public Affairs Journal* (Quarterly).

31738 ■ University of Utah - Kem C. Gardner Policy Institute (CPPA)

411 East South Temple St.
Salt Lake City, UT 84111
Ph: (801)585-5618
Co. E-mail: gardnerinstitute@eccles.utah.edu
URL: http://gardner.utah.edu
Contact: Natalie Gochnour, Associate
E-mail: natalie.gochnour@eccles.utah.edu
Facebook: www.facebook.com/gardnerpolicyinstitute
Linkedin: www.linkedin.com/company/the-policy-institute-at-the-university-of-utah
X (Twitter): x.com/KemGardnerInst

Description: Integral unit of University of Utah. Offers consultation to local, county, and state governments; technical assistance; training. **Scope:** Local and state government finance, organization, and administration; public policy research on education, health, environment, transportation, resources, energy; Western regional policy issues and regional governance. **Founded:** 1979. **Publications:** *Policy briefing papers* (Occasionally); *Policy Perspectives*

(Monthly). **Educational Activities:** Master Public Administration Alumni Conference.

31739 ■ Virginia Commonwealth University - Center for Public Policy
901 Park Ave.
 Richmond, VA 23284-2033
URL: http://scholarscompass.vcu.edu/center-for
 -public-policy

Description: Applied research and public service unit of the Division of Continuing Studies and Public Service, Virginia Commonwealth University. **Scope:** Public policy research, with special attention to health policy, urban and metropolitan development, and state and local government and politics. **Founded:** 1994.

ASSOCIATIONS AND OTHER ORGANIZATIONS

31740 ■ Association for Public Policy Analysis and Management (APPAM)
1100 Vermont Ave. NW Ste. 650
Washington, DC 20005
Ph: (202)496-0130
Co. E-mail: membership@appam.org
URL: http://www.appam.org
Contact: Tara Sheehan, Executive Director
E-mail: tsheehan@appam.org
Facebook: www.facebook.com/appamdc
Linkedin: www.linkedin.com/company/association-for
-public-policy-analysis-&-management
X (Twitter): x.com/APPAM_DC
YouTube: www.youtube.com/user/TheAPPAM

Description: Improves public policy and management by fostering excellence in research and analysis. **Founded:** 1979. **Publications:** *Journal of Policy Analysis and Management (JPAM)* (Quarterly). **Educational Activities:** APPAM Fall Research Conference (Annual). **Awards:** APPAM PhD Dissertation Award (Annual). **Geographic Preference:** Multinational.

31741 ■ Council of PR Firms [PR Council (PRC)]
1460 Broadway, Ste. 8022
New York, NY 10036
Ph: (646)588-0139
Co. E-mail: contact@prcouncil.net
URL: http://prcouncil.net
Contact: Kim Sample, President
E-mail: kim@prcouncil.net
Facebook: www.facebook.com/theprcouncil
Linkedin: www.linkedin.com/company/council-of
-public-relations-firms
X (Twitter): x.com/PRCouncil
Instagram: www.instagram.com/theprcouncil

Description: Strives to build the business of public relations by advocating to non-communications business executives, professors, students and media about the validity of public relations as an effective strategic business tool. Works to set standards for the profession. **Founded:** 1998. **Publications:** *GAP Study* (Annual). **Geographic Preference:** National.

31742 ■ Hispanic Public Relations Association (HPRA)
PO Box 86760
Los Angeles, CA 90086
Ph: (917)880-8702
Co. E-mail: info@hprausa.org
URL: http://hprausa.org
Contact: Sonia Diaz, President
Facebook: www.facebook.com/HPRAusa
Linkedin: www.linkedin.com/company/hispanic-public
-relations-association
X (Twitter): x.com/HPRAusa
Instagram: www.instagram.com/hpra_national

Description: Hispanic professionals in public relations. Promotes a positive image of Hispanics in the media. **Founded:** 1984. **Awards:** HPRA National Scholarship Program (Annual). **Geographic Preference:** National.

31743 ■ National Black Public Relations Society (NBPRS)
14636 Runnymede St.
Van Nuys, CA 91405
Free: 888-491-8833
Co. E-mail: gdprrequest@naylor.com
URL: http://careers.nbprs.org

Description: Black public relations professionals who are either self-employed or employed by advertising agencies, radio and television stations, businesses, or nonprofit organizations. Provides a forum for discussion of topics related to public relations; holds professional development workshops; conducts seminars; maintains speakers' bureau to promote the image of blacks in business. **Founded:** 1998. **Geographic Preference:** National.

31744 ■ Public Relations Society of America (PRSA) - Resource Library
120 Wall St., 21st Fl.
New York, NY 10005-4024
Ph: (212)460-1400
Co. E-mail: memberservices@prsa.org
URL: http://www.prsa.org
Contact: Linda Thomas Brooks, Chief Executive Officer
Facebook: www.facebook.com/PRSANational
Linkedin: www.linkedin.com/company/prsa
X (Twitter): x.com/PRSA
Instagram: www.instagram.com/prsanational

Description: Professional society of public relations practitioners in business and industry, government, associations, hospitals, schools, and nonprofit organizations. Advocates for best practices in the field, as well as greater understanding and adoption of public relations services. Offers job board and networking opportunities. **Scope:** Public relations firm specializes in counseling firms and training programs. **Founded:** 1947. **Holdings:** Articles. **Publications:** "Tactics"; "Professional Development"; "Best Practices"; "How and Why High Technology Companies Use Corporate Identity Principles in Image Building"; "How Much Does My Baby Cost An Analysis of Gender Differences in Income, Career Interruption and Child Bearing"; "Public Relations Practitioners Relationships with Media and Each Other as Moderators of Excellent Health Information and the Local Public Health Agenda". **Training:** PR Boot Camp: Key Concepts and Techniques of Effective Public Relations, New York, Dec, 2009; Not a Bond Cocktail Shaking and Stirring the Right Ingredients for Effective Online Membership Engagement; Jun, 2011; Social Media Its a Jungle Out There, Mar, 2010; Show Me the Members Money The Power of Association and Nonprofit Marketing & Public Relations, July, 2009. **Educational Activities:** PRSA Conferences. **Awards:** Public Relations Professional of the Year Award (Annual); Gold Anvil Award (Annual); Paul M.

Lund Public Service Award (Annual); PRSA Outstanding Educator Award (Annual); Bronze Anvil Awards (Annual); Silver Anvil Awards (Annual); MacEachern Chief Executive Officer Award (Annual); Chester Burger Scholarship for Excellence in Public Relations (Annual). **Geographic Preference:** National.

REFERENCE WORKS

31745 ■ "Backtalk with Terrie M. Williams" in Black Enterprise (Vol. 38, December 2007, No. 5, pp. 204)
Pub: Earl G. Graves Ltd.
Contact: Earl Graves, Jr., President

Ed: Tennille M. Robinson. **Description:** Profile of Terrie M. Williams, president of a public relations agency as well as founder of a youth empowerment organization called Stay Strong Foundation. Williams reflects on her bouts with depression and how the disease impacts sufferers and talks about her book that will inspire others dealing with depression. **Availability:** Online.

31746 ■ "Baseline Metrics CEOs Need for Online Brand Oversight" in South Florida Business Journal (Vol. 34, May 23, 2014, No. 44, pp. 16)
Pub: American City Business Journals, Inc.
Contact: Mike Olivieri, Executive Vice President

Released: Weekly. **Price:** $8, Introductory 4-week offer(Digital & Print). **Description:** Chief executive officers have the option to use metrics that will allow them to monitor their online brands. Social media engagement is an effective customer service metric because it presents a clear assessment of a business social media prowess. Reputation management software, on the other hand, ranks a firm's weekly, hourly, and daily sentiments online. **Availability:** Print; Online.

31747 ■ "BBB Reworks Logo, Grading System" in Crain's Cleveland Business (Vol. 28, October 8, 2007, No. 40, pp. 5)
Pub: Crain Communications Inc.
Contact: K. C. Crain, President

Ed: John Booth. **Description:** During the next year, the Better Business Bureau will adopt a grading system that will establish performance minimums that will make it tougher for some types of businesses to become accredited; this nationwide rebranding effort is part of a campaign to sharpen the Better Business Bureau's image. **Availability:** Online.

31748 ■ "Better ROI Or Your Money Back, Says Buzz Agency" in Advertising Age (Vol. 79, July 14, 2008, No. 7, pp. 1)
Pub: Crain Communications, Inc.
Contact: Jessica Botos, Manager, Marketing
E-mail: jessica.botos@crainsnewyork.com

Ed: Michael Bush. **Description:** Word-of-mouth marketing is discussed as well as the impact on the advertising industry. Although many firms specializing in this form of marketing have opened over the past few years, many marketers are reluctant to try this route. **Availability:** Online.

31749 ■ *"Branding Your Way" in Canadian Business (Vol. 80, February 12, 2007, No. 4, pp. 31)*
Description: The trend in involving consumers in brand marketing by seeking their views through contests or inviting them to produce and submit commercials through Internet is discussed. **Availability:** Online.

31750 ■ *"The Changing Face of the U.S. Consumer" in Advertising Age (Vol. 79, July 7, 2008, No. 26, pp. 1)*
Pub: Advertising Age
Contact: Dan Peres, President
Ed: Peter Francese. **Description:** It is essential for marketers to examine demographic shifts when looking at ways in which to market brands. The average head-of-households is aging and marketers must not continue to ignore them. Statistical data included. **Availability:** Print; Online.

31751 ■ *"Column: It's Time to Take Full Responsibility" in Harvard Business Review (Vol. 88, October 2010, No. 10, pp. 42)*
Pub: Harvard Business Publishing
Contact: Diane Belcher, Managing Director
Ed: Rosabeth Moss Kanter. **Price:** $6, PDF. **Description:** A case for corporate responsibility is cited, focusing on long-term impact and the effects of public accountability. **Availability:** Online; PDF.

31752 ■ *"The Corporation and Private Politics" in Journal of Business Strategy (Vol. 35, May-June 2014, No. 3, pp. 59-62)*
Pub: Emerald Group Publishing Limited
Contact: Erika Valenti, President
Description: Description of how the public pressurizes corporations to reveal their viewpoint on various social issues including same-sex marriages and others, even though the issues have nothing to do with the firm's business. Several guidelines for managing the clash of private issues and corporate reputation have been presented.

31753 ■ *"The Customer Is Always Right Even When He's Wrong" in Contractor (Vol. 57, February 2010, No. 2, pp. 12)*
Ed: Al Schwartz. **Description:** Mechanical contractors should note that customers will make a judgment based upon the impression that they form on their first meeting. Contractors can maintain a professional image by washing their trucks and having the personnel dress uniformly. Contractors have every right to demand that employees clean up and make a better impression on customers. **Availability:** Print; Online.

31754 ■ *"Down on the Boardwalk" in Retail Merchandiser (Vol. 51, September-October 2011, No. 5, pp. 56)*
Description: Classic board game, Monopoly, continues to be the most recognized game brand while staying fresh by entering new markets and gaming platforms for all walks of life. Monopoly is available in over 100 countries, translated into 43 languages and played by more than 1 billion people since its introduction, and the game is tailored to each geographic market it enters. **Availability:** Online.

31755 ■ *"Effective Use of Field Time" in Agency Sales Magazine (Vol. 39, July 2009, No. 7, pp. 40)*
Description: Sales representatives need to consider the value of field visits to themselves and their customers ahead of time. Several anecdotes about field visits from the perspective of manufacturers and sale representatives are presented.

31756 ■ *"Emotional Brand Attachment and Brand Personality: The Relative Importance of the Actual and the Ideal Self" in Journal of Marketing (Vol. 75, July 2011, No. 4, pp. 35)*
Pub: American Marketing Association
Contact: Bennie F. Johnson, Chief Executive Officer

Ed: Bettin Nyffeneger, Lucia Malar, Harley Krohmer, Wayne D. Hoyer. **Description:** A study on whether the brand's personality should match the consumer's actual self or ideal self is presented. Actual self-congruence is found to have the most impact on emotional brand attachment. **Availability:** PDF.

31757 ■ *"Empowered" in Harvard Business Review (Vol. 88, July-August 2010, No. 7-8, pp. 94)*
Pub: Harvard Business Publishing
Contact: Diane Belcher, Managing Director
Ed: Josh Bernoff, Ted Schadler. **Price:** $8.95, PDF. **Description:** HERO concept (highly empowered and resourceful operative) which builds a connection between employees, managers, and IT is outlined. The resultant additional experience and knowledge gained by employees improves customer relationship management. **Availability:** Online; PDF.

31758 ■ *"Exporting Portlandia: Unconventional Brands Carry a Taste of Portland Across U.S." in Business Journal Portland (Vol. 30, January 17, 2014, No. 46, pp. 4)*
Pub: American City Business Journals, Inc.
Contact: Mike Olivieri, Executive Vice President
Description: Some Portland, Oregon-based food companies have been bringing the area's reputation across the U.S. Voodoo Doughnut has opened a branch in Denver, Colorado. Meanwhile, Laughing Planet is opening several West Coast cafes. **Availability:** Print; Online.

31759 ■ *Facebook Marketing: Leveraging Facebook's Features for Your Marketing Campaigns*
Pub: Que Publishing
Ed: Justin R. Levy. **Released:** Third edition. **Price:** $18.21, e-book; $16.18, paperback. **Description:** Detailed steps are given in order to develop, use, and create awareness for any business. The book provides detailed instructions, along with case studies from known brands, for launching marketing campaigns on Facebook. **Availability:** E-book; Print.

31760 ■ *"Gaming Infrastructure Paves Ready Path for Manufacturing" in Memphis Business Journal (No. 35, February 14, 2014, No. 45, pp. 4)*
Pub: American City Business Journals, Inc.
Contact: Mike Olivieri, Executive Vice President
Description: The city of Tunica, Mississippi is trying to expand its reputation as a gaming destination into manufacturing in an effort seek new opportunities for economic development and revenue. German crankshaft manufacturer, Feurer Powertrain, is building a $140 million manufacturing facility that will open in late 2014. **Availability:** Online.

31761 ■ *"Good Questions and the Basics of Selling" in Agency Sales Magazine (Vol. 39, September-October 2009, No. 9, pp. 14)*
Description: Six basic elements to enhance the job of a sales person in regards to his relationship to a customer are presented. **Availability:** Online.

31762 ■ *Groundswell: Winning in a World Transformed by Social Technologies*
Pub: Harvard Business Review Press
Contact: Moderna V. Pfizer, Contact
Ed: Charlene Li, Josh Bernoff. **Released:** June 09, 2011. **Price:** $22, paperback/softbound. **Description:** Individuals are using online social technologies such as blogs, social networking sites, YouTube, and podcasts to discuss products and companies, write their own news, and find their own deals. When consumers you've never met are rating your company's products in public forums with which you have no experience or influence, your company is vulnerable. This book teaches the tools and data necessary to turn this treat into an opportunity. **Availability:** E-book; Print.

31763 ■ *"Hatching Twitter: A True Story of Money, Power, Friendship, and Betrayal"*
Pub: Portfolio Hardcover
Contact: Adrian Zackheim, President
Released: September 05, 2013. **Price:** $18, paperback; $2.18, paperback(100 used from $2.18); $4.28, paperback(55 new from $4.28); $4.39, kindle; $12.99, hardcover; $1.96, hardcover(73 used from $1.96); $8.59, hardcover(9 new from $8.59); $17.50, hardcover(2 collectible from $17.50). **Description:** The first full coverage story covering the four founders of Twitter: Evan Williams, Biz Stone, Jack Dorsey, and Noah Glass, who went from ordinary engineers to wealthy celebrities and entrepreneurs. The story explores their pursuits for money, influence, publicity, and control as Twitter grew larger and more powerful. **Availability:** E-book; Print; Audio.

31764 ■ *"The HBR Interview: "We Had to Own the Mistakes"" in Harvard Business Review (Vol. 88, July-August 2010, No. 7-8, pp. 108)*
Pub: Harvard Business Publishing
Contact: Diane Belcher, Managing Director
Ed: Adi Ignatius. **Description:** Interview with Howard Schultz, CEO of Starbucks, covers topics that include investment in retraining, the impact of competition, premium quality, authenticity, customer services, strategy development, work-and-life issues, and international presence. **Availability:** Online.

31765 ■ *"Hopkins' Security, Reputation Face Challenges in Wake of Slaying" in Baltimore Business Journal (Vol. 28, August 6, 2010, No. 13)*
Pub: Baltimore Business Journal
Contact: Rhonda Pringle, President
E-mail: rpringle@bizjournals.com
Ed: Gary Haber. **Description:** The slaying of Johns Hopkins University researcher Stephen Pitcairn has not tarnished the reputation of the elite school in Baltimore, Maryland among students. Maintaining Hopkins' reputation is important since it is Baltimore's largest employer with nearly 32,000 workers. Insights on the impact of the slaying among the Hopkins' community are also given.

31766 ■ *"How Do You Measure Your PR's Return On Investment?" in Puget Sound Business Journal (Vol. 34, March 21, 2014, No. 49, pp. 9)*
Pub: American City Business Journals, Inc.
Contact: Mike Olivieri, Executive Vice President
Description: The process of measuring public relations and its return on investment (ROI) is difficult because not all expenditures are directed towards media relations and public image. Public relations covers leadership programs, speaking engagements, and word of mouth campaigns. The possibility of linking PR efforts towards bottom line marketing as a goal is discussed. **Availability:** Online.

31767 ■ *"How to Handle a Public Relations Crisis" in Legal Zoom (February 14, 2023)*
URL(s): www.legalzoom.com/articles/how-to-handle-a-public-relations-crisis
Ed: Gwen Moran. **Released:** February 14, 2023. **Description:** Even small businesses are not immune to a pubic relations crisis. Learn how to cope and get your company out of the mess it's in by following the given advice. **Availability:** Online.

31768 ■ *"How Hard Could It Be? The Four Pillars of Organic Growth" in Inc. (January 2008, pp. 69-70)*
Ed: Joel Spolsky. **Description:** Revenue, head count, public relations, and quality are the four most important aspects of any growing business. **Availability:** Online.

31769 ■ *"How I Did It: Timberland's CEO On Standing Up to 65,000 Angry Activists" in Harvard Business Review (Vol. 88, September 2010, No. 9, pp. 39)*
Pub: Harvard Business Publishing
Contact: Diane Belcher, Managing Director

Ed: Jeff Swartz. **Price:** $8.95, PDF. **Description:** Timberland Company avoided a potential boycott by taking a two-way approach. It addressed a supplier issue that posed a threat to the environment, and launched an email campaign to keep Greenpeace activists informed of the development of a new supplier agreement. **Availability:** Online; PDF.

31770 ■ *"How One Company Joins Corporate Public Relations and Community Engagement"* in Denver Business Journal (Vol. 65, January 17, 2014, No. 36, pp. A6)
Pub: American City Business Journals, Inc.
Contact: Mike Olivieri, Executive Vice President

Description: Denver, Colorado-based Barefoot PR was formed by Cori Streetman and Sarah Hogan in 2010 to change corporate views on philanthropy. The partners made a commitment to make community investment the driving force of business. Insights on the next-generation of community relations consultants are also given. **Availability:** Online.

31771 ■ *"How To Be a Twitter Ninja"* in Canadian Business (Vol. 87, October 2014, No. 10, pp. 51)
Description: Robert Palmer, public relations manager at WestJet, shares some rules when it comes to customer engagement on Twitter. He emphasizes the importance of communication when dealing with customer complaints as quickly as possible. **Availability:** Print; Online.

31772 ■ *"How To Live To Be 100: John E. Green Co. Grows Through Diversification"* in Crain's Detroit Business (February 18, 2008)
Pub: Crain Communications Inc.
Contact: Barry Asin, President

Ed: Chad Halcom. **Description:** Continuity, name recognition, and inventiveness are keys to continuing growth for Highland Park, Michigan's John E. Green Company, designer of pipe systems and mechanical contractor. **Availability:** Online.

31773 ■ *If You Have to Cry, Go Outside: And Other Things Your Mother Never Told You*
Pub: HarperCollins Publishers L.L.C.
Contact: Brian Murray, President

Ed: Kelly Cutrone, Meredith Bryan. **Released:** February 02, 2010. **Price:** $10.99, e-book; $7.24, e-book. **Description:** Women's mentor advices on how to make it in one of the most competitive industries in the world, fashion. She has kicked people out of fashion shows, forced some of reality television's shiny start to fire their friends, and built her own company which is one of the most powerful public relations firms in the fashion business. **Availability:** E-book; Print.

31774 ■ *"In My Shoes: A Memoir"*
Pub: Portfolio Hardcover
Contact: Adrian Zackheim, President

Released: October 01, 2013. **Price:** $3.48, kindle; $32.80, hardcover; $0.25, hardcover(49 used from $0.25); $25.60, hardcover (6 new from $25.60); $8. 86, paperback; $1.55, paperback(93 used from $1. 55); $4.01, paperback(49 new from $4.01). **Description:** Profile of Tamara Mellon, woman entrepreneur who built Jimmy Choo into a premier name in the global fashion industry. She addresses her family life, her battles with anxiety and depression, as well as time spend in rehabilitation. She shares her entire life story from her work as a young editor at Vogue to her partnership with shoemaker, Jimmy Choo to her public relationships. She confides what it was like working with an obstinate business partner but also her ability to understand what customers want. **Availability:** E-book; Print; Audio.

31775 ■ *"In the Wake of Pet-Food Crisis, Iams Sales Plummet Nearly 17 Percent"* in Advertising Age (Vol. 78, May 14, 2007, No. 18, pp. 3)
Pub: Crain Communications, Inc.
Contact: Jessica Botos, Manager, Marketing
E-mail: jessica.botos@crainsnewyork.com

Ed: Jack Neff. **Description:** Although the massive U.S. pet-food recall impacted more than 100 brands, Procter & Gamble Co.'s Iams lost more sales and market share than any other industry player. According to Information Resources Inc. data, the brand's sales dropped 16.5 percent in the eight-week period ended April 22. Many analysts feel that the company could have handled the crisis in a better manner. **Availability:** Online.

31776 ■ *"Industrial Buyers' Use of References, Word-of-Mouth and Reputation in Complex Buying Situation"* in Journal of Business & Industrial Marketing (Vol. 29, May 2014, No. 4, pp. 344-352)
Pub: Emerald Group Publishing Limited
Contact: Erika Valenti, President

Description: Exploration of how a buyer can assemble experience-based information dispersed across the business network using customer references, reputation, collegial advice networks, and word-of-mouth, and how this assists in the buying process. Different roles played by these factors are identified and it is suggested that experience-based information sheds light on offerings, suppliers, and problem solving situations in complex buying. **Availability:** Download; PDF; Online.

31777 ■ *It's Not Who You Know - It's Who Knows You!: The Small Business Guide to Raising Your Profits by Raising Your Profile*
Pub: John Wiley & Sons, Inc.
Contact: Christina Van Tassell, Executive Vice President Chief Financial Officer

Ed: David Arvin. **Released:** 2nd edition. **Price:** $8.69, hardcover. **Description:** When it comes to promoting a small business or a brand, it is essential to know how valuable high-profile attention can be. But for most small companies, the cost of hiring an outside firm to increase attention can be too expensive. **Availability:** Print; Online.

31778 ■ *"Kuno Creative to Present the Three Steps of a Successful B2B Social Media Campaign"* in Business Tech & Wireless (August 25, 2011)
Pub: Close-Up Media Inc.
Contact: Caroline S. Moore, President
E-mail: cms@closeupmedia.com

Released: August 24, 2011. **Description:** Kuno Creative, an inbound marketing agency, will host Three Steps of a Successful B2B Social Media Campaign. The firm is a provider of Website development, branding, marketing strategy, public relations, Internet marketing, and inbound marketing. **Availability:** Print; Online.

31779 ■ *"Lessons from SeaWorld's 'Blackfish' Nightmare"* in Orlando Business Journal (Vol. 30, January 3, 2014, No. 28, pp. 7)
Pub: American City Business Journals, Inc.
Contact: Mike Olivieri, Executive Vice President

Released: January 03, 2014. **Price:** $8, introductory 4-week offer(Digital only). **Description:** University of Florida's crisis communications specialist and public relations (PR) professor, W. Timothy Coombs, shares his views about the PR backlash from SeaWorld's refusal to participate in the filming of the documentary 'Blackfish'. Coombs believes SeaWorld must create a public statement that defends its character and actions. **Availability:** Print; Online.

31780 ■ *"The List: Public Relations Agencies"* in South Florida Business Journal (Vol. 35, August 8, 2014, No. 2, pp. 12)
Pub: American City Business Journals, Inc.
Contact: Mike Olivieri, Executive Vice President

Description: Rankings of public relations agencies in the South Florida region are presented. Rankings were based on the 2013 public relations net fee income in the region. **Availability:** Print; Online.

31781 ■ *Media, Organizations and Identity*
Pub: Palgrave Macmillan

Released: First edition. **Description:** The mass media, press, and television are essential in the formation of corporate identity and the promotion of business image and reputation. This book offers a new perspective into the interrelationships between media and organizations over three dimensions: media as business, media in business and business in the media.

31782 ■ *"Microsoft's Diversity Program Clicks into High Speed"* in Hispanic Business (Vol. 30, July-August 2008, No. 7-8, pp. 54)
Ed: Derek Reveron. **Description:** Microsoft's diversity hiring and vendor diversity program to capture more Hispanic consumer and business-to-business market is described. One of the main goals of these programs is to hire more Hispanic executives and managers who will help the company develop and market products and services that will appeal and benefit Hispanic consumers.

31783 ■ *O'Dwyer's Directory of Public Relations Firms*
Pub: J.R. O'Dwyer Company Inc.
Contact: Christine O'Dwyer, Director, Marketing
URL(s): www.odwyerpr.com/pr_firms_database/index _form.php

Ed: Kevin McCauley, Melissa Werbell. **Released:** Annual **Price:** $250, for featured database listing. **Description:** Covers over 1,600 public relations firms; international coverage. Includes list of top 50 public relations firms. **Entries include:** Firm name, address, phone, principal executives, branch and overseas offices, billings, date founded, and 7,750 clients are cross-indexed. **Arrangement:** Geographical by country. **Indexes:** Specialty (beauty and fashions, finance/investor, etc.), geographical, client. **Availability:** Print; Download; Online; PDF.

31784 ■ *"Offer Your Own Authentic Truth"* in South Florida Business Journal (Vol. 34, July 25, 2014, No. 53, pp. 13)
Pub: American City Business Journals, Inc.
Contact: Mike Olivieri, Executive Vice President

Released: Weekly. **Price:** $8, introductory 4-week offer(Digital only). **Description:** Turkel Brands CEO, Bruce Turkel, was born in Miami Beach, Florida and has a bachelor's degree in design at the University of Florida. Turkel was a respected advertising agency owner and executive creative director before he began blogging on marketing and branding. He shares three tips for building a brand and creating a positive public image. **Availability:** Print; Online.

31785 ■ *Public Relations Campaigns: An Integrated Approach*
Ed: Regina M. Luttrell, Luke W. Capizzo. **Released:** March 08, 2018. **Price:** $80.02, Paperback; $68.39, E-book. **Description:** While using case studies and real-life examples, the authors guide the reader into the process of creating a public relations campaign. **Availability:** E-book; Print.

31786 ■ *"Q&A: PSU's Tom Gillpatrick on How Quirkiness Gives Portland Its Edge"* in Business Journal Portland (Vol. 30, January 17, 2014, No. 46, pp. 6)
Pub: American City Business Journals, Inc.
Contact: Mike Olivieri, Executive Vice President

Released: Weekly. **Price:** $4, introductory 4-week offer(Digital only). **Description:** Portland State University Food Industry Leadership Center executive director, Tom Gillpatrick, says consumers now prefer healthier food brands. He also stated the Portland, Oregon's food sector has grown owing to that trend. Gillpatrick added that the state's reputation for being different has also helped the sector. **Availability:** Print; Online.

31787 ■ *"Report: McD's Pepsi Score Best With Young Hispanics"* in Brandweek (Vol. 49, April 21, 2008, No. 16, pp. 8)
Description: According to a new report, in order to reach Hispanic Gen Yers, marketing strategists need to understand this demographic's "bi-dentity," something which has proved an elusive task to many marketers. Another trend is the emergence of Latinas

who have careers, as opposed to just jobs. There is an opportunity to tap this new, young and empowered female market with innovative messaging. Statistical data included. **Availability:** Online.

31788 ■ *"Reputation Warfare"* **in Harvard Business Review (Vol. 88, December 2010, No. 12, pp. 70)**
Pub: Harvard Business Publishing
Contact: Diane Belcher, Managing Director

Ed: Leslie Gaines-Ross. **Price:** $8.95, PDF. **Description:** Steps are presented for addressing attacks on corporate public image. These include responding promptly, avoiding disproportionate displays of force, empowering employees to present the firm's position, and stockpiling credentials to bolster credence. **Availability:** Online; PDF.

31789 ■ *"Restaurants Dish Up Meal Deals To Attract Customers"* **in Crain's Detroit Business (Vol. 24, October 6, 2008, No. 40, pp. 1)**
Pub: Crain Communications Inc.
Contact: Barry Asin, President

Ed: Nathan Skid. **Description:** Restaurateurs are devising many creative and rewarding incentives to get customers to frequent their establishments during this economic crisis. Innovative ways in which even higher-end establishments are drawing in business are discussed. **Availability:** Online.

31790 ■ *"Smart Businesses See Value, and Profit, in Promoting Women"* **in Crain's Chicago Business (Vol. 30, February 2007, No. 6, pp. 30)**
Description: Despite U.S. corporations making little progress in advancing women to leadership positions over the past ten years, enlightened corporate decision makers understand that gender diversity is good business as the highest percentages of women officers yielded, on average, a 34 percent higher total return to shareholders and a 35.1 percent higher return on equity than those firms with the lowest percentages of women officers, according to a 2004 Catalyst study of Fortune 500 companies. **Availability:** Online.

31791 ■ *"Sound Check"* **in Agency Sales Magazine (Vol. 39, August 2009, No. 8, pp. 14)**
Description: Most customers believe salespersons are unable to do well in terms of listening, which is one of the four fundamental competencies of a sales person. Listening is the primary tool to uncover deeper and more powerful needs and motivations of the customer. A guide on how to listen better and improve listening effectiveness is presented. **Availability:** Online.

31792 ■ *"Strategy Migration In a Changing Climate"* **in Harvard Business Review (Vol. 92, May 2014, No. 5, pp. 42)**
Pub: Harvard Business Publishing
Contact: Diane Belcher, Managing Director

Price: $6. **Description:** The CEO of World Wildlife Fund discusses the importance of ensuring reliable source supplies and mitigating reputational and financial risk in promoting corporate sustainability. Forging alliances to achieve goals is also key. **Availability:** Online; PDF.

31793 ■ *"The Tech 100"* **in Canadian Business (Vol. 81, July 21, 2008, No. 11, pp. 48)**
Description: Absolute Software Corp. Day4 Energy Inc., Sandvine Corp., Norsat International Inc. and Call Genie Inc. are the five technology firms included in the annual ranking of top companies in Canada by market capitalization. The services and the one-year total return potential of the companies are presented. **Availability:** Online.

31794 ■ *"Toss the Gum Before You Speak and Other Tips for Presenting to a Potential Principal"* **in Agency Sales Magazine (Vol. 39, July 2009, No. 7, pp. 34)**
Description: When preparing to present to a prospective principal, a salesperson should anticipate the speaking situation and find out in advance the

program events that occur around their speech. They should also practice their material in front of a friend or colleague. **Availability:** Online.

31795 ■ *"Voice: Rebuilding Trust"* **in Business Strategy Review (Vol. 21, Summer 2010, No. 2, pp. 79-80)**
Ed: David De Cremer. **Released:** June 24, 2010. **Description:** The financial world's attempts to rebuild trust are charted. Three steps to jump-start that process are outlined. **Availability:** Print; PDF; Online.

31796 ■ *"What Makes a Great Tweet"* **in Harvard Business Review (Vol. 90, May 2012, No. 5, pp. 36)**
Pub: Harvard Business Review Press
Contact: Moderna V. Pfizer, Contact

Ed: Kurt Luther, Michael Bernstein, Paul Andre. **Price:** $6, PDF. **Description:** A chart uses readership approval percentages to identify the most effective uses of Twitter. Best tweets include amusing random thoughts and self promotion; worst include complaints and presence maintenance. **Availability:** Online; PDF.

31797 ■ *When the Headline Is You: An Insider's Guide to Handling the Media*
Pub: Jossey-Bass

Ed: Jeff Ansell, Jeff Lesson. **Released:** August 01, 2010. **Price:** $29.95, hardcover; $29.95, hardcover. **Description:** How-to guide for executives and other professionals whose high-visibility requires frequent interviews with the media. Tested techniques, tools, and insights for how to respond to all types of media in tough situation are provided. The book also reveals the lessons learned and the pitfalls to avoid by referencing actual news stores from around the world and provides exercises for readers who wish to sharpen their media-handling skills. **Availability:** E-book; Print.

31798 ■ *"Why Does Firm Reputation In Human Resource Policies Influence College Students? The Mechanisms Underlying Job Pursuit Intentions"* **in Human Resource Management (Vol. 51, January-February 2012, No. 1, pp. 121-142)**
Pub: John Wiley & Sons, Inc.
Contact: Christina Van Tassell, Executive Vice President Chief Financial Officer

Ed: Julie Holliday Wayne, Wendy J. Casper. **Released:** January 26, 2012. **Description:** The effects of reputational information about human resource practices of companies on college students seeking employment are examined. The reputation of firms in compensation, work-family, and diversity efforts are found to increase intentions to pursue employment in these firms. **Availability:** Print; PDF; Online.

31799 ■ *"Why Marketing Slogans Matter"* **in Canadian Business (Vol. 85, June 11, 2012, No. 10, pp. 18)**
Ed: Bruce Philp. **Description:** Slogans earn their meaning in popular culture through dramatic beginnings and repetition over the years so marketers should consider whether the brand can earn it before replacing the tag lines. People in the branding business should not use the tag line exercise as a substitute for creating a strategy. **Availability:** Online.

31800 ■ *"You Have to Lead From Everywhere"* **in Harvard Business Review (Vol. 88, November 2010, No. 11, pp. 76)**
Pub: Harvard Business Publishing
Contact: Diane Belcher, Managing Director

Ed: Scott Berinato. **Price:** $8.95, PDF. **Description:** U.S. Coast Guard Admiral Thad W. Allen discusses effective leadership in successful crises management. Topics include influence of media and public perspective, the applicability of military training to the business arena, and the responsibility of a leader to set morale. **Availability:** Online; PDF.

STATISTICAL SOURCES

31801 ■ *Public Relations Firms Industry in the US - Market Research Report*
URL(s): www.ibisworld.com/united-states/market-research-reports/public-relations-firms-industry/

Price: $925. **Description:** Downloadable report analyzing the current and future trends of public relations firms. **Availability:** Online.

TRADE PERIODICALS

31802 ■ *The Levison Letter*
Pub: Ivan Levison and Associates
Contact: Ivan Levison, Contact
E-mail: ivan@levison.com
URL(s): levison.com/backissues.html

Ed: Ivan Levison. **Released:** Monthly **Description:** Offers tips for improving marketing. **Availability:** Print; Online.

VIDEO/AUDIO MEDIA

31803 ■ *The 4 Elements You Need to Build a Bulletproof PR Plan with Billion-Dollar Founder Suneer Madhani*
URL(s): theceoschool.co/241-the-4-elements-you-need-to-build-a-bulletrproof-pr-plan-with-billion-dollar-founder-suneera-madhani

Ed: Suneera Madhani. **Released:** May 15, 2023. **Description:** Podcast discusses the elements of a bulletproof media plan: earned, shared, owned, and paid. Alos offers tips on leveraging these channels for maximum impact, including creating original content, pitching yourself, and building relationships with journalists.

31804 ■ *The How of Business: Megan Bennett - Public Relations*
URL(s): www.thehowofbusiness.com/494-megan-bennett-public-relations

Ed: Henry Lopez. **Released:** October 16, 2023. **Description:** Podcast discusses the role (and challenges) of public relations in small business.

31805 ■ *How to Get PR Coverage for Your Small Business with Melinda Jackson*
URL(s): www.makinggoodpodcast.com/episodes/104

Ed: Lauren Tilden. **Released:** February 08, 2022. **Description:** Podcast defines PR, how to find PR opportunities, how to pitch, and working with influencers. .

31806 ■ *How the Media Industry SHOULD Work for Growing Businesses and Entrepreneurs with Omar Hamdi*
URL(s): www.eofire.com/podcast/omarhamdi

Ed: Jon Lee Dumas. **Released:** January 25, 2024. **Description:** Podcast describes a good PR agent and explains how media coverage can help with lead generation, closing sales, and raising investment.

31807 ■ *How to Pitch Your Business for PR Opportunities with Lucy Werner*
URL(s): www.makinggoodpodcast.com/episodes/146

Ed: Lauren Tilden. **Released:** November 22, 2022. **Description:** Podcast defines PR, how to find the right opportunities, and how to craft your PR pitch.

31808 ■ *PR Hacks You Need to Get Your Business Noticed with Billion Dollar Founder Suneera Madhani*
URL(s): theceoschool.co/the-pr-hacks-you-need-to-get-your-business-noticed

Ed: Suneera Madhani. **Released:** May 15, 2023. **Description:** Podcast dives deeper into leveraging free publicity to build credibility and get people talking about your brand with a focus on authenticity and transparency.

31809 ■ *This Is Small Business: Why Public Relations Matter*
URL(s): www.smallbusiness.amazon/podcast-episodes/ep-50-why-public-relations-matter

Ed: Andrea Marquez. **Released:** March 26, 2024. **Description:** Podcast explains how to implement public relations to mitigate negative impact.

CONSULTANTS

31810 ■ Bitner Group, Inc.

6750 N Andrews Ave., Ste. 200
  Fort Lauderdale, FL 33309
Ph: (954)730-7730
Co. E-mail: info@bitnergroup.com
URL: http://bitnergroup.com
Contact: Gary E. Bitner, President
E-mail: gary@bitnergroup.com
Facebook: www.facebook.com/bitnergroup
Linkedin: www.linkedin.com/company/bitner-group
X (Twitter): x.com/bitnergroup
Instagram: www.instagram.com/bitnergroup
YouTube: www.youtube.com/channel/UCOa7l
  4QJPhMpnDQhAvxBFGw

Description: Provider of media relations, social media management and production of videos and printed materials. **Scope:** A public relations, advertising and marketing consultancy. Serves industries including: travel, technology, telecommunications, financial services, consumer products, health-care, government, automotive, real estate and retail. **Founded:** 2003.

31811 ■ Jeffrey Lant Associates, Inc. (JLA)

50 Follen St., No. 507
  Cambridge, MA 02138
Ph: (617)547-6372
Co. E-mail: drlant@drjeffreylant.com
URL: http://www.drjeffreylant.com

Description: Publishes technical assistance books for nonprofit organizations, consultants, independent professionals and small and home-based businesses. Offers audio cassettes, workshops and consultation services. Also publish the monthly Worlgram newsletter. Reaches market through commission representatives, direct mail, telephone sales and the Internet. Accept unsolicited manuscripts. **Founded:** 1997. **Publications:** "E-mail El Dorado," JLA Publications, 1998; "Web Wealth: How to Turn the World Wide Web Into a Cash Hose for Your Business. Whatever You're Selling," 1997; "Multi-Level Money," JLA Publications, 1994; "No More Cold Calls," JLA Publications, 1997; "Cash Copy"; "How to make at least $100000 a year"; "E-Money". **Training:** Business and personal development, including Establishing and Operating Your Successful Consulting Business; Successfully Promoting Your Small Business and Professional Practice; Succeeding in Your Mail Order Business; Successfully Raising Money for Your Nonprofit Organization from Foundations, Corporations and Individuals; Money Making Marketing: Finding the People Who Need What You're Selling and Making Sure They Buy It; Getting Corporations, Foundations, and Individuals to Give You the Money Your Nonprofit Organization Needs.

31812 ■ Kelley Chunn & Associates (KCA)

PO Box 190871
  Boston, MA 02119
Ph: (617)427-0046
Co. E-mail: kcassociates106@gmail.com
URL: http://www.kelleychunn.com
Contact: Kelley C. Chunn, Contact
Facebook: www.facebook.com/kcaforsocialchange
X (Twitter): x.com/KelleyChunn
Pinterest: www.pinterest.com/kc4info

Description: A consulting firm that specializes in multicultural and cause-related public relations and marketing. It offers cause-related marketing, strategic planning, community relations, corporate communications, guerrilla marketing, event planning and management, public affairs, media relations and training. **Founded:** 1991. **Publications:** "The Tipping point of social marketing Color Magazine"; "Community Voices, Bay State Banner"; "Education: Inner City Slickers," 2006. **Training:** Crisis communications; Guerrilla marketing; Ethnic marketing.

31813 ■ Shannon Staffing Inc.

1590-B Coshocton Ave.
  Mount Vernon, OH 43050
Ph: (740)397-2040
Co. E-mail: mountvernon@shannonstaffing.com
URL: http://www.shannonstaffing.com
Facebook: www.facebook.com/shannonstaffing
Linkedin: www.linkedin.com/company/shannon-s
  taffing-inc.
X (Twitter): x.com/shannonstaffing

Description: Provides human resources recruiting and outplacement counseling services to industries and public sector organizations. **Founded:** 1985. **Publications:** "Powells Rules for Picking People". **Training:** Time Management workshop.

31814 ■ Sparkworks Media

1818 E Yesler Way
  Seattle, WA 98122
Ph: (206)284-5500
Co. E-mail: info@sparkworksmedia.com
URL: http://www.sparkworksmedia.com
Contact: Michel Hansmire, Director
Facebook: www.facebook.com/sparkworksmedia
Linkedin: www.linkedin.com/company/sparkworks
  -media
Instagram: www.instagram.com/sparkworks_media

Description: Firm offers counsel on media and video production for medium and small businesses, governmental and educational institutions and editing and other post-production work as required and distribution and marketing for products produced and full-service production firm for video and new media. **Scope:** Firm offers counsel on media and video production for medium and small businesses, governmental and educational institutions and editing and other post-production work as required and distribution and marketing for products produced and full-service production firm for video and new media. **Founded:** 1979.

INTERNET DATABASES

31815 ■ *Marketing Industry: A Resource Guide*

URL(s): guides.loc.gov/marketing-industry

Description: Provides links to online resources covering the topics of marketing, public relations, and advertising. Users can obtain links to books, academic journals, trade publications, marketing associations, agencies, rankings and awards, brands and advertisements, manufacturers and wholesalers, regulations and ethics, and subscription databases. **Availability:** Online.

RESEARCH CENTERS

31816 ■ Institute for Public Relations (IPR) - Library

PO Box 118400
  Gainesville, FL 32611-8400
Ph: (352)392-0280
Co. E-mail: info@instituteforpr.org
URL: http://www.instituteforpr.org
Contact: Sarah Jackson, Senior Director
Facebook: www.facebook.com/instituteforpr
Linkedin: www.linkedin.com/company/institute-for-pr
X (Twitter): x.com/instituteforpr
Instagram: www.instagram.com/instituteforpr
YouTube: www.youtube.com/c/InstituteforPR

Description: Dedicated to the science beneath the art of public relations. Exists to build and document the intellectual foundations of public relations and to mainstream this knowledge by making it available and useful to all. **Scope:** Measurement and evaluation of public relations. **Founded:** 1956. **Holdings:** Figures not available. **Educational Activities:** IPR Public Relations Executive Forum (Annual). **Awards:** Orangefiery Best Master's Thesis of the Year Award (Annual); IPR Pathfinder Award (Annual); IPR Lifetime Achievement Award (Annual); Ketchum Don Bartholomew Award For Excellence in Public Relations Research (Annual). **Geographic Preference:** National.

ASSOCIATIONS AND OTHER ORGANIZATIONS

31817 ■ Ad Council
815 Second Ave., 9th Fl.
New York, NY 10017
Co. E-mail: privacy@adcouncil.org
URL: http://www.adcouncil.org
Contact: Lisa Sherman, President
Facebook: www.facebook.com/adcouncil
Linkedin: www.linkedin.com/company/the-advertising
  -council
X (Twitter): x.com/adcouncil
Instagram: www.instagram.com/adcouncil
YouTube: www.youtube.com/adcouncil

Description: Produces and promotes public service campaigns on behalf of non-profit organizations and government agencies in issue areas such as improving the quality of life for children, preventative health, education, community well being, environmental preservation and strengthening of families. **Founded:** 1942. **Publications:** *PSA Bulletin* (Bimonthly); *Public Service Advertising Bulletin* (Bimonthly). **Awards:** Ad Council Silver Bell Award (Annual); Advertising Council Public Service Award (Annual). **Geographic Preference:** National.

31818 ■ Advertising Club of New York (ACNY)
989 Avenue of the Americas, 7th Fl.
New York, NY 10018
Ph: (212)533-8080
Co. E-mail: info@theadvertisingclub.org
URL: http://www.theadvertisingclub.org
Contact: Mari Kim Novak, Chairman
Facebook: www.facebook.com/adclubny
X (Twitter): x.com/adclubny
Instagram: www.instagram.com/adclubny

Description: Sponsors educational and public service activities, promotional and public relations projects and talks by celebrities and advertising persons. Conducts annual advertising and marketing course, which offers classes in copywriting, special graphics, verbal communication, advertising production, sale promotion, marketing and management. Sponsors competitions and charitable programs. **Founded:** 1896. **Publications:** *ACNY Membership Roster* (Annual); *Auction Catalogue and Program* (Annual); *ANDY Souvenir Journal* (Annual). **Awards:** ANDY Awards (Annual); AC Silver Medal Award (Annual). **Geographic Preference:** National.

31819 ■ The Advertising Research Foundation (ARF) - Library
432 Park Ave. S 4th Fl.
New York, NY 10016
Ph: (212)751-5656
Fax: (212)689-1859
Co. E-mail: membership@thearf.org
URL: http://thearf.org
Contact: Scott McDonald, Executive
Facebook: www.facebook.com/ARF

Linkedin: www.linkedin.com/company/advertising-research-foundation
X (Twitter): x.com/The_ARF
YouTube: www.youtube.com/user/TheARFvideos

Description: Advertisers, advertising agencies, research organizations, associations, and the media are regular members of the foundation; colleges and universities are associate members. Objectives are to: further scientific practices and promote greater effectiveness of advertising and marketing by means of objective and impartial research. **Scope:** Advertising. **Founded:** 1936. **Holdings:** Figures not available. **Publications:** *Journal of Advertising Research (JAR)* (Quarterly). **Awards:** David Ogilvy Awards (Annual); ARF Rising Star Award (Annual); ARF Innovation Award (Annual); ARF Member Recognition Award (Annual). **Geographic Preference:** National.

31820 ■ Alliance for Women in Media (AWM)
2365 Harrodsburg Rd., A325
Lexington, KY 40504
Ph: (202)750-3664
Fax: (202)750-3664
Co. E-mail: info@allwomeninmedia.org
URL: http://allwomeninmedia.org
Contact: Becky Brooks, President
Facebook: www.facebook.com/allwomeninmedia
X (Twitter): x.com/allwomeninmedia
YouTube: www.youtube.com/user/allwomeninmedia

Description: Committed to supporting women across all media segments, to expand networks, educate and celebrate accomplishments. **Founded:** 1951. **Awards:** The Gracie Award for an National TV Actress in a Leading Role - Comedy or Musical (Annual). **Geographic Preference:** National.

31821 ■ American Academy of Advertising (AAA)
8585 SW 12TH Ln.
Gainesville, FL 32607
Contact: Debbie Treise, Executive Director
E-mail: dtreise@ufl.edu
Facebook: www.facebook.com/AmericanAca
  demyOfAdvertising
X (Twitter): x.com/adscholar

Description: Professional organization for college and university teachers of advertising and for industry professionals who wish to contribute to the development of advertising education. **Founded:** 1958. **Publications:** *Journal of Current Issues & Research in Advertising* (3/year); *American Academy of Advertising--Directory of Members* (Annual); *Journal of Advertising* (5/year); *Journal of Interactive Advertising (JIAD)* (Quarterly; Quarterly); *Proceedings of the Conference of the American Academy of Advertising*; *Membership Roster* (Annual). **Awards:** AAA Distinguished Service Award (Annual); AAA Doctoral Dissertation Grant Competition (Annual); AAA Fellow Award (Annual); AAA Journal of Advertising Best Article Award (Annual); Ivan L. Preston Outstanding Contribution to Research Award (Irregular). **Geographic Preference:** National.

31822 ■ American Advertising Federation (AAF)
1101 K St. NW, Ste. 420
Washington, DC 20005
Ph: (202)898-0089
URL: http://www.aaf.org
Contact: Steve Pacheco, President
Facebook: www.facebook.com/aafnational
Linkedin: www.linkedin.com/company/aafnational
X (Twitter): x.com/AAFNational
Instagram: www.instagram.com/aafnational

Description: Works to advance the business of advertising as a vital and essential part of the American economy and culture through government and public relations; professional development and recognition; community service, social responsibility and high standards; and benefits and services to members. Operates Advertising Hall of Fame, Hall of Achievement, and National Student Advertising Competition. Maintains speaker's bureau. **Founded:** 1905. **Publications:** *Communicator* (Bimonthly); *Newsline* (Monthly); *American Advertising: The American Advertising Federation Magazine* (Quarterly); *AAF Member Newsletter*; *AAF Government Reports*; *American Advertising Federation--Speakers Directory*. **Educational Activities:** American Advertising Federation Annual Conference (Annual); AD-MERICA National Conference (Annual). **Awards:** American Advertising Awards (Annual); AAF Advertising Hall of Fame (Annual); AAF Ovation Awards (Annual); National Student Advertising Competition (Annual); AAF Advertising Hall of Achievement (Annual). **Geographic Preference:** National.

31823 ■ American Association of Advertising Agencies (AAAA)
25 W 45th St., 16th Fl.
New York, NY 10036
Ph: (212)682-2500
Co. E-mail: research@4as.org
URL: http://www.aaaa.org
Contact: Marla Kaplowitz, President
Facebook: www.facebook.com/aaaaorg
Linkedin: www.linkedin.com/company/4as
Instagram: www.instagram.com/4as_presents

Description: Fosters development of the advertising industry; assists member agencies to operate more efficiently and profitably. Sponsors member information and international services. Maintains multiple councils, committees, and forums. Conducts government relations. **Founded:** 1917. **Holdings:** 2,000 books; 300 VF drawers of clippings, reports, and pamphlets. **Publications:** *AAAA Publications Catalog* (Periodic); *The Reporter* (Bimonthly); *Advertising Agency Accounting/Finance/Collaboration Software Directory*; *Cable Broadcast Traffic Guide*; *American Association of Advertising Agencies--Roster and Organization* (Annual). **Awards:** O'Toole Agency Awards (Annual); O'Toole Public Service Award; O'Toole Awards for Creative and Media Excellence; ANA Multicultural Excellence Scholarship Fund (MAIP) (Annual). **Geographic Preference:** National.

31824 ■ American Lutheran Publicity Bureau (ALPB)

PO Box 327
Delhi, NY 13753-0327
Ph: (607)746-7511
URL: http://www.alpb.org
Contact: John Hannah, President
YouTube: www.youtube.com/user/alpb2011

Description: Organized by laymen and pastors of the Lutheran church to publicize its teachings, work, and activities in a movement towards Lutheran unity. Helps Lutherans to explain their faith to non-Lutherans and the unchurched and to discuss important issues in church and society. **Founded:** 1914. **Publications:** Forum Letter (Monthly); Lutheran Forum (Quarterly). **Geographic Preference:** National.

31825 ■ AMIN Worldwide [The Advertising and Marketing Independent Network (AMIN)]

3587 Northshore Dr.
Wayzata, MN 55391
Ph: (613)473-4124
Co. E-mail: contact@aminworldwide.com
URL: http://www.aminworldwide.com
Contact: Ali Sizemore Mahaffy, President
Facebook: www.facebook.com/AMINWorldwide
Linkedin: www.linkedin.com/company/aminworldwide
YouTube: www.youtube.com/channel/UC7S7jayioY9J
6HBEfrlIdjA

Description: Represents independent marketing agencies. **Founded:** 1932. **Geographic Preference:** Multinational.

31826 ■ Association of Free Community Papers (AFCP)

5701 E Cir. Dr., Ste. 347
Cicero, NY 13039
Free: 877-203-2327
Fax: (315)670-3121
Co. E-mail: afcp@afcp.org
URL: http://communitypublishers.com
Contact: Loren Colburn, Executive Director
E-mail: loren@afcp.org
Facebook: www.facebook.com/Association-of-Free
-Community-Papers-149260078439895
X (Twitter): x.oom/afop
Instagram: www.instagram.com/afcpnani
YouTube: www.youtube.com/user/afcp7297

Description: Represents publishers of nearly 3,000 free circulation papers and shopping/advertising guides. Offers national classified advertising placement service and national marketing for industry recognition. Conducts charitable programs. Sponsors competitions and compiles industry statistics. **Publications:** Free Paper INK (Monthly). **Educational Activities:** AFCP Annual Conference & Trade Show (Annual).

31827 ■ Association of Independent Commercial Producers (AICP)

3 W 18th St., 5th Fl.
New York, NY 10011
Ph: (212)929-3000
Fax: (212)929-3359
URL: http://www.aicp.com
Contact: Matt Miller, President
E-mail: mattm@aicp.com
Facebook: www.facebook.com/theAICP
Linkedin: www.linkedin.com/company/2075603
X (Twitter): x.com/aicpproducers
Instagram: www.instagram.com/theaicp
YouTube: www.youtube.com/user/TheAICP

Description: Represents the interests of companies that specialize in producing television commercials for advertisers and agencies, and the businesses that furnish supplies and services to this industry. Serves as a collective voice before government and business councils, and in union negotiations; disseminates information; works to develop industry standards and tools; provides professional development; and markets American production. **Founded:** 1972. **Publications:** Spotted: the AICP Newsletter (Biweekly); AICP Membership Directory. **Educational**

Activities: AICP Show. **Awards:** The AICP Show: The Art and Technique of the American Television Commercial (Annual). **Geographic Preference:** National.

31828 ■ Association of National Advertisers (ANA)

Association of National Advertisers (ANA)
155 E 44th St.
New York, NY 10017
Ph: (212)697-5950
Fax: (212)687-7310
Co. E-mail: info@ana.net
URL: http://www.ana.net
Contact: Christine Manna, President
E-mail: cmanna@ana.net
Facebook: www.facebook.com/ANAmarketers
Linkedin: www.linkedin.com/company/association-of
-national-advertisers
X (Twitter): x.com/anamarketers
Instagram: www.instagram.com/anamarketers

Description: Serves the needs of members by providing marketing and advertising industry leadership in traditional and e-marketing, legislative leadership, information resources, professional development and industry-wide networking. Maintains offices in New York City and Washington, DC. **Founded:** 1910. **Publications:** The Advertiser (Bimonthly); Tie-In Promotion Service (Annual). **Awards:** ANA Multicultural Excellence Awards (Annual). **Geographic Preference:** National.

31829 ■ Geopath

561 7th Ave., 12th Fl.
New York, NY 10018
Ph: (212)972-8075
Co. E-mail: geekout@geopath.org
URL: http://geopath.org
Contact: Kevin Gleason, President
Facebook: www.facebook.com/geopathooh
Linkedin: www.linkedin.com/company/geopath
X (Twitter): x.com/geopathooh
Instagram: www.instagram.com/geopathooh
YouTube: www.youtube.com/channel/UCbxnJ2FK
3IXEUbA8gPdlv2A

Description: Advertisers, advertising agencies, operators of outdoor advertising plants, bus shelter advertising companies, and backlighted display and painted bulletin companies. **Founded:** 1933. **Publications:** Building Accountability for Out of Home Media; TAB Eyes On Out of Home; TABBriefs; What You Should Know About the New TAB Audit. **Educational Activities:** Traffic Audit Bureau for Media Measurement Out of Home Media Conference & Marketing Expo (Annual). **Geographic Preference:** National.

31830 ■ Inflatable Advertising Dealers Association (IADA)

Seattle, WA
URL: http://asapevents.com/why-asap
Contact: Mark Phillips, Founder

Description: Endeavors to be the voice of the inflatable industry. Provides and promotes a better understanding of the functions of inflatable advertising and its values. **Founded:** 1991. **Geographic Preference:** National.

31831 ■ Intermarket Agency Network (IAN)

401 Mendocino Ave.
Santa Rosa, CA 95401
Co. E-mail: info@theengineisred.com
URL: http://www.intermarketnetwork.com
Contact: Alicia Wadas, President

Description: An active network of high-powered marketing/communications agencies in the United States, Canada, Central and South America, and Europe. **Geographic Preference:** National.

31832 ■ International Advertising Association (IAA) - Library

511 Ave. of Americas No. 4017
New York, NY 10011
Ph: (646)849-9908
Co. E-mail: iaa@iaaglobal.org
URL: http://www.iaaglobal.org
Contact: Joel Nettey, President

Facebook: www.facebook.com/InternationalAdver
tisingAssociation
Linkedin: www.linkedin.com/company/international-a
dvertising-association
X (Twitter): x.com/iaa_global
Instagram: www.instagram.com/iaaglobal
YouTube: www.youtube.com/channel/
UCULDmcOgvEd_SyFF0LS_-BQ

Description: Demonstrates to governments and consumers the benefits of advertising as the foundation of diverse, independent media. **Scope:** Advertising. **Founded:** 1938. **Holdings:** Figures not available. **Publications:** IAA National & World News (Quarterly); The Case for Advertising Self-Regulation; IAA Annual Report (Annual); IAA Membership Directory; International Advertising Association--Membership Directory (Continuous). **Awards:** InterAd Student Competition (Annual); Samir Fares Award. **Geographic Preference:** National.

31833 ■ International Communications Agency Network (ICOM)

74 Hwy. 72
Nederland, CO 80466
URL: http://icomagencies.com
Contact: Emma Keenan, Executive Director
Linkedin: www.linkedin.com/company/icomagencies
X (Twitter): x.com/icomagencies

Description: Provides an interchange of management information, international facilities, and branch office service for partner agencies. Provides discounts on syndicated services and access to 1,000 computer databases. **Founded:** 1950. **Publications:** Agency Client Lists (Monthly); The Globe (Monthly); Membership Directory (Annual). **Educational Activities:** International Management Conference. **Geographic Preference:** Multinational.

31834 ■ International Women's Media Foundation (IWMF)

1625 K St. NW, Ste. 1275
Washington, DC 20006
Ph: (202)496-1992
Co. E-mail: info@iwmf.org
URL: http://www.iwmf.org
Contact: Elisa Lees Muñoz, Executive Director
Facebook: www.facebook.com/IWMFpage
X (Twitter): x.com/IWMF
Instagram: www.instagram.com/theiwmf
YouTube: www.youtube.com/user/TheIwmf

Description: Designed to help women fulfill their capacity as leaders within the international news media. **Founded:** 1990. **Publications:** Reporting on HIV/AIDS in Africa: A Manual. **Awards:** Elizabeth Neuffer Fellowship (Annual); IWMF Courage in Journalism Awards (Annual); IWMF Lifetime Achievement Award (Periodic). **Geographic Preference:** Multinational.

31835 ■ Junior Billboard Association (JBA)

1447 N 175
Warsaw, IN 46582
Ph: (574)267-7003
Co. E-mail: eagleoutdoor@eagleoutdoor.com
URL: http://www.juniorbillboard.org
Contact: David Jacobs, Owner
Facebook: www.facebook.com/juniorbillboardassocia
tion

Description: Promotes the use of 8-sheet poster panels in outdoor advertising. (8-sheet signs are smaller than the usual 24-sheet ones, and are most commonly composed of 1 or 3 sheets covering an area of 6 x 12 feet.). **Founded:** 1953. **Publications:** Rates and Allotments: 8 Sheet Poster Panels in the Top Population Ranked Markets (Annual). **Geographic Preference:** National.

31836 ■ Marketing and Advertising Global Network (MAGNET)

Pittsburgh, PA 15202
URL: http://magnetglobal.org
Contact: Melissa Lentz, Chief Executive Officer
E-mail: melissai@magnetglobal.org
Facebook: www.facebook.com/Magnet-Global-Ne
twork-86729467810
Linkedin: www.linkedin.com/company/magnet-global
-network

X (Twitter): x.com/MAGNETGLOBALNET

Description: Aims to bring about, through mutual cooperation, greater accomplishment and efficiency in the management of member advertising agencies. Other goals are: to raise standards of the advertising agency business through the exchange of information relative to agency management and all phases of advertising; to exchange information on all common problems, such as management, sales development, market studies, agency functions, and operations. **Founded:** 1946. **Publications:** *MAGNET Matters* (3/year); *This Week at MAGNET* (Weekly). **Geographic Preference:** Multinational.

31837 ■ National Advertising Review Board (NARB)
7 Times Sq., Fl., 17, Ste. 1705
New York, NY 10036
URL: http://bbbprograms.org/programs/all-programs

Description: Individuals from industry and the public. Sponsored by the National Advertising Review Council for the purpose of sustaining high standards of truth and accuracy in national advertising. Aims to maintain a self-regulatory mechanism that responds constructively to public complaints about national advertising and which significantly improves advertising performance and credibility. **Founded:** 1971. **Publications:** *NARB Panel Reports*. **Geographic Preference:** National.

31838 ■ National Association of Publishers' Representatives, Inc. (NAPR)
206 W 80th St., Lower Level
New York, NY 10024

Description: Independent publishers' representatives selling advertising space for more than one publisher of consumer, industrial, direct response, and trade publications. **Founded:** 1950. **Publications:** *NAPR Newsletter*. **Geographic Preference:** National.

31839 ■ National Hispanic Media Coalition (NHMC)
12825 Philadelphia St.
Whittier, CA 90601
Ph: (626)792-6462
Co. E-mail: info@nhmc.org
URL: http://www.nhmc.org
Contact: Brenda Victoria Castillo, President
Facebook: www.facebook.com/nhmc.org
X (Twitter): x.com/nhmc
Instagram: www.instagram.com/nhmc_org
YouTube: www.youtube.com/user/nhmcorg

Description: Promotes the employment and image of Hispanic Americans in radio, television, and film. **Founded:** 1986. **Publications:** *Positive Images* (Annual). **Awards:** NHMC Impact Awards (Annual). **Geographic Preference:** National.

31840 ■ Out of Home Advertising Association of America, Inc. (OAAA)
1850 M St. NW, Ste. 1040
Washington, DC 20036
Ph: (202)833-5566
Co. E-mail: info@oaaa.org
URL: http://oaaa.org
Contact: Anna Bager, President
E-mail: abager@oaaa.org
Facebook: www.facebook.com/YourOAAA
Linkedin: www.linkedin.com/company/outdoor-advertising-association-of-america
X (Twitter): x.com/YourOAAA
Instagram: www.instagram.com/youroaaa
YouTube: www.youtube.com/user/youroaaa
Pinterest: www.pinterest.com/youroaaa

Description: Firms owning, erecting, and maintaining standardized poster panels and painted display advertising facilities. Aims to provide leadership, services, and standards to promote, protect and advance the outdoor advertising industry. **Founded:** 1891. **Educational Activities:** OOH Media Conference + Expo (Annual). **Awards:** Myles Standish Award (Periodic); L. Ray Vahue Award (Biennial); OBIE Awards (Annual); OAAA Distinguished Achieve-

ment Award of Excellence (Periodic); OAAA Hall of Fame (Annual); Out of Home Media Plan Awards (Annual). **Geographic Preference:** National.

31841 ■ Promotional Products Association International (PPAI) - Library
3125 Skyway Cir. N
Irving, TX 75038
Ph: (972)252-0404
Free: 888-426-7724
URL: http://www.ppai.org
Contact: Dale Denham, President
Facebook: www.facebook.com/PPAI.HQ
Linkedin: www.linkedin.com/company/ppai
X (Twitter): x.com/PPAI_HQ

Description: Promotes industry contacts in 60 countries. Holds executive development and sales training seminars. Conducts research and compiles statistics. Administers industry advertising and public relations program. **Scope:** Products. **Holdings:** Figures not available. **Publications:** *PPAI Newslink* (Semiweekly); *Promotional Products Business (PPB)* (Monthly); *Promotional Products Association International--Membership Directory and Reference Guide* (Annual). **Educational Activities:** PPAI Expo (Annual). **Awards:** PPAI Suppliers Achievement Award (Annual); PPAI Pyramid Award (Annual); PPAI Hall of Fame (Annual); PPAI Technology Awards (Annual). **Geographic Preference:** Multinational; Regional.

31842 ■ Radio Advertising Bureau (RAB) - Reference Collection
400 E Las Colinas Blvd., Ste. 350
Irving, TX 75039
Free: 800-232-3131
Co. E-mail: memberresponse@rab.com
URL: http://www.rab.com
Contact: Erica Farber, President
E-mail: efarber@rab.com
Facebook: www.facebook.com/RadioAdvBureau
Linkedin: www.linkedin.com/company/radio-advertising-bureau
X (Twitter): twitter.com/RadioAdvBureau
Instagram: www.instagram.com/radioadvertisingbureau

Description: Includes radio stations, radio networks, station sales representatives, and allied industry services, such as producers, research firms, schools, and consultants. Calls on advertisers and agencies to promote the sale of radio time as an advertising medium. Sponsors program to increase professionalism of radio salespeople, awarding Certified Radio Marketing Consultant designation to those who pass examination. **Scope:** Radio broadcasting. **Founded:** 1951. **Holdings:** Figures not available. **Publications:** *RAB.com*; *RAB Co-op Directory* (Weekly). **Educational Activities:** Managing Sales Conference. **Awards:** Best of Show (Annual); Radio Marketer of the Year (Annual). **Geographic Preference:** National.

31843 ■ Scenic America (SA)
727 15th St. NW, Ste. 1100
Washington, DC 20005-6029
Ph: (202)792-1300
Co. E-mail: scenic@scenic.org
URL: http://www.scenic.org
Contact: Mark Falzone, President
Facebook: www.facebook.com/ScenicAmerica
Linkedin: www.linkedin.com/company/scenicamerica
Instagram: www.instagram.com/scenicamericaofficial
YouTube: www.youtube.com/channel/UC9V_nJuboM2Rkgt6VAlqAJQ

Description: Safeguards natural beauty and community character through billboard and sign control, appropriate siting of cellular towers and other utilities, promotion of scenic byways, context-sensitive highway design, and protection of scenic landscapes and cityscapes. Advocates for the preservation of scenic beauty, open space, and quality of life. Fights billboard proliferation and other forms of visual pollution. **Founded:** 1982. **Publications:** *Fighting Billboard Blight: An Action Guide for Citizens and Public Officials*; *Getting It Right In the Right-of-Way: Citizen Participation in Context-Sensitive Solutions*; *Power to the People: Strategies for Reducing the Visual Impact*

of Overhead Utilities; *Taming Wireless Telecommunications Towers*; *Tree Conservation*. **Awards:** Stafford Award (Biennial). **Geographic Preference:** National.

31844 ■ She Runs It
89-12 70th Ave.
Forest Hills, NY 11375-6614
Ph: (212)221-7969
Fax: (212)221-8296
Co. E-mail: info@sherunsit.org
URL: http://sherunsit.org
Contact: Lynn Branigan, President
Facebook: www.facebook.com/sherunsitorg
X (Twitter): x.com/sherunsitorg
Instagram: www.instagram.com/sherunsitorg

Description: Women in advertising and related industries that provides a forum for professional growth, serves as catalyst for enhancement and advancement of women; promotes philanthropic endeavors. Conducts events of interest and benefit to members and non-members involved in the industry. Membership concentrated in the metropolitan New York area. **Founded:** 1912. **Awards:** Woman of the Year (Annual); AWNY President's Award (Annual); Crystal Prism Award (Annual). **Geographic Preference:** National.

31845 ■ Television Bureau of Advertising (TVB)
120 Wall St., 15th Fl.
New York, NY 10005-3908
URL: http://www.tvb.org
Contact: Steve Lanzano, President
Linkedin: www.linkedin.com/company/tvb_2
X (Twitter): x.com/TVBTweets

Description: Television stations, station sales representatives, and program producers/syndicates. Strives to increase advertiser dollars to U.S. spot television. Represents television stations to the advertising community. **Founded:** 1954. **Educational Activities:** Television Bureau of Advertising Annual Conference (Annual). **Geographic Preference:** National.

31846 ■ thinkLA
4712 Admiralty Way, Ste. 476
Marina del Rey, CA 90292
Ph: (310)876-0650
Co. E-mail: info@thinkla.org
URL: http://www.thinkla.org
Contact: Jean Freeman, President
Facebook: www.facebook.com/ThinkLA
Linkedin: www.linkedin.com/company/thinkla
X (Twitter): x.com/thinkla
Instagram: www.instagram.com/thinkla
YouTube: www.youtube.com/thinkla

Description: Assists heads of advertising agencies in the Western U.S. to operate their agencies more effectively and profitably. Offers assistance to agency management and staff. Provides a forum for discussion and exchange of information. Promotes members' interests. **Founded:** 1946. **Geographic Preference:** National.

EDUCATIONAL PROGRAMS

31847 ■ Design and Page Layout Skills (Onsite)
National Seminars Training L.L.C. (NST)
14502 W 105th St.
Lenexa, KS 66215
Free: 800-349-1935
Co. E-mail: info@findaseminar.com
URL: http://www.findaseminar.com/tpd/Padgett-Thompson-Seminars.asp
URL(s): www.findaseminar.com/event1.asp?eventID=3401

Description: Workshop teaches participants to create publications, newsletters, brochures, fliers, and reports. **Audience:** Industry Professionals. **Principal Exhibits:** Workshop teaches participants to create publications, newsletters, brochures, fliers, and reports.

REFERENCE WORKS

31848 ■ *"The 6 Best Advertising Strategies for Small Businesses"* in *Entrepreneur (April 20, 2016)*

Ed: Thomas Smale. **Released:** April 20, 2016. **Description:** Provides small business advertising strategies for small businesses so that they can optimize their efforts with effective, low-cost solutions. **Availability:** Online.

31849 ■ *"6 Powerful Sports Marketing Promotions That Are Better Than Google"* in *Forbes (February 6, 2014)*

URL(s): www.forbes.com/sites/markfidelman/2014/0 2/19/6-powerful-sports-marketing-promotions-tha t-are-better-than-google/#43d1b6116603

Ed: Mark Fidelman. **Released:** February 19, 2014. **Description:** Discusses new social media strategies to help sports companies gain a competitive edge in promoting and advertising. **Availability:** Online.

31850 ■ *7 Types of Advertising to Promote Your Small Business Effectively*

Description: Describes seven types of advertising and provides examples within each type for small businesses to use to grow their client base and boost their earnings by reaching a larger audience. **Availability:** Online.

31851 ■ *"10 Effective Local Advertising Ideas for Small Businesses"* in *LOCALiQ Blog (September 22, 2020)*

Ed: Stephanie Heitman. **Released:** September 22, 2020. **Description:** Offers ten local advertising ideas that can help your small business get noticed, get customers, and get growing. **Availability:** Online.

31852 ■ *"11 Free Ways to Get Publicity for Your Small Business"* in *SCORE (August 20, 2020)*

Ed: Brett Farmiloe. **Released:** August 20, 2020. **Description:** Details ideas provided from conversations with thought leaders on how small businesses can get free publicity. **Availability:** Online.

31853 ■ *"23 Low-Budget Marketing Ideas for Small Businesses"* in *The WordStream Blog (September 25, 2020)*

Ed: Megan Marrs. **Released:** September 25, 2020. **Description:** For small businesses who don't have a lot of money to spend on advertising, there are plenty of marketing tactics available that will fit into your marketing budget. This article offers more than twenty marketing ideas for small businesses working on a small budget. **Availability:** Online.

31854 ■ *"1914 Proved to Be Key Year for Chevy"* in *Automotive News (Vol. 86, October 31, 2011, No. 6488, pp. S18)*

Pub: Crain Communications Inc.

Contact: Barry Asin, President

Ed: Jamie LaReau. **Description:** Chevy Bow Tie emblem was born in 1914, creating the brand's image that has carried through to current days. **Availability:** Print; Online.

31855 ■ *"Ampm Focus Has BP Working Overtime"* in *Crain's Chicago Business (April 28, 2008)*

Pub: Crain Communications Inc.

Contact: Barry Asin, President

Ed: John T. Slania. **Description:** Britian's oil giant BP PLC is opening its ampm convenience stores in the Chicago market and has already begun converting most of its 78 Chicago-area gas stations to ampms. The company has also started to franchise the stores to independent operators. BP is promoting the brand with both traditional and unconventional marketing techniques such s real or simulated 3D snacks embedded in bus shelter ads and an in-store Guitar Hero contest featuring finalists from a recent contest at the House of Blues. **Availability:** Online.

31856 ■ *"AVT Featured on TD Waterhouse Market News Website and in Vending Times Magazine"* in *Benzinga.com (August 17, 2011)*

Pub: PR Newswire Association LLC.

Description: AVT Inc. was featured online and in an article reporting the firm's plan to install automated vending machines in high-profile areas including malls, office buildings, stadiums and arenas.

31857 ■ *"BBB Reworks Logo, Grading System"* in *Crain's Cleveland Business (Vol. 28, October 8, 2007, No. 40, pp. 5)*

Pub: Crain Communications Inc.

Contact: K. C. Crain, President

Ed: John Booth. **Description:** During the next year, the Better Business Bureau will adopt a grading system that will establish performance minimums that will make it tougher for some types of businesses to become accredited; this nationwide rebranding effort is part of a campaign to sharpen the Better Business Bureau's image. **Availability:** Online.

31858 ■ *"Ben Hulse"* in *Canadian Business (Vol. 85, August 13, 2012, No. 13, pp. 55)*

Ed: Graham F. Scott. **Description:** Graphic designer Ben Hulse explains the reason for rebranding Canada's Olympic team and how it differs from rebranding a private corporate logo. Hulse discusses his background in music and how he shifted to design. **Availability:** Print; Online.

31859 ■ *"Better ROI Or Your Money Back, Says Buzz Agency"* in *Advertising Age (Vol. 79, July 14, 2008, No. 7, pp. 1)*

Pub: Crain Communications, Inc.

Contact: Jessica Botos, Manager, Marketing

E-mail: jessica.botos@crainsnewyork.com

Ed: Michael Bush. **Description:** Word-of-mouth marketing is discussed as well as the impact on the advertising industry. Although many firms specializing in this form of marketing have opened over the past few years, many marketers are reluctant to try this route. **Availability:** Online.

31860 ■ *"The Buck Stops Here"* in *Canadian Business (Vol. 81, November 10, 2008, No. 19, pp. 25)*

Ed: Sarka Halas. **Description:** Reputation strategist Leslie Gaines-Ross says that minimizing the damage followed by the identification of what went wrong are the first steps that companies need to take when trying to salvage their reputation. Gaines-Ross states that it is up to the CEO to ensure the company's speedy recovery and they need to be at the forefront of the process. **Availability:** Online.

31861 ■ *"Conversations Need to Yield Actions Measured in Dollars"* in *Advertising Age (Vol. 79, July 7, 2008, No. 26, pp. 18)*

Pub: Crain Communications, Inc.

Contact: Jessica Botos, Manager, Marketing

E-mail: jessica.botos@crainsnewyork.com

Ed: Jonathan Salem Baskin. **Description:** New ways in which to market to consumers are discussed. **Availability:** Online.

31862 ■ *"Emotional Brand Attachment and Brand Personality: The Relative Importance of the Actual and the Ideal Self"* in *Journal of Marketing (Vol. 75, July 2011, No. 4, pp. 35)*

Pub: American Marketing Association

Contact: Bennie F. Johnson, Chief Executive Officer

Ed: Bettin Nyffeneger, Lucia Malar, Harley Krohmer, Wayne D. Hoyer. **Description:** A study on whether the brand's personality should match the consumer's actual self or ideal self is presented. Actual self-congruence is found to have the most impact on emotional brand attachment. **Availability:** PDF.

31863 ■ *"Empowered"* in *Harvard Business Review (Vol. 88, July-August 2010, No. 7-8, pp. 94)*

Pub: Harvard Business Publishing

Contact: Diane Belcher, Managing Director

Ed: Josh Bernoff, Ted Schadler. **Price:** $8.95, PDF. **Description:** HERO concept (highly empowered and resourceful operative) which builds a connection

between employees, managers, and IT is outlined. The resultant additional experience and knowledge gained by employees improves customer relationship management. **Availability:** Online; PDF.

31864 ■ *Free Publicity Is Advertising for Your Small Business*

Description: Discusses how publicity can be free advertising for your small business when you see things like feature stories or product/service announcements publishes in print/broadcast media. Also discusses the downside of free publicity in that you cannot control what is said about your company, product, or service. **Availability:** Online.

31865 ■ *"Friday the 13th, a 'Tattoo Holiday"* in *The New York Times (July 13, 2018)*

URL(s): www.nytimes.com/2018/07/13/nyregion/fri day-the-13th-tattoo.html

Ed: Zoe Greenberg. **Released:** July 13, 2018. **Description:** Tattoo shops have developed a new tradition of Friday the 13th tattoos. Shops often release a sheet of pre-designed tats, many of which are only $13 with a suggested lucky $7 tip. The promotions have worked as people line up to get their first tattoo or to add on to their collection. The tradition started in 1996 with "Ink Master" Oliver Peck holding this promotion, and then it escalated when he tattooed the most people in a 24-hour period by tattooing the number 13 on 415 participants on Friday June 13, 2008. **Availability:** Online.

31866 ■ *Groundswell: Winning in a World Transformed by Social Technologies*

Pub: Harvard Business Review Press

Contact: Moderna V. Pfizer, Contact

Ed: Charlene Li, Josh Bernoff. **Released:** June 09, 2011. **Price:** $22, paperback/softbound. **Description:** Individuals are using online social technologies such as blogs, social networking sites, YouTube, and podcasts to discuss products and companies, write their own news, and find their own deals. When consumers you've never met are rating your company's products in public forums with which you have no experience or influence, your company is vulnerable. This book teaches the tools and data necessary to turn this treat into an opportunity. **Availability:** E-book; Print.

31867 ■ *"Half of Canadian Firms to Boost Marketing Budgets"* in *Globe & Mail (January 22, 2007, pp. B1)*

Ed: Keith McArthur. **Description:** The advertising and marketing spending plans of different companies are presented. **Availability:** Online.

31868 ■ *"The HBR Interview: "We Had to Own the Mistakes""* in *Harvard Business Review (Vol. 88, July-August 2010, No. 7-8, pp. 108)*

Pub: Harvard Business Publishing

Contact: Diane Belcher, Managing Director

Ed: Adi Ignatius. **Description:** Interview with Howard Schultz, CEO of Starbucks, covers topics that include investment in retraining, the impact of competition, premium quality, authenticity, customer services, strategy development, work-and-life issues, and international presence. **Availability:** Online.

31869 ■ *"Hennelly Aims to Increase Building Work in Great Lakes Region for Ryan Cos."* in *Crain's Chicago Business (Vol. 34, May 23, 2011, No. 21, pp. 6)*

Pub: Crain Communications Inc.

Contact: Barry Asin, President

Ed: Eddie Baeb. **Description:** Profile of Tim Hennelly, who is working to make Ryan Company known as a pure builder rather than a developer-builder. **Availability:** Print; Online.

31870 ■ *"Hopkins' Security, Reputation Face Challenges in Wake of Slaying"* in *Baltimore Business Journal (Vol. 28, August 6, 2010, No. 13)*

Pub: Baltimore Business Journal

Contact: Rhonda Pringle, President

E-mail: rpringle@bizjournals.com

Ed: Gary Haber. **Description:** The slaying of Johns Hopkins University researcher Stephen Pitcairn has not tarnished the reputation of the elite school in Baltimore, Maryland among students. Maintaining Hopkins' reputation is important since it is Baltimore's largest employer with nearly 32,000 workers. Insights on the impact of the slaying among the Hopkins' community are also given.

31871 ■ *"How I Did It: Best Buy's CEO On Learning to Love Social Media" in Harvard Business Review (Vol. 88, December 2010, No. 12, pp. 43)*
Pub: Harvard Business Publishing
Contact: Diane Belcher, Managing Director

Ed: Brian J. Dunn. **Price:** $8.95, PDF. **Description:** Effective utilization of online social networks to enhance brand identity, connect with consumers, and address bad publicity scenarios is examined. **Availability:** Online; PDF.

31872 ■ *"How I Did It: Timberland's CEO On Standing Up to 65,000 Angry Activists" in Harvard Business Review (Vol. 88, September 2010, No. 9, pp. 39)*
Pub: Harvard Business Publishing
Contact: Diane Belcher, Managing Director

Ed: Jeff Swartz. **Price:** $8.95, PDF. **Description:** Timberland Company avoided a potential boycott by taking a two-way approach. It addressed a supplier issue that posed a threat to the environment, and launched an email campaign to keep Greenpeace activists informed of the development of a new supplier agreement. **Availability:** Online; PDF.

31873 ■ *"How These 12 Small Business Advertising Ideas Can Drive Traffic & ROI" in LYFE Marketing (October 15, 2019)*
Released: October 15, 2019. **Description:** Discusses the many avenues "advertising" can take with the ultimate goal of getting your brand in front of a targeted audience using digital marketing avenues like social media advertising. Offers twelve small business advertising ideas. **Availability:** Online.

31874 ■ *"How To Live To Be 100: John E. Green Co. Grows Through Diversification" in Crain's Detroit Business (February 18, 2008)*
Pub: Crain Communications Inc.
Contact: Barry Asin, President

Ed: Chad Halcom. **Description:** Continuity, name recognition, and inventiveness are keys to continuing growth for Highland Park, Michigan's John E. Green Company, designer of pipe systems and mechanical contractor. **Availability:** Online.

31875 ■ *I Love You More Than My Dog*
Pub: Portfolio
Contact: Adrian Zackheim, President

Ed: Jeanne Bliss. **Released:** October 15, 2009. **Price:** $14.99, E-book. **Description:** Ways to win passionate, loyal and vocal customers in order to build a small business is outlined. **Availability:** E-book; Print.

31876 ■ *If You Have to Cry, Go Outside: And Other Things Your Mother Never Told You*
Pub: HarperCollins Publishers L.L.C.
Contact: Brian Murray, President

Ed: Kelly Cutrone, Meredith Bryan. **Released:** February 02, 2010. **Price:** $10.99, e-book; $7.24, e-book. **Description:** Women's mentor advices on how to make it in one of the most competitive industries in the world, fashion. She has kicked people out of fashion shows, forced some of reality television's shiny start to fire their friends, and built her own company which is one of the most powerful public relations firms in the fashion business. **Availability:** E-book; Print.

31877 ■ *"The Impact of Incomplete Typeface Logos on Perceptions of the Firms" in Journal of Marketing (Vol. 75, July 2011, No. 4, pp. 86)*
Description: A study of the influence of incomplete typeface logos on consumer perceptions of the company is presented. The findings suggest that companies should avoid incomplete typeface logos if perceptions of trustworthiness are critical or if consumers are likely to have a prevention focus. **Availability:** PDF; Online.

31878 ■ *It's Not Who You Know - It's Who Knows You!: The Small Business Guide to Raising Your Profits by Raising Your Profile*
Pub: John Wiley & Sons, Inc.
Contact: Christina Van Tassell, Executive Vice President Chief Financial Officer

Ed: David Arvin. **Released:** 2nd edition. **Price:** $8.69, hardcover. **Description:** When it comes to promoting a small business or a brand, it is essential to know how valuable high-profile attention can be. But for most small companies, the cost of hiring an outside firm to increase attention can be too expensive. **Availability:** Print; Online.

31879 ■ *"Kuno Creative to Present the Three Steps of a Successful B2B Social Media Campaign" in Business Tech & Wireless (August 25, 2011)*
Pub: Close-Up Media Inc.
Contact: Caroline S. Moore, President
E-mail: cms@closeupmedia.com

Released: August 24, 2011. **Description:** Kuno Creative, an inbound marketing agency, will host Three Steps of a Successful B2B Social Media Campaign. The firm is a provider of Website development, branding, marketing strategy, public relations, Internet marketing, and inbound marketing. **Availability:** Print; Online.

31880 ■ *Media, Organizations and Identity*
Pub: Palgrave Macmillan

Released: First edition. **Description:** The mass media, press, and television are essential in the formation of corporate identity and the promotion of business image and reputation. This book offers a new perspective into the interrelationships between media and organizations over three dimensions: media as business, media in business and business in the media.

31881 ■ *"New Sony HD Ads Tout Digital" in Brandweek (Vol. 49, April 21, 2008, No. 16, pp. 5)*
Description: Looking to promote Sony Electronics' digital imaging products, the company has launched another campaign effort known as HDNA, a play on the words high-definition and DNA; originally Sony focused the HDNA campaign on their televisions, the new ads will include still and video cameras as well and marketing efforts will consist of advertising in print, Online, television spots and publicity at various venues across the country. **Availability:** Online.

31882 ■ *Public Relations Campaigns: An Integrated Approach*
Ed: Regina M. Luttrell, Luke W. Capizzo. **Released:** March 08, 2018. **Price:** $80.02, Paperback; $68.39, E-book. **Description:** While using case studies and real-life examples, the authors guide the reader into the process of creating a public relations campaign. **Availability:** E-book; Print.

31883 ■ *"Report: McD's Pepsi Score Best With Young Hispanics" in Brandweek (Vol. 49, April 21, 2008, No. 16, pp. 8)*
Description: According to a new report, in order to reach Hispanic Gen Yers, marketing strategists need to understand this demographic's "bi-dentity," something which has proved an elusive task to many marketers. Another trend is the emergence of Latinas who have careers, as opposed to just jobs. There is an opportunity to tap this new, young and empowered female market with innovative messaging. Statistical data included. **Availability:** Online.

31884 ■ *"Restaurants Dish Up Meal Deals To Attract Customers" in Crain's Detroit Business (Vol. 24, October 6, 2008, No. 40, pp. 1)*
Pub: Crain Communications Inc.
Contact: Barry Asin, President

Ed: Nathan Skid. **Description:** Restaurateurs are devising many creative and rewarding incentives to get customers to frequent their establishments during this economic crisis. Innovative ways in which even higher-end establishments are drawing in business are discussed. **Availability:** Online.

31885 ■ *The Small Business Bible: Everything You Need to Know to Succeed in Your Small Business*
Pub: John Wiley & Sons, Inc.
Contact: Christina Van Tassell, Executive Vice President Chief Financial Officer

Ed: Steven D. Strauss. **Released:** Third edition. **Price:** $22.95, paperback; $14.99, E-book. **Description:** Comprehensive guide to starting and running a successful small business. Topics include bookkeeping and financial management, marketing, publicity, and advertising. **Availability:** E-book; Print.

31886 ■ *"Social Media Advertising for Small Businesses" in The WordStream Blog (July 21, 2020)*
Ed: Dan Shewan. **Released:** July 21, 2020. **Description:** Discusses whether social media advertising is a good fit for your small business, particularly if your advertising budget is stretched thin. This article assess the strengths and weaknesses of four major social networks: Facebook, Twitter, Google+, and LinkedIn and it also covers additional social networks that may be appropriate for your business. **Availability:** Online.

31887 ■ *"Sponsorships, Booths Available for Business Showcase" in Bellingham Business Journal (February 2010, pp. 3)*
Pub: Sound Publishing Inc.
Contact: Josh O'Connor, President

Ed: Lance Henderson. **Description:** Third Annual Spring Business Showcase still have space available for vendors and sponsors. The event gives local businesses the opportunity to increase their visibility and provides a means to increase sales and build relationships.

31888 ■ *Start Your Own Fashion Accessories Business*
Pub: Entrepreneur Media Inc.
Contact: Dan Bova, Director
E-mail: dbova@entrepreneur.com

Ed: Eileen Figure Sandlin. **Released:** Second edition. **Description:** Entrepreneurs wishing to start a fashion accessories business will find important information for setting up a home workshop and office, exploring the market, managing finances, publicizing and advertising the business and more.

31889 ■ *"Too Much Information?" in Black Enterprise (Vol. 37, December 2006, No. 5, pp. 59)*
Pub: Earl G. Graves Ltd.
Contact: Earl Graves, Jr., President

Ed: James C. Johnson. **Description:** African American business owners often face the dilemma of whether or not to divulge their minority status when soliciting new customers and financial institutions. The quality of the products or services is always the key factor and race should never define one's business; however, it is appropriate to market oneself as a minority- or women-owned business, especially if the company is in an industry where those clients are offered top-tier contracts. **Availability:** Online.

31890 ■ *"Want Free Publicity for your Business? Try These 11 Tactics" in Forbes*
Description: Offers information on how to employ the right strategies to gain free publicity for your small business. **Availability:** Online.

31891 ■ *"What Is Publicity?" in The Balance Small Business (September 17, 2020)*
Ed: Laura Lake. **Released:** September 17, 2020. **Description:** Shows the path of how information moves from public relations to target audience and defines how publicity works. Also discusses publicity vs. marketing. **Availability:** Online.

31892 ■ *"What Makes a Great Tweet" in Harvard Business Review (Vol. 90, May 2012, No. 5, pp. 36)*
Pub: Harvard Business Review Press
Contact: Moderna V. Pfizer, Contact
Ed: Kurt Luther, Michael Bernstein, Paul Andre. **Price:** $6, PDF. **Description:** A chart uses readership approval percentages to identify the most effective uses of Twitter. Best tweets include amusing random thoughts and self promotion; worst include complaints and presence maintenance. **Availability:** Online; PDF.

31893 ■ *"What's In Your Toolbox" in Women In Business (Vol. 61, August-September 2009, No. 4, pp. 7)*
Pub: American Business Women's Association
Contact: Rene Street, Executive Director
Ed: Mimi Kopulos. **Description:** Business owners are increasingly turning to using social networking websites, such as Facebook, LinkedIn and Twitter, to promote their companies. The number of adult social media users has increased from 8 percent in 2005 to 35 percent in 2009. **Availability:** Online.

31894 ■ *When the Headline Is You: An Insider's Guide to Handling the Media*
Pub: Jossey-Bass
Ed: Jeff Ansell, Jeff Lesson. **Released:** August 01, 2010. **Price:** $29.95, hardcover; $29.95, hardcover. **Description:** How-to guide for executives and other professionals whose high-visibility requires frequent interviews with the media. Tested techniques, tools, and insights for how to respond to all types of media in tough situation are provided. The book also reveals the lessons learned and the pitfalls to avoid by referencing actual news stores from around the world and provides exercises for readers who wish to sharpen their media-handling skills. **Availability:** E-book; Print.

31895 ■ *"You Have to Lead From Everywhere" in Harvard Business Review (Vol. 88, November 2010, No. 11, pp. 76)*
Pub: Harvard Business Publishing
Contact: Diane Belcher, Managing Director
Ed: Scott Berinato. **Price:** $8.95, PDF. **Description:** U.S. Coast Guard Admiral Thad W. Allen discusses effective leadership in successful crises management. Topics include influence of media and public perspective, the applicability of military training to the business arena, and the responsibility of a leader to set morale. **Availability:** Online; PDF.

CONSULTANTS

31896 ■ **COMsciences Inc.**
Los Angeles, CA
Co. E-mail: info@comsciences.com
URL: http://comsciences.com/comsciences.htm
Contact: Dr. Jack Torobin, Chief Executive Officer
Description: Firm provides strategic advices for products and services for consumer electronic brands. **Scope:** Firm provides strategic advices for products and services for consumer electronic brands. **Founded:** 1989. **Publications:** "Wanted: Radical Thinking," Pmg World Magazine, Mar, 2003. **Special Services:** iKIT®; imovio®.

31897 ■ **Holcomb Gallagher Adams Advertising Inc. [300m]**
4000 Horizons Dr.
  Columbus, OH 43220
Co. E-mail: info@300m.co
URL: http://300m.co
Description: Consults in strategic marketing planning, and new business, brand equity, creative strategy, and media strategy development. Industries served: Consumer goods and services, manufacturing, retail, business-to-business products and services, education, travel, and tourism. **Scope:** Consults in strategic marketing planning, and new business, brand equity, creative strategy, and media strategy development. Industries served: Consumer goods and services, manufacturing, retail, business-to-business products and services, education, travel, and tourism. **Founded:** 1993.

31898 ■ **Westlife Consultants and Advisors**
4 Robert Speck Pkwy.
  Mississauga, ON, Canada L4Z, CA
URL: http://www.westlifeconsultants.com
Contact: Syed N. Hussain, President
E-mail: shussain@westlifeconsultants.com
Linkedin: www.linkedin.com/company/westlife-consultants-&-advisors
Description: Provider of entrepreneurs and businesses with a highly commercial and global perspectives on the international business development ideas under consideration. **Scope:** Provider of entrepreneurs and businesses with a highly commercial and global perspectives on the international business development ideas under consideration. **Founded:** 1992. **Publications:** "Innovative Management"; "Team Building and Leadership"; "Financial Planning"; "Estate Planning"; "Risk Management"; "Export/Import Trade Finance Mechanics"; "Marketing and Sales Management"; "What Your Banker Needs to Know"; "Building A Successful Financial Plan".

COMPUTERIZED DATABASES

31899 ■ *ABI/INFORM*
ProQuest LLC
  789 E Eisenhower Pky.
  Ann Arbor, MI 48108
Ph: (734)761-4700
Free: 800-521-0600
URL: http://www.proquest.com
Contact: Matti Shem Tov, Chief Executive Officer
URL(s): about.proquest.com/en/products-services/abi_inform_complete
Availability: Online. **Type:** Full-text; Bibliographic; Image.

LIBRARIES

31900 ■ **Grey Worldwide Information Center**
200 5th Ave.
  New York, NY 10010
Ph: (212)546-2000
Co. E-mail: hello@grey.com
URL: http://www.grey.com
Facebook: www.facebook.com/GreyGroup
Linkedin: www.linkedin.com/company/grey-group
X (Twitter): x.com/Greygroup
Instagram: www.instagram.com/grey

Description: Advertising and marketing organization. **Scope:** Advertising; marketing; business; new business development. **Services:** Interlibrary loan. **Founded:** 1917. **Holdings:** 500 books; 200 directories.

31901 ■ **Ketchum Advertising - Library Services**
1285 Avenue of the Americas, 4th Fl.
  New York, NY 10019
Ph: (646)935-4100
URL: http://www.ketchum.com
Contact: Mike Doyle, President
X (Twitter): x.com/ketchumpr
Instagram: www.instagram.com/ketchumpr
YouTube: www.youtube.com/user/KetchumPR
Scope: Advertising, marketing, general reference. **Services:** Interlibrary loan. **Holdings:** 1,100 books; 40 VF drawers of marketing material; reference collection; annual reports.

31902 ■ **Martin/Williams Advertising Library**
150 S 5th St., Ste. 900
  Minneapolis, MN 55402
Ph: (612)340-0800
URL: http://www.martinwilliams.com
Contact: Lori Yeager Davis, President
Facebook: www.facebook.com/MartinWilliamsAdvertising
Linkedin: www.linkedin.com/company/martin-williams
X (Twitter): x.com/mwadvertising
Instagram: www.instagram.com/mwadvertising
Description: Branding and advertising agency. **Scope:** Advertising; marketing; business. **Services:** Library open to agency employees and clients; open to the public with special permission. **Founded:** 1977. **Holdings:** Figures not available.

RESEARCH CENTERS

31903 ■ **Boston College (BC) - Carroll School of Management - Center for Corporate Citizenship (CCC)**
140 Commonwealth Ave.
  Chestnut Hill, MA 02467
Ph: (617)552-4545
Co. E-mail: ccc@bc.edu
URL: http://ccc.bc.edu
Contact: Katherine V. Smith, Executive Director
E-mail: kv.smith@bc.edu
Facebook: www.facebook.com/BostonCollegeCCC
Linkedin: www.linkedin.com/company/boston-college-center-for-corporate-citizenship
X (Twitter): x.com/BCCCC
Description: Integral unit of Carroll School of Management, Boston College. Offers contract research and consulting. **Scope:** Research center with products in various fields. Projects include designing corporate social vision, best practice research, analyses of corporate images within local communities, impact of corporation's external affairs on employee behavior, and profiles of community relations professionals. **Founded:** 1985. **Publications:** *Corporate Citizen magazine* (Quarterly); *Center for Corporate Citizenship Research reports*; *Voice of Corporate Citizenship newsletter* (Monthly). **Educational Activities:** The International Corporate Citizenship Conference (Annual).

Purchasing

ASSOCIATIONS AND OTHER ORGANIZATIONS

31904 ■ American Purchasing Society (APS)
8 E Galena Blvd., Ste. 406
Aurora, IL 60506
Ph: (630)859-0250
Fax: (630)859-0270
Co. E-mail: propurch@propurch.com
URL: http://www.american-purchasing.com
Contact: Richard H. Hough, President
X (Twitter): x.com/AmerPurchSoc
Description: Seeks to certify qualified purchasing personnel. Maintains speakers' bureau and placement service. Conducts research programs; compiles statistics including salary surveys. Provides consulting service for purchasing, materials management, and marketing. Conducts seminars and online courses. **Founded:** 1969. **Publications:** *Professional Purchasing* (Monthly); *Annual Report of Purchasing Salaries and Employment Trends* (Annual); *Benchmarking Purchasing* (Annual); *Handbook of Buying and Purchasing Management; How To Get the Best Results from your Purchasing Department* (Biennial). **Awards:** APS Certified Purchasing Professional (Periodic); APS Excellent Supplier Award (Annual). **Geographic Preference:** National.

31905 ■ Institute for Supply Management (ISM) - Library
309 W Elliot Rd., Ste. 113
Tempe, AZ 85284-1556
Ph: (480)752-6276
Fax: (480)752-7890
Co. E-mail: membersvcs@ismworld.org
URL: http://www.ismworld.org
Contact: Thomas Derry, Chief Executive Officer
Facebook: www.facebook.com/InstituteForSupplyManagement
Linkedin: www.linkedin.com/company/institute-for-supply-management
X (Twitter): x.com/ism
Instagram: www.instagram.com/supplymanagement
YouTube: www.youtube.com/ismorg
Description: Represents industrial, commercial and utility firms; educational institutions and government agencies. Disseminates information on procurement. Works to develop more efficient supply management methods. Conducts program for certification as a supply manager. Cosponsors executive purchasing management institutes at Michigan State University and Arizona State University. Provides in-company training. Maintains speakers' bureau and reference service. **Scope:** Management. **Founded:** 1915. **Holdings:** Figures not available. **Publications:** *Chicago Purchasor--Buyers' Guide Issue* (Quarterly); *Chicago Purchasor--Roster Issues* (Annual); *Journal of Supply Chain Management: A Global Review of Purchasing and Supply* (Quarterly); *Inside Supply Management: Resources to Create Your Future* (Bimonthly). **Educational Activities:** International Purchasing; ISM Annual International Supply Management Conference (Annual). **Awards:** J. Shipman

Gold Medal Award (Annual); R. Gene Richter Awards for Leadership and Innovation in Supply Management (Annual). **Geographic Preference:** Local; National.

31906 ■ National Procurement Institute (NPI)
PO Box 2774
Rockport, TX 78381
Ph: (702)989-8095
Co. E-mail: membership@npiconnection.org
URL: http://www.npi-aep.org
Contact: Blake Skiles, President
E-mail: tskiles@rosenbergtx.gov
Facebook: www.facebook.com/npiconnection
Linkedin: www.linkedin.com/company/national-purchasing-institute-inc.
X (Twitter): x.com/NPI_procurement
Description: Purchasing agents, directors of purchasing and procurement, buyers, and others employed by governmental, educational, or other tax-supported agencies. Seeks to improve the field through development of simplified standards of specifications, improved communication, and promotion of uniform purchasing laws. **Founded:** 1968. **Publications:** *Annual Conference Program* (Annual); *Membership Directory* (Annual); *Public Purchasing Review* (Bimonthly). **Educational Activities:** National Procurement Institute Annual Conference (Annual); Annual National Conference (Annual). **Awards:** NPI Achievement of Excellence in Procurement (Annual); Carlton N. Parker Award for Outstanding Service (Annual). **Geographic Preference:** National.

31907 ■ Wisconsin Association for Public Procurement (WAPP)
c/o Dale C. DeNamur, President
Brown County
Green Bay, WI 54305
Ph: (414)659-9006
Free: 800-587-1541
Co. E-mail: members@wapp.org
URL: http://wapp.org
Contact: Dale C. C. DeNamur, President
E-mail: president@wapp.org
Description: Ensures its members to have the growth and makes them still vital in the profession with ongoing educational opportunities. Provides leadership in the pursuance of continuous improvements in public purchasing. Promotes the efficiency of the public procurement profession in the state of Wisconsin. **Founded:** 1943. **Geographic Preference:** State.

EDUCATIONAL PROGRAMS

31908 ■ Fundamentals of Purchasing
URL(s): cmcoutperform.com/files/CMC%20Fall%20Catalogue%202011.pdf
Description: Covers the steps involved in purchasing, negotiating, working with vendors and suppliers, cost and price analysis, and types of purchase contracts. Held in Toronto, ON; and Mississauga, ON. **Audience:** New buyers and experienced buyers who want to review and update basic techniques, as well

as buyers in service, projects, manufacturing, distribution, maintenance and health care. **Principal Exhibits:** Covers the steps involved in purchasing, negotiating, working with vendors and suppliers, cost and price analysis, and types of purchase contracts. Held in Toronto, ON; and Mississauga, ON. **Telecommunication Services:** cmcinfo@cmcoutperform.com.

31909 ■ Fundamentals of Purchasing for the New Buyer (Onsite)
American Management Association (AMA)
1601 Broadway
New York, NY 10019
Ph: (212)586-8100
Free: 800-262-9699
Fax: (212)903-8168
Co. E-mail: customerservice@amanet.org
URL: http://www.amanet.org
Contact: Manny Avramidis, President
URL(s): www.amanet.org/training/seminars/onsite/fundamentals-of-purchasing-for-the-new-buyer.aspx
Facebook: www.facebook.com/AmericanManagementAssn
Linkedin: www.linkedin.com/company/american-management-association
X (Twitter): twitter.com/amanet
Instagram: www.instagram.com/americanmanagementassociation
YouTube: www.youtube.com/user/AmericanManagement
Price: $2,345, Non-members; $2,095, Members; $1,984, General Services Administration (GSA). **Description:** Covers the steps involved in purchasing, negotiating, working with vendors and suppliers, using e-procurement, and the materials management process. **Audience:** Buyers in service, manufacturing, health care or office purchasing agents. **Principal Exhibits:** Covers the steps involved in purchasing, negotiating, working with vendors and suppliers, using e-procurement, and the materials management process. **Telecommunication Services:** customerservice@amanet.org.

31910 ■ How to Bargain & Negotiate with Vendors and Suppliers
Fred Pryor Seminars & CareerTrack
5700 Broadmoor, Ste. 300
Mission, KS 66202
Free: 800-780-8476
Fax: (913)967-8849
Co. E-mail: customerservice@pryor.com
URL: http://www.pryor.com
Contact: Janet Turner, Contact
E-mail: dmca@pryor.com
URL(s): www.pryor.com/training-seminars/bargain-negotiate-vendors-suppliers/?zip=90012
Frequency: Irregular. **Description:** Learn how to get lower prices, quicker delivery, higher quality and better service through negotiation. **Audience:** Business professionals. **Principal Exhibits:** Learn how to get lower prices, quicker delivery, higher quality and better service through negotiation.

TRADE PERIODICALS

31911 ■ *Inside Supply Management:*
Resources to Create Your Future
Pub: Institute for Supply Management
Contact: Thomas Derry, Chief Executive Officer
URL(s): www.ismworld.org/supply-managemen
  t-news-and-reports/news-publications/inside-supply
  -management-magazine
Released: Bimonthly **Description:** Trade magazine
for purchasing and supply managers. **Availability:**
Print; Online.

31912 ■ *Journal of Supply Chain*
Management: A Global Review of Purchasing
and Supply
Pub: Wiley Periodicals Inc.
Contact: Brian Napack, Chief Executive Officer
URL(s): onlinelibrary.wiley.com/journal/1745493X
Released: Quarterly **Price:** $143, Individuals for print
+ online US , Canada; $556, Institutions for print +
online US , Canada; $143, Individuals for print +
online India; $678, Institutions for print + online India;
$122, Individuals for online US , Canada; $494,
Institutions for online US , Canada; $516, Institutions
for print US , Canada; $122, Individuals for online
India; $603, Institutions for online India; $329, Institutions for print India. **Description:** Journal covering all
aspects of supply chain management. Published by
Wiley on behalf of the Institute for Supply Management. **Availability:** Print; PDF; Download; Online.

31913 ■ *Professional Purchasing*
Pub: American Purchasing Society
Contact: Richard H. Hough, President
URL(s): www.american-purchasing.com/propurch
Released: Monthly **Description:** Provides information on policies, procedures, methods, and prices of
purchasing. Features price indexes. Recurring
features include letters to the editor, news of research,
reports of meetings, news of educational opportunities, job listings, book reviews, and notices of publications available. **Availability:** PDF.

TRADE SHOWS AND CONVENTIONS

31914 ■ **ISM Annual International Supply**
Management Conference
Institute for Supply Management (ISM)
  309 W Elliot Rd., Ste. 113
  Tempe, AZ 85284-1556
Ph: (480)752-6276
Fax: (480)752-7890
Co. E-mail: membersvcs@ismworld.org
URL: http://www.ismworld.org
Contact: Thomas Derry, Chief Executive Officer
URL(s): www.ismworld.org/events/conferences-an
  d-events/annual-conference
Frequency: Annual. **Description:** Auctions, business
service, capital equipment, computer hardware/
software, consulting services, e-business services/
software, logistics and transportation, MRO, office
supply, procurement card services. **Audience:**
Industry professionals. **Principal Exhibits:** Auctions,
business service, capital equipment, computer
hardware/software, consulting services, e-business
services/software, logistics and transportation, MRO,
office supply, procurement card services. Dates and
Locations: 2025 Jun 01-03 Rosen Shingle Creek
Hotel & Conference Center, Orlando, FL.

RESEARCH CENTERS

31915 ■ **Arizona State University - CAPS**
Research
09 W Elliot Rd, Ste. No. 113
  Tempe, AZ 85284-1556
Ph: (480)752-2277
Fax: (480)491-7885
URL: http://www.capsresearch.org
Linkedin: www.linkedin.com/company/caps-research
X (Twitter): x.com/CAPSResearch
YouTube: www.youtube.com/c/CAPSResearchOrg
Description: Integral unit of Arizona State University.
Scope: Involves in world-class purchasing, perfor-
mance benchmarks, supplier partnerships, total qual-
ity management, purchasing measurement, non-
traditional purchasing, cycle-time reduction, total cost
models, futures study, and minority business enter-
prise best practices. **Founded:** 1986. **Publications:**
Critical Issue reports (Quarterly); *Practix* (Quarterly);
CAPS research reports.

Remediation

ASSOCIATIONS AND OTHER ORGANIZATIONS

31916 ■ **National Association of Environmental Professionals (NAEP)**
2150 N 107th St., Ste. 205
Seattle, WA 98133
Ph: (206)209-5286
Co. E-mail: office@naep.org
URL: http://www.naep.org
Contact: Rona Spellecacy, President
E-mail: president@naep.org
Facebook: www.facebook.com/National-Association
-of-Environmental-Professionals-267926723515
Linkedin: www.linkedin.com/company/environmen
talprofessionals
X (Twitter): x.com/NAEPtweets
Description: Promotes ethical practice, technical competency, and professional standards in the environment field. Provides access to the latest trends in environmental research, technology, law, and policy. **Founded:** 1975. **Awards:** NAEP National Environmental Excellence Award for Public Involvement and Education (Annual); NAEP Student Award (Annual). **Geographic Preference:** National.

31917 ■ **National Association of Mold Remediators and Inspectors (NAMRI)**
16192 Coastal Hwy.
Lewes, DE 19958
URL: http://www.namri.org/index.php
Description: Seeks to promote professionalism and develop standards of practice for mold professionals in North America. **Founded:** 2005.

31918 ■ **Restoration Industry Association (RIA)**
1120 Rte. 73, Ste. 200
Mount Laurel, NJ 08054
Ph: (856)439-9222
Co. E-mail: info@restorationindustry.org
URL: http://www.restorationindustry.org
Contact: Ben Looper, President
Facebook: www.facebook.com/restorationindustry
X (Twitter): x.com/RIAtweets
YouTube: www.youtube.com/channel/UCXUEIHrn
4wjzwFUv03eMTFg
Description: Conducts educational programs and seminars; operates laboratory. Maintains certification program. **Founded:** 1946. **Publications:** *Cleaning and Restoration--Buyers Guide Issue* (Annual); *Cleaning & Restoration* (Quarterly); *Restoration Industry Association--Membership Directory.* **Educational Activities:** Restoration Industry Association International Restoration Convention & Industry Expo (Annual); RIA Restoration convention and expo (Annual). **Awards:** Helen Bradley Distinguished Service Award (Annual). **Geographic Preference:** National.

REFERENCE WORKS

31919 ■ **"Green Rules To Drive Innovation: Charging for Carbon Can Inspire Conservation, Fuel Competition, and Enhance Competitiveness" in Harvard Business Review (Vol. 90, March 2012, No. 3, pp. 120)**
Pub: Harvard Business Review Press
Contact: Moderna V. Pfizer, Contact

Ed: Daniel C. Esty, Steve Charnovitz. **Price:** $8.95.
Description: Along with carbon emissions charges, other green policy recommendations include expanding domestic renewable power and the use of natural gas, increasing federal funding of clean-energy research, utilizing incentive-based approaches to encourage the adoption of renewable energy, and implementing the World Trade Organization's Doha negotiations on sustainable development. **Availability:** Online; PDF.

TRADE SHOWS AND CONVENTIONS

31920 ■ **SHRM Annual Conference & Exposition**
Society for Human Resource Management (SHRM)
1800 Duke St.
Alexandria, VA 22314
Ph: (703)548-3440
Free: 800-283-7476
Co. E-mail: shrm@shrm.org
URL: http://www.shrm.org
Contact: Johnny C. Taylor, Jr., President
E-mail: shrmceo@shrm.org
URL(s): annual.shrm.org
Frequency: Annual. **Description:** Human resource management products and services; including relocation human resource information systems, recruitment, executive search, temporary/contact personnel employee compensation and benefits, incentive program information, childcare/eldercare, and drug testing information. This is a hybrid event with in-person and virtual options. **Audience:** Human resource professionals. **Principal Exhibits:** Human resource management products and services; including relocation human resource information systems, recruitment, executive search, temporary/contact personnel employee compensation and benefits, incentive program information, childcare/eldercare, and drug testing information. This is a hybrid event with in-person and virtual options. Dates and Locations: 2025 Jun 29-Jul 02 SAN DIEGO CONVENTION CENTER, San Diego, CA. **Telecommunication Services:** gcoffice@shrm.org.

CONSULTANTS

31921 ■ **Ambler Growth Strategy Consultants Inc.**
3432 Reading Ave.
Hammonton, NJ 08037-8008
Fax: (609)567-3810
Description: Growth strategies, strategic assessments, CEO coaching. **Scope:** Growth strategies, strategic assessments, CEO coaching. **Founded:** 1979. **Publications:** "A joint venture can deliver more than growth"; "Achieving competitive advantage"; "Achieving resilience for your business during difficult times"; "Achieving resilient growth during challenging times"; "Acquisitions: A growth strategy to consider"; "Attracting and retaining longterm corporate spon-

sors"; "Celebrate Selling: The Consultative Relationship Way"; "A Joint Venture Can Deliver More Than Growth"; "Achieving Competitive Advantage"; "Achieving Resilience for Your Business During Difficult Times"; "Balancing Revenue Growth with Growth of a Business"; "Capture Your Competitive Advantage"; "Ease Succession Planning"; "Games Employees Play"; "How to Spark Innovation in an Existing Company"; "Managers demands must change with growth"; "Motivating Generation employees"; "Knowing when to hire ratios provide answers"; "Better customer service can bring black ink". **Training:** Strategic Leadership; Managing Innovation; Breaking Through Classic Barriers to Growth; Energize Your Enterprise; Capture Your Competitive Advantage; Four Entrepreneurial Styles; Perservance and Resilience; Real-Time Strategic Planning/RO1. **Special Services:** The Growth Strategist™.

31922 ■ **Effectiveness Resource Group Inc.**
2215 2nd Ave. N
Seattle, WA 98109-2318
Contact: Donald Swartz, Governor
Description: Provider of problem solving help to client organizations in public and private sectors so they can release and mobilize the full potential of their personnel to achieve productive and satisfying results. **Scope:** Provider of problem solving help to client organizations in public and private sectors so they can release and mobilize the full potential of their personnel to achieve productive and satisfying results. **Training:** Life/Work Goals Exploration; Influencing Change Thru Consultation; Designing and Leading Participative Meetings; Designing, Leading and Managing Change; Project Management and Leadership; Performance Management; Productive Management of Differences; Performance Correction.

31923 ■ **Performance Dynamics Group L.L.C.**
50 Virginia Key Dr.
Union Hall, VA 24176
Ph: (732)537-0381
URL: http://mark-green.com
Contact: Mark Green, Contact
Description: Provider of strategic advisors for top level people in businesses and coaches for executive team development and related services such as technology, professional, strategic and business planning, sales force hiring education and development, and much more. **Scope:** Provider of strategic advisors for top level people in businesses and coaches for executive team development and related services such as technology, professional, strategic and business planning, sales force hiring education and development, and much more. **Founded:** 2003. **Training:** Accelerated Approach to Change; Commitment to Quality; Managing Cultural Diversity; The Corporate Energizer; The Power Pole Experience; Team Assessment; Self-Directed Work Teams.

31924 ■ **The Walk The Talk Co.**
PO Box 480
Youngsville, LA 70592

Free: 800-888-2811
Fax: (972)899-9291
Co. E-mail: info@walkthetalk.com
URL: http://www.walkthetalk.com
Contact: Eric Harvey, Founder
Facebook: www.facebook.com/WalkTheTalk.LPDC
X (Twitter): x.com/WalkTheTalk_com
YouTube: www.youtube.com/user/
  WalkTheTalkCompany

Description: Firm engages in performance management system developed by individual responsibility and decision-making instead of disciplinary penalties. **Scope:** Firm engages in performance management system developed by individual responsibility and decision-making instead of disciplinary penalties. **Founded:** 1978. **Publications:** "Positive Discipline"; "Leadership Secrets of Santa Claus"; "Start Right-Stay Right"; "Walk Awhile in My Shoes"; "Listen Up, Leader!"; "Five Star Teamwork"; "Ethics4Everyone"; "Leadership Courage"; "The Manager's Communication Handbook"; "180 Ways to Walk the Recognition Talk"; "The Manager's Coaching Handbook"; "The Best Leadership Advice I Ever Got"; "Power Exchange". **Training:** Walk the Talk; Coaching for Continuous Improvement; Managing Employee Performance; Customized Management Development Forums; Keynote presentations; Leadership Development Workshops; Consulting Services and Publications; Customer service training; Ethics and Values training.

RESEARCH CENTERS

31925 ■ Manchester University - Peace Studies Institute - Program in Conflict Resolution
North Manchester E College Ave.
  North Manchester, IN 46962

URL: http://www.manchester.edu/academics/
  colleges/college-of-arts-humanities/academic
  -programs/peace-studies/peace-studies-home
Contact: Katy Gray Brown, Director
E-mail: klgraybrown@manchester.edu

Description: Integral unit of Manchester University. **Scope:** Peace, societal violence, social responsibility, socially-responsible investing. **Founded:** 1948. **Publications:** *Nonviolent Social Change* (Annual); *Connections Newsletter* (Quarterly). **Educational Activities:** Church as Peacemaker and the Ropchan Lecture series.

Research and Development

START-UP INFORMATION

31926 ■ *"3rd Annual 'OneMedForum NY 2012', July 11th-12th, to Spotlight JOBS Act, Crowdfunding, and Promising Areas for Healthcare Investment"* in *Investment Weekly (June 23, 2012)*

Description: Third annual forum presented by OneMed provided sessions for understanding the changes in regulation due to the new JOBS Act, which will create opportunities for investors and entrepreneurs. Experts in healthcare and life science investments will be featured. Details of the event are covered. **Availability:** Online.

31927 ■ *"Austin, Aggies and Innovation"* in *Austin Business Journal (Vol. 32, April 6, 2012, No. 5, pp. A1)*

Pub: American City Business Journals, Inc.

Contact: Mike Olivieri, Executive Vice President

Ed: Christopher Calnan. **Description:** Texas A and M University System director for new ventures, Jamie Rhodes, has been using his experience as an entrepreneur and angel investor to work with the university's professors, researchers, and new entrepreneurs on commercialization opportunities. Rhodes has a goal to create startups based on research produced at Texas A and M. **Availability:** Online.

31928 ■ *"Made@Mayo: Mayo Professor Doubles As Founder of Text Tech Company"* in *Business Journal (Vol. 32, June 6, 2014, No. 2, pp. 10)*

Pub: American City Business Journals, Inc.

Contact: Mike Olivieri, Executive Vice President

Description: Rochester, Minnesota-based Mayo Clinic Ventures has managed the licensing of Mayo Clinic technologies and invests in startups. Mayo Clinic Ventures has a $100 million growth fund for investing in startups and two smaller funds worth about $500,000 combined. Insights on the stories of Mayo researchers leading startups are also provided. **Availability:** Online.

31929 ■ *"The Startup of Something Big"* in *Philadelphia Business Journal (Vol. 33, July 11, 2014, No. 22, pp. 4)*

Pub: American City Business Journals, Inc.

Contact: Mike Olivieri, Executive Vice President

Released: Weekly. **Price:** $4, Introductory 4-week offer(Digital only). **Description:** Philadelphia is slowly emerging as America's leading innovation district. The South Bank Campus is the city's game changer as University of Pennsylvania and Drexel University, along with others are seeking to harness the merging of innovation and academic pursuits that ultimately translate into new business development. **Availability:** Print; Online.

31930 ■ *"StartX Med Prescribed for Innovation"* in *Silicon Valley/San Jose Business Journal (Vol. 30, June 8, 2012, No. 11, pp. 1)*

Pub: Baltimore Business Journal

Contact: Rhonda Pringle, President

E-mail: rpringle@bizjournals.com

Description: StartX Med is a program started by entrepreneur Divya Nag along with Stanford student-led nonprofit StartX to help medical startups. Under the program, entrepreneurs will have access to wet and dry laboratory space, animal testing and information related to US Food and Drug Adminstration regulations. **Availability:** Print; Online.

31931 ■ *"Tax Credits As Good As Raised Cash for Cyber Firms"* in *Baltimore Business Journal (Vol. 31, March 28, 2014, No. 48, pp. 16)*

Pub: American City Business Journals, Inc.

Contact: Mike Olivieri, Executive Vice President

Price: $4, print. **Description:** The State of Maryland is offering tax incentives to its cyber security startups in order to capitalize on growing talent and to help the budding cyber security sector grow in the state. Three such tax incentives are outlined, including the cyber security investment incentive tax credit, employer security clearance costs tax credit, and research and development tax credit. Mark Vulcan, program manager of tax incentives for DBED describes this as Maryland'Es endeavor to attract a high growth and high wage industry. **Availability:** Print; Online.

31932 ■ *"Troy Patent Law Firm Launches Rent-Free Tech Incubator"* in *Crain's Detroit Business (Vol. 25, June 8, 2009, No. 23, pp. 4)*

Pub: Crain Communications Inc.

Contact: Barry Asin, President

Ed: Tom Henderson. **Description:** Young Basile Hanlon MacFarlane & Helmholdt PC, a patent law firm located in Troy, Michigan has created a small, rent-free technology incubator on site. The incubator will be called North Woodward Tech Incubator and has room for four or five startups. The incubator is for the earliest or pre-seed stage for entrepreneurs who have not yet gotten significant investment capital. **Availability:** Online.

REFERENCE WORKS

31933 ■ *"Airport Adds More Detroit Flavor; Local Brands Bolster Metro Dining, Retail"* in *Crain's Detroit Business (Vol. 30, July 28, 2014, No. 30, pp. 3)*

Pub: Crain Communications Inc.

Contact: Barry Asin, President

Description: Gayle's Chocolates, Hockeytown Café, and National Coney Island have operated at the Detroit Metropolitan Airport for years. Soon new Detroit favorites will be joining the lineup for the enjoyment of both business and leisure travelers with a food court offering local foods and beverages, including wine and 18 craft brewery beers. There will also be a self-serve kiosk where travelers can buy items to take with them. **Availability:** Print; Online.

31934 ■ *"Alberta Star Begins Phase 2 Drilling On Its Eldorado & Contact Lake IOCG & Uranium Projects"* in *Canadian Corporate News (May 16, 2007)*

Description: Profile of Alberta Star Development Corp., a Canadian mineral exploration company that

identifies, acquires, and finances advanced stage exploration projects in Canada, and its current undertaking of its 2007 drill program in which the company intends to begin accelerating its uranium and poly-metallic exploration and drilling activities on all of its drill targets for 2007 now that it has been granted its permits. **Availability:** Online.

31935 ■ *"Apples, Decoded: WSU Scientist Unraveling the Fruit's Genetics"* in *Puget Sound Business Journal (Vol. 29, September 5, 2008, No. 20)*

Description: Washington State University researcher is working to map the apple's genome in order to gain information about how the fruit grows, looks and tastes. His work, funded by a research grant from the US Department of Agriculture and the Washington Apple Commission is crucial to improving the state's position as an apple-producing region. **Availability:** Print; Online.

31936 ■ *"Auctions and Bidding: A Guide for Computer Scientists"* in *ACM Computing Surveys (Vol. 43, Summer 2011, No. 2, pp. 10)*

Pub: Association for Computing Machinery

Contact: Yannis Ioannidis, President

Ed: Simon Parsons, Juan A. Rodriguez-Aguilar, Mark Klein. **Released:** Volume 43 Issue 2. **Price:** $10, Members; $15, Nonmembers; $5, Students. **Description:** There are various actions: single dimensional, multi-dimensional, single-sided, double-sided, first-price, second-price, English, Dutch, Japanese, sealed-bid, and these have been extensively discussed and analyzed in economics literature. This literature is surveyed from a computer science perspective, primarily from the viewpoint of computer scientists who are interested in learning about auction theory, and to provide pointers into the economics literature for those who want a deeper technical understanding. In addition, since auctions are an increasingly important topic in computer science, the article also looks at work on auctions from the computer science literature. The aim is to identify what both bodies of work tell us about creating electronic auctions. **Availability:** Download; PDF.

31937 ■ *"Auxilium Drug's New Use: Putting the Squeeze On Cellulite"* in *Philadelphia Business Journal (Vol. 30, September 16, 2011, No. 31, pp. 1)*

Pub: Philadelphia Business Journal

Contact: Sierra Quinn, Director

E-mail: squinn@bizjournals.com

Ed: John George. **Description:** Auxilium Pharmaceuticals and BioSpecifics Technologies are getting on with their plans of finding new uses for their drug Xiaflex, a possible treatment for cellulite. The two firms have dismissed their pending litigations and mapped out an amended licensing agreement for their search for the potential uses of the drug. **Availability:** Online.

31938 ■ *"Banking on Cord Blood"* in *Business Journal-Serving Phoenix & the Valley of the Sun (Vol. 31, September 10, 2010, No. 1, pp. 1)*

Description: Celebration Stem Cell Centre obtained contracts from Mercy Gilbert Medical Center and its two sister hospitals, St. Joseph Hospital and Medical Center in Phoenix, Arizona and Chandler Regional Medical Center. The contract will facilitate the donation of unused umbilical cord blood for research. **Availability:** PDF; Online.

31939 ■ "Barshop Leading 'Paradigm Shift' In Aging Research" in San Antonio Business Journal (Vol. 28, September 12, 2014, No. 31, pp. 4)
Pub: American City Business Journals, Inc.
Contact: Mike Olivieri, Executive Vice President
Released: September 12, 2014. **Price:** $4, Introductory 4-week offer(Digital & Print). **Description:** The National Institute of Health has given a $7.5 million five-year grant to University of Texas Health Science at San Antonio's Barshop Insitute for Longevity and Aging Studies. The funding was awarded to help researchers accelerate the discoveries of commercial drugs that slow the aging process. **Availability:** Print; Mailing list; Online.

31940 ■ "Better than Advertised: Chip Plant Beats Expectations" in Business Review Albany (Vol. 41, June 27, 2014, No. 14, pp. 4)
Pub: American City Business Journals, Inc.
Contact: Mike Olivieri, Executive Vice President
Released: Weekly. **Price:** $4, introductory 4-week offer(Digital only). **Description:** The $8.5 billion computer chip manufacturing plant and research center of GlobalFoundries in Malta, New York has strengthened the local economy in Saratoga County and helped the local manufacturing and construction industries recover from the recession. The Malta Plant construction project created more than 2,000 direct new construction jobs and over 10,000 indirect positions. **Availability:** Print; Online.

31941 ■ "BioRASI Aims to Fill Larger HQ With More Jobs" in South Florida Business Journal (Vol. 34, April 11, 2014, N. 38, pp. 4)
Pub: American City Business Journals, Inc.
Contact: Mike Olivieri, Executive Vice President
Released: Weekly. **Price:** $8, Introductory 4-week offer(Digital & Print). **Description:** BioRASI has announced plans to hire an additional 20 or 30 workers in Florida in 2014 after moving into a larger headquarters in Aventura. The contract research organization added 40 employees during 2013 and now has 80 working in Florida. Other insights on BioRASI's growing presence in Florida are given. **Availability:** Print; Online.

31942 ■ "Bioscience Hiring Flat in Florida" in South Florida Business Journal (Vol. 34, July 1, 2011, No. 50, pp. 8)
Pub: American City Business Journals, Inc.
Contact: Mike Olivieri, Executive Vice President
Released: Weekly. **Price:** $8, introductory 4-week offer(Digital only); $8, introductory 4-week offer(Digital & Print). **Description:** The bioscience industry in Florida showed little growth in job creation since 2007, despite heavy state investments. The bioscience sector lost 1 percent of its jobs from 2007 to 2010, while the following two years only recovered the losses of previous years. **Availability:** Print; Online.

31943 ■ "Biotechnology Wants a Lead Role" in Business North Carolina (Vol. 28, March 2008, No. 3, pp. 14)
Description: According to experts, North Carolina is poised as a leader in the biotechnology sector. Highlights of a recent roundtable discussion sponsored by the North Carolina Biotechnology Center in Research Triangle Park are presented. **Availability:** Online.

31944 ■ "Border Boletin: UA to Take Lie-Detector Kiosk to Poland" in Arizona Daily Star (September 14, 2010)
Pub: Arizona Daily Star
Contact: John D'Orlando, President
E-mail: jdorlando@tucson.com
Ed: Brady McCombs. **Description:** University of Arizona's National Center for Border Security and Immigration Research will send a team to Warsaw,

Poland to show border guards from 27 European Union countries the center's Avatar Kiosk. The Avatar technology is designed for use at border ports and airports to assist Customs officers detect individuals who are lying. **Availability:** Print; Online.

31945 ■ "Borrowing Brilliance: The Six Steps to Business Innovation by Building on the Ideas of Others
Released: October 05, 2010. **Price:** $16, paperback; $9.99, e-book. **Description:** The author builds the case that cherry-picking the ideas of others is a vital part of the research and development process for any small firm. **Availability:** E-book; Print.

31946 ■ "Bridging the Worlds" in Academy of Management Journal (Vol. 50, No. 5, October 1, 2007, pp. 1043)
Pub: Academy of Management
Contact: Sharon Alvarez, President
Ed: Lise Saari. **Description:** Need to transfer human resource research information published in journals to practitioners and organizations is investigated, along with suggestions on ways of achieving this goal. **Availability:** Electronic publishing; PDF; Download; Online.

31947 ■ "Brown Lab Image of R.I. Innovation" in Providence Business News (Vol. 28, February 24, 2014, No. 47, pp. 1)
Pub: American City Business Journals, Inc.
Contact: Mike Olivieri, Executive Vice President
Released: February 22, 2014. **Description:** The Advanced Baby Imaging Lab at Brown University in Rhode Island is studying infant brain development using magnetic resonance imaging (MRI). The lab is attracting attention from researchers from Europe and California who see potential in Sean C. Deoni's technique to take an MRI of an infant without using sedation. **Availability:** Print; Online.

31948 ■ "Cancer-Fighting Entrepreneurs" in Austin Business Journal (Vol. 31, August 5, 2011, No. 22, pp. 1)
Pub: Austin Business Journal
Contact: Rachel McGrath, Director
E-mail: rmcgrath@bizjournals.com
Ed: Sandra Zaragoza. **Description:** Cancer Prevention and Research Institute of Texas has invested $10 million in recruiting known faculty to the University of Texas. The move is seen to bolster Austin's position as a major cancer research market. The institute has awarded grants to researchers Jonghwan Kim, Guangbin Dong and Kyle Miller. **Availability:** Print; Online.

31949 ■ "Cancer Genome Project Will Put San Antonio In Research Spotlight" in San Antonio Business Journal (Vol. 25, January 27, 2012, No. 53, pp. 1)
Pub: Baltimore Business Journal
Contact: Rhonda Pringle, President
E-mail: rpringle@bizjournals.com
Description: San Antonio, Texas-based South Texas Accelerated Research Therapeutics has been spearheading the development of a new cancer research effort. The San Antonio 1000 Cancer Genome Project will use the genome sequencing process to examine and compare the difference between normal tissue and tissue from some 1,000 tumors. **Availability:** Print; Online.

31950 ■ "Caterpillar to Expand Research, Production in China" in Chicago Tribune (August 27, 2008)
Description: Caterpillar Inc., the Peoria-based heavy-equipment manufacturer, plans to establish a new research-and-development center at the site of its rapidly growing campus in Wuxi. **Availability:** Print; Online.

31951 ■ "The CMO of Consequence" in Business Strategy Review (Vol. 21, Autumn 2010, No. 3, pp. 42)
Ed: D. Eric Boyd, Rajesh K. Chandy, Marcus Cunha, Jr. **Released:** September 29, 2010. **Description:** Do chief marketing officers matter? Some say that CMOs

have limited effect on corporate performance and don't add significant value to the firm. The authors agree that the job in many firms is in great peril, but their research has uncovered why the contributions of some CMOs are invaluable. **Availability:** Print; PDF; Online.

31952 ■ "Commercial Water Efficiency Initiatives Announced" in Contractor (Vol. 56, November 2009, No. 11, pp. 5)
Ed: Robert P. Mader. **Description:** Plumbing engineers John Koeller and Bill Gauley are developing a testing protocol for commercial toilets. The team said commercial toilets should have a higher level of flush performance than residential toilets for certification. The Environmental Protection Agency's WaterSense program wants to expand the program into the commercial/institutional sector. **Availability:** Print; Online.

31953 ■ "Complementary Strengths Fuel Research Duo's Success" in Providence Business News (Vol. 29, June 2, 2014, No. 9, pp. 22)
Pub: American City Business Journals, Inc.
Contact: Mike Olivieri, Executive Vice President
URL(s): pbn.com/complementary-strengths-fuel-research-duos-success96239
Description: Johnna A. Pezzullo and Lynne A. Haughey achieved success with Omega Medical Research through their complementary strengths. The company has been successful and works with pharmaceutical companies like Pfizer and GlaxoSmithKline. **Telecommunication Services:** Daddona@pbn.com.

31954 ■ "Congestion Relief: The Land Use Alternative" in Canadian Business (Vol. 80, February 12, 2007, No. 4, pp. 31)
Description: The development of a satellite-based system for traffic management including paying for parking fees by Skymeter Corp. is discussed. **Availability:** Download; PDF.

31955 ■ "Consumers Want to Learn More About Green Business Efforts Despite Deep Doubt" in Benzinga.com (May 1, 2012)
Pub: Benzinga.com
Contact: Jason Raznick, Founder
Ed: Aaron Wise. **Released:** May 01, 2012. **Description:** According to the third annual Gibbs & Soell Sense & Sustainability Study, 21 percent of Americans think the majority of businesses are working toward sustainable development, while 71 percent of consumer desire more knowledge about things corporations are doing to become sustainable and green. A majority of respondents believe the media is more likely to report green business when they can report bad news. **Availability:** Online.

31956 ■ "Crowdfunding Comes to Science's Aid as Budgets, Grants Face Squeeze" in Economic Times (July 10, 2012)
Pub: Bennett, Coleman & Company Ltd.
Ed: Rituparna Chattterjee. **Description:** Brian L. Fisher, entomologist studying ants in Madagascar raised $10,000 in 45 days from Petridish, a crowdfunding platform for scientists. Crowdfunding is where a group of investors fund projects. **Availability:** Online.

31957 ■ "A Cyber Breach: More Likely Than a Fire" in Philadelphia Business Journal (Vol. 33, June 13, 2014, No. 18, pp. 6)
Pub: American City Business Journals, Inc.
Contact: Mike Olivieri, Executive Vice President
Released: June 13, 2014. **Price:** $4, introductory 4-week offer(Digital only). **Description:** Robert D'Ovidio, an IT, crime and criminal justice system researcher, and Norman Balchunas, director of strategic studies of Drexel Cybersecurity Institute, give their views on cyber security. According to them, the profile of a cyber thief has undergone a change and with it the role of security professionals in corporations globally. They state that a good information security plan that also addresses privacy would be good in security company data. **Availability:** Print; Mailing list; Online.

31958 ■ "Dean Foods: Uh Oh. Here Comes Wal-Mart" in Ice Cream Reporter (Vol. 23, September 20, 2010, No. 10, pp. 8)

Description: Dean Foods promoted Joseph Scalzo to President and Chief Operating Officer to oversee the firm's operational turnaround and near-term strategic initiatives as well as business units. Key functions will include worldwide supply chain and research and development. **Availability:** Online.

31959 ■ "Describing the Entrepreneurial Profile: The Entrepreneurial Aptitude Test (TAI)" in International Journal of Entrepreneurship and Small Business (Vol. 11, November 1, 2010)

Ed: Serena Cubico, Elisa Bortolani, Giuseppe Favretto, Riccardo Sartori. **Description:** An illustration of metric characteristics and selected research applications of an instrument that can be used to define aptitude for an entrepreneurial profile (created in the 1990s) is examined. The entrepreneurial aptitude test (TAI) describes entrepreneurial potential with regard to eight factors. **Availability:** PDF; Online.

31960 ■ "Does America Really Need Manufacturing? Yes, When Production Is Closely Tied to Innovation" in Harvard Business Review (Vol. 90, March 2012, No. 3, pp. 94)

Pub: Harvard Business Review Press
Contact: Moderna V. Pfizer, Contact

Ed: Gary P. Pisano, Willy C. Shih. **Price:** $8.95. **Description:** A framework is presented for assessing when manufacturing and research and development are crucial to innovation and therefore should be kept in close proximity to each other. The framework denotes the degree to which product design data can be separated from manufacturing, and the opportunities to improve manufacturing. **Availability:** Online; PDF.

31961 ■ "Does Spray Tanning Have Side Effects?" in U.S. News & World Report (July 8, 2019)

URL(s): health.usnews.com/conditions/cancer/skin-cancer/articles/spray-tanning-side-effects

Ed: Elaine K. Howley. **Released:** July 08, 2019. **Description:** People who pay for spray tans often ask if it's safe and if there are any side effects. While the process seems to be a healthier option than tanning beds or sitting directly in the sun for hours, the truth is, is that no one really knows for sure. Spray tans acts as a stain on the skin, but there hasn't been many studies done on the process or if there is any risk to the exposure of eyes, lips, mucus membranes, or internal organs. The only assumption is that since these products have been around for years, there hasn't been significant reports of adverse effects. **Availability:** Online.

31962 ■ "Dow AgroSciences Buys Wheat-Breeding Firm in Pacific Northwest" in Farm Industry News (July 29, 2011)

Pub: Informa Business Media, Inc.
Contact: Charlie McCurdy, President

Description: Dow AgroSciences purchased Northwest Plant Breeding Company, a cereals breeding station in Washington in 2011. The acquisition will help Dow expand its Hyland Seeds certified wheat seed program foundation in the Pacific Northwest. Financial terms of the deal were not disclosed. **Availability:** Online.

31963 ■ "DuPont's Pioneer Hi-Bred, Evogene to Develop Rust-Resistant Soybean Varieties" in Farm Industry News (November 22, 2011)

Pub: Informa Business Media, Inc.
Contact: Charlie McCurdy, President

Ed: Karen McMahon. **Description:** DuPont and Evogene have signed a new contract to work together to develop resistance in soybeans to rust. Financial terms of the agreement were not disclosed. **Availability:** Online.

31964 ■ "East Coast Solar" in Contractor (Vol. 57, February 2010, No. 2, pp. 17)

Ed: Dave Yates. **Description:** U.S. Department of Energy's Solar Decathlon lets 20 college student-led teams from around the world compete to design and build a solar-powered home. A mechanical contractor discusses his work as an advisor during the competition. **Availability:** Print; Online.

31965 ■ "EMU, Spark Plan Business Incubator for Ypsilanti" in Crain's Detroit Business (Vol. 23, October 15, 2007, No. 42, pp. 3)

Pub: Crain Communications Inc.
Contact: Barry Asin, President

Ed: Chad Halcom. **Description:** Eastern Michigan University is seeking federal grants and other funding for a new business incubator program that would be in cooperation with Ann Arbor Spark. The site would become a part of a network of three Spark incubator programs with a focus on innovation in biotechnology and pharmaceuticals. **Availability:** Print; Online.

31966 ■ "Entrepreneurial Orientation and Firm Performance: The Unique Impact of Innovativeness, Proactiveness, and Risk-taking" in Journal of Small Business and Entrepreneurship (Vol. 23, Winter 2010, No. 1)

Pub: Canadian Council for Small Business and Entrepreneurship
Contact: John MacRitchie, President

Ed: Patrick M. Kreisera, Justin Davis. **Description:** The article develops a theoretical model of the relationship between firm-level entrepreneurship and firm performance. This model is intended to further clarify the consequences of an 'entrepreneurial orientation', paying particular attention to the differential relationship that exists between the three sub-dimensions of entrepreneurial orientation and firm performance. Included in the theoretical model are other important variables (such as organizational structure and environmental characteristics) that may impact the EO-performance relationship. Propositions are developed regarding the various configurations of the sub-dimensions of EO and organizational structure that would be most appropriate in a given environmental context. Future research may also benefit from considering the important role that organizational strategy and life cycle stage play in this model. The implications of this model for both researchers and managers are discussed.

31967 ■ "Family Business Research: A Strategic Reflection" in International Journal of Entrepreneurship and Small Business (Vol. 12, December 3, 2010, No. 1)

Ed: A. Bakr Ibrahim, Jean B. McGuire. **Description:** Assessment of the growing field of family business and suggestions for an integrated framework. The paper addresses a number of key issues facing family business research. **Availability:** PDF; Download.

31968 ■ "Feeding the Elephants While Searching for Greener Pastures" in Inc. (Volume 32, December 2010, No. 10, pp. 34)

Pub: Mansueto Ventures L.L.C.
Contact: Stephanie Mehta, Chief Executive Officer

Ed: April Joyner. **Released:** December 2010. **Description:** Innovation is the future for small business. A new book, Inside Real Innovation: How the Right Approach Can Move Ideas from R&D to Market - And Get the Economy Moving helps to break down the process by which innovation occurs. **Availability:** Print.

31969 ■ "Five New Scientists Bring Danforth Center $16 Million" in Saint Louis Business Journal (Vol. 32, October 7, 2011, No. 6, pp. 1)

Pub: Saint Louis Business Journal
Contact: Robert Bobroff, President
E-mail: rbobroff@bizjournals.com

Ed: E.B. Solomont. **Description:** Donald Danforth Plant Science Center's appointment of five new lead scientists has increased its federal funding by $16 million. Cornell University scientist Tom Brutnell is one of the five new appointees. **Availability:** Print; Online.

31970 ■ "From Chelsea Machine Shop to Nobel Prize" in Crain's Detroit Business (Vol. 30, October 13, 2014, No. 41, pp. 35)

Pub: Crain Communications Inc.
Contact: Barry Asin, President

Description: Profile of Eric Betzig, one of three scientists recognized with the Nobel Prize in Chemistry for devising ways for microscopes to look into the molecular hearts of living cells. Betzig is an Ann Arbor, Michigan native who performs research in Virginia for the Howard Hughes Medical Institute. **Availability:** Print; Online.

31971 ■ "Funding Drought Stalls Biotech Incubators" in Saint Louis Business Journal (Vol. 31, July 29, 2011, No. 49, pp. 1)

Pub: Saint Louis Business Journal
Contact: Robert Bobroff, President
E-mail: rbobroff@bizjournals.com

Ed: Angela Mueller. **Description:** Economic slowdown took its toll on cash-strapped startups that fill incubators such as the Bio-Research and Development Growth (BRDG) Park in Creve Coeur, Missouri and the Center for Emerging Technologies in Midtown St. Louis. BRDG put a hold on construction of of its two buildings. **Availability:** Print; Online.

31972 ■ "The Future of Work" in Business Strategy Review (Vol. 21, Autumn 2010, No. 3, pp. 16)

Pub: Wiley-Blackwell

Ed: Lynda Gratton. **Released:** August 28, 2017. **Description:** Work is universal. But how, why, where and when we work has never been so open to individual interpretation. The certainties of the past have been replaced by ambiguity, questions and the steady hum of technology. Now, in a groundbreaking research project covering 21 global companies and more than 200 executives, the author is making sense of the future of work. **Availability:** Print; PDF; Online.

31973 ■ "GeneTree.com Unveils New Family Consultation Service in Interpreting Genealogical DNA Data" in Benzinga.com (February 2, 2012)

Description: Family Consultation Services has been launched by GeneTree.com. The service will provide an in-depth examination of genealogical and DNA information to help genealogist help families identify ancestors in specific family lines. The new DNA test called Y-19 will be used by the service. **Availability:** Print; Online.

31974 ■ "Giving Biotech Startups a Hand" in Philadelphia Business Journal (Vol. 28, January 8, 2010, No. 47, pp. 1)

Pub: Philadelphia Business Journal
Contact: Sierra Quinn, Director
E-mail: squinn@bizjournals.com

Ed: John George. **Description:** Elkins Park, Pennsylvania-based BioStrategy Partners is a virtual life sciences incubator that is seeking to improve the dull ranking of Philadelphia in the small business vitality index of life sciences. BioStrategy provides technology and business development services to startup life sciences companies and university-based research projects. **Availability:** Online.

31975 ■ "Grant Program Boosting Biomedical Research" in Providence Business News (Vol. 28, February 24, 2014, No. 47, pp. 3)

Pub: American City Business Journals, Inc.
Contact: Mike Olivieri, Executive Vice President

Released: February 22, 2014. **Description:** The role played by the Institutional Development Award Network of Biomedical Research Excellence (INBRE) is boosting biomedical research in Rhode Island. According to researcher, Niall G. Howlett, procuring startup funding through INBRE led to receiving other grants and working with graduate students who have the potential to become part of the biomedical workforce. **Availability:** Print; Online.

31976 ■ *"Grant Could Help Schools Harness Wind" in Dallas Business Journal (Vol. 37, April 11, 2014, No. 31, pp. 8)*

Pub: American City Business Journals, Inc.

Contact: Mike Olivieri, Executive Vice President

Released: Weekly. Price: $4, introductory 4-week offer(Digital only); $4, introductory 4-week offer(Digital & Print). Description: Five universities led by Texas A&M have received a $2.2 million grant from the Texas Emerging Technologies Fund for use in wind technology research. The research will focus on turbines that feature bigger blades to capture more wind. Technology developed by the universities will eventually be handed to the state. Availability: Print; Online.

31977 ■ *"Group Thinking" in Business Strategy Review (Vol. 23, Spring 2012, No. 1, pp. 48)*

Description: Conflicts and decision making in groups has long been a subject of fascination for Randall Peterson, Professor of Organizational Behavior at London Business School. He talks to Business Strategy Review about what ignited his interest and his latest research and thinking. Availability: Print; Online.

31978 ■ *"GSK Creating Pathways From Academia to Industry" in Philadelphia Business Journal (Vol. 33, March 7, 2014, No. 4, pp. 8)*

Pub: American City Business Journals, Inc.

Contact: Mike Olivieri, Executive Vice President

Released: Weekly. Price: $4, introductory 4-week offer(Digital & Print). Description: The Discovery Fast Track Challenge program of GlaxoSmithKline will expand in 2014 to include scientists in North America and Europe. Scientists will be asked to submit information about their innovative drug research proposals and the winner could be offered a deal with the Discovery Partnerships with Academia team. Availability: Print; Online.

31979 ■ *"Health Science Center's Capital Campaign Will Boost Local Research" in San Antonio Business Journal (Vol. 28, March 14, 2014, No. 5, pp. 8)*

Pub: American City Business Journals, Inc.

Contact: Mike Olivieri, Executive Vice President

Description: The University of Texas Health Science Center at San Antonio's Campaign for the Future of fundraising project has been completed. The Health Science Center is expected to use the money to support research at the South Texas Medical Center. The capital campaign will allow the Health Science Center to become one of the most prominent universities in the U.S. Availability: Print; Online.

31980 ■ *"The Heart of Health Village: innovation Is Key, and to Get It, Florida Hospital Is Wooing Disruptors, Millenials" in Orlando Business Journal (Vol. 30, May 16, 2014, No. 47, pp. 4)*

Pub: American City Business Journals, Inc.

Contact: Mike Olivieri, Executive Vice President

Released: May 16, 2014. Description: The economic impact of Florida Hospital's planned Health Village in downtown Orlando is explored. The 172-acre development aims to bring together business people, scientists for research, and early and mid-stage companies to combine co-working activities in its Medical Innovation Laboratory. Availability: Print; Online.

31981 ■ *"The Hidden Advantages of Quiet Bosses" in Harvard Business Review (Vol. 88, December 2010, No. 12, pp. 28)*

Pub: Harvard Business Publishing

Contact: Diane Belcher, Managing Director

Ed: Adam M. Grant, Francesca Gino, David A. Hofmann. Price: $6, PDF. Description: Research on organizations behavior indicates that, while extroverts most often become managers, introvert managers paired with proactive employees make a highly efficient and effective combination. Availability: Online; PDF.

31982 ■ *"Hope Grows for a Muscular Dystrophy Drug" in Barron's (Vol. 92, August 25, 2012, No. 35, pp. 35)*

Pub: Dow Jones & Company Inc.

Contact: Almar Latour, Chief Executive Officer

Ed: Andrew Bary. Description: The stocks of biotechnology firm Sarepta Therapeutics could gain value if trials for eterpirsen, a drug being developed for Duchenne muscular dystrophy, are successful. The company's stock prices could rise from $10/share to as high as $26/share. Availability: Online.

31983 ■ *"Hopkins' Security, Reputation Face Challenges in Wake of Slaying" in Baltimore Business Journal (Vol. 28, August 6, 2010, No. 13)*

Pub: Baltimore Business Journal

Contact: Rhonda Pringle, President

E-mail: rpringle@bizjournals.com

Ed: Gary Haber. Description: The slaying of Johns Hopkins University researcher Stephen Pitcairn has not tarnished the reputation of the elite school in Baltimore, Maryland among students. Maintaining Hopkins' reputation is important since it is Baltimore's largest employer with nearly 32,000 workers. Insights on the impact of the slaying among the Hopkins' community are also given.

31984 ■ *"Hopkins, University of Maryland, Baltimore Worry Reduced NIH Budget Will Impact Research" in Baltimore Business Journal (Vol. 29, August 19, 2011, No. 15, pp. 1)*

Pub: Boston Business Journal

Contact: Carolyn M. Jones, President

E-mail: cmjones@bizjournals.com

Ed: Scott Dance. Description: The budget for the National Institutes of Health (NIH) is slated to be cut by at least 7.9 percent to $2.5 billion in 2013. This will have a big negative effect on medical and biotech research in Maryland, especially Johns Hopkins University and University of Maryland, Baltimore which could face stiffer completion for grants from the NIH. Availability: Online.

31985 ■ *"How to Conduct a Functional Magnetic Resonance (fMRI) Study in Social Science Research" in MIS Quarterly (Vol. 36, September 2012, No. 3, pp. 811)*

Pub: University of Minnesota Carlson School of Management Management Information Systems Research Center

Ed: Angelika Dimoka. Description: A set of guidelines for conducting functional magnetic resonance imaging studies in social sciences and information systems research is provided. Availability: PDF; Online.

31986 ■ *"How Green Is The Valley?" in Barron's (Vol. 88, July 4, 2008, No. 28, pp. 13)*

Description: San Jose, California has made a good start towards becoming a leader in alternative energy technology through the establishment of United Laboratories' own lab in the city. The certification process for photovoltaic cells will be dramatically shortened with this endeavor. Availability: Print.

31987 ■ *"How Much For a Magic Bullet?" in San Francisco Business Times (Vol. 28, April 25, 2014, No. 40, pp. 4)*

Pub: American City Business Journals, Inc.

Contact: Mike Olivieri, Executive Vice President

Released: April 25, 2014. Price: $4, Introductory 4-Week Offer(Digital & Print). Description: Novel gene therapies developed by San Francisco, California--based research companies entail high prices. Gilead Sciences Inc. developed the hepatitis drug called Sovaldt that is being sold for $1,000 per pill. Health insurers may not be able to finance long-term treatments at these high prices. Availability: Print; Online.

31988 ■ *"Handling New Health Insurance Regulations" in Baltimore Business Journal (Vol. 31, April 25, 2014, No. 52, pp. 25)*

Pub: American City Business Journals, Inc.

Contact: Mike Olivieri, Executive Vice President

Released: March 13, 2014. Description: Research and consulting firm, Mercer, surveyed businesses in January 2014 to examine their employer-sponsored health plans following enrollment in the Affordable Care Act-created exchanges. The survey found employers were taking advantage of a delay to a key regulation in the Act on offering insurance to employees who work at least 30 hours a week. Availability: Print; Online.

31989 ■ *How to Write a Business Plan*

Pub: Kogan Page Ltd.

Contact: Christina Lindeholm, Manager, Sales

Ed: Brian Finch. Released: Seventh edition. Description: Starting with the premise that there's only one chance to make a good impression, this book covers all the issues involved in producing a successful business plan, from profiling competitors to forecasting marketing development. Availability: Print; Electronic publishing.

31990 ■ *"Human Activity Analysis: a Review" in ACM Computing Surveys (Vol. 43, Fall 2011, No. 3, pp. 16)*

Pub: Association for Computing Machinery

Contact: Yannis Ioannidis, President

Ed: J. K. Aggarwal, M. S. Ryoo. Description: Human activity recognition is an important area of computer vision research and is studied in this report. Availability: Download; PDF; Online.

31991 ■ *"iAM Scientist Launches To Provide a Crowdfunding Platform for Science, Technology, and Medicine" in Benzinga.com (July 31, 2012)*

Pub: Benzinga.com

Contact: Jason Raznick, Founder

Ed: Aaron Wise. Description: Medical, technology, and science researchers will be able to seach for funding through the newly launched iAMscientist platform. The sitewill provide a site with funding and shared research opportunities. The new tools, better models, and quicker data collection processes will help make research interdisciplinary, collaborative, data driven, and less predictable. Open Access Funding Platform (OAFP) can be used to solicit funding required to carry out research projects. Availability: Print; Online.

31992 ■ *"Innovation Station" in Canadian Business (Vol. 80, October 8, 2007, No. 20, pp. 42)*

Description: Study and teaching of entrepreneurship at the University of Waterloo is discussed. Research projects in the university are expected to be influential in Canada's economic development. In spite of the success of these studies, financing is still a problem for the university, especially in technological innovations. Availability: Online.

31993 ■ *"Inventive Doctor New Venture Partner" in Houston Business Journal (Vol. 40, January 29, 2010, No. 38, pp. A2)*

Pub: Houston Business Journal

Contact: Bob Charlet, President

E-mail: bcharlet@bizjournals.com

Ed: Ford Gunter. Description: Dr. Billy Cohn, a surgeon from Houston, Texas has been named as venture partner for venture firm Sante Ventures LLC of Austin, Texas. Cohn will be responsible for seeing marketable developing technologies in the medical industry. The motivation for Cohn's naming as venture partner is his development of a minimally invasive therapy for end-stage renal disease. Availability: Print; Online.

31994 ■ *"Jacksonville Doing Well In Growing Economy" in Orlando Business Journal (Vol. 30, June 27, 2014, No. 53, pp. 8)*

Pub: American City Business Journals, Inc.

Contact: Mike Olivieri, Executive Vice President

Released: June 27, 2014. Description: Jerry Mallot is the president of JaxUSA Partnership, the economic development arm of the Jax Chambers. According to Mallot, Northeast Florida's strongest selling points for business site or relocation there include advanced manufacturing, financial services, aviation and aerospace technology, life sciences, logistics and information technology.

31995 ■ *"Kineta Helps Grow Start Group of 5 Biotech Partners" in Puget Sound Business Journal (Vol. 35, June 13, 2014, No. 8, pp. 6)*
Pub: American City Business Journals, Inc.
Contact: Mike Olivieri, Executive Vice President
Description: Kineta Inc is seeking new funding through its KPI Therapeutics. Kineta offers investors a return on their investments after three to five years. KPI Therapeutics is a new collaborative initiative between drug development firms and private investors. KPI's vision is to create a better way to develop early- and mid-stage therapies for patients and will act as an investment group and a strategic research hub. **Availability:** Print; Online.

31996 ■ *"The Life Changers" in Canadian Business (Vol. 81, October 27, 2008, No. 18, pp. 86)*
Description: The first season of 'The Life Changers' was produced in September 2007 to feature stories about research and development (R&D) efforts by universities in Atlantic Canada. The program addresses the need to inform the public about university R&D and its outcomes. **Availability:** Print; Online.

31997 ■ *"Life Sciences Become State's Growth Powerhouse" in Crain's Detroit Business (Vol. 25, June 1, 2009, No. 22, pp. M008)*
Pub: Crain Communications Inc.
Contact: Barry Asin, President
Ed: Amy Lane. **Description:** According to a study conducted by Anderson Economic Group, Michigan's University Research Corridor has helped grow the life sciences industry. Statistical details included. **Availability:** Online.

31998 ■ *"Little Guy is Taking On Potent Competition" in Philadelphia Business Journal (Vol 32, January 10, 2014, No. 48, pp. 4)*
Pub: American City Business Journals, Inc.
Contact: Mike Olivieri, Executive Vice President
Released: Weekly. **Price:** $4, introductory 4-week offer(Digital & Print). **Description:** Auxilium Pharmaceuticals has introduced the erectile dysfunction drug Stendra, which it licensed from Vivus Inc. in a $300 million deal. Auxilium CEO, Adrian Adams, says Stendra has some advantages over competing products. **Availability:** Print; Online.

31999 ■ *"Longwood's FamilLab More Than Just a Hackerspace: It's a Free Form Research and Development Lab" in Orlando Business Journal (Vol. 30, January 17, 2014, No. 30, pp. 4)*
Pub: American City Business Journals, Inc.
Contact: Mike Olivieri, Executive Vice President
Description: FamilLab is a nonprofit hackerspace in Longwood, Florida that has turned into a free-form research and development outfit. The group has at least 70 members who share the same passion for technology and push the limits and boundaries of computer hardware and software, and sometimes start their own business. **Availability:** Print; Online.

32000 ■ *Marketing for Entrepreneurs*
Pub: FT Press
Ed: Jurgen Wolff. **Released:** 1st edition. **Description:** This text identifies marketing as the entire process of researching, creating, distributing and selling a product or service. It isn't about theory and metrics, rather it is a practical guide that starts with the basics of all marketing aspects. **Availability:** Print.

32001 ■ *"A Master Chef's Recipe for Business Success" in Business Strategy Review (Vol. 23, Spring 2012, No. 1, pp. 65)*
Description: Often called the world's greatest chef, Ferran Adria, longtime owner of El Built, Spain's three-star Michelin rated revolutionary restaurant, is now embarking on a new venture: the El Built

Foundation, a place where chefs can create, interact, and discuss their ideas with researchers from other disciplines. He recently spoke at London Business School as part of his tour of a number of select universities to invite students to enter a competition to design an innovative business model for the new Foundation. **Availability:** Print; Online.

32002 ■ *"Med-Tech Vet's Trip From Heart to Sleeve" in Business Journal (Vol. 31, February 14, 2014, No. 38, pp. 8)*
Pub: American City Business Journals, Inc.
Contact: Mike Olivieri, Executive Vice President
Released: February 14, 2014. **Price:** $4, Introductory 4-week offer(Digital & Print). **Description:** Conventus Orthopaedics CEO, Paul Buckman, describes the device which repairs wrist fractures. Buckman reveals plans to use the $17 million venture capital to continue research and development and to conduct clinical studies to justify use of the technology. **Availability:** Print; Online.

32003 ■ *"Medical-Device Firm Targets a Heart-Valve Market in Flux" in Philadelphia Business Journal (Vol. 33, May 9, 2014, No. 13, pp. 9)*
Pub: American City Business Journals, Inc.
Contact: Mike Olivieri, Executive Vice President
Released: May 09, 2014. **Price:** $4, Introductory 4-week offer(Digital only). **Description:** Montgomery County-based medical products company, Thubrikar Aortic Valve Inc., is developing the Optimum TAV, a next-generation transcatheter aortic valve implantation (TAVI) device to treat heart patients with aortic stenosis. The company is raising funds to start clinical testing for the Optimum TAV in 2014, aiming to provide a more durable and efficient transcatheter aortic valve for lower-risk patients. **Availability:** Print; Online.

32004 ■ *"Meet University of Texas' New Business Mind" in Austin Business Journal (Vol. 31, May 13, 2011, No. 10, pp. A1)*
Pub: Austin Business Journal
Contact: Rachel McGrath, Director
E-mail: rmcgrath@bizjournals.com
Ed: Sandra Zaragoza. **Description:** University of Texas (UT) chief commercialization officer, Dr. Richard Miller, has opened a satellite office in Silicon Valley, California in the hopes of luring Californian investors to the science and technology at UT. The satellite office is just one of Miller's efforts to reshape and widen the commercialization of UT-Austin. Insights into Miller's long-term view approach to commercialization are also covered. **Availability:** Online.

32005 ■ *"MIR Growing With Help From Former Pfizer Workers" in Crain's Detroit Business (Vol. 24, January 28, 2008, No. 4, pp. 33)*
Pub: Crain Communications Inc.
Contact: Barry Asin, President
Ed: Tom Henderson. **Description:** Molecular Imaging Research Inc. helps fund research at its parent firm, Molecular Therapeutics Inc. The company provides imaging services and other in vivo and in vitro services to help pharmaceutical companies test new compounds. **Availability:** Print; Online.

32006 ■ *"Monsanto Acquires Targeted-Pest Control Technology Start-Up; Terms Not Disclosed" in Benzinga.com (September 2011)*
Pub: Benzinga.com
Contact: Jason Raznick, Founder
Ed: Eddie Staley. **Description:** Monsanto Company acquired Beelogics, a firm that researches and develops biological tools that control pests and diseases. Research includes a product that will help protect bee health. **Availability:** Online.

32007 ■ *"MPI Expansion Goes Back to Family Roots" in Crain's Detroit Business (Vol. 25, June 1, 2009, No. 22, pp. M007)*
Pub: Crain Communications Inc.
Contact: Barry Asin, President

Ed: Sherri Begin Welch. **Description:** William Parfet, grandson of Upjohn Company founder, is expanding MPI Research's clinical and early clinical research operations into two buildings in Kalamazoo, land which was once part of his grandfather's farm. **Availability:** Print; PDF; Online.

32008 ■ *"The New Face of Aging: Chasing the Secret to Stopping the Clock" in San Francisco Business Times (Vol. 28, January 31, 2014, No. 28, pp. 4)*
Pub: American City Business Journals, Inc.
Contact: Mike Olivieri, Executive Vice President
Released: Weekly. **Price:** $4, Introductory 4-week offer(Digital & Print). **Description:** San Francisco, California-based Calico has built a small team of star scientists to join research for finding the secret to stop human aging, with financial backing from Google. However, the Ellison Medical Foundation has stopped making new grants for aging research. The preventive approach of the aging research is also discussed. **Availability:** Print; Online.

32009 ■ *"New Institutional Accounting and IFRS" in Accounting and Business Research (Vol. 41, Summer 2011, No. 3, pp. 309)*
Pub: Routledge, Taylor & Francis Group
Ed: Peter Wysocki. **Description:** A new framework for institutional accounting research is presented. It has five fundamental components: efficient versus inefficient results, interdependencies, causation, level of analysis, and institutional structure. The use of the framework for evaluation accounting institutions such as the international financial reports standards (IFRS) is discussed. **Availability:** PDF; Online; Download.

32010 ■ *"New Stem Cell Research Awareness Org Launched in Austin" in Austin Business Journal (Vol. 31, June 3, 2011, No. 13, pp. 1)*
Pub: Austin Business Journal
Contact: Rachel McGrath, Director
E-mail: rmcgrath@bizjournals.com
Ed: Sandra Zaragoza. **Description:** MedRebels Foundation was launched in February 2011 with the goal of providing millions of dollars for research funding, education and advocacy for adult stem cell-focused medicine. The foundation, whose major contributor is SpineSmith LP, is a collaboration of other adult stem cell-related companies and nonprofit partners. It hopes to raise $200,000 by the end of 2011. **Availability:** Print; Online.

32011 ■ *"Non-Users Still Inhale Nicotine From E-Cigarettes" in Business First of Buffalo (Vol. 30, February 7, 2014, No. 21, pp. 6)*
Pub: American City Business Journals, Inc.
Contact: Mike Olivieri, Executive Vice President
Released: Weekly. **Price:** $140, Digital & Print; $115, Digital only. **Description:** A group of researchers at Roswell Park Cancer Institute's Department of Health Behavior, led by Maciej Goniewicz, found traces of some potentially dangerous chemical in the vapor of electronic cigarettes. Although smoking e-cigarettes is less harmful than regular cigarettes, non-users are still exposed to nicotine in the same way as secondhand smoke. **Availability:** Print; Online.

32012 ■ *"NSU Seeks Private Partners For New $80M Research Building" in South Florida Business Journal (Vol. 34, February 21, 2014, No. 31, pp. 4)*
Pub: American City Business Journals, Inc.
Contact: Mike Olivieri, Executive Vice President
Released: Weekly. **Price:** $8, Introductory 4-week offer(Digital & Print). **Description:** The $80 million Center for Collaborative Research at Nova Southeastern University hopes to become the largest incubator and wet laboratory space in Broward County, Florida. The center had its groundbreaking on February 13, 2014, and will be open for lease to private companies when it is ready in 22 months. **Availability:** Print; Online.

32013 ■ *"On the Use of Neurophysiological Tools In IS Research: Developing a Research Agenda for NeuroIS"* in MIS Quarterly (Vol. 36, September 2012, No. 3, pp. 679)
Pub: University of Minnesota Carlson School of Management Management Information Systems Research Center
Ed: Angelika Dimoka. Price: $15. Description: The role of neurophysiological tools and neuroimaging tools in information systems research is discussed. Promising application areas and research questions regarding the use of neurophysiological data to benefit information systems researchers are identified. Availability: PDF.

32014 ■ *"The One Thing That's Holding Back Your Wellness Program"* in Employee Benefit News (Vol. 25, December 1, 2011, No. 15, pp. 8)
Pub: SourceMedia LLC
Contact: Gemma Postlethwaite, Chief Executive Officer
Description: A 13-year study shows that women who sat for more than six hours a day were 94 percent more likely to die during the study period. Most women sit at their desks an average of 7.7 hours while at work.

32015 ■ *"Organic Food Industry Goes to College"* in USA Today (April 9, 2012)
Ed: Chuck Raasch. Description: With the organic food industry growing the US Department of Agriculture is has pumped $117 million into organic research in the last three years. According to a recent report by the Organic Farming Research Foundation (OFRF), the number of states committing land for organic research has nearly doubled from 2003 to 2011. Universities offering academic programs in organic farming rose from none to nine. The OFRF supports organic farmers and producers. Availability: Online.

32016 ■ *"Patently Absurd"* in Globe & Mail (January 28, 2006, pp. B4)
Description: An overview of facts about patent dispute between Research In Motion Ltd. and NTP Inc. is presented. Availability: Online.

32017 ■ *"Pet Store Fish Provide Clue to How Alzheimer's Disease May Start"* in Marketwired (July 9, 2012)
Pub: Comtex News Network Inc.
Contact: Kan Devnani, President
Released: August 07, 2012. Description: Western University of Health Sciences in Pomona, California researchers report that studies with zebrafish provided an important clue to understanding how Alzheimer's disease starts. Details of the study are included. Availability: Print; Online.

32018 ■ *"Faster To Dissolve, Faster To Work"* in Philadelphia Business Journal (Vol. 33, March 14, 2014, No. 5, pp. 8)
Pub: American City Business Journals, Inc.
Contact: Mike Olivieri, Executive Vice President
Released: Weekly. Price: $4, introductory 4-week offer(Digital & Print). Description: The U.S. Food and Drug Administration approved Iroko Pharmaceutical's anti-inflammatory drug Tivorbex. The company's technology reformulates a braded drug's active ingredient as submicron particles 20 times smaller than their original size. Iroko also applies the technology to drugs used in oncology. Availability: Print; Online.

32019 ■ *"Physics for Females"* in Occupational Outlook Quarterly (Vol. 55, Summer 2011, No. 2, pp. 22)
Description: Free resources to help females investigate careers in medical physics and health physics are available from the American Physical Society. The booklet is designed for girls in middle and high school and describes the work of 15 women who use physics to solve medical mysteries, discover planets, research new materials, and more. Availability: Print; Online.

32020 ■ *"Preceptis Gets Gopher Angels' Biggest-Ever Investment"* in Business Journal (Vol. 31, January 31, 2014, No. 36, pp. 8)
Pub: American City Business Journals, Inc.
Contact: Mike Olivieri, Executive Vice President
Description: Preceptis Medical Inc. has secured $1.2 million in funding from Gopher Angels. The funding will help Preceptis to finance ongoing clinical studies and general operating expenses. The company develops surgical tools for pediatric ear-tube surgery. Availability: Print; Online.

32021 ■ *"Procter & Gamble vs. IRS: Split Decision"* in Business Courier (Vol. 27, July 16, 2010, No. 11, pp. 1)
Pub: Business Courier
Ed: Jon Newberry. Description: Implications of a court ruling in a $435 million legal dispute between Procter & Gamble Company (P&G) and the Internal Revenue Service (IRS) are discussed. A $21 million win has been realized for P&G for its interpretation of research and development tax credits. However, the said case might involve more than $700 million in P&G tax deductions from 2001 through 2004 that the IRS had disallowed. Availability: Print; Online.

32022 ■ *"Putting 'Extra' in Extra-Silky Shampoo"* in Crain's Chicago Business (Vol. 31, April 28, 2008, No. 17, pp. 37)
Pub: Crain Communications Inc.
Contact: Barry Asin, President
Ed: Phuong Ly. Description: Profile of HallStar Co., a Chicago-based company which develops and manufactures specialty chemicals to upgrade existing products such as hair dye, lotion and deodorant. HallStar has seen its annual earnings rise more than 30 percent since 2002. Availability: Online.

32023 ■ *"The Quest for a Smart Prosthetic"* in Canadian Business (Vol. 83, October 12, 2010, No. 17, pp. 26)
Pub: Rogers Media Inc.
Contact: Neil Spivak, Chief Executive Officer
Ed: Jacqueline Nelson. Description: Information about a two-year research project led by Southern Methodist University (SMU) and funded by the Defense Advance Research Projects Agency (DARPA) is provided. The agency aims to create a 'smart prosthetic' which will improve the lives of military amputees. The planned prosthetic will use a sensor that can carry nerve signals through synthetic channels. Availability: Print; Online.

32024 ■ *"Reading the Public Mind"* in Harvard Business Review (Vol. 88, October 2010, No. 10, pp. 27)
Pub: Harvard Business Publishing
Contact: Diane Belcher, Managing Director
Ed: Andrew O'Connell. Price: $6, PDF. Description: Examination of the various methods for obtaining public opinion and consumer preferences is provided; an outline of the disadvantages and benefits of both are also given. Availability: Online; PDF.

32025 ■ *"Region to Be Named Innovation Hub"* in Business Courier (Vol. 27, July 2, 2010, No. 9, pp. 1)
Pub: Business Courier
Ed: Dan Monk. Description: The selection of Cincinnati's consumer-marketing cluster as a 'Hub of Innovation' by the Ohio Department of Development could boost Cincinnati's chances of receiving $100 million in grants from Ohio's Third Frontier program and other funding sources. Implications of the University of Cincinnati's designation as a Center of Excellence in Advanced Transportation and Aerospace are also discussed. Availability: Print; Online.

32026 ■ *"Region Wins as GE Puts Plants Close to R&D"* in Business Review Albany (Vol. 41, July 4, 2014, No. 15, pp. 8)
Pub: American City Business Journals, Inc.
Contact: Mike Olivieri, Executive Vice President
Description: General Electric Company (GE) invested over $400 million into the expansion of its health care, battery and renewable energy busi-

nesses in the Albany, New York region. The company's local growth secured about 7,000 private-sector jobs in the area and strengthened the relationship between GE research and manufacturing. Availability: Print; Online.

32027 ■ *"Renewable Energy Market Opportunities: Wind Testing"* in PR Newswire (September 22, 2011)
Pub: PR Newswire Association LLC.
Description: Global wind energy test systems markets are discussed. Research conducted covers both non-destructive test equipment and condition monitoring equipment product segments.

32028 ■ *"Research Reports"* in Barron's (Vol. 90, August 23, 2010, No. 34, pp. M13)
Pub: Barron's Editorial & Corporate Headquarters
Description: Shares of Sirius XM Radio, Target and Deere and Company received an eBuyE rating, while shares of Research in Motion got an eNeutralE rating. Availability: Online.

32029 ■ *"Research, Treatment to Expand"* in Philadelphia Business Journal (Vol. 28, June 22, 2012, No. 19, pp. 1)
Pub: Baltimore Business Journal
Contact: Rhonda Pringle, President
E-mail: rpringle@bizjournals.com
Description: Fox Chase Cancer Center and Temple University Health System have been planning several projects once their merger is completed. Their plans include the construction of a unit for cancer patients on the third floor of the Founder's Building at Jeanes Hospital and a granting mechanism to fund research collaborations. Availability: Print; Online.

32030 ■ *"The Right Remedy: Entrepreneur's Success Is a Matter of Life and Death"* in Black Enterprise (Vol. 38, February 2008, No. 7, pp. 46)
Pub: Earl G. Graves Ltd.
Contact: Earl Graves, Jr., President
Ed: Tamara E. Holmes. Description: Profile of Leah Brown, whose company conducts clinical trials to determine if specific drugs will relieve particular symptoms. Her company will also visit physician's offices to make certain doctors are following proper protocol for a clinical trial or will collect data from patients. Availability: Online.

32031 ■ *"RIM Reinforces Claim as Top Dog by Expanding BlackBerry Service"* in Globe & Mail (March 11, 2006, pp. B3)
Ed: Simon Avery. Description: The plans of Research In Motion Ltd. to enhance the features of BlackBerry, through acquisition of Ascendent Systems, are presented. Availability: Online.

32032 ■ *"SABER Research Institute's Steve Nivin"* in San Antonio Business Journal (Vol. 28, April 4, 2014, No. 8, pp. 6)
Pub: American City Business Journals, Inc.
Contact: Mike Olivieri, Executive Vice President
Released: Weekly. Price: $4, Introductory 4-week offer(Digital only). Description: SABER Research Institute director and chief economist, Steve Nivin, shares his views on the potential expansion of Google Fiber's broadband Internet network to San Antonio, Texas. Nivin says Google Fiber should encourage entrepreneurs to start businesses in San Antonio. He also says the chances of fast growth companies being created in the city is enhanced with Google Fiber. Availability: Print; Online.

32033 ■ *"San Antonio Researchers Develop New Laser-Based Imaging System"* in San Antonio Business Journal (Vol. 26, August 24, 2012, No. 30, pp. 1)
Pub: Baltimore Business Journal
Contact: Rhonda Pringle, President
E-mail: rpringle@bizjournals.com
Description: Researchers at the University of Texas Health Science Center at San Antonio in Texas have developed an optical sensor-dependent medical imaging system, which is ready for commercializa-

tion. The laser-based imaging system is expected to improve non-invasive imaging for medical diagnostics. **Availability:** Print; Online.

32034 ■ *"Scientific American Builds Novel Blog Network" in Information Today (Vol. 28, September 2011, No. 8, pp. 12)*
Pub: Information Today Inc.
Contact: Thomas H. Hogan, President

Ed: Kurt Schiller. **Description:** Scientific American launched a new blog network that joins a diverse lineup of bloggers cover various scientific topics under one banner. The blog network includes 60 bloggers providing insights into the ever-changing world of science and technology.

32035 ■ *"Securing our Cyber Status" in San Antonio Business Journal (Vol. 28, May 16, 2014, No. 14, pp. 4)*
Pub: American City Business Journals, Inc.
Contact: Mike Olivieri, Executive Vice President

Released: Weekly. **Price:** $4, introductory 4-week offer(Digital & Print). **Description:** The San Antonio Chamber of Commerce commissioned Deloitte to conduct a study on the local cyber security sector of San Antonio, Texas. Industry insiders are looking forward to securing the status of San Antonio as a top tier cyber city with the results of the study research. **Availability:** Print; Online.

32036 ■ *"The Service Imperative" in Business Horizons (Vol. 51, January-February 2008, No. 1, pp. 39)*
Pub: Elsevier Advanced Technology Publications

Ed: Mary Jo Bitner, Stephen W. Brown. **Description:** The importance of services is growing in developing countries like India and China, but little attention is given to service research, education and innovation. The 'service imperative' seeks to promote the advancement of services. The scope, objectives and philosophy of the service imperative platform are outlined. **Availability:** Online.

32037 ■ *"S.F. Leasing Off to Hottest Start Since 2000" in San Francisco Business Times (Vol. 28, January 17, No. 26, pp. 8)*
Pub: American City Business Journals, Inc.
Contact: Mike Olivieri, Executive Vice President

Description: Figures show that the demand for commercial space in San Francisco, California continues to increase. Companies such as LinkedIn, Trulia, DropBox, and Pinterest are expected to lease around 700,000 square feet of space. Colin Yasukochi, research director at CBRE Group, believes that commercial space is not being constructed fast enough to accommodate demand. **Availability:** Print; Online.

32038 ■ *"Shire Seeking New Digs for Headquarters" in Philadelphia Business Journal (Vol. 30, September 2, 2011, No. 29, pp. 1)*
Pub: Philadelphia Business Journal
Contact: Sierra Quinn, Director
E-mail: squinn@bizjournals.com

Ed: Natalie Kostelni. **Description:** Dublin, Ireland-based Shire PLC announced plans to relocate its North American headquarters from Chesterbrook Corporate Center in Wayne, Pennsylvania and currently evaluating their options. The specialty biopharmaceutical firm is also considering a move to New Jersey or Delaware. **Availability:** Online.

32039 ■ *"Sleep Apnea Pill Nears Human Tests" in Philadelphia Business Journal (Vol. 33, May 9, 2014, No. 13, pp. 8)*
Pub: American City Business Journals, Inc.
Contact: Mike Olivieri, Executive Vice President

Released: Weekly. **Price:** $4, Introductory 4-week offer(Digital & Print). **Description:** Galleon Pharmaceuticals is set to begin human testing of its experimental therapy GAL-160, an oral medicine for sleep apnea, and has already started human testing of GAL-021, an intravenous drug to treat respiratory complications in patients receiving anesthetics and opiate pain medication. Galleon CEO, James C. Man-

nion, hopes that both drugs pass the proof-of-concept stage and move to mid-stage clinical testing in humans by mid-2015. **Availability:** Print; Online.

32040 ■ *"Slow but Steady into the Future" in Barron's (Vol. 88, July 7, 2008, No. 27, pp. M)*
Pub: Dow Jones & Company Inc.
Contact: Almar Latour, Chief Executive Officer

Ed: Mark Veverka. **Description:** Investors are advised to maintain their watch on the shares of business software company NetSuite. The company's chief executive officer, Zach Nelson, claims that the company has a 10-year lead on its competitors with the development of software-as-a service. **Availability:** Online.

32041 ■ *"South Florida Lodging Industry Poised for Strong Growth in 2014" in South Florida Business Journal (Vol. 34, January 3, 2014, No. 24, pp. 3)*
Pub: American City Business Journals, Inc.
Contact: Mike Olivieri, Executive Vice President

Released: Weekly. **Price:** $8, Introductory 4-week offer(Digital & Print). **Description:** Demand for the lodging industry in South Florida is expected to grow in 2014. According to hotel consulting and research firm, PKF Hospitality Research LLC, lodging demand in the U.S. would increase by 2.1 percent by the end of 2013 while airport, resort and suburban areas will achieve the biggest gains in revenue per available room in 2014. **Availability:** Print; Online.

32042 ■ *"'Stalking Horse' Bidder Keeping Plextronics Here" in Pittsburgh Business Times (Vol. 33, March 28, 2014, No. 37, pp. 6)*
Pub: American City Business Journals, Inc.
Contact: Mike Olivieri, Executive Vice President

Released: March 28, 2014. **Price:** $4, Introductory 4-week offer(Digital & Print). **Description:** Chemical company Solvay American has acquired solar and lighting company Plextronics Inc. of Pittsburgh, Pennsylvania. Solvay's research and innovation department is seen as a better fit for Plextronics because it is developing a new technology. **Availability:** Print; Online.

32043 ■ *Start and Run a Delicatessen: Small Business Starters Series*
Description: Information for starting and running a successful delicatessen is provided. Insight is offered into selecting a location, researching the market, writing a business plan and more.

32044 ■ *"Startup Osteosphere Formed to Develop Laboratory Discovery" in Houston Business Journal (Vol. 40, January 8, 2010, No. 35, pp. 1)*
Pub: Houston Business Journal
Contact: Bob Charlet, President
E-mail: bcharlet@bizjournals.com

Ed: Casey Wooten. **Description:** Biotech startup company Osteosphere in Houston, Texas aims to market a technology in which laboratory-grown bone tissues can be processed to appear like a real human bone tissue. The technology was developed by a co-founder of the startup and it can be applied to bone disease and injury treatment. Osteophere's future plans, such as the search for possible investors, is also outlined. **Availability:** Print; Online.

32045 ■ *"Stronger Corn? Take It Off Steroids, Make It All Female" in Farm Industry News (December 5, 2011)*
Pub: Informa Business Media, Inc.
Contact: Charlie McCurdy, President

Ed: Brian Wallheimer. **Description:** Purdue University researcher found that higher improvements in corn crops, and possibly other crops, were yielded when steroids were discontinued. **Availability:** Print; Online.

32046 ■ *"Targeted Technology Raises More Than $40 Million" in San Antonio Business Journal (Vol. 28, September 5, 2014, No. 30, pp. 8)*
Pub: American City Business Journals, Inc.
Contact: Mike Olivieri, Executive Vice President

Released: September 05, 2014. **Price:** $4, introductory 4-week offer(Digital & Print). **Description:** Targeted Technology has raised more than $40 million in venture capital funding for early-stage biotechnology companies in San Antonio, Texas through its Targeted Technology Fund II. Senior managing partner, Paul Castella, recognizes the lack of venture capital funds in the area and the role played by his organization to help these firms. **Availability:** Print; Online.

32047 ■ *"Thinking Aloud" in Business Strategy Review (Vol. 21, Summer 2010, No. 2, pp. 47)*
Description: In each issue we ask an academic to explain the big question on which their research hopes to shed light. Yiorgos Mylonadis looks at how people define and solve problems. **Availability:** Print; Online.

32048 ■ *"Top Worst Weeds in Corn" in Farm Industry News (November 29, 2011)*
Pub: Informa Business Media, Inc.
Contact: Charlie McCurdy, President

Ed: John Pocock. **Description:** Effective weed control for profitable crops is discussed with information from leading weed scientists from the University of Illinois Extension. It is important for farmers to know what their worst weed is in order to choose the best product, or mix of products, to control them. **Availability:** Print; Online.

32049 ■ *"The Trillion Dollar R&D Fix: Most Big Companies Should Spend More On R&D. But How Much More?" in Harvard Business Review (Vol. 90, May 2012, No. 5, pp. 76)*
Pub: Harvard Business Review Press
Contact: Moderna V. Pfizer, Contact

Ed: Anne Marie Knott. **Price:** $8.95. **Description:** Research quotient (RQ) is a new measure for determining research and development investment productivity. The formula utilizes classic regression analysis of expenditures and revenues and yields productivity levels for operations, employees, and R&D. **Availability:** Online; PDF.

32050 ■ *"Trucker Jobs Are Plentiful and Safe . . . but for How Long?" in American Trucker (November 15, 2019)*
URL(s): www.trucker.com/equipment/trucker-jobs-are-plentiful-and-safe-how-long

Ed: Josh Fisher. **Released:** November 15, 2019. **Description:** Automation has been making its way across several industries, but is it going to impact the trucking industry? Technology development is increasing, but it doesn't look like fully automated trucks will be taking over the roads any time soon, and if that does happen, truckers will still be needed in the vehicle. **Availability:** Online.

32051 ■ *"Trust Management of Services in Cloud Environments: Obstacles and Solutions" in ACM Computing Surveys (Vol. 46, Spring 2014, No. 1, pp. 12)*
Pub: Association for Computing Machinery - University of Wyoming
Contact: Ed Seidel, President
E-mail: uwpres@uwyo.edu

Description: Trust management is one of the most challenging issues in the emerging cloud computing area. Over the past few years, many studies have proposed different techniques to address trust management issues. However, despite these past efforts, several trust management issues such as identification, privacy, personalization, integration, security, and scalability have been mostly neglected and need to be addressed before cloud computing can be fully embraced. An overview of the cloud service models and a survey of the main techniques and research prototypes that efficiently support trust management services in cloud environments is presented. Open research issues for trust management in cloud environments is also examined. **Availability:** PDF; Online.

32052 ■ "UA, BP Test Unmanned Aircraft" in Alaska Business Monthly (Vol. 27, October 2011, No. 10, pp. 8)

Pub: Alaska Business Publishing Company Inc.

Contact: Charles Bell, Vice President, Sales and Marketing

E-mail: cbell@akbizmag.com

Ed: Nancy Pounds. Description: University of Alaska Fairbanks Geophysical Institute and BP Exploration Alaska tested the oil-spill capabilities of an unmanned aircraft. The aircraft will be used to gather 3-D ariel data to aid in oil-spill cleanup. Availability: Online.

32053 ■ "U.S. Competitiveness and the Chinese Challenge" in Harvard Business Review (Vol. 90, March 2012, No. 3, pp. 40)

Pub: Harvard Business Review Press

Contact: Moderna V. Pfizer, Contact

Ed: Xu Xiaonian. Price: $6, hardcover. Description: Although China's shift from cntral planningto market-oriented policies has boosted innovation, intellectual property rights and original research are still insufficiently valued. The U.S. has the edge on China in this respect; it remains for the U.S. to restore confidence in its innovation and creativity. Availability: PDF; Online.

32054 ■ U.S. Sourcebook of R & D Spenders

Pub: Schonfeld and Associates Inc.

Contact: Carol Greenhut, President

URL(s): saibooks.com/research-a-development

Released: Annual Price: $395, for book; $495, for book and database. Description: Covers 5,700 public companies in the U.S. That spend money on research and development. Entries include: Company name, address, phone, names and titles of key personnel, financial data, research and development budgets, fiscal year close, Standard Industrial Classification (SIC) code. Arrangement: Geographical by state, then classified by ZIP code. Indexes: Company name. Availability: Print; Online.

32055 ■ "Unveiling the Secrets Behind Hispanic Business' 100 Fastest-Growing Companies" in Hispanic Business (Vol. 30, July-August 2008, No. 7-8, pp. 22)

Ed: Michael Bowker. Description: CEO's of the five fastest growing Hispanic-owned companies discuss the success of their companies; most of them attribute their success to proper investment and diversification, effective innovations and seeing growth opportunities where others see roadblocks. Availability: Online.

32056 ■ "USM Focuses on Turning Science Into New Companies, Cash" in Boston Business Journal (Vol. 29, July 1, 2011, No. 8, pp. 1)

Pub: Boston Business Journal

Contact: Carolyn M. Jones, President

E-mail: cmjones@bizjournals.com

Ed: Alexander Jackson. Description: University System of Maryland gears up to push for its plan for commercializing its scientific discoveries which by 2020 could create 325 companies and double the $1.4 billion the system's eleven schools garner in yearly research grants. It is talking with University of Utah and University Maryland, Baltimore to explore ways to make this plan a reality. Availability: Print; Online.

32057 ■ Values and Opportunities in Social Entrepreneurship

Pub: Palgrave Macmillan

Released: 2010. Price: $89, hardcover; $120, hardcover; $64.99, e-book; $84.99, Softcover. Description: Social entrepreneurship has grown as a research field. This book discusses social entrepreneurship as well as the identification and exploitation of social venturing opportunities. Availability: E-book; Print; PDF; Electronic publishing.

32058 ■ "Variations in R&D Investments of Family and Nonfamily Firms: Behavioral Agency and Myopic Loss Aversion Perspectives" in Academy of Management Journal (Vol. 55, August 1, 2012, No. 4, pp. 976)

Pub: Academy of Management

Contact: Sharon Alvarez, President

Ed: James J. Chrisman, Pankaj C. Patel. Description: The variability in the behavior of family firms is analyzed using the behavioral agency model and the myopic loss aversion framework. Results show that family firms tend to invest less in research and development than nonfamily businesses but the variability of their investments is influenced by family goals and economic goals of the firm. Availability: Electronic publishing; Download; PDF; Online.

32059 ■ "VC Round Will Pay for 'Sham' Surgery Trial" in Business Journal (Vol. 31, April 11, 2014, No. 46, pp. 6)

Pub: American City Business Journals, Inc.

Contact: Mike Olivieri, Executive Vice President

Released: April 11, 2014. Price: $4, Introductory 4-week offer(Digital & Print). Description: Holaira Inc. is preparing for a clinical trial of its technology for treating lung disease after raising $42 million in venture capital. The clinical trial will take place in Europe and will involve about 170 patients. Availability: Print; Online.

32060 ■ "Venture: Nonprofit Aims to Spur New Companies" in South Florida Business Journal (Vol. 34, April 18, 2014, No. 39, pp. 8)

Pub: American City Business Journals, Inc.

Contact: Mike Olivieri, Executive Vice President

Released: Weekly. Price: $8, Introductory 4-week offer(Digital & Print). Description: The Scripps Research Institute has created the Scripps Advance group with an aim to turn early stage research from its scientists in Jupiter, Florida and La Jolla, California into companies and to obtain venture capital funding to support clinical trials. Johnson and Johnson Innovation has become its first collaborator. The terms of the collaboration are also presented. Availability: Print; Online.

32061 ■ "Voices: Breaking the Corruption Habit" in Business Strategy Review (Vol. 21, Autumn 2010, No. 3, pp. 67)

Ed: David De Cremer. Released: September 22, 2010. Description: In times of crisis, it seems natural that people will work together for the common good. David De Cremer cautions that, on the contrary, both economic and social research prove otherwise. He proposes steps for organizations to take to prevent corrupt behaviors. Availability: Print; Electronic publishing; PDF; Online.

32062 ■ "Who Hangs Out Where?" in Harvard Business Review (Vol. 90, July-August 2012, No. 7-8, pp. 34)

Pub: Harvard Business Review Press

Contact: Moderna V. Pfizer, Contact

Price: $6, PDF. Description: A chart breaks down participation in social media gathering places by gender, age group, educational level, and household income. Availability: PDF; Online.

32063 ■ "Why Life Science Needs Its Own Silicon Valley: Human Genomics Won't Reach Its Full Potential Until It Has a Sizable Industry Cluster" in Harvard Business Review (Vol. 90, July-August 2012, No. 7-8, pp. 25)

Pub: Harvard Business Review Press

Contact: Moderna V. Pfizer, Contact

Ed: Fariborz Ghadar, John Sviokla, Dietrich A. Stephan. Price: $6, PDF and hardcover black and white. Description: The creation of an industry cluster will be key to advancing human genomics research. High degrees of specialization via multiple contributors will be needed to generate significant innovations; an accessible, coherent data source will also be necessary. Availability: Print; PDF; Online.

32064 ■ "Why Motivating People Doesn't Work...and What Does: The New Science of Leading, Energizing, and Engaging"

Released: September 30, 2014. Price: $20.95, Nonmembers, PDF e-book; $18.86, Members, electronic publishing; $20.95, Nonmembers, paperback; $18.86, Members, paperback; $24.95, Nonmembers, hardcover; $22.46, Members, hardcover; $20.95, Nonmembers, electronic publishing; $14.67, Members, electronic publishing; $18.95, PDF e-book; $14.67, Members, PDF e-book. Description: Leadership researcher, consultant, and business coach, Susan Fowler, shares the latest research on the nature of human motivation to present a tested model and course of action to help Human Resource leaders and managers guide workers towards motivation that will not only increase productivity and engagement but will provide employees with a sense of purpose and fulfillment. Availability: E-book; Print; PDF; Electronic publishing.

32065 ■ "Winners & Losers" in Canadian Business (Vol. 85, July 16, 2012, No. 11-12, pp. 22)

Description: Canadian Pacific Railway's 4,800 locomotive engineers and conductors walked out in protest of the proposed work rules and pension cuts. Shareholders rejected a $25-million bonus and retention payout to Astral Media chief executive officer Ian Greenburg. The Dragon spacecraft of Space Exploration Technologies delivered supplies and experiments to the International Space Station. Availability: Print.

32066 ■ "You'll Golf Better If You Think Tiger Has Used Your Clubs" in Harvard Business Review (Vol. 90, July-August 2012, No. 7-8, pp. 32)

Pub: Harvard Business Review Press

Contact: Moderna V. Pfizer, Contact

Ed: Sally Linkenauger. Description: Golfers who were told that a professional had used the clubs they were given to use performed better than those who were told nothing about the clubs they were given. They perceived the hole to be 9 percent bigger in diamter than the control group, and were able to sink 32 percent more putts than did the control group.

CONSULTANTS

32067 ■ Medical Imaging Consultants Inc. (MIC)

1037 US Hwy. 46, Ste. G-2
Clifton, NJ 07013-2445
Ph: (973)574 8000
Free: 800-589-5685
Fax: (973)574-8001
Co. E-mail: info@micinfo.com
URL: http://www.micinfo.com
Contact: Philip A. Femano, President

Description: Provider of professional support services in radiology management and comprehensive continuing education programs for radiologic technologists such as professional educators, life scientists, biomedical engineers, and much more. Scope: Provider of professional support services in radiology management and comprehensive continuing education programs for radiologic technologists such as professional educators, life scientists, biomedical engineers, and much more. Founded: 1991. Training: Sectional Anatomy and Imaging Strategies; CT Cross-Trainer; CT Registry Review Program; MR Cross Trainer; MRI Registry Review Program; Digital Mammography Essentials for Technologists; Radiology Trends for Technologists.

32068 ■ Miller, Leiby & Associates P.C.

32 Broadway, 13th Fl.
New York, NY 10004
Ph: (212)227-4200
Fax: (212)504-8369
URL: http://www.millerleiby.com
Contact: Doron Leiby, Partner
Facebook: www.facebook.com/MillerLeibyAssocia tesPc

Linkedin: www.linkedin.com/company/1269719
Instagram: www.instagram.com/millerleiby
Description: Firm is engaged in legal counsel for individuals and businesses. **Scope:** Firm is engaged in legal counsel for individuals and businesses. **Training:** Objectives and standards/recruiting for boards of directors.

FRANCHISES AND BUSINESS OPPORTUNITIES

32069 ■ Supperworks
481 N Service Rd. W, Ste. A24
Oakville, ON, Canada L6M 2V6
Free: 833-278-7737
Co. E-mail: info@supperworks.com
Facebook: www.facebook.com/supperworks
X (Twitter): twitter.com/supperworks
Description: Operator of meal-preparation store. **Founded:** 2005. **Equity Capital Needed:** $250,000-$300,000. **Royalty Fee:** 0.05. **Training:** Includes 3 weeks training.

PUBLICATIONS

32070 ■ *Journal of African Research in Business & Technology (JARBT)*
630 Freedom Business Ctr. Dr., 3rd Fl.
King of Prussia, PA 19406

Fax: (215)867-9992
Co. E-mail: contact@ibimapublishing.com
URL: http://www.ibimapublishing.com
URL(s): ibimapublishing.com/journals/journal-of-african-research-in-business-technology
Released: Latest Edition: Volume 2022. **Description:** Peer-reviewed journal covering business and technology research in Africa. **Availability:** Print; PDF; Online.

LIBRARIES

32071 ■ Allen County Public Library - Business and Technology Department
900 Library Plz.
Fort Wayne, IN 46802
Ph: (260)421-1215
URL: http://acpl.lib.in.us/using-the-library/locations-and-hours
Description: Public library of Allen county. **Scope:** Genealogy. **Services:** Interlibrary loan; copying; Wi-Fi. **Founded:** 1895. **Holdings:** Books; DVDs; Blu-rays; CDs; magazines.

RESEARCH CENTERS

32072 ■ Midwest Research Institute (MRI) - Patterson Library
425 Dr. Martin Luther King, Jr Blvd.
Kansas City, MO 64110

Co. E-mail: info@mriglobal.org
URL: http://www.mriglobal.org
Contact: Martin Nevshemal, Chief Financial Officer
Facebook: www.facebook.com/MRIGlobalResearch
Linkedin: www.linkedin.com/company/mriglobal
X (Twitter): x.com/mriglobal_news
Description: Nonprofit research institute offers scientific services in the areas of national defense, health sciences, agriculture and food safety, engineering, energy, and infrastructure. **Scope:** Nonprofit research institute offers scientific services in the areas of national defense, health sciences, agriculture and food safety, engineering, energy, and infrastructure. **Services:** Interlibrary loan; copying; center open to the public for reference use only and by appointment. **Founded:** 1944. **Holdings:** 22,000 volumes. **Subscriptions:** 100 journals and other serials. **Publications:** *Innovations*; *Midwest Research Institute Annual Report* (Annual).

START-UP INFORMATION

32073 ■ *EBay Income: How ANYONE of Any Age, Location, and/or Background Can Build a Highly Profitable Online Business with eBay*
Pub: Atlantic Publishing Co.
Contact: Dr. Heather L. Johnson, Contact
Description: A complete overview of eBay is given and guides any small company through the entire process of creating the auction and auction strategies, photography, writing copy, text and formatting, multiple sales, programming tricks, PayPal, accounting, creating marketing, merchandising, managing email lists, advertising plans, taxes and sales tax, best time to list items and for how long, sniping programs, international customers, opening a storefront, electronic commerce, buy-it now pricing, keywords, Google marketing and eBay secrets.

32074 ■ *How to Open and Operate a Financially Successful Bookstore on Amazon and Other Web Sites: With Companion CD-ROM*
Pub: Atlantic Publishing Co.
Contact: Dr. Heather L. Johnson, Contact
Description: This book was written for every used book aficionado and bookstore owner who currently wants to take advantage of the massive collection of online resources available to start and run your own online bookstore business.

32075 ■ *"How to Open and Operate a Financially Successful Florist and Floral Business Online and Off"*
Pub: Atlantic Publishing Co.
Contact: Dr. Heather L. Johnson, Contact
Released: Revised second edition. **Description:** A concise and easy to follow guide for opening a retail florist or floral business online or a traditional brick and mortar store. Knowledge shared includes: cost control systems, retail math and competitive pricing, legal concerns, tax reporting requirements and reporting, profit and loss statements, management skills, sales advertising, and marketing techniques, customer service, direct sales, internal marketing ideas, and more. **Availability:** CD-ROM; Print; Online.

32076 ■ *How to Start a Home-Based Online Retail Business*
Ed: Jeremy Shepherd. **Released:** November 08, 2011. **Price:** paperback, softback. **Description:** Information for starting an online retail, home-based business is shared. **Availability:** E-book; Print.

32077 ■ *How to Use the Internet to Advertise, Promote, and Market Your Business or Web Site: With Little or No Money*
Pub: Atlantic Publishing Co.
Contact: Dr. Heather L. Johnson, Contact
Ed: Bruce C. Brown. **Released:** Revised third edition. **Description:** Information is given to help build, promote, and make money from your Website or brick and mortar store using the Internet, with minimal costs.

32078 ■ *"Olive Oil Store and Tap Room To Open In Downtown Boise"* in Idaho Business Review (May 15, 2014)
Pub: BridgeTower Media
Contact: Adam Reinebach, President
Description: Profile of the new olive oil store and tap room called Olivin, which is opening a retail store in Boise, Idaho. The shop will offer various premium olive oils and specialty vinegars. The woman-owned store plans to employ one worker in the startup phase.

32079 ■ *Scrapbooking for Profit: Cashing in on Retail, Home-Based and Internet Opportunities*
Pub: Allworth Press
Contact: Tad Crawford, Founder
Ed: Rebecca Pittman. **Released:** June 01, 2005. **Price:** $16.95, paperback; $19.99, Ebook; $19.95, Paperback. **Description:** Eleven strategies for starting a scrapbooking business, including brick-and-mortar stores, home-based businesses, and online retail and wholesale outlets. **Availability:** E-book; Print.

ASSOCIATIONS AND OTHER ORGANIZATIONS

32080 ■ **International Council of Shopping Centers (ICSC)**
1251 Ave. of the Americas, 45th Fl.
New York, NY 10020-1104
Ph: (646)728-3800
Free: 844-728-4272
Fax: (732)694-1690
Co. E-mail: membership@icsc.com
URL: http://www.icsc.com
Contact: Tom McGee, President
E-mail: tmcgee@icsc.org
Facebook: www.facebook.com/MyICSC
Linkedin: www.linkedin.com/company/icsc
X (Twitter): x.com/icsc
Description: Promotes professional standards of performance in the development, construction, financing, leasing, management, and operation of shopping centers throughout the world. **Founded:** 1957. **Publications:** *Leasing Opportunities*; *International Outlet Journal (IOJ)* (5/year); *Shopping Centers Today (SCT)* (Monthly); *Directory of Products and Services* (Annual); *International Council of Shopping Centers--Membership Directory*; *Value Retail News (VRN)* (10/year). **Awards:** European Shopping Centre Awards (Annual); U.S. Design and Development Awards (Annual); MAXI Awards (Annual). **Geographic Preference:** National.

32081 ■ **Michigan Retailers Association (MRA)**
603 S Washington Ave.
Lansing, MI 48933
Ph: (517)372-5656
Free: 800-366-3699
Fax: (517)372-1303
Co. E-mail: mra@retailers.com
URL: http://www.retailers.com
Contact: Amy Jolley, Director, Human Resources
E-mail: ajolley@retailers.com
Facebook: www.facebook.com/MichiganRetailers
X (Twitter): x.com/michretail
Description: Retail stores and outlets. Promotes the interests of members through legislative and educational activities. **Founded:** 1940. **Publications:** *Michigan Retailer* (Bimonthly). **Geographic Preference:** State.

32082 ■ **National Retail Federation (NRF) - Retail Library**
1101 New York Ave. NW, Ste. 1200
Washington, DC 20005
Ph: (202)783-7971
Free: 800-673-4692
Fax: (202)737-2849
Co. E-mail: contact@nrf.com
URL: http://www.nrf.com
Contact: Matthew R. Shay, President
Facebook: www.facebook.com/NationalRetailFederation
Linkedin: www.linkedin.com/company/national-retail-federation
X (Twitter): x.com/NRFnews
Instagram: www.instagram.com/nrf
YouTube: www.youtube.com/user/NRFInternet
Description: Represents state retail associations, several dozen national retail associations, as well as large and small corporate members representing the breadth and diversity of the retail industry's establishment and employees. Conducts informational and educational conferences related to all phases of retailing including financial planning and cash management, taxation, economic forecasting, expense planning. **Scope:** Careers; economy; loss prevention; mobile; retail trends; store operations; chain restaurants; global; marketing; online; small business; supply chain; consumer trends; human resources; merchandising; public policy; social responsibility; technology. **Founded:** 1911. **Holdings:** Figures Not Available. **Publications:** *Stores*; *NRF Foundation Focus* (Quarterly); *NRF Update* (Monthly); *STORES: The Magazine of NRF* (9/year); *Washington Retail Report* (Weekly); *STORES--Top 100 Retailers Issue* (Annual); *Software SourceBook*. **Educational Activities:** Human Resources Executives Summit; NRF Retail's Big Show (Annual); NRF PROTECT – Retail's Loss Prevention & Cyber Risk Event (Annual); National Retail Federation Annual Convention & Expo (Annual). **Awards:** NRF Gold Medal Award (Annual); NRF International Retailer of the Year (Annual); J. Thomas Weyant Award (Annual); NRF Gold Medal in Retailing (Annual). **Geographic Preference:** National.

32083 ■ **Planning and Visual Education Partnership (PAVE)**
8570 Stirling Rd., Ste. 102-227
Hollywood, FL 33024
Ph: (954)551-9144
Co. E-mail: info@paveglobal.org

URL: http://www.paveglobal.org
Contact: Jerry Fox, President
Facebook: www.facebook.com/PAVEorg
Linkedin: www.linkedin.com/company/paveglobal
X (Twitter): x.com/PAVEorg
Instagram: www.instagram.com/pave_connects

Description: Retail executives, visual merchandisers, store planners, architects. Provides training and networking opportunities. Holds annual design competition; donates proceeds of shows toward financial aid for students. **Founded:** 1992. **Educational Activities:** PAVE Gala (Annual). **Awards:** PAVE Student Design Competition (Annual). **Geographic Preference:** National.

32084 ■ Retail Industry Leaders Association (RILA)
99 M St. SE, Ste. 700
Washington, DC 20003
Ph: (202)869-0200
URL: http://www.rila.org
Contact: Brian Dodge, President
E-mail: brian.dodge@rila.org
Linkedin: www.linkedin.com/company/retail-industry
-leaders-association-rila-
X (Twitter): x.com/RILAtweets
Instagram: www.instagram.com/rila_org

Description: Mass discount retailing chains and suppliers to the mass retail industry. Aims to conduct research and educational programs on every phase of mass retailing. Conducts studies on industry practices and procedures and generates information on all areas of the business. Maintains public affairs program for liaison with government at the state and federal levels. **Founded:** 1969. **Publications:** *RILA Report: Asset Protection* (Bimonthly); *RILA Report: Human Resources*; *RILA Report: IT Community* (Quarterly); *RILA Report: Supply Chain* (Bimonthly); *IMRA Membership Directory and Exposition Guide* (Annual). **Educational Activities:** Retail Asset Protection Conference (Annual). **Geographic Preference:** National; Local.

INCUBATORS/RESEARCH AND TECHNOLOGY PARKS

32085 ■ Plug and Play - Retail Innovation Platform
440 N Wolfe Rd.
Sunnyvale, CA 94085
URL: http://www.plugandplaytechcenter.com/retail
-innovation

Description: An accelerator for startups in the retail industry. Provides support with venture and angel partners, mentorship, a data center, office space, and networking opportunities. The program focuses on e-commerce, in store experiences, supply chain and logistics, process optimization, customer engagement and analysis, payments, sustainability, and hyper-personalization.

32086 ■ XRC Ventures
228 Pk. Ave., S
New York, NY 10003
URL: http://xrcventures.com
Contact: Sam Wils, Director
E-mail: sam@xrclabs.com
Linkedin: www.linkedin.com/company/xrcventures
Instagram: www.instagram.com/xrcventures

Description: An innovation accelerator that provides workspace, access to capital, mentoring, and operational support to emerging companies in the retail and consumer goods industries. **Founded:** 2015.

EDUCATIONAL PROGRAMS

32087 ■ Women Owned in Retail
URL(s): www.wbenc.org/programs/women-owned-in
-retail

Frequency: Irregular. **Description:** Education and outreach for retail-focused women-owned businesses. **Principal Exhibits:** Education and outreach for retail-focused women-owned businesses.

REFERENCE WORKS

32088 ■ *"Three Ways Proposed New $300M-$400M Megamall, Hotel May Change I-Drive"* in Orlando Business Journal (Vol. 30, May 9, 2014, No. 46, pp. 9)
Pub: American City Business Journals, Inc.
Contact: Mike Olivieri, Executive Vice President

Released: Weekly. **Price:** $8, introductory 4-week offer(Digital only). **Description:** A number of ways in which the new 31-story megamall with hotel may transform the North I-Drive corridor in Orlando, Florida are presented. iSquare Mall & Hotel Development LLC applied for approval to construct the upscale, multistory retail mall with 1,253 hotel rooms in two towers. **Availability:** Print; Online.

32089 ■ *"The 12 Best POS Systems for Small Businesses: Our Top Picks for 2023"* in Business News Daily (February 24, 2023)
URL(s): www.businessnewsdaily.com/2955-best-pos
-systems.html
Ed: Jamie Johnson. **Released:** February 24, 2023. **Description:** The best Point-of-Sale systems are reviewed. **Availability:** Online.

32090 ■ *"113D Filings: Investors Report to the SEC"* in Barron's (Vol. 88, March 24, 2008, No. 12, pp. M13)
Pub: Dow Jones & Company Inc.
Contact: Almar Latour, Chief Executive Officer

Released: April 02, 2016. **Description:** HealthCor Management called as problematic the plan of Magellan Health Services to use its high cash balances for acquisitions. Carlson Capital discussed with Energy Partners possible changes in the latter's board. Investor Carl Icahn suggested that Enzon Pharmaceuticals consider selling itself or divest some of its assets. **Availability:** Print; Online.

32091 ■ *"Add Aquatics to Boost Business"* in Pet Product News (Vol. 64, December 2010, No. 12, pp. 20)
Ed: David Lass. **Description:** Pet stores are encouraged to add aquatics departments to increase profitability through repeat sales. This goal can be realized by sourcing, displaying, and maintaining high quality live fish. Other tips regarding the challenges associated with setting up an aquatics department are presented. **Availability:** Online.

32092 ■ *"Ambitious Horse Center Is In the Works for Southeastern Idaho"* in Idaho Business Review (August 25, 2014)
Pub: BridgeTower Media
Contact: Adam Reinebach, President

Price: $99, Digital & Mobile Only(1 Year); $11.99, Print, Digital & Mobile(1 Month); $149, Print, Digital & Mobile(1 Year); $99, Digital & Mobile Only(For 1 Year); $11.99, Print, Digital & Mobile (For 1 Month Intro Rate); $149, Print, Digital & Mobile (For 1 Year). **Description:** Ernest Bleinberger is planning to develop a 167-acre mixed-use project called Horse Station and will be located in Cache Valley, Idaho. Horse Station will include stables for about 250 horses and an arena, along with medical facilities, a hotel, retail shopping center, and a farmers market. **Availability:** Print; Online.

32093 ■ *"Anderson Pitches Liberty Towne Place"* in Business Courier (Vol. 27, June 18, 2010, No. 7, pp. 1)
Pub: Business Courier

Ed: Dan Monk. **Description:** Jeffrey R. Anderson Real Estate Inc.'s plan for a retail center in Butler County, Ohio could have three department stores in the 1.1 million-square-foot property. An outdoor sports retailer is also part of the plans. **Availability:** Print; Online.

32094 ■ *"Aquatic Medications Engender Good Health"* in Pet Product News (Vol. 64, November 2010, No. 11, pp. 47)
Ed: Madelaine Heleine. **Description:** Pet supply manufacturers and retailers have been exerting consumer education and preparedness efforts to help

aquarium hobbyists in tackling ornamental fish disease problems. Aquarium hobbyists have been also assisted in choosing products that facilitate aquarium maintenance before disease attacks their pet fish. **Availability:** Online.

32095 ■ *"Army Surplus Store Rebuilding Again"* in Spokesman-Review (November 17, 2010)
Pub: Spokesman Review
Contact: Kristi Burns, Director
E-mail: kristib@spokesman.com
Ed: Chelsea Bannach. **Description:** Retail business owner, David Arnold Sr., is rebuilding his Army Surplus store in Spokane, Washington after a truck crashed into the building. **Availability:** Print; Online.

32096 ■ *"Attention, Shoppers Take a Deep Breath: Why It Pays to Help Customers Relax"* in Inc. (Vol. 33, November 2011, No. 9, pp. 26)
Pub: Mansueto Ventures L.L.C.
Contact: Stephanie Mehta, Chief Executive Officer
Ed: J.J. McCorvey. **Released:** November 01, 2011. **Description:** According to a current study, along with festive music and decorations for holiday shoppers, some merchants are considering back messages and pedicures to keep customers happy. **Availability:** Online.

32097 ■ *"Austin Group-Buying Site Hones In on Hispanics"* in Austin Business Journal (Vol. 31, July 1, 2011, No. 17, pp. 1)
Pub: Austin Business Journal
Contact: Rachel McGrath, Director
E-mail: rmcgrath@bizjournals.com
Ed: Vicky Garza. **Description:** Descuentl Libre is a new group-buying site from Austin, Texas that targets the Hispanic market, offering discounts of practical items and family-friendly activities. The Hispanic market constitutes 17 percent of the U.S. population and spends $23 billion yearly online. **Availability:** Online.

32098 ■ *"AutoZone Revs Up Sales With Focus on Commercial Market"* in Memphis Business Journal (Vol. 35, January 24, 2014, No. 42, pp. 4)
Pub: American City Business Journals, Inc.
Contact: Mike Olivieri, Executive Vice President
Released: Weekly. **Price:** $4, introductory 4-week offer(Digital & Print). **Description:** Memphis, Tennessee-based automotive parts retailer AutoZone Inc. is focusing its growth on the commercial market after successfully dominating the retail division. The retailer is taking advantage of its strong supply chain to effectively deliver parts to its customers. **Availability:** Print; Online.

32099 ■ *"Ballpark Sales Tax Extension Could Fund New Arena"* in Milwaukee Business Journal (Vol. 27, January 29, 2010, No. 18, pp. A1)
Pub: The Business Journal
Contact: Heather Ladage, President
E-mail: hladage@bizjournals.com
Ed: Mark Kass. **Description:** Milwaukee, Wisconsin-area business executives believe the extension of the Miller Park 0.1 percent sales tax could help fund a new basketball arena to replace the 21-year-old Bradley Center in downtown Milwaukee. However, any sales tax expansion that includes the new basketball arena would need approval by Wisconsin's legislature. **Availability:** Print; Online.

32100 ■ *"Baltimore Shopping Centers Go On the Block as Sellers See Demand"* in Baltimore Business Journal (Vol. 29, September 2, 2011, No. 17, pp. 1)
Pub: Boston Business Journal
Contact: Carolyn M. Jones, President
E-mail: cmjones@bizjournals.com
Ed: Daniel J. Sernovitz. **Description:** Maryland-based investors have been choosing to put their money in the supermarket business. Retail property sales have increased during the second quarter of 2011. **Availability:** Online.

32101 ■ "Bangles, BMWs Elbow Out Delis and Discount Shops" in Crain's New York Business (Vol. 24, January 13, 2008, No. 2, pp. 35)

Pub: Crain Communications, Inc.

Contact: Jessica Botos, Manager, Marketing

E-mail: jessica.botos@crainsnewyork.com

Ed: Wendy Davis. **Description:** Lured by a growing number of affluent residents and high-earning professionals, a number of upscale retailers have opened locations downtown which is driving up rents and forcing out longtime independent merchants.

32102 ■ "Banks, Retailers Squabble Over Fees" in Baltimore Business Journal (Vol. 28, June 18, 2010, No. 6, pp. 1)

Pub: Baltimore Business Journal

Contact: Rhonda Pringle, President

E-mail: rpringle@bizjournals.com

Ed: Gary Haber. **Description:** How an amendment to the financial regulatory reform bill would affect the bankers' and retailers' conflict over interchange fees is discussed. Interchange fees are paid for by retailers every time consumers make purchases through debit cards. Industry estimates indicate that approximately $50 million in such fees are paid by retailers. **Availability:** Print; Online.

32103 ■ "Bass Pro Shops Plans Megastore for Rocklin" in Sacramento Business Journal (Vol. 51, February 14, 2014, No. 51, pp. 4)

Pub: American City Business Journals, Inc.

Contact: Mike Olivieri, Executive Vice President

Description: Bass Pro Shops is set to open its 120,000-square-foot Outdoor World store in Rocklin, California in 2015. The move will allow the Missouri-based outdoor retailer to bring its low prices and friendly, expert service to the sportsmen and women of the area. **Availability:** Online.

32104 ■ "Better Than New Runs on Tried-and-True Model" in Bellingham Business Journal (Vol. February 2010, pp. 16)

Pub: Sound Publishing Inc.

Contact: Josh O'Connor, President

Ed: Ashley Mitchell. **Description:** Profile of family owned Better Than New clothing store that sells overstock items from department stores and clothing manufacturers. The stores location makes it easy to miss and its only advertising is a large sign posted outside. This is the sixth store owned by the couple, Keijeo and Sirba Halmekanqas.

32105 ■ The Big Payback: The History of the Business of Hip-Hop

Ed: Dan Charnas. **Released:** November 01, 2011. **Price:** $17, paperback; $13.99. **Description:** The complete history of hip-hop music is presented, by following the money and the relationship between artist and merchant. In its promise of economic security and creative control for black artist-entrepreneurs, it is the culmination of dreams of black nationalists and civil rights leaders. **Availability:** E-book; Print.

32106 ■ "Birdcage Optimization" in Pet Product News (Vol. 64, November 2010, No. 11, pp. 54)

Ed: Cheryl Reeves. **Description:** Manufacturers have been emphasizing size, security, quality construction, stylish design, and quick cleaning when guiding consumers on making birdcage options. Selecting a birdcage is gaining importance considering that cage purchases have become the highest expense associated with owning a bird. Other avian habitat trends are also examined. **Availability:** Online.

32107 ■ "Bob's Discount Furniture Moving into Harford County, Region" in Baltimore Business Journal (Vol. 27, January 22, 2010, No. 38, pp. 1)

Pub: Baltimore Business Journal

Contact: Rhonda Pringle, President

E-mail: rpringle@bizjournals.com

Ed: Daniel J. Sernovitz. **Description:** Manchester, Connecticut-based Bob's Discount Furniture signed a lease for 672,000 square feet of space in Harford County, Maryland. The site will become the discount furniture retailer's distribution center in mid-Atlantic US. As many as 200 jobs could be generated when the center opens. **Availability:** Print; Online.

32108 ■ "Bodovino Is a World Leader in Self-Service Wine Tasting" in Idaho Business Review (September 8, 2014)

Pub: BridgeTower Media

Contact: Adam Reinebach, President

Description: Bodovino's wine bar and retail shop offers self-service wine tasting for its customers. It is the largest outlet globally for the Italian wine dispenser manufacturer WineEmotion. Visitors to the shop can choose from 144 wines set up in the dispensing machines.

32109 ■ "Bond Hill Cinema Site To See New Life" in Business Courier (Vol. 27, October 29, 2010, No. 26, pp. 1)

Pub: Business Courier

Ed: Dan Monk. **Description:** Avondale, Ohio's Corinthian Baptist Church will redevelop the 30-acre former Showcase Cinema property to a mixed-use site that could feature a college, senior home, and retail. Corinthian Baptist, which is one of the largest African-American churches in the region, is also planning to relocate the church. **Availability:** Print; Online.

32110 ■ "Boom and Bust in the Book Biz" in Canadian Business (Vol. 83, August 17, 2010, No. 13-14, pp. 16)

Pub: Rogers Media Inc.

Contact: Neil Spivak, Chief Executive Officer

Ed: Jordan Timm. **Description:** Electronic book marketplace is booming with Amazon.com's e-book sales for the Kindle e-reader exceeding the hardcover sales. Kobo Inc. has registered early success with its Kobo e-reader and has partnered with Hong Kong telecom giant on an e-book store. **Availability:** Print; Online.

32111 ■ "Borrow Baby Couture Launch Rocks Fasion World - Provides Couture Fashion for Girls" in Benzinga.com (June 18, 2012)

Description: Borrow Baby Couture allows parents, family and friends to rent couture clothing by top fashion designers for girls ages 9 months to 4 years. The retailer has launched an online site. Purchases are wrapped in tissue arriving ready to wear and includes return shipping costs. **Availability:** Online.

32112 ■ "The Bottom Line" in Retail Merchandiser (Vol. 51, July-August 2011, No. 4, pp. 60)

Description: Hanky Panky believes that comfort and style don't have to be mutually exclusive when designing their line of intimate apparel for women. The lingerie retailer was launched in 1977. **Availability:** Print; PDF; Online.

32113 ■ "Buildings to Flank Broken Spoke: Legendary Country Dance Hall To Be Surrounded But Won't Be Touched" in Austin Business Journal (Vol. 32, April 13, 2012, No. 6, pp. 1)

Pub: American City Business Journals, Inc.

Contact: Mike Olivieri, Executive Vice President

Ed: Vicky Garza. **Description:** A $60 million mixed use development tentatively called 704 at the Spoke is being planned along South Lamar Boulevard in Austin, Texas. The plan includes 378 apartments and 20,000 square feet of restaurant and retail space. The project will have the historic Broken Spoke Dance Hall as its hub. **Availability:** Online.

32114 ■ "Business Builders: Tradeshow Attendance Incentives Add Up" in Pet Product News (Vol. 64, December 2010, No. 12, pp. 14)

Ed: Mark E. Battersby. **Description:** Pointers on how pet specialty retailers can claim business travel tax and income tax deductions for expenses paid or incurred in participation at tradeshows, conventions, and meetings are presented. Incentives in form of these deductions could allow pet specialty retailers to gain business benefits, aside from the education and enjoyment involved with the travel. **Availability:** Online.

32115 ■ "Cabela's Plans Outpost Strategy for Smaller Markets" in Pet Product News (Vol. 66, April 2012, No. 4, pp. 21)

Description: Sidney, Nebraska-based outdoor gear retailer Cabela's Inc. plans to launch its first Cabelas Outpost Store, a retail initiative aimed at markets with fewer than 250,000 people. The initial 40,000-square-foot Cabela's Outpost Store is scheduled for a fall 2012 opening in Union Gap, Washington. Online order kiosks are among the features of the new store. **Availability:** Print; Online.

32116 ■ "Cabi to Develop Major Retail Project" in South Florida Business Journal (Vol. 32, July 6, 2012, No. 50, pp. 1)

Pub: Baltimore Business Journal

Contact: Rhonda Pringle, President

E-mail: rpringle@bizjournals.com

Description: Aventura, Florida-based Cabi Developers has received a bankruptcy court approval to begin construction of a major retail project called Capital Brickell Place in the Brickell neighborhood. Mexican real estate developer GICSA will finance the project and Cabi has been talking with retailers like Costco, Targt and Trader Joe's as potential tenants. **Availability:** Print; Online.

32117 ■ "The Call of the City" in Puget Sound Business Journal (Vol. 35, September 5, 2014, No. 20, pp. 16)

Pub: American City Business Journals, Inc.

Contact: Mike Olivieri, Executive Vice President

Description: A number of large companies have moved their headquarters to Seattle, Washington. The area is known to be transit-accessible with mixed-use offices and retail space, making it a great site selection. Seattle also embraces innovations and inventions in area districts that bring a diverse workforce. **Availability:** Print; Online.

32118 ■ "Caribou Coffee Kick-Starts Spring Planting with New Grounds for Your Ground Program in Time for Earth Day" in Ecology, Environment and Conservation Business (May 3, 2014, pp. 5)

Pub: NewsRX LLC.

Contact: Kalani Rosell, Contact

Description: Caribou Coffee is providing customers and local gardening clubs in Minnesota free used espresso ground for their gardens. The Grounds for Your Grounds program allows customers to pick up five-pound recycled bags of used grounds from retail locations for use in their home garden or community garden. The firm is committed to supporting local gardens and gardening organizations with existing reusable resource-espresso grounds. **Availability:** Online.

32119 ■ "The CEO of TJX On How To Train First-Class Buyers" in Harvard Business Review (Vol. 92, May 2014, No. 5, pp. 45)

Pub: Harvard Business Press

Contact: Gabriela Allmi, Regional Manager

E-mail: gabriela.allmi@hbsp.harvard.edu

Released: 2014. **Price:** $8.95. **Description:** The CEO of clothing retailer TJX Companies Inc. emphasizes the importance of buyer training to ensure that store merchandise inventory optimizes consumer response. Buyers must be curious, knowledgeable about customers, and willing to take risks. **Availability:** Print; Online; PDF.

32120 ■ "The CEO of Williams-Sonoma on Blending Instinct with Analysis" in Harvard Business Review (Vol. 92, September 2014, No. 9, pp. 41)

Pub: Harvard Business Publishing

Contact: Diane Belcher, Managing Director

Price: $8.95. **Description:** At Williams-Sonoma Inc., analytics are used to provide customers with experiences that best match their preferences, based on browsing history and/or previous purchases. This data is also used to inform designers, vendors, and distributors of supply and demand patterns. **Availability:** Online; PDF.

32121 ■ *"Citadel EFT (CDFT) Contracts With New Search Engine Optimization (SEO) and Banner Ad Web Marketing Companies"* in Internet Wire (August 8, 2012)
Pub: Comtex News Network Inc.
Contact: Kan Devnani, President
Description: Citafel EFT Inc. provides credit card terminals, online, mail order and retail credit card processing services. The firm has contracted with two Web marketing companies to increase its awareness on the Internet. **Availability:** Print; Online.

32122 ■ *"City May Aid Pop-Up Stores Downtown"* in Austin Business Journal (Vol. 31, August 19, 2011, No. 24, pp. A1)
Pub: Austin Business Journal
Contact: Rachel McGrath, Director
E-mail: rmcgrath@bizjournals.com
Ed: Vicky Garza. **Description:** Temporary retail stores may soon become common in Austin as City Council has urged the city manager to look into the possibility of amending the city codes to permit businesses to temporarily fill the vacant spaces downtown. **Availability:** Print; Online.

32123 ■ *"Clicks Vs. Bricks"* in Birmingham Business Journal (Vol. 31, April 25, 2014, No. 17, pp. 4)
Pub: American City Business Journals, Inc.
Contact: Mike Olivieri, Executive Vice President
Released: May 22, 2018. **Description:** Birmingham, Alabama's retail industry has been evolving as investment to brick-and-mortar stores by mall and shopping center owners double. The hope is that the social shopping experience, economic recovery, and Fair Marketplace legislation for an online sales tax will make co-existence with Internet stores more viable. The survival and expansion of retail are discussed. **Availability:** Print; Online.

32124 ■ *"Coinstar, Inc. and Seattle's Best Coffee Sign Exclusive Agreement to Roll Out Thousands of the New Rubi Kiosks in Grocery, Drug and Mass Channels"* in Marketing Weekly News (June 23 2012, pp. 77)
Pub: PR Newswire Association LLC.
Description: Seattles' Best Coffee, a firm of Starbucks Corporation, has partnered with Coinstar Inc. to install coffee kiosks in grocery, drug and mass merchant retailers featuring Seattle's Best coffee drinks. Rubi kiosk is the third automated kiosk owned by Coinstar. Details of the deal are included.

32125 ■ *"Come Together: A Thematic Collection of Times Articles, Essays, Maps and More About Creating Community"* in Pet Product News (Vol. 64, December 2010, No. 12, pp. 28)
Ed: Lizett Bond. **Description:** Pet supply retailers have posted improved sales and improved customer service by bundling their offerings. Bundling pertains to grouping related items such as collars and leashes into a single unit for marketing purposes. Aside from providing convenience and enhanced product information to customers, bundling has facilitated more efficient purchases. **Availability:** Online.

32126 ■ *"Commercial Builders Take It on the Chin"* in Crain's Chicago Business (Vol. 31, April 28, 2008, No. 17, pp. 16)
Pub: Crain Communications Inc.
Contact: Barry Asin, President
Ed: Alby Gallun. **Description:** Although the health care development sector has seen growth, the rest of Chicago's local commercial building industry has seen steep declines in the first quarter of this year. According to McGraw-Hill Construction, Chicago-area

non-residential construction starts totaled $731 million in the quarter, a 60 percent drop from the year-earlier period. Volume in the retail, office and hotel markets fell by nearly 70 percent. **Availability:** Online.

32127 ■ *"ConsignPro Elevates Nature of Consignment Business, Encourages Designer Resale"* in Internet Wire (May 15, 2012)
Description: Forbes magazine recently highlighted an article on an upscale thrift store located in New York called Designer Resale. The shop features fashion-forward retail merchandies sold on consignment. These new boutique-type resale shops are growing in popularity across the country. **Availability:** Print; Online.

32128 ■ *Consumer Behavior*
Ed: Leon G. Schiffman, Joseph Wisenblit. **Released:** Fifth Edition. **Price:** $276.20, cloth; $112.99, adobe reader. **Description:** Consumer behavior is central to the planning, development and implementation of marketing strategies. **Availability:** Print; Online; PDF.

32129 ■ *"Convenience Store Expanding"* in Clovis News Journal (November 9, 2010)
Description: Allsup's convenience store on North Prince Street in Clovis, New Mexico will expand its facilities. The current building is being demolished to make way for the new construction.

32130 ■ *"Convenience Store Owners Will Request New Zoning Once More"* in Daily Republic (November 1, 2010)
Pub: McClatchy Tribune Information Services
Contact: Patrick J. Talamantes, President
Ed: Tom Lawrence. **Description:** Zoning change has been requested for a proposed convenience store in Mitchell, South Dakota. Details are included. **Availability:** Online.

32131 ■ *"Crowdsourcing their Way into One Big Mess"* in Brandweek (Vol. 51, October 25, 2010, No. 38, pp. 26)
Description: The Gap, was counting on crowdsourcing to provide feedback for its new logo, but it did not prove positive for the retailer. However, a massive outcry of negative opinion, via crowdsourcing, may not always equal valid, constructive criticism. **Availability:** Online.

32132 ■ *"Cyber Thanksgiving Online Shopping a Growing Tradition"* in Marketing Weekly News (December 12, 2009, pp. 137)
Pub: Investment Weekly News
Description: According to e-commerce analysts, Thanksgiving Day is becoming increasingly important to retailers in terms of online sales. Internet marketers are realizing that consumers are already searching for Black Friday sales and if they find deals on the products they are looking for, they are highly likely to make their purchase on Thanksgiving Day instead of waiting. **Availability:** Online.

32133 ■ *Department Stores and Shoe Retailer Directory*
Pub: Chain Store Guide
Contact: Kaitlyn Toner, Account Manager
URL(s): www.chainstoreguide.com/c-69-store-locations.aspxwww.csgis.com
Released: Annual **Price:** $495. **Description:** Covers 6,000 department store companies, 1,600 shoe store companies, jewelry store companies, 95 optical store companies, and 70 leather and luggage store companies in the United States and Canada, with annual sales of $160 billion. **Entries include:** Company name; physical and mailing addresses; phone and fax numbers, company e-mail and web addresses; listing type; total sales; industry sales; total selling square footage; store prototype sizes; total units; units by trade name; trading areas; projected openings and remodeling; self-distributing indicator; distribution center locations; resident buyers' name and location; leased departments area, name, and location; mail order catalog indicator; Internet order processing indicator; private label softlines, hardlines, and credit card indicators; furniture styles and price

lines; average number of checkouts; year founded; public company indicator; parent company name and location; subsidiaries' names and locations; regional and divisional office locations; key personnel with titles; store locations, with address, phone number, and manager name (department stores only); 3,000 personnel email addresses. **Arrangement:** Geographical. **Indexes:** Alphabetical, product lines, exclusions. **Availability:** Print.

32134 ■ *"Design Challenge Seeks to Expand Access"* in Philadelphia Business Journal (Vol. 33, April 25, 2014, No. 11, pp. 7)
Pub: American City Business Journals, Inc.
Contact: Mike Olivieri, Executive Vice President
Description: The Thomas Scattergood Behavioral Health Foundation sponsored the 2014 design challenge on making mental healthcare education, access and services available at retail clinics. The winner was the mental health screening tool, 'Wellness at Your Fingertips', submitted by the Philadelphia Department of Behavioral Health and Intellectual Disability Services in Pennsylvania. **Availability:** Online.

32135 ■ *"Designing Women? Apparel Apparatchic at Kmart"* in Barron's (Vol. 88, March 17, 2008, No. 11, pp. 16)
Pub: Dow Jones & Company Inc.
Contact: Almar Latour, Chief Executive Officer
Ed: Robin Goldwyn Blumenthal. **Description:** Kmart began a nationwide search for women to represent the company in a national advertising campaign. Contestants need to upload their photos to Kmart's website and winners will be chosen by a panel of celebrity judges. The contest aims to reverse preconceived negative notions about the store's quality and service. **Availability:** Online.

32136 ■ *"Developer Backs Out of Major Bastrop Project"* in Austin Business JournalInc. (Vol. 28, December 19, 2008, No. 40, pp. 1)
Description: Weingarten Realty Investors, a Houston, Texas-based real estate company, has backed out of its contract on more than 1 million square feet of retail space at the County Road 304 and State Highway 71 corner in Bastrop, Texas, according to landowner Tom Brundage. Analysts say that the Bastrop area is not ready for big retail projects. **Availability:** Print; Online.

32137 ■ *"The Devolution of Home-Electronics Stores"* in Philadelphia Business Journal (Vol. 28, June 8, 2012, No. 17, pp. 1)
Pub: Baltimore Business Journal
Contact: Rhonda Pringle, President
E-mail: rpringle@bizjournals.com
Description: Philadelphia, Pennsylvania-area consumer electronics stores have mirrored the national trend in which big-box retailers are taking a bigger share of the home-electronics market. However, smaller, locally-based chains are competing in terms of pricing transparency and custom electronics. **Availability:** Print; Online.

32138 ■ *"Dollar General Selects GSI Commerce to Launch Its eCommerce Business"* in Benzinga.com (October 29, 2011)
Pub: Benzinga.com
Contact: Jason Raznick, Founder
Description: Dollar General Corporation chose GSI Commerce, a leading provider of ecommerce and interactive marketing solutions, to launch its online initiative. GSI Commerce is an eBay Inc. company. **Availability:** Online.

32139 ■ *"Dollar Store Growth Presents New Challenge to Larger Mass Retailers"* in Pet Product News (Vol. 66, August 2012, No. 8, pp. 4)
Description: Dollar stores have been rising as a direct competitor to bigger mass-market retailers in the pet market. Aside from focusing on low prices, dollar stores' competitive strategy has been marked by smaller store size and convenience of edited as-

sortments. Other factors that have lured a growing consumer base to dollar stores are described. **Availability:** Online.

32140 ■ *"Dollar Tree Store to Open Mid-July in Shelby Mall" in La Crosse Tribune (June 20, 2010)*
Pub: La Crosse Tribune
Contact: Josh Delarosa, Contact
E-mail: josh.delarosa@lee.net
Ed: Steve Cahalan. **Description:** Dollar Tree Inc. plans to open a new store in the location formerly occupied by Family Dollar.

32141 ■ *"Environmental Working Group Names Whole Foods Market (R) Leading National Retailer for 'Green' Sunscreen" in Ecology, Environment & Conservation Business (June 14, 2014, pp. 5)*
Pub: NewsRX LLC.
Contact: Kalani Rosell, Contact
Description: Whole Foods Market has been named as the leading retailer selling the largest selection of 'green' rated sunscreen to shoppers. **Availability:** Online.

32142 ■ *"Essex Leases Space for Largest Retail Store" in Memphis Business Journal (Vol. 34, September 28, 2012, No. 24, pp. 1)*
Pub: Baltimore Business Journal
Contact: Rhonda Pringle, President
E-mail: rpringle@bizjournals.com
Description: Essex Technology Group Inc. will build its third Memphis, Tennessee-area store in DeSoto County. The company signed a five-year, 69,342-square-foot lease at Stateline Square in Southaven. The new facility, which could open by January 2013, is expected to hire 30-35 employees. **Availability:** Print; Online.

32143 ■ *"New Hotels, Offices Eyed Near SJC" in Silicon Valley/San Jose Business Journal (Vol. 30, June 8, 2012, No. 11, pp. 1)*
Pub: Baltimore Business Journal
Contact: Rhonda Pringle, President
E-mail: rpringle@bizjournals.com
Description: Developer Hunter/Storm LLC plans to break ground on the first phase of the Coleman Highline mixed-use project in San Jose, California by the first quarter of 2013 to take advantage of the growing mass transit and improved market conditions. The project consists of 1.5 million square feet of office space, two hotels and 50,000 square feet of retail space on Coleman Avenue.

32144 ■ *"Experts Strive to Educate on Proper Pet Diets" in Pet Product News (Vol. 64, November 2010, No. 11, pp. 40)*
Ed: Joan Hustace Walker. **Description:** Pet supply manufacturers have been bundling small mammal food and treats with educational sources to help retailers avoid customer misinformation. This action has been motivated by the customer's quest to seek proper nutritional advice for their small mammal pets. **Availability:** Online.

32145 ■ *"Facials for Fido? Retail: Kriser's Pet Store Grows With High-End Pet Products Market" in San Fernando Valley Business Journal (Vol. 17, February 20, 2012, No. 4, pp. 1)*
Description: Sherman Oaks all-natural pet food and supply retailer, Kriser's, is expanding with seven new stores. The company is known for its health options in pet food, tasty treats, and fancy toys by catering to a high-end clientele. They also offer upscale pet grooming services, including blueberry facials and de-shedding treatments. **Availability:** Online.

32146 ■ *"Family Dollar Reaches Preliminary Class Action Settlement" in Benzinga.com (September 12, 2012)*
Pub: Benzinga.com
Contact: Jason Raznick, Founder
Description: Family Dollar Stores Inc. has reached a preliminary settlement with New York store managers. The settlement provides 1,700 managers a

maximum payment of $14 million. A profile of the Family Dollar Stores company is also included. **Availability:** Print; Online.

32147 ■ *"Fifty Percent of Global Online Retail Visits Were to Amazon, eBay and Alibaba in June 2011" in Benzinga.com (October 29, 2011)*
Pub: Benzinga.com
Contact: Jason Raznick, Founder
Description: Current statistics and future forecasts through the year 2015 for Amazon, eBay and Alibaba are explored. **Availability:** Online.

32148 ■ *"Filling the Gap" in Canadian Business (Vol. 80, March 12, 2007, No. 6, pp. 62)*
Ed: Andrew Wahl. **Released:** October 09, 2016. **Description:** The chief executive officer of GAP, Bruce Poon Tip, shares his experience and efforts in the growth of the company to a leading position in Canada. **Availability:** Print; Online.

32149 ■ *"Fire Destroys Surplus Store, Sets Off Live Rounds Near Jacksonville NAS" in Florida Times-Union (December 5, 2010)*
Pub: Florida Times-Union
Ed: John Leacock. **Description:** Fire which caused numerous explosions at a military surplus store near Jacksonville Naval Air Station is under investigation. Heat and flames ignited lighter fluid and set off live rounds of ammunition sold in the store. **Availability:** Print; Online.

32150 ■ *"First Sustainability Standard for Household Portable and Floor Care Appliances Developed to Identify Environmentally Responsible Products" in Ecology, Environment & Conservation Business (September 13, 2014, pp. 39)*
Pub: NewsRX LLC.
Contact: Kalani Rosell, Contact
Description: the Association of Home Appliance Manufacturers (AHAM), CSA Group, and the UL Environment released the AHAM 7002-2014/CSA SPE-7002-14/UL 7002, Sustainability Standard for Household Portable and Floor Care Appliances. This is the first voluntary sustainability standards for these appliances and is the third in a unit of product sustainability standards under development by the group. These standards are intended for use by manufacturers, governments, retailers, and others to identify products conforming to these standards in six key areas: materials, manufacturing and operations, energy consumption during use, end-of-life, consumables, and innovation. **Availability:** Online.

32151 ■ *"Five Reasons Why the Gap Fell Out of Fashion" in Globe & Mail (January 27, 2007, pp. B4)*
Description: The five major market trends that have caused the decline of fashion clothing retailer Gap Inc.'s sales are discussed. The shift in brand, workplace fashion culture, competition, demographics, and consumer preferences have lead to the Gap's brand identity. **Availability:** Online.

32152 ■ *"Fledgling Brands May Take the Fall With Steve & Barry's" in Advertising Age (Vol. 79, July 7, 2008, No. 26, pp. 6)*
Pub: Crain Communications, Inc.
Contact: Jessica Botos, Manager, Marketing
E-mail: jessica.botos@crainsnewyork.com
Ed: Natalie Zmuda. **Description:** Steve & Barry's, a retailer that holds licensing deals with a number of designers and celebrities, may have to declare bankruptcy; this leaves the fate of the retailer's hundreds of licensing deals and exclusive celebrity lines in question. **Availability:** Online.

32153 ■ *"Food as Nature Intended" in Pet Product News (Vol. 64, November 2010, No. 11, pp. 30)*
Ed: Nikki Moustaki. **Description:** Dog owners have been extending their health-consciousness to their pets by seeking natural products that will address their pets' raw food diet. Retailers response to this trend are outlined. **Availability:** Online.

32154 ■ *"Forget Your Pants, Calvin Klein Wants Into Your Bedroom" in Globe & Mail (March 31, 2007, pp. B4)*
Ed: Barrie McKenna. **Description:** The plans of Phillips-Van Heusen Corp. to open more Calvin Klein stores for selling the new ranges of clothing, personal care products, luggage and mattresses are discussed. **Availability:** Online.

32155 ■ *"Fred's Launches New Concept" in Memphis Business Journal (Vol. 34, No. 21, September 07, 2012, pp. 1)*
Pub: Baltimore Business Journal
Contact: Rhonda Pringle, President
E-mail: rpringle@bizjournals.com
Description: Memphis, Tennessee-based Fred's Inc. has opened the Getwell Drug & Dollar, a new store concept that could allow the company to open in smaller markets. The store, which opened in Middleton, is focused primarily on its pharmacy located at the front of the store. **Availability:** Print; Online.

32156 ■ *"From Craft Biz To Wholesale Giant" in Women Entrepreneur (January 19, 2009)*
Description: Advice is given on how to turn a small craft business into a full-time venture; tips to help one transition from a part-time designer to a full-time wholesaler and brand are also included.

32157 ■ *"From New York to Park Avenue: Red Carpet Fashion at a Discount" in Orlando Business Journal (Vol. 30, February 14, 2014, No. 34, pp. 3)*
Pub: American City Business Journals, Inc.
Contact: Mike Olivieri, Executive Vice President
Released: Weekly. **Price:** $8, introductory 4-week offer(Digital & Print). **Description:** Red Carpet Couture & Gems is known for selling high-end discount business attire and accessories. Owner, Caralyce Buford decided to buy from sample sales in New York before opening the store in October 2013. Her retail store caters to women of all sizes. **Availability:** Print; Online.

32158 ■ *"'Frozen' Assets: Refrigeration Goes High Tech as Hussmann Invests $7 Million in Global Hub" in St. Louis Business Journal (Vol. 33, September 21, 2012, No. 4, pp. 1)*
Pub: Baltimore Business Journal
Contact: Rhonda Pringle, President
E-mail: rpringle@bizjournals.com
Description: Hussmann Corporation is spending $7 million to create a high-tech innovation and clients collaboration center that will be called Global Hub, a venue for grocery food retailers, industry trend setters and through leaders. The company is also focusing on tapping the potential of convenience marts and dollar-store retailers. **Availability:** Print.

32159 ■ *"Future Fuzzy at Former Pemco Plant" in Baltimore Business Journal (Vol. 32, July 25, 2014, No. 12, pp. 10)*
Pub: American City Business Journals, Inc.
Contact: Mike Olivieri, Executive Vice President
Released: Weekly. **Price:** $4, introductory 4-week offer(Digital only). **Description:** The abandoned Pemco Corporation site on Eastern Avenue in Southeast Baltimore faces an uncertain future as new owner, MCB Real Estate LLC, fails to specify its prospective development plans for the property. City Councilman, James B. Kraft, wants to restrict the amount of retail space to be built at the Pemco and might even delay filing legislation on the space until MCB provides more details for the 20-acre property. **Availability:** Print; Online.

32160 ■ *"Get On the Shelf: Selling Your Product In Retail Stores" in Black Enterprise (Vol. 44, February 2014, No. 6, pp. 18)*
Pub: Earl G. Graves Ltd.
Contact: Earl Graves, Jr., President
Description: Profile of Arsha and Charles Jones, Washington DC natives, who are selling their Capital City Mumbo Sauce to local retailers as well as big box retailers. The husband and wife team share tips for getting your product into retail establishments.

32161 ■ "Girls Will Gossip: Psst! Buzz About Target" in Barron's (Vol. 89, July 27, 2009, No. 30, pp. 15)
Pub: Dow Jones & Company Inc.
Contact: Almar Latour, Chief Executive Officer
Ed: Katherine Cheng. Description: Target rebutted the rumor that they will disassociate themselves from a line of clothing inspired by the television show 'Gossip Girl'. Target's spokesman says that the retailer intends to remain closely identified with the show. Target's sales should benefit from the hotly anticipated clothing line. Availability: Online.

32162 ■ "The Globe: Let Emerging Market Customers Be Your Teachers" in Harvard Business Review (Vol. 88, December 2010, No. 12, pp. 115)
Pub: Harvard Business Publishing
Contact: Diane Belcher, Managing Director
Ed: Guillermo D'Andrea, David Marcotte, Gwen Dixon Morrison. Price: $8.95, PDF. Description: Examination of effective strategies for emerging markets is presented. These include helping educate customers as well as selling to them, adapting to customers' habits, and focusing brands appropriately. Magazine Luiza, a chain store in Brazil, is used to illustrate these points. Availability: Online; PDF.

32163 ■ "GM's Decision to Boot Dealer Prompts Sale" in Baltimore Business Journal (Vol. 27, November 6, 2009, No. 26, pp. 1)
Pub: Baltimore Business Journal
Contact: Rhonda Pringle, President
E-mail: rpringle@bizjournals.com
Ed: Daniel J. Sernovitz. Description: General Motors Corporation's (GM) decision to strip Baltimore's Anderson Automotive Group Inc. of its GM franchise has prompted the owner, Bruce Mortimer, to close the automotive dealership and sell the land to a developer. The new project could make way for new homes, a shopping center and supermarket. Availability: Print; Online.

32164 ■ "GNC Reaches 'A Pivotal Moment'" in Pittsburgh Business Times (Vol. 34, August 15, 2014, No. 4, pp. 4)
Pub: American City Business Journals, Inc.
Contact: Mike Olivieri, Executive Vice President
Released: Weekly. Price: $4, introductory 4-week offer(Digital & Print). Description: Goldman analyst, Stephen Tanal, states Michael Archbold is taking over as CEO of GNC Holdings Inc. at a pivotal moment as the company shifts from heavy dependence on promotions to sustaining sales growth beyond 2015. Analysts discuss the recent problems faced by the vitamin, health and fitness retailer and the implications of a possible merger between GNC and Archbolds' former company, the Vitamin Shoppe Inc. Availability: Print; Online.

32165 ■ "Green and Clean" in Retail Merchandiser (Vol. 51, July-August 2011, No. 4, pp. 56)
Description: Green Valley Grocery partnered with Paragon Solutions consulting firm to make their stores environmentally green. Availability: Print; Online.

32166 ■ "H&M Offers a Dress for Less" in Canadian Business (Vol. 83, September 14, 2010, No. 15, pp. 20)
Pub: Rogers Media Inc.
Contact: Neil Spivak, Chief Executive Officer
Ed: Laura Cameron. Description: Swedish clothing company H&M has implemented loss leader strategy by pricing some dresses at extremely low prices. The economy has forced retailers to keep prices down despite the increasing cost of manufacturing, partly due to Chinese labor becoming more expensive. How the trend will affect apparel companies is discussed. Availability: Print; Online.

32167 ■ "Hawaii Rides Retail Strength Into New Year" in Pacific Business News (Vol. 51, January 17, 2014, No. 48, pp. 3)
Pub: American City Business Journals, Inc.
Contact: Mike Olivieri, Executive Vice President

Released: Weekly. Price: $4, introductory 4-week offer(Digital only). Description: CBRE Hawaii's Fourth Quarter 2013 Hawaii Retail MarketView shows positive absorption, lower vacancy rates and stable lease rents with large transaction that will accelerate major retail development and redevelopment. Hawaii's real estate market remained strong in 2013. Availability: Print; Online.

32168 ■ "HBC Enlists IBM to Help Dress Up Its On-Line Shopping" in Globe & Mail (February 7, 2006, pp. B3)
Description: The details of management contract between Hudson's Bay Co. and International Business Machines Corp. are presented. Availability: Print; Online.

32169 ■ "Headington Lures High-End Retailers to Downtown Dallas" in Dallas Business Journal (Vol. 35, July 6, 2012, No. 43, pp. 1)
Pub: Baltimore Business Journal
Contact: Rhonda Pringle, President
E-mail: rpringle@bizjournals.com
Ed: Steven R. Thompson. Description: Dallas, Texas-based Headington Companies has leased all of the retail space created with the expansion of The Joule Hotel, to add soft goods retail to downtown Dallas, Texas' revitalization. The company has high-end contemporary brands that include Traffic LA, Tenoversix, and Taschen to fill the retail landscape on Main and Commerce Streets. Availability: Print; Online.

32170 ■ "Health Clinic Expansion Fuels Debate Over Care In Massachusetts" in Boston Business Journal (Vol. 34, June 27, 2014, No. 21, pp. 9)
Pub: American City Business Journals, Inc.
Contact: Mike Olivieri, Executive Vice President
Released: Weekly. Description: The announcement of expansion by several retail health clinics has fueled debate over their quality and competiveness. AFC Doctors Express, a fast-growing chain of retail health clinics, announced its plan to open two new locations in Massachusetts in 2014 and CVS's MinuteClinic announced its intention to open nine additional locations. Concerns are being raised about the cost and quality of this type of healthcare, with a medical society expressing concern that this is fragmented care, not comprehensive care. Availability: Print; Online.

32171 ■ "Hedge Funds Prevail In Merger" in Baltimore Business Journal (Vol. 31, March 21, 2014, No. 47, pp. 8)
Pub: American City Business Journals, Inc.
Contact: Mike Olivieri, Executive Vice President
Released: Weekly. Price: $4, introductory 4-week offer(Digital & Print). Description: Contrary to expectations of the retail experts, after five months of internal strife, Jos. A Bank accepted Men's Wearhouse's offer and closed this hot deal. Men's Wearhouse purchased the Jos. A. Bank Clothiers Inc. for $1.8 billion and is planning to continue both brands. However, this will result in the Greater Baltimore area losing one more corporate headquarters. As the two companies combine operations, Jos. A. Banks stores will close, thus cutting more jobs. Availability: Print; Online.

32172 ■ "Here's How You Boycott Amazon" in Puget Sound Business Journal (Vol. 35, June 13, 2014, No. 8, pp. 12)
Pub: American City Business Journals, Inc.
Contact: Mike Olivieri, Executive Vice President
Description: Critic, Kimberly Mills, says she boycotted Amazon.com because of its lack of corporate philanthropy and poor working conditions. She also boycotted the firm by purchasing directly from the listed company Websites when purchasing retail products, instead of buying directly from Amazon's site. Other online retailers are increasing customer services corporate social responsibility. Availability: Online.

32173 ■ "High Anxiety" in Canadian Business (Vol. 80, November 19, 2007, No. 23, pp. 11)
Description: Value of Canadian dollar continues to rise, and consumers are asking for lower prices of goods. Retailers, on the other hand, are facing concerns over losing sales. The impacts of the rising Canadian dollar on the business sector and consumer behavior are examined. Availability: Online.

32174 ■ "Highmark-Owned Glasses Chain Eyeing Phila. Expansion" in Philadelphia Business Journal (Vol. 28, May 18, 2012, No. 14, pp. 1)
Pub: Baltimore Business Journal
Contact: Rhonda Pringle, President
E-mail: rpringle@bizjournals.com
Description: Pittsburgh, Pennsylvania-based Highmark's subsidiary, Visionworks, has outlined its plan to open 25 stores in the Philadelphia region. The retail eyeglasses store chain has also been trying to recruit opticians to hire in the area. Availability: Print; Online.

32175 ■ "Holiday Sales Look Uncertain for Microsoft and PC Sellers" in Puget Sound Business Journal (Vol. 29, November 28, 2008, No. 32)
Ed: Todd Bishop. Description: Personal computer makers face uncertain holiday sales for 2008 as a result of the weak U.S. economy and a shift toward low-cost computers. Personal computer shipments for the fourth quarter 2008 are forecast to drop 1 percent compared to the same quarter 2007. Availability: Online.

32176 ■ "Holiday Shopping Meets Social Media" in Employee Benefit News (Vol. 25, December 1, 2011, No. 15)
Pub: SourceMedia LLC
Contact: Gemma Postlethwaite, Chief Executive Officer
Ed: Rob J. Thurston. Description: Offering employees access to discount shopping using social media sites for Christmas bonuses, could be the gift that keeps on giving.

32177 ■ "Hoop Culture Opens Showroom, Expands Reach Globally" in Orlando Business Journal (Vol. 30, February 28, 2014, No. 36, pp. 3)
Pub: American City Business Journals, Inc.
Contact: Mike Olivieri, Executive Vice President
Released: Weekly. Description: Hoop Culture Inc. president, Mike Brown, shares how the online basketball apparel retailer/wholesaler online store has expanded globally. He mentions that Orlando, Florida is one of their biggest markets. Availability: Print; Online.

32178 ■ "How Church Street Exchange May Bring Retail, 350 Jobs" in Orlando Business Journal (Vol. 30, February 28, 2014, No. 36, pp. 10)
Pub: American City Business Journals, Inc.
Contact: Mike Olivieri, Executive Vice President
Released: Weekly. Price: $8, introductory 4-week offer(Digital & Print). Description: Nonprofit organization, Canvs, is finalizing a lease for 14,069 square feet of technology-focused co-working space at Church Street Exchange in downtown Orlando, Florida. Jones Lang LaSalle is negotiating for more space than the 87,000-square-foot building has that could bring 300 to 350 high-tech jobs to the area. Availability: Print; Online.

32179 ■ "How Growers Buy" in Farm Industry News (Vol. 42, January 1, 2009, No. 1)
Pub: Informa USA, Inc.
Contact: Stephen A. Carter, Chief Executive Officer
Ed: Karen McMahon. Description: According to a survey regarding the buying habits among large commercial growers, most prefer to purchase from local retailers, customer service is important concerning their decision on who to buy products from, and price and convenience seem to be more important then brand.

32180 ■ *"How I Did It: Best Buy's CEO On Learning to Love Social Media"* in *Harvard Business Review (Vol. 88, December 2010, No. 12, pp. 43)*
Pub: Harvard Business Publishing
Contact: Diane Belcher, Managing Director
Ed: Brian J. Dunn. **Price:** $8.95, PDF. **Description:** Effective utilization of online social networks to enhance brand identity, connect with consumers, and address bad publicity scenarios is examined. **Availability:** Online; PDF.

32181 ■ *"Hunt Valley Towne Center Gears Up for Growth; Ray Lewis Project Scrapped"* in *Baltimore Business Journal (Vol. 30, May 11, 2012, No. 1, pp. 1)*
Pub: American City Business Journals, Inc.
Contact: Mike Olivieri, Executive Vice President
Ed: James Briggs. **Description:** Greenberg Gibbons Commercial Corporation has plans for a 400-unit apartment complex and retail space at Hunt Valley Towne Centre in Baltimore, Maryland. The developer is also considering big-box stores to rent the vacant space that was supposed to be occuped by the failed bowling and entertainment venture MVP Lanes. **Availability:** Print; Online.

32182 ■ *"HVHC's Impact on SA Could Grow as it Pursues Big Expansion"* in *San Antonio Business Journal (Vol. 28, June 20, 2014, No. 19, pp. 8)*
Pub: American City Business Journals, Inc.
Contact: Mike Olivieri, Executive Vice President
Released: Weekly. **Price:** $4, Introductory 4-week offer(Digital & Print). **Description:** HVHC Inc., parent company of several retail eye-care centers in the U.S., is planning to grow its Visionworks footprint by adding at least 360 new stores in the country. The company aims to grow its store count to 1,000 retail outlets across the nation. **Availability:** Print; Online.

32183 ■ *"Iconic Boise Skateboard Shop to Close"* in *Idaho Business Review (August 19, 2014)*
Pub: BridgeTower Media
Contact: Adam Reinebach, President
Description: Lori Wright and Lori Ambur have owned Newt & Harold's for over 30 years. The partners are closing the firm that sold skateboards and snowboards. Wright focused on the marketing and inventory aspects of the retail shop, while Ambur ran the organizational and financial end. Wright and Ambur say they are leaving retail because the industry has faced so many changes since they first opened, particularly competing with online stores.

32184 ■ *"Inland Snaps Up Rival REITs"* in *Crain's Chicago Business (Vol. 31, November 17, 2008, No. 46, pp. 3)*
Pub: Crain Communications Inc.
Contact: Barry Asin, President
Ed: Alby Gallun. **Description:** Discusses Inland American Real Estate Trust Inc., a real estate investment trust that is napping up depressed shares of publicly traded competitors, a possible first step toward taking over these companies; however, with hotel and retail properties accounting for approximately 70 percent of its portfolio, the company could soon face its own difficulties. **Availability:** Online.

32185 ■ *"Inside Out"* in *Playthings (Vol. 107, January 1, 2009, No. 1, pp. 3)*
Description: Mattel signed on as the global master toy licensee for Cartoon Network's The Secret Saturdays while Toy Island signed a deal for wooden toys based on several leading Nick Jr. properties. **Availability:** Print; Online.

32186 ■ *"Internet Sales of Pet Products Increasingly 'Big Box"'* in *Pet Product News (Vol. 66, September 2012, No. 9, pp. 4)*
Description: Internet sales account for nearly 4 percent of the $30 billion U.S. market for pet products in 2011, or about $1.2 billion retail. Meanwhile, overall pet product retail sales growth and overall Internet retail sales growth of 10 percent can be outpaced as

Internet sales of pet products is seen to grow at a 12 percent compound annual rate through 2015. **Availability:** Online.

32187 ■ *"Invest in Energy-Efficient Equipment for Your Pet Store"* in *Pet Product News (Vol. 66, September 2012, No. 9, pp. 72)*
Ed: Leila Meyer. **Description:** Aquatic retailers can achieve business growth by offering lighting products, pumps, heaters, filters, and other aquarium supplies that would help customers realize energy efficiency. Aside from offering an education in energy efficiency as a customer service opportunity, retailers are encouraged to determine what supplies are crucial in helping customers achieve energy usage goals. **Availability:** Online.

32188 ■ *"Izod, Loft Outlets Coming To Tanger"* in *New Hampshire Business Review (Vol. 33, March 25, 2011, No. 6, pp. 30)*
Description: Izod and Lots stores will open at the Tanger Outlet Center in Tilton, New Hampshire. Both stores will feature fashions and accessories. **Availability:** Online.

32189 ■ *"J.C. Penney Head Shops for Shares"* in *Barron's (Vol. 88, July 7, 2008, No. 27, pp. 29)*
Pub: Dow Jones & Company Inc.
Contact: Almar Latour, Chief Executive Officer
Ed: Teresa Rivas. **Description:** Myron Ullman III, chairman and chief executive officer of J.C. Penney, purchased $1 million worth of shares of the company. He now owns 393,140 shares of the company and an additional 1,282 on his 401(k) plan. **Availability:** Online.

32190 ■ *"Jordan Still Soaring"* in *Business Journal Portland (Vol. 30, January 17, 2014, No. 46, pp. 7)*
Pub: American City Business Journals, Inc.
Contact: Mike Olivieri, Executive Vice President
Released: Weekly. **Price:** $4, introductory 4-week offer(Digital only). **Description:** Nike Inc. is planning to open retail stores that will exclusively sell Jordan Brand merchandise. The company is seeking to grow its direct-to-consumer sales to $8 billion by 2017. Nike's capital spending is also expected to increase by 3 to 4 percent. **Availability:** Print; Online.

32191 ■ *"Keep The (Cage) Customer Satisfied"* in *Pet Product News (Vol. 64, December 2010, No. 12, pp. 10)*
Ed: Devon McPhee. **Description:** Windsor, California-based Debbie's Pet Boutique, recipient of Pet Product News International's Outstanding Customer Service Award, has been dedicated to combining topnotch grooming services with a robust retail selection. These features might gain return customers for Debbie's Pet Boutique. **Availability:** Online.

32192 ■ *"Kroger Family of Pharmacies to Offer Health Assessment Kiosks at Locations Nationwide"* in *Entertainment Close-Up (August 22, 2012)*
Pub: Close-Up Media Inc.
Contact: Caroline S. Moore, President
E-mail: cms@closeupmedia.com
Description: Kroger HealthCENTER kiosks will be placed in Kroger Company Family of Pharmacies in 1,950 locations across the country. The kiosks are provided by Styhealthy, a wellness solutions firm and will offer self-use health screening to customers. **Availability:** Online.

32193 ■ *"Lancaster Offers Kiosks to Downtown Businesses: InSite Development is Planning to Lease Up to 20 Retail Units Along Lancaster Boulevard"* in *San Fernando Valley Business Journal (Vol. 17, June 25, 2012, No. 13, pp. 4)*
Pub: CBJ L.P.
Contact: Terri Cunningham, Contact
Ed: Mark Madler. **Description:** At least 20 low-cost kiosks will be installed in downtown Lancaster, California to offer customers a means in which to

purchase items from retailers wanting to sell downtown, but cannot handle the overhead of a new store. **Availability:** PDF; Online.

32194 ■ *The Leadership Challenge: How to Make Extraordinary Things Happen in Organizations*
Pub: Jossey-Bass
Ed: James M. Kouzes, Barry Z. Posner. **Released:** 7th edition. **Price:** $34.95, hardcover; $34.95, hardcover. **Description:** According to research by the authors, people can make extraordinary things happen by liberating the leader within everyone around them. This handbook gives practical tips to aspire leaders in retail, manufacturing, government, community, church and school settings. **Availability:** E-book; Print.

32195 ■ *"Leaning Tower"* in *Business Courier (Vol. 27, June 4, 2010, No. 5, pp. 1)*
Pub: Business Courier
Ed: Jon Newberry. **Description:** New York-based developer Armand Lasky, owner of Tower Place Mall in downtown Cincinnati, Ohio has sued Birmingham, Alabama-based Regions Bank to prevent the bank's foreclosure on the property. Regions Bank claims Lasky was in default on an $18 million loan agreement. Details on the mall's leasing plan are also discussed. **Availability:** Online.

32196 ■ *"Let's Go Team: When a Retail Professional Leads by Example, Everyone Benefits"* in *Black Enterprise (Vol. 41, November 2010, No. 4)*
Pub: Earl G. Graves Ltd.
Contact: Earl Graves, Jr., President
Ed: Aisha I. Jefferson. **Description:** Profile of Derek Jenkins, senior vice president of Target Stores Northeast Region is presented. Jenkins oversees the management of 450 retail stores with nearly 75,000 workers. He shares insight into managing by making sure every interaction with his team counts.

32197 ■ *"Life After Cod"* in *Globe & Mail (March 18, 2006, pp. B1)*
Pub: The Globe & Mail Inc.
Ed: Gordon Pitts. **Description:** Canadian fishing industry is under threat because of Chinese processing competition, high energy costs, rise of powerful retailers and the rise of Canadian dollar value. Fishing industry of Canada is analyzed. **Availability:** Print; PDF; Online.

32198 ■ *"Littleton Firm Chips In On Security Solution"* in *Denver Business Journal (Vol. 65, May 9, 2014, No. 52, pp. A6)*
Pub: American City Business Journals, Inc.
Contact: Mike Olivieri, Executive Vice President
Released: Weekly. **Price:** $4, introductory 4-week offer(Digital & Print). **Description:** CPI Card Group of Littleton, Colorado has been preparing for the nationwide transition to computer chip cards to secure credit and debit cards in the U.S. Banks and merchants in the country need to make the switch by October 2015 or risk being financially liable for fraud if not using the chipped cards in their retail establishments. **Availability:** Print; Online.

32199 ■ *"Loblaw's Apparel Guru No Average Joe"* in *Globe & Mail (March 13, 2006, pp. B1)*
Ed: Marina Strauss. **Description:** The details on Loblaw Companies Ltd., which unveiled Joe Fresh Style line of clothing, are presented. **Availability:** Online.

32200 ■ *"Luxury Still Sells Well"* in *Puget Sound Business Journal (Vol. 29, September 5, 2008, No. 20, pp. 1)*
Description: High fashion retailers are planning to open stores in the Puget Sound area despite the economic slowdown, citing high incomes in the area despite the weak U.S. dollar.

32201 ■ *"Macy's Seeks Balance in All Things Ad-Related"* in *Crain's Chicago Business (Vol. 31, March 31, 2008, No. 13, pp. 19)*
Pub: Crain Communications Inc.
Contact: Barry Asin, President

Ed: Natalie Zmuda. **Description:** Macy's Inc. is seeking to balance its national television campaign with locally tailored promotions and products. **Availability:** Online.

32202 ■ *"Major Golf Retail Show in the Rough for 2010"* in *Orlando Business Journal (Vol. 26, January 15, 2010, No. 33, pp. 1)*
Pub: Orlando Business Journal
Contact: Julie Swyers, Director
E-mail: jswyers@bizjournals.com
Ed: Anjali Fluker. **Description:** The 57th Annual PGA Merchandise Show in Orlando, Florida is projected to attract 39,000 attendees in 2010, compared with 41,000 in 2009. According to the Orange County Convention Center, economic benefits that could be obtained from the 2010 edition of the golf retail show might reach only $77 million, compared with $78 million generated last year. **Availability:** Print; Online.

32203 ■ *"Mall On a Mission: KOP to Get $150 Million Makeover"* in *Philadelphia Business Journal (Vol. 33, March 14, 2014, No. 5, pp. 6)*
Pub: American City Business Journals, Inc.
Contact: Mike Olivieri, Executive Vice President
Released: Weekly. **Price:** $4, introductory 4-week offer(Digital & Print). **Description:** Philadelphia, Pennsylvania-based King of Prussia Mall is set to undergo a $150 million renovation. The plan involves construction of about 250,000 square feet of space for retailers. Mall owner, Simon Property Group, has contracted IMC Construction to handle the project. **Availability:** Print; Online.

32204 ■ *"Marketers Push for Mobile Tuesday as the New Black Friday"* in *Advertising Age (Vol. 79, December 1, 2008, No. 44, pp. 21)*
Pub: Crain Communications, Inc.
Contact: Jessica Botos, Manager, Marketing
E-mail: jessica.botos@crainsnewyork.com
Ed: Natalie Zmuda. **Description:** Marketers are using an innovative approach in an attempt to stimulate business on the Tuesday following Thanksgiving by utilizing consumer's cell phones to alert them of sales or present them with coupons for this typically slow retail business day; with this campaign both advertisers and retailers are hoping to start Mobile Tuesday, another profitable shopping day in line with Black Friday and Cyber Monday. **Availability:** Online.

32205 ■ *"Mars Advertising's Orbit Grows as Other Ad Segments Fall"* in *Crain's Detroit Business (Vol. 25, June 1, 2009, No. 22, pp. 10)*
Pub: Crain Communications Inc.
Contact: Barry Asin, President
Ed: Bill Shea. **Description:** An electrical fire burned at Mars Advertising's headquarters in Southfield, Michigan. The company talks about its plans for regrouping and rebuilding. The family firm specializes in in-store marketing that targets consumers already in the buying mode. **Availability:** Print; Online.

32206 ■ *"Mary Kramer: Good Things Happen When We Buy Local"* in *Crain's Detroit Business (Vol. 24, October 6, 2008, No. 40, pp. 7)*
Pub: Crain Communications Inc.
Contact: Barry Asin, President
Description: Michigan is facing incredibly difficult economic times. One way in which each one of us can help the state and the businesses located here is by purchasing our goods and services from local vendors. The state Agriculture Department projected that if Michigan households earmarked $10 per week in their grocery purchases to made-in-Michigan products, this would generate $30 million a week in economic impact. **Availability:** Online.

32207 ■ *"Maryland Casinos Face Atlantic City's $150M Might"* in *Baltimore Business Journal (Vol. 30, June 1, 2012, No. 4, pp. 1)*
Pub: American City Business Journals, Inc.
Contact: Mike Olivieri, Executive Vice President
Ed: Gary Haber. **Description:** Atlantic City has launched a campaign to attract visitors from the East Coast. The campaign is part of the city's $150 million

marketing plan, which markets the city not for its casinos but as a shopping destination. Executive comments included. **Availability:** Online.

32208 ■ *"Mechanic Theatre's Brutalist Style at Battle's Center"* in *Baltimore Business Journal (Vol. 30, May 11, 2012, No. 1, pp. 1)*
Pub: American City Business Journals, Inc.
Contact: Mike Olivieri, Executive Vice President
Ed: James Briggs. **Description:** David S. Brown Enterprises Ltd. plans to demolish the Morris A. Mechanic Theatre in Baltimore, Maryland and replace it with two 30-story towers that include 600 apartment units, retail, and parking spaces. The local chapter of the American Institute of Architects opposes the proposal and calls for the preservation of the former theatre's brutalist achitecture. **Availability:** Print; Online.

32209 ■ *"Men May Wear the Pants in the Family, But Women Retain the Power of the Purse"* in *Marketing to Women (Vol. 22, August 2009, No. 8)*
Description: Nearly 8 in 10 women say that their opinion holds the most sway in the families' financial decisions. Significant factors that influence women's $100 or more purchases include Online reviews, the opinion of spouse or significant other and expert recommendations. Statistical data included. **Availability:** Print; Online.

32210 ■ *"Metamorphosis Makes Family Dollar a Destination"* in *MMR (Vol. 29, August 20, 2012, No. 13, pp. 8)*
Description: Family Dollar was launched as a store for low-incom customers, but is becoming a mainstream shopping destination for low- and middle-income consumers. Details of the firm are discussed with Howard Levine, chief executive officer. **Availability:** Print.

32211 ■ *"Modern Bride Unveiled Exclusively at JCPenney"* in *Benzinga.com (February 3, 2011)*
Pub: PR Newswire Association LLC.
Description: JCPenney created its new Modern Bride concept in its bridal find jewelry departments. The new shopping experience is a collaboration between the retailer and Conde Nast catering to the bridal customer. **Availability:** Online.

32212 ■ *The Mom & Pop Store: How the Unsung Heroes of the American Economy Are Surviving and Thriving*
Ed: Robert Spector. **Description:** The history of small independent retail enterprises and how mom and pop stores in the U.S. continue to thrive through customer service and renewed community support for local businesses. **Availability:** Audio.

32213 ■ *"More Leading Retailers Using Omniture Conversion Solutions to Boost Sales and Ecommerce Performance"* in *Marketwired (September 22, 2009)*
Pub: Comtex News Network Inc.
Contact: Kan Devnani, President
Description: Many retailers are utilizing Omniture conversion solutions to improve the performance of their ecommerce businesses; recent enhancements to Omniture Merchandising and Omniture Recommendations help clients drive increased conversion to their Internet ventures.

32214 ■ *"More SouthPark Shopping for Charlotte"* in *Charlotte Business Journal (Vol. 25, July 16, 2010, No. 17, pp. 1)*
Pub: Charlotte Business Journal
Contact: Robert Morris, Editor
E-mail: rmorris@bizjournals.com
Ed: Will Boye. **Description:** Charlotte, North Carolina-based Bissel Companies has announced plans to expand its retail presence at the Siskey and Sharon properties in SouthPark. Bissel Companies has requested a rezoning to a mixed-use development classification so that it can utilize the entire ground floor of the Siskey building for restaurant and retail uses. **Availability:** Print; Online.

32215 ■ *"Move Marks KKR's Latest Push into Retail"* in *Globe & Mail (March 13, 2007, pp. B17)*
Ed: Heather Burke. **Description:** Investment giant Kohlberg Kravis Roberts and Co. has finalized a deal to acquire retail store chain Dollar General Corp. for an estimated 6.9 billion dollars. The company will be entering lucrative retail market by this acquisition.

32216 ■ *"A Muddle at Marks & Spencer"* in *Barron's (Vol. 88, July 7, 2008, No. 27, pp. M7)*
Pub: Dow Jones & Company Inc.
Contact: Almar Latour, Chief Executive Officer
Ed: Molly Neal. **Description:** British retail outfit Marks & Spencer is encountering turbulent financial conditions but remains confident in spending 900 million pounds sterling. The company has not made a profit forecast for the first half of 2008 and is suffering from a shrinking cash flow. **Availability:** Online.

32217 ■ *"A Multicategory Model of Consumers' Purchase Incidence, Quantity, and Brand Choice Decisions: Methodological Issues and Implications On Promotional Decisions"* in *Journal of Marketing Research (Vol. 49, August 2012, No. 4, pp. 435)*
Pub: American Marketing Association
Contact: Bennie F. Johnson, Chief Executive Officer
Ed: Nitin Mehta, Yu Ma. **Description:** A multicategory model of consumers' purchase incidence, quantity, and brand choice decisions is presented. The research model allows for cross-category promotion effects in incidence and quantity decisions. Retailers are seen to be better off promoting brands across categories. **Availability:** PDF.

32218 ■ *"National Cattlemen's Beef Association"* in *Retail Merchandiser (Vol. 51, September-October 2011, No. 5, pp. 77)*
Pub: Phoenix Media Corp.
Description: National Cattlemen's Beef Association offers a wide range of tools and information to keep its members informed regarding the state of the beef industry. Their Website provides tools to help cattle producers improve operations. **Availability:** Online.

32219 ■ *"Natural Pet Product Merchandiser Roundtable: Functional Foods and Treats"* in *Pet Product News (Vol. 64, December 2010, No. 12, pp. S1)*
Released: January 18, 2013. **Description:** Executives and business owners from the pet supplies industries deliberate on the role of functional foods in the retail sector. Functional foods pertain to foods with specified health benefits. Insight into marketing functional foods and convincing pet owners to make the transition to these products is examined. **Availability:** Online.

32220 ■ *"Navigating Dog Trainer Partnerships"* in *Pet Product News (Vol. 66, September 2012, No. 9, pp. 47)*
Ed: Steven Appelbaum. **Description:** Benefits and disadvantages of partnerships between pet supplies retailers and dog trainers are discussed. With the proper approach to partnering with dog trainers who are duly specialized in dog behavior modification, pet supplies retailers can realize improved business and stronger customer loyalty. Tips on cross-promoting pet-related services are also provided. **Availability:** Online.

32221 ■ *"Neighborhood Awaits Its 'Very Sexy Building"* in *Dallas Business Journal (Vol. 37, June 27, 2014, No. 42, pp. 12)*
Pub: American City Business Journals, Inc.
Contact: Mike Olivieri, Executive Vice President
Released: Weekly. **Price:** $4, introductory 4-week offer(Digital only). **Description:** Crescent Real Estate Holdings LLC chairman and CEO, John Goff, described the upcoming 20-story, $225 million office and retail tower in Uptown Dallas as a 'sexy addition' to the neighborhood. Goff believes the location offers companies a unique marketing advantage. **Availability:** Print; Online.

32222 ■ *"Neighbors Rally for Dollar Store"* in *Chattanooga Times/Free Press (August 4, 2010)*

Pub: Chattanooga Publishing Company Inc.

Description: Neighbors are rallying to keep the Family Dollar Store in their city open. The proposed new store would expand the grocery portion of its retail discount shop. **Availability:** Print; Online.

32223 ■ *"NetSpend and Family Dollar Announce New Prepaid Card Agreement"* in *GlobeNewswire (May 10, 2012)*

Pub: Comtex News Network Inc.

Contact: Kan Devnani, President

Description: Partnership between Family Dollar and NetSpend will offer customers a NetSpend Visa(R) Prepaid Debit Card to be used at Family Dollar's 7,200 locations. NetSpend is a leading provider of general-purpose reloadable (GPR) prepaid debit cards and other related financial services. **Availability:** Print; Online.

32224 ■ *"New Family Dollar Store Now Open in Hermon"* in *Bangor Daily News (August 12, 2010)*

Pub: Bangor Daily News

Contact: David M. Austin, Contact

Ed: Dawn Gagnon. **Description:** A new Family Dollar Store opened its doors at the newly expanded Hermon Shopping Center in Bangor, Maine. **Availability:** Print; Online.

32225 ■ *"A New Mix of Tenants Settles In Downtown"* in *Crain's New York Business (Vol. 24, January 13, 2008, No. 2, pp. 26)*

Pub: Crain Communications, Inc.

Contact: Jessica Botos, Manager, Marketing

E-mail: jessica.botos@crainsnewyork.com

Ed: Andrew Marks. **Description:** More and more nonfinancial firms are relocating downtown due to the new retailers and restaurants that are reshaping the look and feel of lower Manhattan.

32226 ■ *"New Owner Eyes Big Changes at Brookwood Village"* in *Birmingham Business Journal (Vol. 31, April 4, 2014, No. 14, pp. 10)*

Pub: American City Business Journals, Inc.

Contact: Mike Olivieri, Executive Vice President

Released: Weekly. **Price:** $4, introductory 4-week offer(Digital only). **Description:** New Brookwood Village owner Cypress Equities is planning to renovate the shopping center. It is also considering changes in the shopping center's tenancy, while focusing on the social aspect of shopping. **Availability:** Print; Online.

32227 ■ *"Niche Areas Seeing the Bulk of Retail Activity"* in *San Antonio Business Journal (Vol. 28, August 29, 2014, No. 29, pp. 8)*

Pub: American City Business Journals, Inc.

Contact: Mike Olivieri, Executive Vice President

Released: Weekly. **Price:** $4, introductory 4-week offer(Digital & Print). **Description:** Retail development projects in San Antonio, Texas have been focused on already established areas. Such projects have boosted the local real estate sector. Meanwhile, retail developers have been finding opportunities in redeveloping old retail centers. **Availability:** Print; Online.

32228 ■ *"No Frills - And No Dodge"* in *Crain's Detroit Business (Vol. 24, September 22, 2008, No. 38, pp. 3)*

Pub: Crain Communications Inc.

Contact: Barry Asin, President

Ed: Bradford Wernle. **Description:** Chrysler LLC is in the middle of a business plan known as Project Genesis, a five-year strategy in which the company will reduce the dealer count by combining its Jeep, Chrysler and Dodge brands under one rooftop wherever possible. Not every dealer will be able to arrange this deal because of the investment required to expand stores in which have low-overhead; many of these stores feel that low-overhead structures are

more likely to survive difficult times than the larger stores in which the Genesis consolidation plan intends to implement. **Availability:** Online.

32229 ■ *"Nordstrom Points for Richmond Heights"* in *Saint Louis Business Journal (Vol. 31, August 5, 2011, No. 50, pp. 1)*

Pub: Saint Louis Business Journal

Contact: Robert Bobroff, President

E-mail: rbobroff@bizjournals.com

Ed: E.B. Solomont. **Description:** Nordstrom is set to upgrade its offerings for its second full-line store in St. Louis, Missouri. The new store is expected to benefit nearby shops. **Availability:** Print; Online.

32230 ■ *"No. 300: My Job Is To Solve Every Kind of Crisis"* in *Inc. (Vol. 36, September 2014, No. 7, pp. 72)*

Pub: Mansueto Ventures L.L.C.

Contact: Stephanie Mehta, Chief Executive Officer

Released: September 2014. **Description:** Saima Chowdhury started her integrated sourcing company in New York City after receiving an MBA from Wharton School. Noi Solutions helps retailers manufacture goods in Bangladesh while helping Bangladeshi factories market their capabilities to retailers. Chowdhury discusses the challenges and has learned to remain calm during any crisis. **Availability:** Print; Online.

32231 ■ *"Of Paper Towels and Health Insurance"* in *Philadelphia Business Journal (Vol. 28, May 11, 2012, No. 13, pp. 1)*

Pub: Baltimore Business Journal

Contact: Rhonda Pringle, President

E-mail: rpringle@bizjournals.com

Description: Health insurance companies are using different strategies to take advantage of the demand growth in health coverage in markets such as Philadelphia. Horizon Blue Cross lue Shield of New Jersey, for example, is creating a retail center where customers can get information from specially trained staff about insurance, health and wellness. IBC, on the other hand, has partnered with AAA Mid-Atlantic to market its plan option to AAA members. **Availability:** Print; Online.

32232 ■ *"Offer for Sears Canada 'Inadequate"* in *Globe & Mail (February 10, 2006, pp. B4)*

Description: The financial feasibility of Sears Holdings Corp.'s proposed acquisition of Sears Canada Inc., for $835 million, is discussed. **Availability:** Online.

32233 ■ *On the Make: Clerks and the Quest for Capital in Nineteenth-Century America*

Pub: New York University Press

Contact: Ellen Chodosh, Director

E-mail: ellen.chodosh@nyu.edu

Ed: Brian P. Luskey. **Released:** January 01, 2010. **Price:** $27, paperback; $89, cloth. **Description:** Through exploration into the diaries, newspapers, credit reports, census data, advice literature and fiction, the book presents the origins of the white collar culture, the antebellum clerk. **Availability:** E-book; Print.

32234 ■ *"Online Security Crackdown"* in *Chain Store Age (Vol. 84, July 2008, No. 7, pp. 46)*

Ed: Samantha Murphy. **Description:** Online retailers are beefing up security on their Websites. Cyber thieves use retail systems in order to gain entry to consumer data. David's Bridal operates over 275 bridal showrooms in the U.S. and has a one-stop wedding resource for new brides planning weddings. **Availability:** Online.

32235 ■ *"Options Abound in Winter Wares"* in *Pet Product News (Vol. 64, November 2010, No. 11, pp. 1)*

Ed: Maggie M. Shein. **Description:** Pet supply manufacturers emphasize creating top-notch construction and functional design in creating winter clothing for pets. Meanwhile, retailers and pet owners seek human-inspired style, quality, and versatility for

pets' winter clothing. How retailers generate successful sales of pets' winter clothing outside of traditional brand marketing is also examined. **Availability:** Online.

32236 ■ *"Owners Consider Remodeling Westlake Center"* in *Puget Sound Business Journal (Vol. 33, September 28, 2012, No. 23, pp. 1)*

Pub: Baltimore Business Journal

Contact: Rhonda Pringle, President

E-mail: rpringle@bizjournals.com

Ed: Jeanne Lang Jones. **Description:** General Growth Properties Inc. is considering a major remodel of the Westlake Center shopping mall in Seattle, Washington and international fashion chain Zara is negotiating for space at Westlake. Such activities benefit the city's retailers and landlords along with providing a broader civic benefit to the town square. **Availability:** Print; Online.

32237 ■ *"The Owyhee Is Filling Up Faster Than Expected"* in *Idaho Business Review (September 5, 2014)*

Pub: BridgeTower Media

Contact: Adam Reinebach, President

Description: Clay Carley discusses his idea to renovate the 104-year-old Owyhee Hotel into a modern office, residential and commercial center. He transformed the building's rooftop into an event space for weddings and other celebrations. Carley is the developer and part-owner of the property and reported 3,000 people attending its ribbon cutting. Retail and office space are filling faster than expected and the rooftop venue has already celebrated six weddings.

32238 ■ *"Parkland Approves First "Luxury" Consignment Shop"* in *Sun Sentinel (May 7, 2012)*

Ed: Lisa J. Huriash. **Description:** SincerelyYours is a very upscale consignment shop located in the upscale area of Parkland, Florida. This trend toward high-end luxury consignment boutiques is being seen across the country because consumers of luxury goods can be rid of their items, while those wishing high quality things can purchase at a substantial savings. **Availability:** Print; Online.

32239 ■ *"Pending Shutdown of Coldwater Creek Will Affect Eight Stores In Massachusetts"* in *Boston Business Journal (Vol. 34, April 11, 2014, No. 10)*

Pub: American City Business Journals, Inc.

Contact: Mike Olivieri, Executive Vice President

Released: Weekly. **Description:** Coldwater Creek's pending closure of its stores will adversely affect Massachusetts malls. The women's clothing retailer filed for Chapter 11 bankruptcy to help smooth the pending closures after being unable to find a potential buyer. The company's revenue dropped to $743 million in 2012, down dramatically from the $1.1 billion reported in 2006. **Availability:** Print; Online.

32240 ■ *"Penney's Buys Wal-Mart Site"* in *Crain's Chicago Business (Vol. 31, March 31, 2008, No. 13, pp. 13)*

Pub: Crain Communications Inc.

Contact: Barry Asin, President

Ed: Eddie Baeb. **Description:** J.C. Penny Co. bought the closed Wal-Mart location in Crystal Lake and plans to open a store next year in its push to become more prominent in non-mall locations; Penney plans to expand and renovate the store. **Availability:** Online.

32241 ■ *"People; E-Commerce, Online Games, Mobile Apps"* in *Advertising Age (Vol. 80, October 19, 2009, No. 35, pp. 14)*

Pub: Crain Communications, Inc.

Contact: Jessica Botos, Manager, Marketing

E-mail: jessica.botos@crainsnewyork.com

Ed: Nat Ives. **Description:** Profile of People Magazine and the ways in which the publisher is moving its magazine forward by exploring new concepts in a time of declining newsstand sales and advertising pages; among the strategies are e-commerce such as the brand People Style Watch in which consumers are able highlight clothing and jewelry and then connect to retailers' sites and a channel on Taxi TV, the network of video-touch screens in New Your City taxis. **Availability:** Online.

32242 ■ *"Perfecting Customer Services"* in *Pet Product News (Vol. 64, November 2010, No. 11, pp. 18)*
Ed: Alison Bour. **Description:** Pet supply retailers are encouraged to emphasize customer experience and sales representatives' knowledge of the store's product offerings to foster repeat business. Employee protocols could be implemented to improve customer interaction. Other guidelines on developing a pet supply retail environment that advances repeat business are presented. **Availability:** Online.

32243 ■ *"Phillips Edison Launches $1.8B Retail REIT"* in *Business Courier (Vol. 27, October 15, 2010, No. 24, pp. 1)*
Pub: Business Courier
Ed: Dan Monk. **Description:** Retail center operator Phillips Edison & Company is organizing a real estate investment trust (REIT) to raise $1.8 billion to finance the planned purchase of 150 grocery-centered shopping centers around the U.S. The offering would be Phillips largest. Phillips Edison employs 174 workers and operates 250 shopping centers nationwide. **Availability:** Print; Online.

32244 ■ *"Pink Label: Victoria's Sales Secret"* in *Advertising Age (Vol. 79, July 7, 2008, No. 26, pp. 4)*
Pub: Crain Communications, Inc.
Contact: Jessica Botos, Manager, Marketing
E-mail: jessica.botos@crainsnewyork.com
Ed: Natalie Zmuda. **Description:** Victoria Secret's Pink label accounted for roughly 17 percent of the retailer's total sales last year. The company is launching a Collegiate Collection which will be promoted by a campus tour program. **Availability:** Print; Online.

32245 ■ *"Plan Would Give Face-Lift to Section of Italian Market"* in *Philadelphia Business Journal (Vol. 28, June 29, 2012, No. 20, pp. 1)*
Pub: Baltimore Business Journal
Contact: Rhonda Pringle, President
E-mail: rpringle@bizjournals.com
Description: Midwood Investment & Development is planning construction on a 32,000 square foot shopping center dubbed the Italian Marketplace in South Philadelphia, Pennsylvania. Under the Lower Italian Market Revitalization Plan, the retail space will have improved storefronts,landscaping and bike lanes. It is slated to open in the first half of 2014. **Availability:** Print; Online.

32246 ■ *"Plans for $160M Condo Resort in Wisconsin Dells Moves Forward"* in *Commercial Property News (March 18, 2008)*
Description: Plans for the Grand Cambrian Resort in the Wisconsin Dells is discussed. The luxury condominium resort will include condos, townhomes, and condo-hotel style residences, two water parts, meeting space and indoor entertainment space, as well as a spa, four restaurants and retail offerings. **Availability:** Online.

32247 ■ *"The Power of Online"* in *Advertising Age (Vol. 85, October 13, 2014, No. 21, pp. 4)*
Pub: Crain Communications Inc.
Contact: Barry Asin, President
Description: According to Shop.org, online sales could increase by as much as 11 percent this holiday season. Retailers are not only focusing on when customers will start holiday shopping, but whether they will use online stores or shop at brick-and-mortar stores. Many retailers are expanding their online services using digital showrooms on their Websites. **Availability:** Online.

32248 ■ *"Powering Intelligent Commerce: eCommera Rebrands as OrderDynamics, Helping Retailers Activate Commerce from First Interaction to Fulfillment"* in *Computer Business Week (August 28, 2014, pp. 20)*
Pub: NewsRX LLC.
Contact: Kalani Rosell, Contact

Description: OrderDynamics, a new global brand created by eCommera, is profiled. The firm will continue to provide an integrated suite of software-as-a-service (SaaS) big data products and service that power intelligent commerce for retailers and brands around the world. Details of the integration of the new brand are included. **Availability:** Online.

32249 ■ *"Preleasing Drives Wedgewood Start"* in *Memphis Business Journal (Vol. 33, February 17, 2012, No. 45, pp. 1)*
Pub: Baltimore Business Journal
Contact: Rhonda Pringle, President
E-mail: rpringle@bizjournals.com
Ed: Andy Ashby. **Description:** Austin-Texas-based StoneCrest Investments LLC has started construction on the second phase of its $32 million Wedgewood Commons Shopping Center in Olive Branch at Memphis, Tennessee. The commercial real estate development company has managed to complete enough preleasing to begin construction in the retail center. **Availability:** Print; Online.

32250 ■ *"Progress Means Business"* in *Pet Product News (Vol. 66, September 2012, No. 9, pp. 88)*
Description: Pet supplies retailers are encouraged to promote devices featuring technologies that will assist herp hobbyists to properly monitor temperature, humidity and UVB in tanks with improved control and precision. Customer connction should also be taken into consideration by retailers to generate more sales. Other marketing tips for promoting sophisticated monitoring devices for herp tanks are given. **Availability:** Online.

32251 ■ *"Promotions Create a Path to Better Profit"* in *Pet Product News (Vol. 64, December 2010, No. 12, pp. 1)*
Ed: Joan Hustace Walker. **Description:** Pet store retailers can boost small mammal sales by launching creative marketing and promotions such as social networking and adoption days.

32252 ■ *"Proposed Triangle Redo in Motion"* in *Crain's Cleveland Business (Vol. 28, October 15, 2007, No. 41, pp. 1)*
Pub: Crain Communications Inc.
Contact: K. C. Crain, President
Ed: Stan Bullard. **Description:** Zaremba Homes and MRN Ltd. are partnering to redevelop the so-called Triangle section of University Circle. The proposed project will include a total of 434 new rental and for-sale residential suites and as much as 227,000 square feet of retail and restaurant space. **Availability:** Online.

32253 ■ *"The Proven 3 Step Formula For Growing Retail Profits: Without Having to Resort to Coupons or Discount Sales"*
Pub: CreateSpace
Released: September 24, 2014. **Price:** $4.89, paperback. **Description:** Previously published under the name, "How Some Retailers Make More Money Than Others". Retailers, whether a franchise or independent brand face challenges for increasing sales. An explanation for growing customer base without mass advertising, how to increase each customers spending, and improve gross margins are reported. A proven three-step process for increasing retail profits without the use of coupons or discounts is provided. **Availability:** Print.

32254 ■ *"Recovery on Tap for 2010?"* in *Orlando Business Journal (Vol. 26, January 1, 2010, No. 31, pp. 1)*
Pub: Orlando Business Journal
Contact: Julie Swyers, Director
E-mail: jswyers@bizjournals.com
Ed: Melanie Stawicki Azam, Richard Bilbao, Christopher Boyd, Anjali Fluker. **Description:** Economic forecasts for Central Florida's leading business sectors in 2010 are presented. These sectors include housing, film and TV, sports business, law, restaurants, aviation, tourism and hospitality, banking and finance, commercial real estate, retail, health care,

insurance, higher education, and manufacturing. According to some local executives, Central Florida's economy will slowly recover in 2010. **Availability:** Online.

32255 ■ *"Remington Developer Says Project May Not Include Second Big Box"* in *Baltimore Business Journal (Vol. 30, June 8, 2012, No. 5, pp. 1)*
Pub: American City Business Journals, Inc.
Contact: Mike Olivieri, Executive Vice President
Ed: James Briggs. **Price:** $4, introductory 4-week offer(Digital only). **Description:** WV Urban Developments will proceed with the 25th Street Station retail and housing project in Baltimore, Maryland with Wal-Mart Stores Inc. as the remaining retail anchor occupying 229,383 feet of space. Lowe's Cos. has backed out of the lease due to petitions filed by Wal-Mart components calling to overturn the plan. **Availability:** Print; Online.

32256 ■ *"Rent Check: New Lease on Life for Tenants"* in *Boston Business Journal (Vol. 31, July 29, 2011, No. 27, pp. 1)*
Pub: Boston Business Journal
Contact: Carolyn M. Jones, President
E-mail: cmjones@bizjournals.com
Ed: Lisa Van der Pool. **Description:** Merchants at Newbury Street in Boston, Massachusetts are concerned with the annual increase of already inflated rents that prevent many small businesses from expanding. **Availability:** Print; Online.

32257 ■ *"Report: McD's Pepsi Score Best With Young Hispanics"* in *Brandweek (Vol. 49, April 21, 2008, No. 16, pp. 8)*
Description: According to a new report, in order to reach Hispanic Gen Yers, marketing strategists need to understand this demographic's "bi-dentity," something which has proved an elusive task to many marketers. Another trend is the emergence of Latinas who have careers, as opposed to just jobs. There is an opportunity to tap this new, young and empowered female market with innovative messaging. Statistical data included. **Availability:** Online.

32258 ■ *"Research Reports"* in *Barron's (Vol. 90, August 23, 2010, No. 34, pp. M13)*
Pub: Barron's Editorial & Corporate Headquarters
Description: Shares of Sirius XM Radio, Target and Deere and Company received an eBuyE rating, while shares of Research in Motion got an eNeutralE rating. **Availability:** Online.

32259 ■ *"Retail in Austin Strong, Will Continue to Be"* in *Austin Business JournalInc. (Vol. 29, January 22, 2010, No. 46, pp. 1)*
Pub: Austin Business Journal
Contact: Rachel McGrath, Director
E-mail: rmcgrath@bizjournals.com
Ed: Jacob Dirr. **Description:** Retail sector in Austin, Texas has outpaced the national average in value, mid-tier, high-end and drugs retail sectors, according to a report by Pitney Bowes. The national consulting firm's report has projected growth in every sector until the end of fiscal 2012. Data regarding other sectors is also included. **Availability:** Print; Online.

32260 ■ *"Retail Doesn't Cross Borders: Here's Why and What To Do About It"* in *Harvard Business Review (Vol. 90, April 2012, No. 4, pp. 104)*
Pub: Harvard Business Review Press
Contact: Moderna V. Pfizer, Contact
Ed: Marcel Corstjens, Rajiv Lal. **Description:** Globalization poses challenges for retailers, such as competing directly with well established local businesses. To succeed, retailers should enter markets at the right time, focus not on synergies but on differentiation, and introduce new and innovative products and services.

32261 ■ *"Retail Loyalty in the Digital Age is Focus of Retail Insights Southeast (RISE) Event"* *in GlobeNewswire (August 21, 2012)*
Pub: Comtex News Network Inc.
Contact: Kan Devnani, President
Description: The first annual Retail Insights Southeast (RISE) retail/shopper marketing event was held in Charlotte, North Carolina September 18, 2012. Representatives from retailers such as Family Dollar and Food Lion as well as brands like Coca-Cola, Clorox, Kraft Foods and Unilever were in attendance. **Availability:** Print; Online.

32262 ■ *"Retail Product Management: Buying and Merchandising"*
Pub: Routledge, Taylor & Francis Group
Released: Third edition. **Description:** Due to the rise in Internet use, retailers are facing challenges associated with more informed buyers, technological advances, and the competitive environment. Retail ethics are also examined.

32263 ■ *"Retail Remains Hot as More Stores Browse Around Houston"* *in Houston Business Journal (Vol. 44, January 17, 2014, No. 37, pp. 9A)*
Pub: American City Business Journals, Inc.
Contact: Mike Olivieri, Executive Vice President
Released: Weekly. **Price:** $4, Introductory 4-week offer(Digital & Print). **Description:** Houston, Texas-based Evergreen Commercial Realty president, Lilly Golden, has revealed that the city has 15 new retail projects under construction and about 30 other projects in the pipeline. Golden believes Houston's low vacancy rate and high rent growth in Class A assets cause high demand from investors nationally. The boom in the retail sector is also examined. **Availability:** Print; Online.

32264 ■ *The Retail Revolution: How Wal-Mart Created a Brave New World of Business*
Ed: Nelson Lichtenstein. **Released:** June 08, 2010. **Price:** $20, paperback; $7.99, e-book; $2.84, kindle; $15.89, hardcover; $1.93, hardcover(51 Used from $1.93); $15.86, hardcover(8 New from $15.86); $9.80, hardcover(1 Collectible from $9.80); $1.36, Paperback(50 Used from $1.36); $9.95, Paperback(31 New from $9.95). **Description:** Comprehensive discussion on how Wal-Mart changed retailing, and its place in the changing global economy. **Availability:** E-book; Print.

32265 ■ *"Retail Slump Deflates Greater Cincinnati Development"* *in Business Courier (Vol. 24, February 28, 2008, No. 47, pp. 1)*
Pub: American City Business Journals, Inc.
Contact: Mike Olivieri, Executive Vice President
Ed: Lisa Biank Fasig. **Description:** 2007 sales of the retail industry are the slowest since the year 2003, driving retail stores to reconsider their expansion plans for 2008. A number of retail projects have been delayed, cancelled or altered, including Newport Pavilion, Rivers Crossing, Wal-Mart Supercenters, Legacy Place and Millworks. The impacts of retail slowdown on development projects are analyzed further. **Availability:** Online.

32266 ■ *"Retailers at the Ready to Adopt Mobile Pay Options"* *in Dallas Business Journal (Vol. 35, August 24, 2012, No. 50, pp. 1)*
Pub: Baltimore Business Journal
Contact: Rhonda Pringle, President
E-mail: rpringle@bizjournals.com
Ed: Steven R. Thompson. **Description:** Dallas-Fort Worth-based major retailers have been looking for ways to integrate the apps and mobile technology into their customer experience. The retailers formed the Irving, Texas-based Merchant Customer Exchange to develop mobile payment technology. **Availability:** Print; Online.

32267 ■ *"Retailers Report 'Shrinkage' - Disappearance of Inventory - on the Rise"* *in Arkansas Business (Vol. 26, September 28, 2009, No. 39, pp. 17)*
Pub: Arkansas Business Publishing Group
Contact: Mitch Bettis, President

Ed: Mark Friedman. **Description:** According to a National Retail Security Survey report released last June, retailers across the country have lost about $36.5 billion in shrinkage, most of it at the hands of employees and shoplifters alike. Statistical data included. **Availability:** Online.

32268 ■ *"Retailers Tap into War-Room Creativity of Employees"* *in Globe & Mail (March 12, 2007, pp. B1)*
Ed: Marina Strauss. **Description:** The methods adopted by Canadian Tire Corporation Ltd. to utilize the creative abilities of its employees for innovation during new product development are discussed. **Availability:** Print; Online.

32269 ■ *"Retailers, Your Will, and More"* *in Agency Sales Magazine (Vol. 39, July 2009, No. 7, pp. 46)*
Description: IRS audit guide for small retail businesses is presented. Tips on how to make a will with multiple beneficiaries are discussed together with medical expenses that cannot be deducted.

32270 ■ *"The Return of the Infomercial"* *in Canadian Business (Vol. 83, September 14, 2010, No. 15, pp. 19)*
Pub: Rogers Media Inc.
Contact: Neil Spivak, Chief Executive Officer
Ed: James Cowan. **Description:** Infomercials or direct response ads have helped some products succeed in the marketplace. The success of infomercials is due to the cheap advertising rates, expansion into retail stores and the products' oddball appeal. Insights into the popularity of infomercial products on the Internet and on television are given. **Availability:** Online.

32271 ■ *"Riding High"* *in Small Business Opportunities (November 2008)*
Description: Profile of David Sanborn who found a way to turn his passion for biking into a moneymaking opportunity by opening his own bicycle shops; Sanborn's goal is to become the largest independent bike retailer in the United States.

32272 ■ *"The Rise of Pompei"* *in Retail Merchandiser (Vol. 51, September-October 2011, No. 5, pp. 13)*
Description: Soho creative consulting group follows its C3 philosophy to create an invigorated brand experience that transforms customers from consumers to empowered buyers. Pompei AD is a leading creative consultancy that specializes in design and branding for retail, museum, hospitality, and other sectors. **Availability:** Print; Online.

32273 ■ *"Ritzy Retail"* *in Time (September 17, 2012)*
Ed: Christopher Matthews. **Description:** The continuing impact of the 2008 global economic crisis is evident in shopping mall vacancy rates, currently at 8.9 percent compared to the normal five to six percent prior to 2007. However, malls anchored by high-end, luxury retailers continues to do well because upscale malls target the wealthier demographic. Malls serving low- to middle-income shoppers are lagging because their target consumers cannot afford to shop. These consumers are trading down to discount and dollar stores creating a hollow in the middle of the retail spectrum. **Availability:** Online.

32274 ■ *"Rule of the Masses: Reinventing Fashion Via Crowdsourcing"* *in WWD (Vol. 200, July 26, 2010, No. 17, pp. 1)*
Pub: Conde Nast Publications
Contact: Agnes Chu, President
Ed: Cate T. Corcoran. **Description:** Large apparel brands and retailers are crowdsourcing as a way to increase customer loyalty and to build their businesses. **Availability:** PDF; Download; Online.

32275 ■ *"Same-Day Delivery's Second Act"* *in Inc. (Vol. 36, March 2014, No. 2, pp. 87)*
Pub: Mansueto Ventures L.L.C.
Contact: Stephanie Mehta, Chief Executive Officer

Description: New technology is helping electronic commerce to be reliable and profitable while offering same day delivery. Profiles of delivery services competing for retail contracts include Instacart, Zookal, Postmates, to name a few. Statistical data included. **Availability:** Online.

32276 ■ *"Sears and H&R Block Offer New Tax Preparation Options and Savings Through Tax Season"* *in Benzinga.com (January 30, 2012)*
Description: Individuals preparing their own tax forms can file using www.sears.com/hrblock and receive a 15 percent discount on the purchase of Basic, Deluxe, and Premium H&R Block online editions. H&R Block at Sears also offers free 1040EZ filing online and in Sears stores. Customers filing on the site can also import previous year's tax data from TurboTax and TaxAct Online.

32277 ■ *"Secrets To Trade Show Success"* *in Women Entrepreneur (September 12, 2008)*
Description: Trade shows require an enormous amount of work, but they are an investment that can pay off handsomely because they allow a business to get their product or service in front of their target market. Advice regarding trade shows is given including selecting the correct venue, researching the affair and following up on leads obtained at the event. **Availability:** Online.

32278 ■ *"Sedentary Shoppers: Point, Click, Buy"* *in Barron's (Vol. 90, September 6, 2010, No. 36, pp. 11)*
Pub: Barron's Editorial & Corporate Headquarters
Ed: Vito J. Racanelli. **Description:** Non-travel online retail sales from January to July 2010 increased nine percent which indicates that online shopping for the coming holidays will be good. Online sales are outpacing traditional shopping, but pricing is still critical. **Availability:** Online.

32279 ■ *Selling Online: Canada's Bestselling Guide to Becoming a Successful E-Commerce Merchant*
Description: Helps individuals build online retail enterprises; this updated version includes current tools, information and success strategies, how to launch an online storefront, security, marketing strategies, and mistakes to avoid. **Availability:** Online.

32280 ■ *"Seven Things Great Employers Do (That Others Don't); Unusual, Innovative, and Proven Tactics To Create Productive and Profitable Working Environments"* *in Gallup Business Journal (April 15, 2014)*
Pub: Gallup, Inc.
Contact: Jon Clifton, Chief Executive Officer
Price: $8.95. **Description:** Seven unusual, innovative, and proven tactics that create productive and profitable working environments are examined through researching 32 companies. These firms represented many industries, including healthcare, financial services, hospitality, manufacturing, and retail throughout the world. **Availability:** Print; PDF; Online.

32281 ■ *"Shoppers Targets an Upscale Move"* *in Globe & Mail (January 19, 2007, pp. B4)*
Ed: Marina Strauss. **Description:** Shoppers Drug Mart Corp.'s plan to boost sales of cosmetics and take up global sourcing to offer new products is discussed. **Availability:** Online.

32282 ■ *"ShopSmart: Discounts On Brand-Name Products at Dollar Store"* *in Entertainment Close-Up (July 17, 2012)*
Description: According to a report by ShopSmart magazine, 76 percent of women stated they shopped at a dollar store 3-4 times in the past year. The report also discusses ways shoppers can save money on name brand and private-label products at dollar stores. Dollar stores have gone mainstream by providing retailers with national brand items. **Availability:** Print; Online.

32283 ■ *"Silver Springs Creamery Opens Retail Store" in Bellingham Business Journal (Vol. March 2010, pp. 3)*
Pub: Sound Publishing Inc.
Contact: Josh O'Connor, President
Ed: Isaac Bonnell. **Description:** Eric Sundstrom, owner of Silver Springs Creamery, announced the opening of its on-site retail store that will sell the farm's goat and cow cheese, yogurt, ice cream and flesh milk.

32284 ■ *"Six Sears Board Members to Resign in April" in Globe & Mail (March 1, 2006, pp. B1)*
Ed: Marina Strauss. **Description:** The reasons behind the departure of six board members of Sears Canada Inc. are presented. **Availability:** Online.

32285 ■ *"The Sky's the Limit" in Retail Merchandiser (Vol. 51, July-August 2011, No. 4, pp. 64)*
Description: Mars Retail Group (MRG) is the licensing division handling M&M's Brand Candies. Since taking over the brand they have expanded from 12 licensees to 50 licensees with new offerings. **Availability:** Online.

32286 ■ *"Small Business Sales: 6 Strategies for Prospecting" in Small Business Economic Trends (April 2008, pp. 7)*
Pub: National Federation of Independent Business
Contact: Brad Close, President
Ed: William C. Dunkelberg, Holly Wade. **Description:** Two tables and a graph resenting sales figures of small businesses in the U.S. is presented. Statistics for sales changes and sales expectations are provided. The figures in the graph include data from 1986 to 2008. **Availability:** Print; Online.

32287 ■ *"Smarts Drive Sales" in Pet Product News (Vol. 64, December 2010, No. 12, pp. 1)*
Ed: Karen Shugart. **Description:** Retailers could make smart decisions by deciding how to best attract customers into their stores or resolving whether to nurture in-store or buy herps (reptiles) from suppliers. Paying attention to these smart decisions could help boost customer interest in herps and address customer demands. **Availability:** Online.

32288 ■ *"Staying Social Complements Retail Goals" in Pet Product News (Vol. 66, September 2012, No. 9, pp. 34)*
Description: Pet supplies retailers can take advantage of social media to brand the store and its products and facilitate dialogue with consumers. As these retail goals are realized, profits can be attained. Strategies that can enable pet supplies retailers to create business networks through social media marketing are also presented. **Availability:** Online.

32289 ■ *"Steady Spending In Retail, But Job Losses Are Rising" in Business Week (September 22, 2008, No. 4100, pp. 13)*
Ed: Tara Kalwarski. **Description:** Retail jobs have begun to decline on the national level despite the two percent growth in the industry over the last year; much of the growth has been attributed to the sales of higher-priced oil products.

32290 ■ *"Study: New Moms Build A Lot of Brand Buzz" in Brandweek (Vol. 49, April 21, 2008, No. 16, pp. 7)*
Description: According to a new survey which sampled 1,721 pregnant women and new moms, this demographic is having 109 word-of-mouth conversations per week concerning products, services and brands. Two-thirds of these conversations directly involve brand recommendations. The Internet is driving these word-of-mouth, or W-O-M, conversations among this segment, beating out magazines, television and other forms of media. **Availability:** Online.

32291 ■ *"Suited for Success" in Retail Merchandiser (Vol. 51, July-August 2011, No. 4, pp. 6)*
Description: MyBestFit is a size-matching body scanner that helps consumers find the perfect size clothing for themselves, giving brick and mortar retailers an edge on ecommerce competitors. **Availability:** Online.

32292 ■ *"SunBank Plans Expansion Via Wal-Mart" in Business Journal-Serving Phoenix and the Valley of the Sun (Vol. 10, November 8, 2007)*
Pub: Phoenix Business Journal
Contact: Alex McAlister, Director
E-mail: amcalister@bizjournals.com
Ed: Chris Casacchia. **Description:** SunBank plans to install 12 to 14 branches in Wal-Mart stores in Arizona and hire 100 bankers by the end of 2008. Wal-Mart also offers financial products at other stores through partnerships with other banks. **Availability:** Print; Online.

32293 ■ *"Survey Says Commercial Real Estate Headed for Turbulence" in Commercial Property News (March 17, 2008)*
Description: Commercial real estate sector is declining due to the sluggish U.S. economy. According to a recent survey, national office, retail and hospitality markets are also on the decline. **Availability:** Online.

32294 ■ *"Tapping the 'Well' in Wellness" in Pet Product News (Vol. 64, November 2010, No. 11, pp. 1)*
Ed: Wendy Bedwell-Wilson. **Description:** Healthy food and treats are among the leading wellness products being sought by customers from specialty retailers to keep their pets healthy. With this demand for pet wellness products, retailers suggest making sure that staff know key ingredients to emphasize to customers. Other insights into this trend and ways to engage customers are also discussed. **Availability:** Online.

32295 ■ *"Targeting New Growth" in San Antonio Business Journal (Vol. 28, May 23, 2014, No. 15, pp. 4)*
Pub: American City Business Journals, Inc.
Contact: Mike Olivieri, Executive Vice President
Released: May 23, 2014. **Description:** Reports show that many retailers are discovering new opportunities along Austin Highway in Texas. Observers believe that the rise of multifamily housing contributed to the retail turnaround. However, the increase in property values can have a negative impact on the retail sector. **Availability:** Print; Online.

32296 ■ *"Tax-Free Zones Need Shows: Out-of-State Shoppers Are Key To Success" in Crain's Detroit Business (Vol. 24, January 28, 2008, No. 4)*
Pub: Crain Communications Inc.
Contact: Barry Asin, President
Ed: Daniel Duggan. **Description:** Sales tax-free zones are being considered by Michigan's legislators in order to promote the state as a conference destination. **Availability:** Online.

32297 ■ *"Tax Tip: Streamlining Sales Tax Collections" in Pet Product News (Vol. 66, September 2012, No. 9, pp. 38)*
Ed: Mark E. Battersby. **Description:** Pointers on how pet supplies retailers and managers can streamline sales taxes are presented. Businesses are being challenge by the pressure to collect taxes on goods sold to local customers and competititon from Internet merchants that are not required to collect sales taxes. **Availability:** Online.

32298 ■ *"Teachable Moments: Worth Every Penny" in Pet Product News (Vol. 64, December 2010, No. 12, pp. 34)*
Ed: Cheryl Reeves. **Description:** Pet bird retailers can attain both outreach to customers and enhanced profitability by staging educational events such as the annual Parrot Palooza event of Burlington, New Jersey-based Bird Paradise. Aside from attracting a global audience, Parrot Palooza features seminars, workshops, classes, and bird-related contests. **Availability:** Print; Online.

32299 ■ *"Three Trails Blazes Tax Credit Deal" in The Business Journal-Serving Metropolitan Kansas City (Vol. 27, November 7, 2008, No. 9)*
Description: Three Trails Redevelopment LLC plans to redevelop the Bannister Mall area. The Missouri Development Finance Board is expected to approve

$30 million in tax credits for the project. A verbal agreement on the terms and conditions has already been reached according to the agency's executive director.

32300 ■ *"Tower City Hopes Restrictions on Minors Boost Retail Center" in Crain's Cleveland Business (Vol. 28, November 5, 2007, No. 44)*
Pub: Crain Communications Inc.
Contact: K. C. Crain, President
Ed: John Booth. **Description:** Tower City Center, a shopping mall in downtown Cleveland, hopes to generate more business with their new rules restricting the access of unaccompanied minors after 2:30 p.m. **Availability:** Online.

32301 ■ *"The Trouble With $150,000 Wine" in Barron's (Vol. 88, July 7, 2008, No. 27, pp. 33)*
Pub: Dow Jones & Company Inc.
Contact: Almar Latour, Chief Executive Officer
Ed: Jay Palmer. **Description:** Review of the book, "The Billionaire's Vinegar: The Mystery of the World's Most Expensive Bottle of Wine," which discusses vintners along with the marketing and distribution of wine as well as the winemaking industry as a whole. **Availability:** Online.

32302 ■ *"Tuesday Morning's Corporate Clearance Rack" in Dallas Business Journal (Vol. 37, February 28, 2014, No. 25, pp. 4)*
Pub: American City Business Journals, Inc.
Contact: Mike Olivieri, Executive Vice President
Released: October 30, 2015. **Description:** Tuesday Morning CEO, Michael Rouleau, has been working to help the company recover from its financial problems. Rouleau has improved the shopping experience from garage sale to discount showroom. The company has also been hiring different executives in the past few years. **Availability:** Print; Online.

32303 ■ *"U.S. Retailer Eyes 'Tween' Market" in Globe & Mail (January 30, 2007, pp. B1)*
Ed: Marina Strauss. **Description:** The decision of Tween Brands Inc. (Too Incorporated) to open 100 new stores in Canada as part of its expansion is discussed. The company's focus on targeting girls for its products is detailed. **Availability:** Online.

32304 ■ *"Unused Coupons Still Pay Off" in Harvard Business Review (Vol. 90, May 2012, No. 5, pp. 32)*
Pub: Harvard Business Review Press
Contact: Moderna V. Pfizer, Contact
Ed: Rajkumar Venkatesan, Paul Farris. **Price:** $6, hardcopy and PDF. **Description:** Unredeemed coupons have been found to create a sales lift for retailers as they increase awareness of a retailer or a brand even when consumers do not use them. Redemption rates should still be monitored however to assess campaign effectiveness. **Availability:** Print; Online.

32305 ■ *"Uptick in Clicks: Nordstrom's Online Sales Surging" in Puget Sound Business Journal (Vol. 29, August 22, 2008, No. 18, pp. 1)*
Description: Nordstrom Inc.'s online division grew its sales by 15 percent in the second quarter of 2008, compared to 2007's 4.3 percent in overall decline. The company expects their online net sales to reach $700 million in 2008 capturing eight percent of overall sales. **Availability:** Print; Online.

32306 ■ *"Uptown Goes Local To Fill Final Entertainment District Vacancy" in Birmingham Business Journal (Vol. 31, May 9, 2014, No. 19, pp. 8)*
Pub: American City Business Journals, Inc.
Contact: Mike Olivieri, Executive Vice President
Released: Weekly. **Price:** $4, introductory 4-week offer(Digital & Print). **Description:** A new butcher, beer and wine shop called Bottle & Bone will become the final tenant for the new Uptown entertainment district in Birmingham, Alabama, slated to open by

fall 2014. The shop is owned by Freshfully founder Jen Barnett and will focus on local offerings, particularly fresh meats, wine and beer. **Availability:** Print; Online.

32307 ∎ *"Village at Waugh Chapel $275M Expansion Begins"* in *Baltimore Business Journal (Vol. 28, August 27, 2010, No. 16, pp. 1)*
Pub: Baltimore Business Journal
Contact: Rhonda Pringle, President
E-mail: rpringle@bizjournals.com

Ed: Daniel J. Sernovitz. **Description:** Developer Greenberg Gibbons Corporation has broken ground on a $275 million, 1.2 million-square-foot addition to its Village at the Waugh Chapel mixed-use complex. Aside from creating 2,600 permanent jobs, the addition, named Village South, is expected to lure Target and Wegmans Food Markets to Crofton, Maryland. Funding for this project is discussed. **Availability:** Print.

32308 ∎ *"Wal-Mart China Woes Add Up"* in *Wall Street Journal Eastern Edition (October 17, 2011, pp. B3)*
Pub: Dow Jones & Company Inc.
Contact: Almar Latour, Chief Executive Officer

Ed: Laurie Burkitt. **Description:** Woes for Wal-Mart Inc.'s subsidiary in China are adding up as Wal-Mart China president and chief executive Ed Chan stepped down, as well as the company's senior vice president for human resources, Clara Wong. The company has been charged by regulators with mislabeling pork products, the result which has forced stores to close. Sales in China have been slow at the retail stores. **Availability:** Online.

32309 ∎ *"'Wal-Mart Effect' Feeds Grocer Price Wars"* in *Globe & Mail (March 15, 2007, pp. B14)*
Ed: Marina Strauss. **Description:** The decrease in profit reports by Canadian grocery giants amidst high expansion plans by Wal-Mart Stores Inc. are discussed. This industry is witnessing the most severe pricing competitions in recent times. **Availability:** Print; Online.

32310 ∎ *"Wal-Mart Is Testing Mobile Checkout: App Would Let Shoppers Scan Items, Pay at Kiosks; Giant Saves $12 Million a Year for Every Second It Can Cut"* in *Wall Street Journal. Europe (September 4, 2012, pp. A19)*
Ed: Shelly Banjo. **Description:** Wal-Mart Stores Inc. is testing a new checkout system at some of its US stores that would allow customers to scan items as they browse through stores and pay at self-service kiosks. Wal-Mart estimates savigs of $12 million for every second it cuts from the checkout process. **Availability:** Online.

32311 ∎ *"Wal-Mart Offering In-Store Tax Return Preparation Services"* in *Tax Notes (Vol. 134, January 16, 2012, No. 3, pp. 301)*
Ed: Eric Kroh. **Description:** Wal-Mart is offering tax preparation services to customers in their retail stores. Details of the program included. **Availability:** Online.

32312 ∎ *"Wal-Mart Proposed for Timmerman Plaza"* in *Business Journal-Milwaukee (Vol. 28, December 31, 2010, No. 14, pp. A1)*
Pub: The Business Journal
Contact: Heather Ladage, President
E-mail: hladage@bizjournals.com

Ed: Sean Ryan. **Description:** Dickson, Tennessee-based Gatlin Development Company Inc. owner Franklin C. Gatlin III revealed plans for a new Wal-Mart store in Timmerman Plaza in Milwaukee, Wisconsin. Wal-Mart plans to open up approximately 18 new stores in southeast Wisconsin in 2012 and the Timmerman project is the first of four that Gatlin will submit for city approval. **Availability:** Print; Online.

32313 ∎ *"Wal-Mart Sharpens Focus on Roxbury"* in *Boston Business Journal (Vol. 31, July 8, 2011, No. 24, pp. 1)*
Pub: Boston Business Journal
Contact: Carolyn M. Jones, President
E-mail: cmjones@bizjournals.com

Ed: Mary Moore. **Price:** $4. **Description:** Wal-Mart Stores is boosting its search for a possible location in the Roxbury section of Boston, Massachusetts. The search is focused on underserved communities in terms of jobs and access to reasonably-priced merchandise. The extent Boston's African American community has clashed with Mayor Thomas M. Memino over the accommodations of the retailer in Roxbury is discussed. **Availability:** Print; Online.

32314 ∎ *"Walk-In Retail Clinics Enjoying Robust Health"* in *Memphis Business Journal (Vol. 34, April 27, 2012, No. 2, pp. 1)*
Pub: Baltimore Business Journal
Contact: Rhonda Pringle, President
E-mail: rpringle@bizjournals.com

Description: Walk-in clinics in Memphis, Tennessee have reported increased profits in 2012. Such clinics offer consumers immediate care while retail shopping. **Availability:** Print; Online.

32315 ∎ *"Walmart's New-Store Roll-Out Proving to be Development Magnet"* in *San Antonio Business Journal (Vol. 27, January 24, 2014, No. 51, pp. 4)*
Pub: American City Business Journals, Inc.
Contact: Mike Olivieri, Executive Vice President

Released: Weekly. **Price:** $4, Introductory 4-week offer(Digital & Print). **Description:** Bentonville, Arkansas-based Walmart Stores have developed an aggressive plan to expand its base of business in greater San Antonio, Texas with new Supercenters that opened for business. The Walmart Supercenters are creating an impact on the city's retail market as it spurs the interests of other retailers. Walmart's concept is also examined. **Availability:** Print; Online.

32316 ∎ *"Want Leverage? Multi-Unit Franchisees Deliver Substantial Savings"* in *Franchising World (Vol. 42. October 2010, No. 10, pp. 39)*
Pub: International Franchise Association
Contact: Matthew Haller, President
E-mail: mhaller@franchise.org

Ed: Aziz Hashim. **Description:** Many retail franchises selling the same product are able to buy in bulk. Volume-buying can save money for any franchise. **Availability:** Online.

32317 ∎ *"Web Move Puts Rack Ahead of Pack"* in *Puget Sound Business Journal (Vol. 35, May 16, 2014, No. 4, pp. 8)*
Pub: American City Business Journals, Inc.
Contact: Mike Olivieri, Executive Vice President

Description: Upscale retailer, Norstrom Inc., launched a Website for Nordstrom Rack in the hopes of boosting sales for its discount arm by 10 to 20 percent. Terry Boyle, present of Nordstrom Rack's online store, is not concerned that the site might steal traffic from their retail establishments. **Availability:** Online.

32318 ∎ *"Web Tax Holiday About to End"* in *Silicon Valley/San Jose Business Journal (Vol. 30, September 7, 2012, No. 24, pp. 1)*
Pub: Baltimore Business Journal
Contact: Rhonda Pringle, President
E-mail: rpringle@bizjournals.com

Description: Retailers outside California will be required to charge sales tax to customers in the state making online purchases. It is believed that the sales tax will provide an additional boost for independent booksellers. These sellers claim that they have been at a disadvantage becazuse they were required to automatically charge customers with an 8.375 percent tax. **Availability:** Print; Mailing list; Online.

32319 ∎ *"Wedding Present Shopping - What to Get the Couple Who Have Everything"* in *Benzinga.com (April 19, 2011)*
Released: April 19, 2011. **Description:** Tips for purchasing the perfect wedding gift are outlined. **Availability:** Online.

32320 ∎ *"Well-Heeled Startup Plots Course for a Run at Garmin"* in *Business Journal Portland (Vol. 27, November 12, 2010, No. 37, pp. 1)*
Pub: Portland Business Journal
Contact: Andy Giegerich, Managing Editor
E-mail: agiegerich@bizjournals.com

Description: Oh! Shoes LLC expects to receive about $1.5 million in funding from angel investors, while marketing a new line of high heel shoes that are comfortable, healthy, and attractive. The new line of shoes will use the technology of athletic footwear while having the look of an Italian designer. Oh! Shoes hopes to generate $35 million in sales by 2014. **Availability:** Print; Online.

32321 ∎ *"What Can Michael Brown Do For Biz?"* in *Washington Business Journal (Vol. 31, June 15, 2012, No. 8, pp. 1)*
Pub: Baltimore Business Journal
Contact: Rhonda Pringle, President
E-mail: rpringle@bizjournals.com

Description: Michael Brown, Washington DC's new economic development point man, aims to ease business regulation, speed up retail development, and create opportunities for local contractors. He is also expected to deal with oversight of all housing and economic development issues and agencies within the state. **Availability:** Print; Online.

32322 ∎ *"What the Future Holds for Consumers"* in *Black Enterprise (Vol. 41, August 2010, No. 1, pp. 47)*
Pub: Earl G. Graves Ltd.
Contact: Earl Graves, Jr., President

Ed: Sheiresa Ngo. **Description:** The way people purchase goods and service has changed with technology. With an increased focus on security (as well as privacy and fairness) the U.S. Congress began regulating the credit card industry with the Fair Credit Reporting Act of 1970 and the Credit Card Accountability, Responsibility, and Disclosure (CARD) Act of 2009. **Availability:** Online.

32323 ∎ *"What is an SKU and How Your Small Business Can Use One"* in *Small Business Trends(March 3, 2023)*
URL(s): smallbiztrends.com/2023/03/sku.html
Ed: Samantha Lile. **Released:** March 03, 2023. **Description:** Defines SKU and discusses why small businesses should have them for their products. **Availability:** Online.

32324 ∎ *"What Slump? Davis Likely to Fill Borders Gap Quickly"* in *Sacramento Business Journal (Vol. 28, July 29, 2011, No. 22, pp. 1)*
Pub: Sacramento Business Journal
Contact: Stephanie Fretwell, Director
E-mail: sfretwell@bizjournals.com

Ed: Kelly Johnson. **Description:** The nationwide shutdown of Borders bookstores worry most cities, but not Davis, California, which is experiencing a relatively low retail vacancy rate of 6.3 percent. **Availability:** Online.

32325 ∎ *"What's More Important: Talent or Engagement? A Study With Retailer ANN INC. Seeks To Find the Essential Ingredients To High-Performing Managers and Employees"* in *Gallup Business Journal (April 22, 2014)*
Pub: Gallup, Inc.
Contact: Jon Clifton, Chief Executive Officer

Description: ANN INC. is a leading women's clothing retailer that is exploring the necessary steps to achieving both high-performing managers and employees. The firm found that hiring people with the right talent and engaging them will maximize performance. **Availability:** Online.

32326 ■ "Why the Gap is Stalking Lululemon" in Canadian Business (Vol. 85, August 22, 2012, No. 14, pp. 7)

Ed: Jim Sutherland. **Description:** Lululemon Athletica is facing competition against Gap Inc.'s Athleta as the retail giant plans to have about 50 new shops across Canada by the end of 2012. Athleta is also carrying lines of yoga- and activewear similar to that of Lululemon's and are even located near their stores. **Availability:** Online.

32327 ■ "Why Good Jobs Are Good for Retailers: Some Companies Are Investing In Their Workers and Reaping Healthy Profits" in Harvard Business Review (Vol. 90, January-February 2012, No.1-2, pp. 124)

Pub: Harvard Business Review Press
Contact: Moderna V. Pfizer, Contact

Ed: Zeynep Ton. **Price:** $8.95. **Description:** Four key operational practices can help retailers sever the trade-off between investing in employees and maintaining low prices. These are: offering fewer promotions and SKUs, cross-training workers rather than varifying their number to match customer traffic, eliminating waste while preserving staff, and empowering workers to make prompt decisions. **Availability:** Online; PDF.

32328 ■ "Will mCommerce Make Black Friday Green?" in Retail Merchandiser (Vol. 51, September-October 2011, No. 5, pp. 8)

Description: Retailers speculate the possibilities of mobile commerce and are implementing strategies at their stores. Consumers using mobile devices accounted for only 0.1 percent of visits to retail Websites on Black Friday 2009 and rose to 5.6 percent in 2010; numbers are expected to rise for 2011. **Availability:** Print; Online.

32329 ■ "Worldwide Food Services (EREI) Tests Mini Dollar Store Program" in Marketwired (August 6, 2009)

Pub: Comtex News Network Inc.
Contact: Kan Devnani, President

Description: Mini Dollar Stores and Eagle View LLC, wholly-owned subsidiaries of Worldwide Food Services, Inc., recently met with government officials and purchasing agents to lay out a test program which would distribute Mini Dollar Store items into VA hospital gift shops.

32330 ■ "Young Adults, Childless May Help Fuel Post-Recession Rebound" in Pet Product News (Vol. 64, November 2010, No. 11, pp. 4)

Ed: David Lummis. **Description:** Pet industry retailers and marketers are encouraged to tap into the young adult and childless couple sectors to boost consumer traffic and sales to pre-recession levels. Among young adult owners, pet ownership increased from 40 percent in 2003 to 49 percent in 2009. Meanwhile, the childless couple sector represented 63 percent of all dog/cat owners in 2009. **Availability:** Online.

32331 ■ "Zacks Industry Outlook Highlights: Starbucks, Nike, Big Lots, Deckers Outdoor and Family Dollar Stores" in PR Newswire (August 8, 2012)

Pub: PR Newswire Association LLC.

Description: Zacks takes a look at the retail industry and covers the outlook for this highly competitive sector. Retailers discussed include: Starbucks Corporation, Nike Inc., Big Lots Inc., Deckers Outdoor Corporation, and Family Dollar Stores Inc. **Availability:** Online.

32332 ■ "Zacks Industry Outlook Highlights: Target, Cabela's and Family Dollar Stores" in Marketing Weekly News (April 28, 2012, pp. 351)

Description: Zacks Industry Outlook focuses on retailers such as Target, Cabela's and Family Dollar Stores. An examination of ways retailers are working to improve sales and profits and productivity is given,

including supply-chain management, cost containment, inventory management, and merchandise initiatives. **Availability:** Print; Online.

32333 ■ "Zara Eludes the Pain in Spain: Clothing Giant Inditex Sees Its First-Quarter Profits Rise By 30 Percent" in Canadian Business (Vol. 85, September 17, 2012, No. 14, pp. 67)

Ed: Bryan Borzykowski. **Released:** September 17, 2012. **Description:** Clothing retailer Inditex reported a 30 percent increase in profit in the first quarter of 2012 and 15 percent increase in sales year over year. The company's unique business model was attributed to its growth, which also appeals to income investors.

STATISTICAL SOURCES

32334 ■ Direct-to-Consumer Retailing - US - January 2021

URL(s): store.mintel.com/report/direct-to-consumer-retailing-us-january-2021

Price: $4,366.35. **Description:** Downloadable report discussing the data from direct to consumer shopping. Report includes an executive summary, interactive databook, PowerPoint presentation, infographic overview, report PDF, and previous years data. **Availability:** PDF.

32335 ■ Hispanics: Digital Trends & Impact of COVID-19 One Year Later - US - April 2021

URL(s): store.mintel.com/report/hispanics-digital-trends-impact-of-covid-19-one-year-later-us-april-2021

Price: $4,366.35. **Description:** Downloadable report discussing the impact the COVID-19 pandemic has had on the Hispanic community and their shopping habits. Provides data on Hispanics' approach to technology and attitudes about digital products. Report includes an executive summary, interactive databook, PowerPoint presentation, infographic overview, report PDF, and previous years data. **Availability:** PDF.

32336 ■ RMA Annual Statement Studies

Pub: Risk Management Association
Contact: Nancy Foster, President

Released: Annual. **Description:** Contains composite balance sheets and income statements for more than 360 industries, including the accounting, auditing, and bookkeeping industries. Also contains five years of comparative historical data for discerning trends. Includes 16 commonly used ratios, computed for most of the size groupings for nearly every industry.

32337 ■ U.S. Children's Clothing Market Report 2021

URL(s): store.mintel.com/report/us-childrens-clothing-market-report

Price: $4,366.35. **Description:** Downloadable report covering data analysis of parents and how and why they shop for their children's clothing. Report includes an executive summary, interactive databook, PowerPoint presentation, infographic overview, report PDF, and previous years data. **Availability:** PDF.

32338 ■ U.S. Key Elements of Ecommerce Market Report 2021

URL(s): store.mintel.com/report/us-key-elements-of-ecommerce

Price: $4,366.35. **Description:** Downloadable report providing data on the online shopping habits of US consumers. Report includes an executive summary, interactive databook, PowerPoint presentation, infographic overview, report PDF, and previous years data. **Availability:** PDF.

32339 ■ US Footwear Online Retailing Market Report 2021

URL(s): store.mintel.com/report/us-footwear-online-retailing-market-report

Price: $4,366.35. **Description:** Downloadable report providing data on the online footwear retailing market. Report includes an executive summary, interactive databook, PowerPoint presentation, infographic overview, report PDF, and previous years data. **Availability:** PDF.

32340 ■ US Hispanics: Online Shopping Behaviors Market Report 2021

URL(s): store.mintel.com/report/us-hispanics-online-shopping-behaviors-us-market-report

Price: $4,366.35. **Description:** Downloadable report providing data on the online shopping habits of Hispanics living in the US. Report includes an executive summary, interactive databook, PowerPoint presentation, infographic overview, report PDF, and previous years data. **Availability:** PDF.

32341 ■ US Online Apparel Retailing (Men's and Women's) Market Report 2021

URL(s): store.mintel.com/report/us-online-apparel-retailing-mens-womens-market-report

Price: $4,366.35. **Description:** Downloadable report examining the shopping habits, both online and in-store, for clothing. Details how the Covid-19 pandemic affected shoppers. Report includes and executive summary, interactive databook, PowerPoint presentation, infographic overview, report pdf, and previous years data. **Availability:** PDF.

32342 ■ US Retail and eCommerce & the Impact of COVID-19 - One Year Later 2021

URL(s): store.mintel.com/report/us-state-of-retail-ecommerce-impact-of-covid-19-one-year-later-market-report

Price: $4,366.35. **Description:** Downloadable report featuring analysis of the impact COVID-19 has had on the retail and eCommerce industries. Report includes an executive summary, interactive databook, PowerPoint presentation, infographic overview, report PDF, and previous years data. **Availability:** PDF.

32343 ■ US Shopping Small Business Market Report 2021

URL(s): store.mintel.com/report/us-shopping-small-businesses-market-report

Price: $4,366.35. **Description:** Downloadable report detailing analysis of US consumers regarding their small business shopping habits. Includes a report on how Covid-19 has impacted shoppers, how they shop, and motivations and barriers. **Availability:** PDF.

TRADE PERIODICALS

32344 ■ NSSRA Newsletter

Pub: National Ski and Snowboard Retailers Association
Contact: Julie Pitts, President
URL(s): www.nssra.com/newsletters

Released: Irregular **Description:** Informs ski and snowboard retail stores on critical industry issues such as guidelines and litigation exposure and marketing. **Availability:** Electronic publishing.

VIDEO/AUDIO MEDIA

32345 ■ Elevated Entrepreneurship: Rural Entrepreneurship with Jessi Roberts

URL(s): mikemichalowicz.com/podcast/episode-255-rural-entrepreneurship-with-jessi-roberts

Ed: Mike Michalowiicz. **Released:** June 03, 2019. **Description:** Podcast explains how to create a successful retail and wholesale business despite the challenges of a rural location.

32346 ■ How I Built This: Poshmark: Manish Chandra

URL(s): wondery.com/shows/how-i-built-this/episode/10386-poshmark-manish-chandra

Ed: Guy Raz. **Released:** February 26, 2024. **Description:** Podcast offers a discussion with the founder of Poshmark, an online retailer for second-hand clothes.

32347 ■ Main Street Business Insights: Mindy Bergstrom, Cooks Emporium

URL(s): mainstreet.org/resources/knowledge-hub/podcast/mindy-bergstrom-cooks-emporium

Ed: Matt Wagner. **Released:** September 11, 2024. **Description:** Podcast features a conversation with the owner of kitchen and home goods stores.

32348 ■ *This Is Small Business: Advice Line with Pete Maldonado of Chomps*
URL(s): wondery.com/shows/how-i-built-this/episode/10386-advice-line-with-pete-maldonado-of-chomps
Ed: Guy Raz. **Released:** May 02, 2024. **Description:** Podcast answers questions from a tea shop owner, a bagel slinger, and a salmon seller.

32349 ■ *Trends and Opportunities for Makers and Retail Businesses with Carla Pellicano of Faire*
URL(s): beingboss.club/podcast/trends-and-opportunities-for-makers-and-retail-businesses
Ed: Emily Thompson. **Released:** November 08, 2022. **Description:** Podcast discusses the unique struggles for small business retailers and makers.

TRADE SHOWS AND CONVENTIONS

32350 ■ **Chicago Shoe Market**
URL(s): chicagoshoemarket.com
Frequency: Annual. **Description:** Tradeshow featuring footwear and accessories for retailers. **Principal Exhibits:** Tradeshow featuring footwear and accessories for retailers.

32351 ■ **Independent Retailers Buying Group Spring Trade Show**
URL(s): n2b.goexposoftware.com/events/wbg22sp/goExpo/public/login.php
Frequency: Annual. **Description:** Retailer tradeshow with a focus on shooting sports, sporting goods, and fall/winter apparel and footwear. **Principal Exhibits:** Retailer tradeshow with a focus on shooting sports, sporting goods, and fall/winter apparel and footwear.

32352 ■ **LINK 2022 Retail Supply Chain Conference**
URL(s): www.rila.org/conferences/retail-supply-chain-conference
Description: Networking, talks, and seminars from supply chain industry leaders to discuss and brainstorm ideas on today's challenges. **Audience:** Supply chain executives. **Principal Exhibits:** Networking, talks, and seminars from supply chain industry leaders to discuss and brainstorm ideas on today's challenges.

32353 ■ **Michigan Shoe Market**
URL(s): www.michiganshoeshow.com
Facebook: www.facebook.com/michiganshoemarket
Frequency: Annual. **Description:** Tradeshow featuring shoes and accessories from manufacturers and retailers from Indiana, Ohio, and Michigan. **Audience:** Shoe retailers. **Principal Exhibits:** Tradeshow featuring shoes and accessories from manufacturers and retailers from Indiana, Ohio, and Michigan.

32354 ■ **Mississippi Market Wholesale Show**
URL(s): www.mismag.com/msmarket
Frequency: Annual. **Description:** Vendor show featuring products to order and sell in retail stores. **Principal Exhibits:** Vendor show featuring products to order and sell in retail stores. **Telecommunication Services:** market@mismag.com.

32355 ■ **MRA January Lansing Market**
URL(s): www.midwestreps.org/midwest-reps-shows/january-market-lansing
Frequency: Semimonthly. **Description:** Show featuring outdoor and snow gear for retailers to sell. **Principal Exhibits:** Show featuring outdoor and snow gear for retailers to sell.

32356 ■ **NATSO Connect**
URL(s): www.natso.com/events/natso-connect-2022
Frequency: Annual. **Description:** Expo and meeting to discuss new trends in the truckstop and plaza industry. **Audience:** Truckstop and travel plaza leaders. **Principal Exhibits:** Expo and meeting to discuss new trends in the truckstop and plaza industry.

32357 ■ **Retail Asset Protection Conference**
Retail Industry Leaders Association (RILA)
99 M St. SE, Ste. 700
Washington, DC 20003
Ph: (202)869-0200
URL: http://www.rila.org
Contact: Brian Dodge, President
E-mail: brian.dodge@rila.org
URL(s): www.rila.org/conferences/retail-asset-protection-conference
Frequency: Annual. **Description:** Offer exemplary teaching and training programs. **Audience:** Industry professionals. **Principal Exhibits:** Offer exemplary teaching and training programs. Dates and Locations: 2025 Apr 27-30 Washington, DC. **Telecommunication Services:** tripp.taylor@rila.org.

32358 ■ **StorePoint Fashion**
URL(s): cpmgevents.com/storepointfashion
Frequency: Annual. **Description:** Trade forum where senior-level retailers network with suppliers. **Audience:** Senior-level retailers. **Principal Exhibits:** Trade forum where senior-level retailers network with suppliers.

CONSULTANTS

32359 ■ **Lougheed Resource Group Inc. (LRG)**
17608 Deer Isle Cir.
Winter Garden, FL 34787
Ph: (407)654-1212
Co. E-mail: info@lrgconstruction.com
URL: http://lrgconstruction.com
Contact: Karen Lougheed, Owner
E-mail: karen@lrgconstruction.com
Description: Provider of building diagnostics, forensic and construction document analysis, litigation support, customized on-site risk reduction workshops, and much more for construction fields and trades related to commercial, residential, institutional, industrial, and recreational projects. **Scope:** Provider of building diagnostics, forensic and construction document analysis, litigation support, customized on-site risk reduction workshops, and much more for construction fields and trades related to commercial, residential, institutional, industrial, and recreational projects. **Founded:** 1987.

32360 ■ **The Schallert Group Inc.**
10247 Highland Meadow Cir., Unit 107
Parker, CO 80134
Ph: (970)281-2923
Co. E-mail: info@jonschallert.com
URL: http://www.jonschallert.com
Contact: Jon Schallert, Consultant
Description: Firm offers services such as in-store assessments, development plans to improve store position, differentiated marketing plans for retail groups, group seminars and training to small business owners on improving overall profitability. **Scope:** Firm offers services such as in-store assessments, development plans to improve store position, differentiated marketing plans for retail groups, group seminars and training to small business owners on improving overall profitability. **Founded:** 1996. **Training:** Business Reinvention: The New Normal on Main Street & Every Street, 2010; Driving Customer Traffic and Sales in This Economy with Destination Principles; Turn Any Business Into A Consumer Destination; Win The War Against Retail Superstores; Seven Critical Steps To Reinventing Mom And Pop; Pumping New Life Into A Stagnant Business; Increasing Sales & Profits as a Destination Business, Nov, 2007; Increase Sales & Profits with Branded Marketing, Nov, 2007; Developing Your Destination Business: Creating Design, Direction, and Dominance, Oct, 2006; Making Your Store a Consumer Destination, Nov, 2006; Turn Any Business Into A Consumer Destination; Win The War Against Retail Superstores; Ten Rules For Courting Today's Aging Consumers; The Key to Driving Customer Traffic & Sales in This Economy.

FRANCHISES AND BUSINESS OPPORTUNITIES

32361 ■ **Adam & Eve Stores**
Description: The adult industry is now offering retail store franchise opportunities. With over 30 years experience and over 4 million customers nationwide, you benefit from the Adam & Eve brand name recognized around the country. **No. of Franchise Units:** 33. **Founded:** 1970. **Franchised:** 2004. **Equity Capital Needed:** $192,000-$345,000; cash $50,000. **Franchise Fee:** $30,000. **Training:** Training and support program will show you everything from planning 'open buys' to buying, working with vendors, merchandise inventory control, and the merchandising and display products in your store. Onsite training prior to opening.

32362 ■ **A Buck or Two Stores Ltd. [Buck or Two Plus!]**
11B Director Ct.
Vaughan, ON, Canada L4L 4S5
Ph: (905)265-3160
Fax: (905)265-3161
Co. E-mail: info@extremeretail.ca
URL: http://www.buckortwo.com
URL(s): test.buckortwo.com
Facebook: www.facebook.com/people/Buck-or-Two-Plus-Corporate-Office/100063689437867
Description: Operator of chain of retail stores. **Founded:** 1990. **Franchised:** 1990. **Equity Capital Needed:** $120,000-$225,000. **Franchise Fee:** 25000. **Royalty Fee:** 6% of net sales. **Training:** Includes 10 days training.

32363 ■ **DirectBuy**
8450 Broadway
Merrillville, IN 46410
Ph: (219)682-2083
Co. E-mail: membercares@directbuy.com
URL: http://www.directbuy.com
Facebook: www.facebook.com/DirectBuy
YouTube: www.youtube.com/user/directbuy
Pinterest: www.pinterest.com/directbuy
Description: Firm engages in membership buying services. **Founded:** 1971. **Training:** Provides 9 weeks training and support.

32364 ■ **Discount Sport Nutrition (DSN)**
7324 Gaston Ave., Ste. No. 124-422
Dallas, TX 75214
Ph: (972)489-7925
Free: 833-GET-SWOLE
Fax: (214)292-8619
Co. E-mail: sales@sportsupplements.com
URL: http://www.sportsupplements.com
Contact: Charles Moser, President
Facebook: www.facebook.com/DiscountSportsNutrition
X (Twitter): x.com/DSNutrition
Instagram: www.instagram.com/DSNTULSA
YouTube: www.youtube.com/user/dsnsportsupplements
Description: Nutritional sport supplements retail store. **No. of Franchise Units:** 6. **Founded:** 1998. **Franchised:** 2000. **Equity Capital Needed:** $92,774-$185,344. **Franchise Fee:** $25,000. **Financial Assistance:** Yes **Training:** 3 phase initial hands on training program located at current stores, as well as your location. Provides assistance with site location, leases, layout design, suppliers, advertising, marketing, and ongoing assistance.

32365 ■ **Fully Promoted**
33 Keltic Plz.
Sydney, NS, Canada B1S 1P4
Ph: (902)270-3930
URL: http://fullypromoted.ca
Contact: Michael Brugger, President
Facebook: www.facebook.com/EMECB
Instagram: www.instagram.com/fullypromotedcanada
Description: Manufacturer and distributor of embroidery, screen printing and promotional product such as shopping bags, caps, hats, outwear, T-shirts and much more. **Training:** Includes 2 weeks training at headquarters and 2 weeks onsite.

32366 ■ Giant Tiger/Tigre Geant (GT)
2480 Walkley Rd.
Ottawa, ON, Canada K1G 6A9
Ph: (613)526-2416
Free: 833-848-4437
Co. E-mail: customercare@gianttiger.com
URL: http://www.gianttiger.com
Contact: Paul Wood, President
Facebook: www.facebook.com/GiantTiger
Linkedin: www.linkedin.com/company/giant-tiger
X (Twitter): x.com/gtboutique
Instagram: www.instagram.com/gianttigerstore
YouTube: www.youtube.com/gianttiger
Description: Operator of retail store. **Founded:**
1961. **Training:** Training, site selection, lease
negotiations and advisory council are provided.

32367 ■ Great Canadian Dollar Store (1993) Ltd.
199 Hampton Rd.
Quispamsis, NB, Canada E2E 4L9
Ph: (506)849-4123
Co. E-mail: customer.service@greatcanadiandollars
tore.ca
URL: http://www.dollarstores.com
Contact: Barb Dempster, Manager
E-mail: barb.dempster@greatcanadiandollarstore.ca
Facebook: www.facebook.com/GreatCdnDollarStore
Description: Operator of grocery stores. **Founded:**
1993. **Franchise Fee:** $19,880. **Royalty Fee:** 4%.
Training: Offers training (3P's) and ongoing support.

32368 ■ Marcello's Market & Deli Inc.
1850 Walkley Rd.
Ottawa, ON, Canada
Ph: (613)523-3123
Co. E-mail: info@marcellos.ca
URL: http://marcellos.ca
Facebook: www.facebook.com/marcellosburgers
X (Twitter): x.com/marcellosworld
Instagram: www.instagram.com/marcelloswalkley
Description: Operator of supermarket and restau-
rant. **Franchise Fee:** $25,000. **Royalty Fee:** 0.05.
Training: Provides 4-6 weeks training.

32369 ■ Max Muscle Sports Nutrition
2320 W 54th St. N, Ste. 100
Sioux Falls, SD 57107
Ph: (605)271-2670
Co. E-mail: customerservice@maxmuscle.com
URL: http://maxmuscle.com
Facebook: www.facebook.com/MaxMuscleSportsNu
trition
Instagram: www.instagram.com/maxmusclehq
Description: Producer and retailer of health and fit-
ness muscles products. **Founded:** 1991. **Financial
Assistance:** Yes **Training:** Online nutrition supple-
ments store.

32370 ■ Nicholby's Franchise Systems Inc.
377 Main St.
Markham, ON, Canada L3P 1Z3
Ph: (905)940-1515
Fax: (905)940-1516
Co. E-mail: info@nicholbys.com
URL: http://nicholbys.com
Contact: Rob Kadlovski, President
Description: Operator of retail convenience store.
Founded: 1980. **Training:** Offers 3-4 weeks training
and ongoing support.

32371 ■ Nutrition House Canada Inc.
1200 St. Laurent Blvd.
Ottawa, ON, Canada K1K 3B8
Ph: (604)788-1619
Co. E-mail: customercare@nutritionhouse.com
URL: http://nutritionhouse.com
Facebook: www.facebook.com/nutritionhousecanada
X (Twitter): x.com/nutritionhouse
YouTube: www.youtube.com/channel/UCc4TF
tHDxRgP2sVV9sEBUkA

Pinterest: www.pinterest.com/nutritionhousecanada
Description: Retailer of health, sports nutrition and
body care products. **Founded:** 1979. **Franchised:**
1993. **Training:** Includes 3 weeks training.

32372 ■ Personal Edge
120 Cottage St. SW
Vienna, VA 22180
Ph: (703)587-7678
URL: http://www.thepersonaledge.net
Contact: Sunir Jossan, Owner
Description: Our stores, located in major shopping
malls, feature one of Canada's largest selection of
electric shavers and other personal grooming products, as well as small household appliances and
specialty gifts from leading manufacturers. We have
a unique mix of quality brand name products and
onsite repair services. **No. of Franchise Units:** 64.
Founded: 1959. **Franchised:** 1980. **Equity Capital
Needed:** $50,000-$80,000. **Franchise Fee:** No
franchise fee for new store. **Training:** Includes 6
weeks training.

32373 ■ Place Rosemère
401, Labelle Blvd.
Rosemere, QC, Canada J7A 3T2
Ph: (450)437-0400
Fax: (450)437-7808
Co. E-mail: info@placerosemere.com
URL: http://placerosemere.com/en
Contact: Nelly Medeiros, Manager
Facebook: www.facebook.com/placerosemere
X (Twitter): x.com/PlaceRosemere
Instagram: www.instagram.com/placerosemere
YouTube: www.youtube.com/channel/UC5zloSv
t3NjqQ-L5rpPdtzw
Description: Chain of footwear stores for children.
Founded: 1972. **Training:** Complete training to
franchisees and staff, buying, selling, administration,
merchandising, advertising, etc.

32374 ■ Planet Clean
1609 Derwent Way
Delta, BC, Canada V3M 6K8
Ph: (604)327-1101
URL: http://bunzlch.ca
Description: Distributor of cleaning, sanitation, infec-
tion control products, cleaning tools and professional
equipment. **Founded:** 1982. **Training:** Yes.

32375 ■ Port City Java
Description: Gourmet coffee cafe with wireless web.
No. of Franchise Units: 28. **No. of Company-
Owned Units:** 12. **Founded:** 1995. **Franchised:**
2003. **Equity Capital Needed:** $210,300-$413,900
total investment; $300,000 liquid capital; $500,000
net worth. **Franchise Fee:** $20,000. **Royalty Fee:**
5%. **Financial Assistance:** Yes **Training:** Offers 18
days at headquarters and 14 days at franchisee's
location with ongoing support.

32376 ■ Printwear Xpress
1819 Wazee St.
Denver, CO 80202
Contact: Brian E. Spindel, Contact
Description: Printwear Xpress (PWX) combines
shopping experience, technology & customer service
to deliver a highly competitive business model. PWX
stores are modern, attractive & well merchandised to
help customers select the right product for their
needs. Production is showcased to illustrate the
capabilities of the business & customer service is
second to none. PWX stores are located in neighborhood strip centers & don't require an anchor tenant.
No. of Company-Owned Units: 1. **Founded:** 2007.
Franchised: 2007. **Equity Capital Needed:**
$148,200-$169,600. **Franchise Fee:** $29,900. **Roy-
alty Fee:** 5%. **Financial Assistance:** Yes **Training:**
Offers 1 week classroom in Denver and 1 week onsite
during opening, as well as vendor training.

32377 ■ Saxbys Coffee Worldwide, LLC
Saxbys Coffee Worldwide, LLC
2005 Market St., Ste. 810
Philadelphia, PA 19103
Co. E-mail: support@saxbyscoffee.com
URL: http://www.saxbyscoffee.com/news-item/saxys
-job-fair
Contact: Nick Bayer, Chief Executive Officer
Facebook: www.facebook.com/HelloSaxbys
Linkedin: www.linkedin.com/company/saxbys
X (Twitter): x.com/Saxbys
Instagram: www.instagram.com/saxbys
Description: Coffee retail store, specializing in
gourmet espresso drinks, smoothies, and tea. An af-
fordable initial investment, a rewarding career, a
simple business to own and operate, and an easy
restaurant to staff. **No. of Franchise Units:** 30.
Founded: 2005. **Franchised:** 2003. **Equity Capital
Needed:** $50,000 cash, $200,000 equity. **Franchise
Fee:** $30,000. **Training:** 5 day owner training before
opening the store and a 5 day owner and employee
training upon opening the store.

32378 ■ Tastings-A Wine Experience
50 W Washington St.
Indianapolis, IN 46204
Ph: (317)423-2400
Co. E-mail: indianapolis@tastingsbar.com
URL: http://www.tastingsbar.com
Contact: Jack L. Bailey, Manager
Facebook: www.facebook.com/pages/Tastings-In
dianapolis/200671029067
X (Twitter): x.com/tastingsindy
Instagram: www.instagram.com/tastingsindy
Description: Operator of wine bar and bistro. It offers
menu cocktails, spirits, beer, cigars and foods.
Founded: 2005. **Franchise Fee:** $50,000. **Training:**
Yes. Yes.

32379 ■ Vintage Stock
202 E 32nd St.
Joplin, MO 64804-3802
Ph: (417)623-1550
Co. E-mail: support@vintagestock.com
URL: http://vintagestock.com
Contact: Seth Bayless, Contact
Facebook: www.facebook.com/VintageStock
X (Twitter): x.com/Vintage_Stock
Description: Retailer of movies, video games, music
plus unique items including comic books, collectible
memorabilia, sports and gaming cards. **Founded:**
1980. **Financial Assistance:** Yes **Training:** Offers 1
week of training at headquarters, 2-3 weeks onsite
and ongoing support.

32380 ■ Watch It! Inc.
100 City Ctr. Dr., Ste. 1-151
Mississauga, ON, Canada L5B 2C9
Ph: (905)276-5147
Co. E-mail: squareone@watchit.ca
URL: http://www.watchit.ca
Description: Retailer of watches, sunglasses and
accessories for men and women. **Founded:** 1999.
Training: Yes.

PUBLICATIONS

32381 ■ "Weigh in: 9 ways your store can better support BIPOC-owned brands" in Natural Foods Merchandiser (September 14, 2021)
URL(s): www.newhope.com/natural-foods-merchan
diser
Ed: Melaina Juntti. **Released:** September 14, 2021.
Description: Tips and resources on how to support
BIPOC-owned brands by including their products in
retail spaces.

REFERENCE WORKS

32382 ■ *"5 Ways Entrepreneurs Learn to Manage Risk" in Entrepreneur (February 18, 2015)*

Ed: Joel Trammell. **Released:** February 08, 2015. **Description:** Details five ways in which successful entrepreneurs approach risk. **Availability:** Online.

32383 ■ *"16 Ways Small Businesses Can Tackle Financial Risk Management" in Forbes (July 23, 2020)*

Released: July 23, 2020. **Description:** Experts from Forbes Finance Council share valuable tips to help you get a handle on a future risk management. Also provides financial risk management strategies to adopt. **Availability:** Online.

32384 ■ *"Detecting and Combating Employee Theft" in Wolters Kluwer Expert Insights (Mar 20, 2020)*

URL(s): www.wolterskluwer.com/en/expert-insights/detecting-and-combating-employee-theft

Released: March 20, 2020. **Description:** Discusses how employers can detect employee theft and how to properly handle suspicions within the workplace. Provides information on anti-theft policies. **Availability:** Online.

32385 ■ *"Employee Theft: Identify & Prevent Fraud Embezzlement & Pilfering" in ZenBusiness (Aug. 11, 2021)*

URL(s): www.zenbusiness.com/blog/employee-theft-embezzlement/

Released: August 11, 2021. **Description:** Provides tips on spotting and eliminating employee theft in your small business. **Availability:** Online.

32386 ■ *"Get the Financial Risk-Management Skills You Need to Navigate Uncertain Times" in Entrepreneur (August 21, 2020)*

Released: August 21, 2020. **Description:** Describes a comprehensive eight-course, 23-hour bundle designed to help small business owners pass the Financial Risk Management exam and become a Certified Financial Risk Manager, allowing business owners to take often outsourced resources into their own hands. **Availability:** Online.

32387 ■ *"How Risk Management Can Make Marijuana Businesses Bulletproof (or at Least Bullet Resistant)" in Green Market Report (May 3, 2019)*

Ed: Steve Schain. **Released:** May 03, 2019. **Description:** Many ordinary risk management tools are unavailable to cannabis entrepreneurs because of federal prohibition. This article discusses how, when armed with risk management fundamentals, mari-

juana related businesses can diminish risk, fortify an enterprise's sustained growth, and make money along the way. **Availability:** Online.

32388 ■ *"Identifying and Managing Business Risks" in Investopedia (August 2, 2019)*

Ed: Marc Davis. **Released:** August 02, 2019. **Description:** Describes how to successfully anticipate, identify, manage, and prepare for risks regardless of the size of your business. **Availability:** Online.

32389 ■ *"Risk Management: How Can Small Businesses Handle Crisis" in Full Scale (March 27, 2020)*

Released: March 27, 2020. **Description:** Discusses how careful risk management can help small businesses minimize and ideally prevent the impact of a crisis. **Availability:** Online.

32390 ■ *"Risk Management: How Can You Protect Your Small Business?" in Medium (April 14, 2020)*

Ed: Mahzeb Monica. **Released:** April 14, 2020. **Description:** A risk management guide for small businesses providing information on the process of identifying, evaluating, and responding to risks that would have adverse effects on your business. **Availability:** Online.

32391 ■ *"Small Business Risk Management" in Patriot Software (April 23, 2019)*

Ed: Rachel Blakely-Gray. **Released:** April 23, 2019. **Description:** Discusses prep work involved in small business risk management including a 4-step guide and information on creating a risk management plan. **Availability:** Online.

32392 ■ *"Tips for Small Business Risk Management" in Business Enterprise Mapping (June 27, 2020)*

Released: June 27, 2020. **Description:** Discusses common mistakes that small businesses make when in comes to managing risk. While some risks are harder to plan for than others, it is important to identify the high-risk elements of your business so you can better prepare. **Availability:** Online.

32393 ■ *"What to Do If You Suspect Employee Theft at Your Business" in Insureon Small Business Blog*

URL(s): www.insureon.com/blog/what-to-do-if-you-suspect-employee-theft-at-your-business

Description: Provides information on types of employee theft, what to do when you suspect employee theft, and insurance policy information to protect your small business. **Availability:** Online.

32394 ■ *"What Is Risk Management for Small Business?" in Insureon*

Description: Explains that risk management is the process of identifying and managing threats so that your small business can operate without unexpected interruptions. Discusses risk management planning and insurance. **Availability:** Online.

VIDEO/AUDIO MEDIA

32395 ■ *API Security*

URL(s): www.startuphustlepodcast.com/api-security

Released: December 26, 2023. **Description:** Podcast discusses IT, cybersecurity, and API security risks.

32396 ■ *Building a Secure Startup*

URL(s): www.startuphustlepodcast.com/building-a-secure-startup

Ed: Matt DeCoursey. **Released:** December 07, 2023. **Description:** Podcast explains the importance of data security compliance and how to protect against breaches.

32397 ■ *Data Hoarding Business Hazards*

URL(s): www.startuphustlepodcast.com/data-hoarding-business-hazards

Ed: Matt DeCoursey. **Released:** November 16, 2023. **Description:** Podcast discusses data privacy issues.

32398 ■ *HBR Ideacast: What Venture Capitalists Can Teach Companies about Decision-Making*

URL(s): hbr.org/podcast/2024/05/what-venture-capitalists-can-teach-companies-about-deciison-making

Ed: Alison Beard. **Released:** March 28, 2024. **Description:** Podcast explains how venture capitalists' ability to operationalize risk, embrace disagreement, and remain agile in decision-making translates out of Silcon Valley.

32399 ■ *The How of Business: Ivy Walker - Risk Management*

URL(s): www.thehowofbusiness.com/417-ivy-walker-risk-management

Ed: Henry Lopez. **Released:** April 11, 2022. **Description:** Podcast discusses risks that can impact small businesses and how to counteract or avoid them.

32400 ■ *The How of Business: John Morlan - Risk Management*

URL(s): www.thehowofbusiness.com/471-john-morlan-risk-management

Ed: Henry Lopez. **Released:** May 08, 2023. **Description:** Podcast discusses common risks small businesses owners may overlook, what they should know about safety programs, and how to get better insurance rates.

32401 ■ *Today's Biggest Security Weakness*

URL(s): www.startuphustlepodcast.com/todays-biggest-security-weakness

Released: February 08, 2024. **Description:** Podcast discusses cybersecurity in a dynamic business landscape.

PUBLICATIONS

32402 ■ *Managing Business Risk: A Practical Guide to Protecting Your Business*
45 Gee St., 2nd Fl.
  London EC1V 3RS, United Kingdom
Ph: 44 20 7278-0433

Co. E-mail: kpinfo@koganpage.com
URL: http://www.koganpage.com
Contact: Christina Lindeholm, Manager, Sales
URL(s): www.koganpage.com/risk-compliance/man-
  aging-business-risk-9780749470432
Price: $129.99, for hardback + eBook bundle or eB-
ook or hardback. **Description:** A guide that can help
in identifying potential areas of risk within a business.

Examines the five key areas of risk you need to
consider in today's complex and competitive business market. Drawing on expert advice from leading
risk consultants, lawyers and regulatory authorities, it
shows you how to protect your business against a
rising tide of business risks. **Availability:** E-book;
Print.

START-UP INFORMATION

32403 ■ *How to Start and Run Your Own Corporation: S-Corporations For Small Business Owners*
Pub: HCM Publishing

Ed: Peter I. Hupalo. **Description:** Basics of corporate business structure are explained. Topics include discovering the best business structure for your company; how to decided between an S-Corporation and LLC; choosing the state in which to incorporate, how to form a corporation, angel investing, special issues for one-person corporations, the role of bylaws and corporate minutes, board of directors, taxes, workers' compensation issues, retirement plans, and more. **Availability:** Print.

REFERENCE WORKS

32404 ■ *Choose a Business Structure*
URL(s): www.sba.gov/business-guide/launch-your -business/choose-business-structure

Description: A guide to choosing the best small business structure. Includes information on common business structures, how business structures can be combined, and compares business structures in chart format. **Availability:** Online.

32405 ■ *Choosing the Right Legal Form of Business: The Complete Guide to Becoming a Sole Proprietor, Partnership, LLC, or Corporation*
Pub: Atlantic Publishing Co.
Contact: Dr. Heather L. Johnson, Contact

Ed: Pat Mitchell. **Released:** 2010. **Description:** According to the U.S. Small Business Administration, nearly 250,000 new businesses start up annually; currently there are over nine million small companies in the nation. The importance of choosing the proper legal form of business is stressed. **Availability:** Print; Online.

32406 ■ *Entrepreneurial Finance*
Pub: Pearson Education Inc.
Contact: Andy Bird, Chief Executive Officer

Ed: Philip J. Adelman, Alan M. Marks. **Released:** Sixth edition. **Description:** Financial aspects of running a small business are covered; topics include sole proprietorships, partnerships, limited liability companies, and private corporations. **Availability:** Print; Download; Online.

32407 ■ *Incorporate Your Business: A Legal Guide to Forming a Corporation in Your State*
Pub: Nolo
Contact: Chris Braun, President

Ed: Anthony Mancuso. **Released:** 11th edition. **Price:** $34.99, e-book; $39.99, book and e-book; $34.99, e-book. **Description:** Legal guide to incorporating a business in the U.S., covering all 50 states. **Availability:** E-book; Print.

32408 ■ *"Is It Time to Convert Your Sole Proprietorship to a Corporation or LLC?" in Legal Zoom (March 27, 2023)*
URL(s): www.legalzoom.com/articles/is-it-time-to -convert-your-sole-proprietorship-to-a-corporation -or-llc

Ed: Ann MacDonald. **Released:** March 27, 2023. **Description:** Is it time to switch your small company you founded from a sole proprietorship to a different structure? Discusses the advantages of doing so. **Availability:** Online.

32409 ■ *"The Perils and Pitfalls of S Corporations" in allBusiness*

Ed: Amanda Han. **Description:** Provides in-depth information on one of the most commonly used business structures for small to mid-sized business owners, the S Corporation. Covers strategies as well as common costly mistakes. **Availability:** Online.

32410 ■ *S-Corp Beginner's Guide 2023*

Ed: Steven Carlson. **Released:** January 06, 2023. **Price:** $16.97, paperback. **Description:** Discusses the pros and cons of registering your small business as an S-Corp. **Availability:** Print.

32411 ■ *"S Corporation: Lower Taxes but Limited Growth Potential" in NerdWallet (Oct. 27, 2020)*
URL(s): www.nerdwallet.com/article/small-business/s -corporation-lower-taxes-but-limited-growth-poten tial

Ed: Andrew Wang. **Released:** October 27, 2020. **Description:** Explains what an S Corporation is, who can own an S Corp, pros and cons, and how to start an S Corporation if you decide this is the right designation for your small business. **Availability:** Online.

32412 ■ *"Should Your Small Business Become an S-Corp?" in Brex Blog (Feb. 17, 2021)*
URL(s): www.brex.com/blog/s-corp/

Released: February 17, 2021. **Description:** Explains what an S Corporation is, how it affects the tax status of a business. Provides advantages and disadvantages, explains how to become an S-Corp. **Availability:** Online.

32413 ■ *Simplified Incorporation Kit*

Released: 1st edition. **Description:** Kit includes all the forms, instructions, and information necessary for incorporating any small business in any state (CD-ROM included).

32414 ■ *The Tax Pros and Cons of S Corp Status for Small Business*
URL(s): www.accountingtoday.com/opinion/the-advan tages-of-s-corp-status-for-small-businesses

Ed: Anthony DeStefano. **Released:** November 05, 2020. **Description:** Provides a list of advantages and disadvantages of the four small business entity types so that you can decide which is best for you. **Availability:** Online.

32415 ■ *"To Be or Not To Be an S Corporation" in Modern Machine Shop (Vol. 84, September 2011, No. 4, pp. 38)*
Pub: Gardner Business Media Inc.
Contact: Rick Kline, Jr., President
E-mail: rkline2@gardnerweb.com

Ed: Irving L. Blackman. **Description:** The definitions of both C corporations and S corporations are defined to help any machine shop discover which best suits the owner's business plan. **Availability:** Online.

VIDEO/AUDIO MEDIA

32416 ■ *What Is an S Corp and Should I Become One in 2023?*
URL(s): podcasts.apple.com/us/podcast/what-is-an-s -corp-and-should-i-become-one-in-2023/id137727 6636?i=1000606000323

Ed: Mike Jesowshek. **Released:** July 07, 2023. **Description:** Podcast defines an S-corporation, when to become one, how to set it up, and how to maintain it.

32417 ■ *Why You Shouldn't Be an S Corporation in 2024*
URL(s): podcasts.apple.com/us/podcast/why-you -shouldnt-be-an-s-corporation-in-2024/id137737 6636?i=1000661790362

Ed: Mike Jesowshek. **Released:** July 10, 2024. **Description:** Pocast explains why some business owners should avoid electing S corproation status.

COMPUTERIZED DATABASES

32418 ■ *Federal Income Taxation of S Corporations*
Thomson Reuters (Tax And Accounting) Inc.
  2395 Midway Rd.
  Carrollton, TX 75006
Free: 888-885-0206
URL: http://tax.thomsonreuters.com/en
Contact: Brian Peccarelli, President
URL(s): store.tax.thomsonreuters.com/accounting/ Tax/Federal-Income-Taxation-of-S-Corporations/p/ 100201404

Released: 3/year **Price:** $1,040, Individuals. **Availability:** Print. **Type:** Full-text.

LIBRARIES

32419 ■ **Cornell University - Johnson Graduate School of Management Library**
  101 Sage Hall
  Ithaca, NY 14853
Ph: (607)255-3389
Co. E-mail: mgtref@cornell.edu
URL: http://johnson.library.cornell.edu
Contact: Christina Sheley, Director
E-mail: cms542@cornell.edu

Scope: Business administration and management science; finance; investment; accounting; marketing; managerial economics; operations management and quantitative analysis. **Services:** Interlibrary loan. **Founded:** 1949. **Holdings:** 164,000 volumes; 1,096 non-book materials; 860,000 microfiche; 2,800 microfilm; 450 CD-ROMs.

RESEARCH CENTERS

32420 ■ Coady International Institute - Marie Michael Library
St. Francis Xavier University
   4780 Tompkins Ln.
   Antigonish, NS, Canada B2G 2W5
Ph: (902)867-3960
Free: 866-820-7835
Fax: (902)867-3907
Co. E-mail: coadyadmit@stfx.ca
URL: http://coady.stfx.ca
Contact: Eileen Alma, Executive Director
Facebook: www.facebook.com/CoadyStFX
X (Twitter): x.com/coadystfx
Instagram: www.instagram.com/coadystfx

Description: Works to insure a "full and abundant life for all in a just, inclusive, participatory, and sustainable society" through training of development organization personnel and indigenous peoples affected by development programs. **Scope:** International development, community development, adult education, health education, gender and development, advocacy, microenterprise, microcredit, peacebuilding, evaluation. **Founded:** 1959. **Holdings:** 12,000 books, 800 videos. **Publications:** *Coady International Institute Annual report* (Annual); *Coady Connection* (Quarterly). **Geographic Preference:** Multinational.

32421 ■ Jackson State University (BBER) - Bureau of Business and Economic Research
1400 Lynch St.
   Jackson, MS 39217
Ph: (601)979-2795
Fax: (601)914-0833
URL: http://www.jsums.edu/phonedirectory/s

Description: Integral unit of College of Business at Jackson State University; consulting for local business. **Scope:** Small business, including applied and theoretical studies which contribute to the development of Mississippi business economy. **Publications:** *Annual Demographic Databook* (Annual); *Economic Indicators* (Monthly); *Bureau of Business and Economic Research Reports*.

32422 ■ University of Maryland at College Park - Robert H. Smith School of Business - Dingman Center for Entrepreneurship
2518 Van Munching Hall
   College Park, MD 20742
Ph: (301)405-9545
Co. E-mail: rhsmith-dingman@umd.edu

URL: http://www.rhsmith.umd.edu/centers/dingman
   -center
Contact: Holly DeArmond, Managing Director
E-mail: hdearmond@rhsmith.umd.edu
Facebook: www.facebook.com/DingmanCenter
X (Twitter): x.com/UMD_Dingman
Instagram: www.instagram.com/dingmancenter

Description: Entrepreneurship center of the Robert H. Smith School of Business, University of Maryland at College Park. Offers assistance to emerging growth firms through mentor program and business plan reviews. **Scope:** Entrepreneurship, new venture creation, technology commercialization, and venture capital. **Founded:** 1986. **Publications:** *Newsletters for the entrepreneurial community and for volunteers* (Monthly). **Educational Activities:** Dingman Day Lunches, Offer exemplary teaching programs.; Dingman Center for Entrepreneurship Jumpstart, Three week program aimed at getting students comfortable with start-up culture within the center's experiential learning environment and bringing their business ideas to life.; Dingman Center for Entrepreneurship Industry forums; Dingman Center for Entrepreneurship Networking breakfasts; Dingman Center for Entrepreneurship Seminars; Robert G. Hisaoka Speaker Series (3/year), In entrepreneurship and entrepreneurship concentration in MBA curriculum.; Dingman Center for Entrepreneurship Venture Capital Forums. **Awards:** Pitch Dingman Competition (Annual); Dingman Center for Entrepreneurship MSEC Scholarship.

START-UP INFORMATION

32423 ■ *"9 Strategies to BUILD and GROW Your Author Platform: A Step-by-Step Book Marketing Plan to Get More Exposure and Sales"*

Released: May 04, 2016. **Description:** A nine-step formula for marketing self-published books is presented. The author has sold over 103,000 books using this method since 2008 and continues to grow her customer base through email and followers. **Availability:** Print.

32424 ■ *"Follow the Numbers: It's the Best Way To Spot Problems Before They Become Life-Threatening"* in *Inc.* (January 2008, pp. 63-64)

Ed: Norm Brodsky. **Description:** It is important for any small business to track monthly sales and gross margins by hand for the first year or two. When writing the numbers, be sure to break them out by product category or service type and by customer. **Availability:** Online.

32425 ■ *"How to Open and Operate a Financially Successful Florist and Floral Business Online and Off"*

Pub: Atlantic Publishing Co.
Contact: Dr. Heather L. Johnson, Contact

Released: Revised second edition. **Description:** A concise and easy to follow guide for opening a retail florist or floral business online or a traditional brick and mortar store. Knowledge shared includes: cost control systems, retail math and competitive pricing, legal concerns, tax reporting requirements and reporting, profit and loss statements, management skills, sales advertising, and marketing techniques, customer service, direct sales, internal marketing ideas, and more. **Availability:** CD-ROM; Print; Online.

ASSOCIATIONS AND OTHER ORGANIZATIONS

32426 ■ **American Association of Inside Sales Professionals (AA-ISP)**
18124 Wedge Pkwy., Ste. 2047
  Reno, NV 89511
Free: 800-604-7085
Co. E-mail: info@aa-isp.org
URL: http://www.aa-isp.org
Contact: Todd Caponi, President
Facebook: www.facebook.com/TheAAISP
Linkedin: www.linkedin.com/company/american
  -association-of-inside-sales-professionals
X (Twitter): x.com/aa_isp
YouTube: www.youtube.com/user/OfficialAAISP

Description: Aims to perfect the skills of inside sale professionals. **Founded:** 2009. **Publications:** *Inside Scoop.* **Awards:** AA-ISP Service Provider Awards (Annual). **Geographic Preference:** National.

32427 ■ **Direct Selling Association (DSA)**
1667 K St. NW, Ste. 1100
  Washington, DC 20006-1660
Ph: (202)452-8866
Fax: (202)452-9010
URL: http://www.dsa.org
Contact: Joseph N. Mariano, President
E-mail: jmariano@dsa.org
Facebook: www.facebook.com/DSAssn
Linkedin: www.linkedin.com/company/direct-selling
  -association
X (Twitter): x.com/DSAssn
Instagram: www.instagram.com/directsellingassn
YouTube: www.youtube.com/user/directselling411

Description: Represents manufacturers and distributors selling consumer products through person-to-person sales, by appointment, and through home-party plans. **Founded:** 1910. **Publications:** *State Status Sheet* (Weekly); *Direct Selling Association--Directory* (Annual). **Awards:** DSA Distinguished Service Award (Annual); Vision for Tomorrow (Annual); DSA Hall of Fame Award (Irregular); Vision for Tomorrow Award (Annual); DSA Partnership Award (Annual); DSEF Circle of Honor Award (Annual). **Geographic Preference:** National.

32428 ■ **Direct Selling Education Foundation (DSEF)**
1667 K St. NW, Ste. 1100
  Washington, DC 20006
Ph: (202)452-8866
Fax: (202)452-9015
Co. E-mail: info@dsef.org
URL: http://www.dsef.org
Contact: Gary M. Huggins, Executive Director
E-mail: ghuggins@dsef.org
Facebook: www.facebook.com/TheDSEF
Linkedin: www.linkedin.com/company/direct-selling-e
  ducation-foundation
X (Twitter): x.com/TheDSEF
Instagram: www.instagram.com/the.dsef
YouTube: www.youtube.com/user/TheDSEF

Description: Serves the public interest with education, information, and research, thereby enhancing acceptance and public awareness of direct selling in the global marketplace. **Founded:** 1973. **Publications:** *Direct Selling Association--Active Member List* (Quarterly); *Who's Who in Direct Selling* (Quarterly). **Awards:** DSEF Circle of Honor (Annual). **Geographic Preference:** Multinational.

32429 ■ **Marketing Agencies Association Worldwide (MAA) [MAA WORLDWIDE]**
60 Peachcroft
  Bernardsville, NJ 07924
URL: http://www.maaworldwide.com
Contact: Simon Mahoney, President
E-mail: simonmahoneyuk@outlook.com

Description: Represents the interests of CEOs, presidents, managing directors and principals of top marketing services agencies. Provides opportunity for marketing professionals to meet with peers, raise company profile on both a national and a global platform, and influence the future of industry.

Founded: 1969. **Educational Activities:** Marketing Agencies Association Worldwide Summit (Annual). **Awards:** MAA Worldwide Awards The Globes - Best Integrated Marketing Campaign (Annual). **Geographic Preference:** Multinational.

32430 ■ **National Association of Sales Professionals (NASP)**
2121 Lohmans Crossing Rd., Ste. 504579
  Lakeway, TX 78734
Ph: (512)200-2963
Co. E-mail: support@nasp.com
URL: http://www.nasp.com
Contact: Rod E. Hairston, Chief Executive Officer
Facebook: www.facebook.com/SalesProfession
Linkedin: www.linkedin.com/company/nasp---national
  -association-of-sales-professionals
X (Twitter): x.com/NASPPRO

Description: Professional salespersons. Serves the training, educational, and developmental needs of men and women in sales to earn designation as a Certified Professional Sales Person. **Founded:** 1991. **Geographic Preference:** National.

32431 ■ **National Association of Women Sales Professionals (NAWSP)**
310 S Harrington St.
  Raleigh, NC 27603
Contact: Cynthia Barnes, Chief Executive Officer

Description: Seeks to provide career advancement, sales leadership, and networking opportunities to saleswomen throughout the United States. **Founded:** 2016.

32432 ■ **National Sales Network (NSN)**
3575 Piedmont Rd. NE, Bldg. 15, Ste. 1510
  Atlanta, GA 30305
Ph: (770)551-2734
Co. E-mail: admin@salesnetwork.org
URL: http://www.salesnetwork.org
Contact: Anthony Tuggle, President
Facebook: www.facebook.com/nsnhq
Linkedin: www.linkedin.com/company/national-sales
  -network-headquarters
X (Twitter): x.com/nsnhq
Instagram: www.instagram.com/NSNHQ
YouTube: www.youtube.com/user/SalesNetwork1992

Description: Strives to meet the professional and developmental needs of Black sales and sales management professionals and individuals who want to improve their professional sales skills. **Founded:** 1996.

32433 ■ **The Sales Association**
2460 W 26th Ave., Ste. 245C
  Denver, CO 80211
Ph: (720)259-1250
Fax: (775)370-4055
URL: http://www.salesassociation.org
Contact: Jeffrey Arnold, Executive Director
E-mail: jeff@salesassociation.org
Facebook: www.facebook.com/The-Sales-Associa
  tion-70303869736
X (Twitter): x.com/salesassn

Description: Trade association serving sales and business development professionals from all industries. Offers the Consultative Sales Certification (CSC) program. **Founded:** 2007.

32434 ■ Sales Management Association
1440 Dutch Valley Pl. NE, Ste. 990
  Atlanta, GA 30324
Ph: (404)963-7992
URL: http://salesmanagement.org
Contact: Robert J. Kelly, Chairman
Facebook: www.facebook.com/TheSalesManagementAssociation
Linkedin: www.linkedin.com/company/the-sales-management-association
X (Twitter): x.com/SMAssociation
Instagram: www.instagram.com/smassociation
Description: Promotes career development, communication, techniques, and resources in the field of sales management. Encourages sales practitioners to further hone their skills through training and networking. **Founded:** 2008. **Geographic Preference:** Multinational.

32435 ■ Sales and Marketing Executives International (SMEI) - Library
PO Box 1390
  Sumas, WA 98295
Ph: (312)893-0751
Fax: (312)893-0751
URL: http://www.smei.org
Contact: Willis Turner, Chief Executive Officer
E-mail: willis.turner@smei.org
Facebook: www.facebook.com/smeinternational
Linkedin: www.linkedin.com/groups/45880/profile
X (Twitter): x.com/smeiorg
Description: Undertakes studies in selling and sales management; sponsors sales workshops, rallies, clinics, and seminars. Conducts career education programs, working with teachers, establishing sales clubs and fraternities and cooperating with Junior Achievement and Distributive Education Clubs of America to interest young people in sales careers. **Scope:** Sales; marketing. **Founded:** 1935. **Holdings:** Figures not available. **Educational Activities:** SMEI Conference (Annual). **Awards:** SMEI Distinguished Sales & Marketing Award® (DSMA) (Annual); Don K. Covington, Jr. Award (Annual); Jack Criswell Award (Annual); SMEI Marketing Excellence Awards - Statesman of the Year (Annual); Ken Arbuckle Fellow; SMEI Marketing Excellence Awards - Excellence in Marketing; SMEI Marketing Excellence Awards - Educator of the Year; SMEI Marketing Excellence Awards - Tops in Marketing; SMEI Academy of Achievement Pinnacle Award (Annual); SMEI Chairman's Award (Annual). **Geographic Preference:** Multinational.

32436 ■ World Federation of Direct Selling Associations (WFDSA)
1667 K St. NW, Ste. 1100
  Washington, DC 20006
Ph: (202)416-6442
Fax: (202)747-7528
Co. E-mail: info@wfdsa.org
URL: http://wfdsa.org
Contact: Tamuna Gabilaia, Executive Director
Facebook: www.facebook.com/WorldFedDSA
YouTube: www.youtube.com/channel/UCgM
  5Coulwee41sjY7DeSuOA
Description: An international organization representing the direct-selling industry. Encourages personal relationships and cooperation among people in direct selling. Promotes education through programs and funding. **Founded:** 1978. **Publications:** *Direct Selling World Directory* (Continuous); *WFDSA Newsletters*; *WFDSA World Federation News* (Quarterly). **Awards:** WFDSA Distinguished Service Award (Annual). **Geographic Preference:** Multinational.

EDUCATIONAL PROGRAMS

32437 ■ Advanced Sales Management (Onsite)
American Management Association (AMA)
  1601 Broadway
  New York, NY 10019

Ph: (212)586-8100
Free: 800-262-9699
Fax: (212)903-8168
Co. E-mail: customerservice@amanet.org
URL: http://www.amanet.org
Contact: Manny Avramidis, President
URL(s): www.amanet.org/training/seminars/onsite/advanced-sales-management.aspx
Price: $2,545, Non-members; $2,295, Members; $2,174, General Services Administration (GSA).
Description: Covers increasing productivity and efficiency through team building, adapting to a changing environment, and decision, and problem solving techniques. **Audience:** Seasoned sales managers, decision makers, motivators, communicators, coaches, and counselors. **Principal Exhibits:** Covers increasing productivity and efficiency through team building, adapting to a changing environment, and decision, and problem solving techniques.

32438 ■ AMA Principles of Professional Selling
American Management Association (AMA)
  1601 Broadway
  New York, NY 10019
Ph: (212)586-8100
Free: 800-262-9699
Fax: (212)903-8168
Co. E-mail: customerservice@amanet.org
URL: http://www.amanet.org
Contact: Manny Avramidis, President
URL(s): www.amanet.org/training/seminars/Principles-of-Professional-Selling.aspx
Frequency: Continuous. **Description:** Covers consultative selling, planning the sales process, building relationships with customers, the sales process, utilizing technology, listening skills, telephone techniques, and time management. **Audience:** Sales professionals with a minimum of one year of sales experience. **Principal Exhibits:** Covers consultative selling, planning the sales process, building relationships with customers, the sales process, utilizing technology, listening skills, telephone techniques, and time management. **Telecommunication Services:** customerservice@amanet.org.

32439 ■ AMA Territory and Time Management for Salespeople (Onsite)
URL(s): www.amanet.org/training/seminars/onsite/Territory-and-Time-Management-for-Salespeople.aspx
Description: Covers setting goals, attitude, organizational skills, developing a territory strategy, and increasing productivity. **Audience:** Sales representatives, account executives, sales managers and all sales staff with customer or sales territory management responsibilities. **Principal Exhibits:** Covers setting goals, attitude, organizational skills, developing a territory strategy, and increasing productivity.

32440 ■ The Content Sales Funnel - Creating an Effective Social Media Content Strategy Series
URL(s): cwewbc.ecenterdirect.com/events/977328
Description: This online course offered by the Center for Women and Enterprise discusses brand identity, sales funnel strategy, effective writing, and social media branding. **Audience:** Women who are small business owners. **Principal Exhibits:** This online course offered by the Center for Women and Enterprise discusses brand identity, sales funnel strategy, effective writing, and social media branding.

32441 ■ Cracking New Accounts: High Pay-Off Prospecting (Onsite)
Seminar Information Service Inc. (SIS)
  250 El Camino Real., Ste. 112
  Tustin, CA 92780
Ph: (714)508-0340
Free: 877-736-4636
Fax: (714)734-8027
Co. E-mail: info@seminarinformation.com
URL: http://www.seminarinformation.com
Contact: Catherine Bellizzi, President
URL(s): www.seminarinformation.com

Description: Covers building relationships, winning against competition and maximizing your sales and profit potentials in today's crowded marketplace, including 50 power prospecting techniques and why 85% or more of all sales calls are wasted and how to gain access to anybody at any time. **Audience:** Sales personnel. **Principal Exhibits:** Covers building relationships, winning against competition and maximizing your sales and profit potentials in today's crowded marketplace, including 50 power prospecting techniques and why 85% or more of all sales calls are wasted and how to gain access to anybody at any time. **Telecommunication Services:** info@seminarinformation.com.

32442 ■ The Distinct Advantage (Onsite)
Seminar Information Service Inc. (SIS)
  250 El Camino Real., Ste. 112
  Tustin, CA 92780
Ph: (714)508-0340
Free: 877-736-4636
Fax: (714)734-8027
Co. E-mail: info@seminarinformation.com
URL: http://www.seminarinformation.com
Contact: Catherine Bellizzi, President
URL(s): www.seminarinformation.com/details.cfm?qc=qqbrqd
Description: Provides valuable, innovative, measurable skills that can be put into immediate practice and can dramatically impact the chances of closing a sale-and ultimately the organization's bottom line. **Audience:** Sales executives, account managers, new business developers. **Principal Exhibits:** Provides valuable, innovative, measurable skills that can be put into immediate practice and can dramatically impact the chances of closing a sale-and ultimately the organization's bottom line.

32443 ■ Fundamental Selling Techniques for the New or Prospective Salesperson Level I (Onsite)
Seminar Information Service Inc. (SIS)
  250 El Camino Real., Ste. 112
  Tustin, CA 92780
Ph: (714)508-0340
Free: 877-736-4636
Fax: (714)734-8027
Co. E-mail: info@seminarinformation.com
URL: http://www.seminarinformation.com
Contact: Catherine Bellizzi, President
URL(s): www.seminarinformation.com/details.cfm?qc=qqahhg
Description: Gain the skills and confidence to sell your product or service successfully, including listening and prospecting skills. **Audience:** Salespeople, customer service representative, technical and support staff. **Principal Exhibits:** Gain the skills and confidence to sell your product or service successfully, including listening and prospecting skills.

32444 ■ Mastering the Complex Sale (Onsite)
Seminar Information Service Inc. (SIS)
  250 El Camino Real., Ste. 112
  Tustin, CA 92780
Ph: (714)508-0340
Free: 877-736-4636
Fax: (714)734-8027
Co. E-mail: info@seminarinformation.com
URL: http://www.seminarinformation.com
Contact: Catherine Bellizzi, President
URL(s): www.seminarinformation.com
Description: Seminar that combines the best university level learning with the best of street-smart selling into a proven system for success in the high-stakes sale. **Audience:** Professionals involved in the sales of technology. **Principal Exhibits:** Seminar that combines the best university level learning with the best of street-smart selling into a proven system for success in the high-stakes sale.

32445 ■ Prospecting Strategies to Build a Qualified Pipeline (Onsite)
Seminar Information Service Inc. (SIS)
  250 El Camino Real., Ste. 112
  Tustin, CA 92780
Ph: (714)508-0340
Free: 877-736-4636

Fax: (714)734-8027
Co. E-mail: info@seminarinformation.com
URL: http://www.seminarinformation.com
Contact: Catherine Bellizzi, President
URL(s): www.seminarinformation.com
Description: Learn a proactive approach to successful prospecting by first perfecting your lead qualification followed by practicing your prospecting skills through role-plays, applying your new insights to determine what has value to your qualified customer. **Audience:** Industry professionals, managers. **Principal Exhibits:** Learn a proactive approach to successful prospecting by first perfecting your lead qualification followed by practicing your prospecting skills through role-plays, applying your new insights to determine what has value to your qualified customer.

32446 ▪ Selling to Major Accounts: A Strategic Approach (Onsite)
American Management Association (AMA)
 1601 Broadway
 New York, NY 10019
Ph: (212)586-8100
Free: 800-262-9699
Fax: (212)903-8168
Co. E-mail: customerservice@amanet.org
URL: http://www.amanet.org
Contact: Manny Avramidis, President
URL(s): www.amanet.org/training/seminars/onsite/
 selling-to-major-accounts-a-strategic-approach
 .aspx
Price: $2,345, Non-members; $2,095, Members; $1,984, General Services Administration (GSA). **Description:** Covers strategies for developing successful relationships with major accounts. **Audience:** Sales professionals, including account managers, sales representatives and sales executives. **Principal Exhibits:** Covers strategies for developing successful relationships with major accounts.

32447 ▪ Strategic Sales Negotiations (Onsite)
American Management Association (AMA)
 1601 Broadway
 New York, NY 10019
Ph: (212)586-8100
Free: 800-262-9699
Fax: (212)903-8168
Co. E-mail: customerservice@amanet.org
URL: http://www.amanet.org
Contact: Manny Avramidis, President
URL(s): www.amanet.org/strategic-sales-negotiations
Price: $2,095, Non-members; $1,895, Members; $1,795, General Services Administration (GSA). **Frequency:** Continuous. **Description:** Covers the tools, techniques, and negotiation tactics for effectively influencing a buyer's perception of cost, benefits, and value. **Audience:** Sales professionals, sales managers, account executives, contract negotiators, and anyone involved in negotiation processes. **Principal Exhibits:** Covers the tools, techniques, and negotiation tactics for effectively influencing a buyer's perception of cost, benefits, and value. **Telecommunication Services:** customerservice@amanet.org.

32448 ▪ Successful Sales Skills (Onsite)
Seminar Information Service Inc. (SIS)
 250 El Camino Real., Ste. 112
 Tustin, CA 92780
Ph: (714)508-0340
Free: 877-736-4636
Fax: (714)734-8027
Co. E-mail: info@seminarinformation.com
URL: http://www.seminarinformation.com
Contact: Catherine Bellizzi, President
URL(s): www.seminarinformation.com
Description: Learn how to enhance their ability to deal with buying objections, and refine their skills in closing sales and negotiating win-win agreements leading to long-term relationships with customers. **Audience:** Salespeople, customer service representatives and technical staffs. **Principal Exhibits:** Learn how to enhance their ability to deal with buying objections, and refine their skills in closing sales and negotiating win-win agreements leading to long-term relationships with customers.

32449 ▪ Track Selling System Workshop (Onsite)
Seminar Information Service Inc. (SIS)
 250 El Camino Real., Ste. 112
 Tustin, CA 92780
Ph: (714)508-0340
Free: 877-736-4636
Fax: (714)734-8027
Co. E-mail: info@seminarinformation.com
URL: http://www.seminarinformation.com
Contact: Catherine Bellizzi, President
URL(s): www.seminarinformation.com/details.cfm?qc
 =qqahjv
Description: Teaches salespeople to be customer oriented rather than product-centered, how to translate product/service features into customer benefits, using role playing extensively, and orients and motivates participants towards sales as a profession, and introduces a consultative selling process and a guaranteed method of closing. **Audience:** Salespeople, technical marketing support personnels, service personnel, middle and upper management. **Principal Exhibits:** Teaches salespeople to be customer oriented rather than product-centered, how to translate product/service features into customer benefits, using role playing extensively, and orients and motivates participants towards sales as a profession, and introduces a consultative selling process and a guaranteed method of closing.

REFERENCE WORKS

32450 ▪ 4 Ways AI Is Helping Small Businesses in Sales & Marketing
Ed: Usman Khalil. **Released:** April 03, 2020. **Description:** Discusses how small businesses can utilize artificial intelligence (AI) to help them run their businesses more efficiently, to simplify tasks, to reduce risks and human errors, and to safe on costs. Presents 4 ways in which small businesses are leveraging AI for sales and marketing. **Availability:** Online.

32451 ▪ 5 Simple Strategies to Increase Online Sales in Small Business
URL(s): optimoroute.com/increase-small-business
 -sales/
Released: February 02, 2022. **Description:** Covers how to increase online sales in a small business, how to boost efficiency, and how to handle more customers with your existing workforce. **Availability:** Online.

32452 ▪ 7 Successful Sales Tips for Small Business Owners
URL(s): thekatynews.com/2020/01/16/7-successful
 -sales-tips-for-small-business-owners/
Released: January 16, 2020. **Description:** Details the importance of understanding the sales cycle, creating the perfect elevator pitch, writing a unique sales proposition, overcoming sales objectives, and understanding your audience all in the name of improving your bottom line. **Availability:** Online.

32453 ▪ "8 Things to Try If Your Business Growth Has Stagnated" in Small Business Trends (Jan. 12, 2022)
URL(s): smallbiztrends.com/2022/01/business-growth
 -strategy.html
Ed: Larry Alton. **Released:** January 12, 2022. **Description:** Provides business growth strategies to explore when your small business hits a plateau. **Availability:** Online.

32454 ▪ 9 Sales Techniques That Will Highly Increase Your Success
URL(s): www.clickfunnels.com/blog/successful-sales
 -techniques/
Ed: Holly Flick. **Released:** January 26, 2022. **Description:** A guide for salespeople looking to improve their performance and for sales managers looking to improve the performance of their team. This guide provides details on 9 proven sales techniques. **Availability:** Online.

32455 ▪ 10 Sales Strategies That Small Businesses Can Use
URL(s): www.ringcentral.com/us/en/blog/sales-stra
 tegy/
Description: Presents ten sales strategies that work for small businesses. **Availability:** Online.

32456 ▪ 10 Surprisingly Effective Sales Techniques, Backed by Research
URL(s): corporatevisions.com/selling-techniques/
Ed: Tim Riesterer. **Released:** April 01, 2021. **Description:** Provides a list of ten unique effective and persuasive sales techniques backed by science and research. **Availability:** Online.

32457 ▪ 10 Tips on How to Increase Sales for Your Small Business
URL(s): keap.com/business-success-blog/sales/sales
 -process/how-to-increase-sales
Ed: Twila Grissom, Sam Meenasian, Aaron Stead. **Released:** October 01, 2019. **Description:** Provides secrets to closing sales so that your small business can increase its bottom line. **Availability:** Online.

32458 ▪ "11 Sales Techniques to Help Grow Your Small Business" in Score Blog (Sept. 9, 2021)
URL(s): www.score.org/blog/11-sales-techniques
 -help-grow-your-small-business
Ed: Brett Farmiloe. **Released:** September 09, 2021. **Description:** Provides detail on eleven sales strategies to help grow your small business. **Availability:** Online.

32459 ▪ 31 Days to Greeting Card Marketing Mastery
Price: $17.95, paperback. **Description:** The use of simple greeting cards for marketing and increasing sales is explained. **Availability:** Print.

32460 ▪ "33 FIVERR Power Tips: Featuring Prove Ways to Boost Your Sales and Quit Your Job"
Description: Thirty-three proven methods to increase sales, include directions for setting up an automated buyer email collection system, using a new list to direct market buyers, a system for creating events to boost sales and ways to maximize customer satisfaction.

32461 ▪ 101 Ways to Sell More of Anything to Anyone: Sales Tips for Individuals, Business Owners and Sales Professionals
Pub: Allen and Unwin Proprietary Ltd.
Ed: Andrew Griffiths. **Description:** Tips are shared to help anyone improve sales skills while providing strong customer service. **Availability:** Print.

32462 ▪ "2009 Real Estate in Review: Median Prices Drop, Sales Up" in Bellingham Business Journal (Vol. February 2010, pp. 15)
Description: Bellingham and Whatcom County, Washington saw a rise in home sales in 2008. Single family home sales were up 3.3 percent in Bellingham and 0.5 percent for the entire county. Statistical data included. **Availability:** Print; Online.

32463 ▪ "2010 Book of Lists" in Business Courier (Vol. 26, December 26, 2009, No. 36, pp. 1)
Price: $49.95. **Description:** Rankings of companies and organizations within the business services, education, finance, health care, hospitality and tourism, real estate, and technology industries in the Cincinnati, Ohio-Northern Kentucky area are presented. Rankings are based on sales, business size, or other statistics. **Availability:** PDF; Online.

32464 ▪ "2015 Marketing Calendar for Real Estate Pros: Own It"
Pub: CreateSpace
Released: October 14, 2014. **Price:** $9.56, paperback. **Description:** Real estate agents, mortgage loan agents, and new home builders and site and listing agents are shown how to use low-cost, high yield, proven marketing techniques to create digital real estate listings, find more customers, and sell

more homes. Advice for building a brand and public relations; attracting renters and buyers; developing a good Website; and a digital marketing plan are explained. **Availability:** Print.

32465 ■ *"Add Aquatics to Boost Business"* in *Pet Product News (Vol. 64, December 2010, No. 12, pp. 20)*

Ed: David Lass. **Description:** Pet stores are encouraged to add aquatics departments to increase profitability through repeat sales. This goal can be realized by sourcing, displaying, and maintaining high quality live fish. Other tips regarding the challenges associated with setting up an aquatics department are presented. **Availability:** Online.

32466 ■ *"Advanced Persuasion Techniques for Top Producers, Part 2: Mental Pivots and Mental Removers"* in *Senior Market Advisor (Vol. 13, October 2012, No. 10, pp. 32)*

Description: Two advanced persuasion techniques to help sell and motivate prospects and clients are Mental Pivots and Mental Removers. An examination of mental pivots and mental removers is presented. **Availability:** Online.

32467 ■ *Advanced Selling for Dummies*

Released: 2011. **Description:** This book explores topics such as: visualizing success (includes exercises), investing and reinvesting in your own success, harnessing media and multi-media outlets, calculating risks that stretch your limits, creating lasting relationships, finding balance to avoid burnout and more. This guide is for salespeople who have already read 'Selling for Dummies' and now want forward-thinking, advanced strategies for recharging and reenergizing their careers and their lives. Blogging, Internet leads and virtual assistants are also discussed. **Availability:** emobi; Online; Electronic publishing.

32468 ■ *"Art of the Online Deal"* in *Farm Industry News (March 25, 2011)*

Pub: Informa Business Media, Inc.

Contact: Charlie McCurdy, President

Description: Farmers share advice for shopping online for machinery; photos, clean equipment, the price, equipment details, and online sources topped their list. **Availability:** Print; Online.

32469 ■ *"Austin-Based Insupraise Growing Fast"* in *Austin Business Journal (Vol. 31, April 22, 2011, No. 7, pp. 1)*

Pub: Austin Business Journal

Contact: Rachel McGrath, Director

E-mail: rmcgrath@bizjournals.com

Ed: Sandra Zaragoza. **Description:** Austin, Texas-based Insupraise Inc. is finalizing the purchase of a 24,000-square-foot office at 12116 Jekel Circle. The firm, with 23 salespeople and sales that are growing nearly 300 percent over the past 18 months, will now have room to grow. Insupraise plans to hire 35 new salespersons for its call center. **Availability:** Print; Online.

32470 ■ *"avVaa World Health Care Products Rolls Out Internet Marketing Program"* in *Health and Beauty Close-Up (September 18, 2009)*

Description: avVaa World Health Care Products, Inc., a biotechnology company, manufacturer and distributor of nationally branded therapeutic, natural health care and skin products, has signed an agreement with Online Performance Marketing to launch of an Internet marketing campaign in order to broaden its presence online. The impact of advertising on the Internet to generate an increase in sales is explored. **Availability:** Online.

32471 ■ *"Bad Reviews Can Boost Sales. Here's Why"* in *Harvard Business Review (Vol. 90, April 2012, No. 4, pp. 28)*

Pub: Harvard Business Review Press

Contact: Moderna V. Pfizer, Contact

Ed: Jonah Berger. **Price:** $6. **Description:** Research on positive and negative book reviews found that sales increased for books with bad reviews, as the review itself made people aware of a work they would not have otherwise known about. **Availability:** Online; PDF.

32472 ■ *"Baltimore's Businesses, Latest Stats Show Growth may be an Aberration: Recovery a Ruse?"* in *Baltimore Business Journal (Vol. 28, August 6, 2010, No. 13, pp. 1)*

Pub: Baltimore Business Journal

Contact: Rhonda Pringle, President

E-mail: rpringle@bizjournals.com

Ed: Scott Dance. **Description:** Baltimore, Maryland-area businesses have remained cautious as their optimism faded along with the latest indicators on economic recovery. Economists believe they might be justified with their concern since sales were better, but there is no security that they will stay that way. **Availability:** Print.

32473 ■ *"BayTSP, NTT Data Corp. Enter Into Reseller Pact to Market Online IP Monitoring"* in *Professional Services Close-Up (Sept. 11, 2009)*

Description: Due to incredible interest from distributors and content owners across Asia, NTT Data Corp. will resell BayTSP's online intellectual property monitoring, enforcement, business intelligence and monetization services in Japan.

32474 ■ *"Being All a-Twitter"* in *Canadian Business (Vol. 81, December 8, 2008, No. 21, pp. 22)*

Description: Marketing experts suggest that advertising strategies have to change along with new online social media. Companies are advised to find ways to incorporate social software because workers and customers are expected to continue its use. **Availability:** Print; Online.

32475 ■ *"Better Made's Better Idea: Diversify Despite Rising Costs"* in *Crain's Detroit Business (Vol. 24, September 22, 2008, No. 38, pp. 18)*

Pub: Crain Communications Inc.

Contact: Barry Asin, President

Ed: Nathan Skid. **Description:** Better Made Snack Foods Inc. is planning to expand its product lines and market reach as well as boost manufacturing capability during a time in which the company is being buffeted by rising commodity and fuel costs. The company feels that diversification is the key to maintain sales and growth. **Availability:** Online.

32476 ■ *"Big Trouble at Sony Ericsson"* in *Barron's (Vol. 88, March 24, 2008, No. 12, pp. M9)*

Pub: Dow Jones & Company Inc.

Contact: Almar Latour, Chief Executive Officer

Ed: Angelo Franchini. **Description:** Sony Ericsson is facing trouble as it warned that its sales and net income before taxes will fall by nearly half for the first quarter of 2008. The joint venture of Sony and Ericsson has a global mobile phone market share of nine percent as of 2007, fourth largest in the world. **Availability:** Online.

32477 ■ *"BMW Revs Up for a Rebound"* in *Barron's (Vol. 89, July 13, 2009, No. 28, pp. M7)*

Pub: Dow Jones & Company Inc.

Contact: Almar Latour, Chief Executive Officer

Ed: Jonathan Buck. **Description:** Investors may like BMW's stocks because the company has maintained its balance sheet strength and has an impressive production line of new models that should boost sales in the next few years. The company's sales are also gaining traction, although their vehicle delivery was down 1.7 percent year on year on June 2009, this was still the best monthly sales figure for 2009. **Availability:** Online.

32478 ■ *"Book Yourself Solid: The Fastest, Easiest, and Most Reliable System for Getting More Clients Than You Can Handle"*

Pub: John Wiley & Sons, Inc.

Contact: Christina Van Tassell, Executive Vice President Chief Financial Officer

Released: 3rd edition. **Price:** $22, paperback; $14.99, E-book. **Description:** Self-promotion is essential for successful selling. Strategies, techniques, and skills necessary for success are presented, covering social media marketing strategies for service professionals; pricing models and sales strategies to simplify selling; new networking and outreach plans that take only minutes a day; and new product launches ideas and tactics. **Availability:** E-book; Print.

32479 ■ *"Boom and Bust in the Book Biz"* in *Canadian Business (Vol. 83, August 17, 2010, No. 13-14, pp. 16)*

Pub: Rogers Media Inc.

Contact: Neil Spivak, Chief Executive Officer

Ed: Jordan Timm. **Description:** Electronic book marketplace is booming with Amazon.com's e-book sales for the Kindle e-reader exceeding the hardcover sales. Kobo Inc. has registered early success with its Kobo e-reader and has partnered with Hong Kong telecom giant on an e-book store. **Availability:** Print; Online.

32480 ■ *"BrainScripts for Sales Success: 21 Hidden Principles of Consumer Psychology for Winning New Customers"*

Released: September 10, 2014. **Price:** $22, paperback, softback; $22, e-book. **Description:** Twenty-one techniques of consumer psychology are taught to increase sales and recruit new customers. **Availability:** E-book; Print.

32481 ■ *"Brite-Strike Tactical Launches New Internet Marketing Initiatives"* in *Marketwired (September 15, 2009)*

Pub: Comtex News Network Inc.

Contact: Kan Devnani, President

Description: Brite-Strike Tactical Illumination Products, Inc. has enlisted the expertise of Internet marketing guru Thomas J. McCarthy to help revamp the company's Internet campaign. An outline of the Internet marketing strategy is provided. **Availability:** Print; Online.

32482 ■ *Business Black Belt: Develop the Strength, Flexibility and Agility to Run Your Company*

Price: $15.99. **Description:** Manual offering insights that will enable anyone to become successful in small business. Seventy short chapters included topics such as attitude, management, marketing, selling, employees, money, MBAs, lawyers, consultants, and investors. **Availability:** Print.

32483 ■ *Business Warrior: Strategy for Entrepreneurs*

Price: $9.99. **Description:** Advice to help entrepreneurs understand competitive strategies in order to succeed, focusing on sales, marketing, and personnel management. **Availability:** Print; Download; PDF.

32484 ■ *"Can You Hear Them Now?"* in *Hawaii Business (Vol. 54, August 2008, No. 2, pp. 48)*

Description: Coral Wireless LLC (dba Mobi PCS) is ranked 237 in Hawaii Business' list of the state's top 250 companies for 2008. The company is a local wireless phone provider, which has expanded its market to Oahu, Maui and the Big Island since opening in 2006, offering 13 phones and unlimited texts and calls. Details on the company's sales are provided. **Availability:** Print; Online.

32485 ■ *"Canadian Wine to Ship Across Provincial Borders: Let the Wine Flow Freely. Feds To Allow Shipments Inside Canada"* in *Canadian Business (Vol. 85, August 13, 2012, No. 13, pp. 8)*

Ed: Sarah Barmak. **Description:** The passage of federal Bill C-311 is anticipated to remove restriction on interprovincial wine trade imposed under the

Importation of Intoxicating Liquors Act of 1928. There are claims that legalizing direct-to-consumer selling will not affect liquor store sales. **Availability:** Print; Online.

32486 ■ *"The Carpenter: A Story About the Greatest Success Strategies of All"*
Pub: John Wiley & Sons, Inc.
Contact: Christina Van Tassell, Executive Vice President Chief Financial Officer
Released: May 23, 2014. **Price:** $23, hardcover; $14.99, e-book. **Description:** John Gordon draws upon his with work with business leaders, sales people, professional and college sports teams, nonprofit organizations and schools to share a story that will inspire people to build a better life, career and team with successful business strategies. **Availability:** E-book; Print.

32487 ■ *"The Challenger Sale: Taking Control of the Customer Conversation"*
Pub: Portfolio Hardcover
Contact: Adrian Zackheim, President
Released: November 10, 2011. **Price:** $14.42, hardcover; $2.69, hardcover(258 used from $2.69); $7.45, hardcover(107 new from $7.45); $10.50, hardcover(5 collectible from $10.50); $13.60, paperback; $3.97, paperback(53 used from $3.97); $9.31, paperback(71 new from $9.31); $28.95, hardcover, plus shipping charges; $14.99, e-book; $4.79, kindle. **Description:** The best salespeople not only build relationships with customers, they challenge them. The author challenges conventional sales wisdom that suggests approaching customers with unique information about how they can save or make money by purchasing goods or services from your company; to tailor sales messages to each specific customer's needs. **Availability:** E-book; Print.

32488 ■ *"Characteristics of Great Salespeople"* in Agency Sales Magazine (Vol. 39, November 2009, No. 10, pp. 40)
Description: Tips for managers in order to maximize the performance of their sales personnel are presented through several vignettes. Using performance based commission that rewards success, having business systems that support sales activity, and having an organizational culture that embraces sales as a competitive edge are some suggestions. **Availability:** Online.

32489 ■ *"Charged Up for Sales"* in Charlotte Business Journal (Vol. 25, October 15, 2010, No. 30, pp. 1)
Description: Li-Ion Motors Corporation is set to expand its production lines of electric cars in Sacramento, California. The plan is seen to create up to 600 jobs. The company's total investment is seen to reach $500 million. **Availability:** Print; Online.

32490 ■ *"Close the Deal: The Sandler Sales Institute's 7 Step System for Successful Selling"*
Pub: Nightingale-Conant Corp.
Contact: Vic Conant, Chairman
Description: A seven-step system for regaining control, removing pressure, and closing more sales and generating more profit is outlined.

32491 ■ *"Come Together: A Thematic Collection of Times Articles, Essays, Maps and More About Creating Community"* in Pet Product News (Vol. 64, December 2010, No. 12, pp. 28)
Ed: Lizett Bond. **Description:** Pet supply retailers have posted improved sales and improved customer service by bundling their offerings. Bundling pertains to grouping related items such as collars and leashes into a single unit for marketing purposes. Aside from providing convenience and enhanced product information to customers, bundling has facilitated more efficient purchases. **Availability:** Online.

32492 ■ *The Complete Guide to Google Adwords: Secrets, Techniques, and Strategies You Can Learn to Make Millions*
Pub: Atlantic Publishing Co.
Contact: Dr. Heather L. Johnson, Contact

Released: 2012. **Description:** Google AdWords, when it launched in 2002 signaled a fundamental shift in what the Internet was for so many individuals and companies. Learning and understanding how Google AdWords operates and how it can be optimized for maximum exposure, boosting click through rates, conversions, placement, and selection of the right keywords, can be the key to a successful online business. **Availability:** Print; Online.

32493 ■ *"Conquering the Seven Summits of Sales: From Everest to Every Business, Achieving Peak Performance"*
Pub: Harper Business
Contact: Hollis Heimbouch, Senior Vice President Publisher
Released: October 07, 2014. **Price:** $4.99, e-book; $6.19, hardcover; $0.10, hardcover(39 used from $0.10); $3.75, hardcover(19 new from $3.75); $9.10, kindle. **Description:** Sales professionals are taught to overcome their perceived limitations and strive for success. The guide shows how to define goals, build the right team, commit to a vision, time management, and tracking of progress. **Availability:** E-book; Print.

32494 ■ *Consumer Behavior*
Ed: Leon G. Schiffman, Joseph Wisenblit. **Released:** Fifth Edition. **Price:** $276.20, cloth; $112.99, adobe reader. **Description:** Consumer behavior is central to the planning, development and implementation of marketing strategies. **Availability:** Print; Online; PDF.

32495 ■ *"Consumers Are Still Wary; Here's How To Win Them. The Great Recession Has Left Consumers Worried About Their Financial Future. But the Right Strategies Can Engage Leery Spenders"* in Gallup Business Journal (June 24, 2014)
Pub: Gallup, Inc.
Contact: Jon Clifton, Chief Executive Officer
Description: Because consumers are concerned about their financial futures, they are less likely to spend money. Strategies to increase sales while increasing consumer confidence are outlined. **Availability:** Online.

32496 ■ *Content Rich: Writing Your Way to Wealth on the Web*
Released: 1st Edition. **Description:** A definitive search engine optimization (SEO) copywriting guide for search engine rankings and sales conversion. It includes topics not covered in other books on the subject and targets the small to medium sized business looking for ways to maximize online marketing activities as well as designers and Web developers seeking to incorporate more SEO techniques into design and content.

32497 ■ *"Contractors Debate Maximizing Green Opportunities, Education"* in Contractor (Vol. 56, November 2009, No. 11, pp. 3)
Ed: Robert P. Mader. **Description:** Attendees at the Mechanical Service Contractors Association convention were urged to get involved with their local U.S. Green Building Council chapter by one presenter. Another presenter says that one green opportunity for contractors is the commissioning of new buildings. **Availability:** Print; Online.

32498 ■ *"Coping With a Shrinking Planet"* in Agency Sales Magazine (Vol. 39, December 2009, No. 11, pp. 46)
Description: China and India are forcing big changes in the world and are posing a huge threat to U.S. manufacturers and their sales representatives. Reps may want to consider expanding into these territories. Helping sell American products out of the country presents an opportunity for economic expansion. **Availability:** Online.

32499 ■ *"Counting on Cornhole: Popular Bean Bag Game Brings Crowds to Bars"* in Baltimore Business Journal (Vol. 29, July 15, 2011, No. 10, pp. 1)
Pub: Boston Business Journal
Contact: Carolyn M. Jones, President

E-mail: cmjones@bizjournals.com
Ed: Alexander Jackson. **Description:** Cornhole game is being used by bars to spur business as the games hikes beer and food sales on slow weekdays. The game is played with two cornhole boards facing each other and is played with one or two people on one team who try to place a bag on the board. **Availability:** Print; Online.

32500 ■ *"Courier 250 Companies Hope to Rebound From 2009"* in Business Courier (Vol. 27, July 16, 2010, No. 11, pp. 1)
Pub: Business Courier
Ed: Dan Monk, Jon Newberry. **Description:** Private companies that are featured in the Courier 250 publication have lost almost $4 billion in revenue, while combined sales dropped by 11 percent to 32 billion in 2009. Courier 250 is a guide to public companies, large nonprofits, private firms, and other related entities in Ohio's Cincinnati region. **Availability:** Online.

32501 ■ *"Creating the Perfect Lead Magnet"* in Small Business Trends(November 29, 2022)
URL(s): smallbiztrends.com/2022/11/lead-magnet-2.html
Ed: Holly Chavez. **Released:** November 29, 2022. **Description:** Annie P. Ruggles, founder of Non-Sleazy Sales Academy, is interviewed about creating the perfect lead magnet. **Availability:** Online.

32502 ■ *Crossing the Chasm: Marketing and Selling Disruptive Products to Mainstream Customers*
Pub: HarperCollins Publishers L.L.C.
Contact: Brian Murray, President
Ed: Geoffrey A. Moore. **Released:** 3rd edition. **Price:** $21.99, paperback; $11.99, e-book. **Description:** A guide for marketing in high-technology industries, focusing on the Internet. **Availability:** E-book; Print.

32503 ■ *"Customers Will Pay More For Less"* in (Vol. 90, June 2012, No. 6, pp. 30)
Pub: Harvard Business Review Press
Contact: Moderna V. Pfizer, Contact
Ed: Alexander Chernev. **Price:** $6. **Description:** Research indicates that bundling an expensive product and an inexpensive product together makes customers less willing to pay for them than for a single expensive item. Categorical reasoning makes people perceive the inexpensive item to have a negative impact on the expensive item when presented as a single offering. **Availability:** PDF; Online.

32504 ■ *"Cyber Thanksgiving Online Shopping a Growing Tradition"* in Marketing Weekly News (December 12, 2009, pp. 137)
Pub: Investment Weekly News
Description: According to e-commerce analysts, Thanksgiving Day is becoming increasingly important to retailers in terms of online sales. Internet marketers are realizing that consumers are already searching for Black Friday sales and if they find deals on the products they are looking for, they are highly likely to make their purchase on Thanksgiving Day instead of waiting. **Availability:** Online.

32505 ■ *"Deskside Story: As the Latest Buzzword Suggests, PR Firms Are Happy To Drop By"* in Inc. (December 2007, pp. 70, 73)
Ed: Nitasha Tiku. **Description:** Setting up a meeting between a company's CEO and a journalist is known as deskside and is becoming popular again whereby a publicist offers clients deskside visits, briefings and alerts to help promote public relations for a company. **Availability:** Print; Online.

32506 ■ *"Direct Sales Evolving to 'Hi-Touch, Hi-Tech' Approach"* in Providence Business News (Vol. 29, June 2, 2014, No. 9, pp. 4)
Pub: American City Business Journals, Inc.
Contact: Mike Olivieri, Executive Vice President
Released: May 31, 2014. **Description:** Timothy J. Brown, president of Jamie Oliver at Home North America, is a strong supporter of direct sales and believes direct selling is currently at its prime. Brown

explains direct sales functions and reflects on how the techniques used have evolved from the 1950s Tupperware parties. **Availability:** Print; Online.

32507 ■ *"Discovery Networks" in Brandweek (Vol. 49, April 21, 2008, No. 16, pp. SR9)*

Description: Provides contact information for sales and marketing personnel for the Discovery networks as well as a listing of the station's top programming and an analysis of the current season and the target audience for those programs running in the current season. The networks flagship station returned to the top 10 in 2007, averaging 1.28 million viewers.

32508 ■ *"Distribution Dilemma: Standard Process of Tariff Revisions Across States Can Make Discoms Viable" in Best's Review (Vol. 113, September 2012, No. 5, pp. 15)*

Description: Life insurance companies are addressing the obstacles prohibiting them from increasing sales. **Availability:** Print; Online.

32509 ■ *"Ditch the Discount: 10 Incentives to Drive Sales and Earn New Customers" in Small Business Trends (Jan. 30, 2022)*

URL(s): smallbiztrends.com/2022/01/customer-sales-incentives.html

Released: January 30, 2022. **Description:** Discusses ways in which small businesses can creatively attract new customers by offering incentives rather than deep discounts. **Availability:** Online.

32510 ■ *"Do Social Deal Sites Really Work? A Theme Park Chain Considers Whether the Boost In Ticket Sales Is Worth the Trouble" in Harvard Business Review (Vol. 90, May 2012, No. 5, pp. 139)*

Pub: Harvard Business Review Press

Contact: Moderna V. Pfizer, Contact

Ed: Marco Bertini, Luc Wathieu, Betsy Page Sigman, Michael I. Norton. **Price:** $8.95. **Description:** A fictitious group-purchasing promotion scenario is presented, with contributors providing advice. At issue is whether deal-type promotions compromise the customer experience to the point where it offsets any marketing benefit from the deal. While one approach is to more effectively manage the traffic generated from deals, the other is to more closely target promotions to optimize outcomes. **Availability:** Online; PDF.

32511 ■ *"Does the Hierarchical Position of the Buyer Make a Difference? The Influence of Perceived Adaptive Selling on Customer Satisfaction and Loyalty in a Business-To-Business Context" in Journal of Business & Industrial Marketing (Vol. 29, June 2014, No. 5)*

Pub: Emerald Group Publishing Limited

Contact: Erika Valenti, President

Description: A study to evaluate the influence of adaptive selling on customer satisfaction with the salesperson and the company is examined. The effects of buyer's organizational position on customer satisfaction and loyalty were also analyzed. The results highlighted the positive effects of the perceived adaptive selling and indicated that these effects were stronger when the contact person at the buying company was higher in the hierarchy. **Availability:** Download; Online.

32512 ■ *"Don't Ask To Get Married Before Courting Your Prospect" in South Florida Business Journal (Vol. 34, June 13, 2014, No. 47, pp. 21)*

Pub: American City Business Journals, Inc.

Contact: Mike Olivieri, Executive Vice President

Released: Weekly. **Price:** $8, introductory 4-week offer(Digital only). **Description:** Tips for salesmen when courting prospective buyers are presented. Courting prospects should not be done in haste. Salesmen should ask proper questions to get clients talking. **Availability:** Print; Online.

32513 ■ *"The Don't Do Lists" in Inc. (Vol. 33, October 2011, No. 8, pp. 65)*

Pub: Inc. Magazine

Ed: Jennifer Alsever, Adam Bluestein. **Description:** Ten business leaders and experts share their don't do lists, the things that should be avoided when going on sales calls, planning business lunches, motivating employees and more are presented. **Availability:** Online.

32514 ■ *"Dozens 'Come Alive' in Downtown Chicago" in Green Industry Pro (July 2011)*

Ed: Gregg Wartgow. **Description:** Highlights from the Come Alive Outside training event held in Chicago, Illinois July 14-15, 2011 are shared. Nearly 80 people representing 38 landscape companies attended the event that helps contractors review their services and find ways to sell them in new and various ways. **Availability:** Online.

32515 ■ *eBay Business the Smart Way*

Released: 3rd edition. **Description:** eBay commands ninety percent of all online auction business. Computer and software expert and online entrepreneur shares information to help online sellers get started and move merchandise on eBay. Tips include the best ways to build credibility, find products to sell, manage inventory, create a storefront Website, and more. **Availability:** Print; PDF.

32516 ■ *The eBay Business Start-Up Kit: With 100s of Live Links to All the Information & Tools You Need*

Pub: Nolo

Contact: Chris Braun, President

Ed: Richard Stim. **Description:** Interactive kit that provides in-depth information and practical advice in launching an eBay business. **Availability:** Print.

32517 ■ *EBay Income: How ANYONE of Any Age, Location, and/or Background Can Build a Highly Profitable Online Business with eBay*

Pub: Atlantic Publishing Co.

Contact: Dr. Heather L. Johnson, Contact

Description: A complete overview of eBay is given and guides any small company through the entire process of creating the auction and auction strategies, photography, writing copy, text and formatting, multiple sales, programming tricks, PayPal, accounting, creating marketing, merchandising, managing email lists, advertising plans, taxes and sales tax, best time to list items and for how long, sniping programs, international customers, opening a storefront, electronic commerce, buy-it now pricing, keywords, Google marketing and eBay secrets.

32518 ■ *"Economic Trends for Small Business" in Small Business Economic Trends (April 2008, pp. 1)*

Description: Summary of economic trends for small businesses in the U.S. is presented. Economic indicators such as capital spending, inventories and sales, inflation, and profits are given. Analysis of credit markets is also provided. **Availability:** Online.

32519 ■ *Effective Sales Tactics for Small Businesses*

URL(s): www.onsightapp.com/blog/effective-sales-tactics-small-businesses-2

Description: Provides effective sales tactics for your small business to utilize to increase your bottom line. **Availability:** Online.

32520 ■ *"Effective Use of Field Time" in Agency Sales Magazine (Vol. 39, July 2009, No. 7, pp. 40)*

Description: Sales representatives need to consider the value of field visits to themselves and their customers ahead of time. Several anecdotes about field visits from the perspective of manufacturers and sale representatives are presented.

32521 ■ *"Eight Bucks an Hour" in South Florida Business Journal (Vol. 34, July 11, 2014, No. 51, pp. 13)*

Pub: American City Business Journals, Inc.

Contact: Mike Olivieri, Executive Vice President

Released: Weekly. **Price:** $8, introductory 4-week offer(Digital only). **Description:** Tips on ways to improve entrepreneurial selling behavior are listed. A number of potential activities that entrepreneurs can and should be doing to build business include cold calling, attending networking events, and creating business alliances. **Availability:** Print; Online.

32522 ■ *Electronic Commerce*

Ed: Gary P. Schneider, Bryant Chrzan, Charles McCormick. **Released:** 12th edition. **Price:** $29.49, e-book. **Description:** E-commerce can open the door to more opportunities than ever before for small business. Packed with real-world examples and cases, the book delivers comprehensive coverage of emerging online technologies and trends and their influence on the electronic marketplace. It details how the landscape of online commerce is evolving, changes in the economy and how business and society are responding to those changes. Balancing technological issues with the strategic business aspects of successful e-commerce, the new edition includes expanded coverage of international issues, social networking, mobile commerce, Web 2.0 technologies, and updates on spam, phishing, and identity theft. **Availability:** Print.

32523 ■ *"Emack & Bolio's Founder Blames Brookline Store Closure on Rising Rents" in Ice Cream Reporter (Vol. 23, October 20, 2010, No. 11, pp. 8)*

Released: Weekly. **Description:** Emack & Bolio's is engaging in scent marketing using various odors to help boost sales by attracting consumers with scents appropriate to their products. **Availability:** Print; Online.

32524 ■ *"The End of Solution Sales: The Old Playbook No Longer Works. Star Salespeople Now Seek To Upend the Customer's Current Approach to Doing Business" in Harvard Business Review (Vol. 90, July-August 2012, No. 7-8, pp. 60)*

Pub: Harvard Business Review Press

Contact: Moderna V. Pfizer, Contact

Ed: Brent Adamson, Matthew Dixon, Nicholas Toman. **Price:** $8.95, PDF and hardcover black and white. **Description:** Successful sales representatives have adopted new skill sets that focus on coaching clients rather than providing solutions. They seek out change agents and agile firms undergoing cycles of flux. **Availability:** Print; PDF; Online.

32525 ■ *"Feet on the Street: Reps Are Ready to Hit the Ground Running" in Agency Sales Magazine (Vol. 39, July 2009, No. 7, pp. 12)*

Description: One of the major benefits to manufacturers in working with sales representatives is the concept of synergistic selling where the rep shows his mettle. The rep of today is a solution provider that anticipates and meets the customer's needs.

32526 ■ *"Five Distinct Divisions, One Collective Focus" in Green Industry Pro (Vol. 23, October 2011)*

Ed: Gregg Wartgow. **Description:** Profile of ACLS Inc., an amalgamation of All Commercial Landscape Service (commercial maintenance), All Custom Landscape Service (design/build), Fresno Tree Service, Certified Water Consulting (irrigation), and Tractor Service (disking and flailing services on everything from one-acre lots to hundreds of acres of open land). The firm discusses its rebranding effort in order to increase sales. **Availability:** Online.

32527 ■ *"For Gilead, Growth Beyond AIDS" in Barron's (Vol. 88, June 30, 2008, No. 26, pp. 18)*

Pub: Dow Jones & Company Inc.

Contact: Almar Latour, Chief Executive Officer

Ed: Jay Palmer. **Description:** First-quarter 2008 revenue for Gilead Sciences grew by 22 percent and an earnings gain of 19 percent thanks to their HIV-treatment drugs that comprised over two-thirds of the company's sales in 2007. An analyst has a 12-month target from June, 2008 of 65 per share. The factors behind the company's prospects are also discussed. **Availability:** Online.

32528 ■ *"Formula for Success: Dispelling the Age-Old Myths" in Agency Sales Magazine (Vol. 39, July 2009, No. 7, pp. 26)*
Description: Common misperceptions about selling and salespeople include the idea that anyone can be successful in selling if they work hard enough and that successful salespeople are born that way. In fact, top performers take risks and they invest in themselves. **Availability:** Online.

32529 ■ *The Four Steps to the Epiphany: Successful Strategies for Products that Win*
Pub: John Wiley & Sons, Inc.
Contact: Christina Van Tassell, Executive Vice President Chief Financial Officer
URL(s): www.wiley.com/en-us/The+Four+Steps+to +the+Epiphany%3A+Successful+Strategies+for +Products+that+Win-p-9781119690351
Ed: Steve Blank. **Released:** March 2020. **Price:** $24, e-book; $40, hardcover. **Description:** Helps entrepreneurs starting new businesses understand the four-step Customer Development process, which helps target what is necessary to achieve sales and marketing for your product. **Availability:** E-book; Print.

32530 ■ *"Funds "Friend' Facebook" in Barron's (Vol. 89, July 27, 2009, No. 30, pp. 30)*
Pub: Dow Jones & Company Inc.
Contact: Almar Latour, Chief Executive Officer
Ed: Leslie P. Norton. **Description:** Mutual-fund companies are the latest entrants to the "social media" space and several companies have already set up Facebook and Twitter pages. The use of this technology pose special challenges for compliance and regulators especially since the Financial Industry Regulatory Authority reminds companies that advertising, sales and literature are governed by regulations. **Availability:** Online.

32531 ■ *"Gain the 'Come Alive Outside' Selling Edge" in Green Industry Pro (July 2011)*
Ed: Jim Paluch. **Description:** Marketing the 'Come Alive Outside' slogan can help landscapers to increase their market share by identifying and applying these elements to each customer as well as their workers. **Availability:** Online.

32532 ■ *Getting More: How to Negotiate to Achieve Your Goals in the Real World*
Released: January 04, 2011. **Price:** $26. **Description:** When negotiating, people fail to meet their goals due to focusing on power and the 'win-win' instead of on relationships and perceptions, thus not finding enough things to trade. They think others should be rational when they are dealing with emotions and they get distracted from the real goal.

32533 ■ *"Girls Will Gossip: Psst! Buzz About Target" in Barron's (Vol. 89, July 27, 2009, No. 30, pp. 15)*
Pub: Dow Jones & Company Inc.
Contact: Almar Latour, Chief Executive Officer
Ed: Katherine Cheng. **Description:** Target rebutted the rumor that they will disassociate themselves from a line of clothing inspired by the television show 'Gossip Girl'. Target's spokesman says that the retailer intends to remain closely identified with the show. Target's sales should benefit from the hotly anticipated clothing line. **Availability:** Online.

32534 ■ *"The Globe: Let Emerging Market Customers Be Your Teachers" in Harvard Business Review (Vol. 88, December 2010, No. 12, pp. 115)*
Pub: Harvard Business Publishing
Contact: Diane Belcher, Managing Director
Ed: Guillermo D'Andrea, David Marcotte, Gwen Dixon Morrison. **Price:** $8.95, PDF. **Description:** Examination of effective strategies for emerging markets is presented. These include helping educate customers as well as selling to them, adapting to

customers' habits, and focusing brands appropriately. Magazine Luiza, a chain store in Brazil, is used to illustrate these points. **Availability:** Online; PDF.

32535 ■ *The Golden 120 Seconds of Every Sales Call: A Fresh Innovative Look at the Sales Process*
Pub: NorlightsPress.com
Contact: Dee Justesen, Co-Founder
Ed: Peter G. Dennis. **Released:** Second edition. **Description:** Salespeople who want to find their personal style, gain confidence, and avoid deal-killing mistakes must read this book. It will show both new and experienced sales professionals how to use key fundamentals with every call, every selling interaction, and every opportunity to make something happen. Anyone who sells for a living has experienced the magic moments that can make or break a sales. Advice is given to help recognize, and learn to cultivate, this vital part of the sales process. **Availability:** Print.

32536 ■ *"Good Questions and the Basics of Selling" in Agency Sales Magazine (Vol. 39, September-October 2009, No. 9, pp. 14)*
Description: Six basic elements to enhance the job of a sales person in regards to his relationship to a customer are presented. **Availability:** Online.

32537 ■ *"Harness the Internet to Boost Equipment Sales" in Indoor Comfort Marketing (Vol. 70, July 2011, No. 7, pp. 24)*
Description: Advice is given to increase HVAC/R equipment sales using the Internet. **Availability:** Online.

32538 ■ *"Heavy Duty: The Case Against Packing Lightly" in Crain's Chicago Business (Vol. 31, April 21, 2008, No. 16, pp. 29)*
Pub: Crain Communications Inc.
Contact: Barry Asin, President
Ed: Sarah A. Klein. **Description:** Penelope Biggs, a Northern Trust executive who manages sales teams in North America, Europe and Asia gives advice on traveling abroad for business including time management skills, handling time-zone hops and avoiding jet-lag. **Availability:** Online.

32539 ■ *"Helping Customers Fight Pet Waste" in Pet Product News (Vol. 64, November 2010, No. 11, pp. 52)*
Ed: Sandy Robins. **Description:** Pet cleaning products manufacturers have been enjoying high sales figures by paying attention to changing pet ownership trends and environmental awareness. Meanwhile, the inclusion of user-friendly features in these products has also been boosted by the social role of pets and the media attention to pet waste. How manufacturers have been responding to this demand is explored. **Availability:** Print; Online.

32540 ■ *"How Artificial Intelligence Can Help Small Businesses" in Bplans Blog*
Ed: Nicole Walters. **Description:** Discusses how artificial intelligence is becoming more accessible and more affordable for small businesses and how you can incorporate machine intelligence to make your company more efficient and improve your bottom line. **Availability:** Online.

32541 ■ *How to Build a Winning Sales Team: Tips and Strategies*
URL(s): www.barnesandnoble.com/w/how-to-build-a -winning-sales-team-tips-and-strategies-james -dickson/1143168176?ean=2940185841747
Ed: James Dickson. **Released:** March 04, 2023. **Price:** $4.99, e-book. **Description:** Increasing growth and revenue is usually the main goal of a business, so having a successful sales team will make all the difference. Learn how to develop a sales team with the tips and tools provided in this book. **Availability:** E-book.

32542 ■ *"How to Develop an Active Sales Program" in Green Industry Pro (Vol. 23, September 2011)*
Ed: Gregg Wartgow. **Description:** Craig den Hartog, owner of Emerald Magic Lawn Care located in Holtsville, New York, describes the various marketing

tactics he has developed to increase sales in the current economic environment. Statistical data included. **Availability:** Online.

32543 ■ *"How to Dominate in Residential Maintenance" in Green Industry Pro (Vol. 23, October 2011)*
Ed: Gregg Wartgow. **Description:** Lawn care services were ranked among the most expendable consumer expenditures, according to the National Retail Federation data accumulated in early 2011. This makes it critical for any landscape firm to target sales efforts toward higher-income households and higher-value homes. **Availability:** Online.

32544 ■ *"How Good Advice 'Online' Can Attract Customers" in Indoor Comfort Marketing (Vol. 70, August 2011, No. 8, pp. 20)*
Pub: Spray Technology & Marketing
Contact: Ava Caridad, Director, Editorial
E-mail: acaridad@spraytm.com
Ed: Richard Rutigilano. **Description:** Online marketing tips for heating and cooling small businesses are explained.

32545 ■ *"How to Keep Your Sales from Running Out of Gas" in Agency Sales Magazine (Vol. 39, July 2009, No. 7, pp. 30)*
Description: Salespeople can let the good times deceive them into thinking that success will go on forever. Salespeople and businesses should see prospecting as a strategy for creating a continuing flow of business. **Availability:** Online.

32546 ■ *How to Make Money with Social Media: An Insider's Guide to Using New and Emerging Media to Grow Your Business*
Ed: Jamie Turner, Reshma Shah, PhD. **Released:** 2nd edition. **Description:** Marketers, executives, entrepreneurs are shown more effective ways to utilize Internet social media to make money. This guide brings together both practical strategies and proven execution techniques for driving maximum value from social media marketing. **Availability:** E-book; Print.

32547 ■ *How to Open and Operate a Financially Successful Bookstore on Amazon and Other Web Sites: With Companion CD-ROM*
Pub: Atlantic Publishing Co.
Contact: Dr. Heather L. Johnson, Contact
Description: This book was written for every used book aficionado and bookstore owner who currently wants to take advantage of the massive collection of online resources available to start and run your own online bookstore business.

32548 ■ *"How to Run a Promotion without Running from the Law" in Legal Zoom (March 28, 2023)*
URL(s): www.legalzoom.com/articles/how-to-run-a -promotion-without-running-from-the-law
Ed: Bilal Kaiser. **Released:** March 28, 2023. **Description:** If you are planning on running a sweepstakes or an online contest for your small business, follow these tips so that you make sure your business is in compliance with the law. You will also need to be mindful of data privacy issues. **Availability:** Online.

32549 ■ *"I Brake for Yard Sales: And Flea Markets, Thrift Shops, Auctions, and the Occasional Dumpster"*
Released: April 01, 2012. **Price:** $24.95, Paperback. **Description:** Lara Spencer, self-confessed frugalista and new correspondent, shares her passion for shopping at yard sales, consignment shops, and estate sales for decorating her home as well as her friend's homes. She shares her bargain hunting secrets and tells where to shop, what to look for, how to pay for sales, how to restore items, and how to decorate. **Availability:** E-book; Print.

32550 ■ *"I Hear You're Interested In A..." in Inc. (January 2008, pp. 40-43)*
Ed: Leah Hoffmann. **Description:** Four tips to help any small business generate sales leads online are examined. **Availability:** Online.

32551 ■ *"An Ice Boost in Revenue; Wings Score With Expanded Corporate Sales" in Crain's Detroit Business (Vol. 25, June 1, 2009, No. 22)*
Pub: Crain Communications Inc.
Contact: Barry Asin, President
Ed: Bill Shea. **Description:** Stanley Cup finals always boost business for the Detroit area, even during a recession. The Red Wings corporate office reported corporate sponsorship revenue luxury suite rentals, Legends Club seats and advertising were up 40 percent this year over 2008. **Availability:** Print; Online.

32552 ■ *"If the Opportunity is There, Move Boldly" in Indoor Comfort Marketing (Vol. 70, March 2011, No. 3)*
Pub: Spray Technology & Marketing
Contact: Ava Caridad, Director, Editorial
E-mail: acaridad@spraytm.com
Ed: Richard Rutigliano. **Released:** March 01, 2011. **Description:** Suggestions are offered to help improve air conditioning sales. **Availability:** Print; Online.

32553 ■ *"Increasing Business-to-Business Buyer Word-of-Mouth and Share-of-Purchase" in Journal of Business & Industrial Marketing (Vol. 29, June 2014, No. 5)*
Pub: Emerald Group Publishing Limited
Contact: Erika Valenti, President
Description: The satisfaction-loyalty framework pertaining to word-of-mouth communications and share-of-purchases was examined for situations in which business-to-business buyers are associated with the salesperson as well as the selling firm. The results indicated that satisfaction, loyalty, and WOMC relating to the salesperson directly affect satisfaction, loyalty, and WOMC with the selling firm, and that buyer satisfaction and loyalty also influence their post purchase conduct. **Availability:** Download; Online.

32554 ■ *"Indulgent Parsimony: an Enduring Marketing Approach" in Strategy and Leadership (Vol. 39, March-April 2011, No. 2, pp. 36)*
Pub: Emerald Group Publishing Limited
Contact: Erika Valenti, President
Ed: Kenneth Alan Grossberg. **Description:** Indulgent parsimony (IP), a marketing strategy employed on consumers that are affected by recession, is found to be a relevant and appropriate approach that can help encourage buying. IP involves the selling of cheaper goods and services that allow consumers experience comfort and relief from stress. **Availability:** Download; Online.

32555 ■ *"Info Junkie: Karen Eng" in Crain's Chicago Business (Vol. 34, October 24, 2011, No. 42, pp. 35)*
Pub: Crain Communications Inc.
Contact: Barry Asin, President
Ed: Christina Le Beau. **Description:** Greg Colando, president of Flor Inc., an eco-friendly carpet company located I Chicago discusses his marketing program to increase sales. **Availability:** Online.

32556 ■ *Instant Income: Strategies That Bring in the Cash*
Pub: McGraw-Hill Professional
Ed: Janet Switzer. **Released:** First Edition. **Price:** $24. **Description:** Book covers small business advertising techniques, marketing, joint ventures, and sales. **Availability:** Print.

32557 ■ *"Intentional Networking: Your Guide to Word of Mouth Marketing Greatness"*
Pub: CreateSpace
Released: October 28, 2014. **Price:** $10.55, kindle; paperback ; $7.84, paperback. **Description:** Business owners and salespeople know the power of word of mouth marketing to increase sales. Networking, email communications, social media and referrals are techniques to help build revenue. **Availability:** Print.

32558 ■ *"Intermodal Makes Suppliers Look to Rack Up Big Sales to Distributors" in The Business Journal-Serving Metropolitan Kansas City (August 15, 2008)*
Pub: American City Business Journals, Inc.
Contact: Mike Olivieri, Executive Vice President
Ed: James Dornbrook. **Description:** Suppliers of shelving units, conveyor systems and other equipment used in distribution facilities are expecting new business opportunities along with the planned intermodal projects in the Kansas City area. Suppliers have already observed that small distributors have started to relocate to the city because of the intermodal projects. Demand for shelves and lifts have also increased. **Availability:** Online.

32559 ■ *"Internet Marketing 2.0: Closing the Online Chat Gap" in Agent's Sales Journal (November 2009, pp. 14)*
Ed: Jeff Denenholz. **Description:** Advice regarding the implementation of an Internet marketing strategy for insurance agencies includes how and why to incorporate a chat feature in which a sales agent can communicate in real-time with potential or existing customers. It is important to understand if appropriate response mechanisms are in place to convert leads into actual sales. **Availability:** Print; Online.

32560 ■ *"Investment Market Heats Up on the Eastside" in Puget Sound Business Journal (Vol. 35, August 1, 2014, No. 15, pp. 4)*
Pub: American City Business Journals, Inc.
Contact: Mike Olivieri, Executive Vice President
Released: Weekly. **Price:** $4, Introductory 4-week offer(Digital & Print). **Description:** The real estate investment sales market in Puget Sound, Washington is experiencing growth along with construction activity. Office sales reached $787 million in the first half of the year, while the shortage of office space is driving up rents for office tenants and making the market attractive to investors. **Availability:** Print; Online.

32561 ■ *Islands of Profit in a Sea of Red Ink: Why 40 Percent of Your Business Is Unprofitable and How to Fix It*
Pub: Portfolio
Contact: Adrian Zackheim, President
Ed: Jonathan L. S. Byrnes. **Released:** October 14, 2010. **Price:** $27.95, hardcover; $14.99, e-book. **Description:** Top companies from around the world turn to Jonathan Byrnes to figure out where to find profit for their companies. He shows which parts of a business are worth expanding, and which are just a drain on resources. He has found that roughly 40 percent of any new client's business is unprofitable, and that profit increases of thirty percent or more are within reach. **Availability:** E-book; Print.

32562 ■ *"It's Time for Insurance Carriers To Win More Customers; About One-Third of Insurance Customers are Engaged. This Means the Industry Has a Massive Opportunity to Gain More Business" in Gallup Business Journal (May 28, 2014)*
Pub: Gallup, Inc.
Contact: Jon Clifton, Chief Executive Officer
Description: The insurance industry has the opportunity to engage and increase business and profits. Only one-third of insurance customers are engaged. Tips to help engage customers are offered. **Availability:** Print; Online.

32563 ■ *"Keys to Overcome Fear of Follow-Up" in Agency Sales Magazine (Vol. 39, December 2009, No. 11, pp. 26)*
Description: In order to be more successful at making follow-up calls, salespeople should not take rejection personally and never assume that they are going to annoy prospects if they follow-up. Those that follow-up with prospects stand out among others since few salespeople do this. **Availability:** Online.

32564 ■ *"Leading With Meaning: Beneficiary Contact, Prosocial Impact, and the Performance Effects of Transformational Leadership" in Academy of Management Journal (Vol. 55, April 1, 2012, No. 2, pp. 458)*
Pub: Academy of Management
Contact: Sharon Alvarez, President
Ed: Adam M. Grant. **Description:** Transformational leadership is shown to effectively motivate followers when they interact with the beneficiaries of their work. For instance, beneficiary contact boosted the effects on call center employees' sales and revenue with these findings being extended by a survey study with government employees. How perceived prosocial impact supports a moderated mediation model is discussed. **Availability:** Electronic publishing; Download; PDF; Online.

32565 ■ *"Let's Go Team: When a Retail Professional Leads by Example, Everyone Benefits" in Black Enterprise (Vol. 41, November 2010, No. 4)*
Pub: Earl G. Graves Ltd.
Contact: Earl Graves, Jr., President
Ed: Aisha I. Jefferson. **Description:** Profile of Derek Jenkins, senior vice president of Target Stores Northeast Region is presented. Jenkins oversees the management of 450 retail stores with nearly 75,000 workers. He shares insight into managing by making sure every interaction with his team counts.

32566 ■ *"A Love of Likes: What's a Facebook Nod Worth to a Business? Serious Sales Growth, Say Some" in Boston Business Journal (Vol. 31, July 8, 2011, No. 24, pp. 1)*
Pub: Boston Business Journal
Contact: Carolyn M. Jones, President
E-mail: cmjones@bizjournals.com
Ed: Lisa Van der Pool. **Description:** An increasing number of companies in Boston, Massachusetts have been keen on getting Facebook 'likes' from people. Business owners realize that Facebook 'likes' could generate sales and based on some studies, equate to specific dollar values.

32567 ■ *"Marketing in the Digital World: Here's How to Craft a Smart Online Strategy" in Black Enterprise (Vol. 40, July 2010, No. 12, pp. 47)*
Pub: Earl G. Graves Ltd.
Contact: Earl Graves, Jr., President
Ed: Sonya A. Donaldson. **Description:** Social media is an integral part of any small business plan in addressing marketing, sales, and branding strategies.

32568 ■ *Marketing for Entrepreneurs*
Pub: FT Press
Ed: Jurgen Wolff. **Released:** 1st edition. **Description:** This text identifies marketing as the entire process of researching, creating, distributing and selling a product or service. It isn't about theory and metrics, rather it is a practical guide that starts with the basics of all marketing aspects. **Availability:** Print.

32569 ■ *Marketing Without Money for Small and Midsize Businesses: 300 FREE and Cheap Ways to Increase Your Sales*
Price: $11.25. **Description:** Three hundred practical low-cost or no-cost strategies to increase sales, focusing on free advertising, free marketing assistance, and free referrals to the Internet. **Availability:** Print; Online.

32570 ■ *Mastering the Complex Sale: How to Compete and Win When the Stakes Are High!*
Pub: John Wiley & Sons, Inc.
Contact: Christina Van Tassell, Executive Vice President Chief Financial Officer
Ed: Jeff Thull. **Released:** Second edition. **Price:** $24. 95, hardcover; $16.99, e-book. **Description:** Guide to compete for and win in complex selling, the business-to-business transactions involving multiple decisions by multiple people from multiple perspectives. **Availability:** E-book; Print; Online; PDF.

32571 ■ *"Mobile Discounts: A Matter of Distance and Time" in Harvard Business Review (Vol. 92, May 2014, No. 5, pp. 30)*
Pub: Harvard Business Publishing
Contact: Diane Belcher, Managing Director
Price: $6. **Description:** Geolocation via smartphone enables companies to offer consumers real-time incentives and discounts. Research shows that time and distance are key factors in a customers' receptiveness for these promotions: same day and close proximity increase the odds of a sales purchase. **Availability:** Online; PDF.

32572 ■ *"More Leading Retailers Using Omniture Conversion Solutions to Boost Sales and Ecommerce Performance" in Marketwired (September 22, 2009)*
Pub: Comtex News Network Inc.
Contact: Kan Devnani, President
Description: Many retailers are utilizing Omniture conversion solutions to improve the performance of their ecommerce businesses; recent enhancements to Omniture Merchandising and Omniture Recommendations help clients drive increased conversion to their Internet ventures.

32573 ■ *"Morgan Keegan Feeds Wunderlich" in Memphis Business Journal (Vol. 34, May 18, 2012, No. 5, pp. 1)*
Pub: Baltimore Business Journal
Contact: Rhonda Pringle, President
E-mail: rpringle@bizjournals.com
Ed: Cole Epley. **Description:** Wunderlich Securities Inc. has augmented its equity markets group with a dozen former Morgan Keegan & Company Inc. professionals. Wunderlich assigned ten of the new hires in Memphis, Tennessee while the two joined its institutional sales department in New York. **Availability:** Print; Online.

32574 ■ *"Motivating Salespeople: What Really Works. Companies Fiddle Constantly With Their Incentive Plans - But Most of Their Changes Have Little Effect" in Harvard Business Review (Vol. 90, July-August 2012, No. 7-8, pp. 70)*
Pub: Harvard Business Review Press
Contact: Moderna V. Pfizer, Contact
Ed: Thomas Steenburgh, Michael Ahearne. **Description:** Firms focusing on motivating star performers when core performers are the ones who will make a difference. By taking individual differences into account, firms will realize improved results across the organization.

32575 ■ *"Net Savings Link Announces SpyderShare Inc. Contract for Development of Search Engine Optimization (S.E.O.) Program" in Internet Wire (February 21, 2012)*
Pub: Comtex News Network Inc.
Contact: Kan Devnani, President
Description: Net Savings Link provides electronically deliverable sales incentives for the business market along with improved Web based savings programs for consumers has partnered with SpyderShare Inc. to enhance the firm's presence on the Internet. Details of the partnership are included. **Availability:** Print; Online.

32576 ■ *"NetSpend and Family Dollar Announce New Prepaid Card Agreement" in GlobeNewswire (May 10, 2012)*
Pub: Comtex News Network Inc.
Contact: Kan Devnani, President
Description: Partnership between Family Dollar and NetSpend will offer customers a NetSpend Visa(R) Prepaid Debit Card to be used at Family Dollar's 7,200 locations. NetSpend is a leading provider of general-purpose reloadable (GPR) prepaid debit cards and other related financial services. **Availability:** Print; Online.

32577 ■ *"Never Run Out of Leads" in Senior Market Advisor (Vol. 13, October 2012, No. 10, pp. 34)*
Description: Two basic rules in order to be successful and never run out of sales leads are: 1. always be

in meetings, 2. refer back to rule number one. Meeting with clients and potential clients is essential. **Availability:** Online.

32578 ■ *"New Sales. Simplified: The Essential Handbook for Prospecting and New Business Development"*
Pub: HarperCollins Leadership
Contact: Donald Miller, Chief Executive Officer
Released: September 04, 2012. **Price:** $19.99, Paperback. **Description:** The constant flow of new accounts is essential for any small business to grow and thrive. A proven formula for prospecting; customer-focused selling; proactive telephone calling that leads to face-to-face meetings; the use of email, voicemail, and social media; prevent the buyer's anti-salesperson response; build a rapport; winning sales; communicating with clients; plan time for business development activities; and more. **Availability:** E-book; Print; Audio; Download.

32579 ■ *"NKC Keeps Pace with Auto Industry" in Memphis Business Journal (Vol. 34, September 14, 2012, No. 22, pp. 1)*
Pub: Baltimore Business Journal
Contact: Rhonda Pringle, President
E-mail: rpringle@bizjournals.com
Ed: Michael Sheffield. **Description:** Memphis, Tennessee-based NKC of American Inc. has been expecting sales to increase to about $60 million for 2012 after its revenue dropped to about $20 million during the peak of the recession in 2008-2009. NKC's growth is being driven by new contracts with automotive manufacturers. **Availability:** Print; Online.

32580 ■ *"North American Pet Health Insurance Market Poised for Growth" in Pet Product News (Vol. 64, December 2010, No. 12, pp. 4)*
Ed: David Lummis. **Description:** The pet health insurance market is expected to further grow after posting about $350 million in sales in 2009, a gain of more than $40 million. Pet insurance firms have offered strategies such as product humanization in response to this growth forecast. Meanwhile, pet insurance shoppers have been provided more by insurance firms with wider choices. **Availability:** Online.

32581 ■ *"Norvax University Health Insurance Sales Training and Online Marketing Conference" in Marketwired (January 27, 2010)*
Pub: Comtex News Network Inc.
Contact: Kan Devnani, President
Description: Overview of the Norvax University Marketing and Sales Success Conference Tour which includes insurance sales training seminars, proven and innovative online marketing techniques and a host of additional information and networking opportunities. **Availability:** Print; Online.

32582 ■ *"Not Sales, But a Secret Sauce" in Memphis Business Journal (Vol. 35, March 14, 2014, No. 49, pp. 15)*
Pub: American City Business Journals, Inc.
Contact: Mike Olivieri, Executive Vice President
Released: Weekly. **Price:** $4, introductory 4-week offer(Digital only). **Description:** Farmhouse Marketing LLC creative director, Ben Fent, says businesses should focus on connections instead of sales. He added that businesses should use more visual language in selling. Fant also stated that the key to making a sale is making people see the benefit of a product. **Availability:** Print; Online.

32583 ■ *"Nowspeed and OneSource to Conduct Webinar: How to Develop Social Media Content That Gets Results" in Marketwired (December 14, 2009)*
Pub: Comtex News Network Inc.
Contact: Kan Devnani, President
Description: OneSource, a leading provider of global business information, and Nowspeed, an Internet marketing agency, will conduct a webinar titled "How to Develop Social Media Content That Gets Results" in order to provide marketers insight into how to

develop and optimize effective social media content to get consumer results that translate into purchases and lead generation. **Availability:** Print; Mailing list; Online.

32584 ■ *"On the Go: a Busy Executive Is Always Well-Equipped for Travel" in Black Enterprise (Vol. 40, July 2010, No. 12, pp. 106)*
Pub: Earl G. Graves Ltd.
Contact: Earl Graves, Jr., President
Ed: Sonia Alleyne. **Description:** Successful sales executive, Henry Watkins, shares tips on business travel. **Availability:** Online.

32585 ■ *"The One Thing You Must Get Right When Building a Brand" in Harvard Business Review (Vol. 88, December 2010, No. 12, pp. 80)*
Pub: Harvard Business Publishing
Contact: Diane Belcher, Managing Director
Ed: Patrick Barwise, Sean Meehan. **Price:** $8.95, PDF. **Description:** Four uses for new media include: communicating a clearly defined customer promise, creating trust via delivering on the promise, regularly improving on the promise, and innovating past what is familiar. **Availability:** Online; PDF.

32586 ■ *"Online Book Sales Surpass Bookstores" in Information Today (Vol. 28, September 2011, No. 8, pp. 11)*
Pub: Information Today Inc.
Contact: Thomas H. Hogan, President
Ed: Cindy Martine. **Description:** Online book sales outpaced bookstore purchases in the United States, signaling a shift in the US book industry. Statistical data included.

32587 ■ *"Online Directories: Your Silent Sales Staff" in South Florida Business Journal (Vol. 34, June 20, 2014, No. 48, pp. 14)*
Pub: American City Business Journals, Inc.
Contact: Mike Olivieri, Executive Vice President
Released: Weekly. **Price:** $8, introductory 4-week offer(Digital only). **Description:** The benefits of using online business directories as an extension of the physical sales personnel are explained. Business owners who plan to use online directories to their advantage need to check their listings and links at least once a year and whenever there is a change to the business. **Availability:** Print; Online.

32588 ■ *"Options Abound in Winter Wares" in Pet Product News (Vol. 64, November 2010, No. 11, pp. 1)*
Ed: Maggie M. Shein. **Description:** Pet supply manufacturers emphasize creating top-notch construction and functional design in creating winter clothing for pets. Meanwhile, retailers and pet owners seek human-inspired style, quality, and versatility for pets' winter clothing. How retailers generate successful sales of pets' winter clothing outside of traditional brand marketing is also examined. **Availability:** Online.

32589 ■ *"Outside In: The Power of Putting Customers at the Center of Your Business"*
Description: Customer experience is the most powerful and least understood element of corporate strategy in today's business world. Customer experience is the way your customers perceive their interactions with a company. It drives sales and provides a competitive advantage. **Availability:** Audio.

32590 ■ *"Paid to Persuade: Careers in Sales" in Occupational Outlook Quarterly (Vol. 55, Summer 2011, No. 2, pp. 24)*
Pub: U.S. Department of Labor Bureau of Labor Statistics
Contact: Amrit Kohli, Director
E-mail: kohli.amrit@bls.gov
Ed: Ilka Maria Torpey. **Description:** Sales workers are paid to persuade others to buy goods and services. There were over 13 million wage and salary sales workers in the US in 2010. Wages in sales

careers can vary and some become lucrative, lifelong career positions. Seven sales occupations with annual wages higher than $33,000 are profiled. **Availability:** Online; PDF.

32591 ■ *"Pay or Play: Do Nice (Sales) Guys Finish Last?" in Agency Sales Magazine (Vol. 39, August 2009, No. 8, pp. 8)*
Description: How positive interpersonal relationships among salespersons, program coordinators, and other business-related professions will pay in terms of business success is presented. Business people should know the ideal customers, promise only what they can do, refer out when needed, and follow through with any stated promise. Further insight into these ideas is presented. **Availability:** Online.

32592 ■ *"Perfecting Customer Services" in Pet Product News (Vol. 64, November 2010, No. 11, pp. 18)*
Ed: Alison Bour. **Description:** Pet supply retailers are encouraged to emphasize customer experience and sales representatives' knowledge of the store's product offerings to foster repeat business. Employee protocols could be implemented to improve customer interaction. Other guidelines on developing a pet supply retail environment that advances repeat business are presented. **Availability:** Online.

32593 ■ *"The Perils of Popularity" in Business Strategy Review (Vol. 23, Spring 2012, No. 1, pp. 51)*
Description: The iPhone's worldwide success would seem to be an unqualified win-win for Apple and the mobile operators that sell it. Not so, explains Marco Bertini and Ricardo Cabornero, as mobile operators they must maintain a delicate balance between winning new customers and retaining existing ones. This task is made more difficult when their own brands can actually be diminished by selling the competitor's iPhone. **Availability:** Print; Online.

32594 ■ *"Private Label Manufacturers Association" in Ice Cream Reporter (Vol. 23, July 20, 2010, No. 8, pp. 7)*
Description: Branded frozen dessert manufacturers sold more frozen desserts in terms of sales volume and revenue and market share in 2009. Statistical details included. **Availability:** Print; Online.

32595 ■ *"Progress Means Business" in Pet Product News (Vol. 66, September 2012, No. 9, pp. 88)*
Description: Pet supplies retailers are encouraged to promote devices featuring technologies that will assist herp hobbyists to properly monitor temperature, humidity and UVB in tanks with improved control and precision. Customer connction should also be taken into consideration by retailers to generate more sales. Other marketing tips for promoting sophisticated monitoring devices for herp tanks are given. **Availability:** Online.

32596 ■ *"Promotions Create a Path to Better Profit" in Pet Product News (Vol. 64, December 2010, No. 12, pp. 1)*
Ed: Joan Hustace Walker. **Description:** Pet store retailers can boost small mammal sales by launching creative marketing and promotions such as social networking and adoption days.

32597 ■ *"The Proven 3 Step Formula For Growing Retail Profits: Without Having to Resort to Coupons or Discount Sales"*
Pub: CreateSpace
Released: September 24, 2014. **Price:** $4.89, paperback. **Description:** Previously published under the name, "How Some Retailers Make More Money Than Others". Retailers, whether a franchise or independent brand face challenges for increasing sales. An explanation for growing customer base without mass advertising, how to increase each customers spending, and improve gross margins are reported. A proven three-step process for increasing retail profits without the use of coupons or discounts is provided. **Availability:** Print.

32598 ■ *"A Quick Guide To Putting Employees In The Driver's Seat For Customer Success" in Small Business Trends (March 20, 2023)*
URL(s): smallbiztrends.com/2021/12/business-guide -to-customer-experience.html
Ed: Pratik Dholakiya. **Released:** December 03, 2021. **Description:** A discussion of how to train customer-facing employees. Includes tips on focusing on the customer's needs and also how to treat your employees. **Availability:** Online.

32599 ■ *"Quick Guide VI - How to Sell Coaching"*
Pub: CreateSpace
Released: October 10, 2014. **Price:** $4.99, kindle. **Description:** A sales coach shares her sixteen years of experience to help others increase sales. **Availability:** Print.

32600 ■ *"A Radical Prescription for Sales: The Reps of the Future Won't Work On Commission" in Harvard Business Review (Vol. 90, July-August 2012, No. 7-8, pp. 76)*
Pub: Harvard Business Review Press
Contact: Moderna V. Pfizer, Contact
Ed: Daniel H. Pink. **Price:** $8.95, PDF and hardcover black and white. **Description:** The complexity of sales today has rendered commissions obsolete, as transactions give way to heuristic skills. A more effective way to motivate sales representatives is a combination of 90 percent salary and 10 percent compensation linked to corporate measures rather than individual measures. **Availability:** Print; PDF; Online.

32601 ■ *"Reality Check at the Bottom of the Pyramid: To Succeed in the World's Poorest Markets, Aim For Much Higher Margins and Prices Than You Thought Were Necessary-Or Possible" in Harvard Business Review (Vol. 90, June 2012, No. 6, pp. 120)*
Pub: Harvard Business Review Press
Contact: Moderna V. Pfizer, Contact
Ed: Erik Simanis. **Price:** $8.95, hardcopy black and white. **Description:** Margin-enhancing platforms are identified. Bundling products increases customer access and enables firms to sell more in each transaction. Including services with products creates value for customers and raises each transaction's gross margin. Customer peer groups boost aggregate sales and as a result reduce costs. **Availability:** Print; Online; PDF.

32602 ■ *"Refreshing! A Clearly Canadian Comeback" in Canadian Business (Vol. 79, September 11, 2006, No. 18, pp. 22)*
Pub: Rogers Media Inc.
Contact: Neil Spivak, Chief Executive Officer
Ed: Joe Castaldo. **Description:** Turnaround strategies and initiatives adopted by Canadian Beverage Corp. to boost its declining sales are presented. **Availability:** Print; Online.

32603 ■ *"Rep Contracts: Simple, Clear, Fair" in Agency Sales Magazine (Vol. 39, September-October 2009, No. 9, pp. 3)*
Description: Things that a manufacturer and a sales representative needs to strive for when creating an Agreement for Representation includes an agreement that is simple and complete, one that covers all the needs of both parties and is fair, equitable, and balanced. Sales representatives need to make more sales calls and find new opportunities during this recession.

32604 ■ *"Rep Vs. Direct: Always an Interesting Story" in Agency Sales Magazine (Vol. 39, July 2009, No. 7, pp. 3)*
Description: Manufacturers benefit from outsourcing their field sales to professional sales representatives in the areas of multi-line selling and customer knowledge and relationship. Some misperceptions about sales reps include the belief that they are an additional 'channel' in sales. **Availability:** Online.

32605 ■ *"Reps Have Needs Too!" in Agency Sales Magazine (Vol. 39, December 2009, No. 11, pp. 16)*
Description: There is common information that a sales representatives needs to know prior to choosing a manufacturer to represent. Both parties must keep promises made to customers and prospects. Reps also need the support from the manufacturers and to clear matters regarding their commission. Interviewing tips for representatives to get this vital information are presented. **Availability:** Online.

32606 ■ *"Reps Vs. Factory Direct Sales Force..Which Way to Go?" in Agency Sales Magazine (Vol. 39, September-October 2009, No. 9, pp. 28)*
Description: Hiring independent manufacturers' sales representative is a cost-effective alternative to a direct sales force. Sales reps have predictable sales costs that go up and down with sales, stronger local relationships and better market intelligence. **Availability:** Print; Online.

32607 ■ *"Revisiting Rep Coping Strategies" in Agency Sales Magazine (Vol. 39, December 2009, No. 11, pp. 32)*
Description: Independent manufacturer's representatives should become a well-rounded and complete businessman with continued education. The new type of representative is a problem solver and the resource for answering questions. Employing the concept of synergistic selling is also important to salespeople. **Availability:** Online.

32608 ■ *"The Rise of Pompei" in Retail Merchandiser (Vol. 51, September-October 2011, No. 5, pp. 13)*
Description: Soho creative consulting group follows its C3 philosophy to create an invigorated brand experience that transforms customers from consumers to empowered buyers. Pompei AD is a leading creative consultancy that specializes in design and branding for retail, museum, hospitality, and other sectors. **Availability:** Print; Online.

32609 ■ *"Sales and the Absolute Power of Information" in Agency Sales Magazine (Vol. 39, July 2009, No. 7, pp. 16)*
Description: Having good information can help a sales representative deliver effective sales performance. A process for collecting information about customers, prospects, and competitors is discussed.

32610 ■ *The Sales Bible*
Released: January 01, 2015. **Price:** $17.10, paperback. **Description:** An expert in sales provides the definitive sales reference. **Availability:** Print.

32611 ■ *The Sales Manager's Guide to Greatness: Ten Essential Strategies for Leading Your Team to the Top*
Ed: Kevin F. Davis. **Released:** March 28, 2017. **Price:** $17.55, Hardcover; $8.69, E-book. **Description:** A business leadership book that will guide sales managers towards achieving high results with your team. **Availability:** E-book; Print.

32612 ■ *"Sales Training Programs to Help Your Team Close More Deals" in Business News Daily (March 6, 2023)*
URL(s): www.businessnewsdaily.com/16039-sales -training-programs.html
Ed: Marisa Sanfilippo. **Released:** March 06, 2023. **Description:** Discusses four sales training programs so you can find the one that is right for your sales team. **Availability:** Online.

32613 ■ *"Say Goodbye to Voicemail, Hello To Ribbit Mobile" in Agency Sales Magazine (Vol. 39, November 2009, No. 10, pp. 3)*
Description: Salespeople should think twice before leaving a voicemail. The emerging modern etiquette is to send a text message or to e-mail the customer or client. Communication suggestions for both salespeople and their principals are presented. **Availability:** Print; Online.

32614 ■ *"The Secret Strategy for Meaningful Sales Meetings" in Agency Sales Magazine (Vol. 39, December 2009, No. 11, pp. 40)*

Description: Sales meetings can be made more meaningful by focusing on the end results that the meeting seeks to achieve. Describing the changed behavior that is sought from the sales force and working backwards from there also help make a sales meeting more meaningful. **Availability:** Online.

32615 ■ *"Secrets of the World's Top Sales Performers: Book Summary"*

Description: The author asserts that sales is a unique profession in that it is the only job that requires one to use their own personality to create financial success. Ten sales techniques used by various sectors show how sales people perform in their industry.

32616 ■ *"Sedentary Shoppers: Point, Click, Buy" in Barron's (Vol. 90, September 6, 2010, No. 36, pp. 11)*

Pub: Barron's Editorial & Corporate Headquarters

Ed: Vito J. Racanelli. **Description:** Non-travel online retail sales from January to July 2010 increased nine percent which indicates that online shopping for the coming holidays will be good. Online sales are outpacing traditional shopping, but pricing is still critical. **Availability:** Online.

32617 ■ *"Sell a Movement Within a Smoothie" in Canadian Business (Vol. 87, July 2014, No. 7, pp. 58)*

Description: Vega is a nutritional and fitness supplement maker based in Vancouver, British Columbia that has increased its sales sevenfold from 2008 to 2013, earning the 9th spot in the 2014 Profit 500 ranking of fastest growing companies in Canada. The firm's strategy is to promote its flagship product Vega One using an in-store bicycle-powered blender. **Availability:** Online.

32618 ■ *Selling the Invisible: A Field Guide to Modern Marketing*

Ed: Harry Beckwith. **Released:** March 20, 2012. **Price:** $16, paperback, ($21.00 in canada); $13.98, audiobook abridged library($16.99 in canada); $16. 98, audiobook abridged($19.75 in canada); $9.98, audiobook abridged($12.98 in canada); $9.99, electronic book($9.99 in canada). **Description:** Tips for marketing and selling intangibles such as health care, entertainment, tourism, legal services, and more are provided. **Availability:** audiobook; E-book; Print.

32619 ■ *Selling Online: Canada's Bestselling Guide to Becoming a Successful E-Commerce Merchant*

Description: Helps individuals build online retail enterprises; this updated version includes current tools, information and success strategies, how to launch an online storefront, security, marketing strategies, and mistakes to avoid. **Availability:** Online.

32620 ■ *"Selling With Strengths; Talent Trumps Training" in Gallup Management Journal (March 24, 2011)*

Released: April 03, 2011. **Description:** What are the strengths of salespeople, and how can organizations develop them? What do great sales managers do differently? The authors of, 'Strengths Based Selling' answer these questions and others, including: why money is overrated as a motivator. **Availability:** Print; Online.

32621 ■ *"ShopSmart: Discounts On Brand-Name Products at Dollar Store" in Entertainment Close-Up (July 17, 2012)*

Description: According to a report by ShopSmart magazine, 76 percent of women stated they shopped at a dollar store 3-4 times in the past year. The report also discusses ways shoppers can save money on name brand and private-label products at dollar stores. Dollar stores have gone mainstream by providing retailers with national brand items. **Availability:** Print; Online.

32622 ■ *"Six Steps To Close the Sale" in Birmingham Business Journal (Vol. 31, April 11, 2014, No. 15, pp. 13)*

Pub: American City Business Journals, Inc.
Contact: Mike Olivieri, Executive Vice President

Released: Weekly. **Price:** $4, introductory 4-week offer(Digital only). **Description:** Tips to help salesmen close deals successfully are presented. Sales representatives are advised to be confident in what they are selling, to always ask for business details, avoid blasting the competition, and to show signs of experience. The importance of perseverance is also discussed. **Availability:** Print; Online.

32623 ■ *"Small Budget, Big Impact" in Small Business Opportunities (Summer 2010)*

Pub: Harris Publishing, Inc.
Contact: Janet Chase, Contact

Description: Ways to use social media to get in from of a target audience for small businesses are examined. **Availability:** Online.

32624 ■ *"Small Business Sales: 6 Strategies for Prospecting" in Small Business Economic Trends (April 2008, pp. 7)*

Pub: National Federation of Independent Business
Contact: Brad Close, President

Ed: William C. Dunkelberg, Holly Wade. **Description:** Two tables and a graph resenting sales figures of small businesses in the U.S. is presented. Statistics for sales changes and sales expectations are provided. The figures in the graph include data from 1986 to 2008. **Availability:** Print; Online.

32625 ■ *"Smarts Drive Sales" in Pet Product News (Vol. 64, December 2010, No. 12, pp. 1)*

Ed: Karen Shugart. **Description:** Retailers could make smart decisions by deciding how to best attract customers into their stores or resolving whether to nurture in-store or buy herps (reptiles) from suppliers. Paying attention to these smart decisions could help boost customer interest in herps and address customer demands. **Availability:** Online.

32626 ■ *The Social Media Bible: Tactics, Tools, and Strategies for Business Success*

Pub: John Wiley & Sons, Inc.
Contact: Christina Van Tassell, Executive Vice President Chief Financial Officer

Ed: Lon Safko. **Released:** Third edition. **Price:** $29. 95, paperback; $19.99, E-Book. **Description:** Information is given to build or transform a business into social media, where customers, employees, and prospects connect, collaborate, and champion products and services in order to increase sales and to beat the competition. **Availability:** E-book; Print.

32627 ■ *"Solar Hot Water Sales Are Hot, Hot, Hot" in Contractor (Vol. 56, December 2009, No. 12, pp. 22)*

Ed: Dave Yates. **Description:** Plumbing contractors in the United States can benefit from the increased sales of solar thermal water systems. Licensed plumbers have the base knowledge on the risks associated from heating and storing water. Safety issues associated with solar water heaters are also included. **Availability:** Online.

32628 ■ *"Sound Check" in Agency Sales Magazine (Vol. 39, August 2009, No. 8, pp. 14)*

Description: Most customers believe salespersons are unable to do well in terms of listening, which is one of the four fundamental competencies of a sales person. Listening is the primary tool to uncover deeper and more powerful needs and motivations of the customer. A guide on how to listen better and improve listening effectiveness is presented. **Availability:** Online.

32629 ■ *"The South Looks Yummy to Tastykakes" in Philadelphia Business Journal (Vol. 31, March 30, 2012, No. 7, pp. 1)*

Pub: Baltimore Business Journal
Contact: Rhonda Pringle, President
E-mail: rpringle@bizjournals.com

Description: Tasty Baking Company owner, Flowers Foods, is planning to increase the number of stores selling Tastykake. Sales of Tastykake is expected to grow to as much as $225 million. **Availability:** Print; Online.

32630 ■ *"Sponsorships, Booths Available for Business Showcase" in Bellingham Business Journal (February 2010, pp. 3)*

Pub: Sound Publishing Inc.
Contact: Josh O'Connor, President

Ed: Lance Henderson. **Description:** Third Annual Spring Business Showcase still have space available for vendors and sponsors. The event gives local businesses the opportunity to increase their visibility and provides a means to increase sales and build relationships.

32631 ■ *"Stop Trying to Delight Your Customers" in Harvard Business Review (Vol. 88, July-August 2010, No. 7-8, pp. 116)*

Pub: Harvard Business Publishing
Contact: Diane Belcher, Managing Director

Ed: Matthew Dixon, Karen Freeman, Nicholas Toman. **Price:** $8.95, PDF. **Description:** Importance of resolving issues for customers is key to increasing their loyalty, rather than by exceeding customer expectations. Areas to address include decreasing customer need for follow-up calls, switching service channels, and the potential for negative emotional response. **Availability:** Online; PDF.

32632 ■ *"Strange Brew" in Canadian Business (Vol. 85, June 11, 2012, No. 10, pp. 52)*

Ed: Paul Brent. **Description:** Molson Coors is launching the Coors Light Iced T beer in summer 2012 as part of its effort to improve weak sales in North America. The new product is aimed at female drinkers and is part of an effort to win back sales from wine and spirits. **Availability:** Print; Online.

32633 ■ *Streetwise Small Business Book of Lists: Hundreds of Lists to Help You Reduce Costs, Increase Revenues, and Boost Your Profits!*

Price: Paperback. **Description:** Strategies to help small business owners locate services, increase sales, and lower expenses. **Availability:** Print.

32634 ■ *"Suited for Success" in Retail Merchandiser (Vol. 51, July-August 2011, No. 4, pp. 6)*

Description: MyBestFit is a size-matching body scanner that helps consumers find the perfect size clothing for themselves, giving brick and mortar retailers an edge on ecommerce competitors. **Availability:** Online.

32635 ■ *"Summary. Economic Trends for Small Business" in Small Business Economic Trends (February 2008, pp. 1)*

Pub: National Federation of Independent Business
Contact: Brad Close, President

Ed: William C. Dunkelberg, Holly Wade. **Description:** Summary of economic trends for small businesses in the U.S. is provided. Economic indicators such as capital spending, inventories and sales, inflation, and profits are given. Analysis of credit markets is also provided.

32636 ■ *"Sweet Tea From McDonald's: A Marketing 50 Case Study" in Advertising Age (Vol. 79, November 17, 2008, No. 43, pp. 4)*

Pub: Crain Communications, Inc.
Contact: Jessica Botos, Manager, Marketing
E-mail: jessica.botos@crainsnewyork.com

Ed: Emily Bryson York. **Description:** McDonald's launch of iced coffee and sweat tea, which were promoted via price cuts over the summer, helped to boost sales at the fast-food chain. **Availability:** Online.

32637 ■ "Tap Into Food Truck Trend to Rev Up Sales, Build Buzz" in Nation's Restaurant News (Vol. 45, February 7, 2011, No. 3, pp. 18)
Ed: Brian Sacks. **Description:** Food truck trend is growing, particularly in New York City, Philadelphia, Washington DC, and Los Angeles, California. Man entrepreneurs are using a mobile food component to market their food before opening a restaurant. **Availability:** Print; Online.

32638 ■ "Teachable Moments: Worth Every Penny" in Pet Product News (Vol. 64, December 2010, No. 12, pp. 34)
Ed: Cheryl Reeves. **Description:** Pet bird retailers can attain both outreach to customers and enhanced profitability by staging educational events such as the annual Parrot Palooza event of Burlington, New Jersey-based Bird Paradise. Aside from attracting a global audience, Parrot Palooza features seminars, workshops, classes, and bird-related contests. **Availability:** Print; Online.

32639 ■ "Teaching Sales: Great Sales Professionals are Scarce and Getting Scarcer. Why Aren't Universities Working Harder to Create More?" in (Vol. 90, July-August 2012, No. 7-8, pp. 94)
Pub: Harvard Business Review Press
Contact: Moderna V. Pfizer, Contact
Ed: Suzanne Fogel, David Hoffmeister, Richard Rocco, Daniel P. Strunk. **Price:** $8.95, PDF and hardcover black and white. **Description:** Partnerships between industry and business schools can improve the quality of new sales education programs, increasing access to funding and talent. Industry input to school curricula and scholarly research informing business decisions will produce mutual benefits. **Availability:** Print; PDF; Online.

32640 ■ "Technically Speaking" in Black Enterprise (Vol. 38, February 2008, No. 7, pp. 64)
Pub: Earl G. Graves Ltd.
Contact: Earl Graves, Jr., President
Ed: Sonia Alleyne. **Description:** Marketing manager for Texas Instruments discusses the Strategic Marketing of Technology Products course offered at the California Institute of Technology. The course helps turn products into profits.

32641 ■ "There's Risk, Reward for Business in Baltimore's Edgier Areas: Taking a Chance" in Baltimore Business Journal (Vol. 28, July 16, 2010, No. 10, pp. 1)
Pub: Baltimore Business Journal
Contact: Rhonda Pringle, President
E-mail: rpringle@bizjournals.com
Ed: Scott Dance. **Description:** North Avenue in Baltimore, Maryland is considered a rough neighborhood due to the dangers of prostitution and drug dealing. However, some entrepreneurs have taken the risk of building their businesses on North Avenue as revitalization efforts grow. One of the challenges for businesses in rough neighborhoods is bringing customers to their stores or offices. **Availability:** Print.

32642 ■ "Three Signs Your Biz Needs a COO" in Birmingham Business Journal (Vol. 31, April 18, 2014, No. 16, pp. 10)
Pub: American City Business Journals, Inc.
Contact: Mike Olivieri, Executive Vice President
Description: Business conditions that warrant the recruitment of a chief operations officer are discussed. The halting of growth results in the shifting of focus from operations to sales. Dependence on one or two employees can result in resignations. **Availability:** Print; Online.

32643 ■ "Three Ways to Improve the Prospect's Experience" in South Florida Business Journal (Vol. 35, September 12, 2014, No. 7, pp. 12)
Pub: American City Business Journals, Inc.
Contact: Mike Olivieri, Executive Vice President

Description: Advice on how marketers should get prospective buyers' attention by using Websites is given. Website readability on mobile devices and cell phones should be improved. Marketers should also offer a maximum of two landing pages to increase sales. **Availability:** Online.

32644 ■ "TiVo, Domino's Team to Offer Pizza Ordering by DVR" in Advertising Age (Vol. 79, November 17, 2008, No. 43, pp. 48)
Pub: Crain Communications, Inc.
Contact: Jessica Botos, Manager, Marketing
E-mail: jessica.botos@crainsnewyork.com
Ed: Brian Steinberg. **Description:** Domino's Pizza and TiVo are teaming up to make it possible for customers to order from the restaurant straight from their DVR. The companies see that this kind of interactive television and consumer experience will only serve to generate more sales as the customer can be exposed to a fuller range of menu selections and will not have to interrupt their viewing, while workers can spend more time making the product. **Availability:** Online.

32645 ■ "To Keep Your Customers, Keep It Simple: They Don't Want a 'Relationship' With You. Just Help Them Make Good Choices" in Harvard Business Review (Vol. 90, May 2012, No. 5, pp. 108)
Pub: Harvard Business Review Press
Contact: Moderna V. Pfizer, Contact
Ed: Patrick Spenner, Karen Freeman. **Price:** $8.95. **Description:** Rather than attempt to engage consumers via social media, firms instead should simplify the customer's decision making and assist them through the purchase process. Tips include minimizing the number of purchase-process steps providing reliable product information, and enabling them to easily weigh their options. **Availability:** Online; PDF.

32646 ■ "To Sell Is Human: The Surprising Truth About Moving Others"
Pub: Riverhead Books
Contact: Geoffrey Kloske, President
Released: December 31, 2012. **Description:** The U.S. Bureau of Labor Statistics reports that one in nine Americans form the work sales force. Whether an employee or an entrepreneur, everyone is selling something. The entrepreneur is looking for funders to invest. Pink describes the six successors to the elevator pitch, the three rules for understanding another's perspective, the five frames that can make a message clearer and more persuasive, and more. **Availability:** Print.

32647 ■ "Top Statewide Commercial Real Estate Brokerages" in South Florida Business Journal (Vol. 34, April 4, 2014, No. 37, pp. 14)
Pub: American City Business Journals, Inc.
Contact: Mike Olivieri, Executive Vice President

Description: Rankings of commercial real estate brokerages in South Florida area are presented. Rankings were based on total volume sales and leasing statewide in Florida. The top five real estate executives in the region are also listed. **Availability:** Print; Online.

32648 ■ "Toss the Gum Before You Speak and Other Tips for Presenting to a Potential Principal" in Agency Sales Magazine (Vol. 39, July 2009, No. 7, pp. 34)
Description: When preparing to present to a prospective principal, a salesperson should anticipate the speaking situation and find out in advance the program events that occur around their speech. They should also practice their material in front of a friend or colleague. **Availability:** Online.

32649 ■ "Training: an Investment in Performance Improvement" in Franchising World (Vol. 42, September 2010, No. 9, pp. 22)
Pub: International Franchise Association
Contact: Matthew Haller, President
E-mail: mhaller@franchise.org

Ed: Catherine Monson. **Released:** 2010. **Description:** Advantages of training provided by franchisors that are available to franchisees and their employees are discussed. **Availability:** Online.

32650 ■ "Tweet Me, Friend Me, Make Me Buy" in (Vol. 90, July-August 2012, No. 7-8, pp. 88)
Pub: Harvard Business Review Press
Contact: Moderna V. Pfizer, Contact
Ed: Barbara Giamanco, Kent Gregoire. **Price:** $8.95, PDF and hardcover black and white. **Description:** Sales representatives can make the most out of social media through training on communication skills such as tone, etiquette, and consistency. The most valuable aspects of social media are lead qualification, front-end prospecting, and maintaining post-deal relationships. **Availability:** Print; PDF; Online.

32651 ■ "The Ultimate Sales Letter: Attract New Customers. Boost Your Sales"
Released: February 2011. **Description:** With email and instant communication, sales copy is indispensable to closing a deal. Most sales letters end up in the junk file or wastebasket. Updated text and examples, great headline formulas, and new exercises to be innovative with sales copy along with ways to use graphics successfully from an expert in direct-response copywriting.

32652 ■ "Unleashing the Power of Marketing" in Harvard Business Review (Vol. 88, October 2010, No. 10, pp. 90)
Pub: Harvard Business Publishing
Contact: Diane Belcher, Managing Director
Ed: Beth Comstock, Ranjay Gulati, Stephen Liguori. **Price:** $8.95, PDF. **Description:** Chronicle of the development of General Electric's marketing framework that focused on three key factors: Principles, people and process. GE determined that successful marketing fulfills four functions: instigating, innovating, implementing, and integrating. **Availability:** Online; PDF.

32653 ■ "Unused Coupons Still Pay Off" in Harvard Business Review (Vol. 90, May 2012, No. 5, pp. 32)
Pub: Harvard Business Review Press
Contact: Moderna V. Pfizer, Contact
Ed: Rajkumar Venkatesan, Paul Farris. **Price:** $6, hardcopy and PDF. **Description:** Unredeemed coupons have been found to create a sales lift for retailers as they increase awareness of a retailer or a brand even when consumers do not use them. Redemption rates should still be monitored however to assess campaign effectiveness. **Availability:** Print; Online.

32654 ■ "Use Social Media to Enhance Brand, Business" in Contractor (Vol. 56, December 2009, No. 12, pp. 14)
Ed: Elton Rivas. **Description:** Advice on how plumbing contractors should use online social networks to increase sales is presented including such issues as clearly defining goals and target audience. An additional advantage to this medium is that advertisements can easily be shared with other users.

32655 ■ "The View from the Field: Six Leaders Offer Their Perspectives On Sales Success" in (Vol. 90, July-August 2012, No. 7-8, pp. 101)
Pub: Harvard Business Review Press
Contact: Moderna V. Pfizer, Contact
Ed: Jim Koch, James Farley, Susan Silbermann, Duncan Mac Naughton, Phil Guido, Suresh Goklaney. **Price:** $8.95. **Description:** Six business leaders provide their perspectives on successful selling. Common themes include engaging customers and seeking their input, personalizing their services, ensuring accountability, implementing community outreach, being mindful of cultural and regulatory issues, providing unique offerings, incorporating experiential learning, and properly identifying a customer's needs. **Availability:** Online; PDF.

32656 ■ "Vision Statement: Do You Really Know Who Your Best Salespeople Are?" in Harvard Business Review (Vol. 88, December 2010, No. 12, pp. 34)
Pub: Harvard Business Publishing
Contact: Diane Belcher, Managing Director
Ed: Lynette Ryals, Iain Davies. Price: $6, PDF. Description: Eight salesperson performance types are identified and charted using statistics of their effectiveness in given scenarios. Availability: Online; PDF.

32657 ■ "Web-Based Marketing Excites, Challenges Small Business Use" in Colorado Springs Business Journal (January 20, 2010)
Pub: BridgeTower Media
Contact: Adam Reinebach, President
Ed: Becky Hurley. Description: Business-to-business and consumer-direct firms alike are using the fast-changing Web technologies to increase sales, leads and track consumer behavior but once a company commits to an Online marketing plan, experts believe, they must be prepared to consistently tweak and overhaul content and distribution vehicles in order to keep up. Availability: Online.

32658 ■ "Web Move Puts Rack Ahead of Pack" in Puget Sound Business Journal (Vol. 35, May 16, 2014, No. 4, pp. 8)
Pub: American City Business Journals, Inc.
Contact: Mike Olivieri, Executive Vice President
Description: Upscale retailer, Norstrom Inc., launched a Website for Nordstrom Rack in the hopes of boosting sales for its discount arm by 10 to 20 percent. Terry Boyle, present of Nordstrom Rack's online store, is not concerned that the site might steal traffic from their retail establishments. Availability: Online.

32659 ■ "What Are You Doing Differently?" in Agency Sales Magazine (Vol. 39, December 2009, No. 11, pp. 3)
Description: Strategies that sales representatives can do to plan for a good year include professional development, networking with other reps, and making more sales calls and seeing more people. The end of the year is the perfect time for reps to write or re-write their mission statement and to conduct line profitability. Availability: Print; Download; Online.

32660 ■ "When Are Sales Representatives Also Franchisees?" in Franchise Law Journal (Vol. 27, Winter 2008, No. 3, pp. 151)
Ed: John R.F. Baer, David A. Beyer, Scott P. Weber. Released: Volume 27. Description: Review of the traditional definitions of sales representatives along with information on how these distribution models could fit into various legal tests for a franchise.

32661 ■ "Why Customer Engagement Matters So Much Now; Wary Consumers Will Give More Money to the Businesses they Feel Emotionally Connected To -- While Ignoring Others" in Gallup Business Journal (July 22, 2014)
Pub: Gallup, Inc.
Contact: Jon Clifton, Chief Executive Officer
Description: Gallup's daily tracking of the U.S. economy shows signs of recovery since the crash of 2008. When Americans purchase goods or services, they tend to choose businesses they feel emotionally connected to and might even ignore those that provide no value to them. They expect a company to earn their money. Availability: Print; Online.

32662 ■ "Why CVS May Not Get Burned By Its Tobacco Decision (Part 2); Looking at CVS' Decision To Discontinue Selling Tobacco Products In Purely Dollar Terms Misses the Bigger Picture" in Gallup Business Journal (March 20, 2014)
Pub: Gallup, Inc.
Contact: Jon Clifton, Chief Executive Officer
Description: Drug retailer, CVS, made a strategic play in organizational identity, mission, and purpose when it decided to quit selling cigarettes at its retail stores. The decision to discontinue sales of tobacco products could, long term, strengthen the company's identity in the U.S. marketplace, thus increasing sales. Availability: Print; Online.

32663 ■ "Why You Need a New-Media 'Ringmaster" in Harvard Business Review (Vol. 88, December 2010, No. 12, pp. 78)
Pub: Harvard Business Publishing
Contact: Diane Belcher, Managing Director
Ed: Patrick Spenner. Price: $8.95, PDF. Description: The concept of ringmaster is applied to brand marketing. This concept includes integrative thinking, lean collaboration skills, and high-speed decision cycles. Availability: Online; PDF.

32664 ■ "Will mCommerce Make Black Friday Green?" in Retail Merchandiser (Vol. 51, September-October 2011, No. 5, pp. 8)
Description: Retailers speculate the possibilities of mobile commerce and are implementing strategies at their stores. Consumers using mobile devices accounted for only 0.1 percent of visits to retail Websites on Black Friday 2009 and rose to 5.6 percent in 2010; numbers are expected to rise for 2011. Availability: Print; Online.

32665 ■ "Will Training Help Your Company's Sales Team?" in South Florida Business Journal (Vol. 34, May 16, 2014, No. 43, pp. 17)
Pub: American City Business Journals, Inc.
Contact: Mike Olivieri, Executive Vice President
Released: Weekly. Price: $8, Introductory 4-week offer(Digital & Print). Description: Several factors to consider when training a company's sales team are discussed. Business owners tend to spend more time with bottom-end performers and try to get them to improve when they should instead spend their time and energy with those at the top. Availability: Print; Online.

32666 ■ "Winners Dream: A Journey from Corner Store to Corner Office"
Pub: Simon & Schuster Adult Publishing Group
Contact: Jonathan Karp, President
Released: October 14, 2014. Price: $28.99, hardcover, plus $2.24 shipping charges. Description: Bill McDermott, CEO of the world's largest business software company, SAP, profiles his career. He discusses his career moves, sales strategies, employee incentives to create high performance teams, and the competitive advantages of optimism and hard work. The entrepreneur offers a blueprint for success and the knowledge that the real dream is the journey, not the preconceived destination. Availability: E-book; Print; Download; Audio.

32667 ■ "Women Clicking to Earn Virtual Dollars" in Sales and Marketing Management (November 11, 2009)
Ed: Stacy Straczynski. Description: According to a new report from Internet marketing firm Q Interactive, women are increasingly playing social media games where they are able to click on an ad or sign up for a promotion to earn virtual currency. Research is showing that this kind of marketing may be a potent tool, especially for e-commerce and online stores. Availability: Print; Online.

32668 ■ "Woof Gang Bakery & Grooming Claws Through Recession" in Orlando Business Journal (Vol. 29, July 6, 2012, No. 3, pp. 1)
Pub: Baltimore Business Journal
Contact: Rhonda Pringle, President
E-mail: rpringle@bizjournals.com
Ed: Anjali Fluker. Description: Woof Gang Bakery and Grooming has reported increased sales des;pite the economic crisis. The company is set to open its 30th store by the end of 2012. Availability: Print; Online.

32669 ■ "Young Adults, Childless May Help Fuel Post-Recession Rebound" in Pet Product News (Vol. 64, November 2010, No. 11, pp. 4)
Ed: David Lummis. Description: Pet industry retailers and marketers are encouraged to tap into the young adult and childless couple sectors to boost consumer traffic and sales to pre-recession levels. Among young adult owners, pet ownership increased from 40 percent in 2003 to 49 percent in 2009. Meanwhile, the childless couple sector represented 63 percent of all dog/cat owners in 2009. Availability: Online.

32670 ■ "Your Merchandising and Promotions Exchange: Web Coupon Users Shop More" in Pet Product News (Vol. 66, September 2012, No. 9, pp. 101)
Description: A survey on behalf of Coupons.com shows that consumers who use digital coupons make 22 percent more supermarket trips annually than conventional shoppers and spend 23 percent more per trip. The findings suggest that digital coupon sites should be taken into consideration by brands intending to reach heavy grocery spenders. Availability: Online.

32671 ■ "Zacks Industry Outlook Highlights: Target, Cabela's and Family Dollar Stores" in Marketing Weekly News (April 28, 2012, pp. 351)
Description: Zacks Industry Outlook focuses on retailers such as Target, Cabela's and Family Dollar Stores. An examination of ways retailers are working to improve sales and profits and productivity is given, including supply-chain management, cost containment, inventory management, and merchandise initiatives. Availability: Print; Online.

32672 ■ "Zara Eludes the Pain in Spain: Clothing Giant Inditex Sees Its First-Quarter Profits Rise By 30 Percent" in Canadian Business (Vol. 85, September 17, 2012, No. 14, pp. 67)
Ed: Bryan Borzykowski. Released: September 17, 2012. Description: Clothing retailer Inditex reported a 30 percent increase in profit in the first quarter of 2012 and 15 percent increase in sales year over year. The company's unique business model was attributed to its growth, which also appeals to income investors.

32673 ■ "Zions Offers Step-by-Step Small Business Guidance" in Idaho Business Review (September 1, 2014)
Pub: BridgeTower Media
Contact: Adam Reinebach, President
Description: Zions bank provides small business guidance to clients through its Zions Bank Idaho Business Resource Center. The program helps entrepreneurs learn the basic rules of running a small business. Free courses teach the essentials of finance, marketing and selling, .

32674 ■ "Zoo Entertainment Inc. Aims for the Sky" in Business Courier (Vol. 27, September 24, 2010, No. 21, pp. 1)
Pub: Business Courier
Ed: Dan Monk. Description: Video game company Zoo Entertainment Inc., which is based in Norwood near Cincinnati, Ohio aims to build a strong company and to position itself for future growth. The company reported $27.6 million in revenue for the first half of 2010 and analysts project $100 million in sales for 2011. Availability: Print; Online.

TRADE PERIODICALS

32675 ■ Counterman
Pub: Babcox Media Inc.
Contact: Bill Babcox, Chief Executive Officer
E-mail: bbabcox@babcox.com
URL(s): www.counterman.com
Facebook: www.facebook.com/CountermanMag
X (Twitter): x.com/countermanmag
Instagram: www.instagram.com/countermanmagazine
YouTube: www.youtube.com/channel/UCUWIRti-EtXnYcpwDekTEyA
Ed: Joshua Cable. Released: Monthly Description: Magazine devoted to improving the effectiveness of professional automotive parts counter-sales personnel. Availability: Print; Download; PDF; Online.

32676 ■ Selling Power: Success strategies for sales management
Pub: Personal Selling Power Inc.
URL(s): www.sellingpower.com/magazine
Linkedin: www.linkedin.com/company/selling-power
X (Twitter): x.com/SellingPowerMag
YouTube: www.youtube.com/user/sellingpower
Released: Monthly **Price:** $29, for one-year (12 issues) subscription rate; $49, for 3-year subscription. **Description:** Magazine presenting motivational and sales skills and techniques for sales and marketing executives. **Availability:** Online.

VIDEO/AUDIO MEDIA

32677 ■ The Best Small Business Show: 4 Critical Pre-Sale Tools You Ned to Get More Clients
URL(s): richgee.libsyn.com/254-4-critical-pre-sale-tools-you-need-to-get-more-clients
Ed: rich Gee. **Released:** August 01, 2022. **Description:** Podcast outlines four tools to acquire more clients.

32678 ■ The Best Small Business Show: Closing the Sale - You're Doing It All Wrong
URL(s): richgee.libsyn.com/251-closing-the-sale-youre-doing-it-all-wrong
Ed: Rich Gee. **Released:** July 11, 2022. **Description:** Podcast discusses the game plan for closing a sale.

32679 ■ BS-Free Service Business Show: Stop Selling, Start Solving: For Solopreneurs Who Hate Sleazy Sales
URL(s): bsfreebusiness.com/sleazy-sales
Ed: Maggie Patterson. **Released:** October 14, 2024. **Description:** Podcast explains why selling is really solving a problem.

32680 ■ Conversion Tactics that Win
URL(s): www.startuphustlepodcast.com/conversion-tactics-that-win
Released: November 09, 2023. **Description:** Podcast discusses boosting sales conversion rates; includes maintaining a steady sales funnel, optimizing the process, leveraging upselling techniques, and consistently asking for the sale.

32681 ■ The How of Business: Sales Fundamentals
URL(s): www.thehowofbusiness.com/430-small-business-sales-fundamentals
Ed: Henry Lopez. **Released:** July 11, 2022. **Description:** Podcast defines sales, offers sales misconceptions, and explains the differences between sales and marketing.

32682 ■ Mastering Software Sales
URL(s): www.startuphustlepodcast.com/mastering-software-sales
Ed: Matt Watson. **Released:** June 06, 2024. **Description:** Podcast discusses the sales challenges of SaaS founders: reaching the right audience, closing the deal, finding product-led growth strategies, offering results-oriented demos, and scaling sales with a repeatable process.

32683 ■ A New Sales Paradigm with Jen Szpigel
URL(s): www.makinggoodpodcast.com/episodes/170
Ed: Lauren Tilden. **Released:** April 11, 2023. **Description:** Podcast discusses a new sales paradigm and how to effectively build rapport and relationships.

32684 ■ Nurture Small Business: Sales Success Secrets: Focusing on the Right Activities
URL(s): nurturesmallbusiness.buzzsprout.com/900445/episodes/14182700-sales-success-secrets-focusing-on-the-righ-activities
Ed: Denise Cagan. **Released:** December 25, 2023. **Description:** Podcast offers a conversation with a business coach on the art of effective cold calling.

32685 ■ Sales with Generative AI
URL(s): omny.fm/shows/startup-hustle/sales-with-generative-ai
Ed: Matt Watson. **Released:** September 18, 2023. **Description:** Podcast explores leveraging comments on Linkedin for generating leads and how to build better relationships with your prospects. Features Jason Tan, founder of Engage AI.

32686 ■ Small Biz 101: Sales Spark: Igniting Success in Your Small Business
URL(s): scatteredtostreamlined.com/sales-spark-igniting-success-in-your-small-business-sb023
Ed: Connie Whitesell. **Released:** February 20, 2024. **Description:** Podcast discusses the importance of sales and marketing.

32687 ■ Supercharge Your Sales and Profits with Brian Tracy
URL(s): www.eofire.com/podcast/briantracy3
Ed: Jon Lee Dumas. **Released:** March 12, 2024. **Description:** Podcast discusses important qualities in an entrepreneur, considerations for building a high-profit business, and keys to productivity.

32688 ■ Think Business with Tyler: From Lawn Mowing to Leading with Entrepreneur Matt Shoup
Released: September 18, 2023. **Description:** Podcast discusses the importance of storytelling in sales and how to tell your brand story with a serial entrepreneur.

TRADE SHOWS AND CONVENTIONS

32689 ■ LeadsCon
URL(s): www.leadscon.com
Facebook: www.facebook.com/leadscon
Linkedin: www.linkedin.com/groups/1810842
X (Twitter): twitter.com/leadscon
Description: Talks and workshops focused on generating leads and market strategies for small businesses. **Principal Exhibits:** Talks and workshops focused on generating leads and market strategies for small businesses.

CONSULTANTS

32690 ■ 4th Generation Systems
113 N Grant St.
Barrington, IL 60010
URL: http://www.4thgenerationsystems.com
Contact: Dirk Beveridge, President
E-mail: dirk@4thgenerationsystems.com
Description: Designs and develops marketing, sales, and sales management strategies for mid-market distributors and their suppliers, the companies integrated, multi-appointment learning program incorporates a mix of in-person classroom sessions, online instruction and one-on-one coaching to increase skill development and provide measurable results and greater impact beyond the initial enthusiasm of a single seminar. **Founded:** 1969. **Publications:** "Sales Management: Why the Best are Better," Walsworth, 1992; "The Superman Syndrome"; "Sustaining Resource Selling Skills". **Training:** BOSS-The Mandatory Business Operating System Standards; Sales Management Why The Best Are Better; Proactive Customer Focused Sales; Marketing In The Age Of Technology; Marketing - The Perception of Difference; Why Successful Businesses Don't Stay; Everyone is Part of the Sales Promise.

32691 ■ D.E.I. Management Group Inc.
888 7th Ave., 9th Fl.
New York, NY 10106
Contact: Stephan Schiffman, Chief Executive Officer
Description: Firm offers counsel and training in productivity and goal setting in the corporate setting as well as selling skills and serves telecommunication, financial services, banking services, real-estate and manufacturing. **Scope:** Firm offers counsel and training in productivity and goal setting in the corporate setting as well as selling skills and serves

telecommunication, financial services, banking services, real-estate and manufacturing. **Publications:** "Just Plain Tired," Jun, 2006; "The Sales Manager and the Sale," May, 2006; "The Collaborative Sale," Mar, 2006; "Ten MUSTS For a Successful Speech," Mar, 2006; "Five Stages of the Sales Career," Mar, 2006. **Special Services:** Prospect Management System.

32692 ■ Emerge Natural Sales Solutions
San Francisco, CA
Ph: (415)407-3660
URL: http://www.emergenaturalsalessolutions.com
Contact: Jason Werner, Founder
Facebook: www.facebook.com/emergenaturalsalessolutions
Linkedin: www.linkedin.com/in/jason-werner-2b01a054
X (Twitter): x.com/EmergebyJason
Instagram: www.instagram.com/emergenaturalsalessolutions
Description: A consultant in natural products that provides outsourced sales management solutions for implementing your sales channel in the natural trade.

32693 ■ High Probability Selling (HPS)
Attn. Carl Ingalls
4 Leslie Ln.
Wallingford, PA 19086
Ph: (610)627-9030
Co. E-mail: info@highprobsell.com
URL: http://www.highprobsell.com
Contact: Carl Ingalls, Contact
Facebook: www.facebook.com/HighProbabilitySelling
Linkedin: www.linkedin.com/company/high-probability-selling
X (Twitter): x.com/HighProbSell
YouTube: www.youtube.com/channel/UC3jsAgiQj4qg1XqA9T_mOpw
Description: Firm provides consulting services such as selling process prospecting, disqualifying and completing sales. **Scope:** Firm provides consulting services such as selling process prospecting, disqualifying and completing sales. **Founded:** 1989. **Publications:** "Features vs. Benefits"; "Training the 'D Team'"; "Top 6 Pitfalls of Leaving Voice Mail Messages"; "Building Rapport: Don't"; "The One-Call Close"; "Getting Real About Sales Training"; "Top 10 Reasons Sales Managers Fail"; "Top 10 Reasons Salespeople Fail"; "A Clearly Defined Sales Process Yields Big Results"; "Being "Right" vs. Being Rich"; "Poison Words: The Top 6 Words that Sabotage Sales"; "Overcoming Question Reluctance"; "Top Producers- How They Get There". **Training:** High Probability Selling; High Probability Prospecting and The Power of Experiential Learning; HPS Telecourse: Training in the Basic Process; Overcoming Skepticism and Distrust; How to Turn Cold-Calls into Warm Calls. **Special Services:** Firm engaged in sales process development activities.

32694 ■ Marketing Resource Group Inc.
215 S Washington Sq., Ste. F
Lansing, MI 48933
Ph: (517)372-4400
URL: http://www.mrgmi.com
Contact: Jenell Leonard, Owner
E-mail: jleonard@mrgmi.com
Facebook: www.facebook.com/marketingresourcegroup
Linkedin: www.linkedin.com/company/marketing-resource-group
X (Twitter): x.com/MRGMichigan
Instagram: www.instagram.com/marketingresourcegroup
Description: Provides customized sales skills and field training systems for salespeople, sales managers, executives and non-selling staff and curriculums developed and branded for in-house program to be used with future trainees and new hires and offers pre-screening of sales candidates and strategic consulting. **Founded:** 1995. **Training:** Basic Sales Skills; Consultative Selling; Relationship Selling; Networking to Maximize Your Business; Six Critical

Steps for Every Sales Call; Selling Skills for the Non-Sales Professional; Effective Sales Management; Maximizing Revenue.

32695 ■ Porter Henry & Company Inc.
455 E 86th St., Ste. 37c
  New York, NY 10028
Co. E-mail: sales@porterhenry.com
URL: http://porterhenry.com

Description: Firm provides consulting and custom-designed training in sales and sales management and their work includes sales force studies and needs analysis and systems design. **Scope:** Firm provides consulting and custom-designed training in sales and sales management and their work includes sales force studies and needs analysis and systems design. **Publications:** "The Sales Strategist-6 Break-through Strategies to Win New Business". **Training:** AccountAbility; ManageAbility; SalesAbility: Totaling 25 off- the-shelf programs. Mobliesales/motivation, 1999. Infield reinforcement selling skills and motivational program for sales people.

32696 ■ Sales and Marketing Communications Associates Inc.
2835 W Juneau Ave.
  Milwaukee, WI 53208-2922
Contact: Shelia Payton, Contact

Description: A full-service marketing, public relations, focus group research and advertising company that provides clients with everything from results-oriented ideas to finished programs and materials. **Scope:** A full-service marketing, public relations, focus group research and advertising company that provides clients with everything from results-oriented ideas to finished programs and materials. **Training:** Owning and Operating a Successful Small Business; An Entrepreneur's Guide to Marketing; Getting the Message Across: Effective Business Communications; Planning Your Way to Business Success; To Be or Not To Be(A Business Owner).

32697 ■ The Schallert Group Inc.
10247 Highland Meadow Cir., Unit 107
  Parker, CO 80134
Ph: (970)281-2923
Co. E-mail: info@jonschallert.com
URL: http://www.jonschallert.com
Contact: Jon Schallert, Consultant

Description: Firm offers services such as in-store assessments, development plans to improve store position, differentiated marketing plans for retail groups, group seminars and training to small business owners on improving overall profitability. **Scope:** Firm offers services such as in-store assessments, development plans to improve store position, differentiated marketing plans for retail groups, group seminars and training to small business owners on improving overall profitability. **Founded:** 1996. **Training:** Business Reinvention: The New Normal on Main Street & Every Street, 2010; Driving Customer Traffic and Sales in This Economy with Destination Principles; Turn Any Business Into A Consumer Destination; Win The War Against Retail Superstores; Seven Critical Steps To Reinventing Mom And Pop; Pumping New Life Into A Stagnant Business; Increasing Sales & Profits as a Destination Business, Nov, 2007;

Increase Sales & Profits with Branded Marketing, Nov, 2007; Developing Your Destination Business: Creating Design, Direction, and Dominance, Oct, 2006; Making Your Store a Consumer Destination, Nov, 2006; Turn Any Business Into A Consumer Destination; Win The War Against Retail Superstores; Ten Rules For Courting Today's Aging Consumers; The Key to Driving Customer Traffic & Sales in This Economy.

32698 ■ Westlife Consultants and Advisors
4 Robert Speck Pkwy.
  Mississauga, ON, Canada L4Z, CA
URL: http://www.westlifeconsultants.com
Contact: Syed N. Hussain, President
E-mail: shussain@westlifeconsultants.com
Linkedin: www.linkedin.com/company/westlife-consultants-&-advisors

Description: Provider of entrepreneurs and businesses with a highly commercial and global perspectives on the international business development ideas under consideration. **Scope:** Provider of entrepreneurs and businesses with a highly commercial and global perspectives on the international business development ideas under consideration. **Founded:** 1992. **Publications:** "Innovative Management"; "Team Building and Leadership"; "Financial Planning"; "Estate Planning"; "Risk Management"; "Export/Import Trade Finance Mechanics"; "Marketing and Sales Management"; "What Your Banker Needs to Know"; "Building A Successful Financial Plan".

32699 ■ William Blades L.L.C.
5405 S Abbey
  Mesa, AZ 85212
Ph: (480)556-1467
Co. E-mail: bill@billblades.com
URL: http://www.billblades.com
Contact: William Blades, Contact
E-mail: bill@billblades.com

Description: Firm provides consulting services in sales, sales management, marketing, leadership, corporate culture, and much more. **Scope:** Firm provides consulting services in sales, sales management, marketing, leadership, corporate culture, and much more. **Founded:** 1988. **Publications:** "Selling-The Mother of All Enterprise"; "Leadership Defined"; "Why Do We Make Change So Hard"; "10 Crucial Steps for Sales Management Success"; "In Sales, it's all About Accountability"; "Conversations Of Success"; "Celebrate Selling"; "Vision: Help Your Mind"; "Leadership Defined"; "Managing to Improve: 10 Areas of Emphasis for Workplace Leaders"; "Creativity: Let the Juices Flow in the Workplace"; "Get Bill Blades Philosophy on Boot Camps"; "Great Leadership Grows From a Mixed Bag"; "Self Improvement - The Million Dollar Equation". **Training:** Sales Leadership Culture Creativity; Sales and Management; Coaching for Executives and Sales Managers; Sales and Marketing Action Plans.

FRANCHISES AND BUSINESS OPPORTUNITIES

32700 ■ DEI International L.L.C.
2944 Turpin Woods Ct.
  Cincinnati, OH 45244-3563
Contact: Steve Mulch, Contact

Description: Provider of business development services. **Founded:** 1979. **Training:** Offers 2 weeks home-based training and 2 weeks at headquarters with ongoing support.

32701 ■ Sandler Systems Inc.
300 Red Brook Blvd., Ste. 400
  Owings Mills, MD 21117
Ph: (410)653-1993
Co. E-mail: info@sandler.com
URL: http://www.sandler.com
Contact: Dave Mattson, President
X (Twitter): x.com/SandlerTraining
Instagram: www.instagram.com/sandlertraining
YouTube: www.youtube.com/user/SandlerWorldwide

Description: No. 1 Rated Management Training Franchise by Entrepreneur Magazine 2001. The franchise offered consists of the right to operate a Sandler Sales Institute business devoted to a distinctive style of training persons in the fields of sales and sales management, management consulting, human relations, leadership development, and methods of teaching such subjects through ongoing training, seminars and workshops. **No. of Operating Units:** 250. **Founded:** 1967. **Equity Capital Needed:** Net worth of $200,000-$400,000. **Franchise Fee:** $73,000. **Royalty Fee:** Flat monthly fee based on tenure. **Financial Assistance:** No **Training:** Toll-free hotline for training support, frequent initial training schools, quarterly training conferences, training and operating manuals, newsletter, promotional materials, lead generation, leader's guides.

LIBRARIES

32702 ■ University of Akron - College of Business Administration - Fisher Institute of Professional Selling - Sales Education Learning Library
Akron, OH 44325-4805
Ph: (330)972-7111
Co. E-mail: admissions@uakron.edu
URL: http://www.uakron.edu
Contact: Gary L. Miller, President
Facebook: www.facebook.com/pg/UniversityofAkron
Instagram: www.instagram.com/uakron
YouTube: www.youtube.com/uakron

Scope: Selling and sales management. **Services:** Library open to students. **Founded:** 1870. **Holdings:** Books; audiotapes; CDs; videos.

RESEARCH CENTERS

32703 ■ University of Akron College of Business Administration - Fisher Institute for Professional Selling
259 S Broadway St.
  Akron, OH 44325
URL: http://www.uakron.edu/cba/fisher
X (Twitter): x.com/FisherSales_UA

Description: Integral unit of University of Akron. Offers consulting and corporate training, continuing education courses, and management development courses for sales executives. **Scope:** Professional selling techniques and sales management. **Founded:** 1992. **Educational Activities:** Fisher Institute for Professional Selling Seminars.

Scientific and Technical Research/Development

START-UP INFORMATION

32704 ■ *"3rd Annual 'OneMedForum NY 2012', July 11th-12th, to Spotlight JOBS Act, Crowdfunding, and Promising Areas for Healthcare Investment" in Investment Weekly (June 23, 2012)*
Description: Third annual forum presented by OneMed provided sessions for understanding the changes in regulation due to the new JOBS Act, which will create opportunities for investors and entrepreneurs. Experts in healthcare and life science investments will be featured. Details of the event are covered. **Availability:** Online.

32705 ■ *"Austin, Aggies and Innovation" in Austin Business Journal (Vol. 32, April 6, 2012, No. 5, pp. A1)*
Pub: American City Business Journals, Inc.
Contact: Mike Olivieri, Executive Vice President
Ed: Christopher Calnan. **Description:** Texas A and M University System director for new ventures, Jamie Rhodes, has been using his experience as an entrepreneur and angel investor to work with the university's professors, researchers, and new entrepreneurs on commercialization opportunities. Rhodes has a goal to create startups based on research produced at Texas A and M. **Availability:** Online.

32706 ■ *"Program Boosts 'Breakout' Companies" in Silicon Valley/San Jose Business Journal (Vol. 30, April 20, 2012, No. 4, pp. 1)*
Pub: Baltimore Business Journal
Contact: Rhonda Pringle, President
E-mail: rpringle@bizjournals.com
Description: San Francisco, California-based Thiel Foundation has introduced a new program called Breakout Labs that aims to give small amounts of funding to very early stage science startups. The program is backed by Paypal founder and investor Peter Thiel and had more than 200 applicants. Insights on the initial grant recipients are also given. **Availability:** Print; Online.

32707 ■ *"The Startup of Something Big" in Philadelphia Business Journal (Vol. 33, July 11, 2014, No. 22, pp. 4)*
Pub: American City Business Journals, Inc.
Contact: Mike Olivieri, Executive Vice President
Released: Weekly. **Price:** $4, Introductory 4-week offer(Digital only). **Description:** Philadelphia is slowly emerging as America's leading innovation district. The South Bank Campus is the city's game changer as University of Pennsylvania and Drexel University, along with others are seeking to harness the merging of innovation and academic pursuits that ultimately translate into new business development. **Availability:** Print; Online.

32708 ■ *"StartX Med Prescribed for Innovation" in Silicon Valley/San Jose Business Journal (Vol. 30, June 8, 2012, No. 11, pp. 1)*
Pub: Baltimore Business Journal
Contact: Rhonda Pringle, President
E-mail: rpringle@bizjournals.com
Description: StartX Med is a program started by entrepreneur Divya Nag along with Stanford student-led nonprofit StartX to help medical startups. Under the program, entrepreneurs will have access to wet and dry laboratory space, animal testing and information related to US Food and Drug Adminstration regulations. **Availability:** Print; Online.

32709 ■ *"Troy Patent Law Firm Launches Rent-Free Tech Incubator" in Crain's Detroit Business (Vol. 25, June 8, 2009, No. 23, pp. 4)*
Pub: Crain Communications Inc.
Contact: Barry Asin, President
Ed: Tom Henderson. **Description:** Young Basile Hanlon MacFarlane & Helmholdt PC, a patent law firm located in Troy, Michigan has created a small, rent-free technology incubator on site. The incubator will be called North Woodward Tech Incubator and has room for four or five startups. The incubator is for the earliest or pre-seed stage for entrepreneurs who have not yet gotten significant investment capital. **Availability:** Online.

ASSOCIATIONS AND OTHER ORGANIZATIONS

32710 ■ **American Association for Aerosol Research (AAAR)**
401 Edgewater Pl., Ste. 600
Wakefield, MA 01880
Free: 866-972-7222
Co. E-mail: info@aaar.org
URL: http://www.aaar.org
Contact: V. Faye McNeill, President
Facebook: www.facebook.com/
AmericanAerosolResearch
Linkedin: www.linkedin.com/company/american
-association-for-aerosol-research-inc
X (Twitter): x.com/AmericanAerosol
Description: Represents scientists and engineers associated with universities, technical institutes and private firms; government representatives; interested firms and associations. Promotes aerosol research in areas including industrial processes, air pollution and industrial hygiene. **Scope:** Aerosol research, including global environment, microcontamination, air pollution, instrumentation, aerosol chemistry, material synthesis, aerosol physics, pharmaceutical aerosols, occupational and public health, filtration/separation, atmospheric sciences, combustion, biological aerosols, metrology/standards, indoor air quality, radioactive aerosols, and nuclear safety. **Founded:** 1982. **Publications:** *Aerosol Science & Technology Journal (AS&T)* (Monthly); *American Association for Aerosol Research Directory: Officers and Membership* (Annual); *Particulars* (3/year). **Awards:** Kenneth T. Whitby Award (Annual); David Sinclair Award (Annual); Sheldon K. Friedlander Award (Annual); Thomas T. Mercer Joint Prize (Annual); Benjamin Y.H. Liu Award (Annual). **Geographic Preference:** National.

32711 ■ **American Association of Physical Anthropologists (AABA) [American Association of Biological Anthropologists]**
950 Herndon Pky. Ste. 450
Herndon, VA 20170
Ph: (703)790-1745
Co. E-mail: aapa@burkinc.com
URL: http://physanth.org
Contact: Leslea Hlusko, President
Description: Professional society of physical anthropologists and scientists in closely related fields interested in the advancement of the science of physical anthropology through research and teaching of human variation, paleoanthropology and primatology. **Founded:** 1930. **Publications:** *American Journal of Physical Anthropology--American Association of Physical Anthropologists Membership Directory Issue* (Monthly); *AAPA Newsletter* (Quarterly); *American Journal of Biological Anthropology (AJPA)* (Monthly); *Career Information Bulletin* (Periodic); *Yearbook of Biological Anthropology* (Annual). **Awards:** Charles R. Darwin Lifetime Achievement Award (Annual); William S. Pollitzer Student Travel Award (Annual); The Charles R. Darwin Lifetime Achievement Award (Annual); The Juan Comas Prize; The Ales Hrdlicka Prize; The Mildred Trotter Prize (Annual). **Geographic Preference:** National.

32712 ■ **American Association of State Climatologists (AASC)**
151 Patton Ave., Ste. 120
Asheville, NC 28801
Co. E-mail: info@stateclimate.org
URL: http://stateclimate.org
Description: State-supported climatologists and university-related research climatologists. Promotes applied climatology and climatological services in the U.S. Compiles statistics. **Founded:** 1976. **Geographic Preference:** National.

32713 ■ **Association of Energy Engineers (AEE)**
3168 Mercer University Dr.
Atlanta, GA 30341
Ph: (770)447-5083
Co. E-mail: info@aeecenter.org
URL: http://www.aeecenter.org
Contact: Andres Ortuno, President
Facebook: www.facebook.com/Associa
tionofEnergyEngineers
Linkedin: www.linkedin.com/company/association-of
-energy-engineers
Instagram: www.instagram.com/aeecenter
YouTube: www.youtube.com/user/aee
Description: Engineers, architects, and other professionals with an interest in energy management and cogeneration; manufacturers and industries involved in energy. Promotes the advancement of the profession and contributes to the professional development of members. Sponsors Cogeneration and Competitive Power Institute, Environmental Engineers and Managers Institute, and Demand-Side Management Society. **Founded:** 1977. **Publications:** *Distributed Generation & Alternative Energy Journal* (Quarterly);

Energy Services Marketing News (3/year); *Environmental Engineers and Managers Institute News* (3/year); *Facility Managers Institute News* (3/year). **Educational Activities:** GLOBALCON Expo (Annual); World Energy Engineering Congress (WEEC). **Awards:** Association of Energy Engineers Foundation Scholarship Program (Annual). **Geographic Preference:** Multinational.

32714 ■ Association of Genetic Technologists (AGT)

219 Timberland Trl., Ln.
Rocky Top, TN 37769
Ph: (423)567-4248
Co. E-mail: agtinfonow@gmail.com
URL: http://www.agt-info.org
Contact: Tara Ellingham, President
Facebook: www.facebook.com/AssoGenTech
X (Twitter): x.com/AGTechnologists
YouTube: www.youtube.com/channel/UCCTpScPvM
tDt1LnehH71x9g

Description: Promotes exchange of information among those engaged in classical cytogenetics, molecular and biochemical genetics. Stimulates interest in genetics as a career. **Founded:** 1975. **Publications:** *Association of Genetic Technologists--International Membership Directory; AGT International Membership Directory; Journal of the Association of Genetic Technologists (JAGT)* (Quarterly). **Awards:** AGT Outstanding Achievement Award (Annual). **Geographic Preference:** Multinational.

32715 ■ Federation of American Scientists (FAS)

1112 16th St. NW, Ste. 600
Washington, DC 20036
Ph: (202)454-4660
Co. E-mail: fas@fas.org
URL: http://fas.org
Contact: Gilman Louie, Chairman
E-mail: rbierbau@umich.edu
Facebook: www.facebook.com/fascientists
Linkedin: www.linkedin.com/company/federation-of-american-scientists
X (Twitter): x.com/FAScientists
Instagram: www.instagram.com/fascientists

Description: Natural and social scientists, engineers, and individuals concerned with problems of science and society. **Founded:** 1945. **Publications:** *FAS Public Interest Report* (Quarterly). **Awards:** Hans Bethe Award (Periodic); FAS Public Service Award (Periodic). **Geographic Preference:** National.

32716 ■ National Weather Association (NWA)

3100 Monitor Ave., Ste. 123
Norman, OK 73072
Ph: (405)701-5167
Co. E-mail: nwahelp@nwas.org
URL: http://www.nwas.org
Facebook: www.facebook.com/nwasorg
X (Twitter): x.com/nwas
Instagram: www.instagram.com/nwasorg
YouTube: www.youtube.com/user/NationalWXAssoc

Description: Individuals and groups interested in operational meteorology and related activities. Promotes professionalism in practical meteorology; develops solutions to problems faced by people working in daily weather forecasting activities; acts as a voice for persons in meteorology. Encourages exchange of information and ideas among meteorologists. Provides members with the opportunity to network and to participate in activities related to meteorology. **Founded:** 1975. **Publications:** *National Weather Digest* (Quarterly; Semiannual); *NWA Monthly Newsletter* (Monthly); *Polar Orbiter Satellite Imagery Interpretation.* **Educational Activities:** FLASH Annual Conference (Annual). **Awards:** NWA Broadcaster of the Year (Annual); Larry R. Johnson Special Award (Annual); NWA Member of the Year Award (Annual); NWA Operational Achievement Award (Annual); NWA Public Education Award (Annual); T. Theodore Fujita Research Achievement Award (Annual); Walter J. Bennett Public Service Award (Annual). **Geographic Preference:** National.

32717 ■ Universities Space Research Association (USRA)

425 3rd St., SW, Ste. 950
Washington, DC 20024
Ph: (410)730-2656
Co. E-mail: info@usra.edu
URL: http://www.usra.edu
Contact: Dr. Jeffrey A. Isaacson, President
Facebook: www.facebook.com/UniSpaceResearch
Linkedin: www.linkedin.com/company/usra
X (Twitter): x.com/USRAedu

Description: Represents the International consortium of universities. Fosters cooperation among universities, research organizations and the U.S. government for the advancement of space research. Charter includes provision to acquire, plan, construct and operate laboratories and other facilities for research, development and education associated with space science and technology. Unites NASA engineers and engineering students on design projects for NASA through its educational programs. **Founded:** 1969. **Awards:** Thomas R. McGetchin Memorial Scholarship Award (Annual); John R. Sevier Memorial Scholarship Award (Annual); James B. Willett Educational Memorial Scholarship Award (Annual); Frederick A. Tarantino Memorial Scholarship Award (Annual). **Geographic Preference:** National.

REFERENCE WORKS

32718 ■ "113D Filings: Investors Report to the SEC" in Barron's (Vol. 88, March 24, 2008, No. 12, pp. M13)

Pub: Dow Jones & Company Inc.
Contact: Almar Latour, Chief Executive Officer

Released: April 02, 2016. **Description:** HealthCor Management called as problematic the plan of Magellan Health Services to use its high cash balances for acquisitions. Carlson Capital discussed with Energy Partners possible changes in the latter's board. Investor Carl Icahn suggested that Enzon Pharmaceuticals consider selling itself or divest some of its assets. **Availability:** Print; Online.

32719 ■ "$44M Father/Son Biz Involved in Major Orlando Projects" in Orlando Business Journal (Vol. 31, July 18, 2014, No. 3, pp. 3)

Pub: American City Business Journals, Inc.
Contact: Mike Olivieri, Executive Vice President

Released: Weekly. **Price:** $8, Introductory 4-week offer(Digital & Print). **Description:** Sy and mark Israel, father-son duo of Universal Engineering Sciences, speak about the projects that have been their largest challenges. They also highlight the advice they would give to a family business or a new business startup. **Availability:** Print; Online.

32720 ■ "Abaddon Acquires Pukaskwa Uranium Properties in NW Ontario" in Canadian Corporate News (May 16, 2007)

Description: Rubicon Minerals Corp. has entered into an Option Agreement with Consolidated Abaddon Resources Inc. for the acquisition of Pukaskwa uranium properties and plans to conduct an extensive exploration program to prove out the resource and geological potential of the area. Statistical data included. **Availability:** Online.

32721 ■ "Alcoa: 'Going Where No Materials Scientist Has Gone Before'" in Pittsburgh Business Times (Vol. 33, July 18, 2014, No. 53, pp. 5)

Pub: American City Business Journals, Inc.
Contact: Mike Olivieri, Executive Vice President

Released: Weekly. **Price:** $4, introductory 4-week offer(Digital & Print). **Description:** Alcoa Inc. has signed a $1.1 billion supply agreement with Pratt & Whitney to build the forging for aluminum jet-engine fan blades as well as other parts made with aluminum lithium. This partnership brings together Alcoa's proprietary alloys and unique manufacturing processes with Pratt & Whitney's design, thus forging an aluminum fan blade that is lighter and enables better fuel efficiency. **Availability:** Print; Online.

32722 ■ "American Indian College Fund to Support Environmental Science and Sustainability Programs, Fellowships, and Internships" in Ecology, Environment & Conservation Business (April 12, 2014, pp. 21)

Pub: NewsRX LLC.
Contact: Kalani Rosell, Contact

Description: Tribal colleges serve communities facing environmental issues, such as water quality, energy development, depletion of natural resources, and agricultural management. The American Indian College Fund has created a new Environmental Science and Sustainability Project of $1.35 million grant money to support tribal colleges and universities in select states that underwrite environmental science and sustainability programs of studies. Details of the project are included. **Availability:** Online.

32723 ■ "Angiotech to Buy Top Medical Devices Company" in Globe & Mail (February 1, 2006, pp. B1)

Description: The details on Angiotech Pharmaceuticals Inc.'s acquisition of American Medical Instruments Holdings Inc. are presented. **Availability:** Online.

32724 ■ "Apples, Decoded: WSU Scientist Unraveling the Fruit's Genetics" in Puget Sound Business Journal (Vol. 29, September 5, 2008, No. 20)

Description: Washington State University researcher is working to map the apple's genome in order to gain information about how the fruit grows, looks and tastes. His work, funded by a research grant from the US Department of Agriculture and the Washington Apple Commission is crucial to improving the state's position as an apple-producing region. **Availability:** Print; Online.

32725 ■ "Auctions and Bidding: A Guide for Computer Scientists" in ACM Computing Surveys (Vol. 43, Summer 2011, No. 2, pp. 10)

Pub: Association for Computing Machinery
Contact: Yannis Ioannidis, President

Ed: Simon Parsons, Juan A. Rodriguez-Aguilar, Mark Klein. **Released:** Volume 43 Issue 2. **Price:** $10, Members; $15, Nonmembers; $5, Students. **Description:** There are various actions: single dimensional, multi-dimensional, single-sided, double-sided, first-price, second-price, English, Dutch, Japanese, sealed-bid, and these have been extensively discussed and analyzed in economics literature. This literature is surveyed from a computer science perspective, primarily from the viewpoint of computer scientists who are interested in learning about auction theory, and to provide pointers into the economics literature for those who want a deeper technical understanding. In addition, since auctions are an increasingly important topic in computer science, the article also looks at work on auctions from the computer science literature. The aim is to identify what both bodies of work tell us about creating electronic auctions. **Availability:** Download; PDF.

32726 ■ "Banking on Cord Blood" in Business Journal-Serving Phoenix & the Valley of the Sun (Vol. 31, September 10, 2010, No. 1, pp. 1)

Description: Celebration Stem Cell Centre obtained contracts from Mercy Gilbert Medical Center and its two sister hospitals, St. Joseph Hospital and Medical Center in Phoenix, Arizona and Chandler Regional Medical Center. The contract will facilitate the donation of unused umbilical cord blood for research. **Availability:** PDF; Online.

32727 ■ "BioRASI Aims to Fill Larger HQ With More Jobs" in South Florida Business Journal (Vol. 34, April 11, 2014, N. 38, pp. 4)

Pub: American City Business Journals, Inc.
Contact: Mike Olivieri, Executive Vice President

Released: Weekly. **Price:** $8, Introductory 4-week offer(Digital & Print). **Description:** BioRASI has announced plans to hire an additional 20 or 30 workers in Florida in 2014 after moving into a larger headquarters in Aventura. The contract research organization added 40 employees during 2013 and now has 80 working in Florida. Other insights on BioRASI's growing presence in Florida are given. **Availability:** Print; Online.

32728 ■ "Bioscience Hiring Flat in Florida" in South Florida Business Journal (Vol. 34, July 4, 2014, No. 50, pp. 8)
Pub: American City Business Journals, Inc.
Contact: Mike Olivieri, Executive Vice President
Released: Weekly. **Price:** $8, introductory 4-week offer(Digital only); $8, introductory 4-week offer(Digital & Print). **Description:** The bioscience industry in Florida showed little growth in job creation since 2007, despite heavy state investments. The bioscience sector lost 1 percent of its jobs from 2007 to 2010, while the following two years only recovered the losses of previous years. **Availability:** Print; Online.

32729 ■ "Biotechnology Wants a Lead Role" in Business North Carolina (Vol. 28, March 2008, No. 3, pp. 14)
Description: According to experts, North Carolina is poised as a leader in the biotechnology sector. Highlights of a recent roundtable discussion sponsored by the North Carolina Biotechnology Center in Research Triangle Park are presented. **Availability:** Online.

32730 ■ "Bitumen Oilsands: Slick Science" in Canadian Business (Vol. 81, September 15, 2008, No. 14-15, pp. 55)
Pub: Rogers Media Inc.
Contact: Neil Spivak, Chief Executive Officer
Ed: Andrew Nikiforuk. **Description:** N-Solv Corp's John Nenniger has discovered a better alternative to steam-assisted gravity drainage methods for extracting bitumen. Nenniger's technique also relies on gravity but replaces steam with propane, which leaves behind impurities like asphaltenes and heavy metals that are too dirty to burn. **Availability:** Print; Mailing list; Online.

32731 ■ "Border Boletin: UA to Take Lie-Detector Kiosk to Poland" in Arizona Daily Star (September 14, 2010)
Pub: Arizona Daily Star
Contact: John D'Orlando, President
E-mail: jdorlando@tucson.com
Ed: Brady McCombs. **Description:** University of Arizona's National Center for Border Security and Immigration Research will send a team to Warsaw, Poland to show border guards from 27 European Union countries the center's Avatar Kiosk. The Avatar technology is designed for use at border ports and airports to assist Customs officers detect individuals who are lying. **Availability:** Print; Online.

32732 ■ Borrowing Brilliance: The Six Steps to Business Innovation by Building on the Ideas of Others
Released: October 05, 2010. **Price:** $16, paperback; $9.99, e-book. **Description:** The author builds the case that cherry-picking the ideas of others is a vital part of the research and development process for any small firm. **Availability:** E-book; Print.

32733 ■ "Bridging the Worlds" in Academy of Management Journal (Vol. 50, No. 5, October 1, 2007, pp. 1043)
Pub: Academy of Management
Contact: Sharon Alvarez, President
Ed: Lise Saari. **Description:** Need to transfer human resource research information published in journals to practitioners and organizations is investigated, along with suggestions on ways of achieving this goal. **Availability:** Electronic publishing; PDF; Download; Online.

32734 ■ "Brown Lab Image of R.I. Innovation" in Providence Business News (Vol. 28, February 24, 2014, No. 47, pp. 1)
Pub: American City Business Journals, Inc.
Contact: Mike Olivieri, Executive Vice President

Released: February 22, 2014. **Description:** The Advanced Baby Imaging Lab at Brown University in Rhode Island is studying infant brain development using magnetic resonance imaging (MRI). The lab is attracting attention from researchers from Europe and California who see potential in Sean C. Deoni's technique to take an MRI of an infant without using sedation. **Availability:** Print; Online.

32735 ■ "Cancer-Fighting Entrepreneurs" in Austin Business Journal (Vol. 31, August 5, 2011, No. 22, pp. 1)
Pub: Austin Business Journal
Contact: Rachel McGrath, Director
E-mail: rmcgrath@bizjournals.com
Ed: Sandra Zaragoza. **Description:** Cancer Prevention and Research Institute of Texas has invested $10 million in recruiting known faculty to the University of Texas. The move is seen to bolster Austin's position as a major cancer research market. The institute has awarded grants to researchers Jonghwan Kim, Guangbin Dong and Kyle Miller. **Availability:** Print; Online.

32736 ■ "Cancer Genome Project Will Put San Antonio In Research Spotlight" in San Antonio Business Journal (Vol. 25, January 27, 2012, No. 53, pp. 1)
Pub: Baltimore Business Journal
Contact: Rhonda Pringle, President
E-mail: rpringle@bizjournals.com
Description: San Antonio, Texas-based South Texas Accelerated Research Therapeutics has been spearheading the development of a new cancer research effort. The San Antonio 1000 Cancer Genome Project will use the genome sequencing process to examine and compare the difference between normal tissue and tissue from some 1,000 tumors. **Availability:** Print; Online.

32737 ■ "Caterpillar to Expand Research, Production in China" in Chicago Tribune (August 27, 2008)
Description: Caterpillar Inc., the Peoria-based heavy-equipment manufacturer, plans to establish a new research-and-development center at the site of its rapidly growing campus in Wuxi. **Availability:** Print; Online.

32738 ■ "The CMO of Consequence" in Business Strategy Review (Vol. 21, Autumn 2010, No. 3, pp. 42)
Ed: D. Eric Boyd, Rajesh K. Chandy, Marcus Cunha, Jr. **Released:** September 29, 2010. **Description:** Do chief marketing officers matter? Some say that CMOs have limited effect on corporate performance and don't add significant value to the firm. The authors agree that the job in many firms is in great peril, but their research has uncovered why the contributions of some CMOs are invaluable. **Availability:** Print; PDF; Online.

32739 ■ "The Code-Cracker: Prominent Researcher at Miami Part of Federal Effort to Solve Protein Structures" in Business Courier (Vol. 24, January 10, 2008, No. 40, pp. 1)
Pub: American City Business Journals, Inc.
Contact: Mike Olivieri, Executive Vice President
Ed: James Ritchie. **Description:** Michael Kennedy, a professor in the chemistry and biochemistry department at the Miami University, is a part of the Protein Structure Initiative, a project that is aimed at forming a catalog of three-dimensional protein structures. The initiative is a project of the Northeast Structural Genomics consortium, of which the Miami University is a member. The impacts of the research on drug development are discussed. **Availability:** Print; Online.

32740 ■ "Complementary Strengths Fuel Research Duo's Success" in Providence Business News (Vol. 29, June 2, 2014, No. 9, pp. 22)
Pub: American City Business Journals, Inc.
Contact: Mike Olivieri, Executive Vice President
URL(s): pbn.com/complementary-strengths-fuel-research-duos-success96239

Description: Johnna A. Pezzullo and Lynne A. Haughey achieved success with Omega Medical Research through their complementary strengths. The company has been successful and works with pharmaceutical companies like Pfizer and GlaxoSmithKline. **Telecommunication Services:** Daddona@pbn.com.

32741 ■ "Cost Remains Top Factor In Considering Green Technology" in Canadian Sailings (June 30, 2008)
Description: Improving its environmental performance remains a priority in the shipping industry; however, testing new technologies can prove difficult due to the harsh conditions that ships endure as well as installation which usually requires a dry dock. **Availability:** Online.

32742 ■ "Crowdfunding Comes to Science's Aid as Budgets, Grants Face Squeeze" in Economic Times (July 10, 2012)
Pub: Bennett, Coleman & Company Ltd.
Ed: Rituparna Chattterjee. **Description:** Brian L. Fisher, entomologist studying ants in Madagascar raised $10,000 in 45 days from Petridish, a crowdfunding platform for scientists. Crowdfunding is where a group of investors fund projects. **Availability:** Online.

32743 ■ "Dean Foods: Uh Oh. Here Comes Wal-Mart" in Ice Cream Reporter (Vol. 23, September 20, 2010, No. 10, pp. 8)
Description: Dean Foods promoted Joseph Scalzo to President and Chief Operating Officer to oversee the firm's operational turnaround and near-term strategic initiatives as well as business units. Key functions will include worldwide supply chain and research and development. **Availability:** Online.

32744 ■ "Deere to Open Technology Center in Germany" in Chicago Tribune (September 3, 2008)
Description: Deere & Co. plans to open a technology and innovation center in Germany; details of the company's expansion plans are discussed. **Availability:** Print; Online.

32745 ■ "The Doctor Is In" in Canadian Business (Vol. 80, February 12, 2007, No. 4, pp. 38)
Description: The research at McMaster University to make a pill having imaging devices to takes pictures of any possible cancerous cells in the human body is discussed. **Availability:** Online.

32746 ■ "Does America Really Need Manufacturing? Yes, When Production Is Closely Tied to Innovation" in Harvard Business Review (Vol. 90, March 2012, No. 3, pp. 94)
Pub: Harvard Business Review Press
Contact: Moderna V. Pfizer, Contact
Ed: Gary P. Pisano, Willy C. Shih. **Price:** $8.95. **Description:** A framework is presented for assessing when manufacturing and research and development are crucial to innovation and therefore should be kept in close proximity to each other. The framework denotes the degree to which product design data can be separated from manufacturing, and the opportunities to improve manufacturing. **Availability:** Online; PDF.

32747 ■ "Dow AgroSciences Buys Wheat-Breeding Firm in Pacific Northwest" in Farm Industry News (July 29, 2011)
Pub: Informa Business Media, Inc.
Contact: Charlie McCurdy, President
Description: Dow AgroSciences purchased Northwest Plant Breeding Company, a cereals breeding station in Washington in 2011. The acquisition will help Dow expand its Hyland Seeds certified wheat seed program foundation in the Pacific Northwest. Financial terms of the deal were not disclosed. **Availability:** Online.

32748 ■ *"Drug Trial Halt at YM Sets Stage for Selloff" in Globe & Mail (January 31, 2007, pp. B3)*

Description: The decision of YM Biosciences Inc. to stop its trial of cancer drug tesmilifene and stocks following government concern over the safety of the drug is discussed. **Availability:** Online.

32749 ■ *"DuPont's Pioneer Hi-Bred, Evogene to Develop Rust-Resistant Soybean Varieties" in Farm Industry News (November 22, 2011)*

Pub: Informa Business Media, Inc.

Contact: Charlie McCurdy, President

Ed: Karen McMahon. **Description:** DuPont and Evogene have signed a new contract to work together to develop resistance in soybeans to rust. Financial terms of the agreement were not disclosed. **Availability:** Online.

32750 ■ *"EMU, Spark Plan Business Incubator for Ypsilanti" in Crain's Detroit Business (Vol. 23, October 15, 2007, No. 42, pp. 3)*

Pub: Crain Communications Inc.

Contact: Barry Asin, President

Ed: Chad Halcom. **Description:** Eastern Michigan University is seeking federal grants and other funding for a new business incubator program that would be in cooperation with Ann Arbor Spark. The site would become a part of a network of three Spark incubator programs with a focus on innovation in biotechnology and pharmaceuticals. **Availability:** Print; Online.

32751 ■ *"Entrepreneurial Orientation and Firm Performance: The Unique Impact of Innovativeness, Proactiveness, and Risk-taking" in Journal of Small Business and Entrepreneurship (Vol. 23, Winter 2010, No. 1)*

Pub: Canadian Council for Small Business and Entrepreneurship

Contact: John MacRitchie, President

Ed: Patrick M. Kreisera, Justin Davis. **Description:** The article develops a theoretical model of the relationship between firm-level entrepreneurship and firm performance. This model is intended to further clarify the consequences of an 'entrepreneurial orientation', paying particular attention to the differential relationship that exists between the three sub-dimensions of entrepreneurial orientation and firm performance. Included in the theoretical model are other important variables (such as organizational structure and environmental characteristics) that may impact the EO-performance relationship. Propositions are developed regarding the various configurations of the sub-dimensions of EO and organizational structure that would be most appropriate in a given environmental context. Future research may also benefit from considering the important role that organizational strategy and life cycle stage play in this model. The implications of this model for both researchers and managers are discussed.

32752 ■ *"eResearch Issues Initiating Report on Aldershot Resources Ltd." in Marketwired (May 14, 2007)*

Pub: Comtex News Network Inc.

Contact: Kan Devnani, President

Description: Overview of Bob Weir and Michael Wood's Initiating Report on Aldershot Resources Ltd., a junior Canadian-based uranium exploration company with prospective projects in Canada, Zambia, Australia, and a base metals project in Chile. **Availability:** Print; Online.

32753 ■ *"Family Business Research: A Strategic Reflection" in International Journal of Entrepreneurship and Small Business (Vol. 12, December 3, 2010, No. 1)*

Ed: A. Bakr Ibrahim, Jean B. McGuire. **Description:** Assessment of the growing field of family business and suggestions for an integrated framework. The paper addresses a number of key issues facing family business research. **Availability:** PDF; Download.

32754 ■ *"Feeding the Elephants While Searching for Greener Pastures" in Inc. (Volume 32, December 2010, No. 10, pp. 34)*

Pub: Mansueto Ventures L.L.C.

Contact: Stephanie Mehta, Chief Executive Officer

Ed: April Joyner. **Released:** December 2010. **Description:** Innovation is the future for small business. A new book, Inside Real Innovation: How the Right Approach Can Move Ideas from R&D to Market - And Get the Economy Moving helps to break down the process by which innovation occurs. **Availability:** Print.

32755 ■ *"FinOvation 2009" in Farm Industry News (Vol. 42, January 1, 2009, No. 1)*

Ed: Karen McMahon, Mark Moore, David Hest. **Description:** New and innovative products and technologies are presented.

32756 ■ *"First Venture Reports Proprietary Yeasts Further Reduce Ethyl Carbamate in Sake" in Canadian Corporate News (May 16, 2007)*

Description: First Ventures Technologies Corp., a biotechnology company that develops and commercializes advanced yeast products, confirmed that two of their proprietary yeasts used in the making of sake have yielded reductions in ethyl carbamate compared to previous sake brewing trials.

32757 ■ *"Five New Scientists Bring Danforth Center $16 Million" in Saint Louis Business Journal (Vol. 32, October 7, 2011, No. 6, pp. 1)*

Pub: Saint Louis Business Journal

Contact: Robert Bobroff, President

E-mail: rbobroff@bizjournals.com

Ed: E.B. Solomont. **Description:** Donald Danforth Plant Science Center's appointment of five new lead scientists has increased its federal funding by $16 million. Cornell University scientist Tom Brutnell is one of the five new appointees. **Availability:** Print; Online.

32758 ■ *"For Gilead, Growth Beyond AIDS" in Barron's (Vol. 88, June 30, 2008, No. 26, pp. 18)*

Pub: Dow Jones & Company Inc.

Contact: Almar Latour, Chief Executive Officer

Ed: Jay Palmer. **Description:** First-quarter 2008 revenue for Gilead Sciences grew by 22 percent and an earnings gain of 19 percent thanks to their HIV-treatment drugs that comprised over two-thirds of the company's sales in 2007. An analyst has a 12-month target from June, 2008 of 65 per share. The factors behind the company's prospects are also discussed. **Availability:** Online.

32759 ■ *"From Chelsea Machine Shop to Nobel Prize" in Crain's Detroit Business (Vol. 30, October 13, 2014, No. 41, pp. 35)*

Pub: Crain Communications Inc.

Contact: Barry Asin, President

Description: Profile of Eric Betzig, one of three scientists recognized with the Nobel Prize in Chemistry for devising ways for microscopes to look into the molecular hearts of living cells. Betzig is an Ann Arbor, Michigan native who performs research in Virginia for the Howard Hughes Medical Institute. **Availability:** Print; Online.

32760 ■ *"FSU's OGZEB Is Test Bed for Sustainable Technology" in Contractor (Vol. 56, October 2009, No. 10, pp. 1)*

Ed: Candace Roulo. **Description:** Florida State University has one of 14 off-grid zero emissions buildings (OGZEB) in the U.S.; it was built to research sustainable and alternative energy systems. The building produces electricity from 30 photovoltaic panels and it also has three AET water heating solar panels on the roof. **Availability:** Print; Online.

32761 ■ *"Funding Drought Stalls Biotech Incubators" in Saint Louis Business Journal (Vol. 31, July 29, 2011, No. 49, pp. 1)*

Pub: Saint Louis Business Journal

Contact: Robert Bobroff, President

E-mail: rbobroff@bizjournals.com

Ed: Angela Mueller. **Description:** Economic slowdown took its toll on cash-strapped startups that fill incubators such as the Bio-Research and Development Growth (BRDG) Park in Creve Coeur, Missouri and the Center for Emerging Technologies in Midtown St. Louis. BRDG put a hold on construction of of its two buildings. **Availability:** Print; Online.

32762 ■ *"The Future of Work" in Business Strategy Review (Vol. 21, Autumn 2010, No. 3, pp. 16)*

Pub: Wiley-Blackwell

Ed: Lynda Gratton. **Released:** August 28, 2017. **Description:** Work is universal. But how, why, where and when we work has never been so open to individual interpretation. The certainties of the past have been replaced by ambiguity, questions and the steady hum of technology. Now, in a groundbreaking research project covering 21 global companies and more than 200 executives, the author is making sense of the future of work. **Availability:** Print; PDF; Online.

32763 ■ *"GeneTree.com Unveils New Family Consultation Service in Interpreting Genealogical DNA Data" in Benzinga.com (February 2, 2012)*

Description: Family Consultation Services has been launched by GeneTree.com. The service will provide an in-depth examination of genealogical and DNA information to help genealogist help families identify ancestors in specific family lines. The new DNA test called Y-19 will be used by the service. **Availability:** Print; Online.

32764 ■ *"Giving Biotech Startups a Hand" in Philadelphia Business Journal (Vol. 28, January 8, 2010, No. 47, pp. 1)*

Pub: Philadelphia Business Journal

Contact: Sierra Quinn, Director

E-mail: squinn@bizjournals.com

Ed: John George. **Description:** Elkins Park, Pennsylvania-based BioStrategy Partners is a virtual life sciences incubator that is seeking to improve the dull ranking of Philadelphia in the small business vitality index of life sciences. BioStrategy provides technology and business development services to startup life sciences companies and university based research projects. **Availability:** Online.

32765 ■ *"Good for Business: Houston is a Hot Spot for Economic Growth" in Black Enterprise (Vol. 37, October 2006, No. 3, pp. 216)*

Pub: Earl G. Graves Ltd.

Contact: Earl Graves, Jr., President

Ed: Jeanette Valentine. **Description:** Fast-growing sectors in the biotechnology and healthcare industries are among the driving forces of Houston's economic growth. More than 76,000 small businesses in the area employ about one in four area workers, according to the Small Business Administration. Housing and business costs are 26 and 11 percent below the national average, respectively, garnering the attention of corporate giants.

32766 ■ *"Grant Program Boosting Biomedical Research" in Providence Business News (Vol. 28, February 24, 2014, No. 47, pp. 3)*

Pub: American City Business Journals, Inc.

Contact: Mike Olivieri, Executive Vice President

Released: February 22, 2014. **Description:** The role played by the Institutional Development Award Network of Biomedical Research Excellence (INBRE) is boosting biomedical research in Rhode Island. According to researcher, Niall G. Howlett, procuring startup funding through INBRE led to receiving other grants and working with graduate students who have the potential to become part of the biomedical workforce. **Availability:** Print; Online.

32767 ■ *"Growing Field" in Crain's Detroit Business (Vol. 26, January 11, 2010, No. 2, pp. 3)*

Pub: Crain Communications Inc.

Contact: Barry Asin, President

Description: Detroit's TechTown was awarded a combination loan and grant of $4.1 million from the U.S. Department of Housing and Urban Development to build a 15,000-square-foot stem cell center, a collection of laboratories that will be available to both for-profit companies and university researchers. **Availability:** Online.

32768 ■ "GSK Creating Pathways From Academia to Industry" in Philadelphia Business Journal (Vol. 33, March 7, 2014, No. 4, pp. 8)
Pub: American City Business Journals, Inc.
Contact: Mike Olivieri, Executive Vice President
Released: Weekly. **Price:** $4, introductory 4-week offer(Digital & Print). **Description:** The Discovery Fast Track Challenge program of GlaxoSmithKline will expand in 2014 to include scientists in North America and Europe. Scientists will be asked to submit information about their innovative drug research proposals and the winner could be offered a deal with the Discovery Partnerships with Academia team. **Availability:** Print; Online.

32769 ■ "Health Science Center's Capital Campaign Will Boost Local Research" in San Antonio Business Journal (Vol. 28, March 14, 2014, No. 5, pp. 8)
Pub: American City Business Journals, Inc.
Contact: Mike Olivieri, Executive Vice President
Description: The University of Texas Health Science Center at San Antonio's Campaign for the Future of fundraising project has been completed. The Health Science Center is expected to use the money to support research at the South Texas Medical Center. The capital campaign will allow the Health Science Center to become one of the most prominent universities in the U.S. **Availability:** Print; Online.

32770 ■ "The Heart of Health Village: innovation Is Key, and to Get It, Florida Hospital Is Wooing Disruptors, Millenials" in Orlando Business Journal (Vol. 30, May 16, 2014, No. 47, pp. 4)
Pub: American City Business Journals, Inc.
Contact: Mike Olivieri, Executive Vice President
Released: May 16, 2014. **Description:** The economic impact of Florida Hospital's planned Health Village in downtown Orlando is explored. The 172-acre development aims to bring together business people, scientists for research, and early and mid-stage companies to combine co-working activities in its Medical Innovation Laboratory. **Availability:** Print; Online.

32771 ■ "High Energy: Gaurdie Banister Joins Aera As President and CEO" in Black Enterprise (Vol. 38, July 2008, No. 12, pp. 30)
Pub: Earl G. Graves Ltd.
Contact: Earl Graves, Jr., President
Ed: Brenda Porter. **Description:** Gaurdie Banister Jr. has been appointed president and CEO of Aera Energy L.L.C., becoming one of the first African Americans in the nation to run a major energy corporation. His plans for the firm include utilizing new, sophisticated technologies in order to unlock the 3-1/2 billion barrels of resources the company has on their books in a safe and environmentally friendly way. He also hopes to increase production and maintain cost leadership.

32772 ■ "Hope Grows for a Muscular Dystrophy Drug" in Barron's (Vol. 92, August 25, 2012, No. 35, pp. 35)
Pub: Dow Jones & Company Inc.
Contact: Almar Latour, Chief Executive Officer
Ed: Andrew Bary. **Description:** The stocks of biotechnology firm Sarepta Therapeutics could gain value if trials for eterpirsen, a drug being developed for Duchenne muscular dystrophy, are successful. The company's stock prices could rise from $10/share to as high as $26/share. **Availability:** Online.

32773 ■ "Hopkins' Security, Reputation Face Challenges in Wake of Slaying" in Baltimore Business Journal (Vol. 28, August 6, 2010, No. 13)
Pub: Baltimore Business Journal
Contact: Rhonda Pringle, President

E-mail: rpringle@bizjournals.com
Ed: Gary Haber. **Description:** The slaying of Johns Hopkins University researcher Stephen Pitcairn has not tarnished the reputation of the elite school in Baltimore, Maryland among students. Maintaining Hopkins' reputation is important since it is Baltimore's largest employer with nearly 32,000 workers. Insights on the impact of the slaying among the Hopkins' community are also given.

32774 ■ "Hopkins, University of Maryland, Baltimore Worry Reduced NIH Budget Will Impact Research" in Baltimore Business Journal (Vol. 29, August 19, 2011, No. 15, pp. 1)
Pub: Boston Business Journal
Contact: Carolyn M. Jones, President
E-mail: cmjones@bizjournals.com
Ed: Scott Dance. **Description:** The budget for the National Institutes of Health (NIH) is slated to be cut by at least 7.9 percent to $2.5 billion in 2013. This will have a big negative effect on medical and biotech research in Maryland, especially Johns Hopkins University and University of Maryland, Baltimore which could face stiffer completion for grants from the NIH. **Availability:** Online.

32775 ■ "How Green Is The Valley?" in Barron's (Vol. 88, July 4, 2008, No. 28, pp. 13)
Description: San Jose, California has made a good start towards becoming a leader in alternative energy technology through the establishment of United Laboratories' own lab in the city. The certification process for photovoltaic cells will be dramatically shortened with this endeavor. **Availability:** Print.

32776 ■ "Human Activity Analysis: a Review" in ACM Computing Surveys (Vol. 43, Fall 2011, No. 3, pp. 16)
Pub: Association for Computing Machinery
Contact: Yannis Ioannidis, President
Ed: J. K. Aggarwal, M. S. Ryoo. **Description:** Human activity recognition is an important area of computer vision research and is studied in this report. **Availability:** Download; PDF; Online.

32777 ■ "iAM Scientist Launches To Provide a Crowdfunding Platform for Science, Technology, and Medicine" in Benzinga.com (July 31, 2012)
Pub: Benzinga.com
Contact: Jason Raznick, Founder
Ed: Aaron Wise. **Description:** Medical, technology, and science researchers will be able to seach for funding through the newly launched iAMscientist platform. The sitewill provide a site with funding and shared research opportunities. The new tools, better models, and quicker data collection processes will help make research interdisciplinary, collaborative, data driven, and less predictable. Open Access Funding Platform (OAFP) can be used to solicit funding required to carry out research projects. **Availability:** Print; Online.

32778 ■ "Innovation: A Blood Test on a Chip" in Inc. (Vol. 33, November 2011, No. 9, pp. 42)
Pub: Inc. Magazine
Ed: Christine Chafkin-Lagorio. **Description:** Harvard University researchers have developed a device called the mChip that produces accurate blood tests in about 10 minutes. Plans to apply for FDA approval for the mChip in the US should happen in 2012. **Availability:** Online.

32779 ■ International Research Centers Directory (IRCD)
Pub: Gale, part of Cengage Group
Contact: Paul Gazzolo, General Manager Senior Vice President
URL(s): www.gale.com/ebooks/9781414450391/international-research-centers-directory
Released: Latest edition 23rd. **Description:** Covers over 9,500 research and development facilities maintained outside the United States by governments, universities, or independent organizations, and concerned with all areas of physical, social, and life sciences, technology, business, military science,

public policy, and the humanities. **Entries include:** Facility name, address, phone, fax, telex, e-mail, URLs, name of parent agency or other affiliation, date established, number of staff, type of activity and fields of research, special research facilities, publications, educational activities, services, and library holdings. **Arrangement:** Subject. **Indexes:** Master, subject, personal name and country. **Availability:** E-book; Download. **Type:** Directory.

32780 ■ "Inventive Doctor New Venture Partner" in Houston Business Journal (Vol. 40, January 29, 2010, No. 38, pp. A2)
Pub: Houston Business Journal
Contact: Bob Charlet, President
E-mail: bcharlet@bizjournals.com

Ed: Ford Gunter. **Description:** Dr. Billy Cohn, a surgeon from Houston, Texas has been named as venture partner for venture firm Sante Ventures LLC of Austin, Texas. Cohn will be responsible for seeing marketable developing technologies in the medical industry. The motivation for Cohn's naming as venture partner is his development of a minimally invasive therapy for end-stage renal disease. **Availability:** Print; Online.

32781 ■ "Is Your Employees' BMI Your Business?" in Canadian Business (Vol. 83, September 14, 2010, No. 15, pp. 98)
Pub: Rogers Media Inc.
Contact: Neil Spivak, Chief Executive Officer

Ed: Jacqueline Nelson. **Description:** Canada's Public Health Agency's research shows that there is a solid business case for companies to promote active living to their employees. However, employers must toe the line between being helpful and being invasive. Insights into the issues faces by companies when introducing health programs are discussed. **Availability:** Online.

32782 ■ "Jacksonville Doing Well In Growing Economy" in Orlando Business Journal (Vol. 30, June 27, 2014, No. 53, pp. 8)
Pub: American City Business Journals, Inc.
Contact: Mike Olivieri, Executive Vice President

Released: June 27, 2014. **Description:** Jerry Mallot is the president of JaxUSA Partnership, the economic development arm of the Jax Chambers. According to Mallot, Northeast Florida's strongest selling points for business site or relocation there include advanced manufacturing, financial services, aviation and aerospace technology, life sciences, logistics and information technology.

32783 ■ "The Life Changers" in Canadian Business (Vol. 81, October 27, 2008, No. 18, pp. 86)
Description: The first season of 'The Life Changers' was produced in September 2007 to feature stories about research and development (R&D) efforts by universities in Atlantic Canada. The program addresses the need to inform the public about university R&D and its outcomes. **Availability:** Print; Online.

32784 ■ "Life Sciences Become State's Growth Powerhouse" in Crain's Detroit Business (Vol. 25, June 1, 2009, No. 22, pp. M008)
Pub: Crain Communications Inc.
Contact: Barry Asin, President

Ed: Amy Lane. **Description:** According to a study conducted by Anderson Economic Group, Michigan's University Research Corridor has helped grow the life sciences industry. Statistical details included. **Availability:** Online.

32785 ■ "Live & Learn: Ian Delaney" in Canadian Business (Vol. 81, Summer 2008, No. 9, pp. 168)
Pub: Rogers Media Inc.
Contact: Neil Spivak, Chief Executive Officer

Ed: Joe Castaldo. **Description:** Interview with Ian Delaney who is the executive chairman of chemical company Sherritt International Corp.; Delaney previously worked as chief executive for a holding company owned by Peter Munk. Details of his beliefs, profession and family life are discussed. **Availability:** Online.

32786 ■ *"Longwood's FamilLab More Than Just a Hackerspace: It's a Free Form Research and Development Lab"* in *Orlando Business Journal (Vol. 30, January 17, 2014, No. 30, pp. 4)*
Pub: American City Business Journals, Inc.
Contact: Mike Olivieri, Executive Vice President
Description: FamilLab is a nonprofit hackerspace in Longwood, Florida that has turned into a free-form research and development outfit. The group has at least 70 members who share the same passion for technology and push the limits and boundaries of computer hardware and software, and sometimes start their own business. **Availability:** Print; Online.

32787 ■ *"Looks Like We Made It (In Philadelphia)"* in *Philadelphia Business Journal (Vol. 32, January 24, 2014, No. 50, pp. 4)*
Pub: American City Business Journals, Inc.
Contact: Mike Olivieri, Executive Vice President
Released: Weekly. **Price:** $4, introductory 4-week offer(Digital & Print). **Description:** Philadelphia, Pennsylvania was once viewed as a manufacturing city, and its manufacturing workforce reached 365,000 in the early 1950s. The city is now focusing on advanced manufacturing that requires scientific and technical expertise. The decrease in the number of manufacturing jobs is also examined. **Availability:** Print; Online.

32788 ■ *"Meet University of Texas' New Business Mind"* in *Austin Business Journal (Vol. 31, May 13, 2011, No. 10, pp. A1)*
Pub: Austin Business Journal
Contact: Rachel McGrath, Director
E-mail: rmcgrath@bizjournals.com
Ed: Sandra Zaragoza. **Description:** University of Texas (UT) chief commercialization officer, Dr. Richard Miller, has opened a satellite office in Silicon Valley, California in the hopes of luring Californian investors to the science and technology at UT. The satellite office is just one of Miller's efforts to reshape and widen the commercialization of UT-Austin. Insights into Miller's long-term view approach to commercialization are also covered. **Availability:** Online.

32789 ■ *"MIR Growing With Help From Former Pfizer Workers"* in *Crain's Detroit Business (Vol. 24, January 28, 2008, No. 4, pp. 33)*
Pub: Crain Communications Inc.
Contact: Barry Asin, President
Ed: Tom Henderson. **Description:** Molecular Imaging Research Inc. helps fund research at its parent firm, Molecular Therapeutics Inc. The company provides imaging services and other in vivo and in vitro services to help pharmaceutical companies test new compounds. **Availability:** Print; Online.

32790 ■ *"Monsanto Acquires Targeted-Pest Control Technology Start-Up; Terms Not Disclosed"* in *Benzinga.com (September 2011)*
Pub: Benzinga.com
Contact: Jason Raznick, Founder
Ed: Eddie Staley. **Description:** Monsanto Company acquired Beelogics, a firm that researches and develops biological tools that control pests and diseases. Research includes a product that will help protect bee health. **Availability:** Online.

32791 ■ *"Mosaid Grants First Wireless Patent License To Matsushita"* in *Canadian Electronics (Vol. 23, June-July 2008, No. 5, pp. 1)*
Pub: Annex Buisness Media
Contact: Mike Fredericks, President
Description: Matsushita Electric Industrial Co. Ltd. has been granted a six-and-a-half-year license by Mosaid Technologies Inc. to manufacture the latter's

products. The patent portfolio license agreement covers Mosaid's Wi-Fi, Wi-Max, CDMA-enabled notebook computers and other products.

32792 ■ *"MPI Expansion Goes Back to Family Roots"* in *Crain's Detroit Business (Vol. 25, June 1, 2009, No. 22, pp. M007)*
Pub: Crain Communications Inc.
Contact: Barry Asin, President
Ed: Sherri Begin Welch. **Description:** William Parfet, grandson of Upjohn Company founder, is expanding MPI Research's clinical and early clinical research operations into two buildings in Kalamazoo, land which was once part of his grandfather's farm. **Availability:** Print; PDF; Online.

32793 ■ *"Neuromed Strikes Major Merck Deal"* in *Globe & Mail (March 21, 2006, pp. B1)*
Ed: Leonard Zehr. **Description:** Neuromed Pharmaceuticals Ltd., a spin off of British Columbia University, has struck a drug research deal valued at up to $500 million (U.S) with giant Merck &Co. Inc., the biggest collaboration in Canada. Details of the deal are presented. **Availability:** Online.

32794 ■ *"The New Face of Aging: Chasing the Secret to Stopping the Clock"* in *San Francisco Business Times (Vol. 28, January 31, 2014, No. 28, pp. 4)*
Pub: American City Business Journals, Inc.
Contact: Mike Olivieri, Executive Vice President
Released: Weekly. **Price:** $4, Introductory 4-week offer(Digital & Print). **Description:** San Francisco, California-based Calico has built a small team of star scientists to join research for finding the secret to stop human aging, with financial backing from Google. However, the Ellison Medical Foundation has stopped making new grants for aging research. The preventive approach of the aging research is also discussed. **Availability:** Print; Online.

32795 ■ *"New Institutional Accounting and IFRS"* in *Accounting and Business Research (Vol. 41, Summer 2011, No. 3, pp. 309)*
Pub: Routledge, Taylor & Francis Group
Ed: Peter Wysocki. **Description:** A new framework for institutional accounting research is presented. It has five fundamental components: efficient versus inefficient results, interdependencies, causation, level of analysis, and institutional structure. The use of the framework for evaluation accounting institutions such as the international financial reports standards (IFRS) is discussed. **Availability:** PDF; Online; Download.

32796 ■ *"New Stem Cell Research Awareness Org Launched in Austin"* in *Austin Business Journal (Vol. 31, June 3, 2011, No. 13, pp. 1)*
Pub: Austin Business Journal
Contact: Rachel McGrath, Director
E-mail: rmcgrath@bizjournals.com
Ed: Sandra Zaragoza. **Description:** MedRebels Foundation was launched in February 2011 with the goal of providing millions of dollars for research funding, education and advocacy for adult stem cell-focused medicine. The foundation, whose major contributor is SpineSmith LP, is a collaboration of other adult stem cell-related companies and nonprofit partners. It hopes to raise $200,000 by the end of 2011. **Availability:** Print; Online.

32797 ■ *"No More Ivory Towers: Local Colleges and Universities are Here to Help Your Business"* in *Orlando Business Journal (Vol. 30, February 28, 2014, No. 36, pp. 4)*
Pub: American City Business Journals, Inc.
Contact: Mike Olivieri, Executive Vice President
Released: Weekly. **Price:** $8, Introductory 4-week offer(Digital & Print). **Description:** A number of school leaders in Central Florida share their views on partnering with the business community, boosting science and technology graduates, benefits of a private college, economic development efforts and fixing the higher education construction gridlock. Local universities and colleges have a combined economic impact of $15 billion each year. **Availability:** Print; Online.

32798 ■ *"NSU Seeks Private Partners For New $80M Research Building"* in *South Florida Business Journal (Vol. 34, February 21, 2014, No. 31, pp. 4)*
Pub: American City Business Journals, Inc.
Contact: Mike Olivieri, Executive Vice President
Released: Weekly. **Price:** $8, Introductory 4-week offer(Digital & Print). **Description:** The $80 million Center for Collaborative Research at Nova Southeastern University hopes to become the largest incubator and wet laboratory space in Broward County, Florida. The center had its groundbreaking on February 13, 2014, and will be open for lease to private companies when it is ready in 22 months. **Availability:** Print; Online.

32799 ■ *"The One Thing That's Holding Back Your Wellness Program"* in *Employee Benefit News (Vol. 25, December 1, 2011, No. 15, pp. 8)*
Pub: SourceMedia LLC
Contact: Gemma Postlethwaite, Chief Executive Officer
Description: A 13-year study shows that women who sat for more than six hours a day were 94 percent more likely to die during the study period. Most women sit at their desks an average of 7.7 hours while at work.

32800 ■ *"Optimal Awarded US $256 Thousand Contract to Conduct LiDAR Survey for a Major Electric Utility in the Southwest"* in *Canadian Corporate News*
Description: Optimal Geomatics, a company specializing in the science and technology of analyzing, gathering, interpreting, distributing, and using geographic information, was awarded a new contract from a long-standing electric utility customer in the Southwest to conduct a LiDAR survey for a part of the utility's overhead transmission line system. **Availability:** Print; Online.

32801 ■ *"Organic Food Industry Goes to College"* in *USA Today (April 9, 2012)*
Ed: Chuck Raasch. **Description:** With the organic food industry growing the US Department of Agriculture is has pumped $117 million into organic research in the last three years. According to a recent report by the Organic Farming Research Foundation (OFRF), the number of states committing land for organic research has nearly doubled from 2003 to 2011. Universities offering academic programs in organic farming rose from none to nine. The OFRF supports organic farmers and producers. **Availability:** Online.

32802 ■ *"Pet Store Fish Provide Clue to How Alzheimer's Disease May Start"* in *Marketwired (July 9, 2012)*
Pub: Comtex News Network Inc.
Contact: Kan Devnani, President
Released: August 07, 2012. **Description:** Western University of Health Sciences in Pomona, California researchers report that studies with zebrafish provided an important clue to understanding how Alzheimer's disease starts. Details of the study are included. **Availability:** Print; Online.

32803 ■ *"Faster To Dissolve, Faster To Work"* in *Philadelphia Business Journal (Vol. 33, March 14, 2014, No. 5, pp. 8)*
Pub: American City Business Journals, Inc.
Contact: Mike Olivieri, Executive Vice President
Released: Weekly. **Price:** $4, introductory 4-week offer(Digital & Print). **Description:** The U.S. Food and Drug Administration approved Iroko Pharmaceutical's anti-inflammatory drug Tivorbex. The company's technology reformulates a braded drug's active ingredient as submicron particles 20 times smaller than their original size. Iroko also applies the technology to drugs used in oncology. **Availability:** Print; Online.

32804 ■ *"Physics for Females"* in *Occupational Outlook Quarterly (Vol. 55, Summer 2011, No. 2, pp. 22)*
Description: Free resources to help females investigate careers in medical physics and health physics are available from the American Physical Society.

The booklet is designed for girls in middle and high school and describes the work of 15 women who use physics to solve medical mysteries, discover planets, research new materials, and more. **Availability:** Print; Online.

32805 ■ *"Procter & Gamble vs. IRS: Split Decision" in Business Courier (Vol. 27, July 16, 2010, No. 11, pp. 1)*

Pub: Business Courier

Ed: Jon Newberry. **Description:** Implications of a court ruling in a $435 million legal dispute between Procter & Gamble Company (P&G) and the Internal Revenue Service (IRS) are discussed. A $21 million win has been realized for P&G for its interpretation of research and development tax credits. However, the said case might involve more than $700 million in P&G tax deductions from 2001 through 2004 that the IRS had disallowed. **Availability:** Print; Online.

32806 ■ *"Putting 'Extra' in Extra-Silky Shampoo" in Crain's Chicago Business (Vol. 31, April 28, 2008, No. 17, pp. 37)*

Pub: Crain Communications Inc.

Contact: Barry Asin, President

Ed: Phuong Ly. **Description:** Profile of HallStar Co., a Chicago-based company which develops and manufactures specialty chemicals to upgrade existing products such as hair dye, lotion and deodorant. HallStar has seen its annual earnings rise more than 30 percent since 2002. **Availability:** Online.

32807 ■ *"The Quest for a Smart Prosthetic" in Canadian Business (Vol. 83, October 12, 2010, No. 17, pp. 26)*

Pub: Rogers Media Inc.

Contact: Neil Spivak, Chief Executive Officer

Ed: Jacqueline Nelson. **Description:** Information about a two-year research project led by Southern Methodist University (SMU) and funded by the Defense Advance Research Projects Agency (DARPA) is provided. The agency aims to create a 'smart prosthetic' which will improve the lives of military amputees. The planned prosthetic will use a sensor that can carry nerve signals through synthetic channels. **Availability:** Print; Online.

32808 ■ *"A Questionable Chemical Romance" in Barron's (Vol. 88, July 14, 2008, No. 28, pp. 28)*

Pub: Dow Jones & Company Inc.

Contact: Almar Latour, Chief Executive Officer

Ed: Andrew Bary. **Description:** Dow Chemical paid $78-a-share for the surprise takeover of Rohm & Haas. The acquisition is reducing Dow Chemical's financial flexibility at a time when chemical companies are being affected by high costs and a weak U.S. economy. **Availability:** Online.

32809 ■ *"Reading the Public Mind" in Harvard Business Review (Vol. 88, October 2010, No. 10, pp. 27)*

Pub: Harvard Business Publishing

Contact: Diane Belcher, Managing Director

Ed: Andrew O'Connell. **Price:** $6, PDF. **Description:** Examination of the various methods for obtaining public opinion and consumer preferences is provided; an outline of the disadvantages and benefits of both are also given. **Availability:** Online; PDF.

32810 ■ *"Region to Be Named Innovation Hub" in Business Courier (Vol. 27, July 2, 2010, No. 9, pp. 1)*

Pub: Business Courier

Ed: Dan Monk. **Description:** The selection of Cincinnati's consumer-marketing cluster as a 'Hub of Innovation' by the Ohio Department of Development could boost Cincinnati's chances of receiving $100 million in grants from Ohio's Third Frontier program and other funding sources. Implications of the University of Cincinnati's designation as a Center of Excellence in Advanced Transportation and Aerospace are also discussed. **Availability:** Print; Online.

32811 ■ *"Renewable Energy Market Opportunities: Wind Testing" in PR Newswire (September 22, 2011)*

Pub: PR Newswire Association LLC.

Description: Global wind energy test systems markets are discussed. Research conducted covers both non-destructive test equipment and condition monitoring equipment product segments.

32812 ■ *Research Centers Directory (RCD)*

Pub: Gale, part of Cengage Group

Contact: Paul Gazzolo, General Manager Senior Vice President

URL(s): www.gale.com/ebooks/9781410364777/research-centers-directory

Released: Latest 48 Edition. **Description:** Covers about 17,000 university, government, and other nonprofit research organizations established on a permanent basis to carry on continuing research programs in all areas of study; includes research institutes, laboratories, experiment stations, research parks, technology transfer centers, and other facilities and activities; coverage includes Canada. **Entries include:** Unit name, name of parent institution, address, phone, fax, name of director, e-mail addresses, URLs, year founded, governance, staff, educational activities, public services, sources of support, annual volume of research, principal fields of research, publications, special library facilities, special research facilities. **Arrangement:** Classified by broad subjects, then alphabetical by unit name. **Indexes:** Alphabetical (includes centers, institutions, and keywords), subject, geographical, personal name. **Availability:** E-book; Download.

32813 ■ *"Research Reports" in Barron's (Vol. 88, March 24, 2008, No. 12, pp. M10)*

Pub: Dow Jones & Company Inc.

Contact: Almar Latour, Chief Executive Officer

Ed: Anita Peltonen. **Description:** Investors are recommending purchasing shares of Ampco Pittsburgh due to an expected surge in earnings. Deteriorating credit quality presents problems for the shares of BankAtlantic Bancorp, whose price targets have been lowered from $7 to $5 each. Shares of Helicos Biosciences are expected to move sideways from their $6 level. Statistical data included.

32814 ■ *"Research Reports" in Barron's (Vol. 90, August 23, 2010, No. 34, pp. M13)*

Pub: Barron's Editorial & Corporate Headquarters

Description: Shares of Sirius XM Radio, Target and Deere and Company received an eBuyE rating, while shares of Research in Motion got an eNeutralE rating. **Availability:** Online.

32815 ■ *"The Right Remedy: Entrepreneur's Success Is a Matter of Life and Death" in Black Enterprise (Vol. 38, February 2008, No. 7, pp. 46)*

Pub: Earl G. Graves Ltd.

Contact: Earl Graves, Jr., President

Ed: Tamara E. Holmes. **Description:** Profile of Leah Brown, whose company conducts clinical trials to determine if specific drugs will relieve particular symptoms. Her company will also visit physician's offices to make certain doctors are following proper protocol for a clinical trial or will collect data from patients. **Availability:** Online.

32816 ■ *"Rimfire Minerals Corporation: Jake Gold Project-Drilling Planned for 2007" in Marketwired (May 16, 2007)*

Pub: Comtex News Network Inc.

Contact: Kan Devnani, President

Description: Rimfire Minerals Corporation and Island Arc Exploration Corporation formed a partnership to explore the Jake Property, a high-grade gold prospect with previously unrecognized potential to host economic gold mineralization, located 13 kilometers west of Clearwater, British Columbia. **Availability:** Print; Online.

32817 ■ *"Rising in the East; Research and Development" in The Economist (Vol. 390, January 3, 2009, No. 8612, pp. 47)*

Description: Impressive growth of the technological research and development in Asian countries is discussed. Statistical data included. **Availability:** Online.

32818 ■ *"San Antonio Researchers Develop New Laser-Based Imaging System" in San Antonio Business Journal (Vol. 26, August 24, 2012, No. 30, pp. 1)*

Pub: Baltimore Business Journal

Contact: Rhonda Pringle, President

E-mail: rpringle@bizjournals.com

Description: Researchers at the University of Texas Health Science Center at San Antonio in Texas have developed an optical sensor-dependent medical imaging system, which is ready for commercialization. The laser-based imaging system is expected to improve non-invasive imaging for medical diagnostics. **Availability:** Print; Online.

32819 ■ *"Scientific American Builds Novel Blog Network" in Information Today (Vol. 28, September 2011, No. 8, pp. 12)*

Pub: Information Today Inc.

Contact: Thomas H. Hogan, President

Ed: Kurt Schiller. **Description:** Scientific American launched a new blog network that joins a diverse lineup of bloggers cover various scientific topics under one banner. The blog network includes 60 bloggers providing insights into the ever-changing world of science and technology.

32820 ■ *"Securing our Cyber Status" in San Antonio Business Journal (Vol. 28, May 16, 2014, No. 14, pp. 4)*

Pub: American City Business Journals, Inc.

Contact: Mike Olivieri, Executive Vice President

Released: Weekly. **Price:** $4, introductory 4-week offer(Digital & Print). **Description:** The San Antonio Chamber of Commerce commissioned Deloitte to conduct a study on the local cyber security sector of San Antonio, Texas. Industry insiders are looking forward to securing the status of San Antonio as a top tier cyber city with the results of the study research. **Availability:** Print; Online.

32821 ■ *"Selling Michigan; R&D Pushed as Reason For Chinese To Locate In State" in Crain's Detroit Business (Vol. 24, January 14, 2008)*

Pub: Crain Communications Inc.

Contact: Barry Asin, President

Ed: Marti Benedetti. **Description:** Southeast Michigan Economic Development organizations are working to develop relationships with Chinese manufacturers so they will locate their automotive research and development operations in the state.

32822 ■ *"The Service Imperative" in Business Horizons (Vol. 51, January-February 2008, No. 1, pp. 39)*

Pub: Elsevier Advanced Technology Publications

Ed: Mary Jo Bitner, Stephen W. Brown. **Description:** The importance of services is growing in developing countries like India and China, but little attention is given to service research, education and innovation. The 'service imperative' seeks to promote the advancement of services. The scope, objectives and philosophy of the service imperative platform are outlined. **Availability:** Online.

32823 ■ *"Shire Seeking New Digs for Headquarters" in Philadelphia Business Journal (Vol. 30, September 2, 2011, No. 29, pp. 1)*

Pub: Philadelphia Business Journal

Contact: Sierra Quinn, Director

E-mail: squinn@bizjournals.com

Ed: Natalie Kostelni. **Description:** Dublin, Ireland-based Shire PLC announced plans to relocate its North American headquarters from Chesterbrook Corporate Center in Wayne, Pennsylvania and currently evaluating their options. The specialty biopharmaceutical firm is also considering a move to New Jersey or Delaware. **Availability:** Online.

32824 ■ *"Slow but Steady into the Future"* in *Barron's (Vol. 88, July 7, 2008, No. 27, pp. M)*
Pub: Dow Jones & Company Inc.
Contact: Almar Latour, Chief Executive Officer

Ed: Mark Veverka. **Description:** Investors are advised to maintain their watch on the shares of business software company NetSuite. The company's chief executive officer, Zach Nelson, claims that the company has a 10-year lead on its competitors with the development of software-as-a service. **Availability:** Online.

32825 ■ *"Some Relief Possible Following Painful Week"* in *Barron's (Vol. 88, July 14, 2008, No. 28, pp. M3)*
Pub: Dow Jones & Company Inc.
Contact: Almar Latour, Chief Executive Officer

Ed: Kopin Tan. **Description:** Dow Chemical is offering a 74 percent premium to acquire Rohm & Haas' coatings and electronics materials operations. Frontline amassed a 5.6 percent stake in rival Overseas Shipholding Group and a merger between the two would create a giant global fleet with pricing power. Highlights of the U.S. stock market during the week that ended in July 11, 2008 are discussed. Statistical data included. **Availability:** Online.

32826 ■ *"'Stalking Horse' Bidder Keeping Plextronics Here"* in *Pittsburgh Business Times (Vol. 33, March 28, 2014, No. 37, pp. 6)*
Pub: American City Business Journals, Inc.
Contact: Mike Olivieri, Executive Vice President

Released: March 28, 2014. **Price:** $4, Introductory 4-week offer(Digital & Print). **Description:** Chemical company Solvay American has acquired solar and lighting company Plextronics Inc. of Pittsburgh, Pennsylvania. Solvay's research and innovation department is seen as a better fit for Plextronics because it is developing a new technology. **Availability:** Print; Online.

32827 ■ *"Startup Osteosphere Formed to Develop Laboratory Discovery"* in *Houston Business Journal (Vol. 40, January 8, 2010, No. 35, pp. 1)*
Pub: Houston Business Journal
Contact: Bob Charlet, President
E-mail: bcharlet@bizjournals.com

Ed: Casey Wooten. **Description:** Biotech startup company Osteosphere in Houston, Texas aims to market a technology in which laboratory-grown bone tissues can be processed to appear like a real human bone tissue. The technology was developed by a co-founder of the startup and it can be applied to bone disease and injury treatment. Osteophere's future plans, such as the search for possible investors, is also outlined. **Availability:** Print; Online.

32828 ■ *"Stronger Corn? Take It Off Steroids, Make It All Female"* in *Farm Industry News (December 5, 2011)*
Pub: Informa Business Media, Inc.
Contact: Charlie McCurdy, President

Ed: Brian Wallheimer. **Description:** Purdue University researcher found that higher improvements in corn crops, and possibly other crops, were yielded when steroids were discontinued. **Availability:** Print; Online.

32829 ■ *"Targeted Technology Raises More Than $40 Million"* in *San Antonio Business Journal (Vol. 28, September 5, 2014, No. 30, pp. 8)*
Pub: American City Business Journals, Inc.
Contact: Mike Olivieri, Executive Vice President

Released: September 05, 2014. **Price:** $4, introductory 4-week offer(Digital & Print). **Description:** Targeted Technology has raised more than $40 million in venture capital funding for early-stage biotechnology companies in San Antonio, Texas through its Targeted Technology Fund II. Senior managing

partner, Paul Castella, recognizes the lack of venture capital funds in the area and the role played by his organization to help these firms. **Availability:** Print; Online.

32830 ■ *"The Tech 100"* in *Canadian Business (Vol. 81, July 21, 2008, No. 11, pp. 48)*

Description: Absolute Software Corp. Day4 Energy Inc., Sandvine Corp., Norsat International Inc. and Call Genie Inc. are the five technology firms included in the annual ranking of top companies in Canada by market capitalization. The services and the one-year total return potential of the companies are presented. **Availability:** Online.

32831 ■ *"Tech Coaltion Warns Takeover Spree is Nigh"* in *Globe & Mail (February 6, 2007, pp. B1)*

Ed: Steven Chase. **Description:** The declaration by an alliance of technology-rich companies, that the huge credits that these companies have to endure due to research and development activities may lead to company takeovers, is discussed. **Availability:** Online.

32832 ■ *"Tech Jobs Rebound from Downturn"* in *Denver Business Journal (Vol. 65, March 7, 2014, No. 43, pp. A9)*
Pub: American City Business Journals, Inc.
Contact: Mike Olivieri, Executive Vice President

Released: Weekly. **Price:** $4, Introductory 4-week offer(Digital & Print). **Description:** Denver, Colorado's employment in core technology industries has returned from pre-Great Recession figures. The computer software industry's surging job growth and the slight increase in the broadcasts and telecommunications industry offset the job losses in biotechnology and private aerospace industry from 2008 through 2013. The growth in specific industries is also discussed. **Availability:** Print; Online.

32833 ■ *"Thinking Aloud"* in *Business Strategy Review (Vol. 21, Summer 2010, No. 2, pp. 47)*

Description: In each issue we ask an academic to explain the big question on which their research hopes to shed light. Yiorgos Mylonadis looks at how people define and solve problems. **Availability:** Print; Online.

32834 ■ *"To Build for the Future, Reach Beyond the Skies"* in *Canadian Business (Vol. 83, June 15, 2010, No. 10, pp. 11)*
Pub: Rogers Media Inc.
Contact: Neil Spivak, Chief Executive Officer

Ed: Richard Branson. **Description:** Richard Branson says that tackling an engineering challenge or a scientific venture is a real adventure for an entrepreneur. Branson discusses Virgin's foray into the aviation business and states that at Virgin, they build for the future. **Availability:** Print; Online.

32835 ■ *"Top Worst Weeds in Corn"* in *Farm Industry News (November 29, 2011)*
Pub: Informa Business Media, Inc.
Contact: Charlie McCurdy, President

Ed: John Pocock. **Description:** Effective weed control for profitable crops is discussed with information from leading weed scientists from the University of Illinois Extension. It is important for farmers to know what their worst weed is in order to choose the best product, or mix of products, to control them. **Availability:** Print; Online.

32836 ■ *"Transfusion"* in *Puget Sound Business Journal (Vol. 33, August 31, 2012, No. 19, pp. 1)*

Released: July 12, 2019. **Description:** Seattle, Washington-based nonprofit biotechnology companies have been hiring people with fundraising and scientific skills. The development is part of efforts to find new funding resources. **Availability:** Online.

32837 ■ *"The Trillion Dollar R&D Fix: Most Big Companies Should Spend More On R&D. But How Much More?"* in *Harvard Business Review (Vol. 90, May 2012, No. 5, pp. 76)*
Pub: Harvard Business Review Press
Contact: Moderna V. Pfizer, Contact

Ed: Anne Marie Knott. **Price:** $8.95. **Description:** Research quotient (RQ) is a new measure for determining research and development investment productivity. The formula utilizes classic regression analysis of expenditures and revenues and yields productivity levels for operations, employees, and R&D. **Availability:** Online; PDF.

32838 ■ *"Trust Management of Services in Cloud Environments: Obstacles and Solutions"* in *ACM Computing Surveys (Vol. 46, Spring 2014, No. 1, pp. 12)*
Pub: Association for Computing Machinery - University of Wyoming
Contact: Ed Seidel, President
E-mail: uwpres@uwyo.edu

Description: Trust management is one of the most challenging issues in the emerging cloud computing area. Over the past few years, many studies have proposed different techniques to address trust management issues. However, despite these past efforts, several trust management issues such as identification, privacy, personalization, integration, security, and scalability have been mostly neglected and need to be addressed before cloud computing can be fully embraced. An overview of the cloud service models and a survey of the main techniques and research prototypes that efficiently support trust management services in cloud environments is presented. Open research issues for trust management in cloud environments is also examined. **Availability:** PDF; Online.

32839 ■ *"UA, BP Test Unmanned Aircraft"* in *Alaska Business Monthly (Vol. 27, October 2011, No. 10, pp. 8)*
Pub: Alaska Business Publishing Company Inc.
Contact: Charles Bell, Vice President, Sales and Marketing
E-mail: cbell@akbizmag.com

Ed: Nancy Pounds. **Description:** University of Alaska Fairbanks Geophysical Institute and BP Exploration Alaska tested the oil-spill capabilities of an unmanned aircraft. The aircraft will be used to gather 3-D ariel data to aid in oil-spill cleanup. **Availability:** Online.

32840 ■ *"USM Focuses on Turning Science Into New Companies, Cash"* in *Boston Business Journal (Vol. 29, July 1, 2011, No. 8, pp. 1)*
Pub: Boston Business Journal
Contact: Carolyn M. Jones, President
E-mail: cmjones@bizjournals.com

Ed: Alexander Jackson. **Description:** University System of Maryland gears up to push for its plan for commercializing its scientific discoveries which by 2020 could create 325 companies and double the $1.4 billion the system's eleven schools garner in yearly research grants. It is talking with University of Utah and University Maryland, Baltimore to explore ways to make this plan a reality. **Availability:** Print; Online.

32841 ■ *"UTSA Entrepreneur Program Receives Federal Designation"* in *San Antonio Business Journal (Vol. 28, June 6, 2014, No. 17, pp. 7)*
Pub: American City Business Journals, Inc.
Contact: Mike Olivieri, Executive Vice President

Released: Weekly. **Price:** $4, Introductory 4-week offer(Digital & Print). **Description:** The National Science Foundation has designated the University of Texas at San Antonio (UTSA) as an Innovation Corps Site because of its strong entrepreneurial system through the Center for Innovation and Technology Entrepreneurship. The UTSA expects to see an increase in entrepreneurial activity and successful technology commercialization with such designation. **Availability:** Print; Online.

32842 ■ *Values and Opportunities in Social Entrepreneurship*
Pub: Palgrave Macmillan
Released: 2010. **Price:** $89, hardcover; $120, hardcover; $64.99, e-book; $84.99, Softcover. **Description:** Social entrepreneurship has grown as a research field. This book discusses social entrepreneurship as well as the identification and exploitation of social venturing opportunities. **Availability:** E-book; Print; PDF; Electronic publishing.

32843 ■ *"Venture: Nonprofit Aims to Spur New Companies" in South Florida Business Journal (Vol. 34, April 18, 2014, No. 39, pp. 8)*
Pub: American City Business Journals, Inc.
Contact: Mike Olivieri, Executive Vice President
Released: Weekly. **Price:** $8, Introductory 4-week offer(Digital & Print). **Description:** The Scripps Research Institute has created the Scripps Advance group with an aim to turn early-stage research from its scientists in Jupiter, Florida and La Jolla, California into companies and to obtain venture capital funding to support clinical trials. Johnson and Johnson Innovation has become its first collaborator. The terms of the collaboration are also presented. **Availability:** Print; Online.

32844 ■ *"Voices: Breaking the Corruption Habit" in Business Strategy Review (Vol. 21, Autumn 2010, No. 3, pp. 67)*
Ed: David De Cremer. **Released:** September 22, 2010. **Description:** In times of crisis, it seems natural that people will work together for the common good. David De Cremer cautions that, on the contrary, both economic and social research prove otherwise. He proposes steps for organizations to take to prevent corrupt behaviors. **Availability:** Print; Electronic publishing; PDF; Online.

32845 ■ *"Where the Money Is" in Conde Nast Portfolio (Vol. 2, June 2008, No. 6, pp. 113)*
Description: Revenue generated from treatments for common brain disorders that are currently on the market are listed. **Availability:** Online.

32846 ■ *"Whistling in the Dark" in Canadian Business (Vol. 79, September 25, 2006, No. 19, pp. 17)*
Description: Increasing subsidies for research projects in Canada is discussed. **Availability:** Online.

32847 ■ *"Who Hangs Out Where?" in Harvard Business Review (Vol. 90, July-August 2012, No. 7-8, pp. 34)*
Pub: Harvard Business Review Press
Contact: Moderna V. Pfizer, Contact
Price: $6, PDF. **Description:** A chart breaks down participation in social media gathering places by gender, age group, educational level, and household income. **Availability:** PDF; Online.

32848 ■ *"Why Life Science Needs Its Own Silicon Valley: Human Genomics Won't Reach Its Full Potential Until It Has a Sizable Industry Cluster" in Harvard Business Review (Vol. 90, July-August 2012, No. 7-8, pp. 25)*
Pub: Harvard Business Review Press
Contact: Moderna V. Pfizer, Contact
Ed: Fariborz Ghadar, John Sviokla, Dietrich A. Stephan. **Price:** $6, PDF and hardcover black and white. **Description:** The creation of an industry cluster will be key to advancing human genomics research. High degrees of specialization via multiple contributors will be needed to generate significant innovations; an accessible, coherent data source will also be necessary. **Availability:** Print; PDF; Online.

32849 ■ *"Why Motivating People Doesn't Work...and What Does: The New Science of Leading, Energizing, and Engaging"*
Released: September 30, 2014. **Price:** $20.95, Nonmembers, PDF e-book; $18.86, Members, electronic publishing; $20.95, Nonmembers, paperback; $18.86, Members, paperback; $24.95, Nonmembers, hardcover; $22.46, Members, hardcover; $20.95, Nonmembers, electronic publishing; $14.67, Members, electronic publishing; $18.95, PDF e-book; $14.

67, Members, PDF e-book. **Description:** Leadership researcher, consultant, and business coach, Susan Fowler, shares the latest research on the nature of human motivation to present a tested model and course of action to help Human Resource leaders and managers guide workers towards motivation that will not only increase productivity and engagement but will provide employees with a sense of purpose and fulfillment. **Availability:** E-book; Print; PDF; Electronic publishing.

32850 ■ *"Winners & Losers" in Canadian Business (Vol. 85, July 16, 2012, No. 11-12, pp. 22)*
Description: Canadian Pacific Railway's 4,800 locomotive engineers and conductors walked out in protest of the proposed work rules and pension cuts. Shareholders rejected a $25-million bonus and retention payout to Astral Media chief executive officer Ian Greenburg. The Dragon spacecraft of Space Exploration Technologies delivered supplies and experiments to the International Space Station. **Availability:** Print.

32851 ■ *"You'll Golf Better If You Think Tiger Has Used Your Clubs" in Harvard Business Review (Vol. 90, July-August 2012, No. 7-8, pp. 32)*
Pub: Harvard Business Review Press
Contact: Moderna V. Pfizer, Contact
Ed: Sally Linkenauger. **Description:** Golfers who were told that a professional had used the clubs they were given to use performed better than those who were told nothing about the clubs they were given. They perceived the hole to be 9 percent bigger in diamter than the control group, and were able to sink 32 percent more putts than did the control group.

TRADE PERIODICALS

32852 ■ *Alloy Digest*
Pub: ASM International
Contact: Dr. Judith Todd, President
URL(s): dl.asminternational.org/alloy-digest
Ed: Alok Nayar. **Released:** Monthly **Description:** Periodical providing materials property data on metals and alloys. **Availability:** Print; PDF.

32853 ■ *The Anatomical Record: Advances in Integrative Anatomy and Evolutionary Biology*
Pub: John Wiley & Sons, Inc.
Contact: Christina Van Tassell, Executive Vice President Chief Financial Officer
URL(s): anatomypubs.onlinelibrary.wiley.com/journal/19328494
Facebook: www.facebook.com/anatomical.record
X (Twitter): x.com/AnatRecord
Instagram: www.instagram.com/anatrecord
Ed: Heather F. Smith, PhD. **Released:** Monthly **Price:** $13,375, Institutions for online only US, Canada, India, Japan; $15,020, Institutions for print only, US, Canada, India, Japan; $13,950, Institutions for print and online US, Canada, India, Japan; $7,669, Institutions for print and online. **Description:** Journal covering new discoveries in the morphological aspects of molecular, cellular, developmental, evolutionary, and systems biology. Published by Wiley in cooperation with the American Association of Anatomists. **Availability:** Print; PDF; Download; Online.

32854 ■ *Andrology*
Pub: American Society of Andrology
Contact: Maria Christina W. Avellar, President
URL(s): onlinelibrary.wiley.com/journal/20472927
Released: 8/year **Price:** $1,791, Institutions for online; C$1,791, Institutions for online; $197, Members for online; C$197, Members for online. **Description:** Journal publishing papers on publishes papers on all aspects of andrology, ranging from basic molecular research to the results of clinical investigations. **Availability:** Print; Download; PDF; Online.

32855 ■ *Applied Engineering in Agriculture*
Pub: American Society of Agricultural and Biological Engineers
Contact: Paul H. Heinemann, President
URL(s): www.asabe.org/Applied
Released: 6/year **Price:** $45, Members for outside U.S. postage fees; $45, Nonmembers for outside U.S. postage fees; $195, Members; $345, Nonmembers; $30, Single issue; $390, for outside us. **Description:** Peer-reviewed journal focused on practical applications of current research related to engineering for agricultural, food and biological systems. **Availability:** Print; PDF; Download; Online.

32856 ■ *Biochemistry and Cell Biology*
Pub: Canadian Science Publishing
Contact: Paul Young, Vice Chairman of the Board
URL(s): cdnsciencepub.com/journal/bcb
Ed: Dr. Christopher J. Nelson, Dr. James R. Davie, PhD. **Released:** Bimonthly; February, April, June, August, October and December. **Price:** $1,144, Institutions for online; $1,200, Institutions for online; $322, Individuals for online. **Description:** Scholarly journal on biochemistry research (English and French). **Availability:** Print; PDF; Online.

32857 ■ *Biopolymers*
Pub: Wiley Periodicals Inc.
Contact: Brian Napack, Chief Executive Officer
URL(s): nlinelibrary.wiley.com/journal/10970282
Released: Monthly **Price:** $19,402, Institutions for online US, India, Canada. **Description:** Peer-reviewed journal covering experimental and theoretical research into naturally occurring and synthetic biological macromolecules. **Availability:** Print; Download; Online; PDF.

32858 ■ *Biotechnology Advances: Research Reviews*
Pub: Elsevier Inc.
URL(s): www.sciencedirect.com/journal/biotechnology-advances
Released: 8/year **Price:** $290, Individuals for print us, Canada and India; $4,133, Institutions for print us, Canada and India. **Description:** Multidisciplinary journal covering advances in all aspects of biotechnology, including biotechnology principles and applications in industry, agriculture, medicine, environmental concerns, and regulatory issues. **Availability:** Print; Download; PDF; Online.

32859 ■ *Biotechnology & Bioengineering*
Pub: Wiley Periodicals Inc.
Contact: Brian Napack, Chief Executive Officer
URL(s): analyticalsciencejournals.onlinelibrary.wiley.com/journal/10970290
Released: Monthly; eighteen times a year. **Price:** $18,798, Institutions for print + online US, Canada, Japan; $16,738, Institutions for online only US, Canada, Japan; $17,459, Institutions for print only US, Canada, Japan. **Description:** Journal providing an international forum for original research on all aspects of biochemical and microbial technology, including products, process development and design, and equipment. **Availability:** Print; Download; PDF; Online.

32860 ■ *Brain, Behavior, and Immunity*
Pub: Elsevier B.V.
Contact: Kumsal Bayazit, Chief Executive Officer
URL(s): www.pnirs.org/pnirs-journalwww.sciencedirect.com/journal/brain-behavior-and-immunity
Released: 8/year **Price:** $3,113, Institutions for print per year, US; $510, Individuals for print per year, US. **Description:** International, interdisciplinary, peer-reviewed journal covering basic, experimental, and clinical research related to behavioral, neural, endocrine, and immune system interactions in humans and animals. Official journal of the Psychoneuroimmunology Research Society (PNIRS). **Availability:** Print; PDF; Download; Online.

32861 ■ *Canadian Journal of Chemistry*
Pub: Chemical Institute of Canada
Contact: Josephine Tsang, Executive Director
URL(s): cdnsciencepub.com/journal/cjc
X (Twitter): x.com/CanJChem

Ed: Dr. Yining Huang. **Released:** Monthly **Price:** $668, Individuals for electronic; $2,162, Institutions for electronic; $2,225, Institutions for vol 103. **Description:** Journal on research in chemistry (English and French). **Availability:** Print; PDF; Download; Online.

32862 ■ Cereal Chemistry
Pub: Cereals & Grains Association
Contact: Jennifer S. Robinson, President
URL(s): www.cerealsgrains.org/publications/cc/ Pages/default.aspx
Released: Bimonthly **Price:** $1,730, Institutions for FTE - large: online only US Canada India; $1,943, Institutions for FTE - large: print + online US Canada India; $1,806, Institutions for FTE - large: print only US Canada India; $1,536, Institutions for FTE - medium: online only US Canada India; $1,726, Institutions for FTE - medium: print + online US Canada India; $1,603, Institutions for FTE - medium: print only US Canada India; $1,335, Institutions for FTE - small: online only US Canada India; $1,499, Institutions for FTE - small: print + online US Canada India; $1,393, Institutions for FTE - small: print only US Canada India. **Description:** Journal focusing on cereal chemistry and research on raw materials, processes and products in the cereals area. **Availability:** Print; Download; PDF; Online.

32863 ■ Chemical Engineering Research and Design (ChERD)
Pub: Elsevier Ltd.
Contact: Kumsal Bayazit, Chief Executive Officer
URL(s): www.sciencedirect.com/journal/chemical-engineering-research-and-design
Released: Monthly **Price:** $4,151, Institutions for 1 year print, us, Canada and India; $4,413, Institutions for print 1 year, US, Canada. **Description:** International journal covering experimental and theoretical research in chemical engineering. **Availability:** Print; PDF; Download; Online

32864 ■ Chemical and Petroleum Engineering
Pub: Springer US
Contact: Derk Haank, Chief Executive Officer
URL(s): link.springer.com/journal/10556
Released: Latest Volume 59, Issue 5-6 September 2023. **Description:** Research journal covering chemical and petroleum engineering. A translation of the Russian journal Khimicheskoe: Neftyanoe Mashinostroenie. **Availability:** Print; PDF; Download; Online.

32865 ■ Computer Animation & Virtual Worlds
Pub: John Wiley & Sons Ltd.
Contact: Matthew Kissner, Chief Executive Officer
URL(s): onlinelibrary.wiley.com/journal/1546427x
Ed: Nadia Magnenat Thalmann. **Released:** Continuous **Price:** $3,109, Institutions for online only US Canada India. **Description:** Journal featuring research papers, film case studies, and critiques of the latest uses of computer animation. **Availability:** Print; PDF; Online; Download.

32866 ■ Computing in Science and Engineering (CiSE)
Pub: AIP Publishing LLC
Contact: Alexandra Vance, Chief Executive Officer
URL(s): www.computer.org/csdl/magazine/cs
Facebook: www.facebook.com/CiSEmagazine
X (Twitter): x.com/cisemag
Released: 6/year **Description:** Magazine focusing on physics, medicine, astronomy and other hard sciences. **Availability:** Print; Download; Online.

32867 ■ Cytoskeleton
Pub: Wiley Periodicals Inc.
Contact: Brian Napack, Chief Executive Officer
URL(s): www.wiley.com/en-in/Cytoskeleton-p-978047 1425328onlinelibrary.wiley.com/journal/19493592
Released: Monthly **Price:** $11,425, Institutions for print + online US Canada India; $10,173, Institutions for online US Canada India; $10,611, Institutions for print US Canada India. **Description:** Journal covering all aspects of cytoskeletal research in both healthy and diseased states. **Availability:** Print; PDF; Download; Online.

32868 ■ DNA and Cell Biology
Pub: Mary Ann Liebert Inc. Publishers
Contact: Mary Ann Liebert, Founder
URL(s): home.liebertpub.com/publications/dna-and-cell-biology/13
Released: Monthly **Description:** Medical journal providing research findings in cell biology. **Availability:** Print; Download; PDF; Online.

32869 ■ Earth and Mineral Sciences
Contact: Kelly O. Henry, Editor
URL(s): www.ems.psu.edu
Ed: Kelly O. Henry. **Description:** Magazine covering research on mineral engineering, earth sciences, and materials science and engineering. **Availability:** Print; Download; Online.

32870 ■ Electric Power Components and Systems
Pub: Taylor & Francis Group (Journals)
Contact: Annie Callanan, Chief Executive Officer
URL(s): www.tandfonline.com/journals/uemp20
Released: 20/year. **Price:** $7,494, Institutions for print and online 2024; $2,935, Individuals for print and online; $6,145, Institutions for online only; $2,935, Individuals for print only. **Description:** Journal publishing original theoretical and applied research in electromechanics, electric machines, and power systems. **Availability:** Print; Download; PDF; Online.

32871 ■ Electrical Engineering in Japan (EEJ)
Pub: Wiley Periodicals Inc.
Contact: Brian Napack, Chief Executive Officer
URL(s): onlinelibrary.wiley.com/journal/15206416
Released: Quarterly **Price:** $19,829, Institutions for print and online US, Canada, India; $17,657, Institutions for online only US, Canada, India; $18,417, Institutions for print US, Canada, India. **Description:** An official journal of the Institute of Electrical Engineers of Japan (IEEJ) and an English-language translation of the Transactions of the Institute of Electrical Engineers of Japan. Covers original research findings in electrical engineering with special focus on the science, technology, and applications of electric power. **Availability:** Print; PDF; Download; Online.

32872 ■ Experimental Heat Transfer
Pub: Taylor & Francis Group (Journals)
Contact: Annie Callanan, Chief Executive Officer
URL(s): www.tandfonline.com/journals/ueht20
Released: 7/year **Price:** $2,246, Institutions for print and online; $950, Individuals for print and online; $1,842, Institutions for online only; $950, Individuals for print only. **Description:** Forum for original research on heat and mass transfer and in related fluid flows. **Availability:** Print; Download; PDF; Online.

32873 ■ Geomicrobiology Journal
Pub: Taylor & Francis Group (Journals)
Contact: Annie Callanan, Chief Executive Officer
URL(s): www.tandfonline.com/journals/ugmb20
Ed: William C. Ghiorse. **Released:** 10/year **Price:** $3,371, Institutions for print and online; $963, Individuals for print & online; $2,764, Institutions for online; $963, Individuals for print. **Description:** Journal publishing research and review articles on microbial transformations of materials that comprise the earth's crust. **Availability:** Print; Download; PDF; Online.

32874 ■ Human Mutation: Variation, Informatics, and Disease
Pub: Wiley Periodicals Inc.
Contact: Brian Napack, Chief Executive Officer
URL(s): onlinelibrary.wiley.com/journal/humu
Ed: Garry R. Cutting. **Released:** Volume 2024, Issue 1. **Description:** Peer-reviewed journal covering broad aspects of mutation research in humans. **Availability:** Print; Download; PDF; Online.

32875 ■ IBM Journal of Research and Development
Pub: IEEE-USA
Contact: Peter A. Eckstein, President
URL(s): ieeexplore.ieee.org/xpl/tocresult.jsp ?isnumber=7580579
Released: 6/year **Description:** Technical journal focusing on professional scientific research and engineering developments. **Availability:** Print; Download; PDF; Online.

32876 ■ International Journal of Adaptive Control and Signal Processing
Pub: John Wiley & Sons, Inc.
Contact: Christina Van Tassell, Executive Vice President Chief Financial Officer
URL(s): onlinelibrary.wiley.com/journal/10991115
Ed: Angelo Alessandri, Kartik Ariyur, Lei Guo, Marcello Farina, Rolf Johansson, Andrzej Ordys, Simon Pope, Andrea Lecchini Visintini, Ron Patton, Elizabetta Punta, Gang Tao, Alessandro Casavola, Anthony Rossiter, Mouhacine Benosman, Luigi Chisci. **Released:** Monthly **Price:** $5,196, Institutions for online only US, Canada, India, Japan; $5,836, Institutions for print and online US, Canada, India, Japan; $5,420, Institutions for online US, Canada, India, Japan; $2,767, Institutions for print only. **Description:** Produces content regarding the design, synthesis and application of estimators or controllers for uncertain systems. **Availability:** Print; Download; PDF; Online.

32877 ■ International Journal on Artificial Intelligence Tools
Pub: World Scientific Publishing Co., Inc.
Contact: Max Phua, Managing Director
URL(s): www.worldscinet.com/ijait
Released: 8/year; last volume 33, issue 4. **Price:** $2,008, for online 2024; $2,250, for print + online 2024; $1,894, for online 2023; $2,123, for print + online 2023. **Description:** Journal covering design, development, and testing of AI tools. **Availability:** Print; PDF; Online.

32878 ■ International Journal of Computer Integrated Manufacturing
Pub: Taylor & Francis Group (Journals)
Contact: Annie Callanan, Chief Executive Officer
URL(s): www.tandfonline.com/journals/tcim20
Released: Monthly **Price:** $5,763, Institutions for print and online; $4,726, Institutions for online only. **Description:** Journal containing information of new knowledge, research and applications used in specific manufacturing situations. **Availability:** Print; Download; PDF; Online.

32879 ■ International Journal of Energy Research (IJER)
Pub: John Wiley & Sons Ltd.
Contact: Matthew Kissner, Chief Executive Officer
URL(s): onlinelibrary.wiley.com/journal/ijer
Released: Latest Edition: 2024. **Description:** Multidisciplinary journal providing information on energy research and development. Covers the development and exploitation of both advanced traditional and new energy sources, systems, technologies, and applications. **Availability:** Print; PDF; Download; Online.

32880 ■ International Journal of Hyperthermia
Pub: Society for Thermal Medicine
URL(s): thermaltherapy.org/ebusSFTM/JOURNAL .aspx
Released: 8/year **Description:** Peer-reviewed journal containing information on research and clinical papers on hyperthermia. **Availability:** PDF; Download; Online.

32881 ■ International Journal of Intelligent Systems
Pub: Wiley Periodicals Inc.
Contact: Brian Napack, Chief Executive Officer
URL(s): onlinelibrary.wiley.com/journal/ijiswww.wiley .com/en-in/International+Journal+of+Intelligent+Sys tems-p-9780471541431

Ed: Jin Li. **Released:** Latest Volume 2024, Issue 1. **Description:** International, peer-reviewed journal devoted to the systematic development of the theory necessary for the construction of intelligent systems. Includes research papers, tutorial reviews, and short communications on theoretical as well as developmental issues. **Availability:** Print; PDF; Download; Online.

32882 ■ *Journal of the American Oil Chemists' Society (JAOCS)*

Pub: John Wiley & Sons, Inc.
Contact: Christina Van Tassell, Executive Vice President Chief Financial Officer
URL(s): aocs.onlinelibrary.wiley.com/journal/15589 331www.aocs.org/stay-informed/journals?SSO =True

Released: Monthly **Price:** $1,371, Institutions for print + online US and India, Canada; $1,221, Institutions for online only US and India, Canada; $1,274, Institutions for print only US and India, Canada. **Description:** Peer-reviewed journal focused on fundamental and practical research in the field of fats, oils, oleochemicals, proteins, surfactants, and detergents. **Availability:** Print; Download; PDF; Online.

32883 ■ *Journal of Biochemical and Molecular Toxicology (JBMT)*

Pub: Wiley Periodicals Inc.
Contact: Brian Napack, Chief Executive Officer
URL(s): onlinelibrary.wiley.com/journal/10990461

Released: Monthly **Price:** $1,824, Institutions for online only US, Canada, India and Japan. **Description:** International journal featuring research papers, rapid communications, and mini-reviews focusing on the molecular mechanisms of action and detoxication of exogenous and endogenous chemical toxic agents, including effects on organisms at all stages of development. **Availability:** Print; PDF; Download; Online.

32884 ■ *Journal of Bioenergetics and Biomembranes*

Pub: Springer US
Contact: Derk Haank, Chief Executive Officer
URL(s): link.springer.com/journal/10863

Released: 6/year **Description:** Journal focusing on biological membranes research. **Availability:** Print; PDF; Download; Online.

32885 ■ *Journal of Biological Rhythms (JBR)*

Pub: SAGE Publications
Contact: Tracey Ozmina, President
URL(s): journals.sagepub.com/home/JBR

Released: Bimonthly **Price:** $2,276, Institutions for backfile purchase, e-access; $347, Institutions for combined (print & e-access); $423, Institutions for single issue print; $74, Individuals for single issue print; $2,353, Institutions for print & online; $295, Individuals for online only; $2,306, Institutions for print only; $340, Individuals for print only; $2,000, Institutions for online. **Description:** Peer-reviewed journal covering original research in all aspects of biological rhythms, with a focus on circadian and seasonal rhythms. Official journal of the Society for Research on Biological Rhythms. **Availability:** Print; PDF; Online.

32886 ■ *Journal of Cellular Biochemistry*

Pub: Wiley Periodicals Inc.
Contact: Brian Napack, Chief Executive Officer
URL(s): onlinelibrary.wiley.com/journal/10974644

Released: Eighteen times a year. **Price:** $19,489, Institutions for online only US, Canada, India. **Description:** Scientific journal publishing original research articles and reviews of biochemical and molecular investigations on cells. **Availability:** Print; Online; PDF; Download.

32887 ■ *Journal of Chemical Ecology*

Pub: Springer US
Contact: Derk Haank, Chief Executive Officer
URL(s): link.springer.com/journal/10886

Released: Latest volume 50, Issue 3-4. **Description:** Journal promoting an ecological understanding of the origin, function, and significance of natural chemicals that mediate interactions within and between organisms. **Availability:** Print; PDF; Download; Online.

32888 ■ *Journal of Chemical Technology and Biotechnology (JCTB)*

Pub: Society of Chemical Industry
Contact: Paul Booth, President
URL(s): www.wiley.com/en-in/Journal+of+Chemical +Technology+and+Biotechnology-p-1097 4660scijournals.onlinelibrary.wiley.com/journal/1097 4660

Released: Monthly; 12 issues a year (1 combined). **Price:** $5,316, Institutions for print and online US , Canada , India; $4,734, Institutions for online US , Canada , India; $2,921, Individuals for print US , Canada , India; $4,937, Institutions for print US , Canada , India. **Description:** International, interdisciplinary, peer-reviewed journal covering scientific discoveries and advancements in chemical and biological technology, with a focus on economically and environmentally sustainable industrial processes. Published by Wiley on behalf of SCI (Society of Chemical Industry). **Availability:** Print; Download; PDF; Online.

32889 ■ *Journal of Clinical Microbiology (JCM)*

Pub: American Society for Microbiology
Contact: Virginia L. Miller, President
URL(s): journals.asm.org/journal/jcm
X (Twitter): twitter.com/JClinMicro

Released: Monthly **Price:** $148, Members; $1,012, Institutions for tier a site with 1-200 authorized users; $1,316, Institutions for tier b site with 201-1,500 authorized users; $1,709, Institutions for tier c site with 1,501-3,500 authorized users. **Description:** Journal covering current research in the laboratory diagnosis of human and animal infections and the role of the laboratory in both the management of infectious diseases and the elucidation of the epidemiology of infections. **Availability:** Print; Online; PDF.

32890 ■ *Journal of Communications Technology and Electronics*

Pub: Springer Nature Limited
Contact: Frank Vrancken Peeters, Chief Executive Officer
URL(s): www.pleiades.online/en/journal/comtechlink .springer.com/journal/11487

Released: Monthly **Description:** Journal of research in communications and electronics engineering from the Russian Academy of Sciences. **Availability:** Print; Download; Online.

32891 ■ *Journal of Environmental Engineering*

Pub: Architectural Engineering Institute of ASCE
Contact: Christopher H. Raebel, President
URL(s): ascelibrary.org/journal/joeedu

Ed: Dionysios D. Dionysiou. **Released:** Monthly; volume 150, issue 7. **Price:** $1,810, Institutions for online international; $758, Members for print international; $985, Members for print & online international; $453, Members for online international; $3,740, Institutions for print & online (international); $1,810, Institutions for online (domestic); $2,769, Institutions for print (domestic); $3,674, Institutions for print & online (domestic); $2,835, Institutions for print (international); $476, Members for online (domestic); $692, Members for print (domestic); $919, Members for print & online (domestic). **Description:** Peer-reviewed journal presenting information on the practice and status of research in environmental engineering science, systems engineering, and sanitation. **Availability:** Print; PDF; Download; Online.

32892 ■ *Journal of Investigative Surgery*

Pub: Taylor & Francis Group (Journals)
Contact: Annie Callanan, Chief Executive Officer
URL(s): www.tandfonline.com/journals/iivs20

Released: Continuous **Description:** Open access, peer-reviewed, biomedical research journal dealing with scientific articles for the advancement of surgery, to the ultimate benefit of patient care and rehabilitation. **Availability:** Print; Online; PDF; Download.

32893 ■ *Journal of Labelled Compounds and Radiopharmaceuticals (JLCR)*

Pub: John Wiley & Sons, Inc.
Contact: Christina Van Tassell, Executive Vice President Chief Financial Officer
URL(s): www.wiley.com/en-in/Journal+of+Labelle d+Compounds+and+Radiopharmaceuticals-p-1099 1344analyticalsciencejournals.onlinelibrary.wiley .com/journal/10991344

Released: 14/ year.; Fourteen times a year. **Price:** $9,538, Institutions for online only US, India, Canada, Japan; $9,538, Institutions for online US, Canada, India. **Description:** Journal covering all aspects of research dealing with labeled compound preparation and applications of these compounds, including tracer methods used in medical, pharmacological, biological, biochemical, and chemical research in vitro and in vivo. Official journal of the International Isotope Society. **Availability:** Print; Online; Download; PDF.

32894 ■ *Journal of Materials in Civil Engineering*

Pub: Architectural Engineering Institute of ASCE
Contact: Christopher H. Raebel, President
URL(s): ascelibrary.org/journal/jmcee7

Released: Monthly; volume 36 issue 9. **Price:** $1,395, Institutions for online domestic; $2,134, Institutions for print domestic; $2,832, Institutions for print & online domestic.; $2,200, Institutions for print international; $2,898, Institutions for print & online international; $349, Members for online domestic; $1,395, Institutions for online international; $349, Members for online international; $534, Members for print domestic; $708, Members for print & online domestic; $600, Members for print international; $774, Members for print & online international. **Description:** Journal covering the development, processing, evaluation, applications and performance of construction materials in civil Engineering. **Availability:** Print; PDF; Download; Online.

32895 ■ *Journal of Morphology*

Pub: Wiley Periodicals Inc.
Contact: Brian Napack, Chief Executive Officer
URL(s): onlinelibrary.wiley.com/journal/10974607

Released: Continuous **Price:** $12,148, Institutions for online only US, India, Japan. **Description:** Journal covering original research in cytology, protozoology, embryology, and general morphology. **Availability:** Print; Download; PDF; Online.

32896 ■ *Journal of Natural History*

Pub: Taylor & Francis Group (Journals)
Contact: Annie Callanan, Chief Executive Officer
URL(s): www.tandfonline.com/journals/tnah20

Ed: A. Polaszek. **Released:** 12 quadruple per year. **Price:** $16,300, Institutions for online only. **Description:** Journal publishing papers on research, reviews, opinions and correspondence in systematics and evolutionary and interactive biology, taxonomic works in entomology and zoology, cladistics, experimental taxonomy, parasitology, ecology, behaviour and the interaction of organisms with their environment. **Availability:** Print; Download; PDF; Online.

32897 ■ *Journal of Pharmaceutical Sciences (JPharmSci)*

Pub: American Chemical Society
Contact: Mary K. Carroll, President
URL(s): jpharmsci.org
X (Twitter): x.com/JPharmSciences

Ed: Bradley D. Anderson, Harry G. Brittain. **Released:** Monthly **Price:** $428, Individuals for online only US, Canada, International (12 month). **Description:** Professional journal publishing research articles in the pharmaceutical sciences. **Availability:** Print; Download; PDF; Online.

32898 ■ *Journal of Polymer Science*

Pub: John Wiley & Sons, Inc.

Contact: Christina Van Tassell, Executive Vice President Chief Financial Officer
URL(s): onlinelibrary.wiley.com/journal/26424169
Facebook: www.facebook.com/WileyPolymers
X (Twitter): x.com/JPolymSci
Released: 24/year. **Price:** $39,648, Institutions for print and online US, Canada, India; $35,305, Institutions for online US, Canada, India; $36,823, Institutions for print US, Canada, India. **Description:** International, peer-reviewed journal covering polymer science research, with an emphasis on the physics and chemistry of polymer systems. **Availability:** Print; PDF; Download; Online.

32899 ■ *Journal of Pressure Vessel Technology*
Pub: ASME International
URL(s): www.asme.org/publications-submissions/journals/find-journal/journal-pressure-vessel-technologyasmedigitalcollection.asme.org/pressurevesseltech
Released: Bimonthly; February, April, June, august, October, December. **Price:** $1,058, for list price for print only; $763, for list price for online only; $76.30, Members for online only; $105.80, Members for print only; $25, for print. **Description:** Peer-reviewed journal focusing on pressure vessel research. **Availability:** Print; PDF; Online.

32900 ■ *Journal of Software: Evolution and Process*
Pub: John Wiley & Sons, Inc.
Contact: Christina Van Tassell, Executive Vice President Chief Financial Officer
URL(s): onlinelibrary.wiley.com/journal/20477481
Ed: Xin Peng, Massimiliano Di Penta, Darren Dalcher, Dr. David Raffo. **Released:** 8/year **Price:** $5,151, Institutions for online only US, India, Japan, Canada. **Description:** Journal covering state-of-the-art research and practice papers dealing with the conception, development, testing, management, quality, maintenance, and evolution of software, systems, and services, along with the continuous improvement of processes and capabilities surrounding them. Incorporates Software Process: Improvement and Practice. **Availability:** Print; PDF; Online; Download.

32901 ■ *Journal of Turbomachinery*
Pub: ASME International
URL(s): www.asme.org/publications-submissions/journals/find-journal/journal-turbomachinery/digital-paper
Ed: Kenneth Hall, David C. Wisler. **Released:** Monthly **Price:** $100, Members for online; $1,343, for list price for print; $1,000, for list price for online; $25, for digital paper; $134, Members for print. **Description:** Peer-reviewed journal featuring scholarly research on turbomachinery technology. **Availability:** Print; Online.

32902 ■ *Microscopy Research and Technique (MRT)*
Pub: Wiley Periodicals Inc.
Contact: Brian Napack, Chief Executive Officer
URL(s): analyticalsciencejournals.onlinelibrary.wiley.com/journal/10970029www.wiley.com/en-in/Microscopy+Research+and+Technique-p-9780471559801
Released: Monthly **Price:** $17,063, Institutions for print and online US, Canada, Japan; $15,194, Institutions for online US, Canada, Japan; $15,848, Institutions for print US, Canada, Japan. **Description:** Journal covering research, methodologies, and applications related to all aspects of advanced microscopy. **Availability:** Print; Download; PDF; Online.

32903 ■ *Molecular Physics: An International Journal in the Field of Chemical Physics*
Pub: Taylor & Francis Group (Journals)
Contact: Annie Callanan, Chief Executive Officer
URL(s): www.tandfonline.com/journals/tmph20
Ed: George Jackson. **Released:** Semimonthly; 24 issues per year; volume 122, Issue 10 (2024). **Price:** $19,351, Institutions for print & online; $15,868, Institutions for online only. **Description:** Journal containing information on research papers on chemical physics. **Availability:** Print; Download; PDF; Online.

32904 ■ *Neurobiology of Learning and Memory: An Interdisciplinary Journal*
Pub: Elsevier Inc.
URL(s): www.sciencedirect.com/journal/neurobiology-of-learning-and-memory
Released: 10/year **Price:** $299, Individuals for print US. Canada; $3,422, Institutions for print us. Canada. **Description:** Journal focused on neurobiological mechanisms underlying learning and memory at all levels of analysis ranging from molecular biology to synaptic and neural plasticity and behavior. **Availability:** Print; Download; PDF; Online.

32905 ■ *Numerical Heat Transfer, Part A: Applications: An International Journal of Computation and Methodology*
Pub: Taylor & Francis Group (Journals)
Contact: Annie Callanan, Chief Executive Officer
URL(s): www.tandfonline.com/journals/unht20
Released: 24 Issues per year. **Price:** $15,641, Institutions for print and online; $5,588, Individuals for print and online; $12,826, Institutions for online only; $5,588, Individuals for print only. **Description:** Journal publishing research in the field of heat and mass transfer, and fluid flow. **Availability:** Print; Download; PDF; Online.

32906 ■ *Particulate Science and Technology: An International Journal*
Pub: Taylor & Francis Group (Journals)
Contact: Annie Callanan, Chief Executive Officer
URL(s): www.tandfonline.com/journals/upst20
Released: 8/year **Price:** $1,174, Individuals for print + online; $3,187, Institutions for print & online; $2,613, Institutions for online only; $1,174, Individuals for print only. **Description:** Journal publishing original research and review material dealing with particulate science and technology. **Availability:** Print; Download; PDF; Online.

32907 ■ *The Plant Cell*
Pub: American Society of Plant Biologists
Contact: Katayoon Dehesh, President
URL(s): academic.oup.com/plcell
Facebook: www.facebook.com/ThePlantCell
X (Twitter): twitter.com/ThePlantCell
Ed: Greg Bertoni, Patti Lockhart, Nancy Eckardt. **Released:** Monthly **Price:** $4,507, Institutions for online access -FTE 1,000 to 2,999; $4,259, Institutions for online access FTE under 1K; $5,547, Institutions for online access FTE 3,000 to 9,999; $5,914, Institutions for online access FTE 10,000 and above. **Description:** Academic research journal reporting major advances in plant cellular and molecular biology. **Availability:** Print; PDF; Online.

32908 ■ *Progress in Photovoltaics: Research and Applications*
Pub: John Wiley & Sons Ltd.
Contact: Matthew Kissner, Chief Executive Officer
URL(s): onlinelibrary.wiley.com/journal/1099159x
Released: 8/year **Price:** $4,150, Institutions for print and online US, Canada, India; https://ordering.onlinelibrary.wiley.com/Lite/Subs.aspx?doi=10.1002/(-ISSN)1099-159X&ref=1099-159X; $3,695, Institutions for online US, India, Canada; $3,855, Institutions for print US, India, Canada. **Description:** Journal focusing on practical implementation and research in the field of photovoltaics. **Availability:** Print; PDF; Download; Online.

32909 ■ *The Quarterly Review of Biology (QRB)*
Pub: The University of Chicago Press, Journals Div.
Contact: Ashley Towne, Director
E-mail: atowne@uchicago.edu
URL(s): www.journals.uchicago.edu/toc/qrb/current
X (Twitter): x.com/QRevBiol
Ed: Liliana M. Davalos, Gregory A. Wray, John J. Wiens, James D. Thomson. **Released:** Quarterly; Mar, June, Sep, Dec. **Price:** $29, Students for online 1 year; $48, Individuals for online 1 year; $50, Individuals for print 1 year; $58, Individuals for print and online 1 year; $615, Institutions for print + online very large higher education/large higher education/medium higher education/small higher education/very small higher education/community college/museums/

public library/secondary schools/govt/nonprofit/corporate; $750, Institutions for print + online run museums/public library/secondary schools; $446, Institutions for online museums, public libraries, and secondary schools; $536, Institutions for print + online museums/public library/secondary schools; $652, Institutions for online Run museums/public library/secondary schools; $489, Institutions for online community college and government/non-profit; $1,576, Institutions for print + online run very large higher education; $826, Institutions for print + online run very small higher education; $1,126, Institutions for print + online very large higher education; $590, Institutions for print + online very small higher education; $900, Institutions for print + online run medium higher education; $1,179, Institutions for print + online run large higher education; $862, Institutions for print + online run small higher education; $643, Institutions for print + online medium higher education; $718, Institutions for online Run very small higher education; $616, Institutions for print + online small higher education; $842, Institutions for print + online large higher education; $787, Institutions for print + online run community college; $1,025, Institutions for online very large higher education; $513, Institutions for online very small higher education; $979, Institutions for online very small higher education; $750, Institutions for online Run small higher education; $783, Institutions for online Run large higher education; $562, Institutions for print + online community college; $559, Institutions for online medium higher education; $536, Institutions for online small higher education; $732, Institutions for online large higher education; $1,329, Institutions for print + online run corporate; $685, Institutions for online Run community college; $185, Single issue for individuals and students; $949, Institutions for print + online corporate; $1,155, Institutions for online Run corporate; $825, Institutions for online corporate. **Description:** Journal covering historical, philosophical, and technical treatments of important biological topics. **Availability:** Print; PDF; Online.

32910 ■ *Random Structures & Algorithms*
Pub: Wiley Periodicals Inc.
Contact: Brian Napack, Chief Executive Officer
URL(s): onlinelibrary.wiley.com/journal/10982418
Ed: Joel Spencer, Michal Karonski. **Released:** 8/year **Price:** $2,578, Institutions for online only US, Japan, India, Canada. **Description:** Journal dedicated to covering the latest research on discrete random structures and presenting applications of such research to problems in combinatorics and computer science. **Availability:** Print; Download; Online; PDF.

32911 ■ *Rapid Communications in Mass Spectrometry*
Pub: John Wiley & Sons, Inc.
Contact: Christina Van Tassell, Executive Vice President Chief Financial Officer
URL(s): analyticalsciencejournals.onlinelibrary.wiley.com/journal/10970231
Ed: Prof. Zongwei Cai, Dr. David Goodlett, Dr. Pierre Thibault, Dr. Dietrich Volmer. **Released:** 24/year. **Price:** $15,131, Institutions for print and online US, Japan and India; $13,473, Institutions for online only US, Japan and India; $14,053, Institutions for print only US, Japan and India. **Description:** Journal focused on rapid publication of original research results and ideas on all aspects of the science of gas-phase ions along with all associated scientific disciplines. **Availability:** Print; PDF; Download; Online.

32912 ■ *Reviews in Medical Virology*
Pub: John Wiley & Sons Ltd.
Contact: Matthew Kissner, Chief Executive Officer
URL(s): onlinelibrary.wiley.com/journal/10991654
Ed: Harapan Harapan, Dr. Richard R. Whitley, Dr. Yiming Shao. **Released:** Bimonthly **Price:** $2,300, Institutions for online only US, Canada, India. **Description:** Journal publishing review articles on conceptual or technological advances in diverse areas of virology, including molecular biology, cell biology, replication, pathogenesis, immunology, im-

munization, epidemiology, and diagnosis or treatment of viruses of medical importance. **Availability:** Print; PDF; Online; Download.

32913 ■ *Yeast*
Pub: John Wiley & Sons Ltd.
Contact: Matthew Kissner, Chief Executive Officer
URL(s): onlinelibrary.wiley.com/journal/10970061
X (Twitter): x.com/Yeast_Journal
Released: Monthly **Price:** $6,801, Institutions for print and online US, Canada and India; $6,055, Institutions for online only US, Canada and India; $6,316, Institutions for print only US, Canada and India. **Description:** Peer-reviewed journal for those in the field of yeast biology, covering research and developments related to unicellular fungi. **Availability:** Print; PDF; Download; Online.

32914 ■ *Zoo Biology*
Pub: Wiley Periodicals Inc.
Contact: Brian Napack, Chief Executive Officer
URL(s): onlinelibrary.wiley.com/journal/10982361
Released: Bimonthly **Price:** $4,756, Institutions for print + online, US, Canada, India; $4,235, Institutions for online, US, Canada, India; $4,418, Institutions for print US, Canada, India; $454, Individuals for print US, Canada, India. **Description:** Journal featuring research on wild animals in captive settings. **Availability:** Print; Download; PDF; Online.

VIDEO/AUDIO MEDIA

32915 ■ *Biomanufacturing Tech Hubs*
URL(s): www.startuphustlepodcast.com/biomanufacturing-tech-hubs
Ed: Matt DeCoursey. **Released:** November 30, 2023. **Description:** Podcast discusses the challenges of biomanufacturing tech hubs.

32916 ■ *Entrepreneurial Thought Leaders: Solving for Infrastructure*
URL(s): ecorner.stanford.edu/podcasts/solving-for-infrastructure
Ed: Ravi Belani. **Released:** March 02, 2022. **Description:** Podcast discusses how governments might be an untapped opportunity for Silicon Valley.

TRADE SHOWS AND CONVENTIONS

32917 ■ American Association for Clinical Chemistry Annual Meeting
Association for Diagnostics & Laboratory Medicine (ADLM)
  900 7th St. NW Ste. 400
  Washington, DC 20001
Ph: (202)857-0717
Free: 800-892-1400
Fax: (202)887-5093
Co. E-mail: custserv@aacc.org
URL: http://www.aacc.org
Contact: Anthony Killeen, President
URL(s): meeting.myadlm.org/about
Frequency: Annual; held on july. **Audience:** Clinicians and medical professionals. Dates and Locations: 2025 Jul 27-31 McCormick Place Convention Center, Chicago, IL; 2026 Jul 26-30 Anaheim, CA; 2027 Jul 25-29 McCormick Place Convention Center, Chicago, IL; 2028 Jul 23-27 McCormick Place Convention Center, Chicago, IL. **Telecommunication Services:** custserv@myadlm.org.

32918 ■ American Conference on Crystal Growth and Epitaxy (ACCGE)
American Association for Crystal Growth (AACG)
  10922 Main Range Trl.
  Littleton, CO 80127
Ph: (303)539-6907
Fax: (303)600-5144
Co. E-mail: aacg@comcast.net
URL: http://www.crystalgrowth.org
Contact: Mariya Zhuravleva, President
URL(s): www.crystalgrowth.org/accge24-omvpe22

Frequency: Biennial. **Description:** Apparatus, materials, and services for crystal growth, Epitaxy, lab chemicals, crucibles, furnaces, technical book publishers and software. **Audience:** Engineers, scientists, educators, technologists, marketing representatives, and students. **Principal Exhibits:** Apparatus, materials, and services for crystal growth, Epitaxy, lab chemicals, crucibles, furnaces, technical book publishers and software. **Telecommunication Services:** aacg@comcast.net.

32919 ■ American Transplant Congress (ATC)
American Society of Transplantation (AST)
  1000 Atrium Way, Ste. 400
  Mount Laurel, NJ 08054
Ph: (856)439-9986
Fax: (856)581-9604
Co. E-mail: info@myast.org
URL: http://www.myast.org
Contact: Shandie Covington, Chief Executive Officer
E-mail: scovington@myast.org
URL(s): www.atcmeeting.org
X (Twitter): twitter.com/ATCMeeting
Frequency: Biennial. **Description:** Forum for exchange of new scientific and clinical information relevant to solid organ and tissue transplantation. **Audience:** Physicians, surgeons, scientists, nurses, organ procurement personnel, pharmacists and other transplant professionals. **Principal Exhibits:** Forum for exchange of new scientific and clinical information relevant to solid organ and tissue transplantation. Dates and Locations: 2026 Jun 20-24 Westin Seaport Bostin, Boston, MA. **Telecommunication Services:** program@atcmeeting.org.

32920 ■ ATEA National Conference
URL(s): ateaonline.org/events
Frequency: Annual. **Description:** Disseminate information regarding current issues, trends, and exemplary practices in technical education. **Audience:** Industry professionals. **Principal Exhibits:** Disseminate information regarding current issues, trends, and exemplary practices in technical education.

32921 ■ AVS International Symposium & Exhibition
AVS Science and Technology Society (AVS)
  125 Maiden Ln. 15B, 15th Fl.
  New York, NY 10038
Ph: (212)248-0200
Fax: (212)248-0245
URL: http://avs.org
Contact: Jeannette DeGennaro, Manager, Sales
E-mail: jeannette@avs.org
URL(s): avs70.avs.org
Frequency: Annual. **Description:** Addresses cutting-edge issues associated with materials, processing, and interfaces in the research and manufacturing communities. **Audience:** Scientists and engineers. **Principal Exhibits:** Addresses cutting-edge issues associated with materials, processing, and interfaces in the research and manufacturing communities. Dates and Locations: 2025 Sep 21-26 Charlotte, NC; 2026 Nov 08-13 PA. **Telecommunication Services:** yvonne@avs.org.

32922 ■ Canadian Chemical Engineering Conference
Chemical Institute of Canada (CIC)
  90-2420 Bank St.
  Ottawa, ON, Canada K1V 8S1
Ph: (613)232-6252
Fax: (613)232-5862
Co. E-mail: info@cheminst.ca
URL: http://www.cheminst.ca
Contact: Josephine Tsang, Executive Director
URL(s): www.cheminst.ca/conference/canadian-chemical-engineering-conference-csche-2024
Frequency: Annual. **Description:** Exhibits related to chemical research, development, management, and education. **Audience:** Industry professionals. **Principal Exhibits:** Exhibits related to chemical research, development, management, and education. Dates

and Locations: 2025 Jun 15-19 Carleton University and University of Ottawa, Ottawa, ON. **Telecommunication Services:** cscheconference@cheminst.ca.

32923 ■ Canadian Chemistry Conference and Exhibition
American Chemical Society
  1155 16th St. NW, Ste. 600
  Kearneysville, WV 25430
URL(s): www.cheminst.ca/conference/canadian-chemistry-conference-and-exhibition-csc-2025
Frequency: Annual. **Audience:** Industry professionals. Dates and Locations: 2025 Jun 15-19 Ottawa, ON. **Telecommunication Services:** cscconference@cheminst.ca.

32924 ■ Microscopy Society of America Microscopy & Microanalysis Meeting
Microscopy Society of America (MSA)
  401 Edgewater Pl., Ste. 600
  Wakefield, MA 01880
Ph: (703)234-4115
Fax: (703)234-4147
Co. E-mail: associationmanagement@microscopy.org
URL: http://microscopy.org
Contact: Jay D. Potts, President
URL(s): mmconference.microscopy.org
Frequency: Annual; held in july or august. **Description:** Microscopes and related instruments, equipment, supplies, and services. **Audience:** Medical, biological, metallurgical, and polymer research scientists and technicians, and physicists interested in instrument design and improvement. **Principal Exhibits:** Microscopes and related instruments, equipment, supplies, and services. Dates and Locations: 2025 Jul 27-31 Salt Lake City, UT; 2026 Aug 02-06 Milwaukee, WI. **Telecommunication Services:** meetingmanager@microscopy.org.

32925 ■ SIMB Annual Meeting and Exhibit
Society for Industrial Microbiology and Biotechnology (SIMB)
  3929 Old Lee Hwy., Ste. 92A
  Fairfax, VA 22030
Ph: (703)691-3357
Fax: (703)691-7991
Co. E-mail: membership@simbhq.org
URL: http://www.simbhq.org
Contact: Steve Decker, President
E-mail: steve.decker@nrel.gov
URL(s): www.simbhq.org/annual
Frequency: Annual. **Audience:** Microbial biotechnologists, and industry professionals. **Telecommunication Services:** sponsorship@simbhq.org.

32926 ■ Society of Behavioral Medicine Scientific Sessions
Society of Behavioral Medicine (SBM)
  555 East Wells St., Ste. 1100
  Milwaukee, WI 53202-3823
Ph: (414)918-3156
Free: 866-723-0678
Fax: (414)276-3349
Co. E-mail: info@sbm.org
URL: http://www.sbm.org
Contact: Lindsay Bullock, Executive Director
E-mail: lbullock@sbm.org
URL(s): www.sbm.org/meetings
Frequency: Annual; held in late March or April. **Description:** It provides an opportunity for attendees at all levels of experience to participate in the highest caliber of professional programming devoted to research and practice in the field of behavioral medicine. **Audience:** Physicians, psychologists, nurses and health educators. **Principal Exhibits:** It provides an opportunity for attendees at all levels of experience to participate in the highest caliber of professional programming devoted to research and practice in the field of behavioral medicine. Dates and Locations: 2025 Mar 26-29 Hilton San Francisco Union Square, San Francisco, CA; 2026 Apr 22-25 Hilton Chicago, Chicago, IL; 2027 Apr 14-17 Hilton Atlanta, Atlanta, GA. **Telecommunication Services:** info@sbm.org.

CONSULTANTS

32927 ■ Bio-Technical Resources L.P. (BTR)
1035 S 7th St.
Manitowoc, WI 54220-5301
Ph: (920)684-5518
Fax: (920)684-5519
Co. E-mail: info@biotechresources.com
URL: http://www.biotechresources.com
Contact: Reinhardt A. Rosson, President
Description: Firm provides research and development of industrial fermentation processes service. **Scope:** Services include strain improvement, process development and metabolic engineering. **Founded:** 1962. **Publications:** "A Novel Fungus for the Production of Efficient Cellulases and Hemi-Cellulases," Jun, 2009; "Linoleic Acid Isomerase from Propionibacterium acnes: Purification, Characterization, Molecular Cloning, and Heterologous Expression," 2007; "Purification and Characterization of a Membrane-Bound Linoleic Acid Isomerase from Clostridium sporogenes," 2007; "Metabolic Engineering of Sesquiterpene Metabolism in Yeast," 2007; "Purification and Characterization of a Membrane-Bound Linoleic AcidIsomerase from Clostridium sporogenes," 2007. **Training:** Metabolic Engineering for Industrial Production of Glucosamine and N-Acetylglucosamine, Aug, 2003; Metabolic Engineering of E. coli for the Industrial Production of Glucosamine, Apr, 2003.

32928 ■ BioChem Technology Inc.
1004 9th Ave., Ste. 230
King of Prussia, PA 19406
Ph: (610)768-9360
Co. E-mail: sales@biochemtech.com
URL: http://www.biochemtech.com/about
Description: Firm engages in construction of monitoring, optimization, control of waste water treatment processes, technological optimization services and much more. **Scope:** Firm engages in construction of monitoring, optimization, control of waste water treatment processes, technological optimization services and much more. **Founded:** 1979. **Publications:** "Process Evaluation Provides Optimization and Energy Reduction"; "Effect of Ionic Strength on Ion Selective Electrodes in the Activated Sludge Process". **Training:** A Five Year Case Study of a Feed Forward Nitrogen Reduction Process Control System, Jun, 2009; Alternate DO Control Based on On-line Ammonia Measurement, Jun, 2009.

32929 ■ Education Development Center Inc. (EDC)
300 Fifth Ave., Ste. 2010
Waltham, MA 02451
Ph: (617)969-7100
Fax: (617)969-5979
Co. E-mail: contact@edc.org
URL: http://www.edc.org
Contact: Siobhan Murphy, Chief Executive Officer
Facebook: www.facebook.com/edc.worldwide
Linkedin: www.linkedin.com/company/education
-development-center
X (Twitter): x.com/EDCtweets
YouTube: www.youtube.com/edcworldwide
Description: Delivers programs to address early childhood development, youth workforce development, and suicide prevention. Creates curricula and online courses and conducts surveys. **Scope:** Serves to design, deliver and evaluate innovative programs to address some of the world's most urgent challenges in education, health, and economic opportunity. Renders services to US. and foreign government agencies, private foundations, healthcare sectors, educational institutions, nonprofit organizations, universities, and corporations. **Founded:** 1958. **Publications:** "A Call to Action: HIV/AIDS, Health, Safety, and the Youth Employment Summit"; "A Case Against "Binge" as the Term of Choice: How to Get College Students to Personalize Messages about Dangerous Drinking"; "A Description of Foundation Skills Interventions for Struggling Middle-Grade Readers in Four Urban Northeast and Islands Region School Districts"; "A Guide to Facilitating Cases in Education"; "A Look at Social, Emotional, and Behavioral Screening Tools for Head Start and Early

Head Start"; "A Multifaceted Social Norms Approach to Reduce High-Risk Drinking: Lessons from Hobart and William Smith Colleges"; "The New Media Literacy Handbook"; "Helping Children Outgrow War"; "Worms, Shadows, and Whirlpools: Science in the Early Childhood Classroom"; "Teacher Leadership in Mathematics and Science Casebook and Facilitator's Guide"; "Teachers' Professional Development and the Elementary Mathematics Classroom: Bringing Understandings to Light". **Training:** Designed to Introduce the Materials; To Guide Schools Through the Issues. **Geographic Preference:** Multinational.

32930 ■ Flett Research Ltd.
440 DeSalaberry Ave.
Winnipeg, MB, Canada R2L 0Y7
Ph: (204)667-2505
Fax: (204)667-2505
Co. E-mail: flett@flettresearch.ca
URL: http://www.flettresearch.ca
Contact: Dawn Gilbert, Coordinator
Description: Provider of environmental audits and assessments. Offers contract research and consultation on environmental topics, specializes in limnology, with emphasis in microbiology, bio-geo chemistry and radio-chemistry. **Scope:** Provider of environmental audits and assessments. Offers contract research and consultation on environmental topics, specializes in limnology, with emphasis in microbiology, bio-geo chemistry and radio-chemistry. **Founded:** 1978. **Training:** Comparison of Two Methods for the Measurement of Methyl Mercury Concentrations in Penobscot River Sediments.

32931 ■ Mankind Research Unlimited (MRU) [Mankind Research Foundation]
1315 Apple Ave.
Silver Spring, MD 20910
URL: http://mankindresearchunlimited.weebly.com
Description: Publishes monographs, books, bibliographies and technical reports on health, education and energy resources. **Scope:** Firm provide an organization for scientific development and application of technology that could have positive impact on the health, education, and welfare of mankind. Provide solution to seek and apply futuristic solutions to current problems. Provides services in the areas of advanced sciences, biotechnical, bionic, biocybernetic, biomedical, holistic health, bio immunology, solar energy, accelerated learning, and sensory aids for handicapped. Current specific activities involve research in AIDS, drug abuse, affordable housing, food for the hungry, and literacy and remedial education. **Founded:** 1966.

32932 ■ Midwest Research Institute (MRI) - Patterson Library
425 Dr. Martin Luther King, Jr Blvd.
Kansas City, MO 64110
Co. E-mail: info@mriglobal.org
URL: http://www.mriglobal.org
Contact: Martin Nevshemal, Chief Financial Officer
Facebook: www.facebook.com/MRIGlobalResearch
Linkedin: www.linkedin.com/company/mriglobal
X (Twitter): x.com/mriglobal_news
Description: Nonprofit research institute offers scientific services in the areas of national defense, health sciences, agriculture and food safety, engineering, energy, and infrastructure. **Scope:** Nonprofit research institute offers scientific services in the areas of national defense, health sciences, agriculture and food safety, engineering, energy, and infrastructure. **Services:** Interlibrary loan; copying; center open to the public for reference use only and by appointment. **Founded:** 1944. **Holdings:** 22,000 volumes. **Subscriptions:** 100 journals and other serials. **Publications:** *Innovations*; *Midwest Research Institute Annual Report* (Annual).

PUBLICATIONS

32933 ■ *Developments in Business Simulation and Experiential Learning*
320 Stanley Ave.
Greenwood, SC 29649
Ph: (864)388-8775

Co. E-mail: mfekula@lander.edu
URL: http://absel.org
Contact: Mick Fekula, Executive Director
E-mail: mfekula@lander.edu
URL(s): absel.org/conference-history
Released: Annual **Availability:** Print.

32934 ■ *International Journal of Engineering Business Management (IJEBM)*
1 Oliver's Yard, 55 City Rd.
London EC1Y-1SP, United Kingdom
Contact: Philip John Denvir, Director
URL(s): journals.sagepub.com/home/enb
Ed: Prof. Massimiliano Schiraldi. **Released:** Annual; January-December 2024. **Description:** Peer-reviewed, open access journal covering the design, development, and implementation of new methodologies and technologies in engineering business management. **Availability:** Print; PDF; Download; Online.

32935 ■ *Magnetics Business & Technology (MB&T)*
3773 Cherry Creek N Dr., Ste. 575
Denver, CO 80209
Ph: (720)528-3770
Co. E-mail: general@webcomcommunications.com
URL: http://www.webcomcommunications.com
Contact: David Webster, President
E-mail: david@webcomcommunications.com
URL(s): magneticsmag.com
Facebook: www.facebook.com/MagneticsMagazine
Ed: Shannon Given, Sr. **Released:** 6/year **Price:** $78, for one year USA and Canada; $112, for one year outside USA Canada; $250, for one year outside USA Canada; $176, for three year USA and Canada. **Description:** Trade publication for technical professionals who integrate or utilize magnetic technologies in their products and applications. **Availability:** Print; Online.

32936 ■ *Plunkett's Engineering and Research Industry Almanac: The Only Complete Guide to the Business of Research, Development, and Engineering*
PO Box 541737
Houston, TX 77254-1737
Ph: (713)932-0000
Fax: (713)932-7080
Co. E-mail: customersupport@plunkettresearch.com
URL: http://www.plunkettresearch.com
Contact: Jack W. Plunkett, Chief Executive Officer
URL(s): www.plunkettresearch.com/industries/
engineering-rd-technology-market-research
Released: last edition May 2023. **Price:** $399.99, for print; $399.99, for e-book; $2,495, for single user; $6,995, for 5 users; $1,995, for eBook, enterprise-wide use (instant download). **Description:** Covers 500 of the largest companies involved in research, engineering and development in the biotech, electronics, aerospace and infotech industries. **Entries include:** Name, address, phone, fax, names and titles of key personnel, subsidiary and branch names and locations, financial data, salaries and benefits, description of products/services, overview of company culture/activities. **Indexes:** Industry, location, sales rank, profit rank. **Availability:** Print; Online.

RESEARCH CENTERS

32937 ■ American Defense Institute (ADI)
9316 Craig Ave.
Alexandria, VA 22309
Fax: (202)589-0630
Contact: Eugene B. Mcdaniel, President
Description: Non-partisan public policy foundation promoting a strong national defense. Analyzes and reports on key defense issues. Maintains liaison with members of Congress; offers graduate fellowships and undergraduate internships. **Scope:** Defense and national security policy issues, focusing on the privileges and obligations of citizenship in a free society and America's strength and freedom in the 21st century. Special projects include a military voter program which encourages service personnel to

register and vote. **Founded:** 1983. **Publications:** *ADI Briefing* (Monthly); *ADI Security Review*; *ADI News* (Quarterly). **Geographic Preference:** National.

32938 ■ New Mexico State University Arts and Sciences Research Center

Arts & Sciences Research Ctr., MSC RC
  Las Cruces, NM 88003
Fax: (575)646-4188
URL: http://artsci.nmsu.edu/research/contact-re-
  search-center.html
Contact: James Murphy, Associate
E-mail: murphy@nmsu.edu

Description: Integral unit of College of Arts and Sciences at New Mexico State University. **Scope:** Administers research activities in the arts and physical, natural, and behavioral sciences. Also serves as coordinating center for faculty research in the College. **Founded:** 1959.

32939 ■ San Diego State University - Mount Laguna Observatory (MLO)

5500 Campanile Dr.
  San Diego, CA 92182
Ph: (619)594-1415
URL: http://astronomy.sdsu.edu/mount-laguna
  -observatory-facilities

Description: Integral unit of San Diego State University. **Scope:** San Diego state university library and research center. **Founded:** 1968. **Publications:** *MLOA Newsletter*.

32940 ■ University of Delaware Department of Chemical Engineering - Center for Molecular and Engineering Thermodynamics (CMET)

150 Academy St., 233 Colburn Lab University of
  Delaware
  Newark, DE 19716
Ph: (302)831-0215
Fax: (302)831-1048
URL: http://sites.udel.edu/cmet

Description: Integral unit of Department of Chemical Engineering, University of Delaware. **Scope:** Chemical engineering, including molecular thermodynamics and its applications in environmental problems, purification of pharmaceuticals and biological materials, and new separations technologies. Theoretical research areas also include ab-initio quantum mechanics calculations, Monte Carlo and molecular dynamics simulation and statistical mechanics, development of new applied thermodynamics methods for equations of state and activity coefficients models, and the description of surfactant and micellar solutions. **Founded:** 1992.

32941 ■ University of Toronto - Institute for the History and Philosophy of Science and Technology (IHPST)

91 Charles St. W
  Victoria College, Rm. 316
  Toronto, ON, Canada M5S 1K7

Ph: (416)946-7414
Co. E-mail: ihpst.info@utoronto.ca
URL: http://ihpst.utoronto.ca
Contact: Edward Jones-Imhotep, Director
E-mail: director.ihpst@utoronto.ca
X (Twitter): x.com/uoft_ihpst

Description: Integral unit of University of Toronto. Colloquia and public lectures (biweekly). **Scope:** History and philosophy of science and technology, particularly the history of biology, including classification, invertebrate morphology, Darwinism, and ecology; history of chemistry, including the eighteenth and nineteenth centuries; history of mathematics, including foundation of analysis, eighteenth and nineteenth century mechanics, Joseph Lagrange, Nicolas Sadi Carnot, and Jean Le Rond d'Alembert; history of medicine, including history of social medicine/public health, medicine and national socialism; history of microbiology; history of physics, including Kepler, Descartes, seventeenth through nineteenth century electromagnetism; history of technology, including medieval and Renaissance, eighteenth century French technology and war; medieval and Renaissance science; Science Revolution; the Enlightenment; Victorian science; Romanticism; Canadian science, including Arctic exploration; and philosophy of science, including probability, statistics, experimental science, language, early modern natural philosophy, and foundations of Newtonian dynamics; exact sciences in antiquity. **Founded:** 1967.

START-UP INFORMATION

32942 ■ *"Options Abound in Winter Wares"* in *Pet Product News (Vol. 64, November 2010, No. 11, pp. 1)*

Ed: Maggie M. Shein. **Description:** Pet supply manufacturers emphasize creating top-notch construction and functional design in creating winter clothing for pets. Meanwhile, retailers and pet owners seek human-inspired style, quality, and versatility for pets' winter clothing. How retailers generate successful sales of pets' winter clothing outside of traditional brand marketing is also examined. **Availability:** Online.

REFERENCE WORKS

32943 ■ *"4 Tips for Managing Cash Flow in a Seasonal Business"* in *Entrepreneur (Dec. 9, 2017)*

URL(s): www.entrepreneur.com/article/303368

Ed: Lisa Stevens. **Released:** December 09, 2017. **Description:** Explores strategies that business owners can implement to cope with seasonal downturns and maintain a positive cash flow. **Availability:** Online.

32944 ■ *12 Tips for Managing a Seasonal Business*

URL(s): 10to8.com/blog/tips-for-all-seasonal-businesses/

Released: September 23, 2021. **Description:** Discusses the best way to manage a seasonal business -- by planning. Offers tips on the necessary steps to take such as hiring additional staff and expanding your inventory during peak season, setting realistic goals and mitigating the risk of burnout during busy times, and how to maximize your downtime. **Availability:** Online.

32945 ■ *"20 Best Seasonal Business Ideas for Warm Weather"* in *NerdWallet (Oct. 22, 2020)*

URL(s): www.nerdwallet.com/article/small-business/best-seasonal-business-ideas

Ed: Brian O'Connor. **Released:** October 22, 2020. **Description:** Lists 20 seasonal business ideas for entrepreneurs who prefer warm weather. Also includes information on banking and loan considerations to set your seasonal business up the right way. **Availability:** Online.

32946 ■ *"Best Days and Weekends to Shop for Clothing"* in *U.S. News and World Report (April 23, 2018)*

Ed: Kristin McGrath. **Released:** April 23, 2018. **Description:** General tips for clothes shopping throughout the year and when to hit the stores and online for the best deals to stretch your budget. **Availability:** Online.

32947 ■ *"Celebrate Holiday Spirit With Sparkling Sales"* in *Pet Product News (Vol. 66, September 2012, No. 9, pp. 48)*

Ed: Cheryl Reeves. **Description:** Pet supplies retailers can increase frequency of holiday sales, from

Halloween through New Year's, by integrating creative marketing strategies into merchandise and incentives that elicit customer attention. The impression of fun should also be emphasized on customers. Guidelines for presenting displays and organizing special store-related events are also provided. **Availability:** Print; Online.

32948 ■ *"City May Aid Pop-Up Stores Downtown"* in *Austin Business Journal (Vol. 31, August 19, 2011, No. 24, pp. A1)*

Pub: Austin Business Journal
Contact: Rachel McGrath, Director
E-mail: rmcgrath@bizjournals.com

Ed: Vicky Garza. **Description:** Temporary retail stores may soon become common in Austin as City Council has urged the city manager to look into the possibility of amending the city codes to permit businesses to temporarily fill the vacant spaces downtown. **Availability:** Print; Online.

32949 ■ *"Early Spring Halts Drilling Season"* in *Globe & Mail (March 14, 2007, pp. B14)*

Ed: Norval Scott. **Description:** Decreased petroleum productivity in Canadian oil drilling rigs due to early spring season in western regions is discussed. **Availability:** Online.

32950 ■ *"Farming Starts in December; High-Priced Embryos"* in *Farm Industry News (November 29, 2011)*

Pub: Informa Business Media, Inc.
Contact: Charlie McCurdy, President

Ed: Kent Lock. **Description:** One farmer suggests the season starts in December because one third of his seed and fertilizer for the following year has already been bought and paid for and his cropping mix changes little from one year to another. **Availability:** Print; Online.

32951 ■ *"Have a Seasonal Business? 4 Tips for Year-Round Profitability"* in *Business News Daily (Feb. 14, 2022)*

URL(s): www.businessnewsdaily.com/7394-seasonal-business-stay-profitable.html

Ed: Saige Driver. **Released:** February 14, 2022. **Description:** Provides details on the importance of planning and strategy seasonal businesses owners so that they can remain profitable during the off-season. **Availability:** Online.

32952 ■ *"Here's Why Your Family's Christmas Tree Is So Expensive"* in *USA Today (November 30, 2018)*

Ed: Dalvin Brown. **Released:** November 29, 2018. **Description:** A national shortage on firs, spruces, and pines is causing an increase in Christmas tree prices. The shortage started in 2008 when farmers decided not to plant as many trees due to the Great Recession and people not spending money on a tree. Now that the recession has dwindled, the trees that should have been there are not. Also, recent wildfires and hurricanes have played a role in diminishing the tree supply. **Availability:** Online.

32953 ■ *"Holiday Shopping Meets Social Media"* in *Employee Benefit News (Vol. 25, December 1, 2011, No. 15)*

Pub: SourceMedia LLC
Contact: Gemma Postlethwaite, Chief Executive Officer

Ed: Rob J. Thurston. **Description:** Offering employees access to discount shopping using social media sites for Christmas bonuses, could be the gift that keeps on giving.

32954 ■ *"If Palmer's Is Your Go-To Place to Cut a Christmas Tree, You're Out of Luck This Year"* in *Statesman Journal (October 13, 2019)*

URL(s): www.statesmanjournal.com/story/news/local/mid-valley/2019/10/13/palmers-christmas-tree-farm-closes-after-51-years-family-tradition/3912218002/

Ed: Capi Lynn. **Released:** October 13, 2018. **Description:** Palmer's Christmas Tree Farm is closing after being in business since 1967. **Availability:** Online.

32955 ■ *"Las Vegas Convention and Visitors Authority Kicks Off Halloween Promotion"* in *Travel & Leisure Close-Up (October 8, 2012)*

Description: Las Vegas Convention and Visitors Authority (LVCVA) is promoting the city as the premier destination for Halloween celebrations. LVCVA sites the holiday as a favorite for events and experiences for visitors. **Availability:** Print; Online.

32956 ■ *Managing the Busy Summer Season in a Seasonal Small Business*

URL(s): www.ondeck.com/resources/seasonal-small-business

Ed: Ty Kiisel. **Description:** Explores the necessity of taking a strategic approach to managing your seasonal business and business finances to keep cash flow positive during the slow season. **Availability:** Online.

32957 ■ *Managing Your Time and Resources Most Effectively*

URL(s): www.thehartford.com/business-insurance/strategy/seasonal-business/business-time-management

Description: Presents information on the importance of time management and resource management when operating a seasonal business during both, peak and off-peak season. **Availability:** Online.

32958 ■ *"Playfair Receives Drill Permit for Risby, Yukon Tungsten Deposit"* in *Marketwired (May 16, 2007)*

Pub: Comtex News Network Inc.
Contact: Kan Devnani, President

Description: Playfair Mining announced that it has received a 5 year Class III land use permit from the Mineral Resources Branch, Yukon which will allow the company to carry out a drill program during the upcoming drill season on the company-owned Risby, Yukon tungsten deposit. Statistical data included. **Availability:** Online.

32959 ■ *The Pros and Cons of Running a Seasonal Business*

URL(s): www.sba.gov/blog/pros-cons-running
-seasonal-business

Ed: Jjeoma Nwatu. **Released:** June 08, 2016. **Description:** Provides pros and cons for seasonal business startups to consider when it comes to weathering ups and downs. **Availability:** Online.

32960 ■ *"Pumpkin Spice is Coming Early to Dunkin' and Starbucks" in The New York Times (August 13, 2019)*

URL(s): www.nytimes.com/2019/08/13/business/
pumpkin-spice-starbucks-dunkin.html

Ed: Emily S. Rueb. **Released:** August 13, 2019. **Description:** Is it too soon to start serving pumpkin lattes? Dunkin' and Starbucks don't think so and are rolling out the popular spiced drinks a week earlier than usual this August. This is due to customer feedback and an attempt to capitalize on the popularity of the famous fall beverage. **Availability:** Online.

32961 ■ *"Seasonal Franchises: Strategies to Advance" in Franchising World (Vol. 42, August 2010, No. 8, pp. 50)*

Pub: International Franchise Association
Contact: Matthew Haller, President
E-mail: mhaller@franchise.org

Ed: Jennifery Lemcke. **Price:** $5.99. **Description:** Seasonal franchises, such as tax businesses can be slow during the summer months. Restaurants are slow during the months of January and February. The various challenges faced by seasonal franchises are examined. **Availability:** Online.

32962 ■ *"Sedentary Shoppers: Point, Click, Buy" in Barron's (Vol. 90, September 6, 2010, No. 36, pp. 11)*

Pub: Barron's Editorial & Corporate Headquarters

Ed: Vito J. Racanelli. **Description:** Non-travel online retail sales from January to July 2010 increased nine percent which indicates that online shopping for the coming holidays will be good. Online sales are outpacing traditional shopping, but pricing is still critical. **Availability:** Online.

32963 ■ *The Ultimate Guide for Seasonal Businesses*

URL(s): www.kabbage.com/resource-center/manage/
the-ultimate-guide-for-seasonal-businesses/

Description: A guide to running a seasonal business broken into 5 chapters: expense management, retail business, restaurants, construction businesses, and professional services. Includes information on how to make the most of your busy season and how to keep momentum moving forward during the slower times. **Availability:** Online.

32964 ■ *"Uranerz Acquires Additional Uranium Property Adjoining Nichols Ranch" in Marketwired (May 14, 2007)*

Pub: Comtex News Network Inc.
Contact: Kan Devnani, President

Description: Uranerz Energy Corporation announced the successful leasing of the fee mineral lands that appear to host the "nose" of the oxidation-reduction geochemical front and has the potential for increasing the known uranium mineralization at the Nichols Ranch project which lies west of and adjacent to Uranerz's Nichols Ranch ISR uranium project. **Availability:** Print; Online.

32965 ■ *What You Must Know about Highly Seasonal Businesses*

URL(s): www.fool.com/the-blueprint/seasonal-business/

Released: December 17, 2020. **Description:** Discusses the ins and outs of running a seasonal business. Includes pros and cons, examples of seasonal businesses, and information on the importance of planning. **Availability:** Online.

32966 ■ *"Why Do Stores Put Christmas Decorations Out So Early?" in CheatSheet (October 24, 2018)*

URL(s): www.cheatsheet.com/culture/why-do-stores
-put-christmas-decorations-out-so-early.html

Ed: Chelena Goldman. **Released:** October 04, 2018. **Description:** The "Christmas Creep" originated in the mid-80s and describes how stores sneak their Christmas merchandise onto the shelves earlier in the year. The reason why is simple: competition. Everyone is trying to get a jump on the next store to get consumers' dollars. **Availability:** Online.

32967 ■ *"Why Oil Fell, and How It May Rise" in Globe & Mail (January 18, 2007, pp. B2)*

Ed: Eric Reguly. **Description:** The causes of the decline in oil prices in Canada are discussed, along with prospects of an increase in the same. **Availability:** Print; Online.

32968 ■ *Why Running a Seasonal Business Is Different Than Any Other Kind of Business*

URL(s): www.planday.com/blog/running-seasonal
-business/

Ed: Stymir Masson. **Description:** Discusses how running a seasonal business comes with an array of unique demands and provides pros and cons of running a seasonal business. **Availability:** Online.

32969 ■ *"Will mCommerce Make Black Friday Green?" in Retail Merchandiser (Vol. 51, September-October 2011, No. 5, pp. 8)*

Description: Retailers speculate the possibilities of mobile commerce and are implementing strategies at their stores. Consumers using mobile devices accounted for only 0.1 percent of visits to retail Websites on Black Friday 2009 and rose to 5.6 percent in 2010; numbers are expected to rise for 2011. **Availability:** Print; Online.

VIDEO/AUDIO MEDIA

32970 ■ *This Is Small Business: How to Keep a Seasonal Business Profitable Year-Round*

URL(s): www.smallbusiness.amazon/podcast-episo
des/ep-44-how-to-keep-a-seasonal-business-profi
table-year-round

Ed: Andrea Marquez. **Released:** December 19, 2023. **Description:** Podcast discusses how to leverage slow periods for business growth and the importance of customer loyalty in succeeding during both the high and low seasons.

START-UP INFORMATION

32971 ■ *"The Food Truck Handbook: Start, Grow, and Succeed in the Mobile Food Business"*
Pub: John Wiley & Sons, Inc.
Contact: Christina Van Tassell, Executive Vice President Chief Financial Officer
Released: March 2012. **Price:** $19.95, paperback; $12.99, e-book. **Description:** Food truck businesses have grown so much in popularity, there are actually food truck competitions and was once a television show featuring them. A practical, step-by-step handbook is offered to help an entrepreneur start a mobile food delivery service. Information includes tips on choosing vending locations, opening and closing checklists; creation of a business plan with budget and finding vendor services, daily operation issues; common operating mistakes; and insight into delivery high quality food. **Availability:** E-book; Print.

REFERENCE WORKS

32972 ■ *"AT&T Spend Nears $2 Billion in California With Minority, Women and Disabled Veteran-Owned Businesses in 2011" in Engineering Business Journal (March 21, 2012)*
Description: AT&T reported $2 billion working with diverse suppliers in 2011, representing a consistent annual increase working with minority, women and disabled veteran owned businesses in California. AT&T prides itself on its 44 years leading the way by including minority, women and disabled veteran owned businesses to its supply chain. **Availability:** Print; Online.

32973 ■ *"Benchmark Makes Granduca Entrance" in Houston Business Journal (Vol. 40, January 8, 2010, No. 35, pp. 2)*
Pub: Houston Business Journal
Contact: Bob Charlet, President
E-mail: bcharlet@bizjournals.com
Ed: Jennifer Dawson. **Description:** Houston, Texas-based Interfin Company, owner of the Hotel Granduca, has tapped the services of Benchmark Hospitality International to manage the property. The hiring of Benchmark is part of Interfin's efforts to develop Granduca hotels in other markets. Statistical data included. **Availability:** Print; Online.

32974 ■ *"The Foundations of Supplier Engagement; Companies' Relationships With Their Suppliers Are Vital To Their Success. Here Are the Fundamental Ways Businesses Can Measure and Manage Those Relationships" in Gallup Business Journal (June 26, 2014)*
Pub: Gallup, Inc.
Contact: Jon Clifton, Chief Executive Officer
Description: The global economy has changed the nature of supplier-customer relationships. A company's relationship with their suppliers is critical to success. Fundamental ways any business can measure and manage their relationships with suppliers and become a customer of choice are examined. **Availability:** Print.

32975 ■ *"Is Maid Service Right For Your Home?" in Internet Wire (April 18, 2012)*
Pub: Comtex News Network Inc.
Contact: Kan Devnani, President
Description: Merry Maids service fanchise is discussed. The article helps individuals looking for a cleaning service to investigate the wide range of services offered by each company. **Availability:** Print; Online.

32976 ■ *It's Not Who You Know - It's Who Knows You!: The Small Business Guide to Raising Your Profits by Raising Your Profile*
Pub: John Wiley & Sons, Inc.
Contact: Christina Van Tassell, Executive Vice President Chief Financial Officer
Ed: David Arvin. **Released:** 2nd edition. **Price:** $8.69, hardcover. **Description:** When it comes to promoting a small business or a brand, it is essential to know how valuable high-profile attention can be. But for most small companies, the cost of hiring an outside firm to increase attention can be too expensive. **Availability:** Print; Online.

32977 ■ *"USHCC Applauds 10 Best U.S. Corporations for Veteran-Owned Businesses for 2012" in Economics Week (April 20, 2012, pp. 153)*
Description: The United States Hispanic Chamber of Commerce honored the 2012 National Veteran-Owned Business Association and its 10 Best US Corporations for veteran-owned businesses. The list includes large corporations that engage three million veteran-owned businese as suppliers. The Hispanic Chamber promotes economic growth and development of Hispanic entrepreneurs in the US. **Availability:** Print; Online.

VIDEO/AUDIO MEDIA

32978 ■ *HBR Ideacast: Tech at Work: How to Get the Most Out of Digital Collaboration Tools*
URL(s): hbr.org/podcast/2024/05/tech-at-work-how-to-get-the-most-out-of-digital-collaboration-tools
Ed: Alison Beard. **Released:** November 29, 2022. **Description:** Podcast explains how to match collaboration tools with work tasks and how to know when a technology isn't working for you.

CONSULTANTS

32979 ■ **Expense Control Systems Inc.**
329 Euclid Ave.
Ambler, PA 19002
Contact: John Frustacle, President
Description: Telecommunications consulting firm that specializes in voice and data network analyses, equipment evaluations and accounting services and serves all industries nationwide. **Scope:** Telecommunications consulting firm that specializes in voice and data network analyses, equipment evaluations and accounting services and serves all industries nationwide.

RESEARCH CENTERS

32980 ■ **Indiana Small Business Development Center (ISBDC)**
One North Capitol Ave., Ste., 700
Indianapolis, IN 46204
Free: 888-472-3244
Co. E-mail: leadcenter@isbdc.org
URL: http://isbdc.org
Contact: Andrew Carty, Director
E-mail: ancarty@iedc.in.gov
Facebook: www.facebook.com/isbdc
Linkedin: www.linkedin.com/company/indiana-small-business-development-center-isbdc
X (Twitter): x.com/indiana_sbdc
Description: Providing entrepreneurs with the education, information and tools necessary to build successful businesses. **Scope:** Small business development. **Founded:** 1985. **Geographic Preference:** State.

AGENCY FOR INTERNATIONAL DEVELOPMENT

32981 ■ *"These Are the Best Cities to Be Your Own Boss" in Entrepreneur (October 11, 2017)*

Ed: Nina Zipkin. **Released:** October 11, 2017. **Description:** Discusses how the home base you chose for your startup can contribute significantly to your chances for success. Includes a chart of the top cities for self-employment. **Availability:** Online.

ASSOCIATIONS AND OTHER ORGANIZATIONS

32982 ■ **Coalition to Promote Independent Entrepreneurs**
1025 Connecticut Ave. NW, Ste. 1000
  Washington, DC 20036
Ph: (202)659-0878
Co. E-mail: info@iecoalition.org
URL: http://iccoalition.org
Contact: Russell A. Hollrah, Executive Director
Facebook: www.facebook.com/iecoalition
Linkedin: www.linkedin.com/groups/2223299
X (Twitter): x.com/IECoalition

Description: Individuals, associations, and businesses. Seeks to inform the public and elected representatives about the importance of an individual's right to work as a self-employed person, and to defend an individual's right to contract in this capacity. Develops and/or supports the development of scholarly papers and studies on the importance of preserving the right to work as a self-employed individual, on the historical roots of the right, the economic and social justification for preserving the right, and potential threats to the right.

REFERENCE WORKS

32983 ■ *"3 Business Terms All Self-Employed People Need to Understand" in Due (September 7, 2018)*

Ed: Kara Perez. **Released:** September 07, 2018. **Description:** Discusses three important topics that all self-employed business owners should be aware of: quarterly taxes, bookkeeping, and work agreements. **Availability:** Online.

32984 ■ *"5 Productivity Tools for Self-Employed Internet Entrepreneurs" in Entrepreneur (January 23, 2017)*

Ed: Nathan Resnick. **Released:** January 23, 2017. **Description:** Details five invaluable technology tools for self-employed internet entrepreneurs. **Availability:** Online.

32985 ■ *"5 Steps to Starting a Consulting Business" in Legal Zoom (March 24, 2023)*

URL(s): www.legalzoom.com/articles/5-steps-to-star
  ting-a-consulting-business

Ed: Kylie Ora Lobell. **Released:** March 24, 2023. **Description:** Discusses setting up a consulting business and the steps you should follow to get it going and to find long-term success. **Availability:** Online.

32986 ■ *"Am I Self-Employed or Small Business Owner? What the Heck Am I?" (September, 27, 2016), www.mariettemartinez.com.*

Ed: Mariette Martinez. **Released:** September 27, 2016. **Description:** Provides a list of questions to ask oneself to determine whether they are self-employed or if the are a small business. **Availability:** Online.

32987 ■ *"The Career Shift from Employed to Independent" in Entrepreneur (October 27, 2017)*

Ed: Matthew Baker. **Released:** October 27, 2017. **Description:** Discusses how more and more people are leaving the 9-to-5 job for the opportunity to grow their own business and to work toward career independence. **Availability:** Online.

32988 ■ *"Does Your Home-Based Business Need Business Insurance?" in Legal Zoom (March 22, 2023)*

URL(s): www.legalzoom.com/articles/does-your
  -home-based-business-need-business-insurance

Released: March 22, 2023. **Description:** Discusses the available business insurance small business owners should look into to have themselves covered in case of property damage, liability coverage, and even auto insurance for any company vehicles. **Availability:** Online.

32989 ■ *"Employee vs. Independent Contractor: What Employers Need to Know" in Legal Zoom (March 24, 2023)*

URL(s): www.legalzoom.com/articles/employee-vs-in
  dependent-contractor-what-employers-need-to
  -know

Ed: Diane Faulkner. **Released:** March 24, 2023. **Description:** Discusses the differences between hiring someone as an employee versus an independent contractor. A list of things to look for from the Department of Labor is given. **Availability:** Online.

32990 ■ *"How to Survive Your First Month of Self-Employment" in Due (February 1, 2019)*

Ed: Taylor Gordon. **Released:** January 14, 2019. **Description:** Offers tips on how to survive during the first months of self-employment. **Availability:** Online.

32991 ■ *"Reduce Self-Employment Taxes with a Corporation or LLC" in LegalZoom (September 4, 2020)*

Ed: Jane Haskins. **Released:** September 04, 2020. **Description:** Discusses methods to reduce self-employment taxes by setting up a corporation or an LLC. **Availability:** Online.

32992 ■ *"Self-Employment Taxes" in The Balance Small Business (June 25, 2019)*

Ed: Jean Murray. **Released:** June 25, 2019. **Description:** Discusses how sole proprietorships, LLCs, partnerships, and S corporations pay taxes and how self-employment income affects social security credit. **Availability:** Online.

32993 ■ *Self-Publishing for Dummies*
Pub: John Wiley & Sons, Inc.
Contact: Christina Van Tassell, Executive Vice
  President Chief Financial Officer
URL(s): www.wiley.com/en-us/Self+Publishing+For
  +Dummies%2C+2nd+Edition-p-9781394201273

Ed: Jason R. Rich. **Released:** 2nd edition. **Price:** $24.99, paperback. **Description:** Learn the latest updates in the self-publishing world and get your book out to the market. This guide will take the reader through the initial process of writing all the way to generating publicity for your work. **Availability:** Print.

32994 ■ *"Sole Proprietor vs Independent Contractor Explained" in The Balance Small Business (May 6, 2020)*

Ed: Jean Murray. **Released:** May 06, 2020. **Description:** Discusses the differences between sole proprietorship and independent contractor and how each is required to pay taxes.

32995 ■ *"Tackle Your Taxes Like a Pro" in Entrepreneur (November 6, 2018)*

Ed: Matthew Baker. **Released:** November 06, 2018. **Description:** Offers information on how self-employed people can take control of tax compliance. **Availability:** Online.

32996 ■ *"Top 5 Health Insurance Tips for the Self-Employed" in Legal Zoom (March 24, 2023)*

URL(s): www.legalzoom.com/articles/top-5-health
  -insurance-tips-for-the-self-employed

Ed: Douglas Dalrymple. **Released:** March 24, 2023. **Description:** Self-employed people need to provide their health insurance since there is no big corporation that will give that to them as a benefit. This is often a big expense and the options can be confusing. Included are tips on what to consider. **Availability:** Online.

32997 ■ *"WeWork Closing About 40 Locations in the US" in Small Business Trends(November 16, 2022)*

URL(s): smallbiztrends.com/2022/11/wework-has-an-
  nounced-plans-to-close-around-40-locations-in-the
  -us.html

Ed: Gabrielle Pickard-Whitehead. **Released:** November 16, 2022. **Description:** WeWork, the flexible space provider for self-employed people and others who need a workstation, is closing 40 locations throughout the US. **Availability:** Online.

32998 ■ *"What You Need to Know about Hiring Independent Contractors" in Legal Zoom (March 22, 2023)*

URL(s): www.legalzoom.com/articles/what-you-nee
  d-to-know-about-hiring-independent-contractors

Released: March 23, 2023. **Description:** Independent contractors are an attractive choice for saving some costs, but are they the best choice for your small business? Read about the pros and cons of hiring ICs. **Availability:** Online.

START-UP INFORMATION

32999 ■ *"Allied Brokers of Texas Looking to Fill Private Lending Gap" in San Antonio Business Journal (Vol. 26, March 23, 2012, No. 8, pp. 1)*
Pub: Baltimore Business Journal
Contact: Rhonda Pringle, President
E-mail: rpringle@bizjournals.com
Description: San Antonio, Texas-based Allied Brokers of Texas has announced the expansion of its services to offer private lending. The move would provide direct private financing of $250,000 to $5 million to entrepreneurs looking to buy or sell a small business. Insights into the firm's new subsidiary, Allied Lending Services, are also offered. **Availability:** Print; Online.

REFERENCE WORKS

33000 ■ *"ACE Aims High With Spinoff of Repair Unit" in Globe & Mail (January 31, 2007, pp. B15)*
Description: The decision of ACE Aviation Holdings Inc. to sell its aircraft maintenance division and add workforce at its El Salvador plant is discussed. **Availability:** Online.

33001 ■ *"Algoma Resolves Hedge Fund Fight" in Globe & Mail (March 8, 2006, pp. B1)*
Ed: Greg Keenan. **Description:** Algoma Steel Inc. has ended a dispute with Paulson and Co., a New York hedge fund, by offering to pay $200 million special dividend, appointing new directors, and continue to go for a sale. **Availability:** Print; Online.

33002 ■ *American Bar Association Legal Guide for Small Business: Everything You Need to Know About Small Business, from Start-up to Employment to Financing and Selling*
Released: Second edition. **Description:** The American Bar Association provides insight into financial, health and family issues affecting small business, including start up issues, employment laws, financing a business, and selling a business.

33003 ■ *"Apartment Tower in River North Fetches More Than $90 Million" in Crain's Chicago Business (Vol. 34, October 24, 2011, No. 42, pp. 17)*
Pub: Crain Communications Inc.
Contact: Barry Asin, President
Ed: Alby Gallun. **Description:** Apartment tower in River North was sold for over $90 million to a Texas pension fund adviser. Details are included. **Availability:** Online.

33004 ■ *"Auxilium Drug's New Use: Putting the Squeeze On Cellulite" in Philadelphia Business Journal (Vol. 30, September 16, 2011, No. 31, pp. 1)*
Pub: Philadelphia Business Journal
Contact: Sierra Quinn, Director

E-mail: squinn@bizjournals.com
Ed: John George. **Description:** Auxilium Pharmaceuticals and BioSpecifics Technologies are getting on with their plans of finding new uses for their drug Xiaflex, a possible treatment for cellulite. The two firms have dismissed their pending litigations and mapped out an amended licensing agreement for their search for the potential uses of the drug. **Availability:** Online.

33005 ■ *"BofA May Part With U.S. Trust" in Boston Business Journal (Vol. 31, May 20, 2011, No. 17, pp. 1)*
Pub: Boston Business Journal
Contact: Carolyn M. Jones, President
E-mail: cmjones@bizjournals.com
Ed: Tim McLaughlin. **Description:** Bank of America Corporation is willing to sell its U.S. Trust private banking division to improve its capital ratio. The unit remains to be the corporation's core asset and posted $696 million revenue in the first quarter 2010 in contract with Merrill Lynch Global Wealth Management's $3.5 billion. Analysts say that U.S. Trust would fetch more than $3 billion. **Availability:** Print; Online.

33006 ■ *"Business for Sale: Pocket Change?" in Inc. (Vol. 30, December 2008, No. 12, pp. 28)*
Pub: Mansueto Ventures L.L.C.
Contact: Stephanie Mehta, Chief Executive Officer
Ed: Ryan McCarthy. **Description:** Owner of a chain of nine retail billiard showrooms grew his business by starting to deliver pool tables for Sears. The company, consisting of seven retail locations and two warehouses, is now for sale. Details are included. **Availability:** Online.

33007 ■ *"Caesars Deals a New Reality" in Memphis Business Journal (No. 35, April 4, 2014, No. 52, pp. 4)*
Pub: American City Business Journals, Inc.
Contact: Mike Olivieri, Executive Vice President
Description: Caesars Entertainment Group has announced the closure of the Harrah's Tunica after attempts to sell it failed. Caesars lost $2.9 billion in 2013 after losing $1.5 billion in 2012 and is making moves to control the estimated $20 billion debt. The impact of the convention facility's closure to Tunica, Mississippi is also investigated. **Availability:** Print; Online.

33008 ■ *"Calista Sells Rural Newspapers" in Alaska Business Monthly (Vol. 27, October 2011, No. 10, pp. 8)*
Pub: Alaska Business Publishing Company Inc.
Contact: Charles Bell, Vice President, Sales and Marketing
E-mail: cbell@akbizmag.com
Ed: Nancy Pounds. **Description:** Calista sold its six newspapers, a magazine, shoppers and its printing house. Details of the sales are given.

33009 ■ *"CanWest Plotting Buyback of Newspaper Income Trust" in Globe & Mail (February 7, 2007, pp. B1)*
Description: The CanWest Global Communications Corp.'s decision to sell its media assets in Australia and New Zealand in order to finance its plans of repurchasing its newspaper income trust CanWest MediaWorks Income Fund is discussed. **Availability:** Online.

33010 ■ *"The CEO Poll: Potash Sale Must Be Blocked" in Canadian Business (Vol. 83, October 12, 2010, No. 17, pp. 24)*
Pub: Rogers Media Inc.
Contact: Neil Spivak, Chief Executive Officer
Ed: Kasey Coholan. **Description:** Chief executive officers (CEOs) and corporate leaders in Canada are concerned about the possible sale of Potash Corporation to foreign buyers. A Compas Inc. poll recently asked CEOs whether the Canadian Government should step in to block the sale of the country's largest fertilizer firm. **Availability:** Print; Online.

33011 ■ *The Complete Guide to Buying a Business*
Pub: Nolo
Contact: Chris Braun, President
Ed: Fred S. Steingold. **Released:** 2015. **Description:** Key steps in buying a business are highlighted, focusing on legal issues, tax considerations, approaches for valuing a business, financing, structuring the deal, along with forms and documents for taking ownership are included. **Availability:** Print.

33012 ■ *The Complete Guide to Selling a Business*
Pub: Nolo
Contact: Chris Braun, President
Ed: Fred S. Steingold. **Released:** August 2017. **Description:** When selling a business it is critical that a sales agreement covers all key concerns from price and payment terms to liability protection and restrictions on future competition. **Availability:** Print.

33013 ■ *"Defer Tax with Installment Sale Election" in Business Owner (Vol. 35, September-October 2011, No. 5, pp. 12)*
Description: It is critical to consult with a tax professional before selling any high-value asset in order to minimize taxes. **Availability:** Print; Online.

33014 ■ *Entrepreneur Magazine's Ultimate Guide to Buying or Selling a Business*
Released: Fourth edition. **Description:** Proven strategies to evaluate, negotiate, and buy or sell a small business. Franchise and family business succession planning is included.

33015 ■ *"'Entrepreneurial Spirit' Leads Executives to Form New Tower Company" in South Florida Business Journal (Vol. 34, February 21, 2014, No. 31, pp. 6)*
Pub: American City Business Journals, Inc.
Contact: Mike Olivieri, Executive Vice President

Released: Weekly. **Price:** $8, Introductory 4-week offer(Digital & Print). **Description:** Phoenix Tower International is a new company in Boca Raton, Florida formed by the former executives of Global Tower Partners, a multibillion-dollar company that was sold in October 2013. Phoenix is self-funded and will focused on owning, leasing, and managing cellular phone service towers. **Availability:** Print; Online.

33016 ■ "Fred Weber CEO Tom Dunne: Sales Talks Confidential" in Saint Louis Business Journal (Vol. 32, September 23, 2011, No. 4, pp. 1)
Pub: Saint Louis Business Journal
Contact: Robert Bobroff, President
E-mail: rbobroff@bizjournals.com

Ed: Evan Binns. **Description:** Fred Weber Inc. CEO Tom Dunne Sr. signed a letter of confidentiality as part of an inquiry made by interested party to the construction company. However, Dunne denied the company is in a fire sale and has been continuing to bid for work and has not stopped securing projects. **Availability:** Print; Online.

33017 ■ "The Hard Thing About Hard Things: Building a Business When There Are No Easy Answers"
Pub: HarperCollins Publishers L.L.C.
Contact: Brian Murray, President
Released: 2014. **Price:** $29.99, Hardcover; $14.99, E-book; $23.99, Digital Audiobook Unabridged. **Description:** Cofounder of Andreessen Horowitz and well-respected Silicon Valley entrepreneur, offers advice for building and running a startup small business. Horowitz analyzes issues confronting leaders daily and shares insights he gained from managing, selling, buying investing in, and supervising technology firms. **Availability:** E-book; Print; Download.

33018 ■ "Harleysville Eyes Growth After Nationwide Deal" in Philadelphia Business Journal (Vol. 30, October 7, 2011, No. 34, pp. 1)
Pub: Philadelphia Business Journal
Contact: Sierra Quinn, Director
E-mail: squinn@bizjournals.com

Ed: Jeff Blumenthal. **Price:** $4, introductory 4-week offer(Digital & Print). **Description:** Harleysville Group announced growth plans after the company was sold to Columbus, Ohio-based Nationwide Mutual Insurance Company for about $1.63 billion. Nationwide gained an independent agency platform in 32 states with the Harleysville deal. **Availability:** Print; Online.

33019 ■ "Inmet Selling Nunavut Mining Properties" in Globe & Mail (February 15, 2006, pp. B6)
Ed: Allan Robinson. **Description:** The details on Wolfden Resources Inc.'s acquisition of mining assets of Inmet Mining Corp. are presented. **Availability:** Online.

33020 ■ "Intrawest Puts Itself on Market" in Globe & Mail (March 1, 2006, pp. B1)
Ed: Elizabeth Church. **Description:** The reasons behind the decision of Intrawest Corp. to go for sale or seek partnerships are presented. The company appointed Goldman Sachs & Co. to meet the purpose. **Availability:** Online.

33021 ■ Mergers and Acquisitions from A to Z
Pub: HarperCollins Leadership
Contact: Donald Miller, Chief Executive Officer
Released: 2nd edition. **Price:** $19.99, Paperback. **Description:** Guide for the entire process of mergers and acquisitions, including taxes, accounting, laws, and projected financial gain. **Availability:** E-book; Print.

33022 ■ "My Day" in Business Strategy Review (Vol. 21, Autumn 2010, No. 3, pp. 77)
Ed: Julie Meyer. **Description:** Julie Meyer shots to prominence as cofounder of the entrepreneurial network, First Tuesday. The firm was sold for $50 million in 2000. **Availability:** PDF; Online.

33023 ■ "Neighboring Auto Body Shops Merge as Parks Royal Body Works" in Idaho Business Review (August 26, 2014)
Pub: BridgeTower Media
Contact: Adam Reinebach, President

Description: Parks Royal Body Works and Auto Body Specialists operated next door to each other and were rivals for many years. Ted Vinson, owner of Auto Body, recently sold his business to Ted Thornton's son, Matt in order for Parks Royal to expand. Thornton discusses his company's 13 percent growth in 2013. Details of the purchase are discussed.

33024 ■ "NexCen Brands Sells Chains and Will Liquidate" in Ice Cream Reporter (Vol. 23, August 20, 2010, No. 9, pp. 1)
Description: NexCen Brands is closing the sale of its franchise businesses, which include the frozen dessert chains MaggieMoo's and Marbel Slab Creamery, to Global Franchise Group. **Availability:** Print; Online.

33025 ■ "NuPathe: From Tight On Cash to a Big Payday" in Philadelphia Business Journal (Vol. 33, May 16, 2014, No. 14, pp. 6)
Pub: American City Business Journals, Inc.
Contact: Mike Olivieri, Executive Vice President
Released: Weekly. **Price:** $4, introductory 4-week offer(Digital only). **Description:** Armando Anido, former chief executive officer of NuPathe, shares his perspectives about his brief tenure at the Pennsylvania-based company. He discusses the $144 million sale of the company to Teva Pharmaceuticals. **Availability:** Print; Online.

33026 ■ "Nursing Home Group Put on the Block" in Globe & Mail (February 23, 2006, pp. B1)
Ed: Elizabeth Church. **Description:** The reasons behind the decision of Exetendicare Inc. to go for sale are presented. **Availability:** Online.

33027 ■ "The Ode: S. M. Whitney Co. (1868 – 2010)" in Canadian Business (Vol. 83, October 12, 2010, No. 17, pp. 27)
Pub: Rogers Media Inc.
Contact: Neil Spivak, Chief Executive Officer
Ed: Angelina Chapin. **Released:** October 12, 2010. **Description:** A history of S.M. Whitney Company is presented. The cotton company was opened in 1868. The cotton is sold to textile manufacturers after crops have been picked, ginned and baled. The company closed down in 2010 after chief executive officer Barry Whitney decided to sell his last bale of cotton. **Availability:** Print; Online.

33028 ■ "Points of Light Sells MissionFish to eBay" in Non-Profit Times (Vol. 25, May 15, 2011, No. 7, pp. May 15, 2011)
Description: eBay purchased MissionFish, a subsidiary of Points of Light Institute for $4.5 million. MissionFish allows eBay sellers to give proceeds from sales to their favorite nonprofit organization and helps nonprofits raise funds by selling on eBay. **Availability:** Print; Online.

33029 ■ "Portland's Hilton For Sale" in Business Journal Portland (Vol. 27, October 22, 2010, No. 34, pp. 1)
Pub: Portland Business Journal
Contact: Andy Giegerich, Managing Editor
E-mail: agiegerich@bizjournals.com
Ed: Wendy Culverwell. **Description:** Hilton Portland & Executive Tower, Portland's biggest hotel, is being sold by Cornerstone Real Estate Advisers LLC. Cornerstone hopes to close the deal for the 782-room complex by the end of 2010. Cornerstone contracted Jones Lang LaSalle to manage the sale, but terms to the deal are not available. **Availability:** Print; Online.

33030 ■ "Roy MacDowell Jr. Version 2.0" in Boston Business Journal (Vol. 31, June 10, 2011, No. 20, pp. 1)
Pub: Boston Business Journal
Contact: Carolyn M. Jones, President
E-mail: cmjones@bizjournals.com

Ed: Craig M. Douglas. **Description:** Real estate developer Roy MacDowell is selling his Boston, Massachusetts estate. The asking price for the property is $21.8 million. MacDowell recently suffered setbacks in his finances. **Availability:** Print; Online.

33031 ■ "Sale of Owings Mills Solo Cup Plant Pending" in Boston Business Journal (Vol. 29, June 17, 2011, No. 6, pp. 1)
Pub: Boston Business Journal
Contact: Carolyn M. Jones, President
E-mail: cmjones@bizjournals.com

Ed: Daniel J. Sernovitz. **Released:** Weekly; X. **Price:** $4, Print. **Description:** Baltimore developers Vanguard Equities Inc. and Greenberg Gibbons Commercial have contracted to buy the Solo Cup Company facility in Owing Mills and are now considering several plans for the property. Sale should be completed by September 2011 but no proposed sale terms are disclosed. **Availability:** Print; Online.

33032 ■ "Souled Out" in Canadian Business (Vol. 81, March 3, 2008, No. 3, pp. 35)
Description: According to a survey of over 100 entrepreneurs, 78 percent responded that selling their business was emotionally draining for them. Greig Clark, for example, says that one of the toughest times of his life was selling College Pro Painters, after putting 18 years into that business. The economic impacts of selling out are also examined. **Availability:** Online.

33033 ■ "SunEdison Sells 30MW Spectrum Solar Project To Southern Company and Turner Renewable Energy" in Benzinga.com (September 28, 2012)
Pub: Benzinga.com
Contact: Jason Raznick, Founder
Ed: Paul Quintaro. **Description:** SunEdison sold its Spectrum Solar Project, a 30 MW solar photovoltaic power plant, to Southern Company and Turner Renewable Energy. Construction of the project is planned to begin in October 2012 in Clark County, Nevada. Details are included. **Availability:** Print; Online.

33034 ■ "Symantic Completes Acquisition of VeriSign's Security Business" in Internet Wire (August 9, 2010)
Description: Symantec Corporation acquired VeriSign's identity and authentication business, which includes Secure Sockets Layer (SSL) and Code Signing Certificate Services, the Managed Public Key Infrastructure (MPKI) Services, the VeriSign Trust Seal, the VeriSign Identity Protection (VIP) Authentication Service and the VIP Fraud Protection Service (FDS). The agreement also included a majority stake in VeriSign Japan. **Availability:** Online.

33035 ■ "To Sell or Not To Sell" in Inc. (December 2007, pp. 80)
Ed: Patrick J. Sauer. **Description:** Owner of a private equity discusses the challenges he faces when deciding to sell his family's business. **Availability:** Online.

33036 ■ "Today's Business Sale Climate" in Business Owner (Vol. 35, September-October 2011, No. 5, pp. 10)
Description: Despite the weak economy, there is a surplus of individuals wanting to purchase a small business. The Small Business Administration loan guarantees program helps with its loans for purchase/sale of business assistance. **Availability:** Print; Online.

33037 ■ "The VC Shakeout" in Harvard Business Review (Vol. 88, July-August 2010, No. 7-8, pp. 21)
Pub: Harvard Business Publishing
Contact: Diane Belcher, Managing Director
Ed: Joseph Ghalboun, iDominique Rouzies. **Price:** $6, PDF. **Description:** Authors argue that in order to be successful, venture capital needs to focus less on how to sell a newly acquired investment and more on ways to grow a good company. **Availability:** Online; PDF.

33038 ■ *"Wenmat Sells Last Fitness Clubs" in Sacramento Business Journal (Vol. 31, June 6, 2014, No. 15, pp. 6)*
Pub: American City Business Journals, Inc.
Contact: Mike Olivieri, Executive Vice President
Released: Weekly. **Price:** $4, Introductory 4-week offer(Digital & Print). **Description:** Wenmat Fitness sold all of its health clubs while expanding its presence in Sacramento, California. Fitness Evolution purchased Wenmat's Signature Athletic Club as well as its Incentive Fitness. Meanwhile, California Family Fitness bought two Wenmat locations. **Availability:** Print; Online.

33039 ■ *"Why Your First Suitor Isn't Always the Best" in Business Journal Portland (Vol. 30, January 24, 2014, No. 47, pp. 10)*
Pub: American City Business Journals, Inc.
Contact: Mike Olivieri, Executive Vice President
Released: Weekly. **Price:** $4, Introductory 4-week offer(Digital & Print). **Description:** Norm Duffett of Orca Capital Securities offers tips on how business owners can avoid the downside of selling their business to the first buyer. An auction ensures the owners they got the best available deal. **Availability:** Print; Online.

33040 ■ *"Your Cold Calling?" in Inc. (December 2007, pp. 34)*
Ed: Elaine Appleton Grant. **Description:** Profile of a recreational outfitting company in northern New England with an asking price of $6.185 million, with gross revenue of $9.4 million in 2007. **Availability:** Online.

VIDEO/AUDIO MEDIA

33041 ■ *90 Days After My Acquisition*
URL(s): www.startuphustlepodcast.com/90-days-after-my-acquisition
Ed: Matt Watson. **Released:** March 28, 2024. **Description:** Podcast offers anecdotes about buying out your business partner.

33042 ■ *Be a Profitable Badass Small Business Owner: Is It Time to Shut Down Your Small Business?*
URL(s): traffic.libsyn.com/secure/smallbusinessownercoach/618_time_to_quit.mp3
Ed: Tammy Adams. **Released:** October 14, 2024. **Description:** Podcast discusses whether to keep a business.

33043 ■ *The How of Business: Creating a Business That Can Thrive Without You*
URL(s): www.thehowofbusiness.com/episode-349-john-warrillow
Ed: Henry Lopez. **Released:** January 11, 2021. **Description:** Podcast explains why it's important to build a business ready to sell and steps to take toward that goal, even if you're just starting out.

33044 ■ *The How of Business: David Barnett - Selling Your Business*
URL(s): www.thehowofbusiness.com/episode-172-david-barnett
Ed: Henry Lopez. **Released:** January 15, 2018. **Description:** Podcast offers tips to help prepare for and successfully sell a small business.

33045 ■ *The How of Business: Justine Lackey - Selling Her Small Business*
URL(s): www.thehowofbusiness.com/505-justine-lackey-selling-her-business
Ed: Henry Lopez. **Released:** January 15, 2024. **Description:** Podcast discusses selling a small business.

33046 ■ *The How of Business: Mike Finger - Is Your Business Sellable*
URL(s): www.thehowofbusiness.com/412-mike-finger-sellable-business
Ed: Henry Lopez. **Released:** March 07, 2022. **Description:** Podcast discusses preparing your business for sale, common misconceptions, and determining if you should sell your business.

33047 ■ *How I Built This: Barefoot Wine: Bonnie Harvey and Michael Houlihan*
URL(s): wondery.com/shows/how-i-built-this/episode/10386-barefoot-wine-bonnie-harvey-and-michael-houlihan
Ed: Guy Raz. **Released:** September 16, 2024. **Description:** Podcast explains how Barefoot Wine (founded with almost no knowledge of wine) won over their audience and sold it twenty years after launch.

33048 ■ *Matt Takes the Exit, Matt Goes All In*
URL(s): www.startuphustlepodcast.com/matt-takes-the-exit-matt-goes-all-in
Ed: Matt DeCoursey. **Released:** December 11, 2023. **Description:** Podcast discusses the details of a strategic buyout.

33049 ■ *Profit First Nation: Play for Monopoly Control*
URL(s): www.profitfirstnation.com/episodes/ep-152-play-for-monopoloy-control
Ed: Danielle Mulvey. **Released:** November 28, 2023. **Description:** Podcast discusses pre-planning the sale your business to improve profitability.

33050 ■ *This Is Small Business: How to Prepare for a Business Sale*
URL(s): www.smallbusiness.amazon/podcast-episodes/ep-59-how-to-prepare-for-a-business-sale
Ed: Andrea Marquez. **Released:** May 28, 2024. **Description:** Podcast explains how to increase your business value, who you may need on your team, and when to sell.

CONSULTANTS

33051 ■ **The Blaine Group, Inc.**
8665 Wilshire Blvd., Ste.No. 301
Beverly Hills, CA 90211
Ph: (310)360-1499
Fax: (310)360-1498
URL: http://blainegroupinc.com
Contact: Devon Blaine, President
E-mail: devon@blainegroupinc.com
Description: Provider of communication solutions and services. **Founded:** 1975. **Publications:** "They Don't Want You to Know About".

33052 ■ **Business Team (BT)**
1475 S Bascom Ave., Ste. 113
Campbell, CA 95008
Ph: (408)246-1102
Fax: (408)246-2219
Co. E-mail: sanjose@business-team.com
URL: http://www.business-team.com
Contact: Armstrong Wong, Officer
E-mail: armstrong@business-team.com
Description: A business brokerage firm that specializes in merger, acquisition, and divestiture services for privately held, mid-sized companies. The company's value-added services include business valuation, pre-marketing consultation, and exit strategy planning. **Founded:** 1981. **Training:** Business Valuation Enhancing the Value of Your Company.

33053 ■ **Devries & Associates, P.C.**
3145 Broadway
Kansas City, MO 64111
Ph: (816)561-2555
Fax: (816)561-3939

URL: http://www.devries-law-kc.com
Contact: Coulter F. deVries, Director
Description: Investment banking/financial consulting firm which helps companies solve financial problems and achieve growth and diversification goals. Helps established companies raise capital and assists new and developing companies secure venture capital and create public markets for their stocks. **Scope:** Investment banking/financial consulting firm which helps companies solve financial problems and achieve growth and diversification goals. Helps established companies raise capital and assists new and developing companies secure venture capital and create public markets for their stocks. **Founded:** 1984.

33054 ■ **Management Services & Development Ltd.**
103 Carmalt Ave.
Punxsutawney, PA 15767
URL: http://biz-hub.com
Contact: Richard D. Mowrey, President
Description: Firm provides in valuation and financial services for acquisition or sale of businesses, performs appraisals and facilitates the actual transfer of business ownership, and also specializing in sale of privately owned manufacturing businesses. **Scope:** Firm provides in valuation and financial services for acquisition or sale of businesses, performs appraisals and facilitates the actual transfer of business ownership, and also specializing in sale of privately owned manufacturing businesses. **Publications:** "Business Owner's Journal". **Training:** Exit Planning; How to Determine the Value of Your Business; How to Maximize the Value of Your Business; Success without Stress. **Special Services:** XL Template for Assessment Business Valuation Process.

33055 ■ **Mertz Associates Inc.**
N1629 County Rd. P
Rubicon, WI 53078
URL: http://www.mertz.com
Contact: Linda Mertz, Chief Executive Officer
E-mail: lnda@mertz.com
Description: Firm provides strategic consulting services such as strategic assessments, acquisition strategies, and exit options. **Scope:** Firm provides strategic consulting services such as strategic assessments, acquisition strategies, and exit options. **Publications:** "Why Successful Companies are Launching Acquisition Searches Now"; "On the Block"; "Selling Troubled Divisions and Companies"; "Don't Fear the D Word"; "M and A Multiples: A Key to Value Or a Distraction"; "Savvy CPA Levels the Playing Field"; "M and A Trends Strategic Focus Drives Success".

FRANCHISES AND BUSINESS OPPORTUNITIES

33056 ■ **Upside Group Franchise Consulting Corp.**
11445 E Via Linda, Ste. 2-495
Scottsdale, AZ 85259
Free: 888-445-2882
Co. E-mail: info@upsidefc.com
URL: http://upsidefranchiseconsulting.com
Contact: Mario Altiery, President
Description: Firm engages in full franchise consulting sales development. **Founded:** 2000. **Training:** Yes.

Senior-Owned Business

REFERENCE WORKS

33057 ■ *"3 Types of Grants Available to Seniors"* in *SeniorAdvisor Blog*
URL(s): www.senioradvisor.com/blog/2018/02/types
-of-grants-available-to-seniors/
Ed: Kristen Hicks. **Description:** For seniors who aren't ready to stop working, but could use some help getting a small business going, business grants are available. This article provides tips for applying for grants. **Availability:** Online.

33058 ■ *"5 Businesses You Could Start In Retirement for Under $5,000"* in *Forbes (Feb. 27, 2020)*
URL(s): www.forbes.com/sites/nextavenue/2020/02/
27/5-businesses-you-could-start-in-retirement-for
-under-5000/?sh=5103ea4ff4f3
Released: February 27, 2020. **Description:** Provides information on five low-capital types of startups for retirement businesses. **Availability:** Online.

33059 ■ *"8 Online Business Ideas for Retirees"* in *U.S. News & World Report (Sept. 9, 2020)*
URL(s): money.usnews.com/money/retirement/baby
-boomers/articles/online-business-ideas-for-retirees
Ed: Rachel Hartman. **Released:** September 09, 2020. **Description:** Presents options for retirement businesses and discusses the importance of choosing the right field and carrying out research before launching a business venture in retirement. **Availability:** Online.

33060 ■ *"10 Retirement-Friendly Business Ideas for the Over 50's"* in *Due Blog (Jan. 17, 2022)*
URL(s): due.com/blog/10-retirement-friendly-busi-
ness-ideas-for-the-over-50s/
Ed: Kiara Taylor. **Released:** January 17, 2022. **Description:** Entrepreneurship is possible for those over 50! This article supplies ten business ideas for retirees. **Availability:** Online.

33061 ■ *"10 Small Business Ideas for Retirees"* in *U.S. Chamber of Commerce CO (Oct. 14, 2021)*
URL(s): www.uschamber.com/co/start/business-i
deas/small-business-ideas-for-retirees
Ed: Andrea Forstadt. **Released:** October 14, 2021. **Description:** Reaching retirement age doesn't have to mean the end of your working life. This article presents post-career ideas for entrepreneurs. **Availability:** Online.

33062 ■ *"15 Business Ideas for Senior Citizens"* in *Seniority Live Evergreen Blog*
URL(s): www.seniority.in/blog/15-business-ideas-for
-senior-citizens/
Description: While it can be overwhelming to start a business after retirement, all you need is the initial step. This article presents 15 business ideas, specially crafted for senior citizens that require very little investment. **Availability:** Online.

33063 ■ *"25 Senior Service Business Ideas"* in *Small Business Trends (July 3, 2019)*
Ed: Annie Pilon. **Released:** July 03, 2019. **Description:** Discusses the need for senior services and provides suggestions for small businesses that specialize in senior services. **Availability:** Online.

33064 ■ *Best Business Ideas for Aging Population - 60 TOP Ideas*
Released: November 04, 2019. **Description:** Provides 30 business ideas related to providing services for older people and 30 business ideas that are great examples of work that older people can do to earn extra money when they are retired. **Availability:** Online.

33065 ■ *"Best Businesses for Retirees to Start"* in *ZenBusiness Blog (Aug. 11, 2021)*
URL(s): www.zenbusiness.com/blog/retiree-business
-ideas/
Ed: April Maguire. **Released:** August 11, 2021. **Description:** Retirement businesses are increasingly popular. This article provides ideas for good businesses to start in retirement. **Availability:** Online.

33066 ■ *"Forget Retirement: Senior Citizens are Founding Small Businesses, and Research Shows More of Them are Likely to Succeed Than Young Entrepreneurs"* in *Business Insider (August 12, 2019)*
Ed: Ivan De Luce. **Released:** August 12, 2019. **Description:** Discusses the success that seniors are having with their small businesses as well as the positive impacts of work for seniors. **Availability:** Online.

33067 ■ *"Grants for Senior Citizens Starting a Business"* in *BizFluent (December 31, 2018)*
Ed: Gail Cohen. **Released:** December 31, 2018. **Description:** Provides information on how to obtain grants for seniors who are looking to start a new business. **Availability:** Online.

33068 ■ *"Grey Power: On Target"* in *Canadian Business (Vol. 81, July 22, 2008, No. 12-13, pp. 45)*
Pub: Rogers Media Inc.
Contact: Neil Spivak, Chief Executive Officer
Ed: Calvin Leung. **Description:** Companies such as LavalifePRIME, a dating website devoted to singles 45 and older, discuss the value of marketing and services aimed at Canada's older consumers. One-third of Canada's 33 million people are 50-plus, controlling 77 percent of the countries wealth. **Availability:** Print; Online.

33069 ■ *How to Fund a Business - Info for Seniors*
Description: Provides information for seniors who are looking to start their own business, but who lack the funding to do so. **Availability:** Online.

33070 ■ *"How to Make Money in Retirement: A Guide to Turning a Hobby into a Side Business"* in *business.com (Sept. 7, 2022)*
URL(s): www.business.com/articles/how-make
-money-retirement-hobby/
Released: September 07, 2022. **Description:** Many who want to earn money in retirement turn to their hobbies as jumping-off points for launching a small business. This is a guide to turning a hobby into a side business in retirement. **Availability:** Online.

33071 ■ *"Rebrand, Rebuild, and Recharge Your Business: How This BE 100s CEO Got a New Lease On Life With a Frozen Yogurt Café"* in *Black Enterprise (Vol. 44, March 2014, No. 7, pp. 11)*
Pub: Earl G. Graves Ltd.
Contact: Earl Graves, Jr., President
Description: Profile of Rumia Ambrose-Burbank, chief executive of one of the country's largest minority-owned businesses. Her Troy, Michigan-based firm ranks number 51 on the magazine's 100 Industrial/Service companies and focuses on the maintenance, repair, and operations (MRO) supply side. Ambrose-Burbank opened Sol De Frio, in 2013, a self-serve frozen yogurt dessert shop.

33072 ■ *"Retirement Business Ideas: 12 Ideas for Getting Started After 50"* in *NewRetirement (Feb. 18, 2021)*
URL(s): www.newretirement.com/retirement/re
tirement-business-ideas-for-over-50/
Ed: Derek Sall. **Released:** February 18, 2021. **Description:** Finding success in business after age 50 is more common than one might think. This article provides information for those who like the idea of setting up a retirement purpose/business. **Availability:** Online.

33073 ■ *"Senior-Owned Small Businesses Get a Boost under Kim's Bipartisan Bill"* in *The Ripon Advance (April 26, 2022)*
URL(s): riponadvance.com/stories/senior-owne
d-small-businesses-get-a-boost-under-kims-bipar
tisan-bill/
Released: April 26, 2022. **Description:** Presents information on a bipartisan bill that will establish a training curriculum for older business owners within the Small Business Administration's Office of Entrepreneurial Development. **Availability:** Online.

33074 ■ *"Small Businesses Run by Older Founders Most Likely to Survive"* in *AARP (February 19, 2019)*
Ed: Patrick J. Kiger. **Released:** February 19, 2019. **Description:** Discusses the success that small business owners who are 55 and older and why they may be having that success. **Availability:** Online.

33075 ■ *Starting a Business After Retirement: 12 Business Ideas for the Over 50s*
Ed: Derek Sall. **Released:** March 06, 2018. **Description:** Provides information on starting a business after you retire including information on business ideas,

financial information, buying a business, becoming a franchisee, becoming an Angel investor, and marketing information. **Availability:** Online.

33076 ■ *"These Are the Women Who Really Mean Business" in Canadian Business (Vol. 87, October 2014, No. 10, pp. 67)*

Description: A list of the top 100 women entrepreneurs in Canada are ranked, based on sales, three-year revenue growth rate, and profitability of their businesses is presented. Included in the list are Janet Stimpson of White House Design Company, Inc.; builder, Allison Grafton of Rockwood Custom Homes Inc.; and Janet Jing Di Zhang of Vancouver, BC of New Immigrants Information Services Inc. **Availability:** Online.

33077 ■ *"What to Do in Retirement: 9 Awesome Business Ideas for Seniors" in Senior Outlook Today (May 3, 2020)*

Released: May 03, 2020. **Description:** Provides information and a variety of options for retirees who would like to start their own business. **Availability:** Online.

33078 ■ *"Where to Find Business Loans for Senior Citizens" in Fast Capital 360 (Dec. 2, 2021)*

URL(s): www.fastcapital360.com/blog/business-loans -for-senior-citizens/

Ed: Roy Rasmussen. **Released:** December 2, 2021. **Description:** Provides loan and grant resources for older entrepreneurs as well as tips on how to find the financing you need. **Availability:** Online.

33079 ■ *You're Never Too Old to Get Rich If You Follow These Seven Tips for Starting a Business*

Ed: Jill Cornfield. **Released:** June 25, 2019. **Description:** Provides information for seniors who would like to start their own business post-retirement. **Availability:** Online.

VIDEO/AUDIO MEDIA

33080 ■ *Side Hustle to Small Business: How D.R. Ray Found Entrepreneurial Success Later in Life*

URL(s): www.hiscox.com/side-hustle-to-small-busi ness/dr-fay-mouthy-broad-media-podcast-season-4

Ed: Sanjay Parekh. **Released:** August 07, 2024. **Description:** Podcast features a late-in-life entrepreneur who began a podcast production company.

LIBRARIES

33081 ■ **Virginia Commonwealth University School of Allied Health Professions - Virginia Center on Aging - Information Resources Center**

900 E Leigh St., Ste. 7020
 Richmond, VA 23219

Ph: (804)828-1525

Co. E-mail: vcoa@vcu.edu

URL: http://www.sahp.vcu.edu/vcoa/video-library/in dex.html

Contact: Dr. Edward F. Ansello, Director

E-mail: eansello@vcu.edu

Facebook: www.facebook.com/vcuvcoa

YouTube: www.youtube.com/user/alliedhelp/videos

Scope: Gerontology; mental health; sociology and the politics of aging; geriatrics; family relationships; long-term care; lifelong learning. **Services:** Library open to the public with restrictions (audio/visual materials available to Virginia residents only). **Founded:** 1978. **Holdings:** 1,500 books; 4 archives; 150 videos and DVDs.

START-UP INFORMATION

33082 ■ *"Chem-Dry Carpet Cleaning Franchise on Pace for 120 New Locations In 2014"* in Internet Wire *(September 16, 2014)*
Pub: Comtex News Network Inc.
Contact: Kan Devnani, President
Description: Chem-Dry carpet cleaning franchise is poised to record-setting growth for 2014 with 120 new franchisees. Entrepreneur Magazine named Chem-Dry as the No. 1 carpet cleaning franchise, as well as a top home-based business opportunity with low startup-costs. **Availability:** Online.

33083 ■ *"Fast-Growing Office Pride Franchise Targets Louisville For Expansion"* in Internet Wire *(September 9, 2014)*
Pub: Comtex News Network Inc.
Contact: Kan Devnani, President
Description: Office Pride is a commercial cleaning service that is built on principles that include: honesty, trustworthy service, excellence, and treating everyone with dignity and respect. The commercial cleaning franchise is seeking a developer to help expand its business in Louisville, Kentucky. **Availability:** Online.

33084 ■ *"Fixing Up the Area: Leo Piatz Opens General Repair Business"* in The Dickinson Press *(November 16, 2010)*
Pub: The Dickinson Press
Contact: Joy Schoch, Business Manager
Description: Profile of Leo Piatz, owner of Leo's Repair in Dickinson, North Dakota; Piatz provides welding and fabricating services to farmers and ranchers in the area.

33085 ■ *Your Million-Dollar Idea: From Concept to Marketplace*
Description: Self-taught entrepreneur provides a 12-step plan to make a new product or service a profitable reality.

ASSOCIATIONS AND OTHER ORGANIZATIONS

33086 ■ **Coalition of Service Industries (CSI)**
1707 L St. NW, Ste. 1000
Washington, DC 20036
URL: http://uscsi.org
Contact: Christine Bliss, President
Description: Increases attention to measurement of productivity in services and revises national economic indicators to account for services. Represents US service sector in multilateral trade negotiations. Works with interested groups internationally. **Founded:** 1982. **Geographic Preference:** National.

33087 ■ **Service Industry Association (SIA)**
2164 Historic Decatur Rd., Villa Nineteen
San Diego, CA 92106
Ph: (619)458-9063
Co. E-mail: cbetzner@servicenetwork.org
URL: http://www.servicenetwork.org

Contact: Dwight Strayer, President
Linkedin: www.linkedin.com/company/service-indus
try-association
X (Twitter): x.com/ServiceIndAssoc
Description: Provides a forum for information exchange; strives to enhance the high-technology industry through an open environment of interdependence and cooperation between manufacturers, independent service organizations and users by providing solutions for customers. **Founded:** 1985. **Educational Activities:** SIA Global Executive Summit for Service Leaders (Annual). **Geographic Preference:** National.

REFERENCE WORKS

33088 ■ *"2 New Tools for Safeguarding Your Website: Website Backup Made Simple"* in Inc. *(Vol. 33, September 2011, No. 7, pp. 52)*
Pub: Inc. Magazine
Ed: John Brandon. **Description:** Tools to back up content on a Website are profiled. Vaultpress works only with sites that run on the WordPress publishing platform and CodeGuard works with a variety of publishing platforms and hosting services. **Availability:** Online.

33089 ■ *"2nd Watch Rides AWS Market Maturity to 400% Growth"* in Computer Business Week *(August 28, 2014, pp. 21)*
Description: 2nd Watch reports record earnings for the second quarter of 2014. The firm helps companies develop and implement IT strategies that are based on Amazon Web Services (AWS). Details of the companies business strategies are outlined. **Availability:** Print; Online.

33090 ■ *"85 Amazing Food Business Ideas You Could Start in 2023"* in Small Business Trends *(March 2, 2023)*
URL(s): smallbiztrends.com/2023/03/food-business-i
deas.html
Ed: Annie Pilon. **Released:** March 02, 2023. **Description:** With the food service industry having changed and adapted to new norms after the pandemic, there are available many options for starting your own food-based small business. **Availability:** Online.

33091 ■ *"2010 Book of Lists"* in Business Courier *(Vol. 26, December 26, 2009, No. 36, pp. 1)*
Price: $49.95. **Description:** Rankings of companies and organizations within the business services, education, finance, health care, hospitality and tourism, real estate, and technology industries in the Cincinnati, Ohio-Northern Kentucky area are presented. Rankings are based on sales, business size, or other statistics. **Availability:** PDF; Online.

33092 ■ *"ABM Janitorial Services Receives Service Excellence Award from Jones Lang LaSalle"* in Investment Weekly News *(July 16, 2011, pp. 75)*
Description: ABM Janitorial Services was awarded the 2010 Jones Lang LaSalle Distinction award in the category of Service Excellence. LaSalle is a leading

financial and professional services firm that specializes in real estate services and investment management. The program recognizes supplier partners who play a vital role in LaSalle's aim to provide the highest quality of services, value and innovation to clients. **Availability:** PDF; Online.

33093 ■ *"ACE Agrees to Pay Out $266 Million to Investors"* in Globe & Mail *(February 17, 2006, pp. B1)*
Ed: Brent Jang. **Description:** Canada-based commercial aviation firm ACE Aviation Holdings has agreed to pay 266 million dollars to its investors after filing a bankruptcy one year ago. Complete details of this pay off are discussed. **Availability:** Online.

33094 ■ *"Actiontec and Verizon Team Up for a Smarter Home"* in Ecology,Environment & Conservation Business *(November 5, 2011, pp. 3)*
Pub: Comtex News Network Inc.
Contact: Kan Devnani, President
Description: Verizon is implementing Actiontec Electronics' SG200 Service Gateway as a basic component of its Home Monitoring and Control service. This new smart home service allows customers to remotely check their homes, control locks and appliances, view home-energy use and more using a smartphone, PC, or FiOS TV. **Availability:** Online.

33095 ■ *"Air Canada to Slash 600 Non-Union Jobs"* in Globe & Mail *(February 11, 2006, pp. B3)*
Ed: Brent Jang. **Description:** The reasons behind workforce reduction by ACE Aviation Holdings Inc. at Air Canada are presented. **Availability:** Online.

33096 ■ *"Air Canada's Flight Plan for 777s Excludes India"* in Globe & Mail *(March 28, 2007, pp. B5)*
Ed: Brent Jang. **Description:** The decision of Air Canada to exclude India and to fly its Boeing 777s due to poor economic returns is discussed. **Availability:** Online.

33097 ■ *"All the Trimmings"* in Green Industry Pro *(Vol. 23, March 2011, No. 3, pp. 29)*
Ed: Gregg Wartgow. **Description:** When choosing lawn mowing equipment, it is advised to purchase commercial-grade 21-inch walk mowers rather than less expensive consumer-grade mowers. John Deere is reentering the commercial 21-inch walk behind mower market after a five-year hiatus. **Availability:** Online.

33098 ■ *"Baltimore Grand Prix Week Schedule Filling Up With Galas, Nonprofit Fundraisers"* in Baltimore Business Journal *(Vol. 29, July 22, 2011, No. 11, pp. 1)*
Pub: Boston Business Journal
Contact: Carolyn M. Jones, President
E-mail: cmjones@bizjournals.com

Ed: Alexander Jackson. **Description:** Baltimore, Maryland-based businesses and nonprofit groups have been planning their own events to coincide with the Baltimore Grand Prix during the Labor Day weekend. They also plan to partner with others in hopes of drumming up new business, raising money or to peddle their brands.

33099 ■ *"Baltimore Ravens Back to Business as NFL Lockout Ends" in Baltimore Business Journal (Vol. 29, July 29, 2011, No. 12, pp. 1)*
Pub: Boston Business Journal
Contact: Carolyn M. Jones, President
E-mail: cmjones@bizjournals.com

Ed: Scott Dance. **Description:** The Baltimore Ravens football team has been marketing open sponsorship packages following the end of the National Football League lockout. Team officials are working to get corporate logos and slogans on radio and television commercials and online advertisements. **Availability:** Print; Online.

33100 ■ *"Baltimore's Co-Working Spaces Introduces New Kind of Cubicle Culture" in Baltimore Business Journal (Vol. 29, August 19, 2011, No. 15, pp. 1)*
Pub: Boston Business Journal
Contact: Carolyn M. Jones, President
E-mail: cmjones@bizjournals.com

Ed: Alexander Jackson. **Description:** Beehive Baltimore offers a co-working space where independent freelancers and entrepreneurs can work. There are two other companies that provide the same service and the value of these services to these professional is that it provides them with an office that is both convenient and affordable aside from letting them network with peers.

33101 ■ *"Bankruptcies" in Crain's Detroit Business (Vol. 24, March 24, 2008, No. 12, pp. 6)*
Pub: Crain Communications Inc.
Contact: Barry Asin, President

Description: Current list of business that filed for Chapter 7 or 11 protection in U.S. Bankruptcy Court in Detroit include a construction company, a medical care company, a physical therapy firm and a communications firm. **Availability:** Online.

33102 ■ *"Barbarians Set Bar Low With Lowly Canadian Telco" in Globe & Mail (March 31, 2007, pp. B1)*
Ed: Derek DeCloet. **Description:** The efforts of the private equity fund Kohlberg, Kravis, Roberts and Co. to acquire the Canadian telecommunications firm BCE are described. **Availability:** Online.

33103 ■ *"Bartering Trades on Talents" in Reading Eagle (June 20, 2010)*
Description: Bartering is not just a way of trading goods and services, it can be an essential tool for small business to survive in a bad economy.

33104 ■ *"The Bell Tolls for Thee" in Canadian Business (Vol. 81, March 3, 2008, No. 3, pp. 36)*
Description: Bell Canada has formed the Canadian Coalition for Tomorrow's IT Skills to solve the shortage of technology talent in the country. Canada's total workforce has only around 4%, or 600,000 people employed in information technology-related fields. The aims of the Bell-led coalition, which is supported by different industry associations and 30 corporations, are investigated. **Availability:** Print; Online.

33105 ■ *"Benchmark Makes Granduca Entrance" in Houston Business Journal (Vol. 40, January 8, 2010, No. 35, pp. 2)*
Pub: Houston Business Journal
Contact: Bob Charlet, President
E-mail: bcharlet@bizjournals.com

Ed: Jennifer Dawson. **Description:** Houston, Texas-based Interfin Company, owner of the Hotel Granduca, has tapped the services of Benchmark Hospitality International to manage the property. The

hiring of Benchmark is part of Interfin's efforts to develop Granduca hotels in other markets. Statistical data included. **Availability:** Print; Online.

33106 ■ *"Bernier Open to Telecom Changes" in Globe & Mail (March 22, 2006, pp. B1)*
Ed: Simon Tuck. **Description:** Federal Industry Minister Maxime Bernier of Canada says that he is open to scrapping restrictions on foreign ownership in telecommunications. His views on telecom industry are detailed. **Availability:** Online.

33107 ■ *Beyond Booked Solid: Your Business, Your Life, Your Way-It's All Inside*
Pub: John Wiley & Sons, Inc.
Contact: Christina Van Tassell, Executive Vice President Chief Financial Officer

Ed: Michael Port. **Released:** December 2010. **Price:** $21.99, e-book; $32.50, hardcover. **Description:** Professional service providers and small business owners will discover tactics and strategies for growing and expanding their companies while allowing them to find time to relax and enjoy their lives. Owners will learn to attract new clients and grow profits. **Availability:** E-book; Print; Online; PDF.

33108 ■ *"Big Trouble at Sony Ericsson" in Barron's (Vol. 88, March 24, 2008, No. 12, pp. M9)*
Pub: Dow Jones & Company Inc.
Contact: Almar Latour, Chief Executive Officer

Ed: Angelo Franchini. **Description:** Sony Ericsson is facing trouble as it warned that its sales and net income before taxes will fall by nearly half for the first quarter of 2008. The joint venture of Sony and Ericsson has a global mobile phone market share of nine percent as of 2007, fourth largest in the world. **Availability:** Online.

33109 ■ *"Black Gold: Jobs Aplenty" in Canadian Business (Vol. 79, August 14, 2006, No. 16-17, pp. 57)*
Pub: Rogers Media Inc.
Contact: Neil Spivak, Chief Executive Officer

Ed: Erin Pooley. **Description:** A list of the top ten jobs in the petroleum industry in Canada along with pay and nature of jobs, is presented. **Availability:** Print; Online.

33110 ■ *"Bombardier Wins Chinese Rail Deal" in Globe & Mail (March 20, 2006, pp. B1)*
Ed: Geoffrey York. **Description:** Bombardier Inc. has won a $68 million (U.S) contract to provide railway cars for rapid transit-link between Beijing and its International airport for 2008 Olympics In China. Details of the contract are presented. **Availability:** Print; Online.

33111 ■ *"Book Yourself Solid: The Fastest, Easiest, and Most Reliable System for Getting More Clients Than You Can Handle"*
Pub: John Wiley & Sons, Inc.
Contact: Christina Van Tassell, Executive Vice President Chief Financial Officer

Released: 3rd edition. **Price:** $22, paperback; $14.99, E-book. **Description:** Self-promotion is essential for successful selling. Strategies, techniques, and skills necessary for success are presented, covering social media marketing strategies for service professionals; pricing models and sales strategies to simplify selling; new networking and outreach plans that take only minutes a day; and new product launches ideas and tactics. **Availability:** E-book; Print.

33112 ■ *"Bountiful Barrels: Where to Find $140 Trillion" in Barron's (Vol. 88, July 14, 2008, No. 28, pp. 40)*
Pub: Dow Jones & Company Inc.
Contact: Almar Latour, Chief Executive Officer

Ed: Andrew Bary. **Description:** Surge in oil prices has caused a large transfer of wealth to oil-producing countries thereby reshaping the global economy. Oil reserves of oil exporting countries are now valued at $140 trillion. Economist Stephen Jen believes that

this wealth will be transformed into paper assets as these countries invest in global stocks and bonds. **Availability:** Online.

33113 ■ *"Brief: Janitorial Company Must Pay Back Wages" in Buffalo News (September 24, 2011)*
Description: Knights Facilities Management, located in Michigan, provides grounds maintenance and janitorial services at the Ralph Wilson Stadium in Buffalo, New York. The US Department of Labor ordered the firm to pay $22,000 in back wages and damages to 26 employees for overtime and minimum wage compensation. Details of the company's violation of the Fair Labor Standards Act are included. **Availability:** Online.

33114 ■ *"Built For Growth" in Canadian Business (Vol. 87, July 2014, No. 7, pp. 50)*
Description: The impressive 7,308 percent revenue growth of FourQuest Energy Inc. has earned it the top spot in the 2014 Profit 500 ranking of Canada's fastest growing firms. The Edmonton, Alberta-based company provides mechanical pre-commissioning, shutdown and maintenance for oil-and-gas facilities and diversifying its service offerings and looking to non oil-and-gas verticals as well. **Availability:** Online.

33115 ■ *"Business Diary" in Crain's Detroit Business (Vol. 24, October 6, 2008, No. 40, pp. 23)*
Pub: Crain Communications Inc.
Contact: Barry Asin, President

Description: Detailed listing of acquisitions, expansions, new products, new services, business contracts and startups from the Detroit area is provided. **Availability:** Print; Online.

33116 ■ *"Butane Heated Pressure Washer Offers Diverse Cleaning Options" in Product News Network (March 8, 2011)*
Description: Profile of the Super Max (TM) 6000B power sprayer the can clean with cold or heated water and wet steam. Daimer Industries, provider of janitorial supplies, announced the availability of the machine that offers a variety of cleaning options for a range of applications. **Availability:** Online.

33117 ■ *"California Restaurant Association Sues to Block Berkeley, Calif., Natural Gas Ban" in Nation's Restaurant News (November 22, 2019)*
URL(s): www.nrn.com/operations/california-restauran t-association-sues-block-berkeley-calif-natural-gas -ban

Ed: Lisa Jennings. **Released:** November 22, 2019. **Description:** After Berkeley became the first U.S. city to approve an ordinance to phase out natural gas pipes in new construction in an effort to go all-electric, the California Restaurant Association sued the city due to chefs needing to cook over a fire. In the complaint, the CRA argues that the ordinance in unenforceable due to conflicts with federal and state laws. **Availability:** Online.

33118 ■ *"Can You Hear Them Now?" in Hawaii Business (Vol. 54, August 2008, No. 2, pp. 48)*
Description: Coral Wireless LLC (dba Mobi PCS) is ranked 237 in Hawaii Business' list of the state's top 250 companies for 2008. The company is a local wireless phone provider, which has expanded its market to Oahu, Maui and the Big Island since opening in 2006, offering 13 phones and unlimited texts and calls. Details on the company's sales are provided. **Availability:** Print; Online.

33119 ■ *"Carbon Capture and Storage: Grave Concerns" in Canadian Business (Vol. 81, July 21 2008, No. 11, pp. 25)*
Ed: Andrew Nikiforuk. **Released:** January 01, 2017. **Description:** Air pollution control regulations to reduce greenhouse gasses have been implemented by the Canadian government. The federal government is planning to construct a carbon funeral industry that will store the global warming gases, however the expenditure for the project will be shifted

to the taxpayers. Details of the Bruce Peachy's initiative on how to reduce GHGs are presented. **Availability:** Print; Online.

33120 ■ *"The Case of the Deflated IPO" in Boston Business Journal (Vol. 29, June 24, 2011, No. 7, pp. 1)*
Pub: Boston Business Journal
Contact: Carolyn M. Jones, President
E-mail: cmjones@bizjournals.com
Ed: Scott Dance. **Description:** IPO market is on the rebound from the recession but for some companies in Maryland, the time is not yet ripe to go public. One of the companies that chooses to wait for better timing is SafeNet Inc. and it is eyeing some possible acquisitions while doing so. **Availability:** Print; Online.

33121 ■ *"The Caterer Interview - Patrick Harbour and Nathan Jones" in Caterer & Hotelkeeper (October 28, 2011, No. 288)*
Description: Profiles of Patrick Harbour and Nathan Jones who quit their jobs to start their own catering business. The partners discuss their business strategy when launching their boutique catering firm and ways they are adapting to the slow economy in order to remain successful. **Availability:** Print; Mailing list; Online.

33122 ■ *"The CEO Poll: Fuel for Thought II Canadian Business Leaders on Energy Policy" in Canadian Business (Vol. 81, September 15, 2008, No. 14-15, pp. 12)*
Pub: Rogers Media Inc.
Contact: Neil Spivak, Chief Executive Officer
Ed: Joe Castaldo. **Description:** Most Canadian business leaders worry about the unreliability of the oil supply but feel that Canada is in a better position to benefit from the energy supply crisis than other countries. Many respondents also highlighted the need to invest in renewable energy sources. **Availability:** Online.

33123 ■ *"Certification Experts Germanischer Lloyd Wind Energy Assist NaiKun's Offshore Wind Project" in Marketwired (May 14, 2007)*
Pub: Comtex News Network Inc.
Contact: Kan Devnani, President
Description: Germanischer Lloyd Wind Energy (GL Wind) will examine, inspect, and provide quality management services for the engineering, design, and construction of the offshore wind project planned by NaiKun Wind Development Inc. in northwest British Columbia. **Availability:** Online.

33124 ■ *"Certified Technicians can Increase Bottom Line" in Contractor (Vol. 56, September 2009, No. 9, pp. 37)*
Ed: Ray Isaac. **Description:** Certified technicians increase the value of HVAC firms, a survey by Service Round Table has reported. The increased value has been attributed to fewer callbacks, less warranty work and greater ability to educate consumers. Meanwhile, consumers are willing to pay more for the services of certified technicians. **Availability:** Print; Online.

33125 ■ *"City Seeks More Minorities" in Austin Business Journal Inc. (Vol. 28, November 7, 2008, No. 34, pp. A1)*
Pub: Austin Business Journal
Contact: Rachel McGrath, Director
E-mail: rmcgrath@bizjournals.com
Ed: Jean Kwon. **Description:** Austin, Texas is planning to increase the participation of minority- and women-owned businesses in government contracts. Contractors are required to show 'good faith' to comply with the specified goals. The city is planning to effect the changes in the construction and professional services sector. **Availability:** Print; Online.

33126 ■ *"Columbia's JPB Raising $175M to Acquire Companies, Real Estate" in Boston Business Journal (Vol. 29, May 27, 2011, No. 3, pp. 1)*
Pub: Boston Business Journal
Contact: Carolyn M. Jones, President

E-mail: cmjones@bizjournals.com
Ed: Gary Haber. **Description:** JPB Enterprises is preparing to raise $175 million in its goal of acquiring companies and real estate that are major names in America. The $75 million will be raised for a buyout fund that will target wide range of industries while the $100 million will be used for land investment projects in the Florida Panhandle. Baltimore firms are expected to benefit from this deal. **Availability:** Print; Online.

33127 ■ *"Compelling Opportunities for Investors in Emerging Markets" in Barron's (Vol. 88, March 10, 2008, No. 10, pp. 39)*
Pub: Dow Jones & Company Inc.
Contact: Almar Latour, Chief Executive Officer
Ed: Neil A. Martin. **Description:** Michael L. Reynal, portfolio manager of Principal International Emerging Markets Fund, is bullish on the growth prospects of stocks in emerging markets. He is investing big on energy, steel, and transportation companies. **Availability:** Online.

33128 ■ *"Complete Discovery Source, Inc. (CDS) Receives Minority Owned Business Certification" in Marketwired (December 14, 2010)*
Pub: Comtex News Network Inc.
Contact: Kan Devnani, President
Description: Complete Discovery Source Inc. (CDS) was granted Minority-Owned Business Enterprise status by the New York State Department of Economic Development. The certification provides CDS, an end-to-end eDiscovery services provider, with access to contracting opportunities with 130 government agencies throughout New York state. **Availability:** Print; Online.

33129 ■ *"CPI Corp. Acquires Assets of Bella Pictures" in Benzinga.com (January 28, 2011)*
Pub: PR Newswire Association LLC.
Description: CPI Corporation acquired assets of Bella Pictures Inc., a leading provider of branded wedding photography services. Details of the acquisition are explained. **Availability:** Online.

33130 ■ *"CPR-CN Deal to Ease Vancouver Logjam" in Globe & Mail (January 27, 2006, pp. B4)*
Description: In a bid to lessen West coast port grid lock Canadian Pacific Railway Ltd and Canadian National Railway Co. has agreed to share tracks in the Vancouver region. This will allow the trains to operate more efficiently from the Vancouver Port. **Availability:** Print; Online.

33131 ■ *"Customer Retention is Proportionate to Employee Retention" in Green Industry Pro (Vol. 23, September 2011)*
Description: Presented in a question-answer format, information is provided to help retain customers as well as keeping workers happy. **Availability:** Online.

33132 ■ *"Customized Before Custom Was Cool" in Green Industry Pro (July 2011)*
Ed: Gregg Wartgow. **Description:** Profile of Turf Care Enterprises and owner Kevin Vogeler, who discusses his desire to use more natural programs using little or no chemicals in 1986. At that time, that sector represented 20 percent of his business, today it shares 80 percent. **Availability:** Online.

33133 ■ *"Debt-Collection Agency to Lay Off 368 in Hampton Center" in Virginian-Pilot (December 4, 2010)*
Pub: The Virginian-Pilot
Contact: Kevin Goyette, Director
E-mail: kgoyette@dailypress.com
Ed: Tom Shean. **Description:** NCO Financial Systems Inc., provider of debt-collection and outsourcing services will permanently lay off 368 workers at its Hampton call center in 2011. **Availability:** Print; Online.

33134 ■ *"Deep in the Heart of Drought" in Green Industry Pro (Vol. 23, October 2011)*
Ed: Gregg Wartgow. **Description:** Challenges faced by landscape contractors during the recent drought in Texas are explored. Despite these challenges, opportunity for contractors providing irrigation services has risen. **Availability:** Online.

33135 ■ *Delivering Knock Your Socks Off Service*
Pub: American Management Association
Contact: Manny Avramidis, President
Availability: Print.

33136 ■ *"Designing an Office Around Your Company's Goals How Eventbrite Learned That a Workspace Becomes Much More Than an Office Once Your Team Weighs In" in Inc. (Vol. 36, September 2014, No. 7, pp. 122)*
Pub: Mansueto Ventures L.L.C.
Contact: Stephanie Mehta, Chief Executive Officer
Released: September 2014. **Description:** Julia Hartz, co-founder and president of an online ticketing and event planning service, Eventbrite, shares insight into designing her firm's new office space. She opened suggestions from all employees to come up with the right environment to suit her workers. **Availability:** Print; Online.

33137 ■ *"DIA Contract Sets a Record for Denver Minority, Woman-Owned Business" in Denver Business Journal (Vol. 65, February 21, 2014, No. 41)*
Pub: American City Business Journals, Inc.
Contact: Mike Olivieri, Executive Vice President
Released: Weekly. **Description:** The City of Denver, Colorado has awarded a $39.6 million contract to Burgess Services Inc. to construct a transit and hotel project near the Denver International Airport. Burgess Services is owned by Denise Burgess. This is the largest public contract awarded to a woman0 or minority-owned business in the city's history. **Availability:** Print; Online.

33138 ■ *"Do the Right Thing" in Contractor (Vol. 56, December 2009, No. 12, pp. 16)*
Ed: Robert P. Mader. **Description:** Applewood Plumbing, Heating and Electric has won Contractor magazine's 2009 Contractor of the Year Award. The company has ranked eighth among more than 300 service companies in the United States. A brief history of the company is also provided. **Availability:** Print; Online.

33139 ■ *"Dollar General Selects GSI Commerce to Launch Its eCommerce Business" in Benzinga.com (October 29, 2011)*
Pub: Benzinga.com
Contact: Jason Raznick, Founder
Description: Dollar General Corporation chose GSI Commerce, a leading provider of ecommerce and interactive marketing solutions, to launch its online initiative. GSI Commerce is an eBay Inc. company. **Availability:** Online.

33140 ■ *"Don't Hang Up On FairPoint" in Barron's (Vol. 88, July 7, 2008, No. 27, pp. M5)*
Description: Shares of FairPoint Communications, priced at $6.63 each, are undervalued and should be worth over $12 each. The company increased its size by more than five times by acquiring Verizon's local telephone operations in Vermont, New Hampshire, and Maine, but must switch customers in those areas into their system by the end of September 2007. **Availability:** Online.

33141 ■ *"Don't' Hate the Cable Guy" in Saint Louis Business Journal (Vol. 31, August 5, 2011, No. 50, pp. 1)*
Pub: Saint Louis Business Journal
Contact: Robert Bobroff, President
E-mail: rbobroff@bizjournals.com

Ed: Angela Mueller. **Description:** Charter Communications named John Birrer as senior vice president of customer experience. The company experienced problems with its customer services. **Availability:** Print; Online.

33142 ■ *"Dozens 'Come Alive' in Downtown Chicago"* in Green Industry Pro (July 2011)

Ed: Gregg Wartgow. **Description:** Highlights from the Come Alive Outside training event held in Chicago, Illinois July 14-15, 2011 are shared. Nearly 80 people representing 38 landscape companies attended the event that helps contractors review their services and find ways to sell them in new and various ways. **Availability:** Online.

33143 ■ *"Drilling Deep and Flying High"* in Barron's (Vol. 88, June 30, 2008, No. 26, pp. 34)

Pub: Dow Jones & Company Inc.

Contact: Almar Latour, Chief Executive Officer

Ed: Kenneth Rapoza. **Description:** Shares of Petrobras could rise another 25 percent if the three deepwater wells that the company has found proves as lucrative as some expect. Petrobras will become an oil giant if the reserves are proven. **Availability:** Online.

33144 ■ *"Energy MPLs: Pipeline to Profits"* in Barron's (Vol. 89, July 27, 2009, No. 30, pp. 9)

Pub: Dow Jones & Company Inc.

Contact: Almar Latour, Chief Executive Officer

Ed: Dimitra DeFotis. **Description:** Energy master limited partnership stocks are range-bound in the next few months from July 2009 but there are there are some opportunities that remain. These include Energy Transfer Equity, Enterprise GP holdings, NuStar GP Holdings, and Plains All American Pipeline. **Availability:** Online.

33145 ■ *"Entrepreneurship and Service Innovation"* in Journal of Business & Industrial Marketing (Vol. 29, July 2014, No. 6)

Pub: Emerald Group Publishing Limited

Contact: Erika Valenti, President

Description: An overview of entrepreneurship and service innovation and the association between entrepreneurial orientation, innovation, and entrepreneurship or new entry. Analysis of secondary data was performed and observed that EO (entrepreneurial orientation), innovation, and entrepreneurship feature a triadic connect. EO supports innovation, innovation endorses new venture creation, and it in turn commercializes innovations. **Availability:** Download; Online.

33146 ■ *Exceptional Service, Exceptional Profit: The Secrets of Building a Five-Star Customer Service Organization*

Pub: HarperCollins Leadership

Contact: Donald Miller, Chief Executive Officer

Ed: Leonardo Inghilleri, Micah Solomon. **Released:** April 14, 2010. **Price:** $19.99, paperback. **Description:** Team of insiders share exclusive knowledge of the loyalty-building techniques pioneered by the world's most successful service leaders, including brick-and-mortar stars such as The Ritz-Carlton and Lexus and online success stories such as Netflix and CD Baby. **Availability:** E-book; Print.

33147 ■ *"Executive Decision: XM Mulls Betting the Bank in Competitive Game of Subscriber Growth"* in Globe & Mail (March 18, 2006, pp. B3)

Ed: Grant Robertson. **Description:** Canadian Satellite Radio Inc., XM Canada, president and Chief Operating Officer Stephen Tapp feel that establishing a profile in satellite radio to attract subscribers is a very big challenge. His views on the Canadian radio market are detailed. **Availability:** Print; Online.

33148 ■ *"A Few Points of Contention"* in Barron's (Vol. 88, July 14, 2008, No. 28, pp. 3)

Pub: Dow Jones & Company Inc.

Contact: Almar Latour, Chief Executive Officer

Ed: Michael Santoli. **Description:** Headline inflation tends to revert to the lower core inflation, which excludes food and energy in its calculation over long periods. Prominent private equity figures believe that regulators should allow more than the de facto 10 percent to 25 percent limit of commercial banks to hasten the refunding of the financial sector. **Availability:** Online.

33149 ■ *"Fifth Third Spinoff Eyes More Space"* in Business Courier (Vol. 27, July 16, 2010, No. 11, pp. 1)

Pub: Business Courier

Ed: Dan Monk, Steve Watkins. **Description:** Electronic-funds transfer company Fifth Third Solutions (FTPS), a spinoff of Fifth Third Bancorp, is seeking as much as 200,000 square feet of new office space in Ohio. The bank's sale of 51 percent ownership stake to Boston-based Advent International Corporation has paved the way for the growth of FTPS. How real estate brokers' plans have responded to FTPS' growth mode is discussed. **Availability:** Print; Online.

33150 ■ *"Finding a Way to Continue Growing"* in Green Industry Pro (Vol. 23, March 2011, No. 3, pp. 31)

Ed: Gregg Wartgow. **Description:** Profile of Brett Lemcke, VP of R.M. Landscape located in Rochester, New York. Lemcke tells how his Landscape Industry Certified credentials helped him to grow his business and beat out his competition. **Availability:** Online.

33151 ■ *"Firms Bet On Games To Hike Wellness"* in Business Journal (Vol. 30, June 1, 2012, No. 1, pp. 1)

Pub: American City Business Journals, Inc.

Contact: Mike Olivieri, Executive Vice President

Ed: Katharine Grayson. **Released:** Weekly. **Price:** $4, introductory 4-week offer(Digital only). **Description:** Twin Cities-based firms providing corporate wellness services are integrating games into these programs. These games include friendly competitions between work teams or high-tech smartphone applications. **Availability:** Print; Online.

33152 ■ *"Five Distinct Divisions, One Collective Focus"* in Green Industry Pro (Vol. 23, October 2011)

Ed: Gregg Wartgow. **Description:** Profile of ACLS Inc., an amalgamation of All Commercial Landscape Service (commercial maintenance), All Custom Landscape Service (design/build), Fresno Tree Service, Certified Water Consulting (irrigation), and Tractor Service (disking and flailing services on everything from one-acre lots to hundreds of acres of open land). The firm discusses its rebranding effort in order to increase sales. **Availability:** Online.

33153 ■ *"Fix-It Careers: Jobs in Repair"* in Occupational Outlook Quarterly (Vol. 54, Fall 2010, No. 3, pp. 26)

Pub: U.S. Department of Labor Bureau of Labor Statistics

Contact: Amrit Kohli, Director

E-mail: kohli.amrit@bls.gov

Ed: Elka Maria Torpey. **Description:** Auto mechanics and HVAC technician occupations require repair skills. Advantages for individuals with proper skills are outlined. **Availability:** Online; PDF.

33154 ■ *"Flat or Slight Decline Seen for Nortel 2007 Revenue"* in Globe & Mail (March 17, 2007, pp. B3)

Ed: Catherine McLean. **Description:** The forecast about Nortel Network Corp's decrease in the 2007 revenue and its restructuring to reduce costs is discussed. **Availability:** Online.

33155 ■ *"Flights of Fancy"* in Crain's Chicago Business (Vol. 31, April 21, 2008, No. 16, pp. 27)

Ed: Sarah A. Klein. **Released:** June 17, 2017. **Description:** Due to the competition for business travelers, who account for 30 percent of airline revenue, airlines are offering a number of luxury amenities, especially on long-haul routes. **Availability:** Print; Online.

33156 ■ *"Flying the Unfriendly Skies"* in Crain's Chicago Business (Vol. 31, April 21, 2008, No. 16, pp. 26)

Pub: Crain Communications Inc.

Contact: Barry Asin, President

Ed: Sarah A. Klein. **Description:** Due to the number of Chicago companies and entrepreneurs who are traveling overseas more frequently in order to strengthen ties with customers, companies and oftentimes even business partners, the number of flights leaving O'Hare International Airport for destinations abroad has surged; In 2007, international passengers departing O'Hare totaled 5.7 million, up from 2.4 million in 1990. **Availability:** Online.

33157 ■ *"Forward Motion"* in Green Industry Pro (July 2011)

Ed: Gregg Wartgow. **Description:** Several landscape contractors have joined this publication's Working Smarter Training Challenge over the last year. This process is helping them develop ways to improve work processes, boost morale, drive out waste, reduce costs, improve customer service, and be more competitive. **Availability:** Print; Online.

33158 ■ *"France Telecom Takes Minitel Offline"* in Canadian Business (Vol. 85, August 13, 2012, No. 13, pp. 12)

Ed: Matthew McClearn. **Description:** The Minitel online service was developed to reduce the costs of printing phone directories in the French postal and telecommunications ministry in 1978 and became popular in Paris in 1982. With its user-based halved annually and services declining in its waning years, France Telecom opted to terminate the service on June 30, 2012. **Availability:** Print; Online.

33159 ■ *"Friedland's Next Frontier: Drilling for Oil in Iraq"* in Globe & Mail (April 20, 2007, pp. B1)

Ed: Wendy Stueck. **Description:** The decision of the Canadian oil and gas company Ivanhoe Energy Inc. to partner with the Japanese oil and gas firm INPEX Corp. for the development of heavy oil fields in north central Iraq is discussed. **Availability:** Print; Online.

33160 ■ *"The Future of Work"* in Black Enterprise (Vol. 41, August 2010, No. 1, pp. 65)

Pub: Earl G. Graves Ltd.

Contact: Earl Graves, Jr., President

Ed: Annya M. Lott. **Description:** Technology, globalization, and outsourcing will continue to shape the future of work. Social media is a means for small companies to market goods and services. **Availability:** Online.

33161 ■ *"Gadget of the Week: Easy as a Snap"* in Barron's (Vol. 90, September 13, 2010, No. 37, pp. 35)

Pub: Barron's Editorial & Corporate Headquarters

Ed: Jay Palmer. **Description:** SanMyPhotos.com offers a service whereby people can receive an empty box they can fill with photos then send back to the company to be stored digitally. The photos are returned to the customer with a disc containing the digital photographs. The service costs $150 for one box and $300 for three boxes. **Availability:** Online.

33162 ■ *"Gain the 'Come Alive Outside' Selling Edge"* in Green Industry Pro (July 2011)

Ed: Jim Paluch. **Description:** Marketing the 'Come Alive Outside' slogan can help landscapers to increase their market share by identifying and applying these elements to each customer as well as their workers. **Availability:** Online.

33163 ■ *"Giving Biotech Startups a Hand"* in Philadelphia Business Journal (Vol. 28, January 8, 2010, No. 47, pp. 1)

Pub: Philadelphia Business Journal

Contact: Sierra Quinn, Director

E-mail: squinn@bizjournals.com

Ed: John George. **Description:** Elkins Park, Pennsylvania-based BioStrategy Partners is a virtual life sciences incubator that is seeking to improve the dull ranking of Philadelphia in the small business vitality index of life sciences. BioStrategy provides technology and business development services to startup life sciences companies and university-based research projects. **Availability:** Online.

33164 ■ *"Good Going, Partners"* **in** *Barron's* **(Vol. 89, July 27, 2009, No. 30, pp. M8)**

Pub: Dow Jones & Company Inc.

Contact: Almar Latour, Chief Executive Officer

Ed: Shirley A. Lazo. **Description:** Four master limited partnerships boosted their dividends. Sunoco Logistics raised theirs by 11.2 percent, El Paso Pipeline by 12 percent, Holly Energy upped their dividends by a penny, and Western Gas hiked their dividend to 31 cents per unit. **Availability:** Online.

33165 ■ *"The Green Industry Jobs Gap"* **in** *Green Industry Pro* **(Vol. 23, October 2011)**

Ed: Gregg Wartgow. **Description:** According to the U.S. Bureau of Labor Statistics, the landscaping industry employs over 829,000 workers. According to another private study, the industry would employ more if they were able to find more people interested in performing the required work. **Availability:** Online.

33166 ■ *"Grey Power: On Target"* **in** *Canadian Business* **(Vol. 81, July 22, 2008, No. 12-13, pp. 45)**

Pub: Rogers Media Inc.

Contact: Neil Spivak, Chief Executive Officer

Ed: Calvin Leung. **Description:** Companies such as LavalifePRIME, a dating website devoted to singles 45 and older, discuss the value of marketing and services aimed at Canada's older consumers. One-third of Canada's 33 million people are 50-plus, controlling 77 percent of the countries wealth. **Availability:** Print; Online.

33167 ■ *"Groomers Eye Profit Growth Through Services"* **in** *Pet Product News* **(Vol. 64, December 2010, No. 12, pp. 26)**

Ed: Kathleen M. Mangan. **Description:** Pet groomers can successfully offer add-on services by taking into account insider customer knowledge, store image, and financial analysis in the decision-making process. Many pet groomers have decided to add services such as spa treatments and training due to a slump in the bathing and grooming business. How some pet groomers gained profitability through add-on services is explored. **Availability:** Online.

33168 ■ *"Growth at E Solutions Part of 'Opportunistic' Data Center Market"* **in** *Tampa Bay Business Journal* **(Vol. 30, January 29, 2010, No. 6, pp. 1)**

Pub: Tampa Bay Business Journal

Contact: Ian Anderson, President

E-mail: ianderson@bizjournals.com

Ed: Michael Hinman. **Description:** E Solutions Corporation is experiencing growth amid the economic downturn, with its Park Tower data center occupancy in Tampa Florida expanding from 14,000 square feet to 20,000 square feet. Details on the increased operations fueled by demand for information storage and management services offered by the company are discussed. **Availability:** Print; Online.

33169 ■ *"Headwinds From the New Sod Slow Aer Lingus"* **in** *Barron's* **(Vol. 88, March 10, 2008, No. 10, pp. M6)**

Pub: Dow Jones & Company Inc.

Contact: Almar Latour, Chief Executive Officer

Ed: Sean Walters, Arindam Nag. **Description:** Aer Lingus faces a drop in its share prices with a falling US market, higher jet fuel prices, and lower long-haul passenger load factors. British media companies Johnston Press and Yell Group are suffering from weaker ad revenue and heavier debt payments due to the credit crunch. **Availability:** Online.

33170 ■ *Heart: Building a Great Brand in the Digital Age*

Pub: CreateSpace

Released: September 29, 2014. **Price:** $3.70, paperback. **Description:** Business leader and consultant who works with designers, contractors and service providers in the green industry helps business owners develop and implement company systems and increase revenue. His is a third-generation horticulturist and small business owner and share the challenges of being an entrepreneur. **Availability:** Print.

33171 ■ *"The Heat Is On"* **in** *Crain's Chicago Business* **(Vol. 31, April 28, 2008, No. 17, pp. 4)**

Pub: Crain Communications Inc.

Contact: Barry Asin, President

Ed: Steve Daniels. **Description:** Discusses Nicor Inc., a natural-gas utility serving 2 million customers in Chicago's suburbs, and its potential acquirers; shares of the company have dropped 17 percent this year making Nicor the second-worst among 31 utilities in an index tracked by Standrd & Poor's. Statistical data included.

33172 ■ *"Hey, You Can't Do That"* **in** *Green Industry Pro* **(Vol. 23, September 2011)**

Ed: Rod Dickens. **Description:** Manufacturers of landscape equipment are making better use of energy resources, such as the use of fuel-injection systems instead of carburetors, lightweight materials, better lubricants, advanced battery technology, and innovative engine designs. **Availability:** Online.

33173 ■ *"H.I.G. Capital Announces Acquisition of Next Generation Vending"* **in** *Benzinga.com* **(October 29, 2011)**

Pub: Benzinga.com

Contact: Jason Raznick, Founder

Description: H.I.G. Capital LLC, a leader in global private investments, acquired Next Generation Vending and Food Service Inc. Next Generation is a provider of vending services for corporate and institutional clients in Northeastern United States. **Availability:** Print; PDF; Online.

33174 ■ *"Higher Freight Rates Keep CPR Rolling in Profit"* **in** *Globe & Mail* **(February 1, 2008, pp. B3)**

Description: Canadian Pacific Railway Ltd. posted $135.4 million in revenues for fourth quarter 2005. The company's earnings projections for 2006 and workforce reduction plans are presented. **Availability:** Print; Online.

33175 ■ *"Home Improvement Service Chain Had to Fix Its Own House"* **in** *Crain's Detroit Business* **(Vol. 30, October 13, 2014, No. 41, pp. 15)**

Pub: Crain Communications Inc.

Contact: Barry Asin, President

Description: Mr. Handyman International LLC is the franchising arm for the Mr. Handyman home improvement service chain. The franchises provide smaller home repair and improvement projects, mostly residential with only 15 percent of the jobs being commercial. Statistical data included. **Availability:** Online.

33176 ■ *"Houston (Texas) Computer Repair Adds U-Haul Rentals"* **in** *Benzinga.com* **(March 29, 2012)**

Pub: PR Newswire Association LLC.

Description: Houston Computer Repair has added U-Haul truck and trailer rentals in order to diversify the company. The firm also offers moving equipment and supplies for household furnishings, which includes moving vans, open trailers, closed trailers, furniture pads, appliance dollies, furniture dollies, tow dollies and auto transports. The company also continues to provide computer repair service along with shipping and packaging services. **Availability:** Online.

33177 ■ *"How to Develop an Active Sales Program"* **in** *Green Industry Pro* **(Vol. 23, September 2011)**

Ed: Gregg Wartgow. **Description:** Craig den Hartog, owner of Emerald Magic Lawn Care located in Holtsville, New York, describes the various marketing tactics he has developed to increase sales in the current economic environment. Statistical data included. **Availability:** Online.

33178 ■ *"How to Dominate in Residential Maintenance"* **in** *Green Industry Pro* **(Vol. 23, October 2011)**

Ed: Gregg Wartgow. **Description:** Lawn care services were ranked among the most expendable consumer expenditures, according to the National Retail Federation data accumulated in early 2011. This makes it critical for any landscape firm to target sales efforts toward higher-income households and higher-value homes. **Availability:** Online.

33179 ■ *"How Growers Buy"* **in** *Farm Industry News* **(Vol. 42, January 1, 2009, No. 1)**

Pub: Informa USA, Inc.

Contact: Stephen A. Carter, Chief Executive Officer

Ed: Karen McMahon. **Description:** According to a survey regarding the buying habits among large commercial growers, most prefer to purchase from local retailers, customer service is important concerning their decision on who to buy products from, and price and convenience seem to be more important then brand.

33180 ■ *"How Our Picks Beat The Bear"* **in** *Barron's* **(Vol. 88, July 14, 2008, No. 28, pp. 18)**

Pub: Dow Jones & Company Inc.

Contact: Almar Latour, Chief Executive Officer

Ed: Andrew Bary. **Description:** Performance of the stocks that Barron's covered in the first half of 2008 is discussed; some of the worst picks and most rewarding pans have been in the financial sector while the best plays were in the energy, materials, and the transportation sectors. **Availability:** Online.

33181 ■ *"How To Disaster-Proof Your Business"* **in** *Inc.* **(Vol. 33, September 2011, No. 7, pp. 38)**

Pub: Inc. Magazine

Ed: J.J. McCorvey, Dave Smith. **Description:** Twelve products and services designed to help small businesses run smoothly in the event of a disaster are outlined. **Availability:** Online.

33182 ■ *"Huberman Failing to Keep CTA on Track"* **in** *Crain's Chicago Business* **(Vol. 31, April 21, 2008, No. 16, pp. 22)**

Pub: Crain Communications Inc.

Contact: Barry Asin, President

Description: Discusses the deplorable service of CTA, the Chicago Transit Authority, as well as CTA President Ron Huberman who, up until last week had riders hoping he had the management skills necessary to fix the system's problems; Tuesday's event left hundreds of riders trapped for hours and thousands standing on train platforms along the Blue Line waiting for trains that never came. **Availability:** Online.

33183 ■ *"In Surging Oil Industry, Good Fortune Comes In Stages"* **in** *Barron's* **(Vol. 88, July 7, 2008, No. 27, pp. 12)**

Pub: Dow Jones & Company Inc.

Contact: Almar Latour, Chief Executive Officer

Ed: Sandra Ward. **Description:** Shares of US land oil and gas driller Helmerich and Payne, priced at $69 each, are estimated to be at peak levels. The shares are trading at 17 times 2008 earnings and could be in for some profit taking. **Availability:** Online.

33184 ■ *"Ingrian and Channel Management International Sign Distribution Agreement"* **in** *Canadian Corporate News* **(May 16, 2007)**

Description: Channel Management International (CMI), a Canadian channel management and distribution company, and Ingrian Networks, Inc., the leading provider of data privacy solutions, announced a Canadian distribution agreement to resell Ingrian encryption solutions to the Canadian market. **Availability:** Online.

33185 ■ *"Innovation: A Blood Test on a Chip"* **in Inc. (Vol. 33, November 2011, No. 9, pp. 42)**
Pub: Inc. Magazine

Ed: Christine Chafkin-Lagorio. **Description:** Harvard University researchers have developed a device called the mChip that produces accurate blood tests in about 10 minutes. Plans to apply for FDA approval for the mChip in the US should happen in 2012. **Availability:** Online.

33186 ■ *"IRS Proposing New Tip Reporting Program for Service Business Owners"* **in Small Business Trends(February 7, 2023)**
URL(s): smallbiztrends.com/2023/02/irs-proposing
-new-tip-reporting-program.html
Ed: Gabrielle Pickard-Whitehead. **Released:** February 07, 2023. **Description:** A new program for voluntary tip reporting is discussed. **Availability:** Online.

33187 ■ *"Jacksonville-based Interline Expanding in Janitorial-Sanitation Market"* **in Florida Times-Union (May 10, 2011)**
Pub: Florida Times-Union

Ed: Mark Basch. **Description:** Interline Brands Inc., located in Jacksonville, Florida, aims to grow its business with two recent acquisitions of firms that distribute janitorial and sanitation products. Interline markets and distributes maintenance, repair and operations products. **Availability:** Online.

33188 ■ *"Janitorial Equipment and Supplies US Market"* **in PR Newswire (October 24, 2011)**
Description: United States demand for janitorial equipment and supplies (excluding chemical products) is predicted to rise 2.4 percent per year to $7.6 billion in 2013. New product development will lead to increased sales of higher-value goods in the industry. **Availability:** Print; Online.

33189 ■ *"Juiced on Energy"* **in Barron's (Vol. 88, July 14, 2008, No. 28, pp. 33)**
Pub: Dow Jones & Company Inc.
Contact: Almar Latour, Chief Executive Officer

Ed: Leslie P. Norton. **Description:** Brad Evans and his team at Heartland Value Plus were able to outperform their peers by significantly under-committing to financials and overexposing themselves with energy stocks. Brad Evans believes that there is a lot of value left in energy stocks such as natural gas. **Availability:** Online.

33190 ■ *"Just Be Nice: Providing Good Customer Service"* **in Canadian Business (Vol. 79, October 9, 2006, No. 20, pp. 141)**
Pub: Rogers Media Inc.
Contact: Neil Spivak, Chief Executive Officer

Ed: Joe Castaldo. **Description:** The customer relationship management strategies on customer retention and satisfaction adopted by WestJet are discussed. **Availability:** Print; Online.

33191 ■ *"Just Hang Up"* **in Barron's (Vol. 88, March 10, 2008, No. 10, pp. 45)**
Description: Sprint's shares are expected to continue falling while the company attempts to attract subscribers by cutting prices, cutting earnings in the process. The company faces tougher competition from better-financed AT&T and Verizon Communications.

33192 ■ *"Keeping Railcars 'Busy At All Times' At TTX"* **in Crain's Chicago Business (Vol. 31, April 28, 2008, No. 17, pp. 6)**
Pub: Crain Communications Inc.
Contact: Barry Asin, President

Ed: Bob Tita. **Description:** Profile of the president of Chicago railcar pool operator TTX Co. and his business plan for the company which includes improving fleet management and car purchasing through better use of data on railroad demand. **Availability:** Online.

33193 ■ *"Kinek Offers Secure Prescription Drop-Off For Online Shoppers"* **in Pittsburgh Post-Gazette (June 14, 2012)**
Description: Canadian firm, Kinek, founded in 2009 in New Brunswick, provides drop-off point locations for online shoppers. Med-Fast Pharmacy in Western Pennsylvania joined the Kinek network to provide prescription pickup. The service can be used for most online purchases, including those made on Amazon or eBay. Some drop off sites charge a fee, others are free. **Availability:** Print; Online.

33194 ■ *"Knox County Schools Debate Outsourcing Janitorial Services"* **in (March 29, 2011)**
Description: Custodial services of Knox County Schools in Tennessee may be outsourced in move to save money for the school district. Details of the proposed program are included. **Availability:** Print; Online.

33195 ■ *"Labor of Love"* **in Green Industry Pro (Vol. 23, March 2011, No. 3, pp. 14)**
Ed: Gregg Wartgow. **Description:** Profile of CLS Landscape Management in Chino, California and its owner who started the company when he was 21 years old. Kevin Davis built his landscape firm into a $20 million a year business without using any dedicated salesperson. **Availability:** Online.

33196 ■ *"Local Hotels Brace for Downturn"* **in Crain's Chicago Business (Vol. 31, March 31, 2008, No. 13, pp. 3)**
Pub: Crain Communications Inc.
Contact: Barry Asin, President

Ed: Bob Tita. **Description:** Chicago hotels are seeing a noticeable drop in business-related guests so far this year due to a slumping national economy, tighter corporate expense budgets and higher airfares. **Availability:** Online.

33197 ■ *Low-Budget Online Marketing for Small Business*
Pub: Self-Counsel Press Inc.
Contact: Diana Douglas, Governor

Ed: Holly Berkley. **Released:** 3rd edition. **Price:** C$21.95; $20.95; $20.95; C$21.95; C$12.99; C$21.95. **Description:** Low budget advertising campaigns are presented to help market any small business. **Availability:** CD-ROM; Print; Download; Electronic publishing; PDF.

33198 ■ *"Lower Prices No Shoo-In as Telcos Near Deregulation"* **in Globe & Mail (March 28, 2007, pp. B1)**
Ed: Catherine McLean. **Description:** The fall in market share and low quality of service among other issues that may disallow telecommunication industries in Canada from setting their phone rates is discussed. **Availability:** Online.

33199 ■ *"Market Resource Set for Expansion: Supply Chain Firm to Add Up to 700 Employees"* **in Memphis Business Journal (Vol. 34, May 11, 2012, No. 4, pp. 1)**
Pub: Baltimore Business Journal
Contact: Rhonda Pringle, President
E-mail: rpringle@bizjournals.com

Description: Market Resource Packaging LLC is planning to expand its operation in Memphis, Tennessee under the new ownership of IAM Acquisition. The supply chain services company plans to increase its distribution space from 260,000 square feet to 1 million square feet in three years and to grow its employees from 300 to 1,000 in 18 months. **Availability:** Print; Online.

33200 ■ *Marketing for Entrepreneurs*
Pub: FT Press

Ed: Jurgen Wolff. **Released:** 1st edition. **Description:** This text identifies marketing as the entire process of researching, creating, distributing and selling a product or service. It isn't about theory and metrics, rather it is a practical guide that starts with the basics of all marketing aspects. **Availability:** Print.

33201 ■ *"Mary Kramer: Good Things Happen When We Buy Local"* **in Crain's Detroit Business (Vol. 24, October 6, 2008, No. 40, pp. 7)**
Pub: Crain Communications Inc.
Contact: Barry Asin, President

Description: Michigan is facing incredibly difficult economic times. One way in which each one of us can help the state and the businesses located here is by purchasing our goods and services from local vendors. The state Agriculture Department projected that if Michigan households earmarked $10 per week in their grocery purchases to made-in-Michigan products, this would generate $30 million a week in economic impact. **Availability:** Online.

33202 ■ *"Microsoft's Diversity Program Clicks into High Speed"* **in Hispanic Business (Vol. 30, July-August 2008, No. 7-8, pp. 54)**
Ed: Derek Reveron. **Description:** Microsoft's diversity hiring and vendor diversity program to capture more Hispanic consumer and business-to-business market is described. One of the main goals of these programs is to hire more Hispanic executives and managers who will help the company develop and market products and services that will appeal and benefit Hispanic consumers.

33203 ■ *"A Mixed-Bag Quarter"* **in Barron's (Vol. 88, July 7, 2008, No. 27, pp. 19)**
Description: Seven component companies of the Dow Jones Industrial Average increased their dividend payouts in the second quarter of 2008 despite the weak performance of the index. Five companies in the Dow Jones Transportation index and three in the Dow Jones Utilities also increased their dividends. **Availability:** Online.

33204 ■ *"Monsanto Acquires Targeted-Pest Control Technology Start-Up; Terms Not Disclosed"* **in Benzinga.com (September 2011)**
Pub: Benzinga.com
Contact: Jason Raznick, Founder

Ed: Eddie Staley. **Description:** Monsanto Company acquired Beelogics, a firm that researches and develops biological tools that control pests and diseases. Research includes a product that will help protect bee health. **Availability:** Online.

33205 ■ *"Montgomery & Barnes: a Service-Disabled, Veteran-Owned Small Business"* **in Underground Construction (Vol. 65, October 2010, No. 10)**
Description: Gary Montgomery, chairman of Montgomery and Barnes announced that President Wendell (Buddy) Barnes is now majority owner, thus making the Houston-based civil engineering and consulting services firm, eligible to quality as a Service-Disabled Veteran-Owned Small Business (SDVOSB). **Availability:** Online.

33206 ■ *"The Moral Legitimacy of NGOs as Partners of Corporations"* **in Business Ethics Quarterly (Vol. 21, October 2011, No. 4, pp. 579)**
Ed: Dorothea Baur, Guido Palazzo. **Description:** Partnerships between companies and NGOs have received considerable attention in CSR in the past years. However, the role of NGO legitimacy in such partnerships has thus far been neglected. The article argues that NGOs assume a status as special stakeholders of corporations which act on behalf of the common good. This role requires a particular focus on their moral legitimacy. An introduction to the conceptual framework analyzing the moral legitimacy of NGOs along three dimensions, building on the theory of deliberative democracy. **Availability:** PDF; Online.

33207 ■ *"Most Popular Tools? The Survey Says"* **in Contractor (Vol. 57, February 2010, No. 2, pp. 1)**
Ed: Robert P. Mader. **Description:** According to a survey of individuals in the field, mechanical contractors are purchasing more of their tools at home centers and they are also increasingly working in the

service, repair, and retrofit markets. The survey also found that the reciprocating saw is the most used corded power tool. Additional purchasing habits of mechanical contractors are listed. **Availability:** Print; Online.

33208 ■ *"My Favorite Tool for Managing Expenses"* in Inc. (Volume 32, December 2010, No. 10, pp. 60)
Pub: Inc. Magazine
Ed: J.J. McCorvey. **Description:** Web-based service called Expensify is outlined. The service allows companies to log expenses while away from the office using the service's iPhone application. **Availability:** Online.

33209 ■ *"New Tax Sends Biz Scrambling: Service Levy Will Affect 16,000 Businesses"* in Crain's Detroit Business (October 8, 2007)
Pub: Crain Communications Inc.
Contact: Barry Asin, President
Ed: Amy Lane. **Description:** Legislation that imposes a tax on services in Michigan has business leaders upset. The new law exerts a 6 percent tax on 57 categories of services that affects 16,000 businesses in the state. **Availability:** Online.

33210 ■ *"A New Way to Tell When to Fold 'Em"* in Barron's (Vol. 88, July 7, 2008, No. 27, pp. 27)
Pub: Dow Jones & Company Inc.
Contact: Almar Latour, Chief Executive Officer
Ed: Theresa W. Carey. **Description:** Overview of the Online trading company SmartStops, a firm that aims to tell investors when to sell the shares of a particular company. The company's Web site categorizes stocks as moving up, down, or sideways, and calculates exit points for individual stocks based on an overall market trend. **Availability:** Online.

33211 ■ *"Next-Level E-Commerce"* in Entrepreneur (June 2014)
Pub: Entrepreneur Media Inc.
Contact: Dan Bova, Director
E-mail: dbova@entrepreneur.com
Description: BloomReach's SNAP software enables consumers to see the products they want upon arriving at an e-commerce Website. The software does this by evaluating the users' intent and preferences based on previous site usage. The enterprise-level software, which costs retailers at least $7,500/month, aims to use big data to help consumers choose products based on their intent. The cloud-based service indexes every page on a client's site and automatically generates appropriate content for visitors. The use of machine learning reduces lag time between application and positive results. **Availability:** Print; Online.

33212 ■ *Niche and Grow Rich*
Description: Consultants share insight to entrepreneurs wishing to find a profitable niche market. Authors write that good niche businesses are easy to start and easy to defend from competitors. They also report that finding a successful niche can attract and maintain good customers who are willing to pay more for unique goods and services.

33213 ■ *"Nighttime Shuttle to Connect Detroit, Ferndale, Royal Oak"* in Crain's Detroit Business (Vol. 24, October 6, 2008, No. 40, pp. 24)
Pub: Crain Communications Inc.
Contact: Barry Asin, President
Ed: Nancy Kaffer. **Description:** With hopes of bridging the social gap between the cities and suburbs, Chris Ramos has launched The Night Move, a new shuttle service that will ferry passengers between Royal Oak, Ferndale and downtown Detroit. The cost for a round trip ticket is $12. **Availability:** Online.

33214 ■ *"Nortel Makes Customers Stars in New Campaign"* in Brandweek (Vol. 49, April 21, 2008, No. 16, pp. 8)
Description: Nortel has launched a new television advertising campaign in which the business-to-business communications technology provider cast

senior executives in 30-second TV case studies that show how Nortel's technology helped their businesses innovate. **Availability:** Online.

33215 ■ *"Nortel Outlook Shows Recovery Won't Come Quickly"* in Globe & Mail (March 20, 2007, pp. B4)
Ed: Catherine McLean. **Description:** The forecast about the unlikely recovery of Nortel Networks Corp. from decrease in its share prices is discussed. **Availability:** Online.

33216 ■ *"Nuclear Plans May Stall on Uranium Shortage"* in Globe & Mail (March 22, 2007, pp. B4)
Ed: Shawn McCarthy. **Description:** The poor investments in uranium production and enrichment despite growing demand for it for nuclear energy is discussed. **Availability:** Online.

33217 ■ *"The Ode: CoolBrands (1986 - 2010)"* in Canadian Business (Vol. 83, September 14, 2010, No. 15, pp. 25)
Pub: Rogers Media Inc.
Contact: Neil Spivak, Chief Executive Officer
Ed: Joe Castaldo. **Description:** CoolBrands International Inc.'s merger with Swisher International Inc., a US hygiene products and services company, has formally erased the last traces of the former ice cream company. CoolBrands began as a frozen yogurt stand in 1986 and flourished across the world. How the string of acquisitions and poor corporate governance led to its demise are cited. **Availability:** Online.

33218 ■ *"Offering Service With a :)"* in Puget Sound Business Journal (Vol. 35, July 11, 2014, No. 12, pp. 12)
Pub: American City Business Journals, Inc.
Contact: Mike Olivieri, Executive Vice President
Description: Sorrento Hotel's Sorrento Ambassadors of Memories is an entry level job that allows young people to perform menial tasks for hotel guests. Randall Obrecht, Sorrento's general manager, states that the young workers actually serve as personalized butlers or concierges. The program helps hotel staff deal with high occupancy rates. **Availability:** Online.

33219 ■ *"Oil Markets: A Nasty Russian Tale"* in Canadian Business (Vol. 81, March 3, 2008, No. 3, pp. 85)
Pub: Rogers Media Inc.
Contact: Neil Spivak, Chief Executive Officer
Ed: Andrew Nikiforuk. **Description:** Billionaires Alex Shnaider and Michael Shtaif entered a partnership for an oil venture which ended in a slew of litigations. Cases of breach of contract, injurious falsehood and other related lawsuits were filed against Shnaider. Details of the lawsuits and the other parties involved in the disputes are presented. **Availability:** Online.

33220 ■ *"OK, Bring in the Lawyers"* in Crain's Chicago Business (Vol. 31, November 17, 2008, No. 46, pp. 26)
Pub: Crain Communications Inc.
Contact: Barry Asin, President
Ed: Daniel Rome Levine. **Description:** Bankruptcy attorneys are finding the economic and credit crisis a benefit for their businesses due to the high number of business owners and mortgage holders that are need of their services. One Chicago firm is handling ten times the number of cases they did the previous year and of that about 80 percent of their new clients are related to the real estate sector. **Availability:** Online.

33221 ■ *"The Old Railway is on a Roll"* in Globe & Mail (January 26, 2006, pp. B1)
Description: The reasons behind 5 percent rise in shares for Canadian National Railway Co. are presented. **Availability:** Online.

33222 ■ *"Optima Public Relations Gains Partners"* in Alaska Business Monthly (Vol. 27, October 2011, No. 10, pp. 10)
Pub: Alaska Business Publishing Company Inc.

Contact: Charles Bell, Vice President, Sales and Marketing
E-mail: cbell@akbizmag.com
Ed: Nancy Pounds. **Description:** Optima Public Relations has partnered with Gogerty Marriott of Seattle and Seattle Design Group. **Availability:** Print; Online.

33223 ■ *"Optimal Awarded US $256 Thousand Contract to Conduct LiDAR Survey for a Major Electric Utility in the Southwest"* in Canadian Corporate News
Description: Optimal Geomatics, a company specializing in the science and technology of analyzing, gathering, interpreting, distributing, and using geographic information, was awarded a new contract from a long-standing electric utility customer in the Southwest to conduct a LiDAR survey for a part of the utility's overhead transmission line system. **Availability:** Print; Online.

33224 ■ *"Panel to Call for Reduced Restraints on Telecom Sector"* in Globe & Mail (March 17, 2006, pp. B1)
Ed: Simon Tuck. **Description:** A federal panel called to adopt a more market-friendly approach to the lucrative telecommunications sector in Canada. Details of the report are presented. **Availability:** Online.

33225 ■ *"Panel Calls for 'Fundamental' Change to Telecom Regulation"* in Globe & Mail (March 23, 2006, pp. B1)
Ed: Catherine McLean. **Description:** A federal panel review at Ottawa called for a shakeup of regulations and policies that govern telecommunications companies to contend with sweeping technological changes. Details of the panel review are presented. **Availability:** Print; Online.

33226 ■ *"Patients to Elect to Cut Care"* in The Business Journal-Serving Metropolitan Kansas City (Vol. 27, November 21, 2008, No. 11, pp. 1)
Pub: American City Business Journals, Inc.
Contact: Mike Olivieri, Executive Vice President
Ed: Rob Roberts. **Description:** Patients in Kansas City, Missouri are cutting down on health care services due to the economic crisis. A decline in diagnostic procedures has been observed at Northland Cardiology. Elective reconstructive procedures have also been reduced by 25 percent. Additional information and statistics regarding the healthcare sector is included. **Availability:** Online.

33227 ■ *"The Phone-Service Test: Call Centres"* in Canadian Business (Vol. 79, October 9, 2006, No. 20, pp. 137)
Pub: Rogers Media Inc.
Contact: Neil Spivak, Chief Executive Officer
Ed: Rachel Pulfer. **Description:** Suggestions to improve the customer services provided by airlines through call centers are discussed. **Availability:** Online.

33228 ■ *"Pioneering Strategies for Entrepreneurial Success"* in Business Horizons (Vol. 51, January-February 2008, No. 1, pp. 21)
Pub: Elsevier Advanced Technology Publications
Ed: Candida G. Brush. **Price:** $8.95, hardcopy black and white. **Description:** Entrepreneurs are known for new products, services, processes, markets and industries. In order to achieve success, they have to develop a clear vision, creatively manage finances, and use social skills to persuade others to commit to the venture. Pioneering strategies and their implementation are examined. **Availability:** Print; PDF; Online.

33229 ■ *"Poisoning Relationships: Perceived Unfairness in Channels of Distribution"* in Journal of Marketing (Vol. 75, May 2011, No. 3, pp. 99)
Pub: American Marketing Association
Contact: Bennie F. Johnson, Chief Executive Officer

Ed: Stephen A. Samaha, Robert W. Palmatier, Rajiv P. Dant. **Released:** Volume: 75 issue: 3. **Description:** The effects of perceived unfairness on the relationships among members of distribution channels are examined. Perceived unfairness is found to directly damage relationships, aggravate the negative effects of conflict and opportunism, and undermine the benefits of the contract. **Availability:** PDF.

33230 ■ *"Poor Economy Inspires Rich Alternatives In a Modern, and Tax-Free, Twist on Bartering"* in Houston Chronicle (June 7, 2010)

Pub: Houston Chronicle

Ed: Michael Rubinkam. **Description:** Time banking helps individuals and firms receive goods or services by depositing time dollars into a bank reserved for receipt of goods and services.

33231 ■ *"The Power Brokers"* in Crain's Chicago Business (Vol. 31, April 28, 2008, No. 17, pp. 41)

Pub: Crain Communications Inc.

Contact: Barry Asin, President

Ed: Samantha Stainburn. **Description:** Profile of BlueStar Energy Services Inc., one of the first suppliers to cash in on the deregulation f the electricity market by the Illinois Legislature; last year BlueStar's revenue was $171.1 million, up from $600,000 in 2002, the year the company was founded. **Availability:** Online.

33232 ■ *"Prepare for Your Fourth of July Party With a Maid Service"* in Internet Wire (July 3, 2012)

Pub: Comtex News Network Inc.

Contact: Kan Devnani, President

Description: Merry Maids will assist in preparing a house for special occasions and holiday parties. The firm still specializes in house cleaning, but has expanded its services. Details of services offered are included. **Availability:** Print; Online.

33233 ■ *"Pride Lands Janitorial Work at New Terminal"* in Sacramento Business Journal (Vol. 28, June 10, 2011, No. 15, pp. 1)

Pub: Sacramento Business Journal

Contact: Stephanie Fretwell, Director

E-mail: sfretwell@bizjournals.com

Ed: Kelly Johnson. **Description:** Pride Industries Inc. won the five-year $9.4 million contract to clean the Sacramento International Airport's new Terminal B, which will open in fall 2011. The nonprofit organization posts a revenue of $191 million for 2011 and currently employs more than 2,400 people with disabilities. The contract is expected to provide savings of over $3 million a year to the airport. **Availability:** Online.

33234 ■ *"Problem Solving Requires Total Team Approach"* in Green Industry Pro (Vol. 23, September 2011)

Ed: Bob Coulter. **Description:** Working Smarter Training Challenge teaches that leaders are able to carry out solutions directly into their organization, develop skills and drive business results in key areas by creating a culture of energized workers who are able to take ownership of their performance as well as the performance of the company as a whole. **Availability:** Online.

33235 ■ *Professional Services Marketing: How the Best Firms Build Premier Brands, Thriving Lead Generation Engines, and Cultures of Business Development Success*

Pub: John Wiley & Sons, Inc.

Contact: Christina Van Tassell, Executive Vice President Chief Financial Officer

Ed: Mike Schultz, John E. Doerr, Lee Frederiksen. **Released:** Second edition. **Price:** $29.95, hardcover; $19.99, E-Book. **Description:** Research based on best practices and processes for the professional services industry is presented. The book covers five key areas: creating a custom marketing and growth strategy, establishing a brand, implementing a

marketing communications program, developing a lead strategy, and winning new clients. **Availability:** E-book; Print.

33236 ■ *"Providence Exec Explains Why the Deal with Boeing is the Way of the Future"* in Puget Sound Business Journal (Vol. 35, June 27, 2014, No. 10, pp. 6)

Pub: American City Business Journals, Inc.

Contact: Mike Olivieri, Executive Vice President

Description: Providence-Swedish Accountable Care Organization CEO, Joe Gifford, shares his views on the deal to provide health care to Boeing employees. Gifford says there is opportunity to grow the business if public image spreads showing they offer great quality and service in providing unique healthcare and benefits at a lower cost. Gifford believes meeting directly with the employer customer they create a direct loop of process improvement. **Availability:** Online.

33237 ■ *"Put Power in Your Direct Mail Campaigns"* in Contractor (Vol. 56, September 2009, No. 9, pp. 64)

Ed: Matt Michel. **Description:** Advice on how members of the United States plumbing industry should manage direct mail marketing campaigns is offered. Determining the purpose of a campaign is recommended. Focusing on a single message, product or service is also encouraged. **Availability:** Print; Online.

33238 ■ *"Put Your Heating Cap On"* in Indoor Comfort Marketing (Vol. 70, September 2011, No. 9, pp. 26)

Description: Tools and techniques for HVAC/R technicians servicing boilers are outlined. **Availability:** PDF; Online.

33239 ■ *"Q&A: The CAPP's Greg Stringham"* in Canadian Business (Vol. 81, February 12, 2008, No. 3, pp. 8)

Pub: Rogers Media Inc.

Contact: Neil Spivak, Chief Executive Officer

Ed: Michelle Magnan. **Description:** Canadian Association of Petroleum Producers' Greg Stringham thinks that the new royalty plan will result in companies pulling out their investments for Alberta's conventional oil and gas sector. Stringham adds that Alberta is losing its competitive advantage and companies must study their cost profiles to retrieve that advantage. The effects of the royalty system on Alberta's economy are examined further. **Availability:** Print; Online.

33240 ■ *"Reality Check at the Bottom of the Pyramid: To Succeed in the World's Poorest Markets, Aim For Much Higher Margins and Prices Than You Thought Were Necessary-Or Possible"* in Harvard Business Review (Vol. 90, June 2012, No. 6, pp. 120)

Pub: Harvard Business Review Press

Contact: Moderna V. Pfizer, Contact

Ed: Erik Simanis. **Price:** $8.95, hardcopy black and white. **Description:** Margin-enhancing platforms are identified. Bundling products increases customer access and enables firms to sell more in each transaction. Including services with products creates value for customers and raises each transaction's gross margin. Customer peer groups boost aggregate sales and as a result reduce costs. **Availability:** Print; Online; PDF.

33241 ■ *"Recession and Recovery: Employment Change by Industry"* in Occupational Outlook Quarterly (Vol. 58, Summer 2014, No. 2, pp. 45)

Pub: Government Publishing Office

Contact: Hugh Nathanial Halpern, Director

Description: Data from the U.S. Bureau of Labor Statistics (BLS) is presented showing that most industries added jobs between June 2009 and March 2014, a period spanning the end of the recession into the ongoing economic recovery. The small business trends sow percent change in industry employment

classified by service providing industries, good producing industries, and employment March 2014. **Availability:** Print; Online.

33242 ■ *"Recipe for Disaster?"* in Sacramento Business Journal (Vol. 25, July 4, 2008, No. 18, pp. 1)

Pub: American City Business Journals, Inc.

Contact: Mike Olivieri, Executive Vice President

Ed: Mark Anderson. **Description:** Restaurateurs are challenged with balancing rising operating costs and what customers are willing to pay for their services. Flour prices in 2008 have increased by 46 percent from April 2007. Other views on the situation, as well as trends, forecasts and statistics on sales, outlook on economic conditions, consumer price index, and the typical split of restaurant revenue, are presented. **Availability:** Online.

33243 ■ *"Renren Partners With Recruit to Launch Social Wedding Services"* in Benzinga.com (June 7, 2011)

Pub: PR Newswire Association LLC.

Description: Renren Inc., the leading real name social networking Internet platform in China has partnered with Recruit Company Limited, Japan's largest human resource and classified media group to form a joint venture to build a wedding social media catering to the needs of engaged couples and newlyweds in China.

33244 ■ *"Reports of Banks' Revival were Greatly Exaggerated"* in Barron's (Vol. 88, July 7, 2008, No. 27, pp. L14)

Pub: Dow Jones & Company Inc.

Contact: Almar Latour, Chief Executive Officer

Ed: Jack Willoughby. **Description:** Performance of mutual funds improved for the second quarter of 2008 compared to the previous quarter, registering an average gain of 0.13 percent; funds focusing on natural resources rose the highest, their value rising by an average of 24.50 percent. **Availability:** Online.

33245 ■ *"Restaurant Customers React to First Encounters with a Robot Server"* in Small Business Trends(February 8, 2023)

URL(s): smallbiztrends.com/2023/02/restaurant-customers-react-robot-waiter.html

Ed: Joshua Sophy. **Released:** February 08, 2023. **Description:** Robot waiters are starting to pop up around the country and customers are posting on social media about their encounters and giving feedback. **Availability:** Online.

33246 ■ *"'Resume Mining' Services Can Save Time, Money"* in HR Specialist (Vol. 8, September 2010, No. 9, pp. 7)

Pub: Capitol Information Group Inc.

Contact: Allie Ash, Chief Executive Officer

Description: Low-cost resume mining services can help human resource departments save time and money by searching online resume databases for candidates matching specific job qualifications. **Availability:** PDF; Online.

33247 ■ *"St. Luke's Gets Shot in the Arm From Outpatient Services"* in Saint Louis Business Journal (Vol. 31, August 19, 2011, No. 52, pp. 1)

Pub: Saint Louis Business Journal

Contact: Robert Bobroff, President

E-mail: rbobroff@bizjournals.com

Ed: Angela Mueller, E.B. Solomont. **Description:** St. Louis, Missouri-based St. Luke's Hospital benefited from investing in outpatient services as contained in its latest bond offering. Fitch Ratings gave the bond issuance an A rating. **Availability:** Print; Online.

33248 ■ *"Screening for the Best Stock Screens"* in Barron's (Vol. 90, September 13, 2010, No. 37, pp. 36)

Pub: Barron's Editorial & Corporate Headquarters

Ed: Mike Hogan. **Description:** Pros and cons of the new and revised stock screening tools from Zack, Finviz.com, and GuruFocus are discussed. FinVix.com is more capable for screening through stocks and the service is free. **Availability:** Online.

33249 ■ "Secrets To Trade Show Success" in Women Entrepreneur (September 12, 2008)

Description: Trade shows require an enormous amount of work, but they are an investment that can pay off handsomely because they allow a business to get their product or service in front of their target market. Advice regarding trade shows is given including selecting the correct venue, researching the affair and following up on leads obtained at the event. **Availability:** Online.

33250 ■ "Self-Employment in the United States" in Montly Labor Review (Vol. 133, September 2010, No. 9, pp. 17)

Pub: U.S. Department of Labor Bureau of Labor Statistics

Contact: Amrit Kohli, Director

E-mail: kohli.amrit@bls.gov

Description: Self employment in 2009 in the U.S. continued to be more common among men, Whites, Asians, and older workers and in the agriculture, construction, and services industries. **Availability:** PDF; Online.

33251 ■ Selling the Invisible: A Field Guide to Modern Marketing

Ed: Harry Beckwith. **Released:** March 20, 2012. **Price:** $16, paperback, ($21.00 in canada); $13.98, audiobook abridged library($16.99 in canada); $16.98, audiobook abridged($19.75 in canada); $9.98, audiobook abridged($12.98 in canada); $9.99, electronic book($9.99 in canada). **Description:** Tips for marketing and selling intangibles such as health care, entertainment, tourism, legal services, and more are provided. **Availability:** audiobook; E-book; Print.

33252 ■ "The Service Imperative" in Business Horizons (Vol. 51, January-February 2008, No. 1, pp. 39)

Pub: Elsevier Advanced Technology Publications

Ed: Mary Jo Bitner, Stephen W. Brown. **Description:** The importance of services is growing in developing countries like India and China, but little attention is given to service research, education and innovation. The 'service imperative' seeks to promote the advancement of services. The scope, objectives and philosophy of the service imperative platform are outlined. **Availability:** Online.

33253 ■ "Sharing's Not Just for Start-ups: What Marriott, GE, and Other Traditiional Companies are Learning About the Collaborative Economy" in Harvard Business Review (Vol. 92, September 2014, No. 9, pp. 23)

Pub: Harvard Business Publishing

Contact: Diane Belcher, Managing Director

Ed: Rachel Botsman. **Price:** $6. **Description:** The collaborative economy answers five basic problems companies face: redundancy, broken trust, limited access, waste, and complexity. Online matches eliminate redundancy; peer-to-peer networks boost trust; online training answers access issues; online services can market what other entities are not utilizing (i.e., excess space); and other services can streamline or provide alternative solutions for complex processes. **Availability:** Online; PDF.

33254 ■ "Ship Shape" in Hawaii Business (Vol. 53, January 2008, No. 7, pp. 46)

Ed: David K. Choo. **Description:** Ship Maintenance LLC is in charge of repairing and maintaining the U.S. Navy ships at Pearl Harbor's Middle Noch, having renewed a five-year contract with the navy. Cleaning a ship is a difficult process, which involves degreasing and removal of sensitive items such as guns and missiles. The awards given to Ship Maintenance are also discussed. **Availability:** Online.

33255 ■ "A Simple Old Reg that Needs Dusting Off" in Barron's (Vol. 88, June 30, 2008, No. 26, pp. 35)

Pub: Dow Jones & Company Inc.

Contact: Almar Latour, Chief Executive Officer

Ed: Gene Epstein. **Description:** Senator Joe Lieberman has a point when he accused speculators of inflating the prices of food and fuel futures but introducing legislation to address speculation has an alternative. The senator's committee should instead demand that the Commodity Futures Trading Commission enforce position limits on the maximum number of contracts in a given market per speculative entity. **Availability:** Online.

33256 ■ "The Skype's the Limit" in Canadian Business (Vol. 80, February 12, 2007, No. 4, pp. 70)

Description: The increase in the market share of Skype Technologies S.A.'s Internet phone service to 171 million users is discussed. **Availability:** Print; Online.

33257 ■ "Slow but Steady into the Future" in Barron's (Vol. 88, July 7, 2008, No. 27, pp. M)

Pub: Dow Jones & Company Inc.

Contact: Almar Latour, Chief Executive Officer

Ed: Mark Veverka. **Description:** Investors are advised to maintain their watch on the shares of business software company NetSuite. The company's chief executive officer, Zach Nelson, claims that the company has a 10-year lead on its competitors with the development of software-as-a service. **Availability:** Online.

33258 ■ "Small Businesses Unsure of Impact of New Tax Law" in Crain's Detroit Business (Vol. 23, October 15, 2007, No. 42, pp. 13)

Pub: Crain Communications Inc.

Contact: Barry Asin, President

Ed: Sheena Harrison. **Description:** Small business owners in Michigan are concerned with issues surrounding the proposed increases in state taxes geared at small business, which includes a 6 percent service tax. **Availability:** Online.

33259 ■ "Small Firms Punch Ticket for Growth" in Houston Business Journal (Vol. 40, January 29, 2010, No. 38, pp. 1)

Pub: Houston Business Journal

Contact: Bob Charlet, President

E-mail: bcharlet@bizjournals.com

Ed: Allison Wollam. **Description:** Independent ticket agencies anticipate growth as American and Canadian authorities approved a merger between Ticketmaster and concert promoter Live Nation. Expansion of service offerings and acquisition of venues have also been done by independent ticket agencies in light of the merger. Details of the merger are included. **Availability:** Print; Online.

33260 ■ The Social Media Bible: Tactics, Tools, and Strategies for Business Success

Pub: John Wiley & Sons, Inc.

Contact: Christina Van Tassell, Executive Vice President Chief Financial Officer

Ed: Lon Safko. **Released:** Third edition. **Price:** $29.95, paperback; $19.99, E-Book. **Description:** Information is given to build or transform a business into social media, where customers, employees, and prospects connect, collaborate, and champion products and services in order to increase sales and to beat the competition. **Availability:** E-book; Print.

33261 ■ "A Socko Payout Menu: Rural Phone Carrier Plots to Supercharge Its Shares" in Barron's (Vol. 88, June 30, 2008, No. 26, pp. M5)

Description: CenturyTel boosted its quarterly common payout to 70 cents from 6.75 cents per share die to its strong cash flows and solid balance sheet. Eastman Kodak's plan for a buyback will be partially funded by its $581 million tax refund. CME Group will buyback stocks through 2009 worth $1.1 billion. **Availability:** Online.

33262 ■ "Staffing Firms are Picking Up the Pieces, Seeing Signs of Life" in Milwaukee Business Journal (Vol. 27, February 5, 2010, No. 19)

Pub: The Business Journal

Contact: Heather Ladage, President

E-mail: hladage@bizjournals.com

Ed: Rich Rovito. **Description:** Milwaukee, Wisconsin-based staffing firms are seeing signs of economic rebound as many businesses turned to temporary employees to fill the demands for goods and services. Economic observers believe the growth in temporary staffing is one of the early indicators of economic recovery. **Availability:** Print; Online.

33263 ■ "Stockerts Open Repair Business" in Dickinson Press (July 13, 2010)

Pub: The Dickinson Press

Contact: Joy Schoch, Business Manager

Description: Ed Stockert is opening his new appliance repair firm in Dickinson, North Dakota with his wife Anna.

33264 ■ "Stoneham Drilling Trust Announces Cash Distribution for May 2007" in Canadian Corporate News (May 16, 2007)

Description: Stoneham Drilling Trust, an income trust that provides contract drilling services to natural gas and oil exploration and production companies operating in western Canada, announced that its cash distribution for the period from May 1, 2007 to May 31, 2007 will be $0.15 per trust unit ($1.80 per annum). **Availability:** Print; Online.

33265 ■ "Study: New Moms Build A Lot of Brand Buzz" in Brandweek (Vol. 49, April 21, 2008, No. 16, pp. 7)

Description: According to a new survey which sampled 1,721 pregnant women and new moms, this demographic is having 109 word-of-mouth conversations per week concerning products, services and brands. Two-thirds of these conversations directly involve brand recommendations. The Internet is driving these word-of-mouth, or W-O-M, conversations among this segment, beating out magazines, television and other forms of media. **Availability:** Online.

33266 ■ "Suits Keep Flying in Wireless Service Marketing Wars" in Globe & Mail (March 22, 2007, pp. B3)

Ed: Catherine McLean. **Description:** The suit filed by Telus Corp. against BCE Mobile Communications Inc. over the latter's alleged misleading advertisement in the press is discussed. **Availability:** Print; Online.

33267 ■ "Take This Job and Love It" in Green Industry Pro (Vol. 23, October 2011)

Ed: Gregg Wartgow. **Description:** Details of the lawsuit filed by the Professional Landcare Network (PLANET) against the U.S. Department of Labor are explained. Challenges faced by landscape firms because of employment costs are outlined. Statistical data included. **Availability:** PDF; Online.

33268 ■ "Tax Preparation Made Easier With Carbonite Online Backup" in Investment Weekly News (March 10, 2012, pp. 783)

Pub: PR Newswire Association LLC.

Description: Carbonite, Inc. provides a secure backup protection service, making tax preparation easier for consumers and small- to medium-sized businesses. Details on Carbonite.com and its services are included. **Availability:** Online.

33269 ■ "Teachers, U.S. Fund Providence Made Moves On BCE Buyout" in Globe & Mail (April 10, 2007, pp. B17)

Ed: Boyd Erman, Sinclair Stewart, Jacquie McNish. **Description:** The Ontario Teachers' Pension Plan, the largest shareholder of telecommunications firm BCE Inc., has called for a partnership with buyout firm Providence Equity Partners Inc. in order to acquire BCE Inc. **Availability:** Online.

33270 ■ "Tiny Telecom Big Prize in Bell Aliant Bid Battle" in Globe & Mail (April 4, 2007, pp. B1)

Ed: Catherine McLean. **Description:** The competition between Bell Aliant Regional Communications Income Fund of BCE Inc. and Bragg Communications Inc. to bid for acquiring Amtelecom Income Fund is discussed. **Availability:** Online.

33271 ■ *"To Keep Freight Rolling, Ill. Has to Grease the Hub" in Crain's Chicago Business (Vol. 31, April 21, 2008, No. 16, pp. 22)*
Pub: Crain Communications Inc.
Contact: Barry Asin, President

Ed: Paul O'Connor. **Description:** Discusses the importance of upgrading Chicago's continental-hub freight rail system which is integral to moving international products as well as domestic ones. Global tonnage is expected to double by 2020 and unless more money is designated to upgrade the infrastructure the local and national economy will suffer. **Availability:** Online.

33272 ■ *Trade-Off: The Ever-Present Tension Between Quality and Conscience*
Released: August 17, 2010. **Price:** $15. **Description:** The tension between fidelity (the quality of a consumer's experience) and convenience (the ease of getting and paying for a product) are shown to be the forces that determine the success or failure of new products and services in the marketplace.

33273 ■ *"Travel Leery" in Crain's Chicago Business (Vol. 31, March 31, 2008, No. 13, pp. 3)*
Pub: Crain Communications Inc.
Contact: Barry Asin, President

Ed: John Pletz. **Description:** Due to the rise in airline prices and a possible recession, many companies are starting to change their travel policies and limit travel spending. **Availability:** Online.

33274 ■ *"United's Next Hurdle: Costly Repairs" in Crain's Chicago Business (Vol. 31, April 14, 2008, No. 15, pp. 1)*
Pub: Crain Communications Inc.
Contact: Barry Asin, President

Ed: John Pletz. **Description:** Discusses the recent crackdown by aviation regulators concerning airline safety at United Airlines as well as other carriers. Maintenance costs at United for the upkeep on the company's older planes is severely affecting its bottom line which is already sagging under heavy fuel costs. **Availability:** Online.

33275 ■ *"UPMC Aims to Profit From Billing Angst" in Pittsburgh Business Times (Vol. 33, Jun3 27, 2014, No. 50, pp. 8)*
Pub: American City Business Journals, Inc.
Contact: Mike Olivieri, Executive Vice President

Released: Weekly. **Price:** $4, introductory 4-week offer(Digital only). **Description:** Hospital network UPMC has created a wholly owned, for-profit subsidiary named Ovation Revenue Cycle Solutions that helps medical providers with the complex new Medicare billing codes that take effect October 2015. The service provides revenue-cycle tools designed to help medical groups enhance efficiency, cut rejection rates and reduce time between billing and payment. **Availability:** Print; Online.

33276 ■ *"UPMC Develops Own Billing Solutions" in Pittsburgh Business Times (Vol. 33, January 17, 2014, No. 27, pp. 6)*
Pub: American City Business Journals, Inc.
Contact: Mike Olivieri, Executive Vice President

Description: How University of Pittsburgh Medical Center (UPMC) Health System transformed its accounts payable department by passing its process to a subsidiary, Prodigo Solutions, is discussed. UPMC moved suppliers and purchasers to a shared electronic platform and created a digital marketplace. The system's no purchase order, no pay policy has reduced the number of rogue purchases. **Availability:** Online.

33277 ■ *"VC-Heavy, Revenue-Light Sensicore Sold to GE Division" in Crain's Detroit Business (Vol. 24, April 14, 2008, No. 15, pp. 28)*
Pub: Crain Communications Inc.
Contact: Barry Asin, President

Ed: Tom Henderson. **Description:** General Electric has acquired Sensicore Inc., which although one of Michigan's most successful companies in raising venture capital was unable to generate significant revenue from its handheld water-testing devices. GE is capable of penetrating a larger market than a private company and will be able to take the devices to the municipal marketplace. **Availability:** Online.

33278 ■ *"Virgin Mobile has Big Plans for Year Two" in Globe & Mail (March 6, 2006, pp. B5)*
Ed: Catherine McLean. **Description:** The business growth plans of Virgin Mobile Canada are presented. **Availability:** Online.

33279 ■ *"Wall Street Is No Friend to Radical Innovation" in Harvard Business Review (Vol. 88, July-August 2010, No. 7-8, pp. 28)*
Pub: Harvard Business Publishing
Contact: Diane Belcher, Managing Director

Ed: Julia Kirby. **Price:** $6, PDF. **Description:** Research indicates that investors are skittish about backing a business that proposes significant changes to its product or service status quo. **Availability:** Online; PDF.

33280 ■ *"War Veteran Hit Payoff with Repair Business" in Tulsa World (July 28, 2010)*
Pub: Tulsa World
Contact: Tim Chamberlin, Editor
E-mail: tim.chamberlin@tulsaworld.com

Ed: Tim Stanley. **Description:** Profile of Sam Melton, Korean War veteran and retired Air Force staff sergeant, launched appliance repair stores in the Tulsa, Oklahoma area 50 years ago. **Availability:** Print; Online.

33281 ■ *"Warning Lights Flashing for Air Canada: Carty's Back" in Globe & Mail (February 22, 2006, pp. B1)*
Ed: Brent Jang. **Description:** Air Canada's rival, Donald Carty, former chief oxocutivo officer at American Airlines and new chairman of Toronto based Regco Holdings Inc., launches Porter Airlines Inc. out of Toronto City Center Airport this fall.

33282 ■ *"Water Treatment Player Zenon Goes to GE" in Globe & Mail (March 15, 2006, pp. B1)*
Ed: Leonard Zehr. **Description:** General Electric Co. acquires Ontario-based company, Zenon Environmental Inc., a technology giant in purifying water in northern Canada. **Availability:** Online.

33283 ■ *"Waukesha Firm Hit for $8.9M for Junk Faxes" in Business Journal Milwaukee (Vol. 29, August 3, 2012, No. 45, pp. 1)*
Pub: American City Business Journals, Inc.
Contact: Mike Olivieri, Executive Vice President

Ed: Stacy Vogel Davis. **Released:** Weekly. **Price:** $4, introductory 4-week offer(Digital & Print). **Description:** Waukesha County, Wisconsin-based Easy PC Solutions LLC has been facing an $8.9 million settlement for sending unsolicited faxes to 7,000 health care providers. However, the company won't have to pay since the plaintiffs are expected to go after its insurance company. **Availability:** Print; Online.

33284 ■ *"Way More Than Mowing" in Green Industry Pro (Vol. 23, September 2011)*
Ed: Rod Dickens. **Description:** Shipp Shape Lawn Services located in Sylvester, Georgia now offers aeration, fertilizing and weed control, mulching, yard renovation, flowerbed maintenance, landscaping, as well as irrigation repairs and installation in order to diversify the business and stay competitive. **Availability:** Online.

33285 ■ *"Web Translation Made Simple" in Inc. (Vol. 33, October 2011, No. 8, pp. 44)*
Pub: Inc. Magazine

Ed: Adam Baer. **Description:** Smartling is a Web-based service that translates sites into more than 50 foreign languages. The software will begin translation right after setting up the account. **Availability:** Online.

33286 ■ *"WestJet Gears Up for Domestic Dogfight" in Globe & Mail (May 1, 2007, pp. B6)*
Ed: Brent Jang. **Description:** The effort of WestJet Airlines Ltd. to compete with Air Canada for greater market share of passengers is discussed. **Availability:** Online.

33287 ■ *"What Marketers Misunderstand about Online Reviews: Managers Must Analyze What's Really Driving Buying Decisions - and Adjust Their Strategies Accordingly" in Harvard Business Review (Vol. 92, January-February 2014, No. 1-2, pp. 23)*
Pub: Harvard Business Press
Contact: Gabriela Allmi, Regional Manager
E-mail: gabriela.allmi@hbsp.harvard.edu

Price: $6, hardcopy black and white. **Description:** Companies may overestimate the influence of online reviews, as consumers do not turn to reviews for certain products and services (for example, habitual low-involvement purchases such as groceries). Others' opinions matter more for purchases such as independent restaurants and electronics. **Availability:** Print; PDF; Online.

33288 ■ *"Why Change?" in Canadian Business (Vol. 80, October 8, 2007, No. 20, pp. 9)*
Description: The need for economic change in Canada is discussed. Despite the country's economic growth and low unemployment rate, economic reform is needed in order to maximize its economic potential in the future. Other reasons for the need to further develop its economy, such as the rise of manufacturing and service industries in Asia and the emergence of regional trade pacts in South America are also tackled.

33289 ■ *"Why Customer Engagement Matters So Much Now; Wary Consumers Will Give More Money to the Businesses they Feel Emotionally Connected To -- While Ignoring Others" in Gallup Business Journal (July 22, 2014)*
Pub: Gallup, Inc.
Contact: Jon Clifton, Chief Executive Officer

Description: Gallup's daily tracking of the U.S. economy shows signs of recovery since the crash of 2008. When Americans purchase goods or services, they tend to choose businesses they feel emotionally connected to and might even ignore those that provide no value to them. They expect a company to earn their money. **Availability:** Print; Online.

33290 ■ *"Women as 21st Century Leaders" in Women In Business (Vol. 63, Summer 2011, No. 2, pp. 26)*
Pub: American Business Women's Association
Contact: Rene Street, Executive Director

Ed: Leigh Elmore. **Description:** American Business Women's Association and Park University have partnered to provide a leadership training program to attendees of the 2011 National Women's Leadership Conference. The courses will incorporate introduction to concepts, development of critical thinking skills and direct application through exercises. Comments from executives are also included. **Availability:** Online.

33291 ■ *"Xtium Has Its Head in the Clouds" in Philadelphia Business Journal (Vol. 30, September 23, 2011, No. 32, pp. 1)*
Pub: Philadelphia Business Journal
Contact: Sierra Quinn, Director
E-mail: squinn@bizjournals.com

Ed: Peter Key. **Description:** Philadelphia-based cloud computing firm Xtium LLC received an $11.5 million first-round investment from Boston-Massachusetts-based OpenView Venture Partners. Catering to midsize businesses and unit of bigger firms, Xtium offers disaster-recovery, hosting, and managed-information-technology-infrastructure services. **Availability:** Online.

33292 ■ *"Yammer Gets Serious" in Inc. (Volume 32, December 2010, No. 10, pp. 58)*
Pub: Inc. Magazine

Ed: Eric Markowitz. **Description:** Yammer, an internal social network for companies, allows coworkers to share ideas and documents in real-time. Details of this service are included. **Availability:** Online.

33293 ■ *"You Won't Go Broke Filling Up On The Stock" in Barron's (Vol. 88, July 14, 2008, No. 28, pp. 38)*
Pub: Dow Jones & Company Inc.

Contact: Almar Latour, Chief Executive Officer

Ed: Assif Shameen. **Description:** Due to high economic growth, pro-business policies and a consumption boom, the Middle East is a good place to look for equities. The best ways in which to gain exposure to this market include investing in the real estate industry and telecommunications markets as well as large banks that serve corporations and consumers. **Availability:** Online.

33294 ■ *"You're a What? Wind Turbine Service Technician" in Occupational Outlook Quarterly (Vol. 54, Fall 2010, No. 3, pp. 34)*
Pub: U.S. Department of Labor Bureau of Labor Statistics

Contact: Amrit Kohli, Director
E-mail: kohli.amrit@bls.gov

Ed: Drew Liming. **Description:** Profile of Brandon Johnson, former member of the Air Force, found a career as a wind turbine service technician. **Availability:** Online; PDF.

33295 ■ *"The Zero Marginal Cost Society: The Internet of Things, the Collaborative Commons, and the Eclipse of Capitalism"*
Pub: Palgrave Macmillan

Released: April 04, 2014. **Price:** $18.99, paperback; $9.99, e-book; $29.99, hardcover. **Description:** The emerging Internet of things is speeding society to an ear of nearly free goods and services, causing the rise of a global Collaborative Commons and the eclipse of capitalism. Entrepreneurial dynamism of competitive markets that drives productivity up and marginal costs down, enabling businesses to reduce the price of their goods and services to win consumers and market share is slowly dying. **Availability:** E-book; Print.

VIDEO/AUDIO MEDIA

33296 ■ *BS-Free Service Business Show: 5 Places to Cut the BS in Your Service Business*
URL(s): smallbusinessboss.co/cut-the-bs

Ed: Maggie Patterson. **Released:** September 12, 2022. **Description:** Podcast offers guidelines for building a sustainable service business.

33297 ■ *BS-Free Service Business Show: Awkward Client Situations: What to Do When Things Get Sticky*
URL(s): smallbusinessboss.co/awkward-client-situations

Ed: Maggie Patterson. **Released:** April 11, 2022. **Description:** Podcast explains how to navigate awkward client situations, whether it's unpaid invoices or a mid-project change in direction.

33298 ■ *BS-Free Service Business Show: BS-Free Sustainability for Service Businesses*
URL(s): insidescoop.libsyn.com/bs-free-sustainability-for-service-business

Ed: Maggie Patterson. **Released:** September 05, 2022. **Description:** Podcast explains how to build a sustainable service business.

33299 ■ *BS-Free Service Business Show: Covering Your Ass: Planning for the Unexpected with Julee Yokoyama*
URL(s): smallbusinessboss.co/planning-for-the-unexpected

Ed: Maggie Patterson. **Released:** September 26, 2022. **Description:** Podcast discusses how to plan for the unexpected.

33300 ■ *BS-Free Service Business Show: Creatives, Coaches, and Consultants: The Key Differences Between Different Types of Service Businesses*
URL(s): smallbusinessboss.co/creatives-coaches-and-consultants

Ed: Maggie Patterson. **Released:** June 13, 2022. **Description:** Podcast explains the differences between different types of service businesses.

33301 ■ *BS-Free Service Business Show: Myths of the Microagency*
URL(s): bsfreebusiness.com/microagency

Ed: Maggie Patterson. **Released:** October 23, 2023. **Description:** Podcast dispels common myths about microagencies.

33302 ■ *BS-Free Service Business Show: Putting Sell the Strategy into Action*
URL(s): smallbusinessboss.co/how-to-sell-the-strategy

Ed: Maggie Patterson. **Released:** April 04, 2022. **Description:** Podcast offers examples of how to sell the strategy.

33303 ■ *BS-Free Service Business Show: Sell the Strategy: Stepping Up Your Service Business*
URL(s): smallbusinessboss.co/sell-the-strategy

Ed: Maggie Patterson. **Released:** March 28, 2022. **Description:** Podcast suggests shifts you can make in your business when something has to change but you aren't' sure where to begin.

33304 ■ *BS-Free Service Business Show: The Cult of Scale (and Why Sustainability Is More Important)*
URL(s): smallbusinessboss.co/scale-and-sustainability

Ed: Maggie Patterson. **Released:** August 29, 2022. **Description:** Podcast explains why scaling may not be all it's cracked up to be.

33305 ■ *BS-Free Service Business Show: The Rise of Trauma-Informed Coaching*
URL(s): bsfreebusiness.com/trauma-informed-coaching

Ed: Maggie Patterson. **Released:** December 05, 2022. **Description:** Podcast defines trauma-informed coaching and how to avoid those that falsely claim it.

33306 ■ *BS-Free Service Business Show: The State of Ethical Marketing and Online Business for 2023*
URL(s): smallbusinessboss.co/ethical-marketing-and-online-business

Ed: Maggie Patterson. **Released:** December 12, 2022. **Description:** Podcast describes the state of ethical marketing and online business.

33307 ■ *BS-Free Service Business Show: The Top 10 Awkward Client Moments (and How to Avoid Them)*
URL(s): smallbusinessboss.co/avoid-awkward-client-moments

Ed: Maggie Patterson. **Released:** April 18, 2022. **Description:** Podcast suggests how to avoid awkward client situations.

33308 ■ *Professional on the Go: Do You Have What It Takes to Become a Life Coach?*
URL(s): www.speaker.com/user/11226745/how-to-becoma-a-life-coach

Ed: Chinwe Onyeagoro. **Released:** October 21, 2019. **Description:** Podcast discusses life coach as service profession and explains how it differs from a therapist.

33309 ■ *Professional on the Go: In Dog Trainers We Trust*
URL(s): www.spreaker.com/user/11226745/in-dog-trainers-we-trust

Ed: Chinwe Onyeagoro. **Released:** October 01, 2019. **Description:** Podcast offers advice on becoming a dog trainer.

33310 ■ *Staying Solo: Sorry, Not Sorry: When the Client Is Wrong*
URL(s): bsfreebusiness.com/when-the-client-is-wrong

Ed: Maggie Patterson. **Released:** September 30, 2024. **Description:** Podcast offers tips on handling moments when the client is wrong, how to steer them back on course, and what to do if they won't listen.

FRANCHISES AND BUSINESS OPPORTUNITIES

33311 ■ **1-800-Radiator**
Driven Brands Inc.
4401 Pk. Rd.
Benicia, CA 94510
Ph: (704)377-8855
URL: http://www.drivenbrands.com

Description: Distributor of automotive parts. **Founded:** 1982. **Franchised:** 2003.

33312 ■ **4Refuel**
Ste. 215, 9440-202nd St.
Langley, BC, Canada V1M 4A6

Description: Provider of mobile refueling services and also distributor of trucks and construction equipment. **Founded:** 1995.

33313 ■ **ACFN, the ATM Franchise Business**
255 W Julian St., Ste. 600
San Jose, CA 95110
Free: 888-444-2236
URL: http://atmfranchise.com

Description: The ATM FRANCHISE business. Develop & operate your own private network of ATM machines in hotels and other travel & entertainment based businesses. Potential to earn significant long term residual income. Proven business plan with impressive list of corporate clients. Prior experience not necessary. **No. of Franchise Units:** 210. **Founded:** 1996. **Franchised:** 2003. **Equity Capital Needed:** $40,000. **Franchise Fee:** $25,000. **Financial Assistance:** Yes **Training:** 1 week at corporate office in California and ongoing support in all aspects of operating your ATM network.

33314 ■ **Advanced Maintenance**
2820 N Kerr Ave.
Wilmington, NC 28405
Ph: (910)251-0008
Free: 888-452-9206
Fax: (910)251-0095
URL: http://www.advancedmaintenance.com
Contact: Mike Sellers, Manager
Facebook: www.facebook.com/people/Advanced-Maintenance/100057797763972

Description: Provider of on-site maintenance for fleet vehicles. **Founded:** 2000. **Training:** Yes.

33315 ■ **ChemDry Canada Ltd. (CDC)**
Chilliwack, BC, Canada
Free: 888-243-6379
Co. E-mail: info@chemdry.ca
URL: http://chemdry.ca
Facebook: www.facebook.com/ChemdryCanada
X (Twitter): x.com/chemdrycanada

Description: Provider of home cleaning services such as carpet, upholstery, rugs, pet urine odor removal, tile cleaning. **Founded:** 1978. **Training:** Provides5 days training, including travel and accommodation.

33316 ■ **College Hunks Hauling Junk Inc.**
4756 N Dale Mabry Hwy.
Tampa, FL 33614
Ph: (813)280-3349
Co. E-mail: datarequest@chhj.com
URL: http://www.collegehunkshaulingjunk.com
Contact: Roman Cowan, President
Facebook: www.facebook.com/CollegeHunksHaulingJunk

Linkedin: www.linkedin.com/company/college-hunks
-hauling-junk

X (Twitter): x.com/CollegeHunks

Instagram: www.instagram.com/collegehunks

YouTube: www.youtube.com/channel/UC-zo_ofBvBf
5jTrjpvit_ow

Pinterest: www.pinterest.com/collegehunks

Description: Firm provides stress free moving and junk removal services. **Founded:** 2005. **Franchised:** 2006. **Equity Capital Needed:** $89,300 to $208,200 ; Liquid Capital $50,000. **Franchise Fee:** $40,000 ; $50,000. **Royalty Fee:** 7% of gross sales. **Financial Assistance:** Yes **Training:** Provides 7-10 days training at headquarters, 3 days onsite and ongoing support.

33317 ■ DoodyCalls

Authority Brands
245 Ridge McIntire Rd.
Charlottesville, VA 22903
Free: 800-496-9019
URL: http://www.authoritybrands.com

Description: Firm engages in pet waste removal services. **Founded:** 2000. **Franchised:** 2004. **Financial Assistance:** Yes **Training:** Offers 30 hours training at headquarters and ongoing training as needed.

33318 ■ FirstService Brands, Inc.

1140 Bay St., Ste. 4000
Toronto, ON, Canada M5S 2B4
URL: http://www.fsvbrands.com
Contact: Charlie Chase, President

Description: Firm provides home and business services. **Founded:** 1992.

33319 ■ Flamingo-A-Friend Inc.

110 Crosscut Rd.
Alabaster, AL 35007
Ph: (205)870-1315
Co. E-mail: flamingoafriend@ymail.com
URL: http://birmingham.flamingoafriend.com
Facebook: www.facebook.com/flamingoafriend

Description: Operator of display shop. **Founded:** 1994. **Financial Assistance:** Yes **Training:** Yes.

33320 ■ The Gutter Guys

2547 Fire Rd., Unit. E-5
Egg Harbor Township, NJ 08234
Ph: (609)646-1400
URL: http://thegutterguys.com
Contact: Bill Bradley, Owner

Description: Firm provides gutter cleaning services and also provides gutter doors and repair services. **Financial Assistance:** Yes

33321 ■ Ident-A-Kid

1780 102nd Ave. N, Ste. 100 St.
Saint Petersburg, FL 33716
Ph: (727)577-4646
Free: 800-890-1000
Fax: (727)576-8258
Co. E-mail: info@identakid.com
URL: http://identakid.com
Contact: Robert King, Founder
Facebook: www.facebook.com/IdentakidSA
X (Twitter): x.com/IdentAKid

Description: Provider of laminated child ID cards that contain photograph, fingerprints and physical description. Program is marketed through public and private schools. **Founded:** 1986. **Equity Capital Needed:** $200,000-$500,000. **Financial Assistance:** Yes **Training:** Provides 2 day training session at the distributor's residence. Training includes: The identification process, equipment operation, computer and marketing techniques.

33322 ■ Mr. Appliance Corp.

Neighborly
Crawford, TX 76638
Free: 800-490-7501
Fax: (877)496-2356
URL: http://www.neighborlybrands.com

Description: Home and commercial appliance repair and maintenance. **Founded:** 1996. **Training:** Initial, on-site, finances, recruiting/hiring and employee/technician retention, intra net and ongoing support.

33323 ■ Pirtek USA

1502 N 34th St.
Tampa, FL 33605
Ph: (813)247-6139
URL: http://www.pirtekusa.com
Contact: Kim Gubera, President
Facebook: www.facebook.com/PirtekUSA/timeline

Description: Distributor of hydraulic and industrial hose assemblies and related products. **Founded:** 1980. **Training:** Yes.

33324 ■ Precision Door Service

Free: 877-301-7474
URL: http://www.precisiondoor.net

Description: Garage door repair and installation service. **No. of Franchise Units:** 68. **Founded:** 1997. **Franchised:** 1999. **Equity Capital Needed:** $200,000. **Franchise Fee:** $10,000-$200,000. **Training:** Complete training and ongoing support.

33325 ■ ReCeil It International, Inc.

555 Oak St.
Copiague, NY 11726
Ph: (631)980-7668

Free: 800-234-5464
Co. E-mail: sales@1800ceiling.com
URL: http://www.1800ceiling.com/pages/store-info
-page-walk-ins-welcome
Contact: Glenn Scheel, Chief Executive Officer
Facebook: www.facebook.com/people/
1800ceilingcom/100068073815800
Linkedin: www.linkedin.com/company/receil-it-interna
tional-inc.
X (Twitter): x.com/1800ceilingcom
Instagram: www.instagram.com/1800ceiling
YouTube: www.youtube.com/user/1800ceiling
Pinterest: www.pinterest.com/1800ceilingprod

Description: Firm provides maintenance solutions for ceilings, lightings, and HVAC systems. **Founded:** 1992. **Training:** Provides 5-6 days training at headquarters and ongoing support.

33326 ■ ServiceMaster of Canada Limited

2275 Upper Middle Rd., Ste.,200
Oakville, ON, Canada L6H 0C3
Ph: (905)670-0000
Free: 800-263-5928
Fax: (905)670-0077
Co. E-mail: info@servicemaster.ca
URL: http://www.servicemaster.ca

Description: Provider of residential cleaning, furniture refinishing and facilities management services. **Founded:** 1929. **Financial Assistance:** Yes

33327 ■ Suspended In Time Inc.

122 S Mountain Way Dr.
Orem, UT 84058
Ph: (801)227-0075
Free: 866-756-0059
Co. E-mail: info@suspendedintime.com
URL: http://www.suspendedintime.com
Contact: Rachelle Adams, Contact
E-mail: rachelle@suspendedintime.com
Facebook: www.facebook.com/suspendedintime
X (Twitter): x.com/suspndedintime
Pinterest: www.pinterest.com/suspendedintime

Description: Provider of flower preservation for bridal bouquet, wedding bouquet flowers, preserved funeral floral and more. **Founded:** 1997. **Training:** Training provided at the corporate location 3, 10 hour days, which includes lunch - large discount on room accommodations and ongoing support as long as needed.

33328 ■ Worldwide Wireless

Worldwide Wireless Franchise Services L.L.C.
Dlouha 38
110 00 Prague, Czech Republic
Free: 877-346-3999
Contact: Barry M. Gilbert, Director General

Description: Exclusive Sprint dealership. **Founded:** 1999. **Franchised:** 2006. **Equity Capital Needed:** $75,000-$150,000. **Franchise Fee:** $30,000. **Financial Assistance:** Yes **Training:** Yes.

EARLY STAGE FINANCING

33329 ■ *"Dallas Top-Performing City for Small Business Growth" in Dallas Business Journal (Vol. 37, July 11, 2014, No. 44, pp. 13)*
American City Business Journals, Inc. (ACBJ)
120 W Morehead St.
Charlotte, NC 28202
Co. E-mail: circhelp@bizjournals.com
URL: http://www.acbj.com
Contact: Mike Olivieri, Executive Vice President
Released: Weekly. **Price:** $4, introductory 4-week offer(Digital only). **Description:** Dallas has been ranked as Texas' top-performing metropolitan area for small business job growth in 2014. The 1.07 percent growth rate spike placed Dallas at 104.02 on the index, and it was observed that the market conditions and economy of Dallas made it easier to start a new business. It is reported that though the index indicated a drop, small business job growth in Dallas remained at a record high. **Availability:** Print; Online.

START-UP INFORMATION

33330 ■ *"Consumer Startup Hub Set for Downtown" in Atlanta Business Chronicle (June 13, 2014, pp. 3A)*
Pub: American City Business Journals, Inc.
Contact: Mike Olivieri, Executive Vice President
Description: Michael Tavani, co-founder of Scoutmob, believes that Atlanta is fast becoming the hub for consumer- and design-focused startups. He is planning to locate his consumer-focused startup, Switchyards, in a 1920s building downtown, which will become a hive for mobile app, media, and ecommerce startups. **Availability:** Print; Online.

33331 ■ *"Ex-NFL Players' Game Plan: 2 New Nissan Dealerships" in Crain's Detroit Business (Vol. 30, July 28, 2014, No. 30, pp. 1)*
Pub: Crain Communications Inc.
Contact: Barry Asin, President
Description: All Pro Motors LLC, a New Jersey automobile dealership management company, is bringing National Football League star power to both Dearborn and Clinton Township, Michigan opening new Nissan dealerships. Detail of the new retail stores is revealed. **Availability:** Print; Online.

33332 ■ *"The Food Truck Handbook: Start, Grow, and Succeed in the Mobile Food Business"*
Pub: John Wiley & Sons, Inc.
Contact: Christina Van Tassell, Executive Vice President Chief Financial Officer
Released: March 2012. **Price:** $19.95, paperback; $12.99, e-book. **Description:** Food truck businesses have grown so much in popularity, there are actually food truck competitions and was once a television show featuring them. A practical, step-by-step handbook is offered to help an entrepreneur start a mobile food delivery service. Information includes tips on choosing vending locations, opening and closing checklists; creation of a business plan with budget and finding vendor services, daily operation issues; common operating mistakes; and insight into delivery high quality food. **Availability:** E-book; Print.

33333 ■ *"Old Town Just the First Stop for Carluccio's" in Washington Business Journal (Vol. 33, May 30, 2014, No. 6, pp. 7)*
Pub: American City Business Journals, Inc.
Contact: Mike Olivieri, Executive Vice President
Description: United Kingdom-based Carluccio's announced the opening of its first U.S. location in Old Town Alexandria, Virginia. The Italian restaurant chain reveals plans to open two more restaurants in the region to test out the various styles of their concept. Insights into the selection of the DC are as their first market is examined. **Availability:** Print; Online.

33334 ■ *"So You Want To Be a Food Truck Vendor?" in Philadelphia Business Journal (Vol. 33, August 15, 2014, No. 27, pp. 7)*
Pub: American City Business Journals, Inc.
Contact: Mike Olivieri, Executive Vice President
Released: Weekly. **Price:** $4, introductory 4-week offer(Digital only). **Description:** Food truck vendors assert that the most challenging part of starting a food truck business is acquiring a license as well as the price and number of licenses and permits required. Other costs include additional fees to vend in prime locations, maintenance, and inventory. **Availability:** Print; Online.

33335 ■ *"The Startup of Something Big" in Philadelphia Business Journal (Vol. 33, July 11, 2014, No. 22, pp. 4)*
Pub: American City Business Journals, Inc.
Contact: Mike Olivieri, Executive Vice President
Released: Weekly. **Price:** $4, introductory 4-week offer(Digital only). **Description:** Philadelphia is slowly emerging as America's leading innovation district. The South Bank Campus is the city's game changer as University of Pennsylvania and Drexel University, along with others are seeking to harness the merging of innovation and academic pursuits that ultimately translate into new business development. **Availability:** Print; Online.

33336 ■ *"Tale of Two Tech Facilities" in Business Journal Portland (Vol. 30, January 3, 2014, No. 44, pp. 12)*
Pub: American City Business Journals, Inc.
Contact: Mike Olivieri, Executive Vice President
Released: January 3, 2014. **Description:** The cities of Pittsburgh, Pennsylvania and Portland, Oregon share similarities when it comes to supporting technology startups. Both have been collaborating with the startup community. Portland has the capability to build strong companies due to its local talent pool.

REFERENCE WORKS

33337 ■ *"3 Questions with Andrew Tosh, CEO of GameSim Inc. - and Brother to a Star" in Orlando Business Journal (Vol. 30, April 18, 2014, No. 43, pp. 8)*
Pub: American City Business Journals, Inc.
Contact: Mike Olivieri, Executive Vice President
Released: Weekly. **Price:** $8, introductory 4-week offer(Digital & Print). **Description:** GameSim Inc. CEO, Andrew Tosh, says Orlando, Florida's talent pool is the reason for the company's expansion into the city. He also said that the city government's incentive programs also influenced the video game producer's choice of this location. Tosh added that the firm is set to open satellite office in other states. **Availability:** Print; Online.

33338 ■ *"Aeronautics Seeking New HQ Site" in The Business Journal-Milwaukee (Vol. 25, September 5, 2008, No. 50, pp. 1)*
Description: Milwaukee, Wisconsin-based Aeronautics Corp. of America is planning to move its headquarters to a new site. The company has started to search for a new site. It also plans to consolidate its operations under one roof.

33339 ■ *"Aircraft Maker May Land in Austin" in Austin Business Journal (Vol. 31, April 15, 2011, No. 6, pp. 1)*
Pub: Austin Business Journal
Contact: Rachel McGrath, Director
E-mail: rmcgrath@bizjournals.com
Ed: Jacob Dirr. **Description:** Icon Aircraft Inc. is planning to build a manufacturing facility in Austin, Texas. The company needs 100,000 square feet of space in a new or renovated plant. Executive comments are included. **Availability:** Print; Online.

33340 ■ *"Another California Firm Moving to Austin" in Austin Business Journal (Vol. 31, May 6, 2011, No. 9, pp. 1)*
Pub: Austin Business Journal
Contact: Rachel McGrath, Director
E-mail: rmcgrath@bizjournals.com
Ed: Christopher Calnan. **Description:** Main Street Hub Inc. is planning to build a facility in Austin, Texas. The company helps businesses manage their online reputations. Main Street has selected Aquila Commercial LLC as its real estate broker. **Availability:** Print; Online.

33341 ■ *"Austin: An Oil and Gas Hub? When Drillers Want an Office, This Is the Place" in Austin Business Journal (Vol. 32, April 13, 2012, No. 6, pp. 1)*
Pub: American City Business Journals, Inc.
Contact: Mike Olivieri, Executive Vice President
Ed: Christopher Calnan. **Description:** Austin, Texas is now attracting a greater number of oil and gas companies due to the rising demand for domestically produced energy. The number of these companies that have relocated to Austin has increased sharply and there is no indication that this will end soon. **Availability:** Online.

33342 ■ *"Austin-Based Insuraprise Growing Fast" in Austin Business Journal (Vol. 31, April 22, 2011, No. 7, pp. 1)*
Pub: Austin Business Journal
Contact: Rachel McGrath, Director
E-mail: rmcgrath@bizjournals.com

Ed: Sandra Zaragoza. **Description:** Austin, Texas-based Insuraprise Inc. is finalizing the purchase of a 24,000-square-foot office at 12116 Jekel Circle. The firm, with 23 salespeople and sales that are growing nearly 300 percent over the past 18 months, will now have room to grow. Insuraprise plans to hire 35 new salespersons for its call center. **Availability:** Print; Online.

33343 ■ "Austin Ponders Annexing Formula One Racetrack" in Austin Business Journal (Vol. 31, July 8, 2011, No. 18, pp. 1)
Pub: Austin Business Journal
Contact: Rachel McGrath, Director
E-mail: rmcgrath@bizjournals.com

Ed: Vicky Garza. **Description:** City planners in Austin, Texas are studying the feasibility of annexing the land under and around the Circuit of the Americas Formula One Racetrack being constructed east of the city. The annexation could generate at least $13 million in financial gain over 25 years from property taxes alone. **Availability:** Print; Online.

33344 ■ "Baltimore's Hispanic Businesses Try to Drum Up Cash to Battle Crime Spree" in Baltimore Business Journal (Vol. 28, September 3, 2010, No. 17)
Pub: Baltimore Business Journal
Contact: Rhonda Pringle, President
E-mail: rpringle@bizjournals.com

Ed: Scott Dance. **Description:** Hispanic businesses in Baltimore, Maryland have been raising funds to pay off-duty police officers to patrol a few blocks of Broadway in Fells Point to help curb crime. Efforts to make the area a Latin Town have failed owing to muggings, prostitution and drug dealing. Comments from small business owners are also given. **Availability:** Print; Online.

33345 ■ "Bass Pro Shops Plans Megastore for Rocklin" in Sacramento Business Journal (Vol. 51, February 14, 2014, No. 51, pp. 4)
Pub: American City Business Journals, Inc.
Contact: Mike Olivieri, Executive Vice President

Description: Bass Pro Shops is set to open its 120,000-square-foot Outdoor World store in Rocklin, California in 2015. The move will allow the Missouri-based outdoor retailer to bring its low prices and friendly, expert service to the sportsmen and women of the area. **Availability:** Online.

33346 ■ "Betting On Spec" in San Antonio Business Journal (Vol. 28, April 25, 2014, No. 11, pp. 4)
Pub: American City Business Journals, Inc.
Contact: Mike Olivieri, Executive Vice President

Released: Weekly. **Price:** $4, Introductory 4-week offer(Digital only). **Description:** Real estate broker, Ty Bragg, believes that San Antonio, Texas is lacking space for the industrial-facilities market and that will limit opportunities within the real estate sector. However, Steve Raub of Investment Realty Company, thinks that more companies are noticing the city's industrial market as a site to consider. **Availability:** Print; Online.

33347 ■ "Bob's Discount Furniture Moving into Harford County, Region" in Baltimore Business Journal (Vol. 27, January 22, 2010, No. 38, pp. 1)
Pub: Baltimore Business Journal
Contact: Rhonda Pringle, President
E-mail: rpringle@bizjournals.com

Ed: Daniel J. Sernovitz. **Description:** Manchester, Connecticut-based Bob's Discount Furniture signed a lease for 672,000 square feet of space in Harford County, Maryland. The site will become the discount furniture retailer's distribution center in mid-Atlantic US. As many as 200 jobs could be generated when the center opens. **Availability:** Print; Online.

33348 ■ "Bond Hill Cinema Site To See New Life" in Business Courier (Vol. 27, October 29, 2010, No. 26, pp. 1)
Pub: Business Courier

Ed: Dan Monk. **Description:** Avondale, Ohio's Corinthian Baptist Church will redevelop the 30-acre former Showcase Cinema property to a mixed-use site that could feature a college, senior home, and retail. Corinthian Baptist, which is one of the largest African-American churches in the region, is also planning to relocate the church. **Availability:** Print; Online.

33349 ■ "Bose Seeking Expansion Options in Framingham" in Boston Business Journal (Vol. 34, June 13, 2014, No. 19, pp. 15)
Pub: American City Business Journals, Inc.
Contact: Mike Olivieri, Executive Vice President

Released: Weekly. **Description:** Bose Corporation, the Framingham-based high-end audio products manufacturer, is in talks to buy a 10-acre property near its headquarters. Bose is negotiating with the owner of three buildings on Pennsylvania Avenue near the Bose headquarters. Bose already owns five buildings in Framingham, but is looking at real estate for growth and expansion. **Availability:** Print; Online.

33350 ■ "A Bright Spot: Industrial Space in Demand Again" in Sacramento Business Journal (Vol. 28, October 21, 2011, No. 34, pp. 1)

Description: Sacramento, California's industrial sites have been eyed by potential tenants who are actively seeking space larger than 50,000 square feet. **Availability:** Print; Online.

33351 ■ "Brokerages Seek a Foothold in Charlotte Real Estate Market" in Charlotte Business Journal (Vol. 25, October 15, 2010, No. 30, pp. 1)
Pub: Charlotte Business Journal
Contact: Robert Morris, Editor
E-mail: rmorris@bizjournals.com

Ed: Will Boye. **Description:** Charlotte, North Carolina has become an attractive destination for out-of-town brokerage firms. Colliers International has signed an affiliate deal with Anthony and Company to set up shop in Charlotte. Grubb and Ellis Company, on the other hand, is planning to open an office in the city. **Availability:** Print; Online.

33352 ■ "The Call of the City" in Puget Sound Business Journal (Vol. 35, September 5, 2014, No. 20, pp. 16)
Pub: American City Business Journals, Inc.
Contact: Mike Olivieri, Executive Vice President

Description: A number of large companies have moved their headquarters to Seattle, Washington. The area is known to be transit-accessible with mixed use offices and retail space, making it a great site selection. Seattle also embraces innovations and inventions in area districts that bring a diverse workforce. **Availability:** Print; Online.

33353 ■ "Capital Is a Good Bet as HQ Site, Report Says" in Sacramento Business Journal (Vol. 29, August 17, 2012, No. 25, pp. 1)
Pub: Baltimore Business Journal
Contact: Rhonda Pringle, President
E-mail: rpringle@bizjournals.com

Ed: Sanford Nax. **Description:** Site-selection consultant, John Boyd, has identified the city of Sacramento, California as well positioned to land corporate headquarters but is one of the most expensive cities in North America. He suggests to create incentives specifically to attract headquarters offices from more costl locations in the Bay Area and Southern California.

33354 ■ "Challenges, Responses and Available Resources: Success in Rural Small Businesses" in Journal of Small Business and Entrepreneurship (Vol. 23, Winter 2010, No. 1)
Pub: Canadian Council for Small Business and Entrepreneurship
Contact: John MacRitchie, President

Ed: Lynne Siemens. **Description:** Rural communities and their residents are exploring the potential of small business and entrepreneurship to address the

economic changes they are facing. While these rural areas present many opportunities, business people in these areas face challenges which they must navigate to operate successfully. **Availability:** Download; PDF; Online.

33355 ■ "Chuy's Ready to Serve New Markets" in Austin Business Journal (Vol. 31, June 17, 2011, No. 15, pp. 1)
Pub: Austin Business Journal
Contact: Rachel McGrath, Director
E-mail: rmcgrath@bizjournals.com

Ed: Cody Lyon. **Description:** Chuy's Holdings Inc. plans to expand into the Southeastern United States, particularly in Atlanta, Georgia. The restaurant, which secured $67.5 million in debt financing in May 2011, added 20 stores in five years and plans to open eight locations in 2011. **Availability:** Print; Online.

33356 ■ "Cities Work to Attract Small Biz: Officials Review 'Hoops' and Master Plans" in Crain's Detroit Business (Vol. 25, June 8, 2009, No. 23, pp. 20)
Pub: Crain Communications Inc.
Contact: Barry Asin, President

Ed: Nancy Kaffer. **Description:** Royal Oak and other metropolitan cities are trying to attract small companies to their towns. **Availability:** Print; Online; PDF.

33357 ■ "Cloud City: An Industry - and a Region - On the Rise" in Puget Sound Business Journal (Vol. 34, February 28, 2014, No. 46, pp. 4)
Pub: American City Business Journals, Inc.
Contact: Mike Olivieri, Executive Vice President

Description: Seattle, Washington is experiencing an influx of the world's most innovative cloud companies. Businesses are shifting their applications from in-house servers or private data center into public cloud infrastructure, which is less expensive than buying the servers and managing the data systems. Seattle software companies are taking advantage of this trend and developing products. **Availability:** Online.

33358 ■ "Con Roundup: Novi Eyed for $11 Million, 100-Bed Medilodge" in Crain's Detroit Business (Vol. 25, June 1, 2009, No. 22, pp. M032)
Pub: Crain Communications Inc.
Contact: Barry Asin, President

Description: Novi, Michigan is one of the cities being considered for construction of a new 110-bed skilled nursing facility. Details of the project are included. **Availability:** Online.

33359 ■ "Could UNC Charlotte Be Home to Future Med School?" in Charlotte Business Journal (Vol. 25, July 23, 2010, No. 18, pp. 1)
Pub: Charlotte Business Journal
Contact: Robert Morris, Editor
E-mail: rmorris@bizjournals.com

Ed: Jennifer Thomas. **Description:** University of North Carolina, Charlotte chancellor Phil Dubois is proposing that a medical school be established at the campus. The idea began in 2007 and Dubois' plan is for students to spend all four years in Charlotte and train at the Carolinas Medical Center. **Availability:** Print; Online.

33360 ■ "Couple Hopes to Lead Schlotzsky's Twin Cities Revival" in Business Journal (Vol. 31, January 17, 2014, No. 34, pp. 4)
Pub: American City Business Journals, Inc.
Contact: Mike Olivieri, Executive Vice President

Description: Austin, Texas-based Schlotzsky's announced plans to open six Minnesota locations as it tries to regain its national prominence. The bankruptcy in 2004 and the reduction of its restaurant count had wiped out eight Minnesota restaurants and left only the Edina location. Schlotzsky's six-restaurant deal with the local franchisees is examined. **Availability:** Print; Online.

33361 ■ *"Data Center Operators are Finding San Antonio has the Right Stuff" in San Antonio Business Journal (Vol. 28, February 28, 2014, No. 3, pp. 4)*
Pub: American City Business Journals, Inc.
Contact: Mike Olivieri, Executive Vice President
Released: Weekly. **Price:** $4, Introductory 4-week offer(Digital only). **Description:** A number of data center operators have been opening facilities in San Antonio, Texas. CyrusOne Inc. will build 50,000 square feet of space in the city. Such data centers have also been generating new jobs. **Availability:** Print; Online.

33362 ■ *"Deal Made for Pontiac Home of Film Studio" in Crain's Detroit Business (Vol. 25, June 1, 2009, No. 22, pp. 3)*
Pub: Crain Communications Inc.
Contact: Barry Asin, President
Ed: Daniel Duggan. **Description:** Details of the $75 million movie production and training facility in Pontiac, Michigan are revealed. **Availability:** Print; Online.

33363 ■ *"Editorial: It's Not Perfect; But Illinois a Good Home for Business" in Crain's Chicago Business (Vol. 34, October 24, 2011, No. 42, pp. 18)*
Pub: Crain Communications Inc.
Contact: Barry Asin, President
Description: Focusing on all factors that encompass Illinois' business environment, findings show that Illinois is a good place to start and grow a business. The study focused on corporate income tax rates and the fact that talent, access to capital and customers along with transportation connections are among the important factors the state has for small businesses. **Availability:** Print.

33364 ■ *"Fifth Third Spinoff Eyes More Space" in Business Courier (Vol. 27, July 16, 2010, No. 11, pp. 1)*
Pub: Business Courier
Ed: Dan Monk, Steve Watkins. **Description:** Electronic-funds transfer company Fifth Third Solutions (FTPS), a spinoff of Fifth Third Bancorp, is seeking as much as 200,000 square feet of new office space in Ohio. The bank's sale of 51 percent ownership stake to Boston-based Advent International Corporation has paved the way for the growth of FTPS. How real estate brokers' plans have responded to FTPS' growth mode is discussed. **Availability:** Print; Online.

33365 ■ *"Former Tech Execs Want to Tap Building Trend in Austin" in Austin Business Journal (Vol. 31, May 13, 2011, No. 10, pp. A1)*
Pub: Austin Business Journal
Contact: Rachel McGrath, Director
E-mail: rmcgrath@bizjournals.com
Ed: Cody Lyon. **Description:** Falcon Containers moved to a 51-acre site in Far East Austin, Texas and started construction of a 2,500-square-foot headquarters made from eight 40-foot shipping containers. Falcon's CEO Stephen Shang plans to use his headquarters building as a showroom to attract upscale, urban hipsters. Insights on the construction's environmental and social impact are shared. **Availability:** Print; Online.

33366 ■ *"Franchises with an Eye on Chicago" in Crain's Chicago Business (Vol. 34, March 14, 2011, No. 11, pp. 20)*
Pub: Crain Communications Inc.
Contact: Barry Asin, President
Ed: Kevin McKeough. **Description:** Profiles of franchise companies seeking franchisees for the Chicago area include: Extreme Pita, a sandwich shop; Hand and Stone, offering massage, facial and waxing services; Molly Maid, home-cleaning service; Primrose Schools, private accredited schools for children 6 months to 6 hears and after-school programs; Protect Painters, residential and light-commercial painting contractor; and Wingstop, a restaurant offering chicken wings in nine flavors, fries and side dishes. **Availability:** Online.

33367 ■ *"Good for Business: Houston is a Hot Spot for Economic Growth" in Black Enterprise (Vol. 37, October 2006, No. 3, pp. 216)*
Pub: Earl G. Graves Ltd.
Contact: Earl Graves, Jr., President
Ed: Jeanette Valentine. **Description:** Fast-growing sectors in the biotechnology and healthcare industries are among the driving forces of Houston's economic growth. More than 76,000 small businesses in the area employ about one in four area workers, according to the Small Business Administration. Housing and business costs are 26 and 11 percent below the national average, respectively, garnering the attention of corporate giants.

33368 ■ *"Green Manufacturer Scouts Sites in Greater Cincinnati" in Business Courier (Vol. 27, July 23, 2010, No. 12, pp. 1)*
Pub: Business Courier
Ed: Dan Monk. **Description:** CresaPartners is searching for a manufacturing facility in Cincinnati, Ohio. The company is set to tour about ten sites in the area. **Availability:** Print; Online.

33369 ■ *"Greenlight's Mission: Poach California" in Business Journal Portland (Vol. 26, December 11, 2009, No. 40, pp. 1)*
Pub: Portland Business Journal
Contact: Andy Giegerich, Managing Editor
E-mail: agiegerich@bizjournals.com
Ed: Andy Giegerich. **Description:** Leaders of Greenlight Greater Portland, a privately funded economic development organization, will visit California five times in 2010 in an attempt to lure California businesses to expand or relocate in Oregon. **Availability:** Print; Online.

33370 ■ *"Growth in Sleepy Perryville Hinges on Success of New Casino" in Baltimore Business Journal (Vol. 28, November 19, 2010, No. 28, pp. 1)*
Pub: Baltimore Business Journal
Contact: Rhonda Pringle, President
E-mail: rpringle@bizjournals.com
Ed: Rachel Bernstein. **Description:** Penn National Gaming Company's Hollywood Casino in Perryville, Maryland has been betting on the slot machines to lure slot players to the region to boost the town's growth. The success of Maryland's first casino is expected to lead to the development of land in the area. **Availability:** Print; Online.

33371 ■ *"Houston Tech Company Eyes California for HQ Move" in Houston Business Journal (Vol. 45, July 18, 2014, No. 10, pp. 10A)*
Pub: American City Business Journals, Inc.
Contact: Mike Olivieri, Executive Vice President
Released: Weekly. **Price:** $4, Introductory 4-week offer(Digital & Print). **Description:** Ed Chipul, CEO of Tendenci, a longtime Houston technology company, has stated that they are looking for a headquarters move to California. The decision to move to Silicon Valley is mainly due to a lack of synergy within the venture capital community in Houston. **Availability:** Print; Online.

33372 ■ *"How Church Street Exchange May Bring Retail, 350 Jobs" in Orlando Business Journal (Vol. 30, February 28, 2014, No. 36, pp. 10)*
Pub: American City Business Journals, Inc.
Contact: Mike Olivieri, Executive Vice President
Released: Weekly. **Price:** $8, introductory 4-week offer(Digital & Print). **Description:** Nonprofit organization, Canvs, is finalizing a lease for 14,069 square feet of technology-focused co-working space at Church Street Exchange in downtown Orlando, Florida. Jones Lang LaSalle is negotiating for more space than the 87,000-square-foot building has that could bring 300 to 350 high-tech jobs to the area. **Availability:** Print; Online.

33373 ■ *"How South Florida Can Revive a Flagging Sector" in South Florida Business Journal (Vol. 34, April 4, 2014, No. 37, pp. 10)*
Pub: American City Business Journals, Inc.
Contact: Mike Olivieri, Executive Vice President
Released: Weekly. **Price:** $8, Introductory 4-week offer(Digital & Print). **Description:** South Florida convention centers are trying to address the sluggish demand for conventions to the area by upgrading its facilities and adding hotels. The ancillary revenue generate by the attendees at hotels, restaurants, and other establishments makes a convention as key economic drivers. The efforts to boost the region's position as convention destinations are also addressed. **Availability:** Print; Online.

33374 ■ *How to Start and Run Your Own Corporation: S-Corporations For Small Business Owners*
Pub: HCM Publishing
Ed: Peter I. Hupalo. **Description:** Basics of corporate business structure are explained. Topics include discovering the best business structure for your company; how to decided between an S-Corporation and LLC; choosing the state in which to incorporate, how to form a corporation, angel investing, special issues for one-person corporations, the role of bylaws and corporate minutes, board of directors, taxes, workers' compensation issues, retirement plans, and more. **Availability:** Print.

33375 ■ *"Incentives In Play for Astronautics" in Business Journal-Milwaukee (Vol. 28, November 5, 2010, No. 5, pp. A1)*
Pub: The Business Journal
Contact: Heather Ladage, President
E-mail: hladage@bizjournals.com
Ed: Sean Ryan. **Description:** Astronautics Corporation was offered incentives by local government officials in Milwaukee, Wisconsin and by Brewery Project LLC to move into a building in The Brewery in the city. The company's officials remain indecisive over the offers and incentives. **Availability:** Print; Online.

33376 ■ *"Indiana Collection Agency Announces Expansion Plans" in PaymentsSource (March 23, 2012)*
Description: DECA Financial Services plans to buy a vacant building in Fishers, Indiana and renovate the property. The agency specializes in collection consumer and tax debts for both companies and government agencies. The company plans to hire 140 new employees over the next 3 years. **Availability:** Print; Mailing list.

33377 ■ *"Innovative Trauma Care Sets Up U.S. HQ in San Antonio" in San Antonio Business Journal (Vol. 26, August 31, 2012, No. 31, pp. 1)*
Pub: Baltimore Business Journal
Contact: Rhonda Pringle, President
E-mail: rpringle@bizjournals.com
Description: Canadian biotech firm Innovative Trauma Care (ITC) has selected San Antonio, Texas as the location of its new US headquarters. The selection could boost the reputation of San Antonio region as a hub for medical technology and trauma-related expertise. **Availability:** Print; Online.

33378 ■ *"Insitu May Move to Oregon" in Business Journal Portland (Vol. 27, October 29, 2010, No. 35, pp. 1)*
Pub: Portland Business Journal
Contact: Andy Giegerich, Managing Editor
E-mail: agiegerich@bizjournals.com
Ed: Erik Siemers. **Description:** Bingen, Washington-based Insitu Inc. announced that it has narrowed the search for a new corporate campus into five locations within the Columbia Gorge region. However, state economic development officials are curious whether the company will land in Oregon or Washington. Insights on economic impact of Insitu's decision are also given.

33379 ■ *"Investors Eager to Buy Properties Regionwide"* in *Philadelphia Business Journal (Vol. 33, August 1, 2014, No. 25, pp. 10)*

Pub: American City Business Journals, Inc.

Contact: Mike Olivieri, Executive Vice President

Released: Weekly. **Price:** $4, introductory 4-week offer(Digital only). **Description:** Interest in multifamily homes in the Philadelphia region is growing in 2014, as buyers from across the country view Philadelphia as a key investment market. Investment brokers opine the present trend will continue as pricing remains strong and there are plenty of buyers with a limited number of properties. **Availability:** Print; Online.

33380 ■ *"Jacksonville Doing Well In Growing Economy"* in *Orlando Business Journal (Vol. 30, June 27, 2014, No. 53, pp. 8)*

Pub: American City Business Journals, Inc.

Contact: Mike Olivieri, Executive Vice President

Released: June 27, 2014. **Description:** Jerry Mallot is the president of JaxUSA Partnership, the economic development arm of the Jax Chambers. According to Mallot, Northeast Florida's strongest selling points for business site or relocation there include advanced manufacturing, financial services, aviation and aerospace technology, life sciences, logistics and information technology.

33381 ■ *"Joining the Fiber"* in *San Antonio Business Journal (Vol. 28, April 4, 2014, No. 8, pp. 4)*

Pub: American City Business Journals, Inc.

Contact: Mike Olivieri, Executive Vice President

Released: April 4, 2014. **Description:** San Antonio, Texas leaders have been aggressively pursuing the opportunity to install a Google Fiber network that would deliver gigabit-per-second Internet service to the city. San Antonio is included in Google Fiber's list for possible expansion of its broadband network. The potential benefits of Google Fiber choosing San Antonio as the site for their expansion are examined.

33382 ■ *"Knocking On the World's Door"* in *Business Journal Portland (Vol. 31, March 28, 2014, No. 4, pp. 4)*

Pub: American City Business Journals, Inc.

Contact: Mike Olivieri, Executive Vice President

Released: Weekly. **Price:** $4, introductory 4-week offer(Digital & Print). **Description:** A list of things that the City of Portland, Oregon should do to achieve world-class status is provided. Portland must welcome companies as a site selection, build infrastructure, consider the economic and recreational potential of the Willamette River, allocate more education budget and provide greater access to capital. **Availability:** Print; Online.

33383 ■ *"Kokanee Films World's Longest Beer Commercial: Ready for a 90-Minute Feature Starring the Cast of Kokanee?"* in *Canadian Business (Vol. 85, July 16, 2012, No. 11-12, pp. 11)*

Ed: Jeff Beer. **Description:** Labatt Brewing Company and advertising agency Grip Ltd. produced a feature-length commercial for the Kokanee beer entitled, "The Movie Out Here", which centers on the reunion of friends in a ski town. As part of the marketing campaign, consumers can submit suggestions for props and set locations, audition for parts and vote online for the soundtrack. **Availability:** Online.

33384 ■ *"KXAN Seeks Larger Studio, Office Space in Austin"* in *Austin Business Journal (Vol. 31, May 27, 2011, No. 12, pp. A1)*

Pub: Austin Business Journal

Contact: Rachel McGrath, Director

E-mail: rmcgrath@bizjournals.com

Ed: Cody Lyon. **Description:** Austin NBC affiliate KXAN Television is opting to sell its property north of downtown and relocate to another site. The station is now inspecting possible sites to house its broadcasting facility and employees totaling as many as 200

people. Estimated cost of the construction of the studios and offices is $13 million plus another million in moving the equipment. **Availability:** Print; Online.

33385 ■ *"Luxury Still Sells Well"* in *Puget Sound Business Journal (Vol. 29, September 5, 2008, No. 20, pp. 1)*

Description: High fashion retailers are planning to open stores in the Puget Sound area despite the economic slowdown, citing high incomes in the area despite the weak U.S. dollar.

33386 ■ *"Magpower May Build Solar Panels in Pflugerville"* in *Austin Business Journal (Vol. 31, May 13, 2011, No. 10, pp. A1)*

Pub: Austin Business Journal

Contact: Rachel McGrath, Director

E-mail: rmcgrath@bizjournals.com

Ed: Christopher Calnan. **Description:** RRE Austin Solar LLC CEO Doven Mehta has revealed plans to partner with Portugal-based Magpower SA, only if Austin energy buys electricity from planned solar energy farm in Pflugerville. Austin Energy has received 100 bids from 35 companies to supply 200 megawatts of solar- and wind-generated electricity. **Availability:** Print; Online.

33387 ■ *"M&T On the March?"* in *Baltimore Business Journal (Vol. 28, November 12, 2010, No. 27, pp. 1)*

Pub: Baltimore Business Journal

Contact: Rhonda Pringle, President

E-mail: rpringle@bizjournals.com

Ed: Gary Haber. **Description:** Information on the growth of M&T Bank, as well as its expansion plans are presented. M&T recently acquired Wilmington Trust and took over $500 million in deposits from the failed K Bank. Analysts believe that M&T would continue its expansion through Washington DC and Richmond, Virginia, especially after a bank executive acknowledged that the markets in those areas are attractive. **Availability:** Print; Online.

33388 ■ *"Mapping Out a Career: An Analysis of Geographic Concentration of Occupations"* in *Occupational Outlook Quarterly (Vol. 54, Fall 2010, No. 3, pp. 12)*

Pub: U.S. Department of Labor Bureau of Labor Statistics

Contact: Amrit Kohli, Director

E-mail: kohli.amrit@bls.gov

Ed: Audrey Watson. **Description:** Geographic distribution of occupations is studied, along with lifestyle considerations when choosing a career. **Availability:** PDF; Online.

33389 ■ *"Maryland Casinos Face Atlantic City's $150M Might"* in *Baltimore Business Journal (Vol. 30, June 1, 2012, No. 4, pp. 1)*

Pub: American City Business Journals, Inc.

Contact: Mike Olivieri, Executive Vice President

Ed: Gary Haber. **Description:** Atlantic City has launched a campaign to attract visitors from the East Coast. The campaign is part of the city's $150 million marketing plan, which markets the city not for its casinos but as a shopping destination. Executive comments included. **Availability:** Online.

33390 ■ *"Md.'s Film Industry Professionals have to Leave the State to Find Work: Exiting Stage Left"* in *Baltimore Business Journal (Vol. 28, June 18, 2010, No. 6, pp. 1)*

Pub: Baltimore Business Journal

Contact: Rhonda Pringle, President

E-mail: rpringle@bizjournals.com

Ed: Scott Dance. **Released:** Weekly. **Description:** Film professionals including crew members and actors have been leaving Maryland to find work in other states such as Michigan, Louisiana, and Georgia where bigger budgets and film production incentives are given. Other consequences of this trend in local TV and film production are discussed. **Availability:** Print.

33391 ■ *"Meet University of Texas' New Business Mind"* in *Austin Business Journal (Vol. 31, May 13, 2011, No. 10, pp. A1)*

Pub: Austin Business Journal

Contact: Rachel McGrath, Director

E-mail: rmcgrath@bizjournals.com

Ed: Sandra Zaragoza. **Description:** University of Texas (UT) chief commercialization officer, Dr. Richard Miller, has opened a satellite office in Silicon Valley, California in the hopes of luring Californian investors to the science and technology at UT. The satellite office is just one of Miller's efforts to reshape and widen the commercialization of UT-Austin. Insights into Miller's long-term view approach to commercialization are also covered. **Availability:** Online.

33392 ■ *"Mortgage Servicer Wingspan Portfolio Advisors Makes Mark in Frisco"* in *Dallas Business Journal (Vol. 35, September 7, 2012, No. 52, pp. 1)*

Pub: Baltimore Business Journal

Contact: Rhonda Pringle, President

E-mail: rpringle@bizjournals.com

Ed: Candace Carlisle. **Description:** Carrollton, Texas-based Wingspan Portfolio Advisors LLC has seen rapid growth in its business and the company plans to hire another 500 employees. Wingspan has subleased a 125,000-square-foot building in Firsco, Texa to accommodate the expansion and making it the company's third site in North Texas.

33393 ■ *"Neighborhood Awaits Its 'Very Sexy Building"* in *Dallas Business Journal (Vol. 37, June 27, 2014, No. 42, pp. 12)*

Pub: American City Business Journals, Inc.

Contact: Mike Olivieri, Executive Vice President

Released: Weekly. **Price:** $4, introductory 4-week offer(Digital only). **Description:** Crescent Real Estate Holdings LLC chairman and CEO, John Goff, described the upcoming 20-story, $225 million office and retail tower in Uptown Dallas as a 'sexy addition' to the neighborhood. Goff believes the location offers companies a unique marketing advantage. **Availability:** Print; Online.

33394 ■ *"No Trader Joe's for Mid-South"* in *Memphis Business Journal (Vol. 34, July 13, 2012, No. 13, pp. 1)*

Pub: Baltimore Business Journal

Contact: Rhonda Pringle, President

E-mail: rpringle@bizjournals.com

Ed: Andy Ashby. **Description:** Trader Joe's Company Inc. has been planning 20 new locations in the next 12 months that would be added to its more than 350 stores. However, the specialty grocery store chain has not included Memphis, Tennessee in its two-year plan. **Availability:** Print; Online.

33395 ■ *"Nordstrom Points for Richmond Heights"* in *Saint Louis Business Journal (Vol. 31, August 5, 2011, No. 50, pp. 1)*

Pub: Saint Louis Business Journal

Contact: Robert Bobroff, President

E-mail: rbobroff@bizjournals.com

Ed: E.B. Solomont. **Description:** Nordstrom is set to upgrade its offerings for its second full-line store in St. Louis, Missouri. The new store is expected to benefit nearby shops. **Availability:** Print; Online.

33396 ■ *"Old Ford Plant to Sign New Tenants"* in *Business Courier (Vol. 27, August 13, 2010, No. 15, pp. 1)*

Pub: Business Courier

Ed: Dan Monk. **Description:** Ohio Realty Advisors LLC, a company handling the marketing of the 1.9 million-square-foot former Ford Batavia plant is on the brink of landing one distribution and three manufacturing firms as tenants. These tenants are slated to occupy about 20 percent of the facility and generate as many as 250 jobs in Ohio. **Availability:** Print; Online.

33397 ■ *"One-on-One with Enterprise Florida's Gray Swoope"* in *Orlando Business Journal (Vol. 31, August 15, 2014, No. 7, pp. 4)*

Pub: American City Business Journals, Inc.

Contact: Mike Olivieri, Executive Vice President

Released: Weekly. **Price:** $8, introductory 4-week offer(Digital only); $8, introductory 4-week offer(Digital & Print). **Description:** Gray Swoope is the president and CEO of Enterprise Florida, who is in charge of a $19.9 million operating budget for fiscal year 2014-15 used to attract new businesses, relocations, and expansions to the state. He believes in focusing on game-changing projects that create thousands of jobs, with wages close to $100,000 a year and a capital investment of half-billion dollars by a private sector company. **Availability:** Print; Online.

33398 ■ "Organic Chain Scouting Cincinatti Sites, Including Kenwood" in Business Courier (Vol. 27, December 3, 2010, No. 31, pp. 1)
Pub: Business Courier
Ed: Tom Demeropolis. **Description:** Asheville, North Carolina-based Earth Fare has been planning to add a total of six stores in 2011, including the potential opening of more than one store in the Greater Cincinnati area market. Earth Fare has not named specific locations but Kenwood area was reportedly being considered for its first location. Insights on growing trends toward health food stores are also given. **Availability:** Print; Online.

33399 ■ "Parts, Tooling Manufacturer Machinists Inc. Opts to Expand in South Park" in Puget Sound Business Journal (Vol. 34, February 21, 2014, No. 45, pp. 6)
Pub: American City Business Journals, Inc.
Contact: Mike Olivieri, Executive Vice President
Description: Seattle, Washington-based Machinists Inc. announced an expansion with a seventh building in South Park. The new 20,000-square-foot building will increase the company's footprint to 115,000-square-feet when fully outfitted. The machine manufacturer shares insight into its decision to stay in Seattle rather than relocate is offered. **Availability:** Online.

33400 ■ "Play It Safe At Home, Or Take a Risk Abroad? A US Lease-To-Own Chain Considers Whether To Test Its Business In Mexico" in Harvard Business Review (Vol. 90, January-February 2012, No.1-2, pp. 145)
Pub: Harvard Business Review Press
Contact: Moderna V. Pfizer, Contact
Ed: Michael Chu. **Price:** $8.95, hardcopy black and white. **Description:** A fictitious foreign-market entry scenario is presented, with contributors providing advice. Recommendations include ensuring that expansion will not compromise the firm's core business, and that expansion, while necessary to growth, must be done carefully. **Availability:** Print; Online; PDF.

33401 ■ "PNC Begins Search for New Baltimore-Area Headquarters" in Baltimore Business Journal (Vol. 28, June 4, 2010, No. 4, pp. 1)
Pub: Baltimore Business Journal
Contact: Rhonda Pringle, President
E-mail: rpringle@bizjournals.com
Ed: Daniel J. Sernovitz. **Description:** PNC Financial Services Group Inc. is searching for a new headquarters building in Greater Baltimore, Maryland. The company is seeking about 150,000 square feet for its regional operations. However, PNC could also end up moving out of Baltimore for space in the surrounding suburbs. **Availability:** Print; Online.

33402 ■ "Portland Wooing Under Armour to West Coast Facility" in Baltimore Business Journal (Vol. 27, January 29, 2010, No. 39, pp. 1)
Pub: Baltimore Business Journal
Contact: Rhonda Pringle, President
E-mail: rpringle@bizjournals.com
Ed: Andy Giegerich. **Description:** Baltimore, Maryland sports apparel maker, Under Armour, is planning a west coast expansion with Portland, Oregon among the sites considered to house its apparel and footwear design center. Portland officials counting on the

concentration of nearly 10,000 activewear workers in the city will help lure the company to the city. **Availability:** Print; Online.

33403 ■ "The Promise of the Promised Land" in San Francisco Business Times (Vol. 28, January 3, 2014, No. 24, pp. 4)
Pub: American City Business Journals, Inc.
Contact: Mike Olivieri, Executive Vice President
Released: September 15, 2016. **Price:** $4, print. **Description:** San Francisco Bay Area in California has become the site selection for investment, technology and talent. The financing finding its way to the Bay Area has led to robust job creation, drawing people and increasing the population by 2.6 percent to 805,000. The impact of the Bay Area's technology boon in rents and home prices are also presented. **Availability:** Print; Online.

33404 ■ "Rawlings-Blake Unveils Business Plan for Next Four Years" in Baltimore Business Journal (Vol. 29, September 16, 2011, No. 19, pp. 1)
Pub: Boston Business Journal
Contact: Carolyn M. Jones, President
E-mail: cmjones@bizjournals.com
Ed: Gary Haber. **Description:** Mayor Stephanie Rawlings-Blake of Baltimore, Maryland unveiled her plan to push the economy forward. Her key objectives include giving more support for the city's technology companies and refocusing the Baltimore Development Corporation on job creation and retention. **Availability:** Online.

33405 ■ "Restaurateurs Follow High-End Apartments Into Kendall Square" in Boston Business Journal (Vol. 31, July 22, 2011, No. 26, pp. 3)
Pub: Boston Business Journal
Contact: Carolyn M. Jones, President
E-mail: cmjones@bizjournals.com
Ed: Lisa Van der Pool. **Description:** Kendall Square in Cambridge, Massachusetts is attracting restaurants, 16 of which have opened since 2009. The influx of restaurants is being driven by lower commercial rents.

33406 ■ "Retail Remains Hot as More Stores Browse Around Houston" in Houston Business Journal (Vol. 44, January 17, 2014, No. 37, pp. 9A)
Pub: American City Business Journals, Inc.
Contact: Mike Olivieri, Executive Vice President
Released: Weekly. **Price:** $4, Introductory 4-week offer(Digital & Print). **Description:** Houston, Texas-based Evergreen Commercial Realty president, Lilly Golden, has revealed that the city has 15 new retail projects under construction and about 30 other projects in the pipeline. Golden believes Houston's low vacancy rate and high rent growth in Class A assets cause high demand from investors nationally. The boom in the retail sector is also examined. **Availability:** Print; Online.

33407 ■ "Roseville Investing Big in Downtown" in Sacramento Business Journal (Vol. 28, September 2, 2011, No. 27, pp. 1)
Pub: Sacramento Business Journal
Contact: Stephanie Fretwell, Director
E-mail: sfretwell@bizjournals.com
Ed: Michael Shaw. **Price:** $4, Digital introductory 4-week offer; $4, Print & Digital introductory 4-week offer. **Description:** The city of Roseville, California is planning to invest in downtown development projects. The plan includes a new town square, a venue for a farmers market and an interactive water fountain. **Availability:** Print; Online.

33408 ■ "Roundy's Pushing Chicago Expansion" in Milwaukee Business Journal (Vol. 27, February 12, 2010, No. 20, pp. A1)
Pub: The Business Journal
Contact: Heather Ladage, President
E-mail: hladage@bizjournals.com
Ed: Rich Kirchen. **Description:** Roundy Supermarkets Inc. is expanding in Chicago, Illinois as the Milwaukee-based company is set to open one store

in downtown Chicago and another in the Arlington suburb. The store openings have been pushed back to spring and early summer in 2010 due to the economic downturn. **Availability:** Print; Online.

33409 ■ "S.A. Chasing Tesla, Other Auto-Industry Firms" in San Antonio Business Journal (Vol. 28, April 4, 2014, No. 8, pp. 7)
Pub: American City Business Journals, Inc.
Contact: Mike Olivieri, Executive Vice President
Price: $4, Introductory 4-Week Offer(Digital & Print). **Description:** San Antonio, Texas has joined cities trying to land the $5 billion battery plant of Tesla Motors that could employ 6,500 workers. San Antonio's drive to establish a major auto-industry cluster in the region would be boosted by Tesla's choosing the city as the site for manufacturing batteries. The benefits from the Texas-Mexico Automotive SuperCluster initiative are also explored. **Availability:** Print; Online.

33410 ■ "Shire Seeking New Digs for Headquarters" in Philadelphia Business Journal (Vol. 30, September 2, 2011, No. 29, pp. 1)
Pub: Philadelphia Business Journal
Contact: Sierra Quinn, Director
E-mail: squinn@bizjournals.com
Ed: Natalie Kostelni. **Description:** Dublin, Ireland-based Shire PLC announced plans to relocate its North American headquarters from Chesterbrook Corporate Center in Wayne, Pennsylvania and currently evaluating their options. The specialty biopharmaceutical firm is also considering a move to New Jersey or Delaware. **Availability:** Online.

33411 ■ "The Silvery Moon Moves to Larger Location" in Bellingham Business Journal (Vol. March 2010, pp. 5)
Pub: Sound Publishing Inc.
Contact: Josh O'Connor, President
Ed: Isaac Bonnell. **Description:** Jewelry store, the Silvery Moon, moved to a larger location in order to expand its business. The new location was chosen because it offers the firm more visibility. The store offers find silver and gold pieces and specializes in Pacific Northwest native jewelry.

33412 ■ "South Park Draws Brewers, Vintners" in Puget Sound Business Journal (Vol. 29, August 29, 2008, No. 19, pp. 1)
Description: Craft breweries and wineries are moving into Seattle, Washington's South Park neighborhood due to the area's low rents, convenience, and ample equipment space. These industries bring a more upscale flavor to the heavily industrial area and the tastings and festivals draw people from throughout the Seattle region. **Availability:** Print; Online.

33413 ■ Start and Run a Delicatessen: Small Business Starters Series
Description: Information for starting and running a successful delicatessen is provided. Insight is offered into selecting a location, researching the market, writing a business plan and more.

33414 ■ "State Center Lease Deal High for Md." in Baltimore Business Journal (Vol. 28, August 6, 2010, No. 13, pp. 1)
Pub: Baltimore Business Journal
Contact: Rhonda Pringle, President
E-mail: rpringle@bizjournals.com
Ed: Daniel J. Sernovitz. **Description:** The proposed $1.5 billion State Center development project in Midtown Baltimore might cause the State of Maryland to pay the most expensive rental rates in the city. The state will have to pay an effective rental rate of $34 per square foot, including expenses, on the leasing. Other details of the redevelopment project are discussed. **Availability:** Print; Online.

33415 ■ "Subway Launches Expanded Cafes, Drive-Thru Window Locations" in South Florida Business Journal (Vol. 33, August 10, 2012, No. 2, pp. 1)
Pub: Baltimore Business Journal
Contact: Rhonda Pringle, President

E-mail: rpringle@bizjournals.com

Description: Subway launched its larger cafe concept at Florida Atlantic University and plans to open more drive-thru restaurants in South Florida. This could change preferred leasing locations to Subway franchisees, which are also moving into nontraditional locations. Site selection issues are covered. **Availability:** Print; Online.

33416 ■ *"Suppliers May Follow Fiat: Local Group Says Italian Firms are Inquiring"* in *Crain's Detroit Business (Vol. 25, June 15, 2009, No. 24, pp. 1)*
Pub: Crain Communications Inc.
Contact: Barry Asin, President
Ed: Ryan Beene. **Description:** Italian suppliers to Fiat SpA are looking toward Detroit after the formation of Chrysler Group LLC, the Chrysler-Fiat partnership created from Chrysler's bankruptcy. The Italian American Alliance for Business and Technology is aware of two Italy-based powertrain component suppliers that are considering a move to Detroit. **Availability:** Online.

33417 ■ *"Taylor Tests Land Grant Program"* in *Austin Business Journal (Vol. 31, June 3, 2011, No. 13, pp. 1)*
Pub: Austin Business Journal
Contact: Rachel McGrath, Director
E-mail: rmcgrath@bizjournals.com
Ed: Vicky Garza. **Description:** Taylor Economic Development Corporation implemented a land grant program called Build On Our Lot to lure businesses to Taylor City, Austin, Texas. They are targeting small businesses, especially those in the renewable energy, advanced manufacturing, technical services and food products. Program details are included. **Availability:** Print; Online.

33418 ■ *"Tesla Eyes Two Sites for New Battery-Pack Plant"* in *San Antonio Business Journal (Vol. 28, May 16, 2014, No. 14, pp. 8)*
Pub: American City Business Journals, Inc.
Contact: Mike Olivieri, Executive Vice President
Released: Weekly. **Price:** $4, introductory 4-week offer(Digital only). **Description:** The City of San Antonio, Texas is competing with other cities in five states to land the contract for the $5 million battery-pack plant of Texla Motors. Bill Avila of Bracewell & Giuliani LLPO law firm believes that San Antonio has an edge over some of the cities competing for the Tesla manufacturing plant because of its successful recruitment of Toyota in 2003. **Availability:** Print; Online.

33419 ■ *"There's Risk, Reward for Business in Baltimore's Edgier Areas: Taking a Chance"* in *Baltimore Business Journal (Vol. 28, July 16, 2010, No. 10, pp. 1)*
Pub: Baltimore Business Journal
Contact: Rhonda Pringle, President
E-mail: rpringle@bizjournals.com
Ed: Scott Dance. **Description:** North Avenue in Baltimore, Maryland is considered a rough neighborhood due to the dangers of prostitution and drug dealing. However, some entrepreneurs have taken the risk of building their businesses on North Avenue as revitalization efforts grow. One of the challenges for businesses in rough neighborhoods is bringing customers to their stores or offices. **Availability:** Print.

33420 ■ *"Thriving DFW Big Target for Franchisors"* in *Dallas Business Journal (Vol. 35, March 30, 2012, No. 29, pp. 1)*
Description: Dallas-Fort Worth Metropolitan Area has attracted outside franchisors looking to expand as Texas continues to fare better than other states during the recession. The Internation Franchising Association estimates that there will be 21,772 franchise establishments in DFW in 2012. **Availability:** Print; Online.

33421 ■ *"Vancouver, B.C. Shines - at Seattle's Expense?"* in *Puget Sound Business Journal (Vol. 35, May 9, 2014, No. 3, pp. 6)*
Pub: American City Business Journals, Inc.
Contact: Mike Olivieri, Executive Vice President

Description: Reports show that Vancouver, British Columbia, Canada is becoming Seattle, Washington's biggest competitor because of the British Columbia's business-friendly policies. Microsoft is increasing their number of workers in in Vancouver, while Amazon will open an office in the city. The similarities between Seattle and Vancouver are explored. **Availability:** Online.

33422 ■ *"Wal-Mart Sharpens Focus on Roxbury"* in *Boston Business Journal (Vol. 31, July 8, 2011, No. 24, pp. 1)*
Pub: Boston Business Journal
Contact: Carolyn M. Jones, President
E-mail: cmjones@bizjournals.com
Ed: Mary Moore. **Price:** $4. **Description:** Wal-Mart Stores is boosting its search for a possible location in the Roxbury section of Boston, Massachusetts. The search is focused on underserved communities in terms of jobs and access to reasonably-priced merchandise. The extent Boston's African American community has clashed with Mayor Thomas M. Memino over the accommodations of the retailer in Roxbury is discussed. **Availability:** Print; Online.

33423 ■ *"Why Alabama's Aerospace Is Still Sitting Pretty After 777X"* in *Birmingham Business Journal (Vol. 31, January 10, 2014, No. 2, pp. 3)*
Pub: American City Business Journals, Inc.
Contact: Mike Olivieri, Executive Vice President
Released: Weekly. **Price:** $4, introductory 4-week offer(Digital & Print). **Description:** Alabama's aerospace sector can still benefit from Boeing despite the state's failure to attract the company's 777X project. Boeing is planning to do some of the project's engineering work in Huntsville, Alabama. The company plans to move about 400 engineering jobs to the state. **Availability:** Print; Online.

33424 ■ *"Why Japan Is So Interested In Alabama"* in *Birmingham Business Journal (Vol. 31, August 1, 2014, No. 31, pp. 11)*
Pub: American City Business Journals, Inc.
Contact: Mike Olivieri, Executive Vice President
Description: Kazuo Sunaga, Consul General of Japan in Atlanta, Georgia lists several reasons why Alabama presents several opportunities for Japanese companies, including fewer labor laws, low tax rates and the availability of trained workers. The state's relationship with Japan will be further enhanced when Birmingham hosts the Southeast U.S./Japan Association meeting in 2015, which will be attended by leaders from the business, political, and nonprofit sectors. **Availability:** Print; Online.

TRADE PERIODICALS

33425 ■ *Business Facilities: The Source for Corporate Site Selectors*
Pub: Group C Media Inc.
Contact: Bill Corsini, Director
E-mail: bcorsini@groupc.com
URL(s): businessfacilities.comgroupcmedia.com/print-publications
Facebook: www.facebook.com/BusinessFacilities
Linkedin: www.linkedin.com/company/business-facilities-magazine
X (Twitter): x.com/bizfacilities
Instagram: www.instagram.com/businessfacilitiesmag
YouTube: www.youtube.com/user/businessfacilities
Pinterest: www.pinterest.com/commercial_industry_news/business-facilities-magazine-news
Ed: Mary Ellen McCandless. **Released:** Bimonthly **Price:** $52, Single issue for per year. **Description:** Professional magazine focusing on corporate expansion, commercial/industrial real estate, and economic development. **Availability:** Print; PDF; Download; Online.

33426 ■ *Site Selection Magazine*
Pub: Conway Inc.
Contact: Daniel Boyer, Director
URL(s): siteselection.com
Facebook: www.facebook.com/SiteSelection
Linkedin: www.linkedin.com/company/site-selection-magazine
X (Twitter): x.com/siteSelection

Released: Bimonthly; January, March, May, July, September, November. **Description:** Magazine on real estate and site selectors. **Availability:** Print; Online.

33427 ■ *Urban Land Magazine*
Pub: Urban Land Institute
Contact: Gwyneth Jones Cote, Chief Executive Officer
URL(s): urbanland.uli.org
Released: Quarterly; January, April, July, and September. **Description:** Professional magazine for land use and development practitioners. **Availability:** Print; Online.

CONSULTANTS

33428 ■ **Architectural Research Consultants Inc. (ARC)**
4906 Alameda Blvd. NE, Ste. A
Albuquerque, NM 87113
Ph: (505)842-1254
URL: http://www.arcplanning.com
Contact: John Petronis, President
Facebook: www.facebook.com/arcplanningabq
Linkedin: www.linkedin.com/company/architectural-research-consultants-inc
X (Twitter): x.com/arcplanning
Description: Firm provides architectural consulting services such as planning, architectural programming and research, facility evaluation, and much more. **Scope:** Offers applied research and information services to architects, interior designers and others in the building industry. **Founded:** 1976. **Publications:** "Post-Occupancy Evaluation and edited Facility Programming"; "Programming the Built Environment"; "Building Evaluation"; "Pueblo Style and Regional Architecture"; "Design Intervention: Toward A More Humane Architecture"; "Professional Practice in Facility Programming"; "Design Review: Challenging Urban Aesthetic Control"; "New Directions in Urban Public Housing"; "Directions In Person-Environment Research and Practice"; "Universal Design Handbook"; "Assessing Building Performance"; "Designing for Designers". **Training:** Initiative on Dimensional Tolerances in Construction Surface Compliance Design Issues, Mar, 2007.

33429 ■ **LSA Associates Inc.**
20 Executive Pk., Ste. 200
Irvine, CA 92614
Ph: (949)553-0666
Fax: (949)553-8076
Co. E-mail: irvine@lsa.net
URL: http://lsa.net
Contact: Anthony Petros, President
E-mail: tony.petros@lsa.net
Facebook: www.facebook.com/lsa1976
Linkedin: www.linkedin.com/company/lsa-associates-inc
Description: Provider of planning such as expertise, projects, careers, and much more services. **Scope:** Provider of planning such as expertise, projects, careers, and much more. **Founded:** 1976.

PUBLICATIONS

33430 ■ *Business Facilities: The Location Advisor*
The Galleria
2 Bridge Ave., Ste. 231
Red Bank, NJ 07701
Ph: (732)842-7433
Free: 800-524-0337
Fax: (732)758-6634
URL: http://groupcmedia.com
Contact: Bill Corsini, Director
E-mail: bcorsini@groupc.com
URL(s): businessfacilities.com
Linkedin: www.linkedin.com/company/business-facilities-magazine
YouTube: www.youtube.com/@Businessfacilities
Pinterest: www.pinterest.com/commercial_industry_news/business-facilities-magazine-news
Released: Semiweekly **Description:** Highlights area economic development and site selection news from around the world. **Availability:** Online.

Small Business Development

START-UP INFORMATION

33431 ■ *"Business Diary" in Crain's Detroit Business (Vol. 24, October 6, 2008, No. 40, pp. 23)*
Pub: Crain Communications Inc.
Contact: Barry Asin, President

Description: Detailed listing of acquisitions, expansions, new products, new services, business contracts and startups from the Detroit area is provided. **Availability:** Print; Online.

33432 ■ *Entrepreneur's Information Sourcebook*

Ed: Susan C. Awe. **Released:** January 16, 2012. **Description:** A comprehensive source for those looking to start their own business, which contains information on creating a business plan, marketing and advertising, taxes, and many more relevant topics. Also contains sources for further research.

33433 ■ *The Marketing Plan Handbook*

Ed: Robert W. Bly. **Released:** 2015. **Description:** A beginner's guide to understanding customers and their needs to help form a solid marketing plan for your business. Designed to help your small business outpace your competitors, this book will help you understand the market for your products and develop steps to achieve success. Comes with assignments and examples.

33434 ■ *"Should You Go Into Business With Your Spouse?" in Women Entrepreneur (September 1, 2008)*

Description: Things to consider before starting a business with one's spouse are discussed. Compatible work ethics, clear expectations of one another, long-term goals for the company and the status of the relationship are among the things to consider before starting a business endeavor with a spouse. **Availability:** Online.

33435 ■ *"So You Want to Start a Business? So You Want to Start a Business: What's Your First Move?" in Women Entrepreneur (August 5, 2008)*

Description: Advice for taking an idea and turning it into a legitimate business is given. **Availability:** Online.

33436 ■ *"Spreading Your Wings" in Canadian Business (Vol. 81, March 17, 2008, No. 4, pp. 31)*

Ed: Megan Harman. **Released:** February 09, 2017. **Description:** Financing from angel investors is one avenue that should be explored by startups. Angel investors are typically affluent individuals who invest their own money. Angel investors usually want at least 10 times their initial investment within eight years but they benefit the businesses through their help in decision-making and the industry expertise they provide. **Availability:** Download; Online.

33437 ■ *"UM-Dearborn to Launch Program for Entrepreneurs" in Crain's Detroit Business (Vol. 24, April 14, 2008, No. 15, pp. 7)*
Pub: Crain Communications Inc.
Contact: Barry Asin, President

Ed: Chad Halcom. **Description:** Starting this fall the University of Michigan-Dearborn will begin its Product Realization and Technology Commercialization Program for entrepreneurs and innovators with lab-tested, high-technology products. Ultimately, 20 businesses will each work with the university in creating a customer base, commercializing a new high-tech product or process and connecting with venture capitalists who may invest in the new companies. **Availability:** Online.

ASSOCIATIONS AND OTHER ORGANIZATIONS

33438 ■ **Action for Enterprise (AFE)**
4600 N Fairfax Dr., Ste. 304
Arlington, VA 22203
Ph: (703)243-9172
Fax: (703)243-9123
URL: http://www.actionforenterprise.org
Contact: Frank Lusby, Executive Director

Description: Implements small enterprise development programs, based on a comprehensive analysis of business sectors and the interrelationships of enterprises that function with them. Initiates efforts to develop sustainable business development service providers at the local level. **Founded:** 1991. **Geographic Preference:** Multinational.

33439 ■ **Alabama Business Incubation Network**
1020 9th Ave. SW
Bessemer, AL 35022-4530
Ph: (205)481-2101
Fax: (205)481-2100
Co. E-mail: bessemerincubator@yahoo.com
URL: http://www.nbia.org/resources/directories/u-s-s tate-incubation-associations
Contact: Devron A. Veasley, Chairman

Description: Seeks to advance business incubation and entrepreneurship. Educates businesses and investors on incubator benefits. Provides information, research and networking resources to help members develop and manage successful business incubation programs. **Geographic Preference:** State.

33440 ■ **American Business Association (ABA)**
12444 Powerscourt Dr., Ste. 500A
Saint Louis, MO 63131
Free: 800-992-8044
Co. E-mail: infot@americanbusinessweb.org
URL: http://www.americanbusinessweb.org

Description: Small businesses, self-employed, independent contractors, and entrepreneurs ages 18 and over. Provides benefits and resources to help members with professional, lifestyle, and health-related benefits. **Founded:** 1999.

33441 ■ **American Veteran Owned Business Association (aVOBa)**
1103 W Hibiscus Ave., Ste. 301A
Melbourne, FL 32901
Free: 877-862-5478
Co. E-mail: info@avosba.org
URL: http://avosba.org
Facebook: www.facebook.com/aVOSBa

Description: Seeks to "empower military veterans who own businesses to grow, hire fellow veterans, and give back to military veteran organizations that directly impact the servicemen and women (and their respective families) who proudly served our great nation." Operates the Veteran Owned Business project, an online directory of more than 35,000 U.S. businesses owned by veterans, United States active duty military, reservists, and service disabled veterans (DVBE/SDVOSB) of the United States Army, Air Force, Marines, Navy, Coast Guard, and National Guard. **Founded:** 2008.

33442 ■ **America's Small Business Development Center (ASBDC) [America's SBDC]**
8990 Burke Lake Rd., 2nd Fl.
Burke, VA 22015
Co. E-mail: info@americassbdc.org
URL: http://americassbdc.org
Contact: Charles Rowe, President
E-mail: tee.rowe@americassbdc.org
Facebook: www.facebook.com/ASBDC
Linkedin: www.linkedin.com/company/association-of -small-business-development-centers
X (Twitter): x.com/ASBDC
YouTube: www.youtube.com/user/TheASBDC

Description: Local centers providing advice for those planning to establish a small business. Aims to facilitate information exchange among members and to represent their interests before the federal government. Informs the Small Business Administration on issues of interest to the small business community. **Founded:** 1980. **Geographic Preference:** National.

33443 ■ **Arizona Business Incubation Association**
Flagstaff, AZ
Ph: (602)845-1296
Co. E-mail: debk@azcommerce.com
URL: http://azincubators.org
Facebook: www.facebook.com/pg/azincubators
X (Twitter): twitter.com/azincubators

Description: Promotes effective business incubation in Arizona. Provides professionals with information, education, advocacy and networking opportunities. **Founded:** 2011. **Geographic Preference:** State.

33444 ■ Ashoka Innovators for the Public
2200 Wilson Blvd., Ste. 102, No. 313
  Arlington, VA 22201
Ph: (703)527-8300
URL: http://www.ashoka.org/en-us
Contact: Bill Drayton, Chief Executive Officer
Facebook: www.facebook.com/AshokaUSA
X (Twitter): x.com/ashokaus
Description: Serves as a network for social entrepreneurs and helps them collaborate with like-minded innovators around the world. **Founded:** 1980. **Publications:** *Changemakers.* **Awards:** Ashoka Common Ground Awards (Annual). **Geographic Preference:** Multinational.

33445 ■ Association for Enterprise Opportunity (AEO)
1310 L St. NW, Ste. 830
  Washington, DC 20005
Ph: (202)650-5580
Co. E-mail: info@aeoworks.org
URL: http://www.aeoworks.org
Contact: Connie E. Evans, President
E-mail: cevans@aeoworks.org
Facebook: www.facebook.com/AEO
X (Twitter): x.com/AEOworks
YouTube: www.youtube.com/user/kcrutcher88/videos
Description: Represents microenterprise development organizations serving economically disadvantaged areas across the United States. Promotes improved economic opportunity for aspiring entrepreneurs with limited access to financial resources. Facilitates networking among members; provides training and technical assistance to members; develops and distributes educational materials; conducts advocacy. **Founded:** 1991. **Publications:** *AEO Exchange* (Quarterly). **Geographic Preference:** National; Regional.

33446 ■ Bakersfield Downtown Business Association (DBA)
1675 Chester Ave., Ste. 110
  Bakersfield, CA 93301
Ph: (661)325-5892
Fax: (661)325-7319
Co. E-mail: dbassociation@gmail.com
URL: http://bakersfielddba.com
Contact: Melanie Farmer, President
E-mail: melanie@bakersfielddba.com
Facebook: www.facebook.com/BakersfieldDBA
X (Twitter): x.com/bakersfielddba
Instagram: www.instagram.com/bakersfielddba
Description: Represents small business owners. Promotes the interests of small businesses. Provides government relations services, educational information and member benefit programs. **Founded:** 1954. **Geographic Preference:** Local.

33447 ■ Brentwood Business Owners Association (BBOA)
3325 Saw Mill Run Blvd.
  Pittsburgh, PA 15227
Ph: (412)885-4868
URL: http://bboaonline.com
Description: Represents small business owners. Promotes the interests of small businesses. Provides government relations services, educational information and member benefit programs. **Geographic Preference:** Local.

33448 ■ *Business Barometer*
401-4141 Yonge St.
  Toronto, ON, Canada M2P 2A6
Co. E-mail: cfib@cfib.ca
URL: http://www.cfib-fcei.ca/en
Contact: Dan Kelly, President
URL(s): www.cfib-fcei.ca/en/research-economic
  -analysis/business-barometer
Released: Monthly **Availability:** Print; PDF.

33449 ■ Business Network International Inc. (BNI)
11525 N Community House Rd., No. 475
  Charlotte, NC 28277
Ph: (704)248-4800
Free: 800-825-8286
Co. E-mail: support@bni.com

URL: http://www.bni.com
Contact: Dan Haggerty, President
Linkedin: www.linkedin.com/company/bni
X (Twitter): x.com/bni_official_pg
YouTube: www.youtube.com/user/BNIOfficialChannel
Description: Firm provides consulting services on business, planning and management. **Founded:** 1985.

33450 ■ Canadian Council for Small Business and Entrepreneurship (CCSBE)
6382 Young St.
  Halifax, NS, Canada B3L 2A1
URL: http://ccsbe.org
Contact: John MacRitchie, President
X (Twitter): x.com/ccsbe
Description: Seeks to promote and advance the development of small business and entrepreneurship in Canada. Offers a collaborative platform for the exchange of ideas, research, and best practices among academics, practitioners, and policy influencers for the benefit of Canadian small business and entrepreneurship. **Publications:** *Journal of Small Business & Entrepreneurship* (Bimonthly).

33451 ■ Canadian Federation of Independent Business (CFIB) - Research Library
401-4141 Yonge St.
  Toronto, ON, Canada M2P 2A6
Co. E-mail: cfib@cfib.ca
URL: http://www.cfib-fcei.ca/en
Contact: Dan Kelly, President
Facebook: www.facebook.com/CFIB
Linkedin: www.linkedin.com/company/canadian-fe
  deration-of-independent-business
X (Twitter): x.com/CFIBNews
Instagram: www.instagram.com/cfib_fcei
YouTube: www.youtube.com/user/cfibdotca
Description: Promotes economic well-being of members and seeks to maintain a healthy domestic business climate. **Scope:** Business. **Founded:** 1971. **Holdings:** Figures not available. **Publications:** *Mandate* (Quarterly); *Business Barometer* (Monthly). **Geographic Preference:** National.

33452 ■ Colorado Business Incubation Association
12635 E Montview Blvd., Ste., 100
  Aurora, CO 80045
Contact: Vicki Jenings, Contact
Description: Seeks to advance business incubation and entrepreneurship. Educates businesses and investors on incubator benefits. Provides information, research and networking resources to help members develop and manage successful business incubation programs. **Founded:** 2011. **Geographic Preference:** State.

33453 ■ Cortland County Business Development Corp.
40 Main St., Ste. A
  Cortland, NY 13045
Ph: (607)756-5005
Fax: (607)756-7901
Co. E-mail: info@cortlandbusiness.com
URL: http://www.cortlandbusiness.com
Contact: Garry L. VanGorder, Executive Director
E-mail: garry@cortlandbusiness.com
Facebook: www.facebook.com/profile.php
Description: Seeks to promote business through economic and community development. Assists businesses in their expansion and financing needs. Enhances the quality of life and fosters the growth of good jobs within the community. **Geographic Preference:** Local.

33454 ■ Detroit Economic Club (DEC)
211 W Fort St., Ste. 710
  Detroit, MI 48226
Ph: (313)963-8547
Co. E-mail: info@econclub.org
URL: http://www.econclub.org
Contact: Steve Grigorian, President
E-mail: sgrigorian@econclub.org
Facebook: www.facebook.com/detroiteconomicclub
Linkedin: www.linkedin.com/groups/693427/profile
X (Twitter): x.com/DetEconomicClub

YouTube: www.youtube.com/user/detroi
  teconomicclub
Description: Promotes the discussion and debate of important business, government, and social issues in the Detroit area. **Founded:** 1934. **Geographic Preference:** Local.

33455 ■ District of Columbia Small Business Development Center (DCSBDC)
2600 6th St. NW Rm. 128
  Washington, DC 20059
Ph: (202)806-1551
Fax: (202)806-1777
Co. E-mail: dcsbdc@aedc.net
URL: http://dcsbdc.org
Contact: Carl E. Brown, Jr., Director
E-mail: carl.brown@howard.edu
Facebook: www.facebook.com/DCSBDC
Linkedin: www.linkedin.com/company/dc-small-busi
  ness-development-center-network
X (Twitter): x.com/DCSBDC
Description: Provides free management and technical assistance and affordable training in all phases of business development to District of Columbia based small businesses. **Geographic Preference:** State.

33456 ■ Entrepreneurs Organization (EO)
500 Montgomery St., Ste. 700
  Alexandria, VA 22314
Ph: (703)519-6700
Fax: (703)519-1864
Co. E-mail: info@eonetwork.org
URL: http://www.eonetwork.org
Contact: Carrie Santos, PhD, Chief Executive Officer
Facebook: www.facebook.com/En
  trepreneursOrganization
Linkedin: www.linkedin.com/company/en
  trepreneurs%27-organization
X (Twitter): x.com/EntrepreneurOrg
Instagram: www.instagram.com/entrepreneursorg
YouTube: www.youtube.com/user/EOnetwork
Description: Engages leading entrepreneurs to learn and grow. Serves as a focal point for networking and development of members through small group learning sessions, regular local chapter social and learning events, and global conference-based education programs. **Founded:** 1987. **Publications:** *Overdrive* (Monthly); *Octane* (Quarterly). **Geographic Preference:** Multinational.

33457 ■ The Entrepreneurship Institute (TEI)
4449 E Way
  Columbus, OH 43219
Ph: (614)934-1540
URL: http://www.tei.net
Description: Provides encouragement and assistance to entrepreneurs who operate companies with revenue in excess of $1 million. Unites financial, legal, and community resources to help foster the success of companies. Promotes sharing of information and interaction between members. Operates President's forums and projects which are designed to improve communication between businesses, develop one-to-one business relationships between small and mid-size businesses and local resources, provide networking, and stimulate the growth of existing companies. **Founded:** 1976. **Educational Activities:** The Entrepreneurship Institute Meeting. **Geographic Preference:** National.

33458 ■ Florida Business Incubation Association (FBIA)
12085 Research Dr.
  Alachua, FL 32615
Co. E-mail: fbiamgmt@gmail.com
URL: http://www.fbiaonline.org
Contact: Karl R. LaPan, President
E-mail: klapan@ufl.edu
Facebook: www.facebook.com/FLBIA
Description: Seeks to advance business incubation and entrepreneurship. Educates businesses and investors on incubator benefits. Provides information, research and networking resources to help members develop and manage successful business incubation programs. **Founded:** 1998. **Geographic Preference:** State.

33459 ■ G20 Young Entrepreneurs' Alliance (G20 YEA)

c/o the Centre for Social Innovation
326-192 Spadina Ave.
Toronto, ON, Canada M5T 2C2
Co. E-mail: admin@g20yea.com
URL: http://www.g20yea.com
Facebook: www.facebook.com/G20YEA
Linkedin: www.linkedin.com/company/g20-yea
X (Twitter): x.com/g20_yea
Instagram: www.instagram.com/g20yea
YouTube: www.youtube.com/channel/UC
6eWxfXjmuYUEXMxI7VXguQ
Description: Young entrepreneurs and their supporting organizations around the world. Seeks to support young entrepreneurs at the local, national, and international level, and to promote an environment in which entrepreneurs can grow businesses, create jobs, change lives, and ensure future economic prosperity. Meets each year in advance of the G20 Summit to champion the importance of young entrepreneurs to the G20 member nations and to share members' examples and practices. **Founded:** 2010.

33460 ■ Hacienda Business Park Owners Association

4305 Hacienda Dr., Ste. 330
Pleasanton, CA 94588-2738
Ph: (925)734-6500
Fax: (925)734-6501
Co. E-mail: info@hacienda.org
URL: http://www.hacienda.org
Contact: James Paxson, Agent
Facebook: www.facebook.com/Hacienda-189210
267781138
Linkedin: www.linkedin.com/company/hacienda
X (Twitter): x.com/HaciendaTweet
Description: Represents small business owners. Promotes the interests of small businesses. Provides government relations services, educational information and member benefit programs. **Founded:** 1982. **Geographic Preference:** Local.

33461 ■ HUBZone Contractors National Council [HUBZone Council]

PO Box 355
Oakland, MD 21550
Ph: (240)442-1787
Co. E-mail: info@hubzonecouncil.org
URL: http://hubzonecouncil.org
Contact: Shirley Bailey, Chairman
E-mail: shirley.bailey@mscmgmtservices.com
Facebook: www.facebook.com/hubzone
Linkedin: www.linkedin.com/company/hubzone-con
tractors-national-council
X (Twitter): x.com/HUBZoneCouncil
Instagram: www.instagram.com/hubzone_council
YouTube: www.youtube.com/channel/UCX3uYU
6GaPUwbtg_p_5fTrw
Description: Companies and organizations. Seeks to assist small businesses in promoting job growth, capital investment, and economic development in historically underutilized business zones, known as HUBZones. **Founded:** 2000.

33462 ■ Illinois Department of Commerce & Economic Opportunity - Illinois Small Business Development Center

1011 S 2nd St.
Springfield, IL 62704
Ph: (217)782-7500
URL: http://dceo.illinois.gov/smallbizassistance/
beginhere/sbdc.html
Contact: Ericka White, Director
Description: Statewide network of centers providing information, counseling, and training to existing small business and pre-venture entrepreneurs. **Founded:** 1984. **Geographic Preference:** State.

33463 ■ International Association of Women (IAW)

55 E Monroe St., Ste. 2120
Chicago, IL 60603
Free: 888-852-1600
Co. E-mail: memberservices@iawomen.com
URL: http://www.iawomen.com
Facebook: www.facebook.com/iawomen
Linkedin: www.linkedin.com/company/iawomenhq
X (Twitter): x.com/IAWomenHQ
Instagram: www.instagram.com/iawomen
Description: Serves as network of accomplished women united to achieve professional goals. Provides job listings and a forum for sharing experiences of professional women regarding career success. Promotes an active business and networking community from all industries. **Geographic Preference:** National.

33464 ■ International Business Innovation Association (InBIA)

PO Box 677279
Orlando, FL 32867
Ph: (407)965-5653
Co. E-mail: info@inbia.org
URL: http://inbia.org
Contact: Charles Ross, Chief Executive Officer
E-mail: cross@inbia.org
Facebook: www.facebook.com/TheInBIA
Linkedin: www.linkedin.com/company/theinbia
X (Twitter): x.com/TheInBIA
Instagram: www.instagram.com/TheInBIA
Description: Incubator developers and managers; corporate joint venture partners, venture capital investors; economic development professionals. Helps newly formed businesses to succeed. Educates businesses and investors on incubator benefits; offers specialized training in incubator formation and management. Conducts research and referral services; compiles statistics; publishes information relevant to business incubation and growing companies. **Publications:** *Business Incubators of North America* (Biennial); *NBIA Insights* (Monthly); *NBIA Memberabilia* (Semimonthly); *NBIA Review* (Bimonthly); *NBIA Business Incubation Industry Directory* (Annual). **Awards:** NBIA Incubator Innovation Award (Annual); NBIA Incubator of the Year (Annual); NBIA Outstanding Incubator Client Award (Annual); NBIA Outstanding Incubator Graduate Award. **Geographic Preference:** National; Multinational.

33465 ■ Jackson Growth Alliance (JGA)

1740 Innovation Dr., 227
Carbondale, IL 62903
URL: http://jacksongrowthalliance.org
Contact: Darrell Bryant, Executive Director
E-mail: director@jacksongrowthalliance.org
Facebook: www.facebook.com/jacksongrowthalliance
Description: Seeks to promote business through economic and community development. Assists businesses in their expansion and financing needs. Enhances the quality of life and fosters the growth of good jobs within the community. **Geographic Preference:** Local.

33466 ■ Job Creators Network (JCN)

15455 N Dallas Pky., Ste. 600
Addison, TX 75001
Co. E-mail: info@jobcreatorsnetwork.com
URL: http://www.jobcreatorsnetwork.com
Contact: Alfredo Ortiz, President
Facebook: www.facebook.com/JobCreatorsNetwork
X (Twitter): x.com/JobCreatorsUSA
Instagram: www.instagram.com/jobcreatorsnetwork
YouTube: www.youtube.com/user/JobCreatorsNe
twork
Description: Nonpartisan organization defending small businesses and economic freedom against overreaching government policies. Provides business leaders and entrepreneurs with tools to protect and advance free enterprise.

33467 ■ Ladies Who Launch (LWL)

909 Montgomery St., Ste. 300
San Francisco, CA 94133
Co. E-mail: hello@ladieswholaunch.org
URL: http://www.ladieswholaunch.org
Contact: Jennifer Warren, Executive Director
Facebook: www.facebook.com/LWLGlobal
Linkedin: www.linkedin.com/company/lwlglobal
X (Twitter): x.com/LWLGlobal
Instagram: www.instagram.com/lwlglobal
YouTube: www.youtube.com/channel/UCEDF-5Xk
4U0GT7xmFZDMLoA
Description: Serves as a network for entrepreneurs and businesswomen. **Founded:** 2013.

33468 ■ Lifetime Benefit Solutions (LBS)

333 Butternut Dr.
Syracuse, NY 13214
Free: 800-356-1029
URL: http://www.lifetimebenefitsolutions.com
Contact: Lori Florack, President
Linkedin: www.linkedin.com/company/lifetime-benefi
t-solutions-inc-/about
Description: Represents small businesses (less than 50 employees), the self-employed, and associations of such individuals. Provides services and programs such as group purchasing discounts, health coverage, legislative advocacy, and business and financial support services. **Founded:** 1974. **Publications:** *Capital Crier* (Monthly); *Small-Biz Growth* (Monthly). **Educational Activities:** Small Biz. **Geographic Preference:** National.

33469 ■ Long Island City Partnership (LICP)

27-01 Queens Plz. N, Level B
Long Island City, NY 11101
Ph: (718)786-5300
Co. E-mail: info@licpartnership.org
URL: http://www.longislandcityqueens.com
Contact: Elizabeth Lusskin, President
E-mail: elusskin@licpartnership.org
Facebook: www.facebook.com/LICPartnership
Linkedin: www.linkedin.com/company/licpartnership
X (Twitter): x.com/LICPartnership
Description: Aims to advocate for economic development that benefits Long Island City's industrial, commercial, cultural, and residential sectors. Attracts new businesses and promotes a vibrant and authentic mixed-use community. Serves as the marketing arm of the Long Island City Business Improvement District and the Long Island City Business Development Corporation. **Founded:** 1979. **Geographic Preference:** Local.

33470 ■ Maryland Business Incubation Association (MBIA)

c/o E Shore Entrepreneurship Ctr., 8737 Brooks Dr.,
Ste. 101
Easton, MD 21601
URL: http://mdinnovate.org
Contact: Deb Tillett, Manager
E-mail: dtillett@etcbaltimore.com
Description: Seeks to advance business incubation and entrepreneurship. Educates businesses and investors on incubator benefits. Provides information, research and networking resources to help members develop and manage successful business incubation programs. **Founded:** 2002. **Geographic Preference:** State.

33471 ■ MichBusiness

27700 Hoover Rd.
Warren, MI 48093
Free: 888-277-6464
Fax: (586)393-8810
Co. E-mail: hello@michbusiness.com
URL: http://michbusiness.com
Contact: Jennifer Kluge, President
Facebook: www.facebook.com/michbusiness
Linkedin: www.linkedin.com/company/michbusiness
X (Twitter): x.com/michbusiness
Instagram: www.instagram.com/michbusiness1
YouTube: www.youtube.com/user/
MichBusinessAssoc
Description: Network of business owners that is aimed at promoting and supporting Michigan businesses. **Founded:** 1990. **Publications:** *Corp! Magazine* (Bimonthly). **Educational Activities:** Women Thrive Conference. **Geographic Preference:** State.

33472 ■ Mississippi Business Incubation Association

c/o John Brandon
Mississippi Development Authority
PO Box 849
Jackson, MS 39205-0849
URL: http://inbia.org/about-minneapolis
Contact: Linda Fowler, President

Description: Seeks to advance business incubation and entrepreneurship. Educates businesses and investors on incubator benefits. Provides information, research and networking resources to help members develop and manage successful business incubation programs. **Geographic Preference:** State.

33473 ■ National Association of Business Owners & Entrepreneurs (NABOE)

21732 Brink Meadow Ln.
 Germantown, MD 20876
Ph: (301)873-0448
Co. E-mail: messages@naboe.com
URL: http://naboe.org
Contact: Ronald K. Wills, President
Linkedin: www.linkedin.com/company/national -association-of-business-owners-&-entrepreneurs

Description: Supports small business owners by providing opportunities for education, networking, and information sharing.

33474 ■ National Association of Entrepreneurship (NAE)

OH
Free: 800-497-6950
Co. E-mail: info@naeonline.org
URL: http://naeonline.org

Description: Seeks to advance free enterprise by providing and expanding opportunities for U.S. emerging mid-market companies to grow and succeed in a competitive global economy. Offers peer connectivity, institutional partnerships, and relevant information and education.

33475 ■ National Association for the Self-Employed (NASE)

PO Box 241
 Annapolis Junction, MD 20701-0241
Free: 800-232-6273
Fax: (800)678-4605
URL: http://www.nase.org
Contact: Keith R. Hall, President
Facebook: www.facebook.com/NASEonFB
Linkedin: www.linkedin.com/company/national -association-for-the-self-employed-nase-
X (Twitter): x.com/NASEtweets
Instagram: www.instagram.com/NASEonIG
YouTube: www.youtube.com/user/NASEview
Pinterest: www.pinterest.com/NASEpins

Description: Self-employed and small independent businesspersons. Acts as an advocate at the state and federal levels for self-employed people. Provides discounts on products and services important to self-employed and small business owners. **Founded:** 1981. **Publications:** *Self-Employed OutFront Weekly* (Weekly); *Washington Watch* (Weekly). **Awards:** NASE Future Entrepreneur Award; NASE Dependent Scholarships (Annual).

33476 ■ National Business Association (NBA)

2201 Midway Rd., Ste. 106
 Carrollton, TX 75006
Free: 800-456-0440
Fax: (888)269-4387
Co. E-mail: nba@nationalbusiness.org
URL: http://nationalbusiness.org
Contact: Rick Foster, Contact
Facebook: www.facebook.com/Na tionalBusinessAssoc
Linkedin: www.linkedin.com/company/national-busi ness-association
X (Twitter): x.com/NatlBusAssoc
Instagram: www.instagram.com/na tionalbusinessassoc

Description: Aids members in obtaining government small business and education loans; makes available insurance policies and software in conjunction with the U.S. Small Business Administration. **Founded:** 1982. **Publications:** *Biz Corner* (Weekly); *NBA boss* (Bimonthly). **Geographic Preference:** National.

33477 ■ National Federation of Independent Business (NFIB)

53 Century Blvd., Ste. 250
 Nashville, TN 37214
Ph: (615)874-5288
Free: 800-634-2669
URL: http://www.nfib.com
Contact: Brad Close, President
Linkedin: www.linkedin.com/company/nfib

Description: Aims to promote and protect small and independent businesses throughout the United States through advocacy, resource sharing, and collective purchasing power. **Founded:** 1943. **Educational Activities:** National Association Business Economics Annual Meeting (Annual). **Geographic Preference:** National.

33478 ■ National Federation of Independent Business New Jersey

222 W State St.
 Trenton, NJ 08608
Ph: (609)337-1532
Co. E-mail: eileen.kean@nfib.org
URL: http://www.nfib.com/new-jersey
X (Twitter): x.comcom/nfib_nj

Description: Trade association of small business owners. Conducts lobbying activities. Provides information to the public and small businesses. **Founded:** 1943. **Publications:** *Capitol Coverage* (Quarterly). **Educational Activities:** Small Business Summit (Annual). **Geographic Preference:** State.

33479 ■ National Small Business Association (NSBA)

1156 15th St. NW, Ste. 502
 Washington, DC 20005
Free: 800-345-6728
Co. E-mail: info@nsba.biz
URL: http://www.nsba.biz
Contact: Todd McCracken, President
Facebook: www.facebook.com/NSBAAdvocate
Linkedin: www.linkedin.com/company/2061777
X (Twitter): x.com/NSBAAdvocate

Description: Small businesses including manufacturing, wholesale, retail, service, and other firms. Works to advocate at the federal level on behalf of smaller businesses. **Founded:** 1937. **Educational Activities:** Small Business Meetup Day. **Awards:** Lewis A. Shattuck Small Business Advocate of the Year Award (Annual). **Geographic Preference:** National.

33480 ■ National Veteran-Owned Business Association (NaVOBA)

348 E Main St.
 Lexington, KY 40507
Ph: (724)362-8622
Co. E-mail: inquiries@navoba.org
URL: http://www.navoba.org
Contact: Brian Hall, Secretary
Facebook: www.facebook.com/NaVOBA
Linkedin: www.linkedin.com/company/navoba
X (Twitter): x.com/navoba

Description: Seeks to unite current and future veteran-owned businesses. Acts as the national voice for the veteran business movement. Works to convince corporate America and the government to consider using veteran-owned businesses as preferred vendors. **Founded:** 2007. **Publications:** *Vetrepreneur* (11/year). **Geographic Preference:** National.

33481 ■ New England Business Association (SBANE)

2020 Trapelo Rd., Ste. 172
 Waltham, MA 02451
Ph: (781)890-9070
Fax: (781)890-4567
Co. E-mail: info@newenglandbusiness.org
URL: http://newenglandbusiness.org
Contact: Karim Hill, President
E-mail: karim@newenglandbusiness.org
Linkedin: www.linkedin.com/company-beta/1297172
X (Twitter): x.com/SBANENewEngland
YouTube: www.youtube.com/channel/UCh8G_Ec 3VyiJR-XXbpg21MQ

Description: Aims to provide a legislative voice for small New England businesses at the state and federal levels, and to make practical information available to help business owners grow their companies. Services include networking, educational events, politicals roundtables, and capital connections.

Founded: 1938. **Publications:** *New England Business Association Membership Directory* (Biennial); *SBANE News.*

33482 ■ New Jersey Business Incubation Network (NJBIN)

c/o Anne-Marie Maman, President
 34 Chambers St.
 Princeton, NJ 08542
Ph: (609)258-4499
Co. E-mail: amaman@princeton.edu
URL: http://www.njbin.org
Contact: Anne-Marie Maman, President
E-mail: amaman@princeton.edu
X (Twitter): twitter.com/thenjbin

Description: Seeks to advance business incubation and entrepreneurship. Educates businesses and investors on incubator benefits. Provides information, research and networking resources to help members develop and manage successful business incubation programs. **Geographic Preference:** State.

33483 ■ North Carolina Business Incubators Association (NCBIA)

c/o Nancy Blackman, Secretary
 1551 S Elm-Eugene St.
 Greensboro, NC 27406
Ph: (910)892-2884
Co. E-mail: nljblackman@gmail.com
URL: http://inbia.org/services/resources
Contact: Nancy Blackman, Secretary
E-mail: nljblackman@gmail.com

Description: Seeks to advance business incubation and entrepreneurship. Educates businesses and investors on incubator benefits. Provides information, research and networking resources to help members develop and manage successful business incubation programs. **Founded:** 1996. **Geographic Preference:** State.

33484 ■ Oregon Business Council (OBC)

1100 SW 6th Ave., Ste. 1608
 Portland, OR 97204
Ph: (503)595-7616
URL: http://orbusinesscouncil.org
Contact: Duncan Wyse, President
E-mail: dwyse@orbusinesscouncil.org
YouTube: www.youtube.com/channel/UCj5i 1CpQSRZZad2G0rteQlg

Founded: 1985. **Geographic Preference:** State.

33485 ■ Partners in Business

3500 Old Main Hill
 Logan, UT 84322-3500
Ph: (435)797-2272
Co. E-mail: huntsman@usu.edu
URL: http://www.partners.usu.edu
Contact: Chris Fawson, Executive Director
E-mail: chris.fawson@usu.edu
URL(s): huntsman.usu.edu
Facebook: www.facebook.com/huntsmanschool
Linkedin: www.linkedin.com/school/utah-state -university---jon-m.-huntsman-school-of-business
Instagram: www.instagram.com/huntsmanschool
YouTube: www.youtube.com/user/huntsmanschool

Description: Non-profit organization provides programs of professional business conferences featuring topics on operational excellence, accounting, leadership, human resources and data analytics. **Scope:** Non-profit organization provides programs of professional business conferences featuring topics on operational excellence, accounting, leadership, human resources and data analytics. **Founded:** 1970. **Publications:** "Invading the Cayman Islands and 13 Other Accounting Solutions to the Economic Crisis". **Training:** Women in Business, Feb, 2010; Information Technology, Jan, 2010; Salt Lake Leadership, Nov, 2009; Marketing, Nov, 2009; Customer Service, Nov, 2009; Annual Finance, Oct, 2009; Annual Accounting, Oct, 2009; Restructuring Your Business, Sep, 2009; Operational Excellence, Sep, 2009; Connect yourself and your business to the digital world, Aug, 2009; Entrepreneurs: Defying Gravity, Mar, 2009; Keys to Successfully Restructure Your Business, May, 2009.

33486 ■ River North Business Association (RNBA)
620 N Lasalle St., Ste. 320
Chicago, IL 60654
Ph: (312)645-1047
Fax: (312)645-1151
Co. E-mail: info@greaterrnba.com
URL: http://greaterrnba.com
Contact: Marty Padilla, President
E-mail: president@greaterrnba.com
Facebook: www.facebook.com/Greaterrnba
X (Twitter): x.com/rivernorthchi
Instagram: www.instagram.com/greaterrnba
YouTube: www.youtube.com/user/rnbachicago
Description: Represents businesses and provides member services to help them succeed. **Publications:** *River North Directory* (Annual); *River North News* (Quarterly). **Educational Activities:** Business Exchange and Exposition (Annual); Fraud: Preparing for Holiday Business. **Geographic Preference:** Local.

33487 ■ The Rosie Network
c/o Leona Sublett
15336 Mesa Estates Ct.
Ramona, CA 92065
Co. E-mail: contact@therosienetwork.org
URL: http://www.therosienetwork.org
Contact: Stephanie Brown, Chief Executive Officer
Facebook: www.facebook.com/TheRosieNetwork
Linkedin: www.linkedin.com/company/the-rosie-ne
twork
X (Twitter): x.com/Rosie_Network
Instagram: www.instagram.com/therosienetwork
YouTube: www.youtube.com/channel/UCm_J03rsIR
_LhucNJZZE45g
Pinterest: www.pinterest.com/TheRosieNetwork
Description: Promotes the entrepreneurial efforts of U.S. veterans and military spouses. Seeks to build stronger military families by developing entrepreneurial programs and support services that empower military spouses, transitioning service members, and veterans. **Founded:** 2012.

33488 ■ SEEP Network
1621 N Kent St., Ste. 900
Arlington, VA 22209
Ph: (202)534-1400
Fax: (703)276-1433
Co. E-mail: seep@seepnetwork.org
URL: http://seepnetwork.org/Our-Story
Contact: Alex Sardar, Executive Director
Facebook: www.facebook.com/TheSEEPNetwork
Linkedin: www.linkedin.com/company/the-seep-ne
twork
X (Twitter): x.com/theseepnetwork
Description: Voluntary organizations that support micro and small businesses and microfinance institutions in the developing world; offers publications on best practices. **Founded:** 1985. **Geographic Preference:** Local.

33489 ■ Small Business Majority
1015 15th St. NW, Ste. 450
Washington, DC 20005
Free: 866-597-7431
URL: http://smallbusinessmajority.org
Contact: Geri Aglipay, Director
Facebook: www.facebook.com/
SmallBusinessMajority
Linkedin: www.linkedin.com/company/small-business
-majority
X (Twitter): x.com/SmlBizMajority
Instagram: www.instagram.com/smlbizmajority
YouTube: www.youtube.com/user/
SmlBusinessMajority
Description: National small business advocacy organization that seeks to empower diverse entrepreneurs throughout the United States to build a thriving and equitable economy. Conducts scientific opinion polling, focus groups, and economic research to help educate and inform policymakers, the media, and other stakeholders about key issues impacting small businesses and freelancers, including healthcare, access to capital, taxes, retirement, paid leave and other workforce issues. Provides educational pro-

grams and resources to small business owners, their employees, and self-employed entrepreneurs to empower them to start and grow their enterprises and maximize their economic prosperity. **Founded:** 2005.

33490 ■ Small Business Technology Council (SBTC)
1156 15th St. NW, Ste. 502
Washington, DC 20005
Ph: (202)662-9700
Co. E-mail: press@nsba.biz
URL: http://sbtc.org
Contact: Jere Glover, Executive Director
Facebook: www.facebook.com/NSBAAdvocate
X (Twitter): x.com/NSBAAdvocate
Description: Non-partisan industry association of companies dedicated to promoting the creation and growth of research-intensive, technology-based U.S. small business. Seeks to advance the Small Business Innovation Research (SBIR) Program, which provides over $2.2 billion annually to companies in government R&D contracts. Advocates with the federal government to promote small business technology companies. Offers management support and advanced technology networking opportunities.

33491 ■ Small Giants Community (SGC)
482 Dunston Ct.
Bloomfield Hills, MI 48304
Ph: (313)444-0348
Co. E-mail: hello@smallgiants.org
URL: http://smallgiants.org
Contact: Hamsa Daher, Executive Director
Linkedin: www.linkedin.com/company/small-giants
-community
X (Twitter): x.com/smallgiantsbuzz
YouTube: www.youtube.com/channel/UCh
6uYy8aUCx6cSKMQ0l-gug
Description: Supports entrepreneurs around the world by providing resources, events, mentorship, and networking to enhance and develop their businesses. **Founded:** 2009.

33492 ■ Southern Fauquier Business Owners Association (SFBOA)
PO Box 358
Bealeton, VA 22712
Facebook: www.facebook.com/SoFauquierBusiness
Description: Represents small business owners. Promotes the interests of small businesses. Provides government relations services, educational information and member benefit programs. **Geographic Preference:** Local.

33493 ■ Southwestern Oregon Community College Business Development Center
1988 Newmark Ave.
Coos Bay, OR 97420
URL: http://oregonsbdc.org/centers/southwestern
-sbdc
Contact: Mark Gregory, Director
E-mail: john.bacon@socc.edu
Description: Represents and promotes the small business sector. Provides management assistance to current and prospective small business owners. Helps to improve management skills and expand the products and services of members. **Geographic Preference:** Local.

33494 ■ TechnoServe Inc.
1777 N Kent St.
Arlington, VA 22209
Ph: (202)785-4515
Free: 800-999-6757
Fax: (202)785-4544
Co. E-mail: info@technoserve.org
URL: http://www.technoserve.org
Contact: William Warshauer, President
Facebook: www.facebook.com/TechnoServe
Linkedin: www.linkedin.com/company/technoserve
X (Twitter): x.com/TechnoServe
Instagram: www.instagram.com/technoserve
YouTube: www.youtube.com/user/technoserveglobal
Description: Works to improve the economic and social well-being of low-income people in Latin America, Africa, and Eastern Europe. Provides

agriculture and business training to help the poor build their own self-sustaining enterprises. Provides feasibility assessment; design and implementation of management, production, and financial systems and controls; monitoring and evaluating enterprise performance and impact. **Scope:** Offers management and business advisory services primarily to medium-scale community-based agricultural enterprises and institutions. Helps low-income people. Serves private industries as well as government agencies. **Founded:** 1968. **Publications:** *World Newsletter*. **Geographic Preference:** Multinational.

33495 ■ Texas - Northwest Small Business Development Center (NWTSBDC)
5001 W Loop 289
Lubbock, TX 79414
Ph: (806)745-3973
URL: http://www.depts.ttu.edu/nwtsbdc
Contact: Carla Holland, Executive Director
E-mail: carla.holland@ttu.edu
Description: Represents and promotes the small business sector. Provides management assistance to current and prospective small business owners. Helps to improve management skills and expand the products and services of members. **Geographic Preference:** Local.

33496 ■ United States Veteran Business Alliance (USVBA)
3140 Peacekeeper Way, Ste. 100
McClellan, CA 95652
Free: 888-517-3822
Co. E-mail: info@gousvba.org
URL: http://gousvba.org
Contact: Daniel Connor, President
Facebook: www.facebook.com/NationalUSVBA
Linkedin: www.linkedin.com/in/usvballiance
X (Twitter): x.com/USVBAlliance
Instagram: www.instagram.com/nationalusvba
Description: Provides advocacy, guidance, and resources to support U.S. veteran entrepreneurs in establishing, maintaining, and growing successful businesses. Organizes skill-building and networking events, fosters local chapters nationwide, and helps veterans certify their business for Disabled Veteran Owned Business Enterprise (DVBE) contracts. **Founded:** 1994.

33497 ■ University of Missouri St. Louis SBDC South County
Lafferre Hall
Rm. E2437N, 416 S 6th St.
Columbia, MO 65211
Ph: (873)884-1555
URL: http://sbdc.missouri.edu/locations
Description: Represents and promotes the small business sector. Provides management assistance to current and prospective small business owners. Helps to improve management skills and expand the products and services of members. **Geographic Preference:** Local.

33498 ■ Veteran Business Association
221 Driggs Dr., Ste. 5043
Winter Park, FL 32793
Ph: (407)901-5155
Co. E-mail: support@genesisprivatefund.com
URL: http://veteranbusinessassociation.org
Facebook: www.facebook.com/ve
teranbusinessassociation
X (Twitter): twitter.com/veteranbiz
Instagram: www.instagram.com/Ve
teranBusinessAssociation
Description: Supports veterans, service members, and their spouses who want to launch or buy a business.

33499 ■ Veteran Business Owners Association (VBOA) [Veteran Business Owners Initiative]
200 Springs Rd.
Bedford, MA 01730
Ph: (781)983-3728
Co. E-mail: pinskyg5@gmail.com
URL: http://www.vboa.org
Contact: Colonel Andrea Gayle-Bennett, Secretary

Description: Seeks to assist veterans and their family members in developing and managing a successful business by providing tools and support to leverage the skills and interests of veterans as they become business owners in their communities. Supports members at all levels of business development, from business plan creation to running daily operations. **Founded:** 2004.

33500 ■ Veteran Entrepreneur Alliance (VEA)
1120 S Rackham Way 3rd Fl.
 Meridian, ID 83642
Ph: (208)314-1776
Co. E-mail: info@vealliance.org
URL: http://www.vealliance.org
Contact: Isaac Belden, Executive Director
Facebook: www.facebook.com/vealliance
X (Twitter): x.com/thevealliance
Instagram: www.instagram.com/vealliance

Description: Strives to assist U.S. veterans transition from their military careers into entrepreneurship. Provides resources and support in such areas as business plans, social media marketing, business law, networking, and funding a business.

33501 ■ Veteran Entrepreneurial Training & Resource Network (VETRN)
9 Danforth Ln.
 Norton, MA 02766
Ph: (617)901-6055
Co. E-mail: info@vetrn.org
URL: http://vetrn.org
Contact: Leland Goldberg, President
Facebook: www.facebook.com/vetrnorg
X (Twitter): x.com/vetrn_org
Instagram: www.instagram.com/vetrnorg
YouTube: www.youtube.com/channel/UCbJD
 17xEnVcQU_Y2K1J7GAQ

Description: Seeks to provide veteran small business owners and family members with opportunities to attend veteran-specific educational programs in entrepreneurship in order to gain the skills, resources, mentoring, and networking necessary to grow their own small business. **Founded:** 2013.

33502 ■ Virginia Small Business Development Center (VASBDC)
4031 University Dr., Ste. 100
 Fairfax, VA 22030
Ph: (703)277-7727
Fax: (703)352-8518
Co. E-mail: help@virginiasbdc.org
URL: http://www.virginiasbdc.org
Contact: Jody Keenan, Director
E-mail: jkeenan@gmu.edu
Facebook: www.facebook.com/VASBDC
Linkedin: www.linkedin.com/company/virginia-small
 -business-development-center
X (Twitter): x.com/virginiasbdc
Instagram: www.instagram.com/virginiasbdc
YouTube: www.youtube.com/user/vasbdc

Description: Represents and promotes the small business sector. Provides management assistance to current and prospective small business owners. Helps to improve management skills and expand the products and services of members. **Geographic Preference:** State.

33503 ■ West Kauai Business and Professional Association
PO Box 903
 Waimea, HI 96796
Contact: Eric Nordmeier, President

Description: Promotes the interests of businesses in the western shore of Kauai.

33504 ■ Wyoming Entrepreneur
Dept 3922, 1000 E University Ave.
 Laramie, WY 82071

Description: Assists small business owners and entrepreneurs with assistance to start or grow a business. Provides resources for funding and networking.

SMALL BUSINESS DEVELOPMENT CENTERS

33505 ■ Puerto Rico Small Business and Technology Development Centers San German
Interamerican University Ave.
 San German, PR 00683
Co. E-mail: sangerman@prsbtdc.org
URL: http://prsbtdc.org
Contact: Brenda Rodriguez, Regional Director

Description: Represents and promotes the small business sector. Provides management assistance to current and prospective small business owners. Helps to improve management skills and expand the products and services of members. **Geographic Preference:** Local.

33506 ■ San Diego Regional Economic Development Corp. (SDREDC) - Multimedia Library
530 B St., Ste. 700
 San Diego, CA 92101
Ph: (619)234-8484
Co. E-mail: info@sandiegobusiness.org
URL: http://www.sandiegobusiness.org
Contact: Mark Cafferty, President
E-mail: cafferty@sandiegobusiness.org
Facebook: www.facebook.com/
 SanDiegoRegionalEDC
Linkedin: www.linkedin.com/company/121089
X (Twitter): x.com/sdregionaledc

Description: Works with business agencies, business people and local economic developers and educators in pursuing economic growth and expansion. Provides support and resources for business development needs and programs. Assists in the retention and expansion of existing firms and the attraction of new businesses. **Scope:** Economic development. **Founded:** 1965. **Holdings:** Videos; presentations. **Geographic Preference:** Local.

SMALL BUSINESS ASSISTANCE PROGRAMS

33507 ■ Pursuit (NYBDC)
50 Beaver St., Ste. 500
 Albany, NY 12207
Free: 866-466-9232
Co. E-mail: info@pursuitlending.com
URL: http://pursuitlending.com
Contact: Patrick J. MacKrell, Sr., Chief Executive Officer
E-mail: mackrell@pursuitlending.com
Facebook: www.facebook.com/pursuitlending
Linkedin: www.linkedin.com/company/pursuitlending
X (Twitter): x.com/pursuit_lending

Description: Seeks to promote business through economic and community development. Assists businesses in their expansion and financing needs. Enhances the quality of life and fosters the growth of good jobs within the community. **Founded:** 1955. **Geographic Preference:** State.

33508 ■ Southern Development Council (SDC)
200 Office Pk. Dr., Ste. No 338
 Birmingham, AL 35223
Free: 800-499-3034
URL: http://www.sdcinc.org
Contact: Yolanda Merriweather, Executive Director
E-mail: ymerriweather@sdcinc.org
Facebook: www.facebook.com/SouthernDevelopmen
 tCouncil.Inc
Linkedin: www.linkedin.com/company/southern
 -development-council-inc

Description: Offers loans to small businesses and start-ups for the purchase or construction of buildings and equipment at fixed, low-interest rates for terms from 10-24 years. **Founded:** 1983.

33509 ■ Wisconsin Business Innovator's Support Association (WBIA)
1221 Innovation Dr.
 Whitewater, WI 53190

Ph: (414)587-8425
Co. E-mail: secretary@wbisa.org
URL: http://www.wbisa.org
Contact: Mark Johnson, President
E-mail: president@wbisa.org
Linkedin: www.linkedin.com/company/wbisa
X (Twitter): x.com/WisBISA

Description: Seeks to advance business incubation and entrepreneurship. Educates businesses and investors on incubator benefits. Provides information, research and networking resources to help members develop and manage successful business incubation programs. **Founded:** 1998. **Geographic Preference:** State.

MINORITY BUSINESS ASSISTANCE PROGRAMS

33510 ■ StartingUp Now (SUN)
Chicago, IL
Free: 855-478-2786
Co. E-mail: info@startingupnow.com
URL: http://www.startingupnow.com
Contact: L. Brian Jenkins, President
Facebook: www.facebook.com/StartingUpNow
X (Twitter): x.com/startingupinc
Instagram: www.instagram.com/startingupnow

Description: Provides training, apps, games, and suites of products to help first-time entrepreneurs set up their businesses. Specializes in working with urban, BIPOC, underserved, and under-resourced people and communities.

FINANCING AND LOAN PROGRAMS

33511 ■ Providence Business Loan Fund
444 Westminster St., 3rd Fl.
 Providence, RI 02903
Ph: (401)680-8412
URL: http://providencebusinessloanfund.com
Contact: Tom Hoagland, Executive Director

Description: Promotes economic development for existing and new members of the business community. Seeks to improve the business climate for manufacturers and entrepreneurs through community and legislative actions. **Geographic Preference:** Local.

INCUBATORS/RESEARCH AND TECHNOLOGY PARKS

33512 ■ Business Incubator Association of New York State (BIANYS)
150 State St., Fourth Fl.
 Albany, NY 12201
Ph: (518)207-0427
URL: http://www.bianys.com
Contact: Marc Alessi, Executive Director
E-mail: marc.alessi@bianys.com
Facebook: www.facebook.com/BIAofNY
Linkedin: www.linkedin.com/company/the-business
 -incubator-association-of-new-york-state
X (Twitter): x.com/bianys
Instagram: www.instagram.com/bia.nys

Description: Seeks to advance business incubation and entrepreneurship. Educates businesses and investors on incubator benefits. Provides information, research and networking resources to help members develop and manage successful business incubation programs. **Founded:** 2005. **Geographic Preference:** State.

33513 ■ Connecticut Business Incubator Network (CBIN)
222 Pitkin St.
 East Hartford, CT 06108
URL: http://ccei.uconn.edu/resources/en
 trepreneurship-in-ct
Contact: Gary Wolff, President

Description: Seeks to advance business incubation and entrepreneurship. Educates businesses and investors on incubator benefits. Provides information, research and networking resources to help members develop and manage successful business incubation programs. **Geographic Preference:** State.

33514 ■ Michigan Business Incubator Association (MBIA)
4717 Campus Dr., Ste. 100
  Kalamazoo, MI 49008
Ph: (269)353-1823
Co. E-mail: michigan.incubation@gmail.com
URL: http://www.michiganincubation.org
Contact: Sandra Cochrane, President
Facebook: www.facebook.com/MBIAInfo
X (Twitter): x.com/MBIA_Michigan

Description: Seeks to advance business incubation and entrepreneurship. Educates businesses and investors on incubator benefits. Provides information, research and networking resources to help members develop and manage successful business incubation programs. **Founded:** 1985. **Geographic Preference:** State.

33515 ■ Mifflin County Industrial Development Corp. (MCIDC)
Bldg. 58 Ste. 300., 6395 SR 103 N
  Lewistown, PA 17044
Ph: (717)242-0393
Fax: (717)242-1842
Co. E-mail: mcidc@mcidc.org
URL: http://mcidc.org
Contact: Nick Felice, President
Facebook: www.facebook.com/Mifflin-County-Indus
  trial-Development-Corporation-177741042245883

Description: Promotes economic development by redeveloping and financing Brownfield Parcels and industrial buildings in Mifflin County. **Scope:** Specialists in business planning of start up. Also offers aid in financial applications for variety of manufacturers. Serves private industries as well as government agencies. **Founded:** 1953. **Geographic Preference:** Local.

33516 ■ University of Idaho Research Park (UIRP)
958 S Lochsa St.
  Post Falls, ID 83854
Ph: (208)777-4700
Fax: (208)292-2670
Co. E-mail: uirp@uidaho.edu
URL: http://www.uidaho.edu/cda/uirp

Description: Integral unit of University of Idaho. **Scope:** Water quality and quantity issues; microelectronics and biomolecular research, geography information systems, and technology assistance to small companies. **Founded:** 1997. **Publications:** *UIRP Newsletter* (Quarterly); *UIRP Report.*

EDUCATIONAL PROGRAMS

33517 ■ Business Plan Basics
URL(s): cwewbc.ecenterdirect.com/events/977281

Description: This online class offered by the Center for Women and Enterprise discusses how to write a business plan, plus provides resources and support. **Audience:** Women small business owners. **Principal Exhibits:** This online class offered by the Center for Women and Enterprise discusses how to write a business plan, plus provides resources and support.

33518 ■ The Content Sales Funnel - Creating an Effective Social Media Content Strategy Series
URL(s): cwewbc.ecenterdirect.com/events/977328

Description: This online course offered by the Center for Women and Enterprise discusses brand identity, sales funnel strategy, effective writing, and social media branding. **Audience:** Women who are small business owners. **Principal Exhibits:** This online course offered by the Center for Women and Enterprise discusses brand identity, sales funnel strategy, effective writing, and social media branding.

33519 ■ Content That Drives Sales Across Pinterest and Instagram, Session #1
URL(s): cwewbc.ecenterdirect.com/events/977106

Description: Online class offered by the Center for Women and Enterprise teaching how to create effective content for your small business to be used on social media. **Principal Exhibits:** Online class offered by the Center for Women and Enterprise teaching how to create effective content for your small business to be used on social media.

33520 ■ Content That Drives Sales Across Pinterest and Instragram, Session #2
Description: Online course offered by the Center for Women and Enterprise that shows how to create content and marketing for your small business using Pinterest. **Principal Exhibits:** Online course offered by the Center for Women and Enterprise that shows how to create content and marketing for your small business using Pinterest.

33521 ■ Discovering Your Brand Identity
URL(s): cwewbc.ecenterdirect.com/events/977303

Description: This online class offered by the Center for Women and Enterprise discusses how to develop brand identity, how to reach your audience, and how to use social media. **Audience:** Women who are small business owners. **Principal Exhibits:** This online class offered by the Center for Women and Enterprise discusses how to develop brand identity, how to reach your audience, and how to use social media.

33522 ■ Elevate Your Social Media Marketing and Presence for Engagement and Growth
URL(s): cwewbc.ecenterdirect.com/events/977226

Description: This online class offered by the Center for Women and Enterprise explores how best to use the tools of social media to effectively market your small business. **Audience:** Women who are small-business owners. **Principal Exhibits:** This online class offered by the Center for Women and Enterprise explores how best to use the tools of social media to effectively market your small business.

33523 ■ Grow Your Business Through Government Contracting
URL(s): cwewbc.ecenterdirect.com/events/977308

Description: This online meeting offered by the Center for Women and Enterprise provides information for Veteran business owners to grow their business and discusses helpful verifications and certifications. **Audience:** Small business owners, women, veterens. **Principal Exhibits:** This online meeting offered by the Center for Women and Enterprise provides information for Veteran business owners to grow their business and discusses helpful verifications and certifications.

33524 ■ Is Entrepreneurship Right for You?
URL(s): cwewbc.ecenterdirect.com/events/977133

Description: This online seminar hosted by the Center for Women and Entrepreneurship discusses key points about entrepreneurs and and how they run their businesses. Also gives out a self assessment to help attendees determine if they are a good fit for this type of business. **Audience:** Women small business owners and entrepreneurs. **Principal Exhibits:** This online seminar hosted by the Center for Women and Entrepreneurship discusses key points about entrepreneurs and and how they run their businesses. Also gives out a self assessment to help attendees determine if they are a good fit for this type of business.

33525 ■ Kickstart Your Social Media Blueprint with TikTok and IG Reels, Part I
URL(s): cwewbc.ecenterdirect.com/events/977312

Description: This online workshop offered by the Center for Women and Enterprise provides information on how to use TikTok and Instagram Reels to market your small business and develop and solid social media presence. **Audience:** Women small business owners. **Principal Exhibits:** This online workshop offered by the Center for Women and Enterprise provides information on how to use TikTok and Instagram Reels to market your small business and develop and solid social media presence.

33526 ■ Legal Considerations for Business Owners
URL(s): cwewbc.ecenterdirect.com/events/977282

Description: This workshop provided by the Center for Women and Enterprise gives information on the legal issues that small businesses may face. Covers entity formation, contract basics, IP considerations, and licenses and regulations. **Audience:** Women small business owners. **Principal Exhibits:** This workshop provided by the Center for Women and Enterprise gives information on the legal issues that small businesses may face. Covers entity formation, contract basics, IP considerations, and licenses and regulations.

33527 ■ NextGen The Future of the WBENC Network
URL(s): www.wbenc.org/programs/nextgen

Frequency: Irregular. **Description:** Outreach program to guide the next generation of women small-business owners. **Principal Exhibits:** Outreach program to guide the next generation of women small-business owners.

33528 ■ Planet Mogul
URL(s): www.wbenc.org/programs/planet-mogul

Frequency: Irregular. **Description:** Outreach program for the next generation of entrepreneurs, innovators, and workforce and community leaders. **Principal Exhibits:** Outreach program for the next generation of entrepreneurs, innovators, and workforce and community leaders.

33529 ■ SBA Loan Options and Best Borrowing Practices for Women
URL(s): wewbc.ecenterdirect.com/events/977255

Description: An online class offered by the Center for Women and Enterprise that discusses the different types of SBA loans, their criteria, and how to apply. **Principal Exhibits:** An online class offered by the Center for Women and Enterprise that discusses the different types of SBA loans, their criteria, and how to apply.

33530 ■ Social Media Made Simple
URL(s): cwewbc.ecenterdirect.com/events/977280

Description: This online course gives an introduction on how to use various social media sites to market your small business. **Audience:** Women small business owners. **Principal Exhibits:** This online course gives an introduction on how to use various social media sites to market your small business.

33531 ■ WBENC Allyship Program
URL(s): www.wbenc.org/programs/wbenc-allyship
  -program

Frequency: Irregular. **Description:** Program designed to cultivate inclusion and learn to become better allies to diverse individuals and groups. **Principal Exhibits:** Program designed to cultivate inclusion and learn to become better allies to diverse individuals and groups.

REFERENCE WORKS

33532 ■ *"5 Ways to Get a Free Website for Your Small Business"* in Business 2 Community (September 29, 2021)
URL(s): www.business2community.com/small-busi
  ness/5-ways-to-get-a-free-website-for-your-small
  -business-02433582

Ed: Emmanuel Soroba. **Released:** September 29, 2021. **Description:** Gives an overview of five popular website builders that small businesses can use for free. **Availability:** Online.

33533 ■ *"7 Facebook Tips for Small & Medium-Sized Businesses"* in Business 2 Community (October 1, 2021)
URL(s): www.business2community.com/small-busi
  ness/7-facebook-tips-for-small-medium-sized-busi
  nesses-02433957

Ed: Haiden Hibbert. **Released:** October 01, 2021. **Description:** Tips on how to market your small to medium-sized business using Facebook. **Availability:** Online.

33534 ■ "9 Things You MUST Do Today to Grow Your Small Business" in Small Business Trends (January 22, 2021)

URL(s): smallbiztrends.com/2018/04/how-to-grow-your-small-business.html

Ed: Jeff Charles. **Released:** January 22, 2021. **Description:** Small businesses can grow at a very slow pace or not at all, which is one of the challenges faced by owners. This article gives advice on how to grow your business and the steps you can take right now to get that going. **Availability:** Online.

33535 ■ "25 Social Media Business Ideas" in Small Business Trends(January 26, 2023)

URL(s): smallbiztrends.com/2023/01/social-media-business-ideas.html

Ed: Kevin Ocasio. **Released:** January 26, 2023. **Description:** Social media can provide some good opportunities to start a small business. Discussed are ideas anyone can use to build a social media based business. **Availability:** Online.

33536 ■ "27 Mission Statement Examples" in Small Business Trends (February 27, 2023)

URL(s): smallbiztrends.com/2021/12/mission-statement-examples.html

Released: February 27, 2023. **Description:** Need some inspiration for writing a mission statement for your small business? Peruse these examples from famous companies and see if you can improve your own statement. **Availability:** Online.

33537 ■ "50 Creative Business Ideas to Start in 2023" in Small Business Trends(February 7, 2023)

URL(s): smallbiztrends.com/2023/02/creative-business-ideas.html

Ed: Annie Pilon. **Released:** February 07, 2023. **Description:** A list of 50 small business ideas that are on the creative side and how to best achieve pursuing those ideas. **Availability:** Online.

33538 ■ "50 Handmade Business Ideas to Start in 2023" in Small Business Trends(February 8, 2023)

URL(s): smallbiztrends.com/2023/02/handmade-business-ideas.html

Ed: Annie Pilon. **Released:** February 08, 2023. **Description:** A list of 50 businesses ideas focused on handmade products you can run from your home. **Availability:** Online.

33539 ■ "50 Small Business Grants Available from Kevin Hart's Tequila Brand" in Small Business Trends (March 10, 2023)

URL(s): smallbiztrends.com/2023/03/business-grants-kevin-harts-tequila-brand.html

Ed: Joshua Sophy. **Released:** March 10, 2023. **Description:** Kevin Hart's tequila brand, Gran Coramino Tequila, partnered with the Local Initiatives Support Corporation to sponsor small business grants, worth $10,000 each. Details on how to apply are given. **Availability:** Online.

33540 ■ "$353 Million in SSBCI Funds Going to Small Businesses in 4 States" in Small Business Trends(March 1, 2023)

URL(s): smallbiztrends.com/2023/03/ssbci-funds-for-small-businesses-in-4-states.html

Ed: Gabrielle Pickard-Whitehead. **Released:** March 01, 2023. **Description:** The State Small Business Credit Initiative is releasing four additional state plans, totaling up to $353.4 million. **Availability:** Online.

33541 ■ "$10,000 Grants Available for Women-Owned Businesses" in Small Business Trends(February 4, 2023)

URL(s): smallbiztrends.com/2023/02/latest-small-business-grants-for-women-february-2023.html

Ed: Annie Pilon. **Released:** February 04, 2023. **Description:** Provides details on grants available for women-owned businesses. **Availability:** Online.

33542 ■ "Anxiety Saps Vigor of Small Businesses" in Barron's (Vol. 92, September 15, 2012, No. 38, pp. 36)

Pub: Dow Jones & Company Inc.

Contact: Almar Latour, Chief Executive Officer

Ed: Gene Epstein. **Description:** The Index of Small Business Optimism reveals that optimism among small businesses in the US remains low three years after the 2008-2009 recession. Uncertainty over economic conditionsand government actions could be behind the low optimism as well as no access to credit. **Availability:** Online.

33543 ■ Architecting A Company of Owners: Company Culture By Design

URL(s): www.barnesandnoble.com/w/architecting-a-company-of-owners-daren-martin/11405360 54?ean=2940186604402

Ed: Daren Martin. **Released:** September 05, 2022. **Price:** $9.99, e-book; $24.95, hardcover; $14.99, paperback. **Description:** Companies often deal with employees who have low engagement along with low satisfaction from working at your business. This can be turned around by changing mindsets and engaging your employees as fellow owners. **Availability:** E-book; Print.

33544 ■ "Athletes Face Wins and Losses After Pro Sports" in The Business Journal - Serving Phoenix and the Valley of the Sun (Vol. 29, September 21, 2008, No. 3, pp. 1)

Pub: American City Business Journals, Inc.

Contact: Mike Olivieri, Executive Vice President

Ed: Chris Casacchia. **Description:** Professional athletes like hockey star Jeremy Roenick start businesses, while others like Joel Adamson work to boost local communities. Former athletes were found to be particularly interested with real estate businesses. Other views and information on former athletes and their life after sports are presented. **Availability:** Online.

33545 ■ "Bangles, BMWs Elbow Out Delis and Discount Shops" in Crain's New York Business (Vol. 24, January 13, 2008, No. 2, pp. 35)

Pub: Crain Communications, Inc.

Contact: Jessica Botos, Manager, Marketing

E-mail: jessica.botos@crainsnewyork.com

Ed: Wendy Davis. **Description:** Lured by a growing number of affluent residents and high-earning professionals, a number of upscale retailers have opened locations downtown which is driving up rents and forcing out longtime independent merchants.

33546 ■ "'Biggest Loser' Adds Bit of Muscle to Local Economy" in Crain's Detroit Business (Vol. 26, January 4, 2010, No. 1, pp. 1)

Pub: Crain Communications Inc.

Contact: Barry Asin, President

Ed: Chad Halcom. **Description:** NBC's weight-loss reality show, "The Biggest Loser" has helped the local economy and generated a new crop of local startup businesses due to past contestants that were from the Detroit area. **Availability:** Print; Online.

33547 ■ "Bryan Berg, Target Corp., Senior Vice President, Region 1" in Hawaii Business (Vol. 53, March 2008, No. 9, pp. 28)

Pub: PacificBasin Communications

Contact: Chuck Tindle, Director

E-mail: chuckt@pacificbasin.net

Ed: David K. Choo. **Description:** Bryan Berg, senior vice president at Target Corp.'s Region 1, shares his thoughts about entering the Hawaiian market and Target representatives bringing malasadas when visiting a business in the state. Berg finds the state's aloha spirit interesting and feels that it is important to be respectful of the Hawaiian culture and traditions in doing their business there. **Availability:** Online.

33548 ■ "Business Diary" in Crain's Detroit Business (Vol. 24, October 6, 2008, No. 40, pp. 23)

Pub: Crain Communications Inc.

Contact: Barry Asin, President

Description: Detailed listing of acquisitions, expansions, new products, new services, business contracts and startups from the Detroit area is provided. **Availability:** Print; Online.

33549 ■ "The Business End of Staying in Business" in Contractor (Vol. 56, September 2009, No. 9, pp. 51)

Ed: Al Schwartz. **Description:** Advice on how to manage a new plumbing business in the United States is offered. The transition from being a workman to an employer is seen as one that accompanies a steep learning curve. The importance of managing cash flow is also highlighted. **Availability:** Print; Online.

33550 ■ "Capitol Ideas: Regions to Lansing: Focus on Taxes, Reform, Keeping Talent" in Crain's Detroit Business (Vol. 24, October 6, 2008)

Pub: Crain Communications Inc.

Contact: Barry Asin, President

Ed: Amy Lane. **Description:** Michigan must make bold and dramatic changes in public policy regarding business legislation. The tax structure, unemployment issues and attracting and retaining talent are among the issues the state must confront, especially in this tough economic climate. **Availability:** Online.

33551 ■ "Celebrate Success. Embrace Innovation" in Black Enterprise (Vol. 37, February 2007, No. 7, pp. 145)

Description: 2007 Women of Power Summit provides networking opportunities, empowerment sessions, and nightly entertainment. More than 500 executive women of color are expected to attend this inspiring summit in Phoenix, February 7-10. **Availability:** Print; Online.

33552 ■ "Craft Businesses That Make (the MOST) Money" in Made Urban (April 12, 2018)

URL(s): www.madeurban.com/blog/craft-businesses-that-make-money/

Released: April 12, 2018. **Description:** If you are a crafter and engage in selling your crafts, are you considering all of your costs? It may surprise you how little profit, if any, you are making. Some crafts have a larger demand than others, so there is a bigger chance of making more money by selling those crafts. Included is a list of these types of crafts and a discussion about each one. **Availability:** Online.

33553 ■ "Creating the Perfect Lead Magnet" in Small Business Trends(November 29, 2022)

URL(s): smallbiztrends.com/2022/11/lead-magnet-2.html

Ed: Holly Chavez. **Released:** November 29, 2022. **Description:** Annie P. Ruggles, founder of Non-Sleazy Sales Academy, is interviewed about creating the perfect lead magnet. **Availability:** Online.

33554 ■ Data Strategy: How to Profit from a World of Big Data, Analytics and Artificial Intelligence

Ed: Bernard Marr. **Released:** 2022. **Description:** Details how to use data when setting up and running a business. Includes information on collecting, using, and managing data along with which tools to use. **Availability:** Print.

33555 ■ "David Leonhardt on Hiring a Copywriter for Your Small Business" in Small Business Trends(October 18, 2022)

URL(s): smallbiztrends.com/2022/10/how-to-hire-a-copywriter.html

Ed: Holly Chavez. **Released:** October 21, 2022. **Description:** David Leonhardt, President of The Happy Guy (THGM) Writing Services, discusses the benefits of small businesses hiring copywriters in order to communicate clearly to customers. **Availability:** Online.

33556 ■ "Deep Thoughts: Getting Employees to Think Better Requires a Bit of Creative Thinking Itself" in Canadian Business (March 17, 2008)

Description: Discusses the reason a company needs to make their employees understand that ideas are the stuff of life. For employees to be more creative, they need to cultivate spark moments, play with possibilities, and venture into the unknown. **Availability:** Print; Online; PDF.

33557 ■ "Detroit Pistons, Corporate Sponsors Support Small Businesses Through Grants and Promotions" in Small Business Trends(December 3, 2022)
URL(s): smallbiztrends.com/2022/12/detroit-pistons -small-business-grant.html
Ed: Annie Pilon. **Released:** December 03, 2022. **Description:** Discusses a grant for small businesses sponsored by the Detroit Pistons. **Availability:** Online.

33558 ■ "A Different Kind of Lender Can Get You the Loan You Need" in Small Business Trends(December 26, 2022)
URL(s): smallbiztrends.com/2022/12/impact-inves tment-management.html
Released: December 26, 2022. **Description:** Discusses an alternative to obtaining small business financing — an organization named Equivico. **Availability:** Online.

33559 ■ Different Thinking
Ed: Peter Kreuz, Anja Foerster. **Released:** 2009. **Description:** Offers unconventional techniques and strategies on business operations.

33560 ■ "Dumb Financial Mistakes Business Owners Make and How to Avoid Them" in Small Business Trends(February 20, 2023)
URL(s): smallbiztrends.com/2023/02/financial-mis takes-business-owners-make.html
Released: February 20, 2023. **Description:** President of Business Ventures Corporation, Ruth King, discusses mistakes small business owners typically make and how to avoid them. **Availability:** Online.

33561 ■ "Emerging Tech Companies in One State Can Now Apply for Matching Business Grants" in Small Business Trends (November 5, 2022)
URL(s): smallbiztrends.com/2022/11/matching-grants -for-emerging-tech-companies-in-north-carolina .html
Ed: Annie Pilon. **Released:** November 05, 2022. **Description:** Grants are available for emerging tech businesses in several U.S. states. Details and links are provided in the article. **Availability:** Online.

33562 ■ Entrepreneurship for Dummies
Pub: John Wiley & Sons, Inc.
Contact: Christina Van Tassell, Executive Vice President Chief Financial Officer
Ed: Kathleen Allen. **Released:** 2nd edition. **Price:** $29.99, paperback; $18, e-book. **Description:** A guide to help entrepreneurs get their business up and running. Includes sections on starting a business from beginning to end, testing products, legal requirements, securing funding, and much more. **Availability:** E-book; Print.

33563 ■ From 50 to 500: Mastering the Unique Leadership Challenges of Growing Small Companies
Ed: Jonathan Dapra, Richard Dapra, Jonas Akerman. **Description:** Small business owners will find this book useful as they grow their businesses. It explains key characteristics of companies that are primed for growth and gives a working model how to achieve such growth. **Availability:** Print.

33564 ■ "From Craft Biz To Wholesale Giant" in Women Entrepreneur (January 19, 2009)
Description: Advice is given on how to turn a small craft business into a full-time venture; tips to help one transition from a part-time designer to a full-time wholesaler and brand are also included.

33565 ■ Future of Business Journalism: Why It Matters for Wall Street and Main Street
Ed: Chris Roush. **Released:** 2022. **Description:** Discusses the shift to news that benefits big businesses, leaving small business in the dark about news that would benefit them. **Availability:** Print.

33566 ■ "Grants of Up to $20,000 Available for Building Upgrades, Startup Expenses, and More" in Small Business Trends(February 18, 2023)
URL(s): smallbiztrends.com/2023/02/grants-for-buil ding-upgrades-startup-expenses-and-more.html
Ed: Annie Pilon. **Released:** February 18, 2023. **Description:** Provides details about small business grants available. **Availability:** Online.

33567 ■ "'Groundhog Day' B&B Likely Will Be Converted Into One In Real Life" in Chicago Tribune (October 21, 2008)
Pub: Tribune News Service
Contact: Jack Barry, Vice President, Operations
E-mail: jbarry@tribpub.com
Ed: Carolyn Starks. **Description:** Everton Martin and Karla Stewart Martin have purchased the Victorian house that was featured as a bed-and-breakfast in the 1993 hit move "Groundhog Day"; the couple was initially unaware of the structure's celebrity status when they purchased it with the hope of fulfilling their dream of owning a bed-and-breakfast. **Availability:** Print; Online.

33568 ■ "A Growing Dilemma" in Crain's Cleveland Business (Vol. 28, October 8, 2007, No. 40, pp. 19)
Pub: Crain Communications Inc.
Contact: K. C. Crain, President
Ed: Kimberly Bonvissuto. **Description:** Discusses small business owners who often have to grapple with the decision on whether or not to expand their operations and the importance of a business plan which may help owners with that decision. **Availability:** Online.

33569 ■ Guide to Venture Capital & Private Equity Firms
Pub: Grey House Publishing
Contact: Richard Gottlieb, President
URL(s): www.greyhouse.com/Guide-to-venture-capi tal-and-private-equity-firms
Released: Latest edition; February 2024. **Price:** $395, for softcover. **Description:** Covers 2,300 domestic and international venture capital and private equity firms. **Entries include:** Firm name, address, phone, fax, e-mail, URL, description of services, names and titles of key personnel. **Indexes:** Geographic; Executive Name; Portfolio Company; Industry Preference; College & University. **Availability:** Print; PDF; Online.

33570 ■ "How Deep Listening Will Boost Your Small Business" in Small Business Trends (march 20, 2023)
URL(s): smallbiztrends.com/2023/03/how-deep-lis tening-will-boost-your-small-business.html
Released: March 20, 2023. **Description:** Author and host of the podcast Deep Listening, Oscar Trimboli, discusses how listening affects the relationships small businesses have with customers, employees, and vendors. **Availability:** Online.

33571 ■ "How Federal Interest Rates Are Affecting Small Business Loans" in Small Business Trends(October 11, 2022)
URL(s): smallbiztrends.com/2022/10/small-business -loan-interest-rates.html
Ed: Holly Chavez. **Released:** October 11, 2022. **Description:** Chris Hurn, Founder and CEO of Fountainhead Commercial Capital, is interviewed about federal interest rates and their impact on small business loans. **Availability:** Online.

33572 ■ "How Green Is The Valley?" in Barron's (Vol. 88, July 4, 2008, No. 28, pp. 13)
Description: San Jose, California has made a good start towards becoming a leader in alternative energy technology through the establishment of United Laboratories' own lab in the city. The certification process for photovoltaic cells will be dramatically shortened with this endeavor. **Availability:** Print.

33573 ■ "How to Keep Your Top Employees" in Archery Business (December 14, 2018)
URL(s): www.archerybusiness.com/keep-top -employees
Ed: Phillip M. Perry. **Released:** December 14, 2018. **Description:** A guide on how to retain the best employees to help run your business. Gives tips on recognizing the top performers and how to compensate them so they stay, and points out how to create a respectful and supportive work environment. **Availability:** Online.

33574 ■ "How to Make a Deal In Uncertain Economic Times" in Small Business Trends (November 14, 2022)
URL(s): smallbiztrends.com/2022/11/making-a-deal -in-uncertain-economic-times.html
Released: November 14, 2022. **Description:** The economy may not always be on your side, but that is no reason why you can't still make that business deal go through. Inside are some tips to help you navigate an economic downturn. **Availability:** Online.

33575 ■ How to Optimize Your Small Business Delivery Services
URL(s): optimoroute.com/small-business-delivery -services/
Released: August 26, 2022. **Description:** Discusses the importance of optimizing your small business delivery services and presents three options to choose from and offers information on how to decide which is right for your business. **Availability:** Online.

33576 ■ How To Gather And Use Data For Business Analysis
URL(s): www.barnesandnoble.com/w/how-to-gather -and-use-data-for-business-analysis-m-l-humphrey/ 1141325780?ean=2940160772721
Ed: M.L. Humphrey. **Released:** April 05, 2022. **Price:** $4.99, e-book; $9.99, paperback. **Description:** A guide on collecting your own business data and how to analyze it to see where improvements can be made. **Availability:** E-book; Print.

33577 ■ "In the News: Grants of Up To $20,000 for Small Business Improvements and More" in Small Business Trends(February 24, 2023)
URL(s): smallbiztrends.com/2023/02/small-business -news-roundup-february-24-2023.html
Released: February 24, 2023. **Description:** Provides details on grants available to assist small business with developments and repair projects. **Availability:** Online.

33578 ■ "In the News: Hundreds of Millions of Dollars Available to Small Businesses from SSBCI" in Small Business Trends(March 3, 2023)
URL(s): smallbiztrends.com/2023/03/weeklsmall -business-news-roundup-march-3-2023.html
Released: March 03, 2023. **Description:** Small businesses can apply for funding through the State Small Business Credit Initiative in order to provide help for their long-term survival. **Availability:** Online.

33579 ■ "Inking the Deal" in Slate (October 1, 2014)
URL(s): slate.com/business/2014/10/tattoo-parlors-a -surprisingly-great-small-business-bet.html
Ed: Jesse Dorris. **Released:** October 01, 2014. **Description:** Discusses how tattoo parlors are often a good bet when it comes to opening a small business. Tattoos have been gaining in popularity with the Instagram crowd and their reputations are much higher than they used to be because so many people have tattoos that they have gone mainstream. Local governments are also surprisingly friendly to the industry, making it easier on owners. **Availability:** Online.

33580 ■ "Intrepid Souls: Meet a Few Who've Made the Big Leap" in Crain's Chicago Business (Vol. 31, November 10, 2008, No. 45, pp. 26)
Description: Advice is given from entrepreneurs who have launched businesses in the last year despite the economic crisis. Among the types of businesses

featured are a cooking school, a child day-care center, a children's clothing store and an Internet-based company. **Availability:** Online.

33581 ■ *"The Latest Grant Opportunities for Women- and Minority-Owned Small Businesses"* in Small Business Trends(February 28, 2023)
URL(s): smallbiztrends.com/2023/02/latest-small-business-grants-for-women-and-minority-owned-businesses.html

Ed: Annie Pilon. **Released:** February 28, 2023. **Description:** Information about grants available to women- and minority-owned small businesses is given. **Availability:** Online.

33582 ■ *"Legislators Must Cut Cost of Government"* in Crain's Detroit Business (Vol. 24, October 6, 2008, No. 40, pp. 6)
Pub: Crain Communications Inc.
Contact: Barry Asin, President

Description: Southeast and West Michigan business leaders are setting aside their differences and have proposed clear agendas, ranging from eliminating the Michigan Business Tax to overhauling public employee and retiree benefits and pensions. Lawmakers must also come together to find solutions for the state's economy and discover an entirely new vision for the future of Michigan business. **Availability:** Print; Online.

33583 ■ *"Live and Learn"* in Canadian Business (Vol. 80, April 23, 2007, No. 9, pp. 76)
Description: Paul Anka, a musician, feels that ground work is essential before establishing a company. **Availability:** Print; Online.

33584 ■ *"Look Before You Lease"* in Women Entrepreneur (February 3, 2009)
Description: Top issues to consider before leasing an office space are discussed including: additional charges that may be expected on top of the basic rental price; determining both short- and long-term goals; the cost of improvements to the space; the cost of upkeep; and the conditions of the lease. **Availability:** Online.

33585 ■ *"Minority Auto Suppliers Get Help Diversifying"* in Crain's Detroit Business (Vol. 26, January 11, 2010, No. 2, pp. 3)
Pub: Crain Communications Inc.
Contact: Barry Asin, President

Ed: Sherri Welch. **Description:** Displaced minority auto suppliers are being given assistance by the Kauffman's Foundation Urban Entrepreneur Partnership Detroit program, a three-year effort to assist 150 of the region's suppliers into more diversified businesses. **Availability:** Online.

33586 ■ *"Minority Entrepreneurs Must Make Growth a Priority"* in Crain's Chicago Business (November 12, 2021)
URL(s): www.chicagobusiness.com/equity/minority-entrepreneurs-must-make-growth-priority

Released: November 12, 2021. **Description:** While small businesses are important, now is the time for minority-owned companies to branch out of their comfort zone and redevelop as midsize to large businesses. Doing so will create more jobs and help develop communities. **Availability:** Online.

33587 ■ *"Monique Johnson on the Pros and Cons of Hybrid Events"* in Small Business Trends(November 1, 2022)
URL(s): smallbiztrends.com/2022/11/hybrid-events.html

Ed: Holly Chavez. **Released:** November 01, 2022. **Description:** The founder of Live Video Lab goes over the basics about hybrid business events. **Availability:** Online.

33588 ■ *"Naresh Kumar on Using Heat Maps to Grow Your Business"* in Small Business Trends (August 25, 2022)
URL(s): smallbiztrends.com/2022/08/heat-maps.html

Ed: Holly Chavez. **Released:** August 25, 2022. **Description:** Interview with Naresh Kumar, Zoho Corporation Product Manager, who discusses how small businesses can grow by utilizing heat maps, which is software that shows where website visitors spent their time at the website by recording where they clicked. **Availability:** Online.

33589 ■ *"Pandemic Recovery Grant Programs Launch Additional Funding Rounds"* in Small Business Trends (March 11, 2023)
URL(s): smallbiztrends.com/2023/03/latest-pandemic-recovery-business-grant-programs.html

Ed: Annie Pilon. **Released:** March 11, 2023. **Description:** Some grant programs used in the COVID pandemic are relaunching in order to continue providing funds for struggling small businesses. Details about the grants are included. **Availability:** Online.

33590 ■ *"PayPal and Venmo Launch New Small Business Grant Program for Emerging Businesses"* in Small Business Trends (August 20, 2022)
URL(s): smallbiztrends.com/2022/08/paypal-and-venmo-launch-new-small-business-grant-program.html

Ed: Annie Pilon. **Released:** August 20, 2022. **Description:** PayPal, through the Venmo Small Business Grant, is looking to provide funds to 20 Venmo Business Profile users. **Availability:** Online.

33591 ■ *"Pick A Name, Not Just Any Name"* in Women Entrepreneur (December 17, 2008)
Description: Craft business owners must choose a name that sounds personal since customers who buy hand-made products want to feel that they are buying from an individual rather than an institution. Tips for choosing a name are provided.

33592 ■ *"The Power of Influencer Networks for Education and Small Business"* in Small Business Trends(December 4, 2022)
URL(s): smallbiztrends.com/2022/12/the-power-of-influencer-networks.html

Ed: Gabrielle Pickard-Whitehead. **Released:** December 04, 2022. **Description:** Discusses how influencer networks can benefit your small business. **Availability:** Online.

33593 ■ *Principles of Pricing*
Ed: Rakesh V. Vohra, Lakshman Krishnamurthi. **Released:** 2012. **Description:** Details various pricing strategies, specifically considering the use of auctions, price discrimination, and pricing in a competitive environment.

33594 ■ *"Region and City Need Influx of Youth"* in Crain's Detroit Business (Vol. 24, April 14, 2008, No. 15, pp. 8)
Pub: Crain Communications Inc.
Contact: Barry Asin, President

Description: Discusses an upcoming report from Michigan Future Inc. which finds that young professionals, including those with children, are interested in living in an active urban environment. It also states that because many of those young professionals are entrepreneurial in nature, oftentimes businesses follow. **Availability:** Print; Online.

33595 ■ *"Rural Entrepreneurship Success Factors: An Empirical Investigation in an Emerging Market"* in Journal of Small Business Strategy (Vol. 31, December 1, 2021, No. 4, pp. 5-19)
URL(s): libjournals.mtsu.edu/index.php/jsbs/article/view/2130

Ed: Prince Gyimah, Robert N. Lussier. **Released:** November 16, 2021. **Description:** Discusses the research accomplished on rural small businesses and their economic development on the a global level. **Availability:** PDF; Online.

33596 ■ *Self-Made Boss: Advice, Hacks, and Lessons from Small Business Owners*
Released: 2022. **Description:** Discusses real-life examples of running a small business as told from Square's seller's community.

33597 ■ *"Setting Out on Your Own? Think Franchises"* in Crain's Cleveland Business (Vol. 28, October 8, 2007, No. 40, pp. 20)
Pub: Crain Communications Inc.
Contact: K. C. Crain, President

Description: Franchisers are targeting baby boomers due to their willingness to put up some of their own money to open their own business. According to local franchising expert, Joel Libava, entrepreneurs should expect to pay about 15 to 30 percent of the total cost of starting the franchise out of their own pocket. **Availability:** Online.

33598 ■ *"Side Income: Is It a Hobby or a Business?"* in Money Under 30 (March 12, 2019)
URL(s): www.moneyunder30.com/side-income-hobby-or-a-business

Ed: Amber Gilstrap. **Released:** March 12, 2019. **Description:** A practical discussion of how to determine if your hobby that you love is actually a business. The IRS has some guidelines and questions, and if you meet certain criteria, you can then deduct expenses and report it to the IRS. **Availability:** Online.

33599 ■ *"Small Business Development Centers and Rural Entrepreneurial Development Strategies: Are We Doing Enough for Rural America?"* in Journal of Small Business Strategy (Vol. 31, December 1, 2021, No. 4, 57-63)
URL(s): libjournals.mtsu.edu/index.php/jsbs/article/view/2135

Ed: Timothy C. Dunne, Katie Toyoshima, Michael Byrd. **Released:** November 16, 2021. **Description:** Discusses the research done about business development in rural communities. **Availability:** PDF; Online.

33600 ■ *"Small Business Grants Available for Environmental Upgrades"* in Small Business Trends(December 24, 2022)
URL(s): smallbiztrends.com/2022/12/small-business-grants-environmental-upgrades.html

Ed: Annie Pilon. **Released:** December 24, 2022. **Description:** Small businesses wishing to become more environmentally friendly should investigate these grants that are discussed in this article. **Availability:** Online.

33601 ■ *"Small Business Investment Company Reforms Proposed by SBA to Address Diversity"* in Small Business Trends (October 25, 2022)
URL(s): smallbiztrends.com/2022/10/small-business-investment-company-reforms.html

Ed: Gabrielle Pickard-Whitehead. **Released:** October 25, 2022. **Description:** The Small Business Administration (SBA) proposed new reforms to help reduce financial barriers that many small businesses from underserved communities experience. The new reforms also aim to diversify the Small Business Investment Company (SBIC) program. **Availability:** Online.

33602 ■ *"Small Business Resource Guide for Veterans"* in Business News Daily (October 22, 2020)
Ed: Julianna Lopez. **Released:** October 22, 2020. **Description:** Many veterans choose to go into business for themselves after leaving the armed forces. This article provides several resources veterans can use to get their businesses up and running. **Availability:** Online.

33603 ■ *"Small Business and the Staffing Shortage by Industry"* in Forbes (May 27, 2021)
URL(s): www.forbes.com/sites/williamdunkelberg/2021/05/27/small-business-and-the-staffing-shortage-by-industry/?sh=10a95d7724a3

Ed: William Dunkelberg. **Released:** May 27, 2021. **Description:** Small businesses are struggling to find employees now that Covid shutdowns are a thing of the past. Transportation, communication, and public utilities had the biggest hits to employment. **Availability:** Online.

33604 ■ *"Small Businesses Not Prepared for a Boom" in Small Business Trends(November 13, 2022)*
URL(s): smallbiztrends.com/2022/11/businesses-not-prepared-for-a-boom.html
Ed: Gabrielle Pickard-Whitehead. **Released:** November 13, 2022. **Description:** How to prepare your small businesses for any booms or upticks in sales. **Availability:** Online.

33605 ■ *"Spin Zone: Where Hawaii's Leaders Face Off, Have High-Tech Tax Credits Helped or Hurt Hawaii?" in Hawaii Business (Vol. 53, December 2007, No. 6, pp. 28)*
Pub: PacificBasin Communications
Contact: Chuck Tindle, Director
E-mail: chuckt@pacificbasin.net
Description: Presents the opinons of Channel Capital LLC's Walter R. Roth and Hawaii Venture Capital Association's Bill Spencer concerning the impacts of tax credits. Roth thinks that Act 221 appeals to investors who can earn despite business failure while Spencer thinks that the legislation promotes investments in innovative technology firms. The need to support tax credits is also discussed. **Availability:** Print; Online.

33606 ■ *"Start or Buy? It's a Tough Question for Eager Entrepreneurs" in Crain's Cleveland Business (Vol. 28, October 8, 2007, No. 40, pp. 24)*
Pub: Crain Communications Inc.
Contact: K. C. Crain, President
Ed: David Prizinsky. **Description:** Discusses different approaches to becoming a small business owner. **Availability:** Online.

33607 ■ *Starting a Business All-in-One for Dummies*
Pub: John Wiley & Sons, Inc.
Contact: Christina Van Tassell, Executive Vice President Chief Financial Officer
URL(s): www.wiley.com/en-us/Starting+a+Business+All+in+One+For+Dummies%2C+3rd+Edition-p-9781119868590
Ed: Eric Tyson, Bob Nelson. **Released:** 3rd edition. **Price:** $21, e-book; $34.99, paperback. **Description:** Six books about starting a new business are compiled into this one book. Everything you need to know about setting up a new business, from developing a business model to paying taxes, is covered. **Availability:** E-book; Print.

33608 ■ *Starting a Business QuickStart Guide*
Ed: Ken Colwell. **Released:** February 25, 2019. **Price:** $9.99, e-book; $22.49, paperback. **Description:** A guide explaining all the steps necessary to start your own small business. **Availability:** E-book; Print.

33609 ■ *"Starting and Scaling a Small Business as a Minority Entrepreneur" in Sahan Journal (Nov. 1, 2021)*
Released: November 01, 2021. **Description:** Provides information to support first-time entrepreneurs to launch a successful business. **Availability:** Online.

33610 ■ *Supermaker: Crafting Business on Your Own Terms*
Released: September 08, 2020. **Description:** A guide for entrepreneurs who are interested in starting a small business, especially crafting or maker-centered. Sections on branding, product development, social media marketing, scaling, PR, and customer engagement are included. **Availability:** E-book.

33611 ■ *:Taylor Backman on Using All-in-One Solutions to Lower Cost" in Small Business Trends (August 16, 2022)*
URL(s): smallbiztrends.com/2022/08/using-all-in-one-solutions-to-lower-cost.html

Ed: Holly Chavez. **Released:** August 18, 2022. **Description:** Interview with Taylor Backman, Zoho's Senior Evangelist, to discuss why small businesses should consider buying all-in-one business software. **Availability:** Online.

33612 ■ *"TMC Development Closes $1.1 Million Real Estate Purchase for Mansa, LLC Using SBA 504 Real Estate Financing" in Marketwired (September 17, 2009)*
Pub: Comtex News Network Inc.
Contact: Kan Devnani, President
Description: TMC Development announced the closing of a $1.1 million real estate purchase for Mansa, LLC dba Kwikee Mart, a Napa-based convenience store; TMC helped the company secure a Small Business Administration 504 loan in order to purchase the acquisition of a 3,464 square foot building. SBA created the 504 loan program to provide financing for growing small and medium-sized businesses. **Availability:** Online.

33613 ■ *Twelve-Minute Risk Management: Strategies and Tools Business Owners Need Right Now to Successfully Navigate Today's Business World*
URL(s): www.barnesandnoble.com/w/twelve-minute-risk-management-ivy-walker/1141366299?ean=2940160946580
Released: March 22, 2022. **Price:** $9.99, e-book. **Description:** A guide to help small business owners strategize their business plans and address risk to benefit the company as a whole. **Availability:** E-book.

33614 ■ *"Unveiling the Secrets Behind Hispanic Business' 100 Fastest-Growing Companies" in Hispanic Business (Vol. 30, July-August 2008, No. 7-8, pp. 22)*
Ed: Michael Bowker. **Description:** CEO's of the five fastest growing Hispanic-owned companies discuss the success of their companies; most of them attribute their success to proper investment and diversification, effective innovations and seeing growth opportunities where others see roadblocks. **Availability:** Online.

33615 ■ *"Up to $2 Million in Grants Available for Dairy Businesses, Child Care Centers, and More" in Small Business Trends(February 26, 2023)*
URL(s): smallbiztrends.com/2023/02/grants-for-dairy-businesses-child-care-centers.html
Ed: Annie Pilon. **Released:** February 26, 2023. **Description:** Industry-specific grant programs are available. Details about the grants are given. **Availability:** Online.

33616 ■ *The Upside Within Reach: A New Way to Create a Prosperous Business*
URL(s): www.barnesandnoble.com/w/the-upside-within-reach-drew-morris/1142520510?ean=2940186562757
Ed: Drew Morris. **Released:** October 25, 2022. **Price:** $50, e-book; $50, hardcover. **Description:** Explore the core idea of this guide, which is your business can be more successful by taking into account the unnoticed gaps within the business and making them work for you. **Availability:** E-book; Print.

33617 ■ *"Venture Gap" in Canadian Business (Vol. 81, February 26, 2008, No. 4, pp. 82)*
Pub: Rogers Media Inc.
Contact: Neil Spivak, Chief Executive Officer
Ed: Joe Castaldo. **Description:** Money raised by Canadian venture capitalist firms has been declining since 2001. A strong venture capital market is important if Canada is to build innovative companies. Fixing Canada's tax policy on foreign investments is a start in reviving the industry. **Availability:** Print; Online.

33618 ■ *"Verizon Small Business Opens New Round of Digital Ready Grants" Small Business Trends (March 14, 2023)*
URL(s): smallbiztrends.com/2023/03/verizon-small-business-digital-ready-grants.html

Ed: Lisa Price. **Released:** March 14, 2023. **Description:** Provides details on new grants available to small businesses. **Availability:** Online.

33619 ■ *"A Way Forward for Small Businesses" in Harvard Business Review (April 13, 2020)*
Released: April 13, 2020. **Description:** Details the economic impact of the Coronavirus on small businesses and offers five recommendations for navigating the crisis. **Availability:** Online.

33620 ■ *"Wayne, Oakland Counties Create Own 'Medical Corridor" in Crain's Detroit Business (Vol. 24, October 6, 2008, No. 40, pp. 8)*
Pub: Crain Communications Inc.
Contact: Barry Asin, President
Ed: Jay Greene. **Description:** Woodward Medical Corridor that runs along Woodward Avenue and currently encompasses twelve hospitals and is rapidly growing with additional physician offices, advanced oncology centers and new hospitals. Beaumont Hospital is building a $160 million proton-beam therapy cancer center on its Royal Oak campus in a joint venture with Procure Treatment Centers of Bloomington Ind. That is expected to open in 2010 and will employ approximately 145 new workers. **Availability:** Online.

33621 ■ *"What Is a Vision Statement and How to Write One (+Examples and Template)" in Small Business Trends (February 13, 2023)*
URL(s): smallbiztrends.com/2023/02/vision-statement.html
Released: February 13, 2023. **Description:** Defines and gives examples of vision statements for you to use while starting your small business. **Availability:** Online.

33622 ■ *"YouTube Handles are Here – What it Means for Your Business" in Small Business Trends (October 19, 2022)*
URL(s): smallbiztrends.com/2022/10/youtube-handles.html
Ed: Gabrielle Pickard-Whitehead. **Released:** October 19, 2022. **Description:** YouTube introduced "handles" which will be unique to each creator, including your small business if it has its own channel. Further details about how the handles work are discussed. **Availability:** Online.

STATISTICAL SOURCES

33623 ■ *US Shopping Small Business Market Report 2021*
URL(s): store.mintel.com/report/us-shopping-small-businesses-market-report
Price: $4,366.35. **Description:** Downloadable report detailing analysis of US consumers regarding their small business shopping habits. Includes a report on how Covid-19 has impacted shoppers, how they shop, and motivations and barriers. **Availability:** PDF.

TRADE PERIODICALS

33624 ■ *Business Week Magazine*
Pub: Bloomberg Businessweek
URL(s): www.bloomberg.com/businessweek
Price: Subscriptions are $9 for 12 issues, $40 for 50 issues (print, mobile, tablet). **Description:** Supplies weekly information concerning business, finance, and technology in domestic and international print editions and online. Coverage includes such topics as news analysis and commentary, business trends, social issues, international markets, profiles of important business people, legal affairs, media, computer trends, and personal business. **Availability:** Online.

33625 ■ *Entrepreneur Magazine*
Pub: Entrepreneur Media Inc.
Contact: Dan Bova, Director
E-mail: dbova@entrepreneur.com
URL(s): www.entrepreneur.com/magazine

Released: 6/year **Price:** $10.99, for print and online 1 year; $9.99, for online or print 1 year. **Description:** Magazine covering small business management and operation. **Availability:** Print; Online.

33626 ■ *Entrepreneurship Theory and Practice (ETP)*
Pub: SAGE Publications
Contact: Tracey Ozmina, President
URL(s): journals.sagepub.com/home/ETP
Facebook: www.facebook.com/En trepreneurshipTheoryPractice
Linkedin: www.linkedin.com/company/etpjournal
X (Twitter): x.com/ETPjournal
Released: Bimonthly **Price:** $218, Institutions for single print issue; $41, Individuals for single print issue; $1,150, Institutions for print and online; $187, Individuals for print and online; $1,332, Institutions for print + online; $1,029, Institutions for online only; $1,187, Institutions for print only; $1,211, Institutions for print only; $2,014, Institutions for online. **Description:** Scholarly journal covering original conceptual and empirical research that contributes to the advancement of entrepreneurship. **Availability:** Print; PDF; Download; Online.

33627 ■ *International Journal of Globalisation and Small Business (IJGSB)*
Pub: Inderscience Publishers
URL(s): www.inderscience.com/jhome.php?jcode =ijgsb
Ed: Dr. Susanne Royer. **Released:** Quarterly **Price:** $50, for hardcopy airmail; $861, for online 1 user only; $1,171, for print and online; $3,960.06, for 10 to 14 users; $4,520.25, for 15 to 19 users; $1,463.70, for 2 to 3 users; $2,152.50, for 4 to 5 users; $2,798.25, for 6 to 7 users; $3,400.95, for 8 to 9 users; $310, for multi user; $5,338.20, for 20 plus; $861, for print. **Description:** Peer-reviewed journal aiming to develop, promote and coordinate the research and practice in globalisation and small business management, to help professionals working in the field, small business owners, business educators and policy makers to contribute or disseminate information and to learn from each other's work. **Availability:** Print; PDF; Online.

VIDEO/AUDIO MEDIA

33628 ■ *The How of Business: Jane Allen - Entrepreneur's Lifecycle*
URL(s): www.thehowofbusiness.com/420-jane-allen -entrepreneurs-lifecycle
Ed: Henry Lopez. **Released:** May 16, 2022. **Description:** Podcast offers a discussion with the CEO of the Nashville Entrepreneur Center, a non-profit that connects entrepreneurs with resources needed to increase profitability at any stage.

33629 ■ *The How of Business: Kelly Roach - Principles for Success*
URL(s): www.thehowofbusiness.com/episode-0 21-kelly-roach
Ed: Henry Lopez. **Released:** June 27, 2016. **Description:** Podcast offers tips for small business success.

33630 ■ *The How of Business: Small Business Ideation*
URL(s): www.thehowofbusiness.com/episode-004-i deation
Ed: Henry Lopez. **Released:** April 25, 2016. **Description:** Podcast discusses how to create, develop, and execute new business ideas.

33631 ■ *The How of Business: Steve Alexander - Buying and Growing a Small Business*
URL(s): www.thehowofbusiness.com/episode-007-s teve-alexander
Released: May 19, 2016. **Description:** Podcast offers advice on buying and growing a small business. Features Paul Alexander, owner of Private Water Fishing.

33632 ■ *Main Street Business Insights: Tee Rowe, America's SBDC*
URL(s): mainstreet.org/resources/knowledge-hub/po dcast/tee-rowe-americas-sbdc-2
Ed: Matt Wagner. **Released:** September 25, 2024. **Description:** Podcast features a conversation with the President and CEO of America's Small Business Development Centers (ASBDC).

TRADE SHOWS AND CONVENTIONS

33633 ■ Adobe 99U Conference
URL(s): conference.99u.com
Frequency: Annual. **Description:** Provides workshops, classes, and key topic speakers for creatives, along with small business owners in order to inspire creativity. **Principal Exhibits:** Provides workshops, classes, and key topic speakers for creatives, along with small business owners in order to inspire creativity.

33634 ■ America's SBDC Conference
URL(s): americassbdc.org/future-conferences
Frequency: Annual. **Description:** Provides keynote speeches, workshops, a tradeshow, and networking opportunities for small business owners in order to help grow their businesses. **Principal Exhibits:** Provides keynote speeches, workshops, a tradeshow, and networking opportunities for small business owners in order to help grow their businesses.

33635 ■ Inc. 5000
URL(s): events.inc.com/inc5000-2021
Frequency: Annual. **Description:** Key topics sessions on entrepreneurship and running a business. **Principal Exhibits:** Key topics sessions on entrepreneurship and running a business. **Telecommunication Services:** events@inc.com.

33636 ■ LeadsCon
URL(s): www.leadscon.com
Facebook: www.facebook.com/leadscon
Linkedin: www.linkedin.com/groups/1810842
X (Twitter): twitter.com/leadscon
Description: Talks and workshops focused on generating leads and market strategies for small businesses. **Principal Exhibits:** Talks and workshops focused on generating leads and market strategies for small businesses.

33637 ■ National 8(a) Association Small Business Conference
URL(s): www.national8aassociation.org/new-events/ 2022/1/31/2022-national-8a-association-small -business-conference
Frequency: Annual. **Description:** Educational opportunities, workshops, networking, and other resources for small businesses. **Principal Exhibits:** Educational opportunities, workshops, networking, and other resources for small businesses.

33638 ■ National Small Business Federal Contracting Summit
URL(s): www.asbcc.org
Frequency: Annual. **Description:** Provides education, training, and seminars for small business contractors. **Principal Exhibits:** Provides education, training, and seminars for small business contractors.

33639 ■ Small Business Expo
URL(s): www.thesmallbusinessexpo.com/news/an nouncing-the-2022-small-business-expo-live-in-per son-schedule
Frequency: Annual. **Description:** Seminars and workshops for small business owners. Travels throughout major US cities and hosts virtually. **Audience:** Small business owners, start-ups, and entrepreneurs. **Principal Exhibits:** Seminars and workshops for small business owners. Travels throughout major US cities and hosts virtually.

33640 ■ Small Business Institute Annual Conference
URL(s): www.smallbusinessinstitute.biz/page-18 59789

Price: $595, Early registration. **Frequency:** Annual. **Description:** Conference focused on professional development between business, education, and community. **Principal Exhibits:** Conference focused on professional development between business, education, and community.

33641 ■ Startup Grind
URL(s): startupgrind.tech/conference
Price: $249, Onsite registered, members. **Frequency:** Annual. **Description:** Networking and mentorship for small business owners and startups. **Principal Exhibits:** Networking and mentorship for small business owners and startups.

33642 ■ World Business Forum
URL(s): www.wobi.com/wbf-nyc
Frequency: Annual. **Description:** Talks and forums focused on running a business. Also provides networking opportunities. **Principal Exhibits:** Talks and forums focused on running a business. Also provides networking opportunities.

CONSULTANTS

33643 ■ Alaska Business Development Center Inc. (ABDC)
840 K St., Ste. 202
Anchorage, AK 99501
Ph: (907)562-0335
Free: 800-478-3474
Fax: (907)562-6988
Co. E-mail: info@abdc.org
URL: http://www.abdc.org
Contact: Michelle Kern, President
YouTube: www.youtube.com/channel/UCF 2SoogrnyYDKa64k9ORMEw
Description: Services: Consulting assistance to small businesses and commercial fishers. **Scope:** Services: Consulting assistance to small businesses and commercial fishers. **Founded:** 1978. **Training:** Volunteer Tax & Loan Program.

33644 ■ Anchor Advisors Ltd.
7061 W N Ave. No. 352
Oak Park, IL 60302
Ph: (773)282-7677
URL: http://anchoradvisors.com
Contact: Brad Farris, Principal
Description: Services: Small business consultants. **Founded:** 2001.

33645 ■ Angela Henderson Consulting
The Gap
Brisbane, QLD 4000, Australia
Co. E-mail: info@angelahenderson.com.au
URL: http://www.angelahenderson.com.au
Contact: Angela Henderson, Founder
Linkedin: www.linkedin.com/company/angela-hen derson-consulting
Description: Guides aspiring female entrepreneurs to have the courage, mindset and foundations to build a successful business while embracing their natural gifts and talents, and having the lifestyle they desire. **Scope:** Guides aspiring female entrepreneurs to have the courage, mindset and foundations to build a successful business while embracing their natural gifts and talents, and having the lifestyle they desire. **Founded:** 2016.

33646 ■ Association of Accredited Small Business Consultants (AASBC)
7000 N Mopac Expy., Ste. 200
Austin, TX 78731
Ph: (512)327-4900
Free: 833-327-4901
Co. E-mail: info@aasbc.com
URL: http://www.aasbc.com
Contact: Ashton L. Weinberger, President
Facebook: www.facebook.com/AASBCTX
Linkedin: www.linkedin.com/company/association-of -accredited-small-business-consultants
X (Twitter): x.com/TheAASBC
YouTube: www.youtube.com/user/AASBC

Description: Seeks to train and certify small business and SME (small to medium-sized enterprise) consultants in helping their clients improve operational efficiency, maximize profitability, and create business value. Certifications include the Accredited Small Business Consultant (ASBC) for U.S. members and Accredited SME Consultant (ASMEC) for international members. **Founded:** 2011.

33647 ■ Aurora Management Partners Inc.
1201 Peachtree St., Ste. 1570
  Atlanta, GA 30361
Ph: (704)377-6010
Co. E-mail: info@auroramp.com
URL: http://www.auroramp.com
Contact: David Baker, CTP, Managing Partner
Linkedin: www.linkedin.com/company/aurora
  -management-partners/about

Description: Specializes in turnaround management and reorganization consulting, the company develops strategic initiatives, organize and analyze solutions, deal with creditor issues, review organizational structures and develop time frames for decision making. **Founded:** 2000. **Publications:** "TMA Turnaround of the Year Award, Small Company, Honorable Mention," Nov, 2005; "Back From The Brink - Bland Farms," Progressive Farmer, Oct, 2004; "New Breed of Turnaround Managers," Catalyst Magazine, Aug, 2004; "Key Performance Drivers - Bland Farms," The Produce News, Apr, 2004; "Corporate Governance: Averting Crisis's Before They Happen," ABJ journal, Feb, 2004.

33648 ■ Biomedical Management Resources (BMR)
4131 Fortuna Way
  Salt Lake City, UT 84124
Contact: Ping Fong, Jr., Contact
E-mail: pfongbmr@gmail.com

Description: Provides business development, interim management and executive search services. Assists companies in strategic alliances, corporate partnering, business acquisition. Demonstrated success in identifying recruiting and placing key managers in difficult to hire positions. **Scope:** Provides business development, interim management and executive search services. Assists companies in strategic alliances, corporate partnering, business acquisition. Demonstrated success in identifying recruiting and placing key managers in difficult to hire positions.

33649 ■ Black Business Investment Fund (BBIF)
301 E Pine St., Ste. 175
  Orlando, FL 32801
Ph: (407)649-4780
Co. E-mail: info@bbif.com
URL: http://bbif.com
Contact: Inez Long, President
Facebook: www.facebook.com/bbifflorida
Linkedin: www.linkedin.com/company/bbifflorida
X (Twitter): x.com/bbifflorida

Description: Firm offers business clients a complete business support and growth service package. Primary goal is to provide Black and underserved small business owners with the know-how to successfully operate and manage their business. Provides technical assistance as well as direct, facilitated and guaranteed loans. **Scope:** Firm offers business clients a complete business support and growth service package. Primary goal is to provide Black and underserved small business owners with the know-how to successfully operate and manage their business. Provides technical assistance as well as direct, facilitated and guaranteed loans. **Founded:** 1987. **Training:** BBIF Business Community Outreach Seminar, Apopka, Apr, 2006.

33650 ■ Bryan Media Corp.
5826 S Main St., Ste. 805-A
  Akron, OH 44311
Contact: Roger C. Bryan, Jr., Contact

Description: Business Consultants and Business Coaches in the entire world, Covering almost every segment of business. **Scope:** Business Consultants and Business Coaches in the entire world, Covering almost every segment of business.

33651 ■ The Business Group
369-B 3rd St., Ste. 387
  San Rafael, CA 94901
Ph: (415)491-1896
Fax: (415)459-6472
URL: http://www.businessownerstoolbox.com
Contact: Mike van Horn, President
E-mail: mvh@businessgroup.biz

Description: Our company provides small business owners a resource often reserved for execs of large organizations - problem solving and accountability from savvy independent peers. Management consulting firm providing problem solving and accountability to small business owners. Services include executive coaching, growth management, human resources, and organizational design and development. **Scope:** Our company provides small business owners a resource often reserved for execs of large organizations - problem solving and accountability from savvy independent peers. Management consulting firm providing problem solving and accountability to small business owners. Services include executive coaching, growth management, human resources, and organizational design and development. **Founded:** 1984. **Publications:** "How to Grow Your Business Without Driving Yourself Crazy".

33652 ■ Business Ownership Strategies L.L.C. (BOS)
201 Rossburn Way, 3rd Fl.
  Chapel Hill, NC 27516
Ph: (919)913-8034
URL: http://www.bosacquisitions.com
Contact: Dennis Schaecher, Principal

Description: Firm provides acquisition search assistance to private equity firms, investment groups, and corporations, specialty is matching specific client requirements with proprietary acquisition targets that are not advertised for sale in the public market. Provides business acquisition search assistance to private equity firms, investment groups, and entrepreneurs. **Scope:** Firm provides acquisition search assistance to private equity firms, investment groups, and corporations, specialty is matching specific client requirements with proprietary acquisition targets that are not advertised for sale in the public market. Provides business acquisition search assistance to private equity firms, investment groups, and entrepreneurs. **Founded:** 2004.

33653 ■ CALISO Consulting L.L.C.
400 Commonwealth Dr.
  Warrendale, PA 15096
Free: 877-606-7323
Co. E-mail: training@caliso9000.com
URL: http://www.caliso9000.com/index.shtml
Contact: Tracy Armstrong, Manager

Description: Firm provides consulting and web-based training services. **Scope:** Firm provides consulting and web-based training services. **Founded:** 1996. **Publications:** "In A Nutshell"; "A Practical Approach to Global Safety Certification"; "2000 New Requirements, 28 Requirements Checklist and Compliance Guide "; "Biotechnology from A to Z"; "The CE Mark: Understanding the Medical Device Directive"; "2000 Survival Guide". **Training:** ISO 9001: 2000 Internal Auditor Training, San Jose, Dec, 2007; ISO 9000; ISO/TS 16949; Root Cause Analysis; OHSAS 18001; ISO 13485; ISO 19011.

33654 ■ Carver Peterson Consulting
320 W Ohio St., 3W
  Chicago, IL 60654
Ph: (262)225-8969
URL: http://www.carverpeterson.com
Contact: Scott Peterson, Founder
E-mail: scott@carverpeterson.com
Linkedin: www.linkedin.com/company/carver-pe
  terson-consulting-llc

Description: Offers services to growing businesses to help them reach their true potential. Services include revenue lifecycle assessment, sales stage advancement guidance, and sales advisory and coaching. **Scope:** Offers services to growing businesses to help them reach their true potential. Services include revenue lifecycle assessment, sales stage advancement guidance, and sales advisory and coaching. **Founded:** 2014.

33655 ■ CEO Advisors
848 Brickell Ave., Ste. 603
  Miami, FL 33131
Ph: (305)371-8560
URL: http://www.ceoadvisors.us
Contact: Roberto Arguello, Jr., President
Facebook: www.facebook.com/CEOAdvisors9
Linkedin: www.linkedin.com/company/wix-com

Description: Provider of clients services in strategy, mergers and acquisitions, corporate finance and advisory, supply chain management, government relations and public affairs. **Scope:** Provider of clients services in strategy, mergers and acquisitions, corporate finance and advisory, supply chain management, government relations and public affairs. **Founded:** 1989. **Preferred Investment Size:** $300,000 to $500,000. **Industry Preferences:** Communications and media, computer hardware and software, semiconductors and other electronics, biotechnology, medical and health, consumer related.

33656 ■ Chartered Management Co.
100 Saunders Rd., Ste. 150
  Lake Forest, IL 60045
Contact: William B. Avellone, President

Description: Operations improvement consultants. Specializes in strategic planning, feasibility studies, management audits and reports, profit enhancement, start-up businesses, mergers and acquisitions, joint ventures, divestitures, interim management, crisis management, turnarounds, business process re-engineering, venture capital and due diligence. **Scope:** Operations improvement consultants. Specializes in strategic planning, feasibility studies, management audits and reports, profit enhancement, start-up businesses, mergers and acquisitions, joint ventures, divestitures, interim management, crisis management, turnarounds, business process re-engineering, venture capital and due diligence. **Founded:** 1985.

33657 ■ Clubnet Solutions Inc.
77 City Centre Dr., East Twr., Ste. 501
  Mississauga, ON, Canada L5B 1M5
Ph: (416)992-0909
Co. E-mail: info@clubnet.ca
URL: http://clubnet.ca
Contact: Iliana Rocha, Leader
Facebook: www.facebook.com/clubnetsolutions
Linkedin: www.linkedin.com/company/clubnet-solu
  tions-inc
X (Twitter): x.com/clubnet_inc
Instagram: www.instagram.com/clubnetsolutions

Description: Works as a partner to business leaders looking to transform and scale their businesses profitably. **Scope:** Works as a partner to business leaders looking to transform and scale their businesses profitably. **Founded:** 2019.

33658 ■ Colonial Technology Development Co.
PO Box 264
  Concord, NC 28026
Ph: (470)215-0353
URL: http://www.colonialtdc.com
Contact: Taffy Williams, President

Description: Business consultants focusing on start ups, reorganizations and turnarounds, financing and investment counsel, pharmaceutical and diagnostic discovery and development and commercialization strategies. **Scope:** Business consultants focusing on start ups, reorganizations and turnarounds, financing and investment counsel, pharmaceutical and diagnostic discovery and development and commercialization strategies. **Founded:** 2005.

33659 ■ Comer & Associates L.L.C. (CA)
5255 Holmes Pl.
  Boulder, CO 80303
Ph: (303)786-7986
URL: http://www.comerassociates.com
Contact: Gerald Comer, Contact

Description: Specialize in developing markets and businesses. Marketing support includes developing and writing strategic and tactical business plans, developing and writing focused, effective market plans, researching market potential and competition, implementing targeted marketing tactics to achieve company objectives, conducting customer surveys to determine satisfaction and attitudes toward client. **Scope:** Specialize in developing markets and businesses. Marketing support includes developing and writing strategic and tactical business plans, developing and writing focused, effective market plans, researching market potential and competition, implementing targeted marketing tactics to achieve company objectives, conducting customer surveys to determine satisfaction and attitudes toward client. **Training:** Developing a Strategic Market Plan; Market Research: Defining Your Opportunity; Management and Leadership Effectiveness; Team Building; Developing a Business Plan; How to Close; Using Questions to Sell; Sales System Elements and Checklist; Working With Independent Reps; Features vs. Benefits; Overcoming Objections; Sales Force Automation.

33660 ■ The Consulting CEO
Gold Coast
Brisbane, QLD, Australia
Co. E-mail: hello@theconsultingceo.com
URL: http://theconsultingceo.com
Contact: Elle Crawford, Founder
Instagram: www.instagram.com/theconsultingceo
Pinterest: www.pinterest.com.au/theconsultingceo

Description: Supports female entrepreneurs around the world, helping them ignite their potential so they can enjoy the financial abundance and freedom they're looking for through building a successful business of their own. Trains clients on how to use the power of social media to convert followers into high-ticket clients, while helping them break down their limiting beliefs surrounding success and empowerment. **Scope:** Supports female entrepreneurs around the world, helping them ignite their potential so they can enjoy the financial abundance and freedom they're looking for through building a successful business of their own. Trains clients on how to use the power of social media to convert followers into high-ticket clients, while helping them break down their limiting beliefs surrounding success and empowerment.

33661 ■ Corporate Consulting, Inc.
100 Fillmore St.
Denver, CO 80206
Contact: Devereux C. Josephs, Contact

Description: Engaged in feasibility studies, organizational development, small business management, mergers and acquisitions, joint ventures, divestitures, interim management, crisis management, turnarounds, financing, appraisals valuations and due diligence studies. **Scope:** Engaged in feasibility studies, organizational development, small business management, mergers and acquisitions, joint ventures, divestitures, interim management, crisis management, turnarounds, financing, appraisals valuations and due diligence studies.

33662 ■ CSP Associates Inc.
55 Cambridge Pky., Riverfront 2
Cambridge, MA 02142
Ph: (617)225-2828
Co. E-mail: contact@cspassociates.com
URL: http://www.cspassociates.com
Contact: Logan Slone, Director
Linkedin: www.linkedin.com/company/csp-associates-inc.

Description: Firm provides consulting services to clients in aerospace, defense, and government sectors for transaction and strategic advisory services. **Scope:** Firm provides consulting services to clients in aerospace, defense, and government sectors for transaction and strategic advisory services. **Founded:** 1983.

33663 ■ Dewar Sloan L.L.C.
PO Box 331
Traverse City, MI 49685

Ph: (231)929-4545
Fax: (231)929-4598
URL: http://dewarsloan.com
Contact: Daniel Wolf, President

Description: Business development consulting firm specializes in strategy management, governance, product development, marketing, organization, resource management, business change and conducts applications in advanced product planning, market development, category strategy and business evolution and transition support services, which include organization development, restructuring programs, and corporate redevelopment and smaller company services rendered through SBMP. **Scope:** Business development consulting firm specializes in strategy management, governance, product development, marketing, organization, resource management, business change and conducts applications in advanced product planning, market development, category strategy and business evolution and transition support services, which include organization development, restructuring programs, and corporate redevelopment and smaller company services rendered through SBMP. **Founded:** 1983. **Publications:** "Prepared and Resolved: The Strategic Agenda for Growth, Performance and Change," dsb Publishing, Dec, 2006; "Working Notes and Ideas for Managers". **Training:** Strategy and Governance Concerns; Business Development and Organization Concerns; Leadership Behavior Across Boundaries; Building a Platform for Business Evolution; Operational Conflicts in Strategy Management.

33664 ■ Don Phin, Esq.
114 C. Ave., No. 200
Coronado, CA 92118
Ph: (619)852-4580
URL: http://www.donphin.com
Contact: Don Phin, Contact
E-mail: don@donphin.com
Linkedin: www.linkedin.com/in/donphin
X (Twitter): x.com/donphin12
YouTube: www.youtube.com/donphin

Description: Firm is engaged in consulting services on training, coaching and mentoring for the individuals and small businesses. **Scope:** Firm is engaged in consulting services on training, coaching and mentoring for the individuals and small businesses. **Founded:** 1983. **Publications:** "Doing Business Right!"; "HR That Works!"; "Lawsuit Free! How to Prevent Employee Lawsuits"; "Building Powerful Employment Relationships!"; "Victims, Villains and Heroes: Managing Emotions in The Workplace". **Training:** Doing Business Right!; HR That Works!; Building Powerful Employment Relationships; Lawsuit Free!.

33665 ■ Emerge2 Digital Inc.
554 Parkside Dr.
Waterloo, ON, Canada N2L 5Z4
Ph: (519)886-0100
Free: 888-242-5453
Fax: (519)886-1027
Co. E-mail: sales@emerge2.com
URL: http://emerge2.com
Facebook: www.facebook.com/Emerge2
Linkedin: www.linkedin.com/company/emerge2-digital
X (Twitter): x.com/Emerge2
Instagram: www.instagram.com/emerge2digital

Description: Consultants who develop strategies to grow and enhance small businesses. **Scope:** Consultants who develop strategies to grow and enhance small businesses. **Founded:** 2000.

33666 ■ EmpowerHome Team
11870 W 35th Ave.
Wheat Ridge, CO 80033
URL: http://www.theribblegroup.com
Contact: Gaye Ribble, Contact
Facebook: www.facebook.com/TheRibbleGroup
X (Twitter): twitter.com/theribblegroup
Instagram: www.instagram.com/theribblegroup
YouTube: www.youtube.com/channel/UCd8A4wq-K
5H84yHmArWKbDw

Description: Firm offers business appraisal, brokerage and counseling related services. **Scope:** Firm offers business appraisal, brokerage and counseling related services. **Founded:** 1983.

33667 ■ First Strike Management Consulting Inc. (FSMC)
PO Box 1188
Little River, SC 29566-1188
Ph: (843)385-6338
Co. E-mail: info@fsmc.com
URL: http://www.fsmc.com

Description: Offers proposal management and program management services. Specializes in enterprise systems, management systems, and staff augmentation. Serves the following industries: Nuclear/Fossil Power, Petro-Chemical, Aerospace and Defense, Telecommunications, Engineering and Construction, Information Technology, Golf Course Construction/Management, Utility Engineering/Construction, Civil Works, and Housing Development. **Scope:** Offers proposal management and program management services. Specializes in enterprise systems, management systems, and staff augmentation. Serves the following industries: Nuclear/Fossil Power, Petro-Chemical, Aerospace and Defense, Telecommunications, Engineering and Construction, Information Technology, Golf Course Construction/Management, Utility Engineering/Construction, Civil Works, and Housing Development. **Founded:** 1991. **Publications:** "Project Management for Executives"; "Project Risk Management"; "Project Communications Management"; "Winning Proposals, Four Computer Based Training (CBT) courses"; "Principles of Program Management". **Training:** Preparing Winning Proposals in Response to Government RFPs.

33668 ■ Flagship Technologies, Inc.
14976 Monroe Rd. 1039
Madison, MO 65263-2259
Contact: Mark Wilsdorf, Officer

Description: Company is engaged in developing software products and training materials. **Scope:** Company is engaged in developing software products and training materials. **Publications:** "The Quick-Books Farm Accounting Cookbook"; "Do I Need Quicken. QuickBooks Basic. Or QuickBooks Pro?"; "Getting Rid of Old Account and Class Names"; "Accounts, Categories & Classes Defined"; "Tracking Personal Spending with QuickBooks Equity Accounts"; "Account/Category Setup Basics"; "Classes As Enterprise Profit Centers and Cost Centers"; "Setting Up Classes That Meet Your Information Goals"; "Calculating Rolling Herd Average Milk Production with QuickBooks". **Training:** A Computer for Your Farm; Database Interface Design Techniques for Rapid Scanning by Users; QuickBooks Interfacing Techniques; Then and Now. **Special Services:** ManagePLUS™; FormCalc™.

33669 ■ Franz Schneider & Associates L.L.C.
Lumberton, NJ
Fax: (609)261-1822
URL: http://www.fsmfgnet.com

Description: Specializes in business valuation, executive search, growth management, organizational design, project management and business development. **Scope:** Specializes in business valuation, executive search, growth management, organizational design, project management and business development.

33670 ■ Global Technology Transfer L.L.C.
1500 Dixie Hwy.
Park Hills, KY 41011
Contact: Anthony R. Zembrodt, Sr., Member

Description: Firm specializes in product development, quality assurance, new product development, and total quality management focusing on household chemical specialties, especially air fresheners. Utilizes latest technology from global resources. Specializes in enhancement products for home and automobile. **Scope:** Firm specializes in product development, quality assurance, new product development, and total quality management focusing on household chemical specialties, especially air fresheners. Utilizes latest technology from global resources. Specializes in enhancement products for home and automobile.

33671 ■ Greater Prairie Business Consulting
320 Decker Dr., Ste. 100
Irving, TX 75062
Free: 800-828-7585
Fax: (866)431-3103
Co. E-mail: info@gpbusinesssolutions.com
URL: http://www.greaterprairiebusinessconsulting
.com
Contact: James J. Talerico, Jr., Chief Executive Officer
Facebook: www.facebook.com/grea
terprairiebusinessconsulting
Linkedin: www.linkedin.com/company/greater-prairie
-business-consulting-inc
X (Twitter): x.com/RoadWarriorUSA_
YouTube: www.youtube.com/channel/UCjwAPVMrq
3ef2DcEJ6hNDRg
Description: Provides results-oriented consulting services including financial services, executive coaching, human resources, leadership development and marketing. **Scope:** Provides results-oriented consulting services including financial services, executive coaching, human resources, leadership development and marketing. **Founded:** 2003.

33672 ■ Hewitt Development Enterprises (HDE)
1717 N Bayshore Dr., Ste. 2154
Miami, FL 33132
Ph: (305)372-0941
Fax: (305)372-0941
Co. E-mail: info@hewittdevelopment.com
URL: http://www.hewittdevelopment.com
Contact: Robert G. Hewitt, Contact
E-mail: bob@hewittdevelopment.com
Description: Firm specializes in strategic planning, profit enhancement, startup businesses, interim and crisis management, turnarounds, production planning, just-in-time inventory and project management, serves senior management and acquirers of distressed businesses. **Scope:** Firm specializes in strategic planning, profit enhancement, startup businesses, interim and crisis management, turnarounds, production planning, just-in-time inventory and project management, serves senior management and acquirers of distressed businesses. **Founded:** 1985.

33673 ■ Institute for Management Excellence
Trabuco Canyon, CA 92679
Ph: (949)667-1012
URL: http://www.itstime.com
Contact: Barbara Taylor, Executive Director
Description: Consulting firm and training focuses on improving productivity, using practices and creative techniques. **Scope:** Consulting firm and training focuses on improving productivity, using practices and creative techniques. **Founded:** 1995. **Publications:** "Income Without a Job," 2008; "The Other Side of Midnight, 2000: An Executive Guide to the Year 2000 Problem"; "Concordance to the Michael Teachings"; "Handbook of Small Business Advertising"; "The Personality Game"; "How to Market Yourself for Success". **Training:** The Personality Game; Power Path Seminars; Productivity Plus; Sexual Harassment and Discrimination Prevention; Worker's Comp Cost Reduction; Americans with Disabilities Act; In Search of Identify: Clarifying Corporate Culture.

33674 ■ Interminds & Federer Resources Inc.
PO Box 438
Pasadena, CA 91102
Ph: (512)261-0761
Co. E-mail: yesyoucan@interminds.com
URL: http://www.interminds.com
Description: Firm specializes in feasibility studies, startup businesses, small business management, mergers and acquisitions, joint ventures, divestitures, interim and crisis management, turnarounds, production planning, team building, appraisals, and valuations. **Scope:** Firm specializes in feasibility studies, startup businesses, small business management, mergers and acquisitions, joint ventures, divestitures, interim and crisis management, turnarounds, produc-

tion planning, team building, appraisals, and valuations. **Founded:** 1985. **Publications:** "Yes You Can: How To Be A Success No Matter Who You Are Or Where You're From".

33675 ■ International Money Management Group Inc.
110 Channel Marker Way Ste. 101
Grasonville, MD 21638
Contact: Ernest O. Brittingham, Jr., Contact
Description: Multiservice firm created with the express purpose of guiding and assisting individuals, professionals, small businesses and corporations ineffective management of their business and personal financial planning. **Scope:** Multiservice firm created with the express purpose of guiding and assisting individuals, professionals, small businesses and corporations ineffective management of their business and personal financial planning.

33676 ■ Invanti
2702 S Twyckenham Dr.
South Bend, IN 46614
URL: http://www.invanti.co
Description: Helps aspiring entrepreneurs navigate which problems are the most important to solve. **Scope:** Helps aspiring entrepreneurs navigate which problems are the most important to solve.

33677 ■ Jennifer Cramer Lewis
Vancouver, BC, Canada
URL: http://jennifercramerlewis.com
Contact: Jennifer Cramer Lewis, Founder
E-mail: jennifer@jennifercramerlewis.com
Facebook: www.facebook.com/
jennifercramerlewispersonal
Linkedin: www.linkedin.com/in/jennifercramerlewis
Description: Business and relationship turnaround expert for ambitious female entrepreneurs. Offers experience in Finance, Real Estate, Management, and Investing. **Scope:** Business and relationship turnaround expert for ambitious female entrepreneurs. Offers experience in Finance, Real Estate, Management, and Investing.

33678 ■ Johnston Co.
78 Bedford St.
Lexington, MA 02420
Ph: (781)862-7595
Fax: (781)862-9066
Co. E-mail: info@johnstoncompany.com
URL: http://johnstoncompany.com
Contact: Jim Johnston, Chief Executive Officer
E-mail: jimj@johnstoncompany.com
Description: Firm provides consulting on environmental and workplace services such as LSRP service, property acquisition and redevelopment, engineering and site remediation. **Scope:** Firm provides consulting on environmental and workplace services such as LSRP service, property acquisition and redevelopment, engineering and site remediation. **Publications:** "Why are board meetings such a waste of time," Boston Business Journal, Apr, 2004.

33679 ■ Keecha Harris and Associates
217 Country Club Pk., Ste. 423
Birmingham, AL 35213
Ph: (205)538-7433
URL: http://khandassociates.com
Contact: Keecha Harris, President
Linkedin: www.linkedin.com/company/keecha-harris
-and-associates
X (Twitter): x.com/KHandAssociates
Description: Consultancy specializing in research and evaluation, organizational development, and project management for philanthropy, government, corporations, and nongovernmental organizations. **Scope:** Consultancy specializing in research and evaluation, organizational development, and project management for philanthropy, government, corporations, and nongovernmental organizations.

33680 ■ Mefford, Knutson & Associates Inc. (MKA)
6437 Lyndale Ave. S
Richfield, MN 55423
Co. E-mail: info@mkcconsulting.com

URL: http://mkaconsulting.com
Contact: Jeanette Mefford, Co-Founder
Description: Provider of consulting services to home health and related sectors. **Scope:** Provider of consulting services to home health and related sectors. **Founded:** 1990.

33681 ■ Miller, Leiby & Associates P.C.
32 Broadway, 13th Fl.
New York, NY 10004
Ph: (212)227-4200
Fax: (212)504-8369
URL: http://www.millerleiby.com
Contact: Doron Leiby, Partner
Facebook: www.facebook.com/MillerLeibyAssocia
tesPc
Linkedin: www.linkedin.com/company/1269719
Instagram: www.instagram.com/millerleiby
Description: Firm is engaged in legal counsel for individuals and businesses. **Scope:** Firm is engaged in legal counsel for individuals and businesses. **Training:** Objectives and standards/recruiting for boards of directors.

33682 ■ Murray Dropkin & Associates
390 George St.
New Brunswick, NJ 08901
URL: http://dropkin.com
Contact: Murray Dropkin, Contact
Description: Firm specializes in feasibility studies, business management, business process reengineering, team building, healthcare, and housing. **Scope:** Firm specializes in feasibility studies, business management, business process reengineering, team building, healthcare, and housing. **Publications:** "Bookkeeping for Nonprofits," Jossey Bass, 2005; "Guide to Audits of Nonprofit Organizations," PPC; "The Nonprofit Report," Warren, Gorham & Lamont; "The Budget Building Book for Nonprofits," Jossey-Bass; "The Cash Flow Management Book for Nonprofits," Jossey-Bass.

33683 ■ Next Canada
175 Bloor St. E, Ste. 1800, South Bldg.
Toronto, ON, Canada M4W 3R8
Co. E-mail: info@nextcanada.com
URL: http://www.nextcanada.com
Contact: Reza Satchu, Chairman
Facebook: www.facebook.com/nextcanadaorg
Linkedin: www.linkedin.com/company/next-canada
X (Twitter): x.com/next_canada
Instagram: www.instagram.com/next_canada
Description: Started by entrepreneurs for entrepreneurs, provides a series of life changing experiences and relationships to young Canadians with enormous potential, accelerates the growth trajectory of aspiring and scaling entrepreneurs with education, mentorship, funding and access to Canada's strongest entrepreneurial network. **Founded:** 2010.

33684 ■ Nineteen90 Business Consulting
Sharon Hill, PA
Ph: (215)902-6055
Co. E-mail: info@nineteen90.co
URL: http://www.nineteen90.co
Contact: Kevin Dolce, Chief Executive Officer
Facebook: www.facebook.com/nine
teen90businessconsulting
Instagram: www.instagram.com/nineteen90
_businessconsulting
Description: A full-service business consulting firm that focuses on helping new entrepreneurs to register their businesses as an LLC, C-Corp, S-Corp, or Non-Profit. The firm also offers educational programs that allow entrepreneurs to learn about the different business entities and they provide assistance with writing business plans for all kinds of businesses, no matter the size. **Scope:** A full-service business consulting firm that focuses on helping new entrepreneurs to register their businesses as an LLC, C-Corp, S-Corp, or Non-Profit. The firm also offers educational programs that allow entrepreneurs to learn about the different business entities and they provide assistance with writing business plans for all kinds of businesses, no matter the size.

33685 ■ Norris Bernstein, CMC

9309 Marina Pacifica Dr. N
 Long Beach, CA 90803
Ph: (562)493-5458
Fax: (562)493-5459
Co. E-mail: norris@norrisbernstein.com
URL: http://www.norrisbernstein.com
Contact: Norris Bernstein, Contact
E-mail: norris@norrisbernstein.com

Description: Provider of counsel to help emerging companies develop and grow by analyzing markets, both domestic and international, assessing market position and growth issues, developing and assessing business objectives and strategies, analyzing and implementing marketing programs, reshaping organizational structures to make them more efficient and effective and more. **Founded:** 1977.

33686 ■ Panaram International Trading Co.

126 Greylock Ave.
 Belleville, NJ 07109
Free: 800-872-8695
Co. E-mail: info@usatowl.com
URL: http://usatowl.com
Facebook: www.facebook.com/usatowlcom

Description: Provider of analysis for car wash business and services include promotion, advertising, computer tracking, training, building volume, quality control, and profit centers and will also provide client with a turnkey car wash, if desired, designs systems for cleaning cars and their new specialty is providing turnaround services to small businesses and serves car wash industry small business operations. **Scope:** Provider of analysis for car wash business and services include promotion, advertising, computer tracking, training, building volume, quality control, and profit centers and will also provide client with a turnkey car wash, if desired, designs systems for cleaning cars and their new specialty is providing turnaround services to small businesses and serves car wash industry small business operations. **Training:** Building Volume and Traffic at Your Car Wash; Express Polishing at Your Car Wash; How to Double Your Income as a Car Wash Operator; Car Wash Business Training.

33687 ■ Performance Consultants Group, Inc. (PCG)

1 Innovation Way., Ste. 400
 Newark, DE 19711
Ph: (302)738-7532
Free: 888-724-3578
URL: http://www.pcgius.com

Description: Firm provides consulting services in the areas of strategic planning, profit enhancement, product development, and production planning. **Scope:** Firm provides consulting services in the areas of strategic planning, profit enhancement, product development, and production planning. **Founded:** 1988.

33688 ■ Public Sector Consulting (PSC)

5718 Barlow Rd.
 Sherman, IL 62684
Ph: (217)629-9869
Fax: (217)629-9732
URL: http://www.gotopsc.com

Description: Provider of financial, managerial, and technological products, services and support for new and growing businesses, it provides management services, mobile computing, website and e-commerce, they also provide technology products like notebook specialists, computers, peripherals, telephony, CAD and CAM systems, hardware and software applications and offers special e-commerce packages for independent retailers and service businesses. **Scope:** Provider of financial, managerial, and technological products, services and support for new and growing businesses, it provides management services, mobile computing, website and e-commerce, they also provide technology products like notebook specialists, computers, peripherals, telephony, CAD and CAM systems, hardware and software applications and offers special e-commerce packages for independent retailers and service businesses. **Founded:** 1986. **Publications:** "Economic recovery-The basis for sustainability".

33689 ■ Rose & Crangle Ltd.

102 E Lincoln Ave.
 Lincoln, KS 67455
Contact: S. Jeanne Crangle, Contact

Description: Provider of evaluation, planning and policy analyzes for universities, associations, foundations, governmental agencies and private companies engaged in scientific, technological or educational activities. Special expertise in the development of new institutions. Special skills in providing planning and related group facilitation workshops. **Scope:** Provider of evaluation, planning and policy analyzes for universities, associations, foundations, governmental agencies and private companies engaged in scientific, technological or educational activities. Special expertise in the development of new institutions. Special skills in providing planning and related group facilitation workshops. **Publications:** "Preface to Bulgarian Integration Into Europe and NATO: Issues of Science Policy And research Evaluation Practice," Ios Press, 2006; "Allocating Limited National Resources for Fundamental Research," 2005.

33690 ■ Strand Consulting

925 N LA Brea Ave., Ste. 400
 West Hollywood, CA 90038
Contact: Esther Roth, Chief Executive Officer

Description: A multinational business consultancy that's focused on helping small business owners scale their businesses to make big profits. **Scope:** A multinational business consultancy that's focused on helping small business owners scale their businesses to make big profits.

33691 ■ University CoWork

6127 S University Ave.
 Chicago, IL 60637
Ph: (773)800-9751
URL: http://www.universitycowork.com
Facebook: www.facebook.com/UniversityCoWork
Linkedin: www.linkedin.com/company/universi
  tycowork
X (Twitter): x.com/UniversityCW
Inctagram: www.inctagram.com/UnivorcityCoWork
YouTube: www.youtube.com/channel/UCO5u9Hc
  dCCf_aK8lflvh-Ug

Description: Full-service business development center providing a convenient, fun, and productive work space for entrepreneurs and scholars. Also provides virtual accelerator services. **Scope:** Full-service business development center providing a convenient, fun, and productive work space for entrepreneurs and scholars. Also provides virtual accelerator services. **Founded:** 2018.

33692 ■ University of Missouri - Columbia - Business Research and Information Development Group (BRIDG)

401 Ellis Library
 Columbia, MO 65201
URL: http://muarchives.missouri.edu/c-rg18-s1.html

Description: Integral unit of the University of Missouri—Columbia. **Scope:** Entrepreneurship, small business development and growth. **Founded:** 2001.

33693 ■ Venture Marketing Associates L.L.C.

800 Palisade Ave., Ste. 907
 Fort Lee, NJ 07024
Ph: (201)924-7435
Co. E-mail: venturemkt@aol.com
URL: http://www.venturemarketingassociates.com
Contact: Shep Altshuler, Contact

Description: Business development/franchise consultants. **Scope:** Firm provides business development services for startups or multi-unit operations. **Founded:** 1976. **Training:** Franchise Your Business; How to Research a Franchise Services.

33694 ■ Young & Associates Inc. (YA)

131 E Main St.
 Kent, OH 44240
Ph: (330)678-0524
Free: 800-525-9775
Fax: (330)678-6219
URL: http://www.younginc.com
Contact: Jerry Sutherin, President
Linkedin: www.linkedin.com/company/young
  -&-associates-inc

Description: Offers a wide array of management consulting and outsourcing products and services, including risk management, capital planning, strategic planning, mergers and acquisitions, internal audit, branching and expansion, loan review, information technology, human resources, marketing, and regulatory compliance. **Founded:** 1978. **Publications:** "An Avalanche of New Compliance Regulations," Oct, 2009; "Fair Lending Risk Assessment," May, 2009. **Special Services:** The Compliance Monitoring System™; Compliance Monitoring Update Service™; The Compliance Review Program™; Compliance Review Program Update Service™.

PUBLICATIONS

33695 ■ Advising the Small Business

Ed: Jean L. Batman. **Released:** 2019. **Description:** A guide for lawyers to consult when advising small businesses. Includes forms and documents. **Availability:** Print.

33696 ■ "Digital New Ventures: Assessing the Benefits of Digitalization in Entrepreneurship" in Journal of Small Business Strategy (May 27, 2020)

URL(s): libjournals.mtsu.edu/index.php/jsbs/article/
  view/1543

Ed: Anna Frieda Rosin, Dorian Proksch, Stephan Stubner, Andreas Pinkwart. **Description:** Explores the results from a study conducted on the impact going digital has on the resources of new ventures. **Availability:** PDF.

33697 ■ Entrepreneur Inc.

18061 Fitch
 Irvine, CA 92614
Ph: (212)221-9595
Co. E-mail: entcustserv@cdsfulfillment.com
URL: http://www.entrepreneur.com
Contact: Bill Shaw, President
X (Twitter): x.com/entrepreneur
YouTube: www.youtube.com/user/En
  trepreneurOnline
Pinterest: www.pinterest.com/entrepreneurmedia

Description: Publisher of magazine.

33698 ■ Entrepreneur Media Inc. [Entrepreneur Press]

18061 Fitch
 Irvine, CA 92614
Ph: (212)221-9595
Co. E-mail: events@entrepreneur.com
URL: http://www.entrepreneur.com
Contact: Dan Bova, Director
E-mail: dbova@entrepreneur.com
URL(s): bookstore.entrepreneur.com

Description: Publisher and distributor of books and magazines. **Founded:** 1973. **Publications:** *Bakery*; *Green Entrepreneur*; *Great Big Book of Business Lists*; *How to Start a Business in Arkansas* (Annual); *How to Start a Business in Hawaii* (Annual); *How to Start a Business in Idaho* (Annual); *How to Start a Business in Iowa*; *How to Start a Business in Kansas* (Annual); *Entrepreneur Franchise 500 Ranking* (Annual); *Entrepreneur's Annual Franchise 500 Issue* (Annual); *Business Start-Ups: Smart Ideas for Your Small Business*; *Pet Shop*; *Physical Fitness Center*; *Pizzeria*; *Promotional Marketing*; *PVC Furniture Manufacturing*; *Restaurant Start-Up*; *Sandwich Shop/ Deli*; *SBA Loan Guide*; *Secretarial/Word Processing Service*; *Seminar Promoting*; *Senior Day Care Center*; *Sock Shop*; *Software Store*; *Specialty Advertising*; *Sporting Goods Store*; *Standard Business Forms for the Entrepreneur*; *Start-Up Business Guides*; *Travel Agency*; *How to Start a Business in Kentucky* (Annual); *How to Start a Business in Louisiana* (Annual); *How to Start a Business in Maine* (Annual); *How to Start a Business in Mississippi* (Annual); *How to Start a Business in Montana*; *How to*

Start a Business in Nebraska (Annual); *How to Start a Business in Nevada* (Annual); *How to Start a Business in New Mexico* (Annual); *How to Start a Business in New York City* (Annual); *How to Start a Business in North Dakota*; *How to Start a Business in Ohio* (Annual); *How to Start a Business in Oklahoma* (Annual); *How to Start a Business in Rhode Island* (Annual); *How to Start a Business in South Dakota* (Annual); *How to Start a Business in Utah* (Annual); *How to Start a Business in Vermont* (Annual); *How to Start a Business in West Virginia* (Annual); *How to Start a Business in Wyoming* (Annual); *How to Start a Business in Delaware* (Annual); *How to Start a Business in Alabama*; *How to Start a Business in Alaska* (Annual); *How to Start a Business in District of Columbia* (Annual); *Entrepreneur's Bizstartups. com* (Monthly); *HomeOffice: The Homebased Office Authority* (Bimonthly); *Entrepreneur's Be Your Own Boss*; *Advertising Agency*; *Newsletter Publishing*; *One-Hour Photo Processing Lab* (Daily); *Entrepreneur Magazine* (6/year); *Entrepreneurial Woman* (Monthly); *Entrepreneur: The Small Business Authority*. **Educational Activities:** International Franchise Expo (IFE) (Annual).

33699 ■ *"An Exploratory Study of Executive Factors That Lead To Technology Adoption in Small Businesses"* Journal of Small Business Strategy (May 27, 2020)
URL(s): libjournals.mtsu.edu/index.php/jsbs/article/view/1286
Ed: Sean Reynolds, Felipe Cotrino, Charles Ifedi, Naveen Donthu. **Description:** Examines the results of research regarding the adoption of technology by CEOs and other executives for their small businesses. **Availability:** PDF.

33700 ■ *"Inter-firm Marketing Collaboration in Family Business: The Role of Risk Aversion"* in Journal of Small Business Strategy (April 13, 2021)
URL(s): libjournals.mtsu.edu/index.php/jsbs/article/view/1781
Ed: Maria J. Ibanez. **Released:** April 13, 2021. **Description:** Explores the reasons why family businesses do not collaborate with other small businesses to access resources they may not have readily available. **Availability:** PDF.

33701 ■ *Journal of Small Business and Enterprise Development*
Howard House, Wagon Ln.
  Bingley BD16 1WA, United Kingdom
Ph: 44 1274 777-700
Co. E-mail: support@emeraldinsight.com
URL: http://www.emeraldgrouppublishing.com
Contact: Alice Fleet, Director
URL(s): www.emeraldgrouppublishing.com/journal/jsbed
Ed: Dr. Harry Matlay. **Released:** 7/year **Description:** Journal for leaders of SMEs and academics in the field of entrepreneurship, combining case studies with quality research, providing an authoritative discussion on the developments surrounding small businesses, seeking to explore best practice, investigate strategies for growth, and to assist and inform those responsible for the management of SMEs. **Availability:** Print; PDF; Download; Online.

33702 ■ *Journal of Small Business Strategy (JSBS)*
URL(s): libjournals.mtsu.edu/index.php/jsbs/index
Description: An applied research journal with a focus on the small business/entrepreneurship educator and small business consultants.

33703 ■ *"Marketing Strategies in Family Firms"* in Journal of Small Business Strategy (April 13, 2021)
URL(s): libjournals.mtsu.edu/index.php/jsbs/article/view/2010
Ed: Manuel Alonso Dos Santos, Orlando Llanos Contreras, Raj V. Mahto. **Description:** Explores why family firms do not apply marketing theories and branding concepts. **Availability:** PDF.

33704 ■ *"Reputation and Identity in Family Firms: Current State and Gaps for Future Research"* in Journal of Small Business Strategy (April 13, 2021).
URL(s): libjournals.mtsu.edu/index.php/jsbs/article/view/1742
Ed: Jonathan Cuevas Lizama, Orlando Llanos Contreras, Manuel Alonso Dos Santos. **Released:** April 13, 2021. **Description:** Explores in depth the research regarding the reputation and identity of family businesses and the impact it has on the business. **Availability:** PDF.

33705 ■ *Small Business Institute Journal*
URL(s): www.sbij.org/index.php/SBIJ
Description: Publishes scholarly research articles regarding small business management, entrepreneurship, and field based learning.

33706 ■ *Small Business Trends, LLC*
15275 Collier Blvd., No., 201-367
  Naples, FL 34119
Free: 888-842-1186
Co. E-mail: sbtips@gmail.com
URL: http://smallbiztrends.com
Contact: Anita Campbell, Chief Executive Officer
Facebook: www.facebook.com/smallbusinesstrends
Linkedin: www.linkedin.com/company/small-business-trends
X (Twitter): x.com/smallbiztrends
YouTube: www.youtube.com/c/SmallBusinessTrends
Pinterest: www.pinterest.com/smallbiztrends
Founded: 2003. **Publications:** *BizSugar* (Weekly).

PUBLISHERS

33707 ■ *StartupNation Media Group Inc.*
34300 Woodward Ave., Ste. 200
  Birmingham, MI 48009
Free: 866-597-8278
Co. E-mail: contact@startupnation.com
URL: http://startupnation.com
Contact: Jeff Sloan, Chief Executive Officer
Facebook: www.facebook.com/StartupNation
Linkedin: www.linkedin.com/company/startupnation
X (Twitter): x.com/StartupNation
Instagram: www.instagram.com/startupnationofficial
Description: Multimedia company that provides information for entrepreneurs on how to start, grow, and manage a business. **Founded:** 2002.

COMPUTERIZED DATABASES

33708 ■ *SBA Online*
U.S. Small Business Administration
409 3rd St. SW
  Washington, DC 20416
Ph: (202)205-6766
Free: 800-827-5722
Fax: (202)205-7064
Co. E-mail: answerdesk@sba.gov
URL: http://www.sba.gov
URL(s): www.sba.gov/about-sba/open-government/digital-sba
Description: Contains information on starting up, financing, and expanding small businesses; lists of local Small Business Administration (SBA) offices; how to obtain government contracts; assistance for minority-owned businesses; SBA services such as SCORE (Service Corps of Retired Executives), Small Business Development Centers, and the Small Business Innovation Research program. The database is accessible on the Web. **Availability:** Online. **Type:** Bulletin board; Full-text; Directory.

INTERNET DATABASES

33709 ■ *African Americans in Business and Entrepreneurship: A Resource Guide*
URL(s): guides.loc.gov/african-americans-in-business
Description: A guide providing key topics on the history of African Americans in various business industries. **Availability:** Online.

33710 ■ *DreamBuilder*
URL(s): dreambuilder.org
Description: Provides online educational programs for women small business owners and entrepreneurs. **Availability:** Online.

33711 ■ *Small Business Financing: A Resource Guide*
URL(s): guides.loc.gov/small-business-financing
Description: Provides links to online resources to conduct research on financing options for small businesses and entrepreneurs. Covers the following topics: types of financing, financing by situation, financial management, and avoiding scams. **Availability:** Online.

33712 ■ *Small Business Hub: A Research Guide for Entrepreneurs*
URL(s): guides.loc.gov/small-business-hub
Description: An online guide with links for further research into running a small business. Topics cover a large selection of useful information for entrepreneurs for all stages of setting up a business. Includes resources on planning, finance, location, registering, marketing, managing, growing, and exiting the business. **Availability:** Online.

LIBRARIES

33713 ■ Boston Public Library - Kirstein Business Library & Innovation Center
700 Boylston St.
  Boston, MA 02116
Ph: (617)536-5400
Co. E-mail: businessref@bpl.org
URL: http://www.bpl.org/kbl
Facebook: www.facebook.com/KirsteinBusiness
Linkedin: www.linkedin.com/company/kblic
X (Twitter): x.com/bplkirstein
Scope: Business administration; small business. **Services:** Copying is available through the library's interlibrary loan department; reference faxing up to three pages. **Founded:** 1930. **Holdings:** Mergent Manuals (1935 to present in print; 1909-1997 in microfiche); Commercial and Financial Chronicle, 1957-1987; Bank and Quotation Record, 1928-1987; Standard and Poor's Daily Stock Price Record: New York and American Stock Exchanges, 1962 to present; over-the-counter stocks, 1968 to present; domestic and foreign trade directories; city directories; telephone directories for New England and U.S. cities with populations over 100,000 for New England cities and towns; Standard Stock Market Service, 1921-1922; Standard Stock Offerings, 1925-1939; National Stock Summary, 1927 to present; Standard & Poor's Stock Guide, 1943 to present; New York and American Stock Exchange companies Annual and 10K reports on microfiche (1987-1996); Wall Street Journal on microfilm (latest 10 years); Wall Street Transcript on microfilm (latest 5 years); D-U-N-S Business Identification Service (November 1973 -1995).

33714 ■ Carnegie Library of Pittsburgh Downtown & Business
612 Smithfield St.
  Pittsburgh, PA 15222
Ph: (412)281-7141
URL: http://www.carnegielibrary.org/clp_location/downtown-business
Contact: Andrew Medlar, President
Scope: Local history. **Services:** Library open to the public. **Founded:** 1924. **Holdings:** Books; magazines; CD-ROMs; videos.

33715 ■ Chicago Public Library Central Library - Business/Science/Technology Division
400 S State St.
  Chicago, IL 60605
URL: http://www.chipublib.org/resources/science-technology

Scope: Small business; marketing; technology; sciences; computer science; careers and environmental information. **Services:** Interlibrary loan; library open to the public. **Founded:** 1977. **Holdings:** Figures not available.

33716 ■ Greater Oviedo Chamber of Commerce Business Library
PO Box 621236
  Oviedo, FL 32762
URL: http://www.owsrcc.org
Description: Promotes business in the region of Greater Oviedo. **Founded:** 1995. **Holdings:** 3 books; 10 reports; periodicals.

33717 ■ Indian River Area Library (IRAL)
3546 S Straits Hwy.
  Indian River, MI 49749
Ph: (231)238-8581
Co. E-mail: info@indianriverlibrary.org
URL: http://www.indianriverlibrary.org
Contact: Kelsey Rutkowski, Director
Facebook: www.facebook.com/IndianRiverLibrary
Instagram: www.instagram.com/indianriverarealibrary
Scope: Local history. **Services:** Photocopy; Printer & Copier; Laminating; Faxing; Reciprocal Borrowing Agreement. **Founded:** 1976. **Holdings:** Figures not available.

33718 ■ New York State Small Business Development Center (NYS SBDC) - Library
353 Broadway
  Albany, NY 12246
Ph: (518)944-2840
Free: 800-732-SBDC
Co. E-mail: sonya.smith@nysbdc.org
URL: http://www.nysbdc.org
Contact: Jim Conroy, President
E-mail: jconroy@nybdc.org
Facebook: www.facebook.com/nysbdc
Linkedin: www.linkedin.com/company/422102
X (Twitter): x.com/nyabdo
YouTube: www.youtube.com/c/
  NewYorkSmallBusinessDevelopmentCenter
Pinterest: www.pinterest.com/nyssbdc
Description: Provides expert management and technical assistance to start-up and existing businesses across the state of New York. **Scope:** Small Business Development. **Services:** Library open to members only. **Founded:** 1984. **Holdings:** Figures not available. **Geographic Preference:** State.

33719 ■ Piedmont Technical College Library
Lex Walters Campus
  Bldg. K, 2nd Fl.
  Greenwood, SC 29648-1467
Ph: (864)941-8441
Free: 800-868-5528
Fax: (864)941-8558
Co. E-mail: librarian@ptc.edu
URL: http://www.ptc.edu/college-resources/library
Contact: Hope E. Rivers, President
Facebook: www.facebook.com/PiedmontTech
Linkedin: www.linkedin.com/school/piedmon
  t-technical-college
X (Twitter): x.com/piedmont_tech
Instagram: www.instagram.com/piedmont_tech
YouTube: www.youtube.com/user/Piedmon
  tTechCollege
Description: It offers electronic books, databases, LibGuides, online videos, the state newspaper, and faculty resources. **Scope:** Education; leisure. **Services:** Interlibrary loan; copying; library open to the public. **Founded:** 1966. **Holdings:** Figures not available.

33720 ■ Saskatchewan Research Council (SRC) - Information Services
Bay 2D, 820 51st St., E
  Saskatoon, SK, Canada S7K 0X8
Ph: (306)933-5400
Free: 877-772-7227
Co. E-mail: info@src.sk.ca
URL: http://www.src.sk.ca
Contact: Mike Crabtree, Secretary
X (Twitter): x.com/srcnews

YouTube: www.youtube.com/user/
  saskresearchcouncil
Description: Independent, nonprofit research organization located in Innovation Place research park in Saskatoon, affiliated with the University of Saskatchewan and University of Regina. **Scope:** SRC is Saskatchewan's leading provider of applied R&D and technology commercialization. We take the leading-edge knowledge developed in Saskatchewan and sell it to the world and, at the same time, bring the best knowledge the world has to offer and apply it to the unique Saskatchewan situations. **Services:** Interlibrary loan. **Founded:** 1947. **Holdings:** 8,600 monographs; 3,300 SRC-authored publications. **Publications:** *News Releases*; *SRC Annual report* (Annual).

33721 ■ South College Library
3904 Lonas Dr.
  Knoxville, TN 37909
Ph: (865)251-1832
URL: http://library.south.edu/home
Contact: Anya McKinney, Director, Library Services
E-mail: amckinney@south.edu
Scope: Educational material. **Services:** Interlibrary loan; copying; printing; SDI; library open to South College staff and students. **Holdings:** E-books; print and e-journals; other periodicals; CDs; DVDs; streaming videos.

33722 ■ U.S.D.A. National Agricultural Library - Rural Information Center (RIC)
10301 Baltimore Ave.
  Beltsville, MD 20705
URL: http://www.nal.usda.gov/programs/ric
Scope: Economic development; small business development; city and county government services; government and private grants and funding sources; rural communities; community leadership; natural resources. **Services:** Copying; center open to the public. **Founded:** 1987. **Holdings:** Figures not available.

33723 ■ University of Colorado - Boulder - William M. White Business Library
995 Regent Dr.
  Boulder, CO 80309
Ph: (303)492-8367
Co. E-mail: libraries@colorado.edu
URL: http://www.colorado.edu/libraries/libraries-collec
  tions/business-library
Contact: Rocco Labriola, Manager, Operations
Scope: Business research. **Services:** Interlibrary loan; copying; library open to the public. **Founded:** 1970. **Holdings:** Figures not available.

33724 ■ Warren County Community College Library Special Collections
475 Rte. 57 W
  Washington, NJ 07882
Ph: (908)835-2336
Co. E-mail: wccclibrary@warren.edu
URL: http://warren.libguides.com/c.php?g=789378
Scope: Art; biology; business; chemistry; communications; computer science and graphic design; criminal justice; education; English; history; mathematics; nursing; philosophy and religion; psychology; sociology; world music. **Services:** Interlibrary loan; Q&ANJ, copying; services for the deaf; closed-captioned videos available; library open to the public. **Founded:** 1984. **Holdings:** Figures not available. **Subscriptions:** 200 journals and other serials.

RESEARCH CENTERS

33725 ■ Boston College - Boston College Business Institute (BLI)
140 Commonwealth Ave.
  Chestnut Hill, MA 02467
Co. E-mail: gsasinfo@bc.edu
URL: http://www.bc.edu/bc-web/sites/bc-experience/
  programs/non-credit-programs/business---lea
  dership-institute.html
Description: Integral unit of Boston College. **Scope:** Marketing planning, research, and consultation services for small businesses and start-up ventures.

33726 ■ Boston University (BU) - Institute for Economic Development (IED)
270 Bay State Rd.
  Boston, MA 02215
URL: http://www.bu.edu/econ/research/ied
Contact: Dilip Mookherjee, Director
E-mail: dilipm@bu.edu
Description: Integral unit of Boston University. Offers consulting services. **Scope:** Trade and technology diffusion, international borrowing, fertility, labor migration and labor markets, human capital, economics of the family, social norms and cultural values, agrarian contracts, wage and income inequality, social security, health, tax enforcement, reforms in governance and public enterprises, privatization, monetary union, and comparative business strategy. **Founded:** 1990. **Publications:** *Discussion papers*; *IED Research Review* (Annual). **Educational Activities:** IED Seminar Series (Weekly); IED Northeast University Development Consortium (Annual); IED Public Enterprise Program workshops, seminars (Weekly). **Awards:** IED Research grants (Annual).

33727 ■ Canadian Innovation Centre Resource Centre (CIC)
Waterloo Research & Technology Park Accelerator Ctr.
  295 Hagey Blvd., Ste. 15
  Waterloo, ON, Canada N2L 6R5
Ph: (519)885-5870
Fax: (519)513-2421
Co. E-mail: info@innovationcentre.ca
URL: http://innovationcentre.ca
Contact: E. B. Cross, Chairman
E-mail: tcross@innovationcentre.ca
Linkedin: www.linkedin.com/company/canadian
  -innovation-centre
X (Twitter): x.com/innovationctre
Scope: Technological innovation; invention; entrepreneurship; business start-up; patents; licensing. **Services:** Copying; center open to the public for reference use only. **Founded:** 1975. **Holdings:** Figures not available.

33728 ■ Chamber of Commerce of Metropolitan Montreal - Info Entrepreneurs - Information Center
393 Saint-Jacques St., Ste. 200
  Montreal, QC, Canada H2Y 1N9
Ph: (514)496-4636
Free: 888-576-4444
URL: http://www.infoentrepreneurs.org/en/resource
  -centre
Scope: International trade; statistics; entrepreneur business start-up; commerce. **Services:** Copying; center open to the public. **Founded:** 1994. **Holdings:** Figures not available.

33729 ■ Long Island University - Center for Business Research (CBR)
720 Northern Blvd.
  CW Post Campus
  Brookville, NY 11548
Ph: (516)299-2000
URL: http://www2.liu.edu/cwis/cwp/library/cbr/
  cbrhome.htm
Contact: Kimberly R. Cline, President
Description: Services: Job training and management consulting. **Scope:** Services: Job training and management consulting. **Services:** Center open to Long Island University students, faculty, and business community on a limited schedule. **Founded:** 1978. **Holdings:** 40,000 reference volumes. **Publications:** "Taking Your Business to Canada"; "Logistics Management," 2002.

33730 ■ Louisiana Tech University - Center for Rural Development
Reese Hall, Rm. 101
  305 Wisteria St.
  Ruston, LA 71272
URL: http://www.latech.edu/administration/policies/p
  -5305
Description: Integral unit of Louisiana Tech University. **Scope:** Rural development in Louisiana, focusing on education, technology, small business develop-

ment, rural entrepreneurship, community development, agriculture and forestry, rural health. **Publications:** *Rural Louisiana newsletter* (Quarterly). **Educational Activities:** Outreach, and economic development.

33731 ■ University of Arkansas at Little Rock - Arkansas Economic Development Institute (AEDI)
2801 South University Ave.
  Little Rock, AR 72204
Ph: (501)569-8519
Co. E-mail: grow@youraedi.com
URL: http://youraedi.com
Contact: Jim Youngquist, Executive Director
Facebook: www.facebook.com/ArkansasEDI
Linkedin: www.linkedin.com/company/aredi
X (Twitter): x.com/ArkansasEDI

Description: Integral unit of University of Arkansas at Little Rock. **Scope:** Business and economics, industrial development, labor statistics, demographics, government and taxes, economic development and U.S. census. **Founded:** 1960.

33732 ■ University of Nebraska - Lincoln - Center for Entrepreneurship
730 N 14th St.
  Lincoln, NE 68588-0405
Ph: (402)472-3353
Co. E-mail: entrepreneurship@unl.edu
URL: http://business.unl.edu/academic-programs/center-for-entrepreneurship
Contact: Craig Boesch, Officer
E-mail: boesch@unl.edu
Facebook: www.facebook.com/NebraskaC4E
X (Twitter): x.com/nebraskac4e

Description: Integral unit of University of Nebraska—Lincoln. **Scope:** Management of public and private enterprises, focusing on issues facing entrepreneurship and the franchise industry and the activities and complexities of business, government, and public service. **Founded:** 1983.

33733 ■ University of North Carolina at Charlotte - Urban Institute
9201 University City Blvd.
  Charlotte, NC 28223-0001

Ph: (704)687-1210
Fax: (704)687-5327
Co. E-mail: unccurbaninstitute@uncc.edu
URL: http://ui.charlotte.edu
Contact: Lori Thomas, Executive Director
E-mail: lorithomas@uncc.edu
Facebook: www.facebook.com/CLTUrbanInst
X (Twitter): x.com/CLTUrbanInst

Description: Integral unit of Division of Academic Affairs at University of North Carolina at Charlotte. Offers administration and facilitation of community programs; speakers bureau. **Scope:** Economic development and planning, evaluation research, transportation and growth issues, survey research, needs assessment and citizen opinion surveys; environmental awareness; health care; and regional profiles. **Founded:** 1969. **Publications:** *Urban Institute Annual report*; *Elected Officials Directory*; *Regional HIV/AIDS Resource Directory*; *Urban Outreach Newsletter* (Weekly). **Educational Activities:** Urban Institute Conferences, Covers regional issues.; Urban Institute Conferences, Covers regional issues.

START-UP INFORMATION

33734 ■ *"Local Startup Hits Big Leagues"* in *Austin Business JournalInc. (Vol. 28, December 19, 2008, No. 40, pp. 1)*

Description: Qcue LLC, an Austin, Texas-based company founded in 2007 is developing a software system that can be used by Major League Baseball teams to change the prices of their single-game tickets based on variables affecting demand. The company recently completed a trial with the San Francisco Giants in 2008. **Availability:** Print; Online.

33735 ■ *"Probability Processing Chip: Lyric Semiconductor"* in *Inc. (Volume 32, December 2010, No. 10, pp. 52)*

Pub: Inc. Magazine

Ed: Christine Lagorio. **Description:** Lyric Semiconductor, a start up located in Cambridge, Massachusetts, has developed a computer chip that also uses values that fall between zero and one, resulting in a chip that can process information using probabilities, considering many possible answers that find the best fit. **Availability:** Online.

33736 ■ *"The Rise of Digital Currencies and Atlanta's Key Role"* in *Atlanta Business Chronicle (July 4, 2014, pp. 25A)*

Pub: American City Business Journals, Inc.

Contact: Mike Olivieri, Executive Vice President

Released: Weekly. **Price:** $4, introductory 4-week offer(Digital only). **Description:** Virtual currency bitcoin, which is an Internet protocol that defines a decentralized online payment system is discussed. A description of how bitcoin and other virtual currencies are used and concerns over its future use are examined. A short profile of Atlanta-based startup BitPay, which provides software solutions to help businesses accept bitcoin payments without risking operating cash flow is included. BitPay also enables rapid currency conversion through bitcoin ATMs or kiosks. **Availability:** Print; Online.

33737 ■ *"Startup Lucena Taking On Wall Street"* in *Atlanta Business Chronicle (May 23, 2014, pp. 1A)*

Pub: American City Business Journals, Inc.

Contact: Mike Olivieri, Executive Vice President

Description: Lucena Research is a predictive analytics startup firm developing software for the financial investment sector. The company's software helps investment professionals identify trading strategies and investing trends to reduce risk and increase returns. **Availability:** Print; Online.

ASSOCIATIONS AND OTHER ORGANIZATIONS

33738 ■ **Business Software Alliance (BSA)**
200 Massachusetts Ave., NW
  Ste. 310
  Washington, DC 20001
Ph: (202)872-5500
Fax: (202)872-5501
Co. E-mail: info@bsa.org
URL: http://www.bsa.org
Contact: Victoria A. Espinel, President
Facebook: www.facebook.com/BSATheSof
  twareAlliance
Linkedin: www.linkedin.com/company/bsa-the-sof
  tware-alliance
X (Twitter): x.com/BSAnews
YouTube: www.youtube.com/user/BusinessSftAlli-
  ance

Description: Computer software publishers. Promotes the free world trade of business software by combating international software piracy, advancing intellectual property protection, and increasing market access. **Founded:** 1988. **Publications:** *Guide to Software Management* (Annual); *Software Review* (Quarterly). **Geographic Preference:** National.

EDUCATIONAL PROGRAMS

33739 ■ **Accessible Web Design: Complying with Section 508**
URL(s): www.eeicom.com

Description: Covers what the law is and whom it applies, using HTML and CSS coding techniques to meet the guidelines, creating fluid design that adapts to user needs, using free validation to check site for accessibility, and putting the compliance icon on completed site. **Audience:** Industry professionals. **Principal Exhibits:** Covers what the law is and whom it applies, using HTML and CSS coding techniques to meet the guidelines, creating fluid design that adapts to user needs, using free validation to check site for accessibility, and putting the compliance icon on completed site.

33740 ■ **Adobe Acrobat II (Onsite)**
URL(s): www.eeicom.com

Description: Seminar that covers the advanced features of Adobe Acrobat, focusing on making documents accessible and flexible, incorporating digital signatures and security settings, creating and modifying PDF forms and multimedia presentations, using the engineering and technical features, and using Adobe Acrobat for professional publishing. **Audience:** Industry professionals. **Principal Exhibits:** Seminar that covers the advanced features of Adobe Acrobat, focusing on making documents accessible and flexible, incorporating digital signatures and security settings, creating and modifying PDF forms and multimedia presentations, using the engineering and technical features, and using Adobe Acrobat for professional publishing.

33741 ■ **Adobe Acrobat Section 508 Accessibility (Onsite)**
URL(s): www.eeicom.com

Description: Covers the regulations by the Federal Government's Section 508 accessibility and the features of Adobe Acrobat software designed to meet the regulations, including definition of accessibility, authoring for accessibility, working with existing PDF files, forms, and scanned documents, using the accessibility checker, and tags palette, and testing your PDF files for accessibility. **Audience:** Industry professionals. **Principal Exhibits:** Covers the regulations by the Federal Government's Section 508 accessibility and the features of Adobe Acrobat software designed to meet the regulations, including definition of accessibility, authoring for accessibility, working with existing PDF files, forms, and scanned documents, using the accessibility checker, and tags palette, and testing your PDF files for accessibility.

33742 ■ **Adobe Bridge**
URL(s): www.eeicom.com

Description: Learn the many useful features hidden in Adobe Bridge, the command central for your Creative Suite 4 software, include the settings that help you get the most out of workflow. **Audience:** General public, professionals. **Principal Exhibits:** Learn the many useful features hidden in Adobe Bridge, the command central for your Creative Suite 4 software, include the settings that help you get the most out of workflow.

33743 ■ **Adobe ColdFusion II (Onsite)**
URL(s): www.eeicom.com

Description: Seminar that covers advanced programming techniques, including complex programming concepts such as arrays and loops, deploy application-level security, read information from and write information to text files on server, use the Verify search engine, schedule templates to run on a recurring basis, perform multiple queries as a transaction, and build intelligent "agents" for the Web. **Audience:** Graphic artists, and professionals. **Principal Exhibits:** Seminar that covers advanced programming techniques, including complex programming concepts such as arrays and loops, deploy application-level security, read information from and write information to text files on server, use the Verify search engine, schedule templates to run on a recurring basis, perform multiple queries as a transaction, and build intelligent "agents" for the Web.

33744 ■ **Adobe Creative Suite 5 Bootcamp Training (Onsite)**
URL(s): www.eeicom.com

Description: Covers the interoperability and productively possible between Adobe Photoshop, Illustrator, InDesign, and Acrobat PDF. **Audience:** Industry professionals. **Principal Exhibits:** Covers the interoperability and productively possible between Adobe Photoshop, Illustrator, InDesign, and Acrobat PDF.

33745 ■ **Adobe Fireworks II**
URL(s): www.eeicom.com

Description: Covers Web page designs, including masks to create photomontages, create vector graphics, slicing advanced page designs, generate HTML and JavaScript code, swap images, and create pop-up images. **Audience:** Industry professionals. **Principal Exhibits:** Covers Web page designs, including masks to create photomontages, create vector graphics, slicing advanced page designs, generate HTML and JavaScript code, swap images, and create pop-up images.

33746 ■ Adobe Flash Media Server
URL(s): www.eeicom.com/eei-training-services
Description: Provides experienced Flash developers with the knowledge and hands-on experience they need to build and deliver Streaming and Social Media applications with Flash Media Server 3, with focus on Server Side ActionScript, ActionScript 3 and Flash skills required to build real-world media applications with audio, video, and data that interact with the user. **Audience:** Industry professionals. **Principal Exhibits:** Provides experienced Flash developers with the knowledge and hands-on experience they need to build and deliver Streaming and Social Media applications with Flash Media Server 3, with focus on Server Side ActionScript, ActionScript 3 and Flash skills required to build real-world media applications with audio, video, and data that interact with the user.

33747 ■ Adobe FrameMaker I (Onsite)
URL(s): www.eeicom.com
Description: Learn how to design FrameMaker publication in its entirety, as well as work on a variety of FrameMaker documents. Some topics include understanding FrameMaker interface and screen elements, using paragraph designer to control paragraph formatting, working with character designer, adding color to character and paragraph formats, working with master pages and anchored frames, creating running headers and footers, creating and editing variables and working with table designer and customizing tables. **Audience:** Professionals, students. **Principal Exhibits:** Learn how to design FrameMaker publication in its entirety, as well as work on a variety of FrameMaker documents. Some topics include understanding FrameMaker interface and screen elements, using paragraph designer to control paragraph formatting, working with character designer, adding color to character and paragraph formats, working with master pages and anchored frames, creating running headers and footers, creating and editing variables and working with table designer and customizing tables.

33748 ■ Adobe FrameMaker III: Structured
URL(s): www.eeicom.com
Description: Seminar using Adobe FrameMaker as an authoring tool for creating XML documents, including structured interface and add and edit elements and attributes, documents with structured content EDD (Element Definition Document) and DTD (Document Type Definitions), converting unstructured documents, and the latest tools available for cross-media publishing. **Audience:** Professionals and general public. **Principal Exhibits:** Seminar using Adobe FrameMaker as an authoring tool for creating XML documents, including structured interface and add and edit elements and attributes, documents with structured content EDD (Element Definition Document) and DTD (Document Type Definitions), converting unstructured documents, and the latest tools available for cross-media publishing.

33749 ■ Adobe InDesign CS4 Master Class for Designers Training (Onsite)
URL(s): www.eeicom.com
Description: Master Adobe InDesign CS4's styles, text processing capabilities, table-creation tools, automation features, and in-document creativity enhancements to free up countless hours from smaller tasks and concentrate on designing. **Audience:** Designers. **Principal Exhibits:** Master Adobe InDesign CS4's styles, text processing capabilities, table-creation tools, automation features, and in-document creativity enhancements to free up countless hours from smaller tasks and concentrate on designing.

33750 ■ Adobe InDesign III (Onsite)
URL(s): www.eeicom.com
Description: 2-day seminar that explores the advanced features within Adobe InDesign, including transparency features, feathering, and drop shadows, hyperlinks for PDF or DHTML, create a book list,

formatting an index, generate a table of contents, advanced frame techniques and color management, and XML and other cross-media publishing support. **Audience:** Graphic artists and graphic professionals. **Principal Exhibits:** 2-day seminar that explores the advanced features within Adobe InDesign, including transparency features, feathering, and drop shadows, hyperlinks for PDF or DHTML, create a book list, formatting an index, generate a table of contents, advanced frame techniques and color management, and XML and other cross-media publishing support.

33751 ■ Adobe InDesign with InCopy for Workgroups Training (Onsite)
URL(s): www.eeicom.com
Description: Learn a professional writing and editing program that tightly integrates with Adobe InDesign for a complete solution, including assigning editors to work on parts of pages, spreads, or entire documents in parallel with designers, significantly decreasing the production time for projects. **Audience:** Industry professionals. **Principal Exhibits:** Learn a professional writing and editing program that tightly integrates with Adobe InDesign for a complete solution, including assigning editors to work on parts of pages, spreads, or entire documents in parallel with designers, significantly decreasing the production time for projects.

33752 ■ Adobe InDesign for Long Documents I (Onsite)
URL(s): www.eeicom.com
Description: Learn to publish long documents, such as books or annual reports. Also, explore Adobe InDesign CS4 options in numbering, position figures in relation to text automatically, create running headers or footers, and much more. **Audience:** Industry professionals, general public. **Principal Exhibits:** Learn to publish long documents, such as books or annual reports. Also, explore Adobe InDesign CS4 options in numbering, position figures in relation to text automatically, create running headers or footers, and much more.

33753 ■ Adobe InDesign for Long Documents II (Onsite)
URL(s): www.eeicom.com
Description: Learn all you need to know to work effectively with InDesign CS4, including advanced features. **Audience:** Industry professionals, general public. **Principal Exhibits:** Learn all you need to know to work effectively with InDesign CS4, including advanced features.

33754 ■ Adobe InDesign for Long Documents III (Onsite)
URL(s): www.eeicom.com
Description: Learn to fully exploit all the advanced featured of InDesign CS4 as your integrated workflow and publishing environment. **Audience:** Industry professionals, IT. **Principal Exhibits:** Learn to fully exploit all the advanced featured of InDesign CS4 as your integrated workflow and publishing environment.

33755 ■ Adobe Lightroom Photo Workflow
URL(s): www.eeicom.com
Description: Covers importing and arranging photos, quick edits, developing modules' array of image correction controls, tone curves, black and white conversions, working with Photoshop, slideshow's customizable features, exporting images, and print controls and custom print layouts. **Audience:** Industry professionals. **Principal Exhibits:** Covers importing and arranging photos, quick edits, developing modules' array of image correction controls, tone curves, black and white conversions, working with Photoshop, slideshow's customizable features, exporting images, and print controls and custom print layouts.

33756 ■ Adobe Photoshop for Beginners (Onsite)
Seminar Information Service Inc. (SIS)
  250 El Camino Real., Ste. 112
  Tustin, CA 92780
Ph: (714)508-0340
Free: 877-736-4636
Fax: (714)734-8027

Co. E-mail: info@seminarinformation.com
URL: http://www.seminarinformation.com
Contact: Catherine Bellizzi, President
URL(s): www.seminarinformation.com
Description: Learn how to manipulate images, retouch photos, and cut down time through the entire design process. **Audience:** Those new to photoshop. **Principal Exhibits:** Learn how to manipulate images, retouch photos, and cut down time through the entire design process.

33757 ■ Adobe Photoshop Channels and Masks (Onsite)
URL(s): www.eeicom.com
Description: Learn how to make masks using channels in Adobe Photoshop CS3 to create high quality and accurate selections like the professionals do. **Audience:** Professionals, and general public. **Principal Exhibits:** Learn how to make masks using channels in Adobe Photoshop CS3 to create high quality and accurate selections like the professionals do.

33758 ■ Adobe Photoshop Digital Mastery I (Onsite)
URL(s): www.eeicom.com
Description: Covers techniques for photo recovery, image enhancements, and professional portrait work. **Audience:** Industry professionals. **Principal Exhibits:** Covers techniques for photo recovery, image enhancements, and professional portrait work.

33759 ■ Adobe Photoshop Digital Painting (Onsite)
URL(s): www.eeicom.com
Description: Learn digital painting techniques from adding colors and effects to line art to creating full-on digital paintings in various artistic styles, including watercolor and oil. **Audience:** Professional digital artists, general public. **Principal Exhibits:** Learn digital painting techniques from adding colors and effects to line art to creating full-on digital paintings in various artistic styles, including watercolor and oil.

33760 ■ Adobe Photoshop Extended
URL(s): www.eeicom.com
Description: Covers 3D compositing and texture editing, enhanced vanishing point with 3D support, movie paint, the new animation palette, importing and playing video in Photoshop, video layers, using 2D and 3D measurement tools, scale marker, count tool and combining image stacks. **Audience:** Professionals, and general public. **Principal Exhibits:** Covers 3D compositing and texture editing, enhanced vanishing point with 3D support, movie paint, the new animation palette, importing and playing video in Photoshop, video layers, using 2D and 3D measurement tools, scale marker, count tool and combining image stacks.

33761 ■ Advanced Training for Microsoft Excel (Onsite)
National Seminars Training L.L.C. (NST)
  14502 W 105th St.
  Lenexa, KS 66215
Free: 800-349-1935
Co. E-mail: info@findaseminar.com
URL: http://www.findaseminar.com/tpd/Padge
  tt-Thompson-Seminars.asp
URL(s): findaseminar.com/event1.asp?eventID=10
497
Description: An intensive one-day seminar that teaches the most advanced features of Microsoft Excel. **Audience:** Excel users, and professionals. **Principal Exhibits:** An intensive one-day seminar that teaches the most advanced features of Microsoft Excel.

33762 ■ AJAX Development I (Onsite)
URL(s): www.eeicom.com
Description: Learn how to make dynamic and interactive Web applications using Asynchronous JavaScript and XML (AJAX), including a review of the essential elements of XHTML, CSS, and XML. **Audience:** Industry professionals, IT. **Principal Exhibits:** Learn how to make dynamic and interac-

tive Web applications using Asynchronous JavaScript and XML (AJAX), including a review of the essential elements of XHTML, CSS, and XML.

33763 ■ AJAX Development II (Onsite)
URL(s): www.eeicom.com

Description: In this advanced class explore AJAX in greater depth through topics that include addressing security concerns inherent to AJAX, using XPath and XSLT in your AJAX development, validating form data, managing user sessions, and explore the available AJAX frameworks. **Audience:** Industry professionals, IT. **Principal Exhibits:** In this advanced class explore AJAX in greater depth through topics that include addressing security concerns inherent to AJAX, using XPath and XSLT in your AJAX development, validating form data, managing user sessions, and explore the available AJAX frameworks.

33764 ■ Auditing Business Application Systems (Onsite)
Seminar Information Service Inc. (SIS)
　250 El Camino Real., Ste. 112
　Tustin, CA 92780
Ph: (714)508-0340
Free: 877-736-4636
Fax: (714)734-8027
Co. E-mail: info@seminarinformation.com
URL: http://www.seminarinformation.com
Contact: Catherine Bellizzi, President
URL(s): www.seminarinformation.com

Description: Three-day seminar attendees will learn how to audit and how to develop controls for complex automated applications which use online/real-time, distributed processing, and/or database technologies, including an opportunity to actually prepare an audit plan for a complex application system. **Audience:** Information technology, financial, operations, and business applications auditors and audit managers . **Principal Exhibits:** Three-day seminar attendees will learn how to audit and how to develop controls for complex automated applications which use online/real-time, distributed processing, and/or database technologies, including an opportunity to actually prepare an audit plan for a complex application system.

33765 ■ Business Analysis Essentials (Onsite)
Seminar Information Service Inc. (SIS)
　250 El Camino Real., Ste. 112
　Tustin, CA 92780
Ph: (714)508-0340
Free: 877-736-4636
Fax: (714)734-8027
Co. E-mail: info@seminarinformation.com
URL: http://www.seminarinformation.com
Contact: Catherine Bellizzi, President
URL(s): www.seminarinformation.com/qqbuxn/business-analysis-essentials

Description: Learn to define the scope of work and master requirements-gathering techniques that will work for a variety of projects and audiences. **Audience:** Systems analysts, business analysts, requirements analysts, developers, software engineers, IT project managers, project managers, project analysts, project leaders, senior project managers, team leaders, program managers. **Principal Exhibits:** Learn to define the scope of work and master requirements-gathering techniques that will work for a variety of projects and audiences.

33766 ■ C Programming: Hands-On (Onsite)
Seminar Information Service Inc. (SIS)
　250 El Camino Real., Ste. 112
　Tustin, CA 92780
Ph: (714)508-0340
Free: 877-736-4636
Fax: (714)734-8027
Co. E-mail: info@seminarinformation.com
URL: http://www.seminarinformation.com
Contact: Catherine Bellizzi, President
URL(s): www.seminarinformation.com/qqbtkn/c-programming-hands-on

Description: Learn how to create, compile and run C programs using Visual Studio 2005; write and understand C language constructs, syntax and

classes; leverage the architecture and namespaces of the .NET Framework library; manage the common language infrastructure (CLI) to integrate C with Visual Basic 2005 and C; develop .NET components in C for desktop and distributed multi-tier applications. **Audience:** C programmers, developers and engineers. **Principal Exhibits:** Learn how to create, compile and run C programs using Visual Studio 2005; write and understand C language constructs, syntax and classes; leverage the architecture and namespaces of the .NET Framework library; manage the common language infrastructure (CLI) to integrate C with Visual Basic 2005 and C; develop .NET components in C for desktop and distributed multi-tier applications.

33767 ■ Cascading Style Sheets II
URL(s): www.eeicom.com

Description: Covers the conversion of an HTML Web site to a site that uses Cascading Style Sheets, including text enhancements, link color control, table conversion to precise positioning, layering with text and graphics, DHTML effects, a watermark background image, and validation CSS code. **Audience:** Industry professionals. **Principal Exhibits:** Covers the conversion of an HTML Web site to a site that uses Cascading Style Sheets, including text enhancements, link color control, table conversion to precise positioning, layering with text and graphics, DHTML effects, a watermark background image, and validation CSS code.

33768 ■ Deploying Microsoft Windows Vista Business Desktops (Onsite)
Seminar Information Service Inc. (SIS)
　250 El Camino Real., Ste. 112
　Tustin, CA 92780
Ph: (714)508-0340
Free: 877-736-4636
Fax: (714)734-8027
Co. E-mail: info@seminarinformation.com
URL: http://www.seminarinformation.com
Contact: Catherine Bellizzi, President
URL(s): www.seminarinformation.com

Description: Three-day training to get the knowledge and skills you needed to successfully deploy Windows Vista business desktops throughout your organization. **Audience:** IT professionals, business industry professionals. **Principal Exhibits:** Three-day training to get the knowledge and skills you needed to successfully deploy Windows Vista business desktops throughout your organization.

33769 ■ Designing and Building Great Web Pages: Hands-On (Onsite)
Seminar Information Service Inc. (SIS)
　250 El Camino Real., Ste. 112
　Tustin, CA 92780
Ph: (714)508-0340
Free: 877-736-4636
Fax: (714)734-8027
Co. E-mail: info@seminarinformation.com
URL: http://www.seminarinformation.com
Contact: Catherine Bellizzi, President
URL(s): www.seminarinformation.com

Description: Learn to build powerful Web content that effectively conveys your message; Create graphical content using Photoshop CS2, Fireworks 8 and Flash 8; Develop Web page content with FrontPage and Dreamweaver 8; Generate complex Web pages using Cascading Style Sheets, tables and layers; and Enhance Web pages with special effects and DHTML. **Audience:** IT professionals, designing and building web industry professionals. **Principal Exhibits:** Learn to build powerful Web content that effectively conveys your message; Create graphical content using Photoshop CS2, Fireworks 8 and Flash 8; Develop Web page content with FrontPage and Dreamweaver 8; Generate complex Web pages using Cascading Style Sheets, tables and layers; and Enhance Web pages with special effects and DHTML.

33770 ■ Developing Effective Software Estimation Techniques (Onsite)
Seminar Information Service Inc. (SIS)
　250 El Camino Real., Ste. 112
　Tustin, CA 92780

Ph: (714)508-0340
Free: 877-736-4636
Fax: (714)734-8027
Co. E-mail: info@seminarinformation.com
URL: http://www.seminarinformation.com
Contact: Catherine Bellizzi, President
URL(s): www.seminarinformation.com

Description: Learn how to prepare a software project estimate through an iterative process; Develop an initial estimate using the expert judgment method; Apply historical data for greater precision in an estimate; Refine the size or scope estimate using a component-based method; Perform Function Point calculations to determine the magnitude of a project; Translate a size or scope estimate into a time, schedule and cost estimate. **Audience:** Industry professionals, IT. **Principal Exhibits:** Learn how to prepare a software project estimate through an iterative process; Develop an initial estimate using the expert judgment method; Apply historical data for greater precision in an estimate; Refine the size or scope estimate using a component-based method; Perform Function Point calculations to determine the magnitude of a project; Translate a size or scope estimate into a time, schedule and cost estimate.

33771 ■ Developing SQL Queries for SQL Server: Hands-On (Onsite)
Seminar Information Service Inc. (SIS)
　250 El Camino Real., Ste. 112
　Tustin, CA 92780
Ph: (714)508-0340
Free: 877-736-4636
Fax: (714)734-8027
Co. E-mail: info@seminarinformation.com
URL: http://www.seminarinformation.com
Contact: Catherine Bellizzi, President
URL(s): www.seminarinformation.com/qqbtlv/developing-sql-queries-for-sql-server-hands-on

Description: Learn how to develop complex and robust SQL queries for SQL Server 2005 and SQL Server 2000; Query multiple tables with inner joins, outer joins and self joins; Transform data with built-in functions; Summarize data using aggregation and grouping; Execute analytic functions to calculate ranks; Build simple and correlated sub-queries. **Audience:** Those who are developing systems using SQL Server databases, or who are using SQL to extract and analyze data from SQL Server databases. **Principal Exhibits:** Learn how to develop complex and robust SQL queries for SQL Server 2005 and SQL Server 2000; Query multiple tables with inner joins, outer joins and self joins; Transform data with built-in functions; Summarize data using aggregation and grouping; Execute analytic functions to calculate ranks; Build simple and correlated sub-queries.

33772 ■ Digital Scanning for Production
URL(s): www.eeicom.com

Description: Seminar designed for those using any digital purpose, including direct reproduction or inclusion in page layout programs. **Audience:** Industry professionals. **Principal Exhibits:** Seminar designed for those using any digital purpose, including direct reproduction or inclusion in page layout programs.

33773 ■ Dynamic Web Development I
URL(s): www.eeicom.com

Description: Those already familiar with HTML and how to do some programming will learn to write high-performance Web applications with Microsoft's ASP.NET. Topics include Web forms, controls (HTML, server, Web), ASP.NET application state management, and error handling. **Audience:** Professionals. **Principal Exhibits:** Those already familiar with HTML and how to do some programming will learn to write high-performance Web applications with Microsoft's ASP.NET. Topics include Web forms, controls (HTML, server, Web), ASP.NET application state management, and error handling.

33774 ■ Dynamic Web Development II
URL(s): www.eeicom.com

Description: Explore data binding, data controls and templates, consuming and manipulating data, and creating and managing .NET components and assemblies. **Audience:** Professionals, students. **Princi-**

pal Exhibits: Explore data binding, data controls and templates, consuming and manipulating data, and creating and managing .NET components and assemblies.

33775 ■ EEI Communications Adobe Acrobat 9 for Legal Professionals

URL(s): www.eeicom.com

Description: Designed for lawyers and paralegals who need to incorporate specific legal procedures into their document workflow, including Redaction and Bates numbering. **Audience:** Legal professionals, IT. **Principal Exhibits:** Designed for lawyers and paralegals who need to incorporate specific legal procedures into their document workflow, including Redaction and Bates numbering.

33776 ■ EEI Communications Adobe After Effects II (Onsite)

URL(s): www.eeicom.com

Description: Seminar that builds on the foundation of After Effects I that covers the techniques that production environments use and learn to reverse-engineer popular effects seen on TV, including working with Rotoscoping techniques, keying and mattes, motion matching and video stabilization, 3D layers, cameras, and lights, titling effects and filters, altering time and displacement, and rendering the movies and batching. **Audience:** Adobe After Effects users and industry professionals. **Principal Exhibits:** Seminar that builds on the foundation of After Effects I that covers the techniques that production environments use and learn to reverse-engineer popular effects seen on TV, including working with Rotoscoping techniques, keying and mattes, motion matching and video stabilization, 3D layers, cameras, and lights, titling effects and filters, altering time and displacement, and rendering the movies and batching. **Telecommunication Services:** info@eeicom.com.

33777 ■ EEI Communications Adobe Captivate 3

URL(s): www.eeicom.com

Description: Seminar that teaches how to create professional quality, interactive simulations and software demonstrations without any programming or multimedia knowledge, including basics, captions and timelines, images, pointer paths, buttons, and highlight boxes, movies, rollover captions and rollover images, slide labels and notes, audio, animation, and question slides. **Audience:** Industry professionals. **Principal Exhibits:** Seminar that teaches how to create professional quality, interactive simulations and software demonstrations without any programming or multimedia knowledge, including basics, captions and timelines, images, pointer paths, buttons, and highlight boxes, movies, rollover captions and rollover images, slide labels and notes, audio, animation, and question slides.

33778 ■ EEI Communications Adobe Flash III (Onsite)

URL(s): www.eeicom.com

Description: Covers project creation from planning and development, working with XML, advanced animation and interaction concepts and sound applications, and integrating video with Flash. **Audience:** Adobe flash users and industry professionals. **Principal Exhibits:** Covers project creation from planning and development, working with XML, advanced animation and interaction concepts and sound applications, and integrating video with Flash. **Telecommunication Services:** info@eeicom.com.

33779 ■ EEI Communications Adobe Flex I - Developing Rich Internet Client Applications

URL(s): www.eeicom.com

Description: Introduction to the Flex technology teaches how to develop fully functional, well architected front end for a Rich Internet Application (RIA). **Audience:** Students, and industry professionals. **Principal Exhibits:** Introduction to the Flex technology teaches how to develop fully functional, well architected front end for a Rich Internet Application (RIA).

33780 ■ EEI Communications Adobe Flex II - Data and Communications

URL(s): www.eeicom.com

Description: Learn how your Flex applications exchange data and communicate with remote objects in this hands-on course. **Audience:** Industry professionals, public. **Principal Exhibits:** Learn how your Flex applications exchange data and communicate with remote objects in this hands-on course.

33781 ■ EEI Communications Adobe Flex III - Building Dashboard Applications

URL(s): www.eeicom.com

Description: Learn how to build dashboard applications using Adobe Flex 3 to create highly interactive charts and graphs for data visualization, including creating interactive charts and dynamically controlling the chart data. **Audience:** Industry professionals, public. **Principal Exhibits:** Learn how to build dashboard applications using Adobe Flex 3 to create highly interactive charts and graphs for data visualization, including creating interactive charts and dynamically controlling the chart data.

33782 ■ EEI Communications Apple DVD Studio Pro I (Onsite)

URL(s): www.eeicom.com

Description: Seminar that covers creating menus within DVD Studio Pro, creating slide shows, adding subtitles and closed captioning, multiple language/audio streams, DVD-ROM content and Internet access, options to encode high quality video, creating and working with buttons, overlays, markers, and stories, basic scripting, advanced menu design, working with and creating transitions, using alternate and mixed angles, and Dolby, surround, and PCM audio encoding. **Audience:** Industry professionals. **Principal Exhibits:** Seminar that covers creating menus within DVD Studio Pro, creating slide shows, adding subtitles and closed captioning, multiple language/audio streams, DVD-ROM content and Internet access, options to encode high quality video, creating and working with buttons, overlays, markers, and stories, basic scripting, advanced menu design, working with and creating transitions, using alternate and mixed angles, and Dolby, surround, and PCM audio encoding.

33783 ■ EEI Communications Apple Final Cut Pro Bootcamp (Onsite)

URL(s): www.eeicom.com

Description: Course includes an introduction to Final Cut Pro Interface, basic video editing, importing and exporting video footage, introduction to Soundtrack Pro Interface, basic audio editing, post-production techniques with video, introduction to DVD Studio Pro, introduction to motion, post-production techniques with video, introduction to DVD Studio Pro, and authoring DVDs to your own specifications. **Audience:** Industry professionals, public. **Principal Exhibits:** Course includes an introduction to Final Cut Pro Interface, basic video editing, importing and exporting video footage, introduction to Soundtrack Pro Interface, basic audio editing, post-production techniques with video, introduction to DVD Studio Pro, introduction to motion, post-production techniques with video, introduction to DVD Studio Pro, and authoring DVDs to your own specifications.

33784 ■ EEI Communications Apple Final Cut Pro I (Onsite)

URL(s): www.eeicom.com

Description: Seminar that covers editing using Apple, including working with interface, video standard and HD basics, marking and editing, timeline control, single- and double-sided trimming, master clips, subclips and working with markers, capturing video, importing and exporting assets, working with audio and mixing audio tracks, applying transitions, adding and working with filters, build a composite image, change clip speeds, create motion effects, adding text and graphics, working with and creating animated titles, and finishing and outputting. **Audience:** Industry professionals. **Principal Exhibits:** Seminar that covers editing using Apple, including working with interface, video standard and HD basics,

marking and editing, timeline control, single- and double-sided trimming, master clips, subclips and working with markers, capturing video, importing and exporting assets, working with audio and mixing audio tracks, applying transitions, adding and working with filters, build a composite image, change clip speeds, create motion effects, adding text and graphics, working with and creating animated titles, and finishing and outputting. **Telecommunication Services:** info@eeicom.com.

33785 ■ EEI Communications Apple Final Cut Pro II (Onsite)

URL(s): www.eeicom.com

Description: Learn all you need to know to create your video from concept to completion, including working with the interface, video standard and HD basics, timeline control, single- and double-sided trimming, capturing video and much more. **Audience:** Industry professionals, public. **Principal Exhibits:** Learn all you need to know to create your video from concept to completion, including working with the interface, video standard and HD basics, timeline control, single- and double-sided trimming, capturing video and much more.

33786 ■ EEI Communications Apple Motion I (Onsite)

URL(s): www.eeicom.com

Description: Covers real-time motion graphics, including using generators, working with layers and objects, use and create customized templates, particles and parameter behaviors, blend modes, nonlinear editing and motion, key-framing, audio and setting markers, and create text effects. **Audience:** Industry professionals. **Principal Exhibits:** Covers real-time motion graphics, including using generators, working with layers and objects, use and create customized templates, particles and parameter behaviors, blend modes, nonlinear editing and motion, key-framing, audio and setting markers, and create text effects. **Telecommunication Services:** info@eeicom.com.

33787 ■ EEI Communications ASP.NET with VB.NET and C I (Onsite)

URL(s): www.eeicom.com

Description: Learn to write dynamic, high-performance Web applications with Microsoft's ASP. NET. Topics include introduction of Web forms, controls (HTML, Server, Web), ASP.NET application state management, and error handling. **Audience:** Industry professionals, public. **Principal Exhibits:** Learn to write dynamic, high-performance Web applications with Microsoft's ASP.NET. Topics include introduction of Web forms, controls (HTML, Server, Web), ASP.NET application state management, and error handling.

33788 ■ EEI Communications ASP.NET with VB.NET and C II

URL(s): www.eeicom.com

Description: Hands-on class with those with knowledge of HTML and some programming who want to study data binding, data controls and templates, consuming and manipulating data, and creating and managing .NET components and assemblies. **Audience:** Industry professionals, public, IT. **Principal Exhibits:** Hands-on class with those with knowledge of HTML and some programming who want to study data binding, data controls and templates, consuming and manipulating data, and creating and managing .NET components and assemblies.

33789 ■ EEI Communications ASP.NET with VB.NET C III

URL(s): www.eeicom.com

Description: Hands-on class for those with the knowledge of HTML and some programming background who want to study Web services, localization, Web accessibility, testing and debugging a Web application, and configuring a Web application. **Audience:** Industry professionals, public, IT. **Principal Exhibits:** Hands-on class for those with the knowledge of HTML and some programming background who want to study Web services, localization, Web accessibility, testing and debugging a Web application, and configuring a Web application.

33790 ■ EEI Communications Digital Video Production for Streaming and DVD (Onsite)
URL(s): www.eeicom.com

Description: Seminar the teaches the process of producing video for distribution via the Web, CD, DVD and computer-based presentations, including writing, directing, shooting, recording, capture, edit, and encode/compress effective digital video for training, marketing, internal communications, public information, and other uses. Also, communicate effectively with internal clients/staff, video crews, and editing facilities. **Audience:** Video editors and enthusiasts. **Principal Exhibits:** Seminar the teaches the process of producing video for distribution via the Web, CD, DVD and computer-based presentations, including writing, directing, shooting, recording, capture, edit, and encode/compress effective digital video for training, marketing, internal communications, public information, and other uses. Also, communicate effectively with internal clients/staff, video crews, and editing facilities. **Telecommunication Services:** info@eeicom.com.

33791 ■ EEI Communications Enhanced and Video Podcasts (Onsite)
EEI Communications
66 Canal Center Plz., Ste. 200
Alexandria, VA 22314
Ph: (703)683-0683
Fax: (703)683-4915
Co. E-mail: info@eeicommunications.com
URL: http://eei-alex.com
URL(s): www.eeicom.com

Description: Course includes the pros and cons of enhanced podcasts and video podcasts, creating enhanced podcasts with GarageBand (Mac), creating enhanced podcasts on a PC, creating video podcasts with Final Cut Pro (Mac) with Adobe Audition (PC), Using QuickTime Pro (Mac/PC) in post-production, compression and other troubleshooting issues, keeping production values simple but professional, how to keep video podcasts, and quick, easy downloads. **Audience:** Industry professionals. **Principal Exhibits:** Course includes the pros and cons of enhanced podcasts and video podcasts, creating enhanced podcasts with GarageBand (Mac), creating enhanced podcasts on a PC, creating video podcasts with Final Cut Pro (Mac) with Adobe Audition (PC), Using Quick-Time Pro (Mac/PC) in post-production, compression and other troubleshooting issues, keeping production values simple but professional, how to keep video podcasts, and quick, easy downloads.

33792 ■ EEI Communications Professional Design Techniques with Adobe Creative Suite 4 (CS4)
URL(s): www.eeicom.com

Description: Covers design principles and workflow techniques in real-life projects, including the management of numerous parts, such as stories, data, charts, and images. **Audience:** Industry professionals, public. **Principal Exhibits:** Covers design principles and workflow techniques in real-life projects, including the management of numerous parts, such as stories, data, charts, and images.

33793 ■ EEI Communications Web Design with Adobe Dreamweaver and Photoshop (Onsite)
URL(s): www.eeicom.com

Description: Learn how to create attractive navigation elements and add texture and depth to your Web design, including how to create color palettes, and design clean and well-organized Web page layouts. **Audience:** Web designers. **Principal Exhibits:** Learn how to create attractive navigation elements and add texture and depth to your Web design, including how to create color palettes, and design clean and well-organized Web page layouts.

33794 ■ EEI Communications Writing for the Web II (Onsite)
URL(s): www.eeicom.com

Description: Seminar for persons with 3-5 years' experience as a Web writer or editor, or have completed Writing for the Web I, covering how to define your genre and audience, develop a structure for your Web content, working with subject matter experts who aren't writers, making the most of your writing project, giving and getting feedback, writing links that work for your client, how to write menus so clients can use them, and recasting a print article for the Web. **Audience:** Web writers and editors. **Principal Exhibits:** Seminar for persons with 3-5 years' experience as a Web writer or editor, or have completed Writing for the Web I, covering how to define your genre and audience, develop a structure for your Web content, working with subject matter experts who aren't writers, making the most of your writing project, giving and getting feedback, writing links that work for your client, how to write menus so clients can use them, and recasting a print article for the Web.

33795 ■ The Essentials Of Crystal Reports (Onsite)
Seminar Information Service Inc. (SIS)
250 El Camino Real., Ste. 112
Tustin, CA 92780
Ph: (714)508-0340
Free: 877-736-4636
Fax: (714)734-8027
Co. E-mail: info@seminarinformation.com
URL: http://www.seminarinformation.com
Contact: Catherine Bellizzi, President
URL(s): www.seminarinformation.com/details.cfm?qc
=qqbuqu

Description: Learn to create complex reports containing huge amounts of information to simple reports without being an expert in databases. **Audience:** Industry professionals. **Principal Exhibits:** Learn to create complex reports containing huge amounts of information to simple reports without being an expert in databases.

33796 ■ Forensic Photoshop (Onsite)
URL(s): www.eeicom.com

Description: Designed for law enforcement and Homeland Security personnel that outlines the processes for using Photoshop in a forensic environment. **Audience:** General public, professionals. **Principal Exhibits:** Designed for law enforcement and Homeland Security personnel that outlines the processes for using Photoshop in a forensic environment.

33797 ■ How to Manage an Information Security Program (Onsite)
Seminar Information Service Inc. (SIS)
250 El Camino Real., Ste. 112
Tustin, CA 92780
Ph: (714)508-0340
Free: 877-736-4636
Fax: (714)734-8027
Co. E-mail: info@seminarinformation.com
URL: http://www.seminarinformation.com
Contact: Catherine Bellizzi, President
URL(s): www.seminarinformation.com

Description: Learn the components of a comprehensive plan, covering access control software applications; telecom/network security measures; physical protection of the computer facility; and the legal and regulatory aspects of information security. **Audience:** Industry professionals, persons who mange information security program. **Principal Exhibits:** Learn the components of a comprehensive plan, covering access control software applications; telecom/network security measures; physical protection of the computer facility; and the legal and regulatory aspects of information security.

33798 ■ Introduction to ASP.NET 2.0 Applications
URL(s): www.eeicom.com

Description: Seminar designed for ASP.NET programmers, includes ASP.NET 2.0 applications, master pages, Web parts and personalized API, ADO. NET 2.0 and data-bound controls, membership and role management API, and Web form wizards. **Audience:** Industry professionals. **Principal Exhibits:** Seminar designed for ASP.NET programmers, includes ASP.NET 2.0 applications, master pages, Web parts and personalized API, ADO.NET 2.0 and data-bound controls, membership and role management API, and Web form wizards.

33799 ■ Introduction to .Net and ASP.NET
URL(s): www.eeicom.com

Description: Covers Microsoft.NET and ASP.NET Web pages in both Visual Basic.NET and C (pronounced C-sharp), including Microsoft.Net framework, common language run-time, base framework classes, ADO.NET, ASP.NET, .NET compact framework, XML Web services, and .NET languages. **Audience:** Industry professionals. **Principal Exhibits:** Covers Microsoft.NET and ASP.NET Web pages in both Visual Basic.NET and C (pronounced C-sharp), including Microsoft.Net framework, common language run-time, base framework classes, ADO.NET, ASP. NET, .NET compact framework, XML Web services, and .NET languages.

33800 ■ Introduction to PHP and MySQL
URL(s): www.eeicom.com

Description: Seminar that covers an open-source scripting language for developing database-driven Web sites, including how to download and install PHP on Web server, using PHP to respond to HTML form submissions, sending e-mail messages with PHP, SQL and querying databases with PHP, and managing state information with cookies and sessions. **Audience:** Industry professionals, and general public. **Principal Exhibits:** Seminar that covers an open-source scripting language for developing database-driven Web sites, including how to download and install PHP on Web server, using PHP to respond to HTML form submissions, sending e-mail messages with PHP, SQL and querying databases with PHP, and managing state information with cookies and sessions.

33801 ■ Layout Software Basics (Onsite)
URL(s): www.eeicom.com

Description: Seminar that provides an introduction to publishing and graphics software, including a step-by-step introduction through the terms and tools of applications used by graphic designers, illustrators, photographers, and editors. **Audience:** Industry professionals. **Principal Exhibits:** Seminar that provides an introduction to publishing and graphics software, including a step-by-step introduction through the terms and tools of applications used by graphic designers, illustrators, photographers, and editors.

33802 ■ Mastering Microsoft Excel
Fred Pryor Seminars & CareerTrack
5700 Broadmoor, Ste. 300
Mission, KS 66202
Free: 800-780-8476
Fax: (913)967-8849
Co. E-mail: customerservice@pryor.com
URL: http://www.pryor.com
Contact: Janet Turner, Contact
E-mail: dmca@pryor.com
URL(s): www.pryor.com/training-seminars/mastering
-microsoft-excel

Frequency: Irregular. **Description:** Seminar designed to deliver the most information in the least amount of time, including how to create spreadsheets, input data, perform mathematical calculations, develop workbooks, edit cells, and use formulas, functions, Wizards, and more. **Audience:** Professionals. **Principal Exhibits:** Seminar designed to deliver the most information in the least amount of time, including how to create spreadsheets, input data, perform mathematical calculations, develop workbooks, edit cells, and use formulas, functions, Wizards, and more.

33803 ■ Microsoft Access: A 2-Day Hands-On Workshop
Fred Pryor Seminars & CareerTrack
5700 Broadmoor, Ste. 300
Mission, KS 66202
Free: 800-780-8476
Fax: (913)967-8849

Co. E-mail: customerservice@pryor.com
URL: http://www.pryor.com
Contact: Janet Turner, Contact
E-mail: dmca@pryor.com
URL(s): www.pryor.com/training-seminars/microsof
t-access-basics

Frequency: Irregular. **Description:** Learn how to use features, how to solve problems, and customize Access for the way you work. **Audience:** Access beginners. **Principal Exhibits:** Learn how to use features, how to solve problems, and customize Access for the way you work.

33804 ■ Microsoft Excel

National Seminars Training L.L.C. (NST)
14502 W 105th St.
Lenexa, KS 66215
Free: 800-349-1935
Co. E-mail: info@findaseminar.com
URL: http://www.findaseminar.com/tpd/Padge
tt-Thompson-Seminars.asp
URL(s): www.findaseminar.com/excel-seminar.html

Description: One-day workshop covering ways to get the most out of Excel's features and functions. **Audience:** Industry professionals. **Principal Exhibits:** One-day workshop covering ways to get the most out of Excel's features and functions.

33805 ■ Microsoft Excel 2007 - II (Onsite)

URL(s): www.eeicom.com

Description: Seminar covering the advanced features of Excel, including advanced formulas, Pivot-Tables, and analysis tools, including customizing workbook and toolbars, working with multiple data sources, edit macros, test data, and protect worksheets. **Audience:** General public. **Principal Exhibits:** Seminar covering the advanced features of Excel, including advanced formulas, PivotTables, and analysis tools, including customizing workbook and toolbars, working with multiple data sources, edit macros, test data, and protect worksheets.

33806 ■ Microsoft PowerPoint 2007/2010

Fred Pryor Seminars & CareerTrack
5700 Broadmoor, Ste. 300
Mission, KS 66202
Free: 800-780-8476
Fax: (913)967-8849
Co. E-mail: customerservice@pryor.com
URL: http://www.pryor.com
Contact: Janet Turner, Contact
E-mail: dmca@pryor.com
URL(s): www.pryor.com/training-seminars/microsof
t-powerpoint

Frequency: Irregular. **Description:** Learn to put together well constructed, engaging and entertaining, pleasing to the eye, properly paced, and unmistakable clear in message presentations. **Audience:** Business professionals. **Principal Exhibits:** Learn to put together well constructed, engaging and entertaining, pleasing to the eye, properly paced, and unmistakable clear in message presentations.

33807 ■ Microsoft Project 2007 - II (Onsite)

URL(s): www.eeicom.com

Description: Seminar that covers workload adjustments and developing tracking skills to ensure a successful project completion, including fine-tuning task, resource, and assignment information, reorganizing phases and tasks, analyzing the critical path, leveling over-allocated resources, documenting resource details with reports, create consumption rates, track project progress, create an interim plan, and documenting the project's progress with reports. **Audience:** Industry professionals. **Principal Exhibits:** Seminar that covers workload adjustments and developing tracking skills to ensure a successful project completion, including fine-tuning task, resource, and assignment information, reorganizing phases and tasks, analyzing the critical path, leveling over-allocated resources, documenting resource details with reports, create consumption rates, track project progress, create an interim plan, and documenting the project's progress with reports.

33808 ■ Microsoft SharePoint I - Using SharePoint (Onsite)

URL(s): www.eeicom.com

Description: Learn practical hands-on exercise techniques for using the document and project collaboration tools in Windows SharePoint Services. **Audience:** General public, professionals. **Principal Exhibits:** Learn practical hands-on exercise techniques for using the document and project collaboration tools in Windows SharePoint Services.

33809 ■ Microsoft SharePoint II - Building SharePoint Sites (Onsite)

URL(s): www.eeicom.com

Description: Hands-on class you will learn the skills to design, maintain, and publish a custom SharePoint site. **Audience:** General public, professionals. **Principal Exhibits:** Hands-on class you will learn the skills to design, maintain, and publish a custom SharePoint site.

33810 ■ Microsoft SharePoint III - Installing and Working With SharePoint Server (Onsite)

URL(s): www.eeicom.com

Description: Hands-on class you learn how to create and make modifications that can be applied to all users on the site or to individual users using Microsoft SharePoint controls. **Audience:** General public, and professionals. **Principal Exhibits:** Hands-on class you learn how to create and make modifications that can be applied to all users on the site or to individual users using Microsoft SharePoint controls.

33811 ■ Migrating to Structured Authoring in Adobe Framemaker (Onsite)

URL(s): www.eeicom.com

Description: Learn to work with structured interface view, element catalogs, an understanding of elements and their attributes, edit structured documents, change, merge, split and wrapping of elements, working with paragraph, character, graphic, and table elements, validating documents, adding and editing element definitions, setting up elements with automatic insertion of children, and convert unstructured to structured documents. **Audience:** Professionals. **Principal Exhibits:** Learn to work with structured interface view, element catalogs, an understanding of elements and their attributes, edit structured documents, change, merge, split and wrapping of elements, working with paragraph, character, graphic, and table elements, validating documents, adding and editing element definitions, setting up elements with automatic insertion of children, and convert unstructured to structured documents.

33812 ■ Object-Oriented Programming (OOP) Boot Camp

URL(s): www.eeicom.com

Description: Seminar that teaches what it means to give objects characteristics that can be transferred to, added to, and combined with other objects to make a complete program, including classes and objects, fields, properties, methods, and events, encapsulating, inheritance and polymorphisms, overloading, overriding, and shadowing. **Audience:** Industry professionals. **Principal Exhibits:** Seminar that teaches what it means to give objects characteristics that can be transferred to, added to, and combined with other objects to make a complete program, including classes and objects, fields, properties, methods, and events, encapsulating, inheritance and polymorphisms, overloading, overriding, and shadowing.

33813 ■ Project Management for Software Development - Planning and Managing Successful Projects (Onsite)

Seminar Information Service Inc. (SIS)
250 El Camino Real., Ste. 112
Tustin, CA 92780
Ph: (714)508-0340
Free: 877-736-4636
Fax: (714)734-8027
Co. E-mail: info@seminarinformation.com
URL: http://www.seminarinformation.com
Contact: Catherine Bellizzi, President

URL(s): www.seminarinformation.com/qqafqg/projec
t-management-for-software-development-planning
-and

Description: Learn how to: Deliver successful software projects that support your organization's strategic goals; Match organizational needs to the most effective software development model; Plan and manage projects at each stage of the software development life cycle (SDLC); Create project plans that address real-world management challenges; Develop the skills for tracking and controlling the project deliverables; Focus on key tasks for the everyday management of software projects; Build an effective and committed team and keep them motivated day to day. **Audience:** Industry professionals. **Principal Exhibits:** Learn how to: Deliver successful software projects that support your organization's strategic goals; Match organizational needs to the most effective software development model; Plan and manage projects at each stage of the software development life cycle (SDLC); Create project plans that address real-world management challenges; Develop the skills for tracking and controlling the project deliverables; Focus on key tasks for the everyday management of software projects; Build an effective and committed team and keep them motivated day to day.

33814 ■ Structured Query Language (SQL) I

URL(s): www.eeicom.com

Description: Seminar that covers how to organize and extract information from relational databases, including design relational databases, proper syntax for SQL statements, analyze and organize data, retrieve, insert, update, and delete data, use aggregate functions, write queries from multiple tables, and normalize data. **Audience:** Industry professionals. **Principal Exhibits:** Seminar that covers how to organize and extract information from relational databases, including design relational databases, proper syntax for SQL statements, analyze and organize data, retrieve, insert, update, and delete data, use aggregate functions, write queries from multiple tables, and normalize data.

33815 ■ Structured Query Language (SQL) II

URL(s): www.eeicom.com

Description: Seminar that provides critical information for writing advanced database queries using complex databases, including design sub-queries, data dictionaries, establish database security, create and manage sequences and indexes, and create stored procedures. **Audience:** Industry professionals. **Principal Exhibits:** Seminar that provides critical information for writing advanced database queries using complex databases, including design sub-queries, data dictionaries, establish database security, create and manage sequences and indexes, and create stored procedures.

33816 ■ Typography and Font Management (Onsite)

URL(s): www.eeicom.com

Description: Covers the various electronic typefaces used in desktop publishing applications, including installing, managing, and troubleshooting fonts. **Audience:** Industry professionals. **Principal Exhibits:** Covers the various electronic typefaces used in desktop publishing applications, including installing, managing, and troubleshooting fonts.

33817 ■ VMware Ultimate Bootcamp

URL(s): www.eeicom.com

Description: Hands-on labs designed to expose you to advanced virtualization concepts with VMware V13.5 product suite. Comprehensive class prepares students to become professional virtualization experts with the certification Certified Virtualization Expert (CVE). **Audience:** Professionals. **Principal Exhibits:** Hands-on labs designed to expose you to advanced virtualization concepts with VMware V13.5 product suite. Comprehensive class prepares students to become professional virtualization experts with the certification Certified Virtualization Expert (CVE).

33818 ■ Web Graphics with Adobe Photoshop (Onsite)

URL(s): www.eeicom.com

Description: Covers creating high-quality, low-bandwidth graphics for the Web, including optimizing GIFs and JPEGs, creating transparent GIF graphics and animated GIFs and rollovers, create background tiles and sliced graphics, create navigation bars and buttons, image maps, and correct photographs for the Web. **Audience:** Industry professionals. **Principal Exhibits:** Covers creating high-quality, low-bandwidth graphics for the Web, including optimizing GIFs and JPEGs, creating transparent GIF graphics and animated GIFs and rollovers, create background tiles and sliced graphics, create navigation bars and buttons, image maps, and correct photographs for the Web.

33819 ■ Website Optimization (Onsite)

Seminar Information Service Inc. (SIS)
250 El Camino Real., Ste. 112
Tustin, CA 92780
Ph: (714)508-0340
Free: 877-736-4636
Fax: (714)734-8027
Co. E-mail: info@seminarinformation.com
URL: http://www.seminarinformation.com
Contact: Catherine Bellizzi, President
URL(s): www.seminarinformation.com

Description: Learn how to deliver exceptional service to site visitors, including a friendlier environment, obtain more leads, and integrate social media into your site. **Audience:** Marketing managers, creative directors, marketing strategists, business owners and website graphic designer. **Principal Exhibits:** Learn how to deliver exceptional service to site visitors, including a friendlier environment, obtain more leads, and integrate social media into your site.

33820 ■ XML Development I (Onsite)

URL(s): www.eeicom.com

Description: Covers Extensible Markup Language (XML) that enables the Web designer to create information that is evolvable, including XML structure and syntax, create well-formed XML documents and document type definitions (DTDs) and schemas, valid XML documents, using entities, display using Cascading Style Sheets, data binding, and object model scripts. **Audience:** Web developers and programmers. **Principal Exhibits:** Covers Extensible Markup Language (XML) that enables the Web designer to create information that is evolvable, including XML structure and syntax, create well-formed XML documents and document type definitions (DTDs) and schemas, valid XML documents, using entities, display using Cascading Style Sheets, data binding, and object model scripts.

33821 ■ XML Development II (Onsite)

URL(s): www.eeicom.com

Description: Covers XSLT and how it is used to convert XML data for presentational purposes, modify data structure, and to create non-XML files, including building XSLT applications, transforming XML to HTML, PDF, and Word. **Audience:** Web developers and programmers. **Principal Exhibits:** Covers XSLT and how it is used to convert XML data for presentational purposes, modify data structure, and to create non-XML files, including building XSLT applications, transforming XML to HTML, PDF, and Word.

33822 ■ XML Development III (Onsite)

URL(s): www.eeicom.com

Description: Covers the integration of XML into Web applications using ASP, Cold Fusion, PHP and Java, including guidelines for translating XML structure to a relational database model, rules for modeling, common techniques for storing, transmitting, and displaying content, data access mechanisms that expose relational data as XML, and how to use related technologies when processing XML data. **Audience:** Web developer and programmers. **Principal Exhibits:** Covers the integration of XML into Web applications using ASP, Cold Fusion, PHP and Java, including guidelines for translating XML structure to a relational database model, rules for modeling, common techniques for storing, transmitting, and displaying content, data access mechanisms that expose relational data as XML, and how to use related technologies when processing XML data.

33823 ■ XML Web Services (Onsite)

URL(s): www.eeicom.com

Description: Learn how Web services can enhance your Web site and communication with other companies. **Audience:** Web Designer, students. **Principal Exhibits:** Learn how Web services can enhance your Web site and communication with other companies.

REFERENCE WORKS

33824 ■ "2 New Tools for Safeguarding Your Website: Website Backup Made Simple" in Inc. (Vol. 33, September 2011, No. 7, pp. 52)

Pub: Inc. Magazine

Ed: John Brandon. **Description:** Tools to back up content on a Website are profiled. Vaultpress works only with sites that run on the WordPress publishing platform and CodeGuard works with a variety of publishing platforms and hosting services. **Availability:** Online.

33825 ■ "Abacast, Citadel Strike Radio Ad Deal" in Business Journal Portland (Vol. 27, December 31, 2010, No. 44, pp. 3)

Pub: Portland Business Journal
Contact: Andy Giegerich, Managing Editor
E-mail: agiegerich@bizjournals.com

Ed: Erik Siemers. **Description:** Software firm Abacast Inc. has partnered with Citadel Media to aid the latter's advertising sales. Citadel provides radio networks and syndicated programs to 4,200 affiliate stations. **Availability:** Print; Online.

33826 ■ "Android Users Can Now Manage Life On-the-Go With New AboutOne Family Organizer Companion Application" in PR Newswire (August 1, 2012)

Pub: PR Newswire Association LLC.

Description: AboutOne Family Organizer allows customers to handle family memories and paperwork using android and iPhone mobile phones. The Family Organizer app allows users to organize all household information and is password protected. Details of the app are included. **Availability:** Online.

33827 ■ "Apps For Anybody With an Idea" in Advertising Age (Vol. 79, October 17, 2008, No. 39, pp. 29)

Pub: Crain Communications, Inc.
Contact: Jessica Botos, Manager, Marketing
E-mail: jessica.botos@crainsnewyork.com

Ed: Beth Snyder Bulik. **Description:** Apple's new online App Store is open to anyone with an idea and the ability to write code and many of these developers are not only finding a sense of community through this venue but are also making money since the sales are split with Apple, 30/70 in the developer's favor. **Availability:** Online.

33828 ■ "As Windows 8 Looms, Tech Investors Hold Their Breath" in Barron's (Vol. 92, July 23, 2012, No. 30, pp. 22)

Pub: Dow Jones & Company Inc.
Contact: Almar Latour, Chief Executive Officer

Ed: Tiernan Ray. **Description:** Launch of the Microsoft Windows 8 operating system could affect the stock prices of Microsoft and Intel. The effects of the software's introduction on the market share of personal computers remains uncertain. **Availability:** Online.

33829 ■ "Baseline Metrics CEOs Need for Online Brand Oversight" in South Florida Business Journal (Vol. 34, May 23, 2014, No. 44, pp. 16)

Pub: American City Business Journals, Inc.
Contact: Mike Olivieri, Executive Vice President

Released: Weekly. **Price:** $8, Introductory 4-week offer(Digital & Print). **Description:** Chief executive officers have the option to use metrics that will allow them to monitor their online brands. Social media engagement is an effective customer service metric because it presents a clear assessment of a business social media prowess. Reputation management software, on the other hand, ranks a firm's weekly, hourly, and daily sentiments online. **Availability:** Print; Online.

33830 ■ "BayTSP, NTT Data Corp. Enter Into Reseller Pact to Market Online IP Monitoring" in Professional Services Close-Up (Sept. 11, 2009)

Description: Due to incredible interest from distributors and content owners across Asia, NTT Data Corp. will resell BayTSP's online intellectual property monitoring, enforcement, business intelligence and monetization services in Japan.

33831 ■ "Being All a-Twitter" in Canadian Business (Vol. 81, December 8, 2008, No. 21, pp. 22)

Description: Marketing experts suggest that advertising strategies have to change along with new online social media. Companies are advised to find ways to incorporate social software because workers and customers are expected to continue its use. **Availability:** Print; Online.

33832 ■ "The Best Business Accounting Software Services of 2023" in Business News Daily (March 9, 2023)

URL(s): www.businessnewsdaily.com/7543-best-accounting-software.html

Ed: Erica Sandberg. **Released:** March 09, 2023. **Description:** A review of the best business accounting software out there along with a comparison guide. **Availability:** Online.

33833 ■ "Best iPhone Apps to Manage Your Business Contacts" in Business News Daily (February 21, 2023)

URL(s): www.businessnewsdaily.com/5891-5-iphone-apps-to-manage-your-business-contacts.html

Ed: Jackie Dove. **Released:** February 21, 2023. **Description:** Business owners often have numerous contacts stored in their phone that they need access to throughout the day. Listed are apps that can help them organize their contacts quickly and efficiently. **Availability:** Online.

33834 ■ "The Best Time and Attendance Software of 2023" in Business News Daily (March 9, 2023)

URL(s): www.businessnewsdaily.com/6730-best-time-and-attendance-systems.html

Ed: Jessica Elliott. **Released:** March 09, 2023. **Description:** Looking for a new software for attendance? This guide reviews the best software options out there and provides a comparison chart. **Availability:** Online.

33835 ■ "Beyond Microsoft and Yahoo!: Some M&A Prospects" in Barron's (Vol. 88, March 17, 2008, No. 11, pp. 39)

Pub: Dow Jones & Company Inc.
Contact: Almar Latour, Chief Executive Officer

Ed: Eric J. Savitz. **Description:** Weak quarterly earnings report for Yahoo! could pressure the company's board to cut a deal with Microsoft. Electronic Arts is expected to win its hostile $26-a-share bid for Take-Two Interactive Software. Potential targets and buyers for mergers and acquisitions are mentioned. **Availability:** Online.

33836 ■ "Bitcoin 'Killer App' Or the Currency of the Future?" in Providence Business News (Vol. 28, January 6, 2014, No. 40, pp. 1)

Pub: American City Business Journals, Inc.
Contact: Mike Olivieri, Executive Vice President
URL(s): pbn.com/bitcoin-killer-app-or-the-currency-of-the-future94158

Description: The Providence Bitcoin Meetup has gathered several technology experts to discuss Bitcoin, the popular digital currency. However, software developers, engineers and entrepreneurs see Bitcoin as the next killer app for the Internet and is changing how information and data is stored, shared and verified. The Bitcoin's impact in Rhode Island is examined. **Availability:** Online. **Telecommunication Services:** Anderson@pbn.com.

33837 ■ *"Bringing Healthcare Home"* in *Austin Business Journal (Vol. 34, June 6, 2014, No. 16, pp. B13)*
Pub: American City Business Journals, Inc.
Contact: Mike Olivieri, Executive Vice President
Description: Chris Hester, founder and president of Kinnser Software feels that the company's growth since its inception has been both a blessing and a challenge. He states that his company's policy not to hire people until there's a strong need has increased productiveness of the company and the singular focus on customer service success has driven the company forward. **Availability:** Online.

33838 ■ *"BusinessOnLine Launches New Web-Based Search Engine Optimization Tool: First Link Checker for Google"* in *Marketwired (October 19, 2009)*
Pub: Comtex News Network Inc.
Contact: Kan Devnani, President
Description: First Link Checker, a complimentary new search engine optimization tool that helps site owners optimize their on-page links by understanding which of those links are actually being counted in Google's relevancy algorithm, was developed by BusinessOnLine, a rapidly growing Internet marketing agency. This tool will make it easy for the average web master to ensure that their internal link structure is optimized. **Availability:** Print.

33839 ■ *"CADD Microsystems Launches the CADD Community, Partners with Global eTraining to Provide Online, On-Demand Training for Autodesk Software"* in *Computer Business Week (August 28, 2014, pp. 24)*
Pub: NewsRX LLC.
Contact: Kalani Rosell, Contact
Description: A new online customer-only portal the integrates on-demand training, applications and extension, videos and additional value-added content for customers only was developed by CADD Microsystems. The Autodesk Platinum Partner calls this training program, CADD Community. **Availability:** Online.

33840 ■ *"Certain Predicts 2012 as Breakthrough Year for Events"* in *Internet Wire (January 5, 2012)*
Pub: Comtex News Network Inc.
Contact: Kan Devnani, President
Description: Certain Inc. discusses its threetop predictions for 2012 on technology trends that will promote increased business value in the events industry. Certain Inc. is a leading provider of cloud-based event management software that is used for global meetings and events. **Availability:** Print; Online.

33841 ■ *"Choosing the Right Small Business Software for Collecting Payments"* in *Business 2 Community (October 4, 2021)*
URL(s): www.business2community.com/small-business/choosing-the-right-small-business-software-for-collecting-payments-02434457
Ed: Haiden Hibbert. **Released:** October 04, 2021.
Description: Reviews the reasons a small business needs to choose payment processing software. **Availability:** Online.

33842 ■ *"ClickFuel Unveils Internet Marketing Tools for Small Businesses"* in *Marketwired (October 19, 2009)*
Pub: Comtex News Network Inc.
Contact: Kan Devnani, President
Description: ClickFuel, a firm that manages, designs and tracks marketing campaigns has unveiled a full software suite of affordable services and technology solutions designed to empower small business owners and help them promote and grow their businesses through targeted Internet marketing campaigns. **Availability:** Online.

33843 ■ *"Cloud City: An Industry - and a Region - On the Rise"* in *Puget Sound Business Journal (Vol. 34, February 28, 2014, No. 46, pp. 4)*
Pub: American City Business Journals, Inc.
Contact: Mike Olivieri, Executive Vice President

Description: Seattle, Washington is experiencing an influx of the world's most innovative cloud companies. Businesses are shifting their applications from in-house servers or private data center into public cloud infrastructure, which is less expensive than buying the servers and managing the data systems. Seattle software companies are taking advantage of this trend and developing products. **Availability:** Online.

33844 ■ *"Clouds in the Forecast"* in *Information Today (Vol. 28, September 2011, No. 8, pp. 10)*
Pub: Information Today Inc.
Contact: Thomas H. Hogan, President
Ed: Paula J. Hane. **Description:** Cloud computing is software, applications, and data stored remotely and accessed via the Internet with output displayed on a client device. Recent developments in cloud computing are explored.

33845 ■ *"CradlePoint Is Adding Workers, Seeking More Space"* in *Idaho Business Review (September 3, 2014)*
Pub: BridgeTower Media
Contact: Adam Reinebach, President
Price: $11.99, Print, Digital & Mobile(1 Month); 149, Print, Digital & Mobile(1 Year); 99, Digital & Mobile Only(1 Year); $99, Print, Digital & Mobile(For 1 Year); $9.95, Print, Digital & Mobile (For 1 Month Intro Rate); $149, Print, Digital & Mobile(For 1 Year).
Description: CradlePoint makes networking routers and software, focusing on security for businesses. The firm is hiring new workers at a rate higher than predicted and is seeking new office space in downtown Boise, Idaho. CradlePoint is a major player in the growing wireless service and cloud platform market and is growing faster than its competitors. **Availability:** Print; Online.

33846 ■ *"Design Center Shows Quality of Digital Paper"* in *American Printer (Vol. 128, June 1, 2011, No. 6)*
Description: Digital Design Centers allows printers to customize marketing tools in order to promote their own digital printing capabilities. **Availability:** Online.

33847 ■ *"Eagles Measure Suite Success"* in *Philadelphia Business Journal (Vol. 30, September 9, 2011, No. 30, pp. 1)*
Pub: Philadelphia Business Journal
Contact: Sierra Quinn, Director
E-mail: squinn@bizjournals.com
Ed: John George. **Description:** Philadelphia Eagles have a new software program that helps suite holders keep track of how their suite is being used and whether they are getting a return on their investment. The software allows suite holders to better utilize and distribute their tickets. **Availability:** Online.

33848 ■ *"Elastic Path Software Joins Canada in G20 Young Entrepreneur Summit"* in *Marketwire (June 14, 2010)*
Pub: Comtex News Network Inc.
Contact: Kan Devnani, President
Description: The Canadian Youth Business Foundation hosted the G20 Young Entrepreneur Summit and announced that Harry Chemko of British Columbia's Elastic Path Software will be a member of the Canadian delegation at the G20 Young Entrepreneur Summit. Details are included. **Availability:** Print; Online.

33849 ■ *"The Emergence of Governance In an Open Source Community"* in *Academy of Management Journal (Vol. 50, No. 5, October 1, 2007, pp. 1079)*
Pub: Academy of Management
Contact: Sharon Alvarez, President
Ed: Siobhan O'Mahony, Fabrizio Ferraro. **Description:** Study examined the method of self-governance among small communities producing collective goods, focusing on an open source software community. Results revealed that a combination of bureaucratic and democratic practices helped its governance system. **Availability:** Electronic publishing; PDF; Download; Online.

33850 ■ *"The Evolution of the Laws of Software Evolution: a Discussion Based On a Systematic Literature Review"* in *ACM Computing Surveys (Vol. 46, Summer 2014, No. 2, pp. 28)*
Pub: Association for Computing Machinery - Manor College Student Chapter
Contact: Mary Cecilia Jurasinski, President
Description: After more than 40 years of life, software evolution should be considered as a mature field. However, despite such a long history, many research questions still remain open, and controversial studies about the validity of the laws of software evolution are common. During the first part of these 40 years, the laws themselves evolved to adapt to the changes in both the research and the software industry environments. This process of adaption to new paradigms, standards, and practices stopped about 15 years ago, when the laws were revised for the last time. The current state of affairs about the validity of software laws, how they are perceived by the research community, and the developments and challenges likely to occur in the future are addressed. **Availability:** Print; PDF; Online.

33851 ■ *"Firms Bet On Games To Hike Wellness"* in *Business Journal (Vol. 30, June 1, 2012, No. 1, pp. 1)*
Pub: American City Business Journals, Inc.
Contact: Mike Olivieri, Executive Vice President
Ed: Katharine Grayson. **Released:** Weekly. **Price:** $4, introductory 4-week offer(Digital only). **Description:** Twin Cities-based firms providing corporate wellness services are integrating games into these programs. These games include friendly competitions between work teams or high-tech smartphone applications. **Availability:** Print; Online.

33852 ■ *"Five Easy Ways to Fail: Nothing Like a Weak Team Or An Unrealistic Schedule To Start a Project Off Right"* in *Inc. (November 2007, pp. 85-87)*
Ed: Joel Spolsky. **Description:** Five easy ways to fail meeting a project deadline are discussed by the owner of a software development company: start with second-rate team of developers, set weekly milestones, negotiate a deadline, divide tasks equitably, and work until midnight. **Availability:** Online.

33853 ■ *"Former Owner of Spartanburg Tax Preparation Business Pleads Guilty to Fraud in Multi-Million Dollar Scheme"* in *Internet Wire (January 26, 2012)*
Description: TaxACT tax preparation software includes all e-fileable forms necesary for both simple and complex returns. A full list of forms, that include 1040, 1040A and 1040EZ, Schedules A and B for itemized deductions and interest and dividends, as well as Schedules C, D, E, and F for business owners and investors, can be found at their Website: www.taxact.com. The software also includes free guidance. **Availability:** Online.

33854 ■ *"Free File Alliance & IRS Launch 10th Year of Free Online Tax Preparation Services for Millions of Americans"* in *Economics Week (February 3, 2012, pp. 82)*
Pub: PR Newswire Association LLC.
Description: A coalition of tax software companies have partnered with the Internal Revenue Service to offer the 212 IRS Free File progam. The Free File Alliance offers low-to-moderate income taxpayers free access to online commercial tax preparation software. Details of the program are included. **Availability:** Online.

33855 ■ *"German Win Through Sharing"* in *Canadian Business (Vol. 83, September 14, 2010, No. 15, pp. 16)*
Pub: Rogers Media Inc.
Contact: Neil Spivak, Chief Executive Officer
Ed: Jordan Timm. **Released:** September 14, 2010. **Description:** German economic historian Eckhard Hoffner has a two-volume work showing how German's relaxed attitude toward copyright and intellectual property helped it catch up to industrialized

United Kingdom. Hoffner's research was in response to his interest in the usefulness of software patents. Information on the debate regarding Canada's copyright laws is given. **Availability:** Print; Online.

33856 ■ *"Getting Rid of Global Glitches: Choosing Software For Trade Compliance"* in *Black Enterprise (Vol. 41, September 2010, No. 2, pp. 48)*
Pub: Earl G. Graves Ltd.
Contact: Earl Graves, Jr., President

Ed: Marcia Wade Talbert. **Description:** Compliance software for trading with foreign companies must be compatible with the U.S. Census Bureau's Automated Export System (www.aesdirect.gov). It has to be current with regulatory requirements for any country in the world. Whether owners handle their own compliance or hire a logistics company, they need to be familiar with this software in order to access reports and improve transparency and efficiency of theft supply chain. **Availability:** Online.

33857 ■ *"Growing Encryptics Trades Frisco for Austin"* in *Austin Business Journal (Vol. 34, April 25, 2014, No. 10, pp. A8)*
Pub: American City Business Journals, Inc.
Contact: Mike Olivieri, Executive Vice President

Released: Weekly. **Price:** $4, Introductory 4-week offer(Digital & Print). **Description:** Frisco, Texas-based Encryptics Inc. has announced plans to relocate its headquarters with its 21 employees and negotiating for office space in West Austin's Loop 360 area. Encryptics also plans to increase the number of its employees to about 80 next year. Insights into Encryptics' email security softward area also given. **Availability:** Print; Online.

33858 ■ *"Hatchedlt.com Social Organizer for Families Launches New Phone App at BlogHer '12"* in *PR Newswire (August 3, 2012)*
Pub: PR Newswire Association LLC.

Description: Hatchedlt.com is a free social organizer for families. The new phone app includes two new updates: shareable to do lists and an inbox for members to accept or decline invitations for events or to connect with members.

33859 ■ *"A Heart for Software; Led by Its Upbeat CEO, Menlo Spreads Joy of Technology"* in *Crain's Detroit Business (Vol. 30, October 13, 2014, No. 41, pp. 1)*
Pub: Crain Communications Inc.
Contact: Barry Asin, President

Description: Profile of Rich Sheridan, one of the most prominent names in IT in Ann Arbor, Michigan. Sheridan believes in common-sense solutions and manages his workers to be empowered employees to come up with their own solutions to software coding issues, and he is a consummate salesman and marketer. He runs his company so it goes beyond understanding what the user needs, and managing a great team, to being the front man selling his goods and services. **Availability:** Print; Online.

33860 ■ *"Holiday Sales Look Uncertain for Microsoft and PC Sellers"* in *Puget Sound Business Journal (Vol. 29, November 28, 2008, No. 32)*
Ed: Todd Bishop. **Description:** Personal computer makers face uncertain holiday sales for 2008 as a result of the weak U.S. economy and a shift toward low-cost computers. Personal computer shipments for the fourth quarter 2008 are forecast to drop 1 percent compared to the same quarter 2007. **Availability:** Online.

33861 ■ *"Horse Race: Putting the App in Apple"* in *Inc. (Vol. 30, November 2008, No. 11)*
Pub: Mansueto Ventures L.L.C.
Contact: Stephanie Mehta, Chief Executive Officer

Ed: Nitasha Tiku. **Description:** Aftermarket companies are scrambling to develop games and widgets for Apple's iPhone. Apple launched a kit for developers interested in creating iPhone-specific software

along with the App Store, and an iTunes spinoff. Profiles of various software programs that may be used on the iPhone are given. **Availability:** Online.

33862 ■ *"The Impact of Organizational Context on the Failure of Key and Strategic Account Management Programs"* in *Journal of Business & Industrial Marketing (Vol. 29, June 2014, No. 5)*
Pub: Emerald Group Publishing Limited
Contact: Erika Valenti, President

Description: Examination of how organizational context affects the failure of various account management programs. Two key factors directing the organizational context include formal or hard elements supporting K/SAM programs, and informal and partly cultural or soft elements moderating the implementation. The relationship between organizational elements in K/SAM is illustrated and vital implications for managers are underscored. **Availability:** Download; Online.

33863 ■ *"Inesoft Cash Organizer Desktop: A New Approach to Personal Accounts Bookkeeping"* in *America's Intelligence Wire (August 7, 2012)*
Description: Inesoft Cash Organizer Desktop application is offering a new product for financial management on a home PC and mobile devices. The program supports the classification of money transactions by category, sub-category, project, sub-project, budget planning, and world currencies (including current exchange rates), credit calculators, special reports, and more. Multiple users in the family can use the application. Details of the program are outlined. **Availability:** Online.

33864 ■ *"Innovation Central: Tech, Tweets, and Trolls"* in *Inc. (Vol. 36, September 2014, No. 7, pp. 102)*
Pub: Mansueto Ventures L.L.C.
Contact: Stephanie Mehta, Chief Executive Officer

Description: Results of a survey regarding the ways small business is using technology to grow their businesses is presented. Information covers social media applications, government software patents, trends impacting small business, and the most innovative technology companies. **Availability:** Print; Online.

33865 ■ *"Inside Intel's Effectiveness System for Web Marketing"* in *Advertising Age (Vol. 81, January 25, 2010, No. 4, pp. 4)*
Pub: Crain Communications, Inc.
Contact: Jessica Botos, Manager, Marketing
E-mail: jessica.botos@crainsnewyork.com

Ed: Beth Snyder Bulik. **Description:** Overview of Intel's internally developed program called Value Point System in which the company is using in order to evaluate and measure online marketing effectiveness. **Availability:** Online.

33866 ■ *"Inside Waterloo's Quiet Tech Titan"* in *Canadian Business (Vol. 87, July 2014, No. 7, pp. 39)*
Description: OpenText chief executive officer Mark Barrenechea feels confident about the financial health of the Waterloo, Ontario-based software company. He adds that the company is exploring opportunities by the big data phenomenon. **Availability:** Online.

33867 ■ *"Kinnser: Sales In Overdrive"* in *Austin Business Journal (Vol. 32, March 30, 2012, No. 4, pp. 1)*
Pub: American City Business Journals, Inc.
Contact: Mike Olivieri, Executive Vice President

Ed: Christopher Calnan. **Description:** Kinnser Software Inc.'s receipt of fresh capitalization is seen to enable the company to pursue its acquisition strategy. The company is planning to grow organically. It is also planning to double the number of its employees. **Availability:** Online.

33868 ■ *"Largest North Texas Software Developers"* in *Dallas Business Journal (Vol. 37, January 31, 2014, No. 21, pp. 8)*
Pub: American City Business Journals, Inc.
Contact: Mike Olivieri, Executive Vice President

Released: September 29, 2017. **Description:** The largest software development companies in North Texas as of February 6, 2014, ranked by full time local staff are listed. Sabre got the top spot. Meanwhile, Crossmark ranked second. **Availability:** Print; Online.

33869 ■ *"Lights, Camera, Action: Tools for Creating Video Blogs"* in *Inc. (Volume 32, December 2010, No. 10, pp. 57)*
Pub: Mansueto Ventures L.L.C.
Contact: Stephanie Mehta, Chief Executive Officer

Ed: John Brandon. **Description:** A video blog is a good way to spread company news, talk about products, and stand out among traditional company blogs. New editing software can create two- to four-minute blogs using a webcam and either Windows Live Essentials, Apple iLife 2011, Powerdirector 9 Ultra, or Adobe Visual Communicator 3. **Availability:** Online.

33870 ■ *"Longwood's FamilLab More Than Just a Hackerspace: It's a Free Form Research and Development Lab"* in *Orlando Business Journal (Vol. 30, January 17, 2014, No. 30, pp. 4)*
Pub: American City Business Journals, Inc.
Contact: Mike Olivieri, Executive Vice President

Description: FamilLab is a nonprofit hackerspace in Longwood, Florida that has turned into a free-form research and development outfit. The group has at least 70 members who share the same passion for technology and push the limits and boundaries of computer hardware and software, and sometimes start their own business. **Availability:** Print; Online.

33871 ■ *"Microsoft Goes Macrosoft"* in *Barron's (Vol. 89, July 27, 2009, No. 30, pp. 25)*
Pub: Dow Jones & Company Inc.
Contact: Almar Latour, Chief Executive Officer

Ed: Mark Veverka. **Description:** Microsoft reported a weak quarter on the heels of a tech rally which suggests the economy has not turned around. Marc Andreesen describes his new venture-capital fund as focused on "classic tech" and that historical reference places him in the annals of the last millennium. **Availability:** Online.

33872 ■ *"Microsoft Releases Office Security Updates"* in *Mac World (Vol. 27, November 2010, No. 11, pp. 66)*
Description: Office for Mac and Mac Business Unit are Microsoft's pair of security- and stability-enhancing updates for Office 2008 and Office 2004. The software will improve the stability and compatibility and fixes vulnerabilities that would allow attackers to overwrite Mac's memory with malicious code. **Availability:** Online.

33873 ■ *"Microsoft's Diversity Program Clicks into High Speed"* in *Hispanic Business (Vol. 30, July-August 2008, No. 7-8, pp. 54)*
Ed: Derek Reveron. **Description:** Microsoft's diversity hiring and vendor diversity program to capture more Hispanic consumer and business-to-business market is described. One of the main goals of these programs is to hire more Hispanic executives and managers who will help the company develop and market products and services that will appeal and benefit Hispanic consumers.

33874 ■ *"More Leading Retailers Using Omniture Conversion Solutions to Boost Sales and Ecommerce Performance"* in *Marketwired (September 22, 2009)*
Pub: Comtex News Network Inc.
Contact: Kan Devnani, President

Description: Many retailers are utilizing Omniture conversion solutions to improve the performance of their ecommerce businesses; recent enhancements to Omniture Merchandising and Omniture Recommendations help clients drive increased conversion to their Internet ventures.

33875 ■ *"My Favorite Tool for Organizing Data"* in Inc. (Vol. 33, November 2011, No. 9, pp. 46)
Pub: Inc. Magazine
Ed: Abram Brown. **Description:** Intelligence software firm uses Roambi, a Web-based service that turns spreadsheet data into interactive files for iPhones and iPads. **Availability:** Online.

33876 ■ *"Naresh Kumar on Using Heat Maps to Grow Your Business"* in Small Business Trends (August 25, 2022)
URL(s): smallbiztrends.com/2022/08/heat-maps.html
Ed: Holly Chavez. **Released:** August 25, 2022.
Description: Interview with Naresh Kumar, Zoho Corporation Product Manager, who discusses how small businesses can grow by utilizing heat maps, which is software that shows where website visitors spent their time at the website by recording where they clicked. **Availability:** Online.

33877 ■ *"National Award Goes to eSmartTax.com for Having 'Best Tax Preparation Software' Available to Online Tax Filers"* in Investment Weekly News (February 18, 2012, pp. 706)
Pub: PR Newswire Association LLC.
Description: eSmartTax.com was voted the best tax preparation software in About.com's Reader's Choice Awards 2011. Over 10,000 online tax filers voted for their favorite finance and tax software. eSmartTax. com provides a live online chat where tax professionals can answer specific questions.

33878 ■ *"New Sprint Phone Whets Appetite for Applications, Brings Revenue for Handmark"* in The Business Journal-Serving Metropolitan Kansas City (Vol. 26, July 25, 2008)
Description: Firms supporting the applications of the new Samsung Instinct, which was introduced by Sprint Nextel Corp. in June 2008, have reported usage rates increase for their products. Handmark, whose mobile services Pocket Express comes loaded with Instinct, has redirected employees to meet the rising demand for the services. Other views and information on Instinct, are presented. **Availability:** Print; Online.

33879 ■ *"New Wave of Business Security Products Ushers in the Kaspersky Anti-Malware Protection System"* in Internet Wire (October 26, 2010)
Description: Kaspersky Anti-Malware System provides anti-malware protection that requires minimal in-house resources for small businesses. The system offers a full range of tightly integrated end-to-end protection solutions, ensuring unified protection across an entire network, from endpoint and mobile device protection to file server, mail server, network storage and gateway protection. It provides flexible centralized management, immediate threat visibility and a level of responsiveness not seen in other anti-malware approaches. **Availability:** Print; Online.

33880 ■ *"Next Generation Security Awareness"* in Security Management (Vol. 56, September 2012, No. 9, pp. 32)
Description: Carnegie Mellon University (CMU) has purchased Wombat Security Technologies' PhishGuru to reduce the phishing attacks. CMU also purchased Wombat's two educational games, Anti-Phishing and Anti-Phishing Phyllis, partly due to the PhishGuru's success. Insights on the software-as-a-service solution are also given.

33881 ■ *"Next-Level E-Commerce"* in Entrepreneur (June 2014)
Pub: Entrepreneur Media Inc.
Contact: Dan Bova, Director
E-mail: dbova@entrepreneur.com
Description: BloomReach's SNAP software enables consumers to see the products they want upon arriving at an e-commerce Website. The software does this by evaluating the users' intent and preferences based on previous site usage. The enterprise-level

software, which costs retailers at least $7,500/month, aims to use big data to help consumers choose products based on their intent. The cloud-based service indexes every page on a client's site and automatically generates appropriate content for visitors. The use of machine learning reduces lag time between application and positive results. **Availability:** Print; Online.

33882 ■ *"Nonprofit NAIC Acquires Software Developer as For-Profit Arm"* in Crain's Detroit Business (Vol. 25, June 22, 2009, No. 25, pp. 10)
Pub: Crain Communications Inc.
Contact: Barry Asin, President
Ed: Sherri Begin Welch. **Description:** Details of National Association of Investors Corporation's acquisition of a Massachusetts investment software developer in order to offer more products to investment clubs and individual investors nationwide. **Availability:** Online.

33883 ■ *"Not Your Father's Whiteboard"* in Inc. (Vol. 33, November 2011, No. 9, pp. 50)
Pub: Inc. Magazine
Ed: Adam Baer. **Description:** Sharp's new interactive whiteboard is really a 70-inch touch screen monitor with software for importing presentations from any Windows 7 computer. **Availability:** Online.

33884 ■ *"PayDragon Brings Mobile Payment App to Food-Truck Vendors"* in PaymentsSource (April 16, 2012)
Pub: SourceMedia LLC
Contact: Gemma Postlethwaite, Chief Executive Officer
Ed: David Heun. **Description:** PayDragon is a new App for food truck vendors to collect payments. It is also used by other small merchants. Paperlinks, developed this unit to provide a fast technology that enables consumers to securely order and pay for food with credit and debit cards using email, which elimiantes these steps for the vendors. **Availability:** Print; Online.

33885 ■ *"PC Connection Acquires Cloud Software Provider"* in New Hampshire Business Review (Vol. 33, March 25, 2011, No. 6, pp. 8)
Description: Merrimack-based PC Connection Inc. acquired ValCom Technology, a provider of cloud-based IT service management software. Details of the deal are included. **Availability:** Print; Online.

33886 ■ *"PC Running Slowly? How to Rev Up Your Machine"* in Inc. (Vol. 33, November 2011, No. 9, pp. 46)
Pub: Mansueto Ventures L.L.C.
Contact: Stephanie Mehta, Chief Executive Officer
Ed: John Brandon. **Released:** November 01, 2011.
Description: Software that keeps PCs tuned up and running smoothing are profiled: AUSLO6ICS BOOST-SPEED 5, $50; Tuneup Utilities 2011, $40; Slimware Slimcleaner 1.9, free; and IOBIT Advanced Systemcare Pro 4, $20 a year. **Availability:** Print; Online.

33887 ■ *"The Power of Negative Thinking"* in Inc. (Volume 32, December 2010, No. 10, pp. 43)
Pub: Inc. Magazine
Ed: Jason Fried. **Description:** A Website is software and most businesses have and need a good Website to generate business. Understanding for building a powerful Website is presented. **Availability:** Online.

33888 ■ *"Power Ranger"* in Inc. (November 2007, pp. 131)
Ed: Nitasha Tiku. **Description:** Surveyor software is designed to power down computers when not in use, in order to save energy. **Availability:** Online.

33889 ■ *"Powering Intelligent Commerce: eCommera Rebrands as OrderDynamics, Helping Retailers Activate Commerce from First Interaction to Fulfillment"* in Computer Business Week (August 28, 2014, pp. 20)
Pub: NewsRX LLC.
Contact: Kalani Rosell, Contact

Description: OrderDynamics, a new global brand created by eCommera, is profiled. The firm will continue to provide an integrated suite of software-as-a-service (SaaS) big data products and service that power intelligent commerce for retailers and brands around the world. Details of the integration of the new brand are included. **Availability:** Online.

33890 ■ *"Precision Crop Control with Valley Irrigation/CropMetrics Partnership"* in Farm Industry News (January 6, 2011)
Pub: Informa Business Media, Inc.
Contact: Charlie McCurdy, President
Ed: Karen McMahon. **Description:** Irrigation systems have become a precision farming tool since partnering with agronomic software systems to apply products across the field by prescription. Valley Irrigation and CropMetrics have partnered in order to variably control water, fertilizer and other crop management products through a center pivot irrigation system. **Availability:** Print; Online.

33891 ■ *"Press Release: Trimble Introduces CFX-750 Display"* in Farm Industry News (January 4, 2011)
Description: Trimble is offering a touch screen display called the CFX-750. The new 8-inch full-color display allows farmers to choose the specific guidance, steering and precision agriculture capabilities that best fit their farm's particular needs. The display can be upgraded as business needs change, including the addition of GLONASS capabilities, or the addition of section and rate control for crop inputs such as seed, chemicals and fertilizer. **Availability:** Print; Online.

33892 ■ *"Programs Provide Education and Training"* in Contractor (Vol. 56, September 2009, No. 9, pp. 56)
Ed: William Feldman, Patti Feldman. **Description:** Opportunity Interactive's Showroom v2 software provides uses computer graphics to provide education and training on HVAC equipment and systems. It can draw heat pump balance points for a specific home. Meanwhile, Simutech's HVAC Training Simulators provide trainees with 'hands-on' HVACR training. **Availability:** Print; Online.

33893 ■ *"Providers Ride First Wave of eHealth Dollars"* in Boston Business Journal (Vol. 31, June 10, 2011, No. 20, pp. 1)
Pub: Boston Business Journal
Contact: Carolyn M. Jones, President
E-mail: cmjones@bizjournals.com
Ed: Julie M. Donnelly. **Released:** Weekly. **Description:** Health care providers in Massachusetts implementing electronic medical records technology started receiving federal stimulus funds. Beth Israel Deaconess Medical Center was the first hospital to qualify for the funds. **Availability:** Print.

33894 ■ *QuickBooks 2014 on Demand*
Pub: Que Publishing
Ed: Gail Perry. **Released:** 1st edition. **Price:** $22.39, Members, e-book. **Description:** Step-by-step training for using various small business financial software programs; includes illustrated, full color explanations. **Availability:** watermarked; E-book; Print; Electronic publishing; PDF.

33895 ■ *QuickBooks for the New Bean Counter: Business Owner's Guide 2006*
Description: Profile of QuickBooks software, offering insight into using the software's accounting and bookkeeping functions.

33896 ■ *"Reclaim Your Office"* in Greater Baton Rouge Business Report (Vol. 30, June 12, 2012, No. 22, pp. 12)
Ed: Regina Leeds. **Description:** The 8-Minute Organizer provides easy solutions to simplify life. **Availability:** Online.

33897 ■ *"RES Stakes Its Claim in Area"* in Philadelphia Business Journal (Vol. 28, January 29, 2010, No. 50, pp. 1)
Pub: Philadelphia Business Journal
Contact: Sierra Quinn, Director

E-mail: squinn@bizjournals.com

Ed: Peter Key. **Description:** RES Software Company Inc. of Amsterdam, Netherlands appointed Jim Kirby as president for the Americas and Klaus Besier as chairman in an effort to boost the firm's presence in the US. Brief career profiles of Kirby and Besier are included. RES develops software that allows management of information flow between an organization and its employees regardless of location. **Availability:** Online.

33898 ■ *"Route Optimization Impacts the Bottom Line" in Contractor (Vol. 56, November 2009, No. 11, pp. 48)*

Ed: Dave Beaudry. **Description:** Plumbing and HVAC businesses can save a significant amount of money from route optimization. The process begins with gathering information on a fleet and a routing software tool can determine the effectiveness of current route configurations and identify preferable route plans. **Availability:** Print; Online.

33899 ■ *"Search Engines: Image Conscious" in Canadian Business (Vol. 81, February 26, 2008, No. 4, pp. 36)*

Pub: Rogers Media Inc.

Contact: Neil Spivak, Chief Executive Officer

Ed: Andrew Wahl. **Description:** Idee Inc. is testing an Internet search engine for images that does not rely on tags but compares its visual data to a database of other images. The company was founded and managed by Leila Boujnane as an off-shoot of their risk-management software firm. Their software has already been used by image companies to track copyrighted images and to find images within their own archives. **Availability:** Online.

33900 ■ *"Sears and H&R Block Offer New Tax Preparation Options and Savings Through Tax Season" in Benzinga.com (January 30, 2012)*

Description: Individuals preparing their own tax forms can file using www.sears.com/hrblock and receive a 15 percent discount on the purchase of Basic, Deluxe, and Premium H&R Block online editions. H&R Block at Sears also offers free 1040EZ filing online and in Sears stores. Customers filing on the site can also import previous year's tax data from TurboTax and TaxAct Online.

33901 ■ *"Sense of Discovery" in Business Journal Portland (Vol. 27, November 19, 2010, No. 38, pp. 1)*

Pub: Portland Business Journal

Contact: Andy Giegerich, Managing Editor

E-mail: agiegerich@bizjournals.com

Description: Tigard, Oregon-based Exterro Inc. CEO Bobby Balachandran announced plans to go public without the help of an institutional investor. Balachandran believes Exterro could grow to a $100 million legal compliance software company in the span of three years. Insights on Exterro's growth as market leader in the $1 billion legal governance software market are also given. **Availability:** Print; Online.

33902 ■ *"Slow but Steady into the Future" in Barron's (Vol. 88, July 7, 2008, No. 27, pp. M)*

Pub: Dow Jones & Company Inc.

Contact: Almar Latour, Chief Executive Officer

Ed: Mark Veverka. **Description:** Investors are advised to maintain their watch on the shares of business software company NetSuite. The company's chief executive officer, Zach Nelson, claims that the company has a 10-year lead on its competitors with the development of software-as-a service. **Availability:** Online.

33903 ■ *"Small Is Bountiful for Intuit" in Barron's (Vol. 90, September 13, 2010, No. 37, pp. 22)*

Pub: Barron's Editorial & Corporate Headquarters

Ed: Mark Veverka. **Description:** Finance software maker Intuit wants to tap the underserved small business market. One analyst sees Intuit's shares rising 25 percent to 55 percent in the next 12 months from September 2010. **Availability:** Online.

33904 ■ *"A Software Company's Whimsical Widgets Were an Instant Hit. But Its Core Product Was Getting Overshadowed" in Inc. (January 2008)*

Ed: Alex Salkever. **Description:** A widget designed as a marketing tool tuned into a hit on Facebook. Should ChipIn shift its focus?. **Availability:** Online.

33905 ■ *"Software Developers" in Business Review Albany (Vol. 41, July 18, 2014, No. 17, pp. 9)*

Description: The top software development companies in Albany, New York are ranked by local software revenue in 2013. CMA Consulting Services is listed in the top spot, with GCOM Software following in second place. **Availability:** Online.

33906 ■ *"Software's Last Hurrah" in Canadian Business (Vol. 81, December 24, 2007, No. 1, pp. 27)*

Description: Canada's software industry could be facing a challenge with IBM's acquisition of Cognos, which was the country's last major independent business intelligence company and was also IBM's largest acquisition ever. Next in line to Cognos in terms of prominence is Open Text Corporation, which could also be a possible candidate for acquisition, as analysts predict. **Availability:** Print; Online.

33907 ■ *"Speaking In Tongues: Rosetta Stone's TOTALE Adds 'Social' To Language Learning" in Black Enterprise (Vol. 41, September 2010, No. 2)*

Pub: Earl G. Graves Ltd.

Contact: Earl Graves, Jr., President

Ed: Sonya A. Donaldson. **Description:** As small businesses become more globalized, it is necessary to learn new languages in order to compete. Rosetta Stone's TOTALe is profiled. **Availability:** Online.

33908 ■ *"Spinout Success: New Leadership Steps In At UW's C4C" in Puget Sound Business Journal (Vol. 35, June 27, 2014, No. 10, pp. 11)*

Pub: American City Business Journals, Inc.

Contact: Mike Olivieri, Executive Vice President

Description: University of Washington's Center for Commercialization vice provost, Vikram Jandhyala, talks about his new position with the school. Jandhyala says he plans to build more synergy between the medical school and engineering and between social sciences and computer science. He also says the medical and software industry need to grow to accommodate the volume of data crossing and stored within the Internet. **Availability:** Online.

33909 ■ *"The Story Of Diane Greene" in Barron's (Vol. 88, July 14, 2008, No. 28, pp. 31)*

Pub: Dow Jones & Company Inc.

Contact: Almar Latour, Chief Executive Officer

Ed: Mark Veverka. **Description:** Discusses the ousting of Diane Greene as a chief executive of VMWare, a developer of virtualization software, after the firm went public; in this case Greene, a brilliant engineer, should not be negatively impacted by the decision because it is common for companies to bring in new executive leadership that is more operations oriented after the company goes public. **Availability:** Online.

33910 ■ *"Stoyan Kenderov on Preparing Your Business for Recession" in Small Business Trends (July 26, 2022)*

URL(s): smallbiztrends.com/2022/07/stoyan-kenderov-preparing-your-small-business-for-recession.html

Ed: Holly Chavez. **Released:** July 26, 2022. **Description:** Interview with Stoyan Kenderov, Chief Operating Officer of Plastiq, discusses the necessary resources and tools small businesses can use to help keep their businesses afloat during the recession. **Availability:** Online.

33911 ■ *"A Survey of Combinatorial Testing" in ACM Computing Surveys (Vol. 43, Summer 2011, No. 2, pp. 11)*

Pub: Association for Computing Machinery

Contact: Yannis Ioannidis, President

Ed: Changhai Nie, Hareton Leung. **Description:** Combinatorial Testing (CT) can detect failures triggered by interactions of parameters in the Software Under Test (SUT) with a covering array test suite generated by some sampling mechanisms. Basic concepts and notations of CT are covered. **Availability:** Download; PDF; Online.

33912 ■ *"A Survey of Comparison-Based System-Level Diagnosis" in ACM Computing Surveys (Vol. 43, Fall 2011, No. 3, pp. 22)*

Pub: Association for Computing Machinery

Contact: Yannis Ioannidis, President

Ed: Elias P. Duarte, Jr., Roverli P. Ziwich, Luiz C. P. Albini. **Released:** Volume 43 Issue 3. **Price:** $10, Members; $15, Nonmembers; $5, Students. **Description:** The growing complexity and dependability requirements of hardware, software, and networks demand efficient techniques for discovering disruptive behavior in those systems. Comparison-based diagnosis is a realistic approach to detect faulty units based on the outputs of tasks executed by system units. This survey integrates the vast amount of research efforts that have been produced in this field. **Availability:** Download; PDF.

33913 ■ *"Tejas Gadhia on Using Low-Code or No-Code Apps" in Small Business Trends (August 2, 2022)*

URL(s): smallbiztrends.com/2022/08/tejas-gadhia-using-low-code-no-code-apps.html

Ed: Holly Chavez. **Released:** August 02, 2022. **Description:** Interview with Tejas Gadhia, Zoho Product Manager, as he discusses how small businesses can improve their workflow by implementing low-code and no-code solutions. **Availability:** Online.

33914 ■ *"Thinking Strategically About Technology" in Franchising World (Vol. 42, August 2010, No. 8, pp. 9)*

Pub: International Franchise Association

Contact: Matthew Haller, President

E-mail: mhaller@franchise.org

Ed: Bruce Franson. **Released:** 2010. **Description:** Nearly 25 percent of companies waste money from their technology budget. Most of the budget is spent on non-strategic software. Ways to spend money on technology for any franchise are examined. **Availability:** Online.

33915 ■ *"Three Productivity Solutions" in Contractor (Vol. 57, February 2010, No. 2, pp. 26)*

Ed: William Feldman, Patti Feldman. **Description:** Singletouch is a real-time data capture solution for mechanical and other contractors that work in jobs that require materials and workload tracking. Contractors get information on extreme weather and sudden changes in the cost of materials. The OptimumHVAC optimization software by Optimum Energy is designed to optimize energy savings in commercial buildings. **Availability:** Print; Online.

33916 ■ *"Two Field Service Management Solutions" in Contractor (Vol. 56, November 2009, No. 11, pp. 37)*

Ed: William Feldman, Patti Feldman. **Description:** Bella Solutions Field Service Software v. 4.2 is a web based solution for HVAC service contractors that enables scheduling of emergency, one-time, multi-visit or periodically recurring jobs with drag and drop appointments. VaZing is another web based solution that costs $99 per month for contractors. It can handle line-item discounting and invoices aside from scheduling. **Availability:** Print; Online.

33917 ■ *"Unbound ID Raises $2 Million" in Austin Business JournalInc. (Vol. 28, December 12, 2008, No. 39, pp. 1)*

Description: Austin, Texas-based Unbound ID Corporation has secured $2 million in funding from venture capital firm Silverton Partners. The company has developed identity management software for network directories. The market for identity management technology is expected to grow to more than $12.3 billion by 2014. **Availability:** Print; Online.

33918 ■ *"uTest Discusses the Evolution of Crowdsourcing Models at CrowdConf 2010"* in Marketwired (October 1, 2010)
Pub: Comtex News Network Inc.
Contact: Kan Devnani, President

Description: World's largest software testing marketplace, uTest, announces its first conference dedicated to the emerging field of crowdsourcing along with the future of distributed work. A panel of experts will discuss common misconceptions about crowdsourcing using real-world examples. **Availability:** Print; Mailing list; Online.

33919 ■ *"Web Translation Made Simple"* in Inc. (Vol. 33, October 2011, No. 8, pp. 44)
Pub: Inc. Magazine

Ed: Adam Baer. **Description:** Smartling is a Web-based service that translates sites into more than 50 foreign languages. The software will begin translation right after setting up the account. **Availability:** Online.

33920 ■ *"Wegmans Uses Database for Recall"* in Supermarket News (Vol. 56, September 22, 2008, No. 38)
Pub: Informa USA, Inc.
Contact: Stephen A. Carter, Chief Executive Officer

Ed: Carol Angrisani. **Description:** Wegmans used data obtained through its loyalty card that, in turn, sent automated telephone calls to every customer who had purchased tainted pet food when Mars Petcare recalled dog food products.

33921 ■ *"Winners Dream: A Journey from Corner Store to Corner Office"*
Pub: Simon & Schuster Adult Publishing Group
Contact: Jonathan Karp, President

Released: October 14, 2014. **Price:** $28.99, hardcover, plus $2.24 shipping charges. **Description:** Bill McDermott, CEO of the world's largest business software company, SAP, profiles his career. He discusses his career moves, sales strategies, employee incentives to create high performance teams, and the competitive advantages of optimism and hard work. The entrepreneur offers a blueprint for success and the knowledge that the real dream is the journey, not the preconceived destination. **Availability:** E-book; Print; Download; Audio.

33922 ■ *"Yammer Gets Serious"* in Inc. (Volume 32, December 2010, No. 10, pp. 58)
Pub: Inc. Magazine

Ed: Eric Markowitz. **Description:** Yammer, an internal social network for companies, allows coworkers to share ideas and documents in real-time. Details of this service are included. **Availability:** Online.

33923 ■ *"Your Career: Is It Time for a Change?"* in Rental Product News (Vol. 33, October 2011)

Description: Management software for running a rental business is examined. **Availability:** Online.

TRADE PERIODICALS

33924 ■ *Business Computer Report*
Pub: Lawrence Oakly

Ed: Lawrence Oakly. **Released:** Monthly **Price:** $99, Individuals. **Description:** Reviews business applications software and hardware for IBM and compatible computers.

VIDEO/AUDIO MEDIA

33925 ■ *The Best Small Business Podcast: The Best Time for a Tech Refresh*
URL(s): richgee.libsyn.com/248-the-best-time-for-a-tech-refresh

Ed: Rich Gee. **Released:** June 20, 2022. **Description:** Podcast discusses the best time to refresh you technology.

33926 ■ *The Best Small Business Show: What to Do When Technology Fails You*
URL(s): richgee.libsyn.com/289-what-to-do-when-technology-fails-you

Ed: Rich Gee. **Released:** April 03, 2023. **Description:** Podcast discusses what to do when technology doesn't work for your business.

33927 ■ *The How of Business: Are You Ready to Be Your Own Boss?*
URL(s): www.thehowofbusiness.com/episode-001-ready-to-be-your-own-boss

Ed: Henry Lopez. **Released:** April 18, 2016. **Description:** Podcasts helps you determine if you are prepared to start your own business.

TRADE SHOWS AND CONVENTIONS

33928 ■ **International Symposium on Forms and Business Processes**
Business Forms Management Association (BFMA)
1147 Fleetwood Ave.
Madison, WI 53716-1417
Co. E-mail: bfma@bfma.org
URL: http://www.bfma.org
URL(s): www.bfma.org/?page=TestSymSpon
Description: Business forms and related equipment, software, supplies, and services. **Audience:** Forms designers, forms managers, business process analysts, usability professionals, application designers, workflow analysts, and IT support. **Principal Exhibits:** Business forms and related equipment, software, supplies, and services. **Telecommunication Services:** bfma@bfma.org.

CONSULTANTS

33929 ■ **CheckMark Software Inc.**
323 W Drake Rd., Ste. 100
Fort Collins, CO 80526
Free: 800-444-9922

Fax: (970)225-0611
Co. E-mail: sales@checkmark.com
URL: http://www.checkmark.com
Contact: Mohammed A. Ghani, Contact
X (Twitter): x.com/CheckMark_Inc
YouTube: www.youtube.com/channel/UCpJam_8CH-fjiC4eUG--wSA
Description: Developer of accounting and payroll software. **Scope:** Developer of accounting software tools for small businesses and provides fast, easy to use, affordable accounting and payroll solutions to small and medium sized businesses. Provides payroll software and multiledger integrated accounting software. **Founded:** 1984. **Special Services:** MultiLedger; Payroll.

33930 ■ **ImageOps [DVEO Computer Modules]**
11413 W Bernardo Ct.
San Diego, CA 92127
Ph: (858)613-1818
Fax: (858)613-1815
URL: http://dveo.com
Description: Provider of DVB ASI, Transport Streams, MPEG Encoding, and video over IP solutions. **Scope:** Provider of DVB ASI, Transport Streams, MPEG Encoding, and video over IP solutions. **Founded:** 1982. **Special Services:** QZEO™.

33931 ■ **MoneySoft Inc.**
2415 E Camelback Rd., Ste. 700
Phoenix, AZ 85016
Ph: (602)266-7710
Free: 800-966-7797
Co. E-mail: contact@moneysoft.com
URL: http://moneysoft.com
Linkedin: www.linkedin.com/company/moneysoft-inc-/about
X (Twitter): x.com/MoneySoftUSA
Description: Developer of finance applications software. **Scope:** Specializes in the publication of software for the corporate acquisition and development communities. **Founded:** 1991. **Publications:** "The Price is Right? Or is It?"; "Preparing Financial Projections and Valuations"; "Negotiating Business Acquisitions"; "Managing the Process of Buying a Business"; "The Overpayment Trap"; "Strategies to Avoid the Overpayment Trap"; "The Value, Price and Cost of an Acquisition"; "The Trouble with EBITDA". **Special Services:** Corporate Valuation Professional®; DealSense®; Buy-OutPlan®; Corporate Valuation Professional®; Lightning Deal Reviewer?; Fixed Asset Pro®; Benchmark Pro 2006®; DealSense Plus; Mergerstat?.

33932 ■ **On-Q Software Inc.**
13764 SW 11 St.
Miami, FL 33184
URL: http://www.on-qsoftware.com
Contact: Teresita Cajigas, President

Description: Developer of computer software solutions. **Scope:** Developer of computer software solutions. **Founded:** 1987.

START-UP INFORMATION

33933 ■ *"Kickstarter Funds the Future; Crowdfunding Services Such as Kickstarter Have Been Hailed as a New Way To Get Started In Business and Cut Out the Traditional Money Men"* in Telegraph Online (August 24, 2012)
Pub: Telegraph Media Group Limited
Contact: Nick Hugh, Chief Executive Officer

Ed: Monty Munford. **Description:** More than 530 crowdfunding services are expected to his the net by the end of the year. Crowdfunding helps companies raise money from investors for specific projects. A musician was able to raise over $1 million to fund a new record. **Availability:** Online.

ASSOCIATIONS AND OTHER ORGANIZATIONS

33934 ■ **Academy of Legal Studies in Business (ALSB)**
c/o Daniel Herron, Exec. Secretary
434 Flat Gap Trl.
Cullowhee, NC 20723
Co. E-mail: info@alsb.org
URL: http://www.alsb.org
Contact: Daniel Herron, Executive Secretary
E-mail: herron3653@gmail.com

Description: Teachers of business law and legal environment in colleges and universities. Promotes and encourages business law scholarship and teaching outside of the law school environment. **Founded:** 1924. **Publications:** *American Business Law Journal (ABLJ)* (Quarterly); *Journal of Legal Studies Education (JLSE)* (Semiannual). **Educational Activities:** Alsb Annual Conference (Annual). **Geographic Preference:** Multinational.

33935 ■ **Small Business Legislative Council (SBLC)**
4800 Hampden Ln., 6th Fl.
Bethesda, MD 20814
Ph: (301)652-8302
Co. E-mail: email@sblc.org
URL: http://sblc.org
Contact: Paula Calimafde, President

Description: Serves as an independent coalition of trade and professional associations that share a common commitment to the future of small business. Represents the interests of small businesses in such diverse economic sectors as manufacturing, retailing, distribution, professional and technical services, construction, transportation, and agriculture. **Founded:** 1976. **Geographic Preference:** National.

REFERENCE WORKS

33936 ■ *"5 Things You Should Know If Your Bank Fails"* in Black Enterprise (Vol. 41, December 2010, No. 5, pp. 29)
Pub: Earl G. Graves Ltd.
Contact: Earl Graves, Jr., President

Ed: John Simons. **Description:** The Federal Deposit Insurance Corporation announced that the number of banks in trouble has reached the highest level since March 1993. Advice from the FDIC is cited. Statistical data included. **Availability:** Online.

33937 ■ *"6 Ways Artificial Intelligence Can Transform Your Small Business"* in business.com (April 10, 2020)
Released: April 10, 2020. **Description:** Discusses how you can leverage artificial intelligence (AI) to better serve your business and your customers. **Availability:** Online.

33938 ■ *"ALA: Hot Topics for Librarianship"* in Information Today (Vol. 28, September 2011, No. 8, pp. 17)
Pub: Information Today Inc.
Contact: Thomas H. Hogan, President

Ed: Barbara Brynko. **Description:** Highlights from the American Library Association Annual Conference and Exhibition are listed. Thousands of attendees sought out services, displays, demos, new product rollouts, and freebies. Emerging technology for librarians, staff development, gray literature, interlibrary loans, and next-generation interfaces were among the topics discussed.

33939 ■ *"All Eyes On Iris"* in Canadian Business (Vol. 81, July 22, 2008, No. 12-13, pp. 20)
Description: Provincial governments in Canada are believed to be awaiting Alberta Finance Minister Iris Evans' financial and investment policies as well as Evans' development of a new saving strategy. Alberta is the only Canadian province that is in position to invest in sovereign wealth funds after it eliminated its debt in 2005. **Availability:** Print; Online.

33940 ■ *"Alternative Energy Calls for Alternative Marketing"* in Indoor Comfort Marketing (Vol. 70, June 2011, No. 6, pp. 8)
Pub: Spray Technology & Marketing
Contact: Ava Caridad, Director, Editorial
E-mail: acaridad@spraytm.com

Ed: Richard Rutigliano. **Released:** June 01, 2011. **Description:** Advice for marketing solar energy products and services is given. **Availability:** Print; Online.

33941 ■ *"Analysts: Intel Site May Be Last Major U.S.-Built Fab"* in Business Journal-Serving Phoenix and the Valley of the Sun (October 18, 2007)
Pub: Phoenix Business Journal
Contact: Alex McAlister, Director
E-mail: amcalister@bizjournals.com

Ed: Ty Young. **Description:** Intel's million-square-foot manufacturing facility, called Fab 32, is expected to open in 2007. The plant will mass-produce the 45-nanometer microchip. Industry analysts believe Fab 32 may be the last of its kind to be built in the

U.S., as construction costs are higher in America than in other countries. Intel's future in Chandler is examined. **Availability:** Print; Online.

33942 ■ *"Are You Ignoring Trends That Could Shake Up Your Business?"* in Harvard Business Review (Vol. 88, July-August 2010, No. 7-8, pp. 124)
Pub: Harvard Business Publishing
Contact: Diane Belcher, Managing Director

Ed: Elie Ofek, Luc Wathieu. **Price:** $8.95, PDF. **Description:** Ways for firms to capitalize on trends that might otherwise negatively affect their business are spotlighted. These include using certain aspects of the trend to augment traditional product/service offerings, and combining the trend with the offerings to transcend its traditional category. **Availability:** Online; PDF.

33943 ■ *"As Capital Gains Tax Hike Looms, Baltimore's Merger Activity Percolates"* in Baltimore Business Journal (Vol. 28, August 27, 2010, No. 16, pp. 1)
Pub: Baltimore Business Journal
Contact: Rhonda Pringle, President
E-mail: rpringle@bizjournals.com

Ed: Scott Dance. **Description:** Concerns for higher capital gains taxes in 2011 have been provoking buyers and sellers to engage in mergers and acquisitions activity, which is expected to gain momentum before the end of 2010. Companies that had saved cash during the recession have been taking advantage of the buyer's market. Other trends in local and national mergers and acquisitions activity are presented. **Availability:** Print.

33944 ■ *"As Technology Changes, So Must African American Business"* in Black Enterprise (Vol. 41, August 2010, No. 1, pp. 61)
Pub: Earl G. Graves Ltd.
Contact: Earl Graves, Jr., President

Ed: Sonya A. Donaldson. **Description:** Social media is essential to compete in today's business environment, especially for African American firms. **Availability:** Online.

33945 ■ *"Athletes Face Wins and Losses After Pro Sports"* in The Business Journal - Serving Phoenix and the Valley of the Sun (Vol. 29, September 21, 2008, No. 3, pp. 1)
Pub: American City Business Journals, Inc.
Contact: Mike Olivieri, Executive Vice President

Ed: Chris Casacchia. **Description:** Professional athletes like hockey star Jeremy Roenick start businesses, while others like Joel Adamson work to boost local communities. Former athletes were found to be particularly interested with real estate businesses. Other views and information on former athletes and their life after sports are presented. **Availability:** Online.

33946 ■ "Attracting Veteran-Franchisees To Your System" in Franchising World (Vol. 42, November 2010, No. 11, pp. 53)

Pub: International Franchise Association

Contact: Matthew Haller, President

E-mail: mhaller@franchise.org

Ed: Mary Kennedy Thompson. **Released:** November 01, 2010. **Description:** As military servicemen and women return home, the franchising industry expects an increase in veterans as franchise owners. The Veterans Transition Franchise Initiative, also known as VetFran, is described. **Availability:** Online.

33947 ■ "Auto Asphyxiation" in Canadian Business (Vol. 85, August 13, 2012, No. 13, pp. 38)

Ed: Michael McCullough. **Description:** The declining car ownership and utlization has profound business implications for oil companies and automakers and may bring substantial benefit to other sectors and the economy as a whole. The transition to the post-automotive age may happen in places where there is the will to change transportation practices but not in others. **Availability:** Print; Online.

33948 ■ "AVT Launches New ExpressPay Vending Systems" in Benzinga.com (July 13, 2011)

Description: AVT Inc. has developed a new high-tech vending system that features a touch screen interface and a cashless payment system so users can find what they want easily and pay using a credit card. **Availability:** Print; Online.

33949 ■ Back on the Career Track: A Guide for Stay-At-Home Moms Who Want to Return to Work

Released: August 15, 2008. **Price:** $29.92, paperback. **Description:** For women like themselves who have rejoined the workforce after a prolonged absence, the authors detail seven main steps for reentry; profiles of six women who have successfully re-launched their careers are included. **Availability:** Print.

33950 ■ "Baltimore's Burger Market Sizzling with Newcomers" in Boston Business Journal (Vol. 29, June 10, 2011, No. 5, pp. 1)

Pub: Boston Business Journal

Contact: Carolyn M. Jones, President

E-mail: cmjones@bizjournals.com

Ed: Ryan Sharrow. **Description:** The burger trend in Maryland is on the rise with burger joints either opening up or expanding into several branches. Startup costs for this kind of business range between $250,000 to $400,000. With a growth rate of roughly 17 percent in 2009, this so-called better burger segment of the burger categories is expected to dominate the market for quite some time. **Availability:** Print; Online.

33951 ■ "Baltimore's Co-Working Spaces Introduces New Kind of Cubicle Culture" in Baltimore Business Journal (Vol. 29, August 19, 2011, No. 15, pp. 1)

Pub: Boston Business Journal

Contact: Carolyn M. Jones, President

E-mail: cmjones@bizjournals.com

Ed: Alexander Jackson. **Description:** Beehive Baltimore offers a co-working space where independent freelancers and entrepreneurs can work. There are two other companies that provide the same service and the value of these services to these professional is that it provides them with an office that is both convenient and affordable aside from letting them network with peers.

33952 ■ "Bartering Trades on Talents" in Reading Eagle (June 20, 2010)

Description: Bartering is not just a way of trading goods and services, it can be an essential tool for small business to survive in a bad economy.

33953 ■ "Be Wary of Legal Advice on Internet, Lawyers Warn" in Crain's Detroit Business (Vol. 24, September 22, 2008, No. 38, pp. 16)

Pub: Crain Communications Inc.

Contact: Barry Asin, President

Ed: Harriet Tramer. **Description:** While some lawyers feel that the proliferation of legal information on the Internet can point people in the right direction, others maintain that it simply results in giving false hope, may bring about confusion or worse yet, it sometimes makes their jobs even harder. **Availability:** Online.

33954 ■ "Bed and Breakfast Among Planned Uses for New Bohemia Properties" in Gazette (January 30, 2012)

Description: One of the buildings suffering flood damage in the middle of the New Bohemia district of Cedar Rapids, Iowa area will be converted into a one room bed and breakfast offering food catered by Parlor City. The two-story building will als house commercial business on the first floor and a two-bedroom apartment on the upper level. This concept follows the neighborhood's origins with shop owners living above their small business. **Availability:** Online.

33955 ■ The Big Switch: Rewiring the World, from Edison to Google

Pub: W.W. Norton & Company Ltd.

Contact: Stanley Kubrick, Director

Ed: Nicholas Carr. **Released:** June 10, 2013. **Price:** $16.95, paperback; $26.95, hardcover. **Description:** Companies such as Google, Microsoft, and Amazon.com are building huge centers in order to create massive data centers. Together these centers form a giant computing grid that will deliver the digital universe to scientific labs, companies and homes in the future. This trend could bring about a new, darker phase for the Internet, one where these networks could operate as a fearsome entity that will dominate the lives of individuals worldwide. **Availability:** Print.

33956 ■ "Biodiesel Poised to Regain Growth" in Farm Industry News (January 21, 2011)

Pub: Informa Business Media, Inc.

Contact: Charlie McCurdy, President

Ed: Lynn Grooms. **Description:** According to Gary Haer, vice president of sales and marketing for Renewable Energy Group, the biodiesel industry is positioned to regain growth in 2011 with the reinstatement of the biodiesel blendersa tax credit of $1 per gallon. **Availability:** Print; Online.

33957 ■ "Bioheat - Alternative for Fueling Equipment" in Indoor Comfort Marketing (Vol. 70, May 2011, No. 5, pp. 14)

Description: Profile of Worley and Obetz, supplier of biofuels used as an alternative for fueling industry equipment. **Availability:** Print; Online.

33958 ■ "Biotechs Are Using Back Door to Go Public" in Boston Business Journal (Vol. 31, May 27, 2011, No. 18, pp. 1)

Pub: Boston Business Journal

Contact: Carolyn M. Jones, President

E-mail: cmjones@bizjournals.com

Ed: Julie M. Donnelly. **Description:** Members of Massachusetts' biotechnology sector have been engaging in reverse mergers as an alternative to initial public offerings. Reverse mergers provide access to institutional investors and hedge funds. **Availability:** Print; Online.

33959 ■ "Birdcage Optimization" in Pet Product News (Vol. 64, November 2010, No. 11, pp. 54)

Ed: Cheryl Reeves. **Description:** Manufacturers have been emphasizing size, security, quality construction, stylish design, and quick cleaning when guiding consumers on making birdcage options. Selecting a birdcage is gaining importance considering that cage purchases have become the highest expense associated with owning a bird. Other avian habitat trends are also examined. **Availability:** Online.

33960 ■ "Blue Hill Tavern to Host Baltimore's First Cupcake Camp" in Daily Record (August 10, 2011)

Pub: BridgeTower Media

Contact: Adam Reinebach, President

Ed: Rachel Bernstein. **Description:** Cities joining the trend to host cupcake camps are listed. The camps are open to all individuals wishing to share and eat cupcakes in an open environment.

33961 ■ "Branding Your Way" in Canadian Business (Vol. 80, February 12, 2007, No. 4, pp. 31)

Description: The trend in involving consumers in brand marketing by seeking their views through contests or inviting them to produce and submit commercials through Internet is discussed. **Availability:** Online.

33962 ■ "Bubble Trouble? Many Experts Say Seattle Housing Market Is Headed for a Fall" in Puget Sound Business Journal (Vol. 34, April 18, 2014, No. 53, pp. 4)

Pub: American City Business Journals, Inc.

Contact: Mike Olivieri, Executive Vice President

Description: Redfin disclosed that nearly one third of homes listed in the real estate market in King County, Washington were sold above the listing price in February 2014 and it is forecast that the housing market is headed into a new bubble. Statistics indicate that the trend in rising prices is slowing even in the face of a declining supply of available homes. The impact of international buyers is also discussed.

33963 ■ "Business Stands Firm for Reform: Battle Over 2011 Budget Expected" in Crain's Detroit Business (Vol. 26, January 4, 2010, No. 1, pp. 3)

Pub: Crain Communications Inc.

Contact: Barry Asin, President

Ed: Amy Lane. **Description:** As Michigan faces a new year of budgetary problems, many business groups are preparing to hold firm against tax increases and instead push for enacting spending reforms. **Availability:** Print; Online.

33964 ■ "Campaigner Survey: 46 Percent of Small Businesses Use Email Marketing" in Wireless News (November 21, 2009)

Description: Almost half (46 percent) of small businesses surveyed by Campaigner's 2009 State of Small Business Online Marketing, say that they rely on email marketing to help them find new customers, keep existing ones and grow their businesses. The survey also found that 36 percent of small businesses plan to begin using email marketing over the next year. The trend to utilize Internet marketing tools is allowing small businesses to grow faster and generate higher revenues than those that are not using these mediums. **Availability:** Print; Online.

33965 ■ "Canadian Hydronics Businesses Promote 'Beautiful Heat" in Indoor Comfort Marketing (Vol. 70, September 2011, No. 9, pp. 20)

Pub: Spray Technology & Marketing

Contact: Ava Caridad, Director, Editorial

E-mail: acaridad@spraytm.com

Released: September 01, 2011. **Description:** Canadian hydronics companies are promoting their systems as beautiful heat. Hydronics is the use of water as the heat-transfer medium in heating and cooling system. **Availability:** Print; Online.

33966 ■ "Capitol Ideas: Regions to Lansing: Focus on Taxes, Reform, Keeping Talent" in Crain's Detroit Business (Vol. 24, October 6, 2008)

Pub: Crain Communications Inc.

Contact: Barry Asin, President

Ed: Amy Lane. **Description:** Michigan must make bold and dramatic changes in public policy regarding business legislation. The tax structure, unemployment issues and attracting and retaining talent are among the issues the state must confront, especially in this tough economic climate. **Availability:** Online.

33967 ▪ *"Capturing Generation Y: Ready, Set, Transform" in Credit Union Times (Vol. 21, July 14, 2010, No. 27, pp. 20)*

Ed: Senthil Kumar. **Description:** The financial services sector recognizes that Generation Y will have a definite impact on the way business is conducted in the future. The mindset of Generation Y is social and companies need to use networking tools such as Facebook in order to reach this demographic. **Availability:** Online.

33968 ▪ *"Carbon Capture and Storage: Grave Concerns" in Canadian Business (Vol. 81, July 21 2008, No. 11, pp. 25)*

Ed: Andrew Nikiforuk. **Released:** January 01, 2017. **Description:** Air pollution control regulations to reduce greenhouse gasses have been implemented by the Canadian government. The federal government is planning to construct a carbon funeral industry that will store the global warming gases, however the expenditure for the project will be shifted to the taxpayers. Details of the Bruce Peachy's initiative on how to reduce GHGs are presented. **Availability:** Print; Online.

33969 ▪ *"Cash Deals Are King, But Don't Reign Supreme In Birmingham" in Birmingham Business Journal (Vol. 31, May 16, 2014, No. 20, pp. 6)*

Pub: American City Business Journals, Inc.

Contact: Mike Olivieri, Executive Vice President

Released: Weekly; 16 May 14. **Price:** $4, introductory 4-week offer(Digital & Print). **Description:** Data from market research firm, RealtyTrac found that all-cash transactions in Birmingham, Alabama accounted for less than 31 percent of home sales in the first quarter of 2014, compared with a stronger all-cash transactions recorded by Southern metropolitan areas like Atlanta, Memphis and Charlotte. Ben Chenault of MortgageBanc sees a trend among average home-buyers who prefer cash over finance. **Availability:** Print; Online.

33970 ▪ *"The CEO Poll: Fuel for Thought II Canadian Business Leaders on Energy Policy" in Canadian Business (Vol. 81, September 15, 2008, No. 14-15, pp. 12)*

Pub: Rogers Media Inc.

Contact: Neil Spivak, Chief Executive Officer

Ed: Joe Castaldo. **Description:** Most Canadian business leaders worry about the unreliability of the oil supply but feel that Canada is in a better position to benefit from the energy supply crisis than other countries. Many respondents also highlighted the need to invest in renewable energy sources. **Availability:** Online.

33971 ▪ *"Chandrashekar LSP on How to Deal with Inflation" in Small Business Trends (August 9, 2022)*

URL(s): smallbiztrends.com/2022/08/how-to-deal-with-inflation.html

Ed: Holly Chavez. **Released:** August 09, 2022. **Description:** Interview with Chandrashekar LSP, Senior Evangelist of the Zoho Corporation, to discuss the current high inflation trend and how small businesses can cope. **Availability:** Online.

33972 ▪ *"Child-Care Policy and the Labor Supply of Mothers with Young Children: A Natural Experiment from Canada" in University of Chicago Press (Vol. 26, July 2008, No. 3)*

Description: In 1997, the provincial government of Quebec, the second most populous province in Canada, initiated a new childcare policy. Licensed childcare service providers began offering day care spaces at the reduced fee of $5 per day per child for children aged four. By 2000, the policy applied to all children not in kindergarten. Using annual data (1993-2002) drawn from Statistics Canada's Survey of Labour and Income Dynamics, the results show that the policy had a large and statistically significant impact on the labor supply of mothers with preschool children. **Availability:** PDF.

33973 ▪ *Cities from the Arabian Desert: The Building of Jubail and Yambu in Saudi Arabia*

Ed: Andrea H. Pampanini. **Description:** An overview of Saudi Arabia's government to take control of the nation's natural resources and change the government, educational system, and its culture by evolving into a modern industrial society. **Availability:** Print.

33974 ▪ *"ClickFuel Unveils Internet Marketing Tools for Small Businesses" in Marketwired (October 19, 2009)*

Pub: Comtex News Network Inc.

Contact: Kan Devnani, President

Description: ClickFuel, a firm that manages, designs and tracks marketing campaigns has unveiled a full software suite of affordable services and technology solutions designed to empower small business owners and help them promote and grow their businesses through targeted Internet marketing campaigns. **Availability:** Online.

33975 ▪ *"Cloud City: An Industry - and a Region - On the Rise" in Puget Sound Business Journal (Vol. 34, February 28, 2014, No. 46, pp. 4)*

Pub: American City Business Journals, Inc.

Contact: Mike Olivieri, Executive Vice President

Description: Seattle, Washington is experiencing an influx of the world's most innovative cloud companies. Businesses are shifting their applications from in-house servers or private data center into public cloud infrastructure, which is less expensive than buying the servers and managing the data systems. Seattle software companies are taking advantage of this trend and developing products. **Availability:** Online.

33976 ▪ *"Clouds in the Forecast" in Information Today (Vol. 28, September 2011, No. 8, pp. 10)*

Pub: Information Today Inc.

Contact: Thomas H. Hogan, President

Ed: Paula J. Hane. **Description:** Cloud computing is software, applications, and data stored remotely and accessed via the Internet with output displayed on a client device. Recent developments in cloud computing are explored.

33977 ▪ *"Co-Working a Hit in Seattle Market" in Puget Sound Business Journal (Vol. 34, March 14, 2014, No. 48, pp. 8)*

Pub: American City Business Journals, Inc.

Contact: Mike Olivieri, Executive Vice President

Released: Weekly. **Price:** $4, introductory 4-week offer(Digital & Print). **Description:** Companies in Seattle, Washington are learning about the new trend in co-working. The city's co-working industry continues to grow, which is why competitors have established a trade group. Co-working is the process of sharing office space within business centers. Regus, which manages 21 business centers in the city, plans to introduce private booths called WorkBoxes. **Availability:** Print; Online.

33978 ▪ *"Collection Agency Issues Whitepaper on Legal and Ethical Methods of Collecting on Overdue Accounts" in Marketwired (July 20, 2009)*

Pub: Comtex News Network Inc.

Contact: Kan Devnani, President

Description: American Profit Recovery, a collection agency based in Massachusetts and Michigan, has updated and reissued a whitepaper on what businesses can and cannot do regarding conversing with their customers in an attempt to collect on overdue accounts and payments. A detailed summary on the federal laws associated with collecting on overdue accounts is outlined in such a way that any business owner, manager, or responsible party can easily understand. **Availability:** Print; Online.

33979 ▪ *Comic Shop: The Retail Mavericks Who Gave Us a New Geek Culture*

Ed: Tom Spurgeon. **Released:** October 13, 2017. **Price:** $26.95, Hardcover; $10.20, E-Book. **Description:** Traces the history of the modern comic book

shop from it's origins in the 1970s to today with digital platforms and the evolving retail landscape. **Availability:** E-book; Print.

33980 ▪ *"Comics Retailers Hope to Rebound in 2018" in Publishers Weekly (February 9, 2018)*

URL(s): www.publishersweekly.com/pw/by-topic/industry-news/comics/article/76031-comics-retailers-hope-to-rebound-in-2018.html

Released: February 09, 2018. **Description:** An in-depth look at the state of the comic book store in America. Comic book sales have been trending downward and store owners discuss what's driving this trend and how they, and others, can combat it to grow the industry again. **Availability:** Online.

33981 ▪ *"Commentary. Economic Trends for Small Business" in Small Business Economic Trends (April 2008, pp. 3)*

Description: Commentary on the economic trends for small businesses in the U.S. is presented. Analysis of recession possibilities is given. Reports indicate that the number of business owners citing inflation as their number one problem is at its highest point since 1982.

33982 ▪ *"Congress Ponders Annuity Trusts" in National Underwriter Life & Health (Vol. 114, June 21, 2010, No. 12, pp. 10)*

Ed: Arthur D. Postal. **Description:** Congress is looking over several bills, including the Small Business Jobs Tax Relief Act that would significantly narrow the advantages of using grantor-retained annuity trusts (GRATs) to avoid estate and gift taxes. **Availability:** Online.

33983 ▪ *"Consignment Shops Use Web To Help Sell Used Clothing" in Chattanooga Times/Free Press (March 17, 2012)*

Ed: Carey O'Neil. **Description:** Chattanooga, Tennessee boasts a strong market for consignment shops. Children's clothing and toys are among best sellers. Tips are given to help increase sales for consignment/resale shops. **Availability:** Print; Online.

33984 ▪ *"ConsignPro Elevates Nature of Consignment Business, Encourages Designer Resale" in Internet Wire (May 15, 2012)*

Description: Forbes magazine recently highlighted an article on an upscale thrift store located in New York called Designer Resale. The shop features fashion-forward retail merchandies sold on consignment. These new boutique-type resale shops are growing in popularity across the country. **Availability:** Print; Online.

33985 ▪ *"Consumers Like Green, But Not Mandates" in Business Journal-Milwaukee (Vol. 28, December 10, 2010, No. 10, pp. A1)*

Pub: The Business Journal

Contact: Heather Ladage, President

E-mail: hladage@bizjournals.com

Ed: Sean Ryan. **Description:** Milwaukee, Wisconsin consumers are willing to spend more on green energy, a survey has revealed. Respondents also said they will pay more for efficient cars and appliances. Support for public incentives for homeowners and businesses that reduce energy use has also increased. **Availability:** Print; Online.

33986 ▪ *"Consumers Who Saw a Food Truck This Summer" in Nation's Restaurant News (Vol. 45, September 26, 2011, No. 20, pp. 8)*

Description: A guide to the number of customers encountering food trucks during summer 2011 is presented by region. **Availability:** Online.

33987 ▪ *"Convenience Store Deal for Cardtronics" in American Banker (Vol. 174, July 28, 2009, No. 143, pp. 12)*

Pub: SourceMedia LLC

Contact: Gemma Postlethwaite, Chief Executive Officer

Description: Royal Buying Group, Inc., a convenience store marketing company, has agreed to recommend automated teller machine services from Cardtronics Inc., to its clients.

33988 ■ *"Credit Conditions Improve for Small Businesses"* in Small Business Economic Trends (February 2008, pp. 12)
Pub: National Federation of Independent Business
Contact: Brad Close, President

Ed: William C. Dunkelberg, Holly Wade. **Description:** Graphs and tables that present the credit conditions of small businesses in the U.S. are provided. The tables include figures on availability of loans, interest rates, and expected credit conditions. **Availability:** Print; PDF; Online.

33989 ■ *"Credit Unions Buck Trend, Lend Millions More"* in Saint Louis Business Journal (Vol. 32, September 9, 2011, No. 2, pp. 1)
Pub: Saint Louis Business Journal
Contact: Robert Bobroff, President
E-mail: rbobroff@bizjournals.com

Ed: Greg Edwards. **Description:** St. Louis, Missouri-based credit unions have been making more loans despite the weak economy. Credit unions have made a total of $3.46 billion in outstanding loans as of June 30, 2011. **Availability:** Print; Online.

33990 ■ *"Cremation Popularity On the Rise"* in Memphis Business Journal (Vol. 34, April 13, 2012, No. 53, pp. 1)
Pub: Baltimore Business Journal
Contact: Rhonda Pringle, President
E-mail: rpringle@bizjournals.com

Description: Cremation has growing in popularity in the United States. The economic crisis is seen to drive the current trend. **Availability:** Print; Online.

33991 ■ *"The Critical Need to Reinvent Management"* in Business Strategy Review (Vol. 21, Spring 2010, No. 1, pp. 4)
Ed: Julian Birkinshaw. **Released:** February 09, 2010. **Description:** The author believes that management is undervalued today - and for good reasons. Management, he says, has failed at the big-picture level and thinks it is time to reinvent the profession. **Availability:** Print; PDF; Online.

33992 ■ *"Crude Awakening"* in Canadian Business (Vol. 81, October 27, 2008, No. 18, pp. 14)
Description: Jim Grays believes that a global liquid fuels crisis is coming and hopes the expected transition from oil dependence will be smooth. Charles Maxwell, on the other hand, predicts that a new world economy will arrive in three waves. Views of both experts are examined. **Availability:** Print; Online.

33993 ■ *Currency Internationalization: Global Experiences and Implications for the Renminbi*
Pub: Palgrave Macmillan

Released: First edition. **Description:** A collection of academic studies relating to the potential internationalization of China's remninbi. It also discusses the increasing use of China's remninbi currency in international trade and finance.

33994 ■ *"David Bugs Developer Goliaths"* in Denver Business Journal (Vol. 64, August 17, 2012, No. 13, pp. 1)
Pub: Baltimore Business Journal
Contact: Rhonda Pringle, President
E-mail: rpringle@bizjournals.com

Description: The ordinance allowing citizens to file petitions for the declaration of some Denver buildings as historic is affecting real estate developers. Experts are concerned that these efforts for the preservation of abandoned facilities may become a trend that would hinder new land development projects. Changes in the ordinance are being suggested to ease the impact on developers. **Availability:** Print; Online.

33995 ■ *"A Day Late and a Dollar Short"* in Indoor Comfort Marketing (Vol. 70, March 2011, No. 3, pp. 30)
Description: A discussion involving futures options and fuel oil prices is presented. **Availability:** Online.

33996 ■ *"Death of the PC"* in Canadian Business (Vol. 83, October 12, 2010, No. 17, pp. 44)
Description: The future of the personal computer (PC) is looking bleak as consumers are relying more on new mobile devices instead of their PC. A 'Wall Street Journal' article published in September 2010 reported that the iPad had cannibalized sales of laptops by as much as 50 percent. The emergence of tablet computers running alternative operating systems is also explained. **Availability:** Print; Online.

33997 ■ *"Despite Economic Upheaval Generation Y is Still Feeling Green: RSA Canada Survey"* in CNW Group (October 28, 2010)
Pub: CNW Group Ltd.

Description: Canadian Generation Y individuals believe it is important for their company to be environmentally-friendly and one-third of those surveyed would quit their job if they found their employer was environmentally irresponsible, despite the economy. **Availability:** Online.

33998 ■ *"The Devolution of Home-Electronics Stores"* in Philadelphia Business Journal (Vol. 28, June 8, 2012, No. 17, pp. 1)
Pub: Baltimore Business Journal
Contact: Rhonda Pringle, President
E-mail: rpringle@bizjournals.com

Description: Philadelphia, Pennsylvania-area consumer electronics stores have mirrored the national trend in which big-box retailers are taking a bigger share of the home-electronics market. However, smaller, locally-based chains are competing in terms of pricing transparency and custom electronics. **Availability:** Print; Online.

33999 ■ *"Docs Might Hold Cure for Baltimore-Area Real Estate, Banks"* in Baltimore Business Journal (Vol. 28, November 5, 2010, No. 26, pp. 1)
Pub: Baltimore Business Journal
Contact: Rhonda Pringle, President
E-mail: rpringle@bizjournals.com

Ed: Gary Haber. **Description:** Health care providers, including physicians are purchasing their office space instead of renting it as banks lower interest rates to 6 percent on mortgages for medical offices. The rise in demand offers relief to the commercial real estate market. It has also resulted in a boom in building new medical offices. **Availability:** Print; Online.

34000 ■ *"Drink Up!"* in (Vol. 92, July 23, 2012, No. 30, pp. 19)
Pub: Dow Jones & Company Inc.
Contact: Almar Latour, Chief Executive Officer

Ed: Robin Goldwyn Blumenthal. **Description:** Juice bars in the US are expanding as Americans increase the consumption of fresh vegetable and fruit juices. Coffeehouse chain Starbucks entered the market by introducing Evolution Fresh, a seller of coldpressed vegetable and fruit juices. The health benefits of fresh vegetable and fruit juice, however, remain uncertain. **Availability:** Online.

34001 ■ *"Economic Development: 105 CEOs Depart in July"* in South Florida Business Journal (Vol. 35, August 15, 2014, No. 3, pp. 5)
Pub: American City Business Journals, Inc.
Contact: Mike Olivieri, Executive Vice President

Released: August 15, 2014. **Price:** $4, Introductory 4-Week Offer(Digital & Print). **Description:** Challenger, Gray & Christmas has reported 105 CEO departures in July 2014 and these include seven in Florida. US-based companies announced 766 CEO changes in management during the first seven months of 2014. CEO departure trend by industry are given. **Availability:** Print; Online.

34002 ■ *"Economic Outlook 2009: In Search of New Tools and Initiatives"* in Hispanic Business (January-February 2009, pp. 30, 32)
Ed: Dr. Juan Solana. **Description:** Successful business policies of the past no longer work in this economic climate. New tools and initiatives regarding monetary policy, fiscal policy and a higher multiplier are required to survive the crisis. **Availability:** PDF; Online.

34003 ■ *"Economic Trends for Small Business"* in Small Business Economic Trends (April 2008, pp. 1)
Description: Summary of economic trends for small businesses in the U.S. is presented. Economic indicators such as capital spending, inventories and sales, inflation, and profits are given. Analysis of credit markets is also provided. **Availability:** Online.

34004 ■ *"Effort Is Growing to Offer Healthier Choices in Vending Machines"* in Philadelphia Inquirer (July 29, 2011)
Ed: Don Sapatkin. **Description:** Since Boston's mayor announced a ban on the sale of all sugar sweetened beverages on city properties, it seems more cities, states, hospitals, businesses, and even park systems are following suit. Thus, vending machines are beginning to offer healthier snacks and drinks to consumers.

34005 ■ *Electronic Commerce*
Ed: Gary P. Schneider, Bryant Chrzan, Charles McCormick. **Released:** 12th edition. **Price:** $29.49, e-book. **Description:** E-commerce can open the door to more opportunities than ever before for small business. Packed with real-world examples and cases, the book delivers comprehensive coverage of emerging online technologies and trends and their influence on the electronic marketplace. It details how the landscape of online commerce is evolving, reflecting changes in the economy and how business and society are responding to those changes. Balancing technological issues with the strategic business aspects of successful e-commerce, the new edition includes expanded coverage of international issues, social networking, mobile commerce, Web 2.0 technologies, and updates on spam, phishing, and identity theft. **Availability:** Print.

34006 ■ *Emerging Business Online: Global Markets and the Power of B2B Internet Marketing*
Pub: FT Press

Ed: Lara Fawzy, Lucas Dworski. **Released:** First edition. **Price:** $39.99, Members, watermarked. **Description:** An introduction into ebocube (emerging business online), a comprehensive proven business model for Internet B2B marketing in emerging markets. **Availability:** E-book; Print; Online; PDF; Electronic publishing.

34007 ■ *"Employers See Workers' Comp Rates Rising"* in Sacramento Business Journal (Vol. 28, April 8, 2011, No. 6, pp. 1)
Pub: Sacramento Business Journal
Contact: Stephanie Fretwell, Director
E-mail: sfretwell@bizjournals.com

Ed: Kelly Johnson. **Released:** Weekly. **Price:** $4. **Description:** Employers in California are facing higher workers compensation costs. Increased medical costs and litigation are seen to drive the trend. **Availability:** Online.

34008 ■ *"EPA Finalizes WaterSense for Homes"* in Contractor (Vol. 57, January 2010, No. 1, pp. 70)
Ed: Robert P. Mader. **Description:** U.S. Environmental Protection Agency released its "final" version of the WaterSense for Homes standard. The standard's provisions that affect plumbing contractors include the specification that everything has to be leak tested and final service pressure cannot exceed 60 psi. **Availability:** Print; Online.

34009 ■ *"Experts Strive to Educate on Proper Pet Diets"* in *Pet Product News (Vol. 64, November 2010, No. 11, pp. 40)*

Ed: Joan Hustace Walker. **Description:** Pet supply manufacturers have been bundling small mammal food and treats with educational sources to help retailers avoid customer misinformation. This action has been motivated by the customer's quest to seek proper nutritional advice for their small mammal pets. **Availability:** Online.

34010 ■ *"Extreme Amenities"* in *Puget Sound Business Journal (Vol. 35, May 9, 2014, No. 3, pp. 4)*

Released: Weekly. **Price:** $4, introductory 4-week offer(Digital & Print). **Description:** Reports show that some developers are designing apartment buildings with themes. Alison Jeffries of Red Propeller believes that these buildings will rent faster if they have their own stories. This construction trend of such buildings is expected to appeal to the Millennial generation. **Availability:** Print; Online.

34011 ■ *"Facebook: A Promotional Budget's Best Friend"* in *Women Entrepreneur (February 1, 2009)*

Description: Facebook began as a social networking website but has become a valuable marketing tool for all types of businesses, organizations and causes. Tips are provided for creating a Facebook account and growing one's network on Facebook. **Availability:** Online.

34012 ■ *The Facebook Effect: The Inside Story of the Company That Is Connecting the World*

Ed: David Kirkpatrick. **Released:** 2011. **Price:** $18, paperback; $13.99, e-book. **Description:** There's never been a Website like Facebook: more than 350 million people have accounts, and if the growth rate continues, by 2013 every Internet user worldwide will have his or her own page. No one's had more access to the inner workings of the phenomenon than Kirkpatrick, a senior tech writer at Fortune magazine. Written with the full cooperation of founder Mark Zuckerberg, the book follows the company from its genesis in a Harvard dorm room through its successes over Friendster and MySpace, the expansion of the user base, and Zuckerberg's refusal to sell. **Availability:** E-book; Print.

34013 ■ *"Falling Local Executive Pay Could Suggest a Trend"* in *Tampa Bay Business Journal (Vol. 30, January 15, 2010, No. 4, pp. 1)*

Pub: Tampa Bay Business Journal
Contact: Ian Anderson, President
E-mail: ianderson@bizjournals.com

Ed: Margie Manning. **Description:** Tampa Bay, Florida-based Raymond James Financial Inc. and MarineMax Inc.'s proxy statements have shown the decreasing compensation of the companies' highest paid executives. The falling trend in executive compensation was a result of intensified shareholder scrutiny and the economy. **Availability:** Print; Online.

34014 ■ *"Family Business Research: A Strategic Reflection"* in *International Journal of Entrepreneurship and Small Business (Vol. 12, December 3, 2010, No. 1)*

Ed: A. Bakr Ibrahim, Jean B. McGuire. **Description:** Assessment of the growing field of family business and suggestions for an integrated framework. The paper addresses a number of key issues facing family business research. **Availability:** PDF; Download.

34015 ■ *"Fifty Comic Stores That Have Closed Since January 2017"* in *Bleeding Cool (January 19, 2018)*

URL(s): www.bleedingcool.com/2018/01/19/fifty -comic-stores-closed-since-january-2017/

Ed: Rich Johnston. **Released:** January 19, 2018. **Description:** While some comic book stores are just launching, the trend seems to be downwards. Contained is a list of all fifty stores. **Availability:** Online.

34016 ■ *"Fifty Percent of Global Online Retail Visits Were to Amazon, eBay and Alibaba in June 2011"* in *Benzinga.com (October 29, 2011)*

Pub: Benzinga.com
Contact: Jason Raznick, Founder

Description: Current statistics and future forecasts through the year 2015 for Amazon, eBay and Alibaba are explored. **Availability:** Online.

34017 ■ *"First Food Truck Festival Features Enticing Fare, Frustrating Waits"* in *Saint Paul Pioneer Press (August 6, 2012)*

Pub: McClatchy-Tribune Regional News

Ed: Megan Boldt. **Description:** The first Minnesota Food Truck Fest was held in downtown Minneapolis, Minnesota. Despite best intentions, attendees were left waiting in long lines and two vendors ran out of food in two hours. Fourteen food vendors and 25 craft beer trucks were representing this trend in food service. **Availability:** Print; Online.

34018 ■ *"Five Ways to Make RTK Pay"* in *Farm Industry News (March 25, 2011)*

Pub: Informa Business Media, Inc.
Contact: Charlie McCurdy, President

Ed: David Hest. **Description:** It is important for farmers to decide whether they are seeking greater accuracy or faster payback when upgrading navigation systems. The trend towards higher accuracy continues to grow. **Availability:** Print; Online.

34019 ■ *"Flying the Unfriendly Skies"* in *Crain's Chicago Business (Vol. 31, April 21, 2008, No. 16, pp. 26)*

Pub: Crain Communications Inc.
Contact: Barry Asin, President

Ed: Sarah A. Klein. **Description:** Due to the number of Chicago companies and entrepreneurs who are traveling overseas more frequently in order to strengthen ties with customers, companies and oftentimes even business partners, the number of flights leaving O'Hare International Airport for destinations abroad has surged; In 2007, international passengers departing O'Hare totaled 5.7 million, up from 2.4 million in 1990. **Availability:** Online.

34020 ■ *"Food as Nature Intended"* in *Pet Product News (Vol. 64, November 2010, No. 11, pp. 30)*

Ed: Nikki Moustaki. **Description:** Dog owners have been extending their health-consciousness to their pets by seeking natural products that will address their pets' raw food diet. Retailers response to this trend are outlined. **Availability:** Online.

34021 ■ *"Food Truck Weddings Gain Popularity, Buck Tradition"* in *Tampa Tribune (June 24, 2012)*

Ed: Jeff Houck. **Description:** A new trend crossing the nation is the use of a food truck for feeding guests as wedding receptions. Food trucks allow the bride and groom to provide a more casual atmosphere for their wedding party and is less expensive than a formal dinner. **Availability:** Print; Online.

34022 ■ *"The Foodie Generation Grows Up"* in *Business Review Albany (Vol. 41, August 8, 2014, No. 20, pp. 4)*

Description: Members of Albany, New York's restaurant sector have been meeting the demands of millennials, who have become the catalyst for many of the sector's trends. Some restaurants are serving smaller plates to attract young customers. **Availability:** Print; Online.

34023 ■ *"Foods for Thought"* in *Pet Product News (Vol. 64, December 2010, No. 12, pp. 16)*

Ed: Maddy Heleine. **Description:** Manufacturers have been focused at developing species-specific fish foods due to consumer tendency to assess the benefits of the food they feed their fish. As retailers stock species-specific fish foods, manufacturers have provided in-store items and strategies to assist in efficiently selling these food products. Trends in fish food packaging and ingredients are also discussed. **Availability:** Online.

34024 ■ *"From Fat to Fit"* in *Canadian Business (Vol. 79, September 22, 2006, No. 19, pp. 100)*

Ed: Graham Scott. **Description:** The increase in physical fitness clubs across Canada is discussed. **Availability:** Online.

34025 ■ *"Furniture Making May Come Back--Literally"* in *Business North Carolina (Vol. 28, March 2008, No. 3, pp. 32)*

Pub: Business North Carolina
Contact: Peggy Knaack, Manager
E-mail: pknaack@businessnc.com

Description: Due to the weak U.S. dollar and the fact that lumber processors never left the country, foreign furniture manufacturers are becoming interested in moving manufacturing plants to the U.S. **Availability:** Online.

34026 ■ *"Future Autoworkers will Need Broader Skills"* in *Crain's Detroit Business (Vol. 25, June 8, 2009, No. 23, pp. 13)*

Pub: Crain Communications Inc.
Contact: Barry Asin, President

Ed: Ryan Beene. **Description:** Auto industry observers report that new workers in the industry will need advanced skills and educational backgrounds in engineering and technical fields because jobs in the factories will become more technology-based and multidisciplinary. **Availability:** Online.

34027 ■ *"Future of Diversity: Cultural Inclusion Is a Business Imperative"* in *Black Enterprise (Vol. 41, August 2010, No. 1, pp. 75)*

Pub: Earl G. Graves Ltd.
Contact: Earl Graves, Jr., President

Ed: Annya M. Lott. **Description:** As globalization continues to make the world a smaller place, workforce diversity will be imperative to any small company in order to be sustainable.

34028 ■ *"The Future Is Another Country; Higher Education"* in *The Economist (Vol. 390, January 3, 2009, No. 8612, pp. 43)*

Description: Due to the growth of the global corporation, more ambitious students are studying at universities abroad; the impact of this trend is discussed. **Availability:** Print; Online.

34029 ■ *"The Future of Work"* in *Black Enterprise (Vol. 41, August 2010, No. 1, pp. 65)*

Pub: Earl G. Graves Ltd.
Contact: Earl Graves, Jr., President

Ed: Annya M. Lott. **Description:** Technology, globalization, and outsourcing will continue to shape the future of work. Social media is a means for small companies to market goods and services. **Availability:** Online.

34030 ■ *"The Future of Work"* in *Business Strategy Review (Vol. 21, Autumn 2010, No. 3, pp. 16)*

Pub: Wiley-Blackwell

Ed: Lynda Gratton. **Released:** August 28, 2017. **Description:** Work is universal. But how, why, where and when we work has never been so open to individual interpretation. The certainties of the past have been replaced by ambiguity, questions and the steady hum of technology. Now, in a groundbreaking research project covering 21 global companies and more than 200 executives, the author is making sense of the future of work. **Availability:** Print; PDF; Online.

34031 ■ *"Futures Shock for the CME"* in *Crain's Chicago Business (Vol. 31, November 10, 2008, No. 45, pp. 8)*

Pub: Crain Communications Inc.
Contact: Barry Asin, President

Ed: Ann Saphir. **Description:** Chicago-based CME Group Inc., the largest futures exchange operator in the U.S., is facing a potentially radically altered regulatory landscape as Congress weighs sweeping reform of financial oversight. The possible merger of the CFTC and the Securities and Exchange Commission are among CME's concerns. Other details of possible regulatory measures are provided. **Availability:** Online.

34032 ■ *"The Gender Wage Gap: What Local Firms Plan To Do About It"* in *Orlando Business Journal (Vol. 30, May 2, 2014, No. 45, pp. 4)*
Pub: American City Business Journals, Inc.
Contact: Mike Olivieri, Executive Vice President

Released: Weekly. **Price:** $8, introductory 4-week offer(Digital & Print). **Description:** Reports show that women in Orlando, Florida earn 20 percent less than men. The gender wage gap trend in the city can be attributed to bias and women working in lower-wage positions. Graphs that present information on income gap by education and income gap by industry are also given. **Availability:** Print; Online.

34033 ■ *"Generation Y Chooses the Mobile Web"* in *PR Newswire (November 24, 2010)*
Pub: PR Newswire Association LLC.

Description: Generation Y individuals between the ages of 18 - 27 use their mobile phones to browse the Internet more often than a desktop or laptop computer, according to a survey conducted by Opera, a Web browser company. **Availability:** Print; Online.

34034 ■ *"Generation Y Driving Portland Multifamily"* in *Daily Journal of Commerce, Portland (October 29, 2010)*
Ed: Nick Bjork. **Description:** Generation Y, young adults between the ages of 18-30, are interested in multifamily residents in the Portland, Oregon area. Developers in the area, particularly North Portland, have recognized this trend and are looking into multifamily investments.

34035 ■ *"Getting the Bioheat Word Out"* in *Indoor Comfort Marketing (Vol. 70, September 2011, No. 9, pp. 32)*
Description: Ways to market advanced liquid fuels to the public are outlined. **Availability:** Print; Online.

34036 ■ *"Giving In a New Age"* in *Denver Business Journal (Vol. 65, January 17, 2014, No. 36, pp. A4)*
Pub: American City Business Journals, Inc.
Contact: Mike Olivieri, Executive Vice President

Description: Urban Peak's 921 Project was an online funding event that aims to get 921 people to participate in a group photo to raise awareness about youth homelessness in Denver, Colorado. The project, which was heavily promoted in social media, is symbolic of the sweeping changes in philanthropy in recent years. **Availability:** Online.

34037 ■ *"Global Organic Food"* in *Investment Weekly News (January 21, 2012, pp. 272)*
Description: Research and Markets has added 'Global Organic Food' to its reporting of industry profiles. The report will offer top-line qualitative and quantitative summary information including, market size, description of leading players with key financial metrics and analysis of competitive pressures within the market covering the global organic food market. Market size and segmentation data, textual and graphical analysis of market growth trends, leading companies and macroeconomic information will be provided. **Availability:** Online.

34038 ■ *"Globalization: Canada Tomorrow"* in *Canadian Business (Vol. 80, October 8, 2007, No. 20, pp. 14)*
Description: An assessment of Canada's future in terms of its educational, social, and economic environment is presented. Concerns regarding the country's educational system such as the declining interest in science and technology and the possible lack of teachers in the future are discussed. In terms of its social and economic aspects, the need to support entrepreneurs and other qualified people is explained. **Availability:** Online.

34039 ■ *"Good Companies Launch More New Products"* in *Harvard Business Review (Vol. 90, April 2012, No. 4, pp. 28)*
Pub: Harvard Business Review Press
Contact: Moderna V. Pfizer, Contact

Ed: Xueming Luo, Shuili Du. **Description:** Because corporate social responsibility enhances relationships with outside stakeholders, it gives companies access to a large range of knowledge sources, enabling firms to keep up with innovations and shifts in market preferences.

34040 ■ *"Grey Power: On Target"* in *Canadian Business (Vol. 81, July 22, 2008, No. 12-13, pp. 45)*
Pub: Rogers Media Inc.
Contact: Neil Spivak, Chief Executive Officer

Ed: Calvin Leung. **Description:** Companies such as LavalifePRIME, a dating website devoted to singles 45 and older, discuss the value of marketing and services aimed at Canada's older consumers. One-third of Canada's 33 million people are 50-plus, controlling 77 percent of the countries wealth. **Availability:** Print; Online.

34041 ■ *"Groomers Eye Profit Growth Through Services"* in *Pet Product News (Vol. 64, December 2010, No. 12, pp. 26)*
Ed: Kathleen M. Mangan. **Description:** Pet groomers can successfully offer add-on services by taking into account insider customer knowledge, store image, and financial analysis in the decision-making process. Many pet groomers have decided to add services such as spa treatments and training due to a slump in the bathing and grooming business. How some pet groomers gained profitability through add-on services is explored. **Availability:** Online.

34042 ■ *Groundswell: Winning in a World Transformed by Social Technologies*
Pub: Harvard Business Review Press
Contact: Moderna V. Pfizer, Contact

Ed: Charlene Li, Josh Bernoff. **Released:** June 09, 2011. **Price:** $22, paperback/softbound. **Description:** Individuals are using online social technologies such as blogs, social networking sites, YouTube, and podcasts to discuss products and companies, write their own news, and find their own deals. When consumers you've never met are rating your company's products in public forums with which you have no experience or influence, your company is vulnerable. This book teaches the tools and data necessary to turn this treat into an opportunity. **Availability:** E-book; Print.

34043 ■ *"H&M Offers a Dress for Less"* in *Canadian Business (Vol. 83, September 14, 2010, No. 15, pp. 20)*
Pub: Rogers Media Inc.
Contact: Neil Spivak, Chief Executive Officer

Ed: Laura Cameron. **Description:** Swedish clothing company H&M has implemented loss leader strategy by pricing some dresses at extremely low prices. The economy has forced retailers to keep prices down despite the increasing cost of manufacturing, partly due to Chinese labor becoming more expensive. How the trend will affect apparel companies is discussed. **Availability:** Print; Online.

34044 ■ *"Helping Customers Fight Pet Waste"* in *Pet Product News (Vol. 64, November 2010, No. 11, pp. 52)*
Ed: Sandy Robins. **Description:** Pet cleaning products manufacturers have been enjoying high sales figures by paying attention to changing pet ownership trends and environmental awareness. Meanwhile, the inclusion of user-friendly features in these products has also been boosted by the social role of pets and the media attention to pet waste. How manufacturers have been responding to this demand is explored. **Availability:** Print; Online.

34045 ■ *"Henry Mintzberg: Still the Zealous Skeptic and Scold"* in *Strategy and Leadership (Vol. 39, March-April 2011, No. 2, pp. 4)*
Pub: Emerald Group Publishing Limited
Contact: Erika Valenti, President

Ed: Robert J. Allio. **Description:** Henry Mintzberg, professor at the McGill University in Montreal, Canada, shares his thoughts on issues such as inappropriate methods in management education and on trends in leadership and management. Mintzberg believes that US businesses are facing serious management and leadership challenges. **Availability:** Download; Online.

34046 ■ *"His Record, Not Polls, Is What Matters"* in *Bangor Daily News (October 13, 2010)*
Pub: Bangor Daily News
Contact: David M. Austin, Contact

Ed: Nick Sambides, Jr. **Description:** The Small Business Jobs Tax Relief Act could spur investment in small businesses by increasing capital gains tax cuts for investors in small business in 2010 and increase to $20,000 from $5,000 the deduction for start-up businesses. **Availability:** Print; Online.

34047 ■ *"Historic Is Hot, But Challenging, in Bham"* in *Birmingham Business Journal (Vol. 31, August 1, 2014, No. 31, pp. 10)*
Pub: American City Business Journals, Inc.
Contact: Mike Olivieri, Executive Vice President

Description: Birmingham, Alabama is witnessing a growing trend of restoring old and historic buildings for modern office spaces, driven by the new state credit for the projects. However, developers state that renovation projects present numerous challenges, including complying with current building codes and the use of energy-efficient innovation. **Availability:** Print; Online.

34048 ■ *"Home Sweet (Second) Home"* in *Baltimore Business Journal (Vol. 30, May 25, 2012, No. 3, pp. 1)*
Ed: Leigh Somerville. **Description:** Home prices in Maryland have declined in 2012. A number of affluent homebuyers have been purchasing vacation homes in the state. **Availability:** Print; Online.

34049 ■ *"Home, Sweet Shipping Container"* in *Washington Business Journal (Vol. 33, July 18, 2014, No. 13, pp. 4)*
Pub: American City Business Journals, Inc.
Contact: Mike Olivieri, Executive Vice President

Description: Brookland Equity Group LLC is converting a single-family hom ein Brookland into a three-story, four-unit shipping container apartment building in Washington DC. According to the Department of Consumer Regulatory Affairs, the application was reviewed for lighting, ventilation, insulation, and other construction standards. Discussion on the new micro small living spaces trend is presented. **Availability:** Print; Online.

34050 ■ *Hoover's Vision*
Released: 1st edition. **Description:** Founder of Bookstop Inc. and Hoover's Inc. provides a plan to turn an enterprise into a success by showing entrepreneurs how to address inputs with an open mind in order to see more than what other's envision. Hoover pushes business owners to create and feed a clear and consistent vision by recognizing the importance of history and trends, then helps them find the essential qualities of entrepreneurial leadership. **Availability:** Print.

34051 ■ *"Housing Markets Still Struggling"* in *Montana Business Quarterly (Vol. 49, Spring 2011, No. 1, pp. 17)*
Pub: University of Montana Bureau of Business and Economic Research
Contact: Patrick Barkey, Director
E-mail: patrick.barkey@business.umt.edu

Ed: Scott Rickard. **Released:** Quarterly. **Description:** Montana's economic conditions are a bit better than national averages. Data ranked by state, year-over-year price change, and total price peak is presented, along with statistical data for the entire nation. **Availability:** Online.

34052 ■ *"Houston Doctors Buy In to Medical Timeshares"* in *Houston Business Journal (Vol. 40, December 11, 2009, No. 31, pp. 1)*
Pub: Houston Business Journal
Contact: Bob Charlet, President
E-mail: bcharlet@bizjournals.com

Ed: Mary Ann Azevedo. **Description:** Memorial Hermann Hospital System has leased to doctors three examination rooms and medical office space in the Memorial Hermann Medical Plaza in line with its new timeshare concept. The concept was designed to bring primary care physicians to its Texas Medical Center campus. **Availability:** Print; Online.

34053 ■ *"How Artificial Intelligence Can Help Small Businesses"* in *Bplans Blog*
Ed: Nicole Walters. **Description:** Discusses how artificial intelligence is becoming more accessible and more affordable for small businesses and how you can incorporate machine intelligence to make your company more efficient and improve your bottom line. **Availability:** Online.

34054 ■ *"How Growers Buy"* in *Farm Industry News (Vol. 42, January 1, 2009, No. 1)*
Pub: Informa USA, Inc.
Contact: Stephen A. Carter, Chief Executive Officer

Ed: Karen McMahon. **Description:** According to a survey regarding the buying habits among large commercial growers, most prefer to purchase from local retailers, customer service is important concerning their decision on who to buy products from, and price and convenience seem to be more important then brand.

34055 ■ *"How Many Direct Reports? Senior Leaders, Always Pressed For Time, Are Nonetheless Broadening Their Span of Control"* in *Harvard Business Review (Vol. 90, April 2012, No. 4, pp. 112)*
Pub: Harvard Business Review Press
Contact: Moderna V. Pfizer, Contact

Ed: Gary L. Neilson, Julie M. Wulf. **Price:** $8.95, hardcover. **Description:** A rise in market and geographical complexities has driven an expansion of chief executive officer control during the past 20 years. New executive development options enable CEOs to cross-collaborate, and functional leaders make up 80 percent of new positions reporting to the CEO. **Availability:** PDF; Online.

34056 ■ *"How Marketers Can Tap the Web"* in *Sales and Marketing Management (November 12, 2009)*
Description: Internet marketing strategies require careful planning and tools in order to track success. Businesses are utilizing this trend to attract new clients as well as keep customers they already have satisfied. Advice on website development and design is provided. **Availability:** Online.

34057 ■ *"How to Survive This Mess"* in *Crain's Chicago Business (Vol. 31, April 14, 2008, No. 15, pp. 18)*
Pub: Crain Communications Inc.
Contact: Barry Asin, President

Ed: Christina Le Beau. **Description:** Small business owners can make it through a possible recession with preparations such as reviewing their balance sheet and cash flow every week and spotting trends then reacting quickly to them. **Availability:** Online.

34058 ■ *"How To Get a Loan the Web 2.0 Way"* in *Black Enterprise (Vol. 41, December 2010, No. 5, pp. 23)*
Pub: Earl G. Graves Ltd.
Contact: Earl Graves, Jr., President

Ed: John Simons. **Description:** People are turning to online peer-to-peer network for personal loans as banks are lending less money. **Availability:** Online.

34059 ■ *"How-To Workshops in St. Charles Teach Sewing, Styles"* in *St. Louis Post-Dispatch (September 14, 2010)*
Pub: St. Louis Post-Dispatch LLC.
Contact: Gilbert Bailon, Editor
E-mail: gbailon@post-dispatch.com

Ed: Kalen Ponche. **Description:** Profile of DIY Style Workshop in St. Charles, Missouri, where sewing, designing and teaching is offered. The shop is home base for DIY Style, a Website created by mother and daughter to teach younger people how to sew. **Availability:** Online.

34060 ■ *"The Human Factor"* in *Canadian Business (Vol. 80, October 8, 2007, No. 20, pp. 22)*
Description: David Foot, a demographer and an economics professor at the University of Toronto, talks about Canada's future, including economic and demographic trends. He discusses activities that should be done by businessmen in order to prepare for the future. He also addresses the role of the Canadian government in economic development. **Availability:** Print; Online.

34061 ■ *"HVAC/R Evolution"* in *Indoor Comfort Marketing (Vol. 70, March 2011, No. 3, pp. 14)*
Description: Tools and techniques for heating, ventilation, air conditioning and refrigeration are examined.

34062 ■ *"ICC Works on Prescriptive Green Construction Code"* in *Contractor (Vol. 56, October 2009, No. 10, pp. 1)*
Ed: Robert P. Mader. **Description:** International Code Council launched an initiative to create a green construction code that focuses on existing commercial buildings. The initiative's timeline will include public meetings leading up to a final draft that will be available in 2010. **Availability:** Print; Online.

34063 ■ *Import/Export Kit For Dummies*
Pub: John Wiley & Sons, Inc.
Contact: Christina Van Tassell, Executive Vice President Chief Financial Officer

Ed: John J. Capela. **Released:** 3rd Edition. **Price:** $26.99, paperback; $17.99, E-book. **Description:** Provides entrepreneurs and small- to medium-size businesses with information required to start exporting products globally and importing goods to the U.S. Topics covered include the ins and outs of developing or expanding operations to gain market share, with details on the top ten countries in which America trades, from Canada to Germany to China. **Availability:** E-book; Print.

34064 ■ *"In the Hot Finance Jobs, Women Are Still Shut Out"* in *Harvard Business Review (Vol. 90, July-August 2012, No. 7-8, pp. 30)*
Pub: Harvard Business Review Press
Contact: Moderna V. Pfizer, Contact

Ed: Nori Gerardo Lietz. **Price:** $6, PDF and hardcover black and white. **Description:** Although women constitute a significant proportion of business school graduates, the percentage of senior investment professionals who are female remain in a single-digit figure. Active effort will be needed to change corporate culture and industry awareness to raise this figure. **Availability:** Print; PDF; Online.

34065 ■ *"Indigenous Tourism Operators: The Vanguard of Economic Recovery in the Chatham Islands"* in *International Journal of Entrepreneurship and Small Business (Vol. 10, July 6, 2010, No. 4)*
Ed: Andrew Cardow, Peter Wiltshier. **Description:** Emergent enthusiasm for tourism as a savior for economic development in the Chatham Islands of New Zealand is highlighted. **Availability:** Online.

34066 ■ *"Indoor Tanning Business Is Drying Up, Says National Group"* in *Idaho Business Review (August 20, 2014)*
Pub: BridgeTower Media
Contact: Adam Reinebach, President

Description: According to the Indoor Tanning Association in Washington DC, the recession, a new tax under the Affordable Care Act on indoor tanning businesses, and legislation by states to ban minors using tanning booths, have all contributed to their slow decline. Idaho has lost one-third of the tanning firms that once operated in the state. Statistical data included.

34067 ■ *"Industry Escalates Lobbying Efforts For Loan Program"* in *Crain's Detroit Business (Vol. 24, September 22, 2008, No. 38, pp. 22)*
Pub: Crain Communications Inc.
Contact: Barry Asin, President

Ed: Jay Greene, Ryan Beene, Harry Stoffer. **Description:** Auto suppliers such as Lear Corp., which is best known for vehicle seating, also supplies high-voltage wiring for Ford hybrids and is developing other hybrid components. These suppliers are joining automakers in lobbying for the loan program which would promote the accelerated development of fuel-efficient vehicles. **Availability:** Print; PDF; Online.

34068 ■ *"Innovation Can Be Imperative for Those in Hands-On Trades"* in *Crain's Cleveland Business (Vol. 28, November 12, 2007, No. 45)*
Pub: Crain Communications Inc.
Contact: K. C. Crain, President

Ed: Harriet Tramer. **Description:** Discusses the importance of networking and innovative marketing concerning those in art and restoration trades. **Availability:** Online.

34069 ■ *"Innovation Central: Tech, Tweets, and Trolls"* in *Inc. (Vol. 36, September 2014, No. 7, pp. 102)*
Pub: Mansueto Ventures L.L.C.
Contact: Stephanie Mehta, Chief Executive Officer

Description: Results of a survey regarding the ways small business is using technology to grow their businesses is presented. Information covers social media applications, government software patents, trends impacting small business, and the most innovative technology companies. **Availability:** Print; Online.

34070 ■ *"Intel Joins Movement to Turn Cube Farms Into Wide-Open Spaces"* in *Sacramento Business Journal (Vol. 28, May 27, 2011, No. 13, pp. 1)*
Pub: Sacramento Business Journal
Contact: Stephanie Fretwell, Director
E-mail: sfretwell@bizjournals.com

Ed: Melanie Turner. **Description:** Intel Corporation has remodeled its facility in Folsom, California. The renovation has required some workers to give up their cubicles. Comments from executives are included.

34071 ■ *"Is Business Ethics Getting Better? A Historical Perspective"* in *Business Ethics Quarterly (Vol. 21, April 2011, No. 2, pp. 335)*
Ed: Joanne B. Ciulla. **Released:** Volume 21, Issue 2. **Description:** The question 'Is Business Ethics Getting Better?' as a heuristic for discussing the importance of history in understanding business and ethics is answered. The article uses a number of examples to illustrate how the same ethical problems in business have been around for a long time. It describes early attempts at the Harvard School of Business to use business history as a means of teaching students about moral and social values. In the end, the author suggests that history may be another way to teach ethics, enrich business ethics courses, and develop the perspective and vision in future business leaders. **Availability:** Online.

34072 ■ *"Is Fierce Competition Loosening Standards?"* in *Birmingham Business Journal (Vol. 31, February 14, 2014, No. 7, pp. 6)*
Pub: American City Business Journals, Inc.
Contact: Mike Olivieri, Executive Vice President

Released: Weekly. **Price:** $4, introductory 4-week offer(Digital only). **Description:** Bankers have been seeing an intense competition for business loans in the Birmingham, Alabama market because of the limited number of qualified borrowers. However, some bankers expressed concerns that the trend signals a return to pre-recession habits for lenders. **Availability:** Print; Online.

34073 ■ *"Jobs Data Show Wild Card"* in *Barron's (Vol. 90, September 6, 2010, No. 36, pp. M12)*
Pub: Barron's Editorial & Corporate Headquarters
Ed: Gene Epstein. **Description:** August 2010 jobs report revealed a 54,000 decline in non-farm payrolls and that the unemployment rate remains unchanged at 9.6 percent. The report also shows a welcome rise of 848,999 in the household-data category. The unemployment rate shows a reversed trend where men's 10.6 percent unemployment is higher than women's 8.6 percent rate. **Availability:** Online.

34074 ■ *"KC Incentives Debate Rages on Unabated"* in *The Business Journal-Serving Metropolitan Kansas City (Vol. 26, September 5, 2008, No. 52)*
Pub: American City Business Journals, Inc.
Contact: Mike Olivieri, Executive Vice President
Ed: Rob Roberts. **Description:** Debate on the new economic development and incentives policy adopted by the Kansas City Council is still on. The city's Planned Industrial Expansion Authority has rejected a standard property tax abatement proposal. The real estate development community has opposed the rejection of proposed the tax incentives policy. **Availability:** Online.

34075 ■ *"The Keeper of Records"* in *Black Enterprise (Vol. 41, December 2010, No. 5, pp. 54)*
Pub: Earl G. Graves Ltd.
Contact: Earl Graves, Jr., President
Ed: Denise A. Campbell. **Description:** Medical billing and coding, submission of claims to health insurance companies and Medicare or Medicaid for payment is one of the fastest growing disciplines in healthcare. **Availability:** Online.

34076 ■ *"Keith Crain: Business Must Stand Up And Be Counted"* in *Crain's Detroit Business (Vol. 24, October 6, 2008, No. 40, pp. 6)*
Pub: Crain Communications Inc.
Contact: Barry Asin, President
Description: Discusses the challenges that the new mayor of Detroit faces concerning business, the state of the economy and the exceptionally tight budget the city is running on, which includes a lot of red ink. It is very likely that the city is going to see tax revenues fall substantially in the next few months and business leaders may find it in their favor to lend their support to the new mayor as well as provide him with the executive talent necessary to overcome some of these crucial issues. **Availability:** Online.

34077 ■ *"LA Passes HET Ordinance, California Greens Code"* in *Contractor (Vol. 56, September 2009, No. 9, pp. 1)*
Ed: Candace Roulo. **Description:** Los Angeles City Council has passed a Water Efficiency Requirements ordinance. The law mandates lower low-flow plumbing requirements for plumbing fixtures installed in new buildings and retrofits. Under the ordinance, a toilet's maximum flush volume may not exceed 1.28-gpf. **Availability:** Print; Online.

34078 ■ *"Lawyers Lock Up Cops as Clients"* in *Sacramento Business Journal (Vol. 28, April 8, 2011, No. 6, pp. 1)*
Pub: Sacramento Business Journal
Contact: Stephanie Fretwell, Director
E-mail: sfretwell@bizjournals.com
Ed: Kathy Robertson. **Released:** Weekly. **Price:** $4. **Description:** Sacramento-based law firm Mastagni, Holstedt and Chiurazzi has grown its client base by specializing in law enforcement labor issues. The firm represents 80,000 public sector correctional officers in the US. The firm has been experiencing an increase in new business as public sector employers face huge budget deficits. **Availability:** Online.

34079 ■ *"Layoffs Continue to Be a Drag on Region's Recovery"* in *Philadelphia Business Journal (Vol. 28, January 22, 2010, No. 49, pp. 1)*
Pub: Philadelphia Business Journal
Contact: Sierra Quinn, Director

E-mail: squinn@bizjournals.com
Ed: Athena D. Merritt. **Description:** Mass layoffs continue to hamper Pennsylvania's economic recovery. Job losses are predicted to decline in 2010. **Availability:** Online.

34080 ■ *"Lead-Free Products must Meet Requirements"* in *Contractor (Vol. 56, September 2009, No. 9, pp. 30)*
Ed: Robert Gottermeier. **Description:** United States Environmental Protection Agency's adoption of the Safe Drinking Water Act is aimed at lowering lead extraction levels from plumbing products. Manufacturers have since deleaded brass and bronze potable water products. Meanwhile, California and Vermont have passed a law limiting lead content for potable water conveying plumbing products. **Availability:** Print; Online.

34081 ■ *"Legislators Must Cut Cost of Government"* in *Crain's Detroit Business (Vol. 24, October 6, 2008, No. 40, pp. 6)*
Pub: Crain Communications Inc.
Contact: Barry Asin, President
Description: Southeast and West Michigan business leaders are setting aside their differences and have proposed clear agendas, ranging from eliminating the Michigan Business Tax to overhauling public employee and retiree benefits and pensions. Lawmakers must also come together to find solutions for the state's economy and discover an entirely new vision for the future of Michigan business. **Availability:** Print; Online.

34082 ■ *"The Lost Opportunity for a Canadian Steel Giant"* in *Globe & Mail (April 23, 2007, pp. B1)*
Ed: Greg Keenan. **Description:** The efforts of Algoma Steel Inc. to create a Canadian steel manufacturer that could survive the global trends of consolidation in the steel industry are described. The company's efforts to acquire Stelco Inc., Ivaco Inc. and Slater Steel Inc. are discussed. **Availability:** Print; Online.

34083 ■ *"A Love of Likes: What's a Facebook Nod Worth to a Business? Serious Sales Growth, Say Some"* in *Boston Business Journal (Vol. 31, July 8, 2011, No. 24, pp. 1)*
Pub: Boston Business Journal
Contact: Carolyn M. Jones, President
E-mail: cmjones@bizjournals.com
Ed: Lisa Van der Pool. **Description:** An increasing number of companies in Boston, Massachusetts have been keen on getting Facebook 'likes' from people. Business owners realize that Facebook 'likes' could generate sales and based on some studies, equate to specific dollar values.

34084 ■ *"Make It Yourself: Home Sewing, Gender, and Culture, 1890-1930"* in *Business History Review (Vol. 84, Autumn 2010, No. 3, pp. 602)*
Description: Review of the publication, 'Make It Yourself: Home Sewing, Gender, and Culture, 1890-1930, a nonfiction work. **Availability:** Download; PDF; Online.

34085 ■ *"Managers as Visionaries: a Skill That Can Be Learned"* in *Strategy and Leadership (Vol. 39, September-October 2011, No. 5, pp. 56-58)*
Pub: Emerald Group Publishing Limited
Contact: Erika Valenti, President
Ed: Stephen M. Millett. **Description:** A study uses research findings to examine whether visionary management can be learned. Results conclude that managers can learn visionary management through intuitive pattern recognition of trends and by using scenarios for anticipating and planning for likely future occurrences.

34086 ■ *Managing the Older Worker: How to Prepare for the New Organizational Order*
Pub: Harvard Business Press
Contact: Gabriela Allmi, Regional Manager
E-mail: gabriela.allmi@hbsp.harvard.edu

Ed: Peter Cappelli, Bill Novelli. **Description:** Your organization needs older workers more than ever: They transfer knowledge between generations, transmit your company's values to new hires, make excellent mentors for younger employees, and provide a 'just in time' workforce for special projects. **Availability:** Print; Audio.

34087 ■ *"Mapping Out a Career: An Analysis of Geographic Concentration of Occupations"* in *Occupational Outlook Quarterly (Vol. 54, Fall 2010, No. 3, pp. 12)*
Pub: U.S. Department of Labor Bureau of Labor Statistics
Contact: Amrit Kohli, Director
E-mail: kohli.amrit@bls.gov
Ed: Audrey Watson. **Description:** Geographic distribution of occupations is studied, along with lifestyle considerations when choosing a career. **Availability:** PDF; Online.

34088 ■ *"Market Watch: A Sampling of Advisory Opinion US Stock Price Trends, Economic Effects of Global Trade, Chinese Economic Trends"* in *Barron's (Vol. 92, July 23, 2012, No. 30, pp. M14)*
Ed: Richard M. Salsman, Jack Ablin, Francois Sicart. **Description:** US stocks are considered inexpensive due to their low price-earnings ratios compared to levels before the global financial crisis. The US economy is becoming more dependent on the rest of the worldas a result of global trade. The Chinese economy continues to have strong economic growth despite a slowdown. **Availability:** Online.

34089 ■ *"Marketing in the Digital World: Here's How to Craft a Smart Online Strategy"* in *Black Enterprise (Vol. 40, July 2010, No. 12, pp. 47)*
Pub: Earl G. Graves Ltd.
Contact: Earl Graves, Jr., President
Ed: Sonya A. Donaldson. **Description:** Social media is an integral part of any small business plan in addressing marketing, sales, and branding strategies.

34090 ■ *"Marketing Scholarship 2.0"* in *Journal of Marketing (Vol. 75, July 2011, No. 4, pp. 225)*
Pub: American Marketing Association
Contact: Bennie F. Johnson, Chief Executive Officer
Ed: Richard J. Lutz. **Released:** Volume: 75 issue: 4. **Description:** A study of the implications of changing environment and newer collaborative models for marketing knowledge production and dissemination is presented. Crowdsourcing has become a frequently employed strategy in industry. Academic researchers should collaborate more as well as the academe and industry, to make sure that important problems are being investigated. **Availability:** PDF.

34091 ■ *"Maryland Hospitals Cope with Rare Drop in Patient Admissions"* in *Baltimore Business Journal (Vol. 29, September 23, 2011, No. 20, pp. 1)*
Pub: Boston Business Journal
Contact: Carolyn M. Jones, President
E-mail: cmjones@bizjournals.com
Ed: Scott Dance. **Description:** Admissions to Maryland hospitals have dropped to less than 700,000 in fiscal year 2010 and initial figures for fiscal 2011 show in-patient admissions are now nearing 660,000. The decline can be partly attributed to new ways health insurers are paying hospitals for care and to the financial reward hospitals get for cutting back on admissions. **Availability:** Online.

34092 ■ *"MBT Add-On: Gone by 2012?"* in *Crain's Detroit Business (Vol. 24, October 6, 2008, No. 40, pp. 1)*
Pub: Crain Communications Inc.
Contact: Barry Asin, President
Ed: Amy Lane. **Description:** Discusses the Michigan Business Tax (MBT), which has angered many businesses in the state due to the addition of a 21.99 percent surcharge. Although the tax policy will cut taxes on 63 percent of businesses in the state and represent no tax liability change for another nine

percent of firms, other businesses will see increases of 100 percent or more. This increase means that many business owners will be forced to relocate or close their establishment and others will have to eliminate jobs. Lawmakers are attempting to find a solution to this problem. **Availability:** Print; Online.

34093 ■ *"Md.'s Film Industry Professionals have to Leave the State to Find Work: Exiting Stage Left" in Baltimore Business Journal (Vol. 28, June 18, 2010, No. 6, pp. 1)*
Pub: Baltimore Business Journal
Contact: Rhonda Pringle, President
E-mail: rpringle@bizjournals.com
Ed: Scott Dance. **Released:** Weekly. **Description:** Film professionals including crew members and actors have been leaving Maryland to find work in other states such as Michigan, Louisiana, and Georgia where bigger budgets and film production incentives are given. Other consequences of this trend in local TV and film production are discussed. **Availability:** Print.

34094 ■ *"Medicaid Insurers See Growth in Small Biz Market" in Boston Business Journal (Vol. 31, July 15, 2011, No. 25, pp. 1)*
Pub: Boston Business Journal
Contact: Carolyn M. Jones, President
E-mail: cmjones@bizjournals.com
Ed: Julie M. Donnelly. **Description:** BMC HealthNet Plan announced plans to launch small business products to serve small businesses that are priced out of rising premium rates at large Massachusetts insurers. BMC joined competitors CeltiCare Health Plan and Neighborhood Health Plan in augmenting its core business. **Availability:** Print; Online.

34095 ■ *"Meet the White-Label Cash Kings" in Globe & Mail (April 23, 2007, pp. B1)*
Ed: Tara Perkins, Tavia Grant. **Description:** The services provided by the independent Canadian companies managing automated banking machines are described. The trends of ownership of automated banking machines in Canada are discussed. **Availability:** Online.

34096 ■ *"Men and Menu: A Switch in the Kitchen" in Barron's (Vol. 88, March 24, 2008, No. 12, pp. 17)*
Pub: Dow Jones & Company Inc.
Contact: Almar Latour, Chief Executive Officer
Ed: Robin Goldwyn Blumenthal. **Description:** Men are doing more kitchen duties, with 18 percent of meals at home being made by men in 2007 compared to 11 percent four years previously. Young wives, however, choose to forgo work and stay at home. **Availability:** Online.

34097 ■ *"Messaging Apps: What the New Face of Social Media Means for Brands" in New Generation Latino Consortium (December 2010)*
Ed: Gary Fackler. **Description:** Latina bloggers carve out a new niche in social media that helps preserve their unique cultural identities. **Availability:** Online.

34098 ■ *"Michaud Touts Small-Business Credentials" in Bangor Daily News (September 10, 2010)*
Pub: Bangor Daily News
Contact: David M. Austin, Contact
Ed: Nick Sambides, Jr. **Description:** Mike Michaud, Democrat, is running against a Republican challenger in the 2nd District and states he will support the Small Business Jobs Tax Relief Act if reelected. **Availability:** Print; Online.

34099 ■ *"Millennials Driving New Types of Space" in Philadelphia Business Journal (Vol. 33, April 25, 2014, No. 11, pp. 8)*
Pub: American City Business Journals, Inc.
Contact: Mike Olivieri, Executive Vice President
Description: The trends in the layout of office spaces catering to millennial workers are discussed by a panel of experts at a meeting of the Central Philadelphia Development Corporation and Center City District in Pennsylvania. These tenants like older

buildings with wide open spaces, urban areas and the ability to work by bike or foot and co-working spaces. **Availability:** Online.

34100 ■ *"MoneyGram Hopes Digital Push Will Click With Customers" in Dallas Business Journal (Vol. 37, July 4, 2014, No. 43, pp. 17)*
Pub: American City Business Journals, Inc.
Contact: Mike Olivieri, Executive Vice President
Released: Weekly. **Price:** $4, introductory 4-week offer(Digital only). **Description:** Reports on Money-Gram's recent release of a digital monitoring system, which will allow it to work more closely with customers, is profiled. This digital monitoring system will aggregate data from social media platforms and enable the company to identify customer needs and trends across the money transfer industry. It will help MoneyGram outshine its rivals in the money transfer business. **Availability:** Print; Online.

34101 ■ *"More Brides, Grooms Say 'I Do' to Interracial Marriage" in Black Enterprise (Vol. 41, August 2010, No. 1, pp. 36)*
Pub: Earl G. Graves Ltd.
Contact: Earl Graves, Jr., President
Description: According to a recent survey conducted by Pew Research Center, a record 14.6 percent of all new marriages in the U.S. in 2008 were interracial. Statistical data included.

34102 ■ *"More Small Businesses in Baltimore Willing to Fund Employees' Health Benefits" in Baltimore Business Journal (Vol. 28, June 18, 2010, No. 6, pp. 1)*
Pub: Baltimore Business Journal
Contact: Rhonda Pringle, President
E-mail: rpringle@bizjournals.com
Ed: Scott Graham. **Description:** An increasing number of small businesses in Maryland are tapping into potentially cheaper self-funded health plans instead of providing fully insured benefits to employees through traditional health plans. Self-funded health plans charge employers for health care up to a specified level. Economic implications of self-funded plans to small businesses are discussed.

34103 ■ *"Myths of Deleveraging" in Barron's (Vol. 90, August 23, 2010, No. 34, pp. M14)*
Pub: Barron's Editorial & Corporate Headquarters
Ed: Gene Epstein. **Description:** The opposite is true against reports about deleveraging or the decrease in credit since inflation-adjusted-investment factories and equipment rose 7.8 percent in the first quarter of 2010. On consumer deleveraging, sales of homes through credit is weak but there is a trend towards more realistic homeownership and consumer spending on durable goods rose 8.8 percent. **Availability:** Online.

34104 ■ *"Need Fiber in Your Diet? Pour Some Milk" in Globe & Mail (April 10, 2007, pp. B7)*
Ed: William Illsey Atkinson. **Description:** The growing market and demand for functional foods and neutraceuticals in Canada is discussed. The research being conducted by University of Manitoba's Richardson Centre for Functional Foods and Nutraceuticals to explore new health compounds in food is highlighted. **Availability:** Online.

34105 ■ *"A New Day is Dawning" in Indoor Comfort Marketing (Vol. 70, August 2011, No. 8, pp. 18)*
Description: New trends in the HVAC/R industry regarding biofuels and bioheat are explored. **Availability:** Online.

34106 ■ *"New Food Concepts Flood Market" in Business Journal (Vol. 30, June 8, 2012, No. 2, pp. 1)*
Pub: American City Business Journals, Inc.
Contact: Mike Olivieri, Executive Vice President
Ed: John Vomhof, Jr. **Released:** Weekly. **Price:** $4, introductory 4-week offer(Digital only). **Description:** Twin Cities Metropolitan Area has seen the boom of the frozen yogurt segment over the past few years and the rise of fast casual sandwich shops, which

are helping fuel activity in Minnesota's real estate market. However, there are skeptics who doubt whether all of the new concepts can survive. **Availability:** Print; Online.

34107 ■ *"New Health Care Payment Model Coming to Boise" in Idaho Business Review (August 20, 2014)*
Pub: BridgeTower Media
Contact: Adam Reinebach, President
Description: Direct primary care is coming to the Boise, Idaho area. The process offers patients a range of treatment options, including most wellness and acute care but not hospital visits or some pharmaceuticals, for a monthly membership fee. This trend does not allow health insurance or health savings accounts to pay the monthly fees. Proponents believe direct primary care benefits doctors, patients and the overall health system in many ways.

34108 ■ *"A New Mix of Tenants Settles In Downtown" in Crain's New York Business (Vol. 24, January 13, 2008, No. 2, pp. 26)*
Pub: Crain Communications, Inc.
Contact: Jessica Botos, Manager, Marketing
E-mail: jessica.botos@crainsnewyork.com
Ed: Andrew Marks. **Description:** More and more nonfinancial firms are relocating downtown due to the new retailers and restaurants that are reshaping the look and feel of lower Manhattan.

34109 ■ *"The New Nimble" in Barron's (Vol. 90, August 30, 2010, No. 35, pp. S12)*
Pub: Barron's Editorial & Corporate Headquarters
Ed: Suzanne McGee. **Description:** Financial advisors are making investments based on short-lived market trends due to the uncertainty in the long-term market. This strategy can be demanding and advisors should only try it if they are confident about their skill in spotting short-term trends. **Availability:** Online.

34110 ■ *"New Recession-Proof Internet Marketing Package Allows Businesses to Ramp Up Web Traffic and Profits" in PR Newswire (January 25, 2010)*
Pub: PR Newswire Association LLC.
Description: Profile of Reel Web Design, a leading marketing firm in New York City that caters to small to medium sized businesses with smaller budgets that need substantial return on investment; Reel Web Design offers video production and submission, web design and maintenance and press release writing among additional services. **Availability:** Online.

34111 ■ *The New Role of Regional Management*
Pub: Palgrave Macmillan
Ed: Bjorn Ambos, Bodo B. Schlegelmilch. **Released:** 2010. **Description:** Regional management is becoming more important to companies as they expand globally. This book explores the challenges of European, United States and Asian companies and outlines how regional headquarters can develop into Dynamic Competence Relay centers to master these issues. **Availability:** E-book; Print.

34112 ■ *"Nexstar Super Meeting Breaks Business Barriers" in Contractor (Vol. 56, November 2009, No. 11, pp. 3)*
Ed: Candace Roulo. **Description:** Around 400 Nexstar members met to discuss the trends in the HVAC industry and the economic outlook for 2010. Former lead solo pilot John Foley for the Blue Angels made a presentation on how a business can increase overall productivity based on the culture of the Blue Angels. Some breakout sessions tackled how to optimize workflow and marketing. **Availability:** Print; Online.

34113 ■ *"No Shortage of Challenges for Cross-Border Trade" in Canadian Sailings (June 30, 2008)*
Description: Pros and cons of the North American Free Trade Agreement are examined. The agreement between the U.S. and Canada concerning trade was an essential step toward securing economic growth

for Canadian citizens. Two-way trade between the counties has tripled since the agreement and accounts for 7.1 million American and 3 million Canadian jobs. **Availability:** Print; Online; PDF.

34114 ■ *Non-Standard Employment under Globalization: Flexible Work and Social Security in the Newly Industrializing Countries*

Pub: Palgrave Macmillan

Ed: Koichi Usami. **Released:** First edition. **Description:** Expansion of non-standard employment under globalization is being recognized in all of the newly industrialized countries. The book examines deregulation of labor markets, social protection for nonstandard workers, and social security reforms in accordance with the transformation of employment.

34115 ■ *"Nortel Makes Customers Stars in New Campaign" in Brandweek (Vol. 49, April 21, 2008, No. 16, pp. 8)*

Description: Nortel has launched a new television advertising campaign in which the business-to-business communications technology provider cast senior executives in 30-second TV case studies that show how Nortel's technology helped their businesses innovate. **Availability:** Online.

34116 ■ *"North American Pet Health Insurance Market Poised for Growth" in Pet Product News (Vol. 64, December 2010, No. 12, pp. 4)*

Ed: David Lummis. **Description:** The pet health insurance market is expected to further grow after posting about $350 million in sales in 2009, a gain of more than $40 million. Pet insurance firms have offered strategies such as product humanization in response to this growth forecast. Meanwhile, pet insurance shoppers have been provided more by insurance firms with wider choices. **Availability:** Online.

34117 ■ *"Nowspeed and OneSource to Conduct Webinar: How to Develop Social Media Content That Gets Results" in Marketwired (December 14, 2009)*

Pub: Comtex News Network Inc.

Contact: Kan Devnani, President

Description: OneSource, a leading provider of global business information, and Nowspeed, an Internet marketing agency, will conduct a webinar titled "How to Develop Social Media Content That Gets Results" in order to provide marketers insight into how to develop and optimize effective social media content to get consumer results that translate into purchases and lead generation. **Availability:** Print; Mailing list; Online.

34118 ■ *"Older, But Not Wiser" in Canadian Business (Vol. 85, July 16, 2012, No. 11-12, pp. 54)*

Ed: Matthew McClearn, Michael McCullough. **Description:** Data from Statistics Canada revealed that two-thirds of workers aged 55 and above have some form of debt from mortgage to credit card balance while its one-third among the retired. Some factors contributing to the trend are the decline in borrowing costs, real estate, and older Canadians' car purchasing behavior. **Availability:** Print; Online.

34119 ■ *"On the House: Housing Developers Try to Read Generation Y" in Philadelphia Inquirer (December 2, 2010)*

Pub: The Philadelphia Inquirer

Contact: Elizabeth H. Hughes, Chief Executive Officer

Ed: Al Heavens. **Description:** Results of a survey conducted with Generation Y individuals are examined, focusing on housing developments and whether this particular generation prefers suburban or rural lifestyles. Generation Y encompasses people ages 18 to 32 years old. Statistical data included. **Availability:** Online.

34120 ■ *On the Make: Clerks and the Quest for Capital in Nineteenth-Century America*

Pub: New York University Press

Contact: Ellen Chodosh, Director

E-mail: ellen.chodosh@nyu.edu

Ed: Brian P. Luskey. **Released:** January 01, 2010. **Price:** $27, paperback; $89, cloth. **Description:** Through exploration into the diaries, newspapers, credit reports, census data, advice literature and fiction, the book presents the origins of the white collar culture, the antebellum clerk. **Availability:** E-book; Print.

34121 ■ *"On the Money" in San Antonio Business Journal (Vol. 28, June 27, 2014, No. 20, pp. 4)*

Description: The total compensation for the top 18 highest paid public company CEOs in San Antonio, Texas has increased 11 percent in the 2013 fiscal year to $74.8 million compared to 2012 fiscal year. The average total CEO compensation in the city was $4.15 million, an 11 percent increase from the 2013 list. The trend in the 2014 highest paid CEOs list is discussed. **Availability:** Print; Online.

34122 ■ *"One Hundred Years of Excellence in Business Education: What Have We Learned?" in Business Horizons (January-February 2008)*

Pub: Elsevier Advanced Technology Publications

Ed: Frank Acito, Patricia M. McDougall, Daniel C. Smith. **Description:** Business schools have to be more innovative, efficient and nimble, so that the quality of the next generation of business leaders is improved. The Kelley School of Business, Indiana University has long been a leader in business education. The trends that influence the future of business education and useful success principles are discussed. **Availability:** PDF; Online.

34123 ■ *"Online Book Sales Surpass Bookstores" in Information Today (Vol. 28, September 2011, No. 8, pp. 11)*

Pub: Information Today Inc.

Contact: Thomas H. Hogan, President

Ed: Cindy Martine. **Description:** Online book sales outpaced bookstore purchases in the United States, signaling a shift in the US book industry. Statistical data included.

34124 ■ *"Opportunity Knocks" in Small Business Opportunities (September 2008)*

Description: Profile of YourOffice USA, a franchise that provides home-based and small businesses cost-effective and efficient support through "virtual" offices that are available as much or as little as the client needs it; they also supply necessary tools such as a professional business address, private mailbox service, personalized telephone answering and more that supports clients who want to look, act and operate with an advanced business image. **Availability:** Online.

34125 ■ *"Organic Chain Scouting Cincinatti Sites, Including Kenwood" in Business Courier (Vol. 27, December 3, 2010, No. 31, pp. 1)*

Pub: Business Courier

Ed: Tom Demeropolis. **Description:** Asheville, North Carolina-based Earth Fare has been planning to add a total of six stores in 2011, including the potential opening of more than one store in the Greater Cincinnati area market. Earth Fare has not named specific locations but Kenwood area was reportedly being considered for its first location. Insights on growing trends toward health food stores are also given. **Availability:** Print; Online.

34126 ■ *"Orlando Patents Forecast Biz Diversity and Growth" in Orlando Business Journal (Vol. 30, April 18, 2014, No. 43, pp. 4)*

Pub: American City Business Journals, Inc.

Contact: Mike Olivieri, Executive Vice President

Released: Weekly. **Price:** $8, introductory 4-week offer(Digital & Print). **Description:** Orlando, Florida ranked among cities in the state in terms of number

of patents filed. Around 275 patents were issued to Orlando-based inventors and businesses in 2013. The increase in the number of high technology companies entering the city has contributed to this trend. **Availability:** Print; Online.

34127 ■ *"Outlook In Other Industries" in Crain's Detroit Business (Vol. 30, January 6, 2014, No. 1, pp. 3)*

Pub: Crain Communications Inc.

Contact: Barry Asin, President

Released: January 6, 2014. **Description:** Outlook for industries in the Detroit area are listed, including small business growth, restaurants, defense contracts, nonprofits, transportation, auto suppliers, healthcare, bankruptcy, and government. **Availability:** Print; PDF; Online.

34128 ■ *"Overheating Taking Place? Pay Attention to Details.." in Indoor Comfort Marketing (Vol. 70, March 2011, No. 3)*

Description: Boiler facts are outlined to help the small HVAC company when servicing customers. **Availability:** PDF; Online.

34129 ■ *"Paper Replaces PVC for Gift Cards" in American Printer (Vol. 128, June 1, 2011, No. 6)*

Description: Monadnock Envi Card Stock replaces paper for gift cards, loyalty cards, membership cards, hotel keys and durable signage. This renewable wood fiber alternative to PVC card materials comes from Monadock Paper Mills. **Availability:** Online.

34130 ■ *"Parkland Approves First "Luxury" Consignment Shop" in Sun Sentinel (May 7, 2012)*

Ed: Lisa J. Huriash. **Description:** SincerelyYours is a very upscale consignment shop located in the upscale area of Parkland, Florida. This trend toward high-end luxury consignment boutiques is being seen across the country because consumers of luxury goods can be rid of their items, while those wishing high quality things can purchase at a substantial savings. **Availability:** Print; Online.

34131 ■ *"Pay Heed to 'Smack Stack" in Puget Sound Business Journal (Vol. 35, May 16, 2014, No. 4, pp. 6)*

Pub: American City Business Journals, Inc.

Contact: Mike Olivieri, Executive Vice President

Description: Technology consultant, Geoffrey Moore, discloses the topics he plans to discuss at the annual State of Technology Luncheon held in Washington on May 19, 2014. He will explore the impact of technology and business trends on public-policy making and regulations. **Availability:** Online.

34132 ■ *"PeoplesVC Becomes the 1st Stock-Based Crowdfunding Site to Open Its Doors to Investors" in Investment Weekly (June 23, 2012)*

Description: Peoples VC is the first equity-based crowdfunding site to invite public investors to set up individual crowdfunding investment accounts. Equity-based crowdfunding allows funders to receive stock in return for their investment into companies. In the past, this process was only available to venture capitalists and accredited investors. **Availability:** Print; Online.

34133 ■ *"Pepperidge Farm Getting New Life" in Orlando Business Journal (Vol. 28, August 24, 2012, No. 28, pp. 1)*

Pub: Baltimore Business Journal

Contact: Rhonda Pringle, President

E-mail: rpringle@bizjournals.com

Description: The Pepperidge Farm brand could see renewal with parent company Campbell Soup's hiring of Irene Chang Britt as president. Britt, reputed for growing brands and businesses through her attention on consumer needs and marketplace trends, will be the first woman to lead Pepperidge Farm after founder Margaret Rudkin. Other insights into Britt's career as a business leader are presented. **Availability:** Print; Online.

34134 ■ *The Post-American World*
Pub: W.W. Norton & Company Ltd.
Contact: Stanley Kubrick, Director
Ed: Fareed Zakaria. **Released:** Version 2.0. **Price:** $16.95, paperback; $26.95, hardcover. **Description:** Analyses of the changes taking place as new countries are rising as status players challenging American dominance. **Availability:** Print.

34135 ■ *The Power of Social Innovation: How Civic Entrepreneurs Ignite Community Networks for Good*
Pub: John Wiley & Sons, Inc.
Contact: Christina Van Tassell, Executive Vice President Chief Financial Officer
Ed: Stephen Goldsmith, Tim Burke, Gigi Georges. **Released:** March 01, 2010. **Price:** $44, Hardcover; $35.99, E-Book; $44, hardcover. **Description:** This seminal book provides tools for civic entrepreneurs to create healthier communities and promote innovative solutions to public and social problems. It shows how to effectively tackle the intractable issues facing the country. **Availability:** E-book; Print.

34136 ■ *"A Precious Resource: Investing In the Fate of Fresh Water" in Black Enterprise (Vol. 38, February 2008, No. 7, pp. 44)*
Pub: Earl G. Graves Ltd.
Contact: Earl Graves, Jr., President
Ed: Charles Keenan. **Description:** Despite rising oil prices, water may become the most precious commodity in years to come because the world's supply of drinkable water is dwindling. **Availability:** Online.

34137 ■ *Predictably Irrational: The Hidden Forces That Shape Our Decisions*
Pub: HarperCollins Publishers L.L.C.
Contact: Brian Murray, President
Ed: Dan Ariely. **Released:** April 27, 2014. **Price:** $16.99, trade pb. **Description:** Behaviorists are bringing the economics profession around to realizing that human beings are impulsive, shortsighted and procrastinating in behavior. Economists are using this information to market products to consumers. **Availability:** E-book; Print.

34138 ■ *"Private Equity Firms Focus on Failing Banks" in Baltimore Business Journal (Vol. 28, July 16, 2010, No. 10, pp. 1)*
Pub: Baltimore Business Journal
Contact: Rhonda Pringle, President
E-mail: rpringle@bizjournals.com
Ed: Gary Haber. **Description:** Four deals in which assets of failed banks were acquired by private equity firms have been approved by the Federal Deposit Insurance Corporation in the past couple of years. Bay Bank FSK, for example, purchased Bay National Bank's assets in July 2010. Forecasts on more private equity acquisitions in the community banking industry are given. **Availability:** Print; Online.

34139 ■ *"Professor: More Will Follow CVS Ban on Tobacco" in Philadelphia Business Journal (Vol. 33, February 14, 2014, No. 1, pp. 6)*
Pub: American City Business Journals, Inc.
Contact: Mike Olivieri, Executive Vice President
Released: Weekly. **Price:** $4, introductory 4-week offer(Digital & Print). **Description:** Professor Daniel A. Hussar believes that CVS Caremark's decision to discontinue the sale of tobacco products reflects the company's concern for the health of consumers. He thinks that other drugstores will follow suit. The need for CVS Caremark to emphasize the importance of pharmacists' services is also examined. **Availability:** Print; Online.

34140 ■ *Profiting from Diversity: The Business Advantages and the Obstacles to Achieving Diversity*
Pub: Palgrave Macmillan
Released: First edition. **Description:** Although the benefits of diversity in small business are often discussed, specific ways in which organizations can profit from diversity and some of the obstacles faced are defined.

34141 ■ *"Provinces Tackle E-Waste Problem" in Canadian Electronics (Vol. 23, June-July 2008, No. 4, pp. 1)*
Pub: Action Communication Inc.
Ed: Ken Manchen. **Description:** Canadian provinces are implementing measures concerning the safe and environmentally friendly disposal of electronic waste. Alberta, British Columbia, Nova Scotia, and Saskatchewan impose an e-waste recycling fee on electronic equipment purchases. **Availability:** Online.

34142 ■ *"Quality at Bargain Prices" in Black Enterprise (Vol. 41, December 2010, No. 5, pp. 30)*
Description: Monica L. Walker, CEO of Holland Capital Management, suggests investors to watch prevailing trends in the financial market and to focus on using bottom-up analysis to identify companies meeting their investment criteria. **Availability:** Online.

34143 ■ *"The Rabbi Trust: How to Earn It Now, But Defer the Tax to the Future" in Barron's (Vol. 88, March 24, 2008, No. 12, pp. 55)*
Pub: Dow Jones & Company Inc.
Contact: Almar Latour, Chief Executive Officer
Ed: Joseph F. Gelband. **Description:** Discusses a rabbi trust which is a method of deferring taxes on compensation allowed by the Internal Revenue Service. Funding of the trust is not considered taxable. Other regulations concerning tax deferment are also discussed. **Availability:** Online.

34144 ■ *Race and Entrepreneurial Success: Black-, Asian-, and White-Owned Businesses in the United States*
Pub: The MIT Press
Ed: Robert W. Fairlie, Alicia M. Robb. **Released:** 2008. **Description:** Trends in minority small business ownership are explored, focusing on the importance of human capital, financial capital, and family business background in successful business ownership. **Availability:** E-book; Print; PDF.

34145 ■ *"The Racial Divide and the Class Struggle in the United States" in WorkingUSA (Vol. 11, September 2008, No. 3, pp. 311)*
Description: An examination of questions of race that continue to play such a prominent role in contemporary society is presented, focusing on the undermining of potential solidarity and strength of the working class movement, what sustains racists attitudes, practices and institutions, especially in the face of trends in world economic development. **Availability:** PDF; Online.

34146 ■ *"A Radical Prescription for Sales: The Reps of the Future Won't Work On Commission" in Harvard Business Review (Vol. 90, July-August 2012, No. 7-8, pp. 76)*
Pub: Harvard Business Review Press
Contact: Moderna V. Pfizer, Contact
Ed: Daniel H. Pink. **Price:** $8.95, PDF and hardcover black and white. **Description:** The complexity of sales today has rendered commissions obsolete, as transactions give way to heuristic skills. A more effective way to motivate sales representatives is a combination of 90 percent salary and 10 percent compensation linked to corporate measures rather than individual measures. **Availability:** Print; PDF; Online.

34147 ■ *Reading Financial Reports for Dummies*
Pub: John Wiley & Sons, Inc.
Contact: Christina Van Tassell, Executive Vice President Chief Financial Officer
URL(s): www.amazon.com/gp/product/1119871360/ref=as_li_tl?ie=UTF8&tag=wiley01-20
Ed: Lita Epstein. **Released:** 4th Edition. **Price:** $27.18, paperback; $18, e-book. **Description:** The fourth edition contains more new and updated information. This book is meant as a guide to help the reader interpret and understand financial reports, annual reports, balance sheets, income statements, state-

ments of cash flow and consolidated statements. Real-world examples are given. . **Availability:** E-book; Print.

34148 ■ *"Real Estate Firm Joins Trend Toward Functional Offices" in Pacific Business News (Vol. 52, April 25, 2014, No. 9, pp. 3)*
Pub: American City Business Journals, Inc.
Contact: Mike Olivieri, Executive Vice President
Released: April 25, 2014. **Price:** $4, Introductory 4-Week Offer(Digital & Print). **Description:** CBRE Inc. Hawaii has adopted the Workplace 360 model at its headquarters in downtown Honolulu as part of a companywide effort to support the way its employees work. Employees can choose nine different ways of working including height-adjustable workstations, standard wraparound desk workstations, huddle rooms and conference rooms. **Availability:** Print; Online.

34149 ■ *"Real Estate Funds Raise More Than $350M" in Business Journal Portland (Vol. 27, December 31, 2010, No. 44, pp. 1)*
Pub: Portland Business Journal
Contact: Andy Giegerich, Managing Editor
E-mail: agiegerich@bizjournals.com
Ed: Wendy Culverwell. **Description:** Oregon-based real estate funds have raised around half of the $735 million that was raised by local companies. Investors have been purchasing distressed properties. Commercial real estate prices have declined since 2007. **Availability:** Print; Online.

34150 ■ *"Real Estate Market Still in a Slump" in Montana Business Quarterly (Vol. 49, Summer 2011, No. 2, pp. 15)*
Pub: University of Montana Bureau of Business and Economic Research
Contact: Patrick Barkey, Director
E-mail: patrick.barkey@business.umt.edu
Ed: Patrick M. Barkey. **Released:** Quarterly. **Description:** Montana's housing market is still in decline with no sign of improving in the near future. Statistical data included. **Availability:** Online.

34151 ■ *"Recession and Recovery: Employment Change by Industry" in Occupational Outlook Quarterly (Vol. 58, Summer 2014, No. 2, pp. 45)*
Pub: Government Publishing Office
Contact: Hugh Nathanial Halpern, Director
Description: Data from the U.S. Bureau of Labor Statistics (BLS) is presented showing that most industries added jobs between June 2009 and March 2014, a period spanning the end of the recession into the ongoing economic recovery. The small business trends sow percent change in industry employment classified by service providing industries, good producing industries, and employment March 2014. **Availability:** Print; Online.

34152 ■ *"Remote: Office Not Required"*
Released: 2018. **Description:** The growing trend in working from home, or anywhere else, and the challenges and benefits from working from home are explored. Technology has enabled one in five global workers to telecommute and about ten percent of employees work from home. Some of the advantages in remote jobs is an increase in the talent pool, reduces turnover, lessens a firm's real estate footprint, and improves the ability to conduct business across time zones.

34153 ■ *"Restaurants Dish Up Meal Deals To Attract Customers" in Crain's Detroit Business (Vol. 24, October 6, 2008, No. 40, pp. 1)*
Pub: Crain Communications Inc.
Contact: Barry Asin, President
Ed: Nathan Skid. **Description:** Restaurateurs are devising many creative and rewarding incentives to get customers to frequent their establishments during this economic crisis. Innovative ways in which even higher-end establishments are drawing in business are discussed. **Availability:** Online.

34154 ■ *"A Rise in Rental Units"* in *Philadelphia Business Journal (Vol. 30, October 7, 2011, No. 34, pp. 1)*
Pub: Philadelphia Business Journal
Contact: Sierra Quinn, Director
E-mail: squinn@bizjournals.com

Ed: Natalie Kostelni. **Description:** Housing developers have been stepping up the construction of new apartment complexes throughout the suburbs of Pennsylvania in order to capture growing demand for rental properties. BPG Properties Ltd. has nearly 1,000 new apartments under construction. **Availability:** Online.

34155 ■ *"Rural Employment Trends in Recession and Recovery"*
Pub: CreateSpace
Released: September 24, 2014. **Price:** $10.40, paperback. **Description:** Six years of economic growth in the United States ended with the most severe recession since the Great Depression. The nature and causes of geographic variation, which include differences in the mix of industries supporting a local economy, population growth trends, and demographics of local workforces are examined to trace economic trends in recession and recovery. **Availability:** Print.

34156 ■ *"St. Louis Lending Tumbles $10 Billion Since '08"* in *Saint Louis Business Journal (Vol. 31, August 26, 2011, No. 53, pp. 1)*
Pub: Saint Louis Business Journal
Contact: Robert Bobroff, President
E-mail: rbobroff@bizjournals.com

Ed: Greg Edwards. **Description:** St. Louis, Missouri-based banks lending fell by more than 30 percent in less than three years, from about $30 billion in third and fourth quarters 2008 to about $20 billion in the most recent quarter. However, community banks revealed that they want to lend but there is no loan demand. **Availability:** Print; Online.

34157 ■ *"SEC Report On Rating Agencies Falls Short"* in *Barron's (Vol. 88, July 14, 2008, No. 28, pp. 35)*
Pub: Dow Jones & Company Inc.
Contact: Almar Latour, Chief Executive Officer

Ed: Jack Willoughby. **Description:** The Securities and Exchange Commissions report on credit-rating firms should have drawn attention to the slipshod practices in the offerings of collateralized debt obligations. The report fell short of prescribing correctives for the flawed system of these agencies' relationship with their clients. **Availability:** Online.

34158 ■ *"Sedentary Shoppers: Point, Click, Buy"* in *Barron's (Vol. 90, September 6, 2010, No. 36, pp. 11)*
Pub: Barron's Editorial & Corporate Headquarters

Ed: Vito J. Racanelli. **Description:** Non-travel online retail sales from January to July 2010 increased nine percent which indicates that online shopping for the coming holidays will be good. Online sales are outpacing traditional shopping, but pricing is still critical. **Availability:** Online.

34159 ■ *"Seen & Noted: A Home's Identity in Black and White"* in *Crain's Chicago Business (Vol. 31, April 21, 2008, No. 16, pp. 35)*
Pub: Crain Communications Inc.
Contact: Barry Asin, President

Ed: Lisa Bertagnoli. **Description:** Real estate agents are finding that showing customers a written floor plan is a trend that is growing since many buyers feel that Online virtual tours distort a room. Although floor plans cost up to $500 to have drawn up, they clearly show potential buyers the exact dimensions of rooms and how they connect. **Availability:** Online.

34160 ■ *"Self-Employment in the United States"* in *Montly Labor Review (Vol. 133, September 2010, No. 9, pp. 17)*
Pub: U.S. Department of Labor Bureau of Labor Statistics
Contact: Amrit Kohli, Director

E-mail: kohli.amrit@bls.gov

Description: Self employment in 2009 in the U.S. continued to be more common among men, Whites, Asians, and older workers and in the agriculture, construction, and services industries. **Availability:** PDF; Online.

34161 ■ *"Setting Out on Your Own? Think Franchises"* in *Crain's Cleveland Business (Vol. 28, October 8, 2007, No. 40, pp. 20)*
Pub: Crain Communications Inc.
Contact: K. C. Crain, President

Description: Franchisers are targeting baby boomers due to their willingness to put up some of their own money to open their own business. According to local franchising expert, Joel Libava, entrepreneurs should expect to pay about 15 to 30 percent of the total cost of starting the franchise out of their own pocket. **Availability:** Online.

34162 ■ *Shedworking: The Alternative Workplace Revolution*
Pub: Frances Lincoln Ltd.
Contact: Philip Cooper, Publisher
E-mail: philip.cooper@quarto.com

Ed: Alex Johnson. **Description:** Shedworking is an alternative office space for those working at home. The book features shedworkers and shedbuilders from around the world who are leading this alternative workplace revolution and why this trend is working. **Availability:** Print.

34163 ■ *"Should I or Shouldn't I?"* in *Indoor Comfort Marketing (Vol. 70, February 2011, No. 2, pp. 30)*

Description: Investment tips are shared for investing in futures options. **Availability:** Print; Online.

34164 ■ *Should Your Small Business Invest in AI?*

Ed: Jonathan Herrick. **Description:** Artificial intelligence (AI) can help your small business in a number of ways including virtual assistants, machine learning, marketing strategy, accounting, customer support, chatbots, speech recognition, marketing, and sales. This article discusses how you can use AI in some of these areas. **Availability:** Online.

34165 ■ *"Sign of the Times: Temp-To-Perm Attorneys"* in *HRMagazine (Vol. 54, January 2009, No. 1, pp. 24)*

Description: A growing number of law firms are hiring professional staff on a temp-to-perm basis according to the president of Professional Placement Services in Florida. Firms can save money while testing potential employees on a temporary basis. **Availability:** Print; Online.

34166 ■ *"Single Most Important Problem"* in *Small Business Economic Trends (February 2008, pp. 18)*
Pub: National Federation of Independent Business
Contact: Brad Close, President

Ed: William C. Dunkelberg, Holly Wade. **Description:** Two graphs and a table representing the economic problems encountered by small businesses in the U.S. are presented. The figures presented in the graphs include data from 1974 to 2008. **Availability:** Print; Online; PDF.

34167 ■ *"Slimmer Interiors Make Small Cars Seem Big"* in *Automotive News (Vol. 86, October 31, 2011, No. 6488, pp. 16)*
Pub: Crain Communications Inc.
Contact: Barry Asin, President

Ed: David Sedgwick. **Description:** Cost-conscious buyers want luxury car amenities in their smaller vehicles, so automakers are rethinking interiors. Style, efficiency and value could be the next trend in vehicles. **Availability:** Print; Online.

34168 ■ *"Small Business Capital Outlays"* in *Small Business Economic Trends (July 2010, pp. 16)*
Pub: National Federation of Independent Business
Contact: Brad Close, President

Description: A graph representing actual and planned capital expenditures among small businesses surveyed in the U.S. from January 1986 to June 2010 is given. Tables showing actual capital expenditures, type of capital expenditures made, amount of capital expenditures made, and capital expenditure plans are also presented. **Availability:** Print; PDF; Online.

34169 ■ *"Small Business Compensation"* in *Small Business Economic Trends (February 2008, pp. 10)*
Pub: National Federation of Independent Business
Contact: Brad Close, President

Ed: William C. Dunkelberg, Holly Wade. **Description:** Graphs and tables that present compensation plans and compensation changes of small businesses in the U.S. are provided. The figures include data from 1974 to 2008.

34170 ■ *"Small Business Economic Trends: Moderate Improvement but No Clear Direction"* in *Small Business Economic Trends (March 2008, pp. 3)*
Pub: National Federation of Independent Business
Contact: Brad Close, President

Ed: William C. Dunkelberg, Holly Wade. **Description:** Commentary on the economic trends for small businesses in the U.S. is presented. Analysis of the labor market and low interest rates is given. The effect of the Federal Reserve's policy announcement on small business owner optimism is also discussed. **Availability:** Print; Online.

34171 ■ *"Small Business Employment in 22 Rich Economies"* in *Small Business Economic Trends (January 2008, pp. 9)*
Pub: National Federation of Independent Business
Contact: Brad Close, President

Ed: William C. Dunkelberg, Holly Wade. **Description:** Table from a survey of small businesses in the U.S. is given, representing actual employment changes from January 2002 to December 2007. A graph comparing planned employment and current job openings from January 1986 to December 2007 is also supplied. Tables showing job opening, hiring plans, and qualified applicants for job openings are also presented. **Availability:** Online.

34172 ■ *"Small Business Inventories"* in *Small Business Economic Trends (February 2008, pp. 14)*
Pub: National Federation of Independent Business
Contact: Brad Close, President

Ed: William C. Dunkelberg, Holly Wade. **Description:** Three tables and a graph presenting the inventories of small businesses in the U.S. are given. The tables include figures on actual inventory changes, inventory satisfaction, and inventory plans. **Availability:** Print; Online.

34173 ■ *"Small Business Sales: 6 Strategies for Prospecting"* in *Small Business Economic Trends (April 2008, pp. 7)*
Pub: National Federation of Independent Business
Contact: Brad Close, President

Ed: William C. Dunkelberg, Holly Wade. **Description:** Two tables and a graph resenting sales figures of small businesses in the U.S. is presented. Statistics for sales changes and sales expectations are provided. The figures in the graph include data from 1986 to 2008. **Availability:** Print; Online.

34174 ■ *"Small Changes Can Mean Big Energy Savings"* in *Crain's Cleveland Business (Vol. 28, November 5, 2007, No. 44, pp. 21)*
Pub: Crain Communications Inc.
Contact: K. C. Crain, President

Ed: Harriet Tramer. **Description:** Many Northeast Ohio businesses are taking their cues from the residential real estate market to draw and capitalize on interest in energy efficiency and is regularly taken into account by local architects. **Availability:** Online.

34175 ■ *Social Enterprise: Developing Sustainable Businesses*
Pub: Palgrave Macmillan

Ed: Frank Martin, Marcus Thompson. **Released:** 2010. **Description:** Social enterprises bring people and communities together for economic development and social gain and represent a growing sector of the business community.

34176 ■ *"Social Media By the Numbers: Social-Media Marketing Is All the Rage" in Inc. (Vol. 33, November 2011, No. 9, pp. 70)*
Pub: Inc. Magazine

Ed: J.J. McCorvey, Issie Lapowsky. **Description:** Six strategies to help small businesses use social media sites such as Facebook and Twitter to promote their companies are presented. **Availability:** Online.

34177 ■ *"Social Networks in the Workplace: The Risk and Opportunity of Business 2.0" in Strategy & Leadership (Vol. 38, July-August 2010, No. 4, pp. 50-53)*
Pub: Emerald Inc.

Ed: Daniel Burrus. **Description:** The opinions of futurist Daniel Burrus on a novel trend called 'Business 2.0', which involves the use of social networking applications as business tools, are presented. His suggestion that personal social networking technology can be used by businesses to improve collaboration, problem solving, and leadership communications to achieve continuous value innovation is discussed. **Availability:** Online.

34178 ■ *"Sole Proprietorship Returns, 2008" in SOI Bulletin (Vol. 30, Summer 2010, No. 1, pp. 6)*
Pub: Government Publishing Office
Contact: Hugh Nathanial Halpern, Director

Ed: Adrian Dungan. **Description:** Approximately 22.6 million individual income tax returns reported nonfarm sole proprietorship activity, a 2.2 percent decrease from 2007. Statistical data included. **Availability:** Print; PDF; Online.

34179 ■ *"Sole Proprietorship Returns, 2008 Part 2" in SOI Bulletin (Vol. 30, Summer 2010, No. 1, pp. 27)*
Description: Table of Nonfarm Sole Proprietorships is presented. Statistics are broken down by sector reporting all nonfarm industries as well as agriculture, forestry, hunting and fishing. **Availability:** PDF; Online.

34180 ■ *"Sprinkler Advocates Beat Builders Again" in Contractor (Vol. 56, November 2009, No. 11, pp. 58)*
Ed: Robert P. Mader. **Description:** Proponents of residential fire sprinklers were able to fend off the attempt by the National Association of Home Builders to do away with mandated fire sprinklers on the International Residential Code by the International Code Council (ICC). The ICC's vote on the issue is good news for fire sprinkler contractors and plumbing contractors. **Availability:** Print; Online.

34181 ■ *"Staging a Martini-and-GQ Lifestyle" in Crain's Chicago Business (April 21, 2008)*
Pub: Crain Communications Inc.
Contact: Barry Asin, President

Ed: Kevin Davis. **Description:** Due to the competition of the slumping housing market, home stagers are becoming more prominent and are using creative ways to make an impression beyond de-cluttering, painting and cleaning by using accents such as casually placed magazines, candles and table settings. **Availability:** Online.

34182 ■ *"Start: Punch Fear in the Face, Escape Average and Do Work that Matters"*
Pub: Ramsey Press
Contact: Dave Ramsey, Chief Executive Officer

Released: April 22, 2013. **Price:** $22.99, Hardcover. **Description:** Three things have occurred that have changed the predictable stages of success. Boomers have started second and third careers. Technology has given access to unprecedented number of people who are building online empires, thus changing their

lives. The days of success first, significance later have ended. All stages must be experienced but there are only two paths in life: average and awesome. Tips for building an awesome life or business are included. **Availability:** Print.

34183 ■ *"State Unemployment Fraud Rising Sharply" in Sacramento Business Journal (Vol. 28, October 21, 2011, No. 34, pp. 1)*
Pub: Sacramento Business Journal
Contact: Stephanie Fretwell, Director
E-mail: sfretwell@bizjournals.com

Ed: Michael Shaw. **Description:** California's Employment Development Department has reported that overpayments, especially due to fraud or misrepresentation, have increased from $88 million in 2008 to more than $250 million in 2010. However, criminal prosecutions in 2010 were fewer than in 2008 as the agency struggles to recover the money. **Availability:** Online.

34184 ■ *"Stimulating Fare at the SBA" in Barron's (Vol. 89, July 20, 2009, No. 29, pp. 12)*
Pub: Dow Jones & Company Inc.
Contact: Almar Latour, Chief Executive Officer

Ed: Jim McTague. **Description:** Internet access at the Small Business Administration slowed down on 7 July 2009, apparently caused by employees streaming videos of the Michael Jackson tribute. The agency claims that the event did not disrupt its operations. **Availability:** Online.

34185 ■ *"Succeed With the Right Equipment" in Pet Product News (Vol. 64, November 2010, No. 11, pp. 42)*
Ed: Sandi Cain. **Description:** Grooming shop owners have been focusing on obtaining ergonomic, durable, and efficient products such as restraints, tables, and tubs. These products enhance the way grooming tasks are conducted. Ways pet supply manufacturers have responded to this trend are examined. **Availability:** Online.

34186 ■ *"Sudden Shift Leaves Wells Fargo Vendor Scrambling" in Charlotte Business Journal (Vol. 25, July 9, 2010, No. 16, pp. 1)*
Pub: Charlotte Business Journal
Contact: Robert Morris, Editor
E-mail: rmorris@bizjournals.com

Ed: Adam O'Daniel. **Description:** Rubber stamps vendor Carolina Marking Devices is facing a 30 percent drop in business after banking firm Wells Fargo & Company decided to buy its rubber stamps from another vendor. Carolina Marking Devices had provided rubber to First Union Corporation and its successor Wachovia Corporation, which was eventually acquired by Wells Fargo. Other reactions from Carolina Marking Device owners are given. **Availability:** Print; Online.

34187 ■ *"Summary. Economic Trends for Small Business" in Small Business Economic Trends (February 2008, pp. 1)*
Pub: National Federation of Independent Business
Contact: Brad Close, President

Ed: William C. Dunkelberg, Holly Wade. **Description:** Summary of economic trends for small businesses in the U.S. is provided. Economic indicators such as capital spending, inventories and sales, inflation, and profits are given. Analysis of credit markets is also provided.

34188 ■ *"Take the Right Approach to Concrete Polishing Rentals" in Rental Product News (Vol. 33, June 2011)*
Description: A recent trend in flooring is concrete polishing for a practical, beautiful and sustainable way to decorate homes and businesses. Things to keep in mind when assessing the value of adding concrete polishing equipment to an existing rental store are evaluated. **Availability:** Online.

34189 ■ *"Tap Into Food Truck Trend to Rev Up Sales, Build Buzz" in Nation's Restaurant News (Vol. 45, February 7, 2011, No. 3, pp. 18)*
Ed: Brian Sacks. **Description:** Food truck trend is growing, particularly in New York City, Philadelphia, Washington DC, and Los Angeles, California. Man

entrepreneurs are using a mobile food component to market their food before opening a restaurant. **Availability:** Print; Online.

34190 ■ *"Tapping the 'Well' in Wellness" in Pet Product News (Vol. 64, November 2010, No. 11, pp. 1)*
Ed: Wendy Bedwell-Wilson. **Description:** Healthy food and treats are among the leading wellness products being sought by customers from specialty retailers to keep their pets healthy. With this demand for pet wellness products, retailers suggest making sure that staff know key ingredients to emphasize to customers. Other insights into this trend and ways to engage customers are discussed. **Availability:** Online.

34191 ■ *"Taxis Are Set to Go Hybrid" in Philadelphia Business Journal (Vol. 30, September 16, 2011, No. 31, pp. 1)*
Pub: Philadelphia Business Journal
Contact: Sierra Quinn, Director
E-mail: squinn@bizjournals.com

Ed: Natalie Kostelni. **Description:** Taxis are going hybrid in several major states such as New York, California and Maryland where it is mandated, but it is yet to happen in Philadelphia, Pennsylvania with the exception of one taxi company. Freedom Taxi is awaiting Philadelphia Parking Authority's sign off. **Availability:** Online.

34192 ■ *"Tech Jobs Rebound from Downturn" in Denver Business Journal (Vol. 65, March 7, 2014, No. 43, pp. A9)*
Pub: American City Business Journals, Inc.
Contact: Mike Olivieri, Executive Vice President

Released: Weekly. **Price:** $4, Introductory 4-week offer(Digital & Print). **Description:** Denver, Colorado's employment in core technology industries has returned from pre-Great Recession figures. The computer software industry's surging job growth and the slight increase in the broadcasts and telecommunications industry offset the job losses in biotechnology and private aerospace industry from 2008 through 2013. The growth in specific industries is also discussed. **Availability:** Print; Online.

34193 ■ *"Three Megatrends to Help Your Business Compete in 2014" in South Florida Business Journal (Vol. 34, January 3, 2014, No. 24, pp. 10)*
Pub: American City Business Journals, Inc.
Contact: Mike Olivieri, Executive Vice President

Released: Weekly. **Price:** $8, Introductory 4-week offer(Digital & Print). **Description:** Businesses can improve their competitive edge in 2014 by adapting several mega small business trends in marketing and communications. Brands can use brand bridging to get customers attention, use wearable technology to increase their value, and adapt environmental sustainability and corporate social responsibility to keep their customers. **Availability:** Print; Online.

34194 ■ *"TiVo, Domino's Team to Offer Pizza Ordering by DVR" in Advertising Age (Vol. 79, November 17, 2008, No. 43, pp. 48)*
Pub: Crain Communications, Inc.
Contact: Jessica Botos, Manager, Marketing
E-mail: jessica.botos@crainsnewyork.com

Ed: Brian Steinberg. **Description:** Domino's Pizza and TiVo are teaming up to make it possible for customers to order from the restaurant straight from their DVR. The companies see that this kind of interactive television and consumer experience will only serve to generate more sales as the customer can be exposed to a fuller range of menu selections and will not have to interrupt their viewing, while workers can spend more time making the product. **Availability:** Online.

34195 ■ *"Today's Rx: Solo Physician Practice Loses Appeal" in Dallas Business Journal (Vol. 35, July 13, 2012, No. 44, pp. 1)*
Pub: Baltimore Business Journal
Contact: Rhonda Pringle, President
E-mail: rpringle@bizjournals.com

Ed: Bill Hethcock. Description: The national statistics has shown a trend toward doctors increasingly choosing to work for hospitals, clinics and physician groups. Irving, Texas-based Merritt Hawkins has found in a survey that solo physicians accounted for just one percent of all the firm's searches. Survey details are included. Availability: Print; Online.

34196 ■ "Toll Talker: CEO Takes Stock of His Company, the Housing Market" in Philadelphia Business Journal (Vol. 33, May 9, 2014, No. 13, pp. 4)

Pub: American City Business Journals, Inc.

Contact: Mike Olivieri, Executive Vice President

Released: Weekly. Price: $4, introductory 4-week offer(Digital only). Description: Douglas C. Yearley, Jr., CEO of Toll Brothers Inc. discusses how his company capitalized on the economic recession in the housing market by acquiring large tracts of land between 2008 and 2010, including Shapell Homes in California for $1.2 billion. Yearley believes that while the housing downturn trend led to a rise in apartment living, the concept of home ownership remains relatively strong in the U.S., thus spurring construction. Availability: Print; Online.

34197 ■ "Tower City Hopes Restrictions on Minors Boost Retail Center" in Crain's Cleveland Business (Vol. 28, November 5, 2007, No. 44)

Pub: Crain Communications Inc.

Contact: K. C. Crain, President

Ed: John Booth. Description: Tower City Center, a shopping mall in downtown Cleveland, hopes to generate more business with their new rules restricting the access of unaccompanied minors after 2:30 p.m. Availability: Online.

34198 ■ "The Transparent Supply Chain" in Harvard Business Review (Vol. 88, October 2010, No. 10, pp. 76)

Pub: Harvard Business Publishing

Contact: Diane Belcher, Managing Director

Ed: Steve New. Price: $8.95, PDF. Description: Examination of the use of new technologies to create a transparent supply chain, such as next-generation 2D bar codes in clothing labels that can provide data on a garment's provenance. Availability: Online; PDF.

34199 ■ "Ultra Low Sulfur Diesel: The Promise and the Reality" in Indoor Comfort Marketing (Vol. 70, July 2011, No. 7, pp. 22)

Description: Impacts of ultra low sulfur diesel are examined.

34200 ■ "U.S. Recession Officially Over: Is Recovery Ever Going to Arrive?" in Montana Business Quarterly (Vol. 49, Spring 2011, No. 1, pp. 6)

Pub: University of Montana Bureau of Business and Economic Research

Contact: Patrick Barkey, Director

E-mail: patrick.barkey@business.umt.edu

Ed: Patrick M. Barkey. Released: Quarterly. Description: Ten predictions regarding American's economy for 2012 are listed. Availability: Online.

34201 ■ "Univest Charter Switch Signals Banking Trend" in Philadelphia Business Journal (Vol. 30, September 2, 2011, No. 29, pp. 1)

Pub: Philadelphia Business Journal

Contact: Sierra Quinn, Director

E-mail: squinn@bizjournals.com

Ed: Jeff Blumenthal. Description: Univest Corporation of Pennsylvania changed from a federal to state charter because of cost savings and state agency has greater understanding of the intricacies of the local economy. The Pennsylvania Department of Banking has also received inquiries from seven other banks about doing the same this year. Availability: Online.

34202 ■ "Unretirement: How Baby Boomers are Changing the Way We Think About Work, Community, and the Good Life"

Released: 1st edition. Price: $16.20, paperback; $23.40, hardback; $14.40, ebook. Description: Baby boomers are transforming American economics and society in a positive way. Because boomers are living longer in better health and are extending their work lives, may times with new careers, entrepreneurial ventures, and socially responsible volunteering service. This trend will enrich the American workplace, economy, and the society as a whole for future generations. Availability: E-book; Print; Online.

34203 ■ "Vacation, What Vacation?" in Black Enterprise (Vol. 41, August 2010, No. 1, pp. 36)

Description: Nearly 50 percent of employers expect employees to check in with the office while they are away on vacation.

34204 ■ "Valenti: Roots of Financial Crisis Go Back to 1998" in Crain's Detroit Business (Vol. 24, October 6, 2008, No. 40, pp. 25)

Pub: Crain Communications Inc.

Contact: Barry Asin, President

Ed: Tom Henderson, Nathan Skid. Description: Interview with Sam Valenti III who is the chairman and CEO of Valenti Capital L.L.C., a wealth-management firm; Valenti discusses in detail the history that led up to the current economic crisis as well as his prediction for the future of the country. Availability: Print; Online.

34205 ■ Values and Opportunities in Social Entrepreneurship

Pub: Palgrave Macmillan

Released: 2010. Price: $89, hardcover; $120, hardcover; $64.99, e-book; $84.99, Softcover. Description: Social entrepreneurship has grown as a research field. This book discusses social entrepreneurship as well as the identification and exploitation of social venturing opportunities. Availability: E-book; Print; PDF; Electronic publishing.

34206 ■ "Vistaprint Survey Indicates that Online Marketing Taking Hold Among Small Businesses" in Marketwired (December 10, 2009)

Pub: Comtex News Network Inc.

Contact: Kan Devnani, President

Description: According to a comprehensive survey from Vistaprint N.V., small businesses are very likely to increase their use of Internet marketing strategies such as paid and organic search, email marketing, social media networking and custom websites over the next year. Trends continue to show that more small businesses are indeed adapting to the changing marketplace and are more willing to diversify their marketing strategies than ever before. Availability: Print; Online.

34207 ■ "Volunteers Needed" in Canadian Business (Vol. 81, October 27, 2008, No. 18, pp. 60)

Description: Emissions-targeting regulations focus on the biggest polluters, missing out on other companies that leave carbon footprints in things such as shipping and travel. Some companies in Canada have initiated programs to offset their carbon emissions. Critics claim that offsetting does not reduce emissions and the programs merely justify pollution.

34208 ■ "Wave of Resale, Consignment Shops Pop Up In Springs" in Gazette (March 19, 2012)

Ed: Bill Radford. Description: The depressed economy has spurred the growth of consignment shops across the nation. Colorado Springs, Colorado area urges people to shop at these resale locations because they promote green initiatives by recycling goods. WeeCycle, Knit Wits, Once Upon a Child and Re-Generation, Moutain Equipment Recyclers, and Gearonimo, are among the established consignment stores in the area. Availability: Print.

34209 ■ "Web-Based Marketing Excites, Challenges Small Business Use" in Colorado Springs Business Journal (January 20, 2010)

Pub: BridgeTower Media

Contact: Adam Reinebach, President

Ed: Becky Hurley. Description: Business-to-business and consumer-direct firms alike are using the fast-changing Web technologies to increase sales, leads and track consumer behavior but once a company commits to an Online marketing plan, experts believe, they must be prepared to consistently tweak and overhaul content and distribution vehicles in order to keep up. Availability: Online.

34210 ■ "What Comes After That Job Is Cut?" in Business Review Albany (Vol. 41, August 15, 2014, No. 21, pp. 4)

Released: Weekly. Price: $4, Print. Description: Former KeyBank regional president, Jeff Stone, has joined the list of well-known banking executives who have reinvented themselves as the financial industry transforms around the Albany, NY area. Stone, as well as other leading bank leaders, have transitioned to smaller banks or other industries. Insights into the Banking Industry's Act II are provided. Availability: Print; Online.

34211 ■ "What Does It Costs to Open a Coffee Shop?" in The New York Times (October 17, 2019)

URL(s): www.nytimes.com/2019/10/17/business/cost-to-open-coffee-shop.html

Ed: Julia Rothman, Shaina Feinberg. Released: October 17, 2019. Description: This illustrated article outlines the true costs of opening a coffee shop, the high cost of rent, the price of drinks, and how others in the business stay afloat. Availability: Online.

34212 ■ "What is the Future of Disk Drives, Death or Rebirth?" in ACM Computing Surveys (Vol. 43, Fall 2011, No. 3, pp. 23)

Pub: Association for Computing Machinery

Contact: Yannis Ioannidis, President

Ed: Yuhui Deng. Released: Volume 43 Issue 3. Price: $10, Members; $15, Nonmembers; $5, Students. Description: Disk drives have experienced dramatic development to meet performance requirements since the IBM 1301 disk drive was announced in 1961. However, the performance gap between memory and disk drives has widened to 6 orders of magnitude and continues to widen by about 50 percent per year. Challenges and opportunities facing these storage devices are explored. Availability: Download; PDF.

34213 ■ "What the Future Holds for Consumers" in Black Enterprise (Vol. 41, August 2010, No. 1, pp. 47)

Pub: Earl G. Graves Ltd.

Contact: Earl Graves, Jr., President

Ed: Sheiresa Ngo. Description: The way people purchase goods and service has changed with technology. With an increased focus on security (as well as privacy and fairness) the U.S. Congress began regulating the credit card industry with the Fair Credit Reporting Act of 1970 and the Credit Card Accountability, Responsibility, and Disclosure (CARD) Act of 2009. Availability: Online.

34214 ■ "What Is a Geothermal Heat Pump" in Indoor Comfort Marketing (Vol. 70, August 2011, No. 8, pp. 14)

Description: Examination of geothermal heat pumps is provided, citing new trends in the industry. Availability: Print; Online.

34215 ■ "What's Holding Down Small Business?" in Business Owner (Vol. 35, November-December 2011, No. 6, pp. 3)

Description: According to a recent survey conducted by the National Federation of Independent Business, demand is the number one reason for slow growth to any small business in today's economy. Availability: PDF; Online.

34216 ■ *"Where Small Biz Gets a 'Yes' More Often"* **in Denver Business Journal (Vol. 65, February 28, 2014, No. 42, pp. A10)**
Pub: American City Business Journals, Inc.
Contact: Mike Olivieri, Executive Vice President
Released: Weekly. **Price:** $4, Introductory 4-week offer(Digital & Print). **Description:** The Biz2Credit Small Business Lending Index has found that alternative lenders granted 66.9 percent of funding requests in Colorado compared to the 15.1 percent approval of loans requests by big banks. The big banks' low approval rates were attributed to their less aggressive lending efforts and the state's fewer restrictions on alternative lending. Other findings from the study are discussed. **Availability:** Print; Online.

34217 ■ *"Which Direction are Herbicides Heading?"* **in Farm Industry News (October 11, 2011)**
Pub: Informa Business Media, Inc.
Contact: Charlie McCurdy, President
Ed: Jennifer Shike. **Description:** Currently, one of the best solutions for growers fighting weed resistance may be 2,4-D or other auxin herbicides. **Availability:** Print; Online.

34218 ■ *"Why Top Young Managers Are In a Nonstop Job Hunt"* **in Harvard Business Review (Vol. 90, July-August 2012, No. 7-8, pp. 28)**
Pub: Harvard Business Review Press
Contact: Moderna V. Pfizer, Contact
Ed: Monika Hamori, Jie Cao, Burak Koyuncu. **Price:** $6. **Description:** Managers are moving from firm to firm in part because companies are not addressing formal training, coaching, and mentoring needs. While these are costly, companies might benefit from the investment, as managers may tend to stay longer in firms where they are provided. **Availability:** Online; PDF.

34219 ■ *"Will Home Buyers Pay for Green Features?"* **in Contractor (Vol. 56, October 2009, No. 10, pp. 70)**
Ed: Robert P. Mader. **Description:** National Association of Home Builders commissioned a survey which shows that homeowners are interested in green as long as they do not have to pay much for it. The association did not allow a board member to read the survey which raises questions about how the questions were phrased and how the sample was selected. **Availability:** Print; Online.

34220 ■ *"Women Clicking to Earn Virtual Dollars"* **in Sales and Marketing Management (November 11, 2009)**
Ed: Stacy Straczynski. **Description:** According to a new report from Internet marketing firm Q Interactive, women are increasingly playing social media games where they are able to click on an ad or sign up for a promotion to earn virtual currency. Research is showing that this kind of marketing may be a potent tool, especially for e-commerce and online stores. **Availability:** Print; Online.

34221 ■ *"Words at Work"* **in Information Today (Vol. 26, February 2009, No. 2, pp. 25)**
Description: Current new buzzwords include the following: digital amnesia, or overload by availability, speed and volume of digital information; maternal profiling, a form a discrimination against women; recipe malpractice, a reminder that just because you can turn on a stove it doesn't make you a chef; ringxiety, the act when everyone reaches for their cell phone when one rings; verbing, the practice of turning good nouns into verbs. **Availability:** Print; Online.

34222 ■ *"Work/Life Balance"* **in Dallas Business Journal (Vol. 37, June 20, 2014, No. 41, pp. 4)**
Pub: Routledge, Taylor & Francis Group
Description: Younger generations of corporate employees are increasingly looking for a more engaged workplace community. Research firm, Quantum Workplace, identifies several trends that help to attract and retain employees, including jobs that align with the workers' own values, growth opportunities within the firm, social interactions with co-workers, and employee health benefits. **Availability:** Print; Online.

34223 ■ *"WQA's Leadership Conference Tackles Industry Issues"* **in Contractor (Vol. 56, October 2009, No. 10, pp. 3)**
Ed: Candace Roulo. **Description:** Water Quality Association's Mid-Year Leadership Conference held in Bloomingdale, Illinois in September 2009 tackled lead regulation, water softeners, and product efficiency. The possibility of a WQA green seal was discussed by the Water Sciences Committee and the Government Relations Committee meeting. **Availability:** Online.

34224 ■ *"Xbox 360 Excels As a Media Hub"* **in Hispanic Business (October 2009, pp. 40)**
Ed: Jeremy Nisen. **Description:** Xbox 360 video game console from Microsoft offers games, amazing graphics and state-of-the-art accessories. The trend towards purchase of the Xbox includes more than teenagers.

34225 ■ *"Yao Ming Courts China's Wine Boom"* **in Wall Street Journal Eastern Edition (November 28, 2011, pp. B4)**
Pub: Dow Jones & Company Inc.
Contact: Almar Latour, Chief Executive Officer
Ed: Jason Chow. **Description:** Yao Ming, the former NBA 7-foot 6-inch Chinese basketball star, is set to cash in on the market potential for wine in China. He has created his own winery in California, Yao Family Wines, which will produce wines solely for the Chinese market. **Availability:** Online.

VIDEO/AUDIO MEDIA

34226 ■ *Nurture Small Business: Denise's Opinions: Employee Values In a New Era*
URL(s): nurturesmallbusiness.buzzsprout.com/900
445/episodes/14251029-denise-s-opinions
-employee-values-in-a-new-era
Ed: Denise Cagan. **Released:** January 08, 2024. **Description:** Podcast discusses the positive and negative aspects of workforce trends, including remote and hybrid work models.

34227 ■ *To Niche or Not to Niche: The Pitfalls of Over-Specialization*
URL(s): ducttapemarketing.com/pitfalls-of-over
-specialization
Ed: John Jantsch. **Released:** September 21, 2023. **Description:** Podcast discusses the pros and cons of specialization. Learn how to leverage strategic skills to serve niche audiences.

PUBLICATIONS

34228 ■ *"How to Claim a Google Business Profile"* **in Business 2 Community (October 22, 2021)**
URL(s): www.business2community.com/small-busi-
ness/how-to-claim-a-google-business-profile-02437
585
Ed: Haiden Hibbert. **Description:** Discusses why a small business should set up a Google Business profile and then gives step-by-step instructions on how to complete the process. **Availability:** Online.

LIBRARIES

34229 ■ **Colorado Mountain College - Alpine Campus Library**
1275 Crawford Ave.
  Steamboat Springs, CO 80487
Ph: (970)870-4445
Fax: (970)870-4490
URL: http://library.coloradomtn.edu/c.php?g=298848
&p=1996026
Contact: Tracey Hughes, Director
E-mail: tshughes@coloradomtn.edu

Scope: Small business; hotel and restaurant management; health and fitness; U.S. history and literature; American music; skiing. **Services:** Interlibrary loan; library open to the public; copying. **Founded:** 1981. **Holdings:** 30,000 books; 580 CDs; maps; state documents; CD-ROMs.

34230 ■ **Greater Oviedo Chamber of Commerce Business Library**
PO Box 621236
  Oviedo, FL 32762
URL: http://www.owsrcc.org

Description: Promotes business in the region of Greater Oviedo. **Founded:** 1995. **Holdings:** 3 books; 10 reports; periodicals.

34231 ■ **Indian River Area Library (IRAL)**
3546 S Straits Hwy.
  Indian River, MI 49749
Ph: (231)238-8581
Co. E-mail: info@indianriverlibrary.org
URL: http://www.indianriverlibrary.org
Contact: Kelsey Rutkowski, Director
Facebook: www.facebook.com/IndianRiverLibrary
Instagram: www.instagram.com/indianriverarealibrary

Scope: Local history. **Services:** Photocopy; Printer & Copier; Laminating; Faxing; Reciprocal Borrowing Agreement. **Founded:** 1976. **Holdings:** Figures not available.

34232 ■ **Small Business Administration Reference Library**
409 3rd St. SW
  Washington, DC 20416
URL: http://advocacy.sba.gov/resources/reference
-library

Scope: Small business administration. **Founded:** 1958. **Holdings:** Figures not available.

RESEARCH CENTERS

34233 ■ **Alabama Law Institute (ALI)**
101 Paul W Bryant Dr., E
  Tuscaloosa, AL 35487
URL: http://www.law.ua.edu/directory/department/
  Alabama_Law_Institute
Contact: Clay Hornsby, Contact
E-mail: chornsby@law.ua.edu

Description: State agency of Alabama, located at University of Alabama. Offers basic and advanced law courses. **Scope:** Conducts investigations into state tax structure, evidence, criminal law, business law, probate law, real property, and family law. Develops manuals for legislators, county commissioners, tax assessors and collectors, and other governmental offices. **Founded:** 1967. **Publications:** *Alabama Government Manual* (Quadrennial); *ALI Annual Report* (Annual). **Educational Activities:** ALI Conferences, For state officials.

34234 ■ **Bradley University - Foster College of Business - Center for Business and Economic Research (CBER)**
1501 W Bradley Ave.
  Peoria, IL 61625
Co. E-mail: payroll@bradley.edu
URL: http://www.bradley.edu/academic/undergradcat/
  20192020/fcba-buscourses.dot
Contact: Dr. Stephen Standifird, President
E-mail: president@bradley.edu

Description: Integral unit of Foster College of Business, Bradley University. **Scope:** Coordinates faculty research projects in program evaluation, consumer confidence, economic development, market research, needs assessment, impact analysis, modeling, forecasting, survey research, cost and price modeling, accounting and special purpose information systems, location analysis, financial planning, cost-benefit analysis, performance evaluation and productivity analysis. **Founded:** 1979. **Publications:** *Peoria MSA Business Database Report* (Quarterly); *Peoria MSA Consumer Sentiment.*

34235 ■ East Tennessee State University - Tennessee Small Business Development Center (TSBDC)
112 E Mountcastle Dr.
Johnson City, TN 37601
Ph: (423)439-8505
Co. E-mail: mbays@tsbdc.org
URL: http://tsbdc.org
Contact: Mark Bays, Director
E-mail: baysml@etsu.edu
Facebook: www.facebook.com/TSBDCETSU
Linkedin: www.linkedin.com/company/tsbdc
Description: Integral unit of College of Business and Technology, East Tennessee State University. Provides free Internet access to clients. **Scope:** Small business assistance in the areas of business plans and strategies, financial forecasts, feasibility studies, financial statement analysis, credit establishment and collection policies, inventory. **Founded:** 1984. **Educational Activities:** TSBDC Consulting, technical assistance, and management assistance; TSBDC Workshops, seminars and conferences.

34236 ■ Michigan State University - Institute for Public Policy and Social Research (IPPSR)
509 E Circle Dr., Rm. 321
East Lansing, MI 48824-1226
Ph: (517)355-6672
URL: http://ippsr.msu.edu
Contact: Matt Grossmann, Director
E-mail: grossm63@msu.edu
Facebook: www.facebook.com/Institute-for-Public
-Policy-and-Social-Research-IPPSR
-554215311270962
X (Twitter): x.com/ippsr
Description: Integral unit of College of Social Science at Michigan State University. Offers public policy forums (quarterly). **Scope:** Conducts social and policy research on the national, state, and local levels, focusing on improving the policy process to make governance more effective and developing better policies. **Founded:** 1951. **Publications:** *Policy briefs*; *SOSS Bulletins*.

34237 ■ Pennsylvania Small Business Development Centers (SBDC)
Kutztown University of Pennsylvania
15200 Kutztown Rd., E-Wing, Ste. 24
Kutztown, PA 19530
Free: 877-472-7232
Co. E-mail: sbdc@kutztown.edu
URL: http://www.pasbdc.org
Contact: Ernie Post, Director
E-mail: post@kutztown.edu
Facebook: www.facebook.com/PennsylvaniaSBDC
Linkedin: www.linkedin.com/company/pennsylvania
-small-business-development-centers
X (Twitter): x.com/PASmallBusiness
Description: The Pennsylvania SBDC State Director's office is hosted by the Wharton School at the University of Pennsylvania. The State Director's office is responsible for the administration and oversight of the Pennsylvania system of 18 centers. **Scope:** Helps small businesses improve profitability and increase employment through programs of procurement, international trade, product development, and business law. **Founded:** 1980. **Geographic Preference:** State.

34238 ■ University of Mississippi - Mississippi Small Business Development Center (MSBDC)
122 Jeanette Phillips Dr.
University, MS 38677-1848
Ph: (662)915-5001
Free: 800-725-7232
Fax: (662)915-5650
Co. E-mail: msbdc@olemiss.edu
URL: http://mississippisbdc.org
Contact: Sharon Nichols, Director
E-mail: sknicho1@olemiss.edu
Facebook: www.facebook.com/mississippiSBDC
Linkedin: www.linkedin.com/company/
mississippisbdc
X (Twitter): x.com/mississippiSBDC
Instagram: www.instagram.com/mississippisbdc
Description: Composed of 10 service centers, hosted by five universities and five community colleges in the state of Mississippi. Serves as a one-stop resource center for a variety of counseling, workshops and information for growing businesses and startups. **Scope:** Small business management, including feasibility studies, business law, venture capital, government contracting, and financial, production, and personnel management. **Founded:** 1981. **Publications:** *Going Into Business in Mississippi: An Entrepreneur's Handbook*; *The Mississippi Innovator*; *SBDC Business Beat* (Quarterly). **Educational Activities:** MSBDC Seminars and training on small business development. **Geographic Preference:** State; Local.

34239 ■ University of New Hampshire (UNH) - New Hampshire Small Business Development Center (NHSBDC)
10 Garrison Ave.
Durham, NH 03824
Ph: (603)862-2200
Co. E-mail: nh.sbdc@unh.edu
URL: http://www.nhsbdc.org
Contact: Liz Gray, Director
E-mail: liz.gray@unh.edu
Facebook: www.facebook.com/
NHSmallBusinessDevelopmentCenter
Linkedin: www.linkedin.com/company/nh-sbdc
X (Twitter): x.com/NHSBDC
YouTube: www.youtube.com/user/nhsbdc
Description: Publishes guidebooks of business and marketing data. Reaches market through direct mail. Does not accept unsolicited manuscripts. **Scope:** Provides research support services to small businesses in New Hampshire. **Founded:** 1984. **Publications:** *NHSBDC Annual report* (Annual). **Educational Activities:** NHSBDC Conferences.

34240 ■ World Jurist Association (WJA) - Library
c/o Clark Hill
1001 Pennsylvania Ave. NW Ste. 1300 S
Washington, DC 20004
Co. E-mail: info@worldjurist.org
URL: http://worldjurist.org
Contact: James Black, II, Vice President
X (Twitter): x.com/worldjurist
Description: Seeks to build laws and legal institutions for international cooperation. Conducts Global Work Program to recommend research and voluntary action for development of international law as a basis for promoting the rule of law and the resolution of disputes by peaceful means. **Scope:** Serves as a voluntary international association of the legal profession. **Founded:** 1963. **Holdings:** 50 books and bound periodical volumes; U.N. documents. **Publications:** *Workpapers* (Irregular); *Law/Technology* (Quarterly); *The World Jurist* (Weekly); *Directory of law and judicial systems of nations*; *Pamphlets Series* (Occasionally); *Report Series on Law-making Activities of International Organizations*. **Educational Activities:** Global Economy and the Rule of Law in a Changing World. **Geographic Preference:** National.

REFERENCE WORKS

34241 ■ *"Coronavirus Relief Bill Gives Small Businesses More Time to Cover Payroll Taxes" in CNBC (March 27, 2020)*
Ed: Darla Mercado. **Released:** March 27, 2020. **Description:** Discusses the relief bill that will permit small businesses to defer their share of Social Security payroll taxes in 2020. **Availability:** Online.

34242 ■ *"Do You Own a Small Business? Here's How to Control Your Social Security and Medicare Tax Bills" in MarketWatch (May 21, 2019)*
Ed: Bill Bischoff. **Released:** May 21, 2019. **Description:** Provides information on how to control federal employment taxes on self-employment income. **Availability:** Online.

34243 ■ *"How Can Small Business Owners Reduce Social Security and Medicare Taxes?" in Schroedel, Scullin & Bestic (May 14, 2019)*
Released: May 14, 2019. **Description:** Provides information on lowering your exposure to federal self-employment tax by structuring your business as a subchapter S corporation for federal tax purposes. **Availability:** Online.

34244 ■ *"How Social Security Works for Business Owners" in Due (March 29, 2018)*
Ed: Eric Rosenberg. **Released:** March 29, 2018. **Description:** Details how social security works for business owners. **Availability:** Online.

34245 ■ *"How to Withhold Payroll Taxes for Your Small Business" in SurePayroll (March 14, 2018)*
Ed: Ross Matthews. **Released:** March 14, 2018. **Description:** Walks through the basics of federal income tax, Medicare and Social Security taxes, and state and local taxes for small businesses. **Availability:** Online.

34246 ■ *"Payroll Taxes for Small Businesses: The Basics" in Human Interest Blog (March 26, 2017)*
Ed: Cyndia Zwahlen. **Released:** March 26, 2017. **Description:** Provides information on payroll taxes for small business owners. Provides a tax glossary as well as information on federal and state payroll taxes, employer payroll tax responsibilities, employee payroll tax responsibilities, payroll tax payment schedule and deadlines, how to report payroll taxes, and what to do if you can't pay your payroll taxes. **Availability:** Online.

34247 ■ *"Reducing Small Business Social Security and Medicare Taxes" in Brady Ware & Company (May 8, 2019)*
Released: May 08, 2019. **Description:** Discusses strategies that small business owners can use to reduce social security and Medicare taxes. **Availability:** Online.

34248 ■ *"Self-Employment Taxes" in The Balance Small Business (June 25, 2019)*
Ed: Jean Murray. **Released:** June 25, 2019. **Description:** Discusses how sole proprietorships, LLCs, partnerships, and S corporations pay taxes and how self-employment income affects social security credit. **Availability:** Online.

34249 ■ *"Small Business Tax Changes for 2020" in Pitney Bowes (2020)*
Ed: Barbara Weltman. **Description:** Discusses new tax breaks available to help small businesses and what these tax breaks mean for tax-free income, deferred taxes, tax refunds, and new tax credits. **Availability:** Online.

34250 ■ *"Small Business Tax Obligations: Payroll Taxes" in Investopedia (June 25, 2019)*
Ed: Chizoba Morah. **Released:** June 25, 2019. **Description:** Focuses on the small business owner's obligations with regard to payroll taxes. **Availability:** Online.

34251 ■ *"Social Security for Business Owners" in Fisher Investments (September 13, 2018)*
Released: September 13, 2018. **Description:** Details the nuances involved in managing small business taxes including how benefits are calculated, how Social Security taxes are paid, and what role Social Security will play in a business owner's retirement strategy. **Availability:** Online.

Socially Responsible Business Practices

START-UP INFORMATION

34252 ■ *"Making Social Ventures Work"* in *Harvard Business Review (Vol. 88, September 2010, No. 9, pp. 66)*
Pub: Harvard Business Publishing
Contact: Diane Belcher, Managing Director
Ed: James D. Thompson, Ian C. MacMillan. **Price:** $8.95. **Description:** Five steps are to define, examine the political aspects, focus on discovery-driven planning, develop an appropriate exit strategy, and anticipate unexpected consequences when starting a new social venture. **Availability:** Online; PDF.

34253 ■ *"No. 407: What I Learned in the Military, and What I Had to Unlearn"* in *Inc. (Vol. 36, September 2014, No. 7, pp. 80)*
Pub: Mansueto Ventures L.L.C.
Contact: Stephanie Mehta, Chief Executive Officer
Released: September 2014. **Description:** Profile of William Bailey, who served in the U.S. Army as information manager at the U.S. Military Academy at West Point. Bailey discusses his startup firm, Rapier Solutions, a government contractor providing IT, logistics, and social-work expertise. The firm has developed a new survivor outreach system for the U.S. Army. **Availability:** Print; Online.

34254 ■ *"WIN Home Inspection Garners Recognition as 2012 Military Friendly Franchise by G.I. Jobs Magazine"* in *Entertainment Close-Up (May 21, 2012)*
Description: G.I. Jobs Magazine ranked WIN Home Inspection in the top ten franchises thoughout the United States on its 2012 Military Friendly Franchises. Veterans represent 1/4 of the firm's franchisee base, offering realistic opportunities for vets to become successful. Details of the training and skills involved and what it takes to be selected to launch a WIN franchise are included. **Availability:** Print; Online.

ASSOCIATIONS AND OTHER ORGANIZATIONS

34255 ■ As You Sow Foundation (AYS)
2020 Milvia St., Ste. 500
Berkeley, CA 94704
Ph: (510)735-8158
Co. E-mail: info@asyousow.org
URL: http://www.asyousow.org
Contact: Danielle Fugere, President
Facebook: www.facebook.com/asyousow
Linkedin: www.linkedin.com/company/as-you-sow
X (Twitter): x.com/AsYouSow
Instagram: www.instagram.com/_asyousow_
Description: Dedicated to promoting corporate social responsibility. **Founded:** 1992. **Publications:** *Proxy Preview* (Annual). **Geographic Preference:** National.

34256 ■ Business for Social Responsibility (BSR)
220 Montgomery St., 17th Fl.
San Francisco, CA 94104
Ph: (415)984-3200
Co. E-mail: connect@bsr.org
URL: http://www.bsr.org
Contact: Aron Cramer, President
Facebook: www.facebook.com/BSRorg
Linkedin: www.linkedin.com/company/bsr-business
-for-social-responsibility-
X (Twitter): twitter.com/bsrnews
Instagram: www.Instagram.com/bsrorg
YouTube: www.youtube.com/user/
BusinessSocialResp
Description: Promotes responsible business behavior and serves as a resource to companies striving to make ethical business decisions. **Publications:** *BSR Insight* (Monthly). **Geographic Preference:** Multinational.

34257 ■ Nitem Foundation
15, 1527 Sofia center
Sofia, Bulgaria
Ph: 359 2 943 19 99
Co. E-mail: office@nitem-bg.com
URL: http://www.nitem-bg.com
Facebook: www.facebook.com/NitemCompany
X (Twitter): x.com/NitemBG
Description: A not-for-profit organization that commits its resources to address issues of global social and environmental concern, particularly those that have a major impact and changing through education and support entrepreneurship. **Founded:** 2002.

34258 ■ Vermont Businesses for Social Responsibility (VBSR)
PO Box 1274
Burlington, VT 05402
Ph: (802)870-0868
Co. E-mail: info@vbsr.org
URL: http://vbsr.org
Contact: Roxanne Vought, Executive Director
E-mail: roxannev@vbsr.org
Facebook: www.facebook.com/Vermon
tBusinessesforSocialResponsibility
X (Twitter): x.com/VBSR
Description: An association that recognizes the role of business community in protecting the natural, human, and economic environments thru economic development, education, public influence and networking. **Founded:** 1990. **Publications:** *Business Horizons* (Semiannual); *Sample Practices: Collectible Guide to Innovative Business Practices.* **Educational Activities:** Vermont Businesses for Social Responsibility Conference (Annual); Vermont Businesses for Social Responsibility Workshop (Annual). **Awards:** Terry Ehrich Award (Annual). **Geographic Preference:** State.

34259 ■ *Women & Environments International (WEI)*
192 Spadina Ave., Ste. 400
Toronto, ON, Canada M5T 2C2
Ph: (416)928-0880
Fax: (416)644-0116
Co. E-mail: office@womenshealthyenvironments.ca
URL: http://www.womenshealthyenvironments.ca

Contact: Kanisha Acharya-Patel, Executive Director
URL(s): www.womenshealthyenvironments.ca/par
tnerswww.yorku.ca/weimag/index.html
Released: Semiannual **Price:** $7, Single issue for back issues; $11, for back issue double; $5, for photocopies of out-of-print issues. **Availability:** Print; PDF; Online.

34260 ■ Women's Healthy Environments Network (WHEN)
192 Spadina Ave., Ste. 400
Toronto, ON, Canada M5T 2C2
Ph: (416)928-0880
Fax: (416)644-0116
Co. E-mail: office@womenshealthyenvironments.ca
URL: http://www.womenshealthyenvironments.ca
Contact: Kanisha Acharya-Patel, Executive Director
Facebook: www.facebook.com/WHENonlinex
X (Twitter): x.com/WHENonline
Description: Represents women experts in environmental studies and issues. Works to implement community development projects to improve the environment. Advocates environmental protection, antidiscriminatory zoning practices, and the development of affordable housing. **Founded:** 1994. **Publications:** *Women & Environments International (WEI)* (Semiannual). **Geographic Preference:** National.

EDUCATIONAL PROGRAMS

34261 ■ Institute for Diversity Certification (IDC)
7230 Arbuckle Commons, Ste. 134
Brownsburg, IN 46112
Contact: Leah Smiley, President
Description: Strives to establish and reinforce high standards of qualification for professionals in the field of Diversity and Inclusion (D&I) by offering the Certified Diversity Professional (CDP) and Certified Diversity Executive (CDE) credential programs. **Founded:** 2009.

34262 ■ Social Media
URL(s): www.eeicom.com/tag/social-media
Description: Learn how to model your website and online initiatives to the new Web 2.0 movement, including working with Facebook and Twitter, pros and cons of MySpace, Wikis, working with blogs, and podcasting in a nutshell. **Audience:** General public, professionals. **Principal Exhibits:** Learn how to model your website and online initiatives to the new Web 2.0 movement, including working with Facebook and Twitter, pros and cons of MySpace, Wikis, working with blogs, and podcasting in a nutshell.

REFERENCE WORKS

34263 ■ *"The 3 Pillars of Corporate Sustainability"* in *Investopedia (June 29, 2021)*
URL(s): www.investopedia.com/articles/investing/100
515/three-pillars-corporate-sustainability.asp

Ed: Andrew Beattie. **Released:** June 29, 2021. **Description:** Discusses corporate sustainability for your small business and details the three pillars of sustainable business: environmental, social, and economic. **Availability:** Online.

34264 ■ *"3 Proven Sustainability Practices for Small Businesses"* in Hazardous Waste Experts Blog (March 3, 2015)
Released: March 03, 2015. **Description:** It may feel like a monumental task to become a 'green' company, but small businesses can certainly be a part of this burgeoning movement of corporate social responsibility (CSR). This article details how small businesses can start with small steps. **Availability:** Online.

34265 ■ *"5 Reasons Small Businesses Should Adopt a CSR Strategy & How To Do It"* in America's Charities (Jan. 21, 2021)
URL(s): www.charities.org/news/5-reasons-small -businesses-should-adopt-csr-strategy-how-do-it
Ed: John Allen. **Released:** January 21, 2021. **Description:** Presents five reasons why your small business should adopt a corporate social responsibility (CSR) strategy and how to adapt it to your business. **Availability:** Online.

34266 ■ *"10 Surprising Areas Missed in Small Business Sustainability Programs"* in Cultivating Capital
Description: For small businesses who have already incorporated common sustainability practices like upgraded lighting or recycling, this article provides additional areas in which you can expand your sustainability efforts. **Availability:** Online.

34267 ■ *"Alliance Offers to Help Italian Workers Settle In"* in Crain's Detroit Business (Vol. 25, June 15, 2009, No. 24, pp. 21)
Pub: Crain Communications Inc.
Contact: Barry Asin, President
Ed: Nancy Kaffer. **Description:** Italian American Alliance for Business and Technology will help workers arriving from Italy to transition to their new homes in the Detroit area. **Availability:** Online.

34268 ■ *"Are You a Young Canadian Entrepreneur Looking for Recognition?"* in CNW Group (November 10, 2010)
Pub: Comtex News Network Inc.
Contact: Kan Devnani, President
Description: Business Development Bank of Canada is looking for young Canadian entrepreneurs ages 19 to 35 for its 2011 Young Entrepreneur Awards. The awards pay tribute to remarkable young Canadian entrepreneurs for their creativity, innovative spirit and community development, as well as business success. **Availability:** Online.

34269 ■ *"Arvada Coffee Shop Wants To Be a Model for Employers"* in Denver Business Journal (Vol. 66, May 30, 2014, No. 2, pp. A5)
Pub: American City Business Journals, Inc.
Contact: Mike Olivieri, Executive Vice President
Released: Weekly. **Price:** $4, introductory 4-week offer(Digital only). **Description:** The Steamers Coffee Shop in Arvada, Colorado was initially created to provide work to people with developmental disabilities who are clients of Parker Personal Care Homes Inc. According to owner, Scott Parker, the coffee shop provided the most normal work setting possible to his client. **Availability:** Print; Online.

34270 ■ *"Athletes Face Wins and Losses After Pro Sports"* in The Business Journal - Serving Phoenix and the Valley of the Sun (Vol. 29, September 21, 2008, No. 3, pp. 1)
Pub: American City Business Journals, Inc.
Contact: Mike Olivieri, Executive Vice President
Ed: Chris Casacchia. **Description:** Professional athletes like hockey star Jeremy Roenick start businesses, while others like Joel Adamson work to boost local communities. Former athletes were found to be particularly interested with real estate businesses. Other views and information on former athletes and their life after sports are presented. **Availability:** Online.

34271 ■ *"Attracting Veteran-Franchisees To Your System"* in Franchising World (Vol. 42, November 2010, No. 11, pp. 53)
Pub: International Franchise Association
Contact: Matthew Haller, President
E-mail: mhaller@franchise.org
Ed: Mary Kennedy Thompson. **Released:** November 01, 2010. **Description:** As military servicemen and women return home, the franchising industry expects an increase in veterans as franchise owners. The Veterans Transition Franchise Initiative, also known as VetFran, is described. **Availability:** Online.

34272 ■ *"Automaker Foundations Run Leaner"* in Crain's Detroit Business (Vol. 26, January 11, 2010, No. 2, pp. 1)
Pub: Crain Communications Inc.
Contact: Barry Asin, President
Ed: Sherri Welch. **Description:** Overview of the Detroit automobile industry includes restoring profitability, smarter marketing strategies and philanthropy. Each company comprising the Big 3 is examined, as is their vision for the future. **Availability:** Print; Online.

34273 ■ *"Backtalk with Terrie M. Williams"* in Black Enterprise (Vol. 38, December 2007, No. 5, pp. 204)
Pub: Earl G. Graves Ltd.
Contact: Earl Graves, Jr., President
Ed: Tennille M. Robinson. **Description:** Profile of Terrie M. Williams, president of a public relations agency as well as founder of a youth empowerment organization called Stay Strong Foundation. Williams reflects on her bouts with depression and how the disease impacts sufferers and talks about her book that will inspire others dealing with depression. **Availability:** Online.

34274 ■ *"Banking on Cord Blood"* in Business Journal-Serving Phoenix & the Valley of the Sun (Vol. 31, September 10, 2010, No. 1, pp. 1)
Description: Celebration Stem Cell Centre obtained contracts from Mercy Gilbert Medical Center and its two sister hospitals, St. Joseph Hospital and Medical Center in Phoenix, Arizona and Chandler Regional Medical Center. The contract will facilitate the donation of unused umbilical cord blood for research. **Availability:** PDF; Online.

34275 ■ *"'Bill Feinberg on Building the Model of Success - 'Strive for 100 Percent Satisfaction'"* in South Florida Business Journal (Vol. 34, June 27, 2014, No. 49, pp. 13)
Pub: American City Business Journals, Inc.
Contact: Mike Olivieri, Executive Vice President
Released: Weekly. **Price:** $8, introductory 4-week offer(Digital only). **Description:** Allied Kitchen & Bath president and CEO, Bill Feinberg, is profiled. The entrepreneur discusses his advocacy for helping to find a cure for leukemia and lymphoma. He enjoys cooking and traveling with family. **Availability:** Print; Online.

34276 ■ *"Billion-Dollar Impact: Nonprofit Sector is Economic Powerhouse"* in Business First Buffalo (November 12, 2007, pp. 1)
Pub: Business First
Contact: John Tebeau, Publisher
E-mail: jtebeau@bizjournals.com
Ed: Tracey Drury. **Description:** Western New York has thousands of nonprofit organizations, 240 of which have collective revenue of $1.74 billion based on federal tax returns for the 2005 and 2006 fiscal years. The nonprofit sector has a large impact on WNY's economy, but it is not highly recognized. The financial performance of notable nonprofit organizations is given.

34277 ■ *"Breaking Down the 4 Types of Corporate Social Responsibility"*
URL(s): www.pacificoaks.edu/voices/business/break-ing-down-the-4-types-of-corporate-social -responsibility/

Released: September 23, 2021. **Description:** Discusses four types of corporate social responsibility and how they look in action. **Availability:** Online.

34278 ■ *"Bringing Charities More Bang for Their Buck"* in Crain's Chicago Business (Vol. 34, May 23, 2011, No. 21, pp. 31)
Pub: Crain Communications Inc.
Contact: Barry Asin, President
Ed: Lisa Bertagnoli. **Description:** Marcy-Newberry Association connects charities with manufacturers in order to use excess items such as clothing, janitorial and office supplies. **Availability:** Online.

34279 ■ *Business, Occupations, Professions, & Vocations in the Bible*
Pub: ABC Book Publishing
Ed: Rich Brott. **Price:** $19.99, softcover. **Description:** The important role small business has played in all societies and cultures throughout history is examined. The ingenuity of individuals and their ability to design, craft, manufacture and harvest has kept countries and kingdoms prosperous. **Availability:** Print.

34280 ■ *Business as Usual*
Description: Founder of The Body Shop shares her story and gives her opinion on everything from cynical cosmetic companies to destructive consultants.

34281 ■ *"Campaign Launches to Educate Hispanics on Tax Preparation"* in Economics Week (February 3, 2012, pp. 35)
Pub: NewsRX LLC.
Contact: Kalani Rosell, Contact
Description: Hispanic Access Foundation has partnered with H&R Block to offer a program to help Hispanics file their taxes while avoiding fraud and misinformation. The campaign is called, 'Preparate Para Un Futuro Mejor' (Prepare Yourself for a Better Future) and will help fill the void for tax preparation education for Hispanics. **Availability:** Online.

34282 ■ *"Can We Afford Sustainable Business?"* in MIT Sloan Management Review (Sept. 8, 2021)
URL(s): sloanreview.mit.edu/article/can-we-afford-sus tainable-business/
Released: September 08, 2021. **Description:** Explains how taking a creative approach to pricing can benefit society, the environment, and your small business. **Availability:** Online.

34283 ■ *"Can You Make a Profit and Be Socially Responsible?"* in Business.com (April 8, 2020)
Released: April 08, 2020. **Description:** Discusses how small businesses can be both socially responsible and can make money while doing so. **Availability:** Online.

34284 ■ *"Canadian Pet Charities Won't Go Hungry"* in Pet Product News (Vol. 66, September 2012, No. 9, pp. 15)
Description: Premium dog and cat food manufacturer Petcurean will donate more than 42,000 pounds of Go! and Now Fresh dry foods to 25 animal rescue organizations across Canada. The donation is deemed invaluable to Petcurean's network of dog and cat foster activities. **Availability:** Online.

34285 ■ *"Captain Planet"* in (Vol. 90, June 2012, No. 6, pp. 112)
Pub: Harvard Business Review Press
Contact: Moderna V. Pfizer, Contact
Ed: Paul Polman, Adi Ignatius. **Price:** $8.95, hardcopy black and white. **Description:** Paul Polman, chief executive officer of Unilever N.V., discusses his company's sustainable living plan, which integrates social responsibility with corporate objectives. Topics include sustainable sourcing, abolishing quarterly reporting in favor of long-term perspectives, the impact of the 2008 global economic crisis, and turning a company into a learning organization. **Availability:** Print; Online; PDF.

34286 ■ *"Catholic Charities USA Releases 4th Quarter Snapshot Survey Showing Agencies Save Americans in Need More Than $7 Million per Year through Tax Preparation Assistance"* in *Investment Weekly News* (March 31, 2012, pp. 231)
Pub: PR Newswire Association LLC.

Description: Human services organization, Catholic Charities USA (CCUSA) reports saving low income Americans approximately $7.4 million annually with their free tax preparation assitance program. CCUSA, one of the country's largest human services organizations, believes these numbers reinforce the need for a holistic approach to providing programs and services to those in need.

34287 ■ *"Communication Strategies for Enhancing Perceived Fit in the CSR Sponsorship Context"* in *International Journal of Advertising* (Vol. 31, February 2012, No. 1, pp. 133)
Ed: Yong Seok Sohn, Jin K. Han, Sung-Hack Lee. **Released:** 2012. **Description:** Engaging in corporate social responsibility (CSR) is becoming an increasingly common business practice globally and across industries. By contributing to societal welfare, firms can also enhance their corporate image among its stakeholders, in particular, its customers. For CSR to generate goodwill, consumers generally need to perceive a fit between the sponsoring firm and its CSR. Otherwise, consumers may second-guess the firm's intrinsic CSR motives, which may even evoke a negative reaction. **Availability:** Print; Online.

34288 ■ *"Community Commitment Safeguards Franchising Industry"* in *Franchising World* (Vol. 42, November 2010, No. 11, pp. 38)
Pub: International Franchise Association
Contact: Matthew Haller, President
E-mail: mhaller@franchise.org
Description: Individuals who are dedicated to committing time and resources to bring to the attention of legislators those laws and proposals affecting franchise small businesses are highlighted in a monthly format. **Availability:** Online.

34289 ■ *"Companies Operating at Sea Must Embrace Conservation and Sustainability — And Not Wait to Be Forced Into It"* in *The Conversation* (Oct. 21, 2021)
URL(s): theconversation.com/companies-operating-at-sea-must-embrace-conservation-and-sustainability-and-not-wait-to-be-forced-into-it-168923
Released: October 21, 2021. **Description:** Explores the level of sustainability understanding and innovative problem-solving among companies that operate at sea, including oil and gas, shipping and logistics, mining and minerals, and cruise lines and agriculture. **Availability:** Online.

34290 ■ *"A Company's Good Deeds Can Make Consumers Think Its Products Are Safer"* in *The Conversation* (Feb. 26, 2020)
URL(s): theconversation.com/a-companys-good-deeds-can-make-consumers-think-its-products-are-safer-132234
Released: February 26, 2020. **Description:** Discusses how companies that engage in corporate social responsibility have an impact on their customer base because the customers believe that the business' products or services are safer and of higher quality. **Availability:** Online.

34291 ■ *"The Comprehensive Business Case for Sustainability"* in *Harvard Business Review* (October 21, 2016)
Released: October 21, 2016. **Description:** This article discusses the benefits of placing sustainability practices at the top of your small business list. **Availability:** Online.

34292 ■ *"Conscious Capitalism: Liberating the Heroic Spirit of Business"*
Released: January 07, 2014. **Price:** $12.47, e-book; $16.79, paperback. **Description:** Conscious Capitalism companies include Whole Foods Market, South-west Airlines, Costco, Google, Patagonia, The Container Store, UPS and others. These firms under the four specific tenants to success: higher purpose, stakeholder integration, conscious leadership, and conscious culture and management. These companies are able to create value for all stakeholders, including customers, employees, suppliers, investors, society, and the environment. A new preface by the authors is included. **Availability:** E-book; Print.

34293 ■ *"Consignment Shop Blends Business With a Giving Spirit"* in *Gazette* (January 17, 2012)
Ed: Bill Radford. **Description:** Mountain Equipment Recyclers, located in Colorado Springs, Colorado, sells outdoor gear. Mike Mazzola, owner, has expanded his consignment shop to include a nonprofit entity to raise money for our veterans and their families. So far, he has exceeded his goal by giving five percent of sales of consigned gear and 50 percent of donated gear to three nonprofit organizations: AspenPoint, which helps veterans and their families; The Home Front Cares, supporting families of deployed soliders; and LifeQuest Transitions, which helps soldiers and veterans relearn life skills through cognitive exercises and adventure sports. The funds are split equally to the three agencies. **Availability:** Online.

34294 ■ *"Corporate Responsibility"* in *Professional Services Close-Up* (July 2, 2010)
Description: List of firms awarded the inaugural Best Corporate Citizens in Government Contracting by the Corporate Responsibility Magazine is presented. The list is based on the methodology of the Magazine's Best Corporate Citizen's List, with 324 data points of publicly-available information in seven categories which include: environment, climate change, human rights, philanthropy, employee relations, financial performance, and governance. **Availability:** Online.

34295 ■ *"Corporate Social Responsibility Is Not Only Ethical, But Also A Modern Business Tool"* in *Forbes* (Apr 5, 2021)
URL(s): www.forbes.com/sites/forbeshumanresourcescouncil/2021/04/05/corporate-social-responsibility-is-not-only-ethical-but-also-a-modern-business-tool/?sh=72ae15ca1bfa
Ed: Laura Colombo. **Released:** April 05, 2021. **Description:** Discusses the importance of incorporating socially responsible business practices into your small business plan. **Availability:** Online.

34296 ■ *"Corporate Social Responsibility in Today's Socially and Politically Active World"* in *Reworked* (Apr 2, 2021)
URL(s): www.reworked.co/leadership/corporate-social-responsibility-in-todays-socially-and-politically-active-world/
Ed: Scott Clark. **Released:** April 02, 2021. **Description:** Corporate social responsibility (CSR) is one way a small business can publicly acknowledge its operational values and beliefs. This article discusses the role of CSR in a post-pandemic world. **Availability:** Online.

34297 ■ *"Corporate Social Responsibility and Trade Unions: Perspectives Across Europe"*
Pub: Routledge, Taylor & Francis Group
Released: First edition. **Description:** Although interest in corporate social responsibility (CSR) is focused on the relationship between business and key stakeholders such as NGOs and local communities, the role of trade unions is rarely connected to CSR. Experts discuss the gap in the literature on both CSR and employment relations, namely trade union policies toward CSR as well as union engagement with particular CSR initiatives. The research covers eleven European countries which represent a sample of industrial relations structures across the continent.

34298 ■ *"Corporation, Be Good! The Story of Corporate Social Responsibility"* in *Business and Society* (December 2007, pp. 479-485)
Pub: SAGE Publications
Contact: Tracey Ozmina, President
Ed: David M. Wasieleski. **Description:** Review of the book, "Corporation, Be Good! The Story of Corporate Social Responsibility" is presented. The book examines the importance of corporate responsibility and its economic impact. **Availability:** Download; PDF; Online.

34299 ■ *"The Corporation and Private Politics"* in *Journal of Business Strategy* (Vol. 35, May-June 2014, No. 3, pp. 59-62)
Pub: Emerald Group Publishing Limited
Contact: Erika Valenti, President

Description: Description of how the public pressurizes corporations to reveal their viewpoint on various social issues including same-sex marriages and others, even though the issues have nothing to do with the firm's business. Several guidelines for managing the clash of private issues and corporate reputation have been presented.

34300 ■ *"CR Magazine Taps ITT As a 'Best Corporate Citizen'* in *Government Contracting"* in *Profesional Services Close-Up* (July 30, 2010)
Description: ITT Corporation was named by Corporate Responsibility Magazine as a Best Corporate Citizen in Government Contracting. The list recognizes publicly-traded companies that exemplify transparency and accountability while serving the U.S. government. **Availability:** Print.

34301 ■ *"Death by 1,000 Clicks: Where Electronic Health Records Went Wrong"* in *Kaiser Health News* (March 18, 2019)
URL(s): khn.org/news/death-by-a-thousand-clicks/
Ed: Fred Schulte, Erika Fry. **Released:** March 18, 2019. **Description:** Troubling evidence of health practices that use electronic coding and billing, which has caused issues to patient safety and it's also used to overcharge insurance companies and patients. **Availability:** Online.

34302 ■ *"Defense Mobile Joins Forces with RadioShack to launch New Military Focuses Mobile Service this Fall"* in *Defense & Aerospace Business* (September 10, 2014, pp. 7)
Pub: NewsRX LLC.
Contact: Kalani Rosell, Contact
Description: RadioShack and Defense Mobile Corporation have partnered for RadioShack to be the exclusive national retailer for Defense Mobile's new nationwide 4G LTE mobile services. Defense Mobile was launched by veterans and supported by a 100 percent veteran-staffed Member Service organization and its mobile services are designed to benefit, honor and reward active U.S. military and veterans for their commitment and service. **Availability:** Online.

34303 ■ *"Ditch the Pet Store! MindJolt SGN and The Humane Society of the United States Unleash Fluff Friends Rescue"* in *Benzinga.com* (January 4, 2012)
Pub: Benzinga.com
Contact: Jason Raznick, Founder
Ed: Aaron Wise. **Description:** The Humane Society of the United States has partnered with MindJolt SGN, a multiplatform game developer and distributor, to release a mobile game called Fluff Friends Rescue. The game introduces players to the real-world challenges of rescuing pets by nursing animals back to health while running their own animal shelter.

34304 ■ *"Diversity in Business Awards: Minority Businessperson of the Year and Diversity Corporation of the Year Finalists"* in *ColoradoBiz* (Vol. 30, July 2012, No. 7, pp. 32)
Description: Finalists for the ColoradoBiz 18th annual award presentation are profiled. The journal acknowledges minority businesses and businesspeople as well as firms that have been committed to hiring, contracting, and customer/community service to minorities.

34305 ■ "Doubtful Donors" in Canadian Business (Vol. 81, December 8, 2008, No. 21, pp. 8)

Ed: Denis Seguin. **Description:** Key information on fundraising consultancy Inspire, as well as views and information on charitable organizations in Canada is presented. Inspire designs the financial architecture of charitable foundations in Canada, which was affected by the current financial crisis. Inspire advises foundations to keep existing donors. **Availability:** Online.

34306 ■ "The Effects of Perceived Corporate Social Responsibility on Employee Attitudes" in Business Ethics Quarterly (Vol. 24, April 2014, No. 2, pp. 165)

Pub: Business Ethics Quarterly
Contact: Dawn Elm, Executive Director
E-mail: drelm@stthomas.edu

Description: The impact on employee attitudes and their perceptions of how others outside the organization are treated (i.e., corporate social responsibility) above and beyond the impact of how employees are directly treated by organizations is addressed. Results of a study of 827 employees in 18 organizations show that employee perceptions of corporation social responsibility (CSR) are positively related to organizational commitment with the relationship being partially mediated by work meaningfulness and perceived organizational support (POS) and job satisfaction with work meaningfulness partially mediating the relationship but not POS. **Availability:** Download; PDF; Online.

34307 ■ "Employees Want Genuine Corporate Social Responsibility, Not Greenwashing" in The Conversation (Jan. 29, 2020)

URL(s): theconversation.com/employees-want-genu-ine-corporate-social-responsibility-no t-greenwashing-130435
Released: January 29, 2020. **Description:** Discussion of how employees want their companies to be genuine in their embrace of corporate social responsibility and want to ensure that the company they work for isn't giving a false impression of virtue. **Availability:** Online.

34308 ■ "Enterprise Holdings Hires More Than 4,000 Military Veterans Since Joining 100,000 Jobs Mission Coalition" in Defense & Aerospace Business (September 3, 2014, pp. 9)

Pub: NewsRX LLC.
Contact: Kalani Rosell, Contact

Description: Enterprise Holdings, which owns and operates the Enterprise Rent-A-Car. Alamo Rent A Car and National Car Rental brands has hired more than 4,000 military veterans since joining the 100,000 Jobs Mission coalition in 2012. The company is named after the USS Enterprise, an aircraft carrier, and its commitment to the military goes back almost sixty years. Their Website includes employment opportunities for transitioning military personnel, veterans, members of the National Guard and Reserve and their families. Enterprise Holdings has been designated a Top Veteran-Friendly Company by US Veterans Magazine. **Availability:** Online.

34309 ■ "An Equitable Workforce" in Business Journal Portland (Vol. 31, May 2, 2014, No. 9, pp. 10)

Pub: American City Business Journals, Inc.
Contact: Mike Olivieri, Executive Vice President

Description: Bank of America has awarded the Urban League of Portland a $200,000 unrestricted grant as part of its Neighborhood Builders program. Urban League has been working to revive its workforce development program to tackle unemployment among African Americans in Portland, Oregon. Details of the Urban League's plans are also presented. **Availability:** Online.

34310 ■ "Everybody Wants To Save the World: But When You Start a Charity Overseas, Good Intentions Often Go Awry" in Inc. (December 2007)

Ed: Dalia Fahmy. **Description:** Unique set of challenges faced by small businesses wanting to create

a charity overseas. Five key issues to explore before starting a charity overseas are examined. **Availability:** Online.

34311 ■ "Examples of Social Responsibility Strategies" in Chron (November 9, 2018)

Ed: Lainie Peterson. **Released:** November 09, 2018. **Description:** Not only are business owners expected to provide a quality product or service, but they are also expected to do business ethically and in a way that supports communities. This article discusses different types of socially responsible business initiatives as well as tips on how to implement these initiatives. **Availability:** Online.

34312 ■ "Fairness First" in Canadian Business (Vol. 80, April 23, 2007, No. 9, pp. 45)

Description: The need for the fair treatment of employees from the perspective of employee compensation is discussed. **Availability:** Online.

34313 ■ "Falcons' Blank Kicking Off 'Westside Works' Job Training Program" in Atlanta Business Chronicle (May 30, 2014, pp. 6A)

Pub: American City Business Journals, Inc.
Contact: Mike Olivieri, Executive Vice President

Description: Arthur Blank, owner of the Atlanta Falcons, is kicking off 'Westside Works', an initiative to build a world-class football/soccer stadium in Atlanta and transform the adjacent communities. Westside Works, a partnership between The Arthur M. Blank Family Foundation, the Construction Education Foundation of Georgia, and Integrity CDC will provide construction jobs for at least 100 men and women from the Westside neighborhoods in the next 12 months. The program will also provide job training, skills assessment, adult education programs, interview preparedness, and job placement. **Availability:** Print; Online.

34314 ■ "FIS-Metavante Deal Paying Off for Many" in Business Journal-Milwaukee (Vol. 28, December 17, 2010, No. 11, pp. A1)

Pub: The Business Journal
Contact: Heather Ladage, President
E-mail: hladage@bizjournals.com

Ed: Rich Kirchen. **Description:** Jacksonville, Florida-based Fidelity National Information Services Inc., also known as FIS, has remained committed to Milwaukee, Wisconsin more than a year after purchasing Metavante Technologies Inc. FIS has transferred several operations into Metropolitan Milwaukee and has continued its contribution to charitable organizations in the area. **Availability:** Print; Online.

34315 ■ "Former Tech Execs Want to Tap Building Trend in Austin" in Austin Business Journal (Vol. 31, May 13, 2011, No. 10, pp. A1)

Pub: Austin Business Journal
Contact: Rachel McGrath, Director
E-mail: rmcgrath@bizjournals.com

Ed: Cody Lyon. **Description:** Falcon Containers moved to a 51-acre site in Far East Austin, Texas and started construction of a 2,500-square-foot headquarters made from eight 40-foot shipping containers. Falcon's CEO Stephen Shang plans to use his headquarters building as a showroom to attract upscale, urban hipsters. Insights on the construction's environmental and social impact are shared. **Availability:** Print; Online.

34316 ■ "Free File Alliance & IRS Launch 10th Year of Free Online Tax Preparation Services for Millions of Americans" in Economics Week (February 3, 2012, pp. 82)

Pub: PR Newswire Association LLC.

Description: A coalition of tax software companies have partnered with the Internal Revenue Service to offer the 212 IRS Free File progam. The Free File Alliance offers low-to-moderate income taxpayers free access to online commercial tax preparation software. Details of the program are included. **Availability:** Online.

34317 ■ Giving

Description: The former president describes people and projects that save lives and solve problems around the world.

34318 ■ "Giving In a New Age" in Denver Business Journal (Vol. 65, January 17, 2014, No. 36, pp. A4)

Pub: American City Business Journals, Inc.
Contact: Mike Olivieri, Executive Vice President

Description: Urban Peak's 921 Project was an online funding event that aims to get 921 people to participate in a group photo to raise awareness about youth homelessness in Denver, Colorado. The project, which was heavily promoted in social media, is symbolic of the sweeping changes in philanthropy in recent years. **Availability:** Online.

34319 ■ "The Global Talent Hunt" in Business Strategy Review (Vol. 21, Spring 2010, No. 1, pp. 78)

Ed: Richard Emerton. **Released:** February 09, 2010. **Description:** Richard Emerton explains how the new 'triple context' of economy, environment and society will have profound implications for human resource practices. He suggests that viewing talent as abundant is the right perspective for a manager. **Availability:** Print; PDF; Online.

34320 ■ The Go-Giver: A Little Story About a Powerful Business Idea

Pub: Penguin Publishing Group

Ed: Bob Burg, John David Mann. **Released:** October 20, 2015. **Price:** $16.95, hardcover; $17.99; 11.95, audio. **Description:** Story of an ambitious young man named Joe who yearns for success. The book is a heartwarming tale that brings new relevance to the old proverb, "Give and you shall receive". **Availability:** E-book.

34321 ■ "Good Companies Launch More New Products" in Harvard Business Review (Vol. 90, April 2012, No. 4, pp. 28)

Pub: Harvard Business Review Press
Contact: Moderna V. Pfizer, Contact

Ed: Xueming Luo, Shuili Du. **Description:** Because corporate social responsibility enhances relationships with outside stakeholders, it gives companies access to a large range of knowledge sources, enabling firms to keep up with innovations and shifts in market preferences.

34322 ■ "Greene Street Consignment May Be the Most Happening Area Company You've Never Heard Of" in Philadelphia Inquirer (April 20, 2012)

Ed: Kathy Boccella. **Description:** Greene Street Consignment has grown to seven locations featuring fashionable resale items. Lynne Mastrilli, owner of the boutiques does not use social media to market her business. Her sister, Donna, runs a nonprofit offshoot of the business called Greene Street Animal Rescue. Details of the two businesses are included.

34323 ■ Groundswell: Winning in a World Transformed by Social Technologies

Pub: Harvard Business Review Press
Contact: Moderna V. Pfizer, Contact

Ed: Charlene Li, Josh Bernoff. **Released:** June 09, 2011. **Price:** $22, paperback/softbound. **Description:** Individuals are using online social technologies such as blogs, social networking sites, YouTube, and podcasts to discuss products and companies, write their own news, and find their own deals. When consumers you've never met are rating your company's products in public forums with which you have no experience or influence, your company is vulnerable. This book teaches the tools and data necessary to turn this treat into an opportunity. **Availability:** E-book; Print.

34324 ■ "Halls Give Hospital Drive $11 Million Infusion" in The Business Journal-Serving Metropolitan Kansas City (Vol. 26, July 18, 2008)

Description: Don Hall, chairman of Hallmark Cards Inc., and eight family members have announced that they will give $11 million to Children's Mercy Hospitals and Clinics for its $800 million expansion plan. Hall Family Foundation president Bill Hall that contributions such as that for Children's Mercy reflect the charitable interests of the foundation's board and founders. The possible impacts of the Hall's donation are analyzed.

34325 ■ *"Handbook of Research on Marketing and Social Corporate Responsibility"*
Pub: Edward Elgar Publishing Inc.
Contact: Edward Elgar, Founder Chairman
Released: 2016. **Description:** Corporate Social Responsibility (CSR) is crucial for both small and large companies to promote growth. The complex relationship between marketing and social responsibility, with a focus on marketing as a driver for CSR initiatives is examined.

34326 ■ *"Hansen Mechanical Performs Boiler Upgrade at Zoo"* in *Contractor (Vol. 57, February 2010, No. 2, pp. 7)*
Description: Hansen Mechanical installed a donated boiler in the Brookfield Zoo from Weil-McLain. The boilers were installed in the zoo's 'The Swamp' and 'The Living Coast' exhibits. **Availability:** Print; Online.

34327 ■ *"Health Care Briefs: Survey Says Most Approve of Donating Used Pacemakers to Medically Underserved"* in *Crain's Detroit Business (Vol. 25, June 1, 2009)*
Pub: Crain Communications Inc.
Contact: Barry Asin, President
Description: According to a survey conducted by University of Michigan Cardiovascular Center, 87 percent of those with pacemakers and 71 percent of the general population would donate the device to patients in underserved nations.

34328 ■ *"Here's How You Boycott Amazon"* in *Puget Sound Business Journal (Vol. 35, June 13, 2014, No. 8, pp. 12)*
Pub: American City Business Journals, Inc.
Contact: Mike Olivieri, Executive Vice President
Description: Critic, Kimberly Mills, says she boycotted Amazon.com because of its lack of corporate philanthropy and poor working conditions. She also boycotted the firm by purchasing directly from the listed company Websites when purchasing retail products, instead of buying directly from Amazon's site. Other online retailers are increasing customer services corporate social responsibility. **Availability:** Online.

34329 ■ *"Home Instead Senior Care Awards National Salute to Senior Service Honoree"* in *Professional Services Close-Up (June 8, 2012)*
Description: Home Instead Senior Care presented Clark Paradise with its Salute to Senior Service award. Paradise is an 85-year old volunteer living in Toms River, New Jersey. He founded a mission for the homeless.

34330 ■ *"How Businesses Can Do Well by Doing Good"* in *U.S. News & World Report (Aug. 17, 2021)*
URL(s): www.usnews.com/news/national-news/ar ticles/2021-08-17/how-businesses-can-do-well-by -doing-good
Ed: David Levine. **Released:** August 17, 2021. **Description:** Discusses how meeting the social, environmental, and health needs of the community that your small business serves is both good for society, and how it is also good for your bottome-line!. **Availability:** Online.

34331 ■ *"How One Company Joins Corporate Public Relations and Community Engagement"* in *Denver Business Journal (Vol. 65, January 17, 2014, No. 36, pp. A6)*
Pub: American City Business Journals, Inc.
Contact: Mike Olivieri, Executive Vice President
Description: Denver, Colorado-based Barefoot PR was formed by Cori Streetman and Sarah Hogan in 2010 to change corporate views on philanthropy. The partners made a commitment to make community

investment the driving force of business. Insights on the next-generation of community relations consultants are also given. **Availability:** Online.

34332 ■ *"Howl-o-ween"* in *Decatur Daily (October 25, 2011)*
Description: Animal Friends Humane Society provides free pet food and cat litter to Meals on Wheels clients. **Availability:** Online.

34333 ■ *"Innovating Globally"* in *Business Strategy Review (Vol. 21, Spring 2010, No. 1, pp. 24)*
Ed: Costas Markides, Stuart Crainer. **Description:** Costas Markides has spent over two decades studying business strategy and innovation. Recently, he has been focusing on the bigger picture of how people can address major social problems. Can the techniques used by managers to create innovation inside organizations work with global change?. **Availability:** Download; PDF; Online.

34334 ■ *"KCET Takes On Elder-Care With Robust Your Turn To Care Website"* in *PR Newswire (July 31, 2012)*
Pub: PR Newswire Association LLC.
Description: Your Turn To Care is a new Website created by KCET, the nation's largest independent public television station. The network, serving southern and central California, offers the Website to serve as a resource for families, caregivers and seniors in te US facing the challenges of caring for an ailing or aging loved one. The Website also covers issues involved in aging.

34335 ■ *"Keene: Nominations are Being Sought by the Keene Cities for Climate Protection Committee for the Monadnock Green Business of the Year Award"* in *New Hampshire Business Review (Vol. 34, February 24, 2012, No. 4, pp. 7)*
Released: February 24, 2012. **Description:** Nominations are being sought by the Keene Cities for Climate Protection Committee for the Monadnock Green Business of the Year Award. The award recognizes socially and environmentally responsible companies in the region that have developed innovative practices or programs while contributing to the economic growth of the area.

34336 ■ *The Leadership Challenge: How to Make Extraordinary Things Happen in Organizations*
Pub: Jossey-Bass
Ed: James M. Kouzes, Barry Z. Posner. **Released:** 7th edition. **Price:** $34.95, hardcover; $34.95, hardcover. **Description:** According to research by the authors, people can make extraordinary things happen by liberating the leader within everyone around them. This handbook gives practical tips to aspire leaders in retail, manufacturing, government, community, church and school settings. **Availability:** E-book; Print.

34337 ■ *"A Lifetime of Giving: Food Bank CEO Fights Hunger One Mouth At a Time"* in *Black Enterprise (Vol. 41, November 2010, No. 4, pp. 86)*
Pub: Earl G. Graves Ltd.
Contact: Earl Graves, Jr., President
Ed: Tamara E. Holmes. **Description:** Profile of Valerie Traore, CEO of Food Bank of South Jersey. Traore stresses the importance of volunteerism that she learned from her grandparents. Hunger relief became her passion when she served as a temp office worker for the Maryland Food Bank in Baltimore. She earned her Bachelor's of Science in management and has dedicated herself to a career in nonprofit service. **Availability:** Online.

34338 ■ *"The Loan Arranger"* in *Canadian Business (Vol. 80, October 22, 2007, No. 21, pp. 15)*
Description: Muhammad Yunus received the Nobel Prize in 2006 for the organization that he founded, the Grameen Bank. The bank has helped women in developing countries and has also begun helping mil-

lions of individuals to make loans in the U.S. through the Grameen Bank. An evaluation of the Grameen model is provided. **Availability:** Online.

34339 ■ *"Many in Tech Look to Push More Community Involvement, But Not in Traditional Ways"* in *Boston Business Journal (Vol. 31, August 5, 2011, No. 28, pp. 1)*
Pub: Boston Business Journal
Contact: Carolyn M. Jones, President
E-mail: cmjones@bizjournals.com
Ed: Mary Moore. **Released:** Weekly. **Price:** $4, Introductory 4-Week Offer(Digital Only). **Description:** Entrepreneurs and venture capitalists in Boston have launched Technology Underwriting Greater Good, the tech industry's answer to the criticism that they are not charitable. The foundation finances nonprofits that aid young people through entrepreneurship, education and life experience. Other tech firms in Boston doing charitable works are discussed. **Availability:** Print; Online.

34340 ■ *"Meet the Class of 2014, In their Own Words"* in *South Florida Business Journal (Vol. 34, June 27, 2014, No. 49, pp. 18)*
Pub: American City Business Journals, Inc.
Contact: Mike Olivieri, Executive Vice President
Released: Weekly. **Price:** $8, introductory 4-week offer(Digital & Print). **Description:** Several business leaders and entrepreneurs under the age of 40 who have achieved success and contributed to their community are presented. The honorees of the 40 Under 40 Class of 2014 share their views about personal and professional lives and social responsibilities to their communities. **Availability:** Print; Online.

34341 ■ *Microfranchising: Creating Wealth at the Bottom of the Pyramid*
Pub: Edward Elgar Publishing Inc.
Contact: Edward Elgar, Founder Chairman
Released: 2007. **Description:** Ideas from researchers and social entrepreneurs discusses the movement that moves microfranchising into a mechanism for sustainable poverty reduction on a scale to match microfinance.

34342 ■ *"Military Brides Can Get Free Wedding Gowns"* in *Virginian-Pilot (November 10, 2010)*
Pub: The Virginian-Pilot
Contact: Kevin Goyette, Director
E-mail: kgoyette@dailypress.com
Ed: Jamesetta M. Walker. **Description:** Seventy-five designer wedding gowns will be given to military brides on a first-come, first-served basis at Maya Couture through the Brides Across America's wedding gown giveaway program. Gowns are valued between $500 to $3,000 and are donated by designers Maggie Sottero, Pronovias and Essense of Australia. **Availability:** Online.

34343 ■ *The Mom & Pop Store: How the Unsung Heroes of the American Economy Are Surviving and Thriving*
Ed: Robert Spector. **Description:** The history of small independent retail enterprises and how mom and pop stores in the U.S. continue to thrive through customer service and renewed community support for local businesses. **Availability:** Audio.

34344 ■ *"A New Approach to Funding Social Enterprises: Unbundling Societal Benefits and Financial Returns Can Dramatically Increase Investment"* in *Harvard Business Review (Vol. 90, January-February 2012, No.1-2, pp. 118)*
Pub: Harvard Business Review Press
Contact: Moderna V. Pfizer, Contact
Ed: Bruce Kogut, Antony Bugg-Levine, Nalin Kulatilaka. **Price:** $8.95, PDF and hardcover black and white. **Description:** Identification of a range of financing arrangements that can maximize benefits delivered by social organizations. These include equity, quasi-equity debt, charitable giving, convertible debt, and securitized debt. The claims on assets and types of return for each are defined. **Availability:** Print; PDF; Online.

34345 ■ *"New Economy Initiative Gains Partners"* in *Crain's Detroit Business (Vol. 25, June 1, 2009, No. 22, pp. M014)*
Pub: Crain Communications Inc.
Contact: Barry Asin, President

Ed: Sherri Begin Welch. **Description:** New Economy Initiative is a $100 million philanthropic initiative that focuses on regional economic development. Recent grants awarded to Michigan companies are outlined. **Availability:** Print; Online.

34346 ■ *"New Pet Product Launches IndieGoGo Crowdfunding to Remain American Made"* in *Benzinga.com (June 11, 2012)*
Pub: Benzinga.com
Contact: Jason Raznick, Founder

Ed: Aaron Wise. **Description:** The Supercollar (r) is a new dog collar and leash combination launched on an Indiegogo crowdfunding campaign in order to raise fund to help the firm keep their business in America. The firm is striving to design and manufacture the Supercollar here in the US in order to create and save American jobs. The Supercollar's technology is also discussed. **Availability:** Print; Online.

34347 ■ *"Nonprofit NAIC Acquires Software Developer as For-Profit Arm"* in *Crain's Detroit Business (Vol. 25, June 22, 2009, No. 25, pp. 10)*
Pub: Crain Communications Inc.
Contact: Barry Asin, President

Ed: Sherri Begin Welch. **Description:** Details of National Association of Investors Corporation's acquisition of a Massachusetts investment software developer in order to offer more products to investment clubs and individual investors nationwide. **Availability:** Online.

34348 ■ *"Nonprofits Pressured to Rein in Fundraising Events"* in *Crain's Detroit Business (Vol. 25, June 15, 2009, No. 24, pp. 1)*
Pub: Crain Communications Inc.
Contact: Barry Asin, President

Ed: Sherri Begin Welch. **Description:** Local corporations have asked nonprofits to limit fundraising events in order to cut costs during the recession. **Availability:** Online.

34349 ■ *"One Laptop Per Child Weighs Going For-Profit"* in *Boston Business Journal (Vol. 31, May 20, 2011, No. 17, pp. 1)*
Pub: Boston Business Journal
Contact: Carolyn M. Jones, President
E-mail: cmjones@bizjournals.com

Ed: Mary Moore. **Released:** Weekly. **Price:** $4, Print. **Description:** Nonprofit organization One Laptop Per Child is thinking of shifting into a for-profit structure in order to raise as much as $10 million in capital to achieve its goal of distributing more XO laptops to poor children worldwide. The organization has distributed 2 million computers since 2008 with Uruguay, Peru and Rwanda as its biggest markets. **Availability:** Print; Online.

34350 ■ *"Pet Food Bank 'Shares the Love"'* in *Pet Product News (Vol. 64, December 2010, No. 12, pp. 6)*
Description: Winston-Salem, North Carolina-based nonprofit Share the Love Pet Food Bank has donated 60,000 pounds of pet food since its establishment in 2009. It has been linking pet food manufacturers and rescue groups to supply unsold pet food to needy animals. The nonprofit intends to reach out to more animal welfare groups by building more warehouses. **Availability:** Online.

34351 ■ *"Philanthropy Good For Business"* in *Crain's Detroit Business (Vol. 24, February 18, 2008, No. 7, pp. 14)*
Pub: Crain Communications Inc.
Contact: Barry Asin, President

Ed: Sheena Harrison. **Description:** Profile of Burce McCully, founder of Dynamic Edge Inc., and his views on philanthropy as a key to any small company's suc-

cess. The Ann Arbor, Michigan information technology firm has volunteered and raised funds for many causes since 1999 when the company was founded. **Availability:** Print; Online.

34352 ■ *The Power of Social Innovation: How Civic Entrepreneurs Ignite Community Networks for Good*
Pub: John Wiley & Sons, Inc.
Contact: Christina Van Tassell, Executive Vice President Chief Financial Officer

Ed: Stephen Goldsmith, Tim Burke, Gigi Georges. **Released:** March 01, 2010. **Price:** $44, Hardcover; $35.99, E-Book; $44, hardcover. **Description:** This seminal book provides tools for civic entrepreneurs to create healthier communities and promote innovative solutions to public and social problems. It shows how to effectively tackle the intractable issues facing the country. **Availability:** E-book; Print.

34353 ■ *"Preserving a Nonprofit's Mission: YWCA to Absorb Key Programs as the Boston Center for Community and Justice Fades"* in *Boston Business Journal (Vol. 31, June 17, 2011, No. 21, pp. 3)*
Pub: Boston Business Journal
Contact: Carolyn M. Jones, President
E-mail: cmjones@bizjournals.com

Ed: Mary Moore. **Description:** Young Women's Christian Association Boston (YWCA) agreed to absorb the LeadBoston social issues and youth programs operated by the Boston Center for Community Justice. The BCCJ is scheduled to close after failing to stabilize its finances. **Availability:** Print; Online.

34354 ■ *"Pride Lands Janitorial Work at New Terminal"* in *Sacramento Business Journal (Vol. 28, June 10, 2011, No. 15, pp. 1)*
Pub: Sacramento Business Journal
Contact: Stephanie Fretwell, Director
E-mail: sfretwell@bizjournals.com

Ed: Kelly Johnson. **Description:** Pride Industries Inc. won the five-year $9.4 million contract to clean the Sacramento International Airport's new Terminal B, which will open in fall 2011. The nonprofit organization posts a revenue of $191 million for 2011 and currently employs more than 2,400 people with disabilities. The contract is expected to provide savings of over $3 million a year to the airport. **Availability:** Online.

34355 ■ *"Priority: In Memoriam"* in *Inc. (December 2007, pp. 25-26, 28, 30)*
Ed: Ryan McCarthy. **Description:** Profiles of entrepreneurs who died in 2007; these individuals helped to create some major business trends in the last fifty years, from the advent of socially responsible business to development of quality manufacturing. **Availability:** Online.

34356 ■ *"The Profits of Good Works"* in *Barron's (Vol. 92, September 17, 2012, No. 38, pp. 14)*
Description: The nonprofit organization B Lab is responsible for certifying companies as socially conscious and environmentally friendly. B Lab examines the impact of companies on workers, communities, and the environment as well as their internal governance. **Availability:** Online.

34357 ■ *"Proud Out Loud"* in *Canadian Business (Vol. 80, April 23, 2007, No. 9, pp. 52)*
Description: The role of accomplishments of employees in improving workplace conditions is presented. **Availability:** Online.

34358 ■ *"PSCPets.com Gives Back to Support Military Working Dogs"* in *Pet Product News (Vol. 66, September 2012, No. 9, pp. 17)*
Description: Menomonie, Wisconsin-based online pet health and wellness products supplier PSCPets.com donated on $26.99 bottle of PSCPets Joint Support Military Working Dogs for every $5 donation for the company's Rescue Outreach Program. Each

month, PSCPets.com uses the program to benefit animal welfare causes. How the effort to assist military working dogs started is discussed. **Availability:** Online.

34359 ■ *"Put the Good, the Bad and the Ugly on the Table"* in *South Florida Business Journal (Vol. 35, September 19, 2014, No. 8, pp. 13)*
Pub: American City Business Journals, Inc.
Contact: Mike Olivieri, Executive Vice President

Description: United Way of Broward County chief executive, Kathleen Cannon, says the creation of a macropractice for social work is the most rewarding part of her job. She also said teaching people how to give back is the most challenging part of her role.

34360 ■ *"Readers Share How Sewing Shaped the Fabric of Their Lives"* in *Virginian-Pilot (September 14, 2010)*
Pub: The Virginian-Pilot
Contact: Kevin Goyette, Director
E-mail: kgoyette@dailypress.com

Ed: Jamesetta M. Walker. **Description:** People discuss the ways sewing has help enrich their lives, from public service projects and conventions centered on sewing. **Availability:** Print; Online.

34361 ■ *"Red Cross CEO Mark Beddingfield: This Work Is In His Blood"* in *Birmingham Business Journal (Vol. 31, March 7, 2014, No. 10, pp. 11)*
Pub: American City Business Journals, Inc.
Contact: Mike Olivieri, Executive Vice President

Description: American Red Cross Alabama Region CEO, Mark Beddingfield, says fundraising is the biggest challenge facing nonprofits in view of the weak economy. He believes nonprofits should always be ready to be able to serve clients. Beddingfield added that the organization continues to look for committed volunteers who are willing to serve people. **Availability:** Print; Online.

34362 ■ *"Religious Revival"* in *Canadian Business (Vol. 81, December 8, 2008, No. 21, pp. 57)*
Pub: Rogers Media Inc.
Contact: Neil Spivak, Chief Executive Officer

Ed: Paul Webster. **Description:** Canada-based lawyer Cyndee Todgham Cherniak believes that Canadians wishing to do business in China should have professional competence, as well as cultural and spiritual sensitivity. Chinese government officials also acknowledge the role of religion in China's economy. **Availability:** Online.

34363 ■ *"Research and Markets Offers Report on US Business Traveler's Green, New Technology Views"* in *Airline Industry Information (July 30, 2012)*
Description: The US Business Traveler Expectations of Green and Technology Initiatives in Hotels in 2012 contains comprehensive analysis on US business travelers views on green and technology initiative and socially responsible measures geared towards the business traveler. **Availability:** Print; Online.

34364 ■ *"The Romance of Good Deeds: A Business with a Cause Can Do Good in the World"* in *Inc. (Volume 32, December 2010, No. 10, pp. 47)*
Pub: Inc. Magazine
Ed: Meg Cadoux Hirshberg. **Description:** Entrepreneurship and family relationships are discussed. When a small business has a passion for philanthropy it can help any marriage by creating even greater passion for each other. **Availability:** Online.

34365 ■ *"Sage Advice"* in *Canadian Business (Vol. 80, October 22, 2007, No. 21, pp. 70)*
Description: Seymour Schulich, one of Canada's richest men and generous philanthropist, wrote the book, "Get Smarter: Life and Business Lessons". The business book sold more than 50,000 copies and

now sits on Canada's bestseller's list. Its popularity is attributed to the marketing efforts of the entrepreneur and author. **Availability:** Print; Online.

34366 ■ *"Salvation Army Prepares to Break Ground on South Mountain Community Center"* in The Business Journal - Serving Phoenix and the Valley of the Sun (Vol. 28, September 12, 2008, No. 53, pp. 1)

Pub: Phoenix Business Journal

Contact: Alex McAlister, Director

E-mail: amcalister@bizjournals.com

Ed: Jan Buchholz. **Description:** Construction will begin in early 2009 on an $80 million Ray and Joan Kroc Community Center in Phoenix, Arizona. It will be located adjacent to the Salvation Army, which received a $1.9 billion contribution from Joan Kroc after her death in 2003. This fund will be divided to construct 30 community centers across the country. **Availability:** Print; Online.

34367 ■ *"SECU's Tax Preparation Services Net Members More Than $86 Million in Refunds"* in Economics Week (May 11, 2012)

Description: State Employees' Credit Union (SECU) helped nearly 65,000 North Carolina members file their income taxes in 2012. SECU reports $86 million in refunds and saving members more than $8 million in preparation fees. The credit union promotes its tax preparation services so members can avoid the high fees paid to tax preparers. **Availability:** Print; Online.

34368 ■ *"Shop Happy: Harvesting Happiness Announces Grassroots Crowdfunding Site for HH4Heroes"* in Marketwired (July 2, 2012)

Pub: Comtex News Network Inc.

Contact: Kan Devnani, President

Description: Shop Happy online store has created a fundraising aspect to their customers' shopping experience. Shoppers can assist in helping to heal post combat veterans suffering from PTSD, TBI, MST, andMSA who have served as combat warriors in Operations Iraqi and Enduring Freedom. Lisa Cypers Kamen, founder of Harvesting Happiness believes this program will help both veterans and customers to empower themselves and our veterans in a positive way (HH4Heroes.org).

34369 ■ *"Should Your Small Business Care About CSR? Here's the Honest Answer"* in Digital.com (October 7, 2020)

Ed: Dale Cudmore. **Released:** October 07, 2020. **Description:** More and more businesses are launching initiatives to be more socially responsible. This is the idea behind corporate social responsibility (CSR), which is typically considered a practice for large corporations. However, many small business are now practicing social responsibility and reap the benefits. This article details how small businesses can incorporate CSR into their business practices. **Availability:** Online.

34370 ■ *Social Enterprise: Developing Sustainable Businesses*

Pub: Palgrave Macmillan

Ed: Frank Martin, Marcus Thompson. **Released:** 2010. **Description:** Social enterprises bring people and communities together for economic development and social gain and represent a growing sector of the business community.

34371 ■ *Social Entrepreneurship For Dummies*

Pub: John Wiley & Sons, Inc.

Contact: Christina Van Tassell, Executive Vice President Chief Financial Officer

Ed: Mark Durieux, PhD, Robert Stebbins, PhD. **Released:** April 2010. **Price:** $16.99, E-book; $24.99, paperback. **Description:** Discover ways to bring social entrepreneurship to a small company in today's business environment. Today, a company is not measured by financial performance alone, but also on social entrepreneurship. **Availability:** E-book; Print.

34372 ■ *Social Entrepreneurship: What Everyone Needs to Know*

Ed: David Bornstein, Susan Davis. **Released:** May 27, 2010. **Description:** In development circles, there is now a widespread consensus that social entrepreneurs represent a far better mechanism to respond to needs than we have ever had before, a decentralized and emergent force that remains the best hope for solutions.

34373 ■ *"Socially Responsible Business Practices"* in PurposeMart Blog (June 14, 2021)

URL(s): purposemart.com/corporate-social -responsibility-practices/

Ed: Fidelia Negue. **Released:** June 14, 2021. **Description:** Explains what corporate social responsibility is. Goes into further detail about how it is not only an environmental endeavor, rather it is environmental, economic, and social. **Availability:** Online.

34374 ■ *"SPOILED! Children's Consignment Boutique Now Collecting Donations To Support Baby2Baby & Help Children In Need"* in Benzinga.com (July 30, 2012)

Pub: Benzinga.com

Contact: Jason Raznick, Founder

Ed: Aaron Wise. **Description:** CeCe Hendriks opened her high-end children's consignment store in response to wanting to provide quality clothing for her son. Because children outgrow their clothing so fast, she decided a consignment shop is what all mom's needed. Hendriks offers a 50 percent consignment to donors and if the item isn't sold in 90 days, the consignee can choos to have the item returned or donate it to Baby2Baby. Hendriks also gives 10 percent of proceeds from sales to Baby2Baby, a nonprofit that works with homeles and domestic violence shelters. **Availability:** Online.

34375 ■ *"A Stakeholder--Human Capital Perspective on the Link Between Social Performance and Executive Compensation"* in Business Ethics Quarterly (Vol. 24, January 2014, No. 1, pp. 1)

Pub: Business Ethics Quarterly

Contact: Dawn Elm, Executive Director

E-mail: drelm@stthomas.edu

Description: The link between firm corporate social performance (CSP) and executive compensation could be driven by a sorting effect (a firm's CSP is related to the initial levels of compensation of newly hired executives), or by an incentive effect (incumbent executives are rewarded for past firm CSP). An exploration of the sorting effect of firm CSP on the initial compensation of newly hired executives is discussed. **Availability:** Download; PDF; Online.

34376 ■ *"Stand Out Via Service: How Volunteering Can Boost Your Professional Bottom Line"* in Black Enterprise (Vol. 44, June 2014, No. 10, pp. 42)

Pub: Earl G. Graves Ltd.

Contact: Earl Graves, Jr., President

Description: According to the 2013 Deloitte Volunteer IMPACT Survey, more than three of every four human resource executives volunteer. This strategy can lead to career satisfaction and help a business advance and fuel growth for individuals and the firm. Tips for finding the right volunteer opportunity are included.

34377 ■ *"Steering a Steady Course Through Turbulent Waters"* in Providence Business News (Vol. 29, June 2, 2014, No. 9, pp. 22)

Pub: American City Business Journals, Inc.

Contact: Mike Olivieri, Executive Vice President

URL(s): pbn.com/steering-a-steady-course-through -turbulent-waters97424

Description: Barbara Haynes, Cumulus Broadcasting Market Manager, continues to remain clear sighted amid changing ownership, competition and technology propelling radio through dramatic transformation. Some of the elements that have driven her to success include resilience and dedication to community service.

34378 ■ *"The Sustainability Agenda: Ioannia Ioannou"* in Business Strategy Review (Vol. 25, Summer 2014, No. 2, pp. 16)

Released: June 02, 2014. **Description:** How should academics keep up to date with issues such as corporate responsibility? Ioannis Ioannou of the London School of Business advocates a more interventionist approach to this issue. **Availability:** Print; PDF; Online.

34379 ■ *"Sustainability Is Changing How We Do Business...For the Better"* in Business.com (May 23, 2019)

Ed: Melissa Zehner. **Released:** May 23, 2019. **Description:** Sustainability and credibility now go hand in hand in business. This article discusses how sustainability is transforming businesses from the consumer to the investor. **Availability:** Online.

34380 ■ *"Sustainable Advantage"* in Inc. (Vol. 36, September 2014, No. 7, pp. 86)

Pub: Mansueto Ventures L.L.C.

Contact: Stephanie Mehta, Chief Executive Officer

Price: $8.95, hardcopy black and white. **Description:** Four startup companies committed to providing sustainable, eco-friendly products and services while protecting the environment and bettering human health are profiled. Holganix(TM) offers organic lawn care products; Motiv Power Systems electrifies large vehicles; Clean Energy Collective Solar Power builds lareg community solar panel arrays; and Protein Bar offers healthy alternatives to fast food in its chain of restaurants. The company also works with nonprofits focused on wellness and education and has created 167 Learning Gardens nationwide. **Availability:** Print; PDF; Online.

34381 ■ *"Teksapiens, A Leading SEO Company, Offers Free SEO Consulting Services to Dallas Businesses"* in Wireless News (March 29, 2012)

Description: Dallas-based Web design firm, Teksapiens, offers free search engine optimization to Dallas businesess signing up at DallasBestSEO.com. The free service provides tips to outperform competition when marketing on the Internet. **Availability:** Print; Online.

34382 ■ *"These Clothes Use Outlandish Designs to Trick Facial Recognition Software into Thinking You're Not a Human"* in Business Insider (October 12, 2019)

URL(s): www.businessinsider.com/clothes-accesso -ries-that-outsmart-facial-recognition-tech-2019-10

Ed: Aaron Holmes. **Released:** October 12, 2019. **Description:** With the rise of facial recognition technology, some designers are pushing back by designing clothes and accessories that make faces undetectable. Examples of what confuses this AI technology are given, such as masks and printed material. **Availability:** Online.

34383 ■ *"This Just In: TechTown, Partners Get $1M to Start Tech Exchange"* in Crain's Detroit Business (Vol. 25, June 1, 2009, No. 22, pp. 1)

Pub: Crain Communications Inc.

Contact: Barry Asin, President

Ed: Daniel Duggan. **Description:** Three veterans of the auto industry have partnered to create, Revitalizing Michigan, a nonprofit dedicated to help manufacturers improve their processes. The firm is seeking federal, state and private grants to fund the mission. **Availability:** Print; Online.

34384 ■ *"Three Megatrends to Help Your Business Compete in 2014"* in South Florida Business Journal (Vol. 34, January 3, 2014, No. 24, pp. 10)

Pub: American City Business Journals, Inc.

Contact: Mike Olivieri, Executive Vice President

Released: Weekly. **Price:** $8, Introductory 4-week offer(Digital & Print). **Description:** Businesses can improve their competitive edge in 2014 by adapting several mega small business trends in marketing and communications. Brands can use brand bridging to get customers attention, use wearable technology to increase their value, and adapt environmental sustainability and corporate social responsibility to keep their customers. **Availability:** Print; Online.

34385 ■ *"UB Program Offers Free Tax Preparation" in Buffalo News (January 29, 2012)*

Ed: Jonathan D. Epstein. **Description:** University of Buffalo's Schhol of Management in New York is offering free tax preparation for low-income individuals and families. The program is available on North and South campuses and is designed to help these people save money and collect all refunds in which they are eligible. **Availability:** Online.

34386 ■ *"United Way Offers Free Tax Assistance for Local Low-Income Families" in The Blade (January 6, 2012)*

Pub: Block Communications Inc.

URL(s): www.toledoblade.com

Ed: Kate Giammarise. **Description:** United Way of Greater Toledo, Ohio is offering free income tax preparation for households earning under $50,000 in 2011. United Way has partnered with the Lucas County Commissioner, Tina Skeldon Wozniak; Lucas County Treasurer, Wade Kapszukiewicz; and other social service agencies to help low-income workers in their region. **Availability:** Online.

34387 ■ *"Unretirement: How Baby Boomers are Changing the Way We Think About Work, Community, and the Good Life"*

Released: 1st edition. **Price:** $16.20, paperback; $23.40, hardback; $14.40, ebook. **Description:** Baby boomers are transforming American economics and society in a positive way. Because boomers are living longer in better health and are extending their work lives, may times with new careers, entrepreneurial ventures, and socially responsible volunteering service. This trend will enrich the American workplace, economy, and the society as a whole for future generations. **Availability:** E-book; Print; Online.

34388 ■ *"Urban League Training Program Finds Jobs for Cincinnati's 'Hard to Serve" in Business Courier (Vol. 27, July 2, 2010, No. 9, pp. 1)*

Pub: Business Courier

Ed: Lucy May. **Description:** Stephen Tucker, director of workforce development for the Urban League of Greater Cincinnati, is an example of how ex-offenders can be given chances for employment after service jail sentences. How the Urban Leagues' Solid Opportunities for Advancement job training program helped Tucker and other ex-offenders is discussed. **Availability:** Print; Online.

34389 ■ *"USHCC Applauds 10 Best U.S. Corporations for Veteran-Owned Businesses for 2012" in Economics Week (April 20, 2012, pp. 153)*

Description: The United States Hispanic Chamber of Commerce honored the 2012 National Veteran-Owned Business Association and its 10 Best US Corporations for veteran-owned businesses. The list includes large corporations that engage three million veteran-owned businese as suppliers. The Hispanic Chamber promotes economic growth and development of Hispanic entrepreneurs in the US. **Availability:** Print; Online.

34390 ■ *Values-Centered Entrepreneurs and Their Companies*

Pub: Routledge, Taylor & Francis Group

Ed: David Y. Choi, Edmund Gray. **Released:** First edition. **Description:** A new brand of entrepreneurs has arrived on the business scene, carrying with them a new set of values. They possess a sense of social responsibility, the need to protect the planet, and to do the right thing for all stakeholders.

34391 ■ *Values and Opportunities in Social Entrepreneurship*

Pub: Palgrave Macmillan

Released: 2010. **Price:** $89, hardcover; $120, hardcover; $64.99, e-book; $84.99, Softcover. **Description:** Social entrepreneurship has grown as a research field. This book discusses social entrepreneurship as well as the identification and exploitation of social venturing opportunities. **Availability:** E-book; Print; PDF; Electronic publishing.

34392 ■ *"Veteran-Owned Business Energizes Employees To Give Back" in Investment Weekly News (June 23, 2012, pp. 768)*

Description: Service Disabled Veteran-Owned Small Business (SDVOSB) and Certified (AITC) are commited to American veterans. AITC's staff is composed of 50 percent veterans and sees this model as a means of giving back to the soldiers, a cause they proudly support. Details of programs that support wounded warriors and their families, and are supported by AITC, are described. **Availability:** Print; Online.

34393 ■ *"Veteran-Owned Firm Enlists Street" in Traders (Vol. 25, May 1, 2012, No. 337)*

Description: Academy Securities discusses its vision to give US military veterans a chance at a career on Wall Street. Academy is a veteran owned investment brokerage firm and is pursuing Wall Street professionals willing to mentor veterans. The firm is dedicated to giving back to the veterans who have served the nation and is a certified Service Disabled Veteran Owned Business. **Availability:** Print; Online.

34394 ■ *"Veterans Train to Use Military Skills In Civilian Workforce" in South Florida Business Journal (Vol. 34, April 18, 2014, No. 39, pp. 10)*

Pub: American City Business Journals, Inc.

Contact: Mike Olivieri, Executive Vice President

Released: Weekly. **Price:** $8, Introductory 4-week offer(Digital & Print). **Description:** United Way of Broward County has launched the Mission United program that offers a one-stop shop of information and resources to meet the needs of military veterans. Mission United aims to reduce the jobless rate among veterans by creating two programs to help veterans and connect them with potential employers who are hiring. Details of the job training program is explored. **Availability:** Print; Online.

34395 ■ *"Virtue and Vice" in Entrepreneur (September 2014)*

Pub: Entrepreneur Media Inc.

Contact: Dan Bova, Director

E-mail: dbova@entrepreneur.com

Description: Socially responsible investments (SRI) are rising in the U.S., but many claim that vice funds offer better returns. Vice fund proponents argue that any profitable company deserves a place in a good investment portfolio. SRI proponents emphasize investments that benefit the society. Analysts note that investors who restrict their investment landscape by selecting only vice funds or only SRI funds may lead to lower returns. Other specialized funds attract activist investors supporting advocacies like gender equality or a positive work environment. **Availability:** PDF; Online.

34396 ■ *"Wal-Mart Offering In-Store Tax Return Preparation Services" in Tax Notes (Vol. 134, January 16, 2012, No. 3, pp. 301)*

Ed: Eric Kroh. **Description:** Wal-Mart is offering tax preparation services to customers in their retail stores. Details of the program included. **Availability:** Online.

34397 ■ *"Wal-Mart Sharpens Focus on Roxbury" in Boston Business Journal (Vol. 31, July 8, 2011, No. 24, pp. 1)*

Pub: Boston Business Journal

Contact: Carolyn M. Jones, President

E-mail: cmjones@bizjournals.com

Ed: Mary Moore. **Price:** $4. **Description:** Wal-Mart Stores is boosting its search for a possible location in the Roxbury section of Boston, Massachusetts. The search is focused on underserved communities in terms of jobs and access to reasonably-priced merchandise. The extent Boston's African American

community has clashed with Mayor Thomas M. Memino over the accommodations of the retailer in Roxbury is discussed. **Availability:** Print; Online.

34398 ■ *"Walk-Ins Being Accepted for Free Tax-Preparation Service" in Akron Beacon Journal (January 26, 2012)*

Ed: Betty Lin-Fisher. **Description:** Akron Summit Earned Income Tax Program, despite technical issues, is offering free service to walk in wishing free tax preparation. Details of the program are included. **Availability:** Print.

34399 ■ *"The Walmart Foundation and Leading Nonprofits Launch the MyFreeTaxes Program, Offering Eligible Taxpayers Free Tax Preparation in 2012" in Economics Week (February 10, 2012, pp. 274)*

Pub: PR Newswire Association LLC.

Description: United Way Worldwide, One Economy, and the National Disability Institute's Real Economic Impact Tour received funding in the amount of $4.35 million from Walmart Foundation to provide free tax filing services to eligible U.S. citizens. Earned Income Tax Credit (EITC), SNAP, and WIC elgibility education are also included in the program. The program will not only file income taxes for eligible individuals families, it will also educate them about rights and options. **Availability:** Online.

34400 ■ *"Ways for a Small Business to Show Social Responsibility" in Chron*

URL(s): smallbusiness.chron.com/ways-small-business-show-social-responsibility-60082.html

Ed: Neil Kokemuller. **Description:** Demonstrating socially responsible behavior is must for a small business trying to compete against larger chains. This article discusses ways in which you can incorporate social responsibility into your small business. **Availability:** Online.

34401 ■ *"Wells Fargo and NeighborWorks America Offer Down Payment Assistance: Low- to Middle-Income Consumers Get the Help They Need" in Black Enterprise (Vol. 44, June 2014, No. 10, pp. 34)*

Pub: Earl G. Graves Ltd.

Contact: Earl Graves, Jr., President

Description: A new homeownership program, called NeighborhoodLIFT, helps low to middle income earners obtain mortgages. Currently, the program is present in 25 markets throughout the U.S. and has committed $195 million to those markets. **Availability:** Online.

34402 ■ *"What Big Companies Can Teach Small Business Owners About Sustainability" in Entrepreneur (October 27, 2017)*

Ed: Serenity Gibbons. **Released:** October 27, 2017. **Description:** Companies that have embraced ambitious sustainability goals have invariably found it improves efficiency, employee morale and public perception. This article provides five sustainability lessons that small businesses can learn from top corporations. **Availability:** Online.

34403 ■ *"What Is Corporate Social Responsibility?" in Business News Daily (June 26, 2020)*

Ed: Skye Schooley. **Released:** June 26, 2020. **Description:** Corporate social responsibility (CSR) is a type of business self-regulation with the aim of being socially accountable. This article discusses how small businesses can benefit from using CSR in multiple ways and also provides four types of corporate responsibility your business can practice. **Availability:** Online.

34404 ■ *"What Keeps Global Leaders Up at Night" in Harvard Business Review (Vol. 90, April 2012, No. 4, pp. 32)*

Pub: Harvard Business Review Press

Contact: Moderna V. Pfizer, Contact

Price: $6. **Description:** A chart uses colored squares to portray economic, environmental, geopolitical, societal, and technological concerns of industry leaders, and ranks them according to likelihood and impact. **Availability:** PDF; Online.

34405 ■ "What's That Business? Part of Savers Thrift Store Proceeds Go To Charity" in Duluth News-Tribune (February 27, 2012)

Ed: Candace Renalls. **Description:** Savers Inc., a thrift store that sells housewares, furniture, clothing and collectibles allows customers to pick the charity it would like part of the store's proceeds to be given. The Duluth Savers Store has partnered with the Disabled American Veterans of Minnesota. Details of the stores, their customers and practices are highlighted. **Availability:** Online.

34406 ■ "When Profit Is Not the Incentive" in Business North Carolina (Vol. 28, February 2008, No. 2, pp. 42)
Pub: Business North Carolina
Contact: Peggy Knaack, Manager
E-mail: pknaack@businessnc.com

Ed: Amamda Parry. **Description:** Novant Health is North Carolina's fifth-largest private-sector employer and one of the largest nonprofit companies. Nonprofits grew 35 percent in North Carolina from 1995 to 2003. **Availability:** Online.

34407 ■ "Where New Economy Initiative Grants Have Gone" in Crain's Detroit Business (Vol. 25, June 1, 2009, No. 22, pp. M014)
Pub: Crain Communications Inc.
Contact: Barry Asin, President

Ed: Sherri Begin Welch. **Description:** Listing of grants totaling $20.5 million focusing on talent development, attraction and retention; innovation and entrepreneurship; and shifting to a culture that values learning, work and innovation, is presented. **Availability:** Online; PDF.

34408 ■ Why All Businesses Should Embrace Sustainability

Released: November 2016. **Description:** Sustainability is a business approach to creating long-term value by taking into consideration how a given organization operates in the ecological, social and economic environment. This article discusses corporations who have made strong commitments to sustainability and provides practical recommendations to improve sustainability practices. **Availability:** Online.

34409 ■ Why CSR Is Essential in 2022
URL(s): prowly.com/magazine/why-csr-is-essential-in-2019/

Ed: James Murray. **Description:** Explores why corporate social responsibility will be a critical part of public relations for your small business. **Availability:** Online.

34410 ■ "Why Is Social Responsibility Important in Marketing?" in Investopedia (Dec. 9, 2021)
URL(s): www.investopedia.com/ask/answers/042215/why-social-responsibility-important-marketing.asp

Released: December 09, 2021. **Description:** Explains how social responsibility in marketing works, including examples. Discusses how you can gain small business customers by demonstrating your business' social commitment. **Availability:** Online.

34411 ■ Women Count: A Guide to Changing the World
Pub: Purdue University Press
Contact: Justin Race, Director
E-mail: racej@purdue.edu

Ed: Susan Bulkeley Butler, Bob Keefe. **Released:** September 01, 2010. **Description:** Throughout history, women have struggled to change the workplace, change government, change society. It's time for women to change the world! Whether on the job, in politics, or in their community, there has never been a better time for women to make a difference in the world.

TRADE PERIODICALS

34412 ■ Business Ethics: The Magazine of Corporate Responsibility
Pub: Business Ethics
Contact: Michael Connor, Editor Publisher
URL(s): business-ethics.com
X (Twitter): x.com/BizEthicsMag

Ed: Michael Connor. **Released:** Quarterly **Description:** Business newsletter. **Availability:** Print; Online.

VIDEO/AUDIO MEDIA

34413 ■ 3 Things Social Entrepreneurs Do that Stop Growth
URL(s): www.awarepreneurs.com/podcast/346-social-entrepreneurs-growth

Ed: Paul Zelizer. **Released:** October 08, 2024. **Description:** Podcast discusses balancing social mission with business metrics to ensure long-term viability.

34414 ■ 4 Actions Your Small Business Can Take to Make Change
URL(s): www.makinggoodpodcast.com/episodes/124

Released: June 28, 2022. **Description:** Podcast discusses ways small businesses can take action.

34415 ■ Being Realistic about Social Enterprise Growth
URL(s): www.awarepreneurs.com/podcast/341-social-enterprise-growth

Ed: Paul Zelizer. **Released:** August 27, 2024. **Description:** Podcast offers suggestions for pacing the growth of a social enterprise.

34416 ■ Building a Community
URL(s): omny.fm/shows/startup-hustle/building-a-community

Ed: Lauren Conway. **Released:** September 08, 2023. **Description:** Podcast discusses the challenges and benefits of an inclusive community, how to get it involved in your business, and offering a place of diversity. .

34417 ■ Building Socially Beneficial Companies Leveraging AI with Prashant Samant
URL(s): www.awarepreneurs.com/podcast/298-akido-labs

Ed: Paul Zelizer. **Released:** June 27, 2023. **Description:** Podcast discusses social impact and technology, lessons for entrepreneurs, and the potential of data to address social disparities.

34418 ■ Capital and Exit Strategies for Impact Founders with Miyoko Schinner
URL(s): www.awarepreneurs.com/podcast/336-exit-strategies

Ed: Paul Zelizer. **Released:** May 28, 2024. **Description:** Podcast discusses successful exit strategies for impact founders.

34419 ■ Disruptors for Good: Creating an Entrepreneurial Blueprint for the Next Generation of Farmers
URL(s): share.transistor.fm/s/36df69bd

Description: Podcast offers tips on an entrepreneurial blueprint for regenerative farmers.

34420 ■ Disruptors for Good: Innovative Approach to Upskilling Overlooked and Hidden Talent
URL(s): share.transistor.fm/s/4d252599

Description: Podcast offers tips on upskilling overlooked talent.

34421 ■ Disruptors for Good: Regenerative Farming, Ethical Supply Chains, and Future of Plastic Bottles
URL(s): share.transistor.fm/s/a2929b45

Released: May 01, 2023. **Description:** Podcast discussed regenerative farming, ethical supply chains, and the future of plastic bottles.

34422 ■ Disuptors for Good: Finding Ethical and Sustainable Manufacturers and Suppliers
URL(s): share.transistor.fm/s/bf8e8498

Released: January 31, 2023. **Description:** Podcast discusses connecting brands, manufacturers, and suppliers to help launch sustainable products.

34423 ■ Entrepreneurial Thought Leaders: Build, Don't Break
URL(s): ecorner.stanford.edu/podcasts/build-dont-break

Ed: Tom Byers. **Released:** March 17, 2021. **Description:** Podcast discusses how founders can build responsibly and drive positive social change by measuring impact as much as the financial returns. .

34424 ■ Entrepreneurial Thought Leaders: Derisking Biotech
URL(s): ecorner.stanford.edu/podcasts/derisking-biotech

Ed: Tobey Corey. **Released:** May 18, 2022. **Description:** Podcast discusses how to reduce risk while developing world-changing therapies.

34425 ■ Entrepreneurial Thought Leaders: Diverse Businesses Are Better Businesses
URL(s): ecorner.stanford.edu/podcasts/diverse-businesses-are-better-businesses

Ed: Heidi Roizen. **Released:** April 28, 2021. **Description:** Podcast discusses how diversity helps businesses spot overlooked opportunities.

34426 ■ Entrepreneurial Thought Leaders: Finding Deeper Purpose
URL(s): ecorner.stanford.edu/podcasts/finding-a-deeper-purpose

Ed: Ravi Belani. **Released:** April 13, 2022. **Description:** Podcast explains how companies can articulate a deep purpose and infuse it into company actions.

34427 ■ Entrepreneurial Thought Leaders: Fixing Tech's Gender Gap
URL(s): ecorner.stanford.edu/podcasts/reshma-saujani-girls-who-code-fixing-techs-gender-gap

Ed: Ravi Belani. **Released:** October 27, 2021. **Description:** Podcast offers a conversation with the author of Girls Who Code, who discusses the root causes of the tech gender gap and suggests what could make the field more equitable.

34428 ■ Entrepreneurial Thought Leaders: Innovating Accessibly
URL(s): ecorner.stanford.edu/podcasts/innovating-accessibly

Ed: Ravi Belani. **Released:** October 12, 2022. **Description:** Podcast discusses the importance of approaching accessibility strategically and including the differently abled in employment and innovation.

34429 ■ Entrepreneurial Thought Leaders: Ruthless Empathy
URL(s): ecorner.stanford.edu/podcasts/ruthless-empathy

Released: May 12, 2021. **Description:** Podcast explains how empathetic technology can empower companies to scale social good.

34430 ■ Entrepreneurial Thought Leaders: Transforming Digital Healthcare
URL(s): ecorner.stanford.edu/podcasts/jerrica-kirkley-plume-and-kiki-freedman-hey-jane-transforming-digital-healthcare

Released: November 09, 2022. **Description:** Podcast discusses challenges and opportunities for entrepreneurs who want to build digital healthcare companies but also help underserved patients.

34431 ■ Entrepreneurial Thought Leaders: What is Responsible Innovation?
URL(s): ecorner.stanford.edu/podcasts/jon-zieger-responsible-technology-labs-what-is-responsible-innoation

Ed: Riitta Katila. **Released:** September 01, 2021. **Description:** Podcast discusses developing frameworks for responsible technology innovation and explores what a principled 21st-century technology system looks like.

34432 ■ *How to Build a Regenerative Business with Helen Tremethick*
URL(s): www.makinggoodpodcast.com/episodes/177
Ed: Lauren Tilden. **Released:** May 23, 2023. **Description:** Podcast defines a regenerative business, how to build one, how to make your current business more regenerative, and the role of boundaries in your regenerative business. .

34433 ■ *How I Built This: Reclaiming Food Waste with Jasmine Crowe-Houston of Goodr*
URL(s): wondery.com/shows/how-i-built-this/episode/10386-reclaiming-food-waste-with-jasmine-crowe-houston-of-goodr-2022
Ed: Guy Raz. **Released:** September 12, 2023. **Description:** Podcast offers a conversation with the found of Goodr, which delivers business's unused food those who need it.

34434 ■ *The Intersection Between Community Food and Justice with Erika Allen*
URL(s): www.awarepreneurs.com/podcast/316-community-food
Ed: Paul Zelizer. **Released:** January 09, 2024. **Description:** Podcast discusses youth working in urban growers' collectives and the synergy of community food, wealth, and transportation.

34435 ■ *Mindfully Creating Products that People Really Want with Varshil Patel*
URL(s): www.awarepreneurs.com/podcast/285-therapy-notebooks
Ed: Paul Zelizer. **Description:** Podcast discusses creating mental health notebooks.

34436 ■ *The New Era of Entrepreneurs - Doing Good While Still Making Money with Kurt Long*
URL(s): www.eofire.com/podcast/kurtlong
Ed: Jon Lee Dumas. **Released:** January 10, 2024. **Description:** Podcast explains what it looks like to do good and make money. Discusses B Corp, ESG, and social impact investing.

34437 ■ *Nurture Small Business: Profits with Purpose: Building a Sustainable Social Enterprise*
URL(s): nurturesmallbusiness.buzzsprout.com/900445/episodes/14931113-profits-with-purpose-building-a-sustainable-social-enterprise
Ed: Denise Cagan. **Released:** April 22, 2024. **Description:** Podcast discusses how to balance social impact with sustainable business practices.

34438 ■ *Radical Business with David Gaines*
URL(s): www.awarepreneurs.com/podcast/342-radical-business
Ed: Paul Zelizer. **Released:** September 03, 2024. **Description:** Podcast discusses social impact and purpose-driven businesses.

34439 ■ *The Strategy Hour: Making a Difference and a Profit: Inside Talitha Coffee's Mission-Driven Business*
URL(s): bossproject.com/podcast/making-a-difference-and-a-profit-inside-talitha-cofees-mission-drivin-business
Ed: Abagail Pumphrey. **Released:** November 04, 2024. **Description:** Podcast features a coffee shop owner who explains how to be both profitable and impactful.

34440 ■ *The Tension for Social Entrepreneurs Between Sales and Product Development wit Graham Hill*
URL(s): www.awarepreneurs.com/podcast/280-social-entrepreneurs-sales
Ed: Paul Zelizer. **Released:** January 24, 2023. **Description:** Podcast discusses the tension between sales and product development for social entrepreneurs.

34441 ■ *This Is Small Business: How to Foster Workplace Diversity and Inclusion*
URL(s): www.smallbusiness.amazon/podcast-episodes/ep-24-how-to-foster-workplace-diversity-and-inclusion
Released: April 25, 2023. **Description:** Podcast discusses creating a workplace culture that supports diversity, equity, and inclusion and how to implement diversity into hiring processes to ensure you're selecting the best employees. .

34442 ■ *This Is Small Business: How Your Business Can Have an Impact*
URL(s): www.smallbusiness.amazon/podcast-episodes/bonus-how-your-business-can-have-an-impact
Ed: Andrea Marquez. **Released:** May 01, 2024. **Description:** Podcast discusses what makes a business sustainable, the importance of transparency and authenticity, and how to start a business that does good.

34443 ■ *This Is Small Business: Toyin Leverages Small Business Sucess to Drive Community Impact*
URL(s): www.smallbusiness.amazon/podcast-episodes/ep-23-toyin-leverages-small-business-success-to-drive-community-impact
Ed: Andrea Marquez. **Released:** April 18, 2023. **Description:** Podcast discusses how small business success can drive community impact. Also considers ways to give back to the community with little or no money.

34444 ■ *Toxic Positivity and Leadership in the Impact Space with Satyen Raja*
URL(s): www.awarepreneurs.com/podcast/325-toxic-positivity
Ed: Paul Zelizer. **Released:** March 05, 2024. **Description:** Podcast discusses toxic positivity in leadership and organizations.

INTERNET DATABASES

34445 ■ *Corporate Social Responsibility (CSR): A Resource Guide*
URL(s): guides.loc.gov/corporate-social-responsibility
Description: Provides links to online resources concerning the history of corporate social responsibility to the current day. Also contains links to company and facility information, government resources, journals, and print materials. **Availability:** Online.

RESEARCH CENTERS

34446 ■ **Ethics and Compliance Initiative (ECI)**
8409 Lee Hwy., No. 2175
 Merrifield, VA 22116-8239
Ph: (703)647-2185
Co. E-mail: membership@ethics.org
URL: http://www.ethics.org
Contact: Dr. Patricia J. Harned, Chief Executive Officer
Facebook: www.facebook.com/ECInitiative
Linkedin: www.linkedin.com/company/ecinitiative
X (Twitter): x.com/ECInitiative
Instagram: www.instagram.com/ethicscomplianceinitiative
Description: Managers of ethics, compliance, and business conduct programs. Offers educational business ethics and compliance programs; conducts national research; and provides free job-listing service. **Scope:** Specializes in an integrated program of consulting to establish or modify ethics program or seeking to effectively communicate established values through the organization. Designs services to specifically fit each organization's needs and goals. **Founded:** 1922. **Publications:** Specializes in an integrated program of consulting to establish or modify ethics program or seeking to effectively com-

municate established values through the organization. Designs services to specifically fit each organization's needs and goals. **Educational Activities:** ECI's Annual Conference (Annual); ECOA Sponsoring Partner Forum (Annual). **Awards:** Stanley C. Pace Leadership in Ethics Award (Annual). **Geographic Preference:** National.

34447 ■ **Northwestern University - Kellogg School of Management - Ford Motor Co. Center for Global Citizenship**
2211 Campus Dr.
 Evanston, IL 60208
Co. E-mail: fordcenter@kellogg.northwestern.edu
URL: http://www.kellogg.northwestern.edu/research/ford-center
Description: Integral unit of Kellogg School of Management, Northwestern University. **Scope:** Role of business and its interaction with the social and political environment, focusing on challenges faced by corporations that have become the main agents of global, social and political change. **Founded:** 1994. **Educational Activities:** Ford Motor Co. Center for Global Citizenship Conferences (Irregular), Offer exemplary teaching and training programs.

34448 ■ **Santa Clara University - Markkula Center for Applied Ethics**
Vari Hall, Santa Clara University
 500 El Camino Real
 Santa Clara, CA 95053-0633
Ph: (408)554-5319
Fax: (408)554-2373
Co. E-mail: ethics@scu.edu
URL: http://www.scu.edu/ethics
Contact: Don Heider, Executive Director
Facebook: www.facebook.com/MarkkulaCenterForAppliedEthics
Linkedin: www.linkedin.com/company/markkula
X (Twitter): x.com/scuethics
YouTube: www.youtube.com/user/appliedethicscenter
Description: Integral unit of Santa Clara University operated under its own board of control. Offers consulting for hospitals, businesses, schools, and nonprofit groups (weekly); curriculum development in K-12 character education. **Scope:** Ethics in the areas of biotechnology and health care, education, business, and government. Seeks to increase the understanding of the role of ethics in private and public decision-making processes. **Founded:** 1986. **Publications:** *Ethics Resources*; *At the Center* (Monthly). **Educational Activities:** Business and Organizational Ethics Partnership Meeting, Offers exemplary teaching and training programs.; Lectures (Irregular), Offers exemplary teaching and training programs.; Public Sector Roundtable, By invitation only. **Awards:** Hackworth Grants (Irregular).

34449 ■ **University of Virginia - Darden School of Business - Olsson Center for Applied Ethics**
100 Darden Blvd.
 Charlottesville, VA 22903
Ph: (434)924-7247
Fax: (434)924-6378
Co. E-mail: olssoncenter@darden.virginia.edu
URL: http://www.darden.virginia.edu/olsson
Facebook: www.facebook.com/dardenmba
X (Twitter): x.com/DardenMBA
Instagram: www.instagram.com/dardenmba
YouTube: www.youtube.com/user/dardenmba
Description: Integral unit of University of Virginia. **Scope:** Socio/ethical issues relating to business, including standards of conduct. **Founded:** 1969. **Educational Activities:** Olsson Center for Applied Ethics Lectures and Seminars, Offer exemplary teaching programs.

34450 ■ **W. Michael Hoffman Center for Business Ethics (HCBE)**
175 Forest St.
 Waltham, MA 02452

Ph: (781)891-2981
Fax: (781)891-2988
Co. E-mail: cbeinfo@bentley.edu
URL: http://www.bentley.edu/centers/center-for-business-ethics
Contact: Jeffrey Moriarty, Executive Director
E-mail: jmoriarty@bentley.edu
Facebook: www.facebook.com/bentleyethics
Linkedin: www.linkedin.com/company/bentleyethics
X (Twitter): x.com/BentleyEthics

Description: Integral unit of Bentley College. Offers consulting services. **Scope:** Conducts surveys on topics such as business ethics curriculum and instilling ethical values in corporations. **Founded:** 1976. **Publications:** *Bibliographies on business ethics topics*; *CBE News/Books and surveys*; *CBE Conference proceedings*. **Awards:** W. Michael Hoffman Scholarship in Business Ethics. (Annual).

VENTURE CAPITAL FIRM

34451 ■ *HBR Ideacast: The Growing "Do Good" Economy*
URL(s): hbr.org/podcast/2022/11/the-growing-do-good-economy

Ed: Alison Beard. **Released:** November 29, 2022. **Description:** Podcast explains how incorporating social impact into a for-profit business raises a variety of system dilemmas; also discusses tools to create meaningful change. .

START-UP INFORMATION

34452 ■ *How to Form Your Own California Corporation*
Pub: Nolo
Contact: Chris Braun, President
Ed: Anthony Mancuso. **Released:** 15th edition. **Price:** $31.99, book and e-book; $27.99, e-book (downloadable); $34.99, E-book. **Description:** Instructions and forms required to incorporate any business in the State of California. **Availability:** E-book; Print.

34453 ■ *How to Start and Run Your Own Corporation: S-Corporations For Small Business Owners*
Pub: HCM Publishing
Ed: Peter I. Hupalo. **Description:** Basics of corporate business structure are explained. Topics include discovering the best business structure for your company; how to decided between an S-Corporation and LLC; choosing the state in which to incorporate, how to form a corporation, angel investing, special issues for one-person corporations, the role of bylaws and corporate minutes, board of directors, taxes, workers' compensation issues, retirement plans, and more. **Availability:** Print.

34454 ■ *The Small Business Start-Up Kit*
Pub: Nolo
Contact: Chris Braun, President
Ed: Peri Pakroo. **Released:** 12th edition. **Price:** $20.99, E-book. **Description:** Entrepreneurial advice for launching a new business. Topics include compliance with state regulations, sole proprietorships, partnerships, corporations, limited liability companies, as well as accounting and tax information. **Availability:** E-book; Print; Electronic publishing; PDF.

ASSOCIATIONS AND OTHER ORGANIZATIONS

34455 ■ **Freelancers Union (FU)**
241 37th St., Ste. A326
Brooklyn, NY 11232
Ph: (718)532-1515
Free: 866-569-9900
Co. E-mail: membership@freelancersunion.org
URL: http://freelancersunion.org
Facebook: www.facebook.com/freelancersunion
Linkedin: www.linkedin.com/company/freelancers-union
X (Twitter): x.com/freelancersu
Instagram: www.instagram.com/freelancersu
YouTube: www.youtube.com/user/FreelancersUnion
Description: Promotes the interests of independent workers. Supports the development of effective solutions to health care, retirement, wage security, and other broken systems. Helps the self-employed community in voicing their needs. **Founded:** 1995. **Geographic Preference:** National.

34456 ■ **National Association for the Self-Employed (NASE)**
PO Box 241
Annapolis Junction, MD 20701-0241
Free: 800-232-6273
Fax: (800)678-4605
URL: http://www.nase.org
Contact: Keith R. Hall, President
Facebook: www.facebook.com/NASEonFB
Linkedin: www.linkedin.com/company/national-association-for-the-self-employed-nase-
X (Twitter): x.com/NASEtweets
Instagram: www.instagram.com/NASEonIG
YouTube: www.youtube.com/user/NASEview
Pinterest: www.pinterest.com/NASEpins
Description: Self-employed and small independent businesspersons. Acts as an advocate at the state and federal levels for self-employed people. Provides discounts on products and services important to self-employed and small business owners. **Founded:** 1981. **Publications:** *Self-Employed OutFront Weekly* (Weekly); *Washington Watch* (Weekly). **Awards:** NASE Future Entrepreneur Award; NASE Dependent Scholarships (Annual).

REFERENCE WORKS

34457 ■ *Choosing the Right Legal Form of Business: The Complete Guide to Becoming a Sole Proprietor, Partnership, LLC, or Corporation*
Pub: Atlantic Publishing Co.
Contact: Dr. Heather L. Johnson, Contact
Ed: Pat Mitchell. **Released:** 2010. **Description:** According to the U.S. Small Business Administration, nearly 250,000 new businesses start up annually; currently there are over nine million small companies in the nation. The importance of choosing the proper legal form of business is stressed. **Availability:** Print; Online.

34458 ■ *Entrepreneurial Finance*
Pub: Pearson Education Inc.
Contact: Andy Bird, Chief Executive Officer
Ed: Philip J. Adelman, Alan M. Marks. **Released:** Sixth edition. **Description:** Financial aspects of running a small business are covered; topics include sole proprietorships, partnerships, limited liability companies, and private corporations. **Availability:** Print; Download; Online.

34459 ■ *"Is It Time to Convert Your Sole Proprietorship to a Corporation or LLC?" in Legal Zoom (March 27, 2023)*
URL(s): www.legalzoom.com/articles/is-it-time-to-convert-your-sole-proprietorship-to-a-corporation-or-llc
Ed: Ann MacDonald. **Released:** March 27, 2023. **Description:** Is it time to switch your small company you founded from a sole proprietorship to a different structure? Discusses the advantages of doing so. **Availability:** Online.

34460 ■ *"Managing and Forming a Qualified Joint Venture" in Legal Zoom (March 14, 2023)*
URL(s): www.legalzoom.com/articles/managing-and-forming-a-qualified-joint-venture
Ed: Edward A. Haman, Esq. **Released:** March 14, 2023. **Description:** Explains what a joint venture is and how it could be beneficial to form one if you are part of a married couple. **Availability:** Online.

34461 ■ *Small Business: An Entrepreneur's Plan*
Pub: Nelson Education Ltd.
Contact: Steve Brown, President
Ed: Ronald A. Knowles. **Released:** 7th Canadian edition. **Price:** $111.95, paperback; $67.95, e-book. **Description:** Entrepreneur's guide to planning a small business. **Availability:** E-book; Print.

34462 ■ *"Sole Proprietor vs Independent Contractor Explained" in The Balance Small Business (May 6, 2020)*
Ed: Jean Murray. **Released:** May 06, 2020. **Description:** Discusses the differences between sole proprietorship and independent contractor and how each is required to pay taxes.

34463 ■ *"Sole Proprietorship Returns, 2008" in SOI Bulletin (Vol. 30, Summer 2010, No. 1, pp. 6)*
Pub: Government Publishing Office
Contact: Hugh Nathanial Halpern, Director
Ed: Adrian Dungan. **Description:** Approximately 22.6 million individual income tax returns reported nonfarm sole proprietorship activity, a 2.2 percent decrease from 2007. Statistical data included. **Availability:** Print; PDF; Online.

34464 ■ *"Sole Proprietorship Returns, 2008 Part 2" in SOI Bulletin (Vol. 30, Summer 2010, No. 1, pp. 27)*
Description: Table of Nonfarm Sole Proprietorships is presented. Statistics are broken down by sector reporting all nonfarm industries as well as agriculture, forestry, hunting and fishing. **Availability:** PDF; Online.

34465 ■ *"Symbility Solutions Joins Motion Computing Partner Program" in Marketwired (May 14, 2007)*
Pub: Comtex News Network Inc.
Contact: Kan Devnani, President
Description: Symbility Solutions Inc., a wholly owned subsidiary of Automated Benefits Corp., announced an agreement with Alliance Partner of Motion Computing, a leader in wireless communications and mobile computing, in which both companies will invest in a sales and marketing strategy that focuses specifically on the insurance market. **Availability:** Print; Online.

VIDEO/AUDIO MEDIA

34466 ■ *BS-Free Service Business Show: From Solo to Agency and Back Again with Jules Taggart*
URL(s): bsfreebusiness.com/solo-to-agency

Ed: Maggie Patterson. **Released:** April 01, 2024. **Description:** Podcast offers a conversation with Jules Taggart, who went from solo business owner to agency owner and back to solo again.

34467 ■ BS-Free Service Business Show: Staying Solo: What Every One-Person Business Should Know
URL(s): bsfreebusiness.com/one-person-business

Ed: Maggie Patterson. **Released:** June 17, 2024. **Description:** Podcast discusses how to do less but do it better.

34468 ■ Nurture Small Business: Overcoming Entrepreneur Isolation by Building Authentic Connections
URL(s): nurturesmallbusiness.buzzsprout.com/900445/episodes/15174993-overcoming-entrepreneur-isolation-by-building-authentic-connections

Ed: Denise Cagan. **Released:** June 05, 2024. **Description:** Podcast offers tips on building a thriving support network to fuel both your personal and professional journey.

34469 ■ Profit First Nation: Scaling You
URL(s): www.profitfirstnation.com/episodes/scaling-you

Ed: Danielle Mulvey. **Released:** October 02, 2024. **Description:** Podcast explains how to break the solopreneur mold and scale your business by building the right team.

34470 ■ Side Hustle to Small Business: Improving the Work Environment by Going Solo
URL(s): www.hiscox.com/side-hustle-to-small-business/rita-ernst-podcast-season-3

Ed: Sanjay Parekh. **Released:** May 31, 2023. **Description:** Podcast discusses the decision to become your own boss when unhappy with the corporate environment.

34471 ■ Staying Solo: Bigger is Not Better: Staying Solo as a Strategic Choice
URL(s): bsfreebusiness.com/solo-as-a-strategic-choice

Ed: Maggie Patterson. **Released:** August 26, 2024. **Description:** Podcast discusses why "bigger is bet-ter" may not be accurate and how staying solo is often the best choice for service business owners.

34472 ■ Staying Solo: Grow Your Strategy, Not Your Stress
URL(s): bsfreebusiness.com/growing-your-salary

Ed: Maggie Patterson. **Released:** September 09, 2024. **Description:** Podcast explains how to pay yourself first, increase your salary, and a build a business that works for you.

34473 ■ Staying Solo: Strategy Over Scale: How to Break the Time-Money Trap
URL(s): bsfreebusiness.com/strategy-over-scale

Ed: Maggie Patterson. **Released:** September 02, 2024. **Description:** Podcast discusses the myth of scaling and explains how to use strategy to grow your business without burning out. .

34474 ■ Staying Solo: The Capacity Code: Managing Time and Energay as a Solo Business Owner
URL(s): bsfreebusiness.com/managing-time-and-energy

Ed: Maggie Patterson. **Released:** September 16, 2024. **Description:** Podcast explains how to manage your time, energy, and emotional bandwidth.

ASSOCIATIONS AND OTHER ORGANIZATIONS

34475 ■ Association for Enterprise Opportunity (AEO)
1310 L St. NW, Ste. 830
  Washington, DC 20005
Ph: (202)650-5580
Co. E-mail: info@aeoworks.org
URL: http://www.aeoworks.org
Contact: Connie E. Evans, President
E-mail: cevans@aeoworks.org
Facebook: www.facebook.com/AEO
X (Twitter): x.com/AEOworks
YouTube: www.youtube.com/user/kcrutcher88/videos
Description: Represents microenterprise development organizations serving economically disadvantaged areas across the United States. Promotes improved economic opportunity for aspiring entrepreneurs with limited access to financial resources. Facilitates networking among members; provides training and technical assistance to members; develops and distributes educational materials; conducts advocacy. **Founded:** 1991. **Publications:** *AEO Exchange* (Quarterly) **Geographic Preference:** National; Regional.

34476 ■ Association for Entrepreneurship USA (AFEUSA)
666 Dundee Rd., Ste. 1603
  Northbrook, IL 60062
Free: 844-750-5927
Fax: (888)289-7001
Co. E-mail: info@afeusa.org
URL: http://afeusa.org
Contact: Jack Diehl, President
Facebook: www.facebook.com/AFEUSA
X (Twitter): x.com/AFE_USA_Org
Description: Seeks to serve, support, represent, and promote entrepreneurship for those have (or wish for) the freedom of successfully operating their own business.

34477 ■ Fast Forward
1002A O'Reilly Ave.
  San Francisco, CA 94129
Co. E-mail: info@ffwd.org
URL: http://www.ffwd.org
Contact: Kevin Barenblat, President
Facebook: www.facebook.com/ffwd
Linkedin: www.linkedin.com/company/fast_forward
X (Twitter): x.com/ffwdorg
YouTube: www.youtube.com/user/FfwdOrg
Description: Bridges the technology and nonprofit sectors to build capacity and scale startups.

34478 ■ National Entrepreneurs Association (NEA)
18444 W 10 Mile Rd., No. 103
  Southfield, MI 48075
Ph: (248)416-7278
Co. E-mail: supportstaff@nationalentrepreneurs.org
URL: http://www.nationalentrepreneurs.org
Contact: ZaLonya Allen, President
Facebook: www.facebook.com/National-Entrepreneurs-Association-137536660415863
Linkedin: www.linkedin.com/company/national-entrepreneurs-association
X (Twitter): x.com/NationalEntrep1
YouTube: www.youtube.com/channel/UC0MiAnMYBpFHWeGZ_Z2Cquw
Description: Provides networking and education opportunities to help entrepreneurs create and operate their business successfully.

INCUBATORS/RESEARCH AND TECHNOLOGY PARKS

34479 ■ Evergreen Climate Innovations
20 N Wacker Dr., Ste. 1200
  Chicago, IL 60606
Co. E-mail: info@evergreeninno.org
URL: http://evergreeninno.org
Contact: Erik Birkerts, Chief Executive Officer
Facebook: www.facebook.com/EvergreenClimateInnovations
Linkedin: www.linkedin.com/company/evergreen-climate-innovations
X (Twitter): x.com/evergreen_inno
YouTube: www.youtube.com/channel/UC8t1sHKQ1iczwggoa93zxgw
Description: Supports startups bringing impactful climate technologies to market. Makes seed investments and provide hands-on support to entrepreneurs. **Founded:** 2010.

34480 ■ Green2Gold
1176 Tourmaline Dr.
  Thousand Oaks, CA 91320
Ph: (805)735-7261
Co. E-mail: alan@green2gold.org
URL: http://green2gold.org
X (Twitter): x.com/GOGREEN2GOLD
Description: A non-profit business incubator that provides recommendations and straightforward strategies to help startups achieve their goals. **Founded:** 1970.

34481 ■ U.S. Department of Energy - Office of Energy Efficiency & Renewable Energy - Incubator Program
1000 Independence Ave. SW
  Washington, DC 20585
URL: http://www.energy.gov/eere/solar/incubator-program
Description: Provides early-stage assistance to help startup companies cross technological barriers to commercialization while encouraging private-sector investment. **Founded:** 2007.

REFERENCE WORKS

34482 ■ 3 Alternative Ways to Fund Your Startup
URL(s): www.netsuite.com/portal/business-benchmark-brainyard/industries/articles/entrepreneur/alternative-funding-startup.shtml
Ed: Kris Blackman. **Released:** August 18, 2021. **Description:** Not all businesses are great fits for traditional funding methods. This article explores three alternative funding routes for growing businesses. **Availability:** Online.

34483 ■ "4 Essential Hires if You're Starting a Business in 2020" in Bplans
Ed: Andrew Deen. **Description:** Discusses the importance of investing in the expertise of select professionals with specialized skills in the early stages of your company. **Availability:** Online.

34484 ■ "The 4 Hottest Industries to Start a Businesses in for 2020" in Bplans
Ed: Nina Bamberger. **Description:** Discusses four industries that show the most promise for business startups in 2020: transportation, technology, health and medical, and green products and services. **Availability:** Online.

34485 ■ "5 Business Structures: Find the Right One for Your Small Business" in Business News Daily (April 12, 2022)
URL(s): smallbiztrends.com/2014/01/5-common-business-structures.html
Released: April 12, 2022. **Description:** Five common business structures are discussed with the purpose of providing information to help you choose which structure would benefit your small business the most. **Availability:** Online.

34486 ■ "7 Businesses You Can Start With Almost No Cash" in Entrepreneur (January 5, 2017)
Released: January 05, 2017. **Description:** Provides steps to explore what it takes to formally start a business and details which of those steps cost money. **Availability:** Online.

34487 ■ "7 Places to Incorporate Your Small Business Online" in Small Business Trends (March 18, 2022)
URL(s): smallbiztrends.com/2018/06/incorporate-online.html
Ed: Gabrielle Pickard-Whitehead. **Released:** March 18, 2022. **Description:** Discusses the advantages of forming a LLC for your small businesses and how to do it online. **Availability:** Online.

34488 ■ 7 Sources of Start-up Financing
URL(s): www.bdc.ca/en/articles-tools/start-buy-business/start-business/start-up-financing-sources
Description: Discusses the importance of diversifying your source for small business financing. Provides an overview of seven common sources for startup financing. **Availability:** Online.

34489 ■ "The 10 Most Reliable Ways to Fund a Startup" in Entrepreneur (February 20, 2019)
Ed: Martin Zwilling. **Released:** February 20, 2019. **Description:** Martin Zwilling, veteran funding mentor, discusses ten reliable ways to make startup funding decisions. **Availability:** Online.

34490 ■ "11 Things to Do Before Starting a Business" in Business News Daily (February 21, 2023)
URL(s): www.businessnewsdaily.com/1484-starting-a-business.html
Ed: Stella Morrison. Released: February 21, 2023. Description: Reviews 11 action items small business owners should consider before opening up their own business. Availability: Online.

34491 ■ "13 Small Business Legal Requirements and Tips for Launch" in Legal Zoom (February 15, 2023)
URL(s): www.legalzoom.com/articles/small-business-legal-requirements-and-tips-for-launch
Released: February 15, 2023. Description: Follow this checklist of handy items to accomplish before you launch your small business. Availability: Online.

34492 ■ "26 Great Business Ideas for Entrepreneurs" in Business News Daily (March 8, 2023)
URL(s): www.businessnewsdaily.com/2747-great-business-ideas.html
Ed: Tejas Vemparala. Released: March 08, 2023. Description: If you are thinking about entrepreneurship, check into these ideas to launch a small business. Availability: Online.

34493 ■ "27 Mission Statement Examples" in Small Business Trends (February 27, 2023)
URL(s): smallbiztrends.com/2021/12/mission-statement-examples.html
Released: February 27, 2023. Description: Need some inspiration for writing a mission statement for your small business? Peruse these examples from famous companies and see if you can improve your own statement. Availability: Online.

34494 ■ All Money Is Not Created Equal: How Entrepreneurs Can Crack the Code to Getting the Right Funding for Their Startup
Pub: John Wiley & Sons, Inc.
Contact: Christina Van Tassell, Executive Vice President Chief Financial Officer
URL(s): www.wiley.com/en-us/All+Money+Is+Not+Created+Equal%3A+How+Entrepreneurs+can+Crack+the+Code+to+Getting+the+Right+Funding+for+their+Startup-p-9781119887805
Ed: David A. Spreng, Patricia M. O'Connell. Released: July 2023. Price: $27.95, hardcover. Description: Starting a new businesses requires funding, and often accepting that funding means giving up some ownership of the business. This guide explains how to seek funding that has as little strings attached as possible. Availability: Print.

34495 ■ "Bookkeeping Options for Time-Starved Startups" in Legal Zoom (February 21, 2023)
URL(s): www.legalzoom.com/articles/bookkeeping-options-for-time-starved-startups
Ed: Sandra Beckwith. Released: February 21, 2023. Description: Bookkeeping is an essential part of any business and not everyone has the skills to manage the books. Listed are several options that would work well with startups. Availability: Online.

34496 ■ "Bootstrapping or Equity Funding: Which Is Better for Your Business?" in Business News Daily (February 21, 2023)
URL(s): www.businessnewsdaily.com/11153-start-business-alone-vs-get-investors.html
Ed: Adam Uzialko. Released: February 21, 2023. Description: Lays out the pros and cons of starting your new small business with outside financing or by using your personal funds. Availability: Online.

34497 ■ "Business Partnership Agreement Writing Guide" in Business News Daily (February 21, 2023)
URL(s): www.businessnewsdaily.com/15756-business-partnership-agreement-writing-guide.html
Ed: Adam Uzialko. Released: February 21, 2023. Description: Outlines what to include in a business agreement in case future disputes arise. Availability: Online.

34498 ■ "The Complete Guide to Starting a Business" in Legal Zoom (March 15, 2023)
URL(s): www.legalzoom.com/articles/the-complete-guide-to-starting-a-business
Released: March 15, 2023. Description: A comprehensive guide on the steps needed to start your own business. Availability: Online.

34499 ■ "Developing a Small Business Educational Program for Growing Rural Businesses" in Journal of Small Business Strategy (Vol. 31, December 1, 2021, No. 4, 50-56)
Ed: Timothy L. Pett, John Francis, Wendy Veatch. Released: November 16, 2021. Description: Discusses the research on educational programs to start new businesses in rural communities. Availability: PDF; Online.

34500 ■ Disciplined Entrepreneurship Workbook
Pub: John Wiley & Sons, Inc.
Contact: Christina Van Tassell, Executive Vice President Chief Financial Officer
URL(s): www.wiley.com/en-us/Disciplined+Entrepreneurship+Workbook-p-9781119365792
Ed: Bill Aulet. Released: March 2017. Price: $17; $28, paperback. Description: Used in conjunction with the book Disciplined Entrepreneurship, this workbook will help you grasp key concepts of startup success. Availability: E-book; Print.

34501 ■ Entrepreneurship for Dummies
Pub: John Wiley & Sons, Inc.
Contact: Christina Van Tassell, Executive Vice President Chief Financial Officer
Ed: Kathleen Allen. Released: 2nd edition. Price: $29.99, paperback; $18, e-book. Description: A guide to help entrepreneurs get their business up and running. Includes sections on starting a business from beginning to end, testing products, legal requirements, securing funding, and much more. Availability: E-book; Print.

34502 ■ The Essential Entrepreneur: What It Takes to Start, Scale, and Sell a Successful Business
Pub: John Wiley & Sons, Inc.
Contact: Christina Van Tassell, Executive Vice President Chief Financial Officer
URL(s): www.wiley.com/en-us/The+Essential+Entrepreneur%3A+What+It+Takes+to+Start%2C+Scale%2C+and+Sell+a+Successful+Business-p-9781119984559
Released: November 2022. Price: $13, e-book; $21.99, paperback. Description: Take your business to the next level with the tips included in this guide. Availability: E-book; Print.

34503 ■ "Federal Employer Identification Number (FEIN): How to Get One" in Business News Daily (February 28, 2023)
URL(s): www.businessnewsdaily.com/17-federal-employer-identification-number-criteria.html
Ed: Sean Peek. Released: February 28, 2023. Description: If your small business plans on hiring employees, it will need a federal employer identification number. This article discusses the steps needed to take to obtain that number so your business is compliant. Availability: Online.

34504 ■ "Finding the Right Accountant for Your Small Business" Business News Daily (February 21, 2023)
URL(s): www.businessnewsdaily.com/8039-find-small-business-accountant.html
Ed: Simone Johnson. Released: February 21, 2023. Description: Filing your small business taxes can be daunting, especially if you don't have a background in accounting. This article explains what to look for when choosing an accountant. Availability: Online.

34505 ■ "Finding Startup Success in a Challenging Market" in Food Business News (October 5, 2020)
Ed: Dan Malovany. Released: October 05, 2020. Description: Details how to navigate business startup during economically challenging times. Availability: Online.

34506 ■ "Former Robinhood Employees Launch Parafin, a Finance Startup for Small Business" in The Wall Street Journal (September 29, 2021)
URL(s): www.wsj.com/articles/former-robinhood-employees-launch-parafin-a-finance-startup-for-small-business-11632913201
Released: September 29, 2021. Description: Discusses the new startup, Parafin.

34507 ■ Gorillas Can Dance: Lessons from Microsoft and Other Corporations on Partnering with Startups
Pub: John Wiley & Sons, Inc.
Contact: Christina Van Tassell, Executive Vice President Chief Financial Officer
URL(s): www.wiley.com/en-us/Gorillas+Can+Dance%3A+Lessons+from+Microsoft+and+Other+Corporations+on+Partnering+with+Startups-p-9781119823582
Ed: Shameen Prashantham. Released: September 2021. Price: $18, e-book; $29.95, hardcover. Description: Discusses research about large corporations that partner with startups. Availability: E-book; Print.

34508 ■ "How to Become a Professional Wedding Planner" in The Spruce (October 3, 2019)
Ed: Nina Callaway. Released: October 03, 2019. Description: Includes steps to launch a successful career in wedding planning. Availability: Online.

34509 ■ "How the CEO of Keap Grew His Company from Startup to $120 Million" in Small Business Trends(November 21,2022)
URL(s): smallbiztrends.com/2022/11/interview-with-clate-mask-ceo-of-keap.html
Released: November 21, 2022. Description: Interview with Clate Mask, CEO of Keap. Discussion of Keap's vision, strategy, and growth and how well the company is doing as compared to it's days as a startup. Availability: Online.

34510 ■ "How to Create an LLC" in Small Business Trends (June 29, 2021)
URL(s): smallbiztrends.com/2021/06/how-to-create-an-llc.html
Ed: Lisa Price. Released: September 29, 2021. Description: Discusses the steps small business owners need to take to set up their new company as a LLC. Availability: Online.

34511 ■ "How to Find Your Business Niche" in Business News Daily (February 21, 2023)
URL(s): https://www.businessnewsdaily.com/6748-business-niche-characteristics.html
Ed: Skye Schooley. Released: February 21, 2023. Description: Opening a small business that is just like all the other businesses nearby will not make your company succeed because of the competition. Instead, focus on a niche and research your customer base to provide a product or service that is needed in your area. Availability: Online.

34512 ■ "How the Founder of Grubhub Built a $7 Billion Business" in Small Business Trends (November 7, 2022)
URL(s): smallbiztrends.com/2022/11/interview-with-mike-evans-founder-of-grubhub.html
Released: November 07, 2022. Description: Interview with Mike Evans, the founder of Grubhub. Availability: Online.

34513 ■ "How to Help Your Kid Start a (Legal) Business" in Business News Daily (February 21, 2023)
URL(s): www.businessnewsdaily.com/10278-legal-business-tips-for-kids.html
Ed: Sean Peek. Released: February 21, 2023. Description: Discusses how to set up a legal small business, such as a lemonade stand, for your child. Permits and paperwork are discussed. Availability: Online.

34514 ■ *"How to Manage Your Debt as a Startup"* in *Legal Zoom (February 17, 2023)*

Ed: Marcia Layton Turner. **Released:** February 17, 2023. **Description:** Having business debt while getting your startup going isn't always a bad thing. Follow the advice given here to help keep on top of that debt so that it doesn't consumer you. **Availability:** Online.

34515 ■ *"How Much Does it Cost to Incorporate in Each State?"* in *Business News Daily (June 7, 2016)*

URL(s): smallbiztrends.com/2015/04/much-cos t-incorporate-state.html

Released: June 07, 2016. **Description:** Provides details on each state and their filing fees for incorporating your business there. **Availability:** Online.

34516 ■ *"How to Open a Private Medical Practice, Step by Step"* in *Business News Daily (February 28, 2023)*

URL(s): www.businessnewsdaily.com/8910-opening -a-medical-practice.html

Ed: Max Freedman. **Released:** February 28, 2023. **Description:** Opening a private medical office could be a good choice for certain healthcare professionals. Included is a discussion on how to do that and certain operations that should be considered. **Availability:** Online.

34517 ■ *"How to Overcome Startup Fears and Move Forward with Your Business Goals"* in *Legal Zoom (February 21, 2023)*

URL(s): www.legalzoom.com/articles/how-to -overcome-startup-fears-and-move-forward-with -your-business-goals

Ed: Eliana Perez. **Released:** February 21, 2023. **Description:** Tips for growing your startup and making sure its heading in the right direction. **Availability:** Online.

34518 ■ *"How to Start a Business: A Step-by-Step Guide"* in *Business News Daily (February 23, 2023)*

URL(s): www.businessnewsdaily.com/4686-how-to-s tart-a-business.html

Ed: Joshua Stowers. **Released:** February 28, 2023. **Description:** Outlines the basic steps needed to take to start a small business. **Availability:** Online.

34519 ■ *"How to Start a Business with No Money"* in *Legal Zoom (March 14, 2023)*

URL(s): www.legalzoom.com/articles/how-to-start-a -business-with-no-money

Ed: Katherine Gustafson. **Released:** March 14, 2023. **Description:** Discusses how to start a business without using your own funds. Links to resources are given. **Availability:** Online.

34520 ■ *"How to Start a Business with a Partner"* in *Legal Zoom (March 14, 2023)*

URL(s): www.legalzoom.com/articles/how-to-start-a -business-with-a-partner

Ed: Michelle Kaminsky. **Released:** March 14, 2023. **Description:** Business partnerships can be fragile, so be sure you are doing it right by following the steps listed in this article so you, and your partner, are treated fairly. **Availability:** Online.

34521 ■ *"How to Start a Cleaning Business"* in *Entrepreneur (June 14, 2003)*

Released: June 14, 2003. **Description:** Information on how to start a successful cleaning business. Topics include target market, location, pricing, marketing, and resources. **Availability:** Online.

34522 ■ *"How to Start a Cleaning Business in 7 Steps"* in *JustBusiness (September 15, 2020)*

Ed: Meredith Wood. **Released:** September 15, 2020. **Description:** Provides practical steps for starting a cleaning business including funding, marketing, business planning and budgeting, registering, and finding and maintaining clients. **Availability:** Online.

34523 ■ *"How to Start an Event Planning Business from Home"* in *EventMB (April 30, 2020)*

Ed: Becki Cross. **Released:** April 30, 2020. **Description:** Provides information that acts as a startup kit for anyone wanting to start their own event management company from home. **Availability:** Online.

34524 ■ *How to Start a Food Truck Business in 2020*

Ed: Alex Johnson. **Released:** October 21, 2019. **Price:** $14.97, Paperback; $3.99, E-book. **Description:** An A-Z guide containing the most up-to-date information available on starting a food truck business. **Availability:** E-book; PDF.

34525 ■ *"How to Start a Wedding Planning Business"* in *Startup Jungle*

Ed: Kari Andrews. **Description:** Details how to start a wedding planning business including startup costs, marketing, required skills, license, and tax information. **Availability:** Online.

34526 ■ *"How to Successfully Launch a New Business during Tough Economic Times"* in *Business News Daily (March 6, 2023)*

URL(s): www.businessnewsdaily.com/new-business -during-recession

Ed: Kiara Taylor. **Released:** March 06, 2023. **Description:** When the economy hits a rough patch, many thing now is not the time to launch a new business. Sometimes, though, that is the perfect time because the business may solve a particular need during these times. Tips are given to help make your new venture successful. **Availability:** Online.

34527 ■ *"How To Set Up and Structure Multiple Businesses"* in *Small Business Trends (May 21, 2013)*

Released: May 21, 2013. **Description:** Often, small business owners are able to expand and start new ventures. This article explains how to do that and set up multiple companies. **Availability:** Online.

34528 ■ *"How to Turn Your Idea Into a Product (and Launch It!)"* in *Business News Daily (February 21, 2023)*

URL(s): www.businessnewsdaily.com/8773-turn-your -idea-into-a-product.html

Ed: Kiely Kuligowski. **Released:** February 21, 2023. **Description:** Goes into detail about taking your idea and what to do to make it into a business. **Availability:** Online.

34529 ■ *"How and Why To Get BBB Accreditation"* in *Small Business Trends (August 9, 2021)*

URL(s): smallbiztrends.com/2020/07/bbb-accredite d.html

Ed: Anita Campbell. **Released:** August 09, 2021. **Description:** The Better Business Bureau (BBB) gives accreditation to small businesses. Is this right for your business? This article explains the advantages of having the BBB behind your back. **Availability:** Online.

34530 ■ *"How Will The Startups Created in 2020 Be Different From Startups Build Before?"* in *Protocol (June 27, 2020)*

Ed: Biz Carson. **Released:** June 27, 2020. **Description:** Discusses how the Coronavirus pandemic, economic downturn, and Black Lives Matter movement will shape startups in new ways. **Availability:** Online.

34531 ■ *"The Importance of Healthy Business Relationships"* in *Business News Daily (February 21, 2023)*

URL(s): www.businessnewsdaily.com/10297-healthy -business-relationships.html

Ed: Siri Hedreen. **Released:** February 21, 2023. **Description:** Quality business relationships are important to small businesses, especially those that are just starting out. Expanding your network of customers, clients, suppliers, etc., can be a huge asset as you grow. **Availability:** Online.

34532 ■ *"Incorporated Versus Unincorporated Self Employment"* in *Small Business Trends (January 14, 2014)*

URL(s): smallbiztrends.com/2013/11/incorporate d-versus-unincorporated-self-employment.html

Ed: Scott Shane. **Released:** January 17, 2014. **Description:** Discusses the two types of self employment. **Availability:** Online.

34533 ■ *"Is It Time to Convert Your Sole Proprietorship to a Corporation or LLC?"* in *Legal Zoom (March 27, 2023)*

URL(s): www.legalzoom.com/articles/is-it-time-to -convert-your-sole-proprietorship-to-a-corporation -or-llc

Ed: Ann MacDonald. **Released:** March 27, 2023. **Description:** Is it time to switch your small company you founded from a sole proprietorship to a different structure? Discusses the advantages of doing so. **Availability:** Online.

34534 ■ *"Legal Structure: The Difference Between LLCs And LLPs"* in *Small Business Trends (May 21, 2013)*

URL(s): smallbiztrends.com/2012/04/legal-structure -difference-llc-llp.html

Ed: Nellie Akalp. **Released:** May 21, 2013. **Description:** Explains the differences between setting your small business up as an LLP or as an LLC. **Availability:** Online.

34535 ■ *Limited Liability Companies for Dummies*

Pub: John Wiley & Sons, Inc.

Contact: Christina Van Tassell, Executive Vice President Chief Financial Officer

URL(s): www.wiley.com/en-us/Limited+Liability+Com panies+For+Dummies%2C+4th+Edition-p-978139 4183333

Ed: Jennifer Reuting. **Released:** Fourth edition. **Price:** $29.99, paperback. **Description:** Guide on how to set up an LLC, or limited liability company. Discusses the pros and cons of this structure, how to manage it, and all of the new laws surrounding LLCs. **Availability:** Print.

34536 ■ *LLC Beginner's Guide: The Most Complete and Easy-to-Follow Handbook on How to Form, Manage and Maintain Your Limited Liability Company*

Ed: Steven Carlson. **Released:** October 29, 2022. **Price:** $17.36, paperback; $8.97, e-book. **Description:** A guide that explains the process of setting up a limited liability company (LLC) in simple terms. **Availability:** E-book; Print.

34537 ■ *"Marcia Tiago Shares How to Start and Run a Successful Business in 2023"* in *Home Business (March 2, 2023)*

URL(s): homebusinessmag.com/business-start-up/ how-to-guides/marcia-tiago-shares-how-to-start-run -successful-business-2023/

Released: March 02, 2023. **Description:** Presents Marcia Tiago's best tips for launching a new business. **Availability:** Online.

34538 ■ *"New Business Idea? How to Test It Before Launching"* in *Business News Daily (August 25, 2020)*

Ed: Sammi Caramela. **Released:** August 25, 2020. **Description:** Outlines the importance of testing your business idea for viability. Includes 8 steps. **Availability:** Online.

34539 ■ *Originate, Motivate, Innovate: 7 Steps for Building a Billion Dollar Network*

Pub: John Wiley & Sons, Inc.

Contact: Christina Van Tassell, Executive Vice President Chief Financial Officer

URL(s): www.wiley.com/en-us/Originate%2C+Motiva te%2C+Innovate%3A+7+Steps+for+Building+a+Bil lion+Dollar+Network-p-9781119900542

Ed: Shelly Omilade Bell. **Released:** May 2023. **Price:** $26, hardcover. **Description:** Discusses business funding for women of color in a white male-dominated field. **Availability:** Print.

34540 ■ "Ready to Launch a New Business? Amplify Success with These 4 Tips" in Minority Business Entrepreneur (Vol. 39, Fall, 2022, No. 4, pp.14-15)
URL(s): digital.mbemag.com/?m=53732&i=769780 &p=16&ver=html5
Ed: Rod Robertson. Price: $7.95. Description: Provides information on starting a new business with some helpful tips. Availability: Print; Online.

34541 ■ "Ready to Rent an Office? What You Should Know About Leasing" in Business News Daily (February 21, 2023)
URL(s): www.businessnewsdaily.com/10045-commercial-leasing-tips.html
Ed: Adam Uzialko. Released: February 21, 2023. Description: If you are looking to open a new business or are looking to expand, leasing a commercial space may be what you need. Considerations for what to expect during the process are presented. Availability: Online.

34542 ■ "The Really Big List of Small Business Associations" in Small Business Trends (June 20, 2021)
URL(s): smallbiztrends.com/2018/05/small-business -associations.html
Ed: Annie Pilon. Released: June 20, 2021. Description: Peruse this list of small business associations and see if any can provide you with needed resources. Availability: Online.

34543 ■ "Retailing on a Budget: 8 Brick-and-Mortar Alternatives" in Business News Daily (February 21, 2023)
URL(s): www.businessnewsdaily.com/8191-retail-s tore-alternatives.html
Ed: Nicole Fallon. Released: February 21, 2023. Description: Discusses options for alternatives to buying or renting retail space when it comes to housing your small business. Availability: Online.

34544 ■ "The Right and Wrong Reasons to Incorporate or Form an LLC" in Small Business Trends (February 8, 2016)
URL(s): smallbiztrends.com/2016/02/reasons-to -incorporate-form-llc.html
Ed: Nellie Akalp. Released: February 08, 2016. Description: Not every business needs to be structured as a LLC. This article guides you the reasoning behind incorporation. Availability: Online.

34545 ■ "Should My Business Get a Toll-Free Number?" in Business News Daily (February 21, 2023)
URL(s): www.businessnewsdaily.com/29-should-my -business-get-a-toll-free-number.html
Ed: Adam Uzialko. Released: February 21, 2023. Description: Discusses the pros and cons of obtaining a toll-free number for your small business. Availability: Online.

34546 ■ The Soul of Startups: The Untold Stories of How Founders Affect Culture
Pub: John Wiley & Sons, Inc.
Contact: Christina Van Tassell, Executive Vice President Chief Financial Officer
URL(s): www.wiley.com/en-us/The+Soul+of+Star tups%3A+The+Untold+Stories+of+How+Founders +Affect+Culture-p-9781119885597
Ed: Sophie Theen. Released: July 2022. Price: $18, e-book; $29.95, hardcover. Description: The success of a new startup could hinge on the culture set forth by the founder. This book discusses what it takes to create a situations and environments that employees will be comfortable in and includes an examination of negative situations and how that affects the overall company. Availability: E-book; Print.

34547 ■ "Start Up Boom in the Pandemic Is Growing Stronger" in New York Times (August 19, 2021)
URL(s): www.nytimes.com/2021/08/19/business/star tup-business-creation-pandemic.html
Ed: Ben Casselman. Released: August 19, 2021. Description: Explores the concept of Covid-era startups, which were started by necessity by those who were laid off or lost a job through over means during the pandemic. Boosted by stimulus checks, many people were able to fund a new small business in order to follow passions and new opportunities. Studies showed that women and Black and Hispanic entrepreneurs led the way in pandemic start-ups. Availability: Online.

34548 ■ Start-Up and Emerging Companies: Planning, Financing, and Operating the Successful Business, with Forms on Disk
Pub: ALM Media Properties LLC.
Contact: Bill Carter, Chief Executive Officer
URL(s): www.lawcatalog.com/productdetail/15167/s tart-up-emerging-companies-planning-financing-op erating-the-successful-business-with-forms-on-disk
Released: Updated as needed. Price: $1,235, print + online + ebook; $1,137, online + ebook. Description: Covers a wide variety of business and legal topics relating to new enterprises. Provides information on venture financing, formation of corporations, tax laws, limited liability companies, employee benefits, contracts, and accounting. Includes a CD-ROM containing more than 75 sample legal forms, clauses, agreements, organizational resolutions, and checklists. (Law Journal Press). Availability: E-book; Print; Online.

34549 ■ Start Your Own Event Planning Business
Ed: Cheryl Kimball. Released: 4th Edition. Price: $19.95. Description: Provides advice and tools needed to start, run, and grow a successful event planning business. Availability: Paperback; Print.

34550 ■ Starting a Business All-in-One for Dummies
Pub: John Wiley & Sons, Inc.
Contact: Christina Van Tassell, Executive Vice President Chief Financial Officer
URL(s): www.wiley.com/en-us/Starting+a+Business +All+in+One+For+Dummies%2C+3rd+Edition-p -9781119868590
Ed: Eric Tyson, Bob Nelson. Released: 3rd edition. Price: $21, e-book; $34.99, paperback. Description: Six books about starting a new business are compiled into this one book. Everything you need to know about setting up a new business, from developing a business model to paying taxes, is covered. Availability: E-book; Print.

34551 ■ Startup Boards: A Field Guide to Building and Leading an Effective Board of Directors
Pub: John Wiley & Sons, Inc.
Contact: Christina Van Tassell, Executive Vice President Chief Financial Officer
URL(s): www.wiley.com/en-us/Startup+Boards%3A +A+Field+Guide+to+Building+and+Leading+an +Effective+Board+of+Directors%2C+2nd+Edition-p -9781119859284
Ed: Brad Feld, Matt Blumberg, Mahendra Ramsinghani. Released: 2nd edition. Price: $18, e-book; $29.95, hardcover. Description: A guide to setting up and being part of a board of directors for a startup company. Describes what a board does and how they operate, running meetings, and even what to do when it comes time to part ways. Availability: E-book; Print.

34552 ■ Startup CXO: A Field Guide to Scaling Up Your Company's Critical Functions and Teams
URL(s): www.wiley.com/en-us/Startup+CXO%3A+A +Field+Guide+to+Scaling+Up+Your+Company% 27s+Critical+Functions+and+Teams-p-978111977 2576
Ed: Matt Blumberg, Peter M. Birkeland. Released: June 2021. Price: $18, e-book; $29.95, hardcover. Description: A useful guide for startup companies to use while figuring out their scaling. Availability: E-book; Print.

34553 ■ The Startup Owner's Manual: The Step-By-Step Guide for Building a Great Company
Pub: John Wiley & Sons, Inc.
Contact: Christina Van Tassell, Executive Vice President Chief Financial Officer
URL(s): www.wiley.com/en-us/The+Startup+Owner% 27s+Manual%3A+The+Step+By+Step+Guide+for +Building+a+Great+Company-p-9781119690689
Ed: Steve Blank, Bob Dorf. Released: March 2020. Price: $24, e-book; $40, hardcover. Description: Follow the Customer Development process, which has shown great success and is now taught at prestigious universities. Includes charts, graphs, and seventy-seven checklists to help you get your company off the ground and becoming established. Availability: E-book; Print.

34554 ■ "STARTUP STATISTICS 2023 – The Numbers You Need to Know" in Small Business Trends (December 27, 2022)
URL(s): smallbiztrends.com/2022/12/startup-statistics .html
Ed: Sandeep Babu. Released: December 27, 2022. Description: Educate yourself on the latest statistics on startups. Availability: Online.

34555 ■ "Startups, It's Time to Think Like Camels -- Not Unicorns" in Harvard Business Review (October 16, 2020)
Ed: Alex Lazarow. Released: October 16, 2020. Description: Discusses how startups and innovators can survive in difficult economic conditions using the metaphor of the camel because a camel can survive for long periods without sustenance and can adapt to extreme variations in climate. Availability: Online.

34556 ■ "Sustainable Start-Ups Should Consider Corporate Venture Capital First" in The Conversation
Ed: Deborah de Lange, Dave Valliere. Released: February 27, 2020. Description: Discusses how sustainable start-ups are leading the way with smart business models that have economic, social, and environmental value. Availability: Online.

34557 ■ "Tax and Business Forms You'll Need to Start a Small Business" in Business News Daily (February 21, 2023)
URL(s): www.businessnewsdaily.com/9-tax-and-business-forms-needed-to-start-a-small-business.html
Ed: Andrew Martins. Released: February 21, 2023. Description: Properly filing the right forms is a crucial step in starting a business. This article explains which forms you need based on your company's structure. Availability: Online.

34558 ■ "Tech Startup Challenges (and How to Overcome Them)" in Business News Daily (February 21, 2023)
URL(s): www.businessnewsdaily.com/6265-tech-star tup-challenges.html
Ed: Nicole Fallon. Released: February 21, 2023. Description: Tech startup companies face many challenges, some of them unique to that particular industry. This article discusses overcoming those specific challenges, such as constant changes and upgrades in hardware and software, so that your startup will thrive. Availability: Online.

34559 ■ "Thinking about Names for Your New Business? These 20 Startup Name Generators Could Help" in Small Business Trends (January 27, 2023)
URL(s): smallbiztrends.com/2018/06/startup-name -generator.html
Ed: Annie Pilon. Released: January 27, 2023. Description: Get help with naming your new business with these listed name generators. Availability: Online.

34560 ■ Third Shift Entrepreneur: Keep Your Day Job, Build Your Dream Job
Pub: John Wiley & Sons, Inc.
Contact: Christina Van Tassell, Executive Vice President Chief Financial Officer
URL(s): www.wiley.com/en-us/Third+Shift+En trepreneur%3A+Keep+Your+Day+Job%2C+Buil d+Your+Dream+Job-p-9781119708360

Ed: Todd Connor. **Released:** April 2021. **Price:** $17, e-book; $28, hardcover. **Description:** Conveys techniques entrepreneurs can use to start a business. **Availability:** E-book; Print.

34561 ■ *"Tips on Choosing The Right Location for Your Business" in Business News Daily (February 21, 2023)*

URL(s): www.businessnewsdaily.com/15760-choosing-business-location.html

Ed: Matt D'Angelo. **Released:** February 21, 2023. **Description:** Tips for choosing a great location for your business. This is a decision that is very hard to change, so getting it right the first time is a must. **Availability:** Online.

34562 ■ *"Tips for Entrepreneurs Pitching to Investors" in Legal Zoom (March 14, 2023)*

URL(s): www.legalzoom.com/articles/tips-for-entrepreneurs-pitching-to-investors

Ed: Sandra Beckwith. **Released:** March 14, 2023. **Description:** Startups often need initial funding to get the business off the ground, and entrepreneurs should brush up on these tips to in order to maximize their success in the investor saying yes. **Availability:** Online.

34563 ■ *"Tips and Tools for Great Business Names" in Small Business Trends (December 29, 2022)*

URL(s): smallbiztrends.com/2020/09/business-names.html

Ed: Annie Pilon. **Released:** December 29, 2022. **Description:** Having a hard time thinking of a name for your small business? Check into these online name generators to help you come up with a great name. **Availability:** Online.

34564 ■ *"The Top 4 Tips for Virtual Startups" in Legal Zoom (February 24, 2023)*

URL(s): www.legalzoom.com/articles/the-top-tips-for-virtual-startups

Ed: Brette Sember, J.D. **Released:** February 24, 2023. **Description:** A virtual startup has a rather unique setting since it's all online, so how does one manage employees when everyone is remote? Follow these guidelines to keep your business running smoothly. **Availability:** Online.

34565 ■ *"Top 5 Cities to Launch Your Startup Business" in Legal Zoom (March 21, 2023)*

URL(s): www.legalzoom.com/articles/top-5-cities-to-launch-your-startup-business

Ed: Katherine Gustafson. **Released:** March 21, 2023. **Description:** If you have the opportunity to open your startup anywhere in the U.S., follow the advice and check into these five areas to help maximize your businesses potential. **Availability:** Online.

34566 ■ *"Top Reasons to Incorporate Your Business" in Small Business Trends (August 5, 2014)*

Ed: Nellie Akalp. **Released:** August 05, 2014. **Description:** Provides the reasons why you should incorporate your small business so both you and your business are protected. **Availability:** Online.

34567 ■ *The Unicorn's Shadow: Combating the Dangerous Myths that Hold Back Startups, Founders, and Investors*

URL(s): www.amazon.com/Unicorns-Shadow-Combating-Dangerous-Investors/dp/1613630964/

Ed: Ehtan Mollick. **Released:** June 23, 2020. **Price:** $17.99, paperback; $17.09, e-book. **Description:** Examines what is likely to cause success for startups and encourages entrepreneurs to not focus so much on the "unicorns" of startups — the Googles, Ubers, and other high-profile companies that made it big. **Availability:** E-book; Print.

34568 ■ *"What is a DBA (Doing Business As) and How to Register One" in Business News Daily (February 8, 2023)*

URL(s): smallbiztrends.com/2023/02/dba.html

Ed: Joshua Sophy. **Released:** February 08, 2023. **Description:** Discusses the definition of DBA (Doing Business As) and the pros and cons of setting that up for your small business. **Availability:** Online.

34569 ■ *"What is the Difference Between a Mentor and Coach?" in Small Business Trends (June 7, 2016)*

URL(s): www.smallbiztrends.com/2016/02/difference-mentor-coach.html

Ed: Shubhomita Bose. **Released:** June 07, 2016. **Description:** Small business owners are often encouraged to seek out coaching and mentoring, but what is the difference between the two? This article discusses each one so you can make a solid choice in which one is best for you. **Availability:** Online.

34570 ■ *"What is the Easiest Business to Start?" in Small Business Trends (April 26, 2022)*

URL(s): smallbiztrends.com/2019/08/easiest-business-to-start.html

Released: April 26, 2022. **Description:** Looking for an easy business to start? Those usually fall into the services category, such as consulting. Listed are some ideas to get you started. **Availability:** Online.

34571 ■ *"What Is a C Corporation?" in Business News Daily (February 21, 2023)*

URL(s): www.businessnewsdaily.com/3771-c-corporation.html

Ed: Sean Peek. **Released:** February 21, 2023. **Description:** Discusses the C corporation business structure so you can make in informed decision about setting up your small business. **Availability:** Online.

34572 ■ *"What Is Crowdfunding?" in Business News Daily (February 28, 2023)*

URL(s): www.businessnewsdaily.com/4134-what-is-crowdfunding.html

Ed: Simone Johnson. **Released:** February 28, 2023. **Description:** Defines and discusses crowdfunding in a small business context. **Availability:** Online.

34573 ■ *"What Is a Vision Statement and How to Write One (+Examples and Template)" in Small Business Trends (February 13, 2023)*

URL(s): smallbiztrends.com/2023/02/vision-statement.html

Released: February 13, 2023. **Description:** Defines and gives examples of vision statements for you to use while starting your small business. **Availability:** Online.

34574 ■ *"What Not to Do When Starting a Home-Based Business" in Home Business (March 22, 2023)*

URL(s): homebusinessmag.com/business-start-up/start-up-fundamentals/what-not-do-starting-home-based-business/

Ed: Chandler Peterson. **Released:** March 22, 2023. **Description:** Reviews some helpful tips on home business culture to make your venture a success. **Availability:** Online.

34575 ■ *"What You Need to Build Your Startup" in Minority Business Entrepreneur (Vol. 39, Fall, 2022, No. 4, pp. 12-13)*

URL(s): digital.mbemag.com/?m=53732&i=769780&p=12&ver=html5

Ed: Andrew Ryan. **Price:** $7.95. **Description:** Discusses some of the challenges entrepreneurs face when starting a new business venture. **Availability:** Print; Online.

34576 ■ *"When is the Best Time to Trademark Your Company Name?" in Small Business Trends (June 26, 2014)*

URL(s): smallbiztrends.com/2014/06/best-time-to-get-trademark.html

Ed: Nellie Akalp. **Released:** June 26, 2014. **Description:** Discusses trademarks and when the best time to register your product with the U.S. Patent and Trademark Office. **Availability:** Online.

34577 ■ *"When Do I Need to Register My Business In Another State?" in Small Business Trends (March 8, 2021)*

URL(s): smallbiztrends.com/2014/03/register-business-in-another-state.html

Ed: Nellie Akalp. **Released:** March 08, 2021. **Description:** Provides the particulars on when you will need to register your business in another state in order to follow current laws. **Availability:** Online.

34578 ■ *"When You Need to Find outside Help for Your Business" in Legal Zoom (March 21, 2023)*

URL(s): www.legalzoom.com/articles/when-you-need-to-find-outside-help-for-your-business

Ed: Jane Haskins, Esq. **Released:** March 21, 2023. **Description:** What many people fail to realize is that there is a lot of background work that needs to be done while running a small business and a lot of it takes special knowledge. Having a lawyer, accountant, bookkeeper, and even a business coach is often very beneficial. **Availability:** Online.

34579 ■ *"Your Guide to Getting a Business License" in Business News Daily (February 21, 2023)*

URL(s): www.businessnewsdaily.com/15764-how-to-get-a-business-license.html

Ed: Skye Schooley. **Released:** February 21, 2023. **Description:** This article discusses business licenses, including how to go about obtaining one. **Availability:** Online.

34580 ■ *"Your Ultimate Business Startup Checklist" in Small Business Trends (January 11, 2023)*

Ed: Kevin Ocasio. **Released:** January 11, 2023. **Description:** If you are thinking about starting your own small business, take a look at this checklist and to help you stay organized. **Availability:** Online.

STATISTICAL SOURCES

34581 ■ *"STARTUP STATISTICS 2023 – The Numbers You Need to Know" in Small Business Trends (December 27, 2022)*

URL(s): smallbiztrends.com/2022/12/startup-statistics.html

Ed: Sandeep Babu. **Released:** December 27, 2022. **Description:** Educate yourself on the latest statistics on startups. **Availability:** Online.

VIDEO/AUDIO MEDIA

34582 ■ *3 Challenges Social Impact Startups Face Now with Paul Zelizer*

URL(s): www.awarepreneurs.com/podcast/326-social-impact-startups

Ed: Paul Zelizer. **Released:** March 12, 2024. **Description:** Podcast discusses challenges impact startups face, including access to funding, a regressive social and political landscape, and building awareness/market demand.

34583 ■ *Asking for What You Want, Slack Early Days*

URL(s): www.startuphustlepodcast.com/asking-for-what-you-want-slack-early-days

Ed: Matt Watson. **Released:** June 20, 2024. **Description:** Podcast discusses why entrepreneurs frequently struggle to ask for what they want, how personalized coaching can help them overcome personal hurdles and become better leaders, and how to trust your instincts. .

34584 ■ *Building a Global SaaS Company*

URL(s): www.startuphustlepodcast.com/building-a-global-saas-company

Ed: Matt Watson. **Released:** April 02, 2024. **Description:** Podcast discusses entrepreneurship, the challenges of global markets, and the power of partnerships.

34585 ■ *Christie's Chips*

URL(s): www.thepitch.show/141-christies-chips

Ed: Josh Muccio. **Released:** August 28, 2024. **Description:** Podcast features a pitch for junk food without the junk.

34586 ■ *ChurchSpace: Airbnb for Churches*
URL(s): www.thepitch.show/128-churchspace-airbnb -for-churches

Ed: Josh Muccio. **Released:** April 10, 2024. **Description:** Podcast features ChuchSpace, a church rental marketplace.

34587 ■ *Detroit Top Startups*
URL(s): www.startuphustlepodcast.com/detroit-top-s tartups

Ed: Matt Watson. **Released:** October 18, 2023. **Description:** Podcast shares Detroit startups in industries from digital security to construction.

34588 ■ *Disruptors for Good: Building a Unicorn Tech Company and the Importance of a Co-Founder*
URL(s): share.transistor.fm/s/46aeef23

Ed: Grant Trahant. **Released:** March 27, 2023. **Description:** Podcast discusses building a unicorn tech company and selecting the right co-founder.

34589 ■ *Early Startup Reality Checks*
URL(s): www.startuphustlepodcast.com/early-startup -reality-checks

Ed: Matt Watson. **Released:** December 23, 2023. **Description:** Podcast discusses the early-stage startups, including niche depth and the challenges of business growth.

34590 ■ *Entrepreneurial Thought Leaders: A New Approach to the Great Outdoors*
URL(s): ecorner.stanford.edu/podcasts/a-new-ap proach-to-the-great-outdoors

Ed: Emily Ma. **Released:** January 27, 2021. **Description:** Podcast explains how a simple problem can offer a massive opportunity with the CEO of Hipcamp, a platform for booking outdoor stays.

34591 ■ *Entrepreneurial Thought Leaders: Behind the Scenes of a Mega-Unicorn*
Released: March 01, 2023. **Description:** Podcast explains how a startup can achieve uncommon success even with unconventional approaches.

34592 ■ *Entrepreneurial Thought Leaders: Building Biotech to Last*
URL(s): ecorner.stanford.edu/podcasts/builing-bio tech-to-last
Released: November 23, 2022.

34593 ■ *Entrepreneurial Thought Leaders: Building Startups, Fast and Slow*
URL(s): ecorner.stanford.edu/podcasts/building-star tups-fast-and-slow

Ed: Ravi Belani. **Released:** May 05, 2021. **Description:** Podcast offers advice to innovators who want to create complex products that take longer to prototype.

34594 ■ *Entrepreneurial Thought Leaders: Cody Coleman (Coactive AI) - Starting from 'Why'*
URL(s): ecorner.stanford.edu/podcasts/cody-coleman -coactive-ai-starting-from-why
Released: October 11, 2023. **Description:** Podcast suggests that, before you can build a successful startup, you have to know why you want to build it.

34595 ■ *Entrepreneurial Thought Leaders: David Allemann (On) - Exploration in Sports Technology*
URL(s): stvp.stanford.edu/podcasts/david-allemann -on-exploration-in-sports-technology

Ed: Ravi Belani. **Released:** May 22, 2024. **Description:** Podcast shares how to build a company on a spirit of exploration, innovation, and positivity.

34596 ■ *Entrepreneurial Thought Leaders: Developing a Founder's Mindset*
URL(s): ecorner.stanford.edu/podcasts/alfred-lin-se quoia-capital-developing-a-founders-mindset

Ed: Ravi Belani. **Released:** May 11, 2022. **Description:** Podcast offers advice on identifying worthwhile ideas and sparking excellence in a startup.

34597 ■ *Entrepreneurial Thought Leaders: Driving Innovation*
URL(s): ecorner.stanford.edu/podcasts/driving-innova tion

Ed: Heidi Roizen. **Released:** March 10, 2021. **Description:** Podcast offers a conversation with the CEO of Zoox, who discusses building technology in a crowded market, leading an innovative team, and dealing with skeptics.

34598 ■ *Entrepreneurial Thought Leaders: Entrepreneurship Education Is About More than Startup Creation*
URL(s): ecorner.stanford.edu/podcasts/resaerch -ingsigt-entreprenership-education-is-about-more -than-startup-creation
Released: September 22, 2021. **Description:** Podcast observes that formal entrepreneurship education may have helped raise more funding and scale more quickly but didn't lead to higher rates of startup creation.

34599 ■ *Entrepreneurial Thought Leaders: Ernestine Fu (Brave Capital) - Taking Action for Startup Success*
URL(s): stvp.stanford.edu/podcasts/taking-action-for -startup-success

Ed: Ravi Belani. **Released:** February 14, 2024. **Description:** Podcast discusses how to consider challenges, accept the risks, and embrace the action of entrepreneurship.

34600 ■ *Entrepreneurial Thought Leaders: Garry Tan (Y Combinator) - Unconventional Advice for Founders*
URL(s): stvp.stanford.edu/podcasts/unconventional-a dvice-for-founders

Ed: Ravi Belani. **Released:** October 18, 2023. **Description:** Podcast offers advice for entrepreneurs and startup founders that challenges prevailing wisdom.

34601 ■ *Entrepreneurial Thought Leaders: Innovating for Social Impact*
URL(s): ecorner.stanford.edu/podcasts/irma-olguin-jr -bitwise-industries-and-morgan-simon-candide -group-innovating-for-social-impact

Ed: Chuck Eesley. **Released:** April 20, 2022. **Description:** Podcast suggest high-growth startups and impact investors can work together to creative positive financial and community outcomes.

34602 ■ *Entrepreneurial Thought Leaders: Innovation in Ed-Tech and Biotech*
URL(s): ecorner.stanford.edu/podcasts/daphne-koller -insitro-innovation-in-ed-tech-and-biotech

Ed: Ravi Belani. **Released:** November 10, 2021. **Description:** Podcast explains how to look for opportunities where your skills have disproportionate leverage.

34603 ■ *Entrepreneurial Thought Leaders: Kathleen Eisenhardt (Stanford) - Strategy for New Companies*
URL(s): stvp.stanford.edu/podcasts/kathleen -eisenhardt-standard-strategy-for-new-companies

Ed: Ravi Belani. **Released:** October 18, 2023. **Description:** Podcast offers strategies for new companies in new and disrupted markets.

34604 ■ *Entrepreneurial Thought Leaders: Making Entrepreneurship More Inclusive*
URL(s): ecorner.stanford.edu/podcasts/making-en trepreneurship-more-inclusive

Ed: Ravi Belani. **Released:** March 03, 2021. **Description:** Podcast discusses how advocate for structural change with the founder of Stitch Fix. .

34605 ■ *Entrepreneurial Thought Leaders: Maria Barrera (Clayful) - Mental Health Tech, Mentally Healthy Startups*
URL(s): stvp.stanford.edu/podcasts/maria-barrera -clayful-mental-health-tech-mentally-healthy-star tups

Ed: Ravi Belani. **Released:** May 29, 2024. **Description:** Podcast discusses the journey of building a mental health startup.

34606 ■ *Entrepreneurial Thought Leaders: Problem-Solving for a Unique Market*
URL(s): ecorner.stanford.edu/podcasts/dave-vasen -brightwheel-problem-solving-for-a-unique-market

Ed: Emily Ma. **Released:** February 08, 2023. **Description:** Podcast explains how listening to potential customers' needs can unlock a successful startup idea.

34607 ■ *Entrepreneurial Thought Leaders: Qasar Younis (Applied Intuition) - Radically Pragmatic Insights*
URL(s): stvp.stanford.edu/podcasts/qasar-younis -applied-intuition-radically-pragmatic-insights -explicit

Ed: Ravi Belani. **Released:** April 24, 2024. **Description:** Podcast offers practical advice for aspiring entrepreneurs.

34608 ■ *Entrepreneurial Thought Leaders: Sam Altman (OpenAI) - The Possibilities of AI*
URL(s): stvp.stanford.edu/podcasts/sam-altman -openai-the-possibilities-of-ai

Ed: Ravi Belani. **Released:** May 01, 2024. **Description:** Podcast offers advice for AI entrepreneurs and shares insights on the opportunities and risks of AI tools.

34609 ■ *Entrepreneurial Thought Leaders: Scaling with Resilience*
URL(s): ecorner.stanford.edu/podcasts/scaling-with -resilience

Ed: Ravi Belani. **Released:** April 21, 2021. **Description:** Podcast discusses the challenges of startups and how to find optimism and build a great team despite it.

34610 ■ *Entrepreneurial Thought Leaders: Scaling Sustainable Fashion*
URL(s): ecorner.stanford.edu/podcasts/scaling-sus tainable-fashion

Ed: Ravi Belani. **Released:** October 20, 2021. **Description:** Podcast discusses new ways to connect supply and demand in a new marketplace business.

34611 ■ *Entrepreneurial Thought Leaders: Serial Co-Founders*
URL(s): ecorner.stanford.edu/podcasts/serial-co-foun ders

Ed: Emily Ma. **Released:** February 09, 2022. **Description:** Podcast offers a conversation with someone who founded three startups in15 years.

34612 ■ *Entrepreneurial Thought Leaders: What Investors Want*
URL(s): ecorner.stanford.edu/podcasts/what-inves tors-want

Ed: Ravi Belani. **Released:** November 03, 2021. **Description:** Podcast explains that investors want to see a business than can grow exponentially, evidence of traction, and a concrete business plan.

34613 ■ *Entrepreneurial Thought Leaders: Why Startups Fail*
URL(s): ecorner.stanford.edu/podcasts/tom -eisenmann-harvard-business-school-why-startups -fail

Ed: Tom Byers. **Released:** August 11, 2021. **Description:** Podcast discusses common patterns in failed start-ups with representatives from the Harvard Business School. Also suggests a road map for knowing when to pull the plug and how to fail better.

34614 ■ *From Sales Guy to Tech Founder*
URL(s): www.startuphustlepodcast.com/from-sales -guy-to-tech-founder

Ed: Matt Watson. **Released:** May 07, 2024. **Description:** Podcast discusses the challenges of being a non-tech founder, the importance of networking, and the benefits of white-labeling.

34615 ■ *Get Your Climate Startup Funded with a Great Pitch Deck with Zoë Dove-Many*
URL(s): www.awarepreneurs.com/podcast/316-clima te-pitch-deck

Ed: Paul Zelizer. **Released:** December 19, 2023. **Description:** Podcast discusses funding for climate startups with a brand strategist.

34616 ■ *Handle: The Uncut Pitch*

URL(s): www.thepitch.show/126-handle-the-uncut-pitch

Ed: Josh Muccio. **Released:** November 22, 2023. **Description:** Podcast features the pitch for a snack delivery business.

34617 ■ *HBR Ideacast: Why Entrepreneurs Don't Need Venture Capital to Scale*

URL(s): hbr.org/podcast/2023/06/why-entrepreneurs-dont-need-venture-capital-to-scale

Ed: Alison Beard. **Released:** June 27, 2023. **Description:** Podcast explains how a startup grew without outside money and instead relied on the leverage of influencers, focus on costs, and making tough decisions.

34618 ■ *HBR Ideacast: Why Some Startups Fail to Scale*

URL(s): hbr.org/podcast/2022/12/why-some-start-ups-fail-to-scale

Ed: Alison Beard. **Released:** December 13, 2022. **Description:** Podcast explains how to transition out of the startup phase.

34619 ■ *The How of Business: 7 Start-Up Mistakes*

URL(s): www.thehowofbusiness.com/510-7-startup-mistakes

Ed: Henry Lopez. **Released:** February 19, 2024. **Description:** Podcast discusses how to avoid or minimize common start-up mistakes.

34620 ■ *The How of Business: Courtney Reum - Shortcut Your Startup*

URL(s): www.thehowofbusiness.com/469-courtney-reum-shortcut-your-startup

Ed: Henry Lopez. **Released:** April 24, 2023. **Description:** Podcast offers tips fast-tracking small business success. Also discusses entrepreneur criteria, the role of luck, and how to navigate the fundraising process.

34621 ■ *The How of Business: Erika Tyburski - Health Tech Startup*

URL(s): www.thehowofbusiness.com/401-erika-tyburski-healthcare-startup

Ed: Henry Lopez. **Released:** January 31, 2022. **Description:** Podcast offers a conversation with the founder of a health tech startup.

34622 ■ *The How of Business: Ready to Be Your Own Boss?*

URL(s): www.thehowofbusiness.com/episode-r1-ready-to-be-your-own-boss

Ed: Henry Lopez. **Released:** June 01, 2020. **Description:** Podcast explores what it takes to start your own business.

34623 ■ *The How of Business: Six Startup Myths*

URL(s): www.thehowofbusiness.com/442-six-startup-myths

Ed: Henry Lopez. **Released:** December 19, 2022. **Description:** Podcast outlines myths about small business startups.

34624 ■ *How I Built This: Advice Line: Growing Beyond Your Niche*

URL(s): wondery.com/shows/how-i-built-this/episode/10386-advice-line-growing-beyond-your-niche

Ed: Guy Raz. **Released:** October 10, 2024. **Description:** Podcast offers advice to early-stage founders.

34625 ■ *How I Built This: Advice Line with Mark Ramadan of Sir Kensington's*

URL(s): wondery.com/shows/how-i-built-this/episode/10386-advice-line-with-mark-ramadan

Ed: Guy Raz. **Released:** June 27, 2024. **Description:** Podcast answers questions from founders at different stages in the process.

34626 ■ *How I Built This: Advice Line with Sadie Lincoln of barre3*

URL(s): wondery.com/shows/how-i-built-this/episode/10386-advice-line-with-sadie-lincoln-of-barre3

Ed: Guy Raz. **Released:** September 30, 2024. **Description:** Podcast offers advice to early-stage founders.

34627 ■ *How I Built This: Lily's Sweets: Cynthia Tice*

URL(s): wondery.com/shows/how-i-built-this/episode/10386-lilys-sweets-cynthia-tice

Ed: Guy Raz. **Released:** September 30, 2024. **Description:** Podcast explains how Lily's Sweets was launched with just four employees, a nearly-60-year-old founder, and disastrous early recipes.

34628 ■ *Ignore the Hype - Startup Different with David Sinkinson*

URL(s): www.eofire.com/podcast/davidsinkinson

Ed: Jon Lee Dumas. **Released:** September 26, 2024. **Description:** Podcast discusses startup myths and entrepreneurial challenges.

34629 ■ *Kimoyo: Is This African Startup Venture Backable?*

URL(s): www.thepitch.show/116-kimoyo-is-this-african-startup-venture-backable

Released: August 30, 2023. **Description:** Podcast tracks the pitch for Komoyo Insights, a research analytics platform that gathers feedback from African consumer, despite the fact that it Kimoyo doesn't quite fit the venture mold.

34630 ■ *The Knowledge Project: Brian Halligan: Scaling Culture from Startup to IPO*

URL(s): fs.blog/knowldege-project-podcast/brian-halligan

Ed: Shane Parrish. **Released:** August 06, 2024. **Description:** Podcast discusses leading a company from startup to IPO.

34631 ■ *Lotus: Hardware Hail Mary*

URL(s): www.thepitch.show/117-lotus-hardware-hail-mary

Released: September 06, 2023. **Description:** Podcast tracks the pitch for a ring that converts every home into a smart home using technology found it a TV remote, despite the fact that many VCs avoid investing in hardware startups.

34632 ■ *Midwest Moxie: Autonomous Drones and Video Interviewing: Danny Ellis and Kurt Heikkinen*

URL(s): www.wuwm.com/podcast/midwest-moxie/2023-04-16/autonomous-drones-and-video-interviewing-danny-ellis-and-kurt-heikkinen

Ed: Kathleen Gallagher. **Description:** Podcast discusses how difficult, but ultimately rewarding, a startup can be.

34633 ■ *Midwest Moxie: Curious Robots and Inventory Management: Sankalp Arora*

URL(s): www.wuwm.com/podcast/midwest-moxie/2023/04-23/curious-robots-and-inventory-managemen t-sankalp-arora

Ed: Kathleen Gallagher. **Released:** April 23, 2023. **Description:** Podcast discusses a startup whose software allow autonomous drones to do warehouse inventory management.

34634 ■ *Nurture Small Business: Unleashing Entrepreneurial Magic: Stories of Triumph and Transformation*

URL(s): nurturesmallbusiness.buzzsprout.com/900445/episodes/13934554-unleashing-entrepreneurial-magic-storeis-of-triumph-and-transformation

Ed: Denise Cagan. **Released:** November 23, 2023. **Description:** Podcast offers insights on how to overcome entrepreneurial challenges. Also offers tool suggestions, including goal recipes and time analysis.

34635 ■ *People Engineering*

URL(s): www.startuphustlepodcast.com/people-engineering

Ed: Matt Watson. **Released:** April 10, 2024. **Description:** Podcast discusses navigating startups, avoiding costly mistakes, hiring a team to make your business successful.

34636 ■ *Pittsburgh Top Startups*

URL(s): www.startuphustlepodcast.com/pittsburg-top-startups

Ed: Matt Watson. **Released:** November 22, 2023. **Description:** Podcast shares top startups in Pittsburgh.

34637 ■ *RobeCurls: From TikTok to Target*

URL(s): www.thepitch.show/134-robecurls-from-tiktok-to-target

Ed: Josh Muccio. **Released:** May 29, 2024. **Description:** Podcast features the pitch for a patented line of heatless curling headbands.

34638 ■ *Saving Lives with Medical Device Startups*

URL(s): www.startuphustlepodcast.com/saving-lives-with-medical-device-startups

Ed: Matt Watson. **Released:** January 04, 2024. **Description:** Discusses the challenges of developing medical devices, the dynamics of family collaboration, the intricacies of the EMS sector, and the importance of patents.

34639 ■ *Side Hustle to Small Business: Transitioning form the Startup World to Freelance*

URL(s): www.hiscox.com/side-hustle-to-small-business/jacob-burt-burt-media-podcast-season-3

Ed: Sanjay Parekh. **Released:** June 21, 2023. **Description:** Podcast discusses the transition from startup to freelance.

34640 ■ *Small Business, Big Mindset: The Must-Do Offer Pre-Launch Process*

URL(s): podcast.musclecreative.com/924061/episodes/12426853-the-must-do-offer-pre-launch-process

Ed: Erin Geiger. **Released:** March 14, 2023. **Description:** Podcast explains how pre-launch is about selling your process and not your program.

34641 ■ *Sports Tech and the Value of Startup Communities*

URL(s): www.startuphustlepodcast.com/sports-tech-and-the-value-of-startup-communities

Ed: Matt Watson. **Released:** December 13, 2024. **Description:** Podcast discusses the value of startup communities in Kansas City and elsewhere.

34642 ■ *Start. Scale. Exit. Repeat. What Makes a Startup Successful with Colin Campbell*

URL(s): www.eofire.com/podcast/colincampbell2

Ed: Jon Lee Dumas. **Released:** February 26, 2024. **Description:** Podcast explains what make a startup successful and outlines the sticky note business plan.

34643 ■ *The Startup Santa*

URL(s): www.startuphustlepodcast.com/the-startup-santa

Ed: Andrew Morgans. **Released:** October 25, 2023. **Description:** Podcast offers stories from The Startup Santa. Includes being fired, bankruptcy, and the law of reciprocity.

34644 ■ *Startup Tips for Non-Technical Founders*

URL(s): www.startuphustlepodcast.com/startup-tips-for-non-technical-founders

Ed: Matt Watson. **Released:** January 09, 2024. **Description:** Podcast discusses non-tech founders managing tech startups. Explores product development, feature planning, and managing technical debts.

34645 ■ *Startups for the Rest of Us: Building, Buying, and Selling SaaS Companies*

URL(s): www.startupsfortherestofus.com/epidoses/episode-672-bootstrapping-building-buying-and-selling-saas-companies

Ed: Rob Walling. **Released:** July 22, 2023. **Description:** Podcast discuss the bootstrapper journey, the benefits of buying vs. building, and common pitfalls.

34646 ■ Startups for the Rest of Us: From Side Hustle to Full-Time & Profitable (with Mike Taber)
URL(s): www.startupsfortherestofus.com/epidoses/episode-651-from-side-hustle-to-full-time-profitable-with-mke-taber

Ed: Rob Walling. **Released:** February 2023. **Description:** Podcast discusses the journey from side hustle to full-time entrepreneur.

34647 ■ Startups for the Rest of Us: How to Generate Startup Idea (Plus 8 Ideas You Can Steal)
URL(s): www.startupsfortherestofus.com/episodes/episode-638-how-to-generate-startup-ideas-plus-8-ideas-you-can-steal

Ed: Rob Walling. **Released:** November 26, 2022. **Description:** Podcast discusses how to generate startup ideas and shares some of their own suggestions.

34648 ■ Startups for the Rest of Us: Mock Features, a Failed Launch, Becoming a Freelancer, and More Listener Questions (A Rob Solo Adventure)
URL(s): www.startupsfortherestofus.com/epidoses/episode-679-mock-features-a-failed-launch-becoming-a-freelancer-and-more-listener-question-a-rob-solo-adventurere

Released: September 19, 2023. **Description:** Podcast discusses how to recover from a failed launch, the benefits of phased launches, creating organic content for a SaaS, and what you might encounter during an acquisition in a small startup.

34649 ■ This Is Small Business: How Looking Back Can Lead to Forward-Thinking Business Ideas
URL(s): www.smallbusiness.amazon/podcast-episodes/ep-62-how-looking-back-can-lead-to-forward-thinking-business-ideas

Ed: Andrea Marquez. **Released:** August 06, 2024. **Description:** Podcast discusses how to turn your cultural heritage into a successful business idea. Also considers feedback, pivoting, and turning obstacles Into opportunltles.

34650 ■ This Week in Startups: Angel: Upfront's Mark Suster on the Power of Alignment, Setting Reality, and Raising Capital
URL(s): thisweekinstartups.com/episodes/W91qvM5VaTM

Ed: Molly Wood. **Released:** February 21, 2023. **Description:** Podcast discusses challenges for founders in 2023, raising capital investor strategies, key variables for VCs, mission-aligned founders, and investing principles.

34651 ■ This Week in Startups: Benchmark's Sarah Tavel on the State of VC, AI's Impact on Startups & More!
URL(s): thisweekinstartups.com/episodes/miZBSVvuDDH

Ed: Jason Calacanis. **Released:** September 19, 2023. **Description:** Podcast discusses the current state of venture capital, along with common mistakes and evolving trends.

34652 ■ This Week in Startups: Building a Blood-Testing Startup in 2023 with Vital CEO Vasu Nadella
URL(s): thisweekinstartups.com/episodes/8I8Zl5L8Bna

Ed: Jason Calacanis. **Released:** September 03, 2023. **Description:** Podcast discusses the challenges of scaling a company, integrating AI, and creating accessible lab testing.

34653 ■ This Week in Startups: Developing Drugs to Extend Dog Lifespans with Loyal CEO Celine Halioua
URL(s): thisweekinstartups.com/episodes/TqtKOKdYxVH

Ed: Jason Calacanis. **Released:** August 29, 2023. **Description:** Podcast discusses the science and environmental factors behind drug development for canines; also discusses the challenges of commercialization and the experience as a solo founder.

34654 ■ This Week in Startups: Grammarly CEO Rahul Roy-Chowdhury on the Future of User-Centric Language Tools
URL(s): thisweekinstartups.com/episodes/a98Bv7jwoSw

Ed: Jason Calacanis. **Released:** September 26, 2023. **Description:** Podcast discusses the journey of Grammarly's founder,.

34655 ■ This Week in Startups: Sophia Amoruso on Branding, Raising a Fund, Portfolio Construction & More
URL(s): thisweekinstartups.com/episodes/Vr4FG31Get8

Ed: Molly Wood. **Released:** February 22, 2023. **Description:** Podcast discusses investing experiences, the public fund-raising journey, stages of investing, and explores investing in founders versus ideas.

34656 ■ This Week in Startups: Startup Pitch Competition: Jason Invests $25K
URL(s): thisweekinstartups.com/episodes/46aDAUCywKy

Ed: Jason Calacanis. **Released:** May 22, 2023. **Description:** Podcast offers the kickoff for a pitch competition.

34657 ■ This Week in Startups: State of Early-Stage VC, Finding PMF, Caroline Ellison Testifies & More with Zach Coelius
URL(s): thisweekinstartups.com/episodes/7E9XbTBocGv

Ed: Jason Calacanis. **Description:** Podcast discusses the early stages of venture capital.

34658 ■ This Week in Startups: VenturusAI's Instant MBA & Samantha Wong on Identifying Soon-to-Explode Startup Markets
URL(s): thisweekinstartups.com/episodes/8vY9sQJazlj

Ed: Jason Calacanis. **Released:** July 13, 2023. **Description:** Podcast discusses the evoluiotn of VenturusAI and shares insights on identifying potential startup markets. .

34659 ■ Vital Audio
URL(s): www.thepitch.show/143-vital-audio
Ed: Josh Muccio. **Released:** September 11, 2024. **Description:** Podcast features the pitch for a device that takes someone's vitals with the sound of their voice.

34660 ■ Why Startups Get Stuck & the Pitfalls of Raising Money
URL(s): www.startuphustlepodcast.com/why-startups-get-stuck-the-pitfalls-of-raising-money
Ed: Matt Watson. **Released:** June 11, 2024. **Description:** Podcast discusses fundraising, growth strategies, and avoiding common pitfalls for startups.

34661 ■ The Zero Burnout Social Entrepreneur Launch with Paul Zelizer
URL(s): www.awarepreneurs.com/podcast/318-social-entrepreneur-launch
Ed: Paul Zelizer. **Released:** January 16, 2024. **Description:** Podcast offers ways to mitigate burnout when launching a startup.

TRADE SHOWS AND CONVENTIONS

34662 ■ Startup Grind
URL(s): startupgrind.tech/conference

Price: $249, Onsite registered, members. **Frequency:** Annual. **Description:** Networking and mentorship for small business owners and startups. **Principal Exhibits:** Networking and mentorship for small business owners and startups.

CONSULTANTS

34663 ■ Confidante Consulting
W 103rd St.
New York, NY 10025
Ph: (332)208-2448
URL: http://consultconfidante.com
Description: Management consulting services with a focus toward assisting private equity investors in procuring the best deals, assisting dreamers and startups in finding their way toward success, and talent development. **Scope:** Management consulting services with a focus toward assisting private equity investors in procuring the best deals, assisting dreamers and startups in finding their way toward success, and talent development.

34664 ■ DevelopWell
3301 Richmond Hwy., No. 1090
Alexandria, VA 22305-3044
Co. E-mail: info@developwell.org
URL: http://www.developwell.org
Contact: Holly Witherington, Chief Executive Officer
Facebook: www.facebook.com/developwell
Linkedin: www.linkedin.com/company/developwell
Instagram: www.instagram.com/thedevelopwell
Description: A women-owned and operated coaching and consulting practice that develops leaders and teams in values-driven organizations with a holistic and innovative approach. **Founded:** 2017.

34665 ■ Marisa Moore Nutrition, LLC
2625 Piedmont Rd., Ste. 56-160
Atlanta, GA 30324
Co. E-mail: questions@marisamoore.com
URL: http://marisamoore.com
Contact: Marisa Moore, Contact
E-mail: marisa@marisamoore.com
Facebook: www.facebook.com/MarisaMooreNutrition
X (Twitter): x.com/marisamoore
Instagram: www.instagram.com/MarisaMoore
Pinterest: www.pinterest.com/marisamoore
Description: Food and nutrition expert working on the business side of health and wellness. Works with startups, chefs, food vendors, marketers, food scientists, brand managers, nutritionists, and researchers.

INTERNET DATABASES

34666 ■ Small Business Hub: A Research Guide for Entrepreneurs
URL(s): guides.loc.gov/small-business-hub
Description: An online guide with links for further research into running a small business. Topics cover a large selection of useful information for entrepreneurs for all stages of setting up a business. Includes resources on planning, finance, location, registering, marketing, managing, growing, and exiting the business. **Availability:** Online.

RESEARCH CENTERS

34667 ■ National Council of Entrepreneurial Tech Transfer (NCET2)
2020 Pennsylvania Ave., Ste. 140
Washington, DC 20006
Ph: (202)580-8382
Co. E-mail: support@ncet2.org
URL: http://ncet2.org
Contact: Tony Stanco, Executive Director
E-mail: tony@ncet2.org
Facebook: www.facebook.com/ncet2
Linkedin: www.linkedin.com/company/ncet2
X (Twitter): x.com/ncet2
YouTube: www.youtube.com/channel/UCvRqUzNCHl0tRibnv-rGzpg
Description: Fortune 500 companies and universities. Seeks to utilize university and federal laboratory research in creating, developing, and funding transformative startups that align with corporate business needs.

ASSOCIATIONS AND OTHER ORGANIZATIONS

34668 ▪ Alcoholics Anonymous World Services, Inc. (A.A.) - Library [A.A. World Services Inc.]
475 Riverside Dr., 11th Fl.
W 120th St., 11th & 8th Fl.s
New York, NY 10115
Ph: (212)870-3400
URL: http://www.aa.org
Description: Cardiovascular technologists involved in the allied health professions. Conducts testing of allied health professionals throughout the U.S. and Canada. Provides study guides and reliability and validity testing. Compiles statistics. **Scope:** Alcoholism. **Founded:** 1935. **Holdings:** Figures not available. **Geographic Preference:** Multinational.

34669 ▪ NAADAC: The Association for Addiction Professionals [National Association of Alcoholism and Drug Abuse Counselors]
44 Canal Ctr. Plz., Ste. 301
Alexandria, VA 22314
Ph: (703)741-7686
Fax: (703)741-7698
Co. E-mail: naadac@naadac.org
URL: http://www.naadac.org
Contact: Cynthia Moreno Tuohy, Executive Director
E-mail: naadac@naadac.org
Facebook: www.facebook.com/NAADAC
Linkedin: www.linkedin.com/company/naadac-the-association-for-addiction-professionals
Description: Works to lead, unify, and empower addiction focused professionals to achieve excellence through education, advocacy, knowledge, standards of practice, ethics, professional development and research. **Founded:** 1972. **Publications:** *The Basics of Addiction Counseling: A Desk Reference and Study Guide* (Periodic); *Basics of Addiction Counseling Independent Study Course*; *Advances in Addiction & Recovery* (Quarterly). **Awards:** Lora Roe Memorial Addiction Counselor of the Year (Irregular); Mel Schulstad Professional of the Year (Annual); Organizational Achievement Award (Irregular); William F. (Bill) Callahan Award (Irregular); Enlightenment Award (Annual); NAADAC Medical Professional of the Year (Periodic); NAADAC Organizational Achievement Award (Periodic). **Geographic Preference:** National.

34670 ▪ Narcotics Anonymous (NA)
PO Box 9999
Van Nuys, CA 91409
Ph: (818)773-9999
Fax: (818)700-0700
Co. E-mail: fsmail@na.org
URL: http://www.na.org
Contact: Anthony Edmondson, Executive Director
Description: Aims to recover addicts throughout the world, works to offer help to fellow addicts seeking recovery. Meets regularly to facilitate and stabilize their recovery. Uses 12-step program adapted from Alcoholics Anonymous to aid in the recovery process. **Founded:** 1953. **Publications:** *A Guide to Public Information*; *The NA Way Magazine: The International Journal of Narcotics Anonymous* (Quarterly). **Educational Activities:** World Convention of NA (WCNA) (Biennial). **Geographic Preference:** National.

34671 ▪ National Association of Addiction Treatment Providers (NAATP)
PO Box 271686
  Louisville, CO 80027
Free: 888-574-1008
Co. E-mail: info@naatp.org
URL: http://www.naatp.org
Contact: Marvin Ventrell, Chief Executive Officer
E-mail: mventrell@naatp.org
Facebook: www.facebook.com/nationalassocia tionofaddictiontreatmentproviders
X (Twitter): x.com/NAATPOffice
Instagram: www.instagram.com/naatpofficial
Description: Promotes awareness of chemical dependency as a treatable disease; advocates high standards of health care in substance abuse treatment facilities. Encourages member education. **Founded:** 1970. **Publications:** *Salary Survey* (Biennial). **Awards:** Nelson J. Bradley Life Time Achievement Award (Annual). **Geographic Preference:** National.

34672 ▪ National Association on Drug Abuse Problems (NADAP)
355 Lexington Ave., 2nd Fl.
  New York, NY 10017
Ph: (212)986-1170
Co. E-mail: newsletter@nadap.org
URL: http://www.nadap.org
Contact: John A. Darin, President
Facebook: www.facebook.com/NADAPInc
Linkedin: www.linkedin.com/company/nadap
X (Twitter): x.com/nadap_inc
Instagram: www.instagram.com/nadap_inc
YouTube: www.youtube.com/user/NADAP1971
Description: Serves as an information clearinghouse and referral bureau for corporations and local communities interested in prevention of substance abuse and treatment of substance abusers. **Founded:** 1971. **Publications:** *NADAP News/Report* (Quarterly). **Geographic Preference:** National; Local.

34673 ▪ Substance Abuse Librarians and Information Specialists (SALIS)
PO Box 9513
  Berkeley, CA 94709-0513
Ph: (510)865-6225
Co. E-mail: salis@salis.org
URL: http://salis.org
Contact: Andrea Mitchell, Executive Director
E-mail: amitchell@salis.org
Facebook: www.facebook.com/salis.org
Description: Provides professional development and exchange of information and concerns about access to and dissemination of information on substance abuse. **Founded:** 1978. **Publications:** *SALIS News* (Quarterly); *Substance Abuse Librarians and Informa-tion Specialists Directory* (Triennial). **Educational Activities:** SALIS Annual Conference (Annual). **Geographic Preference:** Multinational.

REFERENCE WORKS

34674 ▪ *"4 Ways You Can Safely Address and Combat Drug Addiction in the Workplace"* in Inc.
URL(s): www.inc.com/serhat-pala/how-your-business-can-join-fight-against-drug-abuse-in-workplace.html
Description: Discusses ways in which small businesses can be proactive in combating substance abuse and drug addiction in the workplace. **Availability:** Online.

34675 ▪ *"Addiction in the Workplace: How Leaders Can Help Create a Path to Recovery"* in Forbes (Oct. 12, 2021)
URL(s): www.forbes.com/sites/ forbesbusinesscouncil/2021/10/12/addiction-in-the-workplace-how-leaders-can-help-create-a-path-to-recovery/?sh=6ec8381f2194
Released: October 12, 2021. **Description:** Addresses the importance of having a path to recovery for employees who are struggling with substance abuse. Offers information on how to employ recovery-friendly small business practices. **Availability:** Online.

34676 ▪ *"Apply These 3 Techniques to Address Addiction in the Workplace"* in Small Business Trends (Dec. 21, 2020)
URL(s): smallbiztrends.com/2018/03/employee-substance-abuse.html
Released: December 21, 2020. **Description:** Discusses the reality of addiction in the small business workplace and provides information on dealing with employee substance abuse. **Availability:** Online.

34677 ▪ *"Cannabis at Work: How Employers Are Reacting to the Legalization of Marijuana"* in Business News Daily (June 10, 2020)
URL(s): www.businessnewsdaily.com/9386-legal-marijuana-employment-practices.html
Released: June 10, 2020. **Description:** Discusses cannabis legalization, workplace drug policies and how employers are responding. **Availability:** Online.

34678 ▪ *"Drugs and Alcohol in the Workplace?"* in Wallace Welch & Willingham Wellness Blog (Jan. 15, 2021)
URL(s): w3ins.com/news/drugs-and-alcohol-in-the-workplace/
Released: January 15, 2021. **Description:** Shares resources on substance abuse in the workplace and how you can legally protect your small business. **Availability:** Online.

34679 ▪ *"Everything Small Business Owners Need to Know About Drug Testing"* in allBusiness
URL(s): www.allbusiness.com/drug-testing-small-businesses-117588-1.html

Description: Discusses the use of drug testing programs for your small business. **Availability:** Online.

34680 ■ *"How to Write a Policy on Substance Abuse in the Workplace" in Workest (Mar 15, 2021)*

URL(s): www.zenefits.com/workest/how-to-write-a -policy-on-substance-abuse-in-the-workplace-free -template/

Released: March 15, 2021. **Description:** Provides information and a template on how to create and enforce strong policies on prohibiting substance abuse in the workplace. **Availability:** Online.

34681 ■ *"Making Sense of Marijuana Use: How Do State Laws Affect Your Business?" in America's SBDC (Aug. 6, 2019)*

URL(s): americassbdc.org/making-sense-of-mari juana-use-how-do-state-laws-affect-your-business/

Released: August 06, 2019. **Description:** Discusses how the legalization of marijuana affects workplace substance abuse and drug testing policies. **Availability:** Online.

34682 ■ *"Why Do Small Businesses Need a Substance Abuse Policy?" in Chron*

URL(s): smallbusiness.chron.com/small-businesses -need-substance-abuse-policy-65444.html

Description: Discusses the importance of having a written substance abuse policy for small businesses. **Availability:** Online.

CONSULTANTS

34683 ■ **Birenbaum & Associates**

906 Olive St., Ste. 1200
 Saint Louis, MO 63101
Ph: (314)241-1445
URL: http://www.birenbaum.org/birenbaum/defaul t.asp
Contact: Dr. Mark Birenbaum, President
X (Twitter): x.com/BirenbaumAssoc

Description: Firm provides solution for not-for-profit associations and coalitions and services includes association management, event management, strategic planning and much more. **Scope:** Firm provides solution for not-for-profit associations and coalitions and services includes association management, event management, strategic planning and much more. **Training:** Alcohol/Drug Abuse Policies for Employers.

34684 ■ **Haynes Associates L.L.C.**

1021 Temple St.
 Charleston, WV 25312
Contact: Richard A. Haynes, Contact

Description: Security management consultant. Offers the following services security surveys and audits, security readiness for labor disputes, investigations, security training and awareness programs, special projects. Industries served: Mining, petroleum, law enforcement, private security companies and government agencies. **Scope:** Security management consultant. Offers the following services security surveys and audits, security readiness for labor disputes, investigations, security training and awareness programs, special projects. Industries served: Mining, petroleum, law enforcement, private security companies and government agencies. **Founded:** 1980. **Publications:** "Let's Talk Security," Kanawha Valley Business Monthly; "The SWAT Cyclopedia" Aug, 1999. **Training:** Personal Protection Workshop: Workplace Violence.

34685 ■ **LifeWorks**

Telus Health
 134 N LaSalle St., Ste. 2200
 Chicago, IL 60602
Ph: (514)665-3050
Free: 877-999-4669
URL: http://www.telushealth.com
Contact: Stephen Liptrap, President
Linkedin: www.linkedin.com/company/lifeworks
X (Twitter): twitter.com/LifeWorks

Description: Services: Employee assistance programs, problem gambling supports, drug testing management and strategic partnerships. **Scope:** Services: Employee assistance programs, problem gambling supports, drug testing management and strategic partnerships. **Founded:** 1982. **Publications:** "Drug Testing in Treatment Settings, Drug Testing in Schools," 2005; "Drug Testing in Correctional Settings," 2005; "Getting Tough on Gateway Drugs: A Guide for the Family"; "A Bridge to Recovery: An Introduction to Twelve-Step Programs"; "The Selfish Brain: Learning from Addiction".

34686 ■ **National Scientific Services**

3411 Philips Dr.
 Baltimore, MD 21208-1827
Contact: Dr. Yale H. Caplan, Owner

Description: Consultant in toxicology, drug and chemical analysis, workplace drug testing and interpretation of toxicology information serves as expert witness in drunk driving and drug testing cases. **Scope:** Consultant in toxicology, drug and chemical analysis, workplace drug testing and interpretation of toxicology information serves as expert witness in drunk driving and drug testing cases. **Publications:** "Garriott's Medicolegal Aspects of Alcohol," Lawyers and Judges Publishing Co.

34687 ■ **TPA technologies**

100 Ledgewood Pl., Ste. 203
 Rockland, MA 02370
Ph: (617)722-6020
Co. E-mail: info@tpatechnologies.com
URL: http://tpatechnologies.com
Contact: Patrick Cox, Chief Executive Officer
X (Twitter): x.com/TPAtechnologies

Description: Firm provides consulting services in information technology and staffing. **Scope:** Firm provides consulting services in information technology and staffing.

LIBRARIES

34688 ■ **Centre for Addiction and Mental Health Library**

100 & 101 Stokes St.
 80 Workman Way
 Toronto, ON, Canada M6J 1H4
Ph: (416)535-8501
Free: 800-463-2338
Co. E-mail: info@camh.ca
URL: http://www.camh.ca
Contact: Deborah Gillis, President
E-mail: deborah.gillis@camh.ca
Facebook: www.facebook.com/CentreforAddictionan dMentalHealth
Linkedin: www.linkedin.com/company/camh
X (Twitter): x.com/CAMHnews
Instagram: www.instagram.com/camhnews
YouTube: www.youtube.com/user/CAMHTV

Scope: Alcoholism; substance use; psychiatric services; mental health. **Services:** Interlibrary loan (in Canada only); AV loan (Ontario only); copying; SDI; library open to the public by appointment only. **Founded:** 1998. **Holdings:** Books; journals; reprints; research reports; government documents and videos.

34689 ■ **Hazelden Betty Ford Foundation - Addiction Research Library**

15251 Pleasant Valley Rd.
 Center City, MN 55012
Free: 866-831-5700
Co. E-mail: info@hazeldenbettyford.org
URL: http://www.hazeldenbettyford.org
Contact: Dr. Joseph Lee, President
Facebook: www.facebook.com/hazeldenbettyfor dfoundation
X (Twitter): x.com/hazldnbettyford
Instagram: www.Instagram.com/hazeldenbettyford
YouTube: www.youtube.com/user/hazeldenbettyford
Pinterest: www.pinterest.com/hazldnbettyford

Description: Provides treatment, recovery, education, and professional services for chemical dependency and other addictive behaviors. **Scope:** History;

contemporary addiction. **Founded:** 1949. **Holdings:** Books. **Publications:** *Hazelden Voice* (Semiannual). **Geographic Preference:** National.

34690 ■ **Maine Department of Health and Human Services (OSAMHS) - Office of Substance Abuse and Mental Health Services - Information and Resource Center**

109 Capitol St. 11 State House Sta.
 Augusta, ME 04333
URL: http://www.maine.gov/dhhs/obh

Scope: Alcohol and drugs - use, abuse, dependency, education, prevention, and training; youth suicide prevention. **Services:** Interlibrary Loan ;copying; Center open to school systems, community organizations, agencies, and professionals. **Holdings:** DVDs.

34691 ■ **National Clearinghouse for Alcohol and Drug Information Library**

PO Box 2345
 Rockville, MD 20847-2345
Ph: (301)468-2600
Free: 800-729-6686

Scope: Alcohol, tobacco, and other drug abuse. **Services:** Interlibrary loan; copying; SDI; library open to the public for reference use only. **Founded:** 1987. **Holdings:** 3721 books; 80,000 cataloged items; 80,000 accessioned items; digitized documents; reports; manuscripts.

34692 ■ **North Conway Institute - Resource Center - Alcohol and Drugs**

107 Denson Dr.
 Austin, TX 78752
URL: http://northconwayinstitute.weebly.com/re-sources.html

Scope: Alcohol; drugs. **Services:** Center open to the public. **Founded:** 1951. **Holdings:** Figures not available. **Subscriptions:** 50 journals and other serials.

34693 ■ **Public Health Institute - Alcohol Research Group (ARG) - Library [National Alcohol Research Center]**

6001 Shellmound St., Ste. 450
 Emeryville, CA 94608
Ph: (510)898-5800
Co. E-mail: info@arg.org
URL: http://arg.org
Contact: Dominique Lampert, Executive Director
Facebook: www.facebook.com/alcoholresearchgroup
Linkedin: www.linkedin.com/company/alcohol -research-group
X (Twitter): x.com/argphi
YouTube: www.youtube.com/channel/UCP7zb 5yyZPL2rztObfDDuxg

Description: National Institute on Alcohol Abuse and Alcoholism-funded research activity, located at the Public Health Institute. Offers consulting and technical assistance; seminars and courses. **Scope:** Epidemiology of alcohol problems and substance abuse, including national studies of the general population, ethnic groups, individuals in treatment, welfare recipients, emergency room patients, and women. Performs research on health services, drinking practices and problems, policy analyses, attitudes concerning drinking, community responses and interventions addressing heavy drinking and alcohol use disorders, dimensions of alcohol dependence and alcohol's role in elevating risks of social and health harms including mortality, morbidity and HIV infection. **Services:** Open to the public by appointment. **Founded:** 1959. **Holdings:** 6,300 books; 60,000 other materials; conference papers; unpublished working papers; documents; 900 books; articles; manuscripts. **Subscriptions:** 200 journals and other serials.

34694 ■ **Rebok Memorial Library**

12501 Old Columbia Pke.
 Silver Spring, MD 20904-6600
URL: http://guides.loc.gov/religion-collections-librar-ies-archives/md-general-conference-seventh-day-a dventists-astr

Scope: Religion; theology. **Services:** Copying; library open to the public with restrictions. **Founded:** 1983. **Subscriptions:** 50 journals and other serials 9,700 books; monographs; CD-ROMS.

34695 ■ South Carolina Department of Mental Health - Earle E. Morris, Jr. Alcohol & Drug Addiction Treatment Center Library
PO Box 485
Columbia, SC 29202
URL: http://scdmh.net
Scope: Alcoholism; drug addiction; group and family therapy. **Services:** Interlibrary loan; library not open to the public. **Founded:** 1975. **Holdings:** 2000 books.

34696 ■ State University of New York at Buffalo - Clinical Research Institute on Addictions (CRIA) - Library
1021 Main St.
Buffalo, NY 14203-1016
Ph: (716)887-2566
Fax: (716)887-2252
URL: http://www.buffalo.edu/cria.html
Contact: Helen Bowman, Librarian
E-mail: jbowman@ria.buffalo.edu
Facebook: www.facebook.com/UBResearchInstitu
teonAddictions
Linkedin: www.linkedin.com/showcase/ub-research
-institute-on-addictions
X (Twitter): x.com/UB_RIA
Description: Integral unit of State University of New York at Buffalo. RIA Clinical Research Center: outpatient facilities. **Scope:** Etiology, course, treatment, and prevention of alcoholism and substance abuse. Studies the following six aspects of substance abuse: normative patterns; biochemical, physiological, psychological, and social antecedents and consequences; biopsychosocial aspects of consumption in early and middle adulthood; family aspects; alcohol-drug interactions; and treatment and prevention strategies. **Services:** Interlibrary loan; copying; reference; library open to the public for reference use only. **Founded:** 1970. **Holdings:** Figures not available. **Publications:** *RIA Annual Report*; *RIA Report* (Semiannual). **Educational Activities:** CRIA Seminars (Irregular), About alcohol, drugs and related issues. **Awards:** RIA Postdoctoral Training Program (Annual).

34697 ■ U.S. Drug Enforcement Administration Library
8701 Morrissette Dr.
Springfield, VA 22152
Ph: (202)307-1000
Free: 800-882-9539
URL: http://www.dea.gov/galleries
Facebook: www.facebook.com/DEAHQ
X (Twitter): twitter.com/DEAHQ
Scope: Narcotic addiction; dangerous drug abuse; law and legislation; law enforcement; drug abuse education; International control. **Services:** Interlibrary loan; Library not open to the public. **Founded:** 1959. **Holdings:** 10,000 books; 40 VF drawers.

RESEARCH CENTERS

34698 ■ Columbia University - Center for Social Policy and Practice in the Workplace [The Workplace Center]
1255 Amsterdam Ave., 11th Fl.
New York, NY 10027
Ph: (212)851-2258
Fax: (212)851-2262
Co. E-mail: workplacecenter@columbia.edu
URL: http://workplacecenter.columbia.edu/home
Contact: Gwyn Kirkbride, Director, Programs
Assistant Director
E-mail: gmk2118@columbia.edu
Description: Integral unit of Columbia University School of Social Work. Offers counseling at the workplace on family and work related problems; employment of people with disabilities; regional Information clearinghouses; written training packages on new social service ideas; continuing education

courses and workshops for social workers. **Scope:** Policy and program issues in the area of work and social welfare policy, including job maintenance of the disabled in the workplace, analysis of Employee Assistance Programs, studies of gender integration, substance abuse in the workplace and programs. Provides a laboratory to test and evaluate service delivery patterns for occupational social workers and offers interdisciplinary training. **Founded:** 1969.

34699 ■ Indiana University Bloomington - Center for Studies of Law in Action
107 S Indiana Ave.
Bloomington, IN 47405-7000
URL: http://criminaljustice.indiana.edu/research/law
-in-action.html
Description: Integral unit of Indiana University Bloomington. **Scope:** Alcohol and transportation, the effects of drugs, pharmacology, and toxicology. **Founded:** 1957.

34700 ■ North Charles Mental Health Research and Training Foundation Inc.
54 Washburn Ave.
Cambridge, MA 02140
Ph: (617)864-0941
Co. E-mail: info@northcharles.org
URL: http://www.northcharles.org
Description: Separately incorporated organization affiliated with Department of Psychiatry, Medical School, Harvard University located at Cambridge Hospital. **Scope:** Mental health and addictions/ substance abuse, including behavioral studies and evaluations of substance abuse trends and treatments. **Founded:** 1971.

34701 ■ Oregon Research Institute (ORI) - Library
3800 Sports Way
Springfield, OR 97477
Ph: (541)484-2123
Co. E-mail: orifacebook@ori.org
URL: http://www.ori.org
Contact: Paul Rohde, President
Facebook: www.facebook.com/OregonResearchInsti
tute
Linkedin: www.linkedin.com/company/oregon-re-
search-institute
YouTube: www.youtube.com/user/
OregonResearchInst
Description: Research center researches on human behavioral mental heath. **Scope:** Researches on behavioral sciences, including studies in tobacco prevention and cessation, compliance with diabetic regimens, children's social skills, personality structure, drug abuse prevention, depression and family interaction. **Founded:** 1960. **Holdings:** Figures not available. **Publications:** *ORI Annual Report* (Annual). **Educational Activities:** ORI Colloquia, Provides an opportunity to present findings to the research community.

34702 ■ Rutgers University - Center of Alcohol & Substance Use Studies (CAS) - Library
607 Allison Rd.
Piscataway, NJ 08854
Ph: (848)445-2190
Fax: (732)445-3500
Co. E-mail: cas_ed@rutgers.edu
URL: http://alcoholstudies.rutgers.edu
Contact: Dr. Denise Hien, Director
E-mail: denise.hien@smithers.rutgers.edu
Facebook: www.facebook.com/RutgersUniversi
tyCAS
X (Twitter): twitter.com/rutgers_cas
Description: Multidisciplinary education and research unit at Rutgers University. Offers consulting and outpatient clinical services. **Scope:** Means to prevent alcohol and other drug misuse, and the incidence and prevalence of normal and problem alcohol consumption in the U.S. and the world. **Services:**

Interlibrary loan; copying; center and library open to the public. **Founded:** 1941. **Holdings:** 80,000 citations. **Publications:** *Monographs of the Rutgers Center of Alcohol Studies*; *National Institute of Alcohol Abuse and Alcoholism-Rutgers University Center of Alcohol Studies (NIAAA-RUCAS) Treatment Series*; *Journal of Studies on Alcohol and Drugs (JSAD)* (Bimonthly). **Educational Activities:** Summer School of Addiction Studies (Annual), Offers students a weeklong professional development experience.

34703 ■ Stanford University - Stanford Prevention Research Center (SPRC)
School of Medicine
3180 Porter Dr., MC 5702
Palo Alto, CA 94304
URL: http://prevention.stanford.edu
Contact: Diana Fox, Division Manager
Description: Research, education, and service organization administered by the School of Medicine, Stanford University. Health improvement classes offered in exercise, smoking cessation, stress management, weight control, and nutrition for University faculty, staff, and families (daily). Offers technical assistance, education, and training for the public, educators, health professionals, and communities (daily); worksite-based strategic planning and research in managed care (daily). **Scope:** Prevention and control of chronic disease. Stresses a public health or community approach to disease prevention and health promotion and seeks methods to improve the overall level of community health by favorably modifying the environmental and personal factors known to influence chronic disease incidence, including blood pressure, blood cholesterol, cigarette use, nutrition, obesity, physical activity, and stress. **Founded:** 1971. **Educational Activities:** SPRC Research Seminar (Weekly (Thurs.)).

34704 ■ State University of New York at Buffalo - Clinical Research Institute on Addictions (CRIA) - Library
1021 Main St.
Buffalo, NY 14203-1016
Ph: (716)887-2566
Fax: (716)887-2252
URL: http://www.buffalo.edu/cria.html
Contact: Helen Bowman, Librarian
E-mail: jbowman@ria.buffalo.edu
Facebook: www.facebook.com/UBResearchInstitu
teonAddictions
Linkedin: www.linkedin.com/showcase/ub-research
-institute-on-addictions
X (Twitter): x.com/UB_RIA
Description: Integral unit of State University of New York at Buffalo. RIA Clinical Research Center: outpatient facilities. **Scope:** Etiology, course, treatment, and prevention of alcoholism and substance abuse. Studies the following six aspects of substance abuse: normative patterns; biochemical, physiological, psychological, and social antecedents and consequences; biopsychosocial aspects of consumption in early and middle adulthood; family aspects; alcohol-drug interactions; and treatment and prevention strategies. **Services:** Interlibrary loan; copying; reference; library open to the public for reference use only. **Founded:** 1970. **Holdings:** Figures not available. **Publications:** *RIA Annual Report*; *RIA Report* (Semiannual). **Educational Activities:** CRIA Seminars (Irregular), About alcohol, drugs and related issues. **Awards:** RIA Postdoctoral Training Program (Annual).

34705 ■ University of Kentucky College of Medicine - Center on Drug and Alcohol Research (CDAR)
643 Maxwelton Ct.
Lexington, KY 40506-0350
Ph: (859)257-1720
Fax: (859)323-1193

URL: http://cdar.uky.edu

Contact: Dr. Sharon Walsh, Director

Description: Integral unit of College of Medicine, University of Kentucky. Offers consulting and technical assistance for the community. **Scope:** Biological, social, and psychological aspects of alcohol and drug abuse; and HIV/AIDS. Conducts household and other surveys. **Founded:** 1990. **Educational Activities:**

CDAR Epidemiology Workgroup; Prevention Research Society Meeting; Rural/Urban Drug Use Continuum.

34706 ■ University of Washington Department of Psychology - Addictive Behaviors Research Center (ABRC)
Seattle, WA

URL: http://depts.washington.edu/abrc

Contact: Dr. Mary Larimer, Director (Acting)

E-mail: larimer@u.washington.edu

Description: Integral unit of Department of Psychology, University of Washington. **Scope:** Addictive behaviors, including topics such as alcohol abuse, smoking, relapse prevention, harm reduction, and skills training. **Founded:** 1980.

REFERENCE WORKS

34707 ■ *"5 Simple Ways to Pinpoint Your Brand's Target Audience" in Business.com (June 4, 2020)*
Ed: Chris Christoff. **Released:** June 04, 2020. **Description:** Provides information for business startups related to the necessity to understand your target market at a fundamental level. **Availability:** Online.

34708 ■ *"6 Ways to Market Your Small Business for Less Than $100" in Entrepreneur (May 30, 2019)*
Ed: Victoria Treyger. **Released:** May 30, 2019. **Description:** Provides six scenarios that outline how to adopt a cheap, but robust marketing plan for your business's growth. **Availability:** Online.

34709 ■ *"10 Ways to Tailor Your Marketing Strategy to Your Business" in Small Business Trends (August 15, 2020)*
Ed: Annie Pilon. **Released:** August 15, 2020. **Description:** Provides tips on how to carefully consider what options are best suited for your products, services, and customers so you can create a market-ing strategy that is completely tailored to your business. **Availability:** Online.

34710 ■ *"Conducting Market Research" in Entrepreneur Press*
Description: Details what is involved in the crucial marketing research step of the product development cycle. **Availability:** Online.

34711 ■ *"Define a Target Market for Your Small Business" in Nolo*
Ed: Peri Pakroo. **Description:** Discusses the importance of defining target customers and a market niche to help your business succeed. **Availability:** Online.

34712 ■ *"Digital Marketing in 2020 - 7 Reasons Why Small Businesses Need It" in Marketo Blog.*
Ed: Anita Sambol. **Description:** A detailed guide on why small business owners should invest in digital marketing. **Availability:** Online.

34713 ■ *"Everyone Is Not a Demographic: A Guide to Target Markets for Small Businesses" in WordStream (February 26, 2020)*
Ed: Dan Shewan. **Released:** February 26, 2020. **Description:** Tips and tricks to help small businesses get the most out of their online advertising. **Availability:** Online.

34714 ■ *"Small Business Marketing Guide: Everything New and Existing Businesses Should Know About Acquiring New Customers" in Business News Daily (August 17, 2020)*
Ed: Jennifer Post. **Released:** August 17, 2020. **Description:** Details core concepts of small business target marketing. **Availability:** Online.

34715 ■ *"Target Marketing and Market Segmentation" in The Balance Small Business (October 27, 2020)*
Ed: Susan Ward. **Released:** October 27, 2020. **Description:** Details how target marketing--breaking a market into segments and then concentrating your marketing efforts on a key segment--can be the key to attracting new business, increasing sales, and making your business a success. **Availability:** Online.

34716 ■ *"Target Marketing: What Is It?" in Bplans*
Ed: Michael Kerr. **Description:** Details what target marketing is and how small businesses can use it to their benefit. **Availability:** Online.

Taxation

START-UP INFORMATION

34717 ■ *"His Record, Not Polls, Is What Matters"* in *Bangor Daily News (October 13, 2010)*
Pub: Bangor Daily News
Contact: David M. Austin, Contact
Ed: Nick Sambides, Jr. **Description:** The Small Business Jobs Tax Relief Act could spur investment in small businesses by increasing capital gains tax cuts for investors in small business in 2010 and increase to $20,000 from $5,000 the deduction for start-up businesses. **Availability:** Print; Online.

34718 ■ *The Small Business Start-Up Kit*
Pub: Nolo
Contact: Chris Braun, President
Ed: Peri Pakroo. **Released:** 12th edition. **Price:** $20.99, E-book. **Description:** Entrepreneurial advice for launching a new business. Topics include compliance with state regulations, sole proprietorships, partnerships, corporations, limited liability companies, as well as accounting and tax information. **Availability:** E-book; Print; Electronic publishing; PDF.

34719 ■ *"Tax Credits As Good As Raised Cash for Cyber Firms"* in *Baltimore Business Journal (Vol. 31, March 28, 2014, No. 48, pp. 16)*
Pub: American City Business Journals, Inc.
Contact: Mike Olivieri, Executive Vice President
Price: $4, print. **Description:** The State of Maryland is offering tax incentives to its cyber security startups in order to capitalize on growing talent and to help the budding cyber security sector grow in the state. Three such tax incentives are outlined, including the cyber security investment incentive tax credit, employer security clearance costs tax credit, and research and development tax credit. Mark Vulcan, program manager of tax incentives for DBED describes this as Maryland'Es endeavor to attract a high growth and high wage industry. **Availability:** Print; Online.

ASSOCIATIONS AND OTHER ORGANIZATIONS

34720 ■ **American Taxation Association (ATA)**
c/o LeAnn Luna, Representative
University of Tennessee-Knoxville
711 Stokely Management Ctr.
Knoxville, TN 37996
URL: http://aaahq.org/ATA
Contact: Jenny Brown, President
Facebook: www.facebook.com/aaahqata
Description: Membership comprises primarily university professors teaching federal income tax, federal estate, and/or gift tax courses; other members are practitioners, including certified public accountants. Seeks to further taxation education. Researches the impact of the tax process, particularly tax code sections, on the social and economic structure of the US. Maintains speakers' bureau. **Founded:** 1974.

Awards: Ray M. Sommerfeld Outstanding Tax Educator Award (Annual); ATA Tax Manuscript Award (Annual); ATA Deloitte Teaching Innovation Award (Annual). **Geographic Preference:** National.

34721 ■ **Tax Executives Institute (TEI)**
1200 G St. NW, Ste. 300
Washington, DC 20005
Ph: (202)638-5601
Fax: (202)638-5607
Co. E-mail: asktei@tei.org
URL: http://www.tei.org
Contact: Mitchell Trager, President
Facebook: www.facebook.com/TaxExecutivesInstitute
Linkedin: www.linkedin.com/company/tax-executives-institute
X (Twitter): x.com/tei_updates
YouTube: www.youtube.com/channel/UCJJVYpl1TASAnZbQN5WUfrg
Description: Professional society of executives administering and directing tax affairs for corporations and businesses. Maintains TEI Education Fund. **Founded:** 1944. **Publications:** *The Tax Executive* (Bimonthly). **Awards:** TEI Distinguished Service Award (Annual). **Geographic Preference:** Multinational.

REFERENCE WORKS

34722 ■ *"5 Steps to Filing Partnership Taxes"* in *Legal Zoom (February 28, 2023)*
URL(s): www.legalzoom.com/articles/5-steps-to-filing-partnership-taxes
Ed: Jane Haskins, Esq. **Released:** February 28, 2023. **Description:** Follow these steps for filing partnership taxes and avoid making some costly mistakes in the process. **Availability:** Online.

34723 ■ *"8 Tax Season Preparation Steps"* in *Business News Daily (March 6, 2023)*
URL(s): www.businessnewsdaily.com/6689-tax-season-prep-steps.html
Ed: Sally Herigstad. **Released:** March 06, 2023. **Description:** Help your small business get through tax season with these tips and details. **Availability:** Online.

34724 ■ *"$100 Million Plan for Jefferson Arms"* in *Saint Louis Business Journal (Vol. 32, October 14, 2011, No. 7, pp. 1)*
Pub: Saint Louis Business Journal
Contact: Robert Bobroff, President
E-mail: rbobroff@bizjournals.com
Ed: Evan Binns. **Description:** Teach for America is planning a $100 million renovation project of the former Jefferson Arms hotel in St. Louis, Missouri. The organization has signed a letter of intent to occupy the space. Financing of the project will be mainly through tax credits. **Availability:** Print; Online.

34725 ■ *"100 Percent Equipment Tax Deduction Deadline Nears"* in *Farm Industry News (December 1, 2010)*
Pub: Informa Business Media, Inc.
Contact: Charlie McCurdy, President
Ed: Karen McMahon. **Description:** Farmers and small business owners are warned that the first deadline for taking advantage of the tax code provision that allows them to deduct the full purchase price of qualified capital expenditures up to $500,000 during the tax year is nearing. **Availability:** Print; Online.

34726 ■ *"2011 Tax Information of Interest"* in *Business Owner (Vol. 35, November-December 2011, No. 6, pp. 10)*
Description: Compilation of 2011 tax information to help small business take advantage of all tax incentives. **Availability:** Print; Online.

34727 ■ *"Acquisition to Give Mylan Tax Benefits, Boost Sales"* in *Pittsburgh Business Times (Vol. 33, July 18, 2014, No. 53, pp. 3)*
Pub: American City Business Journals, Inc.
Contact: Mike Olivieri, Executive Vice President
Released: Weekly. **Price:** $4, introductory 4-week offer(Digital & Print). **Description:** Mylan Inc.'s acquisition of Abbot's foreign specialty and branded generic drug business is a win situation for the company. The acquisition will help Mylan expand and diversify in the largest markets outside the U.S. as well as prove beneficial in growth through enhanced financial flexibility and a more competitive global tax structure. **Availability:** Print; Online.

34728 ■ *"Advantage Capital Partners Awarded $60 Million Allocation in New Markets Tax Credit Program"* in *Economics & Business Week (June 28, 2014, pp. 7)*
Pub: NewsRX LLC.
Contact: Kalani Rosell, Contact
Description: Leading venture capital and small business finance firm, Advantage Capital Partners, was awarded a $60 million allocation in competitive federal New Markets Tax Credit (NMTC) program. This allocation brings the firm's total awards since the program's start in 2002 to $659 million, and maintains the investment firm's leadership role as a top program participant across the nation.

34729 ■ *"All-Star Advice 2010"* in *Black Enterprise (Vol. 41, October 2010, No. 3, pp. 97)*
Pub: Earl G. Graves Ltd.
Contact: Earl Graves, Jr., President
Ed: Renita Burns, Sheiresa Ngo, Marcia Wade Talbert. **Description:** Financial experts share tips on real estate, investing, taxes, insurance and debt management. **Availability:** Online.

34730 ■ *"Allowing Ethanol Tax Incentive to Expire Would Risk Jobs, RFA's Dinneen Says"* in *Farm Industry News (November 3, 2010)*
Pub: Informa Business Media, Inc.
Contact: Charlie McCurdy, President

Ed: Lynn Grooms. **Price:** $4, Print and Online; Special Offers only for 4 weeks. **Description:** Jobs would be at risk if the ethanol tax incentive expires. **Availability:** Print; Online.

34731 ■ *"The Annual Entitlement Lecture Medicare Elephantiasis" in Barron's (March 31, 2008)*
Pub: Dow Jones & Company Inc.
Contact: Almar Latour, Chief Executive Officer
Ed: Thomas G. Donlan. **Description:** Expenditures on Medicare hospital insurance and the revenues available to pay for it have led to a gap of capital valued at $38.6 trillion. Slashing the benefits or raising taxes will not solve the gap which exists unless the government saves the money and invests it in private markets. **Availability:** Online.

34732 ■ *"As Capital Gains Tax Hike Looms, Baltimore's Merger Activity Percolates" in Baltimore Business Journal (Vol. 28, August 27, 2010, No. 16, pp. 1)*
Pub: Baltimore Business Journal
Contact: Rhonda Pringle, President
E-mail: rpringle@bizjournals.com
Ed: Scott Dance. **Description:** Concerns for higher capital gains taxes in 2011 have been provoking buyers and sellers to engage in mergers and acquisitions activity, which is expected to gain momentum before the end of 2010. Companies that had saved cash during the recession have been taking advantage of the buyer's market. Other trends in local and national mergers and acquisitions activity are presented. **Availability:** Print.

34733 ■ *"At-Home Tax Prep Trend Likely to Grow After Pandemic's Boost" in Bloomberg Tax (July 10, 2020)*
Released: July 10, 2020. **Description:** With many businesses closed or people wanting to avoid closed-spaces in an accountant's office during the COVID-19 pandemic, the do-it-yourself tax industry grew. Many people also took advantage of the extra three months given by the government to file taxes and learned how to do so.

34734 ■ *"Austin Ponders Annexing Formula One Racetrack" in Austin Business Journal (Vol. 31, July 8, 2011, No. 18, pp. 1)*
Pub: Austin Business Journal
Contact: Rachel McGrath, Director
E-mail: rmcgrath@bizjournals.com
Ed: Vicky Garza. **Description:** City planners in Austin, Texas are studying the feasibility of annexing the land under and around the Circuit of the Americas Formula One Racetrack being constructed east of the city. The annexation could generate at least $13 million in financial gain over 25 years from property taxes alone. **Availability:** Print; Online.

34735 ■ *"BABs in Bond Land" in Barron's (Vol. 89, July 6, 2009, No. 27, pp. 14)*
Pub: Dow Jones & Company Inc.
Contact: Almar Latour, Chief Executive Officer
Ed: Jim McTague. **Description:** American Recovery and Reinvestment Act has created taxable Build America Bonds (BAB) to finance new construction projects. The issuance of the two varieties of taxable BABs is expected to benefit the municipal bond market. **Availability:** Online.

34736 ■ *"Ballpark Sales Tax Extension Could Fund New Arena" in Milwaukee Business Journal (Vol. 27, January 29, 2010, No. 18, pp. A1)*
Pub: The Business Journal
Contact: Heather Ladage, President
E-mail: hladage@bizjournals.com
Ed: Mark Kass. **Description:** Milwaukee, Wisconsin-area business executives believe the extension of the Miller Park 0.1 percent sales tax could help fund a new basketball arena to replace the 21-year-old Bradley Center in downtown Milwaukee. However, any sales tax expansion that includes the new basketball arena would need approval by Wisconsin's legislature. **Availability:** Print; Online.

34737 ■ *"Baltimore Eyeing Tax Breaks for New Arena" in Boston Business Journal (Vol. 29, June 3, 2011, No. 4, pp. 1)*
Pub: Boston Business Journal
Contact: Carolyn M. Jones, President
E-mail: cmjones@bizjournals.com
Ed: Daniel J. Sernovitz. **Description:** Baltimore City is opting to give millions of dollars in tax breaks and construction loans to a group of private investors led by William Hackerman who is proposing to build a new arena and hotel at the Baltimore Convention Center. The project will cost $500 million with the state putting up another $400 million for the center's expansion.

34738 ■ *"Baltimore's Businesses: Equipment Tax Breaks Help, But Money Still Tight: Weighing the Write-Off" in Baltimore Business Journal (Vol. 28, September 10, 2010, No. 18, pp. 1)*
Pub: Baltimore Business Journal
Contact: Rhonda Pringle, President
E-mail: rpringle@bizjournals.com
Ed: Daniel J. Sernovitz. **Description:** President Barrack Obama has proposed to let business write off their investments in plant and equipment upgrades under a plan aimed at getting the economy going. The plan would allow a company to write off 100 percent of the depreciation for their new investments at one time instead of over several years. **Availability:** Print.

34739 ■ *"Bank On It: New Year, New Estate Plan" in Hawaii Business (Vol. 53, February 2008, No. 8, pp. 54)*
Pub: PacificBasin Communications
Contact: Chuck Tindle, Director
E-mail: chuckt@pacificbasin.net
Ed: Antony M. Orme. **Description:** Discusses the start of the new year which can be a time to revise wills and estate plans as failure to do so may create problems of unequal inheritance and increase in estate tax exemption, which could disinherit beneficiaries. Other circumstances that can prompt changes in wills and estate plans are presented. **Availability:** Print; Online.

34740 ■ *"BETC Backers Plot Future" in Business Journal Portland (Vol. 27, December 10, 2010, No. 41, pp. 1)*
Pub: Portland Business Journal
Contact: Andy Giegerich, Managing Editor
E-mail: agiegerich@bizjournals.com
Ed: Erik Siemers. **Description:** A coalition of clean energy groups and industrial manufacturers have spearheaded a campaign aimed at persuading Oregon legislators that the state's Business Energy Tax Credit (BETC) is vital in job creation. Oregon's BETC grants tax credits for 50 percent of an eligible renewable or clean energy project's cost. However, some legislators propose BETC's abolition. **Availability:** Print; Online.

34741 ■ *"A Better Way to Tax U.S. Businesses" in (Vol. 90, July-August 2012, No. 7-8, pp. 134)*
Pub: Harvard Business Review Press
Contact: Moderna V. Pfizer, Contact
Ed: Mihir A. Desai. **Price:** $8.95, PDF and hardcover black and white. **Description:** Correcting the US corporate tax code will require ending the disconnect between earnings stated to investors and taxable income, implementing rate reductions, eliminating the taxing of overseas income, and securing an agreement by business leaders to acknowledge taxes as a responsibility. **Availability:** Print; PDF; Online.

34742 ■ *"Beyond Repair" in Business First Buffalo (Vol. 28, March 23, 2012, No. 27, pp. 1)*
Pub: American City Business Journals, Inc.
Contact: Mike Olivieri, Executive Vice President
Released: Weekly. **Price:** $140, one year subscription (Print & Digital); $115, one year subscription (Digital Only). **Description:** Episcopal Church Home and Affiliates once ran a thriving senior care community on a Rhode Island Street property located near the Peace Bridge entrance in Buffalo, New York. However, a proposed bridge expansion that would run across the campus has led to the phased shutdown that began seven years ago. Insights on the $14 million liens on the property are also given. **Availability:** Print; Online.

34743 ■ *"Big Tax Breaks for Small Businesses" in Legal Zoom (March 23, 2023)*
URL(s): www.legalzoom.com/articles/big-tax-breaks-for-small-businesses
Ed: Sandra Beckwith. **Released:** March 23, 2023. **Description:** Discusses the changes made to the business tax codes, so you can be informed of the opportunities given to benefit your small business. **Availability:** Online.

34744 ■ *"Big Trouble at Sony Ericsson" in Barron's (Vol. 88, March 24, 2008, No. 12, pp. M9)*
Pub: Dow Jones & Company Inc.
Contact: Almar Latour, Chief Executive Officer
Ed: Angelo Franchini. **Description:** Sony Ericsson is facing trouble as it warned that its sales and net income before taxes will fall by nearly half for the first quarter of 2008. The joint venture of Sony and Ericsson has a global mobile phone market share of nine percent as of 2007, fourth largest in the world. **Availability:** Online.

34745 ■ *"Bills Raise Blues Debate: An Unfair Edge or Level Playing Field?" in Crain's Detroit Business (Vol. 24, January 21, 2008, No. 3)*
Pub: Crain Communications Inc.
Contact: Barry Asin, President
Ed: Sherri Begin. **Description:** Changes in Michigan state law would change the way health insurance can be sold to individuals. Michigan Blue Cross Blue Shield is working to keep its tax-exempt status while staying competitive against for-profit insurers and nonprofit HMOs. **Availability:** Print; Online.

34746 ■ *"Biodiesel Poised to Regain Growth" in Farm Industry News (January 21, 2011)*
Pub: Informa Business Media, Inc.
Contact: Charlie McCurdy, President
Ed: Lynn Grooms. **Description:** According to Gary Haer, vice president of sales and marketing for Renewable Energy Group, the biodiesel industry is positioned to regain growth in 2011 with the reinstatement of the biodiesel blenders a tax credit of $1 per gallon. **Availability:** Print; Online.

34747 ■ *"Birmingham's Turf War" in Birmingham Business Journal (Vol. 31, January 24, 2014, No. 4, pp. 4)*
Pub: American City Business Journals, Inc.
Contact: Mike Olivieri, Executive Vice President
Description: Metropolitan Birmingham, Alabama area incentive battles have been a mainstay for years and smaller cities were forced to compete against cities with larger cash reserves. The fight often means paying up to protect their turf and tax revenue. The rising trend among local municipalities to use incentives to lure companies is discussed. **Availability:** Print; Online.

34748 ■ *"The Bogleheads' Guide to Investing"*
Pub: John Wiley & Sons, Inc.
Contact: Christina Van Tassell, Executive Vice President Chief Financial Officer
Released: Second edition. **Price:** $26.95, hardcover; $17.99, E-Book. **Description:** Advice that provides the first step to successful financial investments includes new information of backdoor Roth IRAs and ETFs as mainstream buy and hold investments, estate taxes and gifting, along with information on the changes in laws regarding Traditional and Roth IRAs and 401k and 403b retirement plans. The author teaches how to craft proven individual investment strategies. **Availability:** E-book; Print.

34749 ■ "Business Builders: Tradeshow Attendance Incentives Add Up" in Pet Product News (Vol. 64, December 2010, No. 12, pp. 14)

Ed: Mark E. Battersby. **Description:** Pointers on how pet specialty retailers can claim business travel tax and income tax deductions for expenses paid or incurred in participation at tradeshows, conventions, and meetings are presented. Incentives in form of these deductions could allow pet specialty retailers to gain business benefits, aside from the education and enjoyment involved with the travel. **Availability:** Online.

34750 ■ "Business Execs Await Walker's Tax Cut Plan" in Business Journal-Milwaukee (Vol. 28, December 17, 2010, No. 11, pp. A1)

Pub: The Business Journal

Contact: Heather Ladage, President

E-mail: hladage@bizjournals.com

Ed: Rich Kirchen. **Description:** Wisconsin governor-elect Scott Walker has to tackle the state's projected $3.3 billion budget deficit, which became the subject of speculation among business groups and state politic watchers. Walker has pledged to reduce the state taxes without driving costs down to the local government and school district level. **Availability:** Print; Online.

34751 ■ "Business Sidestepped Trouble" in Denver Business Journal (Vol. 65, May 9, 2014, No. 52, pp. A8)

Pub: American City Business Journals, Inc.

Contact: Mike Olivieri, Executive Vice President

Released: May 09, 2014. **Description:** A number of business-friendly laws were adopted during the 2014 legislative session Colorado. the legislators passed 11 tax breaks, including the personal property tax break proposal. **Availability:** Print; Online.

34752 ■ "Business Stands Firm for Reform: Battle Over 2011 Budget Expected" in Crain's Detroit Business (Vol. 26, January 4, 2010, No. 1, pp. 3)

Pub: Crain Communications Inc.

Contact: Barry Asin, President

Ed: Amy Lane. **Description:** As Michigan faces a new year of budgetary problems, many business groups are preparing to hold firm against tax increases and instead push for enacting spending reforms. **Availability:** Print; Online.

34753 ■ "Business Tax Complaints Prompt Action" in Sacramento Business Journal (Vol. 28, July 29, 2011, No. 22, pp. 1)

Pub: Sacramento Business Journal

Contact: Stephanie Fretwell, Director

E-mail: sfretwell@bizjournals.com

Ed: Michael Shaw. **Description:** California's Board of Equalization has amended a program to collect taxes from businesses for out-of-state purchases due to a flood of complaints from owners who find the paperwork costly and time consuming. The program was created in 2009 and fell short of expectations as it only brought in $56 million in the first two years against the projected $264 million. **Availability:** Online.

34754 ■ "Calendar" in Crain's Detroit Business (Vol. 24, March 10, 2008, No. 10, pp. 21)

Pub: Crain Communications Inc.

Contact: Barry Asin, President

Description: Listing of events in the Detroit area include conferences addressing entrepreneurialism, economic development, and women business ownership. **Availability:** Print; Online.

34755 ■ "Call for Superblock Jobs Tie-In Lacks Baltimore Backing" in Baltimore Business Journal (Vol. 30, June 1, 2012, No. 4, pp. 1)

Pub: American City Business Journals, Inc.

Contact: Mike Olivieri, Executive Vice President

Ed: James Briggs. **Description:** Officials of Baltimore, Maryland are seen to turn down the proposal to mandate local hiring rules for Lexington Square Partners. The plan is in line with the company's push for tax breaks on its superblock project. **Availability:** Print; Online.

34756 ■ Canadian Small Business Kit for Dummies

Ed: Margaret Kerr, JoAnn Kurtz, Andrew Dagys. **Released:** 4th edition. **Price:** $26.60, paperback; $39.99, paperback. **Description:** Resources include information on changes to laws and taxes for small businesses in Canada. **Availability:** Print; Online.

34757 ■ "Carbon Capture and Storage: Grave Concerns" in Canadian Business (Vol. 81, July 21 2008, No. 11, pp. 25)

Ed: Andrew Nikiforuk. **Released:** January 01, 2017. **Description:** Air pollution control regulations to reduce greenhouse gasses have been implemented by the Canadian government. The federal government is planning to construct a carbon funeral industry that will store the global warming gases, however the expenditure for the project will be shifted to the taxpayers. Details of the Bruce Peachy's initiative on how to reduce GHGs are presented. **Availability:** Print; Online.

34758 ■ "Casinos In Pitch Battle" in Philadelphia Business Journal (Vol. 28, July 20, 2012, No. 23, pp. 1)

Pub: Baltimore Business Journal

Contact: Rhonda Pringle, President

E-mail: rpringle@bizjournals.com

Description: The extent to which casinos in Philadelphia, Pennsylvania have invested in marketing and rebranding effortsin the Philadelphia-Atlantic City markets is explored. These efforts are part of the goal of the casinos to compete for customers considering that casinos contribute about $6 billion in taxes to Pennsylvania. Statistics pertaining to casinos and their advertising expenditures are presented. **Availability:** Print; Online.

34759 ■ "Cautions on Loans with Your Business" in Business Owner (Vol. 35, July-August 2011, No. 4, pp. 5)

Description: Caution must be used when borrowing from or lending to any small business. Tax guidelines for the borrowing and lending practice are also included. **Availability:** Print; Online.

34760 ■ "Central Florida Real Estate Values to Level Out this Year" in Orlando Business Journal (Vol. 29, June 15, 2012, No. 54, pp. 1)

Pub: Baltimore Business Journal

Contact: Rhonda Pringle, President

E-mail: rpringle@bizjournals.com

Ed: Anjali Fluker. **Description:** Property values in Central Florida are stabilizing with only a 1.2 percent decline in combined 2012 taxable values projected in Orange, Seminole, Osceola and Lake Counties, compared with 2011. A stable real estate market is said to be critical for the region, as it makes up 25 percent of the gross metropolitan product. **Availability:** Print; Online.

34761 ■ "CEOs Decry Budget Taxation Change" in Globe & Mail (April 2, 2007, pp. B1)

Ed: Steven Chase. **Description:** The views of the chief executive officers of Canadian firms, on the changes in the country's policy governing the taxation of foreign deals, are presented. **Availability:** Print; Online.

34762 ■ "Chafee Eyes Tax On Travel Sites" in Providence Business News (Vol. 28, March 24, 2014, No. 51, pp. 1)

Pub: American City Business Journals, Inc.

Contact: Mike Olivieri, Executive Vice President

URL(s): pbn.com/chafee-eyes-tax-on-travel-sites9 5903

Description: Rhode Island Governor, Lincoln D. Chafee's 2015 budget will include new tax rules for travel Websites. State officials claim the new regulations will deal with a loophole that has allowed travel Websites to pay less in taxes. Many hotels enter into partnerships with travel Websites in order to sell rooms in bulk. **Availability:** Online. **Telecommunication Services:** Anderson@pbn.com.

34763 ■ "City, County May Kill VC Tax" in Business Journal-Portland (Vol. 24, October 12, 2007, No. 33, pp. 1)

Pub: Portland Business Journal

Contact: Andy Giegerich, Managing Editor

E-mail: agiegerich@bizjournals.com

Ed: Aliza Earnshow. **Description:** City of Portland and Multnomah County in Oregon may soon kill taxes levied on venture capital (VC) firms, which is expected to take place in late October 2007. Capitalists have long been saying that taxation is driving them out of town, but this change is expected to generate more investments and persuade VC firms to relocate within city limits. **Availability:** Print; Online.

34764 ■ "Clarence Firm Gets OK To Make Tobacco Products" in Business First of Buffalo (Vol. 30, March 14, 2014, No. 26, pp. 3)

Pub: American City Business Journals, Inc.

Contact: Mike Olivieri, Executive Vice President

Released: March 14, 2014. **Price:** $4, Introductory 4-Week Offer(Digital & Print). **Description:** Clarence, New York-based 22nd Century Group Inc.'s subsidiary Goodrich Tobacco Company, has received approval from the Alcohol and Tobacco Tax Trade Bureau to produce tobacco products. The approval came after 22nd Century purchased the assets of North Carolina-based Nasco Products LLC, which holds a similar permit. Details of the deal are included. **Availability:** Print; Online.

34765 ■ "Clicks Vs. Bricks" in Birmingham Business Journal (Vol. 31, April 25, 2014, No. 17, pp. 4)

Pub: American City Business Journals, Inc.

Contact: Mike Olivieri, Executive Vice President

Released: May 22, 2018. **Description:** Birmingham, Alabama's retail industry has been evolving as investment to brick-and-mortar stores by mall and shopping center owners double. The hope is that the social shopping experience, economic recovery, and Fair Marketplace legislation for an online sales tax will make co-existence with Internet stores more viable. The survival and expansion of retail are discussed. **Availability:** Print; Online.

34766 ■ The Complete Guide to Buying a Business

Pub: Nolo

Contact: Chris Braun, President

Ed: Fred S. Steingold. **Released:** 2015. **Description:** Key steps in buying a business are highlighted, focusing on legal issues, tax considerations, approaches for valuing a business, financing, structuring the deal, along with forms and documents for taking ownership are included. **Availability:** Print.

34767 ■ "Congress Ponders Annuity Trusts" in National Underwriter Life & Health (Vol. 114, June 21, 2010, No. 12, pp. 10)

Ed: Arthur D. Postal. **Description:** Congress is looking over several bills, including the Small Business Jobs Tax Relief Act that would significantly narrow the advantages of using grantor-retained annuity trusts (GRATs) to avoid estate and gift taxes. **Availability:** Online.

34768 ■ "Council OKs Curtis Park Tax-Credit Plan" in Sacramento Business Journal (Vol. 31, June 13, 2014, No. 16, pp. 3)

Pub: American City Business Journals, Inc.

Contact: Mike Olivieri, Executive Vice President

Released: June 13, 2014. **Description:** The Sacramento City Council of California approved an agreement intended to resolve the dispute over affordable housing tax credits between Bridge Housing and Curtis Park Village developers. Bridge Housing pulled out its application for nine percent tax credits for the rehabilitation of the Sutterview project to allow Curtis Park Court to get the tax credits in July 2014.

34769 ■ *"Battle-Tested Vestas Shrugs Off Ill Winds" in Business Journal Portland (Vol. 30, January 31, 2014, No. 48, pp. 4)*
Pub: American City Business Journals, Inc.
Contact: Mike Olivieri, Executive Vice President
Released: Weekly. **Price:** $4, Introductory 4-week offer(Digital & Print). **Description:** The revenues of Vestas-American Wind Technology are expected to increase by 12 percent in 2014, despite the decline in US turbine sales. The company holds the second-highest market share in the US. However, Vestas is struggling with tax incentives and increased competition. **Availability:** Print; Online.

34770 ■ *"Crazy Tax Deductions That Are Actually Legal" in Business News Daily (March 2, 2023)*
URL(s): www.businessnewsdaily.com/4258-crazy-tax -deduction.html
Ed: Matt D'Angelo. **Released:** March 02, 2023. **Description:** Take advantage of these less-known tax deductions for your small business. **Availability:** Online.

34771 ■ *Deduct It! Lower Your Small Business Taxes*
Pub: Nolo
Contact: Chris Braun, President
Ed: Stephen Fishman. **Released:** 19th edition. **Price:** $17.99, e-book; $19.99, book and e-book; $17.99, E-Book; $19.99, book and e-book; $17.99, e-book. **Description:** Information is provided to help small companies maximize taxable deductions. **Availability:** Handheld; E-book; Print; Electronic publishing; PDF.

34772 ■ *"Defer Tax with Installment Sale Election" in Business Owner (Vol. 35, September-October 2011, No. 5, pp. 12)*
Description: It is critical to consult with a tax professional before selling any high-value asset in order to minimize taxes. **Availability:** Print; Online.

34773 ■ *"Delphi Latest In Fight Over Offshore Tax Shelters" in Crain's Detroit Business (Vol. 30, July 7, 2014, No. 27, pp. 1)*
Pub: Crain Communications Inc.
Contact: Barry Asin, President
Description: Internal Revenue Service is investigating Delphi Automotive and other American companies over the use of offshore tax shelters. The latest in Delphi's dispute with the federal government over tax practices is expected to cost the supplier millions. Delphi manufactures electronics and technologies for vehicles. Apple Inc. and Google Inc. have also been targeted by the IRS for incorporating portions of the businesses offshore allowing them to avoid U.S. taxes as well as other foreign taxes. **Availability:** Online.

34774 ■ *"Developers Tout Benefits of Federal Tax Breaks" in Business First of Buffalo (Vol. 30, March 14, 2014, No. 26, pp. 4)*
Pub: American City Business Journals, Inc.
Contact: Mike Olivieri, Executive Vice President
Released: Weekly. **Price:** $140, Digital & Print; $115, Digital only. **Description:** President Obama has included a Federal tax credit program in the 2015 Federal budget that provides some relief to the local development community. Congressman Mark Higgins promised to support the program that offers tax breaks to urban developers who rehabilitate older buildings with new investments. The tax credit's economic benefits are also discussed. **Availability:** Print; Online.

34775 ■ *"Don't Do Your Business Taxes Before Reading This" in Small Business Trends(February 7, 2023)*
URL(s): smallbiztrends.com/2023/02/business-taxes .html
Ed: Holly Chavez. **Released:** February 07, 2023. **Description:** The author of J.K. Lasser's Small Business Taxes, Barbara Weltman, gives an in-depth interview about small business taxes. **Availability:** Online.

34776 ■ *"Ducking the New Health-Care Taxes" in Barron's (Vol. 92, September 15, 2012, No. 38, pp. 34)*
Pub: Dow Jones & Company Inc.
Contact: Almar Latour, Chief Executive Officer
Ed: Elizabeth Ody. **Description:** Strategies that investors can use to avoid paying higher taxes starting January 2013 are discussed. These include selling assets by December 2012, distributing dividends, purchasing private-placement life insurance and converting individual retirement accounts. **Availability:** Online.

34777 ■ *"Duro Bag to Expand, Add 130 Jobs" in Business Courier (Vol. 27, August 6, 2010, No. 14, pp. 1)*
Pub: Business Courier
Ed: Jon Newberry. **Description:** Duro Bag Manufacturing Company will expand capacity at its Florence, Kentucky plant and will add around 130 jobs over the next few years. The state of Kentucky has given preliminary approval for up to $1 million in tax incentives over 10 years, tied to the creation of new jobs. The company's investment will include new production and packaging equipment and building improvements. **Availability:** Print; Online.

34778 ■ *EBay Income: How ANYONE of Any Age, Location, and/or Background Can Build a Highly Profitable Online Business with eBay*
Pub: Atlantic Publishing Co.
Contact: Dr. Heather L. Johnson, Contact
Description: A complete overview of eBay is given and guides any small company through the entire process of creating the auction and auction strategies, photography, writing copy, text and formatting, multiple sales, programming tricks, PayPal, accounting, creating marketing, merchandising, managing email lists, advertising plans, taxes and sales tax, best time to list items and for how long, sniping programs, international customers, opening a storefront, electronic commerce, buy-it now pricing, keywords, Google marketing and eBay secrets.

34779 ■ *"Economists Warn Against Smart Cap" in Orlando Business Journal (Vol. 29, September 21, 2012, No. 14, pp. 1)*
Pub: Baltimore Business Journal
Contact: Rhonda Pringle, President
E-mail: rpringle@bizjournals.com
Ed: Abraham Aboraya, Richard Bilbao. **Description:** Opponents to the proposed amendment to the Florida State Revenue Limitations warn about the economic impact of the plan to cap state government spending. Under the proposal, the amount of taxes that the state should spend each year will be capped and a rainy day fund will be created where excess revenue collected will be placed. **Availability:** Print; Online.

34780 ■ *"Editorial: It's Not Perfect; But Illinois a Good Home for Business" in Crain's Chicago Business (Vol. 34, October 24, 2011, No. 42, pp. 18)*
Pub: Crain Communications Inc.
Contact: Barry Asin, President
Description: Focusing on all factors that encompass Illinois' business environment, findings show that Illinois is a good place to start and grow a business. The study focused on corporate income tax rates and the fact that talent, access to capital and customers along with transportation connections are among the important factors the state has for small businesses. **Availability:** Print.

34781 ■ *"Eliminating All of Your Estate Tax Burden" in Contractor (Vol. 57, January 2010, No. 1, pp. 48)*
Ed: Irving L. Blackman. **Description:** Suggestions on how family owned businesses can minimize their estate tax burdens are discussed. One of these includes not using life insurance in a business succession plan to move stocks to the children and to never use Section 6166 as part of the overall estate tax plan. **Availability:** Print; Online.

34782 ■ *"Employer Jobless Tax Could Rise" in Sacramento Business Journal (Vol. 28, May 27, 2011, No. 13, pp. 1)*
Pub: Sacramento Business Journal
Contact: Stephanie Fretwell, Director
E-mail: sfretwell@bizjournals.com
Ed: Kathy Robertson. **Description:** The government of California is facing an estimated $16 billion deficit in its unemployment insurance fund. Unemployment insurance spending has exceeded employer contributions to the fund. Statistics on unemployment insurance is included. **Availability:** Online.

34783 ■ *"EPA Grants E15 Waiver for 2001-2006 Vehicles" in Farm Industry News (January 21, 2011)*
Pub: Informa Business Media, Inc.
Contact: Charlie McCurdy, President
Ed: Lynn Grooms. **Description:** U.S. Environmental Protection Agency waived a limitation on selling gasoline that contains more than 10 percent ethanol for model year 2001-2006 cars and light trucks, allowing fuel to contain up to 15 percent ethanol (E15) for these vehicles. **Availability:** Online.

34784 ■ *"Estate Tax Problems may Soon Disappear" in Contractor (Vol. 56, September 2009, No. 9, pp. 60)*
Ed: Irving L. Blackman. **Description:** Advice on how to effectively plan estate tax in the United States. Pending changes to US estate tax laws are seen to resolve inheritance problems. Captive insurance firms can lower property and casualty insurance costs to transfer businesses to children. **Availability:** Print; Online.

34785 ■ *Every Californian's Guide to Estate Planning*
Ed: Liza W. Hanks. **Released:** January 30, 2018. **Price:** $13.59, Paperback; $10.99, E-book. **Description:** A guide to help residents of California understand the basics of estate planning, inheritance, and taxes. **Availability:** E-book; Print.

34786 ■ *"Expect Action on Health Care and the Economy" in Contractor (Vol. 57, January 2010, No. 1, pp. 30)*
Ed: Kevin Schwalb. **Description:** The Plumbing-Heating-Cooling Contractors National Association is working to solidify its standing in the public policy arena as the legislative agenda will focus on health care reform, estate tax and immigration reform, all of which will impact the industries. **Availability:** Print; Online.

34787 ■ *"Experts Discuss New Tax Rules In Webinar to Help Farmers With Year-End Tax Planning" in Farm Industry News (November 22, 2011)*
Pub: Informa Business Media, Inc.
Contact: Charlie McCurdy, President
Description: Section 179 deductions and Bonus Depreciation tax rules for years 2011 and 2012 and how they impact farming operations are available at TractorLife.com. The Website helps farmers maintain and extend the operating lives of their tractors. **Availability:** Print; Online.

34788 ■ *"Expiring Tax Deals Pose Challenges" in Providence Business News (Vol. 29, May 5, 2014, No. 5, pp. 1)*
Pub: American City Business Journals, Inc.
Contact: Mike Olivieri, Executive Vice President
Released: May 03, 2014. **Description:** The expiring property tax stabilization agreements pose significant challenges to businesses and individual homeowners in Providence, Rhode Island. According to an internal auditor report, 71 deals out of the 36 active tax-stabilization incentives valued at $3.5 million are set to expire by 2017. **Availability:** Online.

34789 ■ *"Family Child Care Record-Keeping Guide, Ninth Edition (Redleaf Business Series)"*
Pub: Redleaf Press
Contact: Barbara Yates, President

Released: 9th edition. **Price:** $21.95, soft bound. **Description:** Writer, trainer, lawyer, and consultant provides concise information for home-based family child care (day care) providers. The book covers tracking expenses, being profitable, filing taxes, and meeting government regulations. This resources covers the process of accurate bookkeeping and record-keeping to take advantage of all allowable tax deductions. Changes in depreciation rules, adjustments to food and mileage rates, and clarifications on how to calculate the Time-Space percentage are defined. **Availability:** Print.

34790 ■ *"Federal Employer Identification Number (FEIN): How to Get One"* in Business News Daily (February 28, 2023)
URL(s): www.businessnewsdaily.com/17-federal-employer-identification-number-criteria.html
Ed: Sean Peek. **Released:** February 28, 2023. **Description:** If your small business plans on hiring employees, it will need a federal employer identification number. This article discusses the steps needed to take to obtain that number so your business is compliant. **Availability:** Online.

34791 ■ *"Feds to Pay University Hospital $20M"* in Business Courier (Vol. 27, July 23, 2010, No. 12, pp. 3)
Pub: Business Courier
Ed: James Ritchie. **Description:** The U.S. government is set to pay University Hospital and medical residents who trained there $20 million as part of a tax dispute settlement. Around 1,000 former residents are to receive tax refunds. But the hospital must provide the U.S. Internal Revenue Service with extensive documentation. **Availability:** Print; Mailing list; Online.

34792 ■ *"Fine Wine, Poor Returns"* in Barron's (Vol. 92, September 17, 2012, No. 38, pp. 11)
Description: Investing in wines in not considered a good idea due to irrationally high wine prices. Wine collectors buying wines at very high prices are not expected to make money and are charged with a 28 percent 'collectibles' tax. **Availability:** Online.

34793 ■ *"First Woman To Lead Builders Group"* in Philadelphia Business Journal (Vol. 32, January 31, 2014, No. 51, pp. 8)
Pub: American City Business Journals, Inc.
Contact: Mike Olivieri, Executive Vice President
Released: Weekly. **Price:** $4, introductory 4-week offer(Digital & Print). **Description:** Anne Faldoun, president of the Building Industry Association of Philadelphia (BIA), reveals that she has always been interested in architecture. She shares that she worked at the Dorado Neighborhood Improvement Company after she attended graduate school. Her views about the BIA's policy on tax abatement are also discussed. **Availability:** Print; Online.

34794 ■ *"Five Area Businesses Win State Tax Breaks"* in Crain's Detroit Business (Vol. 25, June 22, 2009, No. 25, pp. 9)
Pub: Crain Communications Inc.
Contact: Barry Asin, President
Ed: Amy Lane. **Description:** Michigan Economic Growth Authority approved tax breaks for five area businesses among 15 across the state. Details of the tax credits are provided. **Availability:** Print; Online.

34795 ■ *"Fuel-Tax Proposal May Be Conversation Starter"* in Sacramento Business Journal (Vol. 31, February 28, 2014, No. 1, pp. 6)
Pub: American City Business Journals, Inc.
Contact: Mike Olivieri, Executive Vice President
Description: Political science professor, Jack Pitney, believes that Senate President pro Tempore, Darrell Steinberg's fuel tax proposal in February 2014 could serve as a conversation starter. Pitney claims that the proposal would lead to a more transparent tax. The bill is expected to exempt small petroleum producers. **Availability:** Online.

34796 ■ *"Gamesa Office Closing Part of Political Reality"* in Pittsburgh Business Times (Vol. 33, February 7, 2014, No. 30, pp. 6)
Pub: American City Business Journals, Inc.
Contact: Mike Olivieri, Executive Vice President
Description: Due to political uncertainty surrounding the production tax credit for wind energy and changes in the supply chain needs in the North America wind market, a Spanish wind blade maker Gamesa will be shutting down its manufacturing unit in Ebesnburg March 31, 2014. The general counsel for Gamesa, Frank Fuselier, stated that optimizing the company's supply chain will help them survive in a market devoid of a production tax credit. **Availability:** Online.

34797 ■ *"Georgia Looking to Expand Film Industry Tax Credits"* in Atlanta Business Chronicle (June 27, 2014, pp. 3A)
Pub: American City Business Journals, Inc.
Contact: Mike Olivieri, Executive Vice President
Released: Weekly. **Price:** $4, introductory 4-week offer(Digital only). **Description:** The lawmakers of the State of Georgia are looking to expand film tax incentives at a time when many states are eliminating or scaling back their film industry tax credits. A recently created legislative study committee will begin meeting to consider proposals to expand Georgia's film tax credit program to encourage an already rapidly growing industry. **Availability:** Print; Online.

34798 ■ *"Getting More Out of Retirement"* in Agency Sales Magazine (Vol. 39, November 2009, No. 10, pp. 48)
Description: Overview of the Tax Increase Prevention and Reconciliation Act, which lets employees convert to a Roth IRA in 2010. The benefits of conversion depend on age and wealth and it is best to consult a tax advisor to determine the best strategy for retirement planners. **Availability:** Print; Online.

34799 ■ *"Goodwill Haunts Local Companies"* in Crain's Chicago Business (Apr. 28, 2008)
Pub: Crain Communications Inc.
Contact: Barry Asin, President
Ed: Ann Saphir. **Description:** Many companies are having to face the reality that they overpaid for acquisitions made in better economic times; investors often dismiss such one-time charges as mere accounting adjustments but writeoffs related to past acquisitions can signal future problems because they mean the expected profits that justified the purchase have not materialized. Writeoffs are particularly worrisome for firms with a lot of debt and whose banks require them to have enough assets to back up their borrowings. **Availability:** Online.

34800 ■ *"Governor Candidates Differ on Oregon's Green Streak"* in Business Journal Portland (Vol. 27, October 22, 2010, No. 34, pp. 1)
Pub: Portland Business Journal
Contact: Andy Giegerich, Managing Editor
E-mail: agiegerich@bizjournals.com
Ed: Andy Giegerich. **Description:** The views of Oregon gubernatorial candidates Chris Dudley and John Kitzhaber on the state's economy and on environmental policies are presented. Both Dudley, who is a Republican, and his Democratic challenger believe that biomass could help drive the state's economy. Both candidates also pledged changes in Oregon's business energy tax credit (BETC) program.

34801 ■ *"High-Tech Job-Apalooza!"* in Orlando Business Journal (Vol. 26, January 15, 2010, No. 33, pp. 1)
Pub: Orlando Business Journal
Contact: Julie Swyers, Director
E-mail: jswyers@bizjournals.com
Ed: Christopher Boyd. **Description:** Science Applications International Corporation, Saab Training USA LLC, CAE USA, and Pelliconi &C.SPA attempt to obtain $939,000 in tax incentives to generate 222 technology and defense-related jobs in Orange

County, Florida. Each job will provide an average salary of $67,000. Future plans of each technology and defense firm are also presented. **Availability:** Print; Online.

34802 ■ *"Hike in Md.'s Alcohol Tax May Be Hard For Lawmakers to Swallow"* in Baltimore Business Journal (Vol. 28, November 19, 2010, No. 28)
Pub: Baltimore Business Journal
Contact: Rhonda Pringle, President
E-mail: rpringle@bizjournals.com
Ed: Emily Mullin. **Description:** Maryland's General Assembly has been reluctant to support a dime-per-drink increase in alcohol tax that was drafted in the 2009 bill if the tax revenue goes into a separate fund. The alcohol tax increase is considered unnecessary by some lawmakers and business leaders due to impending federal spending boosts. **Availability:** Print; Online.

34803 ■ Home Business Tax Deductions: Keep What You Earn
Pub: Nolo
Contact: Chris Braun, President
Ed: Stephen Fishman. **Released:** November 2020. **Price:** $27.99, book and e-book; $24.99, e-book (downloadable). **Description:** Home business tax deductions are outlined. Basic information on the ways various business structures are taxed and how deductions work is included. **Availability:** E-book; Print.

34804 ■ *"How Accountants Break the Bad News about Tax Refunds: with Chocolate and Tissues"* in The Wall Street Journal (March 4, 2019)
URL(s): www.wsj.com/articles/tax-preparers-stock-up-on-tissues-to-deliver-bad-news-about-your-refund-11551715931
Ed: Laura Saunders. **Released:** March 04, 2019. **Description:** Changes in the Treasury Department rules have made it a difficult tax season because many Americans are either getting a lower tax refund, none at all, or are having to pay the IRS. Accountants are preparing to break the bad news as gently as possible and have found ways to soften the blow by offering treats or even just a kind and sympathetic ear. **Availability:** Online.

34805 ■ *"How to Avoid Double Taxation with an S Corporation"* in Small Business Trends (May 22, 2017)
URL(s): smallbiztrends.com/2017/02/double-taxation-s-corporation.html
Ed: Nellie Akalp. **Released:** May 22, 2018. **Description:** Describes how S corporations are taxed and gives tips on how to avoid double taxation. **Availability:** Online.

34806 ■ *"How to Avoid a Tax Audit: 7 Tips for Small Business Owners"* in Legal Zoom (March 2, 2023)
URL(s): www.legalzoom.com/articles/how-to-avoid-a-tax-audit-7-tips-for-small-business-owners
Ed: Jane Haskins, Esq. **Released:** March 02, 2023. **Description:** Follow these tips to help your small business stay clear of an audit from the IRS. **Availability:** Online.

34807 ■ *"How to File for a Business Tax Extension"* in Legal Zoom (February 28, 2023)
URL(s): www.legalzoom.com/articles/how-to-file-for-a-business-tax-extension
Released: February 28, 2023. **Description:** There may come a time when you can't file your business taxes on time, so filing an extension with the IRS is an option to get you through this time. Included are links to file for state extensions as well. **Availability:** Online.

34808 ■ *"How to Issue a 1099 to an LLC"* in Legal Zoom (February 23, 2023)
URL(s): www.legalzoom.com/articles/how-to-issue-a-1099-to-an-llc

Ed: Jane Haskins. **Released:** February 23, 2023. **Description:** Follow these steps to make sure your small business is compliant when it comes to taxes and 1099 forms for your LLC. **Availability:** Online.

34809 ■ *"How to Maximize Your Investment Income"* in *Contractor (Vol. 56, December 2009, No. 12, pp. 33)*
Ed: Irving L. Blackman. **Description:** Private placement life insurance (PPLI) can minimize taxes and protect assets. PPLI is a form of variable universal insurance that is offered privately. Risk of insurance company illiquidity is avoided as investments are placed in separate accounts. **Availability:** Online.

34810 ■ *"How to Open and Operate a Financially Successful Florist and Floral Business Online and Off"*
Pub: Atlantic Publishing Co.
Contact: Dr. Heather L. Johnson, Contact
Released: Revised second edition. **Description:** A concise and easy to follow guide for opening a retail florist or floral business online or a traditional brick and mortar store. Knowledge shared includes: cost control systems, retail math and competitive pricing, legal concerns, tax reporting requirements and reporting, profit and loss statements, management skills, sales advertising, and marketing techniques, customer service, direct sales, internal marketing ideas, and more. **Availability:** CD-ROM; Print; Online.

34811 ■ *"How to Pay Yourself from Your Small Business"* in *Legal Zoom (February 10, 2023)*
URL(s): www.legalzoom.com/articles/how-to-pay -yourself-from-your-small-business
Ed: Jane Haskins, Esq. **Released:** February 10, 2023. **Description:** Getting a small business off the ground is not easy and it can even come with a financial cost to your personal funds. However, consider the given ideas in this article and see if there is a better way so you can pay yourself from money earned through all your hard work. **Availability:** Online.

34812 ■ *How to Pay Zero Taxes: Your Guide to Every Tax Break the IRS Allows*
Released: 2020-2021 edition. **Price:** $12.96, e-book; $24, paperback. **Description:** Simple strategies to save your small business money in taxes, while following the government's tax regulations are covered, for this year and years beyond. The guide covers deductions organized into six categories: exclusions, general deductions, below the line deductions, traditional tax shelters, and super tax shelters. **Availability:** E-book; Print.

34813 ■ *How to Start an Internet Sales Business Without Making the Government Mad*
Pub: Lulu Press Inc.
Ed: Dan Davis. **Released:** October 01, 2011. **Price:** $19.95, paperback; $14.38, PDF; $14.38, e-book. **Description:** Small business guide for launching an Internet sales company. Topics include business structure, licenses, and taxes. **Availability:** E-book; Print; PDF.

34814 ■ *How to Start and Run Your Own Corporation: S-Corporations For Small Business Owners*
Pub: HCM Publishing
Ed: Peter I. Hupalo. **Description:** Basics of corporate business structure are explained. Topics include discovering the best business structure for your company; how to decided between an S-Corporation and LLC; choosing the state in which to incorporate, how to form a corporation, angel investing, special issues for one-person corporations, the role of bylaws and corporate minutes, board of directors, taxes, workers' compensation issues, retirement plans, and more. **Availability:** Print.

34815 ■ *"How Will Home Office Tax Deductions Change When Everyone Is Working Remotely?"* in *Legal Zoom (February 21, 2023)*
URL(s): www.legalzoom.com/articles/how-will-home -office-tax-deductions-change-when-everyone-is -working-remotely

Ed: Katherine Gustafson. **Released:** February 21, 2023. **Description:** Remote work and setting up home offices have become quite popular ever since work from home became mainstream during the COVID pandemic. But, will that change deductions from your taxes if you're setting up an office instead of driving to one?. **Availability:** Online.

34816 ■ *"Income Tax Credit for Business Pushes the Job Creation Button"* in *Idaho Business Review (August 27, 2014)*
Pub: BridgeTower Media
Contact: Adam Reinebach, President
Description: Idaho's new Reimbursement Incentive Act program creates a tax credit for businesses with a qualifying project that will add new jobs that are paid at or above the average wage for work performed. Legislation and technical requirements for small businesses to quality are outlined.

34817 ■ *"Independent Contractor, Sole Proprietor, and LLC Taxes Explained in 100 Pages or Less"*
Description: A small business tax primer which includes information of home office deduction, estimated tax payments, self-employment tax, business retirement plans, numerous business deductions, and audit protection. **Availability:** Print; Online.

34818 ■ *"Indiana Collection Agency Announces Expansion Plans"* in *PaymentsSource (March 23, 2012)*
Description: DECA Financial Services plans to buy a vacant building in Fishers, Indiana and renovate the property. The agency specializes in collection consumer and tax debts for both companies and government agencies. The company plans to hire 140 new employees over the next 3 years. **Availability:** Print; Mailing list.

34819 ■ *"International Benefits Roundup"* in *Employee Benefit News (Vol. 25, December 1, 2011, No. 15)*
Pub: SourceMedia LLC
Contact: Gemma Postlethwaite, Chief Executive Officer
Description: Employee contributions to an employer-sponsored defined contribution plan in Japan are allowed on a tax deductible basic; however, currently employee contributions are not allowed. The defined contribution plan is outlined for better understanding.

34820 ■ *"Investment Firms Unite: Coalition Fights New Tax Law"* in *Black Enterprise (Vol. 38, December 2007, No. 5, pp. 52)*
Description: Minorities working in private equity, real estate and investment management firms have united to form the Access to Capital Coalition to oppose legislation that they feel would adversely affect their ability to attract investments and executives. Details of the group are included. **Availability:** Print; Online.

34821 ■ *"IRS Imposes More Electronic Filing Mandates on Small Businesses"* in *Small Business Trends(March 3, 2023)*
URL(s): smallbiztrends.com/2023/03/irs-electronic -filing-mandates-on-small-businesses.html
Ed: Gabrielle Pickard-Whitehead. **Released:** March 03, 2023. **Description:** The IRS is expanding regulations to require small and medium-sized businesses to file their tax returns electronically instead of using paper forms. **Availability:** Online.

34822 ■ *"IRS Proposing New Tip Reporting Program for Service Business Owners"* in *Small Business Trends(February 7, 2023)*
URL(s): smallbiztrends.com/2023/02/irs-proposing -new-tip-reporting-program.html
Ed: Gabrielle Pickard-Whitehead. **Released:** February 07, 2023. **Description:** A new program for voluntary tip reporting is discussed. **Availability:** Online.

34823 ■ *"IRS Sends Reminder about New 1099 Rules"* in *Small Business Trends(November 9, 2022)*
URL(s): smallbiztrends.com/2022/11/new-1099-k -reporting-rule.html

Ed: Samson Haileyesus. **Released:** November 09, 2022. **Description:** A new 1099 rule will go into effect in 2023. Anyone receiving money through payment cards or third-party networks over $600 will be subjected to a 1099. **Availability:** Online.

34824 ■ *"IRS Updates Dirty Dozen Tax Scams List"* in *Small Business Trends (March 23, 2023)*
URL(s): smallbiztrends.com/2023/03/irs-dirty-dozen -tax-scams-2023.html
Ed: Gabrielle Pickard-Whitehead. **Released:** March 23, 2023. **Description:** With various types of scams infiltrating our emails and texts, the IRS has issued a warning about scammers going after your tax information. **Availability:** Online.

34825 ■ *"Is Mulcair Good for Business?"* in *Canadian Business (Vol. 85, June 11, 2012, No. 10, pp. 20)*
Ed: Sarah Barmak. **Description:** Some of the pronouncements made by New Democratic Party leader Thomas Mulcair suggest that he may be both a friend and an enemy of the Canadian business community. He expressed supportto the energy sector and endorsed lower taxes but also commented on the negative effect of oilsands development. **Availability:** Online.

34826 ■ *"Is Your Tax Pro Worth the Money?"* in *U.S. News & World Report (February 15, 2018)*
URL(s): money.usnews.com/money/personal-finance/ taxes/articles/2018-02-15/is-your-tax-pro-worth-the -money
Ed: Maryalene LaPonsie. **Released:** February 15, 2018. **Description:** Although it may be easier to pay someone to do your taxes, how do you know you are not being taken advantage of? Experts advise doing some research to see what kind of tax professional you need and to meet in person. Set expectations and learn what kind of services will be provided and what price. It's also advisable to look up industry standards for pricing and compare. **Availability:** Online.

34827 ■ *"It's Good To Be King"* in *South Florida Business Journal (Vol. 35, August 29, 2014, No. 6, pp. 12)*
Released: December 01, 2013. **Description:** The $11.4 billion deal that will create a new holding company for Burger King Worldwide and Tim Hortons will be based in Oakville, Ontario, Canada and was met with public outrage. Burger King declares that the merger with the Canadian coffee and doughnut franchise chain was about global growth, not a strategy to avoid millions of dollars in corporate income tax payments to the U.S. government. **Availability:** Print; Online.

34828 ■ *J.K. Lasser's 1001 Deductions and Tax Breaks 2023: Your Complete Guide to Everything Deductible*
Pub: John Wiley & Sons, Inc.
Contact: Christina Van Tassell, Executive Vice President Chief Financial Officer
URL(s): www.wiley.com/en-us/J+K+Lasser%27s+100 1+Deductions+and+Tax+Breaks+2023%3A+Your +Complete+Guide+to+Everything+Deductible-p -9781119931201
Ed: Barbara Weltman. **Released:** November 2022. **Price:** $15, E-book; $25, paperback. **Description:** Recent legislation, the latest tax court rulings, and IRS guidance are all given in this guide for ordinary Americans to help them navigate deductions and tax breaks for their personal tax filings. **Availability:** E-book; Print.

34829 ■ *"JK Lasser's New Rules for Estate, Retirement, and Tax Planning"*
Pub: John Wiley & Sons, Inc.
Contact: Christina Van Tassell, Executive Vice President Chief Financial Officer
Released: 6th Edition. **Price:** $24.95, paperback; $16.99, E-book. **Description:** The authoritative guide to estate, retirement and tax planning is fully updated and reflects the new changes and legal updates.

Estate planning section covers: planning, taxation, investing, wills, executors, trusts, life insurance, retirement planning, Social Security, business planning, succession, asset protection and family limited partnerships. **Availability:** E-book; Print.

34830 ■ "KC Incentives Debate Rages on Unabated" in The Business Journal-Serving Metropolitan Kansas City (Vol. 26, September 5, 2008, No. 52)
Pub: American City Business Journals, Inc.
Contact: Mike Olivieri, Executive Vice President
Ed: Rob Roberts. **Description:** Debate on the new economic development and incentives policy adopted by the Kansas City Council is still on. The city's Planned Industrial Expansion Authority has rejected a standard property tax abatement proposal. The real estate development community has opposed the rejection of proposed the tax incentives policy. **Availability:** Online.

34831 ■ "Keith Crain: Business Must Stand Up And Be Counted" in Crain's Detroit Business (Vol. 24, October 6, 2008, No. 40, pp. 6)
Pub: Crain Communications Inc.
Contact: Barry Asin, President
Description: Discusses the challenges that the new mayor of Detroit faces concerning business, the state of the economy and the exceptionally tight budget the city is running on, which includes a lot of red ink. It is very likely that the city is going to see tax revenues fall substantially in the next few months and business leaders may find it in their favor to lend their support to the new mayor as well as provide him with the executive talent necessary to overcome some of these crucial issues. **Availability:** Online.

34832 ■ "Legislators Must Cut Cost of Government" in Crain's Detroit Business (Vol. 24, October 6, 2008, No. 40, pp. 6)
Pub: Crain Communications Inc.
Contact: Barry Asin, President
Description: Southeast and West Michigan business leaders are setting aside their differences and have proposed clear agendas, ranging from eliminating the Michigan Business Tax to overhauling public employee and retiree benefits and pensions. Lawmakers must also come together to find solutions for the state's economy and discover an entirely new vision for the future of Michigan business. **Availability:** Print; Online.

34833 ■ Limited Liability Companies for Dummies
Pub: John Wiley & Sons, Inc.
Contact: Christina Van Tassell, Executive Vice President Chief Financial Officer
URL(s): www.wiley.com/en-us/Limited+Liability+Companies+For+Dummies%2C+4th+Edition-p-978139 4183333
Ed: Jennifer Reuting. **Released:** Fourth edition. **Price:** $29.99, paperback. **Description:** Guide on how to set up an LLC, or limited liability company. Discusses the pros and cons of this structure, how to manage it, and all of the new laws surrounding LLCs. **Availability:** Print.

34834 ■ "LLC Taxes: Everything You Need to Know" in Small Business Trends (February 14, 2023)
URL(s): smallbiztrends.com/2023/02/llc-taxes.html
Ed: Kevin Ocasio. **Released:** February 14, 2023. **Description:** Provides specifics about the corporate LLC structure and what to expect tax-wise. **Availability:** Online.

34835 ■ "Macroeconomic Policy and U.S. Competitiveness: A Reformed Fiscal Policy Is Vital To Renewing America's Productivity" in Harvard Business Review (Vol. 90, March 2012, No. 3, pp. 112)
Pub: Harvard Business Review Press
Contact: Moderna V. Pfizer, Contact
Ed: Matthew Weinzierl, Richard H.K. Vietor. **Description:** Improving productivity requires increasing physical capital (such as equipment or technology), raising

human capital, or using both of these types of capital more efficiently. The authors promote a plan that blends cuts in defense and health care spending, adjustments to Social Security, and carbon and gas taxes.

34836 ■ "Major Advances in Heat Pump Technology" in Contractor (Vol. 57, January 2010, No. 1, pp. 42)
Ed: Mark Eatherton. **Description:** Tax credits make ground-source heat pump technology more economically feasible. Suggestions on how to choose the right ground-source heat pump technology to install in a house are discussed. **Availability:** Print; Online.

34837 ■ "Make Business Tax Deductions Work for You" in Legal Zoom (February 17, 2023)
URL(s): www.legalzoom.com/articles/make-business-tax-deductions-work-for-you
Ed: Sandra Beckwith. **Released:** February 17, 2023. **Description:** Discusses the deductions the IRS will let small businesses take. **Availability:** Online.

34838 ■ Make Sure It's Deductible
Released: Fourth edition. **Description:** Tax planning, strategies are provided to help small businesses maximize deductions. **Availability:** Print; Online.

34839 ■ "Manitoba Tax Credits Create Film and TV Boom" in Canadian Business (Vol. 85, June 11, 2012, No. 10, pp. 11)
Ed: Lyndsie Bourgon. **Description:** The province of Manitoba offers a 30 percent film and television tax credit on production costs to filmmakers and a 65 percent tax credit for local qualified labor, posting a record $145 million in 2008 and $90 million in 2011. Other Canadian provinces say the boost in film production is only temporary. **Availability:** Print; Online.

34840 ■ "Medical Device Makers Brace for Excise Tax" in Memphis Business Journal (Vol. 34, July 20, 2012, No. 14, pp. 1)
Pub: Baltimore Business Journal
Contact: Rhonda Pringle, President
E-mail: rpringle@bizjournals.com
Ed: Michael Sheffield. **Description:** The US Government's plan to increase excise tax is seen to impact medical device manufacturers. The tax is expected to raise as much as $60 billion over the next 10 years. **Availability:** Print; Online.

34841 ■ "Memphis Pays Healthy Price To Compete for Jobs, Investment" in Memphis Business Journal (Vol. 35, January 3, 2014, No. 39, pp. 4)
Pub: American City Business Journals, Inc.
Contact: Mike Olivieri, Executive Vice President
Released: Weekly. **Price:** $4, introductory 4-week offer(Digital & Print). **Description:** Memphis, Tennessee Mayor A.C. Wharton announced that Economic Development Growth Engine (EDGE) had a solid year and he thinks 2014 will be even better. EDGE has committed $103,718 in pilot-lieu-of-tax property tax reductions for every job created in 2013. The economic development projects in Memphis and in peer cities are also presented. **Availability:** Print; Online.

34842 ■ Mergers and Acquisitions from A to Z
Pub: HarperCollins Leadership
Contact: Donald Miller, Chief Executive Officer
Released: 2nd edition. **Price:** $19.99, Paperback. **Description:** Guide for the entire process of mergers and acquisitions, including taxes, accounting, laws, and projected financial gain. **Availability:** E-book; Print.

34843 ■ "Michaud Touts Small-Business Credentials" in Bangor Daily News (September 10, 2010)
Pub: Bangor Daily News
Contact: David M. Austin, Contact

Ed: Nick Sambides, Jr. **Description:** Mike Michaud, Democrat, is running against a Republican challenger in the 2nd District and states he will support the Small Business Jobs Tax Relief Act if reelected. **Availability:** Print; Online.

34844 ■ "Millennial Spending Influences County Budget" in Puget Sound Business Journal (Vol. 35, September 26, 2014, No. 23, pp. 6)
Pub: American City Business Journals, Inc.
Contact: Mike Olivieri, Executive Vice President
Description: Washington State's tax system has been blamed by King County executive Dow Constantine for its proposed 2015-16 budget that cuts 500 positions. The millennial generation's spending was also partially blamed for the drop in sales tax revenue because they don't buy houses and cars as frequently compared to previous generations. How the millennial generation spends its money is also discussed. **Availability:** Online.

34845 ■ Minding Her Own Business, 4th Ed.
Released: 4th edition. **Description:** A guide to taxes and financial records for women entrepreneurs is presented. **Availability:** E-book; Print.

34846 ■ "More Corporate Welfare?" in Canadian Business (Vol. 80, February 12, 2007, No. 4, pp. 96)
Description: The burden on Canadian taxpayers by governmental efforts to finance loss-making companies in the name of corporate welfare is discussed. **Availability:** Online.

34847 ■ "My Home-Based Business Is Being Audited: Now What?" in Legal Zoom (March 8, 2023)
URL(s): www.legalzoom.com/articles/my-home-based-business-is-being-audited-now-what
Ed: Stephen Sylvester. **Released:** March 08, 2023. **Description:** If your small business is contacted by the IRS to participate in an audit, follow the advice given here to get through the process. **Availability:** Online.

34848 ■ "MyWireless.org Commends Arizona Congressman Trent Franks for Committing to Wireless Tax Relief for American Consumers and Businesses" in PR Newswire (September 21, 2012)
Pub: PR Newswire Association LLC.
Description: MyWireless.org presented Congressman Trent Franks from Arizona with the 2012 Wireless Consumer Hero Award for his work on wireless tax relief for American consumers and businesses. Franks' 'Wireless Tax Fairness Act' (HR 1002) promotes access to wireless networks as a key ingredient of millions of Americans' livelihoods, whether phone, broadband Internet necessary to run a small business. **Availability:** Print; Online.

34849 ■ "New Rule Rankles In Jersey" in Philadelphia Business Journal (Vol. 30, September 16, 2011, No. 31, pp. 1)
Pub: Philadelphia Business Journal
Contact: Sierra Quinn, Director
E-mail: squinn@bizjournals.com
Ed: Jeff Blumenthal. **Description:** A new rule in New Jersey which taxes out-of-state companies that conduct business in the state earned the ire of several banks, mortgage lenders and credit card companies and prompted opponents to threaten to file lawsuits. The new rule is an amendment to New Jersey Division of Taxation's corporate business tax regulation and is retroactive to 2002. Details are given. **Availability:** Online.

34850 ■ "New Tax Sends Biz Scrambling: Service Levy Will Affect 16,000 Businesses" in Crain's Detroit Business (October 8, 2007)
Pub: Crain Communications Inc.
Contact: Barry Asin, President

Ed: Amy Lane. **Description:** Legislation that imposes a tax on services in Michigan has business leaders upset. The new law exerts a 6 percent tax on 57 categories of services that affects 16,000 businesses in the state. **Availability:** Online.

34851 ■ *"No Charlotte Tax Hike, But Plenty of Challenges"* in *Charlotte Business Journal (Vol. 27, June 29, 2012, No. 15, pp. 1)*
Pub: American City Business Journals, Inc.
Contact: Mike Olivieri, Executive Vice President

Ed: Erik Spanberg. **Released:** Weekly. **Price:** $20, Introductory 12-week offer(Digital & Print). **Description:** Charlotte, North Carolina City Council has rejected a proposed tax increase. The move halted investments in roads, business hubs, and major transportation projects. Comments from officials are included. **Availability:** Print; Online.

34852 ■ *"NYPA Grants Aid Area Companies"* in *Business First of Buffalo (Vol. 30, January 10, 2014, No. 17, pp. 6)*
Pub: American City Business Journals, Inc.
Contact: Mike Olivieri, Executive Vice President

Released: Weekly. **Price:** $140, One-Year Print & Digital; $115, One-Year Digital. **Description:** New York Power Authority (NYPA) trustees have approved more than $3.5 million in financial aid to Western New York enterprises. The NYPA and Empire State Development have also funded a package that includes low cost hydropower and $7 million in capital grants and tax credits. The Western New York area manufacturers that were granted aid are also presented. **Availability:** Print; Online.

34853 ■ *"Observers See Different Messages if Voters Reject Ambassador Tax Rebate"* in *Wichita Business Journal (Vol. 27, February 17, 2012, No. 7, pp. 1)*
Pub: Baltimore Business Journal
Contact: Rhonda Pringle, President
E-mail: rpringle@bizjournals.com

Description: Ambassador Hotel's room tax rebate has been put on a referendum in Wichita,Kansas and the rejection is expected to affect future downtown projects. However, the observers differ on the messages of a no vote would send to real estate investors. Insights on the ongoing debate on economic development policy are also given. **Availability:** Print; Online.

34854 ■ *"Pa. Pushes for Collection of Online Sales Tax"* in *Philadelphia Business Journal (Vol. 31, March 2, 2012, No. 3, pp. 1)*
Pub: Baltimore Business Journal
Contact: Rhonda Pringle, President
E-mail: rpringle@bizjournals.com

Description: The government of Pennsylvania is seeking to increase taxes from e-sales. The government estimates that it could lose $380 million in uncollected online sales and use tax to the e-commerce retail sector in 2012. It has also introduced tax forms that instruct taxpayers to report and remit use tax. **Availability:** Print; Online.

34855 ■ *"Pet Care Services in Rhode Island to be Taxed"* in *Pet Product News (Vol. 66, September 2012, No. 9, pp. 1)*

Description: Pet care services will be subject to a 7 percent sales tax in Rhode Island starting October 1, 2012, potentially resulting in more expensive pet boardng, grooming, sitting, and training. The tax is part of the state's efforts to close a $120 million budget deficit. How pet supplies retailers have reacted to the new tax is presented. **Availability:** Online.

34856 ■ *"Phila. Tax Break Aimed at Luring Investment Funds"* in *Philadelphia Business Journal (Vol. 28, April 13, 2012, No. 9, pp. 1)*
Pub: Baltimore Business Journal
Contact: Rhonda Pringle, President
E-mail: rpringle@bizjournals.com

Description: The City Council of Philadelphia adopted a resolution to attract private investment funds to relocate to the city through tax breaks. Two private-equity firms have already expressed interest to relocate in the city. **Availability:** Print; Online.

34857 ■ *"Philadelphia Tourism Push Rising in Fall"* in *Philadelphia Business Journal (Vol. 30, August 26, 2011, No. 28, pp. 1)*
Pub: Philadelphia Business Journal
Contact: Sierra Quinn, Director
E-mail: squinn@bizjournals.com

Ed: Peter Van Allen. **Description:** Philadelphia is offering events for tourists this fall despite massive cuts for tourism promotion. Governor Tim Corbet slashed $5.5 million in funding for the state's tourism-promotion agencies which received $32 million in 2009. The agencies were forced to cooperate and fend for themselves using the hotel taxes that sustain them. **Availability:** Online.

34858 ■ *Plan Your Estate*
Price: $26.49, Paperback; $25.17, E-Book. **Description:** Newly updated to reflect the Tax Cuts and Jobs Acts of 2017, the 14th edition is a complete guide to learning about estate planning. **Availability:** E-book; Print.

34859 ■ *"Planned Rice MLP Latest In Series of Spinoffs"* in *Pittsburgh Business Times (Vol. 34, August 15, 2014, No. 4, pp. 6)*
Pub: American City Business Journals, Inc.
Contact: Mike Olivieri, Executive Vice President
Released: Weekly. **Price:** $4, introductory 4-week offer(Digital & Print). **Description:** Companies such as Rice Energy Inc., EQT Corporation and Consol Energy, are separating their midstream businesses from exploration and production by forming master limited partnerships (MLPs) to gain tax benefits and a higher valuation on midstream assets. However, Kinder Morgan Inc. plans to reorganize and reacquire its three separate MLPs in an effort to streamline the company and remove its distribution incentive rights. **Availability:** Print; Online.

34860 ■ *"Poor Economy Inspires Rich Alternatives In a Modern, and Tax-Free, Twist on Bartering"* in *Houston Chronicle (June 7, 2010)*
Pub: Houston Chronicle
Ed: Michael Rubinkam. **Description:** Time banking helps individuals and firms receive goods or services by depositing time dollars into a bank reserved for receipt of goods and services.

34861 ■ *PPC's Small Business Tax Guide*
Released: January 2005. **Price:** $189.00. **Description:** Business tax laws are covered in an easy to understand format.

34862 ■ *"PPC's Small Business Tax Guide, Vol. 2*
Description: Second volume containing technical guide covering business tax laws. **Availability:** Online.

34863 ■ *"Private Pitfalls"* in *Canadian Business (Vol. 80, October 22, 2007, No. 21, pp. 34)*
Description: Guidelines on how minority shareholders can avoid drawbacks at the time of purchase, during ownership, and when selling shares are discussed; contractual protection, sales taxation and share price are also presented. Investment in a private company entails knowing the party you are buying share from. **Availability:** Print; Online.

34864 ■ *"Procter & Gamble vs. IRS: Split Decision"* in *Business Courier (Vol. 27, July 16, 2010, No. 11, pp. 1)*
Pub: Business Courier
Ed: Jon Newberry. **Description:** Implications of a court ruling in a $435 million legal dispute between Procter & Gamble Company (P&G) and the Internal Revenue Service (IRS) are discussed. A $21 million win has been realized for P&G for its interpretation of research and development tax credits. However, the

said case might involve more than $700 million in P&G tax deductions from 2001 through 2004 that the IRS had disallowed. **Availability:** Print; Online.

34865 ■ *"Publisher Steve Forbes: Small Business Can Flourish in Boise"* in *Idaho Business Review (August 19, 2014)*
Pub: BridgeTower Media
Contact: Adam Reinebach, President

Price: $99, Digital & Mobile Only(1 Year); $11.99, Print, Digital & Mobile(1 Month); $149, Print, Digital & Mobile(1 Year); $99, Digital & Mobile Only(For 1 Year); $11.99, Print, Digital & Mobile (For 1 Month Intro Rate); $149, Print, Digital & Mobile (For 1 Year). **Description:** Steve Forbes spoke at the Zions Bank Small Business Conference in Boise, Idaho. He explored the opportunities for small firms in the area in regards to the global economy. Forbes also addressed taxation and government regulations. **Availability:** Print; Online.

34866 ■ *"Quicken Starter Edition 2008"* in *Black Enterprise (Vol. 38, March 1, 2008, No. 8, pp. 54)*
Pub: Earl G. Graves Ltd.
Contact: Earl Graves, Jr., President

Ed: Dale Coachman. **Description:** Profile of Quicken Starter Edition 2008 offering programs that track spending; it will also categorize tax deductible expenses. **Availability:** Online.

34867 ■ *"The Rabbi Trust: How to Earn It Now, But Defer the Tax to the Future"* in *Barron's (Vol. 88, March 24, 2008, No. 12, pp. 55)*
Pub: Dow Jones & Company Inc.
Contact: Almar Latour, Chief Executive Officer

Ed: Joseph F. Gelband. **Description:** Discusses a rabbi trust which is a method of deferring taxes on compensation allowed by the Internal Revenue Service. Funding of the trust is not considered taxable. Other regulations concerning tax deferment are also discussed. **Availability:** Online.

34868 ■ *"Rawlings-Blake Unveils Business Plan for Next Four Years"* in *Baltimore Business Journal (Vol. 29, September 16, 2011, No. 19, pp. 1)*
Pub: Boston Business Journal
Contact: Carolyn M. Jones, President
E-mail: cmjones@bizjournals.com

Ed: Gary Haber. **Description:** Mayor Stephanie Rawlings-Blake of Baltimore, Maryland unveiled her plan to push the economy forward. Her key objectives include giving more support for the city's technology companies and refocusing the Baltimore Development Corporation on job creation and retention. **Availability:** Online.

34869 ■ *"Realtors Irate Over Tax Plan"* in *Providence Business News (Vol. 26, March 26, 2012, No. 51, pp. 1)*
Pub: American City Business Journals, Inc.
Contact: Mike Olivieri, Executive Vice President
URL(s): pbn.com/realtors-irate-over-tax-plan66344

Ed: Kelly L. Anderson. **Description:** Rhode Island realtors are criticizing Governor Lincoln D. Chafee's plan to tax vacation rentals and bed and breakfast operations. The plan is in line with the state's efforts to balance the 2013 budget. Comments from executives are included.

34870 ■ *Recordkeeping for Business Barter Transactions*
URL(s): www.taxproplus-la.com/10772/Recordkeeping-for-Business-Barter-Transactions/

Description: Discusses appropriate tax reporting and recordkeeping practices when bartering is a part of your small business. **Availability:** Online.

34871 ■ *"Reforms Equal Smaller 401(k)s"* in *Employee Benefit News (Vol. 25, December 1, 2011, No. 15, pp. 19)*
Pub: SourceMedia LLC
Contact: Gemma Postlethwaite, Chief Executive Officer

Ed: Lisa V. Gillespie. **Description:** According to a new analysis by the Employee Benefit Research Institute, two recent proposals to change existing tax treatment of 401(k) retirement plans could cost workers because they would lower their account balances towards retirement.

34872 ■ *"Retailers, Your Will, and More" in Agency Sales Magazine (Vol. 39, July 2009, No. 7, pp. 46)*
Description: IRS audit guide for small retail businesses is presented. Tips on how to make a will with multiple beneficiaries are discussed together with medical expenses that cannot be deducted.

34873 ■ *"Reviving Entrepreneurship: Policy Decisions in 12 Areas Could Nurture - Or Cripple - America's Greatest Asset" in Harvard Business Review (Vol. 90, March 2012, No. 3, pp. 116)*
Pub: Harvard Business Review Press
Contact: Moderna V. Pfizer, Contact

Ed: Josh Lerner, William A. Sahlman. **Price:** $8.95, hardcover. **Description:** Government policies should address entrepreneurship as a process, rather than an act. Several key areas for policymaking include basic and translational science, supply and quality of human capital, information availability, tax treatment of rewards and risks, intellectual property rights, workforce healthcare, and mobility of financial and human capital. **Availability:** PDF; Online.

34874 ■ *"Rocket Lawyer Launches Tax Prep Tool for Small Business Owners" in Small Business Trends(January 22, 2023)*
Ed: Gabrielle Pickard-Whitehead. **Released:** January 22, 2023. **Description:** Small businesses owners can benefit from using the Rocket Tax program by getting paired with tax professionals. **Availability:** Online.

34875 ■ *"Running Your Business: What Do You Need to Do to Retain Good Corporate Standing?" in Legal Zoom (March 28, 2023)*
URL(s): www.legalzoom.com/articles/running-your
-business-what-do-you-need-to-do-to-retain-goo
d-corporate-standing
Ed: Heleigh Bostwick. **Released:** March 28, 2023. **Description:** Discusses obtaining a certificate in good standing from your state in order to prove to customers that your business has complied with tax laws and is current in its filings. **Availability:** Online.

34876 ■ *"S.A. Officials Hunting for Prospects in California" in San Antonio Business Journal (Vol. 26, August 17, 2012, No. 29, pp. 1)*
Released: August 17, 2012. **Description:** Officials of the San Antonio Economic Development Foundation in Texas will meet with 15 or more companies in Los Angeles, California in a bid to convince these businesses to relocated some of their operations to Alamo City. Officials are hoping the companies will recognize the advantages of San Antonio as they face pressures due to increased taxes and added government regulations in California.

34877 ■ *Schaum's Outline of Financial Management*
Pub: McGraw-Hill Professional

Ed: Jae K. Shim, Joel G. Siegel. **Released:** Third edition. **Description:** Rules and regulations governing corporate finance, including the Sarbanes-Oxley Act are discussed. **Availability:** E-book; Print; Download.

34878 ■ *"Seasonal Franchises: Strategies to Advance" in Franchising World (Vol. 42, August 2010, No. 8, pp. 50)*
Pub: International Franchise Association
Contact: Matthew Haller, President
E-mail: mhaller@franchise.org

Ed: Jennifery Lemcke. **Price:** $5.99. **Description:** Seasonal franchises, such as tax businesses can be slow during the summer months. Restaurants are

slow during the months of January and February. The various challenges faced by seasonal franchises are examined. **Availability:** Online.

34879 ■ *Self-Employed Tax Solutions: Quick, Simple, Money-Saving, Audit-Proof Tax and Recordkeeping Basics*
Released: Second edition. **Description:** A simple system for maintaining tax records and filing tax forms for any small business is explored.

34880 ■ *"Self-Employment Taxes" in The Balance Small Business (June 25, 2019)*
Ed: Jean Murray. **Released:** June 25, 2019. **Description:** Discusses how sole proprietorships, LLCs, partnerships, and S corporations pay taxes and how self-employment income affects social security credit. **Availability:** Online.

34881 ■ *"Shear Profit" in Crain's Cleveland Business (Vol. 28, October 29, 2007, No. 43, pp. 3)*
Pub: Crain Communications Inc.
Contact: K. C. Crain, President

Ed: David Bennett. **Description:** Alpaca farms are becoming a very profitable business for a number of Northeast Ohio entrepreneurs due to the high return on initial investments, tax incentives and the rise in demand for the animals. Ohio leads the country in the number of alpaca farms with roughly one-third located in Northeast Ohio. **Availability:** Online.

34882 ■ *"Side Income: Is It a Hobby or a Business?" in Money Under 30 (March 12, 2019)*
URL(s): www.moneyunder30.com/side-income-hobby
-or-a-business
Ed: Amber Gilstrap. **Released:** March 12, 2019. **Description:** A practical discussion of how to determine if your hobby that you love is actually a business. The IRS has some guidelines and questions, and if you meet certain criteria, you can then deduct expenses and report it to the IRS. **Availability:** Online.

34883 ■ *The Small Business Start-Up Kit for California*
Pub: Nolo
Contact: Chris Braun, President

Ed: Peri Pakroo. **Released:** 14th edition. **Price:** $20.99, E-book. **Description:** Handbook covering all aspects of starting a business in California, including information about necessary fees, forms, and taxes. **Availability:** E-book; Print; Download.

34884 ■ *Small Business Taxes for Dummies*
Pub: John Wiley & Sons, Inc.
Contact: Christina Van Tassell, Executive Vice President Chief Financial Officer
URL(s): www.wiley.com/en-us/Small+Business
+Taxes+For+Dummies%2C+3rd+Edition-p-978
1119861164
Ed: Eric Tyson. **Released:** 3rd edition. **Price:** $18, e-book; $29.99, paperback. **Description:** Easy instructions for how to complete small business taxes. Up-to-date information is provided on tax deductions and incentives. **Availability:** E-book; Print.

34885 ■ *"Small Businesses Unsure of Impact of New Tax Law" in Crain's Detroit Business (Vol. 23, October 15, 2007, No. 42, pp. 13)*
Pub: Crain Communications Inc.
Contact: Barry Asin, President

Ed: Sheena Harrison. **Description:** Small business owners in Michigan are concerned with issues surrounding the proposed increases in state taxes geared at small business, which includes a 6 percent service tax. **Availability:** Online.

34886 ■ *Small Time Operator: How to Start Your Own Business, Keep Your Books, Pay Your Taxes, and Stay Out of Trouble*
Ed: Bernard B. Kamoroff. **Released:** 14th edition. **Price:** $18.95, paperback. **Description:** Comprehensive guide for starting any kind of business. **Availability:** Print.

34887 ■ *"Smart Year-End Tax Moves" in Business Owner (Vol. 35, November-December 2011, No. 6, pp. 8)*
Description: Managing small business and individual taxes is more important in a bad economy. It is imperative to seek all tax incentives that apply to your business.

34888 ■ *"A Socko Payout Menu: Rural Phone Carrier Plots to Supercharge Its Shares" in Barron's (Vol. 88, June 30, 2008, No. 26, pp. M5)*
Description: CenturyTel boosted its quarterly common payout to 70 cents from 6.75 cents per share die to its strong cash flows and solid balance sheet. Eastman Kodak's plan for a buyback will be partially funded by its $581 million tax refund. CME Group will buyback stocks through 2009 worth $1.1 billion. **Availability:** Online.

34889 ■ *"Solutions to Family Business Problems" in Contractor (Vol. 56, October 2009, No. 10, pp. 51)*
Ed: Irving L. Blackman. **Description:** Several common business problems that family owned firms face are presented together with their solutions. These problems include giving the children stock bonus options while another discusses the tax burden when a father wants to transfer the business to his son. **Availability:** Print; Online.

34890 ■ *"Some Homeowners Caught in Tax-Code Limbo" in Providence Business News (Vol. 29, June 23, 2014, No. 12, pp. 9)*
Pub: American City Business Journals, Inc.
Contact: Mike Olivieri, Executive Vice President

Released: June 22, 2014. **Description:** The Mortgage Forgiveness Debt Relief Act expired on December 31, 2013 and Congress delayed reauthorizing the tax code, thus impacting homeowners looking for short sales in 2014. Short sellers are unsure whether they will avoid taxation on their forgiven mortgage debt or if the lack of reauthorization by Congress, retroactive to January 1, will lead to large income tax payouts in 2015. **Availability:** Print; Online.

34891 ■ *"Spin Zone: Where Hawaii's Leaders Face Off, Have High-Tech Tax Credits Helped or Hurt Hawaii?" in Hawaii Business (Vol. 53, December 2007, No. 6, pp. 28)*
Pub: PacificBasin Communications
Contact: Chuck Tindle, Director
E-mail: chuckt@pacificbasin.net

Description: Presents the opinons of Channel Capital LLC's Walter R. Roth and Hawaii Venture Capital Association's Bill Spencer concerning the impacts of tax credits. Roth thinks that Act 221 appeals to investors who can earn despite business failure while Spencer thinks that the legislation promotes investments in innovative technology firms. The need to support tax credits is also discussed. **Availability:** Print; Online.

34892 ■ *"Spring Cleaning: Getting Your Business in Order" in Legal Zoom (March 20, 2023)*
URL(s): www.legalzoom.com/articles/spring-cleaning
-getting-your-business-in-order
Ed: Jane Haskins. **Released:** March 20, 2023. **Description:** The spring is a good time to get in the mindset to go over all of your small business documentation and make sure you are in compliance tax-wise. **Availability:** Online.

34893 ■ *"Stadium Developers Seek a Win With the State" in The Business Journal-Serving Metropolitan Kansas City (Vol. 26, August 22, 2008)*
Description: Three Trails Redevelopment LLC is hoping to win $30 million in state tax credits from the Missouri Development Finance Board for the construction of an 18,500-seat Wizards stadium. The project is contingent on state tax incentives and the company remains optimistic about their goal.

34894 ■ *Starting & Running Your Own Horse Business*

Pub: Storey Publishing L.L.C.

Contact: Maribeth Casey, Director

E-mail: maribeth.casey@storey.com

Ed: Mary Ashby McDonald. **Released:** Second edition. **Price:** $19.95, trade paper. **Description:** Insight into starting and running a successful equestrian business is given. The book covers safety, tips for operating a riding school or horse camp, strategies for launching a carriage business, along with tax and insurance advice. **Availability:** E-book; Print.

34895 ■ *"State Aviation Fuel Tax Proposal Runs Into Turbulence" in Crain's Detroit Business (Vol. 25, June 15, 2009, No. 24, pp. 5)*

Pub: Crain Communications Inc.

Contact: Barry Asin, President

Ed: Amy Lane. **Description:** Delta Airlines Inc. is concerned about a proposal that would change the way Michigan taxes aviation fuel. The plan would go from the current cents-per-gallon tax to a percentage tax on the wholesale price of fuel, which would raise the taxes significantly. **Availability:** Online.

34896 ■ *"Surviving an IRS Audit: Tips for Small Businesses" in Agency Sales Magazine (Vol. 39, July 2009, No. 7, pp. 52)*

Description: It is a good idea to enlist the services of a tax professional even if an audit is expected to go smoothly since the IRS is likely to scrutinize the unreported income and personal as well as business expenses of a small business during an audit. **Availability:** Online.

34897 ■ *"Taking the Jump Off the Fiscal Cliff" in Barron's (Vol. 92, August 25, 2012, No. 35, pp. 47)*

Pub: Dow Jones & Company Inc.

Contact: Almar Latour, Chief Executive Officer

Ed: Thomas G. Donlan. **Description:** The arrival of tax increases and spending cuts by the end of 2012 should help the United States reduce its budget deficit. Policy prescriptions advocating looser monetary and fiscal policies are not going to help the country solve its budget problems. **Availability:** Online.

34898 ■ *"Talking Tax: The Horse Business" in Idaho Business Review (September 3, 2014)*

Pub: BridgeTower Media

Contact: Adam Reinebach, President

Description: Tax codes involving a small business that boards, raises, and sells horses are outlined.

34899 ■ *"Tax Breaks Favor Outsiders, Business Owners Object" in Business Review Albany (Vol. 41, August 22, 2014, No. 22, pp. 7)*

Pub: American City Business Journals, Inc.

Contact: Mike Olivieri, Executive Vice President

Released: Weekly. **Price:** $4, introductory 4-week offer(Digital only). **Description:** New York business owners have criticized Governor Andrew Cuomo's Start-Up NY tax-break program. They argue that the existing companies are essentially ignored and they are concerned whether the companies receiving the tax breaks stay longer than ten years. Insights on the Start-Up NY program are included. **Availability:** Print; Online.

34900 ■ *"Tax Breaks for Home-Based Businesses Go Unclaimed" in Legal Zoom (March 29, 2023)*

URL(s): www.legalzoom.com/articles/tax-breaks-for -home-based-businesses-go-unclaimed

Ed: C. Yoder. **Released:** March 29, 2023. **Description:** Discusses how home-based businesses are not claiming items on their taxes when they really should. **Availability:** Online.

34901 ■ *"Tax Credits Drive MO Budget Crisis" in St. Louis Business Journal (Vol. 33, September 14, 2012, No. 3, pp. 1)*

Pub: Baltimore Business Journal

Contact: Rhonda Pringle, President

E-mail: rpringle@bizjournals.com

Description: Tax credits have adversely affected Missouri's annual operating budget. Tax credits were created as an economic incentive tool. **Availability:** Print; Online.

34902 ■ *"Tax-Free Zones Need Shows: Out-of-State Shoppers Are Key To Success" in Crain's Detroit Business (Vol. 24, January 28, 2008, No. 4)*

Pub: Crain Communications Inc.

Contact: Barry Asin, President

Ed: Daniel Duggan. **Description:** Sales tax-free zones are being considered by Michigan's legislators in order to promote the state as a conference destination. **Availability:** Online.

34903 ■ *"Tax Increase Would Leave Heavy Impact" in Memphis Business Journal (Vol. 34, April 27, 2012, No. 2, pp. 1)*

Pub: Baltimore Business Journal

Contact: Rhonda Pringle, President

E-mail: rpringle@bizjournals.com

Description: Memphis, Tennessee Mayor A.C. Wharton's proposed commercial property tax increase is seen to adversely impact owners in the city. Wharton has proposed a one-time, 47-percent property tax increase. **Availability:** Print; Online.

34904 ■ *"Tax Relief Available for Livestock Sold Due to Drought" in Southeast Farm Press (October 4, 2012)*

Description: Designated areas have been identified for farmers and ranchers who were forced to sell draft animals, breeding livestock or dairy animals becuase of drought, flood or other weather relate conditions. These farmers and ranchers have been give more time to defer payment of capital gains taxes on replacement animals. Details of the program are examined.

34905 ■ *Tax Savvy for Small Business*

Pub: Nolo

Contact: Chris Braun, President

Ed: Frederick W. Daily, Jeffrey A. Quinn. **Released:** 22nd edition. **Price:** $31.99, book & e-book; $20.99, E-Book; $23.99; $22.99, E-book. **Description:** Tax strategies for small business. Includes the latest tax numbers and laws as well as current Internal Revenue Service forms and publications. **Availability:** E-book; Print; Electronic publishing; PDF.

34906 ■ *"Tax Tip: Streamlining Sales Tax Collections" in Pet Product News (Vol. 66, September 2012, No. 9, pp. 38)*

Ed: Mark E. Battersby. **Description:** Pointers on how pet supplies retailers and managers can streamline sales taxes are presented. Businesses are being challenge by the pressure to collect taxes on goods sold to local customers and competititon from Internet merchants that are not required to collect sales taxes. **Availability:** Online.

34907 ■ *"Three Trails Blazes Tax Credit Deal" in The Business Journal-Serving Metropolitan Kansas City (Vol. 27, November 7, 2008, No. 9)*

Description: Three Trails Redevelopment LLC plans to redevelop the Bannister Mall area. The Missouri Development Finance Board is expected to approve $30 million in tax credits for the project. A verbal agreement on the terms and conditions has already been reached according to the agency's executive director.

34908 ■ *"To Be or Not To Be an S Corporation" in Modern Machine Shop (Vol. 84, September 2011, No. 4, pp. 38)*

Pub: Gardner Business Media Inc.

Contact: Rick Kline, Jr., President

E-mail: rkline2@gardnerweb.com

Ed: Irving L. Blackman. **Description:** The definitions of both C corporations and S corporations are defined to help any machine shop discover which best suits the owner's business plan. **Availability:** Online.

34909 ■ *The Tools & Techniques of Estate Planning*

Ed: Stephan Leimberg, L. Paul Hood, Edwin P. Morrow. **Released:** January 09, 2019. **Price:** $188, Paperback. **Description:** New updates reflecting changes to tax codes are included in the nineteenth edition of this book for estate planners. Includes easy-to-understand examples and techniques to help your clients make the best decisions for themselves their estates. **Availability:** Print.

34910 ■ *Top Tax Savings Ideas: How to Survive in Today's Tough Tax Environment*

Released: Second edition. **Price:** $16.11. **Description:** Tax deductions, fringe benefits, and tax deferrals for small businesses.

34911 ■ *"A Trader Gets a Better Deal From the IRS Than an Investor" in Barron's (Vol. 88, March 31, 2008, No. 13, pp. 56)*

Pub: Dow Jones & Company Inc.

Contact: Almar Latour, Chief Executive Officer

Ed: Dan McGuire. **Description:** There is a $3,000 a year annual limit to deducting investor's losses and normal investment expenses are purportedly deductible as miscellaneous expenses on Schedule A only to the extent that they exceed two percent of adjusted gross income. Professional gamblers who can use Schedule C are unable deduct a net gaming loss against income from any other sources. **Availability:** Online.

34912 ■ *"Traditional vs. Roth IRA" in Black Enterprise (Vol. 37, October 2006, No. 3, pp. 58)*

Pub: Earl G. Graves Ltd.

Contact: Earl Graves, Jr., President

Ed: K. Parker, Carolyn M. Brown. **Description:** Government taxes the traditional IRAs different than it taxes Roth IRAs. **Availability:** Online.

34913 ■ *"Travel Tears" in Crain's Chicago Business (Vol. 31, November 17, 2008, No. 46, pp. 3)*

Pub: Crain Communications Inc.

Contact: Barry Asin, President

Ed: Bob Tita. **Description:** Hotels, restaurants and conventions are seeing a decline in profits due to corporate travel cutbacks and the sagging economy. City and state revenues derived from taxes on tourism-related industries are also suffering. **Availability:** Online.

34914 ■ *"Trust Tax Under Fire as Drain on Revenue" in Globe & Mail (April 9, 2007, pp. B1)*

Ed: Steven Chase. **Description:** The economic aspects of the implementation of the trust levy by the Canadian government are discussed. The acquisition of Canadian income trusts by Canadian and international financial institutions is described. **Availability:** Online.

34915 ■ *"Unemployment Tax Surge Could Hit Businesses Hard" in Orlando Business Journal (Vol. 26, January 1, 2010, No. 31, pp. 1)*

Pub: Orlando Business Journal

Contact: Julie Swyers, Director

E-mail: jswyers@bizjournals.com

Ed: Christopher Boyd. **Description:** Consequences of the almost 1,100 percent increase in Florida's minimum unemployment compensation insurance tax to businesses in the state are discussed. Employers pay for the said tax, which is used to fund the state's unemployment claims. **Availability:** Print; Online.

34916 ■ *"U.S. Buyer Rescues KCP From Trust Tax Burden" in Globe & Mail (April 3, 2007, pp. B1)*

Ed: Richard Blackwell. **Description:** The economic aspects of the buyout of KCP Income Fund by Caxton-Iseman Capital Inc. are discussed. **Availability:** Online.

34917 ■ "Up In the Air" in The Business Journal-Serving Greater Tampa Bay (Vol. 28, July 18, 2008, No. 30, pp. 1)

Description: Views and information on Busch Gardens and on its future, are presented. The park's 3,769 employees worry for their future, after tourism industry experts have expressed concerns on possible tax cuts and other cost reductions. The future of the park, which ranks number 19 as the most visited park in the world, is expected to have a major impact on the tourism industry. **Availability:** Online.

34918 ■ "Venture Gap" in Canadian Business (Vol. 81, February 26, 2008, No. 4, pp. 82)

Pub: Rogers Media Inc.

Contact: Neil Spivak, Chief Executive Officer

Ed: Joe Castaldo. **Description:** Money raised by Canadian venture capitalist firms has been declining since 2001. A strong venture capital market is important if Canada is to build innovative companies. Fixing Canada's tax policy on foreign investments is a start in reviving the industry. **Availability:** Print; Online.

34919 ■ "Waiting for the Sunset on Taxes" in Memphis Business Journal (Vol. 34, September 28, 2012, No. 24, pp. 1)

Pub: Baltimore Business Journal

Contact: Rhonda Pringle, President

E-mail: rpringle@bizjournals.com

Description: The implementation of the Tax Relief, Unemployment Reauthorization and Job Creation Act of 2010 will end on December 31, 2012. The exemption threshold will fall to $1 million, and the tax rate on transfers above that limit will be at 55 percent. The effect of political uncertainty on tax planning is also discussed. **Availability:** Print; Online.

34920 ■ "Water Efficiency Bills Move Through Congress" in Contractor (Vol. 56, July 2009, No. 7, pp. 20)

Ed: Kevin Schwalb. **Description:** National Association, a plumbing-heating-cooling contractor, was instrumental in drafting the Water Advanced Technologies for Efficient Resource Use Act of 2009 and they are also backing the Water Accountability Tax Efficiency Reinvestment Act. The first bill promotes WaterSense-labeled products while the other promotes water conservation through tax credits. **Availability:** Print; Online.

34921 ■ "The Weeks Ahead" in Crain's New York Business (Vol. 24, January 7, 2008, No. 1, pp. 26)

Description: Listing of events in the Detroit area include conferences addressing entrepreneurialism, economic development, and women business ownership. **Availability:** Print; Online.

34922 ■ "Weyerhaeuser's REIT Decision Shouldn't Scare Investors Away" in Barron's (Vol. 88, June 30, 2008, No. 26, pp. 18)

Pub: Dow Jones & Company Inc.

Contact: Almar Latour, Chief Executive Officer

Ed: Christopher Williams. **Description:** Weyerhaeuser Co.'s management said that a conversion to a real estate investment trust was not likely in 2009 since the move is not tax-efficient as of the moment and would overload its non-timber assets with debt. The company's shares have fallen by 19.5 percent. However, the company remains an asset-rich outfit and its activist shareholder is pushing for change. **Availability:** Online.

34923 ■ "What Business Expenses Do You Need to Track?" in Business News Daily (February 21, 2023)

URL(s): www.businessnewsdaily.com/15745-business-expenses-you-should-track.html

Ed: Adam Uzialko. **Released:** February 21, 2023. **Description:** Discusses the various expenses you need to track as a small business owner. Also goes over the tax-deductible rules. **Availability:** Online.

34924 ■ "What Is an EIN and Does Your Business Need One?" in Legal Zoom (March 15, 2023)

URL(s): www.legalzoom.com/articles/what-is-an-ein-and-does-your-business-need-one

Ed: Boni Peluso. **Released:** March 15, 2023. **Description:** Explains what an EIN is in and discusses why your business needs one. **Availability:** Online.

34925 ■ "What Should You Look For in a Business Bank Account" in Business News Daily (February 21, 2023)

URL(s): www.businessnewsdaily.com/15768-how-to-choose-a-business-bank-account.html

Ed: Julie Ross. **Released:** February 21, 2023. **Description:** Discusses the benefits of opening up a separate business bank account, which will make tax time a lot easier. **Availability:** Online.

34926 ■ "What's the Difference Between a Tax ID Number and a Corporate Number?" in Business News Daily (February 21, 2023)

URL(s): www.businessnewsdaily.com/15094-tax-id-corporate-numbers-explained.html

Ed: Simone Johnson. **Released:** February 21, 2023. **Description:** Discusses the differences between a tax ID number and a corporate number so small business can remain compliant with tax laws. **Availability:** Online.

34927 ■ "Which LLC Taxes Must Your Business File" in Business News Daily (February 28, 2023)

URL(s): www.businessnewsdaily.com/15744-llc-tax-guide.html

Ed: Andrew Martins. **Released:** February 28, 2023. **Description:** Small businesses structured as an LLC file differently during tax time than other businesses. This article guides business owners on what to expect during tax time. **Availability:** Online.

34928 ■ "Why Do I Owe Taxes from My Business despite Receiving No Money?" in Legal Zoom (March 14, 2023)

URL(s): www.legalzoom.com/articles/why-do-i-owe-taxes-from-my-business-despite-receiving-no-money

Ed: Stephen Sylvester. **Released:** March 14, 2023. **Description:** Discussion about business taxes and phantom income, which can affect your business. **Availability:** Online.

34929 ■ "Why Japan Is So Interested In Alabama" in Birmingham Business Journal (Vol. 31, August 1, 2014, No. 31, pp. 11)

Pub: American City Business Journals, Inc.

Contact: Mike Olivieri, Executive Vice President

Description: Kazuo Sunaga, Consul General of Japan in Atlanta, Georgia lists several reasons why Alabama presents several opportunities for Japanese companies, including fewer labor laws, low tax rates and the availability of trained workers. The state's relationship with Japan will be further enhanced when Birmingham hosts the Southeast U.S./Japan Association meeting in 2015, which will be attended by leaders from the business, political, and nonprofit sectors. **Availability:** Print; Online.

34930 ■ "Will Bush Cuts Survive? Tax Thriller in D.C." in Barron's (Vol. 90, August 30, 2010, No. 35, pp. 17)

Pub: Barron's Editorial & Corporate Headquarters

Ed: Jim McTague. **Description:** There are speculations on how Senator Harry Reid can push his bill to raise taxes on the wealthy while retaining the George W. Bush tax rates for the rest. Reid's challenge is to get the 60 votes needed to pass the bill. **Availability:** Online.

34931 ■ "With Measure 2 Defeated, Voters Still Looking for Property Tax Relief" in Dickinson Press (September 8, 2012)

Description: North Dakota voters voted down a measure that would abolish property taxes in the state, but are still seeking tax relief. **Availability:** Online.

34932 ■ Working for Yourself: Law & Taxes for Independent Contractors, Freelancers & Consultants

Pub: Nolo

Contact: Chris Braun, President

Ed: Stephen Fishman. **Released:** 12th Edition. **Price:** $27.99, e-book(downloadable); $34.99, book and e-book; $27.99, E-book. **Description:** In-depth information is shared for contractors, freelancers and consultants involving business law and small business taxes. **Availability:** E-book; Print; Electronic publishing; PDF.

TRADE PERIODICALS

34933 ■ Intertax

URL(s): www.kluwerlawonline.com/toc.php?pubcode=taxi

Released: Monthly **Description:** Journal covering tax information worldwide. **Availability:** Print; Online.

34934 ■ Small Business Taxes and Management

Pub: A/N Group Inc.

Contact: Steven A. Hopfenmuller, Chief Executive Officer

URL(s): www.smbiz.com

Released: Daily; Monday thru Friday. **Description:** Offers current tax news, reviews of recent cases, tax saving tips, and personal financial planning for small business owners. Includes articles on issues such as finance and management. Remarks: Available online only. **Availability:** Print.

VIDEO/AUDIO MEDIA

34935 ■ The How of Business: Matt Chiappetta - Year-End Tax Considerations

URL(s): www.thehowofbusiness.com/501-matt-chiappetta-tax-considerations

Ed: Henry Lopez. **Released:** December 11, 2023. **Description:** Podcast discusses year-end tax considerations for small businesses.

34936 ■ Mastering Accountable Plans: Unlock Tax Savings and Streamline Business Expenses

URL(s): podcasts.apple.com/us/podcast/mastering-accountable-plans-unlock-tax-savings-and/id1377276636?i=10006301686

Ed: Mike Jesowshek. **Released:** October 04, 2023. **Description:** Podcast discusses reimbursement for business-related expenses and devising an accountable plan.

34937 ■ Maximizing Tax Savings with Depreciation and Capitalization Policies for Small Business Owners

URL(s): podcasts.apple.com/us/podcast/maximizing-tax-savings-with-depreciation/id1377376636?i=1000628562867

Ed: Mike Jesowshek. **Released:** September 20, 2023. **Description:** Podcast discusses the power of depreciation and how to leverage it to optimize tax deductions.

34938 ■ Nomad Nation: Thriving as a Location-Independent Entrepreneur with Bobby Casey

URL(s): www.eofire.com/podcast/bobbycasey2

Ed: Jon Lee Dumas. **Released:** October 09, 2024. **Description:** Podcast discusses tax optimization strategies and tips for minimizing tax liabilities as a location-independent entrepreneur.

34939 ■ The Solopreneur Hour: How to Save a TON on Taxes, with Christina Lael

URL(s): solopreneurhour.com/podcast/839-how-to-save-a-ton-on-taxes-with-christina-lael

Ed: Michael O'Neal. **Released:** July 21, 2022. **Description:** Podcast offers five tax-saving strategies.

34940 ■ *This Is Small Business: What You Need to Know About Audits*
URL(s): www.smallbusiness.amazon/podcast-episo des/ep-52-what-you-need-to-know-about-audits
Ed: Andrea Marquez. **Released:** April 09, 2024.
Description: Podcast describes a typical audit, how to navigate it, and when you may need one.

34941 ■ *Top 10 Mid-Year Tax Saving Strategies Every Small Business Owner Must Know*
URL(s): podcasts.apple.com/us/podcast/top-10-mi d-year-tax-saving-strategies-every-small-business/i d1377376636?i=1000621628082
Ed: Mike Jesowshek. **Released:** June 19, 2023.
Description: Podcast offers knowledge and re- sources to help small business owners reduce taxa- tion liabilities and maximize savings.

34942 ■ *What Are Estimated Taxes and How Do I Pay Them?*
URL(s): podcasts.apple.com/us/podcast/what-are-es tmated-taxes-and-how-do-i-pay-them/id137737 6636?i=1000606444314
Ed: Mike Jesowshek. **Released:** March 29, 2023.
Description: Podcast discusses estimated taxes and when to pay them.

34943 ■ *What Year-End Tax Strategies Are Available to Business Owners?*
URL(s): podcasts.apple.com/us/podcast/what-year -end-tax-strategies-are-available-to-business/i d1377376636?i=1000589209385
Ed: Mike Jesowshek. **Released:** December 07, 2022.
Description: Podcast discussed year-end tax strate- gies, including bonus depreciation, credit card reimbursement, buying business equipment, and prepaying expenses.

CONSULTANTS

34944 ■ Crowe Horwath International
Crowe Horwath International
485 Lexington Ave., 11th Fl.
New York, NY 10017-2619
Ph: (212)572-5500
Fax: (212)572-5572
Co. E-mail: mail@crowe.com.kw
URL: http://www.crowe.com
Contact: James L. Powers, Chairman
Linkedin: www.linkedin.com/company/crowe
Description: Services include accounting, auditing, tax, and management consulting provides innovative business solutions in the area of assurance, busi- ness services, consulting, corporate finance, risk management, tax and technology. **Scope:** Services include accounting, auditing, tax, and management consulting provides innovative business solutions in the area of assurance, business services, consulting, corporate finance, risk management, tax and technol- ogy. **Founded:** 1991. **Publications:** "Does Your Busi- ness Have an E-Commerce Strategy"; "Americas Tax Facts," 2007; "Caring Sharing Investing Growing: The Story of Horwath International," Nov, 2006; "How To Franchise Internationally"; "International Tax Planning Manual: Expatriates and Migrants"; "Americas Tax Facts 2007"; "European and Middle East Tax Facts 2008"; "International Offshore Financial Services"; "International Tax Planning Manual: Corporations"; "Asia or Pacific Tax News 2008: Issue 2"; "FOMB: A Quiz for Business Owners". **Training:** Demand Creation Training, Dec, 2006; Marketing, Dec, 2006.

34945 ■ Grant Thornton L.L.P. - Library
Grant Thornton International Ltd. (GTIL)
171 N Clark St., Ste. 200
Chicago, IL 60601
Ph: 44 20 7383 5100
URL: http://www.grantthornton.co.uk
Contact: Seth L. Siegel, Chief Executive Officer
Facebook: www.facebook.com/GrantThorntonUS
Linkedin: www.linkedin.com/company/grant-thornton -llp
X (Twitter): twitter.com/GrantThorntonUS
Instagram: www.instagram.com/grantthorntonusa
YouTube: www.youtube.com/grantthorntonus

Description: Provider of accounting, audit, tax and advisory services. **Scope:** Professional service provider of tax, audit and advisory services. Advisory services are offered in the areas of governance, risk and compliance; forensics, investigations and litiga- tion; Information technology; performance improve- ment; business strategy; restructuring and turn- around; transaction advisory services and valuation. **Services:** Figures not available. **Founded:** 1924. **Educational Activities:** National Association Busi- ness Economics Annual Meeting (Annual); Winter Leadership Conference (Annual).

FRANCHISES AND BUSINESS OPPORTUNITIES

34946 ■ Cash Plus Inc. (CP)
PO Box 2185
Anaheim, CA 92814
Ph: (714)731-2274
Free: 877-227-4758
Fax: (714)731-2099
Co. E-mail: cpcorp@cashplusinc.com
URL: http://cashplusinc.com
Contact: Craig Wells, President
Description: Provider of financial services. **Founded:** 1984. **Training:** Provides training includ- ing easy-to-run computerized operating system, promotions and check verification and payday ad- vance process.

PUBLICATIONS

34947 ■ *Business Organizations with Tax Planning*
NY
URL: http://store.lexisnexis.com/categories/publish- ers/matthew-bender-850
Contact: Mike Walsh, Chief Executive Officer
URL(s): store.lexisnexis.com/products/business -organizations-with-tax-planning-skuusSku10732
Ed: Zolman Cavitch. **Price:** $23,870, for Loose- Leaf:16 loose-leaf volumes; $23,870, for eBook: epub or eBook: mobi. **Description:** Periodic supplementa- tion. In-depth analytical coverage of corporation law and all relevant aspects of federal corporation taxa- tion. **Availability:** CD-ROM; E-book; Print; Electronic publishing; Online; Download.

34948 ■ *"Small Businesses Support Expansive Tax Reforms Needed to Level the Playing Field and Offset the Costs of 'Build Back Better' Plan" in Business2Community (November 3, 2021)*
URL(s): www.business2community.com/small-busi- ness/small-businesses-support-expansive-tax-re- forms-needed-to-level-the-playing-field-and-offse t-the-costs-of-build-back-better-plan-02438911
Ed: John Arensmeyer. **Released:** November 02, 2021. **Description:** Discusses the tax reforms for small businesses within the Build Back Better plan.

COMPUTERIZED DATABASES

34949 ■ *CCH ProSystem fx Tax™*
Wolters Kluwer
90 Sheppard Ave. E, Ste. 300
Toronto, ON, Canada M2N 6X1
Ph: (416)224-2248
URL: http://www.wolterskluwer.com/en-in
Contact: Kevin Entricken, Chief Financial Officer
URL(s): www.wolterskluwer.com/en/solutions/cch -prosystem-fx/tax
Availability: PDF; Download; Online. **Type:** Bulletin board.

34950 ■ *Federal Income Taxation of Corporations and Shareholders*
Thomson Reuters (Tax And Accounting) Inc.
2395 Midway Rd.
Carrollton, TX 75006
Free: 888-885-0206
URL: http://tax.thomsonreuters.com/en
Contact: Brian Peccarelli, President

URL(s): store.tax.thomsonreuters.com/accounting/ Tax/Federal-Income-Taxation-of-Corporations-an d-Shareholders/p/100200943
Released: 3/year **Price:** $1,390, for book, latest updates(One-year subscription,). **Availability:** Print; Online. **Type:** Full-text.

34951 ■ *Federal Income Taxation of S Corporations*
Thomson Reuters (Tax And Accounting) Inc.
2395 Midway Rd.
Carrollton, TX 75006
Free: 888-885-0206
URL: http://tax.thomsonreuters.com/en
Contact: Brian Peccarelli, President
URL(s): store.tax.thomsonreuters.com/accounting/ Tax/Federal-Income-Taxation-of-S-Corporations/p/ 100201404
Released: 3/year **Price:** $1,040, Individuals. **Avail- ability:** Print. **Type:** Full-text.

34952 ■ *Federal Taxes Weekly Alert*
Thomson Reuters (Tax And Accounting) Inc.
2395 Midway Rd.
Carrollton, TX 75006
Free: 888-885-0206
URL: http://tax.thomsonreuters.com/en
Contact: Brian Peccarelli, President
URL(s): store.tax.thomsonreuters.com/accounting/ Tax/US-Tax-Reporter-Estate-and-Gift/p/100200366
Released: Daily **Availability:** Online; PDF. **Type:** Full-text.

34953 ■ *IRS Practice and Procedure*
Thomson Reuters (Tax And Accounting) Inc.
2395 Midway Rd.
Carrollton, TX 75006
Free: 888-885-0206
URL: http://tax.thomsonreuters.com/en
Contact: Brian Peccarelli, President
URL(s): store.tax.thomsonreuters.com/accounting/ Tax/IRS-Practice-and-Procedure/p/100200942
Price: $1,245, Individuals. **Availability:** Print; Online. **Type:** Full-text.

34954 ■ *Limited Liability Companies: Tax & Business Law*
Thomson Reuters (Tax And Accounting) Inc.
2395 Midway Rd.
Carrollton, TX 75006
Free: 888-885-0206
URL: http://tax.thomsonreuters.com/en
Contact: Brian Peccarelli, President
URL(s): store.tax.thomsonreuters.com/accounting/ Tax/Limited-Liability-Companies-Tax-and-Business -Law/p/100201344#:~:text=Limited%20Liability% 20Companies%3A%20Tax%20and%20Business% 20Law%20is%20a%20comprehensive,LLPs)%20an d%20limited%20liability%20limited
Released: Semiannual **Price:** $750, Individuals. **Availability:** E-book; Print; Online. **Type:** Full-text.

LIBRARIES

34955 ■ Arnold & Porter Kaye Scholer LLP - Library
250 W 55th St.
New York, NY 10019-9710
Ph: (212)836-8000
Fax: (212)836-8689
URL: http://www.arnoldporter.com/en
Contact: Arthur E. Brown, Partner
E-mail: arthur.brown@arnoldporter.com
Description: Law firm provides legal services. **Scope:** Law. **Services:** Interlibrary loan; copying; SDI; library open to members of SLA and Law Library Association of Greater New York by appointment. **Founded:** 2017. **Holdings:** 45,546 books; 520 bound periodical volumes; 6220 microfiche; 2007 ultrafiche; 1866 reels of microfilm; 264 VF drawers.; 20,000 books; 400 bound periodical volumes. **Subscrip- tions:** ; 205 journals and other serials; 15 newspa- pers.

34956 ■ Gardiner Roberts L.L.P., Library
22 Adelaide St. W, Ste. 3600
  Toronto, ON, Canada M5H 4E3
Ph: (416)865-6600
Fax: (416)865-6636
Co. E-mail: contactgr@grllp.com
URL: http://www.grllp.com
Contact: Paul Stoyan, Chairman Partner
E-mail: pstoyan@grllp.com
X (Twitter): x.com/grllp

Description: Law firm provides advice in various areas. **Scope:** Law - administrative, civil, commercial, insurance, municipal, real estate, tax; intellectual property; information technology. **Services:** Interlibrary loan; copying; library not open to public. **Founded:** 1920. **Holdings:** 2,000 books; 300 bound periodical volumes; 500 reports; CD-ROMs.

34957 ■ Ross & McBride Library
1 King St., W
  Hamilton, ON, Canada L8P 1A4

Ph: (905)526-9800
Free: 866-526-9800
Fax: (905)526-0732
Co. E-mail: contact@rossmcbride.com
URL: http://www.rossmcbride.com
Contact: Tim R. Parker, General Manager
E-mail: tparker@rossmcbride.com

Scope: Law, taxation. **Services:** Library not open to public. **Founded:** 1894. **Holdings:** Figures not available.

ASSOCIATIONS AND OTHER ORGANIZATIONS

34958 ■ American Productivity & Quality Center (APQC) - Library
123 N Post Oak Ln., Third Fl.
Houston, TX 77024
Ph: (713)681-4020
Free: 800-776-9676
Fax: (713)681-8578
Co. E-mail: communications@apqc.org
URL: http://www.apqc.org
Contact: Lisa Higgins, President
E-mail: lhiggins@apqc.org
Facebook: www.facebook.com/APQCResearch
Linkedin: www.linkedin.com/company/apqc
X (Twitter): x.com/APQC
Instagram: www.instagram.com/apqc_
YouTube: www.youtube.com/channel/UC538mkuA
  tOVzS69ZYSlwHjg
Description: Resource for process and performance improvement. Helps organizations adapt to rapidly changing environments, and succeed in a competitive marketplace. Focuses on productivity, knowledge management, benchmarking, and quality improvement initiatives. Works with member organizations to identify best practices, broadly disseminate findings, and connect individuals with one another and the knowledge and tools they need to succeed. **Scope:** Benchmarking, knowledge management, best practices, organizational effectiveness, performance measurement, K-16 education, productivity, quality, customer-focused systems, shared services, leadership, human resources, organizational development, strategic planning. **Founded:** 1977. **Holdings:** Figures not available. **Publications:** *CenterView Newsletter* (Monthly); *Practice case studies* (Quarterly); *Best Practice.* **Educational Activities:** APQC Conference (Annual); Annual Knowledge Management Conference & Workshop (Annual). **Awards:** Grayson Medal (Annual). **Geographic Preference:** Multinational.

34959 ■ Center for Creative Leadership (CCL) - Library
1 Leadership Pl.
Greensboro, NC 27410
Ph: (336)545-2810
Fax: (336)288-5759
Co. E-mail: unsubscribe@ccl.org
URL: http://www.ccl.org
Contact: Martin Schneider, President
Facebook: www.facebook.com/CenterforCreativeLea
  dership
Linkedin: www.linkedin.com/company/center-for-crea
  tive-leadership
X (Twitter): x.com/CCLdotORG
Description: Promotes behavioral science research and leadership education. **Scope:** Provide training programs in the areas of: leadership development for women and minorities, impact of leadership development programs, emerging leaders, global leaders, high-performing teams, systemic leadership develop-

ment, and evolving concepts of leadership in dynamic systems, and on education and the nonprofit sector. **Founded:** 1970. **Holdings:** Figures not available. **Publications:** *Leadership Resources--A Guide to Training and Development Tools* (Biennial); *Leadership Education: A Source Book of Courses and Programs*; *Center for Creative Leadership Catalog*; *Leadership in Action* (Bimonthly; Semimonthly); *Research Reports* (Periodic). **Educational Activities:** CCL Conferences (Annual). **Awards:** CCL Distinguished Alumni Award (Annual); Kenneth E. Clark Student Research Award (Annual); Walter F. Ulmer, Jr. Applied Research Award (Annual); CCL Leadership Quarterly Award (Annual). **Geographic Preference:** Multinational.

34960 ■ Employers Group (EG) - Reference Library
400 Continental Blvd., Ste. 300
El Segundo, CA 90245
Free: 800-748-8484
Co. E-mail: serviceone@employersgroup.com
URL: http://www.employersgroup.com
Contact: Mark Wilbur, President
E-mail: mwilbur@employersgroup.com
Facebook: www.facebook.com/EmployersGroup
Linkedin: www.linkedin.com/company/employers
  -group
X (Twitter): x.com/EmployersGroup
Description: Provides human resources management services including wage, salary, and benefit surveys; personnel practices surveys; management counseling; management education programs; litigation surveillance; government relations; and research library service. **Scope:** Human resource management. **Founded:** 1896. **Holdings:** Figures not available. **Publications:** *California Wage and Hour GuideAL* (Annual). **Training:** OC - First Time & Frontline Supervisors Boot Camp, 2012; NC - Leadership Essentials & Supervisory Laws, 2012. **Geographic Preference:** National.

34961 ■ Institute for Operations Research and the Management Sciences (INFORMS)
5521 Research Park Dr., Ste. 200
Catonsville, MD 21228
Ph: (443)757-3500
Free: 800-446-3676
Fax: (443)757-3515
Co. E-mail: informs@informs.org
URL: http://www.informs.org
Contact: Jie Xu, President
E-mail: jxu13@gmu.edu
Facebook: www.facebook.com/INFORMSpage
Linkedin: www.linkedin.com/company/informs_2
X (Twitter): x.com/INFORMS
Instagram: www.instagram.com/informs_orms
Description: International scientific society dedicated to improving operational processes, decision-making and management through the application of methods from science and mathematics. Represents operations researchers, management scientists and those working in related fields within engineering and the information, decision, mathematical and social sci-

ences. **Scope:** Improvement of operational processes, decision-making, and management through the application of methods from science and mathematics. **Founded:** 1995. **Publications:** *Management Science* (Monthly); *Manufacturing & Service Operations Management (M&SOM)* (Bimonthly); *INFORMS Journal on Computing (JOC)* (6/year); *Informations Systems Research (ISR)* (Quarterly); *Transportation Science* (Bimonthly); *Annual Comprehensive Index Bibliographic Database*; *INFORMS Membership Directory*; *INFORMS Members Web Pages Database*; *Operations Research* (Bimonthly); *OR/MS Today* (Quarterly); *Decision Analysis* (Quarterly); *INFORMS Bibliographic Database*; *Conference Presentations Database*; *OR/MS Today Resource Directory*; *Operations Management Education Review (OMER)* (Annual); *INFORMS Transactions on Education (ITE)* (3/year); *Mathematics of Operations Research* (Quarterly); *Marketing Science* (Bimonthly); *OR/MS Today Resource Directory*; *INFORMS Presentation Database*; *Working Paper Database*; *INFORMS Journal on Applied Analytics* (Bimonthly); *Marketing Science* (Bimonthly); *Organization Science* (Bimonthly); *ORMS Tomorrow, student newsletter*; *INFORMS OR/MS; Resource Collection: Companies*; *INFORMS OR/MS; Resource Collection: Journals*; *INFORMS OR/MS; Resource Collection: Computer Programs*; *INFORMS OR/MS; Resource Collection: People*; *INFORMS OR/MS; Resource Collection: Resources*; *INFORMS OR/MS; Resource Collection: Conferences*; *INFORMS OR/MS; Resource Collection: Courses*; *INFORMS OR/MS; Resource Collection: Educational Program*; *INFORMS OR/MS; Resource Collection: Societies*; *INFORMS OR/MS; Resource Collection: Job information.* **Educational Activities:** INFORMS Annual Meeting (Annual); George E. Nicholson Student Paper Competition (Annual); INFORMS Business Analytics Conference (Annual); INFORMS Annual Meeting (Annual). **Awards:** Franz Edelman Award for Achievement in Operations Research and the Management Sciences (Annual); INFORMS President's Award (Annual); Frederick W. Lanchester Prize (Annual); Franz Edelman Award for Achievement in Operations Research and the Management Sciences (Annual); George E. Kimball Medal (Annual); Frederick W. Lanchester Prize (Annual); Philip McCord Morse Lectureship Award (Annual); George Nicholson Student Paper Competition (Annual); John von Neumann Theory Prize (Annual); Prize for the Teaching of OR/MS Practice (Annual); George B. Dantzig Dissertation Award (Annual); Saul Gass Expository Writing Award (Annual); President's Award (Annual); Prize for the Teaching of OR/MS Practice (Annual); INFORMS Fellow Award (Annual); Seth Bonder Scholarship for Applied Operations Research in Military Applications (Annual); Franz Edelman Award for Management Science Achievement (Annual); Judith Liebman Award (Annual); INFORMS Moving Spirit Award for Chapters (Annual). **Geographic Preference:** Multinational.

34962 ■ International Society for the Study of Time (ISST)
c/o Lanei Rodemeyer, Treas.
Philosophy Dept.

Duquesne University
600 Forbes Ave.
Pittsburgh, PA 15282
URL: http://studyoftime.org
Contact: Carmen Leccardi, President
Facebook: www.facebook.com/InternationalSocie
tyfortheStudyofTime
X (Twitter): x.com/studyoftime

Description: Scientists and humanists. Explores the idea and experience of time and the role time plays in the physical, organic, intellectual, and social worlds. Encourages interdisciplinary study; provides a forum for exchange of ideas among members. **Founded:** 1966. **Publications:** *KronoScope* (Semiannual); *Time's News* (Annual). **Educational Activities:** International Society for the Study of Time Conference (Triennial). **Awards:** ISST Founder's Prize for New Scholars (Triennial). **Geographic Preference:** Multinational.

34963 ■ Project Management Institute (PMI)
14 Campus Blvd.
  Newtown Square, PA 19073-3299
Ph: (610)356-4600
Fax: (610)356-4647
Co. E-mail: customercare@pmi.org
URL: http://www.pmi.org
Contact: Pierre Le Manh, President
Facebook: www.facebook.com/PMInstitute
Linkedin: www.linkedin.com/company/pminstitute
X (Twitter): x.com/pminstitute
Instagram: www.instagram.com/pmi_org
YouTube: www.youtube.com/c/pmi

Description: Seeks to advance the study, teaching and practice of project management. Establishes project management standards; conducts educational and professional certification courses; bestows Project Management Professional credential upon qualified individuals. Offers educational seminars and global congresses. **Publications:** *Bibliography on the Project Manager and Project Oragnization* (Quarterly); *PM Network* (Monthly); *PMI Today* (Monthly); *Project Management Journal® (PMJ)* (Bimonthly; 6/year); *Project Management Salary Survey.* **Educational Activities:** PMI EMEA Congress; Global Congress North America (Annual). **Awards:** PMI Fellow Award (Irregular); PMO of the Year Award (Annual); PMI Distinguished Contribution Award (Irregular); PMI Linn ~Stuckenbruck Person of the Year Award (Annual); PMI Project of the Year Award (Annual); PMIEF James R. Snyder International Student Paper of the Year Award (Annual).

34964 ■ SHRM Executive Network
1800 Duke St.
  Alexandria, VA 22314
Free: 888-602-3270
Co. E-mail: executivenetwork@shrm.org
URL: http://www.shrm.org/executive
X (Twitter): x.com/TIAonline

Description: Human resource planning professionals representing 160 corporations and 3,000 individual members, including strategic human resources planning and development specialists, staffing analysts, business planners, line managers, and others who function as business partners in the application of strategic human resource management practices. Seeks to increase the impact of human resource planning and management on business and organizational performance. Sponsors program of professional development in human resource planning concepts, techniques, and practices. **Founded:** 1977. **Publications:** *HR People + Strategy Membership*; *People and Strategy* (Quarterly). **Geographic Preference:** National.

34965 ■ Society for Advancement of Management (SAM)
Marshall University - Provost Office 1 John Marshall Dr.
  Huntington, WV 25755
Ph: (407)279-0890
Co. E-mail: sam@samnational.org
URL: http://samnational.org
Contact: Reza Kheirandish, President
Facebook: www.facebook.com/SAMnational

Linkedin: www.linkedin.com/company/samnational
X (Twitter): x.com/SAM_samnational
Instagram: www.instagram.com/samnational_news
Description: Represents management executives in industry commerce, government, and education. Fields of interest include management education, policy and strategy, MIS, international management, administration, budgeting, collective bargaining, distribution, incentives, materials handling, quality control, and training. **Founded:** 1912. **Publications:** *SAM Advanced Management Journal* (Quarterly); *SAM Management In Practice* (Quarterly); *The SAM News International* (Quarterly); *Society for Advancement of Management--International Business Conference Proceedings* (Annual); *Advanced Management Journal* (Quarterly). **Educational Activities:** Society for Advancement of Management Meeting (Annual); Society for Advancement of Management International Business Conference (Annual). **Geographic Preference:** National.

EDUCATIONAL PROGRAMS

34966 ■ Basics of Time Management Workshop (Onsite)
Seminar Information Service Inc. (SIS)
  250 El Camino Real., Ste. 112
  Tustin, CA 92780
Ph: (714)508-0340
Free: 877-736-4636
Fax: (714)734-8027
Co. E-mail: info@seminarinformation.com
URL: http://www.seminarinformation.com
Contact: Catherine Bellizzi, President
URL(s): www.seminarinformation.com/details.cfm?qc
=qqbsll
Description: Identify and overcome barriers to effective time management issues, including proven time management and prioritizing skills to help you concentrate on how to determine how much time, energy and resources is needed. **Audience:** Industry professionals. **Principal Exhibits:** Identify and overcome barriers to effective time management issues, including proven time management and prioritizing skills to help you concentrate on how to determine how much time, energy and resources is needed.

34967 ■ Effective Time Management: Prioritizing for Success (Onsite)
Seminar Information Service Inc. (SIS)
  250 El Camino Real., Ste. 112
  Tustin, CA 92780
Ph: (714)508-0340
Free: 877-736-4636
Fax: (714)734-8027
Co. E-mail: info@seminarinformation.com
URL: http://www.seminarinformation.com
Contact: Catherine Bellizzi, President
URL(s): www.seminarinformation.com/qqbtkh/effec
tive-time-management-prioritizing-for-success
Description: Learn how to: Set goals and priorities that enable you to effectively manage your time; Monitor daily work habits and determine areas for improvement; Plan daily tasks and goals that align with your mission statement; Identify, evaluate and select tools that help with time and priority management; Avoid over-committing yourself and combat procrastination; Balance your professional and personal lives; Implement a personal time-management action plan. **Audience:** Industry professionals and general public. **Principal Exhibits:** Learn how to: Set goals and priorities that enable you to effectively manage your time; Monitor daily work habits and determine areas for improvement; Plan daily tasks and goals that align with your mission statement; Identify, evaluate and select tools that help with time and priority management; Avoid overcommitting yourself and combat procrastination; Balance your professional and personal lives; Implement a personal time-management action plan.

34968 ■ Essential Time Management & Organizational Skills (Onsite)
Seminar Information Service Inc. (SIS)
  250 El Camino Real., Ste. 112
  Tustin, CA 92780

Ph: (714)508-0340
Free: 877-736-4636
Fax: (714)734-8027
Co. E-mail: info@seminarinformation.com
URL: http://www.seminarinformation.com
Contact: Catherine Bellizzi, President
URL(s): www.seminarinformation.com

Description: Time management plan that you will design for yourself; allowing you to build in the flexibility you need to meet work and home commitments. **Audience:** Industry professionals. **Principal Exhibits:** Time management plan that you will design for yourself; allowing you to build in the flexibility you need to meet work and home commitments.

34969 ■ Fred Pryor Seminars & CareerTrack How to Manage Inventories and Cycle Counts
Fred Pryor Seminars & CareerTrack
  5700 Broadmoor, Ste. 300
  Mission, KS 66202
Free: 800-780-8476
Fax: (913)967-8849
Co. E-mail: customerservice@pryor.com
URL: http://www.pryor.com
Contact: Janet Turner, Contact
E-mail: dmca@pryor.com
URL(s): www.pryor.com/mkt_info/seminars/desc/IV
.asp
Description: Cost saving methods and time saving techniques to ensure accurate counts and inventories. **Audience:** Administrative professionals. **Principal Exhibits:** Cost saving methods and time saving techniques to ensure accurate counts and inventories.

34970 ■ Fred Pryor Seminars & CareerTrack Managing Multiple Priorities, Projects, and Deadlines
Fred Pryor Seminars & CareerTrack
  5700 Broadmoor, Ste. 300
  Mission, KS 66202
Free: 800-780-8476
Fax: (913)967-8849
Co. E-mail: customerservice@pryor.com
URL: http://www.pryor.com
Contact: Janet Turner, Contact
E-mail: dmca@pryor.com
URL(s): www.pryor.com/training-seminars/managing
-multiple-priorities-projects-deadlines
Frequency: Irregular. **Description:** Learn to manage multiple demands and priorities, get more done in less time, keep on top of numerous deadlines, and eliminate pressure and stress from your work day. **Audience:** Administrative professionals. **Principal Exhibits:** Learn to manage multiple demands and priorities, get more done in less time, keep on top of numerous deadlines, and eliminate pressure and stress from your work day.

34971 ■ The Indispensable Assistant (Onsite)
Seminar Information Service Inc. (SIS)
  250 El Camino Real., Ste. 112
  Tustin, CA 92780
Ph: (714)508-0340
Free: 877-736-4636
Fax: (714)734-8027
Co. E-mail: info@seminarinformation.com
URL: http://www.seminarinformation.com
Contact: Catherine Bellizzi, President
URL(s): www.seminarinformation.com/details.cfm?qc
=qqayxj
Description: Learn how to juggle multiple projects and priorities; how to keep things running smoothly when the boss is away; how to save time by delegating; and how to identify and overcome personal productivity roadblocks. **Audience:** Administrative assistants, and secretaries. **Principal Exhibits:** Learn how to juggle multiple projects and priorities; how to keep things running smoothly when the boss is away; how to save time by delegating; and how to identify and overcome personal productivity roadblocks.

34972 ■ Managing Information Overload: Techniques for Working Smarter (Onsite)
Seminar Information Service Inc. (SIS)
  250 El Camino Real., Ste. 112
  Tustin, CA 92780

Ph: (714)508-0340
Free: 877-736-4636
Fax: (714)734-8027
Co. E-mail: info@seminarinformation.com
URL: http://www.seminarinformation.com
Contact: Catherine Bellizzi, President
URL(s): www.seminarinformation.com

Description: Learn how to increase your productivity with effective information management skills, apply creative strategies, including mind maps, for processing information, adopt speed-reading techniques to quickly digest reports, and develop advanced memory skills to retain important information. **Audience:** Business industry professionals. **Principal Exhibits:** Learn how to increase your productivity with effective information management skills, apply creative strategies, including mind maps, for processing information, adopt speed-reading techniques to quickly digest reports, and develop advanced memory skills to retain important information.

34973 ■ Managing Multiple Priorities (Onsite)

Seminar Information Service Inc. (SIS)
    250 El Camino Real., Ste. 112
    Tustin, CA 92780
Ph: (714)508-0340
Free: 877-736-4636
Fax: (714)734-8027
Co. E-mail: info@seminarinformation.com
URL: http://www.seminarinformation.com
Contact: Catherine Bellizzi, President
URL(s): www.seminarinformation.com/details.cfm?qc
=qqbeqa

Description: Focus on practical techniques for setting priorities and goals and on how to manage ongoing projects from start to finish. Topics include: handling paperwork systematically, realistic ways to decrease interruptions, and learning to say no. **Audience:** General public. **Principal Exhibits:** Focus on practical techniques for setting priorities and goals and on how to manage ongoing projects from start to finish. Topics include: handling paperwork systematically, realistic ways to decrease interruptions, and learning to say no.

34974 ■ Managing Multiple Projects, Competing Priorities & Tight Deadlines (Onsite)

Seminar Information Service Inc. (SIS)
    250 El Camino Real., Ste. 112
    Tustin, CA 92780
Ph: (714)508-0340
Free: 877-736-4636
Fax: (714)734-8027
Co. E-mail: info@seminarinformation.com
URL: http://www.seminarinformation.com
Contact: Catherine Bellizzi, President
URL(s): www.seminarinformation.com

Description: Skills you need to immediately and effectively deal with multiple projects, expectations, and deadlines without backlog, burnout, and stress. **Audience:** Managers. **Principal Exhibits:** Skills you need to immediately and effectively deal with multiple projects, expectations, and deadlines without backlog, burnout, and stress.

34975 ■ Managing Multiple Projects, Objectives and Deadlines (Onsite)

Seminar Information Service Inc. (SIS)
    250 El Camino Real., Ste. 112
    Tustin, CA 92780
Ph: (714)508-0340
Free: 877-736-4636
Fax: (714)734-8027
Co. E-mail: info@seminarinformation.com
URL: http://www.seminarinformation.com
Contact: Catherine Bellizzi, President
URL(s): www.seminarinformation.com/details.cfm?qc
=qqayxd

Description: Learn organizational skills to help you get more accomplished. **Audience:** Busy managers, supervisors and administrative persons. **Principal Exhibits:** Learn organizational skills to help you get more accomplished.

34976 ■ The Strategic Speed-Reading Advantage for Executives & Legal Professionals

Fred Pryor Seminars & CareerTrack
    5700 Broadmoor, Ste. 300
    Mission, KS 66202
Free: 800-780-8476
Fax: (913)967-8849
Co. E-mail: customerservice@pryor.com
URL: http://www.pryor.com
Contact: Janet Turner, Contact
E-mail: dmca@pryor.com
URL(s): www.pryor.com/mkt_info/seminars/desc/RX
.asp

Description: Learn to organize, prioritize, and absorb volumes of information for effortlessly making critical decisions. **Audience:** Executives and legal professionals. **Principal Exhibits:** Learn to organize, prioritize, and absorb volumes of information for effortlessly making critical decisions.

34977 ■ Time Management (Onsite)

Seminar Information Service Inc. (SIS)
    250 El Camino Real., Ste. 112
    Tustin, CA 92780
Ph: (714)508-0340
Free: 877-736-4636
Fax: (714)734-8027
Co. E-mail: info@seminarinformation.com
URL: http://www.seminarinformation.com
Contact: Catherine Bellizzi, President
URL(s): www.seminarinformation.com/details.cfm?qc
=qqabuk

Description: Learn to determine how your time is being spent, develop strategies for time allocation, create a structure to control time spent on tasks and activities, and prioritize what matters most in your life. **Audience:** Business professionals at all levels. **Principal Exhibits:** Learn to determine how your time is being spent, develop strategies for time allocation, create a structure to control time spent on tasks and activities, and prioritize what matters most in your life.

34978 ■ Time Management Survival Skills (Onsite)

Seminar Information Service Inc. (SIS)
    250 El Camino Real., Ste. 112
    Tustin, CA 92780
Ph: (714)508-0340
Free: 877-736-4636
Fax: (714)734-8027
Co. E-mail: info@seminarinformation.com
URL: http://www.seminarinformation.com
Contact: Catherine Bellizzi, President
URL(s): www.seminarinformation.com/qqbebd/time
-management-survival-skills

Description: Develop a step-by-step action plan and use the latest tools for accomplishing your important goals, objectives, and activities. **Audience:** Professionals and managers. **Principal Exhibits:** Develop a step-by-step action plan and use the latest tools for accomplishing your important goals, objectives, and activities.

REFERENCE WORKS

34979 ■ "100+ Time Saving Tips for Small Businesses" in Small Business Trends(June 16, 2021)

URL(s): smallbiztrends.com/2017/03/time-saving-tips
-small-business.html

Ed: Matt Mansfield. **Released:** June 16, 2021. **Description:** A list of practical time saving tips for small business owners. **Availability:** Online.

34980 ■ "Conquering the Seven Summits of Sales: From Everest to Every Business, Achieving Peak Performance"

Pub: Harper Business
Contact: Hollis Heimbouch, Senior Vice President Publisher

Released: October 07, 2014. **Price:** $4.99, e-book; $6.19, hardcover; $0.10, hardcover(39 used from $0. 10); $3.75, hardcover(19 new from $3.75); $9.10, kindle. **Description:** Sales professionals are taught

to overcome their perceived limitations and strive for success. The guide shows how to define goals, build the right team, commit to a vision, time management, and tracking of progress. **Availability:** E-book; Print.

34981 ■ "Cyberwise" in Black Enterprise (Vol. 40, July 2010, No. 12, pp. 48)

Pub: Earl G. Graves Ltd.
Contact: Earl Graves, Jr., President

Ed: Sonya A. Donaldson. **Description:** Tools to effectively manage time are explored. **Availability:** Online.

34982 ■ "Defend Your Research: The Early Bird Really Does Get the Worm" in Harvard Business Review (Vol. 88, July-August 2010, No. 7-8, pp. 30)

Pub: Harvard Business Publishing
Contact: Diane Belcher, Managing Director

Ed: Christoph Randler. **Price:** $6, PDF. **Description:** Research indicates that those who identify themselves as 'morning people' tend to be more proactive, and thus have a career-development advantage over those who identify themselves as 'night people'. Implications of the research are also discussed. **Availability:** Online; PDF.

34983 ■ "Don't Fear the Phone" in Senior Market Advisor (Vol. 13, October 2012, No. 10, pp. 50)

Description: Investment brokers and financial planning advisors must set aside time to make phone calls to clients as well as prospective clients. The article puts this process into perspective for setting appointments. **Availability:** Online.

34984 ■ "The End of Clock-Punching" in Canadian Business (Vol. 83, September 14, 2010, No. 15, pp. 96)

Pub: Rogers Media Inc.
Contact: Neil Spivak, Chief Executive Officer

Ed: Lyndoic Bourgon. **Description:** Workplace consultant Peter Hadwen is pushing for the transformation of Canada's government departments into results-only work environments (ROWE). ROWE does not require employees to show up to work at a certain time as long as they are meeting goals and achieving results in their jobs. Details of studies regarding ROWE in US companies are examined. **Availability:** Online.

34985 ■ "Fantasy in the Workplace" in Orlando Business Journal (Vol. 28, September 7, 2012, No. 30, pp. 1)

Pub: Baltimore Business Journal
Contact: Rhonda Pringle, President
E-mail: rpringle@bizjournals.com

Description: A 2011 research report from the Fantasy Sports Trade Association shows that participation in fantasy sports increased by 60 percent over the past four years to more than 32 million people over the age of 12. Implications of the increase on employees' workplace productivity and time management as well as employers' monitoring of computer usage are discussed. **Availability:** Print; Online.

34986 ■ "Heavy Duty: The Case Against Packing Lightly" in Crain's Chicago Business (Vol. 31, April 21, 2008, No. 16, pp. 29)

Pub: Crain Communications Inc.
Contact: Barry Asin, President

Ed: Sarah A. Klein. **Description:** Penelope Biggs, a Northern Trust executive who manages sales teams in North America, Europe and Asia gives advice on traveling abroad for business including time management skills, handling time-zone hops and avoiding jet-lag. **Availability:** Online.

34987 ■ "How Busy Executives Manage to Live a Balanced Life" in Influencive(March 20, 2019)

URL(s): www.influencive.com/how-busy-executives
-manage-to-live-a-balanced-life/

Ed: Kiara Williams. **Released:** March 20, 2019. **Description:** Discusses how those in the C-suite are able to run corporations while also maintaining some balance in their personal lives. **Availability:** Online.

34988 ■ *"How Many Direct Reports? Senior Leaders, Always Pressed For Time, Are Nonetheless Broadening Their Span of Control"* in Harvard Business Review (Vol. 90, April 2012, No. 4, pp. 112)

Pub: Harvard Business Review Press

Contact: Moderna V. Pfizer, Contact

Ed: Gary L. Neilson, Julie M. Wulf. **Price:** $8.95, hardcover. **Description:** A rise in market and geographical complexities has driven an expansion of chief executive officer control during the past 20 years. New executive development options enable CEOs to cross-collaborate, and functional leaders make up 80 percent of new positions reporting to the CEO. **Availability:** PDF; Online.

34989 ■ *"Leave It Behind"* in Crain's Chicago Business (Vol. 31, April 21, 2008, No. 16, pp. 32)

Pub: Crain Communications Inc.

Contact: Barry Asin, President

Ed: Sarah A. Klein. **Description:** Patrick Brady who investigates possible violations of the Foreign Corrupt Practices Act has a novel approach when traveling to frequent destinations which allows him to travel with only a carry-on piece of luggage: he leaves suits at dry cleaners in the places he visits most often and since he mainly stays at the same hotels, he also leaves sets of workout clothes and running shoes with hotel staff. **Availability:** Online.

34990 ■ *"Live & Learn: Ian Delaney"* in Canadian Business (Vol. 81, Summer 2008, No. 9, pp. 168)

Pub: Rogers Media Inc.

Contact: Neil Spivak, Chief Executive Officer

Ed: Joe Castaldo. **Description:** Interview with Ian Delaney who is the executive chairman of chemical company Sherritt International Corp.; Delaney previously worked as chief executive for a holding company owned by Peter Munk. Details of his beliefs, profession and family life are discussed. **Availability:** Online.

34991 ■ *"Make It Easier On Yourself"* in Women In Business (Vol. 63, Fall 2011, No. 3, pp. 28)

Pub: American Business Women's Association

Contact: Rene Street, Executive Director

Released: September 22, 2011. **Description:** Getting and staying organized helps avoid wasting time on deciding which priorities to address first. Taking help and avoiding hoarding are examples of how to become organized. The use of technology for organizing priorities is also explained. **Availability:** Online.

34992 ■ *"Managing Yourself: What Brain Science Tells Us About How to Excel"* in Harvard Business Review (Vol. 88, December 2010, No. 12, pp. 123)

Pub: Harvard Business Publishing

Contact: Diane Belcher, Managing Director

Ed: Edward M. Hallowell. **Price:** $8.95, PDF. **Description:** Relevant discoveries in brain research as they apply to boosting employee motivation and organizational effectiveness are explained. Included is a checklist of 15 items for use in assessing the fitness of a person for a particular job, focusing on the intersection of what one likes to do, what one does best, and what increases organizational value. **Availability:** Print; PDF.

34993 ■ *"Monday Organizer: Clean and De-Clutter in 15 Minutes"* in Tulsa World (June 13, 2011)

Pub: The McClatchy Company

Contact: Tony W. Hunter, Chief Executive Officer

Ed: Kim Brown. **Description:** New weekly series highlights practical tips and helpful ideas to simply life by taking 15 minutes to de-clutter your home or office. Paper clutter can be eliminated in 15 minutes by gathering up newspapers and magazines to recycle; sort mail as soon as you receive it and throw away any junk mail at that time. If watching TV, use commercial time to accomplish small tasks. **Availability:** Print; Online.

34994 ■ *"New Sales. Simplified: The Essential Handbook for Prospecting and New Business Development"*

Pub: HarperCollins Leadership

Contact: Donald Miller, Chief Executive Officer

Released: September 04, 2012. **Price:** $19.99, Paperback. **Description:** The constant flow of new accounts is essential for any small business to grow and thrive. A proven formula for prospecting; customer-focused selling; proactive telephone calling that leads to face-to-face meetings; the use of email, voicemail, and social media; prevent the buyer's anti-salesperson response; build a rapport; winning sales; communicating with clients; plan time for business development activities; and more. **Availability:** E-book; Print; Audio; Download.

34995 ■ *"Our Gadget of the Week: Eye Candy From Dell"* in Barron's (Vol. 89, July 27, 2009, No. 30, pp. 26)

Description: Zeo Sleep Coach has a lightweight headband with built-in sensors which measures the user's brain waves and records their sleep patterns. The device details the time the users spends in deep sleep, light sleep and the restorative REM (rapid eye movement) sleep mode. Users can get lifestyle change recommendations from a website to improve their sleep. **Availability:** Online.

34996 ■ *"Pack Mentality: Why Black Can Be Slimming"* in Crain's Chicago Business (Vol. 31, April 21, 2008, No. 16, pp. 31)

Pub: Crain Communications Inc.

Contact: Barry Asin, President

Ed: Sarah A. Klein. **Description:** Jill Smart, the head of human resources for a company with 170,000 employees worldwide, frequently travels to India, London and Singapore; Ms. Smart provides advice concerning efficiency, time management and avoiding jet-lag. **Availability:** Online.

34997 ■ *"Power Play"* in Harvard Business Review (Vol. 88, July-August 2010, No. 7-8, pp. 84)

Pub: Harvard Business Publishing

Contact: Diane Belcher, Managing Director

Ed: Jeffrey Pfeffer. **Price:** $8.95, PDF. **Description:** Guidelines include in-depth understanding of resources at one's disposal, relentlessness that still provides opponents with opportunities to save face, and a determination not to be put off by the processes of politics. **Availability:** Online; PDF.

34998 ■ *"Problem Solving Requires Total Team Approach"* in Green Industry Pro (Vol. 23, September 2011)

Ed: Bob Coulter. **Description:** Working Smarter Training Challenge teaches that leaders are able to carry out solutions directly into their organization, develop skills and drive business results in key areas by creating a culture of energized workers who are able to take ownership of their performance as well as the performance of the company as a whole. **Availability:** Online.

34999 ■ *"Professional Help: Cross That Off Your To-Do List"* in Inc. (November 2007, pp. 89-90, 92)

Ed: Alison Stein Wellner. **Description:** Small business owners are finding that it pays to hire someone to takeover the personal tasks of daily living, including hiring a personal assistant, chauffeur, chef, stylist, pet caregiver, or concierge service. **Availability:** Online.

35000 ■ *"Scrum: The Art of Doing Twice the Work In Half the Time"*

Pub: Penguin Random House

Contact: Nihar Malaviya, Chief Executive Officer

Released: 2014. **Price:** $27, hardcover, plus shipping charges; $16.99, e-book; $35, CD, plus shipping charges; $17.50, audiobook download. **Description:** Scrum is a more efficient way for getting things done, particularly when managing a company. Scrum has

recorded productivity gains as high as 1200 percent and is an excellent time management tool. **Availability:** CD-ROM; E-book; Print; Audio.

35001 ■ *"Should I Stay or Should I Go?"* in Entrepreneur (August 2014)

Pub: Entrepreneur Media Inc.

Contact: Dan Bova, Director

E-mail: dbova@entrepreneur.com

Description: The timing of meeting clients in person is critical to the success of a business venture. Entrepreneurs can save time and money if they know when it is worth seeing the client in person. For Jackie Kimzey of the Institute for Innovation and Entrepreneurship, the best time for a face-to-face meeting with clients is when a business relationship is starting to flourish. Kimzey advises entrepreneurs to consider their budget, the amount of time they have been working together, and the importance of the client to the business. **Availability:** Print; Online.

35002 ■ *"Sleeping with Your Smartphone: How to Break the 24/7 Habit and Change the Way You Work"*

Pub: Harvard Business Review Press

Contact: Moderna V. Pfizer, Contact

Released: May 29, 2012. **Price:** $30, Hardcover/Hardcopy. **Description:** Harvard Business School professor, Leslie Perlow, reveals ways to become more productive after disconnecting from your smartphone. A six-person team was used in an experiment at The Boston Consulting Group, an elite management consulting firm, where teams changed the way they worked and became more efficient and effective by disconnecting. The team was better able to perform and recruit new talent. A step-by-step guide is offered to change your team. **Availability:** E-book; Print.

35003 ■ *Table Talk: The Savvy Girl's Alternative to Networking*

Pub: AuthorHouse Inc.

Contact: William Elliott, President

Ed: Diane Danielson. **Description:** Let's face it. Women and men are different. So why should we all have to network in the same way? And, why should women have to 'network' at all? Between family and work responsibilities, the idea of pressing flesh at some not-very-festive cocktail party is right up there in appeal with a root canal. But what if women could find a way to make career boosting connections that are actually fun? Enter 'table talk', a new way to network for time-pressed, professional women. **Availability:** Print.

35004 ■ *"Time Value of Money Rate of Return"* in Business Owner (Vol. 35, September-October 2011, No. 5, pp. 8)

Description: Estimating value of an income-generating asset or group of assets requires the small business owner to consider concepts such as the time value of money, risk and required rate of return. A brief summary explaining this theory is presented. **Availability:** Print; Online.

35005 ■ *"Vision Statement: Why Mumbai at 1 PM is the Center of the Business World"* in Harvard Business Review (Vol. 88, October 2010, No. 10, pp. 38)

Pub: Harvard Business Publishing

Contact: Diane Belcher, Managing Director

Ed: Michael Segalla. **Price:** $6, PDF. **Description:** A time zone chart is presented for assisting in the planning of international conference calls. **Availability:** Online; PDF.

35006 ■ *"Why Slacking Off Is Great For Business"* in Canadian Business (Vol. 85, August 13, 2012, No. 13, pp. 60)

Ed: Sarah Barmak. **Description:** Procrastination can be good for busy managers to develop creative thinking which may be good for business. Ways to enhance the brain's creative engine including taking a different route to the office, reading a best seller, or playing golf. **Availability:** Print; Online.

35007 ■ *"Your Scarcest Resource: Time Is Money, But Few Organizations Treat It That Way" in Harvard Business Review (Vol. 92, May 2014, No. 5, pp. 74)*
Pub: Harvard Business Press
Contact: Gabriela Allmi, Regional Manager
E-mail: gabriela.allmi@hbsp.harvard.edu
Price: $8.95. **Description:** Optimal management of organizational time involves eight practices. These include a clear and selective agenda, a zero-based time allotment, business cases of every initiative, organizational simplification, decision process standardization, and load management through feedback.
Availability: Online; PDF.

VIDEO/AUDIO MEDIA

35008 ■ *BS-Free Service Business Show: Best-Case Scenario Productivity vs. Reality: The Missing Margin*
URL(s): bsfreebusiness.com/productivity-vs-reality
Ed: Maggie Patterson. **Released:** October 28, 2024.
Description: Podcast explains how ditching best-case planning and creating space for the unexpected can help with time management.

35009 ■ *Elevated Entrepreneurship: Creating More by Doing Less with Kate Northrup*
URL(s): mikemichalowicz.com/podcast/kate-northrup
Ed: Mike Michalowiicz. **Released:** September 16, 2019. **Description:** Podcast offers strategies to do less work and obtain better outcomes.

35010 ■ *Founder Work-Life Balance*
URL(s): www.startuphustlepodcast.com/founder-work-life-balance
Ed: Matt Watson. **Released:** April 17, 2024. **Description:** Podcast discusses work-life balance for entrepreneurs.

35011 ■ *The How of Business: Goal Setting & Time Management*
URL(s): www.thehowofbusiness.com/episode-288-goal-setting-time-management
Ed: Henry Lopez. **Released:** January 06, 2020.
Description: Podcast offers practical tips for setting effective goals, manage your time, and becoming more productive.

35012 ■ *The How of Business: Top 10 Productivity Tools*
URL(s): www.thehowofbusiness.com/episode-544-top-10-productivity-tools

Ed: Henry Lopez. **Released:** November 04, 2024.
Description: Podcast shares top tools to keep small business owners organized and productive.

35013 ■ *The Strategy Hour: How to Deal with Stres and Anxiety - And Still Stay Productive*
URL(s): bossproject.com/podcast/how-to-deal-with-stress-and-anxiety-and-still-stay-productive
Ed: Abagail Pumphrey. **Released:** December 05, 2023. **Description:** Podcast discusses how to cope with stress and anxiety and remain productive.

CONSULTANTS

35014 ■ Associations Plus Inc.
PO Box 11035
Columbia, SC 29211
Ph: (803)252-7128
URL: http://www.associationsplus.com
Contact: Leigh Wickersham, President
E-mail: leigh@associationsplus.com
Description: Offers human resource development services specializing in sales training, support staff training, trade show selling, time management skills and stress management training. **Scope:** Offers human resource development services specializing in sales training, support staff training, trade show selling, time management skills and stress management training. **Training:** Non-verbal Communications; Time/Stress Management; Better Selling Techniques; Trade Show Sales Techniques.

35015 ■ David L. Ward and Associates Inc.
1951 - 47th St., Ste. 179
San Diego, CA 92102
Co. E-mail: dward@wardmosaic.com
URL: http://www.wardmosaic.com
Contact: David L. Ward, Contact
E-mail: dward@wardmosaic.com
Description: Firm specializes in mosaic glass art consulting and provides various seminars on mosaic glass arts. **Scope:** Firm specializes in mosaic glass art consulting and provides various seminars on mosaic glass arts. **Publications:** "Mosaic Glue Comparison Testing". **Training:** Mosaic Glass Art Workshop; How to Turn Your Glass Hobby Into a Money-Making Business.

35016 ■ Quma Learning Systems Inc.
21760 S 220th Pl.
Queen Creek, AZ 85142
URL: http://quma.net/index.html

Contact: Dr. Dennis R. Deaton, Director
Description: Business management firm that works with corporations in developing empowering cultures by laying the foundation of ownership spirit. Specializes in providing principles and tools for maximizing full potential in one's self by becoming more accountable, responsible and committed. **Scope:** Business management firm that works with corporations in developing empowering cultures by laying the foundation of ownership spirit. Specializes in providing principles and tools for maximizing full potential in one's self by becoming more accountable, responsible and committed. **Founded:** 1985. **Publications:** "The Book On Mind Management Discussion Guide"; "The Ownership Spirit Handbook"; "The Book on Mind Management"; "Money: An Owner's Manual". **Training:** The Ownership Spirit; Visioneering; Life Management; Money: An Owner's Manual; Communicating For Success; Sustaining Peak Performance.

35017 ■ Smart Ways to Work
300 Frank H. Ogawa Plz., Ste. 215
Oakland, CA 94612
Free: 800-599-8463
Co. E-mail: odette@smartwaystowork.com
URL: http://www.smartwaystowork.com
Contact: Odette Pollar, Consultant
E-mail: odette@smartwaystowork.com
Description: Provider of consulting, training, and other related services and also analyze performance, speeches, and much more. **Scope:** Provider of consulting, training, and other related services and also analyze performance, speeches, and much more. **Publications:** "Surviving Information Overload driving Information Overload: How to Find, Filter, and Focus on What's Important," Crisp Publications, Sep, 2003; "Take Back Your Life: Smart Ways to Simplify Daily Living," Conari Press, Apr, 1999; "365 Ways to Simplify Your Work Life," Kaplan Business, Aug, 1996; "Dynamics of Diversity: Strategic Programs for Your Organization," Crisp Publications, 1994; "Organizing Your Workspace: A Guide to Personal Productivity," Crisp Publications, May, 1992. **Training:** Managing Multiple Demands: Surviving Ground Zero; Defending Your Life: Balancing Work And Home; Desktop Sprawl: Conquer Your Paper Pile-Up; Getting It All Done: Breaking The Time Bind; To Give or Not To Give: The Delegation Dilemma; Information Happens: Don't Let It Happen On You; Take The Terror Out Of Talk: Secrets To Successful Speaking; To Give or Not To Give: The Delegation Dilemma; Managing Meetings.

Trade Shows/Exhibiting

ASSOCIATIONS AND OTHER ORGANIZATIONS

35018 ■ Exhibit Designers and Producers Association (EDPA)
239 E Michigan Ave., Ste. 212
Paw Paw, MI 49079
Free: 866-806-3372
Co. E-mail: info@edpa.com
URL: http://www.edpa.com
Contact: Dan Serebin, President
Facebook: www.facebook.com/edpassociation
X (Twitter): x.com/EDPAAssociation
YouTube: www.youtube.com/user/EDPAssociation
Description: Firms designing and building exhibits for trade shows and museums. Conducts educational and research programs. **Founded:** 1954. **Publications:** *EDP Action News* (Bimonthly); *EDPA.COMmunications* (Monthly); *EDPA Today* (Quarterly). **Awards:** EDPA Chapter of the Year (Annual); Hazel Hayes Award (Annual); EDPA Ambassador Award (Annual); EDDIE Award (Annual); Michael R. Westcott Designer of the Year Award (Annual). **Geographic Preference:** Multinational.

REFERENCE WORKS

35019 ■ "$3 Million in Repairs Prep Cobo for Auto Show" in Crain's Detroit Business (Vol. 26, January 4, 2010, No. 1, pp. 1)
Pub: Crain Communications Inc.
Contact: Barry Asin, President
Ed: Nancy Kaffer. **Description:** Overview of the six projects priced roughly at $3 million which were needed in order to host the North American International Auto Show; show organizers stated that the work was absolutely necessary to keep the show in the city of Detroit. **Availability:** Print; Online.

35020 ■ "2011 Report on the $9 Billion US Trade Show & Event Planning Services Industry" in Investment Weekly (January 21, 2012, pp. 47)
Description: The US trade show and event planning industry is made up of meeting planners and suppliers. These professionals organize, design, promote, and manage business and consumer trade shows, conferences, and meetings. The US trade show industry represents nearly 4,000 compaines and reports a $9 billion annual revenue. **Availability:** Online.

35021 ■ "Advanced Energy Showcases Industry Leading Inverters and Energy Management Solutions at Solar Power International 2012" in Benzinga.com (September 11, 2012)
Pub: PR Newswire Association LLC.
Description: Advanced Energy Industries Inc. is presenting its energy management solutions suite at the Solar Power International (SPI) conference to be held in Orlando, Florida in September 2012. Details of the conference and this exhibit are included.

35022 ■ "Advice at Entrepreneurs Event: Make Fast Decisions, See Trends" in Crain's Detroit Business (Vol. 30, July 28, 2014, No. 30, pp. 4)
Pub: Crain Communications Inc.
Contact: Barry Asin, President
Description: Crain's entrepreneurial event was held a The Henry Ford in Dearborn, Michigan. Panelists at the event advised entrepreneurs to make fast decisions and to be aware of small business trends in order to be successful. George Matick Chevrolet was honored. Details of the event are covered. **Availability:** PDF; Online.

35023 ■ "ALA: Hot Topics for Librarianship" in Information Today (Vol. 28, September 2011, No. 8, pp. 17)
Pub: Information Today Inc.
Contact: Thomas H. Hogan, President
Ed: Barbara Brynko. **Description:** Highlights from the American Library Association Annual Conference and Exhibition are listed. Thousands of attendees sought out services, displays, demos, new product rollouts, and freebies. Emerging technology for librarians, staff development, gray literature, interlibrary loans, and next-generation interfaces were among the topics discussed.

35024 ■ "Alternative Fuels Take Center Stage at Houston Auto Show" in Houston Business Journal (Vol. 44, January 31, 2014, No. 39, pp. 8)
Pub: American City Business Journals, Inc.
Contact: Mike Olivieri, Executive Vice President
Released: January 31, 2014. **Price:** $4, Introductory 4-Week Offer(Digital & Print). **Description:** An energy summit was held at the Houston Auto Show in Texas on January 22, 2014, where energy executives discussed new technology and initiatives. They considered the market for electric and natural gas-fueled vehicles as well as other options including hydrogen, fuel cells, and biofuels. **Availability:** Print; Online.

35025 ■ "The Art of War for Women" in Hawaii Business (Vol. 54, July 2008, No. 1, pp. 23)
Pub: PacificBasin Communications
Contact: Chuck Tindle, Director
E-mail: chuckt@pacificbasin.net
Ed: Chin-Ning Chu. **Description:** Business consultant Chi-Ning Chu talks about her new book 'The Art of War for Women: Sun Tzu's Ancient Strategies and Wisdom for Winning at Work', which discusses how women can more effectively win in business. She also shares her thoughts about the advantages that women have, which they can use in businesses decisions.

35026 ■ "Attorney Panel Tackles Contract Questions" in Agency Sales Magazine (Vol. 39, September-October 2009, No. 9, pp. 8)
Description: MANAfest conference tackled issues regarding a sales representative's contract. One attorney from the panel advised reps to go through proposed agreements with attorneys who are knowledgeable concerning rep laws. Another attorney advised reps to communicate with a company to ask about their responsibilities if that company is facing financial difficulty. **Availability:** Online.

35027 ■ "Auto Show Aims to Electrify" in Crain's Detroit Business (Vol. 26, January 11, 2010, No. 2, pp. 1)
Pub: Crain Communications Inc.
Contact: Barry Asin, President
Ed: Ryan Beene. **Description:** Overview of the North American International Auto show include sixteen production and concept vehicles including eight from the Detroit 3. High-tech battery suppliers as well as hybrid and electric vehicles will highlight the show. **Availability:** Print; Online.

35028 ■ "Avanti Hosts 19th Annual User's Conference in Washington, DC" in American Printer (Vol. 128, July 1, 2011, No. 7)
Description: Avanti Computer Systems Ltd. hosted its 19th annual users conference in Washington DC. In-plant and commercial printers were in attendance. **Availability:** Online.

35029 ■ "Backer Christmas Trade Show Preview" in Pet Product News (Vol. 66, September 2012, No. 9, pp. 12)
Description: The 46th Annual H.H. Backer Pet Industry Christmas Trade Showand Educational Conference will beheld at the Donald E. Stephens Convention Center in Rosemont, Illinois from October 12-14, 2012. More than 600 pet supply manufacturers and about 9,000 industry professionals will attend. **Availability:** Print; Online.

35030 ■ "Baltimore's Hilton Convention Headquarters Hotel Still Losing Money" in Baltimore Business Journal (Vol. 28, October 15, 2010, No. 23, pp. 1)
Pub: Baltimore Business Journal
Contact: Rhonda Pringle, President
E-mail: rpringle@bizjournals.com
Ed: Daniel J. Sernovitz. **Description:** Baltimore, Maryland-owned Hilton Baltimore Convention Center Hotel has been expected by Baltimore Hotel Corporation to wrap up 2010 with a $9.8 million deficit after completing its first year in operation in the red. The forecast would mark the controversial project's third-straight year of losses.

35031 ■ "The Booth and Beyond: Art Fair Design and the Viewing Experience" in Entrepreneur (September 2014)
Pub: Entrepreneur Media Inc.
Contact: Dan Bova, Director
E-mail: dbova@entrepreneur.com
Description: Entrepreneurs need advance planning before joining trade shows in order to capitalize on the opportunity to present their organization. Steps to ensure a successful trade show event are highlighted. **Availability:** Online.

35032 ■ *"Bottom-Fishing and Speed-Dating in India-How Investors Feel About the Indian Market"* in Barron's (Vol. 88, March 24, 2008, No. 12, pp. M12)

Pub: Dow Jones & Company Inc.

Contact: Almar Latour, Chief Executive Officer

Ed: Elliot Wilson. **Description:** Indian stocks have fallen hard in 2008, with Mumbai's Sensex 30 down 30 percent from its January 2008 peak of 21,000 to 14,995 in March. The India Private Equity Fair 2008 attracted 140 of the world's largest private equity firms and about 24 of India's fastest-growing corporations. Statistical data included. **Availability:** Online.

35033 ■ *"Business Builders: Tradeshow Attendance Incentives Add Up"* in Pet Product News (Vol. 64, December 2010, No. 12, pp. 14)

Ed: Mark E. Battersby. **Description:** Pointers on how pet specialty retailers can claim business travel tax and income tax deductions for expenses paid or incurred in participation at tradeshows, conventions, and meetings are presented. Incentives in form of these deductions could allow pet specialty retailers to gain business benefits, aside from the education and enjoyment involved with the travel. **Availability:** Online.

35034 ■ *"Calendar"* in Crain's Detroit Business (Vol. 24, March 10, 2008, No. 10, pp. 21)

Pub: Crain Communications Inc.

Contact: Barry Asin, President

Description: Listing of events in the Detroit area include conferences addressing entrepreneurialism, economic development, and women business ownership. **Availability:** Print; Online.

35035 ■ *"Can Tech Industry Share Wealth?"* in Puget Sound Business Journal (Vol. 35, May 23, 2014, No. 5, pp. 10)

Pub: American City Business Journals, Inc.

Contact: Mike Olivieri, Executive Vice President

Description: Nearly 700 local technology leaders gathered at the annual State of Technology event organized by Tech Alliance in Washington in May 2014. Trade show speaker, Geoffrey Moore, emphasized the role of the technology industry as a driver of local economies. **Availability:** Online.

35036 ■ *"CarBiz Inc. Speaking At NABD"* in Marketwired (May 14, 2007)

Pub: Comtex News Network Inc.

Contact: Kan Devnani, President

Description: CarBiz Inc., a leading provider of software, consulting, and training solutions to the United States' automotive industry, had two of its executive officers speak at the National Alliance of Buy Here - Pay Here Dealers (NABD), a conference that draws over 2,000 dealers, service providers, and experts from across the United States. **Availability:** Print; Online.

35037 ■ *"Celebrate Success. Embrace Innovation"* in Black Enterprise (Vol. 37, February 2007, No. 7, pp. 145)

Description: 2007 Women of Power Summit provides networking opportunities, empowerment sessions, and nightly entertainment. More than 500 executive women of color are expected to attend this inspiring summit in Phoenix, February 7-10. **Availability:** Print; Online.

35038 ■ *"Certain Predicts 2012 as Breakthrough Year for Events"* in Internet Wire (January 5, 2012)

Pub: Comtex News Network Inc.

Contact: Kan Devnani, President

Description: Certain Inc. discusses its threetop predictions for 2012 on technology trends that will promote increased business value in the events industry. Certain Inc. is a leading provider of cloud-based event management software that is used for global meetings and events. **Availability:** Print; Online.

35039 ■ *"Change Is in the Air"* in Agency Sales Magazine (Vol. 39, August 2009, No. 8, pp. 30)

Description: Highlights of the Power-Motion Technology Representatives Association (PTRA) 37th Annual Conference, which projected an economic upturn, are presented. Allan Bealulieu of the Institute for Trend Research gave the positive news while Manufacturer's Agents National Association (MANA) president Brain Shirley emphasized the need to take advantage of a turnaround. **Availability:** Print; Online.

35040 ■ *"Clusters Last Stand?"* in Canadian Electronics (Vol. 23, February 2008, No. 1, pp. 6)

Description: Survival of technology clusters was the focus of Strategic Microelectronics Council's conference entitled, "The Power of Community: Building Technology Clusters in Canada". Clusters can help foster growth in the microelectronics sector, and it was recognized that government intervention is needed to maintain these clusters. **Availability:** Download; PDF; Online.

35041 ■ *"CommScope and Comsearch to Showcase Innovative Wind Power Solutions at WINDPOWER 2012 in Atlanta"* in Benzinga.com (May 31, 2012)

Pub: Benzinga.com

Contact: Jason Raznick, Founder

Ed: Aaron Wise. **Description:** CommScope Inc. and its subsidiary CommScope will highlight their complete wind power solution products during the WIND-POWER 2012 Conference and Exhibition in Atlanta, Georgia this year. CommScope's wind power products include fiber optic cabling solutions, while Comsearch offers wind energy services that address the siting challenges resulting from complex telecommunications issues. **Availability:** Print; PDF; Online.

35042 ■ *"Conference Calendar"* in Marketing to Women (Vol. 21, April 2008, No. 4, pp. 7)

Description: Listing of current conferences and events concerning women, marketing and business. **Availability:** Print; PDF; Download; Online.

35043 ■ *"Conference To Aid Minority Business Ties"* in Tulsa World (July 24, 2012)

Description: Preview of the 34th Annual Oklahoma Minority Supplier Development Council Business Conference and Opportunity Fair is presented. The event will be held in downtown Tulsa, OK and brings together corporate, government and minority representatives. Business opportunities for minority suppliers will also be presented. **Availability:** Online.

35044 ■ *"Convention Budgeting Best Practices"* in Franchising World (Vol. 42, November 2010, No. 11, pp. 11)

Pub: International Franchise Association

Contact: Matthew Haller, President

E-mail: mhaller@franchise.org

Ed: Steve Friedman. **Description:** Franchise conventions can offer benefits to both franchisor and franchisee in terms of culture-building, professional education and networking. However, these conventions can be costly. Tips for planning a successful franchising convention on a budget are outlined. **Availability:** Online.

35045 ■ *"Convention Ctr. Rehab To Impact Hotels, Eateries"* in Silicon Valley/San Jose Business Journal (Vol. 30, May 18, 2012, No. 8, pp. 1)

Pub: Baltimore Business Journal

Contact: Rhonda Pringle, President

E-mail: rpringle@bizjournals.com

Description: The renovation of the San Jose McEnery Convention Center is seen to adversely impact businesses in the area. Contractors have already demolished the former Martin Luther King Jr. Main Library. Business sales in the area are expected to decline owing to the renovation.

35046 ■ *"Detroit Hosts Conferences on Green Building, IT, Finance"* in Crain's Detroit Business (Vol. 25, June 1, 2009, No. 22, pp. 9)

Pub: Crain Communications Inc.

Contact: Barry Asin, President

Ed: Tom Henderson. **Description:** Detroit will host three conferences in June 2009, one features green technology, one information technology and the third will gather black bankers and financial experts from across the nation. **Availability:** Online.

35047 ■ *"Dow Champions Innovative Energy Solutions for Auto Industry at NAIAS"* in Business of Global Warming (January 25, 2010, pp. 7)

Description: This year's North American International Auto Show in Detroit will host the "Electric Avenue" exhibit sponsored by the Dow Chemical Company. The display will showcase the latest in innovative energy solutions from Dow as well as electric vehicles and the technology supporting them. This marks the first time a non-automotive manufacturer is part of the main floor of the show. **Availability:** Print; PDF; Online.

35048 ■ *"Downtowns Must Court Young, CEOs for Cities President Says"* in Crain's Detroit Business (Vol. 24, October 6, 2008, No. 40, pp. 18)

Description: It is important to produce more college graduates, and keep them in Michigan, according to CEOs for Cities President Carol Coletta when she spoke to a session at the West Michigan Regional Policy Conference which was held in September in Grand Rapids. Ways in which city leaders can connect students to communities, resulting in employees who have vested interest in the region, are also discussed.

35049 ■ *"East-Side Real Estate Forum Detours To Grand Rapids"* in Crain's Detroit Business (Vol. 24, October 6, 2008, No. 40, pp. 17)

Pub: Crain Communications Inc.

Contact: Barry Asin, President

Ed: Daniel Duggan. **Description:** Tom Wackerman was elected chairman of the University of Michigan-Urban Land Institute Real Estate Forum and proposed that the annual conference be held in Grand Rapids due to the brisk economic activity he was finding there; although the idea was initially met with resistance, the plan to introduce East-siders to the West side began receiving more enthusiasm due to the revitalization of the area, which was once considered to have a bleak outlook. Many are hoping to learn the lessons of those who were able to change a negative economic climate into a positive one in which the cooperation of private business and government can work together to accomplish goals. **Availability:** Print; Online.

35050 ■ *"Effective Networking"* in Women in Business (Vol. 64, Summer 2012, No. 2, pp. 50)

Ed: Diane Stafford. **Description:** Tips on effective networking at the 2012 American Business Women's Association National Women's Leadership Conference are suggested. The purpose of networking is to make contacts and build relationships so asking for too much free advice or selling personal services are not advisable. **Availability:** Online.

35051 ■ *"Entrepreneurs Conference Recap: the Business Revolution: Start Focusing On a Growth Strategy For Your Company"* in Black Enterprise (Vol. 45, July-August, 2014, No. 1, pp. 17)

Pub: Earl G. Graves Ltd.

Contact: Earl Graves, Jr., President

Released: 2014. **Description:** Small business owners must concentrate on growth in order to survive using a vision and strategic focus. The 2014 Black Enterprise Entrepreneurs Conference and Expo, sponsored by Nationwide, drew about 1,000 entrepreneurs and professionals.

35052 ■ "Event Will Highlight Underappreciated Rose Wines" in Sacramento Business Journal (Vol. 31, July 18, 2014, No. 21, pp. 4)
Pub: American City Business Journals, Inc.
Contact: Mike Olivieri, Executive Vice President
Released: July 18, 2014. **Description:** The Pink Party is a rose wine tasting event that will be hosted by WineCentric founder and sommelier, Matthew Lewis, in Sacramento, California on July 25, 2014. Lewis hopes that the event will provide a comprehensive understanding of the range of possibilities among difference varieties of these wines.

35053 ■ "Events, Improved Economy Mean Full Hotels in Silicon Valley" in Silicon Valley/San Jose Business Journal (Vol. 30, September 28, 2012, No. 27, pp. 1)
Pub: Baltimore Business Journal
Contact: Rhonda Pringle, President
E-mail: rpringle@bizjournals.com
Description: The increase in hotel occupancy rates in Silicon Valley was attributed to the improving economy and a wide range of local trade shows and events. The city of Santa Clara, California reached an 82 percent occupancy rate in August 2012, while in downtown San Jose, hotels said they started experiencing increased demand since late 2011. **Availability:** Print; Online.

35054 ■ "Ex-Medical Student Stages Career In Event Planning: Barcelona Owner Makes Inroads with Luxury Car Dealerships" in Los Angeles Business Journal (Vol. 34, June 18, 2012, No. 25, pp. 10)
Pub: CBJ L.P.
Contact: Terri Cunningham, Contact
Description: Barcelona Enterprises started as a company designing menus for restaurants, organizing food shows, to planning receptions for luxury car dealers. The fim will be launching the first Las Vegas Chocolate Festival & Pastry Show in July 2012. Presently, the company runs 24 wine and food festivals, organizes events for an upscale dog shampoo maker, and sports car dealerships. **Availability:** Print; Online.

35055 ■ "Four Exhibition Considerations" in American Printer (Vol. 128, August 1, 2011, No. 8)
Description: Four questions to ask at the Graph Expo will help printers improve their own business. **Availability:** Print; Download; PDF.

35056 ■ "Future of Convention and Visitors Bureau In Question" in Houston Business Journal (Vol. 44, April 4, 2014, No. 48, pp. 10)
Pub: American City Business Journals, Inc.
Contact: Mike Olivieri, Executive Vice President
Released: Weekly. **Price:** $4, introductory 4-week offer(Digital & Print). **Description:** Greater Houston Convention and Visitors Bureau (GHCVB) chairwoman Sonia Garza-Monarchi shares her views about the merger talks with Houston First Corporation. Garza-Monarchi says the current proposal is for the continuing existence of the GHCVB board, which approves its own budget and business plan. She also says the members and the board just want an open and fair merger process. **Availability:** Print; Online.

35057 ■ "Grainger Show Highlights Building Green, Economic Recovery" in Contractor (Vol. 57, February 2010, No. 2, pp. 3)
Ed: Candace Roulo. **Description:** Chief U.S. economist told attendees of the Grainger's 2010 Total MRO Solutions National Customer Show that the economic recovery would be subdued. Mechanical contractors who attended the event also learned about building sustainable, green products, and technologies, and economic and business challenges. **Availability:** Print; Online.

35058 ■ "Grand Action Makes Grand Changes in Grand Rapids" in Crain's Detroit Business (Vol. 25, June 1, 2009, No. 22, pp. M012)
Pub: Crain Communications Inc.
Contact: Barry Asin, President

Ed: Amy Lane. **Description:** Businessman Dick DeVos believes that governments are not always the best to lead certain initiatives. That's why, in 1991, he gathered 50 west Michigan community leaders and volunteers to look consider the construction of an arena and expanding or renovating local convention operations. Grand Action has undertaken four major projects in the city. **Availability:** Online.

35059 ■ "Half a World Away" in Tampa Bay Business Journal (Vol. 30, December 4, 2009, No. 50, pp. 1)
Description: Enterprise Florida has offered four trade grants for Florida's marine industry businesses to give them a chance to tap into the Middle East market at the Dubai International Boat Show on March 9 to 13, 2010. The grants pay for 50 percent of the exhibition costs for the qualifying business. **Availability:** Online.

35060 ■ "Hotels Up the Ante in Bid to Lure Visitors" in Sacramento Business Journal (Vol. 29, June 1, 2012, No. 14, pp. 1)
Pub: Baltimore Business Journal
Contact: Rhonda Pringle, President
E-mail: rpringle@bizjournals.com
Description: Hotel owners in Sacramento, California will spend more on marketing the region to convention planners and tourists. The Sacramento Tourism Marketing District is set to replace a 10-year-old marketing business improvement district on July 1, 2012. It is believed that convention and travel business is an economic driver in the city. **Availability:** Print; Online.

35061 ■ "How Detroit Built Its Marquee Auto Show" in Crain's Detroit Business (Vol. 30, January 6, 2014, No. 1, pp. 17)
Pub: Crain Communications Inc.
Contact: Barry Asin, President
Description: Detroit-area automobile dealers and business leaders, along with staff from the Detroit Auto Dealers Association, promoted Detroit as the premier North American International Auto Show event, upstaging New York. Few would have considered cold and snowy Detroit as a January destination, but they succeeded in their marketing campaign and the show has continued to grow since. **Availability:** Online.

35062 ■ "How South Florida Can Revive a Flagging Sector" in South Florida Business Journal (Vol. 34, April 4, 2014, No. 37, pp. 10)
Pub: American City Business Journals, Inc.
Contact: Mike Olivieri, Executive Vice President
Released: Weekly. **Price:** $8, Introductory 4-week offer(Digital & Print). **Description:** South Florida convention centers are trying to address the sluggish demand for conventions to the area by upgrading its facilities and adding hotels. The ancillary revenue generate by the attendees at hotels, restaurants, and other establishments makes a convention as key economic drivers. The efforts to boost the region's position as convention destinations are also addressed. **Availability:** Print; Online.

35063 ■ "How To Find More Customers and Clients with Webinars, Seminars and Workshops"
Pub: CreateSpace
Released: September 27, 2014. **Price:** $2.34, kindle. **Description:** Steps to present successful Webinars, seminars and workshops to market your products at conferences and trade shows are highlighted. A checklist is also provided. **Availability:** Print.

35064 ■ "Javo Beverage to Feature On-Demand Coffee System and Introduce New Specialty Dispensed Beverages at the National Convenience Store Show" in GlobeNewswire (October 20, 2009)
Pub: Comtex News Network Inc.
Contact: Kan Devnani, President
Description: During the National Association of Convenience Store Show (NACS) at the Las Vegas Convention Center, Javo Beverage Company, Inc., a leading provider of premium dispensable coffee and

tea-based beverages to the foodservice industry, will introduce its on-demand hot coffee system as well as a new line of products for the convenience store industry. **Availability:** Online.

35065 ■ "Kuno Creative to Present the Three Steps of a Successful B2B Social Media Campaign" in Business Tech & Wireless (August 25, 2011)
Pub: Close-Up Media Inc.
Contact: Caroline S. Moore, President
E-mail: cms@closeupmedia.com
Released: August 24, 2011. **Description:** Kuno Creative, an inbound marketing agency, will host Three Steps of a Successful B2B Social Media Campaign. The firm is a provider of Website development, branding, marketing strategy, public relations, Internet marketing, and inbound marketing. **Availability:** Print; Online.

35066 ■ "Let's Put On a Show" in Inc. (November 2007, pp. 127)
Ed: Elaine Appleton Grant. **Description:** Profile of Jeff Baker, CEO of Image 4, designer of trade show exhibits. Baker shares details of the firm's commitment to being green. **Availability:** Online.

35067 ■ "Major Golf Retail Show in the Rough for 2010" in Orlando Business Journal (Vol. 26, January 15, 2010, No. 33, pp. 1)
Pub: Orlando Business Journal
Contact: Julie Swyers, Director
E-mail: jswyers@bizjournals.com
Ed: Anjali Fluker. **Description:** The 57th Annual PGA Merchandise Show in Orlando, Florida is projected to attract 39,000 attendees in 2010, compared with 41,000 in 2009. According to the Orange County Convention Center, economic benefits that could be obtained from the 2010 edition of the golf retail show might reach only $77 million, compared with $78 million generated last year. **Availability:** Print; Online.

35068 ■ "Minnesota ABC Event Looks at Government Contracting" in Finance and Commerce Daily Newspaper (November 23, 2010)
Ed: Brian Johnson. **Description:** Minnesota Associated Builders and Contractors hosted an event focusing on doing business with government agencies. Topics included bidding work, awarding jobs, paperwork, guidelines, certifications and upcoming projects. **Availability:** Online.

35069 ■ "The Missing Piece" in Washington Business Journal (Vol. 33, April 25, 2014, No. 1, pp. 6)
Pub: American City Business Journals, Inc.
Contact: Mike Olivieri, Executive Vice President
Description: The hospitality industry is looking forward to the additional business that the opening of the $520 million, 1,175-room Marriott Marquis Hotel in Washington DC will bring. The hotel has signed up a number of first time DC corporate events and 15 citywide conventions for 2016. **Availability:** Online.

35070 ■ "'Nobody Knows What To Do' To Make Money on the Web" in Barron's (Vol. 88, March 17, 2008, No. 11, pp. 40)
Pub: Dow Jones & Company Inc.
Contact: Almar Latour, Chief Executive Officer
Ed: Mark Veverka. **Description:** Attendees of the South by Southwest Interactive conference failed to get an insight on how to make money on the Web from former Walt Disney CEO Michael Eisner when Eisner said there's no proven business model for financing projects. Eisner said he finances his projects with the help of his connections to get product-placement deals. **Availability:** Online.

35071 ■ "Norvax University Health Insurance Sales Training and Online Marketing Conference" in Marketwired (January 27, 2010)
Pub: Comtex News Network Inc.
Contact: Kan Devnani, President

Description: Overview of the Norvax University Marketing and Sales Success Conference Tour which includes insurance sales training seminars, proven and innovative online marketing techniques and a host of additional information and networking opportunities. **Availability:** Print; Online.

35072 ■ *"Nowspeed and OneSource to Conduct Webinar: How to Develop Social Media Content That Gets Results"* in *Marketwired (December 14, 2009)*
Pub: Comtex News Network Inc.
Contact: Kan Devnani, President

Description: OneSource, a leading provider of global business information, and Nowspeed, an Internet marketing agency, will conduct a webinar titled "How to Develop Social Media Content That Gets Results" in order to provide marketers insight into how to develop and optimize effective social media content to get consumer results that translate into purchases and lead generation. **Availability:** Print; Mailing list; Online.

35073 ■ *"O'Loughlin Cuts $6 Million Deal for Chesterfield Doubletree"* in *Saint Louis Business Journal (Vol. 32, September 2, 2011, No. 1, pp. 1)*
Pub: Saint Louis Business Journal
Contact: Robert Bobroff, President
E-mail: rbobroff@bizjournals.com

Ed: Angela Mueller. **Description:** Lodging Hospitality Management (LHM) acquired the Doubletree Hotel and Conference Center in Chesterfield, Missouri and added it as the 18th hotel in its portfolio. LHM chairman and CEO Bob O'Loughlin plans to invest nearly $15 million in the hotel, including $9 for renovation. **Availability:** Print; Online.

35074 ■ *"One World"* in *American Printer (Vol. 128, August 1, 2011, No. 8)*
Description: Graph Expo will highlight entrepreneurs focused on the connection between content, technology and business models. **Availability:** Print; Online.

35075 ■ *"The Open Mobile Summit Opens in San Francisco Today: John Donahoe CEO eBay to Keynote"* in *Benzinga.com (November 2, 2011)*
Pub: Benzinga.com
Contact: Jason Raznick, Founder

Description: eBay's CEO, John Donahoe was keynote speaker at the 4th Annual Open Mobile Summit held in San Francisco, California. eBay is one of the 130 companies participating as speakers at the event.

35076 ■ *"Pay Heed to 'Smack Stack'"* in *Puget Sound Business Journal (Vol. 35, May 16, 2014, No. 4, pp. 6)*
Pub: American City Business Journals, Inc.
Contact: Mike Olivieri, Executive Vice President

Description: Technology consultant, Geoffrey Moore, discloses the topics he plans to discuss at the annual State of Technology Luncheon held in Washington on May 19, 2014. He will explore the impact of technology and business trends on public-policy making and regulations. **Availability:** Online.

35077 ■ *"PHCC Convention, Show Get High Marks"* in *Contractor (Vol. 56, December 2009, No. 12, pp. 1)*
Ed: Robert P. Mader. **Description:** Plumbing-Heating-Cooling Contractors National Association has held its first convention and trade show in New Orleans, Louisiana. Attendees were treated to a variety of seminars and exhibitors during the event. Comments from event organizers are also given. **Availability:** Print; Online.

35078 ■ *"Plan Your Next Event at Newport News Marriott at City Center"* in *Benzinga.com (July 29, 2011)*
Pub: PR Newswire Association LLC.

Description: Newport News Marriott at City Center is promoting itself as the premier venue for business meetings, conventions and weddings.

35079 ■ *"Planned Convention Center Expansion Already Boosting Business"* in *San Antonio Business Journal (Vol. 27, January 3, 2014, No. 48, pp. 6)*
Pub: American City Business Journals, Inc.
Contact: Mike Olivieri, Executive Vice President

Released: Weekly. **Price:** $4, Introductory 4-week offer(Digital only). **Description:** The expansion of Henry B. Gonzalez Convention Center in San Antonio, Texas will be completed in 2016, but the San Antonio Convention and Visitors Bureau has already booked eight businesses as of January 2014 for the facility. The expansion is expected to generate 515,000 square feet of prime contiguous exhibit space. **Availability:** Print; Online.

35080 ■ *"Plumbing, Heating Products Shine at Greenbuild Expo"* in *Contractor (Vol. 56, December 2009, No. 12, pp. 1)*
Ed: Robert P. Mader. **Description:** Greenbuild Show held in Phoenix, Arizona has showcased the latest in plumbing and heating products. Zurn displayed its EcoVantage line of fixtures and valves during the event. Meanwhile, Sloan Valve offered its washdown 1-pint/flush Alphine urinal. **Availability:** Online.

35081 ■ *"PSI Repair Services to Showcase at Windpower Conference and Exhibition"* in *Entertainment Close-Up (May 19, 2012)*
Description: Subsidiary of Phillips Service Industries, PSI Repair Services, will highlight its off-warranty repair support for wind energy operations at the Windpower 2012 Conference and Exhibition. **Availability:** Online.

35082 ■ *"Raising the Game"* in *Birmingham Business Journal (Vol. 31, May 2, 2014, No. 18, pp. 4)*
Pub: American City Business Journals, Inc.
Contact: Mike Olivieri, Executive Vice President

Description: Birmingham, Alabama has grown its reputation in the sports world in recent years by hosting global events that draw tourists and overage from around the world. However, the Metro needs a facilities upgrade to further elevate its game. The long-debated project to replace the Birmingham-Jefferson Convention Complex and Legion Field is also examined. **Availability:** Online.

35083 ■ *"Real-Life Coursework for Real-Life Business People"* in *Women In Business (Vol. 63, Summer 2011, No. 2, pp. 22)*
Pub: American Business Women's Association
Contact: Rene Street, Executive Director

Ed: Leigh Elmore. **Released:** June 22, 2011. **Description:** American Business Women's Association National Women's Leadership Conference provides members with academic business training courses. Members can take a variety of MBA-level courses that are taught by University of Kansas School of Business professors. Courses include marketing, management, leadership and communication and decision making. **Availability:** Print; Online.

35084 ■ *"A Renewed Sisterhood"* in *Women in Business (Vol. 64, Summer 2012, No. 2, pp. 6)*
Ed: Rene Street. **Description:** The American Business Women's Association (ABWA) regional conference highlighted a new sense of enthusiasm and sisterhood as well as effective visioning exercise and breakout sessions. The ABWA National Women's Leadership Conference in October 2012 will feature the graduates of the Kansas University MBA Essentials Program and keynote speakers Bob Eubanks and Francine Ward. **Availability:** Online.

35085 ■ *"Renren Partners With Recruit to Launch Social Wedding Services"* in *Benzinga.com (June 7, 2011)*
Pub: PR Newswire Association LLC.

Description: Renren Inc., the leading real name social networking Internet platform in China has partnered with Recruit Company Limited, Japan's largest

human resource and classified media group to form a joint venture to build a wedding social media catering to the needs of engaged couples and newlyweds in China.

35086 ■ *"RPA Preps for Building Radiant Conference, Show"* in *Contractor (Vol. 57, January 2010, No. 1, pp. 5)*
Description: Radiant Panel Association is accepting registrations for its Building Radiant 2010 Conference and Trade Show. The conference will discuss radiant heating as well as insurance and other legal matters for mechanical contractors. **Availability:** Print; Online.

35087 ■ *"St. Louis Convention Business 'Fully Recovered"* in *St. Louis Business Journal (Vol. 32, July 13, 2012, No. 47, pp. 1)*
Pub: Baltimore Business Journal
Contact: Rhonda Pringle, President
E-mail: rpringle@bizjournals.com

Description: Saint Louis Convention and Visitor Commission (CVC) sales team has booked 479,991 room nights at the America's Center in its fiscal 2012, a 28 percent increased compared with 2011. The CVC also was able to book a major convention with Herbalife for the week when the Saint Loui Rams will travel to London, United Kingdom. **Availability:** Print; Online.

35088 ■ *"Santa Clara Wineries at Odds with County Over Regulations"* in *Silicon Valley/ San Jose Business Journal (Vol. 30, September 7, 2012, No. 24, pp. 1)*
Pub: Baltimore Business Journal
Contact: Rhonda Pringle, President
E-mail: rpringle@bizjournals.com

Description: A proposed ordinance in Santa Clara County, California will change existing winery regulations and implement a sliding fee system for event permits. Officials believe that the government ordinance will improve agricultural tourism, but winery owners claim that it would force them to choose between canceling events and footing the bill for certain costs. **Availability:** Print; Online.

35089 ■ *"Secrets To Trade Show Success"* in *Women Entrepreneur (September 12, 2008)*
Description: Trade shows require an enormous amount of work, but they are an investment that can pay off handsomely because they allow a business to get their product or service in front of their target market. Advice regarding trade shows is given including selecting the correct venue, researching the affair and following up on leads obtained at the event. **Availability:** Online.

35090 ■ *"Sherwin-Williams Workers Forgo Travel for Virtual Trade Show"* in *Crain's Cleveland Business (Vol. 28, October 15, 2007, No. 41, pp. 4)*
Pub: Crain Communications Inc.
Contact: K. C. Crain, President

Ed: John Booth. **Description:** Overview of Cyber-Coating 2007, a cutting-edge virtual three-dimensional trade show that exhibitors such as Sherwin-Williams Co.'s Chemical Coatings Division will take part in by chatting verbally or via text messages in order to exchange information and listen to pitches just like they would on an actual trade show floor. **Availability:** Online.

35091 ■ *"Show and Tell: How Everybody Can Make Extraordinary Presentations"*
Pub: Portfolio Hardcover
Contact: Adrian Zackheim, President

Released: March 01, 2016. **Price:** $19, paperback. **Description:** Whether in a one-on-one meeting, a conference room with strangers, or a lecture hall in front of thousands, giving a presentation can be difficult. Even good speakers can learn from the tips presented. Understanding your audience, organizing your content, building a clear storyline, creating effective visual effects, and channeling fear into fun will help create effective and successful presentations. **Availability:** Print.

35092 ■ *"Social Media Conference NW 2010"
in Bellingham Business Journal (Vol.
February 2010, pp. 3)*
Pub: Sound Publishing Inc.
Contact: Josh O'Connor, President
Ed: Lance Henderson. **Description:** Center for
Economic Vitality (CEV) and the Technology Alliance
Group (TAG) will host the 2010 Social Media Confer-
ence at the McIntyre Hall Performing Arts & Confer-
ence Center in Mt. Vernon, Washington. The event
will provide networking opportunities for attendees.

35093 ■ *"Special Events Pro Mary Tribble
Reveals Secrets of Winning Bids for Political
Convention Business" in Special Events
Magazine (May 30, 2012)*
Ed: Lisa Hurley. **Description:** Mary Tribble, success-
ful event planner, offers tips for winning bids for politi-
cal conventions. Tribble serves as chief of event plan-
ning for the "Charlotte in 2012" convention for the
Democratic National Convention.

35094 ■ *"Sponsorships, Booths Available for
Business Showcase" in Bellingham Business
Journal (February 2010, pp. 3)*
Pub: Sound Publishing Inc.
Contact: Josh O'Connor, President
Ed: Lance Henderson. **Description:** Third Annual
Spring Business Showcase still have space available
for vendors and sponsors. The event gives local busi-
nesses the opportunity to increase their visibility and
provides a means to increase sales and build relation-
ships.

35095 ■ *"State Fairgrounds Adding
Year-Round Attractions" in Crain's Detroit
Business (Vol. 24, February 18, 2008, No. 7,
pp. 17)*
Pub: Crain Communications Inc.
Contact: Barry Asin, President
Ed: Robert Ankeny. **Description:** Michigan State
Fairgrounds and Exposition Center shares its plans
to become a year-round recreation, entertainment
and education center. **Availability:** Print; Online.

35096 ■ *"Tax-Free Zones Need Shows:
Out-of-State Shoppers Are Key To Success"
in Crain's Detroit Business (Vol. 24, January
28, 2008, No. 4)*
Pub: Crain Communications Inc.
Contact: Barry Asin, President
Ed: Daniel Duggan. **Description:** Sales tax-free
zones are being considered by Michigan's legislators
in order to promote the state as a conference destination. **Availability:** Online.

35097 ■ *"Teachable Moments: Worth Every
Penny" in Pet Product News (Vol. 64,
December 2010, No. 12, pp. 34)*
Ed: Cheryl Reeves. **Description:** Pet bird retailers
can attain both outreach to customers and enhanced
profitability by staging educational events such as the
annual Parrot Palooza event of Burlington, New
Jersey-based Bird Paradise. Aside from attracting a
global audience, Parrot Palooza features seminars,
workshops, classes, and bird-related contests. **Availability:** Print; Online.

35098 ■ *"Then and Now" in Washington
Business Journal (Vol. 32, February 21, 2014,
No. 45, pp. 6)*
Pub: Conde Nast Publications
Contact: Agnes Chu, President
Released: January 05, 2016. **Description:** The new
restaurants and bars at Marriott Marquis Hotel in
Washington DC are offering retro lunch-counter items
alongside modern offerings. The conference/conven-
tion center hotel will open across from the Walter E.
Washington Convention Center on May 1, 2014.
Availability: Print; Online.

35099 ■ *"Tic-Tac-Show: Line Up the
Opportunities at Graph Expo" in American
Printer (Vol. 128, August 1, 2011, No. 8)*
Description: Graph Expo has become the US print
industry's main event. There will be as many as 500
exhibitors at this year's event and the Graphic Arts

Show Company lists over 30 co-located events as
well as 53 new sessions in the seminar program's 28
education categories. **Availability:** PDF; Online.

35100 ■ *"Timken Features Solutions at AWEA
WINDPOWER 2012" in PR Newswire (June 3,
2012)*
Pub: PR Newswire Association LLC.
Description: The Timken Company plans to highlight
its products and aftermarket solutions for the wind
industry at the AWEA WINDPOWER 2012 Conference and Exhibition. Timken products help to maximize the performance of wind energy equipment.
Availability: Online.

35101 ■ *"TopGolf Plans Three-Level
Entertainment Center in S.A." in San Antonio
Business Journal (Vol. 27, January 10, 2014,
No. 49, pp. 6)*
Pub: American City Business Journals, Inc.
Contact: Mike Olivieri, Executive Vice President
Released: Weekly. **Price:** $4, Introductory 4-week
offer(Digital & Print). **Description:** TopGolf plans to
construct a golf entertainment complex in San
Antonio, Texas. The proposed facility is expected to
house about 2,900 square feet of private event
space. The entertainment center could also attract
around 400,000 visitors in the facility's first year of
operation. **Availability:** Print; Online.

35102 ■ *"Travel Tears" in Crain's Chicago
Business (Vol. 31, November 17, 2008, No. 46,
pp. 3)*
Pub: Crain Communications Inc.
Contact: Barry Asin, President
Ed: Bob Tita. **Description:** Hotels, restaurants and
conventions are seeing a decline in profits due to
corporate travel cutbacks and the sagging economy.
City and state revenues derived from taxes on
tourism-related industries are also suffering. **Availability:** Online.

35103 ■ *"The Weeks Ahead" in Crain's New
York Business (Vol. 24, January 7, 2008, No.
1, pp. 26)*
Description: Listing of events in the Detroit area
include conferences addressing entrepreneurialism,
economic development, and women business ownership. **Availability:** Print; Online.

35104 ■ *"Welcome to Babesland" in Women
In Business (Vol. 62, June 2010, No. 2, pp. 33)*
Description: Music group, Four Bitchin' Babes will
be performing at the 2010 American Business
Women's Association's National Women's Leader-
ship Conference. The group has been in the industry
for 20 years and has released nine albums. The Four
Bitchin' Babes consist of Sally Fingerett, Nancy Mo-
ran, Deirdre Flint, and Debi Smith. **Availability:**
Online.

35105 ■ *"Where a Dozen Bagels Will Cost
You 45 Bucks" in Philadelphia Business
Journal (Vol. 28, July 6, 2012, No. 21, pp. 1)*
Pub: Baltimore Business Journal
Contact: Rhonda Pringle, President
E-mail: rpringle@bizjournals.com
Description: The Pennsylvania Convention Center is
seen as an expensive place to hold a trade show.
The center is known for its high labor costs. **Availab-
ility:** Print; Online.

35106 ■ *"Women of Power Summit" in Black
Enterprise (Vol. 38, February 2008, No. 7, pp.
163)*
Description: Third annual Women of Power Summit,
hosted by State Farm, will host over 700 executive
women of color offering empowerment sessions, tips
for networking, along with entertainment. **Availability:** Online.

35107 ■ *"Worry No. 1 at Auto Show:
Recession" in Crain's Detroit Business (Vol.
24, January 21, 2008, No. 3, pp. 1)*
Pub: Crain Communications Inc.
Contact: Barry Asin, President

Ed: Brent Snavely. **Description:** Recession fears
clouded activity at the 2008 Annual North American
International Auto Show. Automakers are expecting
to see a drop in sales due to slow holiday retail
spending as well as fallout from the subprime lending
crisis. **Availability:** Online.

35108 ■ *"WQA's Leadership Conference
Tackles Industry Issues" in Contractor (Vol.
56, October 2009, No. 10, pp. 3)*
Ed: Candace Roulo. **Description:** Water Quality Association's Mid-Year Leadership Conference held in
Bloomingdale, Illinois in September 2009 tackled lead
regulation, water softeners, and product efficiency.
The possibility of a WQA green seal was discussed
by the Water Sciences Committee and the Government Relations Committee meeting. **Availability:**
Online.

TRADE PERIODICALS

35109 ■ **Exhibit Builder**
Pub: Exhibit Builder Magazine
URL(s): exhibitbuilder.net
Description: Magazine covering new product infor-
mation and research related to the exhibit building,
including museums and trade shows. **Availability:**
PDF; Online.

TRADE SHOWS AND
CONVENTIONS

35110 ■ **ABA Bank Marketing Conference**
American Bankers Association (ABA)
1120 Connecticut Ave. NW
Washington, DC 20036
Free: 800-226-5377
Co. E-mail: support@aba.com
URL: http://www.aba.com
Contact: Rob Nichols, President
URL(s): www.aba.com/training-events/conferences/
bank-marketing-conference
Frequency: Irregular. **Description:** Marketing metrics, branch development, compliance, marketing
trends, retail banking, customer profitability, branding,
online marketing, employee retention, marketing
research, and payments. **Audience:** Industry professionals. **Principal Exhibits:** Marketing metrics,
branch development, compliance, marketing trends,
retail banking, customer profitability, branding, online
marketing, employee retention, marketing research,
and payments. **Telecommunication Services:** reg-
housing@aba.com.

35111 ■ **ABA/BMA National Conference for
Community Bankers**
Visa Inc.
900 Metro Center B
Foster City, CA 94404
Ph: (650)432-3200
Fax: (650)432-7436
URL: http://www.visa.com
Contact: Rajat Taneja, President
URL(s): www.aba.com/training-events/conferences/
conference-for-community-bankers
Frequency: Annual. **Description:** Products and
services related to investment management, customer service improvements, advertising, asset/li-
ability management, bank management, electronic
data interchange, employee recruitment/training,
insurance, strategic planning models, including
preparation for the 21st century, new revenue
sourhttp://camsfdr.cams.cengage.info:8080/fdr/im-
ages/close.jpgces, cost control techniques, mainframe computers, market research, MCIF technology,
minicomputers in community banking applications,
software: platform, optical disk, and loan pricing,
sweep accounts, and relationship banking for community bankers. **Audience:** Industry professionals.
Principal Exhibits: Products and services related to
investment management, customer service improvements, advertising, asset/liability management, bank
management, electronic data interchange, employee
recruitment/training, insurance, strategic planning
models, including preparation for the 21st century,

new revenue sourhttp://camsfdr.cams.cengage.info:-8080/fdr/images/close.jpgces, cost control techniques, mainframe computers, market research, MCIF technology, minicomputers in community banking applications, software: platform, optical disk, and loan pricing, sweep accounts, and relationship banking for community bankers. **Dates and Locations:** 2025 Feb 16-18 JW Marriott Phoenix Desert Ridge, Phoenix, AZ. **Telecommunication Services:** reghousing@aba.com.

35112 ■ AFP ICONs
StratCom
URL(s): afpicon.com
Frequency: Annual. **Audience:** Fundraising professionals. **Telecommunication Services:** frp@maritz.com.

35113 ■ American Public Health Association Public Health Expo
American Public Health Association (APHA)
800 I St. NW
Washington, DC 20001
Ph: (202)777-2742
Fax: (202)777-2534
Co. E-mail: membership.mail@apha.org
URL: http://www.apha.org
Contact: Ella Greene-Moton, President
URL(s): www.apha.org/Events-and-Meetings/Annual/Program/Public-Health-Expo
Frequency: Annual. **Description:** Share ideas, network and learn about a range of public health topics. Event will be in-person and will host a digital version of the expo a week later. **Audience:** Public health professionals, physicians, nurses, and health administrators. **Principal Exhibits:** Share ideas, network and learn about a range of public health topics. Event will be in-person and will host a digital version of the expo a week later. **Telecommunication Services:** annualmeeting@apha.org.

35114 ■ American Real Estate Society Annual Meeting
American Real Estate Society (ARES)
PO Box 500
Athens, OH 45701
Ph: (740)239-2737
Fax: (740)593-6758
Co. E-mail: membership@aresnet.org
URL: http://www.aresnet.org
Contact: Dr. Spenser J. Robinson, President
E-mail: s.robinson@cmich.edu
URL(s): www.ares.org/page/AnnConf
Frequency: Annual. **Description:** Exhibits relating to decision-making within real estate finance, real estate market analysis, investment, valuation, development, and other areas related to real estate in the private sector. Data providers, book publishers, etc. **Audience:** Industry Professionals. **Principal Exhibits:** Exhibits relating to decision-making within real estate finance, real estate market analysis, investment, valuation, development, and other areas related to real estate in the private sector. Data providers, book publishers, etc. **Dates and Locations:** 2025 Apr 08-12 Loews Ventana Canyon Resort, Tucson, AZ. **Telecommunication Services:** conference@aresnet.org.

35115 ■ American School Health Association National School Health Conference
American School Health Association (ASHA)
501 N Morton St., Ste. 111
Bloomington, IN 47404
Ph: (202)854-1721
Co. E-mail: info@ashaweb.org
URL: http://www.ashaweb.org
Contact: Meagan Shipley, President
URL(s): www.ashaweb.org
X (Twitter): twitter.com/ASHAnews
Frequency: Annual. **Description:** Publications, pharmaceuticals, clinical and medical equipment and supplies, information on health organizations, and health education methods and materials. **Audience:** School nurses, health educators, physicians, teachers, school administrators, dentists, school counselors, physical educators, and school health coordinators. **Principal Exhibits:** Publications,

pharmaceuticals, clinical and medical equipment and supplies, information on health organizations, and health education methods and materials.

35116 ■ Annual ARNOVA Conference
Association for Research on Nonprofit Organizations and Voluntary Action (ARNOVA)
1100 W 42nd St., Ste. 140
Indianapolis, IN 46208
Ph: (317)684-2120
Co. E-mail: conference@arnova.org
URL: http://www.arnova.org
Contact: Emily Barman, President
URL(s): web.cvent.com/event/fabe347c-475b-40e4-9f57-1e1af84d01f7/websitePage:6bc04e53-f251-446f-8190-74a468298cce?locale=en
Frequency: Annual. **Description:** Creates a public conversation on, as well as opportunities for presenting research about, pressing issues and vital opportunities facing the voluntary or nonprofit sector. **Audience:** Industry professionals. **Principal Exhibits:** Creates a public conversation on, as well as opportunities for presenting research about, pressing issues and vital opportunities facing the voluntary or nonprofit sector. **Dates and Locations:** 2025 Nov 20-22 Indianapolis Marriott Downtown, Indianapolis, IN. **Telecommunication Services:** conference@arnova.org.

35117 ■ ApEx
Restaurants Canada
1155 Queen St. W
Toronto, ON, Canada M6J 1J4
Ph: (416)923-8416
Free: 800-387-5649
Fax: (416)923-1450
Co. E-mail: info@restaurantscanada.org
URL: http://www.restaurantscanada.org
Contact: Christian Buhagiar, Co-Chief Executive Officer Co-President
URL(s): www.apextradeshow.ca
Description: Products and services for the restaurant and hospitality industry, as well as institutions, convenience stores, delis and bakeries. **Audience:** Industry professionals. **Principal Exhibits:** Products and services for the restaurant and hospitality industry, as well as institutions, convenience stores, delis and bakeries. **Telecommunication Services:** chuckn@mediaedge.ca.

35118 ■ AQSG Seminar
American Quilt Study Group (AQSG)
1610 L St.
Lincoln, NE 68508-2509
Ph: (402)477-1181
Fax: (402)477-1181
Co. E-mail: aqsg2@americanquiltstudygroup.org
URL: http://www.americanquiltstudygroup.org
Contact: Jayne Steffens, President
URL(s): www.americanquiltstudygroup.org/content.aspx?page_id=22&club_id=267008&module_id=491050
Frequency: Annual. **Description:** Includes presentation of research papers. **Audience:** Enthusiasts and scholars. **Principal Exhibits:** Includes presentation of research papers. **Dates and Locations:** 2025 Oct 15-19 Holiday Inn By the Bay, Portland, ME.

35119 ■ ATEA National Conference
URL(s): ateaonline.org/events
Frequency: Annual. **Description:** Disseminate information regarding current issues, trends, and exemplary practices in technical education. **Audience:** Industry professionals. **Principal Exhibits:** Disseminate information regarding current issues, trends, and exemplary practices in technical education.

35120 ■ Canadian Real Estate Association Annual Conference and Trade Show
Description: Real Estate, financial, printing, and computer business equipment. **Audience:** Real estate professionals, brokers, managers, and corporate representatives from real estate boards across the country. **Principal Exhibits:** Real Estate, financial, printing, and computer business equipment.

35121 ■ Florida RV Supershow
Florida RV Trade Association (FRVTA)
10510 Gibsonton Dr.
Riverview, FL 33578-5434
Ph: (813)741-0488
Fax: (813)741-0688
Co. E-mail: info@frvta.org
URL: http://www.frvta.org
Contact: Dave Kelly, Executive Director
URL(s): www.frvta.org/show/florida-rv-supershow
Price: $10, regular adult admission; free for children under 16. **Frequency:** Annual. **Description:** Exhibits related to recreational vehicle equipment, supplies and services. **Audience:** RV dealers and manufacturers, and general public. **Principal Exhibits:** Exhibits related to recreational vehicle equipment, supplies and services. **Telecommunication Services:** sales@eliteeventsandrentals.com

35122 ■ Game Developers' Conference (GDC)
UBM L.L.C.
2 Penn Plz.
New York, NY 10121
Ph: (212)600-3000
URL: http://www.ubm.com
Contact: Tim Cobbold, Chief Executive Officer
URL(s): www.gdconf.com/about
Price: $1,599, Pre-registered all-access pass; $2,099, Onsite all-access pass. **Frequency:** Annual. **Description:** Equipment, supplies, and services for developers and producers of computer games. **Audience:** Programmers, artists, producers, game designers, audio professionals, and business leaders. **Principal Exhibits:** Equipment, supplies, and services for developers and producers of computer games.

35123 ■ Indexing Society of Canada Annual Conference
Indexing Society of Canada (ISC)
100 Chapel St.
Kitchener, ON, Canada N2H 2T5
Co. E-mail: info@indexers.ca
URL: http://indexers.ca
Contact: Jolanta Komornicka, President
URL(s): conference.indexers.ca
Frequency: Annual. **Description:** Annual national conference covering various topics of interest to indexers. **Audience:** The Society holds its conference and annual general meeting. **Principal Exhibits:** Annual national conference covering various topics of interest to indexers. **Telecommunication Services:** conference@indexers.ca.

35124 ■ Maryland Municipal League Convention
Maryland Municipal League (MML)
1212 W St.
Annapolis, MD 21401
Ph: (410)295-9100
Free: 800-492-7121
Co. E-mail: mml@mdmunicipal.org
URL: http://www.mdmunicipal.org
Contact: Scott A. Hancock, Executive Director
E-mail: scotth@mdmunicipal.org
URL(s): www.mdmunicipal.org/list.aspx?MID=40
Frequency: Annual. **Description:** Office equipment, public works equipment, insurance companies, consulting firms, recreation equipment, computers, engineering firms, police equipment, and code publishers. **Audience:** City and town officials. **Principal Exhibits:** Office equipment, public works equipment, insurance companies, consulting firms, recreation equipment, computers, engineering firms, police equipment, and code publishers.

35125 ■ MFM Annual conference
Media Financial Management Association (MFM)
2365 Harrodsburg Rd., Ste. A325
Lexington, KY 40504
Ph: (847)716-7000
Fax: (847)784-8059
Co. E-mail: info@mediafinance.org
URL: http://www.mediafinance.org
Contact: Joseph J. Annotti, President
E-mail: joe.annotti@mediafinance.org

URL(s): www.mediafinance.org/annual-conference
Frequency: Annual. **Description:** Exhibits relating to the financial management of radio, television, and cable television operations, including issues such as industry - specific software, collection agencies, insurance, investments, banking, accounting firms and music licensing. **Audience:** Financial professionals for media industry. **Principal Exhibits:** Exhibits relating to the financial management of radio, television, and cable television operations, including issues such as industry - specific software, collection agencies, insurance, investments, banking, accounting firms and music licensing. Dates and Locations: 2025 May 18-21 Crystal Gateway Marriott, Arlington, VA. **Telecommunication Services:** info@mediafinance. org.

35126 ■ Michigan Association for Computer Users in Learning Conference

Michigan Association for Computer Users in Learning (MACUL)
  520 S Creyts Rd.
  Lansing, MI 48917
Ph: (517)882-1403
Fax: (517)882-2362
Co. E-mail: macul@macul.org
URL: http://macul.org
Contact: Mark Smith, Executive Director
E-mail: msmith@macul.org
URL(s): maculconference.org
Frequency: Annual; held in March. **Audience:** Educators and students. Dates and Locations: 2025 Mar 19-21 Detroit, MI; 2026 Mar 18-20 Grand Rapids, MI; 2027 Mar 17-19 Detroit, MI. **Telecommunication Services:** msmith@macul.org.

35127 ■ Michigan Interscholastic Athletic Administrators Mid-Winter Conference

Michigan Interscholastic Athletic Administrators Association (MIAAA)
  c/o Karen Leinaar, Executive Director
  PO Box 1708
  Frankfort, MI 49635
Ph: (231)218-6983
Co. E-mail: karenleinaar@gmail.com
URL: http://www.miaaa.com
Contact: Karen Leinaar, Executive Director
E-mail: karenleinaar@gmail.com
URL(s): www.miaaa.com/conferences
Frequency: Annual. **Description:** To bring together athletic directors from all parts of Michigan to discuss new ideas and solutions to problems common to all. **Audience:** Athletic directors and administrators. **Principal Exhibits:** To bring together athletic directors from all parts of Michigan to discuss new ideas and solutions to problems common to all. Dates and Locations: 2025 Mar 13-16; 2026 Mar 19-22; 2027 Mar 18-21. Grand Traverse Resort Hotel, Traverse City, MI. **Telecommunication Services:** tjohnston1977@gmail.com.

35128 ■ Michigan Restaurant Show

Michigan Restaurant & Lodging Association (MRLA)
  225 W Washtenaw St.
  Lansing, MI 48933
Free: 800-968-9668
URL: http://www.mrla.org
Contact: Justin Winslow, President
URL(s): www.mrlashow.org
Frequency: Annual. **Description:** Equipment, supplies, and services for the food service industry. **Audience:** Industry professionals and public. **Principal Exhibits:** Equipment, supplies, and services for the food service industry.

35129 ■ NASPL Annual Conference

North American Association of State and Provincial Lotteries (NASPL)
  7757 Auburn Rd., Unit No. 7
  Concord Township, OH 44077
Ph: (440)361-7962
Co. E-mail: info@nasplhq.org
URL: http://www.naspl.org
Contact: Gretchen Corbin, President
URL(s): www.naspl.org/events

Frequency: Annual. **Description:** Lottery equipment, supplies, and services. **Audience:** Industry professionals. **Principal Exhibits:** Lottery equipment, supplies, and services. Dates and Locations: 2025 Sep 09-12 Niagara Falls, ON; 2026 Sep 21-24 Orlando, FL.

35130 ■ National Agricultural Bankers Conference

CHS Hedging, LLC
  5500 Cenex Dr.
  Inver Grove Heights, MN 55077
Free: 800-328-6530
Co. E-mail: support@chshedging.com
URL: http://chshedging.com
Contact: Nelson Neale, President
URL(s): www.aba.com/training-events/conferences/agricultural-bankers-conference
Frequency: Annual. **Description:** On topics related to latest developments in the agricultural lending business, as well as strategies for better market share, profitability, and customer service. Includes keynote speakers, workshops, and sessions. **Audience:** Industry professionals. **Principal Exhibits:** On topics related to latest developments in the agricultural lending business, as well as strategies for better market share, profitability, and customer service. Includes keynote speakers, workshops, and sessions. **Telecommunication Services:** mrogers@aba.com.

35131 ■ New Jersey League of Municipalities Annual Conference

New Jersey State League of Municipalities (NJLM)
  222 W State St.
  Trenton, NJ 08608
Ph: (609)695-3481
Fax: (609)695-0151
URL: http://www.njlm.org
Contact: Michael F. Cerra, Executive Director
E-mail: mcerra@njlm.org
URL(s): conference.njlm.org/about.html
Frequency: Annual. **Audience:** Technical and professional employees. **Telecommunication Services:** klawrence@njlm.org.

35132 ■ SHRM Annual Conference & Exposition

Society for Human Resource Management (SHRM)
  1800 Duke St.
  Alexandria, VA 22314
Ph: (703)548-3440
Free: 800-283-7476
Co. E-mail: shrm@shrm.org
URL: http://www.shrm.org
Contact: Johnny C. Taylor, Jr., President
E-mail: shrmceo@shrm.org
URL(s): annual.shrm.org
Frequency: Annual. **Description:** Human resource management products and services; including relocation human resource information systems, recruitment, executive search, temporary/contact personnel employee compensation and benefits, incentive program information, childcare/eldercare, and drug testing information. This is a hybrid event with in-person and virtual options. **Audience:** Human resource professionals. **Principal Exhibits:** Human resource management products and services; including relocation human resource information systems, recruitment, executive search, temporary/contact personnel employee compensation and benefits, incentive program information, childcare/eldercare, and drug testing information. This is a hybrid event with in-person and virtual options. Dates and Locations: 2025 Jun 29-Jul 02 SAN DIEGO CONVENTION CENTER, San Diego, CA. **Telecommunication Services:** gcoffice@shrm.org.

35133 ■ South Dakota Association of Realtors Convention

South Dakota Association of Realtors (SDAR)
  2302 Patron Pwy.
  Pierre, SD 57501
Ph: (605)224-0554
Free: 800-227-5877
Fax: (605)224-8975
Co. E-mail: sdar@sdrealtor.org
URL: http://www.sdrealtor.org

Contact: Kyle Lalim, Director
E-mail: soldbykyle@midco.net
URL(s): www.sdrealtor.org/events/realtor-convention-of-the-dakotas
Frequency: Annual. **Description:** Provide information, quality education, and political advocacy. **Audience:** Members and real estate professionals. **Principal Exhibits:** Provide information, quality education, and political advocacy. **Telecommunication Services:** robyn@ndrealtors.com.

35134 ■ Texas Apartment Association Annual Education Conference and Lone Star Expo

Texas Apartment Association (TAA)
  1011 San Jacinto Blvd., Ste. 600
  Austin, TX 78701-1951
Ph: (512)479-6252
Fax: (512)479-6291
URL: http://taa.org
Contact: Clay Hicks, President
URL(s): www.taa.org/conference
Frequency: Annual. **Description:** Goods and services geared to multi-housing professionals, including software, soft goods, and property supplies. **Audience:** Owners and rental operators. **Principal Exhibits:** Goods and services geared to multi-housing professionals, including software, soft goods, and property supplies. Dates and Locations: 2025 May 07-09 Houston, TX. **Telecommunication Services:** conference@taa.org.

35135 ■ Virginia Health Care Association Annual Convention and Trade Show

Virginia Health Care Association (VHCA)
  2112 W Laburnum Ave., Ste. 206
  Richmond, VA 23227
Ph: (804)353-9101
Fax: (804)353-3098
Co. E-mail: info@vhca.org
URL: http://www.vhca.org
Contact: Keith Hare, President
E-mail: keith.hare@vhca.org
URL(s): 2024tradeshow.vhca.org
Frequency: Annual. **Description:** Equipment, supplies, and services for nursing home operations, including food, medical supplies, furniture, computer systems, linen, medical equipment, insurance, pharmaceuticals, optometrists, psychologists, and transportation. **Audience:** Health care professionals and general public. **Principal Exhibits:** Equipment, supplies, and services for nursing home operations, including food, medical supplies, furniture, computer systems, linen, medical equipment, insurance, pharmaceuticals, optometrists, psychologists, and transportation. **Telecommunication Services:** doran.hutchinson@vhca.org.

35136 ■ Wealth Management and Trust Conference

Alpha Core
URL(s): www.aba.com/training-events/conferences/wealth-management-trust-conference
Frequency: Annual. **Description:** Events for the wealth management and trust banking community. **Audience:** Industry professionals. **Principal Exhibits:** Events for the wealth management and trust banking community. Dates and Locations: 2025 Feb 24-26 Manchester Grand Hyatt, San Diego, CA. **Telecommunication Services:** kchancy@aba.com.

35137 ■ Western Food Service & Hospitality Expo Los Angeles

California Restaurant Association (CRA)
  621 Capitol Mall, Ste. 2000
  Sacramento, CA 95814
Free: 800-765-4842
Fax: (916)200-3453
Co. E-mail: membership@calrest.org
URL: http://www.calrest.org
Contact: Jot Condie, President
E-mail: jcondie@calrest.org
URL(s): www.westernfoodexpo.com
Description: Food, equipment, supplies, and services for food service and lodging industries. **Audience:** Restaurant, food service, hospitality and lodging industry professionals. **Principal Exhibits:** Food,

equipment, supplies, and services for food service and lodging industries. **Telecommunication Services:** californiarestaurantshow@xpressreg.net.

35138 ■ WestEx - Colorado Foodservice & Restaurant Conference
Sapporo
1-1, Odori Nishi, Chuo-ku
Sapporo, Hokkaido 060-8703, Japan
URL: http://www.nhk.or.jp
URL(s): www.coloradorestaurant.com/education-even ts/calendar/61_2015-WestEx:-Colorado-Restauran t-&-Foodservice-Conference

Description: Food service and lodging products, equipment, and services. **Audience:** Food service and restaurant industry personnel. **Principal Exhibits:** Food service and lodging products, equipment, and services.

CONSULTANTS

35139 ■ Featherlite Exhibits
7300 32nd Ave. N
Minneapolis, MN 55427
Ph: (763)537-5533
Free: 800-229-5533
URL: http://www.featherlite.com
Facebook: www.facebook.com/featherliteexhibits

X (Twitter): x.com/FeatherliteMN
YouTube: www.youtube.com/user/FeatherliteExhibits
Pinterest: www.pinterest.com/FeatherliteMN

Description: Provides design and fabrication of lightweight trade show displays. **Founded:** 1964. **Special Services:** Computer-aided drafting and design service.

35140 ■ RS+K
155 E Wilson St., Ste. 100
Madison, WI 53703
Ph: (608)827-0701
Co. E-mail: info@rsandk.com
URL: http://www.rsandk.com
Contact: Kay Krebsbach, President
Facebook: www.facebook.com/Reed-Sendecke -Krebsbach-RSK-168244614113
Linkedin: www.linkedin.com/company/r-s-k
X (Twitter): x.com/RSandK_Inc
YouTube: www.youtube.com/channel/ UCOrRIXSU7WwQrMGJssueHHA

Description: Provider of marketing, advertising and design for a communications agency that specialized in creating image and awareness programs for business-to-business clients in the life sciences, computer technology, power quality, filtration, medical equipment, financial services and telecommunications industries. **Scope:** Provider of marketing,

advertising and design for a communications agency that specialized in creating image and awareness programs for business-to-business clients in the life sciences, computer technology, power quality, filtration, medical equipment, financial services and telecommunications industries. **Founded:** 1978.

35141 ■ Together Inc.
3739-A S Peoria
Tulsa, OK 74105
Contact: Bern L. Gentry, Contact

Description: Firm offers services in employee and client self-development training, logo development, lapel pin design, fundraising, public relations, conference and exhibit planning, direct marketing, association management, human resource development, and photography and serves government agencies, education, association and business, public and private schools. **Scope:** Firm offers services in employee and client self-development training, logo development, lapel pin design, fundraising, public relations, conference and exhibit planning, direct marketing, association management, human resource development, and photography and serves government agencies, education, association and business, public and private schools. **Founded:** 1973. **Training:** Adventures in Attitudes; Diversity and Board Training for non-profits. **Special Services:** The Pin Man®.

ASSOCIATIONS AND OTHER ORGANIZATIONS

35142 ■ *Active Voice*
1507-180 Dundas St. W
  Toronto, ON, Canada M5G 1Z8
Ph: (416)975-1379
Co. E-mail: info@editors.ca
URL: http://www.editors.ca
Contact: Natasha Bood, Executive Director
E-mail: executivedirector@editors.ca
URL(s): activevoice.editors.ca
Released: Latest issue Spring/Summer 2019 . **Availability:** Print.

35143 ■ L'Association Canadienne des Relations Industrielles (CIRA) [Canadian Industrial Relations Association (CIRA)]
c/o Jonathan Michaud, Communications Officer
  Universite de Montreal 150, rue Jean-Brillant
  Montreal, QC, Canada H3T 1N8
Co. E-mail: communications.cira@gmail.com
URL: http://www.cira-acri.ca/home
Contact: Jason Foster, President
E-mail: jasonf@athabascau.ca
Facebook: www.facebook.com/CIRAACRI
X (Twitter): x.com/cira_acri
Description: Industrial relations' professionals. Seeks to advance the study and practice of industrial relations. Serves as a forum for the exchange of ideas and information among members; sponsors research. **Awards:** Gérard Dion Award (Annual). **Geographic Preference:** National.

35144 ■ Building and Construction Trades Department - Canadian Office
72 Chamberlain Ave.
  Ottawa, ON, Canada K1S 1V9
Ph: (613)236-0653
URL: http://buildingtrades.ca
Contact: Sean Strickland, Director
Facebook: www.facebook.com/CdnTrades
Linkedin: www.linkedin.com/company/buildingtrades
X (Twitter): x.com/CDNTrades
Instagram: www.instagram.com/cdntrades
YouTube: www.youtube.com/channel/UCVQ6E2v0
  52S2EGA5ZOp5sWA
Description: Individuals working in the building trades. Seeks to obtain optimal conditions of employment for members. Represents members in negotiations with employers. **Founded:** 1896. **Geographic Preference:** National.

35145 ■ Canadian Association of Labour Media (CALM)
196 Rene-Levesque O.
  Quebec, QC, Canada G1R2A5
URL: http://calm.ca
Contact: Tasia Brown, President
X (Twitter): x.com/CanLabourMedia
Description: Media organizations operated by labor unions. Promotes increased awareness of the trade union movement and issues affecting workers.

Serves as a clearinghouse on trade unionism and labor issues. **Founded:** 1976. **Publications:** *CALM-ideas* (Annual). **Geographic Preference:** National.

35146 ■ Canadian Association of Professional Employees (CAPE) [Association canadienne des employés professionnels]
100 Queen St., 4th Fl.
  Ottawa, ON, Canada K1P 1J9
Ph: (613)236-9181
Free: 800-265-9181
Fax: (613)236-6017
Co. E-mail: general@acep-cape.ca
URL: http://www.acep-cape.ca/en
Facebook: www.facebook.com/acepcape
Linkedin: www.linkedin.com/company/acepcape
X (Twitter): x.com/cape_acep
Instagram: www.instagram.com/acep_cape
YouTube: www.youtube.com/channel/UCnGJsFPws
  1sjuQ4sbYZNtfw
Description: Professional and technical employees. Seeks to obtain optimal conditions of employment for members. Represents members in negotiations with employers. **Geographic Preference:** National.

35147 ■ Canadian Labour Congress (CLC) - Library
2841 Riverside Dr.
  Ottawa, ON, Canada K1V 8X7
Ph: (613)521-3400
Free: 800-387-3500
Fax: (613)521-4655
Co. E-mail: media@clcctc.ca
URL: http://canadianlabour.ca
Contact: Bea Bruske, President
E-mail: president-office@clcctc.ca
Facebook: www.facebook.com/clc.ctc
YouTube: www.youtube.com/user/canadianlabour
Description: Seeks to create a just and equitable society. **Scope:** Labor. **Founded:** 1956. **Holdings:** Figures not available. **Publications:** *Canadian Labour* (Quarterly); *C.L.C. Fax-Press* (Weekly); *Sweatshop Alert*; *UI Bulletin* (Periodic). **Geographic Preference:** National.

35148 ■ Canadian Media Guild (CMG)
311 Adelaide St. E, Ste. 101
  Toronto, ON, Canada M5A 1N2
Ph: (416)591-5333
Free: 800-465-4149
Fax: (416)591-5333
Co. E-mail: info@cmg.ca
URL: http://cmg.ca
Contact: Annick Forest, President
E-mail: president@cmg.ca
Facebook: www.facebook.com/cmglaguilde
X (Twitter): x.com/CMGLaGuilde
Description: Employees of press and broadcasting companies and other media outlets. Seeks to secure optimal conditions of employment for members. Represents members in negotiations with employers. **Publications:** *G-Force* (Quarterly). **Awards:** CBC Branch President's Award (Biennial). **Geographic Preference:** National.

35149 ■ Canadian Teachers Federation (CTF) - Library [Fédération canadienne des enseignantes et des enseignants (FCE); Fedration canadienne des enseignantes et des enseignants]
2490 Don Reid Dr.
  Ottawa, ON, Canada K1H 1E1
Ph: (613)232-1505
Fax: (613)232-1886
Co. E-mail: info@ctf-fce.ca
URL: http://www.ctf-fce.ca
Contact: Cassandra Hallett, Executive Director
Facebook: www.facebook.com/CTF.FCE
Linkedin: www.linkedin.com/company/canadian
  -teachers'%E2%80%8B-federation---f%C3%A9
  d.-canadienne-des-enseignantes-et-des
  -enseignants
X (Twitter): x.com/CTFFCE
Instagram: www.instagram.com/ctffce
YouTube: www.youtube.com/channel/UC47tcY23He
  tQCHiyCIHXn1g
Description: Works to ensure that teachers' opinions are considered when national government bodies debate educational legislation. Facilitates communication and cooperation among members. **Scope:** Teachers. **Founded:** 1920. **Holdings:** Figures not available. **Publications:** *Innovations in Teaching: Resumes of the Roy C. Hill Awards Program* (Annual). **Geographic Preference:** National.

35150 ■ Centrale des Syndicats du Quebec (CSQ)
9405 rue Sherbrooke E
  Montreal, QC, Canada H1L 6P3
Ph: (514)356-8888
Free: 800-465-0897
Fax: (514)356-9999
URL: http://www.lacsq.org
Contact: Sonia Ethier, President
Facebook: www.facebook.com/lacsq
X (Twitter): twitter.com/csq_centrale
Instagram: www.instagram.com/lacsq
Description: Represents members in collective bargaining negotiations; promotes members' professional interests. Conducts union education, political action, and research activities. **Publications:** *Nouvelles CSQ*. **Geographic Preference:** National.

35151 ■ Communications Workers of America Canada (CWA)
301-2200 Prince of Wales Dr.
  Ottawa, ON, Canada K2E 6Z9
Ph: (613)820-9777
Free: 877-486-4292
Fax: (613)820-8188
Co. E-mail: info@cwa-scacanada.ca
URL: http://cwacanada.ca
Contact: Martin O'Hanlon, President
E-mail: mohanlon@cwacanada.ca
Facebook: www.facebook.com/cwacanada
X (Twitter): x.com/cwacanada1

Description: Primarily union of journalists and media workers in Canada, as well as social workers and employees in the manufacturing industry. **Founded:** 1995. **Publications:** *TNG Canada Today* (Monthly). **Awards:** Morton Bahr Scholarship (Annual); David S. Barr Award (Annual); Heywood Broun Awards (Annual); Paul Kidd Courage Prize (Annual); Dick Martin Scholarship Award (Annual); CWA Canada/CAJ Awards for Excellence in Labour Reporting (Annual); Charles B. Dale Guild Service Awards; Joe Beirne Foundation Scholarships (Annual); John Belcarz and Dan Zeidler Memorial Scholarships (Annual); CJFE Tara Singh Hayer Memorial Award (Annual); Kurt Schork Awards in International Journalism - Local Reporter (Annual); Union Plus Scholarship Program (Annual). **Geographic Preference:** National.

35152 ■ Confédération des Syndicats Nationaux (CSN) [Confederation of National Trade Unions (CNTU)]
1601 Ave. de Lorimier
  Montreal, QC, Canada H2K 4M5
Free: 866-646-7760
URL: http://www.csn.qc.ca
Facebook: www.facebook.com/LaCSN
X (Twitter): x.com/lacsn
Instagram: www.instagram.com/mouvementcsn
Description: National trade unions representing0 workers. Promotes advancement of the Canadian labor movement. Represents workers in collective bargaining. **Founded:** 1921. **Publications:** *Nouvelles CSN* (Biweekly). **Geographic Preference:** National.

35153 ■ Editors Association of Canada (EAC)
1507-180 Dundas St. W
  Toronto, ON, Canada M5G 1Z8
Ph: (416)975-1379
Co. E-mail: info@editors.ca
URL: http://www.editors.ca
Contact: Natasha Bood, Executive Director
E-mail: executivedirector@editors.ca
Facebook: www.facebook.com/EditorsReviseursCanada
X (Twitter): x.com/editorscanada
Instagram: www.instagram.com/editorscanada
Description: Promotes advancement of the profession of editing, and of members' capabilities. **Founded:** 1978. **Publications:** *Active Voice.* **Awards:** Tom Fairley Award for Editorial Excellence (Annual); Claudette Upton Scholarship (Annual); Lee d'Anjou Volunteer of the Year (Annual); EAC President's Award for Volunteer Service (Annual). **Geographic Preference:** National.

35154 ■ *G-Force*
311 Adelaide St. E, Ste. 101
  Toronto, ON, Canada M5A 1N2
Ph: (416)591-5333
Free: 800-465-4149
Fax: (416)591-5333
Co. E-mail: info@cmg.ca
URL: http://cmg.ca
Contact: Annick Forest, President
E-mail: president@cmg.ca
URL(s): cmg.ca/g-force
Released: Quarterly **Availability:** Online.

35155 ■ *Nouvelles CSQ*
9405 rue Sherbrooke E
  Montreal, QC, Canada H1L 6P3
Ph: (514)356-8888
Free: 800-465-0897
Fax: (514)356-9999
URL: http://www.lacsq.org
Contact: Sonia Ethier, President
URL(s): www.lacsq.org/actualite/magazine-et-revue
  -une-petite-nuance
Description: Consumer magazine for Centrale Des Syndicate du Quebec (CSQ) union members in the Quebec education, health, and social services industries. **Availability:** Print.

35156 ■ *Standing Tall*
Bureau 309
  110 Rue Sainte Therese
  Montreal, QC, Canada H2Y 1E6
Ph: (514)272-2670

Fax: (514)272-8338
Co. E-mail: aafq.info@gmail.com
Contact: Myriam Dumont Robillard, President
Released: Bimonthly **Price:** included in membership dues. **Availability:** Print.

35157 ■ Syndicat Canadien de la Fonction Publique (SCFP) [Canadian Union of Public Employees (CUPE)]
1375 St. Laurent
  Ottawa, ON, Canada K1G 0Z7
Ph: (613)237-1590
Free: 844-242-1590
Fax: (613)237-5508
URL: http://cupe.ca
Contact: Mark Hancock, President
Facebook: www.facebook.com/cupescfp
X (Twitter): x.com/cupenat
Description: Seeks to protect the rights and improve the conditions of employment of members. **Founded:** 1963. **Publications:** *CUPE: It's Your Union*; *Organize* (Periodic). **Geographic Preference:** National.

35158 ■ *Terre de Chez Nous*
555, Roland-Therrien Blvd., Ste. 100
  Longueuil, QC, Canada J4H 3Y9
Ph: (450)679-0530
URL: http://www.upa.qc.ca
Contact: Marcel Groleau, President
URL(s): www.laterre.ca
Facebook: www.facebook.com/laterreca
Linkedin: www.linkedin.com/company/la-terre-de
  -chez-nous
Instagram: www.instagram.com/laterreca
YouTube: www.youtube.com/user/Terredecheznous
Released: Weekly (Wed.) **Price:** $120, for 2 year subscription; $150, for 3 year subscription; $74, for 1 year subscription; $9, for 1 month online. **Availability:** PDF; Download; Online.

35159 ■ Unifor
115 Gordon Baker Rd.
  Toronto, ON, Canada M2H 0A8
Ph: (416)497-4110
Free: 800-268-5763
Co. E-mail: communications@unifor.org
URL: http://www.unifor.org
Contact: Daniel Cloutier, Director
E-mail: daniel.cloutier@unifor.org
Facebook: www.facebook.com/UniforCanada
X (Twitter): x.com/UniforTheUnion
YouTube: www.youtube.com/user/UniforCanada
Description: Trade union. Organizes and conducts collective bargaining for individuals employed in the telecommunications, electrical, electronics, pulp and paper, energy, print and broadcast media, and chemical industries in Canada. **Founded:** 2013. **Publications:** *CAW Contact* (Weekly). **Awards:** Unifor Scholarship Program (Annual).

35160 ■ Union of Canadian Transportation Employees (UCTE)
233 Gilmour St., Ste. 702
  Ottawa, ON, Canada K2P 0P2
Ph: (613)238-4003
Free: 888-542-1850
Co. E-mail: ucte-ucet@psac-afpc.com
URL: http://unioncte.ca
Contact: Teresa Eschuk, President
E-mail: eschukt@psac-afpc.com
Facebook: www.facebook.com/UCTE.UCET
Linkedin: www.linkedin.com/company/ucte-ucet
X (Twitter): x.com/UnionCTE
Instagram: www.instagram.com/ucte.ucet
Description: Individuals employed in the transportation industries. Seeks to obtain optimal conditions of employment for members. Represents members in negotiations with employers. **Founded:** 1969. **Awards:** D. Bennett/W. Weaver Memorial Scholarship (Annual). **Geographic Preference:** National.

35161 ■ Union des Producteurs Agricoles (UPA)
555, Roland-Therrien Blvd., Ste. 100
  Longueuil, QC, Canada J4H 3Y9
Ph: (450)679-0530
URL: http://www.upa.qc.ca

Contact: Marcel Groleau, President
X (Twitter): x.com/upaqc
YouTube: www.youtube.com/user/upa1972
Description: Promotes and supports the interests of agricultural producers throughout Canada. Provides information on updated developments on the farming industry. Works as a communications network among Quebec farmers. Protects the rights of individuals within the agricultural producing community. **Founded:** 1924. **Publications:** *La Terre de Chez Nous*; *Terre de Chez Nous* (Weekly (Wed.)). **Geographic Preference:** National.

35162 ■ United Steelworkers of America - Canadian Branch (USWA) [Metallurgistes Unis d'Amerique]
234 Eglinton Ave. E, 8th Fl.
  Toronto, ON, Canada M4P 1K7
Ph: (416)487-1571
Free: 877-669-8792
Fax: (416)482-5548
Co. E-mail: info@usw.ca
URL: http://www.usw.ca
Contact: Marty Warren, Division Director
Description: Represents the interests of workers in a variety of sectors in Canada. Maintains charitable program. **Founded:** 1942. **Publications:** *Steelabor - Canadian Edition* (Monthly); *Steeleader* (Periodic); *Unionbuilder* (Periodic). **Geographic Preference:** National.

EDUCATIONAL PROGRAMS

35163 ■ Investigation Tools and Techniques: Developing Facts and Evidence (Onsite)
Seminar Information Service Inc. (SIS)
  250 El Camino Real., Ste. 112
  Tustin, CA 92780
Ph: (714)508-0340
Free: 877-736-4636
Fax: (714)734-8027
Co. E-mail: info@seminarinformation.com
URL: http://www.seminarinformation.com
Contact: Catherine Bellizzi, President
URL(s): www.seminarinformation.com
Description: Interactive workshop provides valuable information and tools on how to conduct an investigation of major workplace offenses that may result in immediate termination and that may be the subject of employment litigation. **Audience:** Labor relations, human resource, and operations professionals . **Principal Exhibits:** Interactive workshop provides valuable information and tools on how to conduct an investigation of major workplace offenses that may result in immediate termination and that may be the subject of employment litigation.

35164 ■ The Law of Equal Employment Opportunity (Onsite)
Seminar Information Service Inc. (SIS)
  250 El Camino Real., Ste. 112
  Tustin, CA 92780
Ph: (714)508-0340
Free: 877-736-4636
Fax: (714)734-8027
Co. E-mail: info@seminarinformation.com
URL: http://www.seminarinformation.com
Contact: Catherine Bellizzi, President
URL(s): www.seminarinformation.com/details.cfm?qc
  =qqayrq
Description: Participants examine Equal Employment Opportunity/affirmative action laws and obligations of employers, recent legislation, guidelines, compliance agencies' interpretations, and court decisions and the impact of Equal Employment laws on policies, procedures, and day-to-day operations. **Audience:** EEO, AA, and HR managers. **Principal Exhibits:** Participants examine Equal Employment Opportunity/affirmative action laws and obligations of employers, recent legislation, guidelines, compliance agencies' interpretations, and court decisions and the impact of Equal Employment laws on policies, procedures, and day-to-day operations.

35165 ■ Legal Issues for Managers (Onsite)
Seminar Information Service Inc. (SIS)
  250 El Camino Real., Ste. 112
  Tustin, CA 92780
Ph: (714)508-0340
Free: 877-736-4636
Fax: (714)734-8027
Co. E-mail: info@seminarinformation.com
URL: http://www.seminarinformation.com
Contact: Catherine Bellizzi, President
URL(s): www.seminarinformation.com
Description: Using a case study, practical examples, and discussions participants will explore the law as it relates to making nondiscriminatory employment decisions, compliance with wage and hour laws, safety and health rights and responsibilities, required versus discretionary leaves of absence, managing employees covered by labor agreements, and individual rights and wrongful discharge. **Audience:** Managers. **Principal Exhibits:** Using a case study, practical examples, and discussions participants will explore the law as it relates to making nondiscriminatory employment decisions, compliance with wage and hour laws, safety and health rights and responsibilities, required versus discretionary leaves of absence, managing employees covered by labor agreements, and individual rights and wrongful discharge.

35166 ■ The Service Contract Act (Onsite)
Seminar Information Service Inc. (SIS)
  250 El Camino Real., Ste. 112
  Tustin, CA 92780
Ph: (714)508-0340
Free: 877-736-4636
Fax: (714)734-8027
Co. E-mail: info@seminarinformation.com
URL: http://www.seminarinformation.com
Contact: Catherine Bellizzi, President
URL(s): www.seminarinformation.com/qqanqg/service-contract-act
Description: This course covers the applicable labor requirements, how they are enforced, and how to efficiently incorporate them into contract activities. **Audience:** Government professionals. **Principal Exhibits:** This course covers the applicable labor requirements, how they are enforced, and how to efficiently incorporate them into contract activities.

35167 ■ Wage and Hour Law Compliance (Onsite)
Seminar Information Service Inc. (SIS)
  250 El Camino Real., Ste. 112
  Tustin, CA 92780
Ph: (714)508-0340
Free: 877-736-4636
Fax: (714)734-8027
Co. E-mail: info@seminarinformation.com
URL: http://www.seminarinformation.com
Contact: Catherine Bellizzi, President
URL(s): www.seminarinformation.com
Description: Learn the latest decisions and applications of the Fair Labor Standards Act. **Audience:** HR and payroll professionals. **Principal Exhibits:** Learn the latest decisions and applications of the Fair Labor Standards Act.

REFERENCE WORKS

35168 ■ "4 Visa Programs That Can Help Employers Solve Their Workforce Needs" in U.S. Chamber of Commerce (Nov. 12, 2021)
URL(s): www.uschamber.com/immigration/4-visa-programs-that-can-help-employers-solve-their-workforce-needs
Ed: Jon Baselice. **Released:** November 12, 2021. **Description:** Provides information on four nonimmigrant visa programs small business leaders should know about as they look to fill open positions. **Availability:** Online.

35169 ■ "Air Canada to Slash 600 Non-Union Jobs" in Globe & Mail (February 11, 2006, pp. B3)
Ed: Brent Jang. **Description:** The reasons behind workforce reduction by ACE Aviation Holdings Inc. at Air Canada are presented. **Availability:** Online.

35170 ■ "American Airlines Works to Keep Its Brand Aloft" in Dallas Business Journal (Vol. 35, May 18, 2012, No. 36, pp. 1)
Pub: Baltimore Business Journal
Contact: Rhonda Pringle, President
E-mail: rpringle@bizjournals.com
Ed: Matt Joyce. **Description:** As American Airlines is undergoing restructuring, the company is planning to redesign its international aircraft as part of its marketing strategy. But the airline's efforts to improve its brand image present a challenge made difficult by labor relations. Labor unions representing American Airlines employees are fighting the company over their collective bargaining agreements. **Availability:** Print; Online.

35171 ■ "Apprenticeship: Earn While You Learn" in Occupational Outlook Quarterly (Vol. 54, Fall 2010, No. 3, pp. 24)
Description: Paid training, or apprenticeships, are examined. Registered apprenticeship programs conform to certain guidelines and industry-established training standards and may be run by businesses, trade or professional associations, or partnerships with business and unions. **Availability:** Online.

35172 ■ "Brief: Janitorial Company Must Pay Back Wages" in Buffalo News (September 24, 2011)
Description: Knights Facilities Management, located in Michigan, provides grounds maintenance and janitorial services at the Ralph Wilson Stadium in Buffalo, New York. The US Department of Labor ordered the firm to pay $22,000 in back wages and damages to 26 employees for overtime and minimum wage compensation. Details of the company's violation of the Fair Labor Standards Act are included. **Availability:** Online.

35173 ■ "Builders Aim to Cut Costs: Pushing Changes to Regain Share of Residential Market; Seek Council's Help" in Crain's New York Business
Pub: Crain Communications, Inc.
Contact: Jessica Botos, Manager, Marketing
E-mail: jessica.botos@crainsnewyork.com
Ed: Erik Engquist. **Description:** Union contractors and workers are worried about a decline in their market share for housing so they intend to ask the City Council to impose new safety and benefit standards on all contractors to avoid being undercut by nonunion competitors. **Availability:** Print; Online.

35174 ■ "CAW Hopes to Beat Xstrata Deadline" in Globe & Mail (January 30, 2007, pp. B3)
Description: The decision of Canadian Auto Workers to strike work at Xstrata PLC over wage increase is discussed. **Availability:** Online.

35175 ■ "The CEO of General Electric On Sparking an American Manufacturing Renewal" in Harvard Business Review (Vol. 90, March 2012, No. 3, pp. 43)
Pub: Harvard Business Review Press
Contact: Moderna V. Pfizer, Contact
Ed: Jeffrey R. Immelt. **Price:** $8.95, hardcover. **Description:** General Electric Company utilized human innovation and lean manufactring to improve the firm's competitiveness. By engaging the firm's entire workforce, utilizing technology and improving labor-management relations, GE boosted efficiency and reduced cost and waste. **Availability:** PDF; Online.

35176 ■ "Chrysler Unions Set Up Roadblocks to Private Equity" in Globe & Mail (March 20, 2007, pp. B3)
Ed: Greg Keenan. **Description:** The opposition of the Canadian Auto Workers union and the United Auto Workers to any proposal to sell Chrysler Group is discussed. **Availability:** Online.

35177 ■ "CN Aims for Regional Pacts to Halt Labor Row" in Globe & Mail (April 17, 2007, pp. B2)
Ed: Brent Jang. **Description:** The decision of Canadian National Railway Co. to settle labor dispute with regional unions is discussed. **Availability:** Print; Online.

35178 ■ "Collateral Damage" in Business Courier (Vol. 26, October 16, 2009, No. 25, pp. 1)
Pub: American City Business Journals, Inc.
Contact: Mike Olivieri, Executive Vice President
Ed: Jon Newberry. **Description:** Non-union construction firms representing Ohio Valley Associated Builders and Contractors Inc. have filed cases against unionized shops claiming violations of wage law in Ohio. Defendants say the violations are minor, however, they believe they are caught in the middle of the group's campaign to change the state's wage law. **Availability:** Print; Online.

35179 ■ "Companies Must Set Goals for Diversity" in Crain's Detroit Business (Vol. 24, April 14, 2008, No. 15, pp. 16)
Pub: Crain Communications Inc.
Contact: Barry Asin, President
Ed: Laura Weiner. **Description:** Diversity programs should start with a plan that takes into account exactly what the company wants to accomplish; this may include wanting to increase the bottom line with new contracts or wanting a staff that is more innovative in their ideas due to their varied backgrounds. **Availability:** Online.

35180 ■ "Companies Press Ottawa to End CN Labor Dispute" in Globe & Mail (April 16, 2007, pp. B1)
Ed: Brent Jang. **Description:** The plea of several industries to the Canadian parliament to end the labor dispute at the Canadian National Railway Co. is discussed. **Availability:** Online.

35181 ■ "Contractors Can't Do It Alone, PHCC's Pfeffer Says" in Contractor (Vol. 56, October 2009, No. 10, pp. 3)
Ed: Robert P. Mader. **Description:** President Herbert "Skip" Pfeffer of the Plumbing-Heating-Cooling Contractors National Association says lobbying and education are the services that the association offers that a contractor cannot do individually. Pfeffer says the dues for the association are set up in a manner that allows members to pay monthly. **Availability:** Print; Online.

35182 ■ "Corporate Social Responsibility and Trade Unions: Perspectives Across Europe"
Pub: Routledge, Taylor & Francis Group
Released: First edition. **Description:** Although interest in corporate social responsibility (CSR) is focused on the relationship between business and key stakeholders such as NGOs and local communities, the role of trade unions is rarely connected to CSR. Experts discuss the gap in the literature on both CSR and employment relations, namely trade union policies toward CSR as well as union engagement with particular CSR initiatives. The research covers eleven European countries which represent a sample of industrial relations structures across the continent.

35183 ■ "Councilman Addresses Union Harassment Accusations" in Philadelphia Business Journal (Vol. 33, March 28, 2014, No. 7, pp. 7)
Pub: American City Business Journals, Inc.
Contact: Mike Olivieri, Executive Vice President
Released: Weekly. **Price:** $4, introductory 4-week offer(Digital & Print). **Description:** City Councilman Bobby Heron shares his perspective on the alleged violence and intimidation from building and trade unions in Philadelphia, Pennsylvania. Heron believes that the indictment of the leadership of the Ironworkers Local 401 for harassment was an isolated incident and should not reflect on the good and hardworking building and trades construction workers they represent. **Availability:** Print; Online.

35184 ■ "Counting on Engagement at Ernst & Young" in Workforce Management (Vol. 88, November 16, 2009, No. 12, pp. 25)
Pub: Crain Communications Inc.
Contact: Barry Asin, President

Ed: Ed Frauenheim. **Description:** Employee engagement has been difficult to maintain through the recession but firms such as Ernst & Young have found that the effort to keep their employees loyal has paid off. **Availability:** Print; Online.

35185 ■ *"Cultural Due Diligence"* in *Canadian Business (Vol. 80, April 23, 2007, No. 9, pp. 60)*

Description: The factors to be considered by job seekers during judging good workplace with relation to corporate culture are presented. **Availability:** Download; PDF; Online.

35186 ■ *"Disunion in the House: the Steep Price We Pay"* in *Philadelphia Business Journal (Vol. 33, March 28, 2014, No. 7, pp. 4)*

Pub: American City Business Journals, Inc.

Contact: Mike Olivieri, Executive Vice President

Released: Weekly. **Price:** $4, introductory 4-week offer(Digital & Print). **Description:** Some members of the Ironworkers Local 401 Union in Philadelphia, Pennsylvania face federal indictment on charges of participating in an alleged conspiracy to commit extortion, arson, assault and destruction of property. The alleged motive of their actions was to force construction contractors to hire union ironworkers. **Availability:** Print; Online.

35187 ■ *"Downturn Tests HCL's Pledge to Employees"* in *Workforce Management (Vol. 88, November 16, 2009, No. 12, pp. 23)*

Pub: Crain Communications Inc.

Contact: Barry Asin, President

Ed: Ed Frauenheim. **Description:** HCL Technologies has kept its promise to keep from laying any employees off during the recession which served as a test for the tech firm's Employee First program, which seeks to give workers greater income security as well as a stronger voice in the firm. **Availability:** Online.

35188 ■ *"Empathy: An Entrepreneur's Killer App"* in *Women Entrepreneur (February 3, 2009)*

Description: It is just as important to treat employees with courtesy and respect during bad economic times as it is in a good economy. Employers sometimes take advantage of such bad economic times since they realize that employees are grateful to have a job and cannot just quit and easily find work elsewhere. The importance of empathy in a company's leadership personnel is discussed. **Availability:** Online.

35189 ■ *"Fairness First"* in *Canadian Business (Vol. 80, April 23, 2007, No. 9, pp. 45)*

Description: The need for the fair treatment of employees from the perspective of employee compensation is discussed. **Availability:** Online.

35190 ■ *"Fire Your Agent? Not Yet. Hollywood Writers and Talent Agencies Extend Talks"* in *The New York Times (April 7, 2019)*

URL(s): www.nytimes.com/2019/04/07/business/media/writers-guild-talent-agencies.html

Ed: John Koblin. **Released:** April 07, 2019. **Description:** Writers and agents in Hollywood have been operating under an old agreement from 1976 which is set to expire. The crux of the issue is that the Writers Guild of America is claiming that talent agencies have been enriching themselves at the expensive of the writers. Both sides are meeting to hash out their differences and to come to a new agreement. **Availability:** Online.

35191 ■ *"Get Prepared for New Employee Free Choice Act"* in *HRMagazine (Vol. 53, December 2008, No. 12, pp. 22)*

Description: According to the director of global labor and employee relations with Ingersoll Rand Company, unions may have started having employees signing authorization cards in anticipation of the Employee Free Choice Act. Once signed, the cards are good for one year and employers would have only ten days in which to prepare for bargaining with unions over

the first labor contract. The Act also requires these negotiations be subject to mandatory arbitration if a contract is not reached within 120 days of negotiations with unions, resulting in employers' wage rates, health insurance, retirement benefits and key language about flexibility would be determined by an arbitrator with no vested interest in the success of the company. **Availability:** Print; Online.

35192 ■ *"How Much Profit is Enough?"* in *Automotive News (Vol. 86, October 31, 2011, No. 6488, pp. 12)*

Pub: Crain Communications Inc.

Contact: Barry Asin, President

Description: Workers at the big three automobile companies are unhappy about the issues of class wealth, like the high compensations offered to CEOs. **Availability:** Print; Online.

35193 ■ *"Is Raising CPP Premiums a Good Idea?"* in *Canadian Business (Vol. 83, July 20, 2010, No. 11-12, pp. 37)*

Description: Big labor is pushing for an increase in Canada Pension Plan premiums but pension consultants believe this system is not broken and that the government needs to focus on addressing the low rate of personal retirement savings. If the premiums go up, even those with high savings will be forced to pay more and it could block other plans that really address the real issue. **Availability:** Print; Online.

35194 ■ *"Labor and Management: Working Together for a Stable Future"* in *Alaska Business Monthly (Vol. 27, October 2011, No. 10, pp. 130)*

Pub: Alaska Business Publishing Company Inc.

Contact: Charles Bell, Vice President, Sales and Marketing

E-mail: cbell@akbizmag.com

Ed: Nicole A. Bonham Colby. **Description:** Alaska unions and employers are working to ensure a consistent flow of skilled Alaska workers as current the current workforce reaches retirement age. **Availability:** Print; Online.

35195 ■ *"LaSalle St. Firms Cherry-Pick Talent As Wall St. Tanks"* in *Crain's Chicago Business (Vol. 31, November 17, 2008, No. 46)*

Pub: Crain Communications Inc.

Contact: Barry Asin, President

Ed: H. Lee Murphy. **Description:** Many local businesses are taking advantage of the lay offs that many major Wall Street firms are undergoing in their workforces; these companies see the opportunity to woo talent and expand their staff with quality executives. **Availability:** Online.

35196 ■ *"The Last Word Dirty Work Required"* in *Workforce Management (Vol. 88, November 16, 2009, No. 12, pp. 34)*

Pub: Crain Communications Inc.

Contact: Barry Asin, President

Ed: John Hollon. **Description:** Due to salary freezes, pay cuts, layoffs, buyouts and a number of other stress factors brought about by the recession, employee engagement has been difficult to maintain by managers. **Availability:** Online.

35197 ■ *"Lawyers Lock Up Cops as Clients"* in *Sacramento Business Journal (Vol. 28, April 8, 2011, No. 6, pp. 1)*

Pub: Sacramento Business Journal

Contact: Stephanie Fretwell, Director

E-mail: sfretwell@bizjournals.com

Ed: Kathy Robertson. **Released:** Weekly. **Price:** $4. **Description:** Sacramento-based law firm Mastagni, Holstedt and Chiurazzi has grown its client base by specializing in law enforcement labor issues. The firm represents 80,000 public sector correctional officers in the US. The firm has been experiencing an increase in new business as public sector employers face huge budget deficits. **Availability:** Online.

35198 ■ *"Legislators Must Cut Cost of Government"* in *Crain's Detroit Business (Vol. 24, October 6, 2008, No. 40, pp. 6)*

Pub: Crain Communications Inc.

Contact: Barry Asin, President

Description: Southeast and West Michigan business leaders are setting aside their differences and have proposed clear agendas, ranging from eliminating the Michigan Business Tax to overhauling public employee and retiree benefits and pensions. Lawmakers must also come together to find solutions for the state's economy and discover an entirely new vision for the future of Michigan business. **Availability:** Print; Online.

35199 ■ *"Living in a 'Goldfish Bowl'"* in *WorkingUSA (Vol. 11, June 2008, No. 2, pp. 277)*

Description: Recent changes in laws, regulations and even the reporting format of labor organization annual financial reports in both the U.S. and Australia have received surprisingly little attention, yet they have significantly increased the amount of information available both to union members and the public in general, as reports in both countries are available via government Websites. While such financial reporting laws are extremely rare in European countries, with the exception of the UK and Ireland, the U.S. and Australian reporting systems have become among the most detailed in the world. After reviewing these changes in financial reporting and the availability of these reports, as well as comparing and contrasting the specific reporting requirements of each country, this paper then examines the cost-benefit impact of more detailed financial reporting. **Availability:** Print; Online.

35200 ■ *"Lucky Strikes: Labor-Market Muscle"* in *Barron's (Vol. 92, August 25, 2012, No. 38, pp. 15)*

Pub: Dow Jones & Company Inc.

Contact: Almar Latour, Chief Executive Officer

Ed: Robin Goldwyn Blumenthal. **Description:** An increase in work stoppages in the US indicates rising confidence wrong workers. There were 17 labor strikes involving 1,000 workers or more in the 12 months through July 2012, indicating a greater sense of job security. **Availability:** Online.

35201 ■ *"Managing the Facebookers; Business"* in *The Economist (Vol. 390, January 3, 2009, No. 8612, pp. 10)*

Pub: Economist Newspaper Ltd.

Contact: Lara Boro, Chief Executive Officer

Description: According to a report from PricewaterhouseCoopers, a business consultancy, workers from Generation Y, also known as the Net Generation, are more difficult to recruit and integrate into companies that practice traditional business acumen. 61 percent of chief executive managers say that they have trouble with younger employees who tend to be more narcissistic and more interested in personal fulfillment with a need for frequent feedback and an over-precise set of objectives on the path to promotion which can be hard for managers who are used to a different relationship with their subordinates. Older bosses should prepare to make some concessions to their younger talent since some of the issues that make them happy include cheaper online ways to communicate and additional coaching, both of which are good for business. **Availability:** Online.

35202 ■ *"No End to the Nightmare; America's Car Industry"* in *The Economist (Vol. 390, January 3, 2009, No. 8612, pp. 46)*

Description: Detroit's struggling auto industry and the government loan package is discussed as well as the United Auto Worker union, which is loathed by Senate Republicans. **Availability:** Print; Online.

35203 ■ *"Sheet Metal Union Locals Join Forces: Could Help Local Contractors Compete for Bay Area Jobs"* in *Sacramento Business Journal (Vol. 29, June 29, 2012, No. 18, pp. 1)*

Pub: Baltimore Business Journal

Contact: Rhonda Pringle, President

E-mail: rpringle@bizjournals.com

Description: The Sacramento Local 162 and Local 104 of Sheet Metal Workers International Association in California's Bay Area have merged, leading to an action that is expected to help local contractors compete for jobs in the area. Aside from improving efficiency in operations, the merger could also prevent duplication of services. Other potential benefits of the merger are discussed. **Availability:** Print; Online.

35204 ■ "SLU, Des Peres Hospitals Face Unions" in St. Louis Business Journal (Vol. 32, June 1, 2012, No. 41, pp. 1)
Pub: Baltimore Business Journal
Contact: Rhonda Pringle, President
E-mail: rpringle@bizjournals.com

Description: Executives at St. Louis University (SLU) Hospital and Des Peres Hospital are watching efforts by labor unions to organize workers at the hospitals. The simultaneous campaigns are being led by the California Nurses Association/National Nurses Organizing Committee and SEIU Healthcare. SLU Hospital nurses will vote on union representation on June 7, 2012. **Availability:** Print; Online.

35205 ■ "Steeling for Battle" in Crain's Chicago Business (Vol. 31, April 21, 2008, No. 16, pp. 3)
Pub: Crain Communications Inc.
Contact: Barry Asin, President

Ed: Bob Tita. **Description:** Discusses contract negotiations between the United Steelworkers union and ArcelorMittal USA Inc., the nation's largest steelmaker, and U.S. Steel Corp., the third-largest; the union sees these negotiations as the best chance in two decades to regain lost ground but industry experts predict the companies will try to reduce benefits, demand a separate, lower wage scale for new hires and look for relief from the rising costs for retirees' health insurance coverage. **Availability:** Online.

35206 ■ "The Story Of Diane Greene" in Barron's (Vol. 88, July 14, 2008, No. 28, pp. 31)
Pub: Dow Jones & Company Inc.
Contact: Almar Latour, Chief Executive Officer

Ed: Mark Veverka. **Description:** Discusses the ousting of Diane Greene as a chief executive of VMWare, a developer of virtualization software, after the firm went public; in this case Greene, a brilliant engineer, should not be negatively impacted by the decision because it is common for companies to bring in new executive leadership that is more operations oriented after the company goes public. **Availability:** Online.

35207 ■ "'Those Days In New York Are Over" in Philadelphia Business Journal (Vol. 33, March 28, 2014, No. 7, pp. 6)
Pub: American City Business Journals, Inc.
Contact: Mike Olivieri, Executive Vice President

Released: Weekly. **Price:** $4, introductory 4-week offer(Digital & Print). **Description:** Building Trades Employers' Association of New York president and CEO, Louis J. Coletti, comments on the alleged intimidating union activity in Philadelphia, Pennsylvania to hire union members outlined in a federal indictment against Ironworkers Local 401. Coletti believes the limited open-shop market era will remain in the New York construction industry. **Availability:** Print; Online.

35208 ■ "Tough Year Ahead for Unions" in Philadelphia Business Journal (Vol. 30, January 13, 2012, No. 48, pp. 1)
Pub: Baltimore Business Journal
Contact: Rhonda Pringle, President
E-mail: rpringle@bizjournals.com

Description: Reports show that thousands of union workers in Philadelphia, Pennsylvania are being forced to accept concessions and are facing layoffs. Steelworkers are currently facing the toughest situation because of their lack of bargaining power. Paul

Harrington of Drexel University thinks that the bargaining power of unions will not improve in 2012. **Availability:** Print; Online.

35209 ■ "Union, Heal Thyself" in Canadian Business (Vol. 81, July 21, 2008, No. 11, pp. 9)
Description: General Motors Corp. was offered by the federal government a $250 million fund after the company declared plans to close its facility in Ontario. The government move is geared towards supporting the workers who have refused to support the automotive company. Details of the labor contract between General Motors and the Canadian Auto Workers are presented. **Availability:** Print; Online.

35210 ■ "Unions Pony Up $1 Million for McBride Stimulus" in Saint Louis Business Journal (Vol. 31, July 29, 2011, No. 49, pp. 1)
Pub: Saint Louis Business Journal
Contact: Robert Bobroff, President
E-mail: rbobroff@bizjournals.com

Ed: Evan Binns. **Description:** Carpenters District Council of Greater St. Louis and International Brotherhood of Electrical Workers Local 1 were among the nine unions that agreed to split the cost of nearly $1 million in incentives for homebuyers who purchase homes in McBride communities. McBride & Son has spent over $100,000 to promote the incentive program. **Availability:** Print; Online.

35211 ■ "Verizon, Union Dispute is a Vestige of the Past" in Philadelphia Business Journal (Vol. 30, August 26, 2011, No. 28, pp. 1)
Pub: Philadelphia Business Journal
Contact: Sierra Quinn, Director
E-mail: squinn@bizjournals.com

Ed: Peter Key. **Description:** Verizon is arguing that some of the provisions of its unionized workers' contracts date back to the days before AT&T was forced to spin off its local phone-service providers in 1984. The evolution of Verizon through the years and its relations with its unions are discussed. **Availability:** Online.

35212 ■ What Makes People Tick: How to Understand Yourself and Others
Pub: AWC Business Solutions

Released: February 10, 2015. **Price:** $20.99, large print 16pt edition; $20.99, large print 16pt bold edition; $20.99, super large 18pt bold edition; $20.99, super large 20pt bold edition; $19.99, super large 24pt bold edition. **Description:** Management and Human Resources Development and Psychology expert offers a guide to self-discovery and personal growth. Job Compatibility Indicator is used to pinpoint the most suitable personality for each occupation. **Availability:** Large print.

35213 ■ "Worth His Salt" in Hawaii Business (Vol. 53, January 2008, No. 7, pp. 45)
Pub: PacificBasin Communications
Contact: Chuck Tindle, Director
E-mail: chuckt@pacificbasin.net

Ed: Jolyn Okimoto Rosa. **Description:** Bryan Zada owns three PretzelMaker franchises, whose total loss amounted to $40,000 in 2003. Zada believes that listening to employees was one of the key steps in turning the business around. The efforts made to improve the franchises' products are also given. **Availability:** Online.

35214 ■ "Xstrata and CAW Get Tentative Deal" in Globe & Mail (February 2, 2007, pp. B3)
Description: The agreement between Xstrata PLC and Canadian Auto Workers union over wage hike is discussed. **Availability:** Print; Online.

LIBRARIES

35215 ■ Canadian Labour Congress (CLC) - Library
2841 Riverside Dr.
Ottawa, ON, Canada K1V 8X7
Ph: (613)521-3400

Free: 800-387-3500
Fax: (613)521-4655
Co. E-mail: media@clcctc.ca
URL: http://canadianlabour.ca
Contact: Bea Bruske, President
E-mail: president-office@clcctc.ca
Facebook: www.facebook.com/clc.ctc
YouTube: www.youtube.com/user/canadianlabour

Description: Seeks to create a just and equitable society. **Scope:** Labor. **Founded:** 1956. **Holdings:** Figures not available. **Publications:** *Canadian Labour* (Quarterly); *C.L.C. Fax-Press* (Weekly); *Sweatshop Alert; UI Bulletin* (Periodic). **Geographic Preference:** National.

35216 ■ Federation des Travailleurs et Travailleuses du Quebec - Centre de Documentation
565, boul. Cremazie E, bureau 12100
Montreal, QC, Canada H2M 2W3
URL: http://ftq.qc.ca/articles/tous/tous/document/1

Description: Labour association in Quebec. **Scope:** Labor relations; employment; the economy and public policy. **Services:** Copying; library open to the public. **Subscriptions:** periodicals (includes journals) brochures; audio-visual documents.

35217 ■ Manitoba Department of Labour - Manitoba Labour Board Library
500-175 Hargrave St.
Winnipeg, MB, Canada R3C 3R8
Ph: (204)945-3783
Fax: (204)945-1296
Co. E-mail: mlb@gov.mb.ca
URL: http://www.gov.mb.ca/labour/labbrd/library.html

Description: Establishes the mandate of the Manitoba Labour Board as an independent and autonomous specialist tribunal responsible for the fair and efficient administration. **Scope:** Industrial relations and labor law. **Services:** Library open to the public for reference use only. **Founded:** 1985. **Holdings:** Journals; reports.

35218 ■ York University - Centre for Research on Work and Society (CRWS)
York Research Twr., 6th Fl., 4700 Keele St.
Toronto, ON, Canada M3J 1P3
Ph: (416)736-5612
Fax: (416)736-5916
Co. E-mail: crws@yorku.ca
URL: http://www.yorku.ca/crws
Contact: Stephanie Ross, Director
E-mail: stephr@yorku.ca

Description: Research activity at York University. Offers consulting for government agencies; research for unions and community organizations. **Scope:** Changes in Canadian economic life and work, including global economic integration, industrial relations, health and safety, union structures, corporate practices, changes in daily work life, women and international economic restructuring, young workers, and internationally comparative research in union strategy linking Canada to Eastern and Western Europe, Australia, and South Africa. **Services:** Library open to students, faculty and staff; open by appointment only from May to August. **Holdings:** 500 books; journals; primary and secondary documents and sources. **Publications:** *CRWS Conference Papers*; *CRWS News* (Quarterly); *Working Paper Series*. **Educational Activities:** CRWS Intellectual Forums and Discussions, Focusing on work and the political economy of labor.; CRWS Visiting Scholars Program. **Awards:** CRWS Apprenticeships.

RESEARCH CENTERS

35219 ■ International Labor Rights Forum (ILRF)
1634 I St NW Ste. 1000
Washington, DC 20006
Ph: (202)347-4100
Fax: (202)347-4885
Co. E-mail: laborrights@ilrf.org
URL: http://www.laborrights.org

Contact: Ashwini Sukthankar, President
Facebook: www.facebook.com/Interna
tionalLaborRights
X (Twitter): x.com/ilrf

Description: Seeks to ensure that labor laws are understood and adequately implemented and enforced worldwide. **Scope:** Promotes education and research in labor, business, human rights, religious, and other communities in order to facilitate the advancement of labor rights. **Publications:** *Rugmark After One Year.* **Educational Activities:** ILRF Conferences. **Geographic Preference:** Multinational.

35220 ■ Labor and Employment Relations Association (LERA)
504 East Armory Ave. 121 LER Bldg., MC 504
　Champaign, IL 61820
Ph: (217)333-0072
Fax: (217)244-6500
Co. E-mail: leraoffice@illinois.edu
URL: http://www.leraweb.org
Contact: Emily Smith, Executive Director
E-mail: eesmith@illinois.edu
Facebook: www.facebook.com/LERAssn
X (Twitter): x.com/LERassn
YouTube: www.youtube.com/channel/UCahk-5rdk
　-_5X9-OgpjSHHA

Description: Business persons, union leaders, government officials, lawyers, arbitrators, academics, and others interested in research and exchange of ideas on social, political, economic, legal, and psychological aspects of labor and employment relations. **Scope:** Labor, employment, and the workplace, including employer and employee organization, employment and labor relations, human resources, labor markets, income security, and related fields, including international and comparative dimensions in all pertinent disciplines, including industrial relations, history, economics, political science, psychology, sociology, law, management, labor studies, and others. **Founded:** 1947. **Publications:** *LERA eBulletin* (Bimonthly); *LERA Membership Directory* (Quadrennial); *Perspectives on Work* (Semiannual); *Perspectives on Work* (Annual); *LERA proceedings of the annual meeting* (Annual); *Research Volume* (Annual). **Educational Activities:** LERA Annual Meeting; LERA National Policy Forum (Annual). **Awards:** Thomas A. Kochan and Stephen R. Sleigh Best Dissertation Award (Annual); Susan C. Eaton Scholar-Practitioner Grant (Annual); LERA Outstanding Practitioner Award (Irregular); LERA Lifetime Achievement Award (Annual). **Geographic Preference:** National; Local.

35221 ■ Labor Research Association (LRA)
80 East 11th St.
　New York, NY 10003
Ph: (212)714-1677

Description: Conducts research and provides publications on economic and political issues for trade unions. Sponsors periodic seminars on issues concerning the trade union movement; offers consulting services to labor organizations; compiles statistics. **Scope:** Offers research, strategy, communications and educational services for trade unions. Industries served: labor unions and related industries. **Founded:** 1927. **Geographic Preference:** National.

35222 ■ University of Louisville (LMC) - Labor-Management Center
Ekstrom Library, Lower Level
　Louisville, KY 40292
URL: http://library.louisville.edu/archives/ul-ref/l

Description: Integral unit of College of Business and Public Administration at University of Louisville. Arbitration Advocacy Institute; Institute for ADA Medication; Planning and consulting services. **Scope:** Labor-management relations, equal employment opportunity, economic development issues, and public perceptions of labor relations. **Founded:** 1986. **Publications:** *LMC Newsletter* (Quarterly); *Research publications series.* **Awards:** Labor-Management Center Award (Annual).

Venture Capital and Other Funding

START-UP INFORMATION

35223 ■ *"3rd Annual 'OneMedForum NY 2012', July 11th-12th, to Spotlight JOBS Act, Crowdfunding, and Promising Areas for Healthcare Investment"* in *Investment Weekly (June 23, 2012)*

Description: Third annual forum presented by OneMed provided sessions for understanding the changes in regulation due to the new JOBS Act, which will create opportunities for investors and entrepreneurs. Experts in healthcare and life science investments will be featured. Details of the event are covered. **Availability:** Online.

35224 ■ *"Adventure Capital"* in *Austin Business Journal (Vol. 34, June 20, 2014, No. 18, pp. 4)*

Pub: American City Business Journals, Inc.
Contact: Mike Olivieri, Executive Vice President

Description: Several startup companies in the Austin, Texas area have raised millions of dollars from venture capital firms over several years, without reaching profitability or becoming self-funded. However, while this strategy has been successful for startups such as hologram technology developer Zebra Imaging Inc., others like solar panel maker Helio Volt Corporation and low-power chip maker Calxeda Inc. have been forced to shut down despite receiving substantial amounts of investment capital. **Availability:** Online.

35225 ■ *"Alex Gomez on Leaving Medical School to Launch a Startup"* in *South Florida Business Journal (Vol. 34, May 9, 2014, No. 42, pp. 19)*

Pub: American City Business Journals, Inc.
Contact: Mike Olivieri, Executive Vice President

Description: New Wave Health Care Ventures managing partners, Alex Gomez, shares his views about leaving medical school to launch his startup. Gomez says he always had the spirit of an entrepreneur and business excites him. He knows what he is looking for in investing at startup companies because of his experience with New Wave Surgical Corporation. **Availability:** Print; Online.

35226 ■ *"Alpharetta Seeding Startups To Encourage Job Growth"* in *Atlanta Business Chronicle(June 20, 2014, pp. 3A)*

Pub: American City Business Journals, Inc.
Contact: Mike Olivieri, Executive Vice President

Description: The City of Alpharetta is witnessing several incubators and accelerators that will create the physical and educational infrastructure to convert ideas into sustainable businesses. This will help startups develop a go-to-market strategy, prepare for FDA certification and insurance reimbursement as well as see that the company reaches a point where it can attract private equity or venture capital. **Availability:** Print; Online.

35227 ■ *"Angel Investing Network Launches"* in *Washington Business Journal (Vol. 31, August 31, 2012, No. 19, pp. 1)*

Pub: Baltimore Business Journal
Contact: Rhonda Pringle, President
E-mail: rpringle@bizjournals.com

Description: Dan Mindus, investment director for Virginia's CIT GAP Funds, is launching a network of angel investors, venture capitalists and entrepreneurs. The network, which is expected to have 45 to 50 investors, is in the final stages of formation and could be a source of funds for startups in Washington, DC. **Availability:** Print; Online.

35228 ■ *"Austin, Aggies and Innovation"* in *Austin Business Journal (Vol. 32, April 6, 2012, No. 5, pp. A1)*

Pub: American City Business Journals, Inc.
Contact: Mike Olivieri, Executive Vice President

Ed: Christopher Calnan. **Description:** Texas A and M University System director for new ventures, Jamie Rhodes, has been using his experience as an entrepreneur and angel investor to work with the university's professors, researchers, and new entrepreneurs on commercialization opportunities. Rhodes has a goal to create startups based on research produced at Texas A and M. **Availability:** Online.

35229 ■ *"Austin Welcomes New Program for Entrepreneurs"* in *Austin Business JournalInc. (Vol. 29, February 12, 2010, No. 29, pp. 1)*

Pub: Austin Business Journal
Contact: Rachel McGrath, Director
E-mail: rmcgrath@bizjournals.com

Ed: Christopher Calnan. **Description:** Nonprofit group Economic Development Catalyst Organization (ECDO) is formalizing its BizLaunch mentoring program, which was stated in 2009. The program aims to offer support networks to entrepreneurs and assistance regarding early-stage venture capital. **Availability:** Print; Online.

35230 ■ *"Begslist.org Launches Crowdfunding On Its Website"* in *Computer Business Week (August 2, 2012)*

Description: Donation Website called Begslist has added crowdfunding to its site. Crowdfunding and begging are popular among small startups wishing to procure funding for their new companies. **Availability:** Online.

35231 ■ *"Crowdfunding Becomes Relevant for Medical Start-Ups as TCB Medical Launches Campaign On Idiegogo to Bring Life-Saving Epinephrine Key to Market"* in *PR Newswire (July 31, 2012)*

Pub: PR Newswire Association LLC.

Ed: Hilton Head. **Description:** Startup company, TCB Medical Devices, is hoping to raise money through crowdfunding to launch its life-saving Epinephrine

Key to the marketplace. According to allergist, Thomas C. Beller, MD, epinephrine provides safe and effective relief to allergy sufferers. **Availability:** Online.

35232 ■ *"CrowdFunding Platform, START.ac, Announces It Is Expanding Its International Scope From the US, Canada and the UK to 36 Countries Including Australia, India, Israel, Italy and Africa"* in *Benzinga.com (July 11, 2012)*

Pub: Benzinga.com
Contact: Jason Raznick, Founder

Ed: Aaron Wise. **Description:** START.ac is expanding its CrowdFunding site to include 36 countries and increasing its scope to include business startups, teen projects, as well as medical products. START.ac projects are in the fundraising stage at this point, with 23 percent located outside the United States. **Availability:** Online.

35233 ■ *"Crowdfunding Site Targets Jan. Launch"* in *Crain's Detroit Business (July 9, 2012)*

Pub: Crain Communications Inc.
Contact: Barry Asin, President

Ed: Meghana Keshavan. **Description:** Michigan based RelayFund Inc. incorporates social media with fundraising private equity form small businesses. Before the JOBS Act legislation, it was difficult for small firms to raise money. Crowdfunding connects groups of investors with small startup businesses. **Availability:** Print; Online.

35234 ■ *"EMU, Spark Plan Business Incubator for Ypsilanti"* in *Crain's Detroit Business (Vol. 23, October 15, 2007, No. 42, pp. 3)*

Pub: Crain Communications Inc.
Contact: Barry Asin, President

Ed: Chad Halcom. **Description:** Eastern Michigan University is seeking federal grants and other funding for a new business incubator program that would be in cooperation with Ann Arbor Spark. The site would become a part of a network of three Spark incubator programs with a focus on innovation in biotechnology and pharmaceuticals. **Availability:** Print; Online.

35235 ■ *"Equity 'Crowdfunding' Platform, RelayFund, Launched by Michigan Investor Group"* in *Economics Week (July 20, 2012)*

Description: RelayFund was launched by a group of Michigan venture capitalists, entrepreneurs, and investment bankers to link small investors with startup firms under the new JOBS (Jumpstart Our Business Startups) Act. Crowdfunding is money raised for charities, projects or pre-selling products or services and allows online micro investments for startup companies.

35236 ■ *"Find a Customer To Validate Your Idea"* in *South Florida Business Journal (Vol. 34, May 2, 2014, No. 41, pp. 15)*

Pub: American City Business Journals, Inc.
Contact: Mike Olivieri, Executive Vice President

Released: Weekly. **Price:** $8, Introductory 4-week offer(Digital only). **Description:** Venture Hive founder, Susan Amat, share her views on her mission to nurture the entrepreneurial ecosystem from South Florida to the Americas. Amat says Venture Hive is a safe space where world-class technologists can learn to scale their businesses. Amat is a 40 Under 40 honoree, a White House Champion of Change, chair of Startup Florida, an Emerging Leader and a Woman to Watch. **Availability:** Print; Online.

35237 ■ *"iAM Scientist Launches To Provide a Crowdfunding Platform for Science, Technology, and Medicine" in Benzinga.com (July 31, 2012)*
Pub: Benzinga.com
Contact: Jason Raznick, Founder

Ed: Aaron Wise. **Description:** Medical, technology, and science researchers will be able to seach for funding through the newly launched iAMscientist platform. The sitewill provide a site with funding and shared research opportunities. The new tools, better models, and quicker data collection processes will help make research interdisciplinary, collaborative, data driven, and less predictable. Open Access Funding Platform (OAFP) can be used to solicit funding required to carry out research projects. **Availability:** Print; Online.

35238 ■ *"Kickstarter Funds the Future; Crowdfunding Services Such as Kickstarter Have Been Hailed as a New Way To Get Started In Business and Cut Out the Traditional Money Men" in Telegraph Online (August 24, 2012)*
Pub: Telegraph Media Group Limited
Contact: Nick Hugh, Chief Executive Officer

Ed: Monty Munford. **Description:** More than 530 crowdfunding services are expected to his the net by the end of the year. Crowdfunding helps companies raise money from investors for specific projects. A musician was able to raise over $1 million to fund a new record. **Availability:** Online.

35239 ■ *"Legal Matters: 'Crowdfunding' a Boon for Entrepreneurs, If They Clear Regulatory Hurdles" in Finance and Commerce (July 17, 2012)*
Pub: BridgeTower Media
Contact: Adam Reinebach, President

Ed: Dan Heilman. **Description:** Part of the Jumpstart Our Business Startups Act (JOBS) is crowdfunding, which allows the funding of a company by selling small parts of equity to a group of investors. Kickstarter, a Website for raising funds for business entitites, is primarily used for film and book projects. Most businesses cannot adopt Kickstarter's model because of the legality of receiving investor funds without offering security.

35240 ■ *"Macomb County, OU Eye Business Incubator" in Crain's Detroit Business (Vol. 24, February 11, 2008, No. 6, pp. 1)*
Pub: Crain Communications Inc.
Contact: Barry Asin, President

Ed: Chad Halcom. **Description:** Officials in Macomb County, Michigan are discussing plans to create a defense-themed business incubator in the county. Macomb County was awarded $282,000 in federal budget appropriation for the project. **Availability:** Print; Online.

35241 ■ *"Made@Mayo: Mayo Professor Doubles As Founder of Text Tech Company" in Business Journal (Vol. 32, June 6, 2014, No. 2, pp. 10)*
Pub: American City Business Journals, Inc.
Contact: Mike Olivieri, Executive Vice President

Description: Rochester, Minnesota-based Mayo Clinic Ventures has managed the licensing of Mayo Clinic technologies and invests in startups. Mayo Clinic Ventures has a $100 million growth fund for investing in startups and two smaller funds worth about $500,000 combined. Insights on the stories of Mayo researchers leading startups are also provided. **Availability:** Online.

35242 ■ *"MicroVentures: New Crowdfunding Game Makes Startups the Stars, Prepares Players for a New Kind of Investing" in Health & Beauty Close-Up (July 31, 2012)*
Description: MicroVentures created the MicroVentures Investor Challenge as a game on Facebook. The game features real startups such as AirBnB, Etsy, and Pinterest and players invest in these firms. The game has real startups face off in six weekly rounds and the players act as venture capitalists. One startup and one investor will win the game. **Availability:** Print; Online.

35243 ■ *"New Money for New Ideas" in St. Louis Business Journal (Vol. 33, September 7, 2012, No. 2, pp. 1)*
Pub: Baltimore Business Journal
Contact: Rhonda Pringle, President
E-mail: rpringle@bizjournals.com

Description: Investors have been funding startups in Saint Louis, Missouri. New investments companies have been formed in the area. **Availability:** Print; Online.

35244 ■ *"Oversubscribed: Startup Funds Pour In" in Boston Business Journal (Vol. 31, July 22, 2011, No. 26, pp. 1)*
Pub: Boston Business Journal
Contact: Carolyn M. Jones, President
E-mail: cmjones@bizjournals.com

Ed: Kyle Alspach. **Price:** $4, Introductory 4-Week Offer(Digital Only). **Description:** Companies in Boston, Massachusetts are attracting strong interest from venture capital companies, resulting in increased venture capital funding. About $1.14 billion was invested in local companies during second quarter 2011. **Availability:** Print.

35245 ■ *"Program Boosts 'Breakout' Companies" in Silicon Valley/San Jose Business Journal (Vol. 30, April 20, 2012, No. 4, pp. 1)*
Pub: Baltimore Business Journal
Contact: Rhonda Pringle, President
E-mail: rpringle@bizjournals.com

Description: San Francisco, California-based Thiel Foundation has introduced a new program called Breakout Labs that aims to give small amounts of funding to very early stage science startups. The program is backed by Paypal founder and investor Peter Thiel and had more than 200 applicants. Insights on the initial grant recipients are also given. **Availability:** Print; Online.

35246 ■ *Raising Capital*
Released: Third edition. **Price:** $34.95, Paperback/E-book. **Description:** Corporate attorney provides a comprehensive guide using in-depth, practical advice on raising money to start and grow a business. A 115-page appendix contains samples of financing agreements, forms and questionnaires. **Availability:** E-book; Print.

35247 ■ *"Red McCombs, Partner Rolling Out New Venture Capital Fund" in San Antonio Business Journal (Vol. 26, April 20, 2012, No. 12, pp. 1)*
Pub: Baltimore Business Journal
Contact: Rhonda Pringle, President
E-mail: rpringle@bizjournals.com

Description: Entrepreneur Red McCombs has partnered with businessman Chase Fraser to create a new venture capital fund. This new fund will focus on technology startups in the automotive sector. **Availability:** Print; Online.

35248 ■ *"SEC, NASAA Tell Small Businesses: Wait To Join the 'Crowd': Crowdfunding Is 'Not Yet Legal Until the Commission Appoints Rules', Says SEC's Kim" in Investment Advisor (Vol. 3, August 2012, No. 8, pp. 13)*
Ed: Melanie Waddell. **Description:** Securities and Exchange Commission along with state regulators have advised small businesses and entrepreneurs to wait until the SEC has produced rules governing crowdfunding practices. Until that happens, federal

and state securities laws prohibit publicly accessible Internet securities offerings. An overview of crowdfunding and the JOBS Act is included. **Availability:** Online.

35249 ■ *Seed-Stage Venture Investing: An Insider's Guide to Start-Ups for Scientists, Engineers, and Investors*
Ed: William L. Robbins, Jonathan Lasch. **Released:** 2011. **Description:** Ideas for starting, funding, and managing technology-based firms, also known as, venture capitalists, are featured.

35250 ■ *"So What Is Crowdfunding Anyway? New Legislation by Obama and Congress Relaxes Solicitation by Startups" in Accounting Today (August 6, 2012)*
Ed: Jim Brendel. **Description:** An introduction to crowdfunding provides a concise description to the process in which a group of investors partner to fund small business and startups. Rules from the SEC regarding crowdfunding are expected to be in place by the end of the year. **Availability:** Print; Online.

35251 ■ *"Spreading Your Wings" in Canadian Business (Vol. 81, March 17, 2008, No. 4, pp. 31)*
Ed: Megan Harman. **Released:** February 09, 2017. **Description:** Financing from angel investors is one avenue that should be explored by startups. Angel investors are typically affluent individuals who invest their own money. Angel investors usually want at least 10 times their initial investment within eight years but they benefit the businesses through their help in decision-making and the industry expertise they provide. **Availability:** Download; Online.

35252 ■ *"Staking Claim as Hub for Design" in Providence Business News (Vol. 28, March 17, 2014, No. 50, pp. 1)*
Pub: American City Business Journals, Inc.
Contact: Mike Olivieri, Executive Vice President
URL(s): pbn.com/staking-claim-as-hub-for-design9 5764

Description: Providence, Rhode Island is expected to have two startup accelerators in 2014, even though the city lacks a large technology and venture capital presence. The Providence Design Forward accelerator is a partnership with Rhode Island School of Design and will focus on architecture and interior design entrepreneurship. It is modeled after Boston's MassChallenge. **Availability:** Online.

35253 ■ *"Startup Communities: Building an Entrepreneurial Ecosystem in Your City"*
Pub: John Wiley & Sons, Inc.
Contact: Christina Van Tassell, Executive Vice President Chief Financial Officer

Released: September 2012. **Price:** $17.99, e-book; $26.95, hardcover. **Description:** A guide for building supportive entrepreneurial communities that drive innovation and small business energy. Brad Feld, entrepreneur turned-venture capitalist describes what it takes to create an entrepreneurial community in any city, at any time. He details the four critical principles required to form a sustainable startup community. **Availability:** O-book; E-book; Print; Online; PDF.

35254 ■ *"State Fund That Aids New Companies Likely To Wither" in Crain's Detroit Business (Vol. 24, February 25, 2008, No. 8, pp. 16)*
Pub: Crain Communications Inc.
Contact: Barry Asin, President

Ed: Tom Henderson. **Description:** Officials are committed to fighting to save funding for the statewide Strategic Economic Investment and Commercialization Board which provides pre-seed money to start-up firms. **Availability:** Print; PDF; Online.

35255 ■ *"Take the Money and Run" in Entrepreneur (September 2014)*
Released: February 08, 2011. **Description:** Startup founders are encouraged to ask for more than they think they will need when raising capital. The tendency to think small when it comes to capital or stag-

ing rounds to preserve ownership is a mistake for founders. Securing a large amount of capital in the first round could help save the time and costs associated with raising the next round of funds. Venture capitalists welcome founders who ask for more money because they prefer to go bigger on a single bet and their focus is always on valuation. **Availability:** Online.

35256 ■ *"UM-Dearborn to Launch Program for Entrepreneurs" in Crain's Detroit Business (Vol. 24, April 14, 2008, No. 15, pp. 7)*
Pub: Crain Communications Inc.
Contact: Barry Asin, President
Ed: Chad Halcom. **Description:** Starting this fall the University of Michigan-Dearborn will begin its Product Realization and Technology Commercialization Program for entrepreneurs and innovators with lab-tested, high-technology products. Ultimately, 20 businesses will each work with the university in creating a customer base, commercializing a new high-tech product or process and connecting with venture capitalists who may invest in the new companies. **Availability:** Online.

ASSOCIATIONS AND OTHER ORGANIZATIONS

35257 ■ Acadiana Angels
935 Camellia Blvd., Ste. 200
Lafayette, LA 70508
Contact: Jess Fike, President
Description: Early-stage investor group. Offers educational opportunities to members so they can make informed investment decisions; fosters economic development and job creation in Louisiana; encourages members to contribute to the early-stage entrepreneurial ecosystem in the area. **Investment Policies:** Dynamic growth markets; strong value propositions; sound business plan; scalable companies; clear exit strategy. **Industry Preferences:** Analytics/big data; energy; biotech; digital media; education technology; food/beverage; water management; healthcare; shipping; manufacturing; materials; logistics; SaaS; hospitality.

35258 ■ Angel Capital Association (ACA)
10977 Granada Ln., Ste. 103
Overland Park, KS 66211
Ph: (913)894-4700
Co. E-mail: aca@angelcapitalassociation.org
URL: http://www.angelcapitalassociation.org
Contact: Pat Gouhin, Chief Executive Officer
E-mail: pgouhin@angelcapitalassociation.org
Facebook: www.facebook.com/ACAAngelCapital
X (Twitter): x.com/ACAAngelCapital
Description: Provides professional development, networking and collaboration opportunities for angel investors who belong to member angel groups. Serves as the public policy voice of the angel community and focuses on advancing policies at the state and federal level that support and promotes angel investing. **Founded:** 2004. **Geographic Preference:** National.

35259 ■ Ariel Southeast Angel Partners (ASAP)
11258 Ford Ave., Ste. 2
Richmond Hill, GA 31324
Ph: (912)656-5603
Co. E-mail: hello@asap-invests.com
URL: http://asap-invests.com
Contact: Carl D. Francis, Chairman of the Board
Facebook: www.facebook.com/ArielSAVPartners
Linkedin: www.linkedin.com/company/ariel-savannah-angel-partners
Description: Angel investor group supporting start-up and early-stage high-growth businesses in the Southeast. **Investment Policies:** Potential to exit within 3-5 years.

35260 ■ Atlanta Technology Angels (ATA)
3423 Piedmont Rd., NE
Atlanta, GA 30307
Co. E-mail: info@angelatlanta.com

URL: http://angelatlanta.com
Contact: Steven Lustig, Chief Executive Officer
Facebook: www.facebook.com/AtlantaTechnologyAngels
Linkedin: www.linkedin.com/company/atlanta-technology-angels
X (Twitter): x.com/Angel_Atlanta
YouTube: www.youtube.com/channel/UC_vxDnSkRDw7hyPMp8d108A
Description: Angel investors offering seed- and early-stage capital to high-growth technology companies. **Founded:** 1998. **Preferred Investment Size:** $200,000 to $2,000,000. **Industry Preferences:** Hardware; software; digital media; consumer products and services; financial services; life science; healthcare; CleanTech; industrial technologies.

35261 ■ Backstage Capital
6121 Sunset Blvd.
Los Angeles, CA 90028
URL: http://backstagecapital.com
Contact: Arlan Hamilton, Founder Managing Partner
X (Twitter): x.com/Backstage_Cap
Description: Invests in startups owned by people of color, women, and the LGBT community. **Founded:** 2015.

35262 ■ Beacon Angels
Boston, MA
URL: http://beaconangels.com
Contact: William F. Swiggart, Manager
Description: Angel group for early-stage fast-growing companies. **Founded:** 2006. **Preferred Investment Size:** $50,000 to $400,000.

35263 ■ Bellingham Angel Investors (BAI)
1501 Eldridge Ave.
Bellingham, WA 98225-2801
URL: http://www.bellinghamangelinvestors.com
Contact: Jim Thompson, Governor
Description: Invests in early- or middle-stage companies in the Pacific Northwest and British Columbia, with preference to Whatcom, Skagit, and Island counties. **Founded:** 2005.

35264 ■ Bluegrass Angels (BGA)
330 E Main St., No. 100
Lexington, KY 40507
Co. E-mail: admin@bluegrassangels.com
URL: http://bluegrassangels.com
Contact: Brian Luftman, President
Facebook: www.facebook.com/BluegrassAngelsInvestors
Linkedin: www.linkedin.com/company/bluegrassangels
X (Twitter): x.com/BluegrassAngels
Description: Angel investors for Kentucky startups. Creates new jobs and provides strong financial returns to its members. **Founded:** 2004. **Investment Policies:** Innovative high-tech startups with a scalable business model.

35265 ■ Boise Angel Alliance (BAA)
7154 W State St., No 252
Boise, ID 83714
Ph: (208)629-7290
Co. E-mail: info@boiseangels.org
URL: http://www.boiseangels.org
Contact: Amy Curry, President
E-mail: amy@boiseangels.org
Facebook: www.facebook.com/BoiseAngelAlliance
Instagram: www.instagram.com/BoiseAngels
Description: Identifies and invests in early-stage disruptive companies solving real problems in the Treasure Valley. **Founded:** 2004. **Investment Policies:** Generates revenue (or is nearly there); business models based on a sustainable or unique product, service, or technology; sizable market opportunity; well-defined exit strategy.

35266 ■ Bulldog Angel Network! (BAN)
117 Woodrow Balch Dr.
Huntsville, AL 35806
Ph: (256)682-6190
URL: http://ban.clubexpress.com
Contact: Wade C. Patterson, President
E-mail: wadepat123@gmail.com

Description: Network of Mississippi State University alumni and friends offering angel investments to early-stage companies majority owned by MSU students, faculty, or alumni. **Founded:** 2017.

35267 ■ Canadian Venture Capital and Private Equity Association (CVCA) [Association Canadienne du Capital de Risque et d'Investissement]
372 Bay St.
Toronto, ON, Canada M5H 2W9
Co. E-mail: info@cvca.ca
URL: http://www.cvca.ca
Contact: Kim Furlong, Chief Executive Officer
X (Twitter): x.com/CVCA
Description: Ventures and risks capital companies. Promotes economic growth through provision of capital to emerging businesses. Conducts research; facilitates exchange of information among members; represents the venture capital industry before government agencies, industrial and financial organizations, and the public. **Publications:** *Enterprise* (Quarterly). **Awards:** Deal of the Year Award (Annual); Entrepreneur of the Year Award (Annual); Deal of the Year Award (Annual); Entrepreneur of the Year Award (Annual). **Geographic Preference:** Multinational.

35268 ■ Charleston Angel Partners (CA)
75 Port City Landing, Ste. 110
Mount Pleasant, SC 29464
URL: http://www.chapsc.com
Contact: Will Cruz, Executive Director
Linkedin: www.linkedin.com/company/charleston-angel-partners
Description: Angel investment group for early-stage companies in the Southeast offering innovative solutions to large market problems. **Founded:** 2004. **Industry Preferences:** Medical devices; technology.

35269 ■ Charlottesville Angel Network (CAN)
250 W Main St., Ste. 201
Charlottesville, VA 22902
URL: http://cvilleangelnetwork.net
Contact: Craig Redinger, Contact
Description: Invests in promising startups in technology, software, consumer products, and advanced materials primarily in Virginia; may partner with co-investors on Series A and B rounds. **Preferred Investment Size:** $100,000-$300,000. **Investment Policies:** Innovations and solutions solving market problems. . **Industry Preferences:** SaaS; digital healthcare; biotech; consumer products; clean energy; educational technology.

35270 ■ Chippewa Valley Angel Investors Network, LLC (CVAIN)
PO Box 3232
Eau Claire, WI 54702
Ph: (715)878-9791
URL: http://cvain.com
Description: Equity investment group for startups in the Greater Chippewa Valley area. **Founded:** 2003. **Investment Policies:** High growth potential; strong market position; sustainable competitive advantage; compelling business plan; proprietary technology; strong management team.

35271 ■ Coleman Foundation, Inc.
651 W Washington Blvd., Ste. 306
Chicago, IL 60661
Ph: (312)902-7120
Fax: (312)902-7124
Co. E-mail: info@colemanfoundation.org
URL: http://www.colemanfoundation.org
Contact: Shelley A. Davis, President
E-mail: sdavis@colemanfoundation.org
Facebook: www.facebook.com/ColemanFdn
X (Twitter): x.com/coleman_fdn
Description: Strives to support entrepreneurship, cancer research, housing and education for the handicapped, and diverse educational programs. **Founded:** 1951. **Geographic Preference:** National.

35272 ■ The Collaborative CFO Workgroups
10 S 5th St., Ste. 415
Minneapolis, MN 55402
Ph: (612)338-3828

Co. E-mail: info@collaborative.net
URL: http://www.collaborative.net
Contact: Dan Carr, Founder
Description: A forum of Minnesota finance executives to share, learn, and solve problems.

35273 ■ Council of Development Finance Agencies (CDFA)
100 E Broad St., Ste. 1200
  Columbus, OH 43215
Ph: (614)705-1300
Co. E-mail: info@cdfa.net
URL: http://www.cdfa.net
Contact: Toby Rittner, President
E-mail: trittner@cdfa.net
Linkedin: www.linkedin.com/company/council-of
  -development-finance-agencies
X (Twitter): x.com/CDFA_Update
Description: Works for the advancement of development finance concerns and interests. Represents members of the development finance community from the public, private and non-profit sectors. **Founded:** 1982. **Publications:** Development Finance Review Weekly (Weekly). **Educational Activities:** CDFA National Development Finance Summit (Annual). **Awards:** CDFA Practitioner's Showcase. **Geographic Preference:** National.

35274 ■ Dallas Angel Network (DAN)
5307 E Mockingbird Ln., Ste. 802
  Dallas, TX 75206-5121
Contact: Sammy S. Abdullah, Director
Description: Connects angel investors with high-growth companies and entrepreneurs in Dallas, Houston, and Austin. **Founded:** 2010.

35275 ■ Denton Angels
Denton, TX
Co. E-mail: info@dentonangels.com
URL: http://dentonangels.com
Description: Accredited investor group. Individual members offer capital to high-growth early-stage startups.

35276 ■ digitalundivided
261 Madison Ave., Fl., 9, Ste. 1040
  New York, NY 10016
Co. E-mail: talk@digitalundivided.com
URL: http://digitalundivided.com
Contact: Rodrigo Zavala, President
Facebook: www.facebook.com/digitalundivided
Linkedin: www.linkedin.com/company/digitalundivided
X (Twitter): x.com/digundiv
Instagram: www.instagram.com/digitalundivided
Description: Assists Black and Latino women entrepreneurs with venture funding and providing opportunities via innovation and technology. **Founded:** 2012.

35277 ■ Founders First Capital Partners (FFCP)
9920 Pacific Heights Blvd., Ste. 430
  San Diego, CA 92121
Ph: (858)264-4102
Co. E-mail: info@f1stcp.com
URL: http://foundersfirstcapitalpartners.com
Contact: Kim T. Folsom, Chief Executive Officer
Facebook: www.facebook.com/f1stcp
Linkedin: www.linkedin.com/company/founders-firs
  t-capital-partners
X (Twitter): x.com/f1stcp
Instagram: www.instagram.com/f1stcp
YouTube: www.youtube.com/channel/UCa
  dqC8UNVFH0c_6NBdkE-hA
Description: Venture capital firm providing support to startup companies owned by minorities, women, and military veterans. **Founded:** 2015.

35278 ■ Founders Network
415 Jackson St.
  Hayward, CA 94545
Ph: (415)489-0651
Co. E-mail: info@foundersnetwork.com
URL: http://foundersnetwork.com
Contact: Sonal Puri, Chief Executive Officer
Facebook: www.facebook.com/foundersnetwork

Linkedin: www.linkedin.com/company/founders-ne
  twork
X (Twitter): x.com/foundersnetwork
Instagram: www.instagram.com/foundersnetwork
YouTube: www.youtube.com/user/foundersnetwork
Description: Community of tech start-up founders helping each other through peer mentoring. New members are nominated by current members. **Founded:** 2011.

35279 ■ Frontier Angels (FA)
PO Box 4781
  Bozeman, MT 59772-4781
URL: http://www.frontierangels.com
Contact: Pat LaPointe, Managing Director
Linkedin: www.linkedin.com/company/frontier-angels
Description: Angel investor group for early-stage technology-based companies, primarily in Montana. **Founded:** 2006. **Investment Policies:** Defensible intellectual property; tech-leveraged business model; strong management; market demand. **Industry Preferences:** Software; data/analytics; IoT; edge computing; medical devices; biotech; life sciences; health tech; photonics; ag tech; clean tech; energy tech; consumer tech.

35280 ■ Goldcoast Angel Investors
801 Bricknell Ave., Ste. 900
  Miami, FL 33131
Ph: (305)423-1529
URL: http://goldcoastangels.vc
Contact: Bo Megginson, Managing Partner
Description: Early-stage investment group.

35281 ■ GV Management Company, LLC
Alphabet Inc.
  1600 Amphitheatre Pky.
  Mountain View, CA 94043
Ph: (650)253-0000
URL: http://www.abc.xyz
Contact: David Krane, Chief Executive Officer
Description: Capital venture firm investing in the robotics, transportation, agriculture, and other various industries. **Founded:** 2009.

35282 ■ Harlem Capital Partners (HCP)
1180 Ave. Of The Americas, 8Th Fl.
  New York, NY 10036
Co. E-mail: info@harlom.capital
URL: http://harlem.capital
Contact: Melody Hahm, Director
E-mail: melody@harlem.capital
X (Twitter): x.com/HarlemCapital
Description: Venture capital firm focusing on minority-owned startup companies. **Founded:** 2015.

35283 ■ Hudson Valley Startup Fund (HVSF)
6571 Spring Brook Ln.
  Rhinebeck, NY 12572
Co. E-mail: info@hvstartupfund.com
URL: http://www.hvstartupfund.com
Contact: Tony DiMarco, Manager
Description: Member-managed seed capital fund. Offers funding, business planning, and strategy guidance to high-growth companies in the Hudson Valley. Seeks to generate returns for member investors and grow the entrepreneurial ecosystem. . **Founded:** 2015. **Investment Policies:** Scalable business model; addressable market; clear exit strategy; some kind of competitive advantage.

35284 ■ Humble Ventures
Washington, DC
URL: http://humble.vc
Contact: Ajit Verghese, Co-Founder
X (Twitter): x.com/humbleventures
Description: Venture capital firm focusing on startup businesses owned by women and minority groups.

35285 ■ Investment Company Institute (ICI) - Library
1401 H St. NW, Ste. 1200
  Washington, DC 20005
Ph: (202)326-5800
Co. E-mail: memberservices@ici.org
URL: http://www.ici.org
Contact: Eric J. Pan, President

Facebook: www.facebook.com/ici.org
X (Twitter): x.com/ici
YouTube: www.youtube.com/user/ICIVideo
Description: Represents open-end and closed-end investment companies registered under Investment Company Act of 1940; investment advisers to, and underwriters of, such companies; unit investment trust sponsors; interested others. **Scope:** Legislation, taxation, regulation, economic research marketing, small business, public information. **Founded:** 1940. **Holdings:** Figures not available. **Publications:** The Investment Compant Service Directory (Annual); Trends in Mutual Fund Activity (Monthly); National Association of Investment Companies--Membership Directory (Annual); ICI Membership Directory (Semiannual). **Educational Activities:** Annual General Membership Meeting (GMM) (Annual). **Geographic Preference:** National.

35286 ■ Jumpstart New Jersey Angel Network
New Brunswick, NJ 08901
Ph: (856)813-1440
Co. E-mail: info@jumpstartnj.org
URL: http://www.jumpstartnj.org
Contact: Sharon Waters, Managing Director
E-mail: swaters@jumpstartnj.org
Facebook: www.facebook.com/jumpstartnjangelne
  twork
Linkedin: www.linkedin.com/company/jumpstart-nj
  -angel-network
X (Twitter): x.com/jumpstartangels
Description: Member-led angel investor group for early-stage technology ventures in the mid-Atlantic region. **Founded:** 2002.

35287 ■ Keiretsu Forum
44 Tehama St.
  San Francisco, CA 94104
Co. E-mail: info@keiretsuforum.com
URL: http://www.keiretsuforum.com
Contact: Randy Williams, Chief Executive Officer
Description: Worldwide angel network of capital and resources with more than 50 chapters on three continents. **Founded:** 2000.

35288 ■ Landmark Angels
2 Greenwich Office Pk., Ste. 300
  Greenwich, CT 06831
Ph: (203)552-1445
Co. E-mail: admin@landmarkangels.com
URL: http://www.landmarkangels.com
Contact: William S. Podd, Executive Director
Description: Angel investor group. **Founded:** 2008. **Industry Preferences:** Life science; healthcare services; medical devices; digital health; energy; ed tech; fin tech; ag tech; consumer products.

35289 ■ MaC Venture Capital
6255 Sunset Blvd.
  Los Angeles, CA 90028
URL: http://macventurecapital.com
Contact: Adrian Fenty, Managing Partner
Linkedin: www.linkedin.com/company/mac-venture
  -capital
X (Twitter): x.com/MaCVentureCap
Instagram: www.instagram.com/macventurecap
Description: Early stage venture capital firm investing in minority-owned tech companies. **Founded:** 2019.

35290 ■ Maine Angels (MA)
414 Danforth St.
  Portland, ME 04102
Co. E-mail: contact@maineangels.org
URL: http://www.maineangels.org
Contact: Bill Thomas, Chairman
Linkedin: www.linkedin.com/company/maine-angels
Description: Private equity investors for promising early-stage companies in New England. **Founded:** 2003.

35291 ■ Mid-Atlantic Bio Angels (MABA)
New York, NY
Co. E-mail: info@bioangels.net
URL: http://bioangels.net

Description: Angel investor group for new and emerging life science companies. **Founded:** 2012. **Investment Policies:** Products that will change the standard of care in significant markets; clear exit strategy; proof of concept. **Industry Preferences:** Life sciences: therapeutics, devices, and diagnostics.

35292 ■ MIT Alumni Angels of Boston (MITAAB)
Boston, MA
URL: http://www.mitalumniangels.com
Contact: Wan Li Zhu, Co-Founder Managing Director
Description: Connects MIT alumni investors with entrepreneurs in the Boston area. **Founded:** 2014.

35293 ■ MIT Alumni Angels of New York (MITAANY)
New York, NY
URL: http://www.mitalumniangelsny.com
Contact: Wan Li Zhu, Managing Director Founder
Description: Connects MIT alumni investors with entrepreneurs in the New York area. **Founded:** 2018.

35294 ■ MIT Alumni Angels of Washington DC (MITAADC)
Washington, DC
Co. E-mail: mitalumniangelsdc@gmail.com
URL: http://www.mitalumniangelsdc.com
Contact: Terry Hsiao, Director
Description: Connects MIT alumni investors with entrepreneurs in the Washington DC area. **Founded:** 2018.

35295 ■ MIT Alumni Life Sceince Angels of Boston
Boston, MA
URL: http://mitlifesciangels.com
Contact: Patrick Rivelli, Co-Founder Managing Director
Description: Connects MIT alumni investors with life science entrepreneurs in the Boston area. **Founded:** 2017.

35296 ■ National Association of Development Companies (NADCO)
10319 Westlake Dr., Unit 197
Bethesda, MD 20817
Ph: (202)349-0070
Co. E-mail: news@nadco.org
URL: http://www.nadco.org
Contact: Rhonda Pointon, President
E-mail: rpointon@nadco.org
Facebook: www.facebook.com/NADCO504
Linkedin: www.linkedin.com/company/nadco-national-association-of-development-companies
X (Twitter): x.com/NADCO504
Description: Provides long-term financing to small and medium-sized businesses. **Founded:** 1981. **Publications:** NADCO News (Monthly). **Educational Activities:** Winter Board Meeting (Annual). **Geographic Preference:** National.

35297 ■ National Venture Capital Association (NVCA)
25 Massachusetts Ave. NW, Ste. 730
Washington, DC 20001
Ph: (202)864-5920
Fax: (202)864-5930
Co. E-mail: info@nvca.org
URL: http://nvca.org
Contact: Bobby Franklin, President
E-mail: bfranklin@nvca.org
Facebook: www.facebook.com/nvca.us
Linkedin: www.linkedin.com/company/national-venture-capital-association
X (Twitter): x.com/nvca
YouTube: www.youtube.com/channel/UCP9Q8zxCi2DcWtNnAq45OjA
Description: Venture capital organizations, corporate financiers, and institutional venture capitalists who are responsible for investing private capital in young companies on a professional basis. Fosters a broader understanding of the importance of venture capital to the vitality of the U.S. economy and to stimulate the free flow of capital to young companies. Seeks to improve communications among venture capitalists throughout the country and to improve the general level of knowledge of the venturing process in government, universities, and the business community. **Founded:** 1973. **Publications:** National Venture Capital Association--Membership Directory; National Venture Capital Association--Annual Membership Directory (Annual); The Venture Capital Review (Annual). **Geographic Preference:** National.

35298 ■ North Country Angels (NCA)
60 Lake St., 2nd Fl.
Burlington, VT 05401
Contact: Kenneth H. Merritt, Jr., President
Description: Offers early-stage and seed investments for companies in and around Vermont. Meets once a month to discuss entrepreneurial news, share due diligence activities, build strategic relationships, and review business plans.

35299 ■ Northern Michigan Angels (NMA)
PO Box 1622
Traverse City, MI 49684
URL: http://northernmichiganangels.com
Contact: Jody Trietch, Executive Director
Linkedin: www.linkedin.com/company/northern-michigan-angels
Description: Invests in scalable early-stage companies. **Founded:** 2012.

35300 ■ Oregon Entrepreneurs Network (OEN)
PO Box 6452
Portland, OR 97228
Ph: (503)222-2270
Co. E-mail: info@oen.org
URL: http://www.oen.org
Contact: Amanda Oborne, President
E-mail: amanda@oen.org
Facebook: www.facebook.com/oenorg
Linkedin: www.linkedin.com/company/244877
X (Twitter): x.com/oenorg
Instagram: www.instagram.com/oenorg
YouTube: www.youtube.com/user/orentrepreneurs
Description: Assists entrepreneurs and scalable startups in Oregon by offering funding opportunities, networking, and training. **Founded:** 1991.

35301 ■ Pipeline Angels
1321 Upland Dr., Ste. 5167
Houston, TX 77043
Co. E-mail: info@pipelineangels.com
URL: http://pipelineangels.com
Contact: Natalia Oberti Noguera, Chief Executive Officer
Facebook: www.facebook.com/PipelineAngels
Linkedin: www.linkedin.com/company/pipeline-angels
X (Twitter): x.com/PipelineAngels
Instagram: www.instagram.com/pipelineangels
YouTube: www.youtube.com/c/Pipelineangels
Pinterest: www.pinterest.com/pipelineangels
Description: Angel investment funding for women and non-binary femme social entrepreneurs. Offer angel investment bootcamp, networking, and educational opportunities. **Founded:** 2011.

35302 ■ Precursor Ventures
580 Pacific Ave.
San Francisco, CA 94133
Co. E-mail: hello@precursorvc.com
URL: http://precursorvc.com
Contact: Charles Hudson, Managing Partner
Facebook: www.facebook.com/precursorvc
X (Twitter): x.com/PrecursorVC
Description: Venture capital firm providing funding to technology startups. **Founded:** 2015.

35303 ■ Queen City Angels (QCA)
4555 Lake Forest Dr., Ste. 650
Cincinnati, OH 45242
Ph: (513)373-6972
Co. E-mail: sjacobs@qca.com
URL: http://www.qca.com
Contact: Scott Jacobs, Executive Director
E-mail: sjacobs@qca.com
Linkedin: www.linkedin.com/company/queen-city-angels
X (Twitter): x.com/QueenCityAngels

YouTube: www.youtube.com/channel/UCoedYOaDFNvNZieoSoaSa9A
Description: Offers capital, mentoring, educational programs, and counsel to disruptive startups. **Founded:** 2000.

35304 ■ Rio Grande Valley Angel Network (RGVAN)
307 E Railroad St.
Weslaco, TX 78596
Ph: (956)357-0167
Co. E-mail: laurie.simmons@utrgv.edu
URL: http://www.rgvan.org
Contact: Carlos M. Marin, President
Facebook: www.facebook.com/people/Rio-Grande-Valley-Angel-Network/100076462906423
Linkedin: www.linkedin.com/company/rgvan
X (Twitter): x.com/RGVANGELNETWORK
Description: Offers access to capital for scalable enterprises. Works to develop the economic prosperity of the Rio Grande Valley. **Founded:** 2015.

35305 ■ Rockies Venture Club (RVC)
1415 Pk. Ave. W
Denver, CO 80205
Ph: (720)353-9350
URL: http://rockiesventureclub.wildapricot.org
Contact: Peter Adams, Executive Director
E-mail: peter@rockiesventureclub.org
Description: Angel investing club works to accelerate economic development. Offers events and education. **Founded:** 1985.

35306 ■ San Joaquin Angels (SJA)
c/o San Joaquin Partnership/Business Council In
2800 W March Ln., Ste. 470
Stockton, CA 95219
URL: http://sanjoaquinangels.weebly.com
Contact: Mark Plovnick, President
E-mail: mplovnick@pacific.edu
Description: Angel investment group investing in early-stage companies.

35307 ■ Secured Finance Network (SFNet)
370 7th Ave., Ste. 1801
New York, NY 10001
Ph: (212)792-9390
Fax: (212)564-6053
URL: http://community.cfa.com/home
Contact: Michele Ocejo, Director, Communications
E-mail: mocejo@sfnet.com
URL(s): www.sfnet.comc
Linkedin: www.linkedin.com/company/secured-finance-network
X (Twitter): x.com/SFNet_National
Instagram: www.instagram.com/secured_finance_network
Description: Organizations engaged in asset-based financial services including commercial financing and factoring and lending money on a secured basis to small- and medium-sized business firms. Acts as a forum for information and consideration about ideas, opportunities and legislation concerning asset-based financial services. Seeks to improve the industry's legal and operational procedures. Offers job placement and reference services for members. Sponsors School for Field Examiners and other educational programs. Compiles statistics; conducts seminars and surveys; maintains speaker's bureau and 21 committees. **Founded:** 1944. **Publications:** The Secured Lender (6/year). **Educational Activities:** Annual SFNet Convention (Annual). **Geographic Preference:** Multinational.

35308 ■ SideCar Angels, Inc.
90 Brook St.
Westwood, MA 02090
Contact: Jeffrey M. Stoler, President
Description: Investment organization that seeks to ride "sidecar" with top-tier angel groups and venture capital firms to fund early-stage companies. Membership is limited to accredited investors; by invitation only. **Founded:** 2012. **Investment Policies:** Established and experienced teams; potential to achieve sound financial indicators in a reasonable amount of time; competitive advantage with significant growth potential; scalable projects in fast-growing markets.

35309 ■ Small Business Investor Alliance (SBIA)
529 14th St., NW
Washington, DC 20045
Ph: (202)628-5055
Co. E-mail: info@sbia.org
URL: http://www.sbia.org
Contact: Brett Palmer, President
E-mail: bpalmer@nasbic.org
Linkedin: www.linkedin.com/company/small-business -investor-alliance
X (Twitter): x.com/smallbusinesspe
Description: Firms licensed as Small Business Investment Companies (SBICs) under the Small Business Investment Act of 1958. **Founded:** 1958. **Publications:** NASBIC News (Quarterly); Today's SBICs: Investing in America's Future; Venture Capital: Where to Find It (Annual). **Educational Activities:** Venture Capital Institute for Entrepreneurs (Annual); Small Business Investor Alliance Northeast Private Equity Conference (Annual). **Geographic Preference:** National.

35310 ■ South Coast Angel Network (SCAN)
10201 S Padre Island Dr., Ste. 108
Corpus Christi, TX 78418-4466
Contact: James A. Shiner, Director
Description: Introduces investors to early-stage companies in need of funding.

35311 ■ Spokane Angel Alliance (SAA)
c/o Tom Simpson
518 W Riverside, Ste. 202
Spokane, WA 99201
Ph: (509)953-2989
Co. E-mail: tom@nwva.com
URL: http://www.spokaneangelalliance.com
Contact: Tom Simpson, President
E-mail: tom@nwva.com
Description: Angel investor group for emerging companies in Eastern Washington, Idaho, and Montana.

35312 ■ Texas Venture Association (TxVCA)
PO Box 1131
Austin, TX 78767
URL: http://texasventurealliance.org
Description: Represents the venture capital industry in Texas. **Founded:** 2004.

35313 ■ University of New Hampshire - Peter T. Paul College of Business and Economics - Center for Venture Research (CVR)
10 Garrison Ave.
Durham, NH 03824-3593
Ph: (603)862-3341
Co. E-mail: cvr@unh.edu
URL: http://paulcollege.unh.edu/center-venture -research
Contact: Jeffrey Sohl, Director
E-mail: jeff.sohl@unh.edu
Description: Encourages and conducts research into methods of financing new technology-based industries and firms. **Scope:** Early stage equity financing of entrepreneurial ventures, angels, venture capital and innovation. **Founded:** 1984. **Geographic Preference:** National.

35314 ■ Walnut Ventures
Boston, MA
URL: http://www.walnutventures.com
Contact: Ralph Wagner, Member
Description: Entrepreneurs and executives who invest in and mentor seed and early-stage companies with B2B or B2C products.

35315 ■ West Suburban Angels (WSA)
1750 W Ogden Ave., Unit 4051
Naperville, IL 60567-1254
Co. E-mail: westsuburbanangels@gmail.com
URL: http://www.westsuburbanangels.com
Contact: Kenn Miller, Director
Facebook: www.facebook.com/people/West-Subur-ban-Angels/100067583014610
Linkedin: www.linkedin.com/company/west-suburban -angels
X (Twitter): x.com/wsangels

Description: Connects high-growth early-stage startups looking for capital and mentorship with investors interested in financial return and community impact. **Founded:** 2014. **Industry Preferences:** Innovative information technology; business services; industrial technology; financial services; consumer/industrial products; healthcare services/technology.

35316 ■ Westchester Angels
187 Wolf Rd., Ste. 101
Albany, NY 12205
Description: Angel investment group for early-stage companies. **Founded:** 2015.

35317 ■ Wisconsin Investment Partners (WIP)
PO Box 45919
Madison, WI 53744
Co. E-mail: wip.admin@wisinvpartners.com
URL: http://wisinvpartners.com
Contact: Andrea Dlugos, Manager
Description: Angel investment group for seed- and early-stage startups. **Founded:** 2000.

35318 ■ XLR8HI
900 Fort St. Mall
Honolulu, HI 96813
Co. E-mail: aloha@xlr8hi.com
URL: http://xlr8hi.com
Contact: Tarik Sultan, Member
Facebook: www.facebook.com/Xlr8hi
Linkedin: www.linkedin.com/company/xlr8hi
X (Twitter): x.com/xlr8hi
Instagram: www.instagram.com/xlr8_hi
Description: Promotes a culture of innovation and inclusion in Hawaii's startup community. Offers workspace, workshops, and speakers series. **Founded:** 2012.

REFERENCE WORKS

35319 ■ "2014 Promises Tech IPO Frenzy" in San Francisco Business Times (Vol. 28, January 3, 2014, No. 24, pp. 6)
Pub: American City Business Journals, Inc.
Contact: Mike Olivieri, Executive Vice President
Released: Weekly. **Price:** $4, Introductory 4-week offer(Digital & Print). **Description:** Bay Area-based venture-backed technology companies are expected to fill 2014 with initial public offerings (IPOs) and fuel more venture capital funding in the region. The U.S. IPO market has recorded more than 220 pricings and was the strongest since the dot-com bubble of 2000. California-based technology companies that valued at $1 billion or more are also profiled. **Availability:** Print; Online.

35320 ■ "Advantage Capital Partners Awarded $60 Million Allocation in New Markets Tax Credit Program" in Economics & Business Week (June 28, 2014, pp. 7)
Pub: NewsRX LLC.
Contact: Kalani Rosell, Contact
Description: Leading venture capital and small business finance firm, Advantage Capital Partners, was awarded a $60 million allocation in competitive federal New Markets Tax Credit (NMTC) program. This allocation brings the firm's total awards since the program's start in 2002 to $659 million, and maintains the investment firm's leadership role as a top program participant across the nation.

35321 ■ "Alberta Star Begins Phase 2 Drilling On Its Eldorado & Contact Lake IOCG & Uranium Projects" in Canadian Corporate News (May 16, 2007)
Description: Profile of Alberta Star Development Corp., a Canadian mineral exploration company that identifies, acquires, and finances advanced stage exploration projects in Canada, and its current undertaking of its 2007 drill program in which the company intends to begin accelerating its uranium and poly-metallic exploration and drilling activities on all of its drill targets for 2007 now that it has been granted its permits. **Availability:** Online.

35322 ■ "Biotech Reels In $120M for 1Q" in Philadelphia Business Journal (Vol. 31, March 30, 2012, No. 7, pp. 1)
Pub: Baltimore Business Journal
Contact: Rhonda Pringle, President
E-mail: rpringle@bizjournals.com
Description: Philadelphia, Pennsylvania-based biotechnology firms have raised over $120 million in 2012 by selling stocks and debts. Discovery Laboratories has accounted for more than a third of the total funding. **Availability:** Print; Online.

35323 ■ "California Water Treatment Facility Turns to Solar Power" in Chemical Business Newsbase (September 11, 2012)
Description: Ramona, California municipal water district providing water, sewer, recycled water, fire protection, emergency medical services, and park services to the community has commissioned a 530KWp solar energy installation. Enfinity America Corporation developed and financed the solar panels and EPC services were provided by manufacturer Siliken. **Availability:** Print; Online.

35324 ■ "Canada in 2020 Energy: Mr. Clean" in Canadian Business (Vol. 81, October 27, 2008, No. 18, pp. 74)
Pub: Rogers Media Inc.
Contact: Neil Spivak, Chief Executive Officer
Ed: Rachel Pulfer. **Description:** Profile of Nicholas Parker, co-founder of Cleantech Group LLC, a pioneer in clean technology investing. Cleantech, now a global industry, accounts for 10 percent of all venture capital investments made by U.S. companies in 2007. **Availability:** Print; Online.

35325 ■ "Capital Coming Into City, but Local Money Lags" in Pittsburgh Business Times (Vol. 33, March 21, 2014, No. 36, pp. 4)
Pub: American City Business Journals, Inc.
Contact: Mike Olivieri, Executive Vice President
Released: Weekly. **Price:** $4, Introductory 4-week offer(Digital & Print). **Description:** The strong investment market in Pittsburgh, Pennsylvania was fueled by capital from a combination of angel, venture, corporate and other sources, attracting $338 million in capital to finance 148 deals in 2013, but local money is lagging behind. Lynette Horrell of Ernst & Young notes that local money is not keeping up with the growth of technology companies in Pittsburgh. **Availability:** Print; Online.

35326 ■ "Cash for Kiosks: EcoATM Pulls in Series B Funding" in San Diego Business Journal (Vol. 33, May 7, 2012, No. 19, pp. 10)
Pub: CBJ L.P.
Contact: Terri Cunningham, Contact
Ed: Brad Graves. **Description:** EcoATM received $17 million in Series B venture funds as well as a $1 million grant from the National Science Foundation. The Series B funds will be used to install mall kiosks that offer cash for used cellphones and other small electronic devices. **Availability:** Online.

35327 ■ "Central Valley Local Fund II Has $110M to Invest" in Sacramento Business Journal (Vol. 29, May 25, 2012, No. 13, pp. 1)
Pub: Baltimore Business Journal
Contact: Rhonda Pringle, President
E-mail: rpringle@bizjournals.com
Description: CVF Capital Partners has raised $110 million to fund investments in mature companies. CVF's Central Valley Fund II is twice the size of the fund launched by the company in December 2005. The second hand, which was established by a total of 10 banks and a Mexican equity fund, is considered a vote of confidence in Central Valley industries. **Availability:** Print; Online.

35328 ■ "The Chips Are In" in Business Journal-Portland (Vol. 24, November 2, 2007, No. 35, pp. 1)
Description: The $30 million funding round of Ambric Inc., which brings a total investment of $51 million, is about to close, and its clients are releasing over half-dozen products containing Ambric chips in January

2008. The features of Ambric's semiconductors, its market sectors and market positioning, as well as its investor relations, are discussed. **Availability:** Online.

35329 ■ *"City, County May Kill VC Tax"* in **Business Journal-Portland (Vol. 24, October 12, 2007, No. 33, pp. 1)**
Pub: Portland Business Journal
Contact: Andy Giegerich, Managing Editor
E-mail: agiegerich@bizjournals.com

Ed: Aliza Earnshow. **Description:** City of Portland and Multnomah County in Oregon may soon kill taxes levied on venture capital (VC) firms, which is expected to take place in late October 2007. Capitalists have long been saying that taxation is driving them out of town, but this change is expected to generate more investments and persuade VC firms to relocate within city limits. **Availability:** Print; Online.

35330 ■ *"The Coca-Cola Company and Rise Up Crowdfunding LLC Launch Equity Crowdfunding Resource for Women and Minority-Owned Small Business"* in **Minority Business Entrepreneur (March 7, 2023)**
URL(s): mbemag.com/articles/the-coca-cola-company-and-rise-up-crowdfunding-llc-launch-equity-crowdfunding-resource-for-women-and-minority-owned-small-business/

Ed: Gaby M. Rojas. **Description:** A collaboration between Coca-Cola and Rise Up Crowdfunding is providing a funding portal available to women and minority-owned small businesses if they are need of startup capital. **Availability:** Online.

35331 ■ *"Columbia's JPB Raising $175M to Acquire Companies, Real Estate"* in **Boston Business Journal (Vol. 29, May 27, 2011, No. 3, pp. 1)**
Pub: Boston Business Journal
Contact: Carolyn M. Jones, President
E-mail: cmjones@bizjournals.com

Ed: Gary Haber. **Description:** JPB Enterprises is preparing to raise $175 million in its goal of acquiring companies and real estate that are major names in America. The $75 million will be raised for a buyout fund that will target wide range of industries while the $100 million will be used for land investment projects in the Florida Panhandle. Baltimore firms are expected to benefit from this deal. **Availability:** Print; Online.

35332 ■ *"Crowdfunding Author Thinks Google Will Beat Facebook to the Punch on InvestP2P Acquisition"* in **GlobeNewswire (July 17, 2012)**
Pub: Comtex News Network Inc.
Contact: Kan Devnani, President

Description: Author, Mark Kanter, explores the potentials of crowdfunding Websites, especially InvestP2P (aka: peer to peer lending) in his new book, "Street Smart CEO". Invest P2P has social networking tools built into its system. Kanter predicts Google to acquire InvestP2P.

35333 ■ *"CrowdFunding Made Simple Conference at University of Utah Ignites Ecosystem of Entrepreneurs and Investors"* in **Economics Week (June 29, 2012)**

Description: The first national conference on crowdfunding was held at the University of Utah Guest House and Conference Center May 31 through June 1, 2012. The event, CrowdFunding Made Simple, gathered entrepreneurs, business owners, professional service providers, investors, government officials and students to provide understanding and potential of crowdfunding, including information on the Jumpstart Our Business Startups (JOBS) Act. **Availability:** Print; Online.

35334 ■ *The Directory of Venture Capital & Private Equity Firms*
Pub: Grey House Publishing
Contact: Richard Gottlieb, President

Released: February 01, 2016. **Price:** $250, Softcover. **Description:** Updated and expanded edition that includes new entries offering access to more

than 3,500 domestic and international venture capital and private equity firms; detailed contact information and extensive data on investments and funds is included. **Availability:** Print; Online.

35335 ■ *"EDF Ventures Dissolves Fund, Begins Anew On Investment"* in **Crain's Detroit Business (Vol. 24, February 25, 2008, No. 8, pp. 14)**
Pub: Crain Communications Inc.
Contact: Barry Asin, President

Ed: Tom Henderson. **Description:** EDF Ventures is Michigan's oldest venture capital firm and was part of the second round of investments by the state's 21st Century Investment Fund and the Venture Michigan Fund. **Availability:** Print; Online.

35336 ■ *"The Emerging Capital Market for Nonprofits"* in **Harvard Business Review (Vol. 88, October 2010, No. 10, pp. 110)**
Pub: Harvard Business Publishing
Contact: Diane Belcher, Managing Director

Ed: Robert S. Kaplan, Allen S. Grossman. **Price:** $8.95, PDF. **Description:** Demonstration of how nonprofits can use intermediaries to grow their organizational structures, giving them improved scale and impact is offered. Some intermediaries play a mutual-fund role and conduct due diligence, while others act as venture capital funds and implement strategy. **Availability:** Online; PDF.

35337 ■ *"Equity Crowdfunding Platform Initial Crowd Offering, Inc. Closes Equity Financing with Third-Party Investor"* in **GlobeNewswire (July 18, 2012)**

Description: Initial Crowd Offering Inc. closed third-party equity financing round hat provided capital to finish development of its equity crowdfunding portal to the Website. A private angel investor provided development costs to promote the firm's marketing program. Discussion on equity crowdfunding is included. **Availability:** Print; PDF; Online.

35338 ■ *"Fight Ensues Over Irreplaceable Princess Diana Gowns"* in **Tampa Bay Business Journal (Vol. 30, January 15, 2010, No. 4, pp. 1)**
Pub: Tampa Bay Business Journal
Contact: Ian Anderson, President
E-mail: ianderson@bizjournals.com

Ed: Janet Leiser. **Description:** People's Princess Charitable Foundation Inc. founder Maureen Rorech Dunkel has sought Chapter 11 bankruptcy protection before a state court decides on the fate of the five of 13 Princess Diana Gowns. Dunkel and the nonprofit were sued by Patricia Sullivan of HRH Venture LLC who claimed they defaulted on $1.5 million in loans. **Availability:** Print; Online.

35339 ■ *Financing Your Small Business*

Released: First edition. **Description:** Tips for raising venture capital, dealing with bank officials, and initiating public offerings of stock shares for small business.

35340 ■ *"Firm Raises City's Largest VC Fund In 3 Years"* in **Dallas Business Journal (Vol. 35, July 20, 2012, No. 45, pp. 1)**
Pub: Baltimore Business Journal
Contact: Rhonda Pringle, President
E-mail: rpringle@bizjournals.com

Ed: Jeff Bounds. **Description:** Trailblazer Capital has raised $25 million in commitments for its second fund, the largest fund raised by a Dallas-Fort Worth Metropolitan Area-based ventury company since at least 2009. VC funding has been uncommon in the area since the technology and telecom bubble burst in 2000 and 2001. Insights into Trailblazer's approach to investing is provided. **Availability:** Print; Online.

35341 ■ *"Former Robinhood Employees Launch Parafin, a Finance Startup for Small Business"* in **The Wall Street Journal (September 29, 2021)**
URL(s): www.wsj.com/articles/former-robinhood-employees-launch-parafin-a-finance-startup-for-small-business-11632913201

Released: September 29, 2021. **Description:** Discusses the new startup, Parafin.

35342 ■ *"'Frozen' Assets: Refrigeration Goes High Tech as Hussmann Invests $7 Million in Global Hub"* in **St. Louis Business Journal (Vol. 33, September 21, 2012, No. 4, pp. 1)**
Pub: Baltimore Business Journal
Contact: Rhonda Pringle, President
E-mail: rpringle@bizjournals.com

Description: Hussmann Corporation is spending $7 million to create a high-tech innovation and clients collaboration center that will be called Global Hub, a venue for grocery food retailers, industry trend setters and through leaders. The company is also focusing on tapping the potential of convenience marts and dollar-store retailers. **Availability:** Print.

35343 ■ *"Funders Fuel Explosion of Biotech Activity"* in **Puget Sound Business Journal (Vol. 35, July 11, 2014, No. 12, pp. 3A)**
Pub: American City Business Journals, Inc.
Contact: Mike Olivieri, Executive Vice President

Description: Washington's life sciences industry is experiencing problems due to a lack of support from state lawmakers, but the industry is receiving capital through initial public offerings, partnerships and venture equity. Joel Marcus of Alexandria Real Estate Equities claims that capital flows are at their highest levels since the dot-com bubble. **Availability:** Online.

35344 ■ *"Funding Drought Stalls Biotech Incubators"* in **Saint Louis Business Journal (Vol. 31, July 29, 2011, No. 49, pp. 1)**
Pub: Saint Louis Business Journal
Contact: Robert Bobroff, President
E-mail: rbobroff@bizjournals.com

Ed: Angela Mueller. **Description:** Economic slowdown took its toll on cash-strapped startups that fill incubators such as the Bio-Research and Development Growth (BRDG) Park in Creve Coeur, Missouri and the Center for Emerging Technologies in Midtown St. Louis. BRDG put a hold on construction of of its two buildings. **Availability:** Print; Online.

35345 ■ *"Graduates to the TSX in 2008"* in **Canadian Business (Vol. 81, Summer 2008, No. 9, pp. 79)**

Description: Table showing the market capitalization and stock performance of the companies that jumped to the TSX Venture Exchange is presented. The 17 companies that made the leap to the list will have an easier time raising capital, although leeway must be made in investing since they are still new businesses.

35346 ■ *"Greener Pastures"* in **Canadian Business (Vol. 80, February 12, 2007, No. 4, pp. 69)**

Description: The effort of venture capitalists, including chief executive officer of Fun Technologies Lorne Abony, in successful running of several ventures in diverse fields is discussed. **Availability:** Print; Online.

35347 ■ *"Growing Field"* in **Crain's Detroit Business (Vol. 26, January 11, 2010, No. 2, pp. 3)**
Pub: Crain Communications Inc.
Contact: Barry Asin, President

Description: Detroit's TechTown was awarded a combination loan and grant of $4.1 million from the U.S. Department of Housing and Urban Development to build a 15,000-square-foot stem cell center, a collection of laboratories that will be available to both for-profit companies and university researchers. **Availability:** Online.

35348 ■ *"Growing Number of Angel Investors Filling the Void"* in **Dallas Business Journal (Vol. 35, August 24, 2012, No. 50, pp. 1)**
Pub: Baltimore Business Journal
Contact: Rhonda Pringle, President
E-mail: rpringle@bizjournals.com

Ed: Jeff Bounds. **Description:** Angel investment groups have been in North Texas and helping fill the void left by venture capital companies by putting more money to work than their previous investments. There are now at least seven angel groups active in the Dallas-Fort Worth area as more wealthy North Texas investors become active. **Availability:** Print; Online.

35349 ■ *"Houston Tech Company Eyes California for HQ Move" in Houston Business Journal (Vol. 45, July 18, 2014, No. 10, pp. 10A)*
Pub: American City Business Journals, Inc.
Contact: Mike Olivieri, Executive Vice President

Released: Weekly. **Price:** $4, Introductory 4-week offer(Digital & Print). **Description:** Ed Chipul, CEO of Tendenci, a longtime Houston technology company, has stated that they are looking for a headquarters move to California. The decision to move to Silicon Valley is mainly due to a lack of synergy within the venture capital community in Houston. **Availability:** Print; Online.

35350 ■ *How to Start and Run Your Own Corporation: S-Corporations For Small Business Owners*
Pub: HCM Publishing

Ed: Peter I. Hupalo. **Description:** Basics of corporate business structure are explained. Topics include discovering the best business structure for your company; how to decided between an S-Corporation and LLC; choosing the state in which to incorporate, how to form a corporation, angel investing, special issues for one-person corporations, the role of bylaws and corporate minutes, board of directors, taxes, workers' compensation issues, retirement plans, and more. **Availability:** Print.

35351 ■ *"How to Value Your Startup Business for Equity Financing" in Legal Zoom (March 21, 2023)*
URL(s): www.legalzoom.com/articles/how-to-value -your-startup-business-for-equity-financing

Ed: Thomas M. Dunlap, Esq. **Released:** March 21, 2023. **Description:** Many startups need outside financing in order to stay afloat while the business becomes established, but how does one even begin to value the company and it's assets? Included are tips to get you started in the right direction. **Availability:** Online.

35352 ■ *"In China, Railways to Riches" in Barron's (Vol. 88, July 7, 2008, No. 27, pp. M9)*
Pub: Dow Jones & Company Inc.
Contact: Almar Latour, Chief Executive Officer

Ed: Assif Shameen. **Description:** Shares of Chinese railway companies look to benefit from multimillion-dollar investments aimed at upgrading the Chinese railway network. Investment in the sector is expected to reach $210 billion for the 2006-2010 period. **Availability:** Online.

35353 ■ *"Inside the Mind of an Investor: Lessons from Bill Draper" in Inc. (Volume 32, December 2010, No. 10, pp. 140)*
Pub: Mansueto Ventures L.L.C.
Contact: Stephanie Mehta, Chief Executive Officer

Released: December 01, 2010. **Description:** Profile of the three-generation Draper family, the first venture capital firm west of the Mississippi. **Availability:** Online.

35354 ■ *"Inventive Doctor New Venture Partner" in Houston Business Journal (Vol. 40, January 29, 2010, No. 38, pp. A2)*
Pub: Houston Business Journal
Contact: Bob Charlet, President
E-mail: bcharlet@bizjournals.com

Ed: Ford Gunter. **Description:** Dr. Billy Cohn, a surgeon from Houston, Texas has been named as venture partner for venture firm Sante Ventures LLC of Austin, Texas. Cohn will be responsible for seeing marketable developing technologies in the medical industry. The motivation for Cohn's naming as venture partner is his development of a minimally invasive therapy for end-stage renal disease. **Availability:** Print; Online.

35355 ■ *"Investment Funds: Friends with Money" in Canadian Business (Vol. 81, May 22, 2008, No. 9, pp. 22)*
Pub: Rogers Media Inc.
Contact: Neil Spivak, Chief Executive Officer

Ed: Jeff Stanford. **Description:** Two of the most well connected managers in Canadian capital markets Rob Farquharson and Brian Gibson will launch Panoply Capital Asset Management in June. The investment management company aims to raise a billion dollars from institutions and high-net worth individuals. **Availability:** Print; Online.

35356 ■ *"A League of Their Own" in St. Louis Business Journal (Vol. 32, May 4, 2012, No. 37, pp. 1)*
Pub: Baltimore Business Journal
Contact: Rhonda Pringle, President
E-mail: rpringle@bizjournals.com

Description: Entrepreneurs Brian and Carol Matthews, Jim McKelvey and Rick Holton Jr. have partnered to create Cultivation Capital. The venture capital fund will target technology firms. **Availability:** Print; Online.

35357 ■ *"LISC and Uber Eats Announce Black Restaurant Fund " in Minority Business Entrepreneur (February 2, 2022)*
URL(s): mbemag.com/articles/lisc-and-uber-eats-an-nounce-black-restaurant-fund/

Ed: Gaby M. Rojas. **Description:** The Local Initiatives Support Corporation (LISC) and Uber Eats formed a collaboration that will allow Black restaurant owners acquire financing. These loans do not have fixed repayment terms but will instead focus on allowing the borrower to start paying back after targeted revenue growth is achieved. **Availability:** Online.

35358 ■ *"Many in Tech Look to Push More Community Involvement, But Not in Traditional Ways" in Boston Business Journal (Vol. 31, August 5, 2011, No. 28, pp. 1)*
Pub: Boston Business Journal
Contact: Carolyn M. Jones, President
E-mail: cmjones@bizjournals.com

Ed: Mary Moore. **Released:** Weekly. **Price:** $4, Introductory 4-Week Offer(Digital Only). **Description:** Entrepreneurs and venture capitalists in Boston have launched Technology Underwriting Greater Good, the tech industry's answer to the criticism that they are not charitable. The foundation finances nonprofits that aid young people through entrepreneurship, education and life experience. Other tech firms in Boston doing charitable works are discussed. **Availability:** Print; Online.

35359 ■ *"Med-Tech Vet's Trip From Heart to Sleeve" in Business Journal (Vol. 31, February 14, 2014, No. 38, pp. 8)*
Pub: American City Business Journals, Inc.
Contact: Mike Olivieri, Executive Vice President

Released: February 14, 2014. **Price:** $4, Introductory 4-week offer(Digital & Print). **Description:** Conventus Orthopaedics CEO, Paul Buckman, describes the device which repairs wrist fractures. Buckman reveals plans to use the $17 million venture capital to continue research and development and to conduct clinical studies to justify use of the technology. **Availability:** Print; Online.

35360 ■ *"Meet the Dropouts: the Students Who Chose Start-Ups Over College" in Inc. (Vol. 33, September 2011, No. 7, pp. 32)*
Released: January 09, 2011. **Description:** Profiles of 24 college students who left school in order to work on their own startup companies. Each new company is receiving $100,000 from Peter Thiel, cofounder of PayPal and an angel investor. **Availability:** Online.

35361 ■ *"Meet University of Texas' New Business Mind" in Austin Business Journal (Vol. 31, May 13, 2011, No. 10, pp. A1)*
Pub: Austin Business Journal
Contact: Rachel McGrath, Director
E-mail: rmcgrath@bizjournals.com

Ed: Sandra Zaragoza. **Description:** University of Texas (UT) chief commercialization officer, Dr. Richard Miller, has opened a satellite office in Silicon Valley, California in the hopes of luring Californian investors to the science and technology at UT. The satellite office is just one of Miller's efforts to reshape and widen the commercialization of UT-Austin. Insights into Miller's long-term view approach to commercialization are also covered. **Availability:** Online.

35362 ■ *"Merkle Lands $75M Private-Equity Investment" in Baltimore Business Journal (Vol. 28, October 15, 2010, No. 23, pp. 1)*
Pub: Baltimore Business Journal
Contact: Rhonda Pringle, President
E-mail: rpringle@bizjournals.com

Ed: Gary Haber. **Description:** Baltimore, Maryland-based Merkle has received a $75 million investment from Silicon Valley-based Technology Crossover Ventures. The private equity firm's cash infusion was considered the biggest stake made in a company in the region and provides a healthy sign for Greater Baltimore's company. **Availability:** Print; Online.

35363 ■ *"Michigan Means Growth: Sustaining Growth Through Thick and Thin: Michigan Companies Sustain Growth with Well-Timed Access to Capital" in Inc. (Vol. 36, September 2014, No. 7, pp. 164)*
Pub: Mansueto Ventures L.L.C.
Contact: Stephanie Mehta, Chief Executive Officer

Description: Successful companies possess flexibility, foresight and resources to turn adversity into opportunity. The small businesses in Michigan who have sustained experienced sales growth despite the recession of 2007. The Michigan Economic Development Corporation has introduced three initiatives to help Michigan businesses grow, including venture capital, collateral support and loan participation through the State Small Business Credit Initiative, and cash incentives for businesses looking to invest in urban communities or grow jobs. **Availability:** Print; Online.

35364 ■ *"Microsoft Goes Macrosoft" in Barron's (Vol. 89, July 27, 2009, No. 30, pp. 25)*
Pub: Dow Jones & Company Inc.
Contact: Almar Latour, Chief Executive Officer

Ed: Mark Veverka. **Description:** Microsoft reported a weak quarter on the heels of a tech rally which suggests the economy has not turned around. Marc Andreesen describes his new venture-capital fund as focused on "classic tech" and that historical reference places him in the annals of the last millennium. **Availability:** Online.

35365 ■ *"Mr. Cranky: Glen Hellman Calls It Like He Sees It, Whether D.C. Tech Likes It or Not" in Washington Business Journal (Vol. 31, August 17, 2012, No. 17, pp. 1)*
Pub: Baltimore Business Journal
Contact: Rhonda Pringle, President
E-mail: rpringle@bizjournals.com

Description: Profile of angel investor, Glen Hellman, is presented. Hellman is a veteran of the venture capital industry. His career background and achievements are also included. **Availability:** Print; Online.

35366 ■ *"New Stem Cell Research Awareness Org Launched in Austin" in Austin Business Journal (Vol. 31, June 3, 2011, No. 13, pp. 1)*
Pub: Austin Business Journal
Contact: Rachel McGrath, Director
E-mail: rmcgrath@bizjournals.com

Ed: Sandra Zaragoza. **Description:** MedRebels Foundation was launched in February 2011 with the goal of providing millions of dollars for research funding, education and advocacy for adult stem cell-focused medicine. The foundation, whose major contributor is SpineSmith LP, is a collaboration of other adult stem cell-related companies and nonprofit partners. It hopes to raise $200,000 by the end of 2011. **Availability:** Print; Online.

35367 ■ *"New Ways to Finance Solar Power Projects Expected to Lower Cost of Capital, Cut Electricity Rates, Boost Profits, and Expand Investor Pool"* in PR Newswire (September 28, 2012)

Pub: PR Newswire Association LLC.

Description: Renewable energy companies are examining new ways to finance solar power projects. One such strategy includes the use of the REIT structure as a means to lowering costs of capital, lower the cost of generating solar power by nearly 20 percent. Investors would be more interested in the easy and liquid means in which to own a part of the fast growing solar market. Statistical details included.

35368 ■ *"The Next Frontier"* in San Francisco Business Times (Vol. 28, February 28, 2014, No. 32, pp. 4)

Pub: American City Business Journals, Inc.

Contact: Mike Olivieri, Executive Vice President

Description: The growth of the electronic payments business in San Francisco, California has captured the interest of venture capitalists, entrepreneurs, and other investors. Social media companies like Facebook and Google are expected to expand into electronic payments. Telecommunication companies are also investing in promising startups and joint ventures. **Availability:** Print; Online.

35369 ■ *"N.J. Venture Investing Hits $39M"* in Philadelphia Business Journal (Vol. 28, April 13, 2012, No. 9, pp. 1)

Pub: Baltimore Business Journal

Contact: Rhonda Pringle, President

E-mail: rpringle@bizjournals.com

Description: The New Jersey Economic Development Authority will invest $3 million in Osage Venture Partner III and $2 million in NextStage Capital II. The two are Pennsylvania-based venture capital funds and both now have to establish offices in New Jersey and invest millions in New Jersey companies in return for the investment. **Availability:** Print; Online.

35370 ■ *"'Nobody Knows What To Do' To Make Money on the Web"* in Barron's (Vol. 88, March 17, 2008, No. 11, pp. 40)

Pub: Dow Jones & Company Inc.

Contact: Almar Latour, Chief Executive Officer

Ed: Mark Veverka. **Description:** Attendees of the South by Southwest Interactive conference failed to get an insight on how to make money on the Web from former Walt Disney CEO Michael Eisner when Eisner said there's no proven business model for financing projects. Eisner said he finances his projects with the help of his connections to get product-placement deals. **Availability:** Online.

35371 ■ *"NYC Tops Hub in Tech VC Dollars"* in Boston Business Journal (Vol. 31, August 5, 2011, No. 28, pp. 1)

Pub: Boston Business Journal

Contact: Carolyn M. Jones, President

E-mail: cmjones@bizjournals.com

Ed: Kyle Alspach. **Description:** New York City has been outdoing Boston in terms of venture capital for technology firms since second quarter 2010. New York tech firms raised $865 million during the first two quarters of 2011 against Boston techs' $682 million. Boston has the edge, though, when it comes to hiring engineering talent as it is home to the Massachusetts Institute of Technology. **Availability:** Print; Online.

35372 ■ *Originate, Motivate, Innovate: 7 Steps for Building a Billion Dollar Network*

Pub: John Wiley & Sons, Inc.

Contact: Christina Van Tassell, Executive Vice President Chief Financial Officer

URL(s): www.wiley.com/en-us/Originate%2C+Motivate%2C+Innovate%3A+7+Steps+for+Building+a+Billion+Dollar+Network-p-9781119900542

Ed: Shelly Omilade Bell. **Released:** May 2023. **Price:** $26, hardcover. **Description:** Discusses business funding for women of color in a white male-dominated field. **Availability:** Print.

35373 ■ *"Outside Cash Fuels 'Growth' Tech Deals"* in Washington Business Journal (Vol. 31, September 7, 2012, No. 20, pp. 1)

Pub: Baltimore Business Journal

Contact: Rhonda Pringle, President

E-mail: rpringle@bizjournals.com

Description: Outside investors have been contributing to technology firms' growth in Washington. Technology Crossover Ventures has invested $136 million in Alarm.com. **Availability:** Print; Online.

35374 ■ *"Outside Investors Help Fill Need for North Texas Businesses"* in Dallas Business Journal (Vol. 35, March 16, 2012, No. 27, pp. 1)

Pub: Baltimore Business Journal

Contact: Rhonda Pringle, President

E-mail: rpringle@bizjournals.com

Description: Venture capitalists and private equity firms from outside North Texas have been filling the gap created by scarce capital for companies outside the enrgy and real estate industries. The increase in investments have been attributed to the entrepreneurial culture and gathering of big companies in the Dallas-Fort Worth area. **Availability:** Print; Online.

35375 ■ *"PeoplesVC Becomes the 1st Stock-Based Crowdfunding Site to Open Its Doors to Investors"* in Investment Weekly (June 23, 2012)

Description: Peoples VC is the first equity-based crowdfunding site to invite public investors to set up individual crowdfunding investment accounts. Equity-based crowdfunding allows funders to receive stock in return for their investment into companies. In the past, this process was only available to venture capitalists and accredited investors. **Availability:** Print; Online.

35376 ■ *"The Perks of Going Public"* in Austin Business Journal (Vol. 31, July 15, 2011, No. 19, pp. A17)

Pub: Austin Business Journal

Contact: Rachel McGrath, Director

E-mail: rmcgrath@bizjournals.com

Ed: Christopher Calnan. **Description:** HomeAway Inc. launched a $216 million initial public offering. Austin Ventures has generated more than $32 million from the IPO. **Availability:** Print; Online.

35377 ■ *"Private Equity Firm Links First Arizona Deal"* in Business Journal-Serving Phoenix and the Valley of the Sun (November 2, 2007)

Description: Pacific Investment Partners and Your Source Financial launched a $10 million fund and signed their first deal. The two companies acquires a minority stake in Dreambrands Inc. for $3 million. Dreambrands is using the capital to market its personal lubricant product Carrageenana.

35378 ■ *Raising Capital*

Pub: HarperCollins Leadership

Contact: Donald Miller, Chief Executive Officer

Ed: Andrew J. Sherman. **Released:** 2nd edition. **Availability:** Print.

35379 ■ *"Raptor Opens Austin Office"* in Austin Business Journal (Vol. 31, July 8, 2011, No. 18, pp. 1)

Pub: Austin Business Journal

Contact: Rachel McGrath, Director

E-mail: rmcgrath@bizjournals.com

Ed: Christopher Calnan. **Description:** Boston hedge fund operator Raptor Group launched Raptor Accelerator, a consulting business providing sales and advisory services to early-stage companies in Central Texas. Aside from getting involved with the startups in which the Raptor Group invests, Raptor Accelerator will target firms operating in the sports, media, entertainment, and content technology sectors. **Availability:** Print; Online.

35380 ■ *"RavenBrick Ready to Manufacture Its High-Tech Windows"* in Denver Business Journal (Vol. 64, September 7, 2012, No. 16, pp. 1)

Pub: Baltimore Business Journal

Contact: Rhonda Pringle, President

E-mail: rpringle@bizjournals.com

Description: RavenBrick LLC is set to build a new manufacturing plant in Denver, Colorado. The company manufactures auto-darkening window films. RavenBrick has raised a total of $13.5 million in new investment capital. **Availability:** Print; Online.

35381 ■ *"San Antonio Luring Biotech Firms With Venture Capital"* in San Antonio Business Journal (Vol. 28, August 8, 2014, No. 26, pp. 6)

Pub: American City Business Journals, Inc.

Contact: Mike Olivieri, Executive Vice President

Description: Bluegrass Vascular Technologies Inc. has secured $4.5 million in funding from Targeted Technology Fund II. Under the deal, the company will be required to relocate to San Antonio, Texas. A portion of the funding will be used on regulatory approval submissions for the company's Surfacer Inside-Out Catheter System. **Availability:** Print; Online.

35382 ■ *"SEC Decide if Austin Ventures is VC Firm"* in Austin Business Journal (Vol. 31, June 17, 2011, No. 15, pp. 1)

Pub: Austin Business Journal

Contact: Rachel McGrath, Director

E-mail: rmcgrath@bizjournals.com

Ed: Christopher Calnan. **Description:** Investment firm Austin Ventures could lose its classification as a venture capital firm under a new definition of venture capital by the Securities and Exchange Commission. The reclassification could result in additional expenses for Austin Ventures, which has two-thirds of its investments in growth equity transactions. **Availability:** Print; Online.

35383 ■ *"Seed Funding: Monsanto Plants Millions in Image Advertising"* in Saint Louis Business Journal (Vol. 31, July 29, 2011, No. 49, pp. 1)

Pub: Saint Louis Business Journal

Contact: Robert Bobroff, President

E-mail: rbobroff@bizjournals.com

Ed: Kelsey Volkman. **Description:** Monsanto kicked off a new campaign, 'St. Louis Grown' to show its commitment to the St. Louis, Missouri region after spending millions of dollars in recent years on national advertising campaigns. Monsanto had a marketing budget totaling $839 million in 2010 for both brand and corporate marketing. **Availability:** Print; Online.

35384 ■ *"Seminar on Crowdfunding Set for Aug. 1"* in Gazette (July 25, 2012)

URL(s): gazette.com/seminar-on-crowdfunding-set-for-aug.-1/article/142192#!

Description: Senator Michael Bennet is co-hosting a seminar with Epicentral Coworking on crowdfunding featuring two panels with local entrepreneurs and business owners, legal experts, and representatives from investment firms. The seminar will be held August 1, 2012. **Availability:** Print; Online.

35385 ■ *"A Signaling Theory of Acquisition Premiums: Evidence From IPO Targets"* in Academy of Management Journal (Vol. 55, June 1, 2012, No. 3, pp. 667)

Pub: Academy of Management

Contact: Sharon Alvarez, President

Ed: Jeffrey J. Reuer, Tony W. Tong, Cheng-Wei Wu. **Description:** The value of acquisition premiums that newly public targets capture in post-initial public offering (IPO) acquisitions is investigated. Results reveal greater benefits from signals such as interorganizational relationships for IPO targets selling firms to acquirers from different industries. Associations with prominent alliance partners, venture capitalists and underwriters can also enhance the gains for acquistion targets. **Availability:** Electronic publishing; Download; PDF; Online.

35386 ■ "Slater Progress Stalled" in Providence Business News (Vol. 28, March 10, 2014, No. 49, pp. 1)

Pub: American City Business Journals, Inc.

Contact: Mike Olivieri, Executive Vice President

URL(s): pbn.com/slater-progress-stalled95603

Description: Slater Technology Fund has received only $1.9 million of the $9 million in expected federal funds. However, the venture capital firm decided to invest in some promising technology companies in Providence, Rhode Island. Slater senior managing director, Richard Horan, reveals that uncertainties with respect to grants have delayed private fundraising. **Availability:** Online.

35387 ■ "Startup Osteosphere Formed to Develop Laboratory Discovery" in Houston Business Journal (Vol. 40, January 8, 2010, No. 35, pp. 1)

Pub: Houston Business Journal

Contact: Bob Charlet, President

E-mail: bcharlet@bizjournals.com

Ed: Casey Wooten. **Description:** Biotech startup company Osteosphere in Houston, Texas aims to market a technology in which laboratory-grown bone tissues can be processed to appear like a real human bone tissue. The technology was developed by a co-founder of the startup and it can be applied to bone disease and injury treatment. Osteophere's future plans, such as the search for possible investors, is also outlined. **Availability:** Print; Online.

35388 ■ "State VC Fund To Get At Least $7.5 Million" in Crain's Detroit Business (Vol. 24, February 25, 2008, No. 8, pp. 14)

Pub: Crain Communications Inc.

Contact: Barry Asin, President

Ed: Tom Henderson. **Description:** Michigan's 21st Century Investment Fund is expected to receive $7.5 million, financed by tobacco-settlement money. The Michigan Strategic Fund Board will determine which firms will receive venture capital, which is mandated by legislation to invest the fund within three years. **Availability:** Online.

35389 ■ "Targeted Technology Raises More Than $40 Million" in San Antonio Business Journal (Vol. 28, September 5, 2014, No. 30, pp. 8)

Pub: American City Business Journals, Inc.

Contact: Mike Olivieri, Executive Vice President

Released: September 05, 2014. **Price:** $4, introductory 4-week offer(Digital & Print). **Description:** Targeted Technology has raised more than $40 million in venture capital funding for early-stage biotechnology companies in San Antonio, Texas through its Targeted Technology Fund II. Senior managing partner, Paul Castella, recognizes the lack of venture capital funds in the area and the role played by his organization to help these firms. **Availability:** Print; Online.

35390 ■ "Teakwood Capital Raises $40M to Buy Tech Companies" in Dallas Business Journal (Vol. 35, March 2, 2012, No. 25, pp. 1)

Pub: Baltimore Business Journal

Contact: Rhonda Pringle, President

E-mail: rpringle@bizjournals.com

Description: Dallas, Texas-based private equity firm Teakwood Capital LP has raised $40 million following the raising of $25 million as its initial fund in 2006. Teakwood Capital LP targets the purchase of businesses that apply technology to enhance operational efficiencies of their clients, mainly through software deals. The fund raising process of Teakwood Capital LP is also described. **Availability:** Print; Online.

35391 ■ "TELUS Says No Thanks to Joining BCE Fray" in Globe & Mail (April 24, 2007, pp. B1)

Ed: Eric Reguly, Catherine McLean. **Description:** The causes of the refusal of TELUS Corp. to try and acquire BCE Inc. are discussed. The prospects of the acquisition of TELUS Corp. by private equity funds are discussed, besides the availability of cash with private equity funds. **Availability:** Online.

35392 ■ "Tips for Entrepreneurs Pitching to Investors" in Legal Zoom (March 14, 2023)

URL(s): www.legalzoom.com/articles/tips-for-en trepreneurs-pitching-to-investors

Ed: Sandra Beckwith. **Released:** March 14, 2023. **Description:** Startups often need initial funding to get the business off the ground, and entrepreneurs should brush up on these tips to in order to maximize their success in the investor saying yes. **Availability:** Online.

35393 ■ "Transfusion" in Puget Sound Business Journal (Vol. 33, August 31, 2012, No. 19, pp. 1)

Released: July 12, 2019. **Description:** Seattle, Washington-based nonprofit biotechnology companies have been hiring people with fundraising and scientific skills. The development is part of efforts to find new funding resources. **Availability:** Online.

35394 ■ "Unbound ID Raises $2 Million" in Austin Business JournalInc. (Vol. 28, December 12, 2008, No. 39, pp. 1)

Description: Austin, Texas-based Unbound ID Corporation has secured $2 million in funding from venture capital firm Silverton Partners. The company has developed identity management software for network directories. The market for identity management technology is expected to grow to more than $12.3 billion by 2014. **Availability:** Print; Online.

35395 ■ Values and Opportunities in Social Entrepreneurship

Pub: Palgrave Macmillan

Released: 2010. **Price:** $89, hardcover; $120, hardcover; $64.99, e-book; $84.99, Softcover. **Description:** Social entrepreneurship has grown as a research field. This book discusses social entrepreneurship as well as the identification and exploitation of social venturing opportunities. **Availability:** E-book; Print; PDF; Electronic publishing.

35396 ■ Valuing Early Stage and Venture Backed Companies

Pub: John Wiley & Sons, Inc.

Contact: Christina Van Tassell, Executive Vice President Chief Financial Officer

Ed: Neil J. Beaton. **Released:** March 2010. **Price:** $110, hardcover; $71.99, e-book; $71.99, e-book. **Description:** Valuation techniques that can be used to value early stage companies with complex capital structures are examined. **Availability:** O-book; E-book; Print; PDF.

35397 ■ "VC-Heavy, Revenue-Light Sensicore Sold to GE Division" in Crain's Detroit Business (Vol. 24, April 14, 2008, No. 15, pp. 28)

Pub: Crain Communications Inc.

Contact: Barry Asin, President

Ed: Tom Henderson. **Description:** General Electric has acquired Sensicore Inc., which although one of Michigan's most successful companies in raising venture capital was unable to generate significant revenue from its handheld water-testing devices. GE is capable of penetrating a larger market than a private company and will be able to take the devices to the municipal marketplace. **Availability:** Online.

35398 ■ "VC Money Down In State, Number of Deals Up" in Crain's Detroit Business (Vol. 24, January 28, 2008, No. 4, pp. 18)

Pub: Crain Communications Inc.

Contact: Barry Asin, President

Ed: Tom Henderson. **Description:** Despite the amount of money invested by venture capitalists in Michigan is down, the number of deals rose according to the annual Money Tree report. Venture capital firms invested a combined $105.4 million in 22 deals that involved 19 companies in the state. **Availability:** Online.

35399 ■ "VC Round Will Pay for 'Sham' Surgery Trial" in Business Journal (Vol. 31, April 11, 2014, No. 46, pp. 6)

Pub: American City Business Journals, Inc.

Contact: Mike Olivieri, Executive Vice President

Released: April 11, 2014. **Price:** $4, Introductory 4-week offer(Digital & Print). **Description:** Holaira Inc. is preparing for a clinical trial of its technology for treating lung disease after raising $42 million in venture capital. The clinical trial will take place in Europe and will involve about 170 patients. **Availability:** Print; Online.

35400 ■ "The VC Shakeout" in Harvard Business Review (Vol. 88, July-August 2010, No. 7-8, pp. 21)

Pub: Harvard Business Publishing

Contact: Diane Belcher, Managing Director

Ed: Joseph Ghalboun, iDominique Rouzies. **Price:** $6, PDF. **Description:** Authors argue that in order to be successful, venture capital needs to focus less on how to sell a newly acquired investment and more on ways to grow a good company. **Availability:** Online; PDF.

35401 ■ "Venture Gap" in Canadian Business (Vol. 81, February 26, 2008, No. 4, pp. 82)

Pub: Rogers Media Inc.

Contact: Neil Spivak, Chief Executive Officer

Ed: Joe Castaldo. **Description:** Money raised by Canadian venture capitalist firms has been declining since 2001. A strong venture capital market is important if Canada is to build innovative companies. Fixing Canada's tax policy on foreign investments is a start in reviving the industry. **Availability:** Print; Online.

35402 ■ "Venture: Nonprofit Aims to Spur New Companies" in South Florida Business Journal (Vol. 34, April 18, 2014, No. 39, pp. 8)

Pub: American City Business Journals, Inc.

Contact: Mike Olivieri, Executive Vice President

Released: Weekly. **Price:** $8, Introductory 4-week offer(Digital & Print). **Description:** The Scripps Research Institute has created the Scripps Advance group with an aim to turn early-stage research from its scientists in Jupiter, Florida and La Jolla, California into companies and to obtain venture capital funding to support clinical trials. Johnson and Johnson Innovation has become its first collaborator. The terms of the collaboration are also presented. **Availability:** Print; Online.

35403 ■ "Venturing Into New Territory: Career Experiences of Corporate Venture Capital Managers and Practice Variation" in Academy of Management Journal (Vol. 55, June 1, 2012, No. 3, pp. 563)

Pub: Academy of Management

Contact: Sharon Alvarez, President

Ed: Gina Dokko, Vibha Gaba. **Description:** The role of venture capital managers' experiences in information technology firms' practice variation is investigated. Findings reveal that firms with managers who have practice-specific experience invest more in diverse industries and early-stage startups. The firm's goal orientation also tend to change from financial to strategic when venture capital managers have firm-specific experience and engineering experience. **Availability:** Electronic publishing; Download; PDF; Online.

35404 ■ "Well-Heeled Startup Plots Course for a Run at Garmin" in Business Journal Portland (Vol. 27, November 12, 2010, No. 37, pp. 1)

Pub: Portland Business Journal

Contact: Andy Giegerich, Managing Editor

E-mail: agiegerich@bizjournals.com

Description: Oh! Shoes LLC expects to receive about $1.5 million in funding from angel investors, while marketing a new line of high heel shoes that are comfortable, healthy, and attractive. The new line of shoes will use the technology of athletic footwear while having the look of an Italian designer. Oh! Shoes hopes to generate $35 million in sales by 2014. **Availability:** Print; Online.

35405 ■ "Which Iron Cage? Endo- and Exo-Isomorphism In Corporate Venture Capital Programs" in Academy of Management Journal (Vol. 55, April 1, 2012, No. 2, pp. 477)

Pub: Academy of Management

Contact: Sharon Alvarez, President

Ed: Vangelis Souitaris, Stefania Zerbinati, Grace Liu. **Description:** How organizational units resolve competing forces from different institutional environments is examined in the context of corporate venture capital programs. The organizational structure of units entering a new environment is shown to rely on whether they concentrate isomorphism internally toward a parent corporation or externally toward the industry. Implications on institutional theory are given. **Availability:** Online.

35406 ■ "Xtium Has Its Head in the Clouds" in Philadelphia Business Journal (Vol. 30, September 23, 2011, No. 32, pp. 1)
Pub: Philadelphia Business Journal
Contact: Sierra Quinn, Director
E-mail: squinn@bizjournals.com

Ed: Peter Key. **Description:** Philadelphia-based cloud computing firm Xtium LLC received an $11.5 million first-round investment from Boston-Massachusetts-based OpenView Venture Partners. Catering to midsize businesses and unit of bigger firms, Xtium offers disaster-recovery, hosting, and managed-information-technology-infrastructure services. **Availability:** Online.

TRADE PERIODICALS

35407 ■ Venture Capital and Private Equity
URL(s): thomsonreuters.com/en/products-services/financial/venture-capital-and-private-equity.html
Released: Monthly **Price:** $2,395, Individuals. **Description:** Hard news, analysis and data on the North American private equity market. **Availability:** Print; Online.

VIDEO/AUDIO MEDIA

35408 ■ Brevity: Your AI Pitch Coach
URL(s): www.thepitch.show/114-brevity-your-ai-pitch-coach
Released: May 17, 2023. **Description:** Podcast tracks the pitch for Brevity, AI-powered software to help create a first pitch.

35409 ■ Bridging the Divide Between Funders and Founders with Sarah Sterling
URL(s): www.awarepreneurs.com/podcast/327-funders-and-founders
Ed: Paul Zelizer. **Released:** March 19, 2024. **Description:** Podcast discusses seeking appropriate capital and investors.

35410 ■ Dotcal: The Calendar Wars
URL(s): www.thepitch.show/106-the-calendar-wars
Released: March 08, 2023. **Description:** Podcast tracks the pitch of a scheduling platform and asks if the scheduling market is overbooked.

35411 ■ Dressd: Red Carpet or Red Ocean?
URL(s): www.thepitch.show/104-dressd-red-carpet-or-red-ocean
Released: February 22, 2023. **Description:** Podcast tracks the pitch of a clothing rental company that is going after the sorority girl demographic.

35412 ■ Entrepreneurial Thought Leaders: Breaking the Venture Capital Mold
URL(s): ecorner.stanford.edu/podcasts/breaking-the-venture-capital-mold
Ed: Ravi Belani. **Released:** November 16, 2022. **Description:** Podcast discusses how the venture capital ecosystem is historically limited, but explains how new types of firms are offering opportunities for new types of founders.

35413 ■ Entrepreneurial Thought Leaders: Career Advice from a VC Pro
URL(s): ecorner.stanford.edu/podcasts/connie-chan-andreessen-horowitz-career-advice-from-a-vc-pro
Ed: Ravi Belani. **Released:** March 08, 2023. **Description:** Podcast offers career advice for aspiring venture capitalists.

35414 ■ Entrepreneurial Thought Leaders: Investing at the Cutting Edge
URL(s): ecorner.stanford.edu/podcasts/josh-wolfe-lux-capital-investing-at-the-cutting-edge
Released: June 07, 2023. **Description:** Podcast posits that entrepreneurs who attract venture capital think differently and tackle big problems the few others will.

35415 ■ Entrepreneurial Thought Leaders: New Angel Investing
URL(s): ecorner.stanford.edu/podcasts/ashley-flucas-flucas-ventures-the-new-angel-investing
Ed: Chuck Eesley. **Released:** September 15, 2021. **Description:** Podcast discusses how syndicates, platforms, and digital networks are reshaping angel investing.

35416 ■ Entrepreneurial Thought Leaders: World Positive Investing
URL(s): ecorner.stanford.edu/podcasts/world-positive-investing
Ed: Jack Fuchs. **Released:** November 24, 2021. **Description:** Podcast offers a conversation with a venture capitalist, who suggests scalable businesses can be built by solving humanity's biggest problems.

35417 ■ Gemist: The Crown Jewel of Venture
URL(s): www.thepitch.show/115-gemist-the-crown-jewel-of-venture
Released: August 23, 2023. **Description:** Podcast tracks the pitch for a vertical SaaS design product for jewelers. VCs love this kind of business, but the business has to be flawless.

35418 ■ Get Lost in the AWSM Sauce
URL(s): www.thepitch.show/get-lost-in-the-awsm-sauce
Released: February 15, 2023. **Description:** Podcast tracks the pitch for a sustainable way to make sauce and a futuristic way of getting it on our plates.

35419 ■ HandsDown: The Accelerator Pitch
URL(s): www.thepitch.show/110-handsdown-the-accelerator-pitch
Released: April 05, 2023. **Description:** Podcast tracks the pitch for a social shopping app, but then the investors flip the script and start pitch back, sending it on entirely different path.

35420 ■ HBR Ideacast: The VC Fund Closing Equity Gaps - and Making Money
URL(s): hbr.org/podcast/2023/08/the-vc-fund-closing-equity-gaps-and-making-money
Ed: Alison Beard. **Released:** March 28, 2024. **Description:** Podcast offers a conversation with Kapor Capital, a venture capital firm specializing in tech startups serving low-income and underrepresented communities.

35421 ■ How to Acquire Venture Capital Funding with Paul Jarrett
URL(s): www.eofire.com/podcast/pauljarrett
Ed: Jon Lee Dumas. **Released:** July 03, 2024. **Description:** Podcast explains the difference between bootstrapping and venture capital; how to find venture capital; and mistakes regarding venture capital.

35422 ■ The How of Business: Funding Your Small Business Startup
URL(s): www.thehowofbusiness.com/407-funding-small-business
Ed: Henry Lopez. **Released:** January 31, 2022. **Description:** Podcast discusses how small business are funded, how much is needed, and where to start.

35423 ■ Natrion: The Holy Grail of Battery Tech
URL(s): www.thepitch.show/112-natrion-the-holy-grail-of-battery-tech
Released: April 19, 2023. **Description:** Podcast tracks the pitch for a solid-state battery capable of mass production for electric vehicles and wonders if it's better than the competition.

35424 ■ Nick Mathews CEO and Founder of Mainvest
URL(s): restaurantunstoppable.libsyn.com/1016-nick-mathews-ceo-and-founder-of-mainvest
Ed: Eric Cacciatore. **Released:** August 10, 2023. **Description:** Podcast offers a conversation the founder of Mainvest, an investment platform specializing in community-funded small businesses.

35425 ■ Nurture Small Business: Partner Up by Conquering Your Money Anxiety
URL(s): nurturesmallbusiness.buzzsprout.com/900445/11559296-angel-investors-partner-up-by-conquering-your-money-anxiety
Ed: Denise Cagan. **Released:** October 31, 2022. **Description:** Podcast offers tips on talking to investors, connecting with incubator programs and obtaining grants.

35426 ■ Practical Funding & Founder-Market Fit
URL(s): www.startuphustlepodcast.com/practical-funding-founder-market-fit
Ed: Matt Watson. **Released:** May 01, 2024. **Description:** Podcast explores the challenges or raising money and the drawbacks of venture capital funding.

35427 ■ Pre-Seed Funding
URL(s): www.startuphustlepodcast.com/pre-seed-funding
Released: November 02, 2023. **Description:** Podcast discusses tips and preparations for the pre-seed funding journey and alternative funding options.

35428 ■ Raising Capital Lessons, Big Pharma & Patient Support
URL(s): www.startuphustlepodcast.com/raising-capital-lessons-big-pharma-patient-support
Ed: Matt Watson. **Released:** December 28, 2023. **Description:** Podcast discusses navigating the pharmaceutical industry as a startup founder, the challenges of patient support, and the nuances of pre-product fundraising for VC-backed startups.

35429 ■ Ride iQ: Peloton for Horses
URL(s): www.thepitch.show/121-ride-iq-peloton-for-horses
Released: October 18, 2023. **Description:** Podcast tracks the pitch for audio lessons for horseback riders but wonders if it's too niche.

35430 ■ Side Hustle to Small Business: The Challenge of Raising Funds for Your Small Business
URL(s): www.hiscox.com/side-hustle-to-small-business/raising-funds-your-side-hustle-podcast-season-3
Ed: Sanjay Parekh. **Released:** November 15, 2023. **Description:** Podcast discusses how to raise money, what tools are available for it, and challenges faced.

35431 ■ Stigma: Whose Business Is It Anyway?
URL(s): www.thepitch.show/111-stigma-whose-business-is-it-anyway
Released: April 12, 2023. **Description:** Podcast tracks the pitch for a social app to destigmatize talking about mental health--or maybe it could be Slack app. Is the founder too willing to accommodate the investors?.

35432 ■ Tackling Wealth Inequities
URL(s): omny.fm/shows/startup-hustle/tackling-wealth-inequities
Ed: Lauren Conway. **Released:** September 20, 2023. **Description:** Podcast asks why venture capital and the investor landscape needs to shift focus. Explores bridging the gaps and barriers for historically excluded founders and why profit and social impact aren't mutually exclusive. Features Nassir Criss, Principal at Sixty8 Capital.

35433 ■ Terrascope: A Computer Vision Tale
URL(s): www.thepitch.show/107-terrascope-a-computer-vision-tale

Released: March 15, 2023. **Description:** Podcast tracks the pitch for new rural property search platform, but investors wonder if the innovative technology is wasted on the wrong customer.

35434 ■ Tether: Bodyguard of the Grid
URL(s): www.thepitch.show/102-tether-bodyguard-of-the-grid
Released: February 08, 2023. **Description:** Podcast tracks a nearly perfect pitch, but the VCs worry about the location of the company.

35435 ■ This Is Small Business: How to Attract Investors
URL(s): www.smallbusiness.amazon/podcast-episodes/ep-16-how-to-attract-investors
Ed: Andrea Marquez. **Released:** February 28, 2023. **Description:** Podcast discusses venture capital and angel investments.

35436 ■ Unlocking Capital Opportunities
URL(s): www.startuphustlepodcast.com/unlocking-capital-opportunities
Ed: Lauren Conaway. **Released:** November 15, 2023. **Description:** Podcast discusses why alternative investment is sometimes a better fit than venture capital.

CONSULTANTS

35437 ■ Abrams Valuation Group Inc. (AVGI)
5540 Alcove Ave.
  Valley Village, CA 91607
URL: http://www.abramsvaluation.com/index.html
Contact: Jay B. Abrams, President
E-mail: jay@abramsvaluation.com
Description: Services: Strategic planning and financial analysis. **Scope:** Services: Strategic planning and financial analysis. **Publications:** "Lost Inventory and Lost Profits Damage Formulas in Litigation," Sep, 2004; "The Bias in Annual (vs. Monthly) Discounting is Immaterial," Sep, 2003; "Forecasting Cash Flow: Mathematics of the Payout Ratio," Jun, 2003; "Problems in the QMDM and Comparison to Economic Components Model: A Response to Chris Mercer," Jun, 2002; "Discount Rates as a Function of Log Size and Valuation Error Measurement"

35438 ■ Alpha Capital Partners Ltd.
122 S Michigan Ave., Ste. 1700
  Chicago, IL 60603
Ph: (312)322-9800
Co. E-mail: info@alphacapital.com
URL: http://www.alphacapital.com
Contact: Andrew H. Kalnow, Chief Executive Officer
Description: Private equity investment firm which provides equity financing for promising growth businesses. **Scope:** A venture capital management organization that provides equity financing for promising growth businesses and buyouts or recapitalization of established companies. **Founded:** 1984. **Preferred Investment Size:** $500,000 to $5,000,000. **Industry Preferences:** Computer software and services, consumer related, other products, communications and media, medical and health, biotechnology, semiconductors and other electronics, Internet specific, industrial and energy, and computer hardware.

35439 ■ Andrew Barile Consulting Corporation Inc.
3 Breakfast Ct.
  Savannah, GA 31411
Ph: (619)507-0354
Co. E-mail: abarile@abarileconsult.com
URL: http://abarileconsult.com
Contact: Andrew Barile, President
E-mail: abarile@abarileconsult.com
Facebook: www.facebook.com/barileconsult
Linkedin: www.linkedin.com/in/andrewbarileconsultingcorp
Description: Firm provides insurance and reinsurance consulting services. **Publications:** "Private Power," Apr, 2012; "A Practical Guide to Finite Risk Insurance and Reinsurance," 1995; "A Practical

Guide to Financial Reinsurance," 1991; "Reinsurance and Reinsurance Management," 1981; "The Captive Insurance Company," 1978; "Reinsurance, A Practical Guide," 1978.

35440 ■ Antares Capital Corp.
PO Box 330309
  Miami, FL 33233-0309
Ph: (305)894-2888
Fax: (305)894-3227
Co. E-mail: info@antarescapital.com
URL: http://antarescapital.com
Contact: Randall E. Poliner, Founder
E-mail: rpoliner@antarescapital.com
Description: Private venture capital firm investing equity capital in expansion stage companies and management buyout opportunities for firms headquartered in the Southeast and Texas. **Founded:** 1993. **Investment Policies:** Expansion stage.

35441 ■ Bridgewood Consultants
31876 NW Hwy.
  Farmington Hills, MI 48334
Contact: Deanna Brann, Contact
Description: Firm specializes in assisting service-oriented businesses to develop a professional image, organizational skills, and a structural foundation. **Scope:** Firm specializes in assisting service-oriented businesses to develop a professional image, organizational skills, and a structural foundation. **Publications:** "Don't Give Up Before You've Begun!"; "Invest in Your Success"; "Marketing Our Way"; "Marketing - Sorting Fact from Opinion; and Times, They are a Chang'in - What About You?". **Training:** Make Your Waiting Room Standing Room Only, Sep, 2007; Marketing 101, Sep, 2007; Creating a Lucrative Practice.

35442 ■ The Business Place Ltd.
30 Eglinton Ave. W, Ste. 710
  Mississauga, ON, Canada L5R 3E7
Ph: (905)366-7323
Fax: (905)366-7329
URL: http://thebusinessplace.com
Description: Firm provides buying and selling of businesses, arranging bank financing, venture capital loans/investments, mergers and acquisitions. **Scope:** Firm provides buying and selling of businesses, arranging bank financing, venture capital loans/investments, mergers and acquisitions. **Founded:** 1986.

35443 ■ Business Systems Consulting (BSC)
15 Lincoln St.
  Wakefield, MA 01880
Ph: (781)683-4040
Co. E-mail: info@bizsysconsulting.com
URL: http://www.bizsysconsulting.com
Description: Information technology consultancy is engaged in offering a complete range of services from analysis, planning, and implementation, network installation, process and workflow development to custom software solutions, training, and support, particularly for small- to medium-sized businesses.

35444 ■ Butterflies in Progress L.L.C.
9352 Rockfish Gap Tpke
  Afton, VA 22920
Contact: Cynthia Hurst, Manager
Description: Firm provides feasibility studies and organizational assessments. **Scope:** Firm provides feasibility studies and organizational assessments. **Founded:** 2006.

35445 ■ Canadian Association of Professional Speakers (CAPS)
1370 Don Mills Rd., Ste. 300
  Toronto, ON, Canada M3B 3N7
Ph: (416)847-3355
Free: 877-847-3350
Fax: (416)441-0591
Co. E-mail: info@canadianspeakers.org
URL: http://www.canadianspeakers.org
Contact: Michelle Cederberg, President
X (Twitter): x.com/cdnspeakers
Description: Promotes professional advancement of public speakers. Serves as a forum for the exchange of information on public speaking; facilitates com-

munication among members; sponsors educational programs. **Scope:** Members include Canadian speakers, trainers, consultants and facilitators and seeks to raise their profile and professionalism. Helps members hone their skills at securing more business and in delivering their expertise through education, focused programming and networking. **Founded:** 1997. **Publications:** So To Speak. **Geographic Preference:** National.

35446 ■ Crosslink Capital (CC)
2180 Sand Hill Rd., Ste. 200
  Menlo Park, CA 94025
Ph: (415)617-1800
URL: http://www.crosslinkcapital.com
Contact: Anduena Zhubi, Director, Business Development
Description: Firm provides venture capital investment services. **Scope:** An independent venture capital and investment firm focused on strategic business and technology questions as well as to discuss tactical approaches to addressing these challenges. **Founded:** 1989. **Preferred Investment Size:** $8,000,000 to $20,000,000. **Industry Preferences:** Internet specific, computer software and services, semiconductors and other electronics, communications and media, biotechnology, computer hardware, other products, consumer related, medical and health, industrial and energy.

35447 ■ Design Financial Inc.
5 Belleview Ste. 100
  Mount Clemens, MI 48043
Contact: Anthony G. Forlini, President
E-mail: aforlini@designfinancial.com
Description: Firm provides financial services such as healthcare insurance coverage plans, 401k plans, retirement rollovers, college 529 funding, long-term care plans, and estate planning. **Scope:** Firm provides financial services such as healthcare insurance coverage plans, 401k plans, retirement rollovers, college 529 funding, long-term care plans, and estate planning. **Publications:** "Estates and Trusts"; "Tax Planning"; "Cash Management"; "Retirement"; "Investing"; "Risk Management". **Training:** Retirement; Estate Planning; Tax Strategies; Long Term Care; Financial Management.

35448 ■ Disability Income Concepts Inc. (DIC)
3224 Delk Dr.
  The Villages, FL 32163
Contact: Judith Katz, Director
Description: Provides consultation and expert witness assistance services for disability insurance claims. The company provides sales, marketing, and continuing education seminars for agents and brokers; assistance in designing individual disability policies and guest speaker services for insurance companies. For individuals, it offers claim form consultation, and disability and long term care coverage review, analysis and summary services.

35449 ■ Dominari Holdings Inc.
1 Rockefeller Plz., 11th Fl.
  New York, NY 10020
Ph: (703)992-9325
Co. E-mail: info@aikidopharma.com
URL: http://aikidopharma.com
Contact: Anthony C. Hayes, Chief Executive Officer
Linkedin: www.linkedin.com/spherix
X (Twitter): twitter.com/spherix
Description: An intellectual property company engaged in the ownership, acquisition, development, and monetization of patents, as well as the obtaining of existing rights to already issued patents and pending patent intellectual property assets from inventors and patent owners. Focuses on offering a diversified commercialization platform for protected technologies, with an emphasis on wireless communications and telecommunications sectors, including antenna technology, Wi-Fi, base station functionality, and cellular. **Founded:** 1967. **Publications:** "Viking found no life on Mars, and, just as important, it found why there can be no life". **Special Services:** Naturlose®.

35450 ■ DRS Corp.
8955 S Ridgeline Blvd., Ste. 700
  Highlands Ranch, CO 80129
Ph: (303)306-9200
Fax: (303)309-3945
Co. E-mail: info@drscorp.net
URL: http://www.drscorp.net
Facebook: www.facebook.com/DRS-Engineering
  -Contractors-162733140411992
Linkedin: www.linkedin.com/company/drs-engineer-
  ing-contractors

Description: International high-technology business provides services in venture financing and mergers and acquisitions, managing international telecom-munications expansion, telecommunications mergers and acquisitions, econometrics, futures research including technology assessment, and strategic forecasting for high-technology information and com-munications system corporations. **Scope:** Interna-tional high-technology business provides services in venture financing and mergers and acquisitions, managing international telecommunications expan-sion, telecommunications mergers and acquisitions, econometrics, futures research including technology assessment, and strategic forecasting for high-technology information and communications system corporations. **Founded:** 1997.

35451 ■ ECnow.com Inc.
20660 Stevens Creek Blvd., Ste. 210
  Cupertino, CA 95014
Ph: (408)257-3000
Co. E-mail: info@ecnow.com
URL: http://www.ecnow.com
Contact: Mitchell Levy, President

Description: Management consulting firm provides strategic marketing, speaker, training, and content management services to assist startups, mid-sized and large enterprises with information technology transition services for its employees, partners, and customers. **Publications:** "E-Volve-or-Die.com"; "Happy About Outsourcing"; "Happy About Knowing What to Expect in 2005, 2006, 2007 & 2008"; "Busi-ness Models for the 21st Century", 2002. **Training:** Business and Management Issues. **Special Ser-vices:** Value Framework®; Happy About®.

35452 ■ Integrated Development Consulting
1111 W Mead Ave.
  Salt Lake City, UT 84104
Ph: (801)953-1925
Co. E-mail: integrated100@gmail.com
URL: http://www.integrated-development.biz
Contact: Amy O'Connor, Consultant

Description: Services: Strategic planning and integrated development coaching. **Scope:** Services: Strategic planning and integrated development coaching. **Founded:** 1997.

35453 ■ Jewels by Stacy Appraisals
712 Bancroft Rd., Ste. 436
  Walnut Creek, CA 94598
Ph: (925)393-1962
URL: http://www.jewelry-appraisal.com
Contact: Nancy Stacy, Officer
E-mail: nancy@appraiser.net

Description: Distributor of jewelry items specializes in appraisal services of modern and antique fine jewelry, diamonds, gemstones and watches and also offers useful jewelry and gemstone care, and con-sumer fraud information. **Publications:** "Gem print Goes Hollywood"; "Some Good Advice on Buying Diamonds"; "Gold Buying Scams"; "Cruise Purchases of Jewelry"; "Buying Gemstones in Afghanistan"; "Red Labradorite Scams"; "Tanzanite Scams"; "Shipping jewelry". **Training:** Conquering Comps workshop, San Francisco, Oct, 2009. **Special Services:** Gem-print, Certified Insurance Appraiser.

35454 ■ Mara Perez, Ph.D. Fund Development and Planning Services
Greenbrae, CA 94904
URL: http://www.maraperezconsulting.com
Contact: Mara Perez, Founder

Description: Consultant works with boards and staff leadership of non profit organizations and educational institutions. Areas include Latino affairs, diversity, health, the arts, education, spirituality, the environ-ment and international affairs. Services in fund development, strategic planning, and coalition development. **Scope:** Consultant works with boards and staff leadership of non profit organizations and educational institutions. Areas include Latino affairs, diversity, health, the arts, education, spirituality, the environment and international affairs. Services in fund development, strategic planning, and coalition development. **Founded:** 1995. **Publications:** "De-mocratization's: Comparisons, Confrontations, and Contrasts," MIT Press, 2009; "International migration and the Latino population in the U.S". **Training:** International migration; Wednesday Morning Dia-logue; National Association of Hispanic Realtors.

35455 ■ New York Grant Co. (NYGC)
29 Broadway, Ste. 2222
  New York, NY 10006
Ph: (212)227-8283
Co. E-mail: contact@nygrants.com
URL: http://www.nygrants.com
Contact: Marsha Parris, President
E-mail: marsha@nygrants.com
Linkedin: www.linkedin.com/company/new-york-gran
  t-company
X (Twitter): x.com/newyorkgrantco

Description: Firm is engaged in small commercial industry, not-for-profit and developing communities, economic driving growth through job creation, capital investment, workforce training. **Scope:** Firm is engaged in small commercial industry, not-for-profit and developing communities, economic driving growth through job creation, capital investment, workforce training.

35456 ■ Predictable Futures Inc. (PFI)
11630 Kingsway
  Edmonton, AB, Canada T5G 0X5
Ph: (587)990-1179
URL: http://predictablefutures.com
Contact: Gregg K. Becker, President
Linkedin: www.linkedin.com/company/predictable-fu
  tures-inc.

Description: Firm engages in assisting owners and entrepreneurs of privately-owned family businesses. **Scope:** Firm engages in assisting owners and entrepreneurs of privately-owned family businesses. **Founded:** 1982. **Publications:** "Beyond Survival: A Guide for Business Owners and their Families"; "Achieving Authentic Success"; "Halftime"; "Game Plan"; "How to RETIRE Happy, Wild & Free". **Train-ing:** Family Business Succession-It's All About Plan-ning, Hawaii, Mar, 2006.

35457 ■ Seacoast Capital
55 Ferncroft Rd., Ste. 110
  Danvers, MA 01923
Ph: (978)750-1300
URL: http://www.seacoastcapital.com
Contact: Phil Curatilo, Principal Chief Marketing
  Officer
E-mail: pcuratilo@seacoastcapital.com
Facebook: www.facebook.com/seacoastcapitalpar
  tners
Linkedin: www.linkedin.com/company/seacoas
  t-capital

Description: Provider of investment management services. **Scope:** Invests growth capital in small companies led by strong, entrepreneurial manage-ment teams. Provides follow-on financing for acquisi-tions, internal growth or the execution of roll-out strategies. Assists portfolio companies develop and refine strategic plans, recruit additional management or board talent, access debt or equity capital markets, identify and negotiate acquisitions, develop compen-sation and incentive programs and maximize value for all stakeholders upon exit. **Founded:** 1994. **Preferred Investment Size:** $2,000,000 to $10,000,000. **Industry Preferences:** Other products, Internet specific, consumer related, semiconductors and other electronics, medical and health, industrial and energy, computer software and services.

35458 ■ Strategies for Social Change L.L.C. (SSC)
42-06A Bell Blvd., Ste. 221
  Bayside, NY 11361
Ph: (212)785-0544
Co. E-mail: info@strategiesforsocialchange.com
URL: http://strategiesforsocialchange.com
Contact: Shella Brenner, Officer
Facebook: www.facebook.com/stra
  tegiesforsocialchange
Linkedin: www.linkedin.com/company/strategies-for
  -social-change-llc
X (Twitter): x.com/4SocialChange

Description: Culture-minded firm develops capacity building services, strategies and solutions to help nonprofits increase their resources, maximize strate-gic impact and achieve their mission. **Scope:** Culture-minded firm develops capacity building services, strategies and solutions to help nonprofits increase their resources, maximize strategic impact and achieve their mission. **Publications:** "The Do's and Don'ts of Hiring a Consultant"; "Executive Coaching Works!"; "Characteristics of Highly Effective Organiza-tions". **Training:** Grant Writing and Fund Develop-ment Training; Board Governance and Training Retreat Facilitation; Strategic Planning Training; Cultural Competency Training and Retreat Facilita-tion; Leadership Training and Retreat Facilitation.

35459 ■ Venture Planning Associates, Inc. (VPA)
PO Box 33219
  Reno, NV 89533
Ph: (775)747-8829
Free: 888-404-1212
Co. E-mail: capital@ventureplan.com
URL: http://www.ventureplan.com
Contact: Bill McCready, President

Description: Firm provides basic venture capital, finance and merger, and acquisition consulting services for the business community. **Scope:** Firm provides basic venture capital, finance and merger, and acquisition consulting services for the business community. **Founded:** 1989.

35460 ■ Wall Street Services, Inc.
11 Broadway, Ste. 632
  New York, NY 10004
Contact: Amit K. Giaur, Contact

Description: A staffing agency catering to top tier Manhattan investment banks and legal firms. Special-izes in personnel placement and executive search. Proprietary systems include an instrument for mea-suring key work place attributes, a method for determining what position will inspire and challenge the best available workers, and tools for rapidly matching the right candidate to the job. **Scope:** A staffing agency catering to top tier Manhattan invest-ment banks and legal firms. Specializes in personnel placement and executive search. Proprietary systems include an instrument for measuring key work place attributes, a method for determining what position will inspire and challenge the best available workers, and tools for rapidly matching the right candidate to the job. **Founded:** 1983. **Publications:** "Wall Street Services Editorial".

FRANCHISES AND BUSINESS OPPORTUNITIES

35461 ■ The Entrust Group
555 12th St., Ste. 900
  Oakland, CA 94607
Ph: (510)587-0950
Free: 800-392-9653
Fax: (510)587-0960
Co. E-mail: teg@theentrustgroup.com
URL: http://www.theentrustgroup.com
Contact: Hubert Bromma, Chief Executive Officer
Facebook: www.facebook.com/EntrustGroup
Linkedin: www.linkedin.com/company/the-entrus
  t-group
X (Twitter): x.com/TheEntrustGroup
Instagram: www.instagram.com/theentrustgroup
YouTube: www.youtube.com/user/theentrustgroup

Pinterest: www.pinterest.com/theentrustgroup

Description: Provider of self-directed IRA administration services in business. **Founded:** 1981. **Training:** Yes.

35462 ■ **Innovative Lease Services Inc. (ILS)**
2382 Faraday Ave., Ste. 160
Carlsbad, CA 92008
Contact: Andrew Nere, Chief Executive Officer
Description: Provider of commercial and equipment financing services. **Founded:** 1986.

RESEARCH CENTERS

35463 ■ **St. Louis University - Richard A. Chaifetz School of Business - Chaifetz Center for Entrepreneurship**
1 N Grand Blvd.
Saint Louis, MO 63103
Ph: (314)977-3850
Co. E-mail: ecenter@slu.edu
URL: http://www.slu.edu/business/centers/center-for-entrepreneurship/index.php
Description: Integral unit of John Cook School of Business, St. Louis University. **Scope:** Venture capital, endowed positions in entrepreneurship. **Founded:** 1987. **Educational Activities:** SSCE Billiken Angel Network; SSCE Collegiate Entrepreneurship Organizations; SSCE Gateway Series For Entrepreneurship Research For Faculty (Annual), Discuss and develop ideas and plans on the future of entrepreneurship.; SSCE Habitat For Neighborhood Business. **Awards:** Smurfit-Stone Entrepreneurial Alumni Hall of Fame (Annual).

VENTURE CAPITAL FIRM

35464 ■ **Camelot Venture Group (CVG)**
222 Lakeview Ave., Ste. 1550
West Palm Beach, FL 33401
URL: http://www.camelotvg.com
Contact: Steve Cicurel, Partner
Linkedin: www.linkedin.com/company/camelot-venture-group
Description: Provider of investment management services for consumer companies including online, catalog, retail, technology, financial services and sports management. **Founded:** 2008. **Preferred Investment Size:** $5,000,000 to $150,000,000.

Industry Preferences: Communications and media, computer software and hardware, Internet specific, semiconductors and other electronics, consumer related, financial services, and business service.

35465 ■ **DFJ Frontier [Frontier Venture Capital]**
2101 Pearl St.
Boulder, CO 80302
Ph: (424)354-2244
Co. E-mail: info@frontiervc.com
URL: http://frontiervc.com
Contact: Blair Simpson, Principal
Description: Provider of investment solutions in development stage companies related to software, information services, biotechnology and more. **Founded:** 2002. **Preferred Investment Size:** $100,000 to $1,000,000. **Investment Policies:** Seed and early stage. **Industry Preferences:** Communications and media, computer software, Internet specific, semiconductors and other electronics, biotechnology, consumer related, industrial and energy, financial services, agriculture, forestry and fishing.

35466 ■ **Fifth Wall Ventures**
1 Little W 12th St., 4th Fl.
New York, NY 10014
Co. E-mail: lpinquiry@fifthwall.com
URL: http://fifthwall.com
Contact: Andriy Mykhaylovskyy, Chief Operating Officer Managing Partner
Linkedin: www.linkedin.com/company/fifth-wall-ventures
X (Twitter): x.com/fifthwallvc
Instagram: www.instagram.com/fifthwallvc
YouTube: www.youtube.com/c/FifthWall
Description: Offers an advisory-based approach to venture capital. Advises on and invests in Built World Technology. Connects owners, developers, and operators with entrepreneurs. **Founded:** 2016.

35467 ■ **FIN Capital**
One Sansome St., Ste. 3950
San Francisco, CA 94104
Co. E-mail: info@fin.capital
URL: http://fin.capital
Contact: Chelsea Dodge, Director, Investor Relations
Linkedin: www.linkedin.com/company/finvc
X (Twitter): x.com/FinVentureCap

Description: Venture capital firm. **Founded:** 2018. **Investment Policies:** Typically prefer founders who have invested their own money; potential for rapid scalable growth; compelling, well-articulated strategy; proprietary technology with an early market lead; credible exit strategy; open to mentoring and coaching.

35468 ■ **Golden Angels Investors**
250 N Sunnyslope Rd., Ste. 200
Brookfield, WI 53005
URL: http://goldenangelsinvestors.com
Contact: Tim Keane, Director
E-mail: tim@goldenangelsinvestors.com
Linkedin: www.linkedin.com/company/golden-angels-network
Description: Invests in early-stage technology and emerging growth companies in Wisconsin and Illinois. Members make individual investment decisions. **Founded:** 2002.

35469 ■ **InterWest Partners L.L.C. (IW)**
548 Market St.
San Francisco, CA 94104
Ph: (650)854-8585
Co. E-mail: info@interwest.com
URL: http://www.interwest.com
Contact: Katie Passalacqua, Controller
Description: Provider of venture capital and private equity investment for IT and healthcare businesses. **Founded:** 1979.

35470 ■ **NewtekOne, Inc.**
NewtekOne, Inc.
4800 T Rex Ave., Ste. 120
Boca Raton, FL 33431
Ph: (212)356-9500
Free: 855-763-9835
Co. E-mail: info@newtekone.com
URL: http://www.newtekone.com
Contact: Barry Sloane, President
Facebook: www.facebook.com/tr
Description: Newtek Business Services Inc. is a holding company. The Company provides financial and business services to the small and medium-sized business market. **Founded:** 1998.

35471 ■ **Richmond Global Ventures (RGV)**
750 Hammond St.
Chestnut Hill, MA 02467
Ph: (646)202-3022
Co. E-mail: ventures@rglobal.com
URL: http://www.rglobalventures.com
Contact: David Frazee, Managing Partner
Description: Global venture capital firm.

Wages and Salaries

REFERENCE WORKS

35472 ■ *"3 Things Employers Should Do Before Philadelphia's New Wage History Law Goes Into Effect" in Philadelphia Business Journal (August 18, 2020)*

Ed: Samantha Bononno, Kaleigh Hartigan. **Released:** August 18, 2020. **Description:** The City of Philadelphia will begin enforcing a ban on employers asking for applicants' wage history and setting wages based on past pay per the Philadelphia Wage Equity Ordinance. **Availability:** Online.

35473 ■ *"Employer Costs for Employee Compensation - June 2020" in Bureau of Labor Statistics (September 17, 2020)*

Released: September 17, 2020. **Description:** Provided by the Bureau of Labor Statistics, this report details employer costs for employee compensation. **Availability:** Online.

35474 ■ *"Gender Pay Gap Remains Stagnant" in bizwomen (September 22, 2020)*

Ed: Caitlin Mullen. **Released:** September 22, 2020. **Description:** Addresses the continued gender pay gap based on Census Bureau data and offers information on lobbying for policies designed to improve salary transparency. **Availability:** Online.

35475 ■ *"Guilford County Introduces $20 Million Grant Program for Small Businesses" in Triad Business Journal (June 4, 2020)*
Ed: Daniel Finnegan. **Released:** June 04, 2020. **Description:** Provides information on emergency financial support offered to small businesses in North Carolina through the Guilford CARES Small Business Assistance Grant Program. **Availability:** Online.

35476 ■ *"Here's What the New Overtime Rule Means for Your Business" in Entrepreneur (September 7, 2016)*
Ed: Mike Kappel. **Released:** September 07, 2016. **Description:** Details information on the Department of Labor overtime rule and what it means for small business owners. **Availability:** Online.

35477 ■ *"Here's Why Just 15% of Pennsylvania Small Businesses Plan To Add Staff" in Philadelphia Business Journal (November 7, 2019)*
Ed: Patty Tascarella. **Released:** November 07, 2019. **Description:** Article discussing the fact that more than half of Pennsylvania small and midsize business leaders say it's harder to find qualified employees. **Availability:** Online.

35478 ■ *"How Charlotte's Pilot Program for Incentives Could Boost Small Businesses, Workers' Skills" in Charlotte Business Journal (February 11, 2020)*
Ed: Erik Spanberg. **Released:** February 11, 2020. **Description:** Charlotte, North Carolina is launching a

pilot program that combines incentives for small businesses with an emphasis on providing more equitable access for residents willing to enhance their skills and training. **Availability:** Online.

35479 ■ *"How to Set Salaries" in Entrepreneur*

Ed: Stever Robbins. **Description:** Provides detailed information on how to set salaries for your employees. **Availability:** Online.

35480 ■ *"Small Business Owners Ask: Am I Paying My Employees the Right Salary?" in AllBusiness (September 12, 2020)*

Ed: Rieva Lesonsky. **Released:** February 12, 2020. **Description:** Details information on keeping your best workers and attracting qualified new staff by creating a fair, competitive benefits and pay package. **Availability:** Online.

35481 ■ *"Survey: Mass. Workers to Get Smaller Raises Than Peers Nationally" in The Boston Business Journal (January 14, 2020)*

Ed: Greg Ryan. **Released:** January 14, 2020. **Description:** Information from a survey indicates that Massachusetts businesses are planning to raise employee wages in 2020, but not as much as their counterparts nationwide. **Availability:** Online.

START-UP INFORMATION

35482 ■ *Scrapbooking for Profit: Cashing in on Retail, Home-Based and Internet Opportunities*
Pub: Allworth Press
Contact: Tad Crawford, Founder

Ed: Rebecca Pittman. **Released:** June 01, 2005. **Price:** $16.95, paperback; $19.99, Ebook; $19.95, Paperback. **Description:** Eleven strategies for starting a scrapbooking business, including brick-and-mortar stores, home-based businesses, and online retail and wholesale outlets. **Availability:** E-book; Print.

ASSOCIATIONS AND OTHER ORGANIZATIONS

35483 ■ **Institute for Distribution Excellence**
1325 G St. NW Ste. 1000
  Washington, DC 20005-1000
Co. E-mail: membership@naw.org
URL: http://www.naw.org/naw-institute-for-distribution -excellence
Contact: Patricia A. Lilly, Executive Director
E-mail: plilly@naw.org

Description: Firms that are members of the National Association of Wholesaler-Distributors, wholesalers, and trade associations. Seeks to advance knowledge in the field of wholesale distribution by means of long-range research projects. **Scope:** Wholesale distribution, focusing on long-range projects to advance knowledge in the field. **Publications:** *Facing the Forces of Change: The Road to Opportunity* (Triennial). **Geographic Preference:** National.

35484 ■ **International Federation of Pharmaceutical Wholesalers, Inc. (IFPWI)**
10569 Crestwood Dr.
  Manassas, VA 20109
Ph: (703)331-3714
URL: http://www.ifpw.com
Contact: Mark Parrish, President
E-mail: mark.parrish@ifpw.com
Facebook: www.facebook.com/IFPW1
X (Twitter): x.com/ifpw

Description: Wholesalers and distributors of pharmaceutical products. Promotes efficient delivery of pharmaceuticals to hospitals, physicians, and pharmacists; seeks to increase public awareness of the role played by members in the health care system. Facilitates cooperation and exchange of information among members. **Founded:** 1977. **Geographic Preference:** Multinational.

35485 ■ **Minnesota Beer Wholesalers Association (MBWA)**
222 S 9th St., Ste. 3150
  Minneapolis, MN 55402
URL: http://mnbwa.com
Facebook: www.facebook.com/MnBeerWholesalers

Description: Representatives of state beer wholesale associations. Promotes the welfare of beer association executives and beer wholesalers. Provides speakers; sponsors legislative conferences; compiles statistics. Bestows annual awards. **Founded:** 1945. **Publications:** *WBAE Directory* (Annual). **Geographic Preference:** National.

35486 ■ **National Association of Wholesaler-Distributors (NAW)**
1325 G St. NW, Ste. 1000
  Washington, DC 20005-3100
Ph: (202)872-0885
Fax: (202)785-0586
Co. E-mail: naw@naw.org
URL: http://www.naw.org
Contact: Eric Hoplin, Chief Executive Officer
Linkedin: www.linkedin.com/company/national -association-of-wholesaler-distributors
X (Twitter): x.com/NAWorg
YouTube: www.youtube.com/user/NAWInstitute

Description: Federation of national, state, and regional associations, and individual wholesaler-distributor firms. Represents industry's views to the federal government. Analyzes current and proposed legislation and government regulations affecting the industry. Maintains public relations and media programs and a research foundation. Conducts wholesale executive management courses. **Founded:** 1946. **Publications:** *NAW Annual Report* (Annual); *NAW Report*; *SmartBrief*. **Geographic Preference:** National.

REFERENCE WORKS

35487 ■ *"ABC Supply Company Finally Finds Idaho" in Idaho Business Review (September 17, 2014)*
Pub: BridgeTower Media
Contact: Adam Reinebach, President

Description: The nation's largest wholesale distributor, ABC Supply Company, has entered a store in Idaho. The roofing supply firm has now has stores in 48 states. Franklin Lumber Supply, a home supply chain will be ABCs its major competitor in the area.

35488 ■ *The Big Payback: The History of the Business of Hip-Hop*
Ed: Dan Charnas. **Released:** November 01, 2011. **Price:** $17, paperback; $13.99. **Description:** The complete history of hip-hop music is presented, by following the money and the relationship between artist and merchant. In its promise of economic security and creative control for black artist-entrepreneurs, it is the culmination of dreams of black nationalists and civil rights leaders. **Availability:** E-book; Print.

35489 ■ *"Conscious Capitalism: Liberating the Heroic Spirit of Business"*
Released: January 07, 2014. **Price:** $12.47, e-book; $16.79, paperback. **Description:** Conscious Capitalism companies include Whole Foods Market, Southwest Airlines, Costco, Google, Patagonia, The

Container Store, UPS and others. These firms under the four specific tenants to success: higher purpose, stakeholder integration, conscious leadership, and conscious culture and management. These companies are able to create value for all stakeholders, including customers, employees, suppliers, investors, society, and the environment. A new preface by the authors is included. **Availability:** E-book; Print.

35490 ■ *"From Craft Biz To Wholesale Giant" in Women Entrepreneur (January 19, 2009)*
Description: Advice is given on how to turn a small craft business into a full-time venture; tips to help one transition from a part-time designer to a full-time wholesaler and brand are also included.

35491 ■ *"Hoop Culture Opens Showroom, Expands Reach Globally" in Orlando Business Journal (Vol. 30, February 28, 2014, No. 36, pp. 3)*
Pub: American City Business Journals, Inc.
Contact: Mike Olivieri, Executive Vice President

Released: Weekly. **Description:** Hoop Culture Inc. president, Mike Brown, shares how the online basketball apparel retailer/wholesaler online store has expanded globally. He mentions that Orlando, Florida is one of their biggest markets. **Availability:** Print; Online.

35492 ■ *"How Are Digital Marketplaces Affecting the Wholesale Model?" in Business of Home (November 5, 2019)*
URL(s): businessofhome.com/articles/how-are-digital -marketplaces-affecting-the-wholesale-model

Ed: Warren Shoulberg. **Released:** November 05, 2019. **Description:** Discusses the B2B wholesale initiative in the gift and home markets industry. Typically, wholesalers sold directly to shops via trade shows, seasonal markets, and buying days, but two digital platforms, Faire and ModMart, are now offering an online alternative. **Availability:** Online.

35493 ■ *"Printers to the Trade" in American Printer (Vol. 128, July 1, 2011, No. 7)*
Description: Wholesale printing is discussed. Two wholesale printers share insight into their success, from business philosophies in general to practices that build strong relationships. **Availability:** Online.

STATISTICAL SOURCES

35494 ■ *RMA Annual Statement Studies*
Pub: Risk Management Association
Contact: Nancy Foster, President

Released: Annual. **Description:** Contains composite balance sheets and income statements for more than 360 industries, including the accounting, auditing, and bookkeeping industries. Also contains five years of comparative historical data for discerning trends. Includes 16 commonly used ratios, computed for most of the size groupings for nearly every industry.

VIDEO/AUDIO MEDIA

35495 ■ *Creating a Step-by-Step Small Biz Wholesale Plan*
URL(s): www.makinggoodpodcast.com/episodes/165

Ed: Lauren Tilden. **Released:** March 07, 2023. **Description:** Podcast defines wholesale, explains how to research business to approach as potential clients,and the dos and don'ts of cold emailing.

35496 ■ *Cynthia Wong Founder of Life Raft Treats*
URL(s): restaurantunstoppable.libsyn.com/984-cyn thia-wong-founder-of-life-raft-treats

Ed: Eric Cacciatore. **Released:** April 20, 2023. **Description:** Podcast offers a conversation with someone who burned out in the restaurant industry and now has a wholesale operation.

35497 ■ *The Power of Wholesale with Sarah of Simply Curated*
URL(s): www.makinggoodpodcast.com/episodes/114

Ed: Lauren Tilden. **Released:** April 19, 2022. **Description:** Podcast discusses wholesale strategy.

35498 ■ *Wholesale, Hiring + Taking Your Business Temperature with Katie Hunt*
URL(s): www.makinggoodpodcast.com/episodes/151

Ed: Lauren Tilden. **Released:** December 20, 2022. **Description:** Podcast discusses what the smallest businesses with the greatest wholesale success share in common, what you need to start pitching for wholesale, how to know when you're ready to hire, what it means to take your business temperature, and how to create and annual strategy plan.

TRADE SHOWS AND CONVENTIONS

35499 ■ Oklahoma Super Trade Show
URL(s): oklahomasupertradeshow.com
Frequency: Annual. **Description:** An in-depth tradeshow featuring products from grocers and wholesalers. **Principal Exhibits:** An in-depth tradeshow featuring products from grocers and wholesalers.

FRANCHISES AND BUSINESS OPPORTUNITIES

35500 ■ ProSource Wholesale
13501 Shoreline Dr.
Earth City, MO 63045
Ph: (314)282-4798
Co. E-mail: info@prosourcecalifornia.com
URL: http://www.prosourcewholesale.com
Contact: Dana Hughes, Manager
Facebook: www.facebook.com/prosourcewholesale
Linkedin: www.linkedin.com/company/prosource
-wholesale-floorcoverings
Instagram: www.instagram.com/prosource_wholesale
YouTube: www.youtube.com/user/ProSource2200
Pinterest: www.pinterest.com/pswholesale

Description: Firm provides home remodeling services including flooring, kitchen. **Founded:** 1991. **Franchised:** 1991. **Financial Assistance:** Yes **Training:** Initial training provided at headquarters in St. Louis and ongoing support.

START-UP INFORMATION

35501 ■ *"Cleaning Service Companies in Oklahoma Find Green Market Niche"* in *Journal Record (April 19, 2012)*
Pub: BridgeTower Media
Contact: Adam Reinebach, President

Ed: Brianna Bailey. **Description:** Well Maid was launched in 2010 when owner, Candace Lockett, grew frustrated with trying to find a cleaning service that refrained from using harsh chemicals. Her service uses common household products such as olive oil and baking soda in order to environmentally responsible. Well Maid's green philosophy is helping to grow the new firm.

35502 ■ *"Do Cool Sh*t: Quit Your Day Job, Start Your Own Business, and Live Happily Ever After"*
Pub: Harper Business
Contact: Hollis Heimbouch, Senior Vice President Publisher

Released: January 20, 2015. **Price:** $16.61, hardcover; $11.97, paperback; $11.49, e-book; $3.13, kindle; $0.05, hardcover(99 used from $0.05); $8, hardcover(44 new from $8.00); $2, paperback(76 used from $2.00); $5.47, paperback(64 new from $5.47). **Description:** Serial social entrepreneur, angel investor, and woman business leader, Miki Agrawal, teaches how to start and run a successful new business. She covers all issues from brainstorming, to raising money to getting press without any connections, and still have time to enjoy life. She created WILD, a farm-to-table pizzeria in New York City and Las Vegas. She also partnered in a children's multimedia company called Super Sprowtz--a story-driven nutrition program for children, and she launched a patented high-tech underware business called THINX. Agrawal also discusses the growth in her businesses. **Availability:** E-book; Print.

35503 ■ *"E-Commerce Jewelry Startup Gemvara Won't Pursue Retail Store in Boston"* in *Boston Business Journal (Vol. 34, March 14, 2014, No. 6)*
Pub: American City Business Journals, Inc.
Contact: Mike Olivieri, Executive Vice President

Released: Weekly. **Description:** Janet Holian is CEO of Gemvara, a Boston, Massachusetts-based online jewelry retailer. She ran a pop-up store from November through February and considered opening a traditional brick and mortar store. In the end, Holian decided to focus on the online store. Customers can still make private appointments to Gemvara's One Financial Center location. The company specializes in customizable fine jewelry. **Availability:** Print; Online.

35504 ■ *"Find a Customer To Validate Your Idea"* in *South Florida Business Journal (Vol. 34, May 2, 2014, No. 41, pp. 15)*
Pub: American City Business Journals, Inc.
Contact: Mike Olivieri, Executive Vice President

Released: Weekly. **Price:** $8, Introductory 4-week offer(Digital only). **Description:** Venture Hive founder, Susan Amat, share her views on her mission to nurture the entrepreneurial ecosystem from South Florida to the Americas. Amat says Venture Hive is a safe space where world-class technologists can learn to scale their businesses. Amat is a 40 Under 40 honoree, a White House Champion of Change, chair of Startup Florida, an Emerging Leader and a Woman to Watch. **Availability:** Print; Online.

35505 ■ *"Former WCVB Anchor Bianca De la Garza Discusses the Launch of Her New Media Venture"* in *Boston Business Journal (Vol. 34, June 6, 2014, No. 18, pp. 4)*
Pub: American City Business Journals, Inc.
Contact: Mike Olivieri, Executive Vice President

Released: June 02, 2014. **Description:** News anchor, Bianca de la Garza says career advance ment prompted her to form Lucky Gal Productions LLC. She said her entrepreneurial pursuit will develop a television show focusing on lifestyle and entertainment. De la Garza admits she will miss her co-anchor job at WCVB-TV's morning show, 'EyeOpener'. **Availability:** Print; Online.

35506 ■ *Lean In: Women, Work, and the Will to Lead*
Pub: Knopf Doubleday Publishing Group
Contact: Nan A. Talese, Contact
E-mail: ddaypub@randomhouse.com

Ed: Sheryl Sandberg. **Released:** March 11, 2013. **Description:** The chief operating officer at Facebook examines women's progress in achieving leadership roles and provides solutions to help women fully achieve their goals. **Availability:** Print.

35507 ■ *"Moms Mean Business: A Guide to Creating a Successful Company and Happy Life as a Mom Entrepreneur"*
Pub: Career Press Inc.

Released: October 20, 2014. **Price:** $15.99, Trade Paperback,plus S&H. **Description:** Currently, more women are starting new businesses than men and there are 9 million women-owned businesses in the United States; most of these women are also moms. A guide to help women start and run a successful home-based business is presented. **Availability:** Print.

35508 ■ *"Mount Laurel Woman Launches Venture Into Children's Used Clothing"* in *Philadelphia Inquirer (September 17, 2010)*
Pub: The Philadelphia Inquirer
Contact: Elizabeth H. Hughes, Chief Executive Officer

Ed: Maria Panaritis. **Description:** Profile of Jennifer Frisch, stay-at-home mom turned entrepreneur. Frisch started a used-clothing store Once Upon a Child after opening her franchised Plato's Closet, selling unwanted and used baby clothing and accessories at her new shop, while offering used merchandise to teens at Plato's Closet.

35509 ■ *"No. 64: Scaling the Business Meant Rebuilding a Bridge"* in *Inc. (Vol. 36, September 2014, No. 7, pp. 48)*
Pub: Mansueto Ventures L.L.C.
Contact: Stephanie Mehta, Chief Executive Officer

Released: September 2014. **Description:** Profile of Susan Meitner, mortgage industry veteran who founded Centennial Lending Group, a mortgage lending institution. Meitner and her family helped raise the needed $2.5 million to launch the firm in order to provide loans to new customers. **Availability:** Print; Online.

35510 ■ *"Secure Future"* in *Small Business Opportunities (November 2010)*
Pub: Harris Publishing, Inc.
Contact: Janet Chase, Contact

Ed: Stan Roberts. **Description:** Fed up with the corporate world, this first-time business owner sells security equipment over the phone. Last year, sales hit $4 million. Profile of the founder of SmartWatch Security & Sound, Madelaine Lock is included. **Availability:** Print; Online.

35511 ■ *"Should You Choose a Lump-Sum Pension Payout? Here's How Entrepreneur Ramona Harper Decided"* in *Black Enterprise (Vol. 44, June 2014, No. 10, pp. 27)*
Pub: Earl G. Graves Ltd.
Contact: Earl Graves, Jr., President

Description: Entrepreneur, Ramona Harper, chose a lump sum payout of her pension in order to start a new business. She used $110,000 to start her accessories boutique and put the remaining money into a small business 401(k), which helped her avoid a large tax. Tips to help individuals decide the best way to collect their pension are provided. **Availability:** Online.

35512 ■ *"Upscale Consignment Shop Opens In Brandon"* in *Tampa Tribune (January 25, 2012)*

Ed: Yvette C. Hammett. **Description:** Agape Chic Consignment Boutique opened February 4, 2012. The owners, Dena Ham and Stacy Ulrey Regan became friends working on their children's school PTA. Their business partnership hopes that people walking into their new shop will feel as if they are walking into an upscale boutique. The store offers designer labels in sizes 2-20. **Availability:** Print; Online.

ASSOCIATIONS AND OTHER ORGANIZATIONS

35513 ■ **85 Broads**
12 E 33rd St., 11th Fl.
New York, NY 10016
Ph: (616)517-1160
Co. E-mail: info@ellevatenetwork.com
URL: http://www.ellevatenetwork.com
Contact: Maricella Herrera Avila, Chief Executive Officer

Facebook: www.facebook.com/EllevateNetwork
Linkedin: www.linkedin.com/company/ellevatene
  twork
X (Twitter): x.com/EllevateNtwk
Instagram: www.instagram.com/ellevate_ntwk
Description: Promotes the networking and education of professional women around the world through education, inspiration, and opportunity. Seeks to close the gender achievement gap in business by providing women with a community to lean on and learn from. Partners with companies committed to gender diversity. **Founded:** 1997.

35514 ■ Accounting & Financial Women's Alliance (AFWA)
2365 Harrodsburg Rd., Ste. A325
  Lexington, KY 40504
Ph: (859)219-3532
URL: http://www.afwa.org
Contact: Wendi Christian, President
Facebook: www.facebook.com/AFWANational
Linkedin: www.linkedin.com/company/accounting
  -&-financial-women%27s-alliance
X (Twitter): x.com/afwanational
Instagram: www.instagram.com/afwanational
Description: Works to enable women in all accounting and finance fields to achieve their full potential and to contribute to their profession.

35515 ■ Accounting and Financial Women's Alliance - Billings Chapter
PO Box 20593
  Billings, MT 59104-0593
Co. E-mail: aswabillings@gmail.com
URL: http://www.billingsafwa.org
Contact: Jeremiah L. Rouane, Co-President
E-mail: jrouane@live.com
Description: Aims to increase opportunities and professional growth for women working in all facets of accounting and finance. **Founded:** 1938. **Geographic Preference:** Local.

35516 ■ Accounting and Financial Women's Alliance Birmingham
Birmingham, AL
URL: http://www.afwa.org/birmingham
Contact: Amy Adams, President
E-mail: amyadams6136@gmail.com
Facebook: www.facebook.com/Accounting-Financial
  -Womens-Alliance-Birmingham-Chapter-3557410
  61165916
Description: Aims to increase opportunities and professional growth for women working in all facets of accounting and finance. **Geographic Preference:** Local.

35517 ■ Accounting and Financial Women's Alliance Chicago Chapter
1957 N Dayton St., No. 1
  Chicago, IL 60614
URL: http://www.afwa.org/chicago
Contact: Chelsea Sowers, President
Description: Aims to increase opportunities and professional growth for women working in all facets of accounting and finance. **Founded:** 1938. **Geographic Preference:** Local.

35518 ■ Accounting and Financial Women's Alliance - Denver Chapter
PO Box 2234
  Denver, CO 80201
Ph: (303)588-3303
Co. E-mail: presidentafwadenver1@gmail.com
URL: http://www.afwadenver.org
Contact: Janice Sommers, President
E-mail: presidentafwadenver1@gmail.com
Description: Aims to increase opportunities and professional growth for women working on all facets of accounting and finance. **Founded:** 1938. **Geographic Preference:** Local.

35519 ■ Accounting and Financial Women's Alliance - Flagstaff Chapter
603 N Beaver St.
  Flagstaff, AZ 86001
Co. E-mail: afwaflagstaff@gmail.com
URL: http://www.afwaflagstaff.org

Contact: Karletta Jones, President
E-mail: karletta.jones@nau.edu
Description: Aims to increase opportunities and professional growth for women working on all facets of accounting and finance. **Geographic Preference:** Local.

35520 ■ Accounting and Financial Women's Alliance Houston Chapter (AFWA)
Houston, TX
Co. E-mail: meetings@houstonafwa.org
URL: http://sites.google.com/site/houstonafwa
Contact: Ellie Moore, President
E-mail: president@houstonafwa.org
Description: Seeks to enable women in all accounting and related fields to achieve full personal, professional and economic potential and contribute to the future development of their profession. **Founded:** 1952. **Geographic Preference:** Local.

35521 ■ Accounting and Financial Women's Alliance Milwaukee Chapter
Milwaukee, WI
URL: http://www.milwaukeeafwa.org
Contact: Wendi Hall, President
E-mail: president@milwaukeeafwa.org
Facebook: www.facebook.com/Accounting-Financial
  -Womens-Alliance-Milwaukee-Chapter-138713379
  525306
X (Twitter): x.com/MilwaukeeAFWA
Description: Aims to increase opportunities and professional growth for women working in all facets of accounting and finance. **Geographic Preference:** Local.

35522 ■ Accounting and Financial Women's Alliance - Omaha Chapter
Omaha, NE 68106
Co. E-mail: omahaafwa@gmail.com
URL: http://omahaafwa.org
Contact: Courtney Teeter, President
Facebook: www.facebook.com/OmahaAFWA
X (Twitter): x.com/OmahaAFWA
YouTube: www.youtube.com/user/ASWAHQ
Description: Aims to increase opportunities and professional growth for women working on all facets of accounting and finance. **Founded:** 1976. **Geographic Preference:** Local.

35523 ■ Accounting and Financial Women's Alliance Philadelphia Chapter
c/o Stephanie S Sommers, President
  237 W Lancaster Ave., Ste. 1000
  Devon, PA 19333
Co. E-mail: afwaphilly@gmail.com
URL: http://afwa-phila.org
Contact: Stephanie S. S. Sommers, President
Facebook: www.facebook.com/afwaphilly
Linkedin: www.linkedin.com/company/afwaphilly
Instagram: www.instagram.com/afwaphilly
Description: Aims to increase opportunities and professional growth for women working in all facets of accounting and finance. **Founded:** 1940. **Geographic Preference:** Local.

35524 ■ Accounting and Financial Women's Alliance - San Diego Chapter
c/o Pebbles Dumon
  San Diego, CA 92111
Co. E-mail: membership@afwasandiego.org
URL: http://www.afwasandiego.org
Contact: Pebbles Dumon, Director
E-mail: treasurer@afwasandiego.org
Description: Represents partners in national, regional and local CPA firms, financial officers, controllers, academicians, financial analysts and data processing consultants, recent college graduates and women returning to the work force. Seeks to increase the opportunities for women in all fields of accounting and finance. **Founded:** 1938. **Geographic Preference:** Local.

35525 ■ Accounting and Financial Women's Alliance San Francisco Chapter
San Francisco, CA
URL: http://afwa-sf.org
Contact: Michelle Berthiaume, President

E-mail: president@afwa-sf.org
Description: Aims to increase opportunities and professional growth for women working in all facets of accounting and finance. **Founded:** 1938. **Geographic Preference:** Local.

35526 ■ Accounting and Financial Women's Alliance Silicon Valley Chapter
PO Box 1301
  Santa Clara, CA 95052-1301
Co. E-mail: afwa103@gmail.com
URL: http://www.afwasiliconvalley.org
Contact: Deborah Rosengarten, President
E-mail: debbie@prpcpa.com
Facebook: www.facebook.com/AFWASiliconValley
Description: Increases technical knowledge, skills and abilities keeping members current in their field of expertise by providing career management and transition guidance and assistance. **Founded:** 1976. **Geographic Preference:** Local.

35527 ■ Airport Minority Advisory Council (AMAC)
45 L St. SW
  Washington, DC 20024
Ph: (703)414-2622
Co. E-mail: info@amac-org.com
URL: http://www.amac-org.com
Contact: Simeon Terry, Vice Chairman of the Board
Facebook: www.facebook.com/AirportMinorityA
  dvisoryCouncil
Linkedin: www.linkedin.com/company/airport-minority
  -advisory-council
X (Twitter): x.com/AMAC_ORG
Instagram: www.instagram.com/amac_org
YouTube: www.youtube.com/channel/UCKDJh
  --0mbVOvNltAz9vSiQ
Description: Advocates for equal opportunity for minorities and women in airport contracting and employment. **Founded:** 1984. **Publications:** *AMAC-ESP Informational Brochure.* **Educational Activities:** Annual Airport Business Diversity Conference (Annual). **Awards:** Airport AEC Award (Annual); Airport Concessions Innovation and Inclusion Award (Annual); AMAC Award of the Organization (Annual); AMAC Hall of Fame Award (Annual). **Geographic Preference:** National.

35528 ■ American Academy of Professional Coders (AAPC)
2233 S Presidents Dr., Ste. F
  Salt Lake City, UT 84120
Ph: (801)236-2200
Free: 800-626-2633
Fax: (801)236-2258
Co. E-mail: info@aapc.com
URL: http://www.aapc.com
Contact: Colleen Gianatasio, President
E-mail: colleen.gianatasio@aapcnab.com
Facebook: www.facebook.com/AAPCFan
Linkedin: www.linkedin.com/company/aapc
X (Twitter): x.com/aapcstaff
Instagram: www.instagram.com/aapc_official
YouTube: www.youtube.com/c/AAPCHealthCare
Description: Works to elevate the standards of medical coding by providing ongoing education, certification, networking and recognition. Promotes high standards of physician and outpatient facility coding through education and certification. **Founded:** 1988. **Educational Activities:** HEALTHCON (Annual). **Geographic Preference:** National.

35529 ■ American Business Women's Association (ABWA)
PO Box 4757
  Overland Park, KS 66204-0757
Free: 800-228-0007
Co. E-mail: webmail@abwa.org
URL: http://www.abwa.org
Contact: Rene Street, Executive Director
Facebook: www.facebook.com/ABWA.Na
  tionalOrganization
X (Twitter): x.com/ABWAHQ
Instagram: www.instagram.com/
  americanbusinesswomensassn

Description: Works to bring together business-women of diverse occupations and to provide opportunities for them to help themselves and others grow personally and professionally through leadership, education, and networking support. **Founded:** 1949.

35530 ■ **American Business Women's Association (ABWA) [ABWA Management L.L.C.]**
PO Box 4757
  Overland Park, KS 66204-0757
Free: 800-228-0007
Co. E-mail: webmail@abwa.org
URL: http://www.abwa.org
Contact: Rene Street, Executive Director
Facebook: www.facebook.com/ABWA.NationalOrganization
Linkedin: www.linkedin.com/company/american-business-women-s-association-national
X (Twitter): x.com/ABWAHQ
Instagram: www.instagram.com/americanbusinesswomensassn
Description: Women in business, including women owning or operating their own businesses, women in professions and women employed in any level of government, education, or retailing, manufacturing and service companies. Provides opportunities for businesswomen to help themselves and others grow personally and professionally through leadership, education, networking support and national recognition. **Founded:** 1949. **Publications:** *The Leadership Edge* (Quarterly); *Women in Business*; *American Business Women's Association Directory of Business Owners* (Annual). **Awards:** Top Ten Business Women of ABWA (Annual); Stephen Bufton Memorial Educational Fund (SBMEF) (Annual); ABWA Business Woman of the Year (Annual). **Geographic Preference:** National.

35531 ■ **American Business Women's Association - Big Sky Chapter**
PO Box 4757
  Overland Park, KS 66204-0757
Free: 800-228-0007
URL: http://www.abwa.org/abwa-chapter-express-networks
Description: Promotes and supports the personal and professional development of businesswomen in Montana. **Founded:** 1964.

35532 ■ **American Business Women's Association Cavalier Chapter**
801 E Main St.
  Richmond, VA 23219
URL: http://columbiatriad.abwa.org/scholarships
Contact: Beatrice E. Burton, Contact
E-mail: burtonbeatrice@yahoo.com
Facebook: www.facebook.com/Cavalier-Chapter-of-American-Business-Womens-Association-102855846461120
Description: Provides opportunities for businesswomen to help themselves and others grow personally and professionally through leadership, education, and networking support. **Geographic Preference:** Local.

35533 ■ **American Business Women's Association - Columbia Triad Chapter**
PO Box 1212
  Columbia, SC 29202
URL: http://columbiatriad.abwa.org
Contact: Deborah Brown, Secretary
Description: Promotes and supports the personal and professional development of businesswomen in the Columbia Triad area of South Carolina.

35534 ■ **American Business Women's Association - Coral Springs Charter Chapter**
7801 NW 80th Ave.
  Tamarac, FL 33321
Free: 877-216-9908
Co. E-mail: abwacoralsprings@gmail.com
URL: http://abwa-coralsprings.org
Contact: Sandei Kirshen, President
E-mail: itssandei@aol.com
Facebook: www.facebook.com/abwacs

Linkedin: www.linkedin.com/company/abwacoralsprings
Instagram: www.instagram.com/abwa_cs
Description: Promotes and supports the personal and professional development of businesswomen in the Coral Springs area.

35535 ■ **American Business Women's Association - DC Charter Chapter (ABWA DC)**
PO Box 29602
  Washington, DC 20066
Ph: (301)318-3611
Co. E-mail: dccharterchapter1960@gmail.com
URL: http://www.abwadccharterchapter.com
Contact: Arlene Reese, Contact
Linkedin: www.linkedin.com/in/abwa-dc-charter-chapter-51426a216
Description: Promotes and supports the personal and professional development of businesswomen in the Washington DC area.

35536 ■ **American Business Women's Association - Denver Downtown Chapter**
Denver, CO
Co. E-mail: judithgreen5@live.com
URL: http://www.abwa-denverdowntown.org
Contact: Judith Green, Contact
E-mail: judithgreen5@live.com
Description: Provides opportunities for businesswomen of diverse occupations in the Denver area.

35537 ■ **American Business Women's Association - Dynamic Connections Chapter**
PO Box 1471
  Blue Springs, MO 64013
Co. E-mail: dynamicconnectionsabwa@gmail.com
URL: http://dynamicconnections.abwa.org
Contact: Stacy Arnold, President
E-mail: sandpfamily08@gmai.com
Facebook: www.facebook.com/ABWADynamicConnections
Description: Promotes and supports the personal and professional development of businesswomen in Missouri.

35538 ■ **American Business Women's Association - Greenspoint Chapter**
16945 Northchase Dr., Ste. 1900
  Houston, TX 77060
Ph: (832)314-2216
Co. E-mail: abwa-gp_membershipchair@outlook.com
URL: http://abwa-gpwebsite.wixsite.com/abwa-greenspoint
Contact: Treena Dockery, President
E-mail: abwa-gp_president@outlook.com
Description: Promotes and supports the personal and professional development of businesswomen in the Greenspoint and Greater Houston area.

35539 ■ **American Business Women's Association - Heart of the Piedmont Chapter (ABWA-HOP)**
Greensboro, NC 27410
Co. E-mail: hopn2awba@gmail.com
URL: http://www.hopn2abwa.org
Contact: Debbie McKelvie, President
Facebook: www.facebook.com/abwahop
Linkedin: www.linkedin.com/company/abwa-hop
Description: Promotes and supports the personal and professional development of businesswomen in the Piedmont Triad area of North Carolina. **Founded:** 2009.

35540 ■ **American Business Women's Association - Indianapolis Charter Chapter**
Indianapolis, IN 46220
URL: http://abwaindycharter.org
Description: Promotes and supports the personal and professional development of businesswomen in the Indianapolis area. **Founded:** 1952.

35541 ■ **American Business Women's Association - La Capitale Chapter**
Baton Rouge, LA
URL: http://www.abwabatonrouge.org
Contact: K. J. Callegan, President

Description: Promotes and supports the personal and professional development of businesswomen in the Baton Rouge area.

35542 ■ **American Business Women's Association - La Luz Chapter**
Albuquerque, NM 87113
URL: http://www.abwa.org/abwa-chapters-and-express-networks
Description: Promotes and supports the personal and professional development of businesswomen in the Albuquerque area.

35543 ■ **American Business Women's Association - Maryland Capital Chapter**
PO Box 1955
  Edgewater, MD 21037-7955
Co. E-mail: mdcapabwa@gmail.com
URL: http://www.abwamdcap.org
Contact: Casey Coven, President
E-mail: casey@411totravel.com
Linkedin: www.linkedin.com/company/abwa-maryland-capital-chapter
Instagram: www.instagram.com/abwa_md_capital
Description: Promotes and supports the personal and professional development of businesswomen in the Maryland/DC area. **Founded:** 1970.

35544 ■ **American Business Women's Association - Mo-Kan Chapter**
Lenexa, KS 66215
Co. E-mail: abwamokan@gmail.com
URL: http://www.abwamokan.org
Contact: Kathy Richer, President
Facebook: www.facebook.com/ABWAMoKanChapter
X (Twitter): x.com/AbwaMokan
Instagram: www.instagram.com/abwamokan
Description: Promotes and supports the personal and professional development of businesswomen in the Kansas City area. **Founded:** 1980.

35545 ■ **American Business Women's Association - Na Kilohana 'O Wahine Chapter**
929 Queen St., 2nd f
  Honolulu, HI 96828
Co. E-mail: info@abwahawaii.org
URL: http://www.abwahawaii.org
Contact: Danice Mah, Chairman
Description: Promotes and supports businesswomen in Hawaii through leadership, education, and networking. **Founded:** 1977.

35546 ■ **American Business Women's Association - New York City Chapter**
PO Box 1487
  Amherst, NY 14226
URL: http://www.abwawny.com
Contact: Dr. Katelyn Niemiec Klimek, President
E-mail: abwawnypresident@gmail.com
Description: Promotes and supports the personal and professional development of businesswomen in the New York City area. **Founded:** 1952.

35547 ■ **American Business Women's Association - Novi Oaks Charter Chapter**
Novi, MI 48375
Co. E-mail: novioaksabwa@gmail.com
URL: http://www.novi-abwa.org
Contact: Marcia Green, Treasurer
E-mail: novioaksabwa@gmail.com
Facebook: www.facebook.com/ABWANoviOaks
Description: Promotes and supports the personal and professional development of businesswomen in the Novi area of Michigan. **Founded:** 1990.

35548 ■ **American Business Women's Association - Nutmeg Chapter**
c/o Rita DiMaria
  PO Box 7175
  Prospect, CT 06712-0175
URL: http://abwanutmeg.org/wp
Contact: Rita DiMaria, Contact
Description: Promotes and supports businesswomen in Connecticut through leadership, education, and networking. **Founded:** 1977.

35549 ■ American Business Women's Association - Palm Desert Trendsetter Chapter
77760 Country Club Dr., Ste. I
  Palm Desert, CA 92211
Ph: (760)565-2292
Co. E-mail: info@palmdesertabwa.org
URL: http://palmdesertabwa.org
Instagram: www.instagram.com/abwa_trendsetter
Description: Provides opportunities for business-women of diverse occupations throughout the Coachella Valley.

35550 ■ American Business Women's Association - Pathfinder Chapter
43575 Mission Blvd., No. 409
  Fremont, CA 94539
URL: http://www.abwa-pathfinder.org
Contact: Rebecca Lalwani, President
E-mail: rebecca.lalwani@gmail.com
Facebook: www.facebook.com/AbwaPathfinderChapter
Linkedin: www.linkedin.com/company/american-business-women's-assn
Description: Provides opportunities for business-women to help themselves and others grow personally and professionally through leadership, education, and networking support. **Geographic Preference:** Local.

35551 ■ American Business Women's Association - Quincy Charter Chapter
PO Box 1114
  Quincy, IL 62306
Free: 800-228-0007
Co. E-mail: abwaqcy@gmail.com
URL: http://quincy.abwa.org
Contact: Trina Nkhazi, President
Description: Promotes and supports the personal and professional development of businesswomen in the Quincy, Illinois, area.

35552 ■ American Business Women's Association - Reno Tahoe Express Network
PO Box 20268
  Reno, NV 89515
Free: 800-228-0007
Co. E-mail: renee.mcginnes@renotahoesmg.com
URL: http://renotahoe.abwa.org
Contact: Kathy Powers, President
Description: Promotes and supports the personal and professional development of businesswomen in the Reno area.

35553 ■ American Business Women's Association - River Region Chapter
Montgomery, AL
Co. E-mail: studor1124@aol.com
URL: http://columbiatriad.abwa.org/scholarships
Contact: Susan Crowther, Contact
E-mail: studor1124@aol.com
Description: Provides opportunities for business-women of diverse occupations to help themselves and others grow personally and professionally through leadership, education, networking, and national recognition.

35554 ■ American Business Women's Association - Rochester Charter Chapter
No. 4089
  Rochester, MN 55903
Co. E-mail: abwa.rochester@gmail.com
URL: http://rochester.abwa.org
Contact: Lorlee Steever, President
E-mail: steever.lorlee@gmail.com
Description: Promotes and supports the personal and professional development of businesswomen in the Rochester, Minnesota, area. **Founded:** 2012.

35555 ■ American Business Women's Association - Singing River Charter Chapter
Pascagoula, MS 39581
URL: http://columbiatriad.abwa.org/scholarships
Contact: Pam Knight, Contact
E-mail: knight_pam@yahoo.com

Description: Promotes and supports the personal and professional development of businesswomen in the Jackson County area of Mississippi. **Founded:** 2013.

35556 ■ American Business Women's Association - Smoky Mountain Sevier Chapter
2391 Pky.
  Pigeon Forge, TN 37863
Ph: (865)963-5415
Co. E-mail: abwasevier@gmail.com
URL: http://www.abwasevier.org
Contact: Robin Jones, President
E-mail: michaelrobinjones@yahoo.com
Facebook: www.facebook.com/smokymountainsevier.abwa
X (Twitter): x.com/abwahq
Description: Promotes and supports the personal and professional development of businesswomen in the Sevier County area of Tennessee. **Founded:** 1976.

35557 ■ American Business Women's Association - Territorial Charter Chapter (TCC ABWA)
PO Box 5626
  Yuma, AZ 85366
Ph: (928)261-6505
Co. E-mail: info@mysite.com
URL: http://www.abwayumaaz.org
Contact: Susan James, President
E-mail: susanjamesinsurance@gmail.org
Facebook: www.facebook.com/ABWAYuma
Instagram: www.instagram.com/abwayuma
Description: Provides opportunities for business-women of diverse occupations in the Yuma, Arizona, area.

35558 ■ American Business Women's Association - Tu'Ya Chapter
Oklahoma City, OK
URL: http://tuya.abwa.org
Contact: Kathy Eller, President
E-mail: kathyeller.etc@gmail.com
Facebook: www.facebook.com/AbwaTuYaChapter
Description: Promotes and supports the personal and professional development of businesswomen in the Oklahoma City area. (Tu'Ya is a Chickasaw word meaning "to climb" or "to rise.").

35559 ■ American Business Women's Association - West Des Moines Charter Chapter
West Des Moines, IA
Co. E-mail: aweger@westbankstrong.com
URL: http://westdesmoines.abwa.org
Contact: Susan Dunn, President
E-mail: susandunn@juno.com
Description: Promotes and supports the personal and professional development of businesswomen in the western Des Moines area.

35560 ■ Arab American Business Women's Council (AABWC)
22952 Outer Dr.
  Dearborn, MI 48124
Ph: (313)277-1986
Co. E-mail: info@aawbc.org
URL: http://www.aawbc.org
Contact: Taharah Saad, President
E-mail: tsaad@aawbc.org
Facebook: www.facebook.com/aawbcorg
Linkedin: www.linkedin.com/company/arab-american-women's-business-council
X (Twitter): x.com/aawbc
Instagram: www.instagram.com/aawbc
YouTube: www.youtube.com/channel/UCpwOZRakfrgL4bT7FY-HeNg
Description: Aims to bring together Arab American business women of diverse disciplines and industries. Addresses the needs of Arab American women professionals and business owners. Assists members by providing mentorships, internships, scholarships and professional development programs. **Founded:** 2007. **Geographic Preference:** National.

35561 ■ Arizona Business and Professional Women (Arizona BPW)
Phoenix, AZ
Free: 877-JOI-NBPW
Co. E-mail: aeauguste@aol.com
URL: http://www.bpwaz.org
Contact: Terry Dolan, President
Facebook: www.facebook.com/ArizonaBPW
Description: Represents the interests of business and professional women. Elevates the standards for women in business and professional settings. Promotes equity for all women in the workplace through advocacy, education and information. Provides professional development, networking and career advancement opportunities for working women. **Geographic Preference:** State.

35562 ■ Arkansas Business and Professional Women (AR/BPW)
c/o Debbie Davis, Recording Secretary
  Wynne, AR 72396
Co. E-mail: arkansasbpw@gmail.com
URL: http://arkansasbpw.yolasite.com
Contact: Sarah Akin, President
E-mail: sarah1178@aol.com
Description: Represents the interests of business and professional women. Elevates the standards for women in business and professional settings. Promotes equity for all women in the workplace through advocacy, education and information. Provides professional development, networking and career advancement opportunities for working women. **Founded:** 1919. **Geographic Preference:** State.

35563 ■ Asian Women in Business (AWIB) - Library
125 Lafayette St.
  New York, NY 10013
Co. E-mail: info@awib-sc.org
URL: http://www.awib-sc.org
Instagram: www.instagram.com/asianwomeninbusiness
Description: Asian-American women in business. Seeks to enable Asian-American women to achieve their entrepreneurial potential. Serves as a clearinghouse on issues affecting small business owners; provides technical assistance and other support to members; sponsors business and entrepreneurial education courses. **Scope:** Women; business; Asian American. **Services:** Library open to the public for reference use. **Founded:** 1995. **Holdings:** Articles. **Awards:** AWIB Entrepreneurial Leadership Award (Annual). **Geographic Preference:** National; Regional.

35564 ■ Association for Women in Communications (AWC)
4730 S National Ave., Ste. A1
  Springfield, MO 65810
Ph: (417)409-2492
Co. E-mail: members@womcom.org
URL: http://womcom.org
Contact: Anita K. Parran, Chairman
Description: Professional association of journalism and communications. **Founded:** 1909. **Publications:** *AWC Communique* (Monthly); *The Intercom* (Monthly); *The Matrix* (Quarterly). **Educational Activities:** Association for Women in Communications National Professional Conference (Biennial). **Awards:** AWC Headliner Award (Periodic); AWC Rising Star Award (Annual); AWC International Matrix Award (Biennial); AWC Outstanding Chapter Award (Annual); National Georgina MacDougall Davis Award (Periodic); AWC Outstanding Faculty Advisor Award (Annual); AWC Lifetime Achievement Award (Annual); Ruth Weyand and the Business Pinnacle Award (Periodic); ACW Professional Chapter Awards (Annual); AWC Student Chapter Awards (Annual); Clarion Awards (Annual). **Geographic Preference:** National.

35565 ■ Association for Women in Science (AWIS)
1629 K St., Ste. 300
  Washington, DC 20006
Ph: (202)827-9798

Co. E-mail: awis@awis.org
URL: http://www.awis.org
Contact: Susan Windham-Bannister, President
Facebook: www.facebook.com/Associa
tionforWomeninScience
Linkedin: www.linkedin.com/company/association-for
-women-in-science
X (Twitter): x.com/AWISnational

Description: Promotes equal opportunities for women to enter the scientific workforce and to achieve their career goals; provides educational information to women planning careers in science; networks with other women's groups; monitors scientific legislation and the status of women in science. **Founded:** 1971. **Publications:** *Association for Women in Science Directory*; *AWIS Magazine* (Quarterly); *Taking the Initiative: Report on a Leadership Conference for Women in Science and Engineering*. **Geographic Preference:** National.

35566 ■ Association of Women's Business Centers (AWBC)
10 G St. NE, Ste. 600
Washington, DC 20002
Ph: (202)430-4756
Co. E-mail: info@awbc.org
URL: http://awbc.org
Contact: Corinne Hodges, Chief Executive Officer
Facebook: www.facebook.com/awbc.org
Linkedin: www.linkedin.com/company/awbc
X (Twitter): x.com/AWBC_USA

Description: Aims to develop the collective leadership and power of successful women entrepreneurs. Supports entrepreneurial development among women as a way to achieve economic self-sufficiency. Empowers women business owners by providing education, training, mentoring, business development, and financing opportunities. **Founded:** 1998. **Geographic Preference:** National.

35567 ■ ATHENA International
2425 E Grand River Ave.
Lansing, MI 48912
Ph: (312)580-0111
Co. E-mail: communications@athenainternational
.org
URL: http://www.athenainternational.org
Contact: Traci Corey, President
Facebook: www.facebook.com/ATHENAInternational
Linkedin: www.linkedin.com/company/athena-interna
tional
X (Twitter): x.com/ATHENAleaders
Instagram: www.instagram.com/athena_international

Description: Supports, develops and honors women leaders. Inspires women to achieve their full potential. Creates balance in leadership worldwide. **Founded:** 1982. **Publications:** *The ATHENAIAN* (3/year). **Awards:** The ATHENA Leadership Award (Annual). **Geographic Preference:** Local.

35568 ■ Black Career Women's Network (BCWN)
Cincinnati, OH
Ph: (513)729-9724
URL: http://bcwnetwork.com
Contact: Sherry Sims, Chief Executive Officer
Facebook: www.facebook.com/BCWNetwork
Linkedin: www.linkedin.com/company/bcwnetwork
X (Twitter): x.com/bcwnetwork
Instagram: www.instagram.com/bcwnetwork

Description: A national career development organization dedicated to fostering the professional growth of black women. **Founded:** 2012.

35569 ■ Black Women Business Owners of America (BWBO)
36 E Cameron St., No. 15
Tulsa, OK 74103
Ph: (539)302-2686
Co. E-mail: info@bwboamerica.com
URL: http://www.bwboamerica.com
Contact: Tashia Sumpter, President
Facebook: www.facebook.com/bwboamerica
Linkedin: www.linkedin.com/company/bwboamerica
Instagram: www.instagram.com/bwbo_america

Description: Supports African American women business owners, entrepreneurs, and startup founders across the United States by providing tools, resources, and knowledge needed to grow successful businesses. **Founded:** 2018.

35570 ■ Bozeman Business and Professional Women (BPW)
PO Box 644
Bozeman, MT 59771
Co. E-mail: communications@bozemanbpw.org
URL: http://bozemanbpw.org
Contact: Julie Banuchie, President
E-mail: president@bozemanbpw.org
Facebook: www.facebook.com/bozemanbpw
X (Twitter): x.com/Bozeman_BPW

Description: Represents the interests of business and professional women. Elevates the standards for women in business and professional settings. Promotes equity for all women in the workplace through advocacy, education and information. Provides professional development, networking and career advancement opportunities for working women. **Founded:** 1930. **Geographic Preference:** Local.

35571 ■ Business and Professional Women of Boulder (BPWB)
Boulder, CO
Co. E-mail: ssimmons@bpwboulder.org
URL: http://bpwcolorado.org/boulder
Contact: Barbara Flood, President
E-mail: barbaflood@gmail.com
Facebook: www.facebook.com/BPWBoulder

Description: Represents the interests of business and professional women. Elevates the standards for women in business and professional settings. Promotes equity for all women in the workplace through advocacy, education and information. Provides professional development, networking and career advancement opportunities for working women. **Founded:** 1923. **Geographic Preference:** Local.

35572 ■ Business and Professional Women of Charlotte County
PO Box 510180
Punta Gorda, FL 33951-0180
URL: http://www.angelfire.com/biz6/bluenebula/bpwin
dex.html
Contact: Mary A. Byraki, President

Description: Represents the interests of business and professional women. Elevates the standards for women in business and professional settings. Promotes equity for all women in the workplace through advocacy, education and information. Provides professional development, networking and career advancement opportunities for working women. **Geographic Preference:** Local.

35573 ■ Business and Professional Women - Fayetteville
PO Box 8984
Fayetteville, AR 72703
Co. E-mail: faybpw@hotmail.com
URL: http://sites.google.com/site/fayettevillebpw
Contact: Edwina Hancock, President

Description: Represents the interests of business and professional women. Elevates the standards for women in business and professional settings. Promotes equity for all women in the workplace through advocacy, education and information. Provides professional development, networking and career advancement opportunities for working women. **Founded:** 1924. **Geographic Preference:** Local.

35574 ■ Business and Professional Women - Granite Falls
Granite Falls, NC
URL: http://www.bpwgranitefalls.org
Contact: Ruth Easterling, President

Description: Represents the interests of business and professional women. Elevates the standards for women in business and professional settings. Promotes equity for all women in the workplace through advocacy, education and information. Provides professional development, networking and career advancement opportunities for working women. **Geographic Preference:** Local.

35575 ■ Business and Professional Women/ Jupiter
c/o Lynne Spears, Treasurer
348 Church Rd.
Tequesta, FL 33469
URL: http://www.jupiterbpw.org
Contact: Lynne Spears, Contact
Facebook: www.facebook.com/BPWJupiter
Linkedin: www.linkedin.com/company/business-an
d-professional-women%27s-foundation

Description: Represents the interests of business and professional women. Elevates the standards for women in business and professional settings. Promotes equity for all women in the workplace through advocacy, education and information. Provides professional development, networking and career advancement opportunities for working women. **Geographic Preference:** Local.

35576 ■ Business and Professional Women Michigan (BPW/Michigan)
1372 W Liberty Rd.
Clarklake, MI 49234
Ph: (517)315-7285
Co. E-mail: bpw.michigan@gmail.com
URL: http://bpw-michigan.org
Contact: Amy Courter, President
Facebook: www.facebook.com/bpwmichigan
X (Twitter): twitter.com/BPWMichigan

Description: Advocates for working women and provides networking opportunities.

35577 ■ Business and Professional Women of North Carolina (BPW-NC)
175 BPW Club Rd.
Carrboro, NC 27510
Ph: (252)452-8530
URL: http://bpw-nc.wildapricot.org
Contact: Linda Hardy, Co-President

Description: Represents the interests of business and professional women. Elevates the standards for women in business and professional settings. Promotes equity for all women in the workplace through advocacy, education and information. Provides professional development, networking and career advancement opportunities for working women. **Founded:** 1947. **Geographic Preference:** State.

35578 ■ Business and Professional Women of Raleigh
PO Box 1794
Cary, NC 27512
URL: http://bpwraleigh.org
Contact: Leslie Lemmons, President
E-mail: president@bpwraleigh.org
Facebook: www.facebook.com/BPWtriangle
Instagram: www.instagram.com/bpwtriangle

Description: Represents the interests of business and professional women. Elevates the standards for women in business and professional settings. Promotes equity for all women in the workplace through advocacy, education and information. Provides professional development, networking and career advancement opportunities for working women. **Founded:** 1919. **Geographic Preference:** Local.

35579 ■ Business and Professional Women/ St. Petersburg-Pinellas
400 Beach Dr. NE
Saint Petersburg, FL 33701
Co. E-mail: info@bpwstpetepinellas.org
URL: http://bpwstpetepinellas.org
Contact: Kristin Smith, President
Facebook: www.facebook.com/BPWSPP
X (Twitter): x.com/BPWSPP
Instagram: www.instagram.com/bpwspp

Description: Represents the interests of business and professional women. Elevates the standards for women in business and professional settings. Promotes equity for all women in the workplace through advocacy, education and information. Provides professional development, networking and career advancement opportunities for working women. **Founded:** 2009. **Geographic Preference:** Local.

35580 ■ Business and Professional Women Tallahassee

PO Box 776
Saint Petersburg, FL 33731
URL: http://www.bpwfl.org/about
Contact: Sheri McCandless, President
E-mail: sheri.m@comcast.net

Description: Represents the interests of business and professional women. Elevates the standards for women in business and professional settings. Promotes equity for all women in the workplace through advocacy, education and information. Provides professional development, networking and career advancement opportunities for working women. **Founded:** 1919. **Geographic Preference:** Local.

35581 ■ Business and Professional Women of Tennessee (BPWTN)

1824 Roane State Hwy.
Harriman, TN 37748
Co. E-mail: info@bpwtn.org
URL: http://www.bpwtn.org
Contact: Martha Ervin, President
E-mail: president@bpwtn.org

Description: Represents the interests of business and professional women. Elevates the standards for women in business and professional settings. Promotes equity for all women in the workplace through advocacy, education and information. Provides professional development, networking and career advancement opportunities for working women. **Geographic Preference:** State.

35582 ■ Business and Professional Women Valley Sunset District

1026 Florin Rd., Ste., 370
Sacramento, CA 95831
Co. E-mail: bpwvsd@gmail.com
URL: http://bpwcal.org/valley-sunset-district
Contact: Rosemary Enzer, President

Description: Represents the interests of business and professional women. Elevates the standards for women in business and professional settings. Promotes equity for all women in the workplace through advocacy, education and information. Provides professional development, networking and career advancement opportunities for working women. **Geographic Preference:** Local.

35583 ■ Business and Professional Women/ Vermont (BPW/VT)

PO Box 4172
Saint Johnsbury, VT 05819
URL: http://www.vermontbpw.org
Contact: Alice S. Kitchel, President
E-mail: alice.s.kitchel@gmail.com

Description: Represents the interests of business and professional women. Elevates the standards for women in business and professional settings. Promotes equity for all women in the workplace through advocacy, education and information. Provides professional development, networking and career advancement opportunities for working women. **Geographic Preference:** State.

35584 ■ Business and Professional Women of Washington State (BPW/WA)

WA
URL: http://www.bpwwa.org
Contact: Rosalind Scott, President
E-mail: eastside@bpwwa.org

Description: Represents the interests of business and professional women. Elevates the standards for women in business and professional settings. Promotes equity for all women in the workplace through advocacy, education and information. Provides professional development, networking and career advancement opportunities for working women. **Founded:** 1921. **Geographic Preference:** State.

35585 ■ Business and Professional Women's Club of Canonsburg

Facebook: www.facebook.com/CanonsburgBPW

Description: Represents the interests of business and professional women. Elevates the standards for women in business and professional settings. Promotes equity for all women in the workplace through

advocacy, education and information. Provides professional development, networking and career advancement opportunities for working women. **Founded:** 1931. **Geographic Preference:** Local.

35586 ■ Business and Professional Women's Club of the Lehigh Valley

URL: http://bpwpa.wildapricot.org/page-1839077

Description: Represents the interests of business and professional women. Elevates the standards for women in business and professional settings. Promotes equity for all women in the workplace through advocacy, education and information. Provides professional development, networking and career advancement opportunities for working women. **Founded:** 1947. **Geographic Preference:** Local.

35587 ■ California Conference for Women [Conferences for Women]

2618 San Miguel Dr., No. 476
Newport Beach, CA 92600
URL: http://www.conferencesforwomen.org

Description: Works to promote, communicate, and amplify the influence of women in the workplace and beyond.

35588 ■ Canadian Association of Women Executives and Entrepreneurs (CAWEE) [Association Canadienne des Femmes Cadres et Entrepreneurs]

157 Adelaide St. W, Ste. 106
Toronto, ON, Canada M5H 4E7
Ph: (416)756-0000
Fax: (416)756-0000
Co. E-mail: contact@cawee.net
URL: http://www.cawee.net
Contact: Susan Patterson, President

Description: Seeks to provide opportunities for women to empower other women in the development and advancement of their business and professional lives; which fosters financial independence, professional development and personal satisfaction. **Founded:** 1976. **Publications:** Acclaim (Quarterly). **Awards:** CAWEE Charity of Choice (Annual); CAWEE MBA Scholarship (Annual). **Geographic Preference:** National.

35589 ■ Canadian Federation of Business and Professional Women (CFBPWC) [BPW Canada]

London, ON, Canada N5W 2J8
Co. E-mail: communications@bpwcanada.com
URL: http://bpwcanada.com
Contact: Angie Godin, President
E-mail: president@bpwcanada.com
Facebook: www.facebook.com/canadabpw
Linkedin: www.linkedin.com/in/bpwcanada
X (Twitter): x.com/canadabpw
Instagram: www.instagram.com/canadabpw
YouTube: www.youtube.com/channel/UC6iDC0S _fGD_9aoUPMYywAA

Description: Canadian women engaged in business, the professions, or industry. Works to enhance the economic, social, and employment status of women. Encourages women to become active in government at every level. Strives to improve business service standards. Networks with related organizations to promote common concerns. **Founded:** 1930. **Publications:** Business and Professional Woman (Quarterly). **Educational Activities:** BPW Canada National Convention (Biennial). **Awards:** BPW canada Leadership Award Program (Biennial). **Geographic Preference:** National.

35590 ■ Centre for Women in Business (CWB)

Mt. Saint Vincent University
Ste. 411, Margaret Norrie McCain Ctr.
166 Bedford Hwy.
Halifax, NS, Canada B3M 2J6
Ph: (902)457-6449
Free: 888-776-9022
Co. E-mail: cwb@msvu.ca
URL: http://www.centreforwomeninbusiness.ca
Contact: Tanya Priske, Executive Director
E-mail: tanya.priske@msvu.ca

Facebook: www.facebook.com/cen treforwomeninbusiness
Linkedin: www.linkedin.com/company/cen treforwomeninbusiness
X (Twitter): x.com/cwb_ns
Instagram: www.instagram.com/cwb_ns
YouTube: www.youtube.com/user/Cen treWomenBusiness

Description: Helps women knock down barriers and succeed as entrepreneurs. **Founded:** 1992. **Publications:** Biz Beat (Monthly). **Geographic Preference:** Local.

35591 ■ Colorado Business Women (CBW)

PO Box 5342
Englewood, CO 80155
URL: http://www.coloradobizwomen.com
Contact: Marcia Pinkstaff, President
E-mail: president@coloradobizwomen.com
Facebook: www.facebook.com/Colora doBusinessWomen

Description: Seeks to promote full participation, equity, and economic self-sufficiency for Colorado's working women through involvement in political and legislative issues, community outreach, and personal and professional development. **Founded:** 1919.

35592 ■ ColorComm: Women of Color in Communications

Washington, DC
Co. E-mail: membership@colorcommnetwork.com
URL: http://www.colorcommnetwork.com
Contact: Natalie Boden, Chief Executive Officer
Facebook: www.facebook.com/ColorComm
Linkedin: www.linkedin.com/company/colorcomm-inc
Instagram: www.instagram.com/colorcomm

Description: Supports professional women of color in all areas of communications, including public relations, corporate communications, advertising, media relations, and political communications. Seeks to foster a strong network of leaders by creating mentors/mentees, business relationships, and friendships. **Founded:** 2011.

35593 ■ Concord-Cabarrus Business and Professional Women [Concord-Cabarrus BPW]

Concord, NC
URL: http://bpw-nc.org/page-837235
Contact: Jazmin G. Caldwell, Contact
URL(s): www.bpw-nc.org/Meet_The_BPW_NC_Foun dation_Board
Facebook: www.facebook.com/Concor dCabarrusBPW

Description: Represents the interests of business and professional women. Elevates the standards for women in business and professional settings. Promotes equity for all women in the workplace through advocacy, education and information. Provides professional development, networking and career advancement opportunities for working women. **Geographic Preference:** Local.

35594 ■ digitalundivided

261 Madison Ave., Fl., 9, Ste. 1040
New York, NY 10016
Co. E-mail: talk@digitalundivided.com
URL: http://digitalundivided.com
Contact: Rodrigo Zavala, President
Facebook: www.facebook.com/digitalundivided
Linkedin: www.linkedin.com/company/digitalundivided
X (Twitter): x.com/digundiv
Instagram: www.instagram.com/digitalundivided

Description: Assists Black and Latino women entrepreneurs with venture funding and providing opportunities via innovation and technology. **Founded:** 2012.

35595 ■ The Educational Foundation for Women in Accounting (EFWA)

151 W 4th St., Ste. 222
Cincinnati, OH 45202
Ph: (937)424-3391
Co. E-mail: info@efwa.org
URL: http://www.efwa.org
Contact: Alexandra Miller, President
E-mail: alex@alexmiller-cpa.com

Description: Supports the advancement of women in the accounting profession through funding of education, research, career literature, publications, and other projects. **Founded:** 1966. **Publications:** *The Educator* (Semiannual). **Awards:** Women In Transition Scholarship (Annual); Women In Need Scholarships (Annual); Moss Adams Foundation Scholarship (Annual); Michele L. McDonald Memorial Scholarship (Annual); Rhonda J.B. O'Leary Memorial Scholarship (Annual); EFWA Postgraduate Scholarships (Annual). **Geographic Preference:** National.

35596 ■ eWomenNetwork

14900 Landmark Blvd., Ste. 540
Dallas, TX 75254
Ph: (972)620-9995
Co. E-mail: info@ewomennetwork.com
URL: http://www.ewomennetwork.com
Contact: Sandra Yancey, Chief Executive Officer
Facebook: www.facebook.com/ewomennetwork
Linkedin: www.linkedin.com/company/ewomennetwork
X (Twitter): x.com/eWomenNetwork
YouTube: www.youtube.com/c/eWomenNetwork

Description: Strives to connect and promote female entrepreneurs and their businesses worldwide. Provides members with such resources as networking opportunities, marketing, coaching, events, podcasts, speaking engagements, scholarships, grants, and video production to help grow their businesses. Embraces the mission to "help one million women entrepreneurs each achieve one million dollars in annual revenue.". **Founded:** 2000.

35597 ■ eWomenNetwork - Birmingham Chapter

Birmingham, AL
URL: http://www.ewomennetwork.com/chapters/birmingham-668

Description: Strives to connect and promote female entrepreneurs and their businesses worldwide. Provides members with such resources as networking opportunities, marketing, coaching, events, podcasts, speaking engagements, scholarships, grants, and video production to help grow their businesses.

35598 ■ eWomenNetwork - Boca Raton Chapter

Boca Raton, FL
URL: http://www.ewomennetwork.com/chapters/621

Description: Strives to connect and promote female entrepreneurs and their businesses worldwide. Provides members with such resources as networking opportunities, marketing, coaching, events, podcasts, speaking engagements, scholarships, grants, and video production to help grow their businesses.

35599 ■ eWomenNetwork - Calabasas Chapter

Calabasas, CA
URL: http://www.ewomennetwork.com/chapters/calabasas-665
Contact: Julie Kraschinsky, Managing Director
E-mail: juliekraschinsky@ewomennetwork.com
Facebook: www.facebook.com/ewncalabasas

Description: Strives to connect and promote female entrepreneurs and their businesses worldwide. Provides members with such resources as networking opportunities, marketing, coaching, events, podcasts, speaking engagements, scholarships, grants, and video production to help grow their businesses.

35600 ■ eWomenNetwork - Colorado Springs Chapter

c/o Brenda Layton
  Managing Director
  Colorado Springs, CO
Ph: (719)661-7483
Co. E-mail: brendalayton@ewomennetwork.com
URL: http://www.ewomennetwork.com/chapters/colorado-springs-513
Contact: Brenda Layton, Manager Director
E-mail: brendalayton@ewomennetwork.com
Facebook: www.facebook.com/ewncoloradosprings

Description: Strives to connect and promote female entrepreneurs and their businesses worldwide. Provides members with such resources as networking opportunities, marketing, coaching, events, podcasts, speaking engagements, scholarships, grants, and video production to help grow their businesses.

35601 ■ eWomenNetwork - Denver Chapter

c/o Renee Vejvoda, Managing Director
  Denver, CO
Ph: (720)840-4001
Co. E-mail: reneevejvoda@ewomennetwork.com
URL: http://www.ewomennetwork.com/chapters/denver-654
Contact: Abbey Harrison, Contact
E-mail: abbey@assistforthewin.com
Facebook: www.facebook.com/ewndenver

35602 ■ eWomenNetwork - Ft. Lauderdale Chapter

Fort Lauderdale, FL
URL: http://www.ewomennetwork.com/chapters/ft-lauderdale-515
Contact: Aigerim Kuanysh, Contact
Facebook: www.facebook.com/eWNFtLauderdaleMiami

Description: Strives to connect and promote female entrepreneurs and their businesses worldwide. Provides members with such resources as networking opportunities, marketing, coaching, events, podcasts, speaking engagements, scholarships, grants, and video production to help grow their businesses.

35603 ■ eWomenNetwork - Fresno Chapter

Fresno, CA
URL: http://www.ewomennetwork.com/chapters/fresno-608
Contact: Alison Haugan, Contact

Description: Strives to connect and promote female entrepreneurs and their businesses worldwide. Provides members with such resources as networking opportunities, marketing, coaching, events, podcasts, speaking engagements, scholarships, grants, and video production to help grow their businesses.

35604 ■ eWomenNetwork - Greater Hartford Chapter

Hartford, CT
Ph: (860)227-3054
URL: http://ewomennetwork.com/chapters/greater-hartford-673
Contact: Aina Hoskins, Executive Director
E-mail: ainahoskins@ewomennetwork.com

Description: Strives to connect and promote female entrepreneurs and their businesses worldwide. Provides members with such resources as networking opportunities, marketing, coaching, events, podcasts, speaking engagements, scholarships, grants, and video production to help grow their businesses.

35605 ■ eWomenNetwork - Jacksonville Chapter

Jacksonville, FL
URL: http://www.ewomennetwork.com/chapters/625
Contact: Rebecca Sullivan, Managing Director
E-mail: rebeccasullivan@ewomennetwork.com

Description: Strives to connect and promote female entrepreneurs and their businesses worldwide. Provides members with such resources as networking opportunities, marketing, coaching, events, podcasts, speaking engagements, scholarships, grants, and video production to help grow their businesses.

35606 ■ eWomenNetwork - Ladera Heights Chapter

Ladera Heights, CA
URL: http://www.ewomennetwork.com/chapters/ladera-heights-675
Contact: Melanie Mack, Member

Description: Strives to connect and promote female entrepreneurs and their businesses worldwide. Provides members with such resources as network-

ing opportunities, marketing, coaching, events, podcasts, speaking engagements, scholarships, grants, and video production to help grow their businesses.

35607 ■ eWomenNetwork - Los Angeles Chapter

Los Angeles, CA 90022
Ph: (213)296-4448
URL: http://www.ewomennetwork.com/chapters/los-angeles-588
Contact: Johnell McCauley, Director
E-mail: johnellmccauley@ewomennetwork.com
Facebook: www.facebook.com/ewnlosangeles

Description: Strives to connect and promote female entrepreneurs and their businesses worldwide. Provides members with such resources as networking opportunities, marketing, coaching, events, podcasts, speaking engagements, scholarships, grants, and video production to help grow their businesses.

35608 ■ eWomenNetwork - Miami Chapter

Miami, FL
URL: http://www.ewomennetwork.com/chapters/miami-534

Description: Strives to connect and promote female entrepreneurs and their businesses worldwide. Provides members with such resources as networking opportunities, marketing, coaching, events, podcasts, speaking engagements, scholarships, grants, and video production to help grow their businesses.

35609 ■ eWomenNetwork - Palo Alto Chapter

Palo Alto, CA
URL: http://www.ewomennetwork.com/chapters/543

Description: Strives to connect and promote female entrepreneurs and their businesses worldwide. Provides members with such resources as networking opportunities, marketing, coaching, events, podcasts, speaking engagements, scholarships, grants, and video production to help grow their businesses.

35610 ■ eWomenNetwork - Phoenix/ Scottsdale Chapter

Phoenix, AZ
URL: http://www.ewomennetwork.com/chapters/phoenix-scottsdale-511
Contact: Veronica Bahn, Managing Director
E-mail: veronicabahn@ewomennetwork.com

Description: Strives to connect and promote female entrepreneurs and their businesses worldwide. Provides members with such resources as networking opportunities, marketing, coaching, events, podcasts, speaking engagements, scholarships, grants, and video production to help grow their businesses.

35611 ■ eWomenNetwork - Sacramento Chapter

Sacramento, CA
URL: http://www.ewomennetwork.com/chapters/sacramento-661
Contact: Janet Fish, Managing Director
E-mail: janetfish@ewomennetwork.com

Description: Strives to connect and promote female entrepreneurs and their businesses worldwide. Provides members with such resources as networking opportunities, marketing, coaching, events, podcasts, speaking engagements, scholarships, grants, and video production to help grow their businesses.

35612 ■ eWomenNetwork - San Diego Chapter

San Diego, CA
URL: http://www.ewomennetwork.com/chapters/san-diego-512
Contact: Jenny Harkleroad, Managing Director
E-mail: jennyharkleroad@ewomennetwork.com

Description: Strives to connect and promote female entrepreneurs and their businesses worldwide. Provides members with such resources as networking opportunities, marketing, coaching, events, podcasts, speaking engagements, scholarships, grants, and video production to help grow their businesses.

35613 ■ eWomenNetwork - San Jose Chapter
San Jose, CA
URL: http://www.ewomennetwork.com/chapters/540
Description: Strives to connect and promote female entrepreneurs and their businesses worldwide. Provides members with such resources as networking opportunities, marketing, coaching, events, podcasts, speaking engagements, scholarships, grants, and video production to help grow their businesses.

35614 ■ eWomenNetwork - Tucson Chapter
Tucson, AZ
URL: http://www.ewomennetwork.com/chapters/tucson-581
Contact: Carol Johnson, Manager Director
E-mail: caroljohnson@ewomennetwork.com
Description: Strives to connect and promote female entrepreneurs and their businesses worldwide. Provides members with such resources as networking opportunities, marketing, coaching, events, podcasts, speaking engagements, scholarships, grants, and video production to help grow their businesses.

35615 ■ eWomenNetwork - Washington D.C. Metro Chapter
Washington, DC
URL: http://www.ewomennetwork.com/chapters/washington-dc-metro-728
Contact: Johnell McCauley, Director
E-mail: johnellmccauley@ewomennetwork.com
Description: Strives to connect and promote female entrepreneurs and their businesses worldwide. Provides members with such resources as networking opportunities, marketing, coaching, events, podcasts, speaking engagements, scholarships, grants, and video production to help grow their businesses.

35616 ■ eWomenNetwork - Wilmington Chapter
Wilmington, DE
URL: http://www.ewomennetwork.com/chapters/wilmington-640
Contact: Susan Salter, Managing Director
E-mail: susansalter@ewomennetwork.com
Description: Strives to connect and promote female entrepreneurs and their businesses worldwide. Provides members with such resources as networking opportunities, marketing, coaching, events, podcasts, speaking engagements, scholarships, grants, and video production to help grow their businesses.

35617 ■ Female Entrepreneur Association (FEA)
Carrie & Co.
29a Alderley Rd.
Wilmslow SK9 1HY, United Kingdom
Ph: 44 845 164 5000
Co. E-mail: info@femaleentrepreneurassociation.com
URL: http://femaleentrepreneurassociation.com
Contact: Carrie Green, Founder
Facebook: www.facebook.com/FemaleEntrepreneurAssociation
Pinterest: www.pinterest.co.uk/iamcarriegreen
Description: An international online association with the mission of "inspiring and empowering women from around the world to turn their ideas into a reality, build successful businesses and live a life they love. " Offers weekly inspirational videos, online masterclasses on business topics, and an online networking club for members. **Founded:** 2011. **Publications:** *This Girl Means Business* (Irregular).

35618 ■ Financial Women's Association (FWA)
580 Fifth Ave., Ste. 820
New York, NY 10036
Ph: (212)533-2141

Co. E-mail: fwaoffice@fwa.org
URL: http://www.fwa.org
Contact: Annette Stewart, President
Facebook: www.facebook.com/fwany1956
Linkedin: www.linkedin.com/company/financial-women's-association
X (Twitter): x.com/FWANY
Instagram: www.instagram.com/fwanyc
Description: Promotes the professional development and advancement of all women through education, mentorship, scholarships, networking, and alliances across the financial community. **Founded:** 1956.

35619 ■ Forum for Women Entrepreneurs (FWE)
Room 203, 1961 E
Vancouver, BC, Canada V6T 1Z1
Ph: (604)682-8115
Co. E-mail: info@fwe.ca
URL: http://sba.ubc.ca/forum-women-entrepreneurs-british-columbia-fwe
Description: Strives to energize, educate, mentor, and connect female entrepreneurs in Canada. **Founded:** 2002.

35620 ■ Founders First Capital Partners (FFCP)
9920 Pacific Heights Blvd., Ste. 430
San Diego, CA 92121
Ph: (858)264-4102
Co. E-mail: info@f1stcp.com
URL: http://foundersfirstcapitalpartners.com
Contact: Kim T. Folsom, Chief Executive Officer
Facebook: www.facebook.com/f1stcp
Linkedin: www.linkedin.com/company/founders-first-capital-partners
X (Twitter): x.com/f1stcp
Instagram: www.instagram.com/f1stcp
YouTube: www.youtube.com/channel/UCa dqC8UNVFH0c_6NBdkE-hA
Description: Venture capital firm providing support to startup companies owned by minorities, women, and military veterans. **Founded:** 2015.

35621 ■ Greater Londonderry Business and Professional Women
PO Box 448
Londonderry, NH 03053
Co. E-mail: info@bpwlondonderry.com
URL: http://www.bpwlondonderry.com
Contact: Kristal Diorio, President
Facebook: www.facebook.com/bpwgreaterlondonderry
Description: Represents the interests of business and professional women. Elevates the standards for women in business and professional settings. Promotes equity for all women in the workplace through advocacy, education and information. Provides professional development, networking and career advancement opportunities for working women. **Founded:** 1991. **Geographic Preference:** Local.

35622 ■ Healthcare Businesswomen's Association (HBA)
Bldg. E, Ste. 215
373 Rte. 46 W
Fairfield, NJ 07004
Ph: (973)575-0606
Fax: (973)575-1445
Co. E-mail: info@hbanet.org
URL: http://www.hbanet.org
Contact: Susan M. O'Connor, Chief Executive Officer
E-mail: soconnor@hbanet.org
Facebook: www.facebook.com/HBAnet
X (Twitter): x.com/HBAnet
Instagram: www.instagram.com/hbaimpact
YouTube: www.youtube.com/user/HBAnet
Description: Aims to raise the profile of women as business and thought leaders in healthcare. Facilitates networking forums and offers educational programs to its members. **Founded:** 1977. **Geographic Preference:** Multinational.

35623 ■ Humble Ventures
Washington, DC
URL: http://humble.vc
Contact: Ajit Verghese, Co-Founder

X (Twitter): x.com/humbleventures
Description: Venture capital firm focusing on startup businesses owned by women and minority groups.

35624 ■ Indian American Women Entrepreneurs Association (IAWEA)
1802 Oak Tree Rd.
Edison, NJ 08820
Ph: (347)687-4207
Co. E-mail: info@iawea.net
URL: http://www.iawea.us
Contact: Dr. Nimisha Shukla, Founder
Facebook: www.facebook.com/iaweausa
Linkedin: www.linkedin.com/in/iaweausa
X (Twitter): x.com/iaweausa
Instagram: www.instagram.com/iawea_usa
YouTube: www.youtube.com/channel/UC1kkDJ 2RCKqdctTpallkcwA
Description: Strives to empower Indian American women entrepreneurs and business owners by providing a support network via member interaction and networking events; connecting members with sources of funding for business initiation and expansion; instilling confidence and ownership of accomplishments among members; and changing perceptions and defying social expectations regarding the role of women in the world.

35625 ■ Indiana Business and Professional Women's Club
PO Box 1165
Indiana, PA 15701
Co. E-mail: info@htmlstream.com
URL: http://www.bpwindianapa.org
Description: Represents the interests of business and professional women. Elevates the standards for women in business and professional settings. Promotes equity for all women in the workplace through advocacy, education and information. Provides professional development, networking and career advancement opportunities for working women. **Founded:** 1935. **Geographic Preference:** Local; State.

35626 ■ Jackson Business and Professional Women
PO Box 1020
Jackson, MI 49204
URL: http://jacksonbpw.org
Contact: Robin Vafiadis, President
Description: Represents the interests of business and professional women. Elevates the standards for women in business and professional settings. Promotes equity for all women in the workplace through advocacy, education and information. Provides professional development, networking and career advancement opportunities for working women. **Founded:** 1919. **Geographic Preference:** Local.

35627 ■ Michigan Association for Female Entrepreneurs (MAFE)
12245 Beech Daly Rd.
Redford, MI 48240
Free: 844-490-6233
Co. E-mail: info@mafedetroit.org
URL: http://www.mafedetroit.org
Facebook: www.facebook.com/mafedetroit
X (Twitter): x.com/mafedetroit
YouTube: www.youtube.com/channel/UCSYFKC 3ISegABtsjMQlqXDg
Description: Fosters economic growth of women-owned businesses. Provides a platform for the exchange of information and ideas through networking events, educational workshops and seminars, entrepreneurial training programs, and business support services. Encourages peer-to-peer support for women business owners in a diverse and positive atmosphere. **Founded:** 2003. **Geographic Preference:** State.

35628 ■ Michigan Federation of Business and Professional Women's Clubs (BPW/MI)
1372 W Liberty Rd.
Clarklake, MI 49234
Co. E-mail: bpw.michigan@gmail.com
URL: http://bpw-michigan.org
Contact: Jodi Snyder, Vice President

E-mail: jsnyder@acrolegal.com

X (Twitter): x.com/BPWMichigan

Description: Achieves equity for all women in the workplace through advocacy, education and information. **Founded:** 1919. **Geographic Preference:** State.

35629 ■ Minnesota Business and Professional Women, Inc. (MFBPW) [Minnesota Federation of Business and Professional Women's Clubs, Inc.; Minnesota Business Women]

c/o Faye Crane, Treasurer
1235 S Pokegama Ave.
Grand Rapids, MN 55744-3551

Co. E-mail: info@mnbusinesswomen.org

URL: http://www.mnbusinesswomen.org

Description: Represents the interests of business and professional women. Elevates the standards for women in business and professional settings. Promotes equity for all women in the workplace through advocacy, education and information. Provides professional development, networking and career advancement opportunities for working women. **Founded:** 1920. **Geographic Preference:** State.

35630 ■ National Association of Black Women in Construction, Inc. (NABWIC)

c/o Ann McNeill, Founder
6600 NW 27th Ave. No. 208
Haverhill, FL 33417

URL: http://nabwic.org

Description: Promotes the advancement of black women in the construction industry. Supports aspiring construction executives. Provides advocacy, mentorship and professional development for its members. **Founded:** 1991. **Geographic Preference:** National.

35631 ■ National Association of Christian Women Entrepreneurs (NACWE)

PO Box 1244
McKinney, TX 75070

Ph: (214)491-1991

Co. E-mail: info@nacwe.org

URL: http://nacwe.org

Contact: Heather Rosson, President

Facebook: www.facebook.com/NACWE

Instagram: www.instagram.com/nacwesisters

YouTube: www.youtube.com/channel/UCP8Pp2CCs 5cRcnbJNpmICEQ

Pinterest: www.pinterest.com/NewNACWE

Description: Represents Christian women entrepreneurs in the U.S. and Canada. Engages women entrepreneurs to practice good business ethics. **Founded:** 2010. **Geographic Preference:** Multinational.

35632 ■ National Association for Female Executives (NAFE)

New York, NY

Co. E-mail: lauren.macri@workingmother.com

URL: http://www.workingmother.com/nafe

Contact: Dr. Betty Spence, President

Description: Provides resources and services through education, networking and public advocacy to empower members to achieve career success and financial security. **Founded:** 1972. **Publications:** *NAFE E-Newsletter* (Weekly (Thurs.)); *Executive Female* (Bimonthly). **Geographic Preference:** National.

35633 ■ National Association of Negro Business and Professional Women's Clubs, Inc. (NANBPWC)

1806 New Hampshire Ave. NW
Washington, DC 20009

Ph: (202)483-4206

Fax: (202)462-7253

Co. E-mail: info@nanbpwc.org

URL: http://nanbpwc.org

Contact: Robin Waley, Executive Director

E-mail: executivedirector@nanbpwc.com

Facebook: www.facebook.com/NANBPWC

X (Twitter): x.com/NANBPWC

Instagram: www.instagram.com/nanbpwc

Description: African American women actively engaged in a business or a profession who are committed to rendering service through club programs and activities. Seeks to direct the interest of business and professional women toward united action for improved social and civic conditions, and to provide enriching and ennobling experiences that will encourage freedom, dignity, self-respect, and self-reliance. Offers information and help regarding education, employment, health, housing, legislation, and problems of the aged and the disabled. Sponsors educational assistance program, which includes local and national scholarships. Conducts consumer education and prison reform programs. Maintains youth department clubs. Provides placement services; operates speakers' bureau; compiles statistics. **Founded:** 1935. **Awards:** Dr. Julianne Malveaux Scholarship (Annual); The Dr. Blanca Moore-Velez Woman of Substance Scholarship (Annual); NANBPWC National Scholarship (Annual). **Geographic Preference:** National.

35634 ■ The National Association of Railway Business Women (NARBW)

367 Hinsdale Dr.
Debary, FL 32713

URL: http://www.narbw.org

Contact: Ida Carmouche, President

X (Twitter): x.com/narbw

YouTube: www.youtube.com/narbw

Description: Women who work for railroads. Stimulates interest in the railroad industry. Fosters cooperation and understanding among members and people in related fields; promote good public relations for the railroad industry. Further the educational, social and professional interests of members. Conducts charitable, benevolent, educational, children's service, and social welfare projects. Maintains a residence for retired members at Green Valley, AZ. **Founded:** 1921. **Geographic Preference:** National.

35635 ■ National Association of Women Business Owners (NAWBO)

601 Pennsylvania Ave. NW
S Building, Ste. 900
Washington, DC 20004

Free: 800-556-2926

Fax: (202)403-3788

URL: http://www.nawbo.org

Contact: Ellen Linares, Chairman

Facebook: www.facebook.com/NAWBO

Linkedin: www.linkedin.com/company/nawbo

X (Twitter): x.com/NAWBONational

Instagram: www.instagram.com/nawbonational

YouTube: www.youtube.com/user/nawbonat

Description: Represents and promotes women-owned businesses to shape economic and public policy. **Founded:** 1975. **Educational Activities:** Public Policy Days; National Women's Business Conference (Annual). **Awards:** Gillian Rudd Business Leadership Award (Annual); Susan Hager Legacy Award (Annual); NAWBO/Wells Fargo Trailblazer Award. **Geographic Preference:** National.

35636 ■ National Association of Women Business Owners Atlanta (NAWBO)

6300 Powers Ferry Rd., Ste. 600-247
Atlanta, GA 30339

URL: http://www.nawbo.org/atlanta

Contact: Littie Brown, President

Facebook: www.facebook.com/NAWBOAtlanta

X (Twitter): x.com/nawboatlanta

Description: Seeks to equip Atlanta-area female entrepreneurs and women-owned businesses through programs, training and education. **Founded:** 1975. **Geographic Preference:** Local.

35637 ■ National Association of Women Business Owners Baltimore Regional Chapter (NAWBO)

Baltimore, MD

URL: http://www.nawbo.org/baltimore-regional/par tners/affiliate

Geographic Preference: Local.

35638 ■ National Association of Women Business Owners Buffalo Niagara (NAWBO)

PO Box 1165
Orchard Park, NY 14127

Ph: (716)238-2461

Co. E-mail: info@nawbowny.org

URL: http://nawbowny.org

Contact: Andrea Schillaci, President

Facebook: www.facebook.com/NAWBOWNY

X (Twitter): x.com/nawbowny

Pinterest: www.pinterest.com/nawbowny

Description: Represents and promotes women-owned businesses to shape economic and public policy. **Founded:** 1994. **Geographic Preference:** Local.

35639 ■ National Association of Women Business Owners Central Illinois

PO Box 9404
Peoria, IL 61612-9404

Ph: (309)692-2225

Co. E-mail: newsletter@.org

URL: http://nawbo-cil.org

Contact: Kathryn Spitznagle, President

Description: Represents and promotes women-owned businesses to shape economic and public policy. **Geographic Preference:** Local.

35640 ■ National Association of Women Business Owners Central Jersey

2560 US Hwy 22 No. 150
Scotch Plains, NJ 07076

Co. E-mail: nawbo.ncnj@gmail.com

URL: http://nawbo.org/chapters

Facebook: www.facebook.com/nawbonorthcentralnj

Instagram: www.instagram.com/nawbo_ncnj

Description: Represents and promotes women-owned businesses to shape economic and public policy. **Founded:** 1989. **Geographic Preference:** Local.

35641 ■ National Association of Women Business Owners Chicago [NAWBO Chicago]

4055 W Peterson Ave.
Chicago, IL 60646

Co. E-mail: info@nawbochicago.org

URL: http://www.nawbo.org/chicago

Contact: Elizabeth Colón, President

Facebook: www.facebook.com/nawbochicago

Linkedin: www.linkedin.com/company/nawbo-chicago

X (Twitter): x.com/nawbochicago

YouTube: www.youtube.com/user/NAWBOChicago

Description: Seeks to provide female business owners with leadership, education and networking opportunities. **Founded:** 1978. **Geographic Preference:** Local.

35642 ■ National Association of Women Business Owners Cleveland

321 Florence Rd.
Cleveland, OH 44140

Ph: (440)462-9201

Co. E-mail: info@nawbocleveland.org

URL: http://nawbocleveland.org

Contact: Janet Kendall Kendall White, President

E-mail: president@nawbocleveland.org

Facebook: www.facebook.com/NAWBOCleveland

Linkedin: www.linkedin.com/company/nawbo -cleveland

X (Twitter): x.com/NAWBOCle

Description: Represents and promotes women-owned businesses to shape economic and public policy. **Founded:** 1980. **Geographic Preference:** Local.

35643 ■ National Association of Women Business Owners Columbus Ohio

1201 Dublin Rd., Ste. 153
Columbus, OH 43215

Ph: (614)636-2926

Co. E-mail: info@nawbocolumbusohio.com

URL: http://nawbocolumbusohio.com

Contact: Arien Lawless, Manager

E-mail: arien@nawbocolumbusohio.com

Facebook: www.facebook.com/NawboColumbus

Linkedin: www.linkedin.com/company/nawbo -columbus

X (Twitter): x.com/nawbocolumbus
Instagram: www.instagram.com/nawbocbus
YouTube: www.youtube.com/user/
NAWBOColumbusOhio
Description: Represents and promotes women-owned businesses to shape economic and public policy. **Geographic Preference:** Local.

35644 ■ National Association of Women Business Owners Dallas/Ft. Worth (NAWBO)
10440 N Central Expy., Ste. 800
Dallas, TX 75231
Co. E-mail: dfw@nawbodfw.org
URL: http://www.nawbo.org/dallas-ft-worth
Contact: Teresa Hockett, Co-President
Facebook: www.facebook.com/NAWBODFW
X (Twitter): x.com/nawbodfw
Founded: 1985. **Geographic Preference:** Local.

35645 ■ National Association of Women Business Owners Delaware
PO Box 4657
Greenville, DE 19807-4657
URL: http://www.nawbo.org/delaware
Facebook: www.facebook.com/NawboDelaware
Description: Represents the interests of female entrepreneurs in the state of Delaware. Provides opportunities for members to share mutual experiences, exchange information, and develop business skills. **Geographic Preference:** State.

35646 ■ National Association of Women Business Owners - Greater Detroit Chapter (NAWBO-GDC)
26677 W 12 Mile Rd.
Southfield, MI 48034
Ph: (313)961-4748
Co. E-mail: admin@nawbogdc.org
URL: http://www.nawbogdc.org
Contact: Nicole Lewis, President
E-mail: nicole@nicolelewisandassociates.com
Facebook: www.facebook.com/NAWBOgdc
Linkedin: www.linkedin.com/company/nawbogdc
X (Twitter): x.com/nawbogdc
Instagram: www.instagram.com/nawbogdc
Description: Women business owners and corporate partners seeking networking opportunities, educational seminars, political and economic influence through an organization with a national presence. **Founded:** 1980. **Publications:** *Vision.* **Educational Activities:** Salute to African American Women Business Owners. **Awards:** NAWBO Top 10 Michigan Business Women Awards - Diversity Champion Award (Irregular); NAWBO Top 10 Michigan Business Women Awards - Giving Spirit Award (Irregular); NAWBO Top 10 Michigan Business Women Awards - Global Business Award (Annual); NAWBO Top 10 Michigan Business Women Awards - Pinnacle Award (Irregular); NAWBO Top 10 Michigan Business Women Awards - Rainmaker Award (Annual); NAWBO Top 10 Michigan Business Women Awards - Red-Tape Buster Award (Annual); NAWBO Top 10 Michigan Business Women Awards - Up-and-Coming Award (Annual); NAWBO Top 10 Michigan Business Women Awards - Warrior Award (Annual); NAWBO Top 10 Michigan Business Women Awards - Words of Wisdom Award (Annual); NAWBO Top 10 Michigan Business Women Awards - Greater Good Award (Irregular); NAWBO Top 10 Michigan Business Women Awards - Breakthrough Award (Annual). **Geographic Preference:** Local.

35647 ■ National Association of Women Business Owners - Greater Philadelphia Chapter (NAWBO)
1231 Highland Ave.
Fort Washington, PA 19034
Ph: (215)628-9844
Co. E-mail: info@nawbophiladelphia.org
URL: http://www.nawbophiladelphia.org
Contact: Angela Megasko, President
E-mail: angela@marketviewpoint.com
Facebook: www.facebook.com/NAWBOPhiladelphia
Linkedin: www.linkedin.com/company/nawbo-phila delphia
X (Twitter): x.com/nawbophilly

Instagram: www.instagram.com/nawbophilly
YouTube: www.youtube.com/channel/UCo_9SzSDS 3yBE7slw3M4JRg
Founded: 1983. **Geographic Preference:** Local.

35648 ■ National Association of Women Business Owners Houston
8080 Main St.
Houston, TX 77025
Ph: (832)408-1594
Co. E-mail: administrative@nawbohouston.org
URL: http://nawbohouston.org
Contact: Badra Andrews, President
E-mail: badra@thebougainvilleasrooms.com
Facebook: www.facebook.com/nawbohouston
Linkedin: www.linkedin.com/company/nawbohouston
X (Twitter): x.com/NAWBOHoustonTX
Instagram: www.instagram.com/nawbohoustontx
Description: Represents and promotes women-owned businesses to shape economic and public policy. **Geographic Preference:** Local.

35649 ■ National Association of Women Business Owners - Indianapolis (NAWBO)
101 W Ohio St., Ste. 1580
Indianapolis, IN 46204
Ph: (317)608-0250
Co. E-mail: info@nawboindy.org
URL: http://www.nawboindy.org
Contact: Anne Hathaway, President
Facebook: www.facebook.com/NAWBOIndianapolis
Linkedin: www.linkedin.com/company/nawbo-in dianapolis
X (Twitter): x.com/nawboindy
Description: Represents the interests of all women business owner. **Founded:** 1997. **Geographic Preference:** Local; Regional.

35650 ■ National Association of Women Business Owners - Lexington
3100 Tates Creek Rd.
Lexington, KY 40502
URL: http://nawbokentucky.org
Description: Represents and promotes women-owned businesses to shape economic and public policy. **Geographic Preference:** Local.

35651 ■ National Association of Women Business Owners Los Angeles (NAWBO-LA)
4500 Pk. Granada Ste. 202
Calabasas, CA 91302
URL: http://nawbola.org
Contact: Renee Young, President
Facebook: www.facebook.com/NAWBOLA
Linkedin: www.linkedin.com/company/nawbo-la
X (Twitter): x.com/nawbola
Description: Empowers women entrepreneurs into economic, social and political spheres of leadership by: strengthening the wealth creating capacity of members and promoting economic development within the entrepreneurial community creating innovative and effective changes in the business culture building strategic alliances, coalitions and affiliations transforming public policy and influencing opinion makers. **Founded:** 1979. **Awards:** NAWBO-LA Advocate of the Year Award (Annual); NAWBO-LA Hall of Fame (Annual); NAWBO-LA Rising Star of the Year (Annual); NAWBO-LA Trailblazer of the Year (Annual); Women Business Owner of the Year (Annual). **Geographic Preference:** Local.

35652 ■ National Association of Women Business Owners Miami
1825 Ponce de Leon Blvd., No. 113
Coral Gables, FL 33134
Ph: (407)921-6148
Co. E-mail: nawbomiami@nawbomiami.org
URL: http://nawbomiami.clubexpress.com
Contact: Alma Kadragic, President
Description: Represents and promotes women-owned businesses to shape economic and public policy. **Geographic Preference:** Local.

35653 ■ National Association of Women Business Owners Minnesota (NAWBO-MN)
16526 W 78th St., Ste. 168
Eden Prairie, MN 55346

Ph: (612)326-7772
Co. E-mail: info@nawbo-mn.org
URL: http://www.nawbo.org/minnesota
Contact: Julie Kimble, President
X (Twitter): x.com/NAWBOMN
YouTube: www.youtube.com/channel/ UC09SxFG8Drfx0pPWc4EDTyg
Description: Supports female business owners in Minnesota through education, networking, and resources. **Geographic Preference:** State.

35654 ■ National Association of Women Business Owners Nashville (NAWBO)
2817 W End Ave., No. 126-219
Nashville, TN 37203-1453
Co. E-mail: info@nashvillenawbo.com
URL: http://nashvillenawbo.org
Contact: Paris Love, President
Facebook: www.facebook.com/NashvilleNAWBO
Linkedin: www.linkedin.com/company/nawbo -nashville
X (Twitter): x.com/NashvilleNAWBO
Instagram: www.instagram.com/nashvillenawbo
Description: Represents and promotes women-owned businesses to shape economic and public policy. **Geographic Preference:** Local.

35655 ■ National Association of Women Business Owners New York City (NAWBO-NYC)
244 Fifth Ave., 2nd Fl., Ste. D60
New York, NY 10001
Free: 800-348-0489
Co. E-mail: info@nawbonyc.org
URL: http://www.nawbonyc.org
Contact: Jasmine Sandler, President
E-mail: president@nawbonyc.org
Facebook: www.facebook.com/NAWBONYC
Linkedin: www.linkedin.com/company/nawbo-nyc
X (Twitter): x.com/nawbonyc
Instagram: www.instagram.com/nawbonyc
YouTube: www.youtube.com/channel/UCMKK 1QKKBrIFjiSEiiFoiDg
Description: Inspires and empowers women business owners and promotes and supports the growth of woman owned businesses. As a unified voice, it affects social, political and economic change. Its members are from almost every state and represent most industries and share common interests and concerns. Chapter membership's give you access to local monthly meetings, seminars and a network of women entrepreneurs who can provide information, advice, resources and referrals. Additionally, the organization is represented in more than 50 countries throughout the world by way of its affiliations and alliances. **Founded:** 1985. **Geographic Preference:** Local.

35656 ■ National Association of Women Business Owners - Northern New Mexico
PO Box 30887
Albuquerque, NM 87121
Ph: (505)400-1857
Co. E-mail: communications@nawbonm.org
URL: http://www.nawbonm.org
Contact: Yvonne Wilson, President
Facebook: www.facebook.com/nawbonm
Linkedin: www.linkedin.com/company/nawbo-new -mexico
X (Twitter): x.com/nawbonm
Instagram: www.instagram.com/nawbonm
YouTube: www.youtube.com/channel/UCJaq4CHq 3lPm_fw7bcxl_ZA
Description: Dedicated to the growth and development of all women-owned businesses. **Founded:** 1993. **Publications:** *NAWBO News.* **Geographic Preference:** Local.

35657 ■ National Association of Women Business Owners Orange County (NAWBO-OC)
231 E Alessandro, No. A650
Riverside, CA 92508
Ph: (626)510-4085
Co. E-mail: info@nawbooc.biz
URL: http://nawbooc.biz

Contact: Melissa Northway, President
Facebook: www.facebook.com/Nawbooc
X (Twitter): x.com/nawbooc
Instagram: www.instagram.com/nawbooc
Description: Represents the issues and interests female business owners in Orange County, California. **Founded:** 1991. **Geographic Preference:** Local.

35658 ■ National Association of Women Business Owners Phoenix Metro Chapter
4677 S Lakeshore Dr., Ste. 1
  Tempe, AZ 85282
Ph: (480)289-5768
Co. E-mail: info@nawbophx.org
URL: http://www.nawbo.org/phoenix
Contact: Mary Nutting, Co-President
Facebook: www.facebook.com/NAWBOPhx
X (Twitter): x.com/NAWBOphx
YouTube: www.youtube.com/channel/UC
  3J7f8JiLMmxOc1rliMYr5w
Founded: 1985. **Geographic Preference:** Local.

35659 ■ National Association of Women Business Owners Richmond
PO Box 73201
  North Chesterfield, VA 23235
Ph: (804)510-8560
Co. E-mail: info@nawborichmond.org
URL: http://nawborichmond.org
Contact: Lee Ann Pond, Member
E-mail: lee.ann.pond@engaging-leadership.com
Facebook: www.facebook.com/nawborichmond
YouTube: www.youtube.com/channel/UCywbZ
  -Nix0PXK_ioSUSBp6Q
Description: Represents and promotes women-owned businesses to shape economic and public policy. **Founded:** 1982. **Geographic Preference:** Local.

35660 ■ National Association of Women Business Owners Sacramento Valley
PO Box 189222
  Sacramento, CA 95818
Ph: (916)538-4249
Co. E-mail: info@nawbo-sac.org
URL: http://nawbo-sac.org
Contact: Liliana Bernal, Co-President
Facebook: www.facebook.com/NAWBOSacramento
Linkedin: www.linkedin.com/company/nawbo
  ---sacramento-valley
X (Twitter): x.com/NAWBOsac
Instagram: www.instagram.com/nawbosacramento
Description: Represents and promotes women-owned businesses to shape economic and public policy. **Founded:** 1975. **Geographic Preference:** Local.

35661 ■ National Association of Women Business Owners San Diego
PO Box 880263
  San Diego, CA 92168
Free: 877-866-2926
Co. E-mail: nawbosd@sandiegositepros.com
URL: http://www.nawbo.org/san-diego
Contact: Nichole MacDonald, President
URL(s): www.nawbo.org/california/chapter-about/
  about-nawbo-ca
Facebook: www.facebook.com/NAWBOSanDiego
X (Twitter): twitter.com/NAWBOSanDiego
Founded: 1991. **Geographic Preference:** Local.

35662 ■ National Association of Women Business Owners Sedona-Verde Valley
PO Box 2090
  Sedona, AZ 86339
Ph: (928)301-8288
URL: http://www.nawbo.org/sedona-verde-valley
Facebook: www.facebook.com/NAWBOsvv
X (Twitter): x.com/nawbosvv
Description: Represents and promotes women-owned businesses to shape economic and public policy. **Geographic Preference:** Local.

35663 ■ National Association of Women Business Owners Silicon Valley (NAWBOSV)
PO Box 2696
  Santa Clara, CA 95055-2696

Ph: (408)657-7190
Co. E-mail: info@nawbo-sv.org
URL: http://www.nawbo-sv.org
Contact: Griselda Quezada-Chavez, President
E-mail: president@nawbo-sv.org
Description: Seeks to support and empower female business owners in the Silicon Valley area. Organizes events that provide opportunities to network with other members, interact with corporate partners, develop business relationships, and learn about the latest trends and technologies for building a successful business. **Founded:** 1988. **Geographic Preference:** Local.

35664 ■ National Association of Women Business Owners South Jersey (NAWBO SJ)
PO Box 923
  Marlton, NJ 08053
Co. E-mail: info@nawbosouthjersey.org
URL: http://nawbosouthjersey.org
Contact: Denise Davis, President
Facebook: www.facebook.com/NAWBOSJ
X (Twitter): x.com/nawbosj
Instagram: www.instagram.com/nawbosj
YouTube: www.youtube.com/channel/UCV
  tBCneuaeVzmTuNr8rBKdw
Description: Represents and promotes women-owned businesses to shape economic and public policy. **Founded:** 2003. **Geographic Preference:** Local.

35665 ■ National Association of Women Business Owners Ventura County (NAWBO-VC)
355 N Lantana St., Ste. 449
  Camarillo, CA 93010
Free: 877-629-2682
Co. E-mail: contact@nawbovc.org
URL: http://www.nawbovc.org
Contact: Seana-Marie Sesma, President
Facebook: www.facebook.com/nawbovc
X (Twitter): x.com/NAWBOVC
Instagram: www.instagram.com/nawbovc
Description: Represents and promotes women-owned businesses to shape economic and public policy. **Awards:** NAWBO VC Community Advocate of the Year (Annual); NAWBO VC Education Advocate of the Year (Annual); NAWBO VC Member of the Year (Annual); NAWBO VC Corporate Leader/Partner of the Year (Annual); NAWBO VC Young Woman Entrepreneur (Annual); NAWBO Ventura County Woman Business Owner of the Year (Annual); NAWBO VC Visionary of the Year (Annual); NAWBO VC Innovator of the Year (Annual); NAWBO VC Rising Star of the Year (Annual). **Geographic Preference:** Local.

35666 ■ National Association of Women MBAs (NAWMBA)
PO Box 3425
  Bellevue, WA 98009
Co. E-mail: info@nawmbaseattle.org
URL: http://www.nawmbaseattle.org
Contact: Sylvia Fine, President
E-mail: sylvia@nawmbaseattle.org
Facebook: www.facebook.com/mbawiseattle
X (Twitter): x.com/nawmbaseattle
Instagram: www.instagram.com/nawmba_seattle
YouTube: www.youtube.com/channel/UCKq1KFYTS
  5Q-p9PzL3M7GfQ
Description: Provides networking opportunities for its members. Increases communication among graduate business schools regarding their initiatives to educate and support women in business. **Founded:** 1978. **Geographic Preference:** National.

35667 ■ National Association of Women Sales Professionals (NAWSP)
310 S Harrington St.
  Raleigh, NC 27603
Contact: Cynthia Barnes, Chief Executive Officer
Description: Seeks to provide career advancement, sales leadership, and networking opportunities to saleswomen throughout the United States. **Founded:** 2016.

35668 ■ National Latina Business Women Association (NLBWA)
1107 Fair Oaks Ave.
  South Pasadena, CA 91030
Co. E-mail: info@nlbwa-la.org
URL: http://www.nlbwa-la.org
Contact: Wendy Estrada, President
Facebook: www.facebook.com/NLBWALA
X (Twitter): x.com/NLBWALA
Instagram: www.instagram.com/nlbwala
YouTube: www.youtube.com/channel/UCN5W
  -t4KyLooVD6G_VLZumg
Description: Strives to promote, develop, and support the growth of Latina business owners and professionals. Seeks to create networking and mentoring opportunities for members. **Founded:** 2003. **Geographic Preference:** National.

35669 ■ Nebraska Business and Professional Women (NEBPW)
1703 Brenda Dr.
  Bellevue, NE 68005
Co. E-mail: gweber@neonramp.com
URL: http://nebpw.tripod.com/nebpw/id5.html
Contact: Gail Weger, President
E-mail: gweger@neonramp.com
Description: Represents the interests of business and professional women. Elevates the standards for women in business and professional settings. Promotes equity for all women in the workplace through advocacy, education and information. Provides professional development, networking and career advancement opportunities for working women. **Geographic Preference:** State.

35670 ■ New Jersey Association of Women Business Owners (NJAWBO)
PO Box 133
  Cedar Grove, NJ 07009
Ph: (609)308-2530
Co. E-mail: njawbo@njawbo.org
URL: http://www.njawbo.org
Contact: Bertha Robinson, President
Facebook: www.facebook.com/njawbo
Linkedin: www.linkedin.com/company/njawbo
X (Twitter): x.com/njawbo
Description: Supports and encourages business ownership by women. **Founded:** 1978. **Geographic Preference:** State.

35671 ■ Organization of Women in International Trade (OWIT)
1776 K St., N W, Ste., 200
  Washington, DC 20006
Co. E-mail: admin@owit.org
URL: http://owit.org
Contact: Frida Owinga, President
E-mail: president@owit.org
Facebook: www.facebook.com/OWITIntl
Linkedin: www.linkedin.com/company/organization-of
  -women-in-international-trade-owit-
X (Twitter): x.com/owitintl
Instagram: www.instagram.com/owit_intl
Description: Fosters international trade and the advancement of women in business. Offers educational programs, conventions and other activities to promote the employment of women in international trade. Facilitates networking and exchange of information and ideas among members. **Founded:** 1989. **Geographic Preference:** Local.

35672 ■ Pipeline Angels
1321 Upland Dr., Ste. 5167
  Houston, TX 77043
Co. E-mail: info@pipelineangels.com
URL: http://pipelineangels.com
Contact: Natalia Oberti Noguera, Chief Executive Officer
Facebook: www.facebook.com/PipelineAngels
Linkedin: www.linkedin.com/company/pipeline-angels
X (Twitter): x.com/PipelineAngels
Instagram: www.instagram.com/pipelineangels
YouTube: www.youtube.com/c/Pipelineangels
Pinterest: www.pinterest.com/pipelineangels

Description: Angel investment funding for women and non-binary femme social entrepreneurs. Offer angel investment bootcamp, networking, and educational opportunities. **Founded:** 2011.

35673 ■ Professional Businesswomen of California (PBWC)
2261 Market No. 1600
  San Francisco, CA 94114-1600
Ph: (415)857-2923
Co. E-mail: info@pbwc.org
URL: http://pbwc.org
Contact: Kathleen Brown, President
Facebook: www.facebook.com/officialPBWC
Linkedin: www.linkedin.com/company/pbwc
X (Twitter): x.com/pbwc
Instagram: www.instagram.com/officialpbwc
Description: Dedicated to the advancement of women in the workplace. Promotes professionals and personal growth for professional and businesswomen. Offers a program for high school girls to encourage them to pursue their dreams. **Founded:** 1989. **Publications:** *AFMRD News and Updates* (Quarterly). **Educational Activities:** Professional Businesswomen of California Conference (Annual). **Geographic Preference:** State.

35674 ■ Professional Women of St. Tammany (PWST)
PO Box 831
  Mandeville, LA 70470
Ph: (985)377-3602
Co. E-mail: hello@mypwst.com
URL: http://mypwst.com
Contact: Bailey Martin, President
Facebook: www.facebook.com/ProfessionalWomenStTammany
Linkedin: www.linkedin.com/company/professional-women-of-st-tammany
Description: Represents the interests of business and professional women. Elevates the standards for women in business and professional settings. Promotes equity for all women in the workplace through advocacy, education and information. Provides professional development, networking and career advancement opportunities for working women. **Founded:** 2009. **Geographic Preference:** Local.

35675 ■ Professional Women's Network (PWN)
PO Box 235076
  Honolulu, HI 96823
URL: http://www.pwnhawaii.org
Contact: Nancy Evans Evans Tudor, President
Description: Supports professional and businesswomen in Hawaii. Acts on the premise that mutual support is a necessary factor in bringing about personal growth and business success. **Founded:** 1978. **Awards:** PWN Alex Memorial Scholarship (Annual). **Geographic Preference:** State.

35676 ■ Texas Business and Professional Women's Foundation (TBPWF)
PO Box 70
  Round Rock, TX 78680-0070
Co. E-mail: tbpwf@tbwconnect.com
URL: http://www.texasbpwfoundation.org
Contact: Laura Whisenhunt, Secretary
Facebook: www.facebook.com/TBPWF
X (Twitter): x.com/TexasBPWFoundat
Description: Represents the interests of business and professional women. Elevates the standards for women in business and professional settings. Promotes equity for all women in the workplace through advocacy, education and information. Provides professional development, networking and career advancement opportunities for working women. **Founded:** 2001. **Geographic Preference:** Local.

35677 ■ TiE Women
3975 Freedom Cr., Ste. 230
  Santa Clara, CA 95054
Co. E-mail: info@women.tie.org
URL: http://tiewomen.org
Contact: Richa Naujoks, Contact
Facebook: www.facebook.com/Women.TiE
Linkedin: www.linkedin.com/company/women-tie

X (Twitter): x.com/women_tie
YouTube: www.youtube.com/user/TheTieNetwork
Description: Works to embrace, engage, and empower women entrepreneurs around the world.

35678 ■ United Nations Commission on the Status of Women (CSW)
220 E 42nd St.
  New York, NY 10017
URL: http://www.unwomen.org/en/csw
Description: Intergovernmental body focused on the social, economic, and legal status of women worldwide. Facilitates exchange on local, national, and global issues affecting women; gathers and disseminates information; adopts policy recommendations on gender equality and advancement by women. **Founded:** 1946. **Geographic Preference:** National.

35679 ■ Utah Business and Professional Women
PO Box 561
  Salt Lake City, UT 84110-0561
URL: http://bpwutahfoundation.org
Description: Represents the interests of business and professional women. Elevates the standards for women in business and professional settings. Promotes equity for all women in the workplace through advocacy, education and information. Provides professional development, networking and career advancement opportunities for working women. **Founded:** 1989. **Geographic Preference:** State.

35680 ■ Women Business Owners (WBO)
2311 N 45th St., No. 277
  Seattle, WA 98103
Ph: (206)575-3232
Co. E-mail: info@womenbusinessowners.org
URL: http://www.womenbusinessowners.org
Contact: Tracey Warren, President
Facebook: www.facebook.com/seattlewomenbusinessowners
Linkedin: www.linkedin.com/company/wbo-wa
Instagram: www.instagram.com/wbowwa
Description: Aims to empower, educate, and enhance the lives of children and women business owners throughout the world. Provides programs and workshops on educating future entrepreneurs. Works to develop and encourage entrepreneurship, achievement, and success in business. **Founded:** 2004. **Geographic Preference:** Multinational.

35681 ■ Women Business Owners Connection (WBOC)
4465 E Genesee St., No., 225
  Syracuse, NY 13214
Co. E-mail: info@wboconnection.org
URL: http://www.wboconnection.org
Facebook: www.facebook.com/wboconnection
Instagram: www.instagram.com/wboconnection
Description: Services: Organization that provides connections, education, support and inspiration for women in business.

35682 ■ Women Business Owners Network (WBON)
PO Box 173
  Williston, VT 05495
Ph: (802)503-0219
Co. E-mail: director@wbon.org
URL: http://wbon.org
Contact: Kelly Klein, Treasurer
Facebook: www.facebook.com/wbonvt
Linkedin: www.linkedin.com/company/wbon---women-business-owners-network
X (Twitter): x.com/wbonvt
Description: Offers the opportunity to learn from others and develop relationships. Members discuss problems and triumphs, share questions and resources, and receive advice from other women. **Founded:** 1983. **Geographic Preference:** State.

35683 ■ Women in Development of Greater Boston (WID)
22 Bates Rd., Ste. 224
  Mashpee, MA 02649
Ph: (617)489-6777
Co. E-mail: widgb@widgb.org

URL: http://www.widgb.org
Contact: Katie Quakenbush Spiegel, President
Facebook: www.facebook.com/WIDGB
Linkedin: www.linkedin.com/company/widgb
X (Twitter): x.com/WomeninDevBos
Instagram: www.instagram.com/womenindevbos
Description: Supports women professionals in the fields of development, philanthropy, and fund-raising. **Founded:** 1980.

35684 ■ Women in Development New York (WIDNY)
555 8th Ave., Ste. 1902
  New York, NY 10018
Ph: (212)265-7650
Co. E-mail: widny@widny.org
URL: http://widny.org
Contact: Yolanda F. Johnson, President
Linkedin: www.linkedin.com/company/women-in-development-new-york
X (Twitter): x.com/wid_ny
Instagram: www.instagram.com/wid_ny
Description: Allows women to connect and engage for their professional growth. **Founded:** 1980. **Geographic Preference:** Local.

35685 ■ Women in the Enterprise of Science and Technology (WEST)
1 Broadway, 14th Fl.
  Cambridge, MA 02142
Co. E-mail: info@westorg.org
URL: http://www.westorg.org/about-west
Contact: Karin von Hodenberg, President
X (Twitter): x.com/WESTorg
Description: Seeks to advance women in science and technology. Develops programs that cover issues that are relevant to the career and business issues in the diverse environments of life sciences, biotech, engineering, technology and research. Serves as a forum for men and women, educational institutions, service organizations and corporations. **Founded:** 2000. **Geographic Preference:** National.

35686 ■ Women Impacting Public Policy (WIPP)
PO Box 31279
  San Francisco, CA 94131
Ph: (415)434-4314
Free: 888-488-9477
Fax: (415)434-4331
Co. E-mail: info@wipp.org
URL: http://www.wipp.org
Contact: Candace Waterman, President
Facebook: www.facebook.com/WIPPWeDecide
Linkedin: www.linkedin.com/company/women-impacting-public-policy
X (Twitter): x.com/WIPPWeDecide
Description: Serves as an advocate for women to have a voice in the legislative processes and economic issues involving business matters. **Founded:** 2001. **Geographic Preference:** National.

35687 ■ Women's Business Development Center (WBDC)
8 S Michigan Ave., 4th Fl.
  Chicago, IL 60603
Ph: (312)853-3477
Free: 800-526-0857
Fax: (312)853-0145
Co. E-mail: wbdc@wbdc.org
URL: http://www.wbdc.org/en
Contact: Emilia Dimenco, President
E-mail: edimenco@wbdc.org
Facebook: www.facebook.com/thewbdc
Linkedin: www.linkedin.com/company/women's-business-development-center-chicago
X (Twitter): x.com/WBDC
YouTube: www.youtube.com/user/wbdc1
Description: Provides programs and services to support women's business ownership in Illinois, Iowa, Kansas, Minnesota, Missouri, Nebraska, North Dakota, South Dakota, and Wisconsin. Provides training, certification, technical assistance, and financial support. **Founded:** 1986.

35688 ■ Women's Business Enterprise Alliance (WBEA)
9800 NW Fwy., Ste. 120
Houston, TX 77092-8807
Ph: (713)681-9232
Fax: (713)681-9242
Co. E-mail: wbc@wbea-texas.org
URL: http://www.wbea-texas.org
Contact: Dr. April Day, President
E-mail: aday@wbea-texas.org
Facebook: www.facebook.com/TexasWBEA
Description: Works as third-party certifier of women's business enterprises. Fosters diversity in the world of commerce with programs and policies designed to expand opportunities and eliminate barriers in the marketplace for women business owners. **Founded:** 1995. **Geographic Preference:** Regional.

35689 ■ Women's Business Enterprise Council Pennsylvania - Delaware - South New Jersey
1315 Walnut St., Ste. 1116
Philadelphia, PA 19107
Ph: (215)790-9232
URL: http://wbeceast.com/about
Contact: Elizabeth Walsh, President
Description: Works as third-party certifier of women's business enterprises. Fosters diversity in the world of commerce with programs and policies designed to expand opportunities and eliminate barriers in the marketplace for women business owners. **Founded:** 2000. **Geographic Preference:** Regional.

35690 ■ Women's Business Enterprise Council South (WBEC)
401 Saint Joseph St., Ste. 100
New Orleans, LA 70130
Ph: (504)830-0149
Co. E-mail: info@wbecsouth.org
URL: http://www.wbecsouth.org
Contact: Phala K. Mire, President
E-mail: pkmire@wbecsouth.org
Facebook: www.facebook.com/WBECSouth
Linkedin: www.linkedin.com/company/wbecsouth
X (Twitter): x.com/WBECSouth
Instagram: www.instagram.com/wbecsouthofficial
Description: Works as third-party certifier of women's business enterprises. Fosters diversity in the world of commerce with programs and policies designed to expand opportunities and eliminate barriers in the marketplace for women business owners. **Founded:** 1994. **Geographic Preference:** Regional.

35691 ■ Women's Business Enterprise Council West
1220 S Alma School Rd., Ste. 101
Mesa, AZ 85210
Ph: (480)969-9232
Co. E-mail: office@wbec-west.org
URL: http://wbec-west.com
Contact: Jessica Rosman, Vice President
Facebook: www.facebook.com/wbecwest
X (Twitter): x.com/wbecwest
Description: Works as third-party certifier of women's business enterprises. Fosters diversity in the world of commerce with programs and policies designed to expand opportunities and eliminate barriers in the marketplace for women business owners. **Geographic Preference:** Regional.

35692 ■ Women's Business Enterprise National Council (WBENC)
1120 Connecticut Ave. NW, Ste. 1000
Washington, DC 20036
Ph: (202)872-5515
Co. E-mail: support@wbenc.org
URL: http://www.wbenc.org
Contact: Pamela Prince-Eason, President
E-mail: peason@wbenc.org
Facebook: www.facebook.com/WBENC
Linkedin: www.linkedin.com/company/wbenc
Instagram: www.instagram.com/wbenc
YouTube: www.youtube.com/user/WBENCNews
Description: Works as third-party certifier of women's business enterprises. Fosters diversity in the world of commerce with programs and policies designed to

expand opportunities and eliminate barriers in the marketplace for women business owners. **Founded:** 1997. **Awards:** WBENC Applause Award (Annual); Dorothy B. Brothers Scholarship (Annual); Dorothy B. Brothers Executive Scholarship Program (Annual). **Geographic Preference:** National.

35693 ■ Women's Business Exchange (WBE)
18490 W Old Gages Lake Rd.
Gages Lake, IL 60030
Ph: (847)406-8811
Co. E-mail: wbeinquiries@gmail.com
URL: http://wbe-il.com
Contact: Joelle Pehrson, President
Facebook: www.facebook.com/WomensBusinessExchangeIllinois
Description: Strives to empower women to grow personally and professionally by providing opportunities for learning, leadership, networking, and mentoring. Encourages members to conduct business with each other. **Founded:** 1988.

35694 ■ Women's Business Network, Inc. (WBN)
461 Cochran Rd.
Pittsburgh, PA 15228
Ph: (412)254-3592
Co. E-mail: msc@wbninc.com
URL: http://wbninc.com
Contact: Neha Patel, President
Facebook: www.facebook.com/wbninc
Linkedin: www.linkedin.com/company/womensbusinessnetworkinc
Instagram: www.instagram.com/wbn_inc
YouTube: www.youtube.com/user/WBNInc
Description: Provides an environment of support and assistance for entrepreneurial and established women-owned businesses. **Founded:** 1989. **Geographic Preference:** Local.

35695 ■ Women's Entrepreneurial Opportunity Project, Inc. (WEOP)
250 Georgia Ave., SE, Ste. 213
Atlanta, GA 30312
Ph: (404)681-2497
Co. E-mail: women@weop.org
URL: http://weop.org
Contact: Antionette Ball, Chief Executive Officer
Facebook: www.facebook.com/WEOPinc
X (Twitter): x.com/weopinc
Instagram: www.instagram.com/weopinc
Pinterest: www.pinterest.com/weopinc
Description: Represents the interests of individuals committed to advocate, educate and address the social disparities that impact women. Aims to improve women's family economic self-sufficiency. Provides programs and services for disadvantaged women and girls that promote social change. **Founded:** 1999. **Publications:** *From a Women's Perspective* (Annual). **Geographic Preference:** National.

35696 ■ Women's Regional Publications of America (WRPA)
c/o J. M. Gaffney
San Antonio Woman, 8603 Botts Ln.
San Antonio, TX 78217
Ph: (210)826-5375
URL: http://womensregionalpublications.org
Contact: J. M. Gaffney, Publisher
E-mail: info@sawoman.com
Description: Provides a forum where publishers of women's publications and business directories share information and resources. Increases the visibility, authority, influence and status of women's business for the purpose of promoting growth and support of women. Educates the general public about the need to support women-owned businesses, including equal opportunity employers and contractors. **Founded:** 1986. **Geographic Preference:** National.

35697 ■ Young Women Social Entrepreneurs (YWSE)
459 Broadway
New York, NY 10013
Co. E-mail: info@ywse.org
Facebook: www.facebook.com/YoungWomenSocialEntrepreneurs

Description: Serves women, primarily ages 25-40, with socially conscious agenda who are founders and leaders within businesses, nonprofits, and government organizations. Aims to promote young women entrepreneurs by providing training and development, access to resources, and networking opportunities. **Founded:** 1999. **Geographic Preference:** National.

SMALL BUSINESS ASSISTANCE PROGRAMS

35698 ■ Wisconsin Womens Business Initiative Corp. (WWBIC)
1533 N RiverCtr. Dr.
Milwaukee, WI 53212
Ph: (414)263-5450
Fax: (414)263-5456
Co. E-mail: info@wwbic.com
URL: http://www.wwbic.com
Contact: Wendy K. Baumann, President
E-mail: wendy.baumann@wwbic.com
Facebook: www.facebook.com/WWBIC
Linkedin: www.linkedin.com/company/wwbic
X (Twitter): x.com/WWBIC
Instagram: www.instagram.com/wwbic
YouTube: www.youtube.com/user/TheWWBIC
Description: Firm provides business education and financing to entrepreneurs and small business owners. Programs include small business loans, business education and workshops and much more. **Scope:** Firm provides business education and financing to entrepreneurs and small business owners. Programs include small business loans, business education and workshops and much more. **Founded:** 1987. **Training:** Business Planning - Start Smart; Personal Money Management - Make Your Money Talk; Business Finance Seminar-Madison, Mar, 2012.

35699 ■ Wisconsin Womens Business Initiative Corp. (WWBIC)
2300 S Pk. St., Ste. 103
Madison, WI 53713
Ph: (608)257-5450
Fax: (608)257-5454
URL: http://www.wwbic.com
Contact: Cheryl VandenBurgt, X, Director
Facebook: www.facebook.com/WWBIC
Linkedin: www.linkedin.com/company/wwbic
X (Twitter): x.com/WWBIC
Instagram: www.instagram.com/wwbic
Description: Firm provides targeted individuals interested in starting, strengthening and expanding businesses with access to vital resources and tools such as financial and business education and responsible financial products. **Founded:** 1987.

35700 ■ Wisconsin Womens Business Initiative Corp. (WWBIC)
600 52nd St., Ste. 130
Kenosha, WI 53140
Ph: (262)925-2840
Fax: (262)925-2855
URL: http://www.wwbic.com
Contact: Wendy Baumann, X, President
E-mail: wbaumann@wwbic.com
Facebook: www.facebook.com/WWBIC
Linkedin: www.linkedin.com/company/wwbic
X (Twitter): x.com/WWBIC
Instagram: www.instagram.com/wwbic
YouTube: www.youtube.com/channel/UCGN7oPQGiYnpIv2WgcCzR8A
Description: Firm provides targeted individuals interested in starting, strengthening and expanding businesses with access to vital resources and tools such as financial and business education and responsible financial products. **Founded:** 1987.

FINANCING AND LOAN PROGRAMS

35701 ■ Astia
2164 Hyde St., Ste. 714
San Francisco, CA 94109
Contact: Sharon Vosmek, Chief Executive Officer

Description: Provides funding and expertise for high potential female entrepreneurs.

EDUCATIONAL PROGRAMS

35702 ■ Business Plan Basics
URL(s): cwewbc.ecenterdirect.com/events/977281
Description: This online class offered by the Center for Women and Enterprise discusses how to write a business plan, plus provides resources and support. **Audience:** Women small business owners. **Principal Exhibits:** This online class offered by the Center for Women and Enterprise discusses how to write a business plan, plus provides resources and support.

35703 ■ The Content Sales Funnel - Creating an Effective Social Media Content Strategy Series
URL(s): cwewbc.ecenterdirect.com/events/977328
Description: This online course offered by the Center for Women and Enterprise discusses brand identity, sales funnel strategy, effective writing, and social media branding. **Audience:** Women who are small business owners. **Principal Exhibits:** This online course offered by the Center for Women and Enterprise discusses brand identity, sales funnel strategy, effective writing, and social media branding.

35704 ■ Content That Drives Sales Across Pinterest and Instagram, Session #1
URL(s): cwewbc.ecenterdirect.com/events/977106
Description: Online class offered by the Center for Women and Enterprise teaching how to create effective content for your small business to be used on social media. **Principal Exhibits:** Online class offered by the Center for Women and Enterprise teaching how to create effective content for your small business to be used on social media.

35705 ■ Content That Drives Sales Across Pinterest and Instragram, Session #2
URL(s): cwewbc.ecenterdirect.com/events/977106
Description: Online course offered by the Center for Women and Enterprise that shows how to create content and marketing for your small business using Pinterest. **Principal Exhibits:** Online course offered by the Center for Women and Enterprise that shows how to create content and marketing for your small business using Pinterest.

35706 ■ Discovering Your Brand Identity
URL(s): cwewbc.ecenterdirect.com/events/977303
Description: This online class offered by the Center for Women and Enterprise discusses how to develop brand identity, how to reach your audience, and how to use social media. **Audience:** Women who are small business owners. **Principal Exhibits:** This online class offered by the Center for Women and Enterprise discusses how to develop brand identity, how to reach your audience, and how to use social media.

35707 ■ Elevate Your Social Media Marketing and Presence for Engagement and Growth
URL(s): cwewbc.ecenterdirect.com/events/977226
Description: This online class offered by the Center for Women and Enterprise explores how best to use the tools of social media to effectively market your small business. **Audience:** Women who are small-business owners. **Principal Exhibits:** This online class offered by the Center for Women and Enterprise explores how best to use the tools of social media to effectively market your small business.

35708 ■ Grow Your Business Through Government Contracting
URL(s): cwewbc.ecenterdirect.com/events/977308
Description: This online meeting offered by the Center for Women and Enterprise provides information for Veteran business owners to grow their business and discusses helpful verifications and certifications. **Audience:** Small business owners, women, veterens. **Principal Exhibits:** This online meeting offered by the Center for Women and Enterprise provides information for Veteran business owners to grow their business and discusses helpful verifications and certifications.

35709 ■ How to Land Your First Client, Part 1
URL(s): cwewbc.ecenterdirect.com/events/977256
Frequency: Continuous. **Description:** Online course offered by the Center for Women & Enterprise about content development for marketing your business. **Principal Exhibits:** Online course offered by the Center for Women & Enterprise about content development for marketing your business.

35710 ■ Is Entrepreneurship Right for You?
URL(s): cwewbc.ecenterdirect.com/events/977133
Description: This online seminar hosted by the Center for Women and Entrepreneurship discusses key points about entrepreneurs and and how they run their businesses. Also gives out a self assessment to help attendees determine if they are a good fit for this type of business. **Audience:** Women small business owners and entrepreneurs. **Principal Exhibits:** This online seminar hosted by the Center for Women and Entrepreneurship discusses key points about entrepreneurs and and how they run their businesses. Also gives out a self assessment to help attendees determine if they are a good fit for this type of business.

35711 ■ Kickstart Your Social Media Blueprint with TikTok and IG Reels, Part I
URL(s): cwewbc.ecenterdirect.com/events/977312
Description: This online workshop offered by the Center for Women and Enterprise provides information on how to use TikTok and Instagram Reels to market your small business and develop and solid social media presence. **Audience:** Women small business owners. **Principal Exhibits:** This online workshop offered by the Center for Women and Enterprise provides information on how to use TikTok and Instagram Reels to market your small business and develop and solid social media presence.

35712 ■ Legal Considerations for Business Owners
URL(s): cwewbc.ecenterdirect.com/events/977282
Description: This workshop provided by the Center for Women and Enterprise gives information on the legal issues that small businesses may face. Covers entity formation, contract basics, IP considerations, and licenses and regulations. **Audience:** Women small business owners. **Principal Exhibits:** This workshop provided by the Center for Women and Enterprise gives information on the legal issues that small businesses may face. Covers entity formation, contract basics, IP considerations, and licenses and regulations.

35713 ■ NextGen The Future of the WBENC Network
URL(s): www.wbenc.org/programs/nextgen
Frequency: Irregular. **Description:** Outreach program to guide the next generation of women small-business owners. **Principal Exhibits:** Outreach program to guide the next generation of women small-business owners.

35714 ■ Planet Mogul
URL(s): www.wbenc.org/programs/planet-mogul
Frequency: Irregular. **Description:** Outreach program for the next generation of entrepreneurs, innovators, and workforce and community leaders. **Principal Exhibits:** Outreach program for the next generation of entrepreneurs, innovators, and workforce and community leaders.

35715 ■ SBA Loan Options and Best Borrowing Practices for Women
URL(s): wewbc.ecenterdirect.com/events/977255
Description: An online class offered by the Center for Women and Enterprise that discusses the different types of SBA loans, their criteria, and how to apply. **Principal Exhibits:** An online class offered by the Center for Women and Enterprise that discusses the different types of SBA loans, their criteria, and how to apply.

35716 ■ Social Media Made Simple
URL(s): cwewbc.ecenterdirect.com/events/977280

Description: This online course gives an introduction on how to use various social media sites to market your small business. **Audience:** Women small business owners. **Principal Exhibits:** This online course gives an introduction on how to use various social media sites to market your small business.

35717 ■ Tuck-WBENC Executive Porgram (Tuck I)
URL(s): www.wbenc.org/programs/tuck-wbenc-executive-program
Frequency: Irregular. **Description:** A six-day class for women business owners. Focuses on skill development in operations and leadership and how to apply these skills. **Principal Exhibits:** A six-day class for women business owners. Focuses on skill development in operations and leadership and how to apply these skills.

35718 ■ Tuck-WBENC Strategic Growth Program (Tuck II)
URL(s): www.wbenc.org/programs/tuck-wbenc-strategic-growth-program
Frequency: Irregular. **Description:** A six-day course for students who already graduated from Tuck I. This program focuses on developing and executing a business strategy. **Principal Exhibits:** A six-day course for students who already graduated from Tuck I. This program focuses on developing and executing a business strategy.

35719 ■ WBENC Allyship Program
URL(s): www.wbenc.org/programs/wbenc-allyship-program
Frequency: Irregular. **Description:** Program designed to cultivate inclusion and learn to become better allies to diverse individuals and groups. **Principal Exhibits:** Program designed to cultivate inclusion and learn to become better allies to diverse individuals and groups.

35720 ■ WBENC Business Lab
URL(s): www.wbenc.org/programs/wbenc-business-lab
Frequency: Irregular. **Description:** Interactive program for women business owners and business professionals to engage in business education for personal growth. **Principal Exhibits:** Interactive program for women business owners and business professionals to engage in business education for personal growth.

35721 ■ WBENC Energy Executive Program
URL(s): www.wbenc.org/programs/wbenc-energy-executive-program
Frequency: Irregular. **Description:** A program designed to provide professional development for women in the Energy industry. **Principal Exhibits:** A program designed to provide professional development for women in the Energy industry.

35722 ■ WBENC Industry Spotlight
URL(s): www.wbenc.org/programs/industry-spotlight-series
Frequency: Irregular. **Description:** A series of webinars and resources for women business owners in order to learn about new trends, innovations, and sources of support in the automotive, food & beverage, utilities, healthcare, energy, financial services, and manufacturing sectors. **Principal Exhibits:** A series of webinars and resources for women business owners in order to learn about new trends, innovations, and sources of support in the automotive, food & beverage, utilities, healthcare, energy, financial services, and manufacturing sectors.

35723 ■ WBENC Lift Financial Center of Excellence
URL(s): www.wbenc.org/programs/wbenc-lift-financial-center-of-excellence
Frequency: Irregular. **Description:** Educational program to educate women entrepreneurs on financial business support and funding opportunities. **Principal Exhibits:** Educational program to educate women entrepreneurs on financial business support and funding opportunities.

35724 ■ WeIGNITE

URL(s): www.wbenc.org/programs/weignite
Frequency: Irregular. **Description:** Virtual program presenting business tools to improve operations. **Principal Exhibits:** Virtual program presenting business tools to improve operations.

35725 ■ WeTHRIVE

URL(s): www.wbenc.org/programs/wethrive
Frequency: Irregular. **Description:** Virtual 8-week program for members of WBENC to help improve across five disciplines: Leadership and Communication, Financial Management, Business Strategy, Operations and Human Resources, and Marketing and Sales. **Principal Exhibits:** Virtual 8-week program for members of WBENC to help improve across five disciplines: Leadership and Communication, Financial Management, Business Strategy, Operations and Human Resources, and Marketing and Sales.

35726 ■ Women of Color Program

URL(s): www.wbenc.org/programs/women-of-color -program
Frequency: Irregular. **Description:** Outreach and development for women of color entrepreneurs. **Principal Exhibits:** Outreach and development for women of color entrepreneurs.

35727 ■ Women Owned in Retail

URL(s): www.wbenc.org/programs/women-owned-in -retail
Frequency: Irregular. **Description:** Education and outreach for retail-focused women-owned businesses. **Principal Exhibits:** Education and outreach for retail-focused women-owned businesses.

35728 ■ Women & Pride

URL(s): www.wbenc.org/programs/women-and-pride
Frequency: Irregular. **Description:** A virtual outreach and development program for strengthening the LQBTQ+ entrepreneurs and business professionals within the WBENC network. Focuses on: Advocacy and Allyship, Community Building, Education and Development, and Resources. **Principal Exhibits:** A virtual outreach and development program for strengthening the LQBTQ+ entrepreneurs and business professionals within the WBENC network. Focuses on: Advocacy and Allyship, Community Building, Education and Development, and Resources.

35729 ■ Women in Technology

URL(s): www.wbenc.org/programs/women-in -technology
Frequency: Irregular. **Description:** Presented by Dell Technologies, this virtual program will help women grow their technology businesses. **Principal Exhibits:** Presented by Dell Technologies, this virtual program will help women grow their technology businesses.

35730 ■ Women in Technology Summit

Women in Technology International (WITI)
11500 Olympic Blvd., Ste. 400
Los Angeles, CA 90064
Ph: (818)788-9484
Fax: (818)788-9410
Co. E-mail: member-info@corp.witi.com
URL: http://witi.com
Contact: David Leighton, President
URL(s): summit.witi.com

Frequency: Annual. **Description:** Offer exemplary teaching and training programs. **Audience:** Executive women, entrepreneurs, and technology thought leaders. **Principal Exhibits:** Offer exemplary teaching and training programs. **Telecommunication Services:** support@corp.witi.com.

REFERENCE WORKS

35731 ■ "5 Reasons Why Right Now Is Prime Time for Women-Owned Businesses" in GoSite Blog (March 8, 2021)

URL(s): www.gosite.com/blog/5-reasons-why-righ t-now-is-prime-time-for-women-owned-businesses

Ed: Bailey Keppel. **Released:** March 08, 2021. **Description:** Provides information on why this is a great time for women-owned businesses. Includes details on financing opportunities to networking groups, trends, statistics, and resources. **Availability:** Online.

35732 ■ "9 Grants for Black Women Entrepreneurs" by Now Corp.

URL(s): nowcorp.com/grants
Description: Discusses the fastest-growing group of small business owners -- black women. Provides information on grants that are specifically for black women entrepreneurs. **Availability:** Online.

35733 ■ 10 Everyday Actions to Make the Workplace More Inclusive for Women

URL(s): www.kornferry.com/insights/featured-topics/ diversity-equity-inclusion/10-everyday-actions-to -make-the-workplace-more-inclusive-for-women
Released: April 04, 2022. **Description:** Proposes ten everyday actions of inclusion that you can take to ensure that your workplace is more inclusive for women. **Availability:** Online.

35734 ■ "AG Warns Slots MBE Plan Risky" in Boston Business Journal (Vol. 29, May 27, 2011, No. 3, pp. 1)

Description: Attorney General Doug Gansler states that the law extending the minority business program on slots parlors contracting through 2018 could be open to lawsuits. He recommended that the state should conduct a study proving that minority- and women-owned businesses do not get a fair share in the gaming industry before it signs the bill to avoid lawsuits from majority-owned firms. **Availability:** Print; Online.

35735 ■ "The AHA Moment" in Hispanic Business (December 2010)

Description: An interview with Gisela Girard on how competitive market conditions push buttons. Girard stepped down from her 18-month position as chairwoman the Association of Hispanic Advertising Agencies. She has more than 20 years of experience in advertising and research marketing. **Availability:** Print; Online.

35736 ■ "Are You Ready for a Transformation?" in Women Entrepreneur (November 28, 2008)

Description: Marlene J. Waldock, an expert in women's empowerment and reinvention, discusses brand modification and what a business owner should consider before attempting to change or modify their brand. **Availability:** Online.

35737 ■ The Art of War for Women: Sun Tzu's Ultimate Guide to Winning Without Confrontation

Pub: Doubleday

Ed: Chin-ning Chu. **Released:** February 09, 2010. **Price:** $15, paperback; $11.99, e-book. **Description:** According to the author, the workplace is a battlefield for women. She offers a strategy for women to succeed in business. **Availability:** E-book; Print.

35738 ■ "AT&T Spend Nears $2 Billion in California With Minority, Women and Disabled Veteran-Owned Businesses in 2011" in Engineering Business Journal (March 21, 2012)

Description: AT&T reported $2 billion working with diverse suppliers in 2011, representing a consistent annual increase working with minority, women and disabled veteran owned businesses in California. AT&T prides itself on its 44 years leading the way by including minority, women and disabled veteran owned businesses to its supply chain. **Availability:** Print; Online.

35739 ■ "Attention Businesswomen! International Trade Isn't Just for Large Businesses" in Minority Business Entrepreneur (Vol. 39, Fall, 2022, No. 4, pp. 56-57)

URL(s): digital.mbemag.com/?m=53732&i=769780 &p=56&ver=html5

Ed: Camille Richardson. **Price:** $7.95. **Description:** The U.S. Department of Commerce's International Trade Administration is poised to help women-owned businesses develop their business through exports. **Availability:** Print; Online.

35740 ■ Back on the Career Track: A Guide for Stay-At-Home Moms Who Want to Return to Work

Released: August 15, 2008. **Price:** $29.92, paperback. **Description:** For women like themselves who have rejoined the workforce after a prolonged absence, the authors detail seven main steps for reentry; profiles of six women who have successfully re-launched their careers are included. **Availability:** Print.

35741 ■ "Backtalk with Terrie M. Williams" in Black Enterprise (Vol. 38, December 2007, No. 5, pp. 204)

Pub: Earl G. Graves Ltd.
Contact: Earl Graves, Jr., President

Ed: Tennille M. Robinson. **Description:** Profile of Terrie M. Williams, president of a public relations agency as well as founder of a youth empowerment organization called Stay Strong Foundation. Williams reflects on her bouts with depression and how the disease impacts sufferers and talks about her book that will inspire others dealing with depression. **Availability:** Online.

35742 ■ "Because Kids Need To Be Heard: Tina Wells: Buzz Marketing Group: Voorhees, New Jersey" in Inc. (Volume 32, December 2010)

Pub: Mansueto Ventures L.L.C.
Contact: Stephanie Mehta, Chief Executive Officer

Ed: Tamara Schweitzer. **Released:** December 01, 2010. **Description:** Profile of Tina Wells, founder and CEO of Buzz Marketing Group, who writes a tween book series called Mackenzie Blue to reach young girls. **Availability:** Online.

35743 ■ "The Best Grants for Women-Owned Businesses" in Nav Blog (June 2, 2022)

URL(s): www.nav.com/blog/9-best-small-business -grants-for-women-34414/

Ed: Imani Bashir. **Released:** June 02, 2022. **Description:** Women face inordinate challenges and find themselves behind their male counterparts when it comes to business ownership and funding. This article provides information on small business grants for women that can help your business reach the next level. **Availability:** Online.

35744 ■ "Black-Woman Owned Tech Company Introduces First Two-Part Charging System Portable Device" in Minority Business Entrepreneur (February 2, 2022)

URL(s): mbemag.com/articles/black-woman-owne d-tech-company-introduces-first-two-part-charging -system-portable-device/

Ed: Gaby M. Rojas. **Description:** Sparkee has announced its new charging device, Sparkee puck, on Kickstarter. This black-woman-owned tech company designed a small device that doesn't take up much room while it charges your electronic devices. **Availability:** Online.

35745 ■ "Business Books for Women" in Small Business Trends(October 31, 2022)

URL(s): smallbiztrends.com/2020/10/business-books -for-women.html?utm_content=vc-true

Ed: Ivana Taylor. **Released:** October 31, 2022. **Description:** Includes a list and descriptions about business books that women entrepreneurs and small business owners would benefit from reading. **Availability:** Online.

35746 ■ "Business Grants from Papaya Available to Women Small Business Owners" in Small Business Trends (March 9, 2023)

Ed: Joshua Sophy. **Released:** March 09, 2023. **Description:** The financial technology startup, Papaya, is offering the Female Founder Grant. **Availability:** Online.

35747 ■ *Business as Usual*

Description: Founder of The Body Shop shares her story and gives her opinion on everything from cynical cosmetic companies to destructive consultants.

35748 ■ *"Businesses Owned by Women Grow Twice as Fast" in Business News Daily (Sept. 23, 2019)*

URL(s): www.businessnewsdaily.com/15289-women -owned-business-growth.html

Ed: Andrew Martins. **Released:** September 23, 2019. **Description:** Provides data points on women-owned businesses and their continued effectiveness as economic drivers. **Availability:** Online.

35749 ■ *"Calendar" in Crain's Detroit Business (Vol. 24, March 10, 2008, No. 10, pp. 21)*

Pub: Crain Communications Inc.

Contact: Barry Asin, President

Description: Listing of events in the Detroit area include conferences addressing entrepreneurialism, economic development, and women business ownership. **Availability:** Print; Online.

35750 ■ *"Cancer Survivor Becomes Marathoner, Author" in Business Journal-Serving Phoenix & the Valley of the Sun (Vol. 30, August 20, 2010, No. 50, pp. 1)*

Pub: Phoenix Business Journal

Contact: Alex McAlister, Director

E-mail: amcalister@bizjournals.com

Ed: Angela Gonzales. **Description:** Cancer survivor Helene Neville has finished a record-breaking 2,520-mile run in 93 days and then celebrated her 50th birthday despite being diagnosed with Hodgkins' lymphoma in 1991. Neveille, who is also a Phoenix area registered nurse, made stops along the way to promote her book, 'Nurses in Shape'. Neville also discusses how she fought her cancer through running. **Availability:** Print; Online.

35751 ■ *"Capital One and Count Me In for Women's Economic Independence to Launch Program to Support Women Veteran-Owned Small Businesses Across the U.S." in Investment Weekly News (June 23, 2012, pp. 210)*

Description: Capital One Financial Corporation partnered with Count Me In for Women's Economic Independence to help create a new small business training program for women veteran business owners. The not-for-profit providers of business education and resources for women is commited to helping women veterans to succeed. **Availability:** Print; Online.

35752 ■ *"Car Dealer Closings: Immoral, Slow-Death" in Crain's Detroit Business (Vol. 25, June 8, 2009, No. 23)*

Pub: Crain Communications Inc.

Contact: Barry Asin, President

Ed: Daniel Duggan. **Description:** Colleen McDonald discusses the closing of her two Chrysler dealerships located in Taylor and Livonia, Michigan, along with her Farmington Hills store, Holiday Chevrolet. **Availability:** Print; Online.

35753 ■ *"Celebrate Success. Embrace Innovation" in Black Enterprise (Vol. 37, February 2007, No. 7, pp. 145)*

Description: 2007 Women of Power Summit provides networking opportunities, empowerment sessions, and nightly entertainment. More than 500 executive women of color are expected to attend this inspiring summit in Phoenix, February 7-10. **Availability:** Print; Online.

35754 ■ *"City Seeks More Minorities" in Austin Business Journal Inc. (Vol. 28, November 7, 2008, No. 34, pp. A1)*

Pub: Austin Business Journal

Contact: Rachel McGrath, Director

E-mail: rmcgrath@bizjournals.com

Ed: Jean Kwon. **Description:** Austin, Texas is planning to increase the participation of minority- and women-owned businesses in government contracts.

Contractors are required to show 'good faith' to comply with the specified goals. The city is planning to effect the changes in the construction and professional services sector. **Availability:** Print; Online.

35755 ■ *"Conference Calendar" in Marketing to Women (Vol. 21, April 2008, No. 4, pp. 7)*

Description: Listing of current conferences and events concerning women, marketing and business. **Availability:** Print; PDF; Download; Online.

35756 ■ *"Conference Networking Tips" in Women In Business (Vol. 66, Summer 2014, No. 1, pp. 14)*

Ed: Diane Stafford. **Description:** American Business Women's Association will hold its National Women's Leadership Conference from October 30, 2014 to November 1, 2014 in Overland, Kansas. Attendees are advised to study the conference agenda before the event. Participants also need to become good listeners when other attendees introduce themselves. **Availability:** Online.

35757 ■ *"Consignment Shop Opens In Spring Township To Serve Hard-To-Find Sizes" in Reading Eagle (June 16, 2012)*

Ed: Shannon Simcox. **Description:** BeautiFull Figure is a plus-size consignment store located in Spring Township, Pennsylvania. The owner, Elizabeth Reach, is also a full-time student. Many consignment shops will not accept clothing over size 16 and Reach saw an opportunity to serve plus-size women. She offers 50-50 split of profits on consigned items. **Availability:** Print; Online.

35758 ■ *"A Conversation with: Renea Butler" in Crain's Detroit Business (Vol. 25, June 8, 2009, No. 23, pp. 12)*

Pub: Crain Communications Inc.

Contact: Barry Asin, President

Ed: Ryan Beene. **Description:** Renea Butler, vice president of administration and human resources for Real Estate One Inc. in Southfield as well as vice president for public relations for the Human Resource Association of Greater Detroit, talks about how the economy has affected human resource services. **Availability:** Print; Online.

35759 ■ *"Cupcake Maker Explains Tricks of the Trade" in Chattanooga Times/Free Press (September 6, 2011)*

Pub: Chattanooga Publishing Company Inc.

Ed: Holly Leber. **Description:** Sunny Burden, head baker at Whipped Cupcakes in Chattanooga, Tennessee creates themed cupcakes as well as traditional ones. Burden finds baking therapeutic. **Availability:** Online.

35760 ■ *"The Cutest Houston-Made Kids' Clothes Will Soon Come in Mom Versions" in Houstonia (August 7, 2019)*

URL(s): www.houstoniamag.com/articles/2019/8/7/ bee-and-birdie-kids-clothes-etsy-shop

Ed: Abby Ledoux. **Released:** August 07, 2019. **Description:** The small online shop, Bee + Birdie has made a name for itself selling affordable toddler clothing that has a more subdued aesthetic instead of the in-your-face fashion that most stores carry. With its current success, the brand is now launching "mom" versions of their fashions. **Availability:** Online.

35761 ■ *"Designing an Office Around Your Company's Goals How Eventbrite Learned That a Workspace Becomes Much More Than an Office Once Your Team Weighs In" in Inc. (Vol. 36, September 2014, No. 7, pp. 122)*

Pub: Mansueto Ventures L.L.C.

Contact: Stephanie Mehta, Chief Executive Officer

Released: September 2014. **Description:** Julia Hartz, co-founder and president of an online ticketing and event planning service, Eventbrite, shares insight into designing her firm's new office space. She opened suggestions from all employees to come up with the right environment to suit her workers. **Availability:** Print; Online.

35762 ■ *"Developing the Next Generation of Rosies" in Employee Benefit News (Vol. 25, November 1, 2011, No. 14, pp. 36)*

Pub: SourceMedia LLC

Contact: Gemma Postlethwaite, Chief Executive Officer

Ed: Kathleen Koster. **Description:** According to the research group Catalyst, women made up 46.7 percent of the American workforce in 2010, however only 14.4 percent was Fortune 500 executive officers and 15.7 percent held Fortune 500 board seats. Statistical data included.

35763 ■ *"DIA Contract Sets a Record for Denver Minority, Woman-Owned Business" in Denver Business Journal (Vol. 65, February 21, 2014, No. 41)*

Pub: American City Business Journals, Inc.

Contact: Mike Olivieri, Executive Vice President

Released: Weekly. **Description:** The City of Denver, Colorado has awarded a $39.6 million contract to Burgess Services Inc. to construct a transit and hotel project near the Denver International Airport. Burgess Services is owned by Denise Burgess. This is the largest public contract awarded to a woman0 or minority-owned business in the city's history. **Availability:** Print; Online.

35764 ■ *Divas Doing Business: What the Guidebooks Don't Tell You About Being A Woman Entrepreneur*

Pub: Nouveau Connoisseurs Corporation

Contact: Monique Hayward, President

Ed: Monique Hayward. **Description:** A must-read for any woman who's currently running a business or is thinking of starting one.

35765 ■ *"DMW Gets MBE Certification" in Wireless News (July 29, 2012)*

Description: Towson, Maryland's Daft McCune Walker (DMW) received the Minority Business Enterprise (MBE) Certification from the State of Maryland for Engineering, Surveying, Environmental and CAD services. The firm is a multidisciplinary consulting organization and is woman-owned. **Availability:** Print; Online.

35766 ■ *"Dr. Melanie Brown" in Women in Business (Vol. 65, Winter 2013, No. 3, pp. 40)*

Description: Milestones in the career of Melanie Brown, PhD, are highlighted in light of her selection as the 2014 American Business Woman of American Business Women's Association (ABWA). An ABWA member since 2007, Dr. Brown is also the Information Technology Strategic and Analytics Manager at CenterPoint Energy. **Availability:** Print; Online.

35767 ■ *"Does Diversity Pay Dividends?" in Canadian Business (Vol. 87, October 2014, No. 10, pp. 89)*

Description: The growing interest in gender diversity-based investing can be driven in part by a rising number of women investors with progressive ideals. Alex Johnston of Catalyst Canada advocacy group predict the use of a diversity-based approach by institutional investors. **Availability:** Online.

35768 ■ *"Don't Quit When The Road Gets Bumpy" in Women Entrepreneur (November 25, 2008)*

Description: Discusses techniques four women entrepreneurs are utilizing to keep their businesses successful despite the credit crunch and the economic downturn.

35769 ■ *"Dress Professionally Cool for Summer" in Women In Business (Vol. 62, June 2010, No. 2, pp. 38)*

Description: Summer clothing for business and career women is discussed with regard to traditional and relaxed work places. Fabric considerations, tips on choosing blazers and a list of clothes and other items that are not appropriate for the workplace are presented. **Availability:** Print; Online.

35770 ■ *"Edible Endeavors"* in Black Enterprise (March 1, 2008)
Pub: Earl G. Graves Ltd.
Contact: Earl Graves, Jr., President

Ed: Carolyn M. Brown. **Description:** Profile of Jacqueline Frazer, woman entrepreneur who turned her love for cooking into a catering business. She is chef and owner of Command Performance in New York City. The firm works with more than 50 clients annually and generates annual revenues of about $350,000. **Availability:** Online.

35771 ■ *"Effective Networking"* in Women in Business (Vol. 64, Summer 2012, No. 2, pp. 50)

Ed: Diane Stafford. **Description:** Tips on effective networking at the 2012 American Business Women's Association National Women's Leadership Conference are suggested. The purpose of networking is to make contacts and build relationships so asking for too much free advice or selling personal services are not advisable. **Availability:** Online.

35772 ■ *"Entrepreneur Says Spirituality Has Been a Key to Her Success"* in Business First Columbus (Vol. 25, October 17, 2008, No. 8, pp. 1)

Description: Profile of Carolyn Williams Francis, CEO of Williams Interior Designs Inc. She outlines her mantra for success in her furniture design business, but emphasizes that faith has taken her business to greater heights.

35773 ■ *"The Evolution of Carolyn Elman"* in Women In Business (Vol. 62, September 2010, No. 3, pp. 11)
Pub: American Business Women's Association
Contact: Rene Street, Executive Director

Ed: Leigh Elmore. **Description:** Carolyn Elman, former executive director of the American Business Women's Association (ABWA), provides an overview of her career. Elman grew up with the Association, and it was part of her family's existence. She believes that the ABWA provides women the opportunity to learn and improve their skills in business.

35774 ■ *"An Examination of Rural and Female-Led Firms: A Resource Approach"* in Journal of Small Business Strategy (Vol. 31, December 1, 2021, No. 4, 20-39)
URL(s): libjournals.mtsu.edu/index.php/jsbs/article/view/2131

Ed: Marcos Segantini, Lori A. Dickes. **Released:** November 16, 2021. **Description:** Discusses funding for rural businesses and for those that are women-led. **Availability:** PDF; Online.

35775 ■ *"The Federal Government Is Making a New Investment in Women-Owned Small Businesses"* in The 19th (Dec. 7, 2021)
URL(s): 19thnews.org/2021/12/office-womens-business-ownership-investment-small-businesses/

Ed: Chabeli Carrazana. **Released:** December 07, 2021. **Description:** Discusses the changing role of the Small Business Administration as it works to support women entrepreneurs in their communities, offers training, and helps with federal contracts and financing. **Availability:** Online.

35776 ■ *"Federal Grants for Women: Multiple Grants for Entrepreneurs"* by Now Corp.
URL(s): nowcorp.com/federal-grants-women

Description: Discusses alternative financing options, such as federal grant programs, that have been created to fill the gender funding gap for women-owned small businesses. **Availability:** Online.

35777 ■ *Female Entrepreneurship in East and South-East Asia: Opportunities and Challenges*

Ed: Philippe Debroux. **Released:** 2010. **Description:** A detailed study of female entrepreneurship in Asia, where public authorities are slowly realizing the importance of women as workers and entrepreneurs. **Availability:** E-book; Print.

35778 ■ *"Filling the Business Gap"* in Hispanic Business (December 2010)

Description: New York group seeks to increase state diversity supplier spending to help create jobs and boost the economy. According to a recent study, six out of 10 small business owners will increase capital spending but delay hiring in 2011. However, potential job creation is good among businesses owned by women and minorities. **Availability:** Print; Online.

35779 ■ *"Financial Woes Continue to Plague Nearly Half of Women Small Business Owners"* in bizwomen (Oct. 8, 2021)
URL(s): www.bizjournals.com/bizwomen/news/latest-news/2021/10/women-business-owners-finances.html?page=all

Ed: Caitlin Mullen. **Released:** October 08, 2021. **Description:** Details how women entrepreneurs continue to deal with the economic fallout of the pandemic as well as optimism for the future. **Availability:** Online.

35780 ■ *"First Woman To Lead Builders Group"* in Philadelphia Business Journal (Vol. 32, January 31, 2014, No. 51, pp. 8)
Pub: American City Business Journals, Inc.
Contact: Mike Olivieri, Executive Vice President

Released: Weekly. **Price:** $4, introductory 4-week offer(Digital & Print). **Description:** Anne Faldoun, president of the Building Industry Association of Philadelphia (BIA), reveals that she has always been interested in architecture. She shares that she worked at the Dorado Neighborhood Improvement Company after she attended graduate school. Her views about the BIA's policy on tax abatement are also discussed. **Availability:** Print; Online.

35781 ■ *"Floral-Design Kiosk Business Blossoming"* in Colorado Springs Business Journal (September 24, 2010)
Pub: Dolan Media Newswires

Ed: Monica Mendoza. **Description:** Profile of Shellie Greto and her mother Jackie Martin who started a wholesale flower business in their garage. The do-it-yourself floral arrangement firm started a kiosk business in supermarkets called Complete Design. **Availability:** Online.

35782 ■ *"For Giving Us a Way To Say Yes To Solar: Lynn Jurich and Edward Fenster"* in Inc. (Volume 32, December 2010, No. 10, pp. 110)
Pub: Mansueto Ventures L.L.C.
Contact: Stephanie Mehta, Chief Executive Officer

Ed: Leigh Buchanan. **Released:** December 01, 2010. **Description:** Profile of entrepreneurs Lynn Jurich and Edward Fenster, cofounders of SunRun. The firm installs solar panels at little or no cost and homeowners sign 20-year contracts to buy power at a fixed price. **Availability:** Online.

35783 ■ *"Former Dell Exec Turns Entrepreneur, Buys Travel Agency"* in Austin Business Journal (Vol. 34, May 9, 2014, No. 12, pp. 9)
Pub: American City Business Journals, Inc.
Contact: Mike Olivieri, Executive Vice President

Released: Weekly. **Price:** $4, Introductory 4-week offer(Digital & Print). **Description:** Robin Goad, former sales executive for Dell Inc., is buying Tramex Travel of Austin, Texas. She hopes to reinvent the travel agency into a corporate powerhouse it once was when she worked there in the 1990s before working for Dell. **Availability:** Print; Online.

35784 ■ *The Foundations of Female Entrepreneurship: Enterprise, Home and Household in London, c. 1800-1870*
Pub: Routledge, Taylor & Francis Group

Ed: Alison Kay. **Released:** First edition. **Description:** This book argues that active business did not exclude women from 1747 to 1880, although careful representation was necessary and this has obscured the similarities of women's businesses to those of many male business owners.

35785 ■ *"From Craft Biz To Wholesale Giant"* in Women Entrepreneur (January 19, 2009)

Description: Advice is given on how to turn a small craft business into a full-time venture; tips to help one transition from a part-time designer to a full-time wholesaler and brand are also included.

35786 ■ *"From New York to Park Avenue: Red Carpet Fashion at a Discount"* in Orlando Business Journal (Vol. 30, February 14, 2014, No. 34, pp. 3)
Pub: American City Business Journals, Inc.
Contact: Mike Olivieri, Executive Vice President

Released: Weekly. **Price:** $8, introductory 4-week offer(Digital & Print). **Description:** Red Carpet Couture & Gems is known for selling high-end discount business attire and accessories. Owner, Caralyce Buford decided to buy from sample sales in New York before opening the store in October 2013. Her retail store caters to women of all sizes. **Availability:** Print; Online.

35787 ■ *"Furniture Restoration and Design Firm Holds Grand Opening in Dunbar"* in Charleston Gazette-Mail (July 18, 2019)
URL(s): www.wvgazettemail.com/dailymailwv/daily_mail_news/furniture-restoration-and-design-firm-holds-grand-opening-in-dunbar/article_ad3e4568-871e-5c74-983f-6e3ace21bfbe.html

Ed: Clint Thomas. **Released:** July 18, 2019. **Description:** Appalachian Restoration and Design Company held it's grand opening on July 16. Owner Christina Deaton has been restoring furniture for well over a decade and decided it was time to open up a shop, which also included hand-painted vintage and antique furniture. **Availability:** Online.

35788 ■ *"Gabrielle Union Providing $75K in Business Grants to Black Women Owned Companies"* in Small Business Trends (March 14, 2023)
URL(s): smallbiztrends.com/2023/03/75k-in-business-grants-to-black-women-owned-companies.html

Ed: Gabrielle Pickard-Whitehead. **Released:** March 14, 2023. **Description:** Black women-owned companies are eligible for business grants from actress and entrepreneur Gabrielle Union. **Availability:** Online.

35789 ■ *"Greene Street Consignment May Be the Most Happening Area Company You've Never Heard Of"* in Philadelphia Inquirer (April 20, 2012)

Ed: Kathy Boccella. **Description:** Greene Street Consignment has grown to seven locations featuring fashionable resale items. Lynne Mastrilli, owner of the boutiques does not use social media to market her business. Her sister, Donna, runs a nonprofit offshoot of the business called Greene Street Animal Rescue. Details of the two businesses are included.

35790 ■ *"Grooming Your Online Persona"* in Women In Business (Vol. 62, June 2010, No. 2, pp. 36)

Description: Employees' use of online social networks could become a basis on how their employers, clients, or business partners would judge them. Personal details, pictures and other online data should be filtered to avoid inappropriate or uncomfortable situations and distinguish personal from professional or work life. **Availability:** Online.

35791 ■ *"HBR Case Study: Play It Safe or Take a Stand?"* in Harvard Business Review (Vol. 88, November 2010, No. 11, pp. 139)
Pub: Harvard Business Publishing
Contact: Diane Belcher, Managing Director

Ed: Trish Gorman Clifford, Jay Barney. **Price:** $8.95, PDF. **Description:** A fictitious leadership scenario is presented, with contributors providing comments and recommendations. A female executive ponders whether to assert a point of view on a new venture. Both experts agree that after providing careful analysis of pros and cons, the executive should come to a well-informed conclusion. **Availability:** Online; PDF.

35792 ■ *"Her Aim Is True"* in *Senior Market Advisor (Vol. 13, October 2012, No. 10, pp. 40)*

Description: Profile of Rebecca True, president of True Capital Advisors, discusses her approach to broad marketing plans for her company. True emphasizes on building relationships with women business owners and executives. **Availability:** Print; Online.

35793 ■ *"Hollywood Baskets To Gift Nominees For the 2012 Teen Choice Awards July 22nd"* in *PR Newswire (July 16, 2012)*

Pub: PR Newswire Association LLC.

Description: Lisa Gal,founder of Hollywood Baskets, provided gift bags to the celebrities attending the 2012 Teen Choice Awards. **Availability:** Online.

35794 ■ *"Home Health Franchise Expands Across S. Fla."* in *South Florida Business Journal (Vol. 34, January 24, 2014, No. 27, pp. 5)*

Pub: American City Business Journals, Inc.

Contact: Mike Olivieri, Executive Vice President

Released: Weekly. **Price:** $8, Introductory 4-week offer(Digital & Print). **Description:** Lucy Robellos' Synergy HomeCare franchise in South Florida is experiencing strong growth. The business has 90 active caregiver, and Robellow plans to hire 90 six to ten employees a month for her firm in 2014. She reveals that Synergy aims to keep its clients in the comfort of their own home. **Availability:** Print; Online.

35795 ■ *"How Far Have Women Come?"* in *Women in Business (Vol. 64, Fall 2012, No. 3, pp. 13)*

Description: Discrimination against women still exists in the workplace despite the fact that women have gained greater access to good-paying, rewarding careers. The role of the American Business Women's Association is to provide women with the knowledge, attitude, skills and habits to help them achieve their personal and professional goals amid the challenging times. **Availability:** Print; Online.

35796 ■ *"How I Became a Serial Entrepreneur"* in *Baltimore Business Journal (Vol. 31, April 18, 2014, No. 51, pp. 26)*

Pub: American City Business Journals, Inc.

Contact: Mike Olivieri, Executive Vice President

Description: Dr. Lisa Beth Ferstenberg, a physician by training, teaches a course at the Maryland Center for Entrepreneurship in Columbia to help CEOs attract prospective investors. Dr. Ferstenberg is also the chief medical officer at Sequella Inc. She reflects on the kind of personality required to become a successful entrepreneur and the mistakes entrepreneurs make in raising capital funding. **Availability:** Print; Online.

35797 ■ *"How I Did It: Bobbi Brown, Founder and CEO, Bobbi Brown Cosmetics"* in *Inc. (November 2007, pp. 110-112)*

Ed: Athena Schindelheim. **Description:** Profile of Bobbi Brown, CEO and founder of Bobbi Brown Cosmetics, designed to highlight a woman's natural look. Brown opened her first freestanding retail store recently that houses a makeup artistry school in the back. **Availability:** Online.

35798 ■ *"How I... Operate a Food Truck on the Streets of Honolulu"* in *Pacific Business News (Vol. 21, July 18, 2014, No. 21, pp. 19)*

Pub: American City Business Journals, Inc.

Contact: Mike Olivieri, Executive Vice President

Released: Weekly. **Price:** $4, Introductory 4-week offer(Digital only). **Description:** Jennifer Hino, co-owner of The Girls Who Bake Next Door, believes that social media is important as it helps create and reach a wider customer base for her business, which she runs out of a food truck in Honolulu. She also posts photos on the site, which helps reinforce her brand. **Availability:** Print; Online.

35799 ■ *"How Investors React When Women Join Boards"* in *Harvard Business Review (Vol. 88, July-August 2010, No. 7-8, pp. 24)*

Pub: Harvard Business Publishing

Contact: Diane Belcher, Managing Director

Ed: Andrew O'Connell. **Price:** $6, PDF. **Description:** Research reveals a cognitive bias in blockholders regarding the presence of women on boards of directors despite evidence showing that diversity improves results. **Availability:** Online; PDF.

35800 ■ *"How Ivanah Thomas Founded a $5 Million Business - While Working Nights"* in *Orlando Business Journal (Vol. 30, April 18, 2014, No. 43, pp. 3)*

Pub: American City Business Journals, Inc.

Contact: Mike Olivieri, Executive Vice President

Released: Weekly. **Price:** $8, introductory 4-week offer(Digital & Print). **Description:** Caring First Inc. founder, Ivanah Thomas, says her drive to serve people in their home rather than them being institutionalized lead to the establishment of her firm. She added that she ran the home care business by herself during its early years. Thomas also stated her social status posed challenges for the company. **Availability:** Print; Online.

35801 ■ *"How One Company Joins Corporate Public Relations and Community Engagement"* in *Denver Business Journal (Vol. 65, January 17, 2014, No. 36, pp. A6)*

Pub: American City Business Journals, Inc.

Contact: Mike Olivieri, Executive Vice President

Description: Denver, Colorado-based Barefoot PR was formed by Cori Streetman and Sarah Hogan in 2010 to change corporate views on philanthropy. The partners made a commitment to make community investment the driving force of business. Insights on the next-generation of community relations consultants are also given. **Availability:** Online.

35802 ■ *How to Run Your Business Like a Girl: Successful Strategies from Entrepreneurial Women Who Made It Happen*

Description: Tour of three women entrepreneurs and their successful companies.

35803 ■ *"How to Set Up an Effective Home Office"* in *Women Entrepreneur (August 22, 2008)*

Description: Checklist provides ways in which one can arrange their home office to provide the greatest efficiency which will allow maximum productivity and as a result the greater the chance of success. **Availability:** Online.

35804 ■ *How Women Are Rethinking the Tattoo Parlor*

URL(s): www.nytimes.com/2018/02/28/style/women -tattoo-artists.html

Released: February 28, 2018. **Description:** Nice Tattoo Parlor in Brooklyn is looking to change how people view tattoo parlors by using chic decor and a staff of friendly female artists. Women have been interested in tattoos and are making a bigger impact in the industry, either through getting a tattoo or by becoming an artist. **Availability:** Online.

35805 ■ *"I Tried to Live Off Women-Owned Businesses. Turns Out, Men Still Run Everything"* in *Time (July 22, 2021)*

URL(s): time.com/6081259/women-owned-busi-nesses-rare/

Ed: Alana Semuels. **Released:** July 22, 2021. **Description:** Provides information on many facets of the women-owned business industry. **Availability:** Online.

35806 ■ *"Iconic Boise Skateboard Shop to Close"* in *Idaho Business Review (August 19, 2014)*

Pub: BridgeTower Media

Contact: Adam Reinebach, President

Description: Lori Wright and Lori Ambur have owned Newt & Harold's for over 30 years. The partners are closing the firm that sold skateboards and snowboards. Wright focused on the marketing and inventory aspects of the retail shop, while Ambur ran the organizational and financial end. Wright and Ambur say they are leaving retail because the industry has faced so many changes since they first opened, particularly competing with online stores.

35807 ■ *If You Have to Cry, Go Outside: And Other Things Your Mother Never Told You*

Pub: HarperCollins Publishers L.L.C.

Contact: Brian Murray, President

Ed: Kelly Cutrone, Meredith Bryan. **Released:** February 02, 2010. **Price:** $10.99, e-book; $7.24, e-book. **Description:** Women's mentor advices on how to make it in one of the most competitive industries in the world, fashion. She has kicked people out of fashion shows, forced some of reality television's shiny start to fire their friends, and built her own company which is one of the most powerful public relations firms in the fashion business. **Availability:** E-book; Print.

35808 ■ *"In the Hot Finance Jobs, Women Are Still Shut Out"* in *Harvard Business Review (Vol. 90, July-August 2012, No. 7-8, pp. 30)*

Pub: Harvard Business Review Press

Contact: Moderna V. Pfizer, Contact

Ed: Nori Gerardo Lietz. **Price:** $6, PDF and hardcover black and white. **Description:** Although women constitute a significant proportion of business school graduates, the percentage of senior investment professionals who are female remain in a single-digit figure. Active effort will be needed to change corporate culture and industry awareness to raise this figure. **Availability:** Print; PDF; Online.

35809 ■ *"In My Shoes: A Memoir"*

Pub: Portfolio Hardcover

Contact: Adrian Zackheim, President

Released: October 01, 2013. **Price:** $3.48, kindle; $32.80, hardcover; $0.25, hardcover(49 used from $0.25); $25.60, hardcover (6 new from $25.60); $8.86, paperback; $1.55, paperback(93 used from $1.55); $4.01, paperback(49 new from $4.01). **Description:** Profile of Tamara Mellon, woman entrepreneur who built Jimmy Choo into a premier name in the global fashion industry. She addresses her family life, her battles with anxiety and depression, as well as time spend in rehabilitation. She shares her entire life story from her work as a young editor at Vogue to her partnership with shoemaker, Jimmy Choo to her public relationships. She confides what it was like working with an obstinate business partner but also her ability to understand what customers want. **Availability:** E-book; Print; Audio.

35810 ■ *"In the Raw: Karyn Calabrese Brings Healthy Dining to a New Sophisticated Level"* in *Black Enterprise (Vol. 41, September 2010)*

Pub: Earl G. Graves Ltd.

Contact: Earl Graves, Jr., President

Ed: Sonia Alleyne. **Description:** Profile of Karyn Calabrese whose businesses are based in Chicago, Illinois. Calabrese has launched a complete line of products (vitamins and beauty items), services (spa, chiropractic, and acupuncture treatments), and restaurants to bring health dining and lifestyles to a better level. **Availability:** Online.

35811 ■ *"It's Never Too Late: Entrepreneurial Spirit Drives Older Women"* in *USA Today (Jan. 6, 2021)*

URL(s): www.usatoday.com/story/money/business/20 21/01/06/older-women-starting-businesses-its -never-too-late/4130883001/

Ed: Mariel Padilla. **Released:** January 06, 2021. **Description:** Discusses the entrepreneurial spirit of older women. **Availability:** Online.

35812 ■ *"Juicy Couture (1997-2014) Couldn't Evolve When Its Cachet Dried Up"* in *Canadian Business (Vol. 87, July 2014, No. 7, pp. 16)*

Description: Fashion brand Juicy Couture was started by Pamela Skaist-Ley and Gela Nash-Taylor in Los Angeles, California in 1997 and was acquired by Fifth & Pacific Companies in 2003. Fifth & Pacific put Juicy Couture up for sale in fall 2013, with Authentic Brands Group owning the rights to the brand name for $195 million. The last of the Canadian outlets will close June 30, 2014. **Availability:** Online.

35813 ■ *"Katie's Cupcakes to Celebrate One-Year Anniversary"* in *Bellingham Business Journal (Vol. March 2010, pp. 3)*
Pub: Sound Publishing Inc.
Contact: Josh O'Connor, President

Ed: Lance Henderson. **Description:** Katie Swanson, owner of Katie's Cupcakes, celebrated her firm's one-year anniversary with a fundraiser for the Whatcom Humane Society by offering free specialty cupcakes and other special events to the public. The specialty cupcakes will feature either a paw or bone and will be available throughout the month of March.

35814 ■ *"The Latest Grant Opportunities for Women- and Minority-Owned Small Businesses"* in *Small Business Trends(February 28, 2023)*
URL(s): smallbiztrends.com/2023/02/latest-small-business-grants-for-women-and-minority-owned-businesses.html

Ed: Annie Pilon. **Released:** February 28, 2023. **Description:** Information about grants available to women- and minority-owned small businesses is given. **Availability:** Online.

35815 ■ *"Lean In: Women, Work, and the Will to Lead"*
Pub: Penguin Random House
Contact: Nihar Malaviya, Chief Executive Officer

Released: March 11, 2013. **Price:** $24.95, hardcover; $12.99, e-book; $35, CD; $17.50, audiobook download; $24.95, hardcover; $12.99, e-book. **Description:** Sheryl Sandberg is the COO of Facebook and ranked as one of the fifty most powerful women in business. She addresses the fact that despite the advances for women, men still hold most of the leadership positions in business. Sandberg addresses this issue using anecdotes, hard data and compelling research to delve through the layers of ambiguity and bias encompassing choices of working women. **Availability:** audiobook download; CD-ROM; E-book; Print.

35816 ■ *"A Lifetime of Giving: Food Bank CEO Fights Hunger One Mouth At a Time"* in *Black Enterprise (Vol. 41, November 2010, No. 4, pp. 66)*
Pub: Earl G. Graves Ltd.
Contact: Earl Graves, Jr., President

Ed: Tamara E. Holmes. **Description:** Profile of Valerie Traore, CEO of Food Bank of South Jersey. Traore stresses the importance of volunteerism that she learned from her grandparents. Hunger relief became her passion when she served as a temp office worker for the Maryland Food Bank in Baltimore. She earned her Bachelor's of Science in management and has dedicated herself to a career in nonprofit service. **Availability:** Online.

35817 ■ *"Longmont's Comida Food Truck Now a Brick-and-Mortar Restaurant, Too"* in *Las Cruces Sun-News (February 17, 2012)*
Pub: Tribune News Service
Contact: Jack Barry, Vice President, Operations
E-mail: jbarry@tribpub.com

Ed: Tony Kindelspire. **Description:** Rayme Rosello discusses her plans to open her new Mexican-style restaurant, Comida Cantina, which grew from her pink food truck. Rosello started her food truck in 2010 and has frequented neighborhood parties as well as office parks to build her business. Details of the new restaurant are provided. **Availability:** Print; Online.

35818 ■ *"Longtime Advocacy for Green Skin Care Is Paying Off"* in *Providence Business News (Vol. 29, June 2, 2014, No. 9, pp. 24)*
Pub: American City Business Journals, Inc.
Contact: Mike Olivieri, Executive Vice President

Released: February 01, 2014. **Description:** Brenda Brock, entrepreneur and founder of Farmaesthetics, achieved success with her line of green, sustainable skin care products. She is now expanding her business to start new outlets. **Availability:** Print; Online.

35819 ■ *"Maryland Nonprofits May Lose Minority Business Enterprise Status"* in *Baltimore Business Journal (Vol. 29, September 2, 2011, No. 17, pp. 1)*
Pub: Boston Business Journal
Contact: Carolyn M. Jones, President
E-mail: cmjones@bizjournals.com

Ed: Scott Dance. **Description:** A business group has been pushing to bar nonprofits from Maryland's Minority Business program. Nonprofits have been found to take a large portion of state contracts intended for women- and minority-owned businesses. The group is also crafting proposed legislation to remove nonprofits from the program. **Availability:** Online.

35820 ■ *Minding Her Own Business, 4th Ed.*
Released: 4th edition. **Description:** A guide to taxes and financial records for women entrepreneurs is presented. **Availability:** E-book; Print.

35821 ■ *Minority Women Entrepreneurs: How Outsider Status Can Lead to Better Business Practices*
Ed: Mary Godwyn, Donna Stoddard. **Released:** September 08, 2017. **Description:** Minority women in the US start businesses at a faster rate then non-minority men and women. This book explores their success and how they use their outside status to develop business practices that benefit not only their company, but their communities. **Availability:** E-book.

35822 ■ *"Mixing Business and Pleasure On the Green"* in *Black Enterprise (Vol. 41, October 2010, No. 3, pp. 65)*
Description: Glow Golf, sponsored by Glow Sports, will offer instruction to 150 female corporate executives and entrepreneurs to learn the fundamentals of the game of golf. **Availability:** Print; Online.

35823 ■ *"My Day"* in *Business Strategy Review (Vol. 21, Autumn 2010, No. 3, pp. 77)*
Ed: Julie Meyer. **Description:** Julie Meyer shots to prominence as cofounder of the entrepreneurial network, First Tuesday. The firm was sold for $50 million in 2000. **Availability:** PDF; Online.

35824 ■ *My Life From Scratch: A Sweet Journey of Starting Over, One Cake at a Time*
Pub: Broadway Business

Ed: Gesine Bullock-Prado. **Released:** June 08, 2010. **Price:** $15, paperback; $10.99, e-book. **Description:** Lively account of Old World recipes, Bullock-Prado, a former Hollywood film developer and sister to actress Sandra Bullock, recounts the joys and heartbreak of running her own patisserie in Montpelier, Vermont. Having fled Los Angeles with her husband, Ray for the simpler pleasures of a small town near the Green Mountains, she opened her own bake shop, Gesine Confectionary in 2004, mostly on the fame of the macaroons she refashioned from her German mother's favorite almond treat, mandelhoernchen (and the casual mention of her sister in an interview). Her memoir follows one day in a busy baker's life, from waking at 3 a.m. to prepare the batter and bake her croissants, scones, and sticky buns, before opening her shop at 7 a.m., through the hectic lunch, and 3 p.m. tea time. **Availability:** E-book; Print.

35825 ■ *National Directory of Woman-Owned Business Firms*
Pub: Business Research Services, Inc.
URL(s): www.sba8a.com/order.htm

Price: $499, for 1 year; $299, for 6 month. **Description:** Covers 30,000 woman-owned businesses. **Entries include:** Company name, address, phone, name and title of contact, minority group, certification status, date founded, number of employees, description of products or services, sales volume, government contracting experience, references. **Arrangement:** Standard Industrial Classification (SIC) code, geographical. **Indexes:** Alphabetical by company. **Availability:** Online. **Type:** Directory.

35826 ■ *"New Beat for Marley's Daughter: Offspring of Reggae Royalty Opens Vintage Clothing Shop with Pal"* in *Los Angeles Business Journal (Vol. 34, March 12, 2012, No. 11, pp. 3)*
Pub: CBJ L.P.
Contact: Laura Garrett, Vice President Publisher
E-mail: garrett@ocbj.com

Ed: Bethany Firnhaber. **Description:** Karen Marley, daughter of famous reggae musician Bob Marley, explains her passion for vintage clothing. Karen and her fried Monique Aquino have partnered to open a resale consignment store in Los Angeles selling designer and vintage clothing. **Availability:** Online.

35827 ■ *"New Biz Mixes Paint, Wine; Will It Yield Green?"* in *Crain's Detroit Business (Vol. 30, September 8, 2014, No. 36, pp. 6)*
Pub: Crain Communications Inc.
Contact: Barry Asin, President

Description: Profile of Leanna Haun, owner of Picasso's Grapevine in downtown Clarkston, Michigan. Haun describes her business as one part wine, one part paint, and one part entertainment. Sessions include as many as ten people who are given instruction to paint a picture while enjoying wine and conversation with others. **Availability:** Print; Online.

35828 ■ *"New Generation Deans Lead Atlanta Area Business Schools Into the Future"* in *Atlanta Business Chronicle (July 25, 2014, pp. 3A)*
Pub: American City Business Journals, Inc.
Contact: Mike Olivieri, Executive Vice President

Released: Weekly. **Price:** $4, introductory 4-week offer(Digital only). **Description:** An interview with five business school deans from Georgia share their views on the future of business education, changing business education needs, and other issues affecting the Atlanta area business schools. The growing demands for greater global competences, good communication skills across various cultures, and other challenges faced by the students and employers are discussed. Other topics include the role of women in the corporate world. **Availability:** Print; Online.

35829 ■ *"On the Green: Sheila Johnson Adds $35 Million Golf Resort To Her Expanding Portfolio"* in *Black Enterprise (January 2008)*
Pub: Earl G. Graves Ltd.
Contact: Earl Graves, Jr., President

Ed: Donna M. Owens. **Description:** Profile of Sheila Johnson, CEO of Salamander Hospitality LLC, made history when she purchased the Innisbrook Resort and Golf Club, making her the first African American woman to own this type of property. The resort includes four championship golf courses, six swimming pools, four restaurants, eleven tennis courts, three conference halls, and a nature preserve. **Availability:** Online.

35830 ■ *"On Your Marks, American Airlines, Now Vote! Contest Creating Possibilities and Opportunities for Delray Beach Wedding Planner"* in *Benzinga.com (2011)*
Pub: Benzinga.com
Contact: Jason Raznick, Founder

Description: Wedding planner, Aviva Samuels, owner of Kiss the Planner boutique wedding and event planning agency in Florida, says that winning this contest would help her increase her knowledge base and provide in-depth, personal experience offering more destination wedding destinations.

35831 ■ *"The One Thing That's Holding Back Your Wellness Program"* in *Employee Benefit News (Vol. 25, December 1, 2011, No. 15, pp. 8)*
Pub: SourceMedia LLC
Contact: Gemma Postlethwaite, Chief Executive Officer

Description: A 13-year study shows that women who sat for more than six hours a day were 94 percent more likely to die during the study period. Most women sit at their desks an average of 7.7 hours while at work.

35832 ■ "Organic Food Company's a Hit With the Sippy-Cup Crowd" in Investor's Business Daily (March 27, 2012, pp. A5)
Description: Cofounder Annie Withy of Annie's Homegrown Inc. is profiled along with the firm's packaged foods that appeal to children. Statistical data included. **Availability:** Online.

35833 ■ "Packing Chic" in Black Enterprise (Vol. 38, February 2008, No. 7, pp. 154)
Pub: Earl G. Graves Ltd.
Contact: Earl Graves, Jr., President
Ed: Sonia Alleyne. **Description:** Profile of Angela Theodora's leather overnight bags that offer a variety of smart compartments for the business traveler.

35834 ■ "Passionate About Empowering Women" in Women In Business (Vol. 63, Spring 2011, No. 1, pp. 24)
Pub: American Business Women's Association
Contact: Rene Street, Executive Director
Ed: Leigh Elmore. **Released:** March 22, 2011. **Description:** Krazy Coupon Ladies cofounder Joanie Demer shares her views about her book, 'Pick Another Checkout Lane, Honey', which she coauthored with Heather Wheeler. Demer believes using coupons is for everyone who wants to save money. She also believes that extreme couponing is not an exercise for those who lack organizational ability since it requires planning and discipline. **Availability:** Online.

35835 ■ "Pedal to the Medal" in Small Business Opportunities (Summer 2010)
Description: Profile of Darlene Miller who became and partner and eventually took over Permac Industries, a firm that specializes in precision machine products. **Availability:** Print; Online.

35836 ■ "Pepperidge Farm Getting New Life" in Orlando Business Journal (Vol. 28, August 24, 2012, No. 28, pp. 1)
Pub: Baltimore Business Journal
Contact: Rhonda Pringle, President
E-mail: rpringle@bizjournals.com
Description: The Pepperidge Farm brand could see renewal with parent company Campbell Soup's hiring of Irene Chang Britt as president. Britt, reputed for growing brands and businesses through her attention on consumer needs and marketplace trends, will be the first woman to lead Pepperidge Farm after founder Margaret Rudkin. Other insights into Britt's career as a business leader are presented. **Availability:** Print; Online.

35837 ■ "Person To Watch: Wedding Planner Brings Energy to Her Job" in Chattanooga Times/Free Press (April 24, 2012)
Ed: Karen Nazor Hill. **Description:** Profile of Morgan Holland, 28-year-old founder of Soirees of Chattanooga. Weddings are a large part of Holland's event planning business, with parties for nonprofits, birthday parties, and private parties making up the other 15 percent. **Availability:** Print; Online.

35838 ■ "Physics for Females" in Occupational Outlook Quarterly (Vol. 55, Summer 2011, No. 2, pp. 22)
Description: Free resources to help females investigate careers in medical physics and health physics are available from the American Physical Society. The booklet is designed for girls in middle and high school and describes the work of 15 women who use physics to solve medical mysteries, discover planets, research new materials, and more. **Availability:** Print; Online.

35839 ■ The Pocket MBA: A Woman's Playbook for Succeeding in Business
Pub: John Wiley & Sons, Inc.
Contact: Christina Van Tassell, Executive Vice President Chief Financial Officer
URL(s): www.wiley.com/en-us/The+Pocket+MBA%3A +A+Woman%27s+Playbook+for+Succeeding+in +Business-p-9781394194575

Ed: Jodi Cottle. **Released:** July 2023. **Price:** $15.86, paperback. **Description:** With the goal of helping women boost their businesses and leadership skills, this book discusses the challenges women face in the business world. **Availability:** Print.

35840 ■ "Politicians Who Really Get Business: Meet Four of the Entrepreneurs Running for Congress" in Inc. (Vol. 34, September 2012, No. 7, pp. 21)
Ed: Ryan Underwood. **Description:** Businessman Mitt Romney is running for President of the United States. Profiles of three entrepreneurs running for Congress and one for the Senate in the 2012 elections include: John Dennis (Rep.), 12th District, California; Jim Graves (Dem.), 6th District, Minnesota; Thomas Massie (Rep.), 4th District, Kentucky; and Linda McMahon (Rep.), US Senate, Connecticut. **Availability:** Online.

35841 ■ "Presenting the Bizwomen 100, leading in their business communities" in Bizwomen (March 27, 2023)
URL(s): www.bizjournals.com/bizwomen/news/profiles-strategies/2023/03/bizwomen-100.html
Ed: Betsey Guzior. **Released:** March 27, 2023. **Description:** A list of 100 businesswomen who are entrepreneurs along with being committed to their local communities and serving them in some manner. **Availability:** Online.

35842 ■ "Program for Women Entrepreneurs: Tips for Surviving this Economy" in Crain's Detroit Business (Vol. 25, June 22, 2009, No. 25)
Pub: Crain Communications Inc.
Contact: Barry Asin, President
Description: Michigan Leadership Institute for Women Entrepreneurs will hold its third and final program, "Tough Times are Temporary, but Tough People are Permanent" at the Davenport University in Livonia, Michigan. **Availability:** Online.

35843 ■ "Real-Life Coursework for Real-Life Business People" in Women In Business (Vol. 63, Summer 2011, No. 2, pp. 22)
Pub: American Business Women's Association
Contact: Rene Street, Executive Director
Ed: Leigh Elmore. **Released:** June 22, 2011. **Description:** American Business Women's Association National Women's Leadership Conference provides members with academic business training courses. Members can take a variety of MBA-level courses that are taught by University of Kansas School of Business professors. Courses include marketing, management, leadership and communication and decision making. **Availability:** Print; Online.

35844 ■ "Rebrand, Rebuild, and Recharge Your Business: How This BE 100s CEO Got a New Lease On Life With a Frozen Yogurt Café" in Black Enterprise (Vol. 44, March 2014, No. 7, pp. 11)
Pub: Earl G. Graves Ltd.
Contact: Earl Graves, Jr., President
Description: Profile of Rumia Ambrose-Burbank, chief executive of one of the country's largest minority-owned businesses. Her Troy, Michigan-based firm ranks number 51 on the magazine's 100 Industrial/Service companies and focuses on the maintenance, repair, and operations (MRO) supply side. Ambrose-Burbank opened Sol De Frio, in 2013, a self-serve frozen yogurt dessert shop.

35845 ■ "A Renewed Sisterhood" in Women in Business (Vol. 64, Summer 2012, No. 2, pp. 6)
Ed: Rene Street. **Description:** The American Business Women's Association (ABWA) regional conference highlighted a new sense of enthusiasm and sisterhood as well as effective visioning exercise and breakout sessions. The ABWA National Women's Leadership Conference in October 2012 will feature the graduates of the Kansas University MBA Essentials Program and keynote speakers Bob Eubanks and Francine Ward. **Availability:** Online.

35846 ■ "The Right Remedy: Entrepreneur's Success Is a Matter of Life and Death" in Black Enterprise (Vol. 38, February 2008, No. 7, pp. 46)
Pub: Earl G. Graves Ltd.
Contact: Earl Graves, Jr., President
Ed: Tamara E. Holmes. **Description:** Profile of Leah Brown, whose company conducts clinical trials to determine if specific drugs will relieve particular symptoms. Her company will also visit physician's offices to make certain doctors are following proper protocol for a clinical trial or will collect data from patients. **Availability:** Online.

35847 ■ "The Road Warrior: Pamela Rodgers Kept Rodgers Chevrolet On Course Despite Numerous Obstacles" in Black Enterprise (Vol. 44, June 2014, No. 10, pp. 76)
Pub: Earl G. Graves Ltd.
Contact: Earl Graves, Jr., President
Description: Profile of Pamela Rodgers, who built her company into one of General Motor's flagship franchises and ranked among the largest black-owned dealerships. Rodgers addresses the importance of customer service in order to grow her business. She is a 30-year veteran with her Chevrolet dealership located in the Detroit area.

35848 ■ "Sacred Success: A Course in Financial Miracles"
Pub: BenBella Books Inc.
Contact: Aida Herrera, Director
E-mail: aida@benbellabooks.com
Released: October 01, 2014. **Price:** $17.46, hardcover; $11.87, paperback; $12.99, e-book(MOBI); $12.99, e-book(PDF), plus shipping charge; $12.99, E-Book (EPUB) ; $12.99, e-book(electronic publishing). **Description:** A leading expert on women and money helps women to take control of the finances and lose their fear or ambivalence towards it. It is a tutorial for taking charge of a woman's life along with financial investing success. **Availability:** E-book; Print; Electronic publishing; PDF; Online.

35849 ■ "Sallie Krawcheck: Women Are the Untapped Recipe for Business Success" in Idaho Business Review (August 20, 2014)
Pub: BridgeTower Media
Contact: Adam Reinebach, President
Price: $99, Digital & Mobile Only(1 Year); $11.99, Print, Digital & Mobile(1 Year); $149, Print, Digital & Mobile(1 Year); $99, Digital & Mobile Only(For 1 Year); $11.99, Print, Digital & Mobile (For 1 Month Intro Rate); $149, Print, Digital & Mobile (For 1 Year). **Description:** Salle Krawcheck spoke at the Zions Bank Small Business Conference at the Riverside Hotel in Boise, Idaho. She addressed the power of women as customers as well as the fact that 40 percent of business startups are by women. Statistical data included. **Availability:** Print; Online.

35850 ■ The Savvy Gal's Guide to Online Networking: Or What Would Jane Austen Do?
Pub: Booklocker.com Inc.
Ed: Diane K. Danielson, Lindsey Pollak. **Description:** It is a truth universally acknowledged that a woman in search of a fabulous career must be in want of networking opportunities. Or so Jane Austen would say if she were writing, or more likely, blogging today. So begins the must-read guide to networking in the 21st Century. Authors and networking experts share the nuts, bolts and savvy secrets that business-women need in order to use technology to build professional relationships. **Availability:** Print; Online; PDF.

35851 ■ "SBA Opens Program to Get Women Owned Businesses Federal Contracts" in Small Business Trends (August 30, 2022)
URL(s): smallbiztrends.com/2022/08/sba-governmen t-contracting-education-initiative-women-en trepreneurs-challengeher.html
Ed: Gabrielle Pickard-Whitehead. **Released:** October 04, 2022. **Description:** The Small Business Association (SBA) opened up a new program titled ChallengeHer to help women small business owners win federal contracts. **Availability:** Online.

35852 ■ *"Score a Home Run for Women-Owned Small Businesses"* in AZ Big Media (July 24, 2018)
URL(s): azbigmedia.com/business/small-business/score-a-home-run-for-women-owned-small-businesses/
Ed: Sarah O'Keefe. **Released:** July 24, 2018. **Description:** Discusses resources that the federal government provides to equalize the playing field and reduce hurdles that hinder the entrepreneurial efforts of women in small business. **Availability:** Online.

35853 ■ *"Secrets To Trade Show Success"* in Women Entrepreneur (September 12, 2008)
Description: Trade shows require an enormous amount of work, but they are an investment that can pay off handsomely because they allow a business to get their product or service in front of their target market. Advice regarding trade shows is given including selecting the correct venue, researching the affair and following up on leads obtained at the event. **Availability:** Online.

35854 ■ *"Shari's Berries Founder Shuts Last Store"* in Sacramento Business Journal (Vol. 28, September 2, 2011, No. 27, pp. 1)
Pub: Sacramento Business Journal
Contact: Stephanie Fretwell, Director
E-mail: sfretwell@bizjournals.com
Ed: Kelly Johnson. **Description:** Sacramento, California-based Shari's Berries owner Shari Fitzpatrick closed the company's last three stores called The Berry Factory. Fitzpatrick also filed for business bankruptcy protection. The weak economy is blamed for the company's failure. **Availability:** Online.

35855 ■ *"Small-Business Grants for Women: Best Options for Free Funding"* in NerdWallet (Oct. 14, 2022)
URL(s): www.nerdwallet.com/article/small-business/small-business-grants-for-women
Ed: Randa Kriss. **Released:** October 14, 2022. **Description:** Presents information on business grants for women entrepreneurs, which are essentially free financing, as opposed to small business loans or other types of debt-based funding. Lists 17 places female entrepreneurs can look for small business grants. **Availability:** Online.

35856 ■ *Smart Women Finish Rich*
Pub: Currency
Contact: Penny Simon, Contact
E-mail: psimon@randomhouse.com
Ed: David Bach. **Released:** September 18, 2018. **Price:** $17, paperback. **Description:** A nine-step program designed to show how to spend wisely and secure a rich financial future and to build up financial confidence before embarking on an entrepreneurial journey. **Availability:** E-book; Print.

35857 ■ *"So You Want to Start a Business? So You Want to Start a Business: What's Your First Move?"* in Women Entrepreneur (August 5, 2008)
Description: Advice for taking an idea and turning it into a legitimate business is given. **Availability:** Online.

35858 ■ *"SPOILED! Children's Consignment Boutique Now Collecting Donations To Support Baby2Baby & Help Children In Need"* in Benzinga.com (July 30, 2012)
Pub: Benzinga.com
Contact: Jason Raznick, Founder
Ed: Aaron Wise. **Description:** CeCe Hendriks opened her high-end children's consignment store in response to wanting to provide quality clothing for her son. Because children outgrow their clothing so fast, she decided a consignment shop is what all mom's needed. Hendriks offers a 50 percent consignment to donors and if the item isn't sold in 90 days, the consignee can choos to have the item returned or donate it to Baby2Baby. Hendriks also gives 10 percent of proceeds from sales to Baby2Baby, a nonprofit that works with homeles and domestic violence shelters. **Availability:** Online.

35859 ■ *"Start 2022 with a Bang with These Grants"* in Small Business News (Dec. 31, 2021)
URL(s): smallbiztrends.com/2021/12/in-the-news-start-2022-with-a-bang-with-these-grants.html
Released: December 31, 2021. **Description:** Discusses grants that are available to small businesses in many cities throughout the United States. Includes information about requirements for businesses affected by the pandemic as well as women and minority-owed businesses. **Availability:** Online.

35860 ■ *"A Step Up"* in Black Enterprise (Vol. 38, January 2008, No. 6, pp. 53)
Pub: Earl G. Graves Ltd.
Contact: Earl Graves, Jr., President
Ed: Aisha Sylvester. **Description:** Professional black women can get advice from a nonprofit program called ASCENT: Leading Multicultural Women to the Top. ASCENT's sessions last six months and are held at both Tuck School of Business at Dartmouth and UCLA Anderson School of Management.

35861 ■ *"Strengthen the Support for Women in Biz"* in Crain's Detroit Business (Vol. 30, September 8, 2014, No. 36, pp. 1)
Pub: Crain Communications Inc.
Contact: Barry Asin, President
Description: According to the 2014 State of Women-Owned Businesses Report, the number of woman-owned businesses has almost doubled since 1997. The report was commissioned by American Express Open. Statistical data included. **Availability:** Online.

35862 ■ *"Susan Leger Ferraro Built a $7.2 Million Day Care Business: Now She Wants To Expand-And Cash Out"* in Inc. (January 2008, pp. 50-53)
Ed: Dalia Fahmy. **Description:** Profile of Susan Leger Ferraro who wants to expand her chain of day care centers into Florida and California and sell part of her 87 percent stake to reduce financial risk. **Availability:** Online.

35863 ■ *"Sylvie Collection Offers a Feminine Perspective and Voice in Male Dominated Bridal Industry"* in Benzinga.com (October 29, 2011)
Description: Bridal jewelry designer Sylvie Levine has created over 1,000 customizable styles of engagement rings and wedding bands and is reaching out to prospective new brides through a new Website, interactive social media campaign and monthly trunk show appearances. **Availability:** Online.

35864 ■ *Table Talk: The Savvy Girl's Alternative to Networking*
Pub: AuthorHouse Inc.
Contact: William Elliott, President
Ed: Diane Danielson. **Description:** Let's face it. Women and men are different. So why should we all have to network in the same way? And, why should women have to 'network' at all? Between family and work responsibilities, the idea of pressing flesh at some not-very-festive cocktail party is right up there in appeal with a root canal. But what if women could find a way to make career boosting connections that are actually fun? Enter 'table talk', a new way to network for time-pressed, professional women. **Availability:** Print.

35865 ■ *"Ten Ways to Save on Business Travel"* in Women Entrepreneur (November 21, 2008)
Description: Advice regarding ways in which to save money when traveling for business is given. **Availability:** Online.

35866 ■ *"These Are the Women Who Really Mean Business"* in Canadian Business (Vol. 87, October 2014, No. 10, pp. 67)
Description: A list of the top 100 women entrepreneurs in Canada are ranked, based on sales, three-year revenue growth rate, and profitability of their businesses is presented. Included in the list are Janet Stimpson of White House Design Company, Inc.;

builder, Allison Grafton of Rockwood Custom Homes Inc.; and Janet Jing Di Zhang of Vancouver, BC of New Immigrants Information Services Inc. **Availability:** Online.

35867 ■ *"To Live and Thrive in L.A."* in Canadian Business (Vol. 81, October 13, 2008, No. 17, pp. 78)
Description: Toronto entrepreneur Shereen Arazm thrived in Los Angeles, California as the queen of nightlife. Arazm holds or has held ownership stakes in bars, nightspots and restaurants that include the Geisha House, Concorde, Shag, Parc and Central, and Terroni L.A. **Availability:** Online.

35868 ■ *"Too Much Information?"* in Black Enterprise (Vol. 37, December 2006, No. 5, pp. 59)
Pub: Earl G. Graves Ltd.
Contact: Earl Graves, Jr., President
Ed: James C. Johnson. **Description:** African American business owners often face the dilemma of whether or not to divulge their minority status when soliciting new customers and financial institutions. The quality of the products or services is always the key factor and race should never define one's business; however, it is appropriate to market oneself as a minority- or women-owned business, especially if the company is in an industry where those clients are offered top-tier contracts. **Availability:** Online.

35869 ■ *"Top Challenges Female Entrepreneurs Need to Overcome"* in Legal Zoom (February 21, 2023)
URL(s): www.legalzoom.com/articles/top-challenges-female-entrepreneurs-need-to-overcome
Ed: Jenn Morson. **Released:** February 21, 2023. **Description:** Discusses the challenges that women entrepreneurs face in the workplace. Maintaining a work-life balance and finding a support system are featured. **Availability:** Online.

35870 ■ *"Top Women In Tech: Whether It's Mobile or Engineering, These Mavens Are Making an Impact on Today's Tech Scene"* in Black Enterprise (Vol. 44, February 2014, No. 6, pp. 29)
Pub: Earl G. Graves Ltd.
Contact: Earl Graves, Jr., President
Description: There are fewer women than men in technology, science, engineering, and mathematics professions. As part of the magazine's Women of Power coverage, three successful minority women in their fields are profiled.

35871 ■ *"Transitioning From Hobbyist to Entrepreneur: Teen Designer Creates Custom and Handmade Jewelry for the Everyday Diva"* in Black Enterprise (Vol. 44, March 2014, No. 7, pp. 14)
Pub: Earl G. Graves Ltd.
Contact: Earl Graves, Jr., President
Description: Profile of Jaya Kiere Johnson, who states that every one of her jewelry creations represents a generation of black female entrepreneurship in her life, from her mother to her great-grandmother. The young entrepreneur tells how she was inspired while designing and creating handmade jewelry in high school.

35872 ■ *"Truffles & Trifles' Marci Arthur Plans YouTube Channel, Cookbook"* in Orlando Business Journal (Vol. 30, May 2, 2014, No. 45, pp. 3)
Pub: American City Business Journals, Inc.
Contact: Mike Olivieri, Executive Vice President
Released: Weekly. **Price:** $8, introductory 4-week offer(Digital & Print). **Description:** Marci Arthur, founder of Truffles & Trifles Cooking School, plans to create a YouTube channel and publish a cookbook. Arthur believes that the survival of her business can be attributed to the devotion and integrity of her employees. Reports show that the school has been receiving donations from sponsors such as Wolf Appliances and Sub-Zero. **Availability:** Print; Online.

35873 ■ "Union Pacific Railroad Receives Minority Business Exchange Award of Excellence" in News Bites US (July 7, 2012)

Description: Union Pacific Railroad was given the Award of Excellence at the 2012 Iowa Minority Business Exchange held in Des Moines, Iowa. The award is part of the Wisconsin Iowa and Central Illinois Minority Supplier Development Council. Union Pacific has a history of purchasing from minority- and women-owned businesses. **Availability:** Print; Online.

35874 ■ "The Weeks Ahead" in Crain's New York Business (Vol. 24, January 7, 2008, No. 1, pp. 26)

Description: Listing of events in the Detroit area include conferences addressing entrepreneurialism, economic development, and women business ownership. **Availability:** Print; Online.

35875 ■ "Welcome to Babesland" in Women In Business (Vol. 62, June 2010, No. 2, pp. 33)

Description: Music group, Four Bitchin' Babes will be performing at the 2010 American Business Women's Association's National Women's Leadership Conference. The group has been in the industry for 20 years and has released nine albums. The Four Bitchin' Babes consist of Sally Fingerett, Nancy Moran, Deirdre Flint, and Debi Smith. **Availability:** Online.

35876 ■ "What Managers Can Do to Keep Women in Engineering" in Harvard Business Review (June 12, 2018)

URL(s): hbr.org/2018/06/what-managers-can-do-to -keep-women-in-engineering

Ed: Dulini Fernando, Laurie Cohen, Joanne Duberley. **Released:** June 12, 2018. **Description:** Discusses what keeps women engineers in their current jobs and to be successful in their field. Many women leave the engineering jobs they worked hard to obtain, so how do companies retain women?. **Availability:** Online.

35877 ■ "Where Do Women Stand? Leaders Don't Skirt the Issue" in Birmingham Business Journal (Vol. 31, April 4, 2014, No. 14, pp. 4)

Pub: American City Business Journals, Inc.

Contact: Mike Olivieri, Executive Vice President

Description: Women business executives discuss ways women are faring in the workplace. City Paper Company's Cathy Friedman says equality remains the biggest challenge for women in the workplace. Mayer Electric Supply's Nancy Goedecke, believes company's should encourage women to try new things. **Availability:** Print; Online.

35878 ■ "Where Women Business Owners Turn for Encouragement and Inspiration" in Legal Zoom (March 14, 2023)

URL(s): www.legalzoom.com/articles/where-women -business-owners-turn-for-encouragement-an d-inspiration

Ed: Gwen Moran. **Released:** March 14, 2023. **Description:** Several mentors and consultants, books and podcasts, and community members are all discussed in this article articulating where women entrepreneurs turn to when they need to hear some enouragement. **Availability:** Online.

35879 ■ "Why I Stopped Firing Everyone and Started Being a Better Boss" in Inc. (Vol. 34, September 2012, No. 7, pp. 86)

Pub: Mansueto Ventures L.L.C.

Contact: Stephanie Mehta, Chief Executive Officer

Ed: April Joyner. **Released:** August 28, 2012. **Description:** Indigo Johnson, former Marine, discusses her management style when starting her business. She fired employees regularly. Johnson enrolled in a PhD program in leadership and established a better hiring program and learned to utilize her workers' strengths. **Availability:** Print; Online.

35880 ■ "Why Investing in Women-Led Startups Is the Smart Move" in Entrepreneur (March 8, 2018)

URL(s): www.entrepreneur.com/article/309555

Ed: David Nethero. **Released:** March 08, 2018. **Description:** Discusses advantages of investing in women-owned business. **Availability:** Online.

35881 ■ "Why Men Still Get More Promotions Than Women" in Harvard Business Review (Vol. 88, September 2010, No. 9, pp. 80)

Pub: Harvard Business Publishing

Contact: Diane Belcher, Managing Director

Ed: Herminia Ibarra, Nancy M. Carter, Christine Silva. **Price:** $8.95, PDF. **Description:** Sponsorship, rather than mentoring, is identified as the main difference in why men still receive more promotions than women. Active executive sponsorship is key to fostering career advancement. **Availability:** Online; PDF.

35882 ■ "Woman-Owned Firm 3D Strategic Management to Operate New Location of Orlando Business Center" in Orlando Business Journal (November 10, 2021)

URL(s): www.bizjournals.com/orlando/news/2021/11/ 10/3d-strategic-management-to-operate-minority -center.html

Ed: Anjali Fluker. **Released:** November 10, 2021. **Description:** A business development training center is under new management. Discussion of the woman-owned firm and their goals for this project are given. **Availability:** Online.

35883 ■ "Women as 21st Century Leaders" in Women In Business (Vol. 63, Summer 2011, No. 2, pp. 26)

Pub: American Business Women's Association

Contact: Rene Street, Executive Director

Ed: Leigh Elmore. **Description:** American Business Women's Association and Park University have partnered to provide a leadership training program to attendees of the 2011 National Women's Leadership Conference. The courses will incorporate introduction to concepts, development of critical thinking skills and direct application through exercises. Comments from executives are also included. **Availability:** Online.

35884 ■ "Women Are Crushing the Gender Pay Gap" in Legal Zoom (March 16, 2023)

URL(s): www.legalzoom.com/articles/women-are -crushing-the-gender-pay-gap

Ed: Gwen Moran. **Released:** March 16, 2023. **Description:** A report on the state of the Gender Pay Gap and discusses the disparity that is still happening. **Availability:** Online.

35885 ■ "Women in Business Networking Begins in North Fulton" in Atlanta Business Chronicle (July 25, 2014, pp. 2B)

Pub: American City Business Journals, Inc.

Contact: Mike Olivieri, Executive Vice President

Released: Weekly. **Price:** $4, introductory 4-week offer(Digital only). **Description:** Deborah Lanham, the director of membership services with the Greater Fulton Chamber of Commerce, is spearheading a number of key programs including the new eWomen in Business Networking event. Lanham discusses the vision and purpose of Women in Business, the events leading to the conception of the program, the fall event on gender diversification, and their goals for the upcoming year. **Availability:** Print; Online.

35886 ■ "Women Business Owners: Where We Stand Now" in SCORE Association Blog (Oct. 12, 2021)

URL(s): www.score.org/blog/women-business -owners-where-we-stand-now

Ed: Rieva Lesonsky. **Released:** October 12, 2021. **Description:** Discusses the current state of women business owners including funding, stress, and the gender gap. **Availability:** Online.

35887 ■ Women Count: A Guide to Changing the World

Pub: Purdue University Press

Contact: Justin Race, Director

E-mail: racej@purdue.edu

Ed: Susan Bulkeley Butler, Bob Keefe. **Released:** September 01, 2010. **Description:** Throughout history, women have struggled to change the workplace, change government, change society. It's time for women to change the world! Whether on the job, in politics, or in their community, there has never been a better time for women to make a difference in the world.

35888 ■ Women Entrepreneurs in The Global Marketplace

Pub: Edward Elgar Publishing Inc.

Contact: Edward Elgar, Founder Chairman

Ed: Andrea E. Smith-Hunter. **Released:** 2013. **Description:** Focus is on women entrepreneurs; information includes human capital, network structures and financial capital, with comparative analysis across racial lines.

35889 ■ "Women and Higher Education" in Montly Labor Review (Vol. 133, September 2010, No. 9, pp. 70)

Pub: U.S. Department of Labor Bureau of Labor Statistics

Contact: Amrit Kohli, Director

E-mail: kohli.amrit@bls.gov

Description: The increase in people going to college has been mostly among women. Statistical data included. **Availability:** Online; PDF.

35890 ■ "Women-Owned Small Business Resources" in SBDC Net (Nov. 16, 2021)

URL(s): www.sbdcnet.org/small-business-information -center/women-owned-small-business-resources/

Released: November 16, 2021. **Description:** Provides links to resources for women-owned small business. Includes federal resources, associations and organizations, and financial resources. **Availability:** Online.

35891 ■ "Women of Power Summit" in Black Enterprise (Vol. 38, February 2008, No. 7, pp. 163)

Description: Third annual Women of Power Summit, hosted by State Farm, will host over 700 executive women of color offering empowerment sessions, tips for networking, along with entertainment. **Availability:** Online.

35892 ■ "Women Up: Kathleen Ligocki of Harvest Power Inc." in Boston Business Journal (Vol.. 34, April 11, 2014, No. 10)

Pub: American City Business Journals, Inc.

Contact: Mike Olivieri, Executive Vice President

Released: Weekly. **Price:** $4, introductory 4-week offer(Digital & Print). **Description:** Kathleen Ligocki is the CEO of Harvest Power Inc. of Massachusetts. The company diverts organic waste destined for landfills and produces green energy and soil enrichment products. The company was founded in 2008 and reported sales of over $130 million in 2013. **Availability:** Print; Online.

35893 ■ "Women's Initiative for Self Employment Honors Home Instead Senior Care Owner as 2012 Woman Entrepreneur of the Year" in Marketwired (September 11, 2012)

Pub: Comtex News Network Inc.

Contact: Kan Devnani, President

Ed: Michelle Rogers. **Description:** Women's Initiative for Self Employment has bestowed its 2012 Woman Entrepreneur of the Year award on Michelle Rogers, owner of Home Instead Senior Care. The Women's Initiative is a nonprofit organization celebrating eight female business owners in the Silicon Valley Region annually. Home Instead Senior Care provides in-home care for seniors in the Bay Area of northern California. **Availability:** Online.

TRADE PERIODICALS

35894 ■ The Facilitator

URL(s): www.thefacilitator.com

Released: Quarterly **Price:** $35, U.S.; $35, Institutions; $40, Out of country. **Description:** Provides articles written by facilitators that are designed to link facilitators from around the world in a forum of sharing, networking, and communicating. Includes updates on training, automated meeting tools, and resources. Recurring features include tips and techniques, a calendar of events, reports of meetings, news of educational opportunities, book reviews, and notices of publications available. **Availability:** Print.

35895 ■ Multicultural Marketing News (MMN)
Pub: Multicultural Marketing Resources Inc.
Contact: Lisa Skriloff, President
E-mail: lisa@multicultural.com
URL(s): multicultural.com/newsletter-category/mul
ticultural-marketing-news

Released: Monthly **Description:** Covers minority- and women-owned businesses and corporations that sell to them. Provides story ideas, diverse resources for journalists, and contacts for marketing executives. Recurring features include a calendar of events, business profiles, and a feature on a trend in multicultural marketing. **Availability:** Online.

VIDEO/AUDIO MEDIA

35896 ■ Building Up Women, Building Communities
URL(s): www.startuphustlepodcast.com/building-up
-women-building-communities

Ed: Matt Watson. **Released:** March 27, 2024. **Description:** Podcast explains how entrepreneurship impacts communities.

35897 ■ Disrupting Male-Dominated Fields
URL(s): omny.fm/shows/startup-hustle/disrupting
-male-dominated-fields

Ed: Lauren Conaway. **Released:** August 17, 2023. **Description:** Podcast discusses disrupting male-dominated fields and the startup environment in Las Vegas with Brooke Fiumara, co-founder and Co-CEO of OPTX.

35898 ■ Elevated Entrepreneurship: A Female Entrepreneur's Perspective with Michelle Pippin
URL(s). mikemichalowicz.com/podcast/a-female-en
trepreneurs-perspective-with-michelle-pippin

Ed: Mike Michalowiicz. **Released:** October 28, 2019. **Description:** Podcast discusses what it takes to be a successful female entrepreneur.

35899 ■ Female Small Business Owners Embrace Equity of International Women's Day
URL(s): podcast.imanet.org/217

Ed: Yvonne Barber. **Released:** March 08, 2023. **Description:** Podcasts reflects on how the Covid pandemic affected female small business owners and how they used management accounting strategies to become more resilient.

35900 ■ From Side Hustle to Small Business: Samantha Besnoff, Your Financial Maven
URL(s): www.hiscox.com/side-hustle-to-small-busi
ness/samantha-besnoff-your-financial-maven-po
dcast-season-4

Ed: Sanjay Parekh. **Released:** October 02, 2024. **Description:** Podcast features the owner of an accounting business.

35901 ■ How to Find Your Purpose with Jessica Huie
URL(s): www.makinggoodpodcast.com/episodes/248
Ed: Lauren Tilden. **Released:** July 16, 2024. **Description:** Podcast discusses how to balance motherhood and entrepreneurship, defines purpose and transformational visibility, and explains the connection between visibility and impact.

35902 ■ Main Street Business Insights: Lindsay Goodson McDonald, Keith McDonald Plumbing
URL(s): mainstreet.org/resources/knowledge-hub/po
dcast/lindsay-goodson-mcdonald-keith-mcdonal
d-plumbing

Ed: Matt Wagner. **Released:** September 20, 2023. **Description:** Podcast discusses a woman-owned business in a male-dominated industry.

35903 ■ Marketplace: Immigrant Woman Are Increasingly Running Their Own Businesses
URL(s): www.marketplace.org/2023/06/06/immigran
t-women-are-increasingly-running-their-own
-businesses

Ed: Elizabeth Trovall. **Released:** June 06, 2023. **Description:** Discusses immigrant women starting their own businesses.

35904 ■ Nurture Small Business: Nesha Pai: Kicking Your Obstacles to the Curb
URL(s): nurturesmallbusiness.buzzsprout.com/900
445/episodes/14829811-nesha-pai-kcking-your-obs
tacles-to-the-curb

Ed: Denise Cagan. **Released:** April 08, 2024. **Description:** Podcast offers advice (particularly on handing adversity) for female entrepreneurs juggling multiple businesses.

35905 ■ Nurture Small Business: The Perfectionism Trap: A Guide to Entrepreneurial Success
URL(s): nurturesmallbusiness.buzzsprout.com/900
445/episodes/13985674-the-perfectionism-trap-a
-guide-to-entrepreneurial-success

Ed: Denise Cagan. **Released:** December 11, 2023. **Description:** Podcast shares the experience of a female business owner and how she dealt with overvaluing expertise and striving for perfection.

35906 ■ Overcoming Doubt and Imposter Syndrome
URL(s): www.startuphustlepodcast.com/overcoming
-doubt-and-imposter-syndrome

Ed: Lauren Conway. **Released:** October 11, 2023. **Description:** Podcast offers a conversation on conquering doubt and imposter syndrome as female entrepreneurs.

35907 ■ Side Hustle to Small Business: Building a Strong Foundation for Her New Creative Agency
URL(s): www.hiscox.com/side-hustle-to-small-busi
ness/heather-gibbons-inmo-creative-podcast-sea
son-3

Ed: Sanjay Parekh. **Released:** April 26, 2023. **Description:** Podcast offers conversation with the co-founder of a full-service creative agency committed to building a foundation of systems and processes aligned with their beliefs, values, and mission.

35908 ■ Side Hustle to Small Business: Creating Inclusive Spaces for Women to Collaborate
URL(s): www.hiscox.com/side-hustle-to-small-busi
ness/eileen-lee-lola-podcast-season-3

Ed: Sanjay Parekh. **Released:** September 27, 2023. **Description:** Podcast features the founder of an all-inclusive working space in Atlanta.

35909 ■ Side Hustle to Small Business: Launching a New Business in the Midst of a Maternity Leave
URL(s): www.hiscox.com/side-hustle-to-small-busi
ness/dominique-elkind-nixi-city-podcast-season-4

Ed: Sanjay Parekh. **Released:** July 17, 2024. **Description:** Podcast features a mother who founded a play center after noticing a lack of third spaces for parents of very young children when she was on maternity leave.

35910 ■ The Small Business School Podcast: Empowering Women Entrepreneurs with Erin Sisko
URL(s): podcasts.apple.com/us/podcast/empowering
-women-entrepreneurs-with-erin-sisko/id1695210
366?i=1000651286930

Ed: Staci Millard. **Released:** April 03, 2024. **Description:** Podcast discussing the importance of aligning business activities with personal values, women's access to capital, the role of networking, and the power of community. .

35911 ■ Think Business with Tyler: Chelsea Husum Reveals Success Secrets in Male-Dominated Construction World
URL(s): thinktyler.com/podcast_episode/chelsea
-husum-reveals-success

Ed: Tyler Martin. **Released:** May 06, 2024. **Description:** Podcast discusses the challenges in the construction industry, including personnel and management, cash flow, and assumption made about a woman leading in a male-dominated field.

35912 ■ This Is Small Business: Strategies for Success as a Woman in Business
URL(s): www.smallbusiness.amazon/podcast-episo
des/ep-47-strategies-for-success-as-a-woman-in
-business

Ed: Andrea Marquez. **Released:** March 04, 2024. **Description:** Podcast explains how being a woman in business can be challenging but can also be a journey of empowerment and growth with the right tools.

35913 ■ Why Women Need to Put Themselves Forward for Leadership
URL(s): www.startuphustlepodcast.com/why-women
-need-to-put-themselves-forward-for-leadership

Ed: Lauren Conaway. **Released:** December 26, 2023. **Description:** Podcast discusses why women should actively pursue leadership roles, navigating the challenges women encounter in business, and demystifies gender equity, diversity, and equality.

TRADE SHOWS AND CONVENTIONS

35914 ■ American Business Women's Association Convention
URL(s): www.abwa.org

Description: Equipment, supplies, and services for women in business. **Audience:** Working women and women business owners. **Principal Exhibits:** Equipment, supplies, and services for women in business.

35915 ■ Annual IAIP Convention
International Association of Insurance Professionals (IAIP)
One Glenlake Pkwy., Ste. 1200
Atlanta, GA 30328
Ph: (404)789-3153
Free: 800-766-6249
Fax: (404)240-0998
Co. E-mail: membership@iaip-ins.org
URL: http://www.internationalinsuranceprofessionals
.org/default.aspx
Contact: Tammy Wascher, President
URL(s): iaipconvention.com

Frequency: Annual. **Description:** Learn the hottest industry trends, share best practices and gather fresh ideas. **Audience:** Insurance professionals. **Principal Exhibits:** Learn the hottest industry trends, share best practices and gather fresh ideas. **Telecommunication Services:** ahammerli@iaip-ins.org.

35916 ■ Business Boutique
URL(s): www.ramseysolutions.com/business/busi-
ness-boutique

Frequency: Annual. **Description:** Seminars and educational opportunities for women interested in learning about running a small business, online shop, retail storefront, side-hustle, or freelance business. **Principal Exhibits:** Seminars and educational opportunities for women interested in learning about running a small business, online shop, retail storefront, side-hustle, or freelance business.

35917 ■ eWomen Network Conference
URL(s): www.ewnconf.com
Facebook: www.facebook.com/ewomennetwork
X (Twitter): twitter.com/ewomennetwork
Instagram: www.instagram.com/ewomennetwork

Frequency: Annual. **Description:** Key topic sessions for women business owners. **Audience:** Women business owners and entrepreneurs. **Principal Exhibits:** Key topic sessions for women business owners.

35918 ■ WBENC Collegiate Accelerator
URL(s): www.wbenc.org/programs/collegiate
-accelerator
Frequency: Annual. **Description:** A program for female founders and small-business owners. **Audience:** Students. **Principal Exhibits:** A program for female founders and small-business owners.

CONSULTANTS

35919 ■ Avita & Associates
5257 NE MLK, Ste. 201
  Portland, OR 97211
Ph: (503)998-9560
Co. E-mail: info@avitabiz.com
URL: http://www.avitabiz.com
Contact: Kedma Ough, Director
Description: Women-owned economic development firm dedicated to serving the interests of women, minorities, and persons with disabilities. Offers consulting and financial services.

35920 ■ DevelopWell
3301 Richmond Hwy., No. 1090
  Alexandria, VA 22305-3044
Co. E-mail: info@developwell.org
URL: http://www.developwell.org
Contact: Holly Witherington, Chief Executive Officer
Facebook: www.facebook.com/developwell
Linkedin: www.linkedin.com/company/developwell
Instagram: www.instagram.com/thedevelopwell
Description: A women-owned and operated coaching and consulting practice that develops leaders and teams in values-driven organizations with a holistic and innovative approach. **Founded:** 2017.

35921 ■ LoudBird LLC
456 N 1200 W
  Salt Lake City, UT 84116
URL: http://loudbirdmarketing.com
Contact: Clair Jones, Founder
Facebook: www.facebook.com/loudbirdmarketing
Instagram: www.instagram.com/loudbirdmarketing
YouTube: www.youtube.com/channel/UCAY2Kp
ttXmBb-5QBl1TJjFg
Pinterest: www.pinterest.com/loudbirdmarketing
Description: Small business marketing agency whose services include branding, SEO, websites, content, social media, copywriting, advertising, and training.

35922 ■ Ms.Tech Co.
222 W Merchandise Mart Plz., Ste.1212
  Chicago, IL 60654
URL: http://mstech.co
Contact: Nathaly Salas, President
Description: Provides women in technology ventures and innovative companies the inspiration, knowledge and connections to reach their full potential. **Founded:** 2010.

35923 ■ The Nova Collective
1819 W Grand Ave., Ste. 203
  Chicago, IL 60622
Free: 866-383-4463
Co. E-mail: connect@thenovacollective.com
URL: http://thenovacollective.com
Facebook: www.facebook.com/thenovacollective
Linkedin: www.linkedin.com/company/thenovacollec
tive
X (Twitter): x.com/findnova
Instagram: www.instagram.com/findnova
Description: Works to make the world a more inclusive place by helping businesses build and sustain diversity, equity, and inclusion (DEI) programs with real impact.

35924 ■ She+ Geeks Out, LLC
68 Harrison Ave. No 605
  Boston, MA 02111
Co. E-mail: hello@shegeeksout.com
URL: http://www.shegeeksout.com
Contact: Akyanna Smith-Gonzalez, Program
  Manager
Linkedin: www.linkedin.com/company/she-geeks-out
X (Twitter): x.com/shegeeksout
Instagram: www.instagram.com/shegeeksout

Description: Works to abolish inequity in the workplace. Supports businesses in their diversity, equity, and inclusion efforts by providing them with the knowledge, skills, and tools to create an inclusive environment. **Founded:** 2015.

PUBLICATIONS

35925 ■ BusinessWoman
3912 Abel Dr.
  Columbia, PA 17512
Ph: (717)285-1350
Co. E-mail: info@businesswomanpa.com
URL: http://www.businesswomanpa.com
Contact: Donna Anderson, President
E-mail: danderson@onlinepub.com
Facebook: www.facebook.com/BWMagazine
X (Twitter): x.com/BusinessWomanPA
YouTube: www.youtube.com/user/OnLinePublishers
Pinterest: www.pinterest.com/womensexpos
Description: Publisher of monthly magazine covering community and information, business. **Publications:** *Business Woman Resource Directory.*

35926 ■ *Enterprising Women: The Magazine for Women Business Owners*
1135 Kildaire Rd., Ste. 200
  Cary, NC 27511
Ph: (919)362-1551
Co. E-mail: info@enterprisingwomen.com
URL: http://www.enterprisingwomen.com
Contact: Monica S. Smiley, President
URL(s): enterprisingwomen.com/online-magazines
Facebook: www.facebook.com/EnterprisingWomen
Linkedin: www.linkedin.com/company/enterprising
-women-magazine
X (Twitter): x.com/ewmagazine
Instagram: www.instagram.com/enterprisingwomen
YouTube: www.youtube.com/user/En
terprisingWomenMag
Ed: Monica Smiley. **Released:** Quarterly **Price:** $20, U.S. for annual print; $40, U.S. for 2 year; $45, for 1 year international; $90, for 2 year international. **Description:** Magazine for women entrepreneurs. **Availability:** Print; Online.

COMPUTERIZED DATABASES

35927 ■ *National Directory of Woman-Owned Business Firms*
Business Research Services, Inc.
  7720 Wisconsin Ave., Ste. 213
  Bethesda, MD 20814
Ph: (301)229-5561
Free: 800-845-8420
Fax: (301)229-6133
Co. E-mail: brspubs@sba8a.com
URL: http://www.sba8a.com
URL(s): www.sba8a.com/order.htm
Price: $499, for 1 year; $299, for 6 month. **Description:** Covers 30,000 woman-owned businesses. **Entries include:** Company name, address, phone, name and title of contact, minority group, certification status, date founded, number of employees, description of products or services, sales volume, government contracting experience, references. **Arrangement:** Standard Industrial Classification (SIC) code, geographical. **Indexes:** Alphabetical by company. **Availability:** Online. **Type:** Directory.

INTERNET DATABASES

35928 ■ *DreamBuilder*
URL(s): dreambuilder.org
Description: Provides online educational programs for women small business owners and entrepreneurs. **Availability:** Online.

35929 ■ *Women in Business and the Workforce*
URL(s): guides.loc.gov/women-business-workforce
Description: Includes links to primary and secondary resources about women in business, industry, commerce, and entrepreneurship. Provides research into the history of women in the workforce along with reports and statistics. **Availability:** Online.

RESEARCH CENTERS

35930 ■ Business and Professional Women's Foundation (BPW) - The Willard Wirtz Labor Library
1030 15th St. NW, Ste. B1, Ste. 148
  Washington, DC 20005
Ph: (202)293-1100
Co. E-mail: foundation@bpwfoundation.org
URL: http://bpwfoundation.org
Facebook: www.facebook.com/BPWFoundation
Linkedin: www.linkedin.com/company/business-an
d-professional-women's-foundation
X (Twitter): x.com/BPW_CEO
Description: Dedicated to improving the economic status of working women through their integration into all occupations. Conducts and supports research on women and work, with special emphasis on economic issues. Maintains Marguerite Rawalt Resource Center of 20,000 items on economic issues involving women and work and provides public reference and referral service. Formerly National Federation of Business and Professional Women's Clubs. **Scope:** Workingwomen in America and its issues. **Founded:** 1919. **Holdings:** Figures not available. **Publications:** *Business Woman*; *Headquarters News*; *Legislative Hotline*; *Workingwomen Speak Out*. **Educational Activities:** Policy and Action Conference. **Awards:** BPW Foundation Career Advancement Scholarships (Annual). **Geographic Preference:** National.

35931 ■ National Women's Business Council (NWBC)
409 3rd St. SW
  Washington, DC 20416
Ph: (202)205-3850
Co. E-mail: info@nwbc.gov
URL: http://www.nwbc.gov
Contact: Maria Rios, President
Facebook: www.facebook.com/NWBCgov
Linkedin: www.linkedin.com/company/nwbcgov
X (Twitter): x.com/NWBC
YouTube: www.youtube.com/channel/UCBIGsDHm
3GELPDI8oNDsPqg/featured
Description: Women business owners. Strives to promote initiatives, policies, and programs designed to support women's business enterprises. **Membership:** Council consists of fifteen members: the chair, appointed by the President of the United States; four owners of small businesses who are of the same political party as the President; four owners of small businesses who are not of the same political party as the President; and six representatives of national women's business organizations, including representatives of women's business center sites. Members serve three-year terms. Carla Harris, Managing Director and Senior Client Advisor, Morgan Stanley, chairs the Council. **Scope:** Business and economic issues of importance to women business owners. **Founded:** 1988. **Publications:** *Study of Women-Owned and Led Businesses*; *Support for Women's Enterprise Development in the United States: Lessons Learned*, by the Council's Executive Director, Julie Weeks; *Engage!* (Monthly); *NWBC Reports*. **Educational Activities:** NWBC Seminars; Women's Business Connection. **Geographic Preference:** National.

35932 ■ University of Illinois at Chicago - Center for Urban Economic Development (CUED)
412 S Peoria St., MC 348
  Chicago, IL 60607
Co. E-mail: cued@uic.edu
URL: http://cued.uic.edu
Contact: Dr. Nik Theodore, Director
E-mail: theodore@uic.edu
Description: Integral unit of College of Urban Planning and Public Affairs, University of Illinois at Chicago. Offers program evaluations and technical assistance; research services to community organizations. **Scope:** Economic development, labor market research, technical assistance to community organizations and governments, immigration, globalization of the economy. **Founded:** 1978. **Publications:** *CUED Manuals*; *CUED Technical Reports*.

ASSOCIATIONS AND OTHER ORGANIZATIONS

35933 ■ National Safety Council (NSC) - Library
1121 Spring Lake Dr.
Itasca, IL 60143-3201
Ph: (630)285-1121
Free: 800-621-7615
Co. E-mail: customerservice@nsc.org
URL: http://www.nsc.org/home
Contact: Mark Vergnano, President
Facebook: www.facebook.com/NatlSafetyCouncil
Linkedin: www.linkedin.com/company/national-safety
-council
X (Twitter): x.com/NSCsafety
Instagram: www.instagram.com/nationalsafetycouncil
YouTube: www.youtube.com/user/NatlSafetyCouncil
Description: Promotes injury reduction by providing a forum for the exchange of safety and health ideas, techniques, and experiences and the discussion of injury prevention methods. Offers courses in first aid, occupational safety and traffic safety. Maintains extensive library on health and safety subjects. Publishes books on occupational safety, health topics, emergency planning, first-aid, traffic, school, farm, labor, youth, transportation and public (governmental) employee safety. **Scope:** Roadway safety. **Services:** Library access to members for free. **Founded:** 1913. **Holdings:** 174,000 books, research reports, articles; papers; clippings and pamphlets. **Publications:** *Injury Facts*; *Safeworker* (Monthly); *Safety and Health* (Monthly); *Today's Supervisor* (Monthly); *Traffic Safety* (Monthly; Bimonthly); *Safe Driver* (Monthly); *Construction Division Newsletter* (Bimonthly); *Safety & Health--Industrial Hygiene Buyers' Guide Issue*; *Safety & Health--Safety Equipment Buyers' Guide Issue*. **Educational Activities:** NSC Congress & Expo (Annual). **Awards:** USPS Safe Driver Awards (Annual); NSC Occupational Excellence Achievement Award (Periodic). **Geographic Preference:** National.

35934 ■ Voluntary Protection Programs Participants' Association (VPPPA)
8116 Arlington Blvd., No. 210
Falls Church, VA 22042
Ph: (703)761-1146
Co. E-mail: communications@vpppa.org
URL: http://vpppa.org
Contact: Chris Williams, Executive Director
E-mail: cwilliams@vpppa.org
Facebook: www.facebook.com/VPPPA
Linkedin: www.linkedin.com/company/vpppa-inc-
X (Twitter): x.com/VPPPA
Instagram: www.instagram.com/vpppa_inc
Description: Companies participating in Voluntary Protection Programs and other workplace environmental protection, health, and safety programs. Promotes cooperation between labor, management, and government agencies to insure safe and environmentally sustainable workplaces. Works closely with federal environmental and safety agencies to develop and implement cooperative programs; provides information on environmental health and workplace safety to congressional committees considering legislation. **Founded:** 1985. **Publications:** *VPPPA On the Wire* (Bimonthly); *Safety News Network (SNN)* (Biweekly); *VPPPA Washington Update* (Monthly). **Awards:** VPPPA Stephen Brown Scholarship (Annual); William "Sully" Sullivan Scholarship (Annual); VPPPA June Brothers Scholarship (Annual); VPPPA Safety & Health Achievement Program (Annual); VPPPA Safety and Health Outreach Award (Annual); VPP Innovation Award (Annual); VPP Outreach Award (Annual). **Geographic Preference:** National.

EDUCATIONAL PROGRAMS

35935 ■ Fred Pryor Seminars & CareerTrack OSHA Compliance
Fred Pryor Seminars & CareerTrack
5700 Broadmoor, Ste. 300
Mission, KS 66202
Free: 800-780-8476
Fax: (913)967-8849
Co. E-mail: customerservice@pryor.com
URL: http://www.pryor.com
Contact: Janet Turner, Contact
E-mail: dmca@pryor.com
URL(s): www.pryor.com/training-seminars/osha
-compliance
Frequency: Irregular. **Description:** Learn cost effective methods for getting your organization into compliance, how to expand the effectiveness of your safety training program, learn how to keep records required by OSHA, and how to assess your organization for a variety of hazards. **Audience:** Safety and security directors, facility managers and directors, human resources personnel, small business owners, supervisors and managers, controllers. **Principal Exhibits:** Learn cost effective methods for getting your organization into compliance, how to expand the effectiveness of your safety training program, learn how to keep records required by OSHA, and how to assess your organization for a variety of hazards.

35936 ■ OSHA 30-Hour Compliance Course (Onsite)
URL(s): www.pryor.com/training-seminars/osha-30
-hour-compliance
Description: A practical, hands-on experience you need to pinpoint hidden or overlooked safety and health issues, address them, and become fully compliant with OSHA's general industry standards. **Audience:** Professionals. **Principal Exhibits:** A practical, hands-on experience you need to pinpoint hidden or overlooked safety and health issues, address them, and become fully compliant with OSHA's general industry standards.

35937 ■ OSHA Compliance and Training for Medical and Dental (Onsite)
Seminar Information Service Inc. (SIS)
250 El Camino Real., Ste. 112
Tustin, CA 92780
Ph: (714)508-0340
Free: 877-736-4636
Fax: (714)734-8027
Co. E-mail: info@seminarinformation.com
URL: http://www.seminarinformation.com
Contact: Catherine Bellizzi, President
URL(s): www.seminarinformation.com/search.cfm?tx
=osha%20compliance
Description: Covers everything you need to ensure compliance with all OSHA standards and requirements. **Audience:** Nurses, hygienists, business and office managers, safety and risk managers, administrators, medical assistants, all lab personnel, medical technologists, dentists, dental assistants, physicians, physician assistants and nurse practitioners. **Principal Exhibits:** Covers everything you need to ensure compliance with all OSHA standards and requirements.

35938 ■ OSHA Compliance & Workplace Safety (Onsite)
Seminar Information Service Inc. (SIS)
250 El Camino Real., Ste. 112
Tustin, CA 92780
Ph: (714)508-0340
Free: 877-736-4636
Fax: (714)734-8027
Co. E-mail: info@seminarinformation.com
URL: http://www.seminarinformation.com
Contact: Catherine Bellizzi, President
URL(s): www.seminarinformation.com/details.cfm?qc
=qqbpaq
Description: Comprehensive update in OSHA's ever-changing requirements and innovative methods other organizations are successfully using to meet these stringent standards. **Audience:** Safety Managers, facility managers, human resource personnel, business owners, and supervisors. **Principal Exhibits:** Comprehensive update in OSHA's ever-changing requirements and innovative methods other organizations are successfully using to meet these stringent standards.

REFERENCE WORKS

35939 ■ *"Be Safe: CSE Requires a Series of Steps"* in Contractor (Vol. 56, October 2009, No. 10, pp. 40)
Ed: Dave Yates. **Description:** Confined Space Entry claims 91 lives each year and plumbers can prevent this by following several steps starting with the use of a four-gas analyzer which costs $1,262. It measures oxygen levels, as well as combustible gases, carbon monoxide, and hydrogen sulfide. **Availability:** Print; Online.

35940 ■ *"The CEO of Anglo American On Getting Serious About Safety"* in (Vol. 90, June 2012, No. 6, pp. 43)
Pub: Harvard Business Review Press
Contact: Moderna V. Pfizer, Contact
Ed: Cynthia Carroll. **Price:** $8.95, PDF and hardcover black and white. **Description:** The author discusses her decision to shut down Anglo American PLC's

platinum mine, the world's largest, for a complete overhaul of the firm's safety procedures. This involved a thorough retraining of the mine's workforce, replacing nearly all of the managers, and promoting the changes throughout the rest of the industry. **Availability:** Print; PDF; Online.

35941 ■ *"A Coffee Shop Owner's Guide to Handling Food & Dairy Allergies"* in Perfect Daily Grind (November 1, 2019)
URL(s): www.perfectdailygrind.com/2019/11/a-coffee-shop-owners-guide-to-handling-food-dairy-allergies/

Ed: Janice Kanniah. **Released:** November 01, 2019. **Description:** A practical guide to understanding common food allergies and how best to handle your coffee shop around this issue. **Availability:** Online.

35942 ■ *"CSE: Contractors Are Always Responsible"* in Contractor (Vol. 56, November 2009, No. 11, pp. 34)
Ed: Dave Yates. **Description:** Plumbing contractors should purchase a long snorkel hose, a tripod with manual-crank hoist, and a sump pump in order to prevent accidents associated with Confined Space Entry. Liability issues surrounding confined space entry prevention and accidents are discussed. **Availability:** Print; Online.

35943 ■ *"Employers See Workers' Comp Rates Rising"* in Sacramento Business Journal (Vol. 28, April 8, 2011, No. 6, pp. 1)
Pub: Sacramento Business Journal
Contact: Stephanie Fretwell, Director
E-mail: sfretwell@bizjournals.com
Ed: Kelly Johnson. **Released:** Weekly. **Price:** $4. **Description:** Employers in California are facing higher workers compensation costs. Increased medical costs and litigation are seen to drive the trend. **Availability:** Online.

35944 ■ *"Explainer: The Rules for Shooting on Film Sets"* in The Conversation (January 25, 2017)
URL(s): theconversation.com/explainer-the-rules-for-shooting-on-film-sets-71797
Ed: David Court, Peter Millynn. **Released:** January 25, 2017. **Description:** Movies often feature characters using firearms to shoot each other, but who is responsible for ensuring safety on the set? Many safety protocols must be followed, especially in the use of blanks, which has caused injury and even death on some sets. **Availability:** Online.

35945 ■ *"Footage Shows Workers Concerned About Hard Rock New Orleans Before Deadly Collapse"* in ConstructionDive (October 18, 2019)
URL(s): www.constructiondive.com/news/footage-shows-workers-concerned-about-hard-rock-new-orleans-before-deadly-c/565338/
Ed: Kim Slowey. **Released:** October 18, 2019. **Description:** On October 12, three people died and 30 others were injured when a portion of the Hard Rock Hotel in New Orleans fell. Video has surfaced showing workers concerned about the shoring holding up a concrete slab on the upper floors. An expert points out some general observations about the incident. **Availability:** Online.

35946 ■ *"How to Make Your Coffee Shop More Accessible"* in Perfect Daily Grind (August 12, 2019)
URL(s): www.perfectdailygrind.com/2019/08/how-to-make-your-coffee-shop-more-accessible/
Ed: Tasmin Grant. **Released:** August 12, 2019. **Description:** Addresses how coffee shops can make improvements in regards to accessibility for customers and employees with disabilities and impairments. **Availability:** Online.

35947 ■ *"Huberman Failing to Keep CTA on Track"* in Crain's Chicago Business (Vol. 31, April 21, 2008, No. 16, pp. 22)
Pub: Crain Communications Inc.
Contact: Barry Asin, President

Description: Discusses the deplorable service of CTA, the Chicago Transit Authority, as well as CTA President Ron Huberman who, up until last week had riders hoping he had the management skills necessary to fix the system's problems; Tuesday's event left hundreds of riders trapped for hours and thousands standing on train platforms along the Blue Line waiting for trains that never came. **Availability:** Online.

35948 ■ *"'Human Error' Cited for Deadly Google Seattle Crane Collapse, 3 Firms Fined $107K"* in ConstructionDive (October 21, 2019)
URL(s): www.constructiondive.com/news/human-error-cited-for-deadly-google-seattle-crane-collapse-3-firms-fined/565416/
Ed: Kim Slowey. **Released:** October 21, 2019. **Description:** Three contractors were fined a total of $107,200 over the deadly tower crane collapse at the Google office project in Seattle. Four people were killed. It was determined that the contractors and their workers ignored the proper instructions for dismantling the crane, causing it to weaken and fall. **Availability:** Online.

35949 ■ *"NIOSH Teams with Staffing Association to Promote Temp Worker Safety and Health"* in Safety+Health (August 30, 2021)
URL(s): www.safetyandhealthmagazine.com/articles/21653-niosh-teams-with-staffing-association-to-promote-temp-worker-safety-and-health
Released: August 30, 2021. **Description:** Key safety issues are being promoted between a multi-year partnership between the National Institute for Occupational Safety & Health, and temp agencies in order to better protect all workers. **Availability:** Online.

35950 ■ *"The One Thing That's Holding Back Your Wellness Program"* in Employee Benefit News (Vol. 25, December 1, 2011, No. 15, pp. 8)
Pub: SourceMedia LLC
Contact: Gemma Postlethwaite, Chief Executive Officer
Description: A 13-year study shows that women who sat for more than six hours a day were 94 percent more likely to die during the study period. Most women sit at their desks an average of 7.7 hours while at work.

35951 ■ *"The Price of Citizenship"* in Canadian Business (Vol. 79, August 14, 2006, No. 16-17, pp. 13)
Description: Safety and insurance benefits provided by the Canadian government to Canadian passport holders returning from Lebanon, is discussed. **Availability:** Print; Online.

35952 ■ *"Project Managers' Creed: Learn It, Live It"* in Contractor (Vol. 56, November 2009, No. 11, pp. 46)
Ed: H. Kent Craig. **Description:** Project managers should take the health and safety of their subordinates above all else. A manager should deal with the things that distract him from his job before starting a day on the site. The manager should maintain a comfortable and relaxed attitude with his employees. **Availability:** Print; Online.

35953 ■ *"Solar Hot Water Sales Are Hot, Hot, Hot"* in Contractor (Vol. 56, December 2009, No. 12, pp. 22)
Ed: Dave Yates. **Description:** Plumbing contractors in the United States can benefit from the increased sales of solar thermal water systems. Licensed plumbers have the base knowledge on the risks associated from heating and storing water. Safety issues associated with solar water heaters are also included. **Availability:** Online.

35954 ■ *"United's Next Hurdle: Costly Repairs"* in Crain's Chicago Business (Vol. 31, April 14, 2008, No. 15, pp. 1)
Pub: Crain Communications Inc.
Contact: Barry Asin, President

Ed: John Pletz. **Description:** Discusses the recent crackdown by aviation regulators concerning airline safety at United Airlines as well as other carriers. Maintenance costs at United for the upkeep on the company's older planes is severely affecting its bottom line which is already sagging under heavy fuel costs. **Availability:** Online.

TRADE PERIODICALS

35955 ■ *Occupational Health & Safety*
Pub: 1105 Media Inc.
Contact: Rajeev Kapur, Chief Executive Officer
URL(s): ohsonline.com/Home.aspx
Facebook: www.facebook.com/ohsmag
Linkedin: www.linkedin.com/company/occupational-health-and-safety-magazine
X (Twitter): x.com/OccHealthSafety
Ed: Jerry Laws. **Released:** 7/year; Feb/Mar, Apr/May, June, Jul/Aug, Sep, Oct and Nov/Dec. **Description:** Magazine covering federal and state regulation of occupational health and safety. **Availability:** Print; Download; PDF; Online.

35956 ■ *Safety Compliance Alert*
Pub: American Future Systems Inc.
Contact: Edward G. Rendell, Governor
URL(s): www.pbp.com/divisions/publishing/newsletters/regulations-compliance/safety-compliance-alert
Released: Semimonthly **Description:** Presents real world examples to help safety professionals avoid accidents and fires, reduce costs, and comply with changing OSHA rules. Recurring features include news of research, a calendar of events, news of educational opportunities, and a column titled Sharpen Your Judgment. **Availability:** Online.

35957 ■ *Work & Stress*
Pub: Routledge, Taylor & Francis Group
URL(s): www.tandfonline.com/journals/twst20
Ed: Toon Taris. **Released:** Quarterly **Price:** $1,109, Institutions for print and online; $909, Institutions for online only; $505, Individuals for print only. **Description:** Peer-reviewed journal focusing on psychological, social, organizational aspects of occupational and environmental Health stress and safety Management. **Availability:** Print; Download; PDF; Online.

VIDEO/AUDIO MEDIA

35958 ■ *The How of Business: Kevin Ring - Workers' Compensation Insurance*
URL(s): www.thehowofbusiness.com/497-kevin-ring-workers-compensation-insurance
Ed: Henry Lopez. **Released:** November 04, 2023. **Description:** Podcast discusses the importance of understanding and managing workers' compensation insurance to balance both employee safety/benefits and the financial impact.

CONSULTANTS

35959 ■ Caliche Ltd.
PO Box 107
Magnolia, TX 77353-0107
Ph: (281)356-6038
Free: 800-683-1046
Fax: (281)356-6224
Co. E-mail: calicheltd@calicheltd.com
URL: http://calicheltd.com
Contact: Frank M. Parker, III, Partner
Facebook: www.facebook.com/CalicheLtd
X (Twitter): x.com/CalicheLtd
Description: Safety, health and environmental management consulting company provides comprehensive environmental services including air, soil and water monitoring and analysis, emission and ventilation studies, asbestos and lead-based paint consulting, environmental site assessments, industrial hygiene and safety audits, indoor air quality and underground storage tank closures. **Founded:** 1980.

Training: How You Can Get the Most of Your Industrial Hygiene Assessment: A Systematic and Comprehensive Approach to Exposure Assessment, Aug, 2007.

35960 ■ Charp Associates Inc.
39 Maple Ave.
Upper Darby, PA 19082
Contact: Solomon Charp, President
Description: Provider of consulting, analysis and design services and serve the manufacturing and industrial, transportation, occupational safety, legal and insurance industries. **Scope:** Provider of consulting, analysis and design services and serve the manufacturing and industrial, transportation, occupational safety, legal and insurance industries. **Publications:** "Technological Horizons in Education".

35961 ■ Cocciardi & Associates Inc.
4 Kacey Ct.
Mechanicsburg, PA 17055
Ph: (717)766-4500
Fax: (717)766-3999
Co. E-mail: info@cocciardi.com
URL: http://www.cocciardi.com
Contact: Greg Cameron, Project Manager
E-mail: gcameron@cocciardi.com
Linkedin: www.linkedin.com/company/cocciardi-and-associates-inc-
Description: Provides safety, health consulting and management services such as training and education services. **Founded:** 1988. **Publications:** "Guidebook on Pennsylvania Environmental Laws & Regulations; Storage Tank Compliance: Above Ground and Underground," The Pennsylvania Chamber of Business and Industry, 2009; "Briefing's on Hospital Safety," Health Care Pro, 2009; "Flammable and Combustible Liquids Hazards in the Workplace: OSHA Requirements Put Focus on Safe Storage," 2008; "Creating Isolation Surge Capacity," Rusting Publications, 2008; "Arc Flash Hazards and Protecting Your Employees," Nov, 2008; "United States Department of Homeland Security (DHS) Chemical Facility AntiTerrorism Rule," Sep, 2008; "Mold Contamination and Its Regulatory Status in Pennsylvania," Aug, 2006; "Arc Flash Hazards and How to Protect Your Employees," Feb, 2006; "Hidden Benefits of Training," Jun, 2005; "Terrorism Response Field Guide," Jones and Bartlett, 2003; "Terrorism Response Training Manual," Jones and Bartlett, 2003; "Emergency Response Team Manual," National Fire Protection Association, 2004.

35962 ■ Don Phin, Esq.
114 C. Ave., No. 200
Coronado, CA 92118
Ph: (619)852-4580
URL: http://www.donphin.com
Contact: Don Phin, Contact
E-mail: don@donphin.com
Linkedin: www.linkedin.com/in/donphin
X (Twitter): x.com/donphin12
YouTube: www.youtube.com/donphin
Description: Firm is engaged in consulting services on training, coaching and mentoring for the individuals and small businesses. **Scope:** Firm is engaged in consulting services on training, coaching and mentoring for the individuals and small businesses. **Founded:** 1983. **Publications:** "Doing Business Right!"; "HR That Works!"; "Lawsuit Free! How to Prevent Employee Lawsuits"; "Building Powerful Employment Relationships!"; "Victims, Villains and Heroes: Managing Emotions in The Workplace". **Training:** Doing Business Right!; HR That Works!; Building Powerful Employment Relationships; Lawsuit Free!.

35963 ■ Environmental Assessment Services Inc.
201 E 5th St. 2500 Central Trust Ctr.
Cincinnati, OH 45202
Contact: Larry H. McMillin, Contact
Description: Offers environmental and health and safety services in compliance auditing, program management and implementation, field services and real estate assessment. **Scope:** Offers environmental

and health and safety services in compliance auditing, program management and implementation, field services and real estate assessment.

35964 ■ Environmental Support Network Inc. (ESN)
PO Box 36448
Canton, OH 44735
Ph: (330)494-0905
URL: http://www.environmental-support.com
Contact: William Racine, Contact
Description: Provides environmental, health and safety consulting and project management services. These include compliance auditing and remediation specifications concerning air, groundwater and soil quality. Also offers health and safety reviews, asbestos and lead-based paint handling, noise sampling, industrial permitting and UST management. Industries served: education, finance, industry and government. **Scope:** Provides environmental, health and safety consulting and project management services. These include compliance auditing and remediation specifications concerning air, groundwater and soil quality. Also offers health and safety reviews, asbestos and lead-based paint handling, noise sampling, industrial permitting and UST management. Industries served: education, finance, industry and government. **Founded:** 1989. **Training:** Environmental Health and Safety Management in Ohio; Managing Compliance in Ohio; Environmental Site Remediation in Ohio and Surrounding States; Conducting ESAs by ASTM Standards; Health and Safety Management in the Medical Setting; Exposure Monitoring in Schools and Public Buildings.

35965 ■ Error Analysis Inc.
5173 Waring Rd., Ste. 157
San Diego, CA 92120
Ph: (619)464-4427
Co. E-mail: info@erroranalysis.com
URL: http://www.erroranalysis.com
Contact: Dr. Joseph Cohen, Consultant
E-mail: joe@erroranalysis.com
Description: Research and consulting in the fields of human factors, safety and accident reconstruction. Provides consulting and expert witness services to attorneys, the insurance industry and businesses throughout the world. **Scope:** Research and consulting in the fields of human factors, safety and accident reconstruction. Provides consulting and expert witness services to attorneys, the insurance industry and businesses throughout the world. **Publications:** "Participation on voluntary committees for standards and codes by forensic practitioners: A win-win combination,"2011; "Ergonomics in Design,"2011; "Stairway falls: An ergonomics analysis of 80 cases," Professional Safety, 2009; "The practice of forensic human factors/ergonomics and related safety professions," Lawyers & Judges Publishing Company, 2009. **Training:** The role of a just culture, American Society of Safety Engineers, Costa Mesa, TCA, Jan, 2009; Common trends in slip and falls, Las Vegas, NV, Sep, 2008; Safety; Risk Management; Premises and Product Liability.

35966 ■ Fox Fire Safety, Inc.
4605 LincolnWay E
Mishawaka, IN 46544
Ph: (574)258-5479
Fax: (574)674-0911
URL: http://www.foxfiresafetyinc.com
Contact: John Kwist, Account Manager
E-mail: jkwist@foxfiresafetyinc.com
Facebook: www.facebook.com/foxfiresafety
Description: Provider of fire protection and fire suppression needs in a range of systems and their services include installation of fire protection equipment, hydrostatic testing, fire demonstration and serves all industries. **Scope:** Provider of fire protection and fire suppression needs in a range of systems and their services include installation of fire protection equipment, hydrostatic testing, fire demonstration and serves all industries. **Founded:** 1986.

35967 ■ Humanics ErgoSystems Inc.
10202 La Costa Dr.
Austin, TX 78747-1103

Ph: (818)345-3746
Co. E-mail: ergoquestions@gmail.com
URL: http://www.humanics-es.com
Contact: Rani Lueder, Principal Founder
E-mail: rani@humanics-es.com
Description: Firm is engaged in ergonomics consulting services such as occupational ergonomics, research and design of products and places for adults children and people with disabilities. **Scope:** Firm is engaged in ergonomics consulting services such as occupational ergonomics, research and design of products and places for adults children and people with disabilities. **Founded:** 1982. **Publications:** "The Future of Ergonomics in Children's Education," IEA 2009; "Ergonomics for Children; designing products and places for toddlers to teens," 2007; "Are Children just Little Adults? Child growth, development and age-related risk," Dec, 2003; "Rethinking Sitting," Oct, 2003; "Revisiting Ergonomics," May, 2003. **Training:** Teaching elder design, Las Vegas, Jul, 2008; Ergonomic considerations in seated work activities, University of California, Los Angeles, Jun, 2008; Rethinking back support: Sacral, lumbar or live backs, Dec, 2007; Adjunct Faculty, Human Factors and Design, 2006; Zen sitting and Western seating, 2005; Behavioral ergonomics, Oct, 2005; Sitting & seating in Zenmonasteries, Sep, 2005; Walking in their shoe.

35968 ■ Leonard R. Friedman Risk Management Inc.
1979 Marcus Ave., Ste. E100
Lake Success, NY 11042
Contact: Alice B. Weiss, Chief Executive Officer
Description: Provider of independent insurance and risk management and also provides related services. **Scope:** Provider of independent insurance and risk management and also provides related services.

35969 ■ Safety Management Services (SMS)
1847 W 9000 S, Ste. 205
West Jordan, UT 84088
Ph: (801)567-0456
Fax: (801)567-0457
URL: http://smsenergetics.com
Contact: Robert Ford, President
Facebook: www.facebook.com/safetymanagementservices
Linkedin: www.linkedin.com/company/safety-management-services-inc
Description: Provider of safety consulting services including evaluating safety policies and procedures to determine degree of effectiveness, advises on compliance with OSHA standards and provides safety programs for managers, supervisors, and workers. **Scope:** Provider of safety consulting services including evaluating safety policies and procedures to determine degree of effectiveness, advises on compliance with OSHA standards and provides safety programs for managers, supervisors, and workers. **Founded:** 1998. **Publications:** "What Can Go Wrong?," International Cranes magazine, Apr, 1994. **Training:** Federal OSHA Construction Safety and Health Course for Trainers, University of California, San Diego; OSHA 10-Hour Construction Safety Course; 90-Hour Construction Safety Management Certificate Course - 1991 to 1993; Fall Protection; Confined Space Standards; Cranes and Rigging; Scaffold or Trenching and Excavation; and Safe Construction Work Practices.

LIBRARIES

35970 ■ Ameren Corporation - Library
Ameren Corporation
1901 Chouteau Ave.
Saint Louis, MO 63103
Ph: (314)621-3222
Free: 800-255-2237
Fax: (314)554-2401
Co. E-mail: invest@ameren.com
URL: http://www.ameren.com
Contact: Martin J. Lyons, Jr., President
Facebook: www.facebook.com/AmerenCorp
Linkedin: www.linkedin.com/company/ameren
X (Twitter): twitter.com/amerencorp

Description: A public utility holding company that operates through Ameren Missouri and Ameren Illinois. Ameren Missouri operates a rate-regulated electric generation, transmission, and distribution business and a rate-regulated natural gas transmission and distribution business in Missouri. Ameren Illinois operates rate-regulated electric and natural gas transmission and distribution businesses in Illinois. **Scope:** Business, the environment, engineering, occupational safety and health, nuclear power, public utilities, public-private power. **Founded:** 1997. **Holdings:** Figures not available.

35971 ■ Bloomberg Industry Group - Library
Bloomberg Industry Group
1801 S Bell St.
Arlington, VA 22202
Ph: (703)341-1818
URL: http://www.bloombergindustry.com
Contact: Josh Eastright, Chief Executive Officer
X (Twitter): x.com/BBGIndustry
Instagram: www.instagram.com/bloombergindustry

Description: Provides information and solutions to legal, tax, compliance, government affairs, and government contracting professionals. **Scope:** Law; labor-management relations; economics; government regulation; business; the environment; industrial safety and health. **Services:** Interlibrary loan; library open by special arrangement only. **Founded:** 1929. **Holdings:** More than 80 computer-readable databases are maintained.; 20,000 volumes. **Publications:** *Directory of U. S. Labor Organizations*; *Environment Reporter*; *Federal Contracts Report™* (Continuous); *Government Employee Relations Report*; *International Trade Reporter* (Daily); *Patent, Trademark & Copyright Journal®*; *Weekly Report* (Weekly); *United States Law Week®*; *Banking Daily™*; *Daily Environment Report™*; *Pension & Benefits Daily™*; *Securities Law Daily™*; *Labor Relations Week*; *Antitrust & Trade Regulation Daily™*; *Compensation Planning Journal*; *Estates, Gifts, and Trust Journal* (Bimonthly); *Tax Management Memorandum*; *Real Estate Journal* (Monthly); *Foreign Income Portfolios Library* (Weekly); *International Environment Reporter™*; *International Trade Reporter* (Weekly); *Spill Reporting Procedures Guide*; *Directory of State and Federal Courts, Judges and Clerks*; *Occupational Safety & Health Reporter™* (Daily); *HR-focus* (Monthly); *BNA Online* (Bimonthly); *Product Safety and Liability Reporter™*; *BNA Pension & Benefits Reporter* (Weekly); *Employee Benefits Cases*; *Labor Relations Week*; *Union Labor Report Newsletter ®*; *Wages and Hours*; *Biotechnology Research Directory: 400 Faculty Profiles*; *United States Patents Quarterly*; *International Trade Reporter Decisions* (Weekly); *Affirmative Action Compliance Manual for Federal Contractors* (Monthly); *Antitrust and Trade Regulation Resource Center* (Continuous); *Fair Employment Practices*; *BNA Pension and Benefits Reporter* (Weekly); *BNA Policy and Practice Series* (Biweekly); *Wage and Hour Laws: A State-by-State Survey, Third Edition*; *BNA's Banking Report: Legal and Regulatory Developments in the Financial Services Industry* (Weekly); *Daily Report for Executives* (Daily); *Daily Report for Executives* (Daily); *BNA's Medicare Report* (Weekly); *BNA's Health Care Policy Report* (Weekly); *Health Insurance Report* (Weekly); *Medical Research Law & Policy Report* (Semimonthly); *U.S. Income Portfolios Library*; *Antitrust & Trade Regulation Daily™*; *Banking Report™*; *Pension & Benefits Reporter™*; *Chemical Regulation Reporter™*; *Daily Report for Executives* (Daily); *Daily Labor Report* (Daily); *Daily Tax Report*; *Securities Regulation & Law Report*; *Health Care Daily Report™*; *Medicare Report*; *Health Care Policy Report*; *Bankruptcy Law Reporter™*; *Class Action Litigation Report®*; *Computer Technology Law Report®*; *Construction Labor Report*; *Corporate Governance Library*; *Electronic Commerce & Law Report™*; *Employee Benefits Cases*; *Environment & Safety Resource Center™* (Daily); *Family Law Reporter®*; *State Health Care Regulatory Alert* (Daily); *Pharmaceutical Law & Industry Report®* (Continuous; Weekly); *Product Safety & Liability Reporter™*; *Toxics Law Reporter™*; *Criminal Law Reporter*; *Employment Discrimination Report*; *Corpo-*

rate Law Daily™; *Compensation Planning Journal* (Monthly); *Tax Practice Adviser* (Monthly); *United States Law Week: A National Survey of Current Law*; *BNA's Environment Library on CD*; *BNA's Safety Library on CD*; *Telecommunications Law Resource Center™*; *Patent, Trademark and Copyright Rules Service*; *BNA LRR Arbitrators' Biographies*; *Labor Relations Reference Manual*; *Research & Custom Solutions*; *Air Pollution Control* (Biweekly); *Union Labor Report* (Biweekly); *Managing 401(k) Plans(tm)* (Monthly); *Air Pollution Control Guide™* (Continuous); *Water Pollution Control Guide™* (Daily); *Canadian Environment & Safety Library™* (Daily); *Waste Management Guide™* (Daily); *Health Law & Business Library(tm)*; *Health Law Reporter™* (Weekly); *Export Reference Library*; *Health Care Fraud Report™*; *Compensation & Benefits Library*; *Payroll Library*; *HR Library(tm)* (Continuous); *BNA's Patent, Trademark & Copyright Journal*; *Daily Labor Report* (Daily); *BNA's Directory of State Administrative Codes and Registers*; *Collective Bargaining Contract Library*; *Collective Bargaining Contract Settlements*; *Directory of U.S. Labor Organizations* (Annual); *Tax Management International Forum*; *ABA/BNA Lawyers' Manual on Professional Conduct™* (Continuous); *BNA's Directory of State and Federal Courts, Judges, and Clerks* (Annual); *Collective Bargaining Negotiations and Contracts* (Biweekly); *Human Resources Report* (Weekly; Continuous); *Guide to State Environmental Programs* (Irregular); *Chemical Regulation Reporter: A Weekly Review of Activity Affecting Chemical Users and Manufacturers* (Monthly; Daily); *Government Employee Relations Report* (Weekly); *Labor Relations Reporter*; *International Trade Reporter Export Reference Manual*; *Tax Management International Forum* (Quarterly).

35972 ■ Cogswell College Library [Cogswell Polytechnical College]
191 Baypointe Pky.
San Jose, CA 95134
Co. E-mail: library@usv.edu
URL: http://usv.edu/student-life/library

Description: Sillicon valley Cogswell college library. **Scope:** Art; animation; software engineering; digital audio technology. **Services:** Interlibrary loan; copying; library open to the public for reference use only. **Holdings:** Books; CDs; DVDs; e-books; digital journals; articles.

35973 ■ Cornell University - School of Industrial and Labor Relations - Martin P. Catherwood Library
229 Ives Hall Tower Rd.
Ithaca, NY 14853
Ph: (607)255-5435
Co. E-mail: ilrcirc@cornell.edu
URL: http://catherwood.library.cornell.edu
Contact: Jim DelRosso, Assistant Director
E-mail: jdd10@cornell.edu
Facebook: www.facebook.com/cathlib
X (Twitter): x.com/catherwoodlibe
Instagram: www.instagram.com/kheelcenter

Scope: Labor and employment. **Services:** Interlibrary loan; copying; library open to the public. **Founded:** 1945. **Subscriptions:** 1,500 journals and other serials 250,000 volumes; microforms; media items; manuscripts; 350,000 photographs; archives.

35974 ■ The Hartford Financial Services Group Loss Control Library
690 Asylum Ave.
Hartford, CT 06155
URL: http://www.thehartford.com/loss-control

Scope: Safety engineering; toxicology; chemistry; fire protection; transportation; occupational safety and health; industrial hygiene; ergonomics; risk management. **Services:** Interlibrary loan; library open to the public by special arrangement only. **Founded:** 1810. **Holdings:** Figures not available.

35975 ■ Industrial Health Foundation (IHF) [American Industrial Hygiene Foundation]
3120 Fairview Pk. Dr., Ste. 360
Falls Church, VA 22042
Ph: (703)849-8888
Fax: (703)207-3561

URL: http://www.aiha.org/get-involved/aih-foundation
Facebook: www.facebook.com/AIHFoundation
Linkedin: www.linkedin.com/company/aiha
X (Twitter): x.com/AIHA

Description: Publishes proceedings of technical meetings. Offers a monthly abstract service. Does not accept unsolicited manuscripts.

35976 ■ Insurance Institute for Business And Home Safety (IBHS) - Hurricane Video Library
4775 East Fowler Ave.
Tampa, FL 33617
Ph: (813)286-3400
Co. E-mail: info@ibhs.org
URL: http://ibhs.org
Contact: Roy E. Wright, President
Facebook: www.facebook.com/disasterprep
Linkedin: www.linkedin.com/company/institute-for-business-&-home-safety
X (Twitter): x.com/disastersafety
YouTube: www.youtube.com/user/ibhsdotorg

Description: Aims to reduce the social and economic effects of natural disasters and other property losses by conducting research and advocating improved construction, maintenance and preparation. **Scope:** To conduct objective, scientific research to identify and promote the most effective ways to strengthen homes, businesses and communities against natural disasters and other causes of loss. **Founded:** 1977. **Holdings:** Videos. **Publications:** *Disaster Safety Review*; *IBHS Annual report*.

35977 ■ International Union of Operating Engineers (IUOE)
1125 17th St. NW
Washington, DC 20036
Ph: (202)429-9100
URL: http://www.iuoe.org
Contact: James T. Callahan, President

Description: Represents operating engineers, stationary engineers, nurses, and other health industry workers engaged in a wide variety of occupations. **Founded:** 1896. **Publications:** *International Operating Engineer* (Quarterly). **Geographic Preference:** National.

35978 ■ J.J. Keller & Associates Inc. - Editorial Resource Center - Research & Technical Library
3003 W Breezewood Ln.
Neenah, WI 54957
Free: 877-564-2333
Fax: (800)727-7516
Co. E-mail: compliancelibrarysupport@jjkeller.com
URL: http://www.jjkeller.com
Contact: Rustin Keller, President
Facebook: www.facebook.com/JJKellerAssoc
X (Twitter): x.com/JJKeller
YouTube: www.youtube.com/channel/UCIruR_EJGIqS25_6b-2Jc7A

Scope: Transportation; motor carrier regulations; workplace safety regulations and practices; hazardous materials; hazardous wastes; industry regulations and compliance; food safety; human resources. **Services:** Copying; library open to the public by referral. **Founded:** 1953. **Holdings:** 8,000 books, 500 periodicals; 7,600 books, AV programs, and government documents (Department of Transportation, Environmental Protection Agency, and Department of Labor).

35979 ■ Lakehead University Resource Centre for Occupational Health and Safety
955 Oliver Rd.
Thunder Bay, ON, Canada P7B 5E1
URL: http://www.lakeheadu.ca/faculty-and-staff/departments/services/hr/health-safety/tb

Description: Lakehead university resource center. for occupational health and safety. **Scope:** Occupational health and safety; the environment. **Services:** Interlibrary loan; copying; library open to the public. **Founded:** 1978. **Subscriptions:** journals 10,000 books and articles.

35980 ■ Manitoba Department of Labour & Immigration-Workplace Safety and Health Division-Client Resource Centre
200-401 York Ave.
Winnipeg, MB, Canada R3C 0P8
Ph: (204)957-7233
Free: 855-957-7233
Co. E-mail: wshcompl@gov.mb.ca
URL: http://www.gov.mb.ca/justice/courts/mep/clien t_resources.html
Description: Manitoba association for its labours. **Scope:** Legal and education information. **Services:** Library not open to the public. **Holdings:** Figures not available.

35981 ■ Montana Tech of the University of Montana - Library
1300 W Pk. St.
Butte, MT 59701
Free: 800-445-8324
URL: http://www.mtech.edu
Contact: Leslie Dickerson, Executive Director
Facebook: www.facebook.com/montanatech
Linkedin: www.linkedin.com/school/montana-tech
X (Twitter): x.com/montana_tech
Instagram: www.instagram.com/montana_tech
YouTube: www.youtube.com/user/mtechpr
Description: Engaged in research and development. **Scope:** Biological sciences; business; chemistry; computer science and software engineering; environmental issues; healthcare; mathematics and statistics; metallurgy and materials engineering; microbiology; mining engineering; nursing; petroleum engineering. **Services:** Interlibrary loan. **Founded:** 1896. **Holdings:** 20,000 state documents; books; e-books; e-journals; e-newspapers; journals; government documents; maps; atlases; patents; yearbooks; student newspapers; alumni publications. **Publications:** The Technocrat.

35982 ■ National Safety Council (NSC) - Library
1121 Spring Lake Dr.
Itasca, IL 60143-3201
Ph: (630)285-1121
Free: 800-621-7615
Co. E-mail: customerservice@nsc.org
URL: http://www.nsc.org/home
Contact: Mark Vergnano, President
Facebook: www.facebook.com/NatlSafetyCouncil
Linkedin: www.linkedin.com/company/national-safety -council
X (Twitter): x.com/NSCsafety
Instagram: www.instagram.com/nationalsafetycouncil
YouTube: www.youtube.com/user/NatlSafetyCouncil
Description: Promotes injury reduction by providing a forum for the exchange of safety and health ideas, techniques, and experiences and the discussion of injury prevention methods. Offers courses in first aid, occupational safety and traffic safety. Maintains extensive library on health and safety subjects. Publishes books on occupational safety, health topics, emergency planning, first-aid, traffic, school, farm, labor, youth, transportation and public (governmental) employee safety. **Scope:** Roadway safety. **Services:** Library access to members for free. **Founded:** 1913. **Holdings:** 174,000 books, research reports, articles; papers; clippings and pamphlets. **Publications:** Injury Facts; Safeworker (Monthly); Safety and Health (Monthly); Today's Supervisor (Monthly); Traffic Safety (Monthly; Bimonthly); Safe Driver (Monthly); Construction Division Newsletter (Bimonthly); Safety & Health--Industrial Hygiene Buyers' Guide Issue; Safety & Health--Safety Equipment Buyers' Guide Issue. **Educational Activities:** NSC Congress & Expo (Annual). **Awards:** USPS Safe Driver Awards (Annual); NSC Occupational Excellence Achievement Award (Periodic). **Geographic Preference:** National.

35983 ■ New Mexico Department of Environment - NMED Library
1190 S St. Francis Dr., Ste. N4050
Santa Fe, NM 87505
URL: http://www.env.nm.gov

Scope: Health and the environment. **Services:** Open to the public. **Founded:** 1980. **Holdings:** Figures not available.

35984 ■ New York State Office of Fire Prevention and Control - Academy of Fire Science (AFS) - Library
600 College Ave.
Montour Falls, NY 14865-9634
Ph: (607)535-7136
Fax: (607)535-4841
URL: http://www.dhses.ny.gov/fire-prevention-an d-control-training
Scope: Fire; arson investigation; building codes; construction; EMS; rescue; fire suppression; fire protection engineering and HazMat. **Services:** Interlibrary loan; copying; answers to email, mail and telephone inquiries from patrons in New York state; library open to the public. **Founded:** 1971. **Holdings:** Books; journal; photocopies; audio-visual.

35985 ■ North Carolina Department of Labor (NCDOL) - Occupational Safety and Health Div. - Education, Training and Technical Assistance Bureau - Charles H. Livengood, Jr. Memorial Library
Old Revenue Bldg.
Raleigh, NC 27699-1101
Ph: (919)707-7880
Co. E-mail: dol.library@labor.nc.gov
URL: http://www.labor.nc.gov/safety-and-health/li brary
Scope: Labor law and history; occupational safety; health and training. **Services:** Interlibrary loan; copying; SDI; library open to the public by appointment. **Subscriptions:** 120 journals 14,000 volumes; 1500 videos and DVDs; vertical files; state government documents; 10,000 labor-related print titles.

35986 ■ Ohio Bureau of Workers' Compensation - BWC Library
30 W Spring St.
Columbus, OH 43215-2256
Ph: (614)466-7388
Co. E-mail: library@bwc.ohio.gov
URL: http://info.bwc.ohio.gov/for-employers/safety-an d-training/safety-video-library
Scope: Occupational safety; industrial hygiene; workers' compensation; occupational rehabilitation. **Services:** Interlibrary loan; copying; center open to the public. **Founded:** 1974. **Holdings:** 6,000 books; 850 standards; 650 subject headings; 900 videos; 200 magazines and newsletters. **Subscriptions:** 100 journals and other serials.

35987 ■ Triodyne Inc. (TI) - Library
450 Skokie Blvd., Ste. 604
Northbrook, IL 60062
Ph: (847)677-4730
Co. E-mail: infoserv@triodyne.com
URL: http://www.triodyne.com
Description: Provider of mechanical engineering consulting services. **Scope:** Provider of mechanical engineering consulting services. **Founded:** 1969. **Holdings:** Figures not available. **Publications:** "Center of Excellence"; "The Triodyne Safety Bulletin"; "The Triodyne Safety Alert"; "The Triodyne Safety Brief"; "The Triodyne Safety Abstract".

35988 ■ U.S. Department of Labor-Occupational Safety & Health Administration-Region III Library
OSHA 1835 Market St.
Philadelphia, PA 19103
Ph: (215)861-4900
Fax: (215)861-4904
URL: http://www.osha.gov/contactus/bystate/region3
Description: Aims to assure safe and healthful working conditions for working men and women by setting and enforcing standards and by providing training, outreach, education and assistance. **Founded:** 1971.

35989 ■ U.S. Department of Labor - Occupational Safety and Health Administration - Region VIII Library
200 Constitution Ave. NW
Washington, DC 20210

URL: http://www.osha.gov
Scope: Occupational safety; occupational health; OSHA regulations; any questions about OSHA - federal or state. **Services:** Interlibrary loan; copying; library open to the public for reference use only; OSHA publications are distributed from this office (one copy per request/title). Help with using OSHA's public website (http://www.osha.gov). **Holdings:** 600 books; 1,100 reports.

35990 ■ U.S. Department of Labor - Occupational Safety & Health Administration - Region X Library
300 Fifth Ave., Ste. 1260
Seattle, WA 98104
URL: http://www.osha.gov/alliances/regional/region 10/agreement_20100527
Contact: Lewis McChord, Contact
Founded: 1970.

35991 ■ U.S. Dept. of Labor - OSHA Billings Area Office Library
c/o Art Hazen, Area Director
2900 4th Ave. N, Ste. 303
Billings, MT 59101
Ph: (406)247-7494
Fax: (406)247-7499
URL: http://www.osha.gov
Contact: Art Hazen, Director
Scope: Safety and health in the workplace. **Services:** Library open to the public. **Founded:** 1974. **Holdings:** 500 books.

35992 ■ U.S. Department of Labor - OSHA Technical Data Center (TDC)
200 Constitution Ave. NW, Rm. N-3508
Washington, DC 20210
Ph: (202)693-2350
Fax: (202)693-1648
Co. E-mail: technicaldatacenter@dol.gov
URL: http://www.osha.gov/contactus/byoffice/dtsem/ technical-data-center
Scope: Occupational safety and health; biology; chemistry; engineering; science and toxicology. **Services:** Interlibrary loan; Open to the public with Valid ID. **Founded:** 1971. **Holdings:** Books; journal.

35993 ■ University of California, Berkeley - School of Public Health - Labor Occupational Health Program Library
1995 University Ave.
Suite 300, Rm. 3318, MC7358
Berkeley, CA 94704-7358
Ph: (510)642-5507
Fax: (510)643-5698
Co. E-mail: lohp@berkeley.edu
URL: http://lohp.org/resources/library
Contact: Laura Stock, Director
E-mail: lstock@berkeley.edu
Facebook: www.facebook.com/LaborOccupa tionalHealthProgram
Linkedin: www.linkedin.com/company/the-labor -occupational-health-program/
X (Twitter): twitter.com/ucberkeleylohp
Instagram: www.instagram.com/ucberkeleylohp/
Scope: Workplace health and safety.; chemical hazards; worker's rights. **Services:** Library open to the public for reference use only (technical assistance by phone and e-mail). **Founded:** 1974. **Holdings:** 10,000 books, pamphlets, periodicals, and videos.

35994 ■ WorkSafeNB - Communications Department
1 Portland St.
Saint John, NB, Canada E2L 3X9
Free: 800-999-9775
Co. E-mail: communications@ws-ts.nb.ca
URL: http://www.worksafenb.ca/about-us/news-an d-events/events
Description: Committed to promoting healthy and safe workplaces for New Brunswick's workers and employers. **Scope:** Social affairs; education; occupational health and safety; training; mining safety. **Holdings:** Figures not available.

RESEARCH CENTERS

35995 ■ National Farm Medicine Center (NFMC)

1000 North Oak Ave.
 Marshfield, WI 54449-5790
Ph: (715)389-4999
Free: 800-662-6900
Fax: (715)389-4996
Co. E-mail: nfmcsh@mcrf.mfldclin.edu
URL: http://www.marshfieldresearch.org/nfmc
Contact: Casper Bendixsen, Director
E-mail: bendixsen.casper@mcrf.mfldclin.edu
Facebook: www.facebook.com/farmmedicine
X (Twitter): x.com/FarmMedicine
YouTube: www.youtube.com/channel/UCZEzrl
 4OVfBXLP5ER4hGJnQ
Pinterest: www.pinterest.com/nationalfarmmed

Description: Integral unit of Marshfield Clinic, Division of Research and Education. **Scope:** Human health and safety associated with rural and agricultural work, life and environment. **Founded:** 1981. **Publications:** *Cultivate* (Semiannual); *Nurture newsletter* (Quarterly); *Progress Report*; *Year in Review annual report* (Annual).

35996 ■ University of Michigan - College of Engineering - Department of Industrial and Operations Engineering - Center for Ergonomics

1205 Beal Ave.
 Ann Arbor, MI 48109-2117
Ph: (734)763-2243
Fax: (734)764-3451
Co. E-mail: centerforergonomics@umich.edu
URL: http://c4e.engin.umich.edu
Contact: Yili Liu, Director
E-mail: yililiu@umich.edu

Description: Integral unit of Department of Industrial and Operations Engineering, College of Engineering, University of Michigan. Offers 15 one- to five-day courses for engineers, managers, and occupational health professionals. **Scope:** Ergonomics and safety engineering, including studies on contemporary techniques and methods necessary to minimize occupational health and safety problems and maximize human-hardware performance capability. **Founded:** 1959.

35997 ■ University of Utah - Rocky Mountain Center for Occupational and Environmental Health (RMCOEH) [National Institute for Occupational Safety and Health Education and Research Center]

250 E 200 S Ste. 100
 Salt Lake City, UT 84111
Ph: (801)581-4800
URL: http://rmcoeh.com
Contact: Heidi Slack, Associate Director
E-mail: heidi.slack@utah.edu
Facebook: www.facebook.com/RMCOEH
Linkedin: www.linkedin.com/company/rmcoeh
Instagram: www.instagram.com/rmcoeh

Description: National Institute for Occupational Safety and Health-established Education and Research Center, located at University of Utah. Offers consulting for federal, state, and local governments, industry, and other organizations. **Scope:** Occupational and environmental health and safety with emphasis on exposure assessment, environmental epidemiology, asbestos-related health problems, musculoskeletal and other injury evaluation and prevention, and ergonomic aspects of the work environment. **Founded:** 1977.

START-UP INFORMATION

35998 ■ *"Campus CEOs: Young and the Restless" in Business Journal Portland (Vol. 30, February 21, 2014, No. 50, pp. 4)*
Pub: American City Business Journals, Inc.
Contact: Mike Olivieri, Executive Vice President

Released: Weekly. **Price:** $4, Introductory 4-week offer(Digital & Print). **Description:** A number of startups in Portland, Oregon were created by young entrepreneurs while still attending college. The University of Oregon and Portland State University are developing courses designed to launch the entrepreneurial ambitions of their students. **Availability:** Print; Online.

35999 ■ *"Entrepreneurs Take Different Paths, but Arrive at Same Place" in Business Journal Portland (Vol. 30, February 14, 2014, No. 50, pp. 6)*
Pub: American City Business Journals, Inc.
Contact: Mike Olivieri, Executive Vice President

Released: Weekly. **Price:** $4, Introductory 4-week offer(Digital & Print). **Description:** Several young entrepreneurs in Portland, Oregon describe how they started their own businesses while attending college. They discuss the challenges of balancing their studies and their companies. **Availability:** Print; Online.

36000 ■ *"The New CEO: 185 Easy-To-Set-Up Businesses for Youth and Adult Entrepreneurs"*
Pub: CreateSpace

Released: September 09, 2014. **Price:** $7.12, paperback. **Description:** Regardless of age, this book will help anyone wishing to launch and run a small business. **Availability:** E-book; Print.

36001 ■ *"On Their Own: Bronx High School Students Open a Bank Branch" in Black Enterprise (Vol. 38, February 2008, No. 7, pp. 42)*
Pub: Earl G. Graves Ltd.
Contact: Earl Graves, Jr., President

Ed: Jessica Jones. **Description:** Students at Fordham Leadership Academy for Business and Technology in New York City opened a student-run bank branch at their high school. The business paid high school seniors $11 per hour to work as tellers. Students were also taught interviewing basics. **Availability:** Online.

36002 ■ *"The Startup Blueprint: The Young Entrepreneur's Step-by-Step Guide To Starting Your Own Business"*
Pub: CreateSpace

Released: October 21, 2014. **Description:** Careful planning and smart execution is required to start a new business. More than 90 percent of new business fail with the first three years. Practical tips and advice are offered to help young entrepreneurs successfully start a new business. **Availability:** Print.

ASSOCIATIONS AND OTHER ORGANIZATIONS

36003 ■ **Entrepreneurs Organization (EO)**
500 Montgomery St., Ste. 700
Alexandria, VA 22314
Ph: (703)519-6700
Fax: (703)519-1864
Co. E-mail: info@eonetwork.org
URL: http://www.eonetwork.org
Contact: Carrie Santos, PhD, Chief Executive Officer
Facebook: www.facebook.com/EntrepreneursOrganization
Linkedin: www.linkedin.com/company/entrepreneurs%27-organization
X (Twitter): x.com/EntrepreneurOrg
Instagram: www.instagram.com/entrepreneursorg
YouTube: www.youtube.com/user/EOnetwork

Description: Engages leading entrepreneurs to learn and grow. Serves as a focal point for networking and development of members through small group learning sessions, regular local chapter social and learning events, and global conference-based education programs. **Founded:** 1987. **Publications:** *Overdrive* (Monthly); *Octane* (Quarterly). **Geographic Preference:** Multinational.

36004 ■ **Network for Teaching Entrepreneurship (NFTE)**
120 Wall St., 18th Fl.
New York, NY 10005
Ph: (212)232-3333
Co. E-mail: nfte@nfte.com
URL: http://www.nfte.com
Contact: J. D. LaRock, President
Facebook: www.facebook.com/NFTE
Linkedin: www.linkedin.com/company/network-for-teaching-entrepreneurship
X (Twitter): x.com/NFTE
Instagram: www.instagram.com/nfte
YouTube: www.youtube.com/user/NFTEGlobal

Description: Devoted to teaching entrepreneurship education to low-income young people, ages 11 through 18. **Founded:** 1987. **Geographic Preference:** Multinational.

36005 ■ **Ronnia Langston Foundation, Inc. (RLF)**
3948 Legacy Dr., Ste. 106
Plano, TX 75023
Ph: (469)213-0618
Fax: (469)730-2050
Co. E-mail: info@ronnialangstonfoundation.org
URL: http://ronnialangstonfoundation.org
Contact: Ronnia Langston, Chief Executive Officer
X (Twitter): x.com/rrlfoundation
Instagram: www.instagram.com/ronnialangston

Description: Transforms the lives of youth around the world through mentoring, financial literacy, and entrepreneurship programs. **Founded:** 2013.

36006 ■ **Young Entrepreneur Council (YEC)**
177 Huntington Ave., Ste. 1703, PMB 52536
Boston, MA 02115
Ph: (484)403-0736
Co. E-mail: info@yec.co
URL: http://yec.co
Contact: Scott Gerber, Co-Founder
Facebook: www.facebook.com/theyec
Linkedin: www.linkedin.com/company/yec
X (Twitter): x.com/YEC
Instagram: www.instagram.com/yec

Description: Invitation-only organization for young, successful entrepreneurs engaged in providing personal and professional guidance. **Founded:** 2010.

36007 ■ **Young Entrepreneur Society (YES)**
3333 W 39th St.
Erie, PA 16506

Description: Fosters the growth and improvement of individuals who make up the workforce and/or create new businesses through entrepreneurial thinking. Offers community outreach initiatives, healthcare training programs, workforce solutions, hospitality training, and STEM initiatives.

36008 ■ **Young Presidents' Organization (YPO)**
225 E John Carpenter Fwy., Ste. 500
Irving, TX 75062
Ph: (972)587-1500
Free: 800-773-7976
Co. E-mail: askypo@ypo.org
URL: http://www.ypo.org
Contact: Rafi Demirjian, Chairman
Facebook: www.facebook.com/youngpresorg
Linkedin: www.linkedin.com/company/ypoglobal
X (Twitter): x.com/YPO
Instagram: www.instagram.com/ypoglobal
YouTube: www.youtube.com/user/YPOvideo

Description: Presidents or chief executive officers of corporations with minimum of 50 employees; each member must have been elected president before his/her 40th birthday and must retire by June 30th the year after his/her 50th birthday. Assists members in becoming better presidents through education and idea exchange. Conducts courses for members and spouses, in business, arts and sciences, world affairs, and family and community life, during a given year at various locations, including graduate business schools. **Founded:** 1950. **Geographic Preference:** Multinational.

REFERENCE WORKS

36009 ■ *"3 Lessons on Launching From 3 Young, Early-Stage Founders" in Entrepreneur (Sept. 1, 2020)*
URL(s): www.entrepreneur.com/slideshow/355252

Released: September 01, 2020. **Description:** Conversations with three up-and-coming thinkers, inventors, and entrepreneurs and their advice for taking action of your own. **Availability:** Online.

36010 ■ "10 Successful Young Entrepreneurs" in Investopedia (Apr 11, 2021)
URL(s): www.investopedia.com/10-successful-young-entrepreneurs-4773310
Released: April 11, 2021. **Description:** Provides information on entrepreneurship for young adults. Includes examples of ten successful young entrepreneurs. **Availability:** Online.

36011 ■ "21 Success Tips for Young and Aspiring Entrepreneurs" in Entrepreneur
URL(s): www.entrepreneur.com/article/247540
Ed: Sujan Patel. **Description:** Provides twenty-one tips for young entrepreneurs to help you get started. **Availability:** Online.

36012 ■ "Are You a Young Canadian Entrepreneur Looking for Recognition?" in CNW Group (November 10, 2010)
Pub: Comtex News Network Inc.
Contact: Kan Devnani, President
Description: Business Development Bank of Canada is looking for young Canadian entrepreneurs ages 19 to 35 for its 2011 Young Entrepreneur Awards. The awards pay tribute to remarkable young Canadian entrepreneurs for their creativity, innovative spirit and community development, as well as business success. **Availability:** Online.

36013 ■ "Brooklyn-Bred Business Owner Starts Student-Entrepreneur Grant in Immigrant Parents' Names" in Entrepreneur (March 3, 2021)
URL(s): www.entrepreneur.com/article/366284
Ed: Kenny Herzog. **Released:** March 03, 2021. **Description:** Presents a Brooklyn-Bred business owner who started a student-entrepreneur grant as a forum for networking and mentorship. **Availability:** Online.

36014 ■ "Business Ideas for Teens - 30 Teen Business Ideas" in TRUiC (Feb. 4, 2022)
URL(s): howtostartanllc.com/business-ideas/categories/30-business-ideas-for-teens
Released: February 04, 2022. **Description:** Breaks down teen business ideas into seven categories and ranks their startup costs, required skill level, and earning potential. **Availability:** Online.

36015 ■ Capitalism for Kids: Growing Up to Be Your Own Boss
Pub: Bluestocking Press
Contact: Karl Hess, Contact
Ed: Karl Hess. **Price:** $14.95, paperback, plus $9.95 for shipping charges. **Description:** Capitalism, democratic socialism, socialism, communism, and totalitarianism is explained to children. The book explains to young people how to build a profitable business. **Availability:** Print.

36016 ■ "Combating Reverse Ageism as a Young Entrepreneur" in Entrepreneur (Sept. 11, 2018)
URL(s): www.entrepreneur.com/article/319603
Ed: Matt Rizzetta. **Released:** September 11, 2018. **Description:** Offers lessons learned from an entrepreneur for young entrepreneurs. Discusses challenges that young entrepreneurs face when it comes to age, inexperience, and reverse ageism. **Availability:** Online.

36017 ■ "Companies Founded by Amazing Young Entrepreneurs" in Business News Daily (Sept. 8, 2019)
URL(s): www.businessnewsdaily.com/5051-young-entrepreneurs.html
Ed: Jennifer Post. **Released:** September 08, 2019. **Description:** Provides information on 15 companies founded by young entrepreneurs. **Availability:** Online.

36018 ■ "Consignment Shop Opens In Spring Township To Serve Hard-To-Find Sizes" in Reading Eagle (June 16, 2012)
Ed: Shannon Simcox. **Description:** BeautiFull Figure is a plus-size consignment store located in Spring Township, Pennsylvania. The owner, Elizabeth

Reach, is also a full-time student. Many consignment shops will not accept clothing over size 16 and Reach saw an opportunity to serve plus-size women. She offers 50-50 split of profits on consigned items. **Availability:** Print; Online.

36019 ■ "Elastic Path Software Joins Canada in G20 Young Entrepreneur Summit" in Marketwire (June 14, 2010)
Pub: Comtex News Network Inc.
Contact: Kan Devnani, President
Description: The Canadian Youth Business Foundation hosted the G20 Young Entrepreneur Summit and announced that Harry Chemko of British Columbia's Elastic Path Software will be a member of the Canadian delegation at the G20 Young Entrepreneur Summit. Details are included. **Availability:** Print; Online.

36020 ■ "Four Tactics Young Tech Entrepreneurs Should Keep In Mind to Ensure the Long-Term Success of Their Startups" in Entrepreneur (May 3, 2021)
URL(s): www.entrepreneur.com/article/370880
Ed: Wissam Youssef. **Released:** May 03, 2021. **Description:** Shares essential lessons with the next generation of tech entrepreneurs to help as they shape their dreams of entrepreneurship. **Availability:** Online.

36021 ■ "G20 Young Entrepreneur Alliance Signs Charter Outlining Commitment to Entrepreneurship" in Marketwire (November 10, 2010)
Pub: Comtex News Network Inc.
Contact: Kan Devnani, President
Description: G20 Young Entrepreneur Summit members created a charter document that outlines their support for the G20 process to include entrepreneurship on its agenda. Details of the Summit are included. **Availability:** Online.

36022 ■ Generation Hustle: Young entrepreneurs got creative during the pandemic
URL(s): www.cnbc.com/2021/08/03/generation-hustle-young-entrepreneurs-got-creative-during-the-pandemic.html
Ed: Ryan Waterman Aldana. **Released:** August 03, 2021. **Description:** Explores young entrepreneurs who, during the pandemic, adapted to digital technology and the flexibility of remote work who saw opportunities to create their own businesses. **Availability:** Online.

36023 ■ "How 15 People in Their 20s Built Million-Dollar Businesses" in Entrepreneur (Aug. 24, 2021)
URL(s): www.entrepreneur.com/slideshow/380002
Released: August 24, 2021. **Description:** Shares stories of fifteen young entrepreneurs who have built companies that are making the world a kinder, better place. **Availability:** Online.

36024 ■ "How to Lead Kids Down a Path to Entrepreneurship in 2021" in Entrepreneur (Jan. 17, 2021)
URL(s): www.entrepreneur.com/article/362093
Ed: Paul Gunn, Jr. **Released:** January 17, 2021. **Description:** Article discusses how parents can nurture their kids' inner-entrepreneur. **Availability:** Online.

36025 ■ "Labor of Love" in Green Industry Pro (Vol. 23, March 2011, No. 3, pp. 14)
Ed: Gregg Wartgow. **Description:** Profile of CLS Landscape Management in Chino, California and its owner who started the company when he was 21 years old. Kevin Davis built his landscape firm into a $20 million a year business without using any dedicated salesperson. **Availability:** Online.

36026 ■ "The Lessons I Learned As a Teen Entrepreneur" in Entrepreneur (July 1, 2021)
URL(s): www.entrepreneur.com/article/374363

Ed: Milan Kordestani. **Released:** July 01, 2021. **Description:** Offers advice for young entrepreneurs on how to avoid pitfalls and start their professional endeavors on the right footing. **Availability:** Online.

36027 ■ "Many in Tech Look to Push More Community Involvement, But Not in Traditional Ways" in Boston Business Journal (Vol. 31, August 5, 2011, No. 28, pp. 1)
Pub: Boston Business Journal
Contact: Carolyn M. Jones, President
E-mail: cmjones@bizjournals.com
Ed: Mary Moore. **Released:** Weekly. **Price:** $4, Introductory 4-Week Offer(Digital Only). **Description:** Entrepreneurs and venture capitalists in Boston have launched Technology Underwriting Greater Good, the tech industry's answer to the criticism that they are not charitable. The foundation finances nonprofits that aid young people through entrepreneurship, education and life experience. Other tech firms in Boston doing charitable works are discussed. **Availability:** Print; Online.

36028 ■ "Meet the Class of 2014, In their Own Words" in South Florida Business Journal (Vol. 34, June 27, 2014, No. 49, pp. 18)
Pub: American City Business Journals, Inc.
Contact: Mike Olivieri, Executive Vice President
Released: Weekly. **Price:** $8, introductory 4-week offer(Digital & Print). **Description:** Several business leaders and entrepreneurs under the age of 40 who have achieved success and contributed to their community are presented. The honorees of the 40 Under 40 Class of 2014 share their views about personal and professional lives and social responsibilities to their communities. **Availability:** Print; Online.

36029 ■ "Meet the Dropouts: the Students Who Chose Start-Ups Over College" in Inc. (Vol. 33, September 2011, No. 7, pp. 32)
Released: January 09, 2011. **Description:** Profiles of 24 college students who left school in order to work on their own startup companies. Each new company is receiving $100,000 from Peter Thiel, cofounder of PayPal and an angel investor. **Availability:** Online.

36030 ■ "Success in Business: A Guide for Young Entrepreneurs" in Women in Technology International (Nov. 22, 2021)
URL(s): witi.com/articles/1965/Success-in-Business-:-A-Guide-for-Young-Entrepreneurs/
Ed: Naomi Cook. **Released:** November 22, 2021. **Description:** Provides seven ways for young entrepreneurs to succeed in business with planning, preparation, and management. **Availability:** Online.

36031 ■ "Top 5 Lessons From a Kid Entrepreneur (Pay Attention, Public Schools!)" in Entrepreneur (May 13, 2020)
URL(s): www.entrepreneur.com/article/350052
Ed: George Deeb. **Released:** May 13, 2020. **Description:** Details the journey of young entrepreneur, Brendan Cox, and provides his top five lessons that he'd like to share with aspiring young entrepreneurs. **Availability:** Online.

36032 ■ "Transitioning From Hobbyist to Entrepreneur: Teen Designer Creates Custom and Handmade Jewelry for the Everyday Diva" in Black Enterprise (Vol. 44, March 2014, No. 7, pp. 14)
Pub: Earl G. Graves Ltd.
Contact: Earl Graves, Jr., President
Description: Profile of Jaya Kiere Johnson, who states that every one of her jewelry creations represents a generation of black female entrepreneurship in her life, from her mother to her great-grandmother. The young entrepreneur tells how she was inspired while designing and creating handmade jewelry in high school.

36033 ■ "Young Entrepreneur Gets Some Recognition and Some Help for College" in Philadelphia Inquirer (August 30, 2010)
Pub: The Philadelphia Inquirer

Contact: Elizabeth H. Hughes, Chief Executive Officer

Ed: Susan Snyder. **Description:** Profile of Zachary Gosling, age 18, who launched an online auction Website from his bedroom, using advertising and sponsorship funds rather than charging fees to users.

36034 ■ *"Young Entrepreneur's Business Plan? An Ice Cream Boat? Really Floats: Maine at Work" in Portland Press Herald (August 9, 2010)*
Pub: Portland Press Herald
Contact: Lisa DeSisto, Chief Executive Officer

Ed: Ray Routhier. **Description:** Profile of Jake Viola, founder of and ice cream boat located near Portland, Maine. Viola is a sophomore at Yale University and sells ice cream from his pontoon boat on Little Sebago lake. **Availability:** Print; Online.

36035 ■ *"Young Millionaires" in Entrepreneur (Vol. 35, October 2007, No. 10, pp. 76)*
Pub: Entrepreneur Media Inc.
Contact: Dan Bova, Director
E-mail: dbova@entrepreneur.com

Ed: Jason Ankeny. **Description:** Young successful entrepreneurs of 2007 were chosen to talk about their success story and their business strategies in the past and those for the future. Among those featured are Kelly Flatley, Brendan Synnott, Herman Flores, Myles Kovacs, Haythem Haddad, Jim Wetzel, Lance Lawson, Jacob DeHart, Jake Nickell, Tim Vanderhook, Chris Vanderhook, Russell Vanderhook, Megan Duckett, Brad Sugars, John Vechey, Brian Fiete, Jason Kapalka, Nathan Jones, Devon Rifkin, Ryan Black, Ed Nichols, Jeremy Black, Amy Smilovic, Bob Shallenberger, and John Cavanagh.

VIDEO/AUDIO MEDIA

36036 ■ *Emily Eldh Owner of The Muffin Drop*
URL(s): restarantunstoppable.libsyn.com/995-emily -eldh-owner-of-the-muffin-drop

Ed: Eric Cacciatore. **Released:** May 29, 2023. **Description:** Podcast follows a young adult who began making gluten-free muffins out of her parents' home and now offers pop-ups, wholesale, and nationwide shipping.

36037 ■ *How I Built My Small Business: Duran Morley - No College? No Problem. 17-Year-Old Started VanSpeed Instead*
URL(s): www.annemcginty.com/transcripts/ duranmorley

Ed: Anne McGinty. **Released:** October 08, 2024. **Description:** Podcast features the founder of a van conversion business.

36038 ■ *The Solopreneur Hour: Charliee Cannon Built a Drone Empire Using Alibaba at Age 22, Then Cashed Out*
URL(s): solopreneurhour.com/podcast/872-charlie -cannon-built-a-drone-empire-using-alibaba-at-age -22-then-cashed-out

Ed: Michael O'Neal. **Released:** July 25, 2022. **Description:** Podcast features a conversation with a freeskier-turned-entrepreneur.

36039 ■ *The Solopreneur Hour: Lauren Tickner Is Redefining the Rules of How to Be a Young Entrepreneur*
URL(s): solopreneurhour.com/podcast/854-lauren -tickner-is-redefining-the-rules-of-how-to-be-a -young-entrepreneur

Ed: Michael O'Neal. **Released:** November 14, 2022. **Description:** Podcast features a young woman who went from being a fitness influencer to a young entrepreneur.State Listings